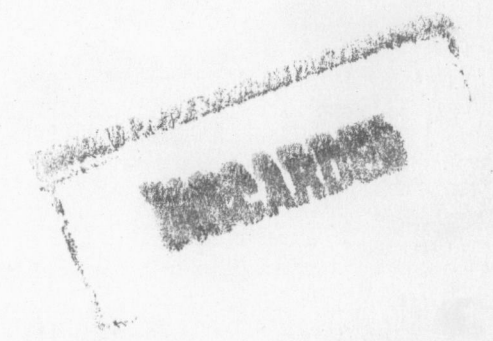

HANDBOOK
of
BIOLOGICAL DATA

EDITED BY

WILLIAM S. SPECTOR

Prepared under the Direction of the Committee

on the Handbook of Biological Data

DIVISION OF BIOLOGY AND AGRICULTURE

THE NATIONAL ACADEMY OF SCIENCES

THE NATIONAL RESEARCH COUNCIL

W. B. SAUNDERS COMPANY

Philadelphia and London

Foreword

Seven years ago the National Academy of Sciences-National Research Council contracted with the Wright Air Development Center, United States Air Force, to gather and compile for publication, in handbook form, basic established data in the biological and medical sciences. The principal objective of the Handbook, like that of similar volumes in the fields of engineering and physical sciences, is to serve the student, the teacher, and the expert who seeks information outside his own area of specialization. Another aim has been to produce as comprehensive a work as possible and, at the same time, keep it from becoming unwieldly in size and prohibitive in cost. To achieve this goal it has been necessary to condense some 20,000 sheets of data into the present number of tables, and, further, to condense each table to the point where only the most generally useful, informative, and comprehensive material would be included. Therefore, the data as presented are by no means complete, and the limitations of space and time have disallowed inclusion of many subjects of obvious importance.* Also, by the very nature of the subject material, certain of the tables will appear elementary to the expert in the field, while to the student — a beginner in the subject of the table — or to an expert in another field, the same data may seem extremely complex. For the compiler, who cannot possess an expert knowledge of all fields in the bio-sciences, the task of choosing for publication not only the subject areas, but also data within these areas, would have been utterly impossible without the unprecedented cooperation of some 17,000 biological scientists who gave freely of their time to serve as advisers, appraisers, contributors, and reviewers.

From the onset of the project, direction of the work was entrusted to the Committee on the Handbook of Biological Data, operating under the Division of Biology and Agriculture of the National Research Council. Membership of the Committee is representative of major fields in the biological sciences. The Committee, seeking the highest degree of authenticity, recognized that a specialist in a given field can best exercise the critical judgment necessary for evaluation of data in that field. He is also best able to identify those values derived from the most acceptable methods of measurement and those having the greatest likelihood, or actual history, of reproducibility in competent hands. The Committee accordingly prescribed that in selection and review of data, broadest collaboration be sought among outstanding investigators in each of the many areas of the biological sciences.

With the generous assistance of the Council's Office of Scientific Personnel, a "Panel of Appraisers," comprised of thousands of experts statistically proportioned into groups in relation to the various bio-science populations, was established to submit and grade table titles for inclusion in the Handbook and to suggest names of authorities to act as contributors. Each contributor to the Handbook was recommended by at least three experts in his field. Data received in the Handbook Office were compiled and reconciled into the Handbook format and resubmitted to the original contributors, as well as to a review panel — one panel for each table — for verification and authentication. By this procedure it has been possible to strip from the tables most of the questionable or borderline material, leaving for final presentation to the user only what is considered as fact or accepted as reliable theory by those who are competent to judge.

The tables in this Handbook represent the actual correlated contributions of more than 4,000 scientists and the counsel of an additional 13,000. In the face of this overwhelming response and devotion to the science, the compiler feels humble indeed.

The Handbook of Biological Data was prepared under USAF Contract No. 33(038)-2174 between the National Academy of Sciences and the Wright Air Development Center — to which funds were also contributed by the Department of the Army and the Department of the Navy — and Contract No. AT(49-1)-626 between the National Academy of Sciences and the Atomic Energy Commission. The first of the two contracts was administered under the direction of the Aero Medical Laboratory as Project 7158, Dr. J. W. Heim, Project Director, and the second, by Dr. John C. Bugher, former Director, Division of Biology and Medicine, Atomic Energy Commission.

Acknowledgment is made, on behalf of the Handbook Committee and the National Academy of Sciences-National Research Council, to Wright Air Development Center, Office of the Surgeon General of the Army, Office of Naval Research, and Division of Biology and Medicine of the Atomic Energy Commission, for the foresight and scientific judgment inherent in the commission to prepare this Handbook; to the scientists of the Smithsonian Institution for their most valuable assistance in problems of taxonomy; to the thousands of biologists all over the world who, as contributors and reviewers, made possible the completion of this edition; and to the thousands of others, unlisted, who so willingly responded to requests for advice. Acknowledgment is also made to the present and former members of the Handbook Staff for their loyalty to a most tedious and exacting task.

W. S. S.

---

*These, as well as more detailed coverage of areas in this Handbook, will be published in monographs dealing with such special fields as growth and reproduction, circulation and respiration, plant and animal physiology, biophysical and biochemical characteristics, and aquatic biology. Already in print are "Standard Values in Blood" (1952), "Standard Values in Nutrition and Metabolism" (1954), and Volume I of a five-volume "Handbook of Toxicology."

Contributors and Reviewers

1. JOHN ABAJIAN, University of Vermont
2. B. C. ABBOTT, Marine Biological Laboratories, Plymouth, England
3. CHARLES H. ABBOTT, 208 Avenue G, Redondo Beach, Cal.
4. R. TUCKER ABBOTT, Academy of Natural Sciences, Philadelphia
5. NEVA M. ABELSON, Children's Hospital, Philadelphia
6. MICHAEL ABERCROMBIE, University of London
7. JOHN N. ABERSOLD, American Smelting and Refining Co., El Paso, Texas
8. L. G. ABOOD, University of Illinois College of Medicine
9. SIDNEY ABRAHAM, Department of Health, Education & Welfare, Washington, D. C.
10. DAVID I. ABRAMSON, University of Illinois College of Medicine
11. HAROLD A. ABRAMSON, Mount Sinai Hospital, N. Y. C.
12. D. ACKERMANN, University of Würzburg
13. G. L. ADA, Royal Melbourne Hospital, Australia
14. A. ELIZABETH ADAMS, Mount Holyoke College
15. GAIL D. ADAMS, University of California, San Francisco
16. MARK ADAMS, New York University
17. W. H. F. ADDISON, 286 E. Sidney Ave., Mount Vernon, N.Y.
18. EDWARD A. ADELBERG, University of California, Berkeley
19. FRANCIS H. ADLER, 313 S. 17th St., Philadelphia
20. HARRY F. ADLER, 274 W. Ware Blvd., San Antonio, Texas
21. EDWARD F. ADOLPH, University of Rochester
22. GUY W. ADRIANCE, Texas Agricultural and Mechanical College
23. JOHN ADRIANI, Charity Hospital of Louisiana, New Orleans
24. PAUL C. AEBERSOLD, Oak Ridge National Laboratory
25. H. AEBI, University of Bern
26. BJÖRN AFZELIUS, Karolinska Institute, Stockholm
27. PAUL M. AGGELER, University of California, San Francisco
28. GILBERT H. AHLGREN, Rutgers University
29. G. C. AINSWORTH, University College of the South West, Exeter, England
30. THOMAS H. G. AITKEN, Trinidad Regional Virus Laboratory, Port-of-Spain
31. ANTHONY A. ALBANESE, St. Luke's Hospital, Greenwich, Conn.
32. JULIETTE O. ALBANESE, St. Luke's Hospital, Greenwich, Conn.
33. HARRY G. ALBAUM, Brooklyn College
34. D. ALBE-FESSARD, Biological Station, Arcachon, France
35. A. ALBERT, Mayo Clinic
36. WILLIAM A. ALBRECHT, University of Missouri
37. DANIEL G. ALDRICH, Jr., University of California, Davis
38. FREDERICK A. ALDRICH, Academy of Natural Sciences, Philadelphia
39. BENJAMIN ALEXANDER, Beth Israel Hospital, Boston
40. FRANZ ALEXANDER, Institute for Psychoanalysis, Chicago
41. G. V. ALEXANDER, University of California, Los Angeles
42. MARTIN ALEXANDER, University of Wisconsin
43. ROBERT S. ALEXANDER, Medical College of Georgia
44. H. A. ALLARD, 3000 7th St. N., Arlington, Va.
45. W. C. ALLEE (Deceased)
46. EMMA G. ALLEN, University of Pennsylvania
47. FRANK ALLEN, University of Manitoba
48. FRED H. ALLEN, Jr., Blood Grouping Laboratory, 300 Longwood Ave., Boston
49. GEORGE S. ALLEN, University of British Columbia
50. M. B. ALLEN, University of California, Berkeley
51. O. N. ALLEN, University of Wisconsin
52. PAUL H. ALLEN, Pan-American Agricultural School Tegucigalpa, Honduras
53. PAUL J. ALLEN, University of Wisconsin
54. WILLIAM W. ALLEN, University of California, Berkeley
55. GORDON A. ALLES, California Institute of Technology
56. W. B. ALLINGTON, University of Nebraska
57. JAMES B. ALLISON, Rutgers University
58. H. J. ALMQUIST, The Grange Co., Modesto, Cal.
59. JOHN O. ALMQUIST, Pennsylvania State University
60. THOMAS P. ALMY, Cornell University Medical College
61. JOHN B. ALSEVER, U. S. Public Health Service, Washington, D. C.
62. HOWARD L. ALT, Northwestern University Medical College
63. MARIO ALTAMIRANO, Columbia University
64. NICHOLAS M. ALTER, Margaret Hague Maternity Hospital, Jersey City
65. PAUL D. ALTLAND, National Institute of Arthritis and Metabolic Diseases
66. FRANZ ALTMANN, Columbia University
67. MARK D. ALTSCHULE, McLean Hospital, Waverly, Mass.
68. WALTER C. ALVAREZ, 700 N. Michigan Ave., Chicago
69. ELLSWORTH C. ALVORD, Jr., Walter Reed Army Medical Center
70. DEAN AMADON, American Museum of Natural History
71. WILLIAM R. AMBERSON, University of Maryland
72. CHARLES T. AMBROSE, Johns Hopkins University
73. CLARA M. AMBRUS, Roswell Park Memorial Institute, Buffalo
74. JULIAN L. AMBRUS, Roswell Park Memorial Institute, Buffalo
75. LOUISE BATES AMES, Yale University
76. AXEL L. ANDERSEN, U. S. Department of Agriculture, East Lansing
77. BERTIL G. ANDERSON, Pennsylvania State University
78. DONALD B. ANDERSON, North Carolina State College
79. EDGAR ANDERSON, Missouri Botanical Gardens, St. Louis
80. FREDERICK N. ANDERSON, Purdue University
81. HAMILTON H. ANDERSON, University of California, San Francisco
82. IRVING H. ANDERSON, University of Michigan
83. R. J. ANDERSON, Yale University
84. W. H. ANDERSON, Smithsonian Institution
85. WILLIAM W. ANDERSON, U.S. Fish and Wildlife Service, Brunswick, Ga.
86. A. ANDREJEW, Institute of Physical and Chemical Biology, Paris
87. REUBIN ANDRES, Johns Hopkins University
88. MARJORY I. ANDRESEN, 1604 Capitol Ave., Cheyenne, Wyo.
89. P. H. ANDRESEN, Bispebjerg Hospital, Copenhagen
90. WARREN ANDREW, Bowman Gray School of Medicine
91. H. G. ANDREWARTHA, University of Adelaide
92. F. N. ANDREWS, Purdue University
93. CHRISTIAN B. ANFINSEN, Jr., National Heart Institute
94. LUIS ANGELONE, Washington University
95. CLIFFORD A. ANGERER, Ohio State University
96. A. W. ANGULO, Hahnemann Medical College
97. BARRY J. ANSON, Northwestern University Medical School
98. J. W. APPLE, University of Wisconsin
99. MILO D. APPLEMAN, University of Southern California
100. R. M. ARCHIBALD, Rockefeller Institute for Medical Research
101. L. B. AREY, Northwestern University Medical School
102. KUNITARO ARIMOTO, National Institute of Nutrition, Tokyo
103. PETER A. ARK, University of California, Berkeley
104. JOSEPH M. ARMER, Incarnate Word College, San Antonio, Texas
105. ARTHUR R. ARMSTRONG, Hamilton, Ontario
106. S. HOWARD ARMSTRONG, Jr., Cook County Hospital, Chicago
107. WALLACE D. ARMSTRONG, University of Minnesota
108. CARLO ARNAUDI, University of Milan
109. JOHN H. ARNETT, 6200 Ardleigh St., Philadelphia
110. DANIEL I. ARNON, University of California, Berkeley
111. S. ARONOFF, Iowa State College
112. J. G. ARROWOOD, Massachusetts Memorial Hospital, Boston
113. JOHN M. ARTHUR, Boyce Thompson Institute for Plant Research
114. CAMILLO ARTOM, Bowman Gray School of Medicine
115. J. F. ARTUSIO, Cornell University Medical College
116. S. A. ASDELL, Cornell University
117. CONRADO F. ASENJO, University of Puerto Rico
118. FRANK G. ASHBROOK, U. S. Fish and Wildlife Service, Washington, D. C.
119. WINIFRED M. ASHBY, St. Elizabeth's Hospital, Washington, D. C.
120. R. ASHCROFT, University of Durham
121. RICHARD ASHMAN, 5902 Marshall Foch St., New Orleans
122. V. S. ASMUNDSON, University of California, Davis
123. ERLING ASMUSSEN, University of Copenhagen
124. PER-OLAF ÅSTRAND, Physiological Institute, Stockholm
125. LAWRENCE ATKIN, Fleischmann Laboratories, Stamford, Conn.
126. H. J. ATKINSON, Department of Agriculture, Ottawa
127. MEYER ATLAS, Yeshiva University
128. C. AUERBACH, University of Edinburgh
129. WALDO C. AULT, U. S. Department of Agriculture, Philadelphia
130. C. R. AUSTIN, National Institute for Medical Research, London
131. MARY L. AUSTIN, Wellesley College
132. OLIVER L. AUSTIN, Jr., North Eastham, Mass.
133. JAMES K. AVERY, University of Michigan
134. DOMINGO M. AVIADO, Jr., University of Pennsylvania
135. JORGE AWAPARA, University of Texas
136. ALVIN D. AYERS, U. S. Salinity Laboratory, Riverside, Cal.
137. FRANK H. BABERS, U. S. Department of Agriculture, Beltsville
138. H. BACCHUS, George Washington University
139. JAMES E. BACHER, University of California, San Francisco
140. C. S. BACHOFER, University of Notre Dame
141. HOWARD L. BACHRACH, U.S. Department of Agriculture, Greenport, N. Y.
142. MYRON P. BACKUS, University of Wisconsin
143. OSCAR G. BACON, University of California, Davis
144. VINTON W. BACON, State Water Pollution Control Board, Sacramento
145. HENRY BADEER, American University of Beirut
146. ERIC BAER, University of Toronto
147. ANNA M. BAETJER, Johns Hopkins University
148. B. K. BAGCHI, University of Michigan
149. R. E. BAGDON, American Cyanamid Co., N. Y. C.
150. WILLARD E. BAIER, Sunkist Growers, Inc., Ontario, Cal.

151. B. L. BAILEY, Oklahoma Medical Research Foundation, Oklahoma City
152. IRVING W. BAILEY, Harvard University
153. LOWELL F. BAILEY, University of Arkansas
154. PERCIVAL BAILEY, University of Illinois College of Medicine
155. REEVE M. BAILEY, University of Michigan
156. JOSHUA L. BAILEY, Jr., 4435 Ampudia St., San Diego
157. C. H. BAKER, Medical Research Council, Cambridge, England
158. CARL BAKER, University of California, Berkeley
159. F. S. BAKER, University of California, Berkeley
160. GLADYS LUCILLE BAKER
161. KENNETH F. BAKER, University of California, Berkeley
162. W. BAKER, University of Bristol
163. W. A. BAKER, U. S. Department of Agriculture, Beltsville
164. A. L. BAKKE, Iowa State College
165. WILLIAM BALAMUTH, University of California, Berkeley
166. R. T. BALCH, U. S. Department of Agriculture, Houma, La.
167. HENRY I. BALDWIN, New Hampshire Forestry and Recreation Commission, Concord
168. PAUL H. BALDWIN, Colorado Agricultural and Mechanical College
169. ERIC G. BALL, Harvard Medical School
170. ERNEST BALL, University of North Carolina
171. GORDON H. BALL, University of California, Los Angeles
172. MIKE BALL, Field & Stream Magazine, N. Y. C.
173. ELMER J. BALLINTINE, 10515 Carnegie Ave., Cleveland
174. ARNOLD KENT BALLS, Purdue University
175. ROBERT S. BANDURSKI, Michigan State University
176. I. BANGA, University of Budapest
177. HARLAN P. BANKS, Cornell University
178. ALVAN L. BARACH, Columbia University
179. KILE BARBEHENN, Army Chemical Center, Md.
180. S. A. BARBER, Purdue University
181. JOHN KIRBY BARE, College of William and Mary
182. ROBERT R. BARER, Oxford University
183. A. CLIFFORD BARGER, Harvard Medical School
184. H. A. BARKER, University of California, Berkeley
185. HENRY D. BARKER, U. S. Department of Agriculture, Beltsville
186. S. B. BARKER, University of Alabama Medical Center
187. ALMA W. BARKSDALE, New York Botanical Garden
188. H. L. BARNETT, West Virginia University
189. HENRY L. BARNETT, New York Hospital
190. MARION I. BARNHART, Wayne State University
191. D. A. BARNUM, Ontario Veterinary College

192. HAROLD W. BARRETT, University of Kansas
193. WILLIAM C. BARRETT, Boston University
194. DONALD H. BARRON, Yale University
195. S. BARSKY, University of Illinois College of Medicine
196. FLOYD E. BARTELL, University of Michigan
197. GEORGE W. BARTELMEZ, Carnegie Institution of Washington, Baltimore
198. H. BARTELS, University of Tübingen
199. LAWRENCE M. BARTLETT, University of Massachusetts
200. S. HOWARD BARTLEY, Michigan State University
201. LELA V. BARTON, Boyce Thompson Institute for Plant Research
202. A. F. BARTSCH, U.S. Public Health Service, Cincinnati
203. R. K. BARUA, Assam Medical College, Dibrugarh, India
204. J. T. BASHOUR, Stauffer Chemical Company, N.Y.C.
205. DAVID E. BASS, U.S. Quartermaster Research and Development Center, Natick, Mass.
206. LOUIS N. BASS, Iowa State College
207. DAVID L. BASSETT, Stanford University School of Medicine
208. T. H. BAST, University of Wisconsin
209. K. P. BASU, Indian Dairy Research Institute, Bangalore
210. A. J. BATEMAN, Christie Hospital, Manchester, England
211. ROGER G. BATES, National Bureau of Standards
212. L. P. BATJER, U.S. Department of Agriculture, Wenatchee, Wash.
213. WALTER BAUER, Massachusetts General Hospital, Boston
214. C. A. BAUMANN, University of Wisconsin
215. F. C. BAWDEN, Rothamsted Experiment Station, Harpenden, England
216. DOW V. BAXTER, University of Michigan
217. FREDERICK M. BAYER, Smithsonian Institution
218. NANCY BAYLEY, National Institute of Mental Health
219. H. C. BAZETT (Deceased)
220. ELIOT F. BEACH, Metropolitan Life Insurance Co., N.Y.C.
221. DESMOND BEALL, Ayerst Laboratories, Inc., Rouses Point, N.Y.
222. HAROLD W. BEAMS, State University of Iowa
223. WILLIAM B. BEAN, State University of Iowa
224. FIRMAN E. BEAR, Rutgers University
225. JOSEPH W. BEARD, Duke University
226. RAIMON L. BEARD, Connecticut Agricultural Experiment Station, New Haven
227. CLARISSA H. BEATTY, University of Oregon Medical School
228. R. A. BEATTY, Institute of Animal Genetics, Edinburgh
229. CHARLES O. BECHTOL, Yale University
230. STANLEY D. BECK, University of Wisconsin
231. B. A. BECKER, Armour Laboratories, Chicago

232. BERNARD BECKER, Washington University
233. ELERY R. BECKER, Iowa State College
234. R. FREDERICK BECKER, Duke University
235. EDWARD L. BECKMAN, U.S. Naval Air Development Center, Johnsville, Pa.
236. HARRY BECKMAN, Marquette University
237. SAMUEL P. BEDSON, London Hospital, England
238. HENRY K. BEECHER, Harvard Medical School
239. C. H. BEEK, Hospital St. Loannes de Deo, The Hague
240. A. B. R. BEEMSTER, Institute for Research in Plant Pathology, Wageningen, The Netherlands
241. JAMES R. BEER, University of Minnesota
242. ROLAND F. BEERS, Jr., Massachusetts Institute of Technology
243. ERNEST BEERSTECHER, Jr., University of Texas Dental Branch
244. HERBERT C. BEESKOW, Michigan State University
245. KENNETH C. BEESON, U.S. Department of Agriculture, Ithaca, N.Y.
246. W. M. BEESON, Purdue University
247. CHARLES F. BEGG, Columbia University
248. ALBERT R. BEHNKE, U.S. Naval Radiological Defense Laboratory, San Francisco
249. CHARLES F. BEHRENS, U.S. Naval Base, Charleston, S. C.
250. HOWARD T. BEHRMAN, 2 East 69th St., N. Y. C.
251. LLOYD M. BEIDLER, Florida State University
252. WALTER M. BEJUKI, Prev. of Det. Ctr., N.A.S.-N.R.C.
253. HARWOOD S. BELDING, University of Pittsburgh
254. MORRIS BELKIN, National Cancer Institute
255. EMILY J. BELL, Vanderbilt University
256. G. H. BELL, University of St. Andrews
257. J. FREDERICK BELL, National Microbiological Institute, Hamilton, Mont.
258. J. MILTON BELL, University of Saskatchewan
259. W. DEXTER BALLAMY, General Electric Co., Schenectady, N. Y.
260. FRANK C. BELLROSE, Illinois Natural History Society, Urbana
261. F. L. BEMAN, Ohio State University
262. BELLE J. BENCHLEY, Zoological Society of San Diego
263. MAURICE BENDER, Rutgers University
264. HARRIS M. BENEDICT, Stanford Research Institute
265. E. S. BENEKE, Michigan State University
266. F. B. BENJAMIN, University of Illinois College of Medicine
267. LEONARD BENNETCH
268. C. W. BENNETT, U.S. Department of Agriculture, Salinas, Cal.
269. GEORGE W. BENNETT, Illinois Natural History Survey Division, Urbana
270. LESLIE R. BENNETT, University of California, Los Angeles

271. JOSEPH BENOTTI, Pratt Diagnostic Hospital, Boston
272. EDWARD H. BENSLEY, Montreal General Hospital
273. ANDREW A. BENSON, Pennsylvania State University
274. LYMAN BENSON, Pomona College
275. SETH B. BENSON, University of California, Berkeley
276. EUGENE S. BERESTON, 2406 Eutaw Place, Baltimore
277. CLARENCE P. BERG, State University of Iowa
278. OLAF BERGEIM, University of Illinois College of Medicine
279. ANDREW J. BERGER, University of Michigan
280. A. D. BERGNER, Army Chemical Center, Md.
281. E. ALEXANDER BERGSTROM 37 Old Brook Rd., W. Hartford, Conn.
282. JOSEPH BERKSON, Mayo Clinic
283. ROBERT W. BERLINER, National Heart Institute
284. H. J. BERMAN, Boston University
285. LAWRENCE BERMAN, Wayne State University
286. ROBERT M. BERNE, Western Reserve University
287. PETER BERNFELD, Tufts College Medical School
288. FREDERICK BERNHEIM, Duke University
289. LEON BERNSTEIN, U. S. Salinity Laboratory, Riverside, Cal.
290. L. JOE BERRY, Bryn Mawr College
291. W. T. C. BERRY, Ministry of Health, London
292. J. BERTHET, University of Louvain
293. OTTO A. BESSEY, University of Texas Medical Branch
294. SAMUEL P. BESSMAN
295. CHARLES H. BEST, University of Toronto
296. MAURICE M. BEST, Louisville General Hospital
297. FRANK H. BETHELL, University of Michigan
298. E. J. BETT
299. K. H. BEYER, Sharp and Dohme, Inc., West Point, Pa.
300. F. R. BHARUCHA, Institute of Science, Bombay
301. JACOB B. BIALE, University of California, Los Angeles
302. T. GEORGE BIDDER, Western Reserve University
303. ORLIN BIDDULPH, State College of Washington
304. RICHARD BIEBL, University of Vienna
305. JACOB BIELY, University of British Columbia
306. JOHN J. BIESELE, Sloan-Kettering Institute for Cancer Research
307. ARTHUR BING, Cornell University, Farmingdale, N.Y.
308. FRANKLIN C. BING, 30 W. Washington St., Chicago
309. RICHARD J. BING, Medical College of Alabama
310. E. F. BINKERD, Armour and Co., Chicago
311. L. C. BIRCH, University of Sydney
312. H. R. BIRD, University of Wisconsin
313. ORSON D. BIRD, Parke, Davis and Co., Detroit
314. ROBERT M. BIRD, University of Oklahoma Medical School

315. CHARLES J. BIRKELAND, University of Illinois
316. JORGEN M. BIRKELAND, Ohio State University
317. G. R. BISBY, Commonwealth Mycological Institute, Kew, England
318. FRITZ E. BISCHOFF, Cottage Hospital, Santa Barbara, Cal.
319. DAVID W. BISHOP, Carnegie Institution of Washington, Baltimore
320. HARLOW BISHOP, Lederle Laboratories, Pearl River, N.Y.
321. JACK G. BISHOP, Baylor University Dental School
322. F. C. BISHOPP, U. S. Department of Agriculture, Brownsville, Texas
323. GEORGE H. BISHOPS, Washington University
324. JOEL BITMAN, U. S. Department of Agriculture, Beltsville
325. J. OWEN BLACHE, Homer G. Phillips Hospital, St. Louis
326. EDGAR C. BLACK, University of British Columbia
327. JOHN W. BLACK, Ohio State University
328. LINDSAY M. BLACK, University of Illinois
329. R. M. BLACK
330. VIRGINIA S. BLACK, 1726 Western Parkway, Vancouver
331. G. E. BLACKMAN, Oxford University
332. A. C. BLACKWOOD, Prairie Regional Laboratory, Saskatoon
333. ALBERT P. BLAIR, University of Tulsa
334. J. R. BLAIR, Army Medical Research Laboratory, Fort Knox, Ky.
335. MARY G. BLAIR, 102 N. School St., Fayetteville, Ark.
336. S. F. BLAKE, U. S. Department of Agriculture, Beltsville
337. WILLIAM D. BLAKE, University of Oregon Medical School
338. J. L. BLAKELY, Jamell Chinchilla Ranch
339. WILLIAM S. BLAKEMORE, University of Pennsylvania
340. E. W. BLANCHARD, Schieffelin and Co., N. Y. C.
341. FRED C. BLANCK, U. S. Department of Agriculture, Pittsburgh
342. RICHARD J. BLANDAU, University of Washington
343. HARRY F. BLANEY, 6407 Maryland Dr., Los Angeles
344. IRVINE H. BLANK, Harvard Medical School
345. W. BLASIUS, Physiological Institute, Giessen, Germany
346. GLENN W. BLAYDES, Ohio State University
347. CLIFTON R. BLINCOE, University of Missouri
348. LAWRENCE R. BLINKS, National Science Foundation
349. CHESTER I. BLISS, Connecticut Agricultural Experiment Station, New Haven
350. KONRAD E. BLOCH, Harvard University
351. ROBERT BLOCH, University of Pennsylvania
352. MATTHEW H. BLOCK, University of Colorado School of Medicine
353. RICHARD J. BLOCK, New York Medical College
354. W. D. BLOCK, University of Michigan
355. TRUMAN G. BLOCKER, University of Texas Medical Branch

356. MARVIN L. BLOOM, Pratt Diagnostic Hospital, Boston
357. WILLIAM BLOOM, University of Chicago
358. WALTER R. BLOOR, University of Rochester
359. HERMAN T. BLUMENTHAL, Jewish Hospital of St. Louis
360. HERMAN L. BLUMGART, Harvard Medical School
361. VIVIAN R. BOARDMAN, U. S. Food and Drug Administration, Washington, D. C.
362. ROBERT D. BOCHE, 503-5th St., Davis, Cal.
363. FLORANTE C. BOCOBO, University of Michigan
364. DAVID BODIAN, Johns Hopkins University
365. PAUL BOEDER, Harvard Medical School
366. ENZO BOERI, Zoological Station, Naples
367. BENT G. BÖVING, Carnegie Institution of Washington, Baltimore
368. CHARLES M. BOGERT, American Museum of Natural History
369. RICHARD H. BOHNING, Ohio State University
370. NESTOR BOHONAS, Lederle Laboratories, Pearl River, N. Y.
371. GUSTAV BOHSTEDT, University of Wisconsin
372. JESSE L. BOLLMAN, Mayo Clinic
373. LEE BONAR, University of California, Berkeley
374. KELSHAW BONHAM, 5240 18th Ave., NE, Seattle
375. EDWARD W. BONN, Texas Game and Fish Commission, Denison
376. JAMES F. BONNER, California Institute of Technology
377. WALTER D. BONNER, Jr., Cornell University
378. J. BONNE-WEPSTER, Institute of Tropical Hygiene, Amsterdam
379. DESMOND D. BONNYCASTLE, Yale University
380. WALTER M. BOOKER, Howard University
381. C. H. BOOKHOUT, Duke University
382. D. M. BOONE
383. WALTER M. BOOTHBY (Deceased)
384. L. E. BOPST, University of Maryland
385. PAUL BOQUET, Pasteur Institute, Garches, France
386. F. H. BORMANN, Duke University
387. HANS BORNSCHEIN, University of Vienna
388. H. A. BORTHWICK, U. S. Department of Agriculture, Beltsville
389. DAVID K. BOSSHARDT, Sharp and Dohme, Inc., West Point, Pa.
390. ROBERT V. BOUCHER, Pennsylvania State University
391. M. BOUILLENNE, University of Liege
392. RAYMOND LÉON EUGENE BOUILLENNE, University of Liege
393. F. BOURLIÈRE, 8, rue Huysmans, Paris
394. A. A. BOURNE, London Hospital Medical College, England
395. H. H. M. BOWMAN, University of Toledo

396. RUSSEL O. BOWMAN, Baylor University
397. J. M. BOWNESS, University of Malaya
398. L. L. BOYARSKY, University of Kentucky
399. EDITH BOYD, University of Colorado School of Medicine
400. ELIZABETH M. BOYD, Mount Holyoke College
401. JAMES D. BOYD, Cambridge University
402. WILLIAM C. BOYD, Boston University
403. EDWARD A. BOYDEN, University of Washington
404. FRANK P. BOYLE, Cornell University
405. WILLIAM S. BOYLE, Utah State Agricultural College
406. DAMON BOYNTON, Cornell University
407. EMIL BOZLER, Ohio State University
408. J. W. BRADBEER, University of Durham
409. DOROTHY BRADBURY, U.S. Department of Agriculture, Peoria, Ill.
410. JAMES T. BRADBURY, State University of Iowa
411. WILLIAM B. BRADLEY, American Institute of Baking, Chicago
412. CARL B. BRAESTRUP, City Department of Hospitals, N.Y.C.
413. D. E. BRAGDON, University of Virginia
414. B. L. BRAGE, South Dakota State College
415. ARTHUR N. BRAGG, University of Oklahoma
416. REGINALD T. BRAIN, 132 Harley St., London
417. W. J. BRAKEL, Ohio State University
418. CHARLES E. BRAMBEL, 1504 Park Ave., Baltimore
419. ERWIN BRAND, Columbia University
420. ALLEN D. BRANDT, Bethlehem Steel Co., Inc., Bethlehem, Pa.
421. K. D. BRASE, New York Agricultural Experiment Station, Geneva
422. BAYARD H. BRATTSTROM, University of California, Los Angeles
423. ALFRED BRAUER, University of Kentucky
424. J. WERNER BRAUN, Rutgers University
425. R. I. BRAWN, McGill University
426. R. W. BRAY, University of Wisconsin
427. GEORGE BRECHER, National Institutes of Health
428. GERHARD A. BRECHER, Western Reserve University
429. GOODWIN M. BREININ, New York University
430. J. R. BRETT, Pacific Biological Station, Nanaimo, B. C.
431. WILLIS R. BREWER, University of Arizona
432. C. S. BRIDGMAN, University of Wisconsin
433. CHARLES F. BRIDGMAN, University of California, Los Angeles
434. HEINRICH BRIEGER, Jefferson Medical College
435. PHILIP A. BRIEGLEB, U.S. Forest Service, New Orleans
436. W. G. BRIERLEY, University of Minnesota
437. DAVID R. BRIGGS, University of Minnesota

438. GEORGE M. BRIGGS, National Institute of Arthritis and Metabolic Diseases
439. W. M. BRIGHT, Lever Bros., Edgewater, N. J.
440. WORTHIE E. BRILES, Texas Agricultural and Mechanical College
441. FRANK BRINK, Jr., Rockefeller Institute for Medical Research
442. R. ALEXANDER BRINK, University of Wisconsin
443. KENNETH M. BRINKHOUS, University of North Carolina
444. C. J. C. BRITTON, 35 Harley St., London
445. MAX E. BRITTON, Northwestern University
446. JOHN R. BROBECK, University of Pennsylvania
447. MICHEL BROCHART, National Veterinary School, Alfort, France
448. VERNON E. BROCK, Territorial Division of Fish and Game, Honolulu
449. BERNARD B. BRODIE, National Heart Institute
450. WILLIAM A. BRODSKY, University of Louisville
451. SAMUEL BRODY, University of Missouri
452. F. W. BRONISCH, University of Heidelberg
453. M. M. BROOKE, U. S. Public Health Service, Chamblee, Ga.
454. JOHN R. BROOKS, Harvard Medical School
455. M. M. BROOKS, University of California, Berkeley
456. S. C. BROOKS (Deceased)
457. LUCIEN BROUHA, E. I. du Pont de Nemours and Co., Wilmington, Del.
458. GORONWY O. BROUN, St. Louis University
459. JEROME BROWER, State Department of Health, St. Paul
460. A. W. A. BROWN, University of Western Ontario
461. ARNOLD L. BROWN, Jr., Presbyterian Hospital, Chicago
462. C. J. D. BROWN, Montana State College
463. DUGALD E. S. BROWN, University of Michigan
464. FRANK A. BROWN, Jr., Northwestern University
465. GEORGE B. BROWN, Sloan-Kettering Institute for Cancer Research
466. HARLEY P. BROWN, University of Oklahoma
467. J. M. A. BROWN, University of Durham
468. JAMES W. BROWN, Camp Detrick, Md.
469. M. VERTNER BROWN, City College of New York
470. R. A. BROWN, Parke, Davis and Co., Detroit
471. R. W. BROWN, Smithsonian Institution
472. RELIS B. BROWN, Lawrence College
473. ROBERT K. BROWN, Harvard Medical School
474. ROYAL L. BROWN, 3956 Oakwood Place, Riverside, Cal.
475. RUSSELL G. BROWN, University of Maryland
476. WILLIAM E. BROWN
477. WILLIAM L. BROWN, Pioneer Hi-Bred Corn Co., Johnston, Iowa
478. KATHARINE A. BROWNELL, Ohio State University

479. I. BROWNING, American Optical Co., Buffalo
480. T. C. BROYER, University of California, Berkeley
481. JOSEF BROZEK, University of Minnesota
482. AUSTIN M. BRUES, Argonne National Laboratory
483. CHARLES T. BRUES, Harvard University
484. JOHN M. BRUHN, Medical College of Alabama
485. ROBERT BRUN, University of Geneva
486. D. W. BRUNER, Cornell University
487. H. D. BRUNER, Emory University
488. ROSEMARY BRUNETTI, California Department of Public Health, Berkeley
489. HOWARD G. BRUNSMAN, U.S. Bureau of the Census
490. ROYAL B. BRUNSON, Montana State University
491. WILLIAM R. BRYAN, National Cancer Institute
492. MARVIN P. BRYANT, U. S. Department of Agriculture, Beltsville
493. VERNON BRYSON, National Science Foundation
494. DOROTHY JEAN BUCHANAN, Vanderbilt University
495. FRITZ BUCHTHAL, University of Copenhagen
496. J. B. BUCK, National Institutes of Health
497. ELEANOR E. BUCKLEY, Wyeth Laboratories, Philadelphia
498. WOLFGANG BÜCHERL, Butantan Institute, São Paulo
499. KONRAD J. J. BUETTNER, University of Washington
500. EDNA M. BUHRER, U. S. Department of Agriculture, Beltsville
501. KENNETH BULLOCK, University of Manchester
502. THEODORE H. BULLOCK, University of California, Los Angeles
503. HARVEY L. BUMGARDNER, North Carolina State College
504. G. E. BURCH, Tulane University
505. HELEN B. BURCH, Washington University
506. JOHN C. BURCH, Vanderbilt University
507. Walter J. Burdette, University of Missouri
508. H. O. BURDICK, Alfred University
509. ALFRED BURGER, University of Virginia
510. HOVEY M. BURGESS, General Foods Corp., Kankakee, Ill.
511. DEAN BURK, National Institutes of Health
512. BERTHA S. BURKE, Harvard School of Public Health
513. W. H. BURKHOLDER, Cornell University
514. B. D. BURKS, Smithsonian Institution
515. GEORGE W. BURNETT, Walter Reed Army Medical Center
516. LEE BURNETT, Lenox Hill Hospital, N. Y. C.
517. GEORGE W. BURNS, Ohio Wesleyan University
518. PATTON WRIGHT BURNS, Texas Agricultural and Mechanical College
519. M. BURSTEIN, Faculty of Medicine, Paris
520. ROBERT H. BURRIS, University of Wisconsin

521. WISE BURROUGHS, Iowa State College
522. ROGER E. BURROWS, U. S. Fish and Wildlife Service, Entiaf, Wash.
523. HANS BURSTRÖM, University of Lund
524. WILLIAM H. BURT, University of Michigan
525. ALAN C. BURTON, University of Western Ontario
526. D. BURTON, University of Leeds
527. MILTON BURTON, University of Notre Dame
528. R. L. BUSBEY, U. S. Department of Agriculture, Beltsville
529. P. BUSER, Collège de France
530. R. C. BUSHLAND, U. S. Department of Agriculture, Kerrville, Texas
531. JOHN BUSHNELL, Ohio Agricultural Experimental Station, Wooster
532. E. R. BUSKIRK, Quartermaster Research and Development Center, Natick, Mass.
533. ROBERT A. BUSSABARGER
534. ALLAN M. BUTLER, Massachusetts General Hospital, Boston
535. LEONARD BUTLER, University of Toronto
536. PHILIP A. BUTLER, U. S. Fish and Wildlife Service, Pensacola, Fla.
537. EDWARD M. BUTT, University of Southern California
538. F. H. BUTT, Cornell University
539. HUGH R. BUTT, Mayo Foundation
540. HENRY M. BUTZEL, Jr., Union College
541. SANFORD O. BYERS, Mount Zion Hospital, San Francisco
542. CHESTER L. BYRD, Jr., Cook County Hospital, Chicago

543. C. A. CABELL, U. S. Department of Agriculture, Beltsville
544. ANTHONY CACCESE, State University of New York, Brooklyn
545. FRED R. CAGLE, Tulane University
546. PAUL CALABRISI, George Washington University
547. PHILIP CALCAGNO, University of Buffalo
548. BENJAMIN CALESNICK, Hahnemann Medical College
549. JOHN B. CALHOUN, National Institute of Mental Health
550. ENOCH CALLAWAY, University of Maryland School of Medicine
551. ROBERT L. CALLISON, Department of the Army, Washington, D. C.
552. MELVIN CALVIN, University of California, Berkeley
553. G. R. CAMERON, University College Hospital Medical School, London
554. HUGH S. CAMERON, University of California, Davis
555. JAMES W. CAMERON, University of California, Riverside
556. A. F. CAMP, University of Florida, Lake Alfred
557. BERRY CAMPBELL, University of Minnesota
558. C. J. CAMPBELL, Hercules Powder Co., Wilmington, Del.
559. JACK J. R. CAMPBELL, University of British Columbia
560. J. D. CAMPOS, Aglipay Colleges, Inc., Philippine Islands

561. E. S. CANELLAKIS, University of Wisconsin
562. C. Y. CANNON, Iowa State College
563. ORSON S. CANNON, Utah State Agricultural College
564. ABRAHAM CANTAROW, Jefferson Medical College
565. EDWARD C. CANTINO, University of Pennsylvania
566. SIMEON T. CANTRIL, Swedish Hospital, Seattle
567. ATTILIO CANZANELLI, Tufts College Medical School
568. SAMUEL M. CAPLIN, University of Rochester
569. RAYMOND CARHART, Northwestern University
570. G. CLIFFORD CARL, Office of Provincial Museum, Victoria, B.C.
571. KENNETH D. CARLANDER, Iowa State College
572. J. GORDON CARLSON, University of Tennessee
573. A. J. CARMICHAEL, Ontario Tree Seed Plant, Angus
574. ROBERT L. CAROLUS, Michigan State University
575. FRANK G. CARPENTER, Cornell University Medical College
576. JOHN B. CARPENTER, U. S. Department of Agriculture, Indio, Cal.
577. M. B. CARPENTER, New York University
578. THORNE M. CARPENTER, 142 Birch Tree Dr., Westwood, Mass.
579. A. F. CARR, Jr., University of Florida
580. C. JELLEFF CARR, Purdue University
581. MELBOURNE R. CARRIKER, University of North Carolina
582. W. E. CARROLL, University of Illinois
583. CHRISTOPHER CARRUTHERS, Roswell Park Memorial Institute, Buffalo
584. L. J. CARSCALLEN, College of Medical Evangelists
585. S. CARSWELL, National Institute for Medical Research, London
586. NEAL M. CARTER, Pacific Fisheries Experimental Station, Vancouver
587. F. A. CARTIER, Air Force ROTC, Maxwell AFB, Alabama
588. GEORGE E. CARTWRIGHT, University of Utah
589. O. L. CARTWRIGHT, Smithsonian Institution
590. ALBERT E. CASEY, Baptist Hospital, Birmingham
591. C. D. CASKEY, CO-OP Mills, Inc., Baltimore
592. ERNEST W. CASPARI, Wesleyan University
593. WILLIAM A. CASSEL, Hahnemann Medical College
594. W. G. B. CASSELMAN, University of Toronto
595. W. O. CASTER, University of Minnesota
596. EDWARD S. CASTLE, Harvard University
597. W. E. CASTLE, University of California, Berkeley
598. H. R. CATCHPOLE, University of Illinois College of Medicine
599. WILLIAM F. CATON, Harvard Medical School
600. BORIS CATZ, 6423 Wilshire Blvd., Los Angeles
601. NELLE B. CAUSEY, University of Arkansas

602. A. J. E. CAVE, Medical College of St. Bartholomew's Hospital, London
603. DAVID CAYER, Bowman Gray School of Medicine
604. LEOPOLD R. CERECEDO, Fordham University
605. FENNER A. CHACE, Jr., Smithsonian Institution
606. L. C. CHADWICK, Ohio State University
607. LEIGH S. CHADWICK, Army Chemical Center, Md.
608. CARLOS CHAGAS, University of Brazil
609. I. L. CHAIKOFF, University of California, Berkeley
610. ALEJANDRO CHAIT, Institute of Medicine, Cordoba, Argentina
611. LESLIE A. CHAMBERS, U.S. Public Health Service, Cincinnati
612. ROBERT CHAMBERS, 425 Riverside Dr., N. Y. C.
613. WILLIAM H. CHAMBERS, Army Chemical Center, Md.
614. BRITTON CHANCE, University of Pennsylvania
615. C. W. CHANG, New Mexico Agricultural and Mechanical College
616. FREDERIC C. CHANG, University of Tennessee
617. J. P. CHANG, University of Kansas Medical School
618. JANIE CHANG, Cleveland Clinic
619. M. C. CHANG, Worcester Foundation for Experimental Biology
620. SHIH L. CHANG, U. S. Public Health Service, Cincinnati
621. ALFRED CHANUTIN, University of Virginia
622. ALPHONSE CHAPANIS, Bell Telephone Laboratories, Murray Hill, N. J.
623. EDWARD A. CHAPIN, Harvard University
624. JOHN L. CHAPIN, University of Colorado Medical Center
625. HUGH CHAPLIN, Jr., National Microbiological Institute
626. ARTHUR B. CHAPMAN, University of Wisconsin
627. ARTHUR G. CHAPMAN, U.S. Forest Service, Columbus, Ohio
628. DON W. CHAPMAN, U. S. Army Hospital, Neubrücke, Germany
629. EUGENE R. CHAPMAN, 304 Primero Dr., San Antonio, Texas
630. H. D. CHAPMAN, University of California, Riverside
631. HAROLD W. CHAPMAN, University of Nebraska
632. LAWRENCE B. CHAPMAN, Princeton, Mass.
633. W. P. CHAPMAN, Massachusetts General Hospital, Boston
634. HARRY A. CHARIPPER, New York University
635. R. CHARR (Deceased)
636. SAMUEL W. CHASE, Western Reserve University
637. SARAH CHASTAIN, University of California, Los Angeles
638. CHARLOTTE CHATFIELD, U. N. Food and Agricultural Organization, Rome
639. R. CHATTERJEE, Medical College, Calcutta
640. P. CHAUCHARD, University of Paris

641. VERNON H. CHELDELIN, Oregon State College
642. JAMES YU-PING CHEN, Marquette University
643. K. K. CHEN, Eli Lilly and Co., Indianapolis
644. TZE TUAN CHEN, University of Southern California
645. RALPH H. CHENEY, Brooklyn College
646. SIDNEY S. CHERNICK, National Institute of Arthritis and Metabolic Diseases
647. AMOZ I. CHERNOFF, Washington University
648. R. B. CHERRY, Harvard University
649. LEON C. CHESLEY, State University of New York College of Medicine, Brooklyn
650. K. STARR CHESTER, Alton Box Board Co., Alton, Ill.
651. ANDRÉ CHEVALLIER, University of Strasbourg
652. L. CHEVILLARD, Collège de France
653. HARRIETTE CHICK, Lister Institute of Preventive Medicine, Cambridge, England
654. NORMAN F. CHILDERS, Rutgers University
655. E. C. CHILDS, Cambridge University
656. J. S. CHOWHAN, Central Drugs Laboratory, Calcutta
657. CLYDE M. CHRISTENSEN, University of Minnesota
658. E. HOHWÜ CHRISTENSEN, Physiological Institute, Stockholm
659. HALVOR N. CHRISTENSEN, Tufts College Medical College
660. J. J. CHRISTENSEN, University of Minnesota
661. P. AGERHOLM CHRISTENSEN, South African Institute for Medical Research, Johannesburg
662. R. P. CHRISTENSEN, U. S. Department of Agriculture, Washington, D. C.
663. J. R. CHRISTIE, University of Florida
664. LEON CHURNEY, Louisiana State University School of Medicine
665. JOSEPH CHUSID, St. Vincent's Hospital, N. Y. C.
666. EDWIN A. CIESLAK, University of Minnesota
667. GRACE L. CLAPP, Windsor Locks, Conn.
668. AUSTIN H. CLARK, Smithsonian Institution
669. DANIEL G. CLARK, Cornell University
670. EDGAR W. CLARK, U. S. Department of Agriculture, Brownsville, Texas
671. ELIOT R. CLARK, University of Pennsylvania
672. ERNEST D. CLARK, National Canners Assoc., Seattle
673. F. M. CLARK, University of Illinois
674. HERBERT C. CLARK, Gorgas Memorial Laboratory, Panama
675. J. BENNETT CLARK, University of Oklahoma
676. L. J. CLARK, U. S. Department of Agriculture, Beltsville
677. PAUL F. CLARK, University of Wisconsin
678. J. F. GATES CLARKE, Smithsonian Institution
679. N. A. CLARKE, U. S. Public Health Service, Cincinnati
680. NORMAN E. CLARKE, Providence Hospital, Detroit

681. H. J. CLAUSEN, University of South Dakota
682. LeROY W. CLEMENCE, Abbott Laboratories, North Chicago
683. K. A. CLENDENNING, Charles F. Kettering Foundation
684. ROBERT C. CLEVERDON, University of Connecticut
685. DORIS H. CLOUET, Thayer Veterans Administration Hospital, Nashville
686. CHARLES S. COAKLEY, George Washington University
687. G. ROBERT COATNEY, National Institutes of Health
688. STANLEY COBB, Harvard University
689. DORIS M. COCHRAN, Smithsonian Institution
690. KENNETH COCHRAN, University of Chicago
691. CHARLES F. CODE, Mayo Clinic
692. WESLEY R. COE, Scripps Institution of Oceanograph
693. GEORGE W. COFFEY, Petinsure of Virginia, Alexandria
694. DAVID L. COFFIN, Angell Memorial Animal Hospital, Boston
695. ROBERT D. COGHILL, Abbott Laboratories, North Chicago
696. PHILIP P. COHEN, University of Wisconsin
697. SEYMOUR S. COHEN, University of Pennsylvania
698. SYLVAN I. COHEN, Gallowhur Chemical Co., Ossining, N. Y.
699. EDWIN J. COHN (Deceased)
700. JEROME E. COHN, Bellevue Hospital, N. Y. C.
701. ROBERT COHN, U. S. Naval Hospital, Bethesda, Md.
702. T. S. COILE, Duke University
703. HAROLD H. COLE, University of California, Davis
704. J. WAYNE COLE, Glidden Co., Chicago
705. JONATHAN O. COLE, National Research Council
706. KENNETH S. COLE, National Institute of Neurological Diseases and Blindness
707. LaMONT C. COLE, Cornell University
708. LEONARD J. COLE, U. S. Naval Radiological Defense Laboratory, San Francisco
709. WARREN H. COLE, University of Illinois College of Medicine
710. WILLIAM H. COLE, Rutgers University
711. ALLAN L. COLEMAN, Bureau of Industrial Hygiene, Hartford, Conn.
712. H. BRUCE COLLIER, University of Alberta
713. H. O. J. COLLIER, Allen and Hanburys Ltd., Ware, England
714. F. D. COLLINS, Australian National University
715. G. H. COLLINS, Clemson College
716. SELWYN D. COLLINS, U. S. Public Health Service, Washington, D. C.
717. NICHOLAS F. COLOVOS, University of New Hampshire
718. SIDNEY P. COLOWICK, Johns Hopkins University
719. ARTHUR L. COLWIN, Queens College, Flushing, N. Y.
720. GERALD F. COMBS, University of Maryland
721. MANDRED W. COMFORT, Mayo Clinic
722. BARRY COMMONER, Washington University

723. JULIUS H. COMROE, Jr., University of Pennsylvania
724. NORMAN F. CONANT, Duke University
725. ROGER CONANT, Philadelphia Zoological Garden
726. RUTH E. CONKLIN, Vassar College
727. BERNARD E. CONLEY, American Medical Assoc., Chicago
728. C. LOCKARD CONLEY, Johns Hopkins University
729. ERIC E. CONN, University of California, Berkeley
730. HAROLD J. CONN, Cornell University
731. ARTHUR CONNOR
732. CARL M. CONRAD, U. S. Department of Agriculture, New Orleans
733. H. R. CONRAD, Ohio Agricultural Experiment Station, Wooster
734. WILLIAM V. CONSOLAZIO, National Science Foundation
735. W. G. CONWAY, St. Louis Zoological Park
736. BRUCE J. COOIL, University of Hawaii
737. A. STANLEY COOK, Ayerst, McKenna and Harrison Ltd., N. Y. C.
738. ROBERT P. COOK, University of St. Andrews
739. W. C. COOK, U. S. Department of Agriculture, Walla Walla, Wash.
740. W. H. COOK, National Research Council, Ottawa
741. WILLIAM COOKE, U. S. Public Health Service, Cincinnati
742. THOMAS B. COOLIDGE, University of Chicago
743. JULIUS M. COON, University of Chicago
744. CALLIE MAE COONS, U. S. Department of Agriculture, Washington, D. C.
745. G. H. COONS, U. S. Department of Agriculture, Beltsville
746. G. A. COOPER, Smithsonian Institution
747. H. R. COOPER, National Naval Medical Center
748. HERBERT P. COOPER, Clemson Agricultural College
749. J. P. COOPER, University College of Wales
750. WILLIAM C. COOPER, U. S. Department of Agriculture, Welasco, Texas
751. W. M. COPENHAVER, Columbia University
752. G. COPPÉE, University of Liege
753. A. C. CORCORAN, Cleveland Clinic
754. CARL F. CORI, Washington University
755. NORMAL L. CORKILL, Aden Protectorate Health Service Hdqrs., Mukalla
756. RALPH C. CORLEY, Purdue University
757. JOHN O. CORLISS, University of Illinois
758. J. F. CORMACK, Army Medical Nutrition Laboratory, Denver
759. THEODORE CORNBLEET, University of Illinois College of Medicine
760. A. CORNELL, Mount Sinai Hospital, N. Y. C.
761. GEORGE W. CORNER, Rockefeller Institute for Medical Research
762. IVOR CORNMAN, Hazleton Laboratories, Falls Church, Va.

763. BERNARD W. CORSON, New Hampshire Fish and Game Department, Concord
764. ERNEST COTLOVE, Harvard Medical School
765. CLARENCE COTTAM, U. S. Fish and Wildlife Service, Washington, D. C.
766. RICHARD T. COTTON, U. S. Department of Agriculture, Washington, D. C.
767. J. N. COUCH, University of North Carolina
768. J. R. COUCH, Texas Agricultural and Mechanical College
769. D. A. COULT, University of Liverpool
770. EARL W. COUNT, Hamilton College
771. ANDRÉ COURNAND, Columbia University
772. F. C. COURTICE, Sydney Hospital, Australia
773. I. McT. COWAN, University of British Columbia
774. JOHN C. COWAN, U. S. Department of Agriculture, Peoria, Ill.
775. W. ALLEN COWAN, University of Connecticut
776. R. F. COWING, Pondville Hospital, Walpole, Mass.
777. RAYMOND B. COWLES, University of California, Los Angeles
778. GERALD J. COX, University of Pittsburgh
779. GERTRUDE M. COX, North Carolina State College
780. R. T. COX, Johns Hopkins University
781. VICTOR COXON, Oxford University
782. D. GLEN CRABTREE, Motomco, Inc., N. Y. C.
783. W. A. CRAFT, Iowa State College
784. A. S. CRAFTS, University of California, Davis
785. EDWARD C. CRAFTS, U. S. Department of Agriculture, Washington, D. C.
786. ROGER C. CRAFTS, University of Cincinnati
787. F. N. CRAIG, Army Chemical Center, Md.
788. RODERICK CRAIG, University of California, Berkeley
789. WINCHELL McK. CRAIG, Mayo Clinic
790. A. H. CRAIGE, Jr., Pitman-Moore Co., Indianapolis
791. J. H. CRAIGIE, Department of Agriculture, Ottawa
792. ELOISE B. CRAM, National Microbiological Institute
793. MARIAN CRAMER, University of California, Riverside
794. MARTIN CRAMER
795. CHARLES W. CRAMPTON, 471 Park Ave., N. Y. C.
796. E. W. CRAMPTON, McGill University
797. LEE S. CRANDALL, New York Zoological Park
798. L. A. CRANDALL, Jr., Miles-Ames Research Laboratory, Elkhart, Ind.
799. ROBERT K. CRANE, Washington University
800. W. W. CRAVENS, University of Wisconsin
801. JOHN D. CRAWFORD, Massachusetts General Hospital, Boston
802. JOHN T. CREIGHTON, University of Florida
803. ADOLPH J. CRESKOFF, University of Pennsylvania

804. EUGENE P. CRONKITE, Brookhaven National Laboratory
805. H. ROBERT CROOKSHANK, Texas Technical College
806. GLEN G. CROSBIE, Zoological Society of San Diego
807. GERMAIN CROSSMAN, Bausch and Lomb Optical Co., Rochester
808. JAMES F. CROW, University of Wisconsin
809. R. M. CROWN, Louisiana State University
810. FRANK A. CSONKA, U. S. Department of Agriculture, Beltsville
811. J. N. CUMINGS, National Hospital, London
812. ALVIN J. CUMMINS, University of Pennsylvania
813. T. J. CUNHA, University of Florida
814. CHARLES H. CUNNINGHAM, Michigan State University
815. PERRY T. CUPPS, University of California, Davis
816. ROSCOE F. CUOZZO, University of Maine
817. HAROLD R. CURRAN, U. S. Department of Agriculture, Washington, D. C.
818. H. B. CURRIER, University of California, Davis
819. ARTHUR H. CURTIS, Northwestern University Medical School
820. HOWARD J. CURTIS, Brookhaven National Laboratory
821. L. K. CUTKOMP, University of Minnesota
822. RICHARD D. CUTTER, 300 Homer Ave., Palo Alto, Cal.
823. VICTOR M. CUTTER, University of North Carolina, Greensboro
824. WINDSOR C. CUTTING, Stanford University School of Medicine

825. G. M. DACK, University of Chicago
826. FLOYD S. DAFT, National Institute of Arthritis and Metabolic Diseases
827. R. L. DAGGETT, George Lueders and Co., N. Y. C.
828. A. ORVILLE DAHL, University of Minnesota
829. GENEVA A. DALAND, Boston City Hospital
830. H. E. DALE, University of Missouri
831. GILBERT J. DALLDORF, New York State Department of Health, Albany
832. M. J. DALLEMAGNE, University of Liege
833. FRANCESCO D'AMATO, University of Pisa
834. WILLIAM DAMESHEK, Tufts College Medical School
835. C. H. DANFORTH, Stanford University
836. WILLIAM F. DANFORTH, Illinois Institute of Technology
837. SAVINO A. D'ANGELO, Jefferson Medical College
838. LOUIS J. DANIEL, Cornell University
839. LUCILLE DANIELS, Stanford University
840. T. C. DANIELS, University of California, San Francisco
841. ARNOLD DANKNER, 110 S. Central Ave., Clayton, Mo.
842. T. C. DANOWSKI, University of Pittsburgh
843. PIERRE DANSEREAU, University of Montreal

844. RICHARD T. DARBY, Quartermaster Research and Development Center, Natick, Mass.
845. WILLIAM J. DARBY, Vanderbilt University
846. ROBERT C. DARLING, Columbia University
847. C. D. DARLINGTON, Oxford University
848. HENRY T. DARLINGTON, Michigan State University
849. R. M. DARNELL, Marquette University
850. DANIEL C. DARROW, Yale University
851. H. J. A. DARTNALL, Institute of Ophthalmology, London
852. R. DAUBENMIRE, State College of Washington
853. B. F. DAUBERT, General Foods Corp., Hoboken, N. J.
854. C. C. DAUER, U. S. Public Health Service, Washington, D. C.
855. JACK W. DAUGHERTY, Rice Institute
856. HORACE W. DAVENPORT, University of Michigan
857. ROBERT J. DAVEY, U. S. Department of Agriculture, Beltsville
858. PAUL R. DAVID, University of Oklahoma
859. BERNARD DAVIDOW, U. S. Food and Drug Administration, Washington, D. C.
860. ISRAEL DAVIDSOHN, Mount Sinai Hospital, N. Y. C.
861. CHARLES S. DAVIDSON, Harvard Medical School
862. J. N. DAVIDSON, University of Glasgow
863. LEONARD T. DAVIDSON, University of Louisville
864. DEAN F. DAVIES, American Cancer Society, Inc., N. Y. C.
865. W. MORLEY DAVIES, Ministry of Agriculture and Fisheries, London
866. BERNARD D. DAVIS, New York University
867. CHARLES C. DAVIS, Western Reserve University
868. DAVID E. DAVIS, Johns Hopkins University
869. DONALD E. DAVIS, Alabama Polytechnic Institute
870. GORDON DAVIS, National Microbiological Institute, Hamilton, Mont.
871. HALLOWELL DAVIS, Central Institute for the Deaf, St. Louis
872. JOHN H. DAVIS, University of Florida
873. RUSSELL E. DAVIS, U. S. Department of Agriculture, Beltsville
874. HUGH DAVSON, 12 Tregunter Rd., London
875. THOMAS R. DAWBER, Faulkner Hospital, Boston
876. A. R. DAWE, University of Wisconsin
877. G. S. DAWES, Nuffield Institute for Medical Research, Oxford
878. ALDEN B. DAWSON, Harvard University
879. R. M. C. DAWSON, Oxford University
880. HARRY G. DAY, Indiana University
881. PAUL L. DAY, University of Arkansas Medical Center
882. RICHARD L. DAY, Babies Hospital, N. Y. C.
883. HOWARD G. DAYMAN, University of Buffalo

884. WILLIAM A. DAYTON, U. S. Department of Agriculture, Washington, D. C.
885. WILLIAM C. DEAMER, University of California, San Francisco
886. ROBERT B. DEAN, Borden Co., Bainbridge, N. Y.
887. F. E. DEATHERAGE, Ohio State University
888. PAUL H. DeBACH, University of California, Riverside
889. EDWIN J. deBEER, Wellcome Research Laboratories
890. BENJAMIN DeBOER, University of North Dakota
891. CARL J. DeBOER, The Upjohn Co., Kalamazoo, Mich.
892. ALBERT DECKER, New York Medical College
893. JOHN P. DECKER, New York State College of Forestry, Syracuse
894. JENS DEDICHEN, Rikshospitalet, Oslo
895. FLOYD DE EDS, U. S. Department of Agriculture, Albany, Cal.
896. EDWARD S. DEEVEY, Jr., Yale University
897. ARTHUR C. DeGRAFF, New York University
898. WILLIAM B. DEICHMANN, University of Miami
899. RUSSELL N. DeJONG, University of Michigan
900. ELEANOR DELFS, Johns Hopkins University
901. ALBERT L. DeLISLE, South Hadley Falls, Mass.
902. C. JOSEPH DeLOR, Ohio State University
903. EUGENE A. DELWICHE, Cornell University
904. Q. B. DeMARSH, University of Washington
905. B. DE MEILLON, South African Institute for Medical Research, Johannesburg
906. G. C. DeMELLO, Lederle Laboratories, Pearl River, N. Y.
907. MILISLAV DEMEREC, Carnegie Institution of Washington, Cold Spring Harbor, N. Y.
908. MÁRTHE DEMERS, University of Montreal
909. EDWARD W. DEMPSEY, Washington University
910. JOHN DEMPSHER, University of Pennsylvania
911. EVERETT R. DEMPSTER, University of California, Berk.
912. PETER DENES, University of London
913. R. A. DENO, University of Michigan
914. PAUL M. DENSEN, University of Pittsburgh
915. ORVILLE F. DENSTEDT, McGill University
916. E. R. deONG, U. S. Department of Agriculture, Albany, Cal.
917. ELMER DeRITTER, Hoffman-La Roche, Inc., Nutley, N. J.
918. EDUARDO deROBERTIS, Institute for Biological Investigation, Montevideo
919. R. S. de ROPP, Lederle Laboratories, Pearl River, N. Y.
920. J. H. DE SMET, University of Ghent
921. HERBERT C. DESSAUER, Louisiana State University Medical School
922. GEZA deTAKATS, University of Illinois College of Medicine
923. VINCENT G. DETHIER, Johns Hopkins University

924. HARRY J. DEUEL, University of Southern California
925. HAROLD F. DEUTSCH, University of Wisconsin
926. MARSHALL E. DEUTSCH, Warner-Chilcott Research Laboratories, Morris Plains, N. J.
927. ROBERT H. DEWEY, Commercial Solvents Corp., Terre Haute, Ind.
928. VIRGINIA C. DEWEY, Amherst College
929. J. J. DUYVENE De WIT, University of the Orange Free State
930. JAMES B. DeWITT, U. S. Fish and Wildlife Service, Laurel, Md.
931. ROBERT M. DeWITT, University of Florida
932. S. T. DEXTER, Michigan State University
933. LOUIS K. DIAMOND, Harvard Medical School
934. MARIO UMBERTO DIANZANI, University of Genoa
935. FRANK DICKENS, Middlesex Hospital Medical School, London
936. G. E. DICKERSON, Kimber Farms, Inc., Niles, Cal.
937. BENJAMIN DICKSTEIN, University of Pennsylvania
938. W. J. DIECKMANN, University of Chicago
939. W. W. DIEHL, U. S. Department of Agriculture, Beltsville
940. HENRY DIETRICH, Cornell University
941. LEMUEL W. DIGGS, University of Tennessee
942. JOSEPH H. DiLEO, New York Foundling Hospital
943. DAVID B. DILL, Army Chemical Center, Md.
944. ALBERT E. DIMOND, Connecticut Agricultural Experiment Station, New Haven
945. JAMES S. DINNING, University of Pittsburgh
946. JOSEPH R. DiPALMA, Hahnemann Medical College
947. ZACHARIAS DISCHE, Columbia University
948. HOWARD J. DITTMER, University of New Mexico
949. CARL DJERASSI, Wayne State University
950. AFRANIO DO AMARAL, Butantan Institute, São Paulo
951. CHARLES A. DOAN, Ohio State University
952. L. G. DOBSON, Ryerson Institute of Technology, London
953. BERNARD O. DODGE, New York Botanical Garden
954. CARROLL W. DODGE, Washington University
955. RAYMOND N. DOETSCH, University of Maryland
956. VINCENT P. DOLE, Rockefeller Institute for Medical Research
957. M. J. L. DOLS, University of Amsterdam
958. R. DOMINGUEZ, St. Luke's Hospital, Cleveland
959. L. V. DOMM, Loyola University, Chicago
960. LAUREN R. DONALDSON, University of Washington
961. J. DONE, Medical Research Council, London
962. EILEEN L. DONOHOE, Mill Race Farm, Clinton, N. J.
963. HUGO DONOSO, Johns Hopkins University
964. C. G. DONOVAN, U. S. Department of Agriculture, Beltsville

965. DAVID J. DORAN, U. S. Department of Agriculture, Beltsville
966. ALBERT DORFMAN, University of Chicago
967. RALPH I. DORFMAN, Worcester Foundation for Experimental Biology
968. ERNST J. DORNFELD, Oregon State College
969. C. K. DORSEY, West Virginia University
970. KELVIN DORWARD, U.S. Department of Agriculture, Washington, D. C.
971. PETER DOUDOROFF, Oregon State College
972. ELLSWORTH C. DOUGHERTY, University of California, Berkeley
973. THOMAS F. DOUGHERTY, University of Utah
974. H. C. DOUGLAS, University of Washington
975. JAMES R. DOUGLAS, University of California, Davis
976. ALEXANDER L. DOUNCE, University of Rochester
977. ANDREW H. DOWDY, University of California, Los Angeles
978. CORA M. DOWNS, University of Kansas
979. R. J. DOWNS, U. S. Department of Agriculture, Beltsville
980. WILBUR G. DOWNS, Trinidad Regional Virus Laboratory, Port-of-Spain
981. WILLIAM L. DOYLE, University of Chicago
982. BYRD K. DOZIER, University of Tennessee
983. DAVID L. DRABKIN, University of Pennsylvania
984. W. F. DREA, Foundation for Tuberculosis Research, Colorado Springs
985. H. E. DREGNE, New Mexico College of Agriculture and Mechanic Arts
986. DAVID A. DREILING, Mount Sinai Hospital, N. Y. C.
987. ROBERT H. DREISBACH, Stanford University School of Medicine
988. N. B. DREYER, Women's Medical College of Philadelphia
989. VICTOR A. DRILL, G. D. Searle and Co., Chicago
990. CECIL K. DRINKER, Box 502, Falmouth, Mass.
991. C. M. DRIVER, Crops Research Division, Christchurch, New Zealand
992. LESTER DRUBIN, Veterans Administration Hospital, Northport, N. Y.
993. I. N. DUBIN, Armed Forces Institute of Pathology
994. LOUIS I. DUBLIN, Metropolitan Life Insurance Co., N.Y.C.
995. EUGENE F. DuBOIS, 1300 York Avenue, N. Y. C.
996. KENNETH P. DuBOIS, University of Chicago
997. R. C. DuBOIS, 129 Haws Lane, Chestnut Hill, Pa.
998. M. DUBUISSON, University of Liege
999. H. DuBUY, National Microbiological Institute
1000. CHARLES J. DUCA, 535-2nd Ave., N. Y. C.
1001. HORACE C. DUDLEY, U. S. Naval Hospital, St. Albans, N. Y.
1002. R. A. DUDLEY, U. S. Atomic Energy Commission

1003. HELEN E. DUELL, Smith, Kline and French Laboratories, Philadelphia
1004. JAMES DUFFUS, U. S. Department of Agriculture, Salinas, Cal.
1005. T. L. DUGGAN, Loyola University, New Orleans
1006. BENJAMIN M. DUGGAR, Lederle Laboratories, Pearl River, N. Y.
1007. OLIVER H. DUGGINS, Washington University
1008. KENNETH L. DUKE, Duke University
1009. W. STEWART DUKE-ELDER, University of London
1010. H. H. DUKES, Cornell University
1011. FRANK L. DULEY, U.S. Department of Agriculture, Lincoln, Neb.
1012. MAXMILIAN GEORGE DUMAN, St. Vincent College, Latrobe, Pa.
1013. MAXWELL J. DUNBAR, McGill University
1014. C. W. DUNCAN, Michigan State University
1015. JOHN C. DUNEGAN, U.S. Department of Agriculture, Beltsville
1016. GEORGE DUNGAN, University of Illinois
1017. A. A. DUNHAM, Brookhaven National Laboratory
1018. JACK S. DUNLAP, State College of Washington
1019. CECIL G. DUNN, Massachusetts Institute of Technology
1020. HALBERT L. DUNN, National Office of Vital Statistics
1021. L. C. DUNN, Columbia University
1022. MAX S. DUNN, University of California, Los Angeles
1023. EDWIN B. DUNPHY, Massachusetts Eye and Ear Infirmary, Boston
1024. ASUNCIÓN DUPLÁN, Social Security Service, Mexico City
1025. MARGARET V. DUPRÉ, State University of New York, Buffalo
1026. FRANCISCO DURAN-REYNALS, Yale University
1027. ABRAHAM DURY, Bradford Hospital, Bradford, Pa.
1028. PIERRE DUSTIN, Jr., Free University of Brussels
1029. J. D. DUTCHER, Squibb Institute for Medical Research, New Brunswick, N. J.
1030. W. C. DUTTON, Dow Chemical Co., Midland, Mich.
1031. VINCENT duVIGNEAUD, Cornell University Medical College
1032. W. J. DYER, Technological Station, Halifax, N. S.
1033. J. R. DYMOND, University of Toronto
1034. ANDREW P. D'ZMURA, University of Pittsburgh

1035. G. S. EADIE, Duke University
1036. RICHARD D. EADS, Texas State Department of Health, Austin
1037. ROBERT E. EAKIN, University of Texas
1038. A. J. EAMES, Cornell University
1039. F. R. EARLE, U.S. Department of Agriculture, Peoria, Ill.
1040. I. P. EARLE, U.S. Department of Agriculture, Beltsville

1041. WILTON R. EARLE, National Cancer Institute
1042. ERNEST B. EARLEY, University of Illinois
1043. M. D. EASTHAM, Queen's College, Dundee, Scotland
1044. DEXTER M. EASTON, Florida State University
1045. FRANK M. EATON, U. S. Department of Agriculture, College Station, Texas
1046. ORSON N. EATON, 4320 Clagett Rd., Hyattsville, Md.
1047. J. C. ECCLES, Australian National University
1048. FRODE ECKARDT, International Station of Geobotany, Montpellier, France
1049. R. E. ECKHARDT, Esso Research and Engineering Co., Linden, N. J.
1050. ENRIQUE E. ECKER, Western Reserve University
1051. SOPHIA H. ECKERSON, Pleasant Valley, Conn.
1052. RICHARD W. ECKSTEIN, Western Reserve University
1053. NATHAN B. EDDY, National Institutes of Health
1054. I. S. EDELMAN, University of California, San Francisco
1055. ABRAHAM EDELMAN, Nuclear Science and Engineering Corp., Pittsburgh
1056. H. E. EDERSTROM, University of North Dakota
1057. S. A. EDGAR, Alabama Polytechnic Institute
1058. JOHN T. EDSALL, Harvard University
1059. CAROLYN T. EDWARDS, Medical College of Virginia
1060. EDWARD A. EDWARDS, Harvard Medical School
1061. ERNEST P. EDWARDS, Box 611, Amherst, Va.
1062. WARD EDWARDS, Institute for Cooperative Research, Baltimore
1063. J. P. EGAN, Indiana University
1064. HAROLD E. EGGERS, Nebraska State Health Department, Omaha
1065. CHARLES F. EHRET, Argonne National Laboratory
1066. WILLIAM E. EHRICH, University of Pennsylvania
1067. HARRY C. EHRMANTRAUT, Stanford Research Institute
1068. F. W. EICHBAUM, R. Marque de Itu 58, São Paulo
1069. LILLIAN EICHELBERGER, University of Chicago
1070. C. J. EIDE, University of Minnesota
1071. WILLIAM J. EISENMENGER, 39 Dana St., Amherst, Mass.
1072. A. EISENSTARK, Kansas State College
1073. A. EL-ANI, Prairie Regional Laboratory, Saskatoon
1074. DONALD ELDREDGE, Central Institute for the Deaf, St. Louis
1075. LOUIS K. ELFMAN, 6330 Lebanon Ave., Philadelphia
1076. HERBERT ELFTMAN, Columbia University
1077. EDWARD I. ELISBERG, Northwestern University School of Medicine
1078. H. B. ELLENBERGER, University of Vermont
1079. F. P. ELLINGER, Naval Medical Research Institute
1080. ALFRED M. ELLIOTT, University of Michigan
1081. CHARLOTTE ELLIOTT, Lanham, Md.

1082. E. C. ELLIOTT, State College of Washington
1083. EWING W. ELLIOTT, APO 403, c/o PM, N.Y.C.
1084. F. I. ELLIOTT, American Foundation for the Study of Genetics, Madison, Wis.
1085. HENRY W. ELLIOTT, University of California, San Francisco
1086. K. A. C. ELLIOTT, Montreal Neurological Institute
1087. HAZEL R. ELLIS, Keuka College
1088. N. R. ELLIS, U.S. Department of Agriculture, Beltsville
1089. ORWYN H. ELLIS, 523 W. Sixth St., Los Angeles
1090. R. W. B. ELLIS, 18 Blackett Pl., Edinburgh
1091. ROBERT ELMAN, Washington University
1092. E. F. ELSLAGER, Parke, Davis and Co., Detroit
1093. J. P. ELTING, Kendall Cotton Mills, Paw Creek, N. C.
1094. NORMAN W. ELTON, Army Chemical Center, Md.
1095. CONRAD A. ELVEHJEM, University of Wisconsin
1096. DAVID ELWYN, Harvard Medical School
1097. GLADYS A. EMERSON, Merck Institute for Therapeutic Research, Rahway, N. J.
1098. RALPH W. EMERSON, University of California, Berkeley
1099. FREDERICK E. EMERY, University of Arkansas School of Medicine
1100. WILLIAM H. EMIG, University of Pittsburgh
1101. JOHN T. EMLEN, Jr., University of Wisconsin
1102. EDWIN EMMA, Beth Israel Hospital, N. Y. C.
1103. VICTOR M. EMMEL, University of Rochester
1104. E. M. EMMERT, University of Kentucky
1105. C. W. EMMONS, National Institutes of Health
1106. A. R. G. EMSLIE, Department of Agriculture, Ottawa
1107. S. L. EMSWELLER, U. S. Department of Agriculture, Beltsville
1108. ROBERT K. ENDERS, Swarthmore College
1109. KENNETH M. ENDICOTT, National Institutes of Health
1110. R. W. ENGEL, Virginia Agricultural Experiment Station, Blacksburg
1111. MARY ALLEN ENGLE, New York Hospital
1112. EARL T. ENGLE, Columbia University
1113. ARTHUR R. ENGLISH, Pfizer Therapeutic Institute, Maywood, N. J.
1114. BORIS EPHRUSSI, University of Paris
1115. EMANUEL EPSTEIN, U. S. Department of Agriculture, Beltsville
1116. LEWIS W: ERDMAN, U.S. Department of Agriculture, Beltsville
1117. ERVIN ERDOES, University of Pittsburgh
1118. DAVID R. ERGLE, Texas Agricultural Experiment Station, College Station
1119. CARL ERHARDT, City Department of Health, N. Y. C.
1120. RALPH O. ERICKSON, University of Pennsylvania

1121. JOSEPH ERLANGER, Washington University
1122. ARTHUR C. ERNSTENE, Cleveland Clinic
1123. BENJAMIN H. ERSHOFF, Emory W. Thurston Laboratories, Los Angeles
1124. F. ERVIN, Tulane University
1125. KATHERINE ESAU, University of California, Davis
1126. ROBERTO F. ESCAMILLA, 655 Sutter St., San Francisco
1127. PAUL H. ESCHMEYER, U. S. Fish and Wildlife Service, Ann Arbor, Mich.
1128. C. ESCOFFIER-LAMBIOTTE, 8 Rue Murillo, Paris
1129. HIRAM E. ESSEX, Mayo Foundation
1130. E. O. ESSIG, University of California, Berkeley
1131. J. RUSSEL ESTY, National Canners Assoc., Berkeley, Cal.
1132. JOHN L. ETCHELLS, U.S. Food Fermentation Laboratory, Raleigh, N. C.
1133. J. EUGSTER, University of Bern
1134. E. A. EVANS, Jr., University of Chicago
1135. F. GAYNOR EVANS, Wayne State University
1136. H. E. EVANS, Cornell University
1137. H. J. EVANS, North Carolina State College
1138. MORGAN W. EVANS, 701 N. Beuer St., Wooster, Ohio
1139. ROBERT JOHN EVANS, Michigan State University
1140. ROBLEY D. EVANS, Massachusetts Institute of Technology
1141. TITUS C. EVANS, State University of Iowa
1142. JOHN W. EVERETT, Duke University
1143. MARK R. EVERETT, University of Oklahoma Medical School
1144. W. J. EVERSOLE, University of New Mexico
1145. HENRY E. EVERT, State University of New York College of Medicine, Brooklyn
1146. G. YUAN EWART, Kekaha Sugar Co., Kauai, Hawaii
1147. LORA EWING, Springfield College
1148. FRANCIS H. EYRE, U.S. Forest Service, Washington, D. C.
1149. HENRY EYRING, University of Utah
1150. H. CLYDE EYSTER, Charles F. Kettering Foundation
1151. C. EZRIN, University of Toronto

1152. A. FAHN, Royal Botanical Gardens, Kew, England
1153. MYRON F. FAIR, Oak Ridge National Laboratory
1154. LAWRENCE T. FAIRHALL, Pine Orchard, Conn.
1155. A. A. FALCONER, Hopkins Marine Station
1156. HARRIET FANCHER, University of Missouri
1157. U. FANO, National Bureau of Standards
1158. PAUL FANTL, Alfred Hospital, Melbourne
1159. LIONEL FARBER, University of California, San Francisco
1160. CHESTER J. FARMER, Northwestern University Medical School
1161. DONALD S. FARNER, State College of Washington

1162. DEAN FARNSWORTH, U. S. Naval Base, New London, Conn.
1163. EUGENE FARNSWORTH, Syracuse University
1164. R. F. FARQUHARSON, University of Toronto
1165. C. L. FARRAR, University of Wisconsin
1166. GEORGE FARRAR, Wyeth Laboratories, Philadelphia
1167. EDMOND J. FARRIS, Wistar Institute of Anatomy and Biology, Philadelphia
1168. ERNEST CARROLL FAUST, Tulane University
1169. R. W. FAY, U.S. Public Health Service, Savannah, Ga.
1170. JOSEPH F. FAZEKAS, Gallinger Municipal Hospital, Washington, D. C.
1171. ROBERT E. FEENEY, University of Nebraska
1172. LOUIS FEINSTEIN, U.S. Department of Agriculture, Beltsville
1173. HARRY A. FELDMAN, Syracuse University
1174. MILTON FELDSTEIN, University of Buffalo
1175. FRANCES E. FELIN, U.S. Fish and Wildlife Service, La Jolla, Cal.
1176. A. E. FELLER, Western Reserve University
1177. PAUL F. FENTON, Brown University
1178. CHARLOTTE FERENCZ, Johns Hopkins University
1179. CHARLES L. FERGUS, Pennsylvania State University
1180. J. K. W. FERGUSON, University of Toronto
1181. JOHN H. FERGUSON, University of North Carolina
1182. ROLAND M. FERRY, Harvard University
1183. DOROTHY FETTER, Brooklyn College
1184. JOHN FIDDES, 3842 W. 19th St., Vancouver
1185. JOHN C. FIDLER, Ditton Laboratory, Kent, England
1186. E. A. FIEGER, Louisiana State University
1187. JOHN B. FIELD, University of Southern California
1188. L. F. FIESER, Harvard University
1189. GILES F. FILLEY, University of Colorado Medical Center
1190. CLEMENT A. FINCH, University of Washington
1191. MARGARET L. FINCKE, Oregon State College
1192. JACOB FINE, Beth Israel Hospital, Boston
1193. MILTON FINGERMAN, Tulane University
1194. M. H. FINLAYSON, Capetown, South Africa
1195. HARLAN I. FIRMINGER, University of Kansas Medical Center
1196. EDWARD E. FISCHEL, Bronx Hospital, N. Y. C.
1197. ALBERT FISCHER, Carlsbergfondets Biological Institute, Copenhagen
1198. ERNST FISCHER, Medical College of Virginia
1199. RONALD A. FISHER, Cambridge University
1200. A. A. FISK, Permanente Medical Group, San Francisco
1201. HENRY S. FITCH, University of Kansas

1202. JOHN E. FITCH, State Fisheries Laboratory, Terminal Island, Cal.
1203. J. W. FITTS, Iowa State College
1204. WILLIAM FITTS, Jr., University of Pennsylvania
1205. STANLEY E. FLANDERS, University of California, Riverside
1206. A. FLEISCH, University of Lausanne
1207. LAUNCE J. FLEMISTER, Swarthmore College
1208. SARAH C. FLEMISTER, Swarthmore College
1209. PETER FLESCH, University of Pennsylvania
1210. C. A. FLESCHNER, University of California, Riverside
1211. HEWITT G. FLETCHER, Jr., National Institute of Arthritis and Metabolic Diseases
1212. JOEL E. FLETCHER, U. S. Department of Agriculture, Tucson
1213. LOUIS B. FLEXNER, University of Pennsylvania
1214. LEWIS H. FLINT, Louisiana State University
1215. HERVÉ P. FLOCH, Pasteur Institute, Cayenne, French Guiana
1216. EUNICE V. FLOCK, Mayo Clinic
1217. HOWARD FLOREY, Oxford University
1218. LLOYD J. FLORIO, University of Colorado Medical Center
1219. MARCEL FLORKIN, University of Liege
1220. C. FREDERIC FLUHMANN, Stanford University School of Medicine
1221. DONALD J. FLUKE, Brookhaven National Laboratory
1222. JOHN A. FLUNO, U.S. Department of Agriculture, Orlando, Fla.
1223. PIERO P. FOA, Chicago Medical School
1224. G. E. FOGG, University College, London
1225. LLOYD C. FOGG, Pondville Hospital, Walpole, Mass.
1226. JAMES FOLCH-PI, McLean Hospital, Waverly, Mass.
1227. S. J. FOLLEY, National Institute for Research in Dairying, Shinfield, England
1228. RICHARD H. FOLLIS, Jr., Armed Forces Institute of Pathology
1229. RICHARD H. FOOTE, U.S. Department of Agriculture, Washington, D. C.
1230. E. B. FORBES, Pennsylvania State University
1231. JAMES FORBES, Fordham University
1232. THOMAS FORBES, Yale University
1233. W. H. FORBES, Harvard School of Public Health
1234. HARRY FOREMAN, Los Alamos Scientific Laboratory
1235. ANDREW P. M. FORREST, University of Glasgow
1236. R. E. FORSTER, University of Pennsylvania
1237. R. P. FORSTER, Dartmouth College
1238. HENRY FORTMANN, Pennsylvania State University
1239. DOROTHY FORWARD, University of Toronto
1240. F. RAYMOND FOSBERG, National Research Council

1241. W. F. FOSHAG, Smithsonian Institution
1242. A. O. FOSTER, U. S. Department of Agriculture, Beltsville
1243. ADRIANCE S. FOSTER, University of California, Berkeley
1244. DEAN FOSTER, United States Testing Co., Hoboken, N. J.
1245. JACKSON W. FOSTER, University of Texas
1246. E. EUGENE FOWLER, U.S. Atomic Energy Commission, Oak Ridge
1247. NOBLE O. FOWLER, Emory University
1248. WARD S. FOWLER, Mayo Foundation
1249. WILLIS M. FOWLER, State University of Iowa
1250. ARTHUR L. FOX, Colgate-Palmolive Co., Jersey City
1251. BERNARD H. FOX, 5712 Crawford Dr., Rockville, Md.
1252. DENIS L. FOX, Scripps Institute of Oceanography
1253. J. A. FOX, The Upjohn Co., Kalamazoo, Mich.
1254. L. E. FOX, University of Florida
1255. SIDNEY W. FOX, Iowa State College
1256. GOTTFRIED S. FRAENKEL, University of Illinois
1257. SAUL FRANCES, Wells Laboratories, Inc., Jersey City
1258. CARL C. FRANCIS, Western Reserve University
1259. JAMES FRANCK, University of Chicago
1260. ARCHIE FRANK, U.S. Department of Agriculture, Beltsville
1261. H. A. FRANK, Beth Israel Hospital, Boston
1262. PETER W. FRANK, University of Missouri
1263. K. J. FRANKLIN, Medical College of St. Bartholomew's Hospital, London
1264. ÅKE FRANZÉN, University of Uppsala
1265. RICHARD M. FRAPS, U.S. Department of Agriculture, Beltsville
1266. F. CLARKE FRASER, McGill University
1267. A. C. FRAZER, University of Birmingham
1268. JOHN C. FRAZIER, Kansas State College
1269. JEROME F. FREDRICK, Dodge Chemical Co., N. Y. C.
1270. ALFRED H. FREE, Miles-Ames Research Laboratory, Elkhart, Ind.
1271. S. CHARLES FREED, 450 Sutter St., San Francisco
1272. A. STONE FREEDBERG, Beth Israel Hospital, Boston
1273. REINO S. FREEMAN, University of Toronto
1274. SMITH FREEMAN, Northwestern University Medical School
1275. WALTER FREEMAN, George Washington University
1276. HENRY C. FREIMUTH, Office of the Chief Medical Examiner, Baltimore
1277. EDWARD D. FREIS, Georgetown University
1278. C. S. FRENCH, Carnegie Institution of Washington, Stanford, Cal.
1279. CYRUS E. FRENCH, Pennsylvania State University
1280. ALBERT W. FRENKEL, University of Minnesota
1281. CHARLES N. FREY, Massachusetts Institute of Technology

1282. A. FREY-WYSSLING, Federal Institute of Technology, Zurich

1283. HUGO FRICKE, Argonne National Laboratory

1284. PAUL H. FRIED, 1812 Spruce St., Philadelphia

1285. FELIX FRIEDBERG, Howard University

1286. HYMER L. FRIEDELL, Western Reserve University

1287. THEODORE E. FRIEDEMANN, Army Medical Nutrition Laboratory, Denver

1288. EARL FRIEDEN, Florida State University

1289. ARNOLD P. FRIEDMAN, Montefiore Hospital, N. Y. C.

1290. LORRAINE FRIEDMAN, Tulane University

1291. SYDNEY M. FRIEDMAN, University of British Columbia

1292. HERBERT FRIEDMANN, Smithsonian Institution

1293. NILS FRIES, University of Uppsala

1294. HUBERT FRINGS, Pennsylvania State University

1295. MABEL FRINGS, Pennsylvania State University

1296. HARRY K. FRITCHMANN, II University of California, Berkeley

1297. J. C. FRITZ, Dawe's Laboratories, Elgin, Ill.

1298. MARTIN FROBISHER, U.S. Public Health Service, Tenafly, N. J.

1299. D. V. FROST, Abbott Laboratories, North Chicago

1300. JOSEPH S. FRUTON, Yale University

1301. F. E. J. FRY, University of Toronto

1302. WAYNE L. FRY, Geological Survey of Canada, Ottawa

1303. FREDERICK A. FUHRMAN, Stanford University

1304. GEORGE I. FUJIMOTO, University of Utah

1305. MARGARET H. FULFORD, University of Cincinnati

1306. ALBERT FULLER, Milwaukee Public Museum

1307. HENRY S. FULLER, Walter Reed Army Medical Center

1308. E. H. FULLING, New York Botanical Garden

1309. GEORGE P. FULTON, Boston University

1310. JOHN F. FULTON, Yale University

1311. ROBERT W. FULTON, University of Wisconsin

1312. LYMAN FUORT, Harris Research Laboratories, Inc., Washington, D. C.

1313. M. G. F. FUORTES, Walter Reed Army Medical Center

1314. DEANE P. FURMAN, University of California, Berkeley

1315. J. R. FURR, U.S. Department of Agriculture, Indio, Cal.

1316. JACOB FURTH, Harvard Medical School

1317. BEVERLY W. GABRIO, University of Washington

1318. E. A. GAENSLER, Boston City Hospital

1319. H. GAFFRON, University of Chicago

1320. ALFRED GAJDOS, University of Paris

1321. ROBERT GALAMBOS, Army Medical Service Graduate School

1322. MORTON GALDSTON, New York University

1323. LORRAINE GALL, National Dairy Research Laboratories, Inc., Oakdale, N. Y.

1324. FRED W. GALLAGHER, University of Vermont

1325. ARTHUR W. GALSTON, Yale University

1326. PAUL S. GALTSOFF, U.S. Fish and Wildlife Service, Woods Hole, Mass.

1327. MILDRED M. GALTON, U.S. Public Health Service, Chamblee, Ga.

1328. JAMES L. GAMBLE, Harvard Medical School

1329. CHARLES P. GANDAL, New York Zoological Society

1330. SOLOMON GARB, Cornell University Medical College

1331. MARY S. GARDINER, Bryn Mawr College

1332. MARY V. GARDNER, 72 Rugby Pl., Woodbury, N. J.

1333. V. R. GARDNER, Michigan State University

1334. WALTER H. GARDNER, State College of Washington

1335. WILLIAM U. GARDNER, Yale University

1336. STANLEY M. GARN, Antioch College

1337. W. R. GARNER, Johns Hopkins University

1338. W. W. GARNER, 1367 Parkwood Pl., NW, Washington, D. C.

1339. U. S. GARRIGUS, University of Illinois

1340. W. P. GARRIGUS, University of Kentucky

1341. HERBERT S. GASSER, Rockefeller Institute for Medical Research

1342. H. GASTAUT, International Federation of Electroencephalographic and Clinical Neurophysiological Societies, Marseilles

1343. R. RUGGLES GATES, 18 Concord Ave., Cambridge, Mass.

1344. HUGH G. GAUCH, University of Maryland

1345. MARIO GAUDINO, New York University

1346. ARDEN R. GAUFIN, University of Utah

1347. ROBERT GAUNT, Ciba Pharmaceutical Co., Summit, N. J.

1348. R. J. GAUTHERET, University of Paris

1349. JAMES A. GAVAN, Medical College of South Carolina

1350. JOHN M. GEARY, Gunter Air Force Base, Ala.

1351. E. M. K. GEILING, University of Chicago

1352. QUENTIN M. GEIMAN, Stanford University School of Medicine

1353. T. A. GEISSMAN, University of California, Los Angeles

1354. BENJAMIN R. GENDEL, Veterans Administration Hospital, Memphis

1355. LUCILLE K. GEORG, U. S. Public Health Service, Chamblee, Ga.

1356. R. W. GERARD, University of Illinois College of Medicine

1357. J. GERGELY, Massachusetts General Hospital, Boston

1358. SHELBY D. GERKING, Indiana University

1359. GERALD C. GERLOFF, University of Wisconsin

1360. RICHARD W. GERRY, University of Maine

1361. ISIDORE GERSH, University of Illinois College of Medicine

1362. STANLEY N. GERSHOFF, Harvard School of Public Health

1363. MENARD M. GERTLER, New York Medical College

1364. S. R. GEVORKIANTZ, U. S. Forest Service, St. Paul

1365. GEORGE O. GEY, Johns Hopkins University

1366. ROBERT P. GEYER, Harvard School of Public Health

1367. DAVID M. GIBSON, University of Wisconsin

1368. JOHN G. GIBSON, Harvard Medical School

1369. JOEL GIDDENS, University of Georgia

1370. FREDERIC A. GIERE, Luther College

1371. ARTHUR C. GIESE, Stanford University

1372. WARREN GIFFORD, University of Arkansas

1373. FRANK A. GILBERT, Battelle Memorial Institute, Columbus

1374. R. B. GILLILAND, A. Guinness Son and Co., Ltd., Dublin

1375. LAUREN G. GILMAN, University of Miami

1376. ARTHUR S. GILSON, Washington University

1377. HAROLD S. GINSBERG, Western Reserve University

1378. DOUGLAS J. GIORGIO, St. Mary's Hospital, Evansville, Ind.

1379. RAYMOND E. GIRTON, Purdue University

1380. DAVID GITLIN, Harvard Medical School

1381. W. E. GIZYNSKI, U.S. Naval Hospital, Newport, R. I.

1382. GRACE GLANCE, Smithsonian Institution

1383. E. M. GLASER, University of Malaya

1384. KURT GLASER, 3646 N. Hermitage St., Chicago

1385. S. J. GLASS, Cedars of Lebanon Hospital, Los Angeles

1386. OTTO GLASSER, Cleveland Clinic Foundation

1387. W. J. GLECKLER, 2191 El Camino Real, San Mateo, Cal.

1388. WALDO S. GLOCK, Macalester College

1389. P. GLOOR

1390. G. C. GLOSER, Washington University

1391. ALFRED GLUCKSMANN, Cambridge University

1392. DAVID R. GODDARD, University of Pennsylvania

1393. C. W. GOFF, 30 Farmington Ave., Hartford, Conn.

1394. RICHARD A. GOFF, University of Oklahoma

1395. COLEMAN J. GOIN, University of Florida

1396. NORMAN I. GOLD, Peter Bent Brigham Hospital, Boston

1397. LEO R. GOLDBAUM, Walter Reed Army Medical Center

1398. RAYMOND W. GOLDBLUM, 3500 Fifth Ave., Pittsburgh

1399. DAVID E. GOLDMAN, Naval Medical Research Institute

1400. M. R. GOLDMAN, Montefiore and Passavant Hospital, Pittsburgh

1401. GRACE A. GOLDSMITH, Tulane University

1402. ROBERT GOLDSTEIN, Central Institute for the Deaf, St. Louis

1403. EUGENE GOLDWASSER, University of Chicago

1404. JOSEPH W. GOLDZIEHER, Southwest Foundation for Research and Education, San Antonio, Texas

1405. GEORGE GOMORI, University of Chicago

1406. CLARENCE J. GOODNIGHT, Purdue University

1407. T. W. GOODWIN, University of Liverpool

1408. ALLAN V. N. GOODYER, Yale University

1409. H. A. GORDON, University of Notre Dame

1410. HAROLD T. GORDON, University of California, Berkeley

1411. J. J. GORDON, Bristol Mental Hospital, England

1412. MORRIS A. GORDON, Medical College of South Carolina

1413. PAUL R. GORHAM, National Research Council, Ottawa

1414. RICHARD GORLIN, U. S. Naval Hospital, Portsmouth, Va.

1415. WILLIS A. GORTNER, Pineapple Research Institute, Honolulu

1416. CHARLES M. GOSS, Louisiana State University School of Medicine

1417. HAROLD GOSS, University of California, Davis

1418. LEONARD J. GOSS, New York Zoological Society

1419. RAYMOND GOSSELIN, Psychoanalytic Quarterly, N.Y.C.

1420. ROBERT A. GOSSELIN, University of Rochester

1421. JOSEPH S. GOTS, University of Pennsylvania

1422. DAVID GOTTLIEB, University of Illinois

1423. BERNARD S. GOULD, Massachusetts Institute of Technology

1424. DAVID GOULD, Schering Corporation, Bloomfield, N. J.

1425. WILLIAM M. GOVIER, The Upjohn Co., Kalamazoo, Mich.

1426. K. K. GOVIND, Municipal Laboratory, Fort Bombay

1427. B. GRAD, McGill University

1428. S. GRAFF, Presbyterian Hospital, N. Y. C.

1429. ALASTAIR GRAHAM, University of Reading

1430. BRUCE G. GRAHAM, University of Michigan

1431. CLAIRE E. GRAHAM, Wilson Laboratories, Chicago

1432. JOHN B. GRAHAM, University of North Carolina

1433. H. C. GRAM, Sundby Hospital, Copenhagen

1434. PHILIP GRANETT, Rutgers University

1435. S. GRANICK, Rockefeller Institute for Medical Research

1436. RAGNAR ARTHUR GRANIT, Karolinska Institute, Stockholm

1437. VERNE GRANT, Rancho Santa Ana Botanic Garden, Claremont, Cal.

1438. EDMOND GRASSET, Institute of Hygiene, Geneva

1439. CHARLES MURRAY GRATZ, 115 E. 61st St., N. Y. C.

1440. CHARLES R. GRAU, University of California, Berkeley

1441. CHARLES H. GRAY, University of London

1442. HORACE GRAY, 222 Olive Mill Lane, Santa Barbara, Cal.

1443. JOHN S. GRAY, Northwestern University Medical School

1444. L. H. GRAY, Mt. Vernon Hospital, Northwood, England

1445. M. GENEVA GRAY, Arthur D. Little, Inc., Cambridge, Mass.

1446. SEYMOUR J. GRAY, Peter Bent Brigham Hospital, Boston
1447. J. GRAYDON, Commonwealth Serum Laboratories, Parkville, Australia
1448. JOHN GRAYSON, University of Bristol
1449. G. A. GREATHOUSE, Orlando Research, Inc., Orlando, Fla.
1450. DAVID E. GREEN, University of Wisconsin
1451. HAROLD D. GREEN, Bowman School of Medicine
1452. HARRY GREEN, Wills Eye Hospital, Philadelphia
1453. JESSE R. GREEN, Anaconda Copper Mining Co., Bozeman, Mont.
1454. STANLEY GREEN, 1415 N. Taft St., Arlington, Va.
1455. WILLARD W. GREEN, University of Maryland
1456. DAVID M. GREENBERG, University of California, Berkeley
1457. LOUIS D. GREENBERG, University of California, San Francisco
1458. W. D. GREENBERG, University of California, San Francisco
1459. ROBERT B. GREENBLATT, Medical College of Georgia
1460. ISIDOR GREENWALD, New York University
1461. TIBOR J. GREENWALT, Milwaukee Blood Center, Inc.
1462. ALAN W. GREENWOOD, Agricultural Research Council, Edinburgh
1463. SHELDON B. GREER, Columbia University
1464. DONALD E. GREGG, Walter Reed Army Medical Center
1465. F. G. GREGORY, Imperial College of Science and Technology, London
1466. ROBERT G. GRENELL, University of Maryland School of Medicine
1467. WALTER F. GRETHER, Wright Air Development Center, Dayton, Ohio
1468. VICTOR A. GREULACH, University of North Carolina
1469. G. D. GREVILLE, Cambridge University
1470. SYLVIA F. GRIEM, University of Chicago
1471. DONALD R. GRIFFIN, Cornell University
1472. E. HARRISON GRIFFIN, Kings County Hospital, Brooklyn
1473. JOHN QUINTON GRIFFITH, Jr., Griffith Foundation for Medical Research, Inc., Philadelphia
1474. WENDELL H. GRIFFITH, Jr., University of California, Los Angeles
1475. WILLIAM H. GRIGGS, University of California, Davis
1476. ROY A. GRIZZELL, Jr., Kentucky Woodlands National Wildlife Refuge, Golden Pond
1477. ARTHUR GROLLMAN, Southwestern Medical College
1478. DANIEL S. GROSCH, North Carolina State College
1479. ALBERT C. GROSCHKE, The Borden Co., N. Y. C.
1480. JACOB GROSSMAN, Montefiore Hospital, N. Y. C.
1481. JAMES D. GROSSMAN, Ohio State University
1482. MORTON I. GROSSMAN, Veterans Administration Center, Los Angeles
1483. ROBERT D. GROVE, National Office of Vital Statistics

1484. CHARLES M. GRUBER, College of Medical Evangelists
1485. PETER GRUENWALD, Margaret Hague Maternity Hospital, Jersey City
1486. ROBERT H. GRUMMER, University of Wisconsin
1487. R. GRUNN, Motomco, Inc., N. Y. C.
1488. N. B. GUERRANT, Pennsylvania State University
1489. G. MASON GUEST, University of Texas Medical Branch
1490. H. R. GUILBERT, University of California, Davis
1491. W. R. GUILD, Yale University
1492. THOR W. GULLICKSON, University of Minnesota
1493. JAMES GUNCKEL, Rutgers University
1494. GORDON GUNTER, Gulf Coast Research Laboratory, Ocean Springs, Miss.
1495. F. A. GUNTHER, University of California, Riverside
1496. RALPH GUNTHER, University of California, Berkeley
1497. LILLIAN GURALNICK, National Office of Vital Statistics
1498. FRANK N. GURD, Harvard Medical School
1499. SAMUEL GURIN, University of Pennsylvania
1500. ASHLEY B. GURNEY, Smithsonian Institution
1501. F. G. GUSTAFSON, University of Michigan
1502. PAUL H. GUTH, Beaumont Army Hospital, El Paso, Texas
1503. SYLVESTER K. GUTH, General Electric Co., Cleveland
1504. ALEXANDER B. GUTMAN, Mount Sinai Hospital, N.Y.C.
1505. ALAN F. GUTTMACHER, Mount Sinai Hospital, N.Y.C.
1506. E. S. GUZMAN BARRON, University of Chicago
1507. L. GYERMEK, Pharmaco-Industrial Research Institute, Budapest
1508. PAUL GYORGY, University of Pennsylvania

1509. HARVEY B. HAAG, Medical College of Virginia
1510. J. R. HAAG, Oregon State College
1511. A. J. HAAGEN-SMIT, California Institute of Technology
1512. A. R. C. HAAS, University of California, Riverside
1513. THEODOR PHILIPP HAAS, Philadelphia College of Pharmacy and Science
1514. F. W. HAASIS, Box 1265, Carmel, Cal.
1515. SOL HABERMAN, Blood Grouping Laboratory, 300 Longwood Ave., Boston
1516. ERNST HABERMANN, University of Würzburg
1517. W. X. HACKMAN, Zoological Museum, Helsinki
1518. WILLIAM HAENSZEL, State Department of Health, Hartford, Conn.
1519. ERNEST C. HAGAN, U. S. Food and Drug Administration, Washington, D. C.
1520. HAROLD R. HAGAN, Box 312, Alma, Neb.
1521. ROBERT M. HAGAN, University of California, Davis
1522. W. A. HAGAN, Cornell University
1523. CHARLES W. HAGEN, Jr., Indiana University

1524. KENNETH S. HAGEN, University of California, Albany
1525. NORMA C. HAGMAN, Harvard School of Public Health
1526. PAUL F. HAHN, Meharry Medical College
1527. C. H. HAKANSSON, University of Copenhagen
1528. FRANZ HALBERG, University of Minnesota
1529. CARLYN HALDE, University of California, Los Angeles
1530. JOHN HALDI, Emory University
1531. DONALD E. HALE, Cleveland Clinic
1532. DAVID HALER, 27 Weymouth St., London
1533. THOMAS J. HALEY, University of California, Los Angeles
1534. D. A. HALL, University of Leeds
1535. E. K. HALL, University of Louisville
1536. E. RAYMOND HALL, University of Kansas
1537. FRANK G. HALL, Duke University
1538. R. P. HALL, New York University
1539. RAYMOND E. HALL, University of Kansas
1540. W. C. HALL, Texas Agricultural and Mechanical College
1541. W. J. HALL, U. S. Department of Agriculture, Beltsville
1542. H. L. J. HALLER, U.S. Department of Agriculture, Washington, D. C.
1543. BRUCE W. HALSTEAD, College of Medical Evangelists
1544. JOHN E. HALVER, U.S. Fish and Wildlife Service, Cook, Wash.
1545. THOMAS H. HAM, Western Reserve University
1546. JAMES I. HAMBLETON, U.S. Department of Agriculture, Beltsville
1547. W. E. HAMBOURGER, G. D. Searle and Co., Chicago
1548. FRANK E. HAMERSLAG, Wyeth Institute for Medical Research, Philadelphia
1549. HOWARD L. HAMILTON, Iowa State College
1550. JOSEPH G. HAMILTON, University of California, Berkeley
1551. PAUL B. HAMILTON, Alfred I. du Pont Institute, Wilmington, Del.
1552. W. J. HAMILTON, University of London
1553. W. J. HAMILTON, Jr., Cornell University
1554. WILLIAM F. HAMILTON, University of Georgia School of Medicine
1555. H. T. HAMMEL, University of Pennsylvania
1556. KARL C. HAMMER, University of California, Los Angeles
1557. JOHN HAMMOND, Cambridge University
1558. PAUL B. HAMMOND, University of Minnesota
1559. O. L. HAMNER, Michigan State University
1560. G. HAMOIR, University of Liege
1561. C. J. HAMRE
1562. PHILIP HANDLER, Duke University
1563. CHARLES O. HANDLEY, Jr., Smithsonian Institution
1564. MARTIN E. HANKE, University of Chicago
1565. JOHN H. HANKS, Harvard Medical School

1566. HARRY W. HANN, University of Michigan
1567. WILLIAM H. HANNA, Yater Clinic, Washington, D. C.
1568. SAM L. HANSARD, University of Tennessee, Oak Ridge
1569. ROY HANSBERRY, Shell Development Co., Modesto, Cal.
1570. CORWIN HANSCH, Pomona College
1571. WILLIAM HANSEL, Cornell University
1572. ELMER HANSEN, Oregon State College
1573. EARL D. HANSON, Yale University
1574. ROBERT P. HANSON, University of Wisconsin
1575. ROGER W. HANSON, University of Alabama
1576. W. D. HANSON, University of Florida
1577. FRED HARBERT, Jefferson Medical College
1578. MARGARET M. HARD, State College of Washington
1579. K. ALBERT HARDEN, Howard University
1580. ESTHER HARDENBERGH, Naval Medical Research Institute
1581. PAUL L. HARDING, U.S. Department of Agriculture, Orlando, Fla.
1582. JAMES D. HARDY, University of Pennsylvania
1583. ROSS HARDY, Long Beach State College
1584. JOHN W. HARMAN, University of Wisconsin
1585. PINCKNEY J. HARMAN, New York University
1586. A. A. HARPER, University of Durham
1587. E. O. HARPER, Jefferson Medical College
1588. HAROLD A. HARPER, University of San Francisco
1589. E. S. HARRAR, Duke University
1590. GEORGE T. HARRELL, University of Florida
1591. JAMES F. HARRINGTON, University of California, Davis
1592. DANIEL L. HARRIS, University of Chicago
1593. JOHN E. HARRIS, University of Oregon Medical School
1594. L. MARSHALL HARRIS, U.S. Naval Hospital, Newport, R.I.
1595. LORIN E. HARRIS, Utah State Agricultural College
1596. PHILIP L. HARRIS, Distillation Products, Inc., W. Rochester, N. Y.
1597. ROBERT S. HARRIS, Massachusetts Institute of Technology
1598. RUTH HARRIS, Columbia Presbyterian Medical Center, N. Y. C.
1599. VAN T. HARRIS, U.S. Fish and Wildlife Service, Lafayette, La.
1600. WILFRED HARRIS, 11 Chester Terrace, London
1601. FRANK HARRISON, Southwestern Medical School
1602. R. J. HARRISON, London Hospital Medical College
1603. BENJAMIN HARROW, College of the City of New York
1604. E. J. HART, Argonne National Laboratory
1605. J. SANFORD HART, National Research Council of Canada
1606. ROBERT A. HARTE, Sharp and Dohme, Inc., Glenolden, Pa.

1607. R. L. HARTLES, University of Liverpool
1608. CARL HARTLEY, U.S. Department of Agriculture, Beltsville
1609. H. K. HARTLINE, Rockefeller Institute for Medical Research
1610. CARL G. HARTMAN, Ortho Research Foundation, Raritan, N. J.
1611. FRANK A. HARTMAN, Ohio State University
1612. OLGA HARTMAN, University of Southern California
1613. W. STANLEY HARTROFT, Washington University
1614. NORMAN HARTWEG, University of Michigan
1615. JONATHAN L. HARTWELL, National Cancer Institute
1616. A. L. HARVEY, U.S. Department of Agriculture, Beltsville
1617. D. HARVEY, Rowett Research Institute, Bucksburn, Scotland
1618. E. NEWTON HARVEY, Princeton University
1619. GEORGE T. HARVEY, Saulte Sainte Marie, Ontario
1620. H. J. HARWOOD, Armour and Co., Chicago
1621. ARTHUR L. HASKINS, Washington University
1622. CARYL P. HASKINS, Haskins Laboratories, N. Y. C.
1623. R. H. HASKINS, Prairie Regional Laboratory, Saskatoon
1624. G. A. D. HASLEWOOD, Guy's Hospital Medical School, London
1625. CHARLES C. HASSETT, Army Chemical Center, Md.
1626. A. BAIRD HASTINGS, Harvard Medical School
1627. ANNA B. HASTINGS, British Museum of Natural History
1628. ELLSWORTH B. HASTINGS, Montana State College
1629. THEODORE F. HATCH, University of Pittsburgh
1630. EDWARD S. HATHAWAY, Tulane University
1631. MILICENT HATHAWAY, U.S. Department of Agriculture, Washington, D. C.
1632. NIELS HAUGAARD, University of Pennsylvania
1633. FELIX HAUROWITZ, Indiana University
1634. W. PAUL HAVENS, Jr., Jefferson Medical College
1635. PHILIP B. HAWK, 750 W. 50th St., Miami Beach, Fla.
1636. ROSEMARY D. HAWKINS, 1595 Decarie Blvd., Montreal
1637. W. W. HAWKINS, National Research Council, Halifax, N.S.
1638. D. C. HAWTHORNE, California Institute of Technology
1639. FRANCIS T. HAXO, Scripps Institution of Oceanography
1640. JAMES HAY, Harvard University
1641. M. HAYAKAWA, University of Hirosaki
1642. MYKOLA H. HAYDAK, University of Minnesota
1643. WEBB HAYMAKER, Armed Forces Institute of Pathology
1644. WILLIAM C. HAYNES, U.S. Department of Agriculture, Peoria, Ill.
1645. FRANK A. HAYS, University of Massachusetts
1646. HERMAN E. HAYWARD, U. S. Department of Agriculture, Riverside, Cal.
1647. ALBERT B. HEAGY, University of Maryland
1648. C. WRIGHT HEATH, Tufts College

1649. ROBERT G. HEATH, Tulane University
1650. HANS. H. HECHT, University of Utah
1651. FRANK J. HECK, Mayo Clinic
1652. L. D. HEDGECOCK, Mayo Clinic
1653. JOEL W. HEDGPETH, Scripps Institution of Oceanography
1654. ALBERT H. HEGNAUER, Boston University
1655. D. MARK HEGSTED, Harvard School of Public Health
1656. MICHAEL HEIDELBERGER, Columbia University
1657. FORDYCE HEILMAN, Mayo Clinic
1658. WERNER G. HEIM, University of California, Los Angeles
1659. C. R. HEISLER, Western Reserve University
1660. C. E. HEIT, New York Agricultural Experiment Station, Geneva
1661. LESLIE HELLERMAN, Johns Hopkins University
1662. JOHN D. HELM, 720 Columbia Ave., Lancaster, Pa.
1663. ALLAN HEMINGWAY, University of California, Los Angeles
1664. EDWARD HENDERSON, Schering Corp., Bloomfield, N. J.
1665. JAMES H. M. HENDERSON, Tuskegee Institute
1666. L. M. HENDERSON, University of Illinois
1667. LAVANIEL L. HENDERSON, Tuskegee Institute
1668. STERLING B. HENDRICKS, U. S. Department of Agriculture, Beltsville
1669. E. B. HENDRY, Western Infirmary, Glasgow
1670. NORBERT HENNING, University of Würzburg
1671. CHARLES E. HENRY, Institute of Living, Hartford, Conn.
1672. FRANKLIN M. HENRY, University of California, Berkeley
1673. JOHN HENSALA, University of Maryland School of Medicine
1674. AUSTIN F. HENSCHEL, Quartermaster Research and Development Center, Natick, Mass.
1675. GEORGE H. HEPTING, U. S. Forest Service, Asheville, N.C.
1676. WILLIAM B. HERMS (Deceased)
1677. THOMAS HERNANDEZ, Louisiana State University
1678. C. JUDSON HERRICK, 236 Morning Side Dr., Grand Rapids, Mich.
1679. RAYMOND C. HERRIN, University of Wisconsin
1680. L. P. HERRINGTON, Yale University
1681. GEORGE R. HERRMANN, University of Texas Medical Branch
1682. ROY G. HERRMAN, Eli Lilly & Co., Indianapolis
1683. A. D. HERSHEY, Carnegie Institution of Washington, Cold Spring Harbor, N. Y.
1684. S. G. HERSHEY, 235 E. 22nd St., N. Y. C.
1685. MELVILLE J. HERSKOVITS, Northwestern University
1686. ARTHUR T. HERTIG, Harvard Medical School
1687. ROY HERTZ, National Cancer Institute
1688. H. T. E. HERTZBERG, Wright Air Development Center, Dayton, Ohio

1689. WALTER C. HESS, Georgetown University
1690. C. O. HESSE, University of California, Davis
1691. DUNCAN C. HETHERINGTON, Duke University
1692. HERBERT O. HETZER, U.S. Department of Agriculture, Beltsville
1693. G. F. HEUSER, Cornell University
1694. GEORGE HEVESY, University of Copenhagen
1695. E. A. HEWITT, Iowa State College
1696. G. FLETCHER HEWITT, Jr., National Institute of Arthritis and Metabolic Diseases
1697. HAROLD B. HEWITT, Westminster Medical School, London
1698. OLIVER H. HEWITT, Cornell University
1699. C. HEYMANS, University of Ghent
1700. A. N. J. HEYN, Clemson Agricultural College
1701. F. HEYROTH, University of Cincinnati
1702. ANTONIN HEYROVSKY, University Hospital, Prague
1703. C. W. HIATT, Walter Reed Army Medical Center
1704. EDWIN P. HIATT, University of North Carolina
1705. HOPE HIBBARD, Oberlin College
1706. JOHN W. HIBBS, Ohio Agricultural Experiment Station, Wooster
1707. JOHN B. HICKAM, Duke University
1708. JOSEPH J. HICKEY, University of Wisconsin
1709. RICHARD J. HICKEY, University of Pennsylvania
1710. SAMUEL P. HICKS, New England Deaconess Hospital, Boston
1711. STANLEY W. HIER, Wilson Laboratories, Chicago
1712. W. A. HIESTAND, Purdue University
1713. GEORGE M. HIGGINS, Mayo Foundation
1714. N. C. HIGHTOWER, Scott and White Clinic, Temple, Texas
1715. L. BODINE HIGLEY, State University of Iowa
1716. JOHN D. HILCHEY, Boyce Thompson Institute for Plant Research
1717. E. M. HILDEBRAND, U.S. Department of Agriculture, Beltsville
1718. ALBERT C. HILDEBRANDT, University of Wisconsin
1719. CHARLES H. HILL, University of North Carolina
1720. ROBERT M. HILL, University of Colorado School of Medicine
1721. MARY HILTZ, University of Manitoba
1722. HAROLD E. HIMWICH, Galesburg State Research Hospital, Ill.
1723. WILLIAMINA A. HIMWICH, Galesburg State Research Hospital, Ill.
1724. H. M. HINES, State University of Iowa
1725. MARION HINES, Emory University
1726. FRANK HINMAN, Jr., University of California, San Francisco
1727. ELLY HINREINER, University of California, Davis

1728. TAYLOR HINTON, University of California, Los Angeles
1729. HILDE E. HIRSCH, Washington University
1730. S. HIRSCH, Free University of Brussels
1731. NELL HIRSCHBERG, State Laboratory of Hygiene, Raleigh, N. C.
1732. JOHN S. HIRSCHBOECK, Marquette University
1733. A. A. HIRSH, U. S. Department of Agriculture
1734. A. E. HITCHCOCK, Boyce Thompson Institute for Plant Research
1735. DAVID I. HITCHCOCK, Yale University
1736. GEORGE H. HITCHINGS, Wellcome Research Laboratories, Tuckahoe, N. Y.
1737. KOICHI HIWATASHI, Tohoku University, Sendai, Japan
1738. E. H. HIXON, University of North Carolina
1739. O. F. HIXON, Laboratory of Vitamin Technology, Chicago
1740. BRUCE M. HOBSON, Usher Institute, Edinburgh
1741. LAWRENCE B. HOBSON, Squibb Institute for Medical Research, New Brunswick, N.J.
1742. P. HOBSON, Rowett Research Institute, Bucksburn, Scotland
1743. HANS HOCH, Medical College of Virginia
1744. RAYMOND J. HOCK, Arctic Health Research Center, Anchorage, Alaska
1745. ROBERT C. HOCKETT, 72 Howell Ave., Larchmont, N.Y.
1746. GEORGE M. HOCKING, Alabama Polytechnic Institute
1747. HAROLD C. HODGE, University of Rochester
1748. PAUL C. HODGES, University of Chicago
1749. W. E. HODGES, University of Toronto
1750. A. L. HODGKIN, Cambridge University
1751. PAUL F. A. HOEFER, Presbyterian Hospital, N.Y.C.
1752. WILLARD M. HOEHN, G. D. Searle and Co., Chicago
1753. NORMAND L. HOERR, Western Reserve University
1754. A. W. HOFER, Cornell University
1755. F. W. HOFFBAUER, University of Minnesota
1756. C. H. HOFFMAN, U. S. Department of Agriculture, Beltsville
1757. JOSEPH G. HOFFMAN, Roswell Park Memorial Institute, Buffalo
1758. DONALD F. HOFFMEISTER, University of Illinois
1759. ALBERT G. HOGAN, University of Missouri
1760. LOWELL E. HOKIN, McGill University
1761. E. S. HOLDSWORTH, National Institute for Research in Dairying, Shinfield, England
1762. ALEXANDER HOLLAENDER, Oak Ridge National Laboratory
1763. ALBERT H. HOLLAND, Jr., U.S. Food and Drug Administration, Washington, D. C.
1764. JOHN M. HOLLAND, Rohm and Haas Co., Philadelphia
1765. FRANKLIN HOLLANDER, Mount Sinai Hospital, N.Y.C.
1766. K. T. HOLLEY, Georgia Experiment Station, Experiment

1767. H. H. HOLMAN, Agricultural Research Council, Compton, England
1768. F. O. HOLMES, Rockefeller Institute for Medical Research
1769. JOSEPH H. HOLMES, University of Colorado School of Medicine
1770. P. HOLMES, University of Western Australia
1771. A. S. HOLT, University of Illinois
1772. JOHANNES HOLTFRETER, University of Rochester
1773. D. E. HOLTGRAVE, University of Louisville
1774. GEORGE G. HOLZ, Jr., Syracuse University
1775. ICIE MACY HOOBLER, Merrill-Palmer School, Detroit
1776. DONALD W. HOOD, Texas Agricultural and Mechanical College
1777. J. D. HOOD, National Hospital, London
1778. DAVENPORT HOOKER, University of Pittsburgh
1779. EMMET T. HOOPER, University of Michigan
1780. SAM R. HOOVER, U. S. Department of Agriculture, Philadelphia
1781. DWIGHT L. HOPKINS (Deceased)
1782. GILES E. HOPKINS, The Wool Bureau, Inc., N. Y. C.
1783. SEWELL H. HOPKINS, Texas Agricultural and Mechanical College
1784. T. H. HOPPER, U. S. Department of Agriculture, New Orleans
1785. CARL A. HOPPERT, Michigan State University
1786. THOMAS J. HORDER
1787. BERNARD L. HORECKER, National Institutes of Health
1788. MILLARD J. HORN, U. S. Department of Agriculture, Beltsville
1789. JAMES G. HORSFALL, Connecticut Agricultural Experiment Station, New Haven
1790. WILLIAM R. HORSFALL, University of Illinois
1791. STEVEN M. HORVATH, State University of Iowa
1792. M. K. HORWITT, Elgin State Hospital, Ill.
1793. ORVILLE HORWITZ, University of Pennsylvania
1794. W. M. HOSKINS, University of California, Berkeley
1795. C. RILEY HOUCK, University of Tennessee, Memphis
1796. A. HOUGH, National Institutes of Health
1797. G. V. C. HOUGHLAND, U. S. Department of Agriculture, Beltsville
1798. B. A. HOUSSAY, Institute of Biology and Experimental Medicine, Buenos Aires
1799. HOWARD L. HOUSE, Department of Agriculture, Belleville, Ontario
1800. EARL E. HOUSEMAN, U. S. Department of Agriculture, Washington, D. C.
1801. WILLIAM HOVANITZ, University of San Francisco
1802. E. L. HOVE, Alabama Polytechnic Institute
1803. C. C. HOWARD, 18 Prospect Park West, Brooklyn
1804. R. PALMER HOWARD, University of Oklahoma Medical School

1805. RICHARD A. HOWARD, Harvard University
1806. ROBERT S. HOWARD, University of Delaware
1807. EUGENE E. HOWE, Merck and Co., Rahway, N. J.
1808. PAUL E. HOWE, U. S. Department of Agriculture, Beltsville
1809. A. B. HOWELL, Alna, Maine
1810. D. E. HOWELL, Oklahoma Agricultural and Mechanical College
1811. DAVID S. HOWELL, National Heart Institute
1812. ROBERT W. HOWELL, U. S. Department of Agriculture, Urbana, Ill.
1813. GUNTER HOXTER, Hospital das Clinicas, São Paulo
1814. AVERY S. HOYT, U. S. Department of Agriculture, Washington, D. C.
1815. DONALD M. HUBBARD, University of Cincinnati
1816. RUTH HUBBARD, Harvard University
1817. L. L. HUBER, Pennsylvania State University
1818. MARTIN R. HUBERTY, University of California, Los Angeles
1819. FRANK M. HUENNEKENS, University of Washington
1820. THEODORE F. HUETER, Massachusetts Institute of Technology
1821. C. F. HUFFMAN, Michigan State University
1822. A. ST. G. HUGGETT, University of London
1823. CHARLES B. HUGGINS, University of Chicago
1824. KENNETH H. HUGHES, University of California, Albany
1825. WALTER HUGHES, Johns Hopkins University
1826. WILLIAM F. HUGHES, University of Illinois College of Medicine
1827. C. N. HUHTANEN, National Dairy Research Laboratories, Oakdale, N. Y.
1828. F. HUIDOBRO, Catholic University of Chile
1829. FRED H. HULL, University of Florida
1830. HERBERT M. HULL, U. S. Department of Agriculture, Tucson
1831. ROBERT N. HULL, Eli Lilly and Co., Indianapolis
1832. HAROLD R. HULPIEU, Indiana University School of Medicine
1833. HAROLD J. HUMM, Duke University
1834. GEORGE F. HUMPHREY, University of Sydney
1835. R. R. HUMPHREY, University of Buffalo
1836. T. HUMPHREY, University of Pittsburgh
1837. FRANK P. HUNGATE, General Electric Co., Richland, Wash.
1838. GERALD F. HUNGERFORD, George Washington University
1839. J. N. HUNT, Guy's Hospital, London
1840. THOMAS E. HUNT, University of Alabama
1841. F. R. HUNTER, University of Illinois College of Medicine
1842. G. HUNTER, Stoke Mandeville Hospital, Aylesbury, England
1843. JOHN HUNTER, Defense Research Medical Laboratories, Toronto
1844. MATTHEW C. HUNTER, Hunter Laboratories, Metairie, La.

1845. NORVELL W. HUNTER, Morgan State College
1846. CHARLES D. HURD, Northwestern University
1847. V. O. HURME, Forsyth Dental Infirmary for Children, Boston
1848. W. W. HURST, University of Oregon Medical School
1849. W. J. HUSA, University of Florida
1850. JOHN O. HUTCHENS, University of Chicago
1851. G. EVELYN HUTCHINSON, Yale University
1852. S. H. HUTNER, Haskins Laboratories, N. Y. C.
1853. F. B. HUTT, Cornell University
1854. A. F. HUXLEY, Cambridge University
1855. C. LEE HUYCK, St. Louis College of Pharmacy
1856. HEMAN L. IBSEN, Kansas State College
1857. DAVID R. IDLER, Pacific Fisheries Experimental Station, Vancouver
1858. ALBERTA ILIFF, University of Colorado School of Medicine
1859. DWIGHT J. INGLE, University of Chicago
1860. C. T. INGOLD, University of London
1861. MARYLOU INGRAM, University of Rochester
1862. W. R. INGRAM, State University of Iowa
1863. DON D. IRISH, Dow Chemical Co., Midland, Mich.
1864. H. M. IRVIN, U. S. Department of Agriculture, Beltsville
1865. J. LOGAN IRVIN, University of North Carolina
1866. M. R. IRWIN, University of Wisconsin
1867. LEO A. ISAAC, U. S. Forest Service, Portland, Ore.
1868. H. S. ISBELL, National Bureau of Standards
1869. DUANE ISLEY, Iowa State College
1870. MARTIN C. G. ISRAËLS, Royal Infirmary, Manchester, England
1871. S. S. IVANOFF, Mississippi State College
1872. MARGARET IVES, American Can Co., Maywood, Ill.
1873. A. C. IVY, University of Illinois College of Medicine
1874. IWAO IWAMURA, University of Mirjazaki, Japan
1875. VINCENTE JABONERO, National Institute of Medical Sciences, Oviedo, Spain
1876. F. G. JACKSON
1877. GEORGE GEE JACKSON, University of Illinois College of Medicine
1878. K. D. JACOB, U. S. Department of Agriculture, Beltsville
1879. M. H. JACOBS, University of Pennsylvania
1880. LEON O. JACOBSON, University of Chicago
1881. LOUIS JACOBSON, University of California, Berkeley
1882. W. JACOBSON, Cambridge University
1883. JAY JACOBY, Ohio State University
1884. WERNER G. JAFFÉE, National Institute of Nutrition, Caracas
1885. W. O. JAMES, Oxford University

1886. E. W. JAMESON, Jr., University of California, Davis
1887. BERNARD J. JANDORF, Army Chemical Center, Md.
1888. LEONARD L. JANSEN, U. S. Department of Agriculture, Beltsville
1889. L. B. JAQUES, University of Saskatchewan
1890. R. JAQUES, CIBA Ltd., Basle
1891. F. G. JARVIS, Idaho State College
1892. HERBERT H. JASPER, McGill University
1893. W. E. JEFFERSON, University of Texas
1894. HAROLD J. JEGHERS, Georgetown University
1895. DALE W. JENKINS, Camp Detrick, Md.
1896. PAUL JENNER, U. S. Food and Drug Administration, Washington, D. C.
1897. MARSHALL W. JENNISON, Syracuse University
1898. HANS JENNY, University of California, Berkeley
1899. C. O. JENSEN, Pennsylvania State University
1900. D. D. JENSEN, University of California, Berkeley
1901. GEORGE B. JERZY-GLASS, New York Medical College
1902. WALTER W. JETTER, Latrobe Hospital Assoc., Latrobe, Pa.
1903. S. V. JOB, Central Marine Fisheries Research Laboratory, Mandapam Camp, S. India
1904. IVAR JOHANSSON, University of Uppsala
1905. CAROL J. JOHNS, Johns Hopkins University
1906. B. CONNOR JOHNSON, University of Illinois
1907. C. M. JOHNSON, University of California, Berkeley
1908. CARL H. JOHNSON, University of Florida
1909. CHARLES G. JOHNSON, Wayne State University
1910. DAVID H. JOHNSON, Smithsonian Institution
1911. ELTON L. JOHNSON, University of Minnesota
1912. FRANK H. JOHNSON, Princeton University
1913. JULIUS JOHNSON, Dow Chemical Co., Midland, Mich.
1914. L. P. V. JOHNSON, University of Alberta
1915. PAUL E. JOHNSON, National Research Council
1916. PHYLLIS T. JOHNSON, Smithsonian Institution
1917. R. W. JOHNSON, U. S. Department of Agriculture, Peoria, Ill.
1918. RICHARD P. JOHNSON, Valley Forge Army Hospital, Phoenixville, Pa.
1919. ROBERT E. JOHNSON, University of Illinois
1920. T. EARLE JOHNSON, University of Alabama
1921. WILLIAM S. JOHNSON, Rohm and Haas Co., Philadelphia
1922. WILLIS H. JOHNSON, Wabash College
1923. FRANCES A. JOHNSTON, Cornell University
1924. M. W. JOHNSTON, University of Toronto
1925. ROBERT L. JOHNSTON, Caylor-Nickel Clinic, Bluffton, Ind.
1926. DONALD B. JOHNSTONE, University of Vermont

1927. NORMAN H. JOLLIFFE, Columbia University
1928. ANNE K. JONES
1929. F. AVERY JONES, Central Middlesex Hospital, London
1930. F. NOWELL JONES, University of California, Los Angeles
1931. JACK COLVARD JONES, National Microbiological Institute
1932. L. MEYER JONES, Iowa State College
1933. OLIVER P. JONES, University of Buffalo
1934. H. E. JORDAN, University of Virginia
1935. NORMAN R. JOSEPH, University of Illinois College of Medicine
1936. HOWARD R. JOSEPHSON, U.S. Forest Service, Washington, D. C.
1937. M. A. JOSLYN, University of California, Berkeley
1938. HUDSON JOST, University of Georgia
1939. DEANE B. JUDD, National Bureau of Standards
1940. WESLEY P. JUDKINS, Virginia Polytechnic Institute
1941. R. W. JUGENHEIMER, University of Illinois
1942. MORLEY A. JULL, University of Maryland
1943. O. L. JUSTICE, U. S. Department of Agriculture, Beltsville
1944. ELVIN A. KABAT, Columbia University
1945. B. M. KAGAN, Michael Reese Hospital, Chicago
1946. REUBEN L. KAHN, University of Michigan
1947. BETTY F. KALISZEWSKI, Boston University
1948. KURT KALLE, German Hydrographical Institution, Hamburg
1949. M. V. KAMAT, Haffkine Institute, Bombay
1950. W. G. KAMMLADE, University of Illinois
1951. ELIZABETH M. KAMPA, Scripps Institution of Oceanography
1952. OTTO F. KAMPMEIER, College of Medical Evangelists
1953. GERALD S. KANTER, Albany Medical College
1954. A. A. KAPLAN, State University of New York College of Medicine, Brooklyn
1955. NATHAN O. KAPLAN, Johns Hopkins University
1956. ROBERT M. KARK, University of Illinois
1957. ROBERT E. KARPER, Texas Agricultural and Mechanical College, Lubbock
1958. PETER V. KARPOVICH, Springfield College
1959. LEO KARTMAN, U. S. Public Health Service, San Francisco
1960. B. KASSANIS, Rothamsted Experiment Station, Harpenden, England
1961. JOE KASTELIC, Iowa State College
1962. K. C. KATES
1963. MAX KATZ, U. S. Public Health Service, Corvallis, Ore.
1964. SOLOMON KATZENELBOGEN, George Washington University
1965. FRANK H. KAUFERT, University of Minnesota
1966. HANS KAUNITZ, Columbia University
1967. FREDERICK W. KAVANAGH, Eli Lilly and Co., Indianapolis
1968. R. KAWASAKI, University of Hirosaki

1969. KINGSLEY KAY, Department of National Health and Welfare, Ottawa
1970. SIDNEY KAYE, State Department of Health, Richmond, Va.
1971. CLYDE W. KEARNS, University of Illinois
1972. GEORGE H. KELKER, Utah State Agricultural College
1973. AARON KELLNER, New York Hospital
1974. REMINGTON KELLOGG, Smithsonian Institution
1975. J. A. KELLY, Dow Chemical Co., Midland, Mich.
1976. R. EMMET KELLY, Monsanto Chemical Co., St. Louis
1977. SALLY M. KELLY, New York State Department of Health, Albany
1978. WILLIAM D. KELLY, University of Minnesota
1979. ARTHUR KELMAN, North Carolina State College
1980. ARTHUR R. KEMMERER, University of Arizona
1981. N. E. KEMP, University of Michigan
1982. W. N. KEMP, 2414 Main St., Vancouver
1983. W. F. F. KEMSLEY
1984. E. E. KENAGA, Dow Chemical Co., Midland, Mich.
1985. JAMES I. KENDALL, College of the City of New York
1986. S. CHARLES KENDEIGH, University of Illinois
1987. J. F. KENDRICK, U.S. Department of Agriculture, Washington, D. C.
1988. DONALD KENNEDY, Harvard University
1989. IRVIN KERLAN, U. S. Food and Drug Administration, Washington, D. C.
1990. STANLEY E. KERR, American University of Beirut
1991. BRINA KESSEL, University of Alaska
1992. S. KESSLER, National Drug Co., Philadelphia
1993. ERNEST B. KESTER, U. S. Department of Agriculture, Berkeley, Cal.
1994. JAMES W. KESTERSON, University of Florida, Lake Alfred
1995. SEYMOUR S. KETY, National Institute of Mental Health
1996. R. D. KEYNES, Cambridge University
1997. ANCEL KEYS, University of Minnesota
1998. TEOFIL KHEIM, Washington University
1999. H. H. KIBLER, University of Missouri
2000. GEORGE W. KIDDER, Amherst College
2001. T. A. KIESSELBACH, University of Nebraska
2002. H. KIKKAWA, University of Osaka
2003. JOHN H. KILBUCK, Dried Fruit Assoc., Fresno, Cal.
2004. J. E. KINDRED, University of Virginia
2005. ALLEN L. KING, Dartmouth College
2006. C. G. KING, Nutrition Foundation, Inc., N. Y. C.
2007. E. J. KING, Hammersmith Hospital, London
2008. J. H. KING, Walter Reed Army Medical Center
2009. MURRAY V. KING, Polytechnic Institute of Brooklyn
2010. THOMAS H. KING, University of Minnesota

2011. WALTER C. KING, University of Michigan
2012. H. E. KINGMAN, Wyoming Hereford Ranch, Cheyenne
2013. LAURANCE W. KINSELL, Alameda County Hospital, Oakland, Cal.
2014. V. EVERETT KINSEY, Kresge Eye Institute, Detroit
2015. D. C. KIPLINGER, Ohio State University
2016. JOHN ESBEN KIRK, Washington University
2017. DON KIRKHAM, Iowa State College
2018. WILLIAM R. KIRKHAM, University of Missouri
2019. HENRY KIRKPATRICK
2020. JOSEPH B. KIRSNER, University of Chicago
2021. BRUNO KISCH, 845 West End Ave., N. Y. C.
2022. WALTER KISIELESKI, Argonne National Laboratories
2023. GEORGE W. KISKER, University of Cincinnati
2024. A. G. KITCHELL, University of Durham
2025. LAURENCE M. KLAUBER, 233 W. Juniper St., San Diego
2026. MAX KLEIBER, University of California, Davis
2027. J. RAYMOND KLEIN, Brookhaven National Laboratory
2028. RICHARD M. KLEIN, New York Botanical Garden
2029. ISRAEL S. KLEINER, New York Medical College
2030. LEWIS H. KLEINHOLZ, Reed College
2031. NATHANIEL KLEITMAN, University of Chicago
2032. W. O. KLINGMAN, University of Virginia
2033. ARNOLD KLOPPER, Medical Research Council, Edinburgh
2034. I. M. KLOTZ, Northwestern University
2035. G. G. KNAPPEIS, University of Copenhagen
2036. GEORGES KNAYSI, Cornell University
2037. C. A. KNIGHT, University of California, Berkeley
2038. KENNETH L. KNIGHT, Department of the Navy, Washington, D. C.
2039. PATRICIA F. KNIGHT, University of California, Los Angeles
2040. STANLEY G. KNIGHT, University of Wisconsin
2041. E. F. KNIPLING, U.S. Department of Agriculture, Beltsville
2042. IRVING W. KNOBLOCH, Michigan State University
2043. FRANK P. KNOWLTON, 1356 Westmoreland Ave., Syracuse
2044. HERBERT KNUTSON, Kansas State College
2045. OSAMU KOBAYASHI, Mie Medical College, Tsu City, Japan
2046. ROBERT M. KOCH, University of Nebraska, Ft. Robinson
2047. CHARLES D. KOCHAKIAN, University of Oklahoma Medical Center
2048. ERICH KÖHLER, Government Establishment for Farming and Forestry Research, Celle, Germany
2049. GEORGE B. KOELLE, University of Pennsylvania
2050. VIRGIL L. KOENIG, Veterans Administration Research Hospital, Chicago
2051. HELMUT KOHNKE, Purdue University

2052. M. KOJIMA, Niigata University School of Medicine
2053. PAUL KOLACHOV, Joseph E. Seagram and Sons, Inc., Louisville
2054. DOV KOLLER, Hebrew University
2055. P. C. KOLLER, Royal Cancer Hospital, London
2056. JERRY J. KOLLROS, State University of Iowa
2057. SIMON A. KOMAROV, Temple University
2058. DAVID R. KOMINZ, National Institutes of Health
2059. W. H. W. Komp (Deceased)
2060. KINSUKI KONDO, University of Kyoto
2061. D. J. KOOYMAN, Procter and Gamble Co., Cincinnati
2062. THEODORE KOPPANYI, Georgetown University
2063. V. KORENCHEVSKY, Oxford University
2064. SEYMOUR KORKES, Duke University
2065. H. KORMAN, Beth Israel Hospital, Boston
2066. S. I. KORNHAUSER, University of Louisville
2067. STEWART A. KOSER, University of Chicago
2068. DANIEL E. KOSHLAND, Brookhaven National Laboratory
2069. FREDERIC J. KOTTKE, University of Minnesota
2070. R. H. KOUGH, University of Pennsylvania
2071. WILLIAM B. KOUNTZ, Washington University
2072. L. M. KOZLOFF, University of Chicago
2073. THEODORE T. KOZOWSKI, University of Massachusetts
2074. ROY R. KRACKE (Deceased)
2075. AMIHUD KRAMER, University of Maryland
2076. PAUL J. KRAMER, Duke University
2077. B. A. KRANTZ, U. S. Department of Agriculture, Billings, Mont.
2078. JOHN C. KRANTZ, Jr., University of Maryland School of Medicine
2079. KERMIT KRANTZ, University of Vermont
2080. WILLIAM A. KRATZ, Trinity University, San Antonio, Texas
2081. F. H. KRATZER, University of California, Davis
2082. E. J. KRAUS, Oregon State College
2083. ARLINGTON C. KRAUSE, University of Chicago
2084. R. F. KRAUSE, West Virginia University
2085. BEATRICE KRAUSS, Pineapple Research Institute, Honolulu
2086. ROBERT W. KRAUSS, University of Maryland
2087. HEINRICH KRAUT, Max Planck Institute of Work Physiology, Dortmund
2088. H. F. KRAYBILL, Army Medical Nutrition Laboratory, Denver
2089. H. ROBERT KREAR, Emlenton, Pa.
2090. H. A. KREBS, Oxford University
2091. WILLARD A. KREHL, Yale University

2092. WENDELL J. S. KREIG, Northwestern University School of Medicine
2093. WILLIAM A. KREUTZER, Shell Development Co., Modesto, Cal.
2094. CARL H. KRIEGER, Wisconsin Alumni Research Foundation, Madison
2095. CHARLES J. KRISTER, E. I. du Pont de Nemours and Co., Wilmington, Del.
2096. WILTON M. KROGMAN, University of Pennsylvania
2097. KARL V. KROMBEIN, Smithsonian Institution
2098. STEPHEN KROP, Army Chemical Center, Md.
2099. FRIEDRICH KRÜGER, University of Münster
2100. HUGO KRUEGER, Oregon State College
2101. KEATHA K. KRUEGER, University of South Dakota
2102. VLADIMIR N. KRUKOVSKY, Cornell University
2103. WENDELL KRULL, Oklahoma Agriculture and Mechanical College
2104. MARCUS A. KRUPP, Palo Alto Medical Research Foundation, Cal.
2105. VLADISLAV KRUTA, Charles University
2106. H. E. KUBITSCHEK, Argonne National Laboratory
2107. KATHRYN D. KUCK, 23135 Cole St., Roseville, Mich.
2108. STEPHEN W. KUFFLER, Johns Hopkins University
2109. OTTO E. KUGLER, University of Illinois
2110. M. H. KUIZENGA, The Upjohn Co., Kalamazoo, Mich.
2111. M. E. KULKARNI, Haffkine Institute, Bombay
2112. ERNEST KUN, Tulane University
2113. M. M. KUNDE, Northwestern University Medical School
2114. DHIRENDRA KUNDU, National Research Council
2115. MOSES KUNITZ, Rockefeller Institute for Medical Research
2116. EDWARD C. KUNKLE, Duke University
2117. ALBERT KUNTZ, St. Louis University
2118. PETER T. KUO, University of Pennsylvania
2119. ALFRED B. KUPFERBERG, Ortho Research Foundation, Raritan, N. J.
2120. N. B. KURNICK, Veterans Administration Hospital, Long Beach, Cal.
2121. ADRIAN C. KUYPER, Wayne State University
2122. SVEN ANCHER KVORNING, University of Copenhagen

2123. DANIEL H. LABBY, University of Oregon Medical School
2124. ERNEST A. LACHNER, Smithsonian Institution
2125. ROBERT W. LACKEY, Southwestern Medical College
2126. KARL F. LAGLER, University of Michigan
2127. KEITH J. LAIDLER, Catholic University of America
2128. ABEL LAJTHA, Columbia University
2129. KOLOMAN LAKI, National Institute of Arthritis and Metabolic Diseases
2130. JOSEPH J. LALICH, University of Wisconsin

2131. CARL LAMANNA, Johns Hopkins University
2132. CHRISTIAN J. LAMBERSTEN, University of Pennsylvania
2133. JOSÉ A. LAMELAS, Valdecilla Hospital, Santander, Spain
2134. J. OLIVER LAMPEN, Squibb Institute for Medical Research, New Brunswick, N. J.
2135. HAROLD LAMPORT, Yale University
2136. LOUIS LAMY, Pasteur Institute, Paris
2137. L. Y. LANCASTER, University of Kentucky
2138. WALTER LANDAUER, University of Connecticut
2139. CARNEY LANDIS, New York State Psychiatric Institute, N. Y. C.
2140. THOMAS H. LANGLOIS, Ohio State University
2141. A. F. LANGLYKKE, Squibb Institute for Medical Research, New Brunswick, N. J.
2142. EDWIN M. LANSFORD, Jr., University of Texas
2143. HENRY A. LARDY, University of Wisconsin
2144. EDWARD J. LARGENT, University of Cincinnati
2145. IRA La RIVERS, University of Nevada
2146. SIGURD LARSEN, Laboratory of Agricultural Chemistry, Copenhagen
2147. D. L. LARSON, Walter Reed Army Medical Center
2148. EDWARD LARSON, University of Miami
2149. GEORGE R. La RUE, U. S. Department of Agriculture, Beltsville
2150. GABRIEL W. LASKER, Wayne State University
2151. AMELIA R. LASKEY, 1521 Graybar Lane, Nashville, Tenn.
2152. SVEN H. LASSEN, 3720 Floresta Way, Los Angeles
2153. ANDREW LASSLO, Emory University
2154. JULES H. LAST, Northwestern University Medical School
2155. HOMER B. LATIMER, University of Kansas
2156. WALTER L. LATSHAW, 1803 Yale Ave., Salt Lake City
2157. JOHN S. LATTA, University of Nebraska Medical School
2158. M. LATYSZEWSKI, Institute of Animal Gentics, Edinburgh
2159. F. U. LAUBER, Mount Sinai Hospital, N. Y. C.
2160. MAX A. LAUFFER, University of Pittsburgh
2161. J. R. LAUGHNAN, University of Missouri
2162. HENRY D. LAUSON, Albert Einstein College of Medicine
2163. LLOYD W. LAW, National Cancer Institute
2164. DONALD B. LAWRENCE, University of Minnesota
2165. JOHN S. LAWRENCE, University of California, Los Angeles
2166. MERLE LAWRENCE, University of Michigan
2167. W. DERBY LAWS, Texas Research Foundation, Renner
2168. HAMPDEN C. LAWSON, University of Louisville
2169. HENRY D. LAWSON, Cornell University Medical College
2170. ALFRED H. LAWTON, Office of the Air Surgeon General, Washington, D. C.

2171. R. W. LAWTON, U.S. Naval Air Development Center, Johnsville, Pa.
2172. JAMES N. LAYNE, University of Florida
2173. ARNOLD LAZAROW, University of Minnesota
2174. JULIAN G. LEACH, West Virginia University
2175. JAMES H. LEATHEM, Rutgers University
2176. BYRD S. LEAVELL, University of Virginia
2177. RUSSELL K. LeBARRON, State Forest and Range Experiment Station, Placerville, Cal.
2178. CURT LEBEN, University of Wisconsin
2179. C. P. LEBLOND, McGill University
2180. RAOUL LECOQ, Hospital Center, St.-Germain-en-Laye, France
2181. JOSHUA LEDERBERG, University of Wisconsin
2182. E. LEDERER, Institute of Physical and Chemical Biology, Paris
2183. G. A. LEDINGHAM, Prairie Regional Laboratory, Saskatoon
2184. DOUGLAS H. K. LEE, Johns Hopkins University
2185. MILTON O. LEE, American Psysiological Society, Washington, D. C.
2186. A. D. LEES, Cambridge University
2187. W. M. LEES, Chicago Municipal Tuberculosis Sanitarium
2188. J. E. LEGATES, North Carolina State College
2189. C. W. LEGGATT, Department of Agriculture, Ottawa
2190. ARNOLD J. LEHMAN, U. S. Food and Drug Administration, Washington, D. C.
2191. GUNTHER LEHMAN, Max Planck Institute of Work Physiology, Dortmund
2192. A. L. LEHNINGER, University of Chicago
2193. HENRY M. LEICESTER, College of Physicians and Surgeons, San Francisco
2194. ISABELLA LEITCH, Rowett Research Institute, Bucksburn, Scotland
2195. M. RUDOLF LEMBERG, Royal North Shore Hospital, Sydney
2196. CHESTER D. LEONARD, University of Florida, Lake Alfred
2197. SAMUEL L. LEONARD, Cornell University
2198. WARREN H. LEONARD, Colorado Agricultural and Mechanical College
2199. JACK R. LEONARDS, Western Reserve University
2200. CHARLES A. LEONE, University of Kansas
2201. G. A. LePAGE, University of Wisconsin
2202. A. C. LEOPOLD, Purdue University
2203. A. STARKER LEOPOLD, University of California, Berkeley
2204. IRVING H. LEOPOLD, University of Pennsylvania
2205. EUGENE LEPESCHKIN, University of Vermont
2206. I. MICHAEL LERNER, University of California, Berkeley
2207. GEORGE V. Le ROY, University of Chicago
2208. J. W. LESLEY, University of California, Riverside

2209. I. LESLIE, University of Glasgow
2210. ALBERT LEVAN, University of Lund
2211. STANLEY LEVEY, University Hospitals of Cleveland
2212. ELAINE LEVI, University of California, Los Angeles
2213. ERWIN LEVIN, Western Reserve University
2214. MYRON LEVINE, University of Illinois
2215. NORMAN D. LEVINE, University of Illinois
2216. PHILIP LEVINE, Ortho Research Foundation, Raritan, N. J.
2217. VICTOR E. LEVINE, Creighton University
2218. J. LEVITT, University of Missouri
2219. G. A. LEVVY, Rowett Research Institute, Bucksburn, Scotland
2220. LOUIS LEVY, Georgetown University
2221. MATTHEW N. LEVY, Albany Medical College
2222. MILTON LEVY, New York University
2223. RUTH J. LEVY, Veterans Administration Hospital, Seattle
2224. RALPH F. LEWERS, Fritzsche Brothers, Inc., N. Y. C.
2225. RALPH A. LEWIN, Marine Biological Laboratory, Woods Hole, Mass.
2226. C. N. LEWIS, U. S. Food and Drug Administration, Washington, D. C.
2227. HOWARD B. LEWIS
2228. JESSICA H. LEWIS, University of North Carolina
2229. RALPH W. LEWIS, Michigan State University
2230. BERT R. LEXEN, U.S. Forest Service, Washington, D. C.
2231. S. S. LICHTMAN, Cornell University Medical College
2232. MORRIS LIEBERMAN, U. S. Department of Agriculture, Beltsville
2233. DANIEL LIEBOWITZ, Sequoia Medical Group, Redwood City, Cal.
2234. HIRSCH R. LIEBOWITZ, New York University
2235. AMOS E. LIGHT, Wellcome Research Laboratories, Tuckahoe, N. Y.
2236. JOSEPH L. LILIENTHAL, Johns Hopkins University
2237. R. D. LILLIE, National Institute of Arthritis and Metabolic Diseases
2238. J. H. LILLY, Iowa State College
2239. VIRGIL GREEN LILLY, West Virginia University
2240. LOUIS R. LIMARZI, University of Illinois College of Medicine
2241. P. LIMASSET, Central Plant Pathology Station, Versailles, France
2242. CARL C. LINDEGREN, Southern Illinois University
2243. A. W. LINDQUIST, U. S. Department of Agriculture, Beltsville
2244. JEAN M. LINDSDALE, Robles del Rio, Cal.
2245. A. A. LINDSEY, Purdue University
2246. C. R. LINEGAR, Squibb Institute for Medical Research, New Brunswick, N. J.

2247. HANS LINEWEAVER, U. S. Department of Agriculture, Albany, Cal.

2248. GILBERT LING, University of Illinois College of Medicine

2249. ROGER P. LINK, University of Illinois

2250. ARTHUR LINKSZ, Manhattan Eye, Ear and Throat Hospital

2251. FRITZ LIPMANN, Massachusetts General Hospital, Boston

2252. WILLIAM F. LIPP, 40 North Street, Buffalo

2253. RICHARD W. LIPPMAN, 414 N. Camden Dr., Beverly Hills, Cal.

2254. ELBERT L. LITTLE, Jr., U.S. Forest Service, Washington, D. C.

2255. JOHN E. LITTLE, University of Vermont

2256. J. MAXWELL LITTLE, Bowman Gray School of Medicine

2257. GEORGE R. LIVERMORE, Jr., 820 Medical Arts Bldg., Memphis

2258. GEORGE LIVINGSTON, National Research Council

2259. CHARLES W. LLOYD, Syracuse University

2260. WALTER C. LOBITZ, Jr., Hitchock Clinic, Hanover, N.H.

2261. OTTO E. LOBSTEIN, University of Southern California

2262. JOHN LOCHHEAD, University of Vermont

2263. DAN H. LOCKARD, J. I. Holcomb Co., Indianapolis

2264. JOHN F. LOCKE, Jr., Mississippi State College

2265. JOHN B. LOEFER, Office of Naval Research, Pasadena, Cal.

2266. WALTER F. LOEHWING, State University of Iowa

2267. IRENE E. LOEWENFELD, Columbia University

2268. J. E. LOGAN, Department of National Health and Welfare, Ottawa

2269. MILAN A. LOGAN, University of Cincinnati

2270. ELNA A. LOMBARD, Medical College of Georgia

2271. IRVING M. LONDON, Columbia University

2272. C. N. H. LONG, Yale University

2273. J. E. LONG, Army Medical Nutrition Laboratory, Denver

2274. L. G. LONGSWORTH, Rockefeller Institute for Medical Research

2275. WALTER E. LOOMIS, Iowa State College

2276. JOSEPH M. LOONEY, Veterans Administration Regional Office, Boston

2277. VICTOR L. LOOSANOFF, U.S. Fish and Wildlife Service, Milford, Conn.

2278. J. K. LOOSLI, Cornell University

2279. M. S. LOPUSNIAK, University of Pennsylvania

2280. O. A. LORENZ, University of California, Davis

2281. ALLAN L. LORINCZ, University of Chicago

2282. HUBERT S. LORING, Stanford University

2283. R. M. LOVE, Torry Research Station, Aberdeen, Scotland

2284. H. B. LOVELL, University of Louisville

2285. ARTHUR LOVERIDGE, Harvard University

2286. J. A. LOVERN, Torry Research Station, Aberdeen, Scotland

2287. ROY L. LOVVORN, U. S. Department of Agriculture, Beltsville

2288. BARBARA W. LOW, Harvard Medical School

2289. FRANK N. LOW, Louisiana State University

2290. SETH H. LOW, Route 2, Gaithersburg, Md.

2291. CHARLES U. LOWE, University of Buffalo

2292. J. L. LOWE, Syracuse University

2293. OTTO LOWENSTEIN, Columbia University

2294. E. W. LOWRANCE, University of Missouri

2295. ALFRED M. LUCAS, U.S. Department of Agriculture, East Lansing, Mich.

2296. E. H. LUCAS, Michigan State University

2297. HENRY L. LUCAS, Jr., North Carolina State College

2298. MIRIAM SCOTT LUCAS, Michigan State University

2299. SALVATORE P. LUCIA, University of California, San Francisco

2300. BALDUIN LUCKÉ, University of Pennsylvania

2301. T. D. LUCKEY, University of Missouri

2302. DANIEL LUDWIG, Fordham University

2303. RICHARD W. LUECKE, Michigan State University

2304. HEINZ LÜLLMANN, University of Mainz

2305. ULRICH C. LUFT, Randolph Air Force Base

2306. ALDO A. LUISADA, Chicago Medical School

2307. FRANCIS D. W. LUKENS, University of Pennsylvania

2308. ALFRED LUND, University of Copenhagen

2309. HORACE O. LUND, University of Georgia

2310. WALTER O. LUNDBERG, Hormel Institute, Austin, Minn.

2311. HAROLD P. LUNDGREN, U.S. Department of Agriculture, Albany, Cal.

2312. FRANK LUNDQUIST, University of Copenhagen

2313. JOHN S. LUNDY, Mayo Clinic

2314. S. E. LURIA, University of Illinois

2315. MOSES H. LURIE, Harvard Medical School

2316. JAY L. LUSH, Iowa State College

2317. B. J. LUYET, St. Louis University

2318. ANDRÉ LWOFF, Pasteur Institute, Paris

2319. MARGUERITE LWOFF, Pasteur Institute, Paris

2320. CARL M. LYMAN, Texas Agricultural and Mechanical College

2321. CHARLES P. LYMAN, Harvard University

2322. ELDIN V. LYNN, Massachusetts College of Pharmacy

2323. R. B. LYNN, Postgraduate Medical School of London

2324. W. GARDNER LYNN, Catholic University of America

2325. CHARLES J. LYON, Dartmouth College

2326. W. R. LYONS, University of California, Berkeley

2327. D. L. MacADAM, Eastman Kodak Co., Rochester, N. Y.

2328. A. B. MACALLUM, University of Western Ontario

2329. R. H. McBEE, Montana State College

2330. ROBERT A. McCABE, University of Wisconsin

2331. KEITH B. McCALL, Michigan State Department of Health, Lansing

2332. ARTHUR C. McCALLA, University of Alberta

2333. R. A. McCANCE, Cambridge University

2334. ROSS C. MacCARDLE, National Cancer Institute

2335. MORLEY G. McCARTNEY, Ohio Agricultural Experiment Station, Wooster

2336. BENJAMIN McCASHLAND, University of Nebraska Medical School

2337. CLIVE M. McCAY, Cornell University

2338. EVAN W. McCHESNEY, Sterling-Winthrop Research Institute, Rensselaer, N. Y.

2339. R. M. McCLUNG, New York Zoological Society

2340. FRANK J. McCLURE, National Institute of Dental Research

2341. KENNETH P. McCONNELL, Veterans Administration Hospital, Louisville

2342. MACK H. McCORMICK, Eli Lilly and Co., Indianapolis

2343. GRAYSON P. McCOUCH, University of Pennsylvania

2344. J. W. McCUBBIN, Cleveland Clinic

2345. I. McCULLOCH, University of Southern California

2346. F. HAROLD McCUTCHEON, University of Pennsylvania

2347. ERNEST G. McDANIEL

2348. L. H. McDANIELS, Cornell University

2349. EMMA J. McDONALD, National Bureau of Standards

2350. RODERICK P. MacDONALD, Harper Hospital, Detroit

2351. E. C. MacDOWELL, Cold Spring Harbor, N. Y.

2352. W. C. McDUFFIE, U. S. Department of Agriculture, Beltsville

2353. WILLIAM D. McELROY, Johns Hopkins University

2354. AMYAN MACFADYEN, Oxford University

2355. WILLIAM J. McGANITY, Vanderbilt University

2356. W. T. McGEORGE, University of Arizona

2357. R. W. McGILVERY, University of Wisconsin

2358. D. I. McGILVRAY, Purdue University

2359. G. E. MacGINITIE, California Institute of Technology

2360. JAMES McGINNIS, State College of Washington

2361. T. E. MACHELLA, University of Pennsylvania

2362. E. W. McHENRY, University of Toronto

2363. WILLARD MACHLE, 816 S.E. 25th Ave., Fort Lauderdale, Fla.

2364. LEONARD MACHLIS, University of California, Berkeley

2365. J. L. McHUGH, Virginia Fisheries Laboratory, Gloucester Point

2366. WAYNE J. McILRATH, University of Chicago

2367. R. J. McILROY, Tocklai Experimental Station, Cinnamara, Assam, India

2368. H. McILWAIN, University of London

2369. JUNIUS M. McINTIRE, Quartermaster Food and Container Institute, Chicago

2370. ROSS McINTYRE, University of Nebraska Medical School

2371. RALPH W. McKEE, University of California, Los Angeles

2372. COSMOS G. MACKENZIE, University of Colorado

2373. FRED F. McKENZIE, Oregon State College

2374. JOHN M. McKIBBIN, Syracuse University

2375. G. MACKINNEY, University of California, Berkeley

2376. H. H. McKINNEY, U. S. Department of Agriculture, Beltsville

2377. A. D. McLAREN, University of California, Berkeley

2378. BARBARA A. McLAREN, University of Toronto

2379. FRANKLIN C. McLEAN, University of Chicago

2380. DONALD M. MacLEOD, Insect Pathology Laboratory, Saulte Ste. Marie, Ont.

2381. JOHN McLEOD, Cornell University Medical College

2382. W. F. McLIMANS, The Upjohn Co., Kalamazoo, Mich.

2383. E. S. McLOUD, S. C. Johnson and Son, Inc., Racine, Wis.

2384. J. F. A. McMANUS, University of Alabama

2385. THOMAS L. McMEEKIN, U. S. Department of Agriculture, Philadelphia

2386. JAMES E. McMURTREY, Jr., U. S. Department of Agriculture, Beltsville

2387. HUGH C. McPHEE, U. S. Department of Agriculture, Washington, D. C.

2388. IRVINE McQUARRIE, University of Minnesota

2389. W. E. McQUILKIN, U. S. Forest Service, Kingston, Pa.

2390. W. H. McSHAN, University of Wisconsin

2391. B. J. McSHERRY, Ontario Veterinary College

2392. ROBERT W. MacVICAR, Oklahoma Agricultural and Mechanical College

2393. MALCOLM H. McVICKAR, National Fertilizer Assoc., Washington, D. C.

2394. WILLIAM O. MADDOCK, Wayne State University

2395. GERTRUDE MAENGYN-DAVIES, Georgetown University

2396. THOMAS B. MAGATH, Mayo Clinic

2397. H. E. MAGEE, Ministry of Health, London

2398. G. E. MAGNI, University of Paris

2399. HORACE W. MAGOUN, University of California, Los Angeles

2400. G. G. MAHER, Ohio State University

2401. J. P. MAHLSTEDE, Iowa State College

2402. G. B. MAINLAND, Alabama Polytechnic Institute

2403. SAJIRO MAKINO, University of Hokkaido

2404. N. S. R. MALUF, Veterans Administration Hospital, Houston

2405. SERGE MAMY, Smithsonian Institution

2406. EVELYN B. MAN, Yale University

2407. BENJAMIN MANDEL, Public Health Research Institute of the City of New York, Inc.

2408. P. MANDEL, University of Strasbourg

2409. GABRIEL R. MANDELS, Quartermaster Research and Development Center, Natick, Mass.

2410. JEANNE F. MANERY, University of Toronto

2411. PAUL C. MANGELSDORF, Harvard University

2412. T. MANN, Cambridge University

2413. WILLIAM M. MANN, National Zoological Park, Washington, D. C.

2414. ISAAC H. MANNING, Jr., University of North Carolina

2415. R. H. MANSKE, Dominion Rubber Co., Ltd., Guelph, Ont.

2416. HAROLD W. MANTER, University of Nebraska

2417. L. W. MAPSON, Cambridge University

2418. KARL MARAMOROSCH, Rockefeller Institute for Medical Research

2419. JOHN P. MARBARGER, University of Illinois College of Medicine

2420. ALEXANDER MARBLE, New England Deaconess Hospital, Boston

2421. MARION M. MARESH, University of Colorado School of Medicine

2422. S. MARGOLIN, Schering Corp., Bloomfield, N. J.

2423. LEONIDAS D. MARINELLI, Argonne National Laboratory

2424. KLARE S. MARKLEY, Institute of Inter-American Affairs, Rio de Janeiro

2425. J. G. M. MARQUENIE, Samuel Mullerstraat 33a, Rotterdam

2426. JOHN C. MARR, U. S. Fish and Wildlife Service, La Jolla, Cal.

2427. J. R. MARRACK, London Rd., Sawbridgeworth, England

2428. C. R. MARSHALL, Weybridge Park House, Weybridge, England

2429. H. L. MARSHALL, Olin Mathieson Chemical Co., Baltimore

2430. LAWRENCE M. MARSHALL, Howard University

2431. S. M. MARSHALL, Marine Station, Millport, Scotland

2432. DOUGLAS MARSLAND, New York University

2433. HEDLEY R. MARSTON, Commonwealth Scientific and Industrial Research Organization, Adelaide, Australia

2434. PAUL C. MARTH, U. S. Department of Agriculture, Beltsville

2435. ALBERT MARTIN, Jr., Veterans Administration Hospital, Pittsburgh

2436. CONSTANCE R. MARTIN, Creedmoor Institute for Psychobiologic Studies, Philadelphia

2437. GUSTAV J. MARTIN, National Drug Co., Philadelphia

2438. H. MARTIN, Science Service Laboratory, London, Ont.

2439. S. J. MARTIN, St. Francis' Hospital, Hartford, Conn.

2440. W. EDGAR MARTIN, U. S. Office of Education, Washington, D. C.

2441. ITALO MARTIRANI, Hospital das Clinicas, São Paulo

2442. BERNARD S. MARTOF, University of Georgia

2443. JOHN A. MASELLI, Fleischmann Laboratories, Stamford, Conn.

2444. EDWARD C. MASON, University of Oklahoma Medical School

2445. KARL E. MASON, University of Rochester

2446. MERLE MASON, University of Michigan

2447. BENEDICT F. MASSELL, House of the Good Samaritan, Boston

2448. MAURY MASSLER, University of Illinois College of Dentistry

2449. ARTHUR M. MASTER, Columbia University

2450. JOHN R. MATCHETT, U. S. Department of Agriculture, Washington, D. C.

2451. K. MATHER, University of Birmingham

2452. DON R. MATHIESON, Mayo Clinic

2453. SAMUEL A. MATTHEWS, Williams College

2454. MARJORIE R. MATTICE, 358 Norwich Dr., W. Hollywood, Cal.

2455. KARL F. MATTIL, Swift and Co., Chicago

2456. THOMAS W. MATTINGLY, Walter Reed Army Hospital

2457. NORMAN T. MATTOX, University of Southern California

2458. EDWIN B. MATZKE, Columbia University

2459. ANNA MAURIZIO, Dairy Research Establishment, Bern

2460. C. A. MAWSON, Atomic Energy of Canada, Ltd., Chalk River

2461. DENNIS T. MAYER, University of Missouri

2462. JEAN MAYER, Harvard School of Public Health

2463. H. S. MAYERSON, Tulane University

2464. L. A. MAYNARD, Cornell University

2465. ERNST MAYR, Harvard University

2466. D. V. B. MAZZIA, Cornell University

2467. ALBERT R. MEAD, University of Arizona

2468. SEDGWICK MEAD, Washington University

2469. J. C. MEDCOF, Atlantic Biological Station, St. Andrews, N. B.

2470. H. MEGGE, University of Wisconsin

2471. ALTON MEISTER, National Cancer Institute

2472. HENRY E. MELENEY, Louisiana State University

2473. W. J. MELLEN, University of Delaware

2474. ROBERT C. MELLORS, Sloan-Kettering Institute for Cancer Research

2475. JOSEPH L. MELNICK, Yale University

2476. PHILIP E. MELTZER, 285 Commonwealth Ave., Boston

2477. THEODORE H. MENDELL, Mount Sinai Hospital, Philadelphia

2478. A. MENDELOFF, Washington University

2479. MILTON MENDLOWITZ, Mount Sinai Hospital, N. Y. C.

2480. VALY MENKIN, Temple University

2481. FRANK MERCER, St. Louis College of Pharmacy

2482. HOWARD V. MEREDITH, State University of Iowa

2483. J. V. MERRICK, Penrose Research Laboratory, Philadelphia

2484. A. L. MERRILL, U. S. Department of Agriculture, Washington, D. C.

2485. JOHN R. MERRIMAN, 636 Church St., Evanston, Ill.

2486. H. HOUSTON MERRITT, Columbia University

2487. ROBERT L. METCALF, University of California, Riverside

2488. A. J. METCALFE, Department of Health, Canberra

2489. FRED A. METTLER, Columbia University

2490. HELMUT METZNER, University of Göttingen

2491. BERNARD S. MEYER, Ohio State University

2492. K. F. MEYER, University of California, San Francisco

2493. MARION P. MEYER, University of Wisconsin

2494. MARVIN C. MEYER, University of Maine

2495. OVID O. MEYER, University of Wisconsin

2496. S. J. MEYER, 109 N. Wabash Ave., Chicago

2497. THOMAS O. MEYER, State College of Washington

2498. GEORGE S. MEYERS, Stanford University

2499. A. S. MICHAEL, U. S. Department of Agriculture, Beltsville

2500. CHARLES G. MICHEAU, Army Chemical Center, Md.

2501. BURLYN E. MICHEL, State University of Iowa

2502. A. E. MICHELBACHER, University of California, Berkeley

2503. NICHOLAS A. MICHELS, Jefferson Medical College

2504. OLAF MICKELSEN, National Institute of Arthritis and Metabolic Diseases

2505. JOHN T. MIDDLETON, University of California, Riverside

2506. EDWARD C. MIGDALSKI, Yale University

2507. R. MIKAMI, University of Hirosaki

2508. PAUL W. MILES, Washington University

2509. ALDEN H. MILLER, University of California, Berkeley

2510. CARLOS O. MILLER, University of Wisconsin

2511. DAVID F. MILLER, Ohio State University

2512. DONALD F. MILLER, National Research Council

2513. H. A. MILLER, State Department of Agriculture, Raleigh, N. C.

2514. HARRY MILLER, General Foods Corp., Kankakee, Ill.

2515. JOHN H. MILLER, 8806 Wolberton Rd., Baltimore

2516. JULIAN C. MILLER, Louisiana State University

2517. MALCOLM R. MILLER, Stanford University

2518. RICHARD B. MILLER, University of Alberta

2519. RUTH A. MILLER, Louisiana State University

2520. CLARENCE A. MILLS, University of Cincinnati

2521. HARLOW B. MILLS, University of Illinois

2522. JOHN P. MILLS, Equitable Life Assurance Society, N. Y. C.

2523. RUSSELL C. MILLS, University of Kansas

2524. KELSEY C. MILNER, National Microbiological Institute, Hamilton, Mont.

2525. C. E. MINARIK, Camp Detrick, Md.

2526. ALLEN H. MINOR, Lenox Hill Hospital, N. Y. C.

2527. WILLIAM H. MINSHALL, Department of Agriculture, Ottawa

2528. SHERMAN A. MINTON, Jr., Indiana University Medical Center

2529. NICHOLAS T. MIROV, University of California, Berkeley

2530. I. ARTHUR MIRSKY, University of Pittsburgh

2531. H. H. MITCHELL, University of Illinois

2532. HERSCHEL K. MITCHELL, California Institute of Technology

2533. JOHN W. MITCHELL, U. S. Department of Agriculture, Beltsville

2534. WALTER MODELL, Cornell University Medical College

2535. IRINA MODLIBOWSKA, Research Station, East Malling, England

2536. BEN C. MOFFETT, Jr., University of Alabama

2537. DANIEL B. MOFFETT, 1150 Connecticut Ave., Washington, D. C.

2538. ARTHUR D. MOINAT, Colorado State College of Education

2539. HAROLD N. MOLDENKE, 15 Glenbrook Ave., Yonkers, N.Y.

2540. GEORGE W. MOLNAR, Army Medical Research Laboratory, Fort Knox, Ky.

2541. GAIRDNER B. MOMENT, Goucher College

2542. W. F. H. M. MOMMAERTS, Western Reserve University

2543. JOSEPH MONACHINO, New York Botanical Garden

2544. WILLIAM MONTAGNA, Brown University

2545. FLORENCE MOOG, Washington University

2546. H. H. MOON, U. S. Department of Agriculture, Beltsville

2547. PARRY MOON, Massachusetts Institute of Technology

2548. A. R. MOORE, Hopkins Marine Station

2549. BETTY C. MOORE, Columbia University

2550. CARL V. MOORE, Washington University

2551. DAN H. MOORE, Columbia University

2552. FRANCIS D. MOORE, Harvard Medical School

2553. J. D. MOORE, University of Wisconsin

2554. JOHN A. MOORE, Columbia University

2555. LANE A. MOORE, U. S. Department of Agriculture, Beltsville

2556. RICHARD O. MOORE, Ohio State University

2557. STANFORD MOORE, Rockefeller Institute for Medical Research

2558. W. G. MOORE, Loyola University, New Orleans

2559. RAY MOREE, State College of Washington

2560. LAURENCE E. MOREHOUSE, University of Southern California

2561. GEORGES M. MOREL, Central Plant Pathology Station, Versailles, France
2562. AGNES FAY MORGAN, University of California, Berkeley
2563. F. G. MORGAN, Commonwealth Serum Laboratories, Parkville, Australia
2564. J. F. MORGAN, Department of National Health and Welfare, Ottawa
2565. KARL Z. MORGAN, Oak Ridge National Laboratory
2566. M. W. MORGAN, Jr., University of California, Berkeley
2567. I. M. MORIYAMA, National Office of Vital Statistics, Washington, D. C.
2568. THOMAS G. MORRIONE, New York University
2569. C. CHRISTOPHER MORRIS, University of Texas Medical Branch
2570. HAROLD P. MORRIS, National Cancer Institute
2571. LESLIE E. MORRIS, Beth Israel Hospital, Boston
2572. MARK L. MORRIS, 1500 MacVicar St., Topeka, Kan.
2573. MELVIN S. MORRIS, Montana State University
2574. F. B. MORRISON, Cornell University
2575. IRA R. MORRISON, 118 N. 5th St., Atchison, Kan.
2576. PETER R. MORRISON, University of Wisconsin
2577. PAUL E. MORROW, University of Rochester
2578. MINERVA MORSE, University of Chicago
2579. OTTO A. MORTENSEN, University of Wisconsin
2580. JULIA F. MORTON, University of Miami
2581. NEWTON E. MORTON, University of Wisconsin
2582. ERWIN H. MOSBACH, Goldwater Memorial Hospital, N. Y. C.
2583. HENRY S. MOSBY, Virginia Polytechnic Institute
2584. HERMANN A. MOSER, Carnegie Institution of Washington, Cold Spring Harbor, N. Y.
2585. HAROLD E. MOSES, Purdue University
2586. ROBERT E. MOSHER, Providence Hospital, Detroit
2587. D. A. A. MOSSEL, Central Institute for Nutrition Research, Utrecht
2588. HARLAND W. MOSSMAN, University of Wisconsin
2589. KOITI MOTOKAWA, Tohuku University
2590. JAMES W. MOULDER, University of Chicago
2591. A. L. MOXON, Ohio Agricultural Experiment Station, Wooster
2592. ANDREW J. MOYER, U. S. Department of Agriculture, Peoria, Ill.
2593. CARL A. MOYER, Southwestern Medical School
2594. ELIZABETH K. MOYER, Boston University
2595. EMIL M. MRAK, University of California, Davis
2596. GILBERT H. MUDGE, Columbia University
2597. JUSTUS F. MUELLER, Syracuse University
2598. W. C. MUENSCHER, Cornell University
2599. CARL F. W. MUESEBECK, Smithsonian Institution

2600. JOSEPH C. MUHLER, Indiana University
2601. ROBERT M. MUIR, State University of Iowa
2602. S. R. MUKHERJEE, University of Edinburgh
2603. E. G. MULDER, Agriculture Experiment Station, Groningen
2604. MICHAEL G. MULINOS, New York Medical School
2605. RICHARD M. MULLIGAN, University of Colorado School of Medicine
2606. LORIN J. MULLINS, Purdue University
2607. THORNTON T. MUNGER, 2755 S.W. Buena Vista Dr., Portland, Ore.
2608. HAZEL E. MUNSELL, 8 N. Main St., Monson, Mass.
2609. E. MUNTWYLER, State University of New York College of Medicine, Brooklyn
2610. JOHN A. MUNTZ, Western Reserve University
2611. GARTH I. MURPHY, U. S. Fish and Wildlife Service, Honolulu
2612. R. C. MURPHY, American Museum of Natural History
2613. K. E. MURRAY, Commonwealth Scientific and Industrial Research Organization, Melbourne
2614. MARGARET MURRAY, Columbia University
2615. R. W. MURRAY, University of Birmingham
2616. JYTTE MUUS, Mount Holyoke College
2617. EARL H. MYERS, University of California, Berkeley
2618. GEORGE S. MYERS, Stanford University
2619. JACK MYERS, University of Texas

2620. S. M. NABRIT, Atlanta University
2621. ELI M. NADEL, National Cancer Institute
2622. JOHN P. NAFE, Florida State University
2623. B. NAGANNA, Andhra Medical College, India
2624. LOUIS H. NAHUM, Yale University
2625. A. V. NALBANDOV, University of Illinois
2626. THOMAS W. NALE, Union Carbide and Carbon Corp., N. Y. C.
2627. JAMES F. NANCE, University of Illinois
2628. DAVID L. NANNEY, University of Michigan
2629. ROLAND M. NARDONE, Catholic University of America
2630. ALVIN N. NASON, Johns Hopkins University
2631. HANS N. NAUMANN, Veterans Administration Hospital, Jackson, Miss.
2632. U. G. NAYAK, National Chemical Laboratory of India, Poona
2633. AUBREY NAYLOR, Yale University
2634. H. NECHELES, Michael Reese Hospital, Chicago
2635. GERALD M. NEEDHAM, Mayo Clinic
2636. JAMES G. NEEDHAM, Cornell University
2637. JAMES V. NEEL, University of Michigan
2638. WILLIAM O. NEGHERBON, National Research Council

2639. KENNETH A. NEILAND, University of California, Los Angeles
2640. CATHERINE NEILL, 4 View Rd., London
2641. ARTHUR C. NEISH, Prairie Regional Laboratory, Saskatoon
2642. JEAN H. NELBACH, Yale University
2643. E. M. NELSON, U. S. Food and Drug Administration, Washington, D. C.
2644. MARJORIE M. NELSON, University of California, Berkeley
2645. WERNER L. NELSON, North Carolina State College
2646. RALPH B. NESTLER, U. S. Department of Agriculture, Washington, D. C.
2647. ERWIN NETER, Children's Hospital, Buffalo
2648. HANS NEURATH, University of Washington
2649. W. B. NEVENS, University of Illinois
2650. JOSEPH L. NEWCOMER, University of Maryland
2651. VICTOR D. NEWCOMER, University of California, Los Angeles
2652. ROBERT R. NEWELL, Stanford University School of Medicine
2653. HARRISON E. NEWLIN, Midwest Research Institute, Kansas City, Mo.
2654. ELLIOT V. NEWMAN, Vanderbilt University
2655. RUSSELL W. NEWMAN, Quartermaster Research and Development Center, Natick, Mass.
2656. ROY C. NEWTON, Swift and Co., Chicago
2657. MARGARET M. NICE, 5725 Harper Ave., Chicago
2658. D. J. D. NICHOLAS, Johns Hopkins University
2659. J. S. NICHOLAS, Yale University
2660. D. C. NICHOLSON, King's College Hospital Medical School, London
2661. WALTER J. NICKERSON, Rutgers University
2662. E. NICOLAI, University of Leeds
2663. PAUL A. NICOLL, Indiana University
2664. WILLIAM NIEDERMEIER, Hillman Hospital, Birmingham
2665. C. OVERGAARD NIELSEN, Molslaboratoriet Femmöller, Jylland, Denmark
2666. J. M. NIELSEN, University of California, Los Angeles
2667. J. R. NIELSON, Stanford University
2668. WILLIAM T. NIEMER, Creighton University
2669. G. T. NIGHTINGALE, Hawaiian Pineapple Experiment Station, Honolulu
2670. HUGO W. NILSON, U.S. Fish and Wildlife Service, College Park, Md.
2671. LESLIE F. NIMS, Brookhaven National Laboratory
2672. J. P. NITSCH, Harvard University
2673. CHARLES R. NOBACK, Columbia University
2674. G. R. NOGGLE, Charles F. Kettering Foundation
2675. JERRE L. NOLAND, Veterans Administration Center, Wood, Wis.

2676. LOWELL E. NOLAND, University of Wisconsin
2677. RAY O. NOOJIN, Medical College of Alabama
2678. LEONARD NORCIA, Hormel Institute, Austin, Minn.
2679. F. F. NORD, Fordham University
2680. JEAN NORDMANN, University of Strasbourg
2681. L. C. NORRIS, Cornell University
2682. WILLIAM P. NORRIS, Argonne National Laboratory
2683. E. H. NORTHEY, Davis and Geck, Inc., Danbury, Conn.
2684. JOHN H. NORTHROP, University of California, Berkeley
2685. D. W. NORTHUP, West Virginia University
2686. L. J. NOTKIN, Jewish General Hospital, Montreal
2687. G. DAVID NOVELLI, Western Reserve University
2688. ALEX B. NOVIKOFF, University of Vermont
2689. E. NOVITSKI, University of Missouri
2690. J. C. NURCH, Vanderbilt University
2691. G. E. NUTILE, Associated Seed Growers, Inc., Twin Falls, Idaho

2692. R. OBERHOLZER, University of Zurich
2693. J. P. O'BRIEN, University of Sydney
2694. RUTH O'BRIEN, U. S. Department of Agriculture, Washington, D. C.
2695. SEVERO OCHOA, New York University
2696. SIDNEY OCHS, University of Illinois College of Medicine
2697. R. J. O'CONNOR, Westminister School of Medicine, London
2698. GUNNAR ÖSTERGREN, University of Lund
2699. FRANKLIN OFFNER, U. S. Naval Hospital, Bethesda
2700. COLM Ó hEOCHA, Scripps Institution of Oceanography
2701. E. A. OHLER, Temple University
2702. MARGARET A. OHLSON, Michigan State University
2703. YOSHIRO OKAMI, National Institute of Health, Tokyo
2704. JOSEPH C. O'KELLEY, University of Alabama
2705. RUTH OKEY, University of California, Berkeley
2706. G. OKUNZUA, University of Birmingham
2707. O. OLBRICH, General Hospital, Sunderland, England
2708. JAMES L. O'LEARY, Washington University
2709. LINDSAY OLIVE, Columbia University
2710. W. T. OLIVER, Ontario Veterinary College
2711. CHARLES E. OLMSTED, University of Chicago
2712. BERNARD J. O'LOUGHLIN, University of California, Los Angeles
2713. N. S. OLSEN, Thayer Veterans Administration Hospital, Nashville
2714. F. C. W. OLSON, Florida State University
2715. RODNEY A. OLSON, National Institute of Arthritis and Metabolic Diseases
2716. WILLARD C. OLSON, University of Michigan

2717. JOHN OLWIN, University of Illinois College of Medicine

2718. E. Opitz (Deceased)

2719. JANE OPPENHEIMER, Bryn Mawr College

2720. NELSON K. ORDWAY, University of North Carolina

2721. JACK ORLOFF, National Heart Institute

2722. GEORGE G. ORNSTEIN, 965 5th Ave., N. Y. C.

2723. F. L. O'ROURKE, Michigan State University

2724. A. P. ORR, Marine Station, Millport, Scotland

2725. JAMES M. ORTEN, Wayne State University

2726. STAFFORD L. OSBORNE, Northwestern University Medical School

2727. BERNARD L. OSER, Food Research Laboratory, Inc., Long Island City, N. Y.

2728. EDWIN E. OSGOOD, University of Oregon Medical School

2729. ARTHUR OSOL, Philadelphia College of Pharmacy and Science

2730. KURT A. OSTER, McKesson and Robbins Laboratories, Bridgeport, Conn.

2731. ARNOLD ERWIN OSTERBERG, Abbott Laboratories, North Chicago

2732. HAJIMA OTA, U. S. Department of Agriculture, Beltsville

2733. ARTHUR B. OTIS, Johns Hopkins University

2734. GILBERT F. OTTO, Abbott Laboratories, North Chicago

2735. RICHARD R. OVERMAN, University of Tennessee College of Medicine

2736. HAROLD OWEN, University of Minnesota

2737. PHILIP S. OWEN, National Research Council

2738. P. A. OWREN, Rikshospitalet, Oslo

2739. A. C. PABST, Socony-Vacuum Oil Co., N. Y. C.

2740. DONALD M. PACE, University of Nebraska

2741. NELLO PACE, University of California, Berkeley

2742. J. PAGANO, Squibb Institute for Medical Research, New Brunswick, N. J.

2743. IRVINE H. PAGE, Cleveland Clinic Foundation

2744. ROBERT M. PAGE, Stanford University

2745. I. M. PALLIN, Jewish Hospital of Brooklyn

2746. DWIGHT M. PALMER, Ohio State University

2747. HAIG P. PAPAZIAN, Yale University

2748. JOHN R. PAPPENHEIMER, Harvard Medical School

2749. HAROLD E. B. PARDEE, 772 Park Ave., N. Y. C.

2750. DAVID PARETSKY, University of Kansas

2751. SOPHY PARFIN, Smithsonian Institution

2752. THOMAS PARK, University of Chicago

2753. J. PARKER, University of Idaho

2754. J. R. PARKER, U. S. Department of Agriculture, Bozeman, Mont.

2755. MARION W. PARKER, U. S. Department of Agriculture, Beltsville

2756. RAYMOND C. PARKER, University of Toronto

2757. A. S. PARKES, National Institute for Medical Research, London

2758. A. K. PARPART, Princeton University

2759. MARY S. PARSHLEY, Columbia University

2760. R. C. PARSIL, Olin Mathieson Chemical Co., N. Y. C.

2761. J. I. PASCAL (Deceased)

2762. KARL E. PASCHKIS, Jefferson Medical College

2763. HARVEY M. PATT, Argonne National Laboratory

2764. BRADLEY M. PATTEN, University of Michigan

2765. JOHN A. PATTEN, Middle Tennessee State College

2766. JOHN L. PATTERSON, Jr., Medical College of Virginia

2767. ROBERT L. PATTON, Cornell University

2768. SCOTT S. PAULEY, University of Minnesota

2769. PAUL L. PAVCEK, Washington University

2770. T. K. PAVLYCHENKO, American Chemical Paint Co., Saskatoon, Sask.

2771. LOYAL C. PAYNE, Iowa State College

2772. A. S. PEARSE (Deceased)

2773. GEORGE A. PEARSON, U. S. Salinity Laboratory, Riverside, Cal.

2774. OLIVER P. PEARSON, University of California, Berkeley

2775. PAUL B. PEARSON, U. S. Atomic Energy Commission, Washington, D. C.

2776. WILLIAM N. PEARSON, Vanderbilt University

2777. DANIEL C. PEASE, University of California, Los Angeles

2778. J. THOMAS PEDLOW, University of Maine

2779. MICHAEL PEECH, Cornell University

2780. ALBERT A. F. PEEL, Victoria Infirmary, Glasgow

2781. C. N. PEISS, St. Louis University

2782. MICHAEL J. PELCZAR, University of Maryland

2783. J. A. PELLER, University of Toronto

2784. RÉAL L. PELLETIER, McGill University

2785. CAROLYN A. PELLETT, McKesson and Robbins, Inc., Bridgeport, Conn.

2786. WILLIAM T. PENFOUND, University of Oklahoma

2787. KENNETH E. PENROD, Duke University

2788. J. H. PEPPER, Montana State College

2789. C. B. PERKINS (Deceased)

2790. JOHN F. PERKINS, Jr., University of Chicago

2791. M. PERKINS, Lincoln Park Zoo, Chicago

2792. D. PERLMAN, Princeton University

2793. GERTRUDE E. PERLMANN, Rockefeller Institute for Medical Research

2794. ERNST PESCHEL, Duke University

2795. HAROLD G. PETERING, The Upjohn Co., Kalamazoo, Mich.

2796. MARY L. PETERMAN, Sloan-Kettering Institute for Cancer Research

2797. JOHN H. PETERS, Veterans Administration Hospital, Atlanta

2798. JOHN P. PETERS (Deceased)

2799. LYSLE H. PETERSON, University of Pennsylvania

2800. MERLIN H. PETERSON, Abbott Laboratories, North Chicago

2801. GEORGE A. PETRIDES, Michigan State University

2802. ASENATH PETRIE, University of London

2803. G. PETROSINI, University of Naples

2804. ALEXANDER PETRUNKEVITCH, Yale University

2805. L. BRADLEY PETT, Department of National Health and Welfare, Ottawa

2806. C. K. PETTER, Lake County Tuberculosis Sanatorium, Waukegan, Ill.

2807. ROBERT E. PFADT, University of Wyoming

2808. CARL PFAFFMAN, Brown University

2809. CARL C. PFEIFFER, Emory University

2810. NORMA E. PFEIFFER, Boyce Thompson Institute for Plant Research

2811. CORNELIUS B. PHILIP, National Microbiological Institute, Hamilton, Mont.

2812. ARTHUR M. PHILLIPS, Jr., U. S. Fish and Wildlife Service, Cortland, N. Y.

2813. P. H. PHILLIPS, University of Wisconsin

2814. BERNARD O. PHINNEY, University of California, Los Angeles

2815. ESTHER F. PHIPARD, U. S. Department of Agriculture, Washington, D. C.

2816. WILLIAM F. PICKETT, Kansas State College

2817. GRACE E. PICKFORD, Yale University

2818. W. H. PIERRE, Iowa State College

2819. KARL A. PIEZ, National Institutes of Health

2820. WARD W. PIGMAN, University of Alabama

2821. PAUL-EMILE PILET, University of Lausanne

2822. MAXON Y. PILLOW, U. S. Forest Products Laboratory, Madison, Wis.

2823. GREGORY PINCUS, Worcester Foundation for Experimental Biology

2824. ANTOINETTE PIRIE, Oxford University

2825. N. W. PIRIE, Rothamsted Experiment Station, Harpenden, England

2826. P. P. PIRONE, New York Botanical Garden

2827. A. PISEK, University of Innsbruck

2828. WESLEY S. PLATNER, University of Missouri

2829. B. C. PLATT, Antibiotics Research Station, Clevedon, England

2830. DAVID PLATT, University of Alabama Medical Center

2831. G. W. E. PLAUT, University of Wisconsin

2832. ALBERT A. PLENTL, Columbia University

2833. H. H. PLOUGH, Amherst College

2834. CLAUS MUNK PLUM, University of Copenhagen

2835. ORDA A. PLUNKETT, University of California, Los Angeles

2836. DONALD G. POCOCK, Vanderbilt University

2837. G. G. POHLMAN, West Virginia University

2838. SAMUEL M. POILEY, National Institutes of Health

2839. S. H. POLAYES, Cumberland Hospital, Brooklyn

2840. CASH B. POLLARD, University of Florida

2841. LEWIS J. POLLOCK, Northwestern University Medical School

2842. ALFRED POLSON, Veterinary Research Laboratory, Onderstepoort, Transvaal

2843. ELIZABETH POMERENE, St. Luke's Hospital, Cleveland

2844. J. H. POMEROY, Argonne National Laboratory

2845. SEYMOUR POMPER, Fleischmann Laboratories, Stamford, Conn.

2846. ERIC PONDER, Nassau Hospital, Mineola, N. Y.

2847. CHARLES F. POOLE, University of Hawaii

2848. A. L. POPE, University of Wisconsin

2849. RICHARD A. POPHAM, Ohio State University

2850. HENRY W. POPP, Pennsylvania State University

2851. HANS POPPER, Cook County Hospital, Chicago

2852. NANDOR PORGES, U. S. Department of Agriculture, Philadelphia

2853. J. R. PORTER, State University of Iowa

2854. JOHN N. PORTER, Lederle Laboratories, Pearl River, N. Y.

2855. JOHN W. PORTER, General Electric Co., Richland, Wash.

2856. KEITH R. PORTER, Rockefeller Institute for Medical Research

2857. RENO PORTER, Veterans Administration Hospital, Richmond, Va.

2858. THELMA PORTER, University of Chicago

2859. VAN R. POTTER, University of Wisconsin

2860. SAMUEL R. POTTINGER, U. S. Fish and Wildlife Service, East Boston

2861. CARL G. POTTS, U. S. Department of Agriculture, Beltsville

2862. GLENN S. POUND, University of Wisconsin

2863. E. L. POWERS, Argonne National Laboratory

2864. JUSTIN L. POWERS, American Pharmaceutical Assoc., Washington, D. C.

2865. M. R. N. PRASAD, Central College, Bangalore, India

2866. ELMER B. PRATT, University of Colorado Medical Center

2867. JOHN J. PRATT, Jr., Quartermaster Research and Development Center, Natick, Mass.

2868. ROBERTSON PRATT, University of California, San Francisco

2869. I. A. PREECE, The Journal of the Institute of Brewing, Edinburgh

2870. KENNETH W. PRESCOTT, Kansas City Museum

2871. EDWARD PRESS, The American Public Health Assoc., N.Y.

2872. R. D. PRESTON, University of Leeds
2873. E. W. PRICE, U. S. Department of Agriculture, Washington, D. C.
2874. W. C. PRICE, University of Pittsburgh
2875. E. G. PRINGSHEIM, Cambridge University
2876. G. E. PRINTY, University of Illinois
2877. GORDON H. PRITHAM, Pennsylvania State University
2878. B. E. PROCTOR, Massachusetts Institute of Technology
2879. C. LADD PROSSER, University of Illinois
2880. LUIGI PROVASOLI, Haskins Laboratories, N. Y. C.
2881. LOUIS M. PRUESS, Lederle Laboratories, Pearl River, N. Y.
2882. HELEN B. PRYOR, Stanford University
2883. HOWARD E. PULLING, Wellesley College
2884. NATESAIER PURSHOTTAM, Harvard School of Public Health
2885. E. R. PURVIS, Rutgers University
2886. FRANK W. PUTNAM, University of Chicago
2887. LOREN S. PUTNAM, Ohio State University

2888. K. D. QUARTERMAN, U. S. Public Health Service, Savannah, Ga.
2889. J. H. QUASTEL, Montreal General Hospital
2890. ARMAND J. QUICK, Marquette University
2891. J. J. QUILLIGAN, Jr., Southwestern Medical School
2892. EDITH H. QUIMBY, Columbia University
2893. DANIEL P. QUIRING, Western Reserve University

2894. W. RAAB, University of Vermont
2895. JOHN RAAF, University of Oregon Medical School
2896. HERMINIO R. RABANAL, Bureau of Fisheries, Manila
2897. GLENN S. RADIDEAU, University of Texas
2898. EUGENE RABINOWITCH, University of Illinois
2899. R. R. RACE, The Lister Institute, London
2900. R. D. RADELEFF, U. S. Department of Agriculture, Kerrville, Texas
2901. SIDNEY RAFFEL, Stanford University
2902. H. A. RAFSKY, Lenox Hill Hospital, N. Y. C.
2903. HERMANN RAHN, University of Rochester
2904. OTTO RAHN, Idaho State College
2905. CYRIL RAINBOW, University of Birmingham
2906. HAROLD RAISTRICK, University of London
2907. NATHAN B. RAKIETEN, South Shore Analytical and Research Laboratory, Inc., Islip, N. Y.
2908. GEORGE J. RALEIGH, Cornell University
2909. DAVID P. RALL, National Cancer Institute
2910. M. RAMAUT, University of Liege
2911. ELIZABETH M. RAMSEY, Carnegie Institution of Washington, Baltimore

2912. A. L. RAND, Chicago Natural History Museum
2913. WALTER C. RANDALL, St. Louis University
2914. WILLIAM A. RANDALL, U.S. Food and Drug Administration, Washington, D. C.
2915. HUGH W. RANDEL, Gunter Air Force Base, Montgomery, Ala.
2916. C. I. RANDLES, Ohio State University
2917. L. F. RANDOLPH, Cornell University
2918. OTTO F. RANKE, University of Erlangen
2919. S. L. RANSOM, University of Durham
2920. M. NARAYANA RAO, Central Food Technological Research Institute, Mysore, India
2921. S. S. RAO, Haffkine Institute, Bombay
2922. JOHN R. RAPER, Harvard University
2923. KENNETH B. RAPER, University of Wisconsin
2924. SAMUEL RAPOPORT, University of Cincinnati
2925. B. A. RASMUSEN, University of California, Davis
2926. A. F. RASMUSSEN, Jr., University of California, Los Angeles
2927. THEODORE RASMUSSEN, McGill University
2928. W. P. RATCHFORD, U. S. Department of Agriculture, Philadelphia
2929. HERBERT L. RATCLIFFE, University of Pennsylvania
2930. E. N. RATHBUN, University of California, Berkeley
2931. I. S. RAVDIN, University of Pennsylvania
2932. A. RAVINA, Hospital Beaujon, Paris
2933. W. W. RAY, University of Nebraska
2934. DANIEL READY, Camp Detrick, Frederick, Md.
2935. JOHN W. REBUCK, Henry Ford Hospital, Detroit
2936. ALFRED C. REDFIELD, Woods Hole Oceanographic Institution
2937. WALTER REDISCH, New York University
2938. J. H. REDISKE, General Electric Co., Richland, Wash.
2939. JAMES R. REDMOND, Braddock Heights, Md.
2940. RALPH P. REECE, Rutgers University
2941. T. EDWARD REED, University of Michigan
2942. CHARLES W. REES, National Microbiological Institute
2943. K. REES, University College, London
2944. ALBERT M. REESE, West Virginia University
2945. E. T. REESE, Quartermaster Research and Development Center, Natick, Mass.
2946. HARALD A. REHDER, Smithsonian Institution
2947. WARREN S. REHM, Jr., University of Louisville
2948. CARL REICH, Lenox Hill Hospital, N. Y. C.
2949. HANS REICH, University of Wisconsin
2950. MARY ELIZABETH REID, National Institute of Arthritis and Metabolic Diseases
2951. MIRIAM REINER, District of Columbia General Hospital

2952. EDWARD G. REINHARD, Catholic University of America
2953. WILLIAM O. REINHARDT, University of California, Berkeley
2954. EDWARD H. REISNER, Jr., New York University
2955. F. J. REITHEL, Queen's University, Belfast
2956. PAUL E. REKERS, 176 S. Goodman St., Rochester, N.Y.
2957. ALICE GERTRUDE RENFREW Mellon Institute, Pittsburgh
2958. ALBERT E. RENOLD, Peter Bent Brigham Hospital, Boston
2959. WALTER REUTHER, U. S. Department of Agriculture, Orlando, Fla.
2960. RANDALL W. REYER, University of Pittsburgh
2961. JAMES A. REYNIERS, University of Notre Dame
2962. ALBERT E. REYNOLDS, De Pauw University
2963. EARLE L. REYNOLDS, Atomic Bomb Casualty Commission, San Francisco
2964. MONICA REYNOLDS, University of Pennsylvania
2965. SAMUEL R. M. REYNOLDS, Carnegie Institution of Washington, Baltimore
2966. B. T. RHEINS, Ohio State University
2967. ALBERT O. RHOAD, King Ranch, Kingsville, Texas
2968. M. M. RHOADES, University of Illinois
2969. E. L. RICE, University of Oklahoma
2970. ELDON E. RICE, Swift and Co., Chicago
2971. A. GLENN RICHARDS, University of Minnesota
2972. AUTE RICHARDS, 2950 East Mabel, Tucson
2973. DICKINSON RICHARDS, Jr., Bellevue Hospital, N. Y. C.
2974. FRANCIS A. RICHARDS, Woods Hole Oceanographic Institute
2975. MERFYN RICHARDS, National Research Laboratories, Saskatoon
2976. OSCAR W. RICHARDS, Jr., American Optical Co., Southbridge, Mass.
2977. R. E. RICHARDS, Australian Institute of Anatomy, Canberra
2978. R. K. RICHARDS, Abbott Laboratories, North Chicago
2979. R. RUTH RICHARDS, 3936 Graceland Ave., Indianapolis
2980. ALFRED W. RICHARDSON, Indiana University
2981. DRAYFORD RICHARDSON, Kansas State College
2982. DAN A. RICHERT, Syracuse University
2983. J. E. RICHMOND, University of Rochester
2984. KENNETH M. RICHTER, University of Oklahoma Medical School
2985. PAUL O. RICHTER, Oregon State College
2986. RICHARD B. RICHTER, University of Chicago
2987. R. RICHTERICH, Boston University
2988. NELSON K. RICHTMYER, National Institutes of Health
2989. CHARLES M. RICK, Jr., University of California, Davis
2990. WILLIAM E. RICKER, Pacific Biological Station, Nanaimo, B. C.

2991. FREDERICK RIDLEY, 80 Harley St., London
2992. F. RIEDERS, Jefferson Medical College
2993. VICTOR H. RIES, Ohio State University
2994. AUSTIN H. RIESEN, University of Chicago
2995. R. H. RIGDON, University of Texas Medical Branch
2996. F. I. RIGHTER, University of California, Berkeley
2997. FRED L. RIGHTS, Wayne State University
2998. A. J. RIKER, University of Wisconsin
2999. EDGAR F. RILEY, State University of Iowa
3000. GORDON A. RILEY, Yale University
3001. RICHARD L. RILEY, Johns Hopkins University
3002. CLAUDE RIMINGTON, University College Hospital Medical School, London
3003. JAMES F. RINEHART, University of California, San Francisco
3004. WILLIAM H. RISER, Jr., Medical College of Alabama
3005. PAUL L. RISLEY, University of Oregon
3006. J. M. RITCHIE, National Institute for Medical Research, London
3007. DAVID RITTENBERG, Columbia University
3008. ERNEST G. RITZMAN, University of New Hampshire
3009. H. L. RIVA, Walter Reed Army Medical Center
3010. THOMAS M. RIVERS, Rockefeller Institute for Medical Research
3011. JEAN RIVIERE, University of Bordeaux
3012. C. C. ROAN, Kansas State College
3013. JANE SANDS ROBB, Syracuse University
3014. CHANDLER S. ROBBINS, U.S. Fish and Wildlife Service, Laurel, Md.
3015. W. REI ROBBINS, Rutgers University
3016. WILLIAM J. ROBBINS, New York Botanical Garden
3017. E. A. HOUGHTON ROBERTS, Tocklai Experimental Station, Cinnamara, Assam, India
3018. ELMER ROBERTS, University of Illinois
3019. R. H. ROBERTS, University of Wisconsin
3020. SIDNEY ROBERTS, University of California, Los Angeles
3021. J. D. ROBERTSON, University of Glasgow
3022. R. N. ROBERTSON, Commonwealth Scientific and Industrial Research Organization, Homebush, Australia
3023. ALLEN D. ROBINSON, University of Manitoba
3024. FLORENCE BELL ROBINSON, University of Illinois
3025. G. N. ROBINSON, University of Nottingham
3026. H. E. ROBINSON, Swift and Co., Chicago
3027. HAMILTON B. G. ROBINSON, Ohio State University
3028. KATHLEEN ROBINSON, University of Queensland
3029. ROBERT A. ROBINSON, Johns Hopkins University
3030. S. W. ROBINSON, Ohio State University

3031. SID ROBINSON, Indiana University
3032. RICHARD O. ROBLIN, American Cyanamid Co., N. Y. C.
3033. J. M. ROBSON, Guy's Hospital, London
3034. A. ROCHE, University of Paris
3035. JOHN ROCK, Free Hospital for Women, Brookline, Mass.
3036. MORRIS ROCKSTEIN, New York University
3037. SIMON RODBARD, University of Buffalo
3038. EUGENE I. ROE, U. S. Forest Service, Grand Rapids, Minn.
3039. JOSEPH H. ROE, George Washington University
3040. KENNETH D. ROEDER, Tufts College
3041. WILLIAM G. ROESSLER, Army Chemical Center, Md.
3042. DONALD P. ROGERS, New York Botanical Garden
3043. WILLIAM M. ROGERS, Columbia University
3044. WILLIAM P. ROGERS, University of Adelaide
3045. WILLIAM M. ROGOFF, South Dakota State College
3046. E. ROHRMANN, Eli Lilly and Co., Indianapolis
3047. PAAVO ROINE, University of Helsinki
3048. G. N. ROLINSON, Boots Pure Drug Co., Ltd., West Bridgford, England
3049. REED C. ROLLINS, Harvard University
3050. A. L. ROMANOFF, Cornell University
3051. ALFRED S. ROMER, Harvard University
3052. EVANS ROMNEY, University of California, Los Angeles
3053. G. LYNN ROMOSER, University of Maryland
3054. PAUL G. ROOFE, University of Kansas
3055. EDWARD C. ROOSEN-RUNGE, University of Washington
3056. RAYMOND W. ROOT, College of the City of New York
3057. MARION W. ROPES, Massachusetts General Hospital, Boston
3058. WILLIAM C. ROSE, University of Illinois
3059. HAROLD J. ROSEN, Montreal Neurological Institute
3060. FRANCIS F. ROSENBAUM, Marquette University
3061. HANS R. ROSENBERG, E. I. du Pont de Nemours and Co., Inc., Newark, Del.
3062. WALTER A. ROSENBLITH, Massachusetts Institute of Technology
3063. ARTURO ROSENBLUETH, Institute of Cardiology, Mexico City
3064. PAUL ROSENFALCK, University of Copenhagen
3065. JORGE ROSENKRANZ, Syntex, S. A., Mexico City
3066. LAWRENCE ROSNER, Laboratory of Vitamin Technology, Chicago
3067. A. FRANK ROSS, Cornell University
3068. LUCILLE J. ROSS, 801 West End Ave., N. Y. C.
3069. MORRIS H. ROSS, Biochemical Research Foundation, Newark, Del.
3070. VICTORIA ROSSETTI, R. Marques de Itu 58, São Paulo
3071. G. VICTOR ROSSI, National Drug Co., Philadelphia

3072. R. J. ROSSITER, University of Western Ontario
3073. CLAYTON O. ROST, University of Minnesota
3074. ADOLPH ROSTENBERG, Jr., University of Illinois College of Medicine
3075. JAMES L. A. ROTH, University of Pennsylvania
3076. JAY S. ROTH, Cambridge University
3077. PAUL ROTHEMUND, Charles F. Kettering Foundation
3078. ALEXANDER ROTHEN, Rockefeller Institute for Medical Research
3079. STEPHEN ROTHMAN, University of Chicago
3080. LORD ROTHSCHILD, Cambridge University
3081. A. ROTHSTEIN, University of Rochester
3082. GEORGE A. ROUNSEFELL, U. S. Fish and Wildlife Service, Woods Hole, Mass.
3083. PHYLLIS M. ROUNTREE, Royal Prince Albert Hospital, Camperdown, Australia
3084. R. D. ROUSE, Alabama Polytechnic Institute
3085. D. G. ROUX, Leather Industries Research Institute, Grahamstown, South Africa
3086. V. K. ROWE, Dow Chemical Co., Midland, Mich.
3087. I. W. ROWLANDS, Agricultural Research Council, Cambridge, England
3088. S. ROWLANDS, St. Mary's Hospital Medical School, London
3089. LOYD A. ROYAL, International Pacific Salmon Fisheries Commission, New Westminster, B. C.
3090. MITCHELL I. RUBIN, Children's Hospital, Buffalo
3091. S. H. RUBIN, Hoffman-La Roche, Inc., Nutley, N. J.
3092. ROBERT R. RUCKER, University of Washington
3093. PAUL O. RUDOLF, U. S. Forest Service, St. Paul
3094. G. D. RUEHLE, Subtropical Experiment Station, Homestead, Fla.
3095. H. RUFELT, University of Lund
3096. JULIAN M. RUFFIN, Duke University
3097. ROBERTS RUGH, Columbia University
3098. OLIN RULON, Northwestern University
3099. MEREDITH RUNNER, Roswell Park Memorial Institute, Buffalo
3100. ARTHUR RUSKIN, University of Texas Medical Branch
3101. L. L. RUSOFF, Louisiana State University
3102. E. W. RUSSELL, Oxford University
3103. FINDLAY E. RUSSELL, College of Medical Evangelists
3104. JANE A. RUSSELL, Emory University
3105. PAUL F. RUSSELL, Rockefeller Foundation
3106. WALTER C. RUSSELL, Rutgers University
3107. JOHN H. RUST, University of Chicago
3108. ELBERT B. RUTH, Johns Hopkins University
3109. ALFRED RUTISHAUSER, University of Zurich

3110. DAVID A. RYTAND, Stanford University Hospital, San Francisco
3111. JEAN SABINE, Los Alamos Scientific Laboratory, New Mexico
3112. JACOB SACKS, University of Arkansas
3113. V. SADASIVAN, Municipal Buildings, Fort Bombay
3114. SAUL B. SAILA, State Department of Agriculture and Conservation, Providence
3115. R. I. SAILER, Smithsonian Institution
3116. W. ST. AMAND, Oak Ridge National Laboratory
3117. PAUL R. SALERNO, Western Reserve University
3118. EDWARD SALISBURY, Royal Botanic Gardens, Kew, England
3119. H. J. SALLACH, University of Wisconsin
3120. KURT SALOMON, University of Rochester
3121. PAUL SALTMAN, California Institute of Technology
3122. MAURICE SALTZMAN, Temple University
3123. SAMUEL B. SALVIN, National Microbiological Institute, Hamilton, Mont.
3124. JOSEPH SAMACHSON, Jewish Hospital of Brooklyn
3125. H. G. SAMMONS, University of Birmingham
3126. JESSE SAMPSON, University of Illinois
3127. JOHN J. SAMPSON, University of California, San Francisco
3128. MAX SAMTER, University of Illinois College of Medicine
3129. ARYEH H. SAMUEL, Ventura College
3130. GEORGE SAMUELS, University of Puerto Rico
3131. LEO T. SAMUELS, University of Utah
3132. MURRAY SANDERS, University of Miami
3133. GLEN C. SANDERSON, Iowa Conservation Commission, Marion
3134. DAVID J. SANDWEISS, 9739 Dexter Blvd., Detroit
3135. J. G. SANDZA, Stauffer Chemical Co., Chauncey, N.Y.
3136. SIDNEY SAPERSTEIN, The Borden Co., Yonkers, N. Y.
3137. OTTO SAPHIR, Michael Reese Hospital, Chicago
3138. HERBERT P. SARETT, Mead Johnson and Co., Evansville, Ind.
3139. IRA SARKAR, University of Calcutta
3140. N. K. SARKAR, School of Tropical Medicine, Calcutta
3141. MERRITT P. SARLES, Catholic University of America
3142. J. N. SASSER, North Carolina State College
3143. H. E. SAUBERLICH, Alabama Polytechnic Institute
3144. VINCENT SAUCHELLI, Davison Chemical Corp., Baltimore
3145. FRANCIS J. SAUNDERS, G. D. Searle and Co., Chicago
3146. J. B. deC. M. SAUNDERS, University of California, San Francisco
3147. JEAN SAVEL, University of Paris
3148. PAUL B. SAWIN, Roscoe B. Jackson Memorial Laboratory

3149. CHARLES H. SAWYER, University of California, Los Angeles
3150. KARL SAX, Harvard University
3151. GEORGE SAYERS, Western Reserve University
3152. J. D. SAYRE, Ohio Agricultural Experiment Station, Wooster
3153. GEORGE D. SCARSETH, American Farm Research Assoc., Lafayette, Ind.
3154. ARNOLD EDWARD SCHAEFER, National Institutes of Health
3155. HERBERT C. SCHAEFER, Ralston-Purina Co., St. Louis
3156. A. A. SCHAEFFER, Temple University
3157. B. SCHAERFFENBERG, University of Graz
3158. DAVID E. SCHAFER, University of Minnesota
3159. C. S. SCHAFFNER, University of Maryland
3160. ALBERT SCHATZ, National Agricultural College, Bucks County, Pa.
3161. V. SCHATZ, National Agricultural College, Bucks County, Pa.
3162. A. M. SCHECHTMAN, University of California, Los Angeles
3163. BRADLEY T. SCHEER, University of Oregon
3164. THEODORE C. SCHEFFER, U. S. Forest Products Laboratory, Madison, Wis.
3165. ARNOLD H. SCHEIN, University of Vermont
3166. PERITZ SCHEINBERG, University of Miami
3167. S. L. SCHEINBERG, University of Wisconsin
3168. RUDOLF SCHENCK, University of Marburg
3169. BERNARD SCHEPARTZ, Jefferson Medical College
3170. JEAN SCHERRER, Collège de France
3171. OLE A. SCHJEIDE, University of California, Los Angeles
3172. RUDI SCHMID, University of Minnesota
3173. CARL F. SCHMIDT, University of Pennsylvania
3174. KARL P. SCHMIDT, Chicago Natural History Museum
3175. L. H. SCHMIDT, Christ Hospital, Cincinnati
3176. KNUT SCHMIDT-NIELSEN, Duke University
3177. O. T. SCHMIDT, University of Heidelberg
3178. RUDOLF G. SCHMIEDER, University of Pennsylvania
3179. FRANCIS O. SCHMITT, Massachusetts Institute of Technology
3180. MEYER D. SCHNALL, Mount Sinai Hospital, N. Y. C.
3181. BURCH H. SCHNEIDER, State College of Washington
3182. R. U. SCHOCK, Abbott Laboratories, North Chicago
3183. HENRY W. SCHOENBORN, University of Georgia
3184. GORDON M. SCHOEPFLE, Washington University
3185. WERNER H. A. SCHÖTTLER, Butantan Institute, São Paulo
3186. P. F. SCHOLANDER, Woods Hole Oceanographic Institution
3187. P. G. SCHOLEFIELD, Montreal General Hospital
3188. W. H. SCHOPFER, University of Bern
3189. FRANZ SCHRADER, Columbia University

3190. E. SCHREIDER, School of Advanced Studies, Paris

3191. L. H. SCHREINER, Mayo Clinic

3192. GILBERT H. SCHUBERT, U.S. Forest Service, Berkeley, Cal.

3193. JACK SCHUBERT, Argonne National Laboratory

3194. HOWARD A. SCHUCK, U. S. Department of the Air Force, Washington, D. C.

3195. ADOLPH H. SCHULTZ, University of Zurich

3196. ALFRED S. SCHULTZ, Fleischmann Laboratories, Stamford, Conn.

3197. JACK SCHULTZ, Institute for Cancer Research, Philadelphia

3198. LEONARD P. SCHULTZ, Smithsonian Institution

3199. MAX O. SCHULTZE, University of Minnesota

3200. F. X. SCHUMACHER, Duke University

3201. ROBERT E. SCHUMACHER, Minnesota Department of Conservation, St. Paul

3202. ROBERT S. SCHWAB, Massachusetts General Hospital, Boston

3203. HERMAN P. SCHWAN, University of Pennsylvania

3204. H. H. SCHWARDT, Cornell University

3205. L. H. SCHWARTE, Iowa State College

3206. BENJAMIN SCHWARTZ, U.S. Department of Agriculture, Beltsville

3207. IRVING L. SCHWARTZ, Rockefeller Institute for Medical Research

3208. LOUIS SCHWARTZ, 915 19th St., N. W., Washington, D. C.

3209. STEVEN O. SCHWARTZ, Hektoen Institute for Medical Research, Chicago

3210. KLAUS SCHWARZ, National Institute of Arthritis and Metabolic Diseases

3211. B. S. SCHWEIGERT, American Meat Industry Foundation, Chicago

3212. GEORGE W. SCHWERT, Duke University

3213. LOUIS J. SCIARINI, Yale University

3214. FRANCIS SCOFIELD, National Paint, Varnish, and Lacquer Assoc., Washington, D. C.

3215. DONALD SCOTT, Jr., University of Pennsylvania

3216. F. M. SCOTT, University of California, Los Angeles

3217. J. P. SCOTT, Roscoe B. Jackson Memorial Laboratory

3218. JANET D. SCOTT, Interscience Encyclopedia, Inc., Brooklyn

3219. JOHN C. SCOTT, Hahnemann Medical College

3220. LELAND E. SCOTT, University of Maryland

3221. MILTON L. SCOTT, Cornell University

3222. RALPH C. SCOTT, University of Cincinnati

3223. RALPH W. SCOTT, University of Wisconsin

3224. RONALD B. SCOTT, Freedman's Hospital, Washington, D. C.

3225. ROBERT O. SCOW, National Institutes of Health

3226. HARVEY I. SCUDDER, U. S. Public Health Service, Savannah, Ga.

3227. JOHN A. SEALANDER, Jr., University of Arkansas

3228. O. H. SEARS, University of Illinois

3229. OLDRICH K. SEBEK, The Upjohn Co., Kalamazoo, Mich.

3230. WALTER H. SEEGERS, Wayne State University

3231. ALBERT SEGALOFF, Alton Ochsner Medical Foundation, New Orleans

3232. FLORENCE B. SEIBERT, Henry Phipps Institute, Philadelphia

3233. JOSEPH SEIFTER, Wyeth Institute for Applied Biochemistry, Philadelphia

3234. VÁCLAV SELIGER, Charles University

3235. EWALD E. SELKURT, Western Reserve University

3236. W. A. SELLE, University of California, Los Angeles

3237. GEORGE P. SELLMER, Upsala College

3238. HANS SELYE, University of Montreal

3239. ARTHUR SELZER, 450 Sutter St., San Francisco

3240. JULIUS SENDROY, Jr., National Naval Medical Center

3241. JOHN SENIOR, University of Pennsylvania

3242. T. R. SESHADRI, University of Delhi

3243. RICHARD B. SETLOW, Yale University

3244. HENRY W. SETZER, Smithsonian Institution

3245. M. G. SEVAG, University of Pennsylvania

3246. ELMER L. SEVERINGHAUS, Hoffmann-LaRoche, Inc., Nutley, N. J.

3247. JOHN W. SEVERINGHAUS, National Institutes of Health

3248. SIMON SEVITT, Birmingham Accident Hospital, England

3249. ROGER SEVY, 6809 Emlen St., Philadelphia

3250. RICHARD M. SHACKELFORD, University of Wisconsin

3251. ALBERT R. SHADLE, University of Buffalo

3252. C. BOYD SHAFFER, American Cyanamid Co., Stamford, Conn.

3253. CARL F. SHAFFER, Baylor University Medical College

3254. G. F. SHAMBAUGH, 55 E. Washington St., Chicago

3255. S. J. SHANE, Point Edward Hospital, Sydney, N. S.

3256. A. M. SHANES, National Institutes of Health

3257. ROYAL L. SHANKS, University of Tennessee

3258. FREDERICK A. SHANNON, Box 276, Wickenburg, Ariz.

3259. H. L. SHANTZ, 464 Paseo Del Descanso, Santa Barbara, Cal.

3260. HERBERT SHAPIRO, Wills Hospital, Philadelphia

3261. L. H. SHAPIRO, Mount Sinai Hospital, N. Y. C.

3262. SAM SHAPIRO, U. S. Public Health Service, Washington, D. C.

3263. LEO SHAPOVALOV, California Department of Fish and Game, Sacramento

3264. LEONARD SHARE, Western Reserve University

3265. JOHN R. SHAVER, California Institute of Technology

3266. A. C. SHAW, Skinners School, Tunbridge Wells, England

3267. CHARLES E. SHAW, Zoological Society of San Diego

3268. JAMES H. SHAW, Harvard School of Dental Medicine

3269. WARREN C. SHAW, U. S. Department of Agriculture, Beltsville

3270. CORNELIUS B. SHEAR, U. S. Department of Agriculture, Gainesville, Fla.

3271. G. M. SHEAR, Virginia Agricultural Experiment Station, Blacksburg

3272. MURRAY J. SHEAR, National Cancer Institute

3273. WILLIAM H. SHELDON, Columbia University

3274. E. KOST SHELTON, 921 Westwood Blvd., Los Angeles

3275. DAVID SHEMIN, Columbia University

3276. HENRY A. SHENKIN, 255 S. 17th St., Philadelphia

3277. G. DONALD SHERMAN, University of Hawaii

3278. JAMES M. SHERMAN, Cornell University

3279. LANDRUM B. SHETTLES, Columbia University

3280. FREDERICK E. SHIDEMAN, University of Wisconsin

3281. LORA M. SHIELDS, New Mexico Highlands University

3282. B. M. SHINN, Armour and Co., Chicago

3283. ROBERT E. SHIPLEY, Indianapolis General Hospital

3284. HAROLD G. SHIRK, Prev. of Det. Ctr., N.A.S.-N.R.C.

3285. HARDY L. SHIRLEY, Syracuse University

3286. JOHN W. SHIVE, Rutgers University

3287. WILLIAM SHIVE, University of Texas

3288. SIMON SHLAER, Los Alamos Scientific Laboratory, New Mexico

3289. NATHAN W. SHOCK, Baltimore City Hospitals

3290. MARY S. SHORB, University of Maryland

3291. F. W. SHORT, Parke, Davis and Co., Detroit

3292. EDWARD W. SHRIGLEY, Indiana University Medical Center

3293. PING SHU, Prairie Regional Laboratory, Saskatoon

3294. C. R. SHUMAN, Temple University

3295. CARL N. SHUSTER, Jr., University of Delaware

3296. FRANK K. SHUTTLEWORTH, City College of New York

3297. CHARLES G. SIBLEY, Cornell University

3298. C. P. SIDERIS, Pineapple Research Institute, Honolulu

3299. ARTHUR A. SIEBENS, State University of New York College of Medicine, Brooklyn

3300. JACK M. SIEGEL, Pabst Laboratories, Milwaukee

3301. R. W. SIEGEL, Reed College

3302. DALE H. SIELING, University of Massachusetts

3303. ARTHUR F. SIEVER, U. S. Department of Agriculture, Beltsville

3304. R. SIGHTS, Washington University

3305. KARL M. SILBERSCHMIDT, Biological Institute, São Paulo

3306. DEMITRA J. SILIDES, Harvard School of Public Health

3307. S. D. SILVER, Army Chemical Center, Md.

3308. MILTON SILVERMAN, National Institutes of Health

3309. S. RICHARD SILVERMAN, Central Institute for the Deaf, St. Louis

3310. F. A. SIMEONE, Western Reserve University

3311. E. G. SIMMONS, Quartermaster Research and Development Center, Natick, Mass.

3312. SAMUEL W. SIMMONS, U. S. Public Health Service, Atlanta

3313. HENRY S. SIMS, Columbia University

3314. HENRI SIMONNET, National Veterinary School, Paris

3315. ERNST SIMONSON, University of Minnesota

3316. WALTER E. SIMONSON, 5104 26th Ave., South Minneapolis

3317. F. J. SIMPSON

3318. JEAN I. SIMPSON, Syracuse University

3319. JENNIE L. S. SIMPSON, Hunter College

3320. S. D. SIMPSON

3321. H. M. SINCLAIR, Oxford University

3322. F. M. SINEX, Brookhaven National Laboratory

3323. LEON SINGER, University of Minnesota

3324. RICHARD B. SINGER, New England Mutual Life Insurance Co., Boston

3325. ROLAND SINGER, University of Cape Town

3326. THOMAS P. SINGER, University of Wisconsin

3327. A. O. SINGLETON, University of Texas Medical Branch

3328. E. P. SINGSEN, University of Connecticut

3329. WILLIAM SIRI, University of California, Berkeley

3330. C. SIRONVAL, University of Liege

3331. JONAS H. SIROTA, 120 N. Fourth St., San Jose, Cal.

3332. GRANT E. SITA, Allied Chemical and Dye Corp., N. Y. C.

3333. JOHN W. SITES, University of Florida, Lake Alfred

3334. IRWIN W. SIZER, Massachusetts Institute of Technology

3335. P. D. SKAAR, Long Island Biological Assoc., Cold Spring Harbor, N. Y.

3336. O. SKAUG, Medical College of Virginia

3337. FOLKE SKOOG, University of Wisconsin

3338. STANLEY C. SKORNYA, McGill University

3339. N. SKREB, Faculty of Medicine, Zagreb

3340. CHARLES A. SLANETZ, Columbia University

3341. GEORGE L. SLATE, New York Agricultural Experiment Station, Geneva

3342. E. C. SLATER, University of Amsterdam

3343. HERMAN M. SLATIS, Argonne National Laboratory

3344. R. F. SLECHTA, Worcester Foundation for Experimental Biology

3345. ELEANOR H. SLIFER, State University of Iowa

3346. S. J. SLINGER, Ontario Agricultural College

3347. G. H. SLOANE-STANLEY, McLean Hospital, Waverley, Mass.

3348. K. H. SLOTTA, Box 4790, São Paulo

3349. NORMAN SLOVIK, Jewish Hospital of Brooklyn

3350. JOSEPH E. SMADEL, Walter Reed Army Medical Center

3351. J. SMALL, Queen's University, Belfast

3352. LYNDON F. SMALL, National Institute of Arthritis and Metabolic Diseases
3353. ARLAN E. S. SMITH, University of California, Los Angeles
3354. ARTHUR H. SMITH, Wayne State University
3355. CARL C. SMITH, Christ Hospital, Cincinnati
3356. CARROLL N. SMITH, U. S. Department of Agriculture, Orlando, Fla.
3357. CLEMENT A. SMITH, Harvard Medical School
3358. DURWOOD J. SMITH, University of Vermont
3359. EMIL L. SMITH, University of Utah
3360. FRANK A. SMITH, University of Rochester
3361. GILBERT M. SMITH, Stanford University
3362. HOBART M. SMITH, University of Illinois
3363. HOMER W. SMITH, New York University
3364. KENNETH M. SMITH, Agricultural Research Council, Cambridge, England
3365. LYMAN SMITH, Smithsonian Institution
3366. NATHAN R. SMITH, U. S. Department of Agriculture, Sarasota, Fla.
3367. OLIVE WATKINS SMITH, Free Hospital for Women, Brookline, Mass.
3368. PAUL F. SMITH, U. S. Department of Agriculture, Orlando, Fla.
3369. PAUL G. SMITH, University of California, Davis
3370. RALPH I. SMITH, University of California, Berkeley
3371. ROGER C. SMITH, Kansas State College
3372. ROLAND F. SMITH, State Department of Conservation and Economic Development, Trenton, N. J.
3373. S. E. SMITH, Cornell University
3374. SAM C. SMITH, University of Oklahoma Medical School
3375. W. L. SMITH, Jr., U. S. Department of Agriculture, Beltsville
3376. REGINALD H. SMITHWICK, Boston University
3377. ROBERT M. SMOCK, Cornell University
3378. HENRY F. SMYTH, Jr., Mellon Institute, Pittsburgh
3379. J. D. SMYTH, University of Dublin
3380. GEORGE W. SNEDECOR, Iowa State College
3381. ESMOND E. SNELL, University of Texas
3382. GEORGE D. SNELL, Roscoe B. Jackson Memorial Laboratory
3383. RAY S. SNIDER, Northwestern University Medical School
3384. CHARLES E. SNOW, University of Kentucky
3385. F. W. SNYDER, Box 226, East Lansing, Mich.
3386. LAURENCE H. SNYDER, University of Oklahoma
3387. WILLIAM S. SNYDER, University of California, Berkeley
3388. ALBERT E. SOBEL, Jewish Hospital of Brooklyn
3389. HARRY SOBOTKA, Mount Sinai Hospital, N. Y. C.
3390. ARTHUR SOHVAL, 1155 Park Avenue, N. Y. C.

3391. A. SOKOLOFF, University of Chicago
3392. LEON SOKOLOFF, National Institute of Arthritis and Metabolic Diseases
3393. TORALD SOLLMANN, Western Reserve University
3394. MORRIS SOLOTOROVSKY, Merck Institute for Therapeutic Research, Rahway, N.J.
3395. MATHILDE SOLOWEY, Camp Detrick, Md.
3396. G. FRED SOMERS, University of Delaware
3397. T. M. SONNEBORN, Indiana University
3398. RALPH R. SONNENSCHEIN, University of California, Los Angeles
3399. LESTER W. SONTAG, Antioch College
3400. ROBERT K. SOOST, University of California, Riverside
3401. CONSTANTINE SOROKIN, University of Maryland
3402. JOHN C. SOWDEN, Washington University
3403. BASIL C. SOYENKOFF, New York University
3404. S. SPANGLER, University of Texas
3405. C. R. SPEALMAN, Civil Aeronautics Administration, Washington, D. C.
3406. DAMON A. SPENCER, U. S. Department of Agriculture, Beltsville
3407. MERRILL P. SPENCER, Bowman Gray School of Medicine
3408. WARREN M. SPERRY, New York State Psychiatric Institute, N. Y. C.
3409. SAMUEL S. SPICER, National Institutes of Health
3410. MORTIMER SPIEGELMAN, Metropolitan Life Insurance Co., N. Y. C.
3411. CHARLES J. SPIEGL, University of Rochester
3412. LESLIE SPIER, Box 880, Santa Cruz, Cal.
3413. HERMAN T. SPIETH, University of California, Riverside
3414. H. SPITZER, Max Planck Institute of Work Physiology, Dortmund
3415. MATTIE RAE SPIVEY, National Institutes of Health
3416. H. J. SPOOR, New York Medical College
3417. GEORGE F. SPRAGUE, Iowa State College
3418. HOWARD B. SPRAGUE, 1180 Beacon St., Brookline, Mass.
3419. RANDALL G. SPRAGUE, Mayo Clinic
3420. STEPHEN H. SPURR, University of Michigan
3421. M. STACEY, University of Birmingham
3422. MAURICE V. STACK, Dental Hospital, Bristol, England
3423. RALPH W. STACY, Ohio State University
3424. WILLIAM C. STADIE, University of Pennsylvania
3425. ARTHUR L. STAHL, University of Miami
3426. MARK A. STAHMANN, University of Wisconsin
3427. HERBERT L. STAHNKE, Arizona State College
3428. E. C. STAKMAN, University of Minnesota
3429. TREVOR STAMP, Hammersmith Hospital, London
3430. J. FISHER STANFIELD, Miami University, Ohio

3431. ROGER Y. STANIER, University of California, Berkeley
3432. W. W. STANLEY, University of Tennessee
3433. WENDELL M. STANLEY, University of California, Berkeley
3434. J. NEWELL STANNARD, University of Rochester
3435. MAURICE E. STANSBY, U. S. Fish and Wildlife Service, Seattle
3436. FREDERICK J. STARE, Harvard Medical School
3437. EGON STARK, Purdue University
3438. MORTIMER P. STARR, University of California, Davis
3439. JOSEPH STASNEY, Jefferson Medical College
3440. JOHN F. STAUFFER, University of Wisconsin
3441. GENEVIEVE STEARNS, State University of Iowa
3442. G. LEDYARD STEBBINS, Jr., University of California, Davis
3443. ROBERT C. STEBBINS, University of California, Berkeley
3444. BETTY L. STEELE, Iowa State College
3445. RICHARD STEELE, Rohm and Haas Co., Philadelphia
3446. V. STEENSBERG, Naesgaard Agricultural College, Denmark
3447. WILLIAM C. STEERE, Stanford University
3448. MARIO STEFANINI, St. Elizabeth's Hospital, Brighton, Mass.
3449. FREDERICK STEIGMANN, Cook County Hospital, Chicago
3450. W. H. STEIN, Rockefeller Institute for Medical Research
3451. GEORGE P. STEINBAUER, Michigan State University
3452. H. STEINBERG, New York Hospital
3453. ROBERT A. STEINBERG, U.S. Department of Agriculture, Beltsville
3454. ARTHUR STEINDLER, Mercy Hospital, Iowa City
3455. ARTHUR H. STEINHAUS, George Williams College
3456. EDWARD A. STEINHAUS, University of California, Berkeley
3457. J. VERNON STEINLE, S. C. Johnson and Sons, Inc., Racine, Wis.
3458. J. E. STENTON, National Parks of Canada, Banff
3459. WILLIAM STEPKA, Medical College of Virginia
3460. CURT STERN, University of California, Berkeley
3461. EDWARD S. STERN, J. F. Macfarlan and Co., Ltd., Edinburgh
3462. JAN STERN, Fountain Hospital, London
3463. JOSEPH R. STERN, Western Reserve University
3464. DeWITT STETTEN, Jr., National Institute of Arthritis and Metabolic Diseases
3465. ORIN A. STEVENS, North Dakota State College
3466. S. S. STEVENS, Harvard University
3467. JAMES A. F. STEVENSON, University of Western Ontario
3468. JOHN A. STEVENSON, U. S. Department of Agriculture, Beltsville
3469. F. C. STEWARD, Cornell University
3470. IVAN STEWART, University of Florida

3471. M. A. STEWART, University of California, Berkeley
3472. WILLIAM S. STEWART, University of California, Riverside
3473. J. CLIFFORD STICKNEY, West Virginia University
3474. HAZEL K. STIEBELING, U.S. Department of Agriculture, Washington, D. C.
3475. WALTER STILES, 17 Elsley Rd., Reading, England
3476. R. H. STINSON, University of Western Ontario
3477. C. CHESTER STOCK, Sloan-Kettering Institute for Cancer Research
3478. FRANK H. STODOLA, U. S. Department of Agriculture, Peoria, Ill.
3479. HERBERT STOENNER, National Microbiological Institute, Hamilton, Mont.
3480. ALLEN W. STOKES, Utah State Agricultural College
3481. J. L. STOKES, U. S. Department of Agriculture, Albany, Cal.
3482. HERBERT E. STOKINGER, U. S. Public Health Service, Cincinnati
3483. E. L. ROBERT STOKSTAD, Lederle Laboratories, Pearl River, N. Y.
3484. H. H. STONAKER, Colorado Agricultural and Mechanical College
3485. ALAN STONE, Smithsonian Institution
3486. H. H. STONE, University of Pennsylvania
3487. JULIUS STONE
3488. ROBERT S. STONE, University of California, San Francisco
3489. JOHN B. STORER, Los Alamos Scientific Laboratory, New Mexico
3490. ROBERT M. STORM, Oregon State College
3491. CLARA A. STORVICK, Oregon State College
3492. ELMER H. STOTZ, University of Rochester
3493. PERRY R. STOUT, Kearney Foundation of Soil Science, Oakland, Cal.
3494. VERNON T. STOUTMEYER, University of California, Los Angeles
3495. E. L. STOVER, Eastern Illinois State College
3496. CLARENCE M. STOWE, Jr., University of Minnesota
3497. ROBERT E. STOWELL, University of Kansas Medical Center
3498. HAROLD H. STRAIN, Argonne National Laboratory
3499. FRITZ STRAUSS, University of Bern
3500. MAURICE B. STRAUSS, Veterans Administration Hospital, Boston
3501. H. E. STREET, University of Manchester
3502. BERNARD L. STREHLER, University of Chicago
3503. G. H. STRINGFIELD, Ohio Agricultural Experiment Station, Wooster
3504. EDWARD H. STRISOWER, 924 Clayton St., San Francisco
3505. FRANK A. STROMSTEN, State University of Iowa
3506. F. M. STRONG, University of Wisconsin
3507. LAURENCE E. STRONG, Earlham College

3508. R. M. STRONG, Chicago Natural History Museum
3509. ROBERT C. STROUD, Medical College of South Carolina
3510. B. E. STRUCKMEYER, University of Wisconsin
3511. MAX M. STRUMIA, University of Pennsylvania
3512. HAROLD C. STUART, Harvard School of Public Health
3513. FREDERICK W. STUEWER, Michigan Department of Conservation, Lansing
3514. PAUL K. STUMPF, University of California, Berkeley
3515. SOMERS H. STURGIS, Peter Bent Brigham Hospital, Boston
3516. PAUL D. STURKIE, Rutgers University
3517. E. E. SUCKLING, State University of New York College of Medicine, Brooklyn
3518. J. A. SULLIVAN, University of Toronto
3519. WALTER E. SULLIVAN, University of Colorado Medical Center
3520. MARION B. SULZBERGER, New York University
3521. WILLIAM H. SUMMERSON, Army Chemical Center, Md.
3522. JAMES B. SUMNER (Deceased)
3523. Y. P. SUN, Shell Development Co., Denver
3524. F. WILLIAM SUNDERMANN, Jefferson Medical College
3525. ALEXANDER R. SURREY, Sterling-Winthrop Research Institute, Renssalaer, N. Y.
3526. ADOLPH SURTSHIN, Washington University
3527. MITZI SUSKIND, Rockland State Hospital, Orangeburg, N. Y.
3528. JEROME SUTIN, University of California, Los Angeles
3529. H. U. SVERDRUP, Norwegian Polar Institute, Oslo
3530. ARTHUR SVIHLA, University of Washington
3531. JASON R. SWALLEN, Smithsonian Institution
3532. T. V. SWAMY, Tata Iron and Steel Co., Ltd., Jamshedpur, India
3533. C. A. SWANSON, Ohio State University
3534. ERIC W. SWANSON, University of Tennessee
3535. JACOB H. SWARTZ, Harvard Medical School
3536. EARL SWARTZLANDER, 805 Peachtree St., Atlanta
3537. W. W. SWETT, U. S. Department of Agriculture, Beltsville
3538. RAYMOND W. SWIFT, Pennsylvania State University
3539. H. S. SWINGLE, Alabama Polytechnic Institute
3540. V. P. SYDENSTRICKER, Medical College of Georgia
3541. J. F. SYKES, U. S. Department of Agriculture, Beltsville
3542. JOHN C. SYLVESTER, Abbott Laboratories, North Chicago
3543. J. E. SYLVESTRE, Department of National Health and Welfare, Quebec
3544. P. SYMONDS, National Institutes of Health
3545. ALBERT SZENT-GYORGYI, Marine Biological Laboratory, Woods Hole, Mass.
3546. WACLAW SZYBALSKI, Rutgers University
3547. MATTHEW TABACK, City Health Department, Baltimore

3548. RICHARD TABER, University of California, Berkeley
3549. HENRY TAGNON, Sloan-Kettering Institute for Cancer Research
3550. NOZOMI TAKEMURA, University of Osaka
3551. MASUICHI TAKINO, Kyoto Imperial University
3552. TIMOTHY R. TALBOT, Jr., University of Pennsylvania
3553. JOHN H. TALBOTT, University of Buffalo
3554. W. H. TALIAFERRO, University of Chicago
3555. FRED W. TANNER, Jr., Charles Pfizer and Co., Inc., Brooklyn
3556. VASCO M. TANNER, Brigham Young University
3557. KATHARINE TANSLEY, Institute of Ophthalmology, London
3558. A. L. TAPPEL, University of California, Davis
3559. CLARENCE M. TARZWELL, U. S. Public Health Service, Cincinnati
3560. I. TASAKI, National Institute of Neurological Diseases and Blindness
3561. E. L. TATUM, Stanford University
3562. DAVID TAUB, Merck and Co., Rahway, N. J.
3563. HENRY TAUBER, U. S. Public Health Service, Chapel Hill, N. C.
3564. ALBERT L. TAYLOR, U. S. Department of Agriculture, Beltsville
3565. ALTON R. TAYLOR, Parke, Davis and Co., Detroit
3566. ARAVILLA M. TAYLOR, Andes, N. Y.
3567. CRAIG L. TAYLOR, University of California, Los Angeles
3568. E. P. TAYLOR, Allen and Hanburys Ltd., Ware, England
3569. F. H. L. TAYLOR, Harvard Medical School
3570. HENRY L. TAYLOR, University of Minnesota
3571. J. D. TAYLOR, Abbott Laboratories, North Chicago
3572. LAURISTON TAYLOR, National Bureau of Standards, Washington, D. C.
3573. M. WIGHT TAYLOR, Rutgers University
3574. MARIE CLARK TAYLOR, Howard University
3575. ROBERT D. TAYLOR, Medical Center, Marshfield, Wis.
3576. ROBERT E. TAYLOR, University of Illinois College of Medicine
3577. STERLING A. TAYLOR, Utah State Agricultural College
3578. T. G. TAYLOR, University of Reading
3579. HORACE S. TELFORD, State College of Washington
3580. GEORGE S. TEMPLETON, U. S. Department of Agriculture, Fontana, Cal.
3581. J. D. TERESI, U. S. Naval Radiological Defense Laboratory, San Francisco
3582. CLAIR E. TERRILL, U. S. Department of Agriculture, Beltsville
3583. STANLEY W. TERRILL, University of Illinois
3584. LUTHER L. TERRY, National Heart Institute
3585. S. J. THANNHAUSER, Tufts College Medical School
3586. ETHEL THEWLIS, University of Wisconsin

3587. FRED P. THIEME, University of Michigan
3588. CLINTON H. THIENES, Huntington Memorial Hospital, Pasadena, Cal.
3589. KENNETH V. THIMANN, Harvard University
3590. J. EARL THOMAS, Jefferson Medical College
3591. J. WILLIAM THOMAS, U. S. Department of Agriculture, Beltsville
3592. M. THOMAS, King's College, Newcastle-on-Tyne 2, England
3593. R. P. THOMAS, University of Maryland
3594. ROY C. THOMAS, 537 Bloomington Ave., Wooster, Ohio
3595. H. J. THOME, E. I. du Pont de Nemours and Co., Inc., Wilmington, Del.
3596. GEORGE G. THOMPSON, Syracuse University
3597. JESSE E. THOMPSON, Boston University
3598. PAUL E. THOMPSON, Parke, Davis and Co., Detroit
3599. PAUL E. THOMPSON, U. S. Fish and Wildlife Service, Washington, D. C.
3600. RANDALL L. THOMPSON, Sterling-Winthrop Research Institute, Renssalaer, N. Y.
3601. J. D. THOMSON, Iowa State College
3602. JOHN F. THOMSON, Argonne National Laboratory
3603. H. H. THORNBERRY, University of Illinois
3604. D. W. THORNE, Utah State Agricultural College
3605. GERALD THORNE, U. S. Department of Agriculture, Salt Lake City
3606. R. S. W. THORNE, Alfred Jørgensen Laboratory of Fermentology, Copenhagen
3607. BRUCE THORNTON, Colorado Agricultural Experiment Station, Fort Collins
3608. CHARLES S. THORNTON, Kenyon College
3609. M. K. THORNTON, Texas Agricultural and Mechanical College
3610. THOMAS B. THORSON, University of Nebraska
3611. T. H. THUNG, Institute for Research in Plant Pathology, Wageningen, The Netherlands
3612. JOHN F. THURLOW, Cumberland Mills, Maine
3613. HERBERT C. TIDWELL, Southwestern Medical School
3614. L. H. TIFFANY, Northwestern University
3615. JOHN F. TIGHE, U. S. Food and Drug Administration, Washington, D. C.
3616. ALLEN D. TILLMAN, Oklahoma Agricultural and Mechanical College
3617. MILES A. TINKER, University of Minnesota
3618. ERNEST R. TINKHAM, Box 306, Indio, Cal.
3619. HARRY W. TITUS, Lime Crest Research Laboratory, Newton, N. J.
3620. CORNELIUS A. TOBIAS, University of California, Berkeley
3621. NORMAN TOBIAS, St. Louis University
3622. ELEANOR J. TOBIE, National Microbiological Institute
3623. L. M. TOCANTINS, Jefferson Medical College
3624. ALLEN R. TODD, Cambridge University

3625. FRANK E. TODD, U. S. Department of Agriculture, Tucson
3626. W. R. TODD, University of Oregon Medical School
3627. N. EDWARD TOLBERT, Oak Ridge National Laboratory
3628. L. J. TOLMACH, University of Colorado Medical Center
3629. A. E. TOMHAVE, University of Delaware
3630. C. M. TOMPKINS, 1517 Le Roy Ave., Berkeley, Cal.
3631. EDNA H. TOMPKINS, New England Deaconess Hospital, Boston
3632. EBEN O. TOOLE, U.S. Department of Agriculture, Beltsville
3633. HERBERT A. TOOPS, Ohio State University
3634. HARRISON B. TORDOFF, University of Kansas
3635. JOHN G. TORREY, University of California, Berkeley
3636. T. W. TORREY, Indiana University
3637. HENRY R. TOTTEN, University of North Carolina
3638. JOHN R. TOTTER, Oak Ridge National Laboratory
3639. DEE TOURTELLOTTE, Knox Gelatin Co., Inc., Camden, N. J.
3640. RALPH M. TOVELL, Hartford Hospital, Conn.
3641. BERNARD TOWERS, Cambridge University
3642. WILLIAM TRAGER, Rockefeller Institute for Medical Research
3643. EDGAR N. TRANSEAU, Ohio State University
3644. EUGENE F. TRAUB, Metropolitan Hospital, N. Y. C.
3645. J. J. TRAVERS, Stauffer Chemical Co., N. Y. C.
3646. B. V. TRAVIS, Cornell University
3647. SAM F. TRELEASE, Columbia University
3648. HARRY C. TRELOGAN, U. S. Department of Agriculture, Washington, D. C.
3649. E. R. TRETHEWIE, University of Melbourne
3650. GEORGE W. TRIMBERGER, Cornell University
3651. PHELPS TRIX, Wyandotte Chemical Corp., Wyandotte, Mich.
3652. WALTER TROLL, New York University
3653. FRANCIS G. TROMBA, U. S. Department of Agriculture, Beltsville
3654. MILDRED TROTTER, Washington University
3655. R. C. TRUEX, Hahnemann Medical College
3656. EMIL TRUOG, University of Wisconsin
3657. E. V. TRUTER, University of Leeds
3658. K. K. TSUBOI, Columbia University
3659. HAROLD B. TUKEY, New York Agricultural Experiment Station, Geneva
3660. HENRY J. TUMEN, 1900 Rittenhouse Sq., Philadelphia
3661. A. V. TUNISON, U. S. Fish and Wildlife Service, Washington, D. C.
3662. RONALD TUPPER, Medical College of St. Bartholomew's Hospital, London
3663. CHARLES W. TURNER, University of Missouri

3664. JOHN S. TURNER, University of Melbourne
3665. R. B. TURNER, Rice Institute
3666. ROBERT A. TURNER, State University of New York College of Medicine, Brooklyn
3667. ROBERT S. TURNER, Stanford University
3668. FRANKLIN M. TURRELL, University of California, Riverside
3669. J. W. TURRENTINE, 1102 16th St., NW, Washington, D. C.
3670. DAVID B. TYLER, University of Puerto Rico
3671. L. J. TYLER, Cornell University
3672. R. TYSLOW, Ortho Research Foundation, Raritan, N. J.
3673. WILLIAM J. TYZNIK, Ohio Agricultural Experiment Station, Wooster

3674. ALBERT ULRICH, University of California, Berkeley
3675. R. ULRICH, Cold Research Station, Meudon, France
3676. H. E. UMBARGER, Harvard Medical School
3677. CHARLES J. UMBERGER, New York University
3678. WAYNE W. UMBREIT, Merck Institute for Therapeutic Research, Rahway, N. J.
3679. B. M. L. UNDERHILL, Chase Farm Hospital, Enfield, England
3680. LELAND A. UNDERKOFLER, Takamine Laboratory, Inc., Clifton, N. J.
3681. LESTER J. UNGER, New York University
3682. W. G. UNGLAUB, Tulane University
3683. A. C. UPTON, Oak Ridge National Laboratory
3684. F. URBACH, Roswell Park Memorial Institute, Buffalo
3685. SYUNRO UTIDA, Kyoto Imperial University
3686. J. R. UZZMAN, U. S. Fish and Wildlife Service, Seattle

3687. DERRICK T. VAIL, Northwestern University Medical School
3688. F. G. VALDECASAS, University of Barcelona
3689. WILLIAM N. VALENTINE, University of California, Los Angeles
3690. K. B. VALLANCE, University of Liverpool
3691. BERT L. VALLEE, Massachusetts Institute of Technology
3692. J. T. VAN BRUGGEN, University of Oregon Medical School
3693. N. L. VANDEMARK, University of Illinois
3694. J. VANDER, Faulkner Hospital, Boston
3695. J. P. H. van der WANT, Institute for Research in Plant Pathology, Wageningen, The Netherlands
3696. J. J. A. VAN de VELDE, University of Ghent
3697. G. C. van DRIMMELEN, University of Pretoria
3698. FRANCES O. VAN DUYNE, University of Illinois
3699. M. van EEKELEN, Central Institute of Nutrition, Utrecht
3700. J. van EYS, University of Illinois
3701. D. S. VAN FLEET, University of Missouri
3702. RICHARD G. VAN GELDER, American Museum of Natural History

3703. A. van HARREVELD, California Institute of Technology
3704. J. M. VAN LANEN, Hiram Walker & Sons, Inc., Peoria, Ill.
3705. EDWARD J. VAN LIERE, West Virginia University
3706. J. VAN OVERBEEK, Shell Oil Company, Modesto, Cal.
3707. JOHN F. VAN PILSUM, University of Utah
3708. C. E. VAN ROOYEN, University of Toronto
3709. GEORGE H. VANSELL (Deceased)
3710. DONALD D. VAN SLYKE, Brookhaven National Laboratory
3711. GERTRUDE van WAGENEN, Yale University
3712. W. J. van WAGTENDONK, Indiana University
3713. D. VARIAKOJIS, University of Illinois College of Medicine
3714. J. E. VARNER, Ohio State University
3715. HARRY M. VARS, University of Pennsylvania
3716. STUART J. VAUGHAN, University of Buffalo
3717. F. J. VEIHMEYER, University of California, Davis
3718. SIDNEY F. VELICK, Washington University
3719. OLE VENGE, University of Uppsala
3720. BIRGIT VENNESLAND, University of Chicago
3721. ELEANOR H. VENNING, McGill University
3722. F. VERZAR, University of Basle
3723. WALTER G. VENZKE, Ohio State University
3724. JACOB VERDUIN, Ohio State University, Put-in-Bay
3725. MATTHEW F. VESSEL, San Jose State College
3726. CARL S. VESTLING, University of Illinois
3727. GASTON VIAUD, University of Strasbourg
3728. HUBERT B. VICKERY, Connecticut Agricultural Experiment Station, New Haven
3729. GEORGE P. VIERHELLER, St. Louis Zoological Park
3730. CLAUDE A. VILLEE, Harvard Medical School
3731. GILBERTO G. VILLELA, Oswald Cruz Institute, Rio de Janeiro
3732. RICHARD W. VILTER, University of Cincinnati
3733. ROBERT W. VIRTUE, Colorado General Hospital, Denver
3734. HELEN S. VISHNIAC, Yale University
3735. WOLF VISHNIAC, Yale University
3736. MAURICE B. VISSCHER, University of Minnesota
3737. VADIM D. VLADYKOV, Department of Fisheries, Quebec
3738. ARNO VOELKEL, Waldhaus Neurological Clinic, Berlin
3739. HOWARD H. VOGEL, Jr., Argonne National Laboratory
3740. GAYLORD M. VOLK, University of Florida
3741. NORMAN J. VOLK, Purdue University
3742. ERWIN P. VOLLMER, Naval Medical Research Institute
3743. LUDWIG von BERTALANFFY, Mount Sinai Hospital, Los Angeles

3744. GERHARDT von BONIN, University of Illinois College of Medicine
3745. THEODOR von BRAND, National Microbiological Institute
3746. U. S. von EULER, Physiological Institute, Stockholm
3747. W. F. von OETTINGEN, National Institutes of Health
3748. A. LeROY VORIS, National Research Council
3749. BERT J. VOS, U.S. Food and Drug Administration, Washington, D. C.
3750. PAUL D. VOTH, University of Chicago
3751. M. VULPÉ, McGill University
3752. JAMES WADDELL, E.I. du Pont de Nemours & Co., Newark, Del.
3753. CECIL H. WADLEIGH, U. S. Department of Agriculture, Beltsville
3754. F. M. WADLEY, 3215 Albemarle St., Arlington, Va.
3755. JAMES R. WADSWORTH, University of Vermont
3756. A. C. WAGENKNECHT, Cornell University
3757. H. G. WAGNER, Johns Hopkins University
3758. RICHARD WAGNER, Tufts College Medical School
3759. WALTER W. WAINIO, Rutgers University
3760. HARRY A. WAISMAN, University of Wisconsin
3761. PHILIP C. WAKELEY, U. S. Department of Agriculture, New Orleans
3762. GEORGE WALD, Harvard University
3763. LIONEL A. WALFORD, U. S. Fish and Wildlife Service, Washington, D. C.
3764. BURNHAM S. WALKER, Boston University
3765. D. A. WALKER, University of Durham
3766. ERNEST P. WALKER, National Zoological Park, Washington, D. C.
3767. HENRY WALKER, University of Alabama
3768. J. C. WALKER, University of Wisconsin
3769. LEVA B. WALKER, University of Nebraska
3770. RICHARD B. WALKER, University of Washington
3771. SHEPPARD M. WALKER, University of Louisville
3772. LAWRENCE H. WALKINSHAW, 1730 Wolverine Tower, Battle Creek, Mich.
3773. M. E. WALLACE, Cambridge University
3774. WILLIAM M. WALLACE, Western Reserve University
3775. H. WALLICK, Merck and Co., Inc., Rahway, N. J.
3776. WALTER B. WALLIN, University of Minnesota
3777. MACKENZIE WALSER, National Heart Institute
3778. W. GREY WALTER, Burden Neurological Institute, Bristol, England
3779. I. W. WANDER, University of Florida, Lake Alfred
3780. C. C. WANG, University of Illinois College of Medicine
3781. H. W. WANG
3782. JUSTUS C. WARD, U. S. Department of Agriculture, Washington, D. C.

3783. WILFRED H. WARD, U. S. Department of Agriculture, Albany, Cal.
3784. ROBERT A. WARDLE, University of Manitoba
3785. JOSEPH WARKANY, Children's Hospital Research Foundation, Cincinnati
3786. CAROL WARNER
3787. EMORY D. WARNER, State University of Iowa
3788. R. G. WARNER, Cornell University
3789. ROBERT C. WARNER, New York University
3790. DON C. WARREN, Kimber Farms Inc., Niles, Cal.
3791. NEIL D. WARREN, University of Southern California
3792. SHIELDS WARREN, New England Deaconess Hospital, Boston
3793. STAFFORD L. WARREN, University of California, Los Angeles
3794. ALBIN H. WARTH, 29 York Court, Baltimore
3795. BRUCE L. WARWICK, Texas Agricultural Experiment Station, McGregor
3796. ALFRED H. WASHBURN, University of Colorado School of Medicine
3797. S. L. WASHBURN, University of Chicago
3798. D. WATERHOUSE, Commonwealth Scientific and Industrial Research Organization, Canberra
3799. ALLYN J. WATERMAN, Williams College
3800. LELAND A. WATSON, Maico Co., Minneapolis
3801. R. JANET WATSON, State University of New York College of Medicine, Brooklyn
3802. BERNICE K. WATT, U. S. Department of Agriculture, Washington, D. C.
3803. DEAN D. WATT, Southeast Louisiana Hospital, Mandeville
3804. JAMES C. WATT, University of Toronto
3805. R. W. E. WATTS, Medical College of St. Bartholomew's Hospital, London
3806. VICTOR M. WATTS, University of Arkansas
3807. THEODORE R. WAUGH, McGill University
3808. E. LEONG WAY, University of California, San Francisco
3809. KATHERINE WAY, National Research Council
3810. E. R. WAYGOOD, McGill University
3811. CHARITY WAYMOUTH, Roscoe B. Jackson Memorial Laboratory
3812. JOHN L. WEAGLEY, Upper Ionia Rd., Mendham, N. J.
3813. JOHN E. WEAVER, University of Nebraska
3814. ROBERT J. WEAVER, University of California, Davis
3815. A. WEBER, University of Tübingen
3816. D. R. WEBSTER, Royal Victoria Hospital, Montreal
3817. STEWART H. WEBSTER, National Institutes of Health
3818. P. H. WECHSBERG, University of Illinois College of Medicine
3819. DAVID WECHSLER, New York University
3820. RICHARD L. WECHSLER, University of Pennsylvania

3821. RALPH J. WEDGWOOD, Quartermaster Climatic Research Laboratory, Lawrence, Mass.
3822. THEODORE E. WEICHSELBAUM, Washington University
3823. ROBERT H. WEIDMAN, Placerville, Cal.
3824. S. M. WEIDMAN, University of Leeds
3825. LEOPOLD WEIL, U. S. Department of Agriculture, Philadelphia
3826. WILLIAM WEILL, Jr., Army Chemical Center, Md.
3827. H. WEIL-MALHERBE, Runwell Hospital, Essex, England
3828. EUGENE D. WEINBERG, Indiana University
3829. AARON L. WEINBERGER, U.S. Department of Agriculture, Washington, D. C.
3830. HERBERT WEINER, Walter Reed Army Medical Center
3831. SIDNEY WEINHOUSE, Institute for Cancer Research, Philadelphia
3832. ERNEST O. WEINMAN, University of California, Los Angeles
3833. JACOB J. WEINSTEIN, 900 17th St., NW, Washington, D. C.
3834. ROBERT L. WEINTRAUB, Camp Detrick, Md.
3835. T. WEIS-FOGH, University of Copenhagen
3836. BENJAMIN WEISS, Harper Hospital, Detroit
3837. FREEMAN A. WEISS, American Type Culture Collection, Washington, D. C.
3838. HARRY B. WEISS, New Jersey Department of Agriculture, Trenton
3839. K. WEISS
3840. HENRY WELCH, U. S. Food and Drug Administration, Washington, D. C.
3841. EDWIN M. WELLER, University of California, Los Angeles
3842. H. J. WELLMAN
3843. BENJAMIN B. WELLS, University of Arkansas Medical School
3844. L. J. WELLS, University of Minnesota
3845. SHIRLEY WELLS, University of Oklahoma Medical Center
3846. I. D. WELT, National Research Council
3847. D. H. WENRICH, University of Pennsylvania
3848. F. W. WENT, California Institute of Technology
3849. BERNICE M. WENZEL, 10638 Holman Ave., Los Angeles
3850. CHESTER H. WERKMAN, Iowa State College
3851. LARS WERKÖ, St. Erik's Hospital, Stockholm
3852. CARL J. WESSEL, Prev. of Det. Ctr., N.A.S.-N.R.C.
3853. LAURENCE G. WESSON, Massachusetts Institute of Technology
3854. CLARK D. WEST, University of Cincinnati
3855. EDWARD S. WEST, University of Oregon Medical School
3856. ERDMAN WEST, University of Florida
3857. RALPH H. WETMORE, Harvard University
3858. NORMAN C. WETZEL, 2358 Ardleigh Dr., Cleveland Heights
3859. E. G. WEVER, Princeton University

3860. F. W. WEYMOUTH, Los Angeles College of Optometry
3861. G. W. WHARTON, University of Maryland
3862. V. R. WHEATLEY, St. Bartholomew's Hospital Medical Center, London
3863. H. E. WHEELER, Louisiana State University
3864. EDGAR T. WHERRY, University of Pennsylvania
3865. ALMA J. WHIFFEN, The Upjohn Co., Kalamazoo, Mich.
3866. ROY L. WHISTLER, Purdue University
3867. ELLIS H. WHITAKER, State Teachers College, Oneonta, N. Y.
3868. LIONEL E. H. WHITBY, Cambridge University
3869. ABRAHAM WHITE, Albert Einstein Medical School
3870. GLADYS R. WHITE, National Bureau of Standards
3871. I. G. WHITE, University of Sydney
3872. JAMES C. WHITE, Massachusetts General Hospital, Boston
3873. JOHN WHITE, University of Birmingham
3874. PAUL DUDLEY WHITE, Massachusetts General Hospital, Boston
3875. PHILIP R. WHITE, Roscoe B. Jackson Memorial Laboratory
3876. ROBERT M. WHITE, Quartermaster Research & Development Command, Natick, Mass.
3877. H. L. K. WHITEHOUSE, Cambridge University
3878. G. B. WHITFIELD, Jr., The Upjohn Co., Kalamazoo, Mich.
3879. L. A. WHITFORD, North Carolina State College
3880. P. W. WHITING, University of Pennsylvania
3881. JOHN B. WHITNEY, Jr., Clemson Agricultural College
3882. ROBERT H. WHITTAKER, General Electric Co., Richland, Wash.
3883. JAMES L. WHITTENBERGER, Harvard School of Public Health
3884. RALPH WICHTERMAN, Temple University
3885. LYNFERD J. WICKERMAN, U. S. Department of Agriculture, Peoria, Ill.
3886. LESTER F. WICKS, Veterans Administration Hospital, Jefferson Barracks, Mo.
3887. E. M. WIDDOWSON, Cambridge University
3888. THEODORE M. WIDRIG, U.S. Fish and Wildlife Service, La Jolla, Cal.
3889. ALEXANDER S. WIENER, 64 Rutland Rd., Brooklyn
3890. FLOYD J. WIERCINSKI, Hahnemann Medical College
3891. C. A. G. WIERSMA, California Institute of Technology
3892. A. C. WIESE, University of Idaho
3893. C. J. WIGGERS, Western Reserve University
3894. CHARLES G. WILBER, Army Chemical Center, Md.
3895. HAROLD L. WILCKE, Ralston-Purina Co., St. Louis
3896. L. V. WILCOX, U. S. Salinity Laboratory, Riverside
3897. ALAN WILD, Commonwealth Scientific & Industrial Research Organization, Canberra
3898. S. A. WILDE, University of Wisconsin

3899. WALTER S. WILDE, Tulane University
3900. RUSSELL M. WILDER, Mayo Clinic
3901. A. L. WILDS, University of Wisconsin
3902. D. R. WILKIE, University College, London
3903. LAWSON WILKINS, Johns Hopkins University
3904. LOUIS P. WILKS, Velsicol Corp., Chicago
3905. C. J. WILLARD, Ohio State University
3906. E. L. WILLETT, American Foundation for the Study of Genetics, Madison, Wis.
3907. AUSTIN B. WILLIAMS, University of Illinois, Chicago
3908. BERT C. WILLIAMS (Deceased)
3909. EDWARD F. WILLIAMS, Jr., University of Tennessee
3910. HAROLD H. WILLIAMS, Cornell University
3911. J. N. WILLIAMS, Jr., University of Wisconsin
3912. J. W. WILLIAMS, University of Wisconsin
3913. R. T. WILLIAMS, St. Mary's Hospital Medical School, London
3914. ROGER J. WILLIAMS, University of Texas
3915. ROY G. WILLIAMS, University of Pennsylvania
3916. W. R. WILLIAMSON
3917. E. D. WILLS, Medical College of St. Bartholomew's Hospital, London
3918. C. W. WILSON, Sunkist Growers, Inc., Ontario, Cal.
3919. CHARLES C. WILSON, University of Georgia
3920. D. WRIGHT WILSON, University of Pennsylvania
3921. G. B. WILSON, Michigan State University
3922. J. DEAN WILSON, Ohio Agricultural Experiment Station, Wooster
3923. J. WALTER WILSON, Brown University
3924. JAMES L. WILSON, University of Michigan
3925. PERRY W. WILSON, University of Wisconsin
3926. SLOAN J. WILSON, University of Kansas Medical Center
3927. VICTOR J. WILSON, Rockefeller Institute for Medical Research
3928. WILLIAM A. WIMSATT, Cornell University
3929. MARTIN M. WINBURY, G. D. Searle & Co., Chicago
3930. C. F. WINCHESTER, U. S. Department of Agriculture, Beltsville
3931. WILLIAM F. WINDLE, National Institute of Neurological Diseases and Blindness
3932. BERTRAM WINER
3933. O. WINGE, University of Copenhagen
3934. TRAVIS WINSOR, 3875 Wilshire Blvd., Los Angeles
3935. A. R. WINTER, Ohio State University
3936. CHARLES A. WINTER, Merck Institute for Therapeutic Research, Rahway, N. J.
3937. L. M. WINTERS, University of Minnesota
3938. O. WINTERSTEINER, Squibb Institute for Medical Research, New Brunswick, N. J.
3939. MAX M. WINTROBE, University of Utah

3940. RICHARD J. WINZLER, University of Illinois College of Medicine
3941. Z. T. WIRTSCHAFTER
3942. GEORGE B. WISLOCKI, Harvard Medical School
3943. ERNEST WITEBSKY, University of Buffalo
3944. TORBEN K. WITH, County Hospital, Svendborg, Denmark
3945. ALICE P. WITHROW, Smithsonian Institution
3946. ROBERT B. WITHROW, Smithsonian Institution
3947. EDWARD S. WITOWSKI, Jr., Georgetown University Hospital
3948. EMIL WITSCHI, Iowa State College
3949. HAROLD WITTCOFF, General Mills, Inc., Minneapolis
3950. JONATHAN B. WITTENBERG, Western Reserve University
3951. SYLVAN H. WITTWER, Michigan State University
3952. MICHAEL G. WOHL, Temple University
3953. DONALD E. WOHLSCHLAG, Stanford University
3954. L. D. WOJCIK, Harvard Medical School
3955. S. BURT WOLBACH, Children's Hospital, Boston
3956. A. V. WOLF, Walter Reed Army Medical Center
3957. FREDERICK A. WOLF, Duke University
3958. FREDERICK T. WOLF, Vanderbilt University
3959. LOUIS E. WOLF, New York State Fish Hatchery, Rome
3960. MARK A. WOLF, Dow Chemical Co., Midland, Mich.
3961. JAMES A. WOLFE, Babies Hospital, N. Y. C.
3962. HAROLD R. WOLFE, University of Wisconsin
3963. D. O. WOLFENBARGER, University of Florida, Homestead
3964. DOROTHY WOLFF, Manhattan Eye, Ear and Throat Hospital
3965. RENÉ WOLFF, University of Nancy
3966. MELVILLE L. WOLFROM, Ohio State University
3967. ALBERT WOLFSON, Northwestern University
3968. MADELYN WOMACK, U. S. Department of Agriculture, Washington, D. C.
3969. EARL H. WOOD, Mayo Clinic
3970. JOHN L. WOOD, University of Tennessee
3971. SHERWIN F. WOOD, Los Angeles City College
3972. HERN Q. WOODARD, Memorial Hospital, N. Y. C.
3973. RUSSELL T. WOODBURNE, University of Michigan
3974. ANGUS M. WOODBURY, University of Utah
3975. ROBERT A. WOODBURY, University of Tennessee
3976. ALAN H. WOODCOCK, Quartermaster Research and Development Center, Natick, Mass.
3977. BARNES WOODHALL, Duke University
3978. MARK W. WOODS, National Cancer Institute
3979. EDWARD R. WOODWARD, University of California, Los Angeles
3980. D. W. WOOLLEY, Rockefeller Institute for Medical Research
3981. HAROLD A. WOOSTER, Mellon Institute, Pittsburgh

3982. I. D. P. WOOTTON, University of London
3983. W. G. WORKMAN, National Microbiological Institute
3984. LEONARD G. WORLEY, Brooklyn College
3985. ALBERT HAZEN WRIGHT, Cornell University
3986. CLAUDE-STARR WRIGHT, Medical College of Georgia
3987. ERNEST B. WRIGHT, University of Rochester
3988. H. PAYLING WRIGHT, University College Hospital Medical School, London
3989. JONATHAN W. WRIGHT, U.S. Forest Service, Philadelphia
3990. LEMUEL D. WRIGHT, Sharp & Dohme, Inc., West Point, Pa.
3991. NORMAN C. WRIGHT, Ministry of Food, London
3992. SEWALL WRIGHT, University of Wisconsin
3993. W. D. WRIGHT, Imperial College, London
3994. S. H. WU, Oregon State College
3995. DONALD WYMAN, Harvard University
3996. E. STATEN WYNNE, Anderson Hospital & Tumor Institute, Houston
3997. ORVILLE WYSS, University of Texas

3998. C. P. YAGLOU, Harvard School of Public Health
3999. TAKASHI YAMAGUCHI, Kanegasaki Hospital, Kanegasaki, Japan
4000. KINTARO YANAGI, Tokyo Medical and Dental University
4001. CHARLES YANOFSKY, Western Reserve University
4002. J. A. YARBROUGH, Ohio State University
4003. G. YASUZUMI, University of Osaka
4004. M. M. YEOMAN, University of Durham
4005. CHARLES F. YOCOM, Humboldt State College
4006. L. EDWIN YOCUM, George Washington University
4007. J. M. YOFFEY, University of Bristol
4008. GEORGE T. YORK, U. S. Department of Agriculture, Ames, Iowa
4009. JOHN B. YOUMANS, Vanderbilt University
4010. E. GORDON YOUNG, National Research Council, Halifax, N.S.
4011. FRANK N. YOUNG, Indiana University
4012. I. MAUREEN YOUNG, St. Thomas's Hospital, London

4013. MARTIN D. YOUNG, U. S. Public Health Service, Columbia, S. C.
4014. R. J. YOUNG, University of Toronto
4015. R. S. YOUNG, Mond Nickel Co., Ltd., Clydach, England
4016. WILLIAM C. YOUNG, University of Kansas
4017. HEBER W. YOUNGKEN, Jr., University of Washington
4018. HOWARD R. YOUSE, DePauw University
4019. STEPHEN ZAMENHOF, Columbia University
4020. M. X. ZARROW, Purdue University
4021. H. L. ZAUDER, Bronx Municipal Hospital Center, N.Y.C.
4022. WILLIAM J. ZAUMEYER, U. S. Department of Agriculture, Beltsville
4023. S. H. ZBARSKY, University of British Columbia
4024. GUSTAV ZECHEL, University of Illinois College of Medicine
4025. L. ZECHMEISTER, California Institute of Technology
4026. THEODORE N. ZEKMAN, University of Illinois College of Medicine

4027. JOHN H. ZELLER, U. S. Department of Agriculture, Beltsville
4028. GEORGE A. ZENTMEYER, University of California, Riverside
4029. E. ZEUTHEN, University of Copenhagen
4030. MILDRED R. ZIEGLER, University of Minnesota
4031. KENNETH L. ZIERLER, Johns Hopkins University
4032. ARNOLD A. ZIMMERMAN, University of Illinois College of Medicine
4033. P. W. ZIMMERMAN, Boyce Thompson Institute for Plant Research
4034. ISADORE ZIPKIN, National Institutes of Health
4035. RAYMOND E. ZIRKLE, University of Chicago
4036. CLAUDE E. ZoBELL, Scripps Institution of Oceanography
4037. WILLIAM D. ZOETHOUT, South Laguna, Cal.
4038. F. P. ZSCHEILE, University of California, Davis
4039. LOIS M. ZUCKER, Columbia University
4040. THEODORE F. ZUCKER, Columbia University
4041. RAYMUND L. ZWEMER, UNESCO, Paris

Contents

Numbers in parentheses immediately following titles refer to principal contributors and correspond with those listed on pages v - xxx. Additional contributors and reviewers for each table are listed in the Contributor-Reviewer Index, pages 544, 545.

III. DEVELOPMENT AND MORPHOLOGY

IV. NUTRITION, DIGESTION, AND METABOLISM

V. RESPIRATION AND CIRCULATION

VI. OTHER PHYSIOLOGICAL ACTIVITIES AND PERFORMANCES

VII. BIOLOGICALLY ACTIVE COMPOUNDS

VIII. ENVIRONMENT AND SURVIVAL

IX. SYMBIOSIS AND PARASITISM

X. ECOLOGY AND BIOGEOGRAPHY

Introduction

"Without generalization there is no meaning, and without concreteness there is no significance."

... A. N. Whitehead

This Handbook presents tabular data and certain graphs, charts, and diagrams in the broad general areas of plant, animal, and pre-clinical medical sciences. The guiding principle for inclusion of material was its basic importance or wide general interest, and its adaptability to tabular presentation. The fact that certain of the data may already have been compiled and published was not regarded as a reason for excluding them from the Handbook. Unfortunately, some fundamental material has had to be omitted, either because in condensing 20,000 sheets of data into some 500 pages certain subject areas suffered extreme curtailment, or because efforts to secure the needed information were unsuccessful, or because certain tables arrived in the Handbook office too late to allow the processing requisite to publication. Inability to publish material that a contributor may have spent hours in compiling is cause for deepest regret, and every attempt will be made to include it in a revision of this volume or in one of the specialized monographs.

In considering presentational sequence of subject material, any one of a number of patterns could be followed. The one chosen appeared the most logical — first, chemical and physical data, then intra- or sub-cellular biology, followed by information on organs and organisms, growth and function, environmental effects, and, finally, distribution. The Table of Contents shows, for convenience of the user, a demarcation into ten categories. Within the book itself, however, no such clear-cut boundaries exist, and there is a gradual transition from one table or area to the next.

The chief objective in the preparation of this material in tabular form has been clarity of presentation. Where the subject matter of a table was considered to be inherently difficult for the non-specialist, effort has been made, in explanatory headnotes and footnotes, to resolve some of the difficulties. Certain of the tables contain symbols and terms peculiar to the fields of those tables. For each of these a glossary is included as an integral part of the table. In many instances information originally within the table itself has been moved into footnotes to simplify the structure of the table. Taxonomy, general definitions, symbols, and conversion factors, are covered in the Appendix.

One of the greatest difficulties encountered in the compilation of biological data is the element of variability. With few exceptions — and these clearly indicated — numerical values for variables are means, or adjusted means, of a group of measured values. To give these values significance, every effort has been made to present with the value an upper and lower estimate of the 95% range. The 95% range has been selected in preference to the standard deviation as better suited to the needs of the user who is not a specialist in the field from which a value has been drawn. The 95% range is a direct representation of the ordinary* range of variation, to be had only by further calculation if the standard deviation alone is available. The latter has the disadvantage of not being readily available, in many instances, and of giving biased limits for the 95% range when a variable has a skewed distribution. The statistically-minded reader who might wish to make further calculations from values in these tables may not care to proceed without facts on comparability and number of measurements. Unfortunately space does not permit including here such collateral information. Bibliographic references, available from the indicated contributor or from the Handbook Office, will lead to the original data where the desired material should be found.

The 95% range may be estimated in several ways, the method depending on the information available. The types of estimate most commonly encountered are listed below. The letter designations (a, b, c, d) will be found as superscripts identifying ranges given in the tables. ** Range data as commonly encountered, including estimates of the 95% range, represent a mixture of the variability existing between individuals and the variability existing within individuals.

(a) By the method of greatest accuracy, the 95% range is obtained by fitting a recognized type of frequency curve to a group of measured values and excluding the extreme 2.5% of area under the curve at each end. (See sketch.) Estimate is made by this procedure only when the group of values is relatively large.

(b) By a less accurate method, the 95% range is estimated by a simple statistical calculation, assuming a normal distribution and using the standard deviation. This estimate is used when the group of values is too small for curve fitting, as is usually the case.

(c) A third and still less accurate procedure for gauging the 95% range is simply to take as range limits the highest value and lowest value of the reported sample group of measurements. It underestimates the 95% range for small samples (three or four values) and overestimates for larger sample sizes, but may be used in preference to the preceding method (b) when the sample shows convincing evidence that the variable is asymmetrical in distribution.

(d) The upper and lower limits of the ordinary range of variation, as estimated by an investigator experienced in measuring the quantity in question and based solely on general experience, constitute still another estimate of the 95% range. The reliability of limits so placed, although not as sound as with the methods listed above, should not be underestimated.

In some instances range data were not available; in others estimates of the 95% range are given, but information on the manner of estimate is lacking. Effort to assemble both types of missing information is continuing.

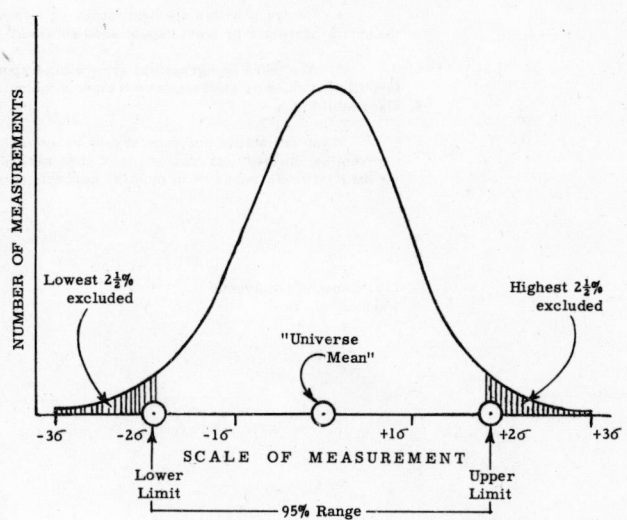

---

*To the clinician, equivalent, with reservations, to "normal and borderline."

**For details of these and other estimates the user is referred to standard texts on statistical methods.

QUESTIONNAIRE

TO THE USER OF

"THE HANDBOOK OF BIOLOGICAL DATA"

This volume is a first edition, comparable to first editions of other handbooks, particularly those in the physical sciences, in the sense that its initial presentation should offer a compilation not only useful in itself, but also one indicative of even greater service through improved future editions. Not yet subjected as a whole to the test of use and criticism by the scientific public, the book may be characterized by certain imbalances including areas treated too extensively or cursorily and remnant errors of commission or omission. We are convinced the persons best qualified to assist toward refined, superior future editions are those who, through study and use of this volume, have remarked such shortcomings. The following questions should receive particular attention by persons using this book. Your thoughts on them will be gratefully received at any time.

1. Has this first edition neglected to cover any general areas or specific tables, of fundamental usefulness to workers in the many biological sciences, that should be treated in a "handbook"?

2. Has it included areas not of this basic importance and utility, and of too specialized a nature for such a volume?

3. How might the coverage in certain areas, presently treated, be made more sound by expansion, contraction, or other types of revision?

4. Can gaps within specific tables be eliminated by incorporating material from the extant literature or from unpublished sources?

5. Are there typographical errors in any portion of the book, or definite errors of fact (i.e., values or statements you know to be untrue) that should be replaced in a revised edition?

If you are able to supplement your recommendations, we should appreciate receiving from you suggestions on sources of data needed for any revisions -- or preferably the data with references -- to modify, correct, or expand this initial presentation.

The Editor

2101 Constitution Avenue
Washington, D. C.

2

TABLES

Data in each of the following tables are, in the judgment of the contributors and reviewers, established fact or recognized theory, free of controversial material, and represent the consensus of expert judgment and experience in the special field from which the table is drawn. It is recognized, however, that all biological data are subject to continuing revision as investigators improve techniques and make more measurements. The user of this book is warned against attributing significance to small differences among species, or even within the same species while uniformity in methods of measurement is yet to be attained, and, particularly, where there may be marked differences in the size, age, or condition of the test samples.

Improper balance in coverage, despite the best efforts of thousands of advisors, may still persist, and many gaps remain to be filled. An appeal is made, particularly to the teacher and the specialist, to advise the compiler on the inclusion of important basic information that has been omitted, or on the deletion of material that may, for one reason or another, be considered as less useful to the student or non-specialist.

The user in general -- from the beginner to the expert -- is invited to submit any values or ranges he feels should be given consideration. It is hoped that such persons will participate in the development of a second edition with improved balance, better coverage, and elimination of errors.

1. STANDARD SOLUTIONS: pH_s [1]

	Temp °C	HCl 0.1 M	Tetroxalate [2]	Tartrate [3]	Phthalate [4]	Phosphate [5]	Borax [6]
1	0	1.10	1.67		4.01	6.98	9.46
2	5	1.10	1.67		4.01	6.95	9.39
3	10	1.10	1.67		4.00	6.92	9.33
4	15	1.10	1.67		4.00	6.90	9.27
5	20	1.10	1.68		4.00	6.88	9.22
6	25	1.10	1.68	3.56	4.01	6.86	9.18
7	30	1.10	1.69	3.55	4.01	6.85	9.14
8	35	1.10	1.69	3.55	4.02	6.84	9.10
9	40	1.10	1.70	3.54	4.03	6.84	9.07
10	45	1.10	1.70	3.55	4.04	6.83	9.04
11	50	1.10	1.71	3.55	4.06	6.83	9.01
12	55	1.11	1.72	3.55	4.08	6.84	8.99
13	60	1.11	1.73	3.57	4.10	6.84	8.96
14	70	1.11		3.59	4.12	6.85	8.92
15	80	1.11		3.61	4.16	6.86	8.88
16	90	1.12			4.20	6.86	8.85
17	95	1.12			4.22	6.87	8.83

/1/ pH_s is defined as $-\log f_H m_H$, where f_H is the activity coefficient of hydrogen ion, and m_H is the concentration of hydrogen ion on the molal scale. /2/ 0.05M potassium tetroxalate. /3/ $KHC_4H_4O_6$, saturated solution at 25°C. /4/ 0.05M $KHC_8H_4O_4$. /5/ 0.025M KH_2PO_4 and 0.025M Na_2HPO_4. /6/ 0.01M.

2. ACID-BASE INDICATORS: pH RANGES

	Indicator [1]	pH Range	Acid Color	Alkaline Color
1	Thymol blue (acid range)	1.2-2.8	Red	Yellow
2	Tropeolin 00	1.3-3.2	Red	Yellow
3	Dimethyl yellow	2.9-4.0	Red	Yellow
4	Methyl orange	3.1-4.4	Red	Orange-yellow
5	Bromphenol blue	3.0-4.6	Yellow	Purple
6	Bromcresol green	3.8-5.4	Yellow	Blue
7	Methyl red	4.4-6.2	Red	Yellow
8	Bromthymol blue	6.0-7.6	Yellow	Blue
9	Phenol red	6.4-8.2	Yellow	Red
10	Neutral red	6.8-8.0	Red	Yellow
11	Thymol blue (alk. range)	8.0-9.6	Yellow	Blue
12	Phenolphthalein	8.0-9.8	Colorless	Red-violet
13	Thymolphthalein	9.3-10.5	Colorless	Blue
14	Alizarin yellow	10.1-11.1	Yellow	Lilac
15	Nitramine	10.8-12.8	Colorless	Orange-brown
16	Tropeolin 0	11.1-12.7	Yellow	Orange-brown
17	Trinitrobenzoic acid	12.0-13.4	Colorless	Orange-red

/1/ A solution containing 0.1 percent indicator is satisfactory. Water is a suitable solvent for all the indicators listed except dimethyl yellow, neutral red, phenolphthalein, thymolphthalein, and nitramine; 70 - 90% ethanol should be used to dissolve these indicators.

3. BUFFER SOLUTIONS: pH RANGES

	Acidic Component	Alkaline Component	pH Range
1	Hydrochloric acid	Glycine	1.0-3.7
2	Hydrochloric acid	Potassium hydrogen phthalate	2.2-4.0
3	Citric acid	Disodium hydrogen phosphate	2.2-8.0
4	Acetic acid	Sodium acetate	3.7-5.6
5	Potassium hydrogen phthalate	Sodium hydroxide	4.0-6.2
6	Potassium dihydrogen phosphate	Sodium hydroxide	5.8-8.0
7	Boric acid	Borax	6.8-9.2
8	Diethylbarbituric acid	Sodium diethylbarbiturate	7.0-9.2
9	Hydrochloric acid	Borax	7.6-9.2
10	Glycine	Sodium hydroxide	8.2-10.1
11	Borax	Sodium hydroxide	9.2-11.0
12	Disodium hydrogen phosphate	Sodium hydroxide	11.0-12.0

4. OXIDATION-REDUCTION (REDOX) POTENTIALS
E_O at pH 7.0 and 30° C.

	Indicator	E_O (volts)		Indicator	E_O (volts)
1	(Standard oxygen electrode)	+0.810	16	Gallocyanine	0.021
2	Phenol-m-sulfonate-indo-2,6-dichlorophenol	0.273	17	Methylene blue	0.011
3	m-Bromphenol indophenol	0.248	18	Janus green (a)	-0.011
4	o-Bromphenol indophenol	0.230	19	Ciba scarlet sulfonate	-0.036
5	Phenol indophenol	0.227	20	Pyocyanine	-0.040
6	Phenol blue	0.224	21	Indigo tetrasulfonate	-0.046
7	2,6-Dibromphenol indophenol	0.218	22	Methyl capri blue	-0.060
8	m-Cresol indophenol	0.208	23	Indigo trisulfonate	-0.081
9	o-Cresol indophenol	0.191	24	Nile blue	-0.122
10	Thymol indophenol	0.174	25	Gallophenine	-0.142
11	2,6-Dibromphenol indoguaicol	0.159	26	Brilliant alizarine blue	-0.173
12	1-Naphthol-2-sulfonate indophenol	0.123	27	Phenosafranine	-0.252
13	Toluylene blue	0.115	28	Dimethyl phenosafranine	-0.260
14	Thionine (Lauth's violet)	0.063	29	Tetramethyl phenosafranine	-0.273
15	Brilliant cresyl blue	0.047	30	Safranine T	-0.289
			31	Neutral red	-0.325
			32	Viologens	-0.400
			33	(Standard hydrogen electrode)	-0.421

5. ORGANIC SYSTEMS: NORMAL OXIDATION-REDUCTION POTENTIALS

	System	Potential E'_O [1] volts	pH
1	Epinephrine	0.808	0.0
2	Cytochrome a	0.29	7.4
3	Cytochrome c	0.26	5-8
4	Cytochrome b	-0.04	7.4
5	Reductone	0.282	0.0
6	2,6-Dichloroindophenol	0.217	7.0
7	Hemoglobin	0.152	7.0
8	Ascorbic acid	0.136	4.59
9	Methylene blue	0.011	7.0
10	Succinate-fumarate	-0.015	6.7
11	Pyocyanine	-0.034	7.0
12	Flavoprotein (yellow enzyme)	-0.059	7.0
13	Alcohol-acetaldehyde	-0.090	7.45
14	Hemin	-0.114	6.99
15	Lactate-pyruvate	-0.186	7.01
16	Riboflavin	-0.208	7.0
17	Phthiocol	-0.208	7.32
18	Cystine-cysteine	-0.227	7.15
19	Glutathione	-0.233	7.15
20	Coenzyme I	-0.325	7.4

/1/ Symbol used for systems in which H^+ ions are involved.

6. IONIC SYSTEMS: NORMAL OXIDATION-REDUCTION POTENTIALS AT 25°C

	Oxidation-Reduction System	Electrode Reaction	Normal Potential E_O, volts
1	Co^{+++}—Co^{++}	$Co^{++} \rightleftharpoons Co^{+++} +e$	1.817
2	Ce^{++++}—Ce^{+++}	$Ce^{+++} \rightleftharpoons Ce^{++++} +e$	1.55
3	Cl_2—Cl^-	$Cl^- \rightleftharpoons \frac{1}{2} Cl_2 + e$	1.3583
4	Sn^{2++++}—Sn^{++}	$Sn^{++} \rightleftharpoons Sn^{++++} + 2e$	1.256
5	Tl^{+++}—Tl^+	$Tl^+ \rightleftharpoons Tl^{+++} + 2e$	1.211
6	Br_2—Br^-	$Br^- \rightleftharpoons \frac{1}{2} Br_2 + e$	1.0648
7	Hg_2^{++}—Hg^{++}	$\frac{1}{2} Hg_2^{++} \rightleftharpoons Hg^{++} +e$	0.9011
8	O_2 (1 atm.) — OH^- at pH 7	$OH^- \rightleftharpoons \frac{1}{2} H_2O + 1/4 O_2 +e$	0.810
9	Fe^{+++}—Fe^{++}	$Fe^{++} \rightleftharpoons Fe^{+++} +e$	0.7477
10	MnO_4^-—$MnO_4^=$	$MnO_4^= \rightleftharpoons MnO_4^- +e$	0.664
11	I_2—I^-Mn	$I^- \rightleftharpoons \frac{1}{2} I_2 + e$	0.5345
12	Cu^{++}—Cu^+	$Cu^+ \rightleftharpoons Cu^{++} +e$	0.455
13	Ti^{+++}—Ti^{++}	$Ti^{++} \rightleftharpoons Ti^{+++} +e$	0.37
14	H_2(1 atm.)—H^+	$\frac{1}{2}H_2 \rightleftharpoons H^+ +e$	0.0000 [1]
15	$HCN + H_2O$ — $HCNO + H^+$	$HCN + H_2O \rightleftharpoons HCNO + 2H^+ +2e$	0.0
16	Pb—Pb^{++}	$Pb \rightleftharpoons Pb^{++} + 2e$	-0.126
17	Mn—Mn^{++}	$Mn \rightleftharpoons Mn^{++} +2e$	-1.1
18	Al—Al^{+++}	$Al \rightleftharpoons Al^{+++} +3e$	-1.7
19	Mg—Mg^{++}	$Mg \rightleftharpoons Mg^{++} +2e$	-2.4
20	K—K^+	$K \rightleftharpoons K^+ +e$	-2.924

/1/ Reference electrode.

7. ACIDS AND BASES: DISSOCIATION CONSTANTS

Values are for determinations at 25°C, unless otherwise indicated.

Acids

	Acid	Formula	Constant for 1st Hydrogen	Constant for 2nd Hydrogen
1	Acetic	$C_2H_4O_2$	1.75×10^{-5}	
2	α-Alanine	$C_3H_7O_2N$	9×10^{-10}	
3	Arsenic	H_3AsO_4	5×10^{-3}	4×10^{-5}; 6×10^{-10} (3H)
4	Arsenious	$HAsO_2$	6×10^{-10}	
5	Barbituric	$C_4H_4O_3N$	1.05×10^{-4}	
6	Benzoic	$C_7H_6O_2$	6.3×10^{-5}	
7	Boric	H_3BO_3	6.4×10^{-10}	
8	Bromacetic	$C_2H_3O_2Br$	1.38×10^{-3}	
9	Butyric	$C_4H_8O_2$	1.48×10^{-5}	
10	Carbonic[1]	H_2CO_3	3.5×10^{-7}	4.4×10^{-11}
11	Chloracetic	$C_2H_3O_2Cl$	1.4×10^{-3}	
12	Citric	$C_6H_8O_7$	8.4×10^{-4}	1.8×10^{-5}; 4×10^{-6} (3H)
13	Dichloracetic	$C_2H_2O_2Cl_2$	5×10^{-2}	
14	Formic	CH_2O_2	1.76×10^{-4}	
15	Fumaric	$C_4H_4O_4$	1×10^{-3}	3×10^{-5}
16	Hippuric	$C_9H_9O_3N$	2.3×10^{-4}	
17	Hydrocyanic	CHN	7.2×10^{-10}	
18	Hydroquinone[1]	$C_6H_6O_2$	1.1×10^{-10}	
19	Hydrosulfuric[1]	H_2S	9.1×10^{-8}	1.2×10^{-15}
20	Hydrazoic	HN_3	1.9×10^{-5}	
21	Hypochlorous[2]	$HOCl$	3.7×10^{-8}	
22	Iodic	HIO_3	1.9×10^{-1}	
23	Isobutyric	$C_4H_8O_2$	1.5×10^{-5}	
24	Isovaleric	$C_5H_{10}O_2$	1.7×10^{-5}	
25	Lactic	$C_3H_6O_3$	1.38×10^{-4}	
26	Maleic	$C_4H_4O_4$	1.5×10^{-2}	2.6×10^{-7}
27	Malic	$C_4H_6O_5$	4×10^{-4}	9×10^{-6}
28	Malonic	$C_3H_4O_4$	1.61×10^{-3}	2.1×10^{-6}
29	Mandelic	$C_8H_8O_3$	4.29×10^{-4}	
30	Nicotinic	$C_6H_5O_2N$	1.4×10^{-5}	
31	Nitrous[1]	HNO_2	4×10^{-4}	
32	Oxalic	$H_2C_2O_4$	6.5×10^{-2}	6.1×10^{-5}
33	Periodic	HIO_4	2.3×10^{-2}	
34	Phenol	C_6H_6O	1.3×10^{-10}	
35	Phosphoric[1]	H_3PO_4	1.1×10^{-2}	7.5×10^{-8}; 4.8×10^{-13} (3H)
36	Phosphorous	H_3PO_3	7×10^{-3}	2×10^{-5}
37	Phthalic	$C_8H_6O_4$	1.26×10^{-3}	3.1×10^{-6}
38	Picolinic	$C_6H_5O_2N$	3×10^{-6}	
39	Picric[1]	$C_6H_3O_7N_3$	1.6×10^{-1}	
40	Propionic	$C_3H_6O_2$	1.4×10^{-5}	
41	Salicylic	$C_7H_6O_3$	1.06×10^{-3}	1×10^{-13}
42	Selenious	H_2SeO_3	3×10^{-3}	5×10^{-8}
43	Succinic	$C_4H_6O_4$	6.6×10^{-5}	2.8×10^{-6}
44	Sulfanilic	$C_6H_7O_3NS$	6.2×10^{-4}	
45	Sulfuric[1]	H_2SO_4		2×10^{-2}
46	Sulfurous	H_2SO_3	1.7×10^{-2}	5×10^{-6}
47	Tartaric	$C_4H_6O_6$	1.1×10^{-3}	6.9×10^{-5}
48	Trichloracetic[1]	$C_2HO_2Cl_3$	2×10^{-1}	
49	Uric	$C_5H_4O_3N_4$	1.5×10^{-6}	
50	Valeric	$C_5H_{10}O_2$	1.6×10^{-5}	

Bases

	Base	Formula	Constant for 1st Hydroxyl	Constant for 2nd Hydroxyl
51	Acetamide	C_2H_5ON	3.1×10^{-15}	
52	Acetanilide[3]	C_8H_9ON	4.1×10^{-14}	
53	α-Alanine	$C_3H_7O_2N$	5.1×10^{-12}	
54	o-Aminobenzoic	$C_7H_7O_2N$	1.4×10^{-12}	
55	Ammonium hydroxide	NH_4OH	1.8×10^{-5}	
56	Aniline	C_6H_7N	4.6×10^{-10}	
57	Arsenious oxide	As_2O_3	1×10^{-14}	
58	Beryllium hydroxide	$Be(OH)_2$		5×10^{-11}
59	Brucine	$C_{23}H_{26}O_4N_2$	7.2×10^{-4}	2.5×10^{-11}
60	Butylamine, sec.	$C_4H_{11}N$	4.4×10^{-4}	
61	Caffeine[3]	$C_8H_{10}O_2N_4$	4.1×10^{-14}	
62	Cinchonine[4]	$C_{19}H_{22}ON_2$	1.6×10^{-7}	3.3×10^{-10}
63	Cocaine	$C_{17}H_{21}O_4N$	4×10^{-7}	
64	Diethylbenzylamine	$C_{11}H_{17}N$	3.6×10^{-5}	
65	Diethylamine	$C_4H_{11}N$	1.26×10^{-3}	
66	Diisoamylamine	$C_{10}H_{23}N$	9.6×10^{-4}	
67	Diisobutylamine	$C_8H_{19}N$	4.8×10^{-4}	
68	Dimethylamine	C_2H_7N	5.2×10^{-4}	
69	Dimethylbenzylamine	$C_9H_{13}N$	1.05×10^{-5}	
70	Dipropylamine	$C_6H_{15}N$	1.02×10^{-3}	
71	Ethylamine	C_2H_7N	5.6×10^{-4}	
72	Ethylenediamine	$C_2H_8N_2$	8.5×10^{-5}	
73	Hydrazine	$N_2H_4 \cdot H_2O$	3×10^{-6}	
74	Isoamylamine	$C_5H_{13}N$	5×10^{-4}	
75	Isobutylamine	$C_4H_{11}N$	3.1×10^{-4}	
76	Isopropylamine	C_3H_9N	5.3×10^{-4}	
77	Lead hydroxide	$Pb(OH)_2$		3×10^{8}
78	Methylamine	CH_5N	5×10^{-4}	
79	Methyldiethylamine	$C_5H_{13}N$	2.7×10^{-4}	
80	α-Naphthylamine	$C_{10}H_9N$	9.9×10^{-11}	
81	β-Naphthylamine	$C_{10}H_9N$	2×10^{-10}	
82	o-Phenylenediamine	$C_6H_8N_2$	3.3×10^{-10}	
83	Phenylhydrazine[3]	$C_6H_8N_2$	1.6×10^{-9}	
84	Piperidine	$C_5H_{11}N$	1.6×10^{-3}	
85	Propylamine (norm.)	C_3H_9N	4.7×10^{-4}	
86	Pyridine	C_5H_5N	2.3×10^{-9}	
87	Quinine[4]	$C_{20}H_{24}O_2N_2$	2.2×10^{-7}	3.3×10^{-10}
88	Quinoline	C_9H_7N	1×10^{-9}	
89	Semicarbazide[3]	CH_5ON_3	2.7×10^{-11}	
90	Silver hydroxide	$AgOH$	1.1×10^{-4}	
91	Strychnine[4]	$C_{21}H_{22}O_4N_2$	1×10^{-7}	6×10^{-11}
92	Tetramethylenediamine	$C_4H_{12}N_2$	5.1×10^{-4}	
93	Thiourea	CH_4N_2S	1.1×10^{-15}	
94	m-Toluidine	C_7H_9N	5.5×10^{-10}	
95	o-Toluidine	C_7H_9N	3.3×10^{-10}	
96	p-Toluidine	C_7H_9N	2×10^{-9}	
97	Triethylamine	$C_6H_{15}N$	6.4×10^{-4}	
98	Triisobutylamine	$C_{12}H_{27}N$	2.6×10^{-4}	
99	Trimethylamine	C_3H_9N	7.4×10^{-5}	
100	Trimethylenediamine	$C_3H_{10}N_2$	3.5×10^{-4}	
101	Tripropylamine	$C_9H_{21}N$	5.5×10^{-4}	
102	Urea	CH_4ON_2	1.5×10^{-14}	
103	Zinc hydroxide	$Zn(OH)_2$		1.5×10^{-9}

/1/ At 18°C. /2/ At 17°C. /3/ At 40°C. /4/ At 15°C.

8. AMINO ACIDS: IONIZATION CONSTANTS AND pH VALUES

Determinations were made at the isoelectric points of the amino acids in water at 25°C.

	Amino Acid	Classical				Zwitterionic				Acidic				pH
		pk_{a1}	pk_{a2}	pk_{b1}	pk_{b2}	pK_{A1}	pK_{A2}	pK_{B1}	pP_{B2}	pK_1	pK_2	pK_3	pK_4	
1	DL-Alanine	9.866		11.649		2.348		4.131		2.348	9.866			6.107
2	L-Arginine	12.48	9.82	4.96	11.99	2.01	3.86	1.52	4.96	2.01	9.04	12.48		10.76
3	L-Aspartic acid	3.86	9.82	11.93		2.10	3.86	4.18		2.10	3.86	9.82		2.98
4	L-Cystine	8.00	10.25	11.95	12.96	1.04	2.05	3.75	6.00	1.04	2.05	8.00	10.25	5.02
5	L-Diiodotyrosine	6.48	7.82	11.88		2.12	6.48	6.18		2.12	6.48	7.82		4.29
6	L-Glutamic acid	4.07	9.47	11.90		2.10	4.07	4.53		2.10	4.07	9.47		3.08
7	Glycine	9.778		11.647		2.350		4.219		2.350	9.778			6.064
8	L-Histidine	9.18		7.90	12.23	1.77		4.82	7.90	1.77	6.10	9.18		7.64
9	Hydroxy-L-proline	9.73		12.08		1.92		4.27		1.92	9.73			5.82
10	DL-Isoleucine	9.758		11.679		2.318		4.239		2.318	9.758			6.038
11	DL-Leucine	9.744		11.669		2.328		4.253		2.328	9.744			6.036
12	L-Lysine	10.53		5.05	11.82	2.18		3.47	5.05	2.18	8.95	10.53		9.47
13	DL-Methionine	9.21		11.72		2.28		4.79		2.28	9.21			5.74
14	DL-Phenylalanine	9.24		11.42		2.58		4.76		2.58	9.24			5.91
15	L-Proline	10.60		12.0		2.00		3.40		2.00	10.60			6.3
16	DL-Serine	9.15		11.79		2.21		4.85		2.21	9.15			5.68
17	L-Tryptophan	9.39		11.62		2.38		4.61		2.38	9.39			5.88
18	L-Tyrosine	9.11	10.07	11.80		2.20	9.11	3.93		2.20	9.11	10.07		5.63
19	DL-Valine	9.719		11.711		2.286		4.278		2.286	9.719			6.002

9. CARBOHYDRATES: PHYSICAL AND CHEMICAL CHARACTERISTICS

Part 1: NATURAL MONOSACCHARIDES: ALDOSES[1,2]

No.	Substance[3]	MP °C	$[\alpha]_D$, degrees[4]
1	D-Glyceraldehyde ($C_3H_6O_3$)	(sirup)	+13.5±0.5 (sirup)
2	D-Glyceraldehyde dimethyl acetal	BP_{14}, 124-127	+21.8 (c 6.5, H_2O)
3	2,3-O-Isopropylidene-D-glyceraldehyde	$BP_{0.8}$, 18-20	+64.9 (c 5.7, C_6H_6)
4	D-Glyceraldehyde dimethone	199-201	+197.5 (c 0.7, C_2H_5O)
5	D-L-Glyceraldehyde dimethone	197.5 (clouds at 190, melts at 210-211)	
6	D-Glyceraldehyde 2,4-dinitrophenylhydrazone	155-156	
7	D-L-Glyceraldehyde 2,4-dinitrophenylhydrazone	166-167	
8	D-L-Glyceraldehyde 2,4-dinitrophenylosazone	310-311	
9	D-Glyceraldehyde semicarbazone	133	
10	D-Glyceraldehyde, 3,3-bis-C-(hydroxymethyl)- (apiose) ($C_5H_{10}O_5$) Apionic acid		+5.6 (c 10) [150°] (sirup) / -20 → -34.6 (H_2O)
11			
12	Apionic acid phenylhydrazide	127	+30 (H_2O)
13	Apiose benzyl phenylhydrazone	137-138	-78.5 (c 5, C_5H_5N)[579]
14	β-D-Arabinose ($C_5H_{10}O_5$)	155	-175 → -103 [16°]
15	D-Arabinose benzylphenyl-hydrazone	177-178	+14.4 (CH_3OH)
16	D-Arabinose p-bromophenyl-hydrazone	163	
17	D-Arabinose diphenylhydrazone	206	
18	Tri-O-acetyl-β-D-arabopyranosyl	139	-283.4 ($CHCl_3$)
19	Methyl α-D-arabofuranoside	65-67	+123 / -241.1 (c 1.2, H_2O)
20	Methyl β-D-arabopyranoside	168	-205 (c 1.6, CH_3OH)
21	Methyl 2-O-methyl-β-D-arabinoside	62-63	-102 (c 1.5, H_2O)
22	2-O-Methyl-D-arabinose	Sirup	-17.0 (c 1, H_2O)
23	2-O-Methyl-D-arabinose p-toluenesulfonylhydrazone	143 d.	
24	2,4-Di-O-methyl-D-arabinose	Sirup	-30.8 (c 2.4, H_2O)
25	2,4-Di-O-methyl-D-arabinose anilide	142-143	
26	Methyl 2,3,5-tri-O-methyl-D-arabofuranoside	Sirup	+80.4 (c 1.1, H_2O) [15°]
27	2,3,5-Tri-O-methyl-D-arabofuranose	Sirup	+40 (c 2.9, CH_3OH) [14°] / +55.4 → +105
28	α-L-Arabinose ($C_5H_{10}O_5$)	158 amorph.	+190.6 → 104.5
	(See also β-D-arabinose for hydrazones and bromides)		
29	β-L-Arabinose ($C_5H_{10}O_5$)	160	
64	L-Lyxose, 3-C-formyl-5-deoxy- (streptose) ($C_6H_{10}O_5$) (concluded)	186-188	+26 (c 0.5, CH_3OH)
65	2,3-Di-O-acetyl-L-streptosonic acid monolactone	135-136	+14 (c 0.5, H_2O) → -23.7
66	L-Streptosonic acid diamide	87	
67	D-Ribose ($C_5H_{10}O_5$)		+10.3 (c 1, C_2H_5OH), 19.3 (c 1, C_5H_5N) -26.5 (c 3, C_2H_5OH)
68	D-Ribose p-bromophenyl hydrazone	164-165	
69	D-Ribose benzylphenyl-hydrazone	127-128	
70	1,2,3,5-Tetra-O-acetyl-D-ribofuranoside	82	-12.6 (c 12, $CHCl_3$)
71	Tetra-O-acetyl-D-ribo-pyranoside	110	-52 (c 3, $CHCl_3$)
72	Methyl D-ribofuranoside	Sirup	+13.1 (c 1.9, CH_3OH)
73	Methyl D-ribopyranoside	83-84	-39.5 ($CHCl_3$) -113.6 (c 1, CH_3OH)
74	Methyl 2,3,4-Tri-O-methyl-D-ribopyranoside	Sirup	-35 (c 2.5, H_2O)
75	2,3,4-Tri-O-methyl-D-ribopyranose	85-86	-51 → -40 (c 1, H_2O)
76	Methyl 2,3,5-tri-O-methyl-D-ribofuranoside	Sirup	+59.1 (c 4.7, CH_3OH)
77	2,3,5-Tri-O-methyl-D-ribofuranose	Sirup	+41.1 (c 1, CH_3OH)
78	2,3,5-Tri-O-methyl-D-ribose anilide	56.5	
79	β-D-Ribose, 2-deoxy- (β-D-erythro-2-deoxyaldopentose) ($C_5H_{10}O_4$)	96-98	-91 → -58 (c 2, C_5H_5N)
80	2-Deoxy-D-ribose benzyl-phenylhydrazone	128	-17.5 (c 2, C_5H_5N)
81	2-Deoxy-D-ribose p-nitro-phenylhydrazone	160	-11.1 [14°] (c 0.1, C_2H_5OH)
82	2-Deoxy-D-ribose anilide	175-176	+20.5 (C_2H_5OH)
83	1,3,4-Tri-O-acetyl-2-deoxy-D-ribopyranoside	98	-171.8 (c 0.5, $CHCl_3$)
84	Methyl 2-deoxy-D-ribo-furanoside (α, β mixture)	Sirup	+38.4 (c 0.6, CH_3COOH)
85	Methyl 3,5-di-O-p-tolylsulfonyl-D-ribofuranoside (α, β mixture)	Sirup	-121 (c 0.4, $CHCl_3$)
86	Methyl 3-4-di-O-p-tolylsulfonyl-β-D-ribopyranoside	104-107	-115.5 (c 6.7, $CHCl_3$)
87	D-Ribose, 3-4-di-O-hydroxymethyl-D- (hamamelose) ($C_6H_{12}O_6$)	165-166	-7.1 [578] / +144 [578] (c 4, C_5H_5N)
88	Hamamelose p-nitrophenyl hydrazone	Sirup	-75 (c 5, CH_3OH)
89	Methyl hamameloside	Sirup	
90	Methyl tri-O-acetyl hamameloside	72.5	-34.8 [Hg] (c 4.1, C_2H_5OH)
91	Ammonium hamamelonate	152	-3.9 [578] (c 10, H_2O)
122	α-D-Xylose ($C_5H_{10}O_5$) (concluded)	155-157	-40 [70°] (c 0.7, $CH_3COOC_2H_5$)
123	2,4-Di-O-methyl-D-xylose anilide	170	-82 (dioxane)
124	Methyl 2,4-di-O-methyl-3-O-p-tolylsulfonyl-β-D-xylopyranoside	88	-58.9 (c 1, $CHCl_3$)
125	Methyl 2,4-di-O-methyl-3-O-p-tolylsulfonyl-β-D-xylopyranoside	75-76	+28.8 (c 1, $CHCl_3$)
126	Methyl 2,5-di-O-methyl-α-D-xylofuranoside	Sirup	+54.3
127	Methyl 2,5-di-O-methyl-β-D-xylopyranoside	Sirup	-56 (c 2.3, $CHCl_3$)
128	2,5-Di-O-methyl-D-xylo-furanose	Sirup	+46 (c 1.2, H_2O)
129	Methyl 2,5-di-O-methyl-3-O-p-tolylsulfonyl-α-D-xylofuranoside	Sirup	+34.7 [17°] (c 2, $CHCl_3$)
130	Methyl 2,5-di-O-methyl-3-O-p-tolylsulfonyl-β-D-xylofuranoside	Sirup	-49.9 [18°] (c 1.8, $CHCl_3$)
131	Methyl 3,4-di-O-methyl-β-D-xylopyranoside	89-90	-82 (c 2.1, $CHCl_3$)
132	3,4-Di-O-methyl-D-xylose	Sirup	+24.9 → +20.5 (c 2.2, H_2O)
133	Methyl 3,4-di-O-methyl-2-O-p-tolylsulfonyl-β-D-xylopyranoside	105	-34.8 (c 1.6, $CHCl_3$)
134	3,5-Di-O-methyl-D-xylose	Sirup	+25 (c 1.1, H_2O)
135	Methyl 2,3,4-tri-O-methyl-β-D-xylopyranoside	49-50	-73 (c 0.8, $CHCl_3$)
136	Methyl 2,3,4-tri-O-methyl-α-D-xylopyranoside	Sirup	+86 (c 2, CH_3OH)
137	Methyl 2,3,4-tri-O-methyl-α-D-xylopyranoside (with some β?)	91-92	+49.5 (c 1.2, HCl-alc) / +64 → +18 (c 1, H_2O)
138	2,3,4-Tri-O-methyl-α-D-xylopyranose	Sirup	+32 (c 0.8, CH_3OH)
139	2,3,5-Tri-O-methyl-D-xylofuranose	Sirup	+24.7 → +29.5 (H_2O)
140	1,2,3,5-Tetra-O-acetyl-D-xylofuranose	Sirup	+56 (c 2, C_2H_5OH)
141	D-Allose, 6-deoxy- ($C_6H_{12}O_6$)	140-143	+1.6 [18°] (c 0.6)
142	6-Deoxy-D-allose p-bromophenylhydrazone	138-140	
143	1,2,3,4-Tetra-O-acetyl-6-deoxy-D-allopyranose	109-110	+10.4 (c 2, $CHCl_3$)
144	D-Allose, 2,6-dideoxy- (digitoxose) (2,6-dideoxy-D-altrose) ($C_6H_{12}O_4$)		
145	Digitoxose phenylhydrazone	110	+46.4
146	Digitoxose oxime	204-209	+215 (C_5H_5N, C_2H_5OH)
147	D-Allose, 2,6-dideoxy-3-O-methyl- (cymarose) ($C_7H_{14}O_4$)	102	+52
148	Methyl α-D-cymaroside	93; 34-36	+210±2 [14°] (c 1.3, CH_3OH)

No.	Compound	M.p. (°C)	[α]D
30	(See also β-D-arabinose for hydrazones and bromides)		
31	Tetra-O-acetyl-α-L-arabo-pyranoside	97	+42.5 (c 3, $CHCl_3$)
	Tetra-O-acetyl-β-L-arabo-pyranoside	86	+147.2 (c 5, $CHCl_3$)
32	2,3,4,5-Tetra-O-acetyl-L-arabinose	113-115	-65.6 (c 4, $CHCl_3$)
33	Methyl α-L-arabofuranoside	Sirup	-125 (c 1.2, H_2O)
34	Methyl α-L-arabopyranoside	131	+17.3 (c 3, H_2O)
35	Methyl β-L-arabopyranoside	166-169	+245 (c 7, H_2O)
36	Methyl 2-O-methyl-β-L-arabo-pyranoside	63-65	+208 (c 2.5, CH_3OH)
37	2-O-Methyl-L-arabinose	Sirup	+100 (c 5, H_2O)
38	2-O-Methyl-L-arabinose phenylhydrazone	114-116	+110 (c 3.6, H_2O)
39	3-O-Methyl-L-arabinose	Sirup	
40	3-O-Methyl-L-arabinose anilide	117	+107 (c 1, H_2O)
41	2,3-Di-O-methyl-L-arabinose	Sirup	
42	2,3-Di-O-methyl-L-arabinose anilide	139	+30.85
43	2,4-Di-O-methyl-L-arabinose	Sirup	-60 (c 1, H_2O)
44	Methyl 2,5-di-O-methyl-L-arabofuranoside	Sirup	-2 (c 1, H_2O)
45	2,5-Di-O-methyl-L-arabinose[6]	Sirup	+210.6 (c 3.8, $CHCl_3$)
46	Methyl 3,4-di-O-methyl-β-L-arabopyranoside	Sirup	+116 (c 4.2, H_2O)
47	3,4-Di-O-methyl-L-arabinose	Sirup	+46.2 (c 1, H_2O)
48	Methyl 2,3,4-tri-O-methyl-α-L-arabopyranoside	46-48	+250 (c 1, H_2O)
49	Methyl 2,3,4-tri-O-methyl-β-L-arabopyranoside	44-46	+127 (c 8, H_2O)
50	2,3,4-Tri-O-methyl-L-arabinose	Sirup	
51	2,3,5-Tri-O-methyl-L-arabinose	Sirup	0 (c 1, H_2O)
52	Tri-O-acetyl-β-L-arabo-pyranosyl bromide	139	+287.1 (c 2, $CHCl_3$)
53	D-, L-Arabinose ($C_5H_{10}O_5$) (See D- and L-arabinose for derivatives)	163.5-164.5	None
54	α-L-Lyxose ($C_5H_{10}O_5$)	105	+5.8 → +13.5
55	α-L-Lyxose p-bromophenyl-hydrazone[7]	157	
56	L-Lyxose p-nitrophenyl-hydrazone	172	+25 ($CHCl_3$)
57	Tetra-O-acetyl-α-D-lyxose[7]	93-94	+59.4 (c 5, H_2O)
58	Methyl α-D-lyxopyranoside[7]	108-109	-128.1 (c 2, H_2O)
59	Methyl β-D-lyxopyranoside	118	+10 [546I]
60	Methyl 2,3,4-tri-O-methyl-D-lyxoside[7]	Sirup	-10 (c 2.6, H_2O)
61	2,3,4-Tri-O-methyl-D-lyxose[7]	79	-22 (c 2, H_2O)
62	2,3,5-Tri-O-methyl-D-lyxose[7]	Sirup	+39 (c 1, H_2O)
63	L-Lyxose, 3-C-Formyl-5-deoxy-(streptose); L-Streptosonic acid monolactone ($C_6H_{10}O_5$)	146-148	-37 (c 0.7, H_2O)

No.	Compound	M.p. (°C)	[α]D
92	Hamamelonic acid phenylhydrazide	202-203	+35.2 [578] (c 4, 50% CH_3COOH, C_5H_5N)
93	α-D-Xylose ($C_5H_{10}O_5$)	145	+93.6 → +18.8
94	D-Xylose p-nitro phenylhydrazone	156	
95	D-Xylose benzylphenyl-hydrazone	99	-20.3 (CH_3OH)
96	D-Xylose p-bromophenyl-hydrazone	128	-20.7 (H_2O)
97	1,2,3,4-Tetra-O-acetyl-α-D-xylopyranose	59	+89.3 (c 5, $CHCl_3$)
98	1,2,3,4-Tetra-O-acetyl-β-D-xylopyranoside	128	-24.7 (c 5, $CHCl_3$)
99	2,3,4,5-Tetra-O-acetyl-aldehydo-D-xylose	87-89	-15.9 [26°] (c 4, $CHCl_3$)
100	Methyl D-xyloside (furanose form?)	Sirup	+62.8 (C_2H_5OH)
101	Methyl α-D-xylopyranoside	90-92	+153.9 (c 11, H_2O)
102	Methyl β-D-xylopyranoside	157	-65.5 (c 13, H_2O)
103	Methyl 2-O-methyl-β-D-pyranoside	111-112	-67.7 (c 1.4, $CHCl_3$)
104	2-O-Methyl-β-D-xylose	132-133	-23.9 → +35.9 (c 2, H_2O)
105	3-O-Methyl-α-D-xylose	103-104	+55 → +17 (c 2, H_2O)
106	3-O-Methyl-α-D-xylose	95	+45 → +19 (c 1.6, H_2O)
107	3-O-Methyl-α-D-xylose	98-101	
108	3-O-Methyl-D-xylose anilide	137	
109	5-O-Methyl-D-xylose	Sirup	
110	1,2-O-Isopropylidene-3-O-p-tolylsulfonyl-D-xylose	81-82	+32.8 → +36 (c 2.4, $CHCl_3$)
111	Methyl 3-O-p-tolylsulfonyl-5-O-methyl-β-D-xylofurano-side	89	-31.8 (c 2.4, $CHCl_3$)
112	Methyl 3-O-p-tolylsulfonyl-5-O-methyl-β-D-xylofurano-side	Sirup	-51.7 [18°] (c 1.8, $CHCl_3$)
113	Methyl 2,3-di-O-methyl-D-xyloside (β form?)	Sirup	+44.5 [17°] (c 2.2, $CHCl_3$)
114	Methyl 2,3-di-O-methyl-D-xyloside (α form?)	Sirup	+61.8 (c 1.2, $CHCl_3$)
115	2,3-Di-O-methyl-D-xylose	79-80	-5.8 (c 2.2, $CHCl_3$)
116	Methyl 2,3-di-O-methyl-4-O-p-tolylsulfonyl-β-D-xylopyranoside	56-59	+70 → +23 (c 1, H_2O) [159]
117	Methyl 2,4-di-O-methyl-β-D-xylopyranoside	77.5-78.5	-8.8 (c 2.5, $CHCl_3$)
118	Methyl 2,4-di-O-methyl-β-D-xylopyranoside	60-61	-70 (c 1, $CHCl_3$)
119	2,4-Di-O-methyl-D-xylose	108	-82.4 (c 1.4, $CHCl_3$)
120	2,4-Di-O-methyl-D-xylose (β form?)	111	-30 (c 2, H_2O)
121	2,4-Di-O-methyl-D-xylose	116-118	-13 → +23 (c 2, H_2O); -26 (c 1, $CHCl_3$)

No.	Compound	M.p. (°C)	[α]D
149	D-Cymaronic acid phenylhydrazide	155-156	+1.4±3, [16°] (c 0.7, CH_3OH)
150	Antiarose ($C_6H_{12}O_5$)		Levo -30
151	Antiaronic acid lactone		
152	Antiaronic acid phenylhy-drazide	143-145	
153	α-D-Galactose ($C_6H_{12}O_6$) See β-D-galactose	167	+150.7 → +80.2
154	β-D-Galactose ($C_6H_{12}O_6$)		+52.8 → +80.2
155	D-Galactose o-tolylhydra-zone	176	
156	D-Galactose p-bromo-phenylhydrazone	166-167	
157	D-Galactose p-nitro phenylhydrazone	196-197	
158	D-Galactose benzylphenyl-hydrazone	157-158	-25 [26°] (c 4, $CHCl_3$)
159	2,3,4,5,6-Penta-O-acetyl-aldehydo-D-galactose	121	+61.2 (c 4, $CHCl_3$)
160	1,2,3,5,6-Penta-O-acetyl-α-D-galactofuranoside	87	
161	1,2,3,4,6-Penta-O-acetyl-β-D-galactofuranoside	98	-41.6 ($CHCl_3$)
162	1,2,3,4,6-Penta-O-acetyl-α-D galactopyranoside	96	+106.7 (c 3, $CHCl_3$)
163	1,2,3,4,6-Penta-O-acetyl-β-D-galactopyranoside	142	+25 ($CHCl_3$)
164	Methyl α-D-galactopyrano-side monohydrate	110	+179.3 (c 9, H_2O)
165	Methyl β-D-galacto-pyranoside	178	0 (c 10, H_2O)
166	Methyl 2-O-methyl-α-D-galactopyranoside	Sirup	+180 (c 3.5, CH_3OH)
167	Methyl 2-O-methyl-β-D-galactopyranoside	131-132	+1.7 (c 11, H_2O)
168	2-O-Methyl-β-D-galactopyranose	147-149	+53 → +86.2 (c 5, H_2O)
169	Methyl 3-O-methyl-β-D-galactopyranoside	Sirup	+31.9 → +108.6 (c 5, H_2O)
170	α-D-Galactopyranose, 3-O-methyl-; 3-O-methyl-α-D-galactopyranose ($C_7H_{14}O_6$)	144-147	+150.6 → +108.6 (c 1.5, H_2O)
171	4-O-Methyl-β-D-galactopyranose	207	+62 → +92 (H_2O)
172	Methyl 6-O-methyl-β-D-galactofuranoside (?)	Sirup	-78.7 (c 3.3, H_2O)
173	6-O-Methyl-α-D-galactofuranoside	113-114	+137 → +77 (c 3, H_2O)
174	Methyl 2,3-di-O-methyl-α-D-galactopyranose	Sirup	+210 (H_2O)
175	Methyl 2,3-di-O-methyl-β-D-galactopyranose	Sirup	+23 (H_2O)
176	2,3-Di-O-methyl-α-D-galactopyranose	Sirup	+57 → +105 (H_2O)
177	Methyl 2,4-di-O-methyl-α-D-galactopyranose	105	+142 (c 1.1, H_2O)
178	Methyl 2,4-di-O-methyl-β-D-galactopyranose		+23
179	2,4-Di-O-methyl-D-galactopyranose	165-166	0 (c 1.8, H_2O) → +122 (c 1.7, H_2O)
180	Methyl 2,6-di-O-methyl-β-D-galactopyranose	103	+85.6 (c 1.7, H_2O)
181	2,6-Di-O-methyl-β-D-galactopyranose	72; 106-108	-22 (c 1, $CHCl_3$); +45 → +88 (c 5.4, H_2O)

Part I: NATURAL MONOSACCHARIDES: ALDOSES[1,2] (Continued)

	Substance[3]	MP °C	$[\alpha]_D$, degrees[4]		Substance[3]	MP °C	$[\alpha]_D$, degrees[4]		Substance[3]	MP °C	$[\alpha]_D$, degrees[4]
182	α-D-Galactopyranose, 3-O-methyl ($C_7H_{14}O_6$) (concluded)	128-130	+46.8 → +87.5 (c 6.3, H_2O)	233	L-Galactose ($C_6H_{12}O_6$) (See derivatives of D-galactose)		(See D-galactose)	289	β-D-Glucose ($C_6H_{12}O_6$) (concluded) 4,6-Di-O-methyl-α-D-glucose	156-158	+110 → +65.7
183	2,6-Di-O-methyl-β-D-galactopyranose	102-103	-9.1 (c 6.2, $CHCl_3$)	234	L-Galactose[8], 3,6-anhydro-($C_6H_{10}O_5$)	82	+75 [14°] (c 5.6, H_2O)	290	5,6-Di-O-methyl-D-galactose → glucose	Sirup	+4.0 [32°] (c 2, H_2O)
184	Methyl 3,4-di-O-methyl-β-D-galactopyranoside	164-166	+95 → +117 (c 6.5, H_2O)	235	2,4-Di-O-methyl-3,6-anhydro-L-galactose	Sirup	-23	291	Methyl 2,3,4-tri-O-methyl-β-D-glucopyranoside	93-94	-19.6 (c 5, H_2O)
185	3,4-Di-O-methyl-β-D-galactopyranose	140	-41.5 (c 4, $CHCl_3$)	236	Methyl 3,6-anhydro-β-L-galactoside	118	-113.5 (c 1, H_2O)	292	2,3,4-Tri-O-methyl-D-glucose	Sirup	+50 (c 4, H_2O)
186	Methyl 4,6-di-O-methyl-β-D-galactopyranose	131-133	+133 → +76.9 (c 2.4, H_2O)	237	α-L-Galactose, 6-deoxy-(L-fucose)($C_6H_{12}O_5$)	145	-124.1 → -76.4	293	Methyl 2,3,5-tri-O-methyl-D-glucose	Sirup	-11 (c 1.8, H_2O)
187	4,6-Di-O-methyl-α-D-galactopyranose	30	+198.4 (c 1, H_2O)	238	Methyl α-L-fucoside (See also D-galactose, 6-deoxy-)	154-156	-197 [15°] (c 1.1, H_2O)	294	2,3,5-Tri-O-methyl-D-glucose	Sirup	+17 (c 1.8, H_2O)
188	Methyl 2,3,4-tri-O-methyl-α-D-galactopyranoside	85	+154.1 → +122 (c 2, H_2O)	239	Methyl 3-O-methyl-α-L-fucopyranoside	130-132	-173 [14°]	295	Methyl 2,3,6-tri-O-methyl-α-D-glucoside		+149 (c 2, CH_3OH)
189	2,3,4-Tri-O-methyl-α-D-galactopyranose		-55 (c 1.2, H_2O)	240	3-O-Methyl-L-fucose	Sirup	-94 [15°] (c 0.4, H_2O)	296	Methyl 2,3,6-tri-O-methyl-β-D-glucopyranoside	58-60	-48 (c 5, $CHCl_3$)
190	Methyl 2,3,5-tri-O-methyl-D-galactofuranoside	Sirup	-5 (c 0.8, H_2O)	241	Methyl 2,3,-di-O-methyl-α-L-fucopyranoside	49-51	-190 [15°] (c 0.5, H_2O)	297	2,3,6-Tri-O-methyl-D-glucose	121-123	+90 → +70.5 (H_2O)
191	2,3,5-Tri-O-methyl-D-galactose	144	+18 [14°] (c 1.2, C_2H_5OH)	242	2,3-Di-O-methyl-L-fucose	Sirup	+4.6 [15°] (c 1.4, H_2O)	298	Methyl 2,4,6-tri-O-methyl-β-D-glucopyranoside	70-71	-27.4 (c 5, $CHCl_3$)
192	Methyl 2,3,6-tri-O-methyl-D-galactose	Sirup	+87 (H_2O)	243	Methyl 3,4-di-O-methyl-α-L-fucopyranoside	100	-213 (c 3, H_2O)	299	2,4,6-Tri-O-methyl-α-D-glucose	123	+89.7 → +71.9 (c 2, H_2O)
193	2,3,6-Tri-O-methyl-D-galactonic acid phenylhydrazide	175	-62.4 (c 1, --)	244	3,4-Di-O-methyl-L-fucose	76, 82	-118 [15°] (c 1.3, H_2O)	300	Methyl 3,4,6-tri-O-methyl-β-D-glucopyranoside	52-53	-16.4 (c 2, $CHCl_3$)
194	Methyl 2,4,6-tri-O-methyl-α-D-galactopyranoside	73-74	+163.9 (c 1, H_2O)	245	Methyl 2,3,4-tri-O-methyl-α-L-fucopyranoside	97-98	-209 (H_2O)	301	3,4,6-Tri-O-methyl-α-D-glucose	76-77	+91.9 → +77.4 (c 2, H_2O)
195	Methyl 2,4,6-tri-O-methyl-β-D-galactopyranoside	111-112	-40.9 (c 5, $CHCl_3$)	246	Methyl 2,3,4-tri-O-methyl-β-L-fucopyranoside	101.5-102.5	-21 (c 1.1, H_2O)	302	Methyl 3,4,6-tri-O-methyl-β-D-glucofuranoside	97-98	+41.1 → +77.5 (c 1.6, H_2O)
196	2,4,6-Tri-O-methyl-α-D-galactopyranose	102-105	+124 → +90.4 (c 3.4, H_2O)	247	2,3,4-Tri-O-methyl-α-L-fucose	36-37	-184 → -128	303	Methyl 3,5,6-tri-O-methyl-α-D-glucofuranoside	Sirup	+93 (c 3.1, CH_3OH)
197	3,4,6-Tri-O-methyl-D-galactopyranose	Sirup	-4.3 (c 4.2, CH_3OH)	248	Methyl β-L-fucoside	120-122	+15.1 (c 2, H_2O)	304	Methyl 3,5,6-tri-O-methyl-β-D-glucofuranoside	Sirup	-87 (c 2.8, CH_3OH)
198	3,4,6-Tri-O-methyl-D-galactonic acid lactone	Sirup	+46.8 (c 2.5, H_2O)	249	D,L-Galactose ($C_6H_{12}O_6$)	143-144, 163	None	305	3,5,6-Tri-O-methyl-D-glucose	Sirup	-25.9 (c 1, H_2O)
199	Methyl 2,3,4,6-tetra-O-methyl-α-D-galactopyranoside	Sirup	+190 (H_2O)	250	α-D-Glucose ($C_6H_{12}O_6$) (See derivatives of D-galactose)	146	+112.2 → +52.7	306	Methyl tetra-O-methyl-α-D-glucopyranoside	Sirup	+147.2 (c 10, H_2O)
200	Methyl 2,3,4,6-tetra-O-methyl-β-D-galactopyranoside	48-49	+18.7 (H_2O)	251	α-D-Glucose monohydrate ($C_6H_{12}O_6 \cdot H_2O$)	83	+102 → +52.7	307	Methyl tetra-O-methyl-β-D-glucopyranoside	40-41	-17.3 (c 4, H_2O)
201	2,3,4,6-Tetra-O-methyl-α-D-galactopyranose	71	+142 → +118 (H_2O)	252	D-Glucose p-bromophenyl-hydrazone	164-166		308	Tetra-O-methyl-α-D-glucopyranose	88-89	+100 → +83.3 (H_2O)
202	Methyl 2,3,5,6-tetra-O-methyl-D-galactoside	Sirup	-45.2	253	β-D-Glucose ($C_6H_{12}O_6$) (See also β-D-glucose)	148-150	+18.7 → +52.7	309	Tetra-O-methyl-β-D-glucopyranose	50	+73.1 → +83.1 (c 5, H_2O)
203	Methyl 2,3,5,6-tetra-O-methyl-D-galactoside	48-48.5	+19.6 (c 1, H_2O)	254	D-Glucose p-nitrophenyl-hydrazone	189	+21.5 (C_5H_5N, C_2H_5OH)	310	Methyl tetra-O-methyl-α-D-glucofuranoside	11	+107 [18°] (c 0.7, H_2O)
204	2,3,5,6-Tetra-O-methyl-D-galactose	Sirup	-21.2 (c 2, H_2O)	255	D-Glucose benzylphenyl-hydrazone	150, 158	+101.6 (c 5, $CHCl_3$)	311	Methyl tetra-O-methyl-β-D-glucofuranoside	Sirup	-72.7 (CH_3OH)
205	2,3,5,6-Tetra-O-methyl-D-galactonic acid lactone	Sirup	-27.1 (c 1.5, H_2O)	256	Penta-O-acetyl-α-D-glucopyranose	114	+101.6 (c 5, $CHCl_3$)	312	Tetra-O-methyl-D-glucofuranose	Sirup	-7.6 (c 0.9, H_2O)
				257	Penta-O-acetyl-β-D-glucopyranose	135	+3.8 (c 7, $CHCl_3$)	313	D-Glucose, 6-benzoyl-(vaccinin) ($C_{13}H_{16}O_7$)	Amorph.	+48 (C_2H_5OH)
				258	Penta-O-acetyl-aldehydo-D-glucose	119-120	-4.2 (c 3, $CHCl_3$)	314	1,2,3,4-Tetra-O-acetyl-6-O-benzoyl-β-D-glucose	132	+32.9 ($CHCl_3$)
206	D-Galactose, 2-amino-2-deoxy-(chondrosamine) (galactosamine) ($C_6H_{13}NO_5$) α-D-Galactosamine hydrochloride	185	+121 → +80 (c 2, HCl-H_2O)	259	Methyl α-D-glucofuranoside	62-63	+118 (c 5, H_2O)	315	D-Glucose, 2-deoxy-($C_6H_{12}O_5$)	148	+46.6 [18°]
								316	2-Deoxy-D-glucose benzyl-phenylhydrazone	158-159	
								317	α-D-Glucose, 2-deoxy-2-amino-(chitosamine) (glucosamine) ($C_6H_{13}NO_5$)	88	+100 → +47.5

Table (continued) — first group (No. 207–233):

No.	Compound	M.p.	Rotation
207	β-D-Galactosamine hydrochloride	187	+44.5 → +80 (c 2, HCl·H₂O)
208	N-Acetyl-D-galactosamine	120–122	+115 → +80 (H₂O)
209	N-(2,4-Dinitrophenyl)-D-galactosamine	184–186	+84 [5461] (c 1, 80% C₂H₅OH)
210	1,3,4,6-Tetra-O-acetyl-N-acetyl-α-D-galactosamine	178	+102 [5461] (c 1.6, CHCl₃)
211	1,3,4,6-Tetra-O-acetyl-N-acetyl-β-D-galactosamine	235	+10 (c 1, CHCl₃)
212	Methyl N-acetyl-α-D-galactosaminide	217–218	+170 (CHCl₃)
213	Methyl 3,4,6-Tri-O-methyl-α-D-galactosaminide hydrochloride	227	+150.3 (c 3.6, CH₃OH)
214	3,4,6-Tri-O-methyl-D-galactosamine hydrochloride	178	+114 (c 1, H₂O)
215	Methyl 3,4,6-Tri-O-methyl-N-acetyl-α-D-galactosaminide	185	+121 (c 1.4, CHCl₃)
216	Methyl 3,4,6-Tri-O-methyl-N-acetyl-β-D-galactosaminide	232	+7 (c 1, CHCl₃)
217	N-(2-Hydroxyl-1-napthylidene)-D-galactosamine	175–178	+287 → +258 [CH₃OH] [5461]
218	α-D-Galactose, 6-deoxy- (rhodeose)(C₆H₁₂O₅)	140–145	+127 (c 10)
219	D-Fucose benzylphenyl-hydrazone	178–179	-14.9 (c 0.4, CH₃OH)
220	D-Fucose p-bromophenyl-hydrazone	184	
221	Methyl α-D-fucoside	155–156	+190 (c 4.2, H₂O)
222	Methyl β-D-fucoside	120	-14.0 (c 0.8, H₂O)
223	2-O-Methyl-D-fucose	155–161	+73 → +87 (c 1.3, H₂O)
224	Methyl 2,3,4-tri-O-methyl-β-D-fucopyranoside	93–98	+11.2 (c 1, H₂O)
225	2,3,4-Tri-O-methyl-D-fucose	Sirup	+106 (c 1, H₂O)
226	2,3,4-Tri-O-methyl-D-fucose hydrate	65	+183 → +128.8 (H₂O)
227	D-Galactose, 6-deoxy-3-O-methyl- (digitalose) (C₇H₁₄O₅)	106, 119; 137–138	+106
228	Digitalonic acid lactone	Sirup	-83 (c 3.2, CH₃COCH₃)
229	Methyl 3-O-methyl-α-D-fucopyranoside	Sirup	+124.4 (c 0.9, CH₃COCH₃)
230	Methyl 3-O-methyl-β-D-fucopyranoside	97–99	
231	D-Galactose, 2,6-dideoxy-3-O-methyl- (diginose) (C₇H₁₄O₄)	90–92; Sirup	+56e4
232	Diginonic acid lactone	137	-30 [14°] (c 2, CH₃COCH₃)
233	S-Benzylthiuronium salt of diginonic acid	137	-9.2 (CH₃OH)

Table (continued) — second group (No. 260–288):

No.	Compound	M.p.	Rotation
260	Methyl β-D-glucofuranoside	Sirup	-77 (H₂O)
261	Methyl α-D-glucopyranoside	166	+158.9 (c 10, H₂O)
262	Methyl β-D-glucopyranoside	105	-34.2 (c 10, H₂O)
263	Methyl 2-O-methyl-α-D-glucopyranoside	147–148	+155 (c 0.7, H₂O)
264	Methyl 2-O-methyl-β-D-glucopyranoside	97–98	-37.5 (c 5, H₂O)
265	2-O-Methyl-β-D-glucose	157–158	+2 → +65.3 (c 2, H₂O)
266	Methyl 3-O-methyl-β-D-glucopyranoside	Sirup	-26 (c 5.5, H₂O)
267	3-O-Methyl-α-D-glucose	160–161	+104.3 → +55.3 (c 1, H₂O)
268	3-O-Methyl-β-D-glucose	130–132	+31.9 → +55.1 (c 1, H₂O)
269	4-O-Methyl-D-glucose	Sirup	+53 (c 2, H₂O)
270	5-O-Methyl-D-glucose	Sirup	-10.6 (c 2, C₂H₅OH)
271	Methyl 6-O-methyl-α-D-glucopyranoside	Sirup	+127.9 (c 5, H₂O)
272	Methyl 6-O-methyl-β-D-glucopyranoside	133–135	-27.0 (c 5)
273	6-O-Methyl-α-D-glucose	143–145	+110 → +55 (c 3, H₂O)
274	Methyl 2,3-di-O-methyl-α-D-glucopyranoside	80–82	+142.6 (c 5, H₂O)
275	Methyl 2,3-di-O-methyl-β-D-glucopyranoside	62–64	-36.6 (c 5, H₂O)
276	2,3-O-Methyl-α-D-glucose	85–87	+81.9 → +48.3 (c 1, CH₃COCH₃)
277	2,3-O-Methyl-β-D-glucose	108–110	+5.9 → +50.9 (c 4, CH₃COCH₃)
278	Methyl-2,4-di-O-methyl-α-D-glucopyranoside	79–81	+159, +186 (c 0.3–1, CH₃COCH₃)
279	Methyl 2,4-di-O-methyl-β-D-glucopyranoside	124	-16.5 [29°] (c 0.5, CH₃COCH₃)
280	Methyl 2,6-di-O-methyl-α-D-glucopyranoside	Sirup	+154 (c 1.5, CH₃OH)
281	Methyl 2,6-di-O-methyl-β-D-glucopyranoside	50–52	-43.5 (c 11, CHCl₃)
282	2,6-Di-O-methyl-D-glucose	Sirup	+58.2 (c 2.7, H₂O)
283	Methyl 3,4-di-O-methyl-β-D-glucopyranoside	79–81	-11.9 (c 5, H₂O)
284	3,4-Di-O-methyl-D-glucose	113	+64.9 → +94.8 (c 1, H₂O)
285	Methyl 3,6-di-O-methyl-β-D-glucopyranoside	Sirup	+55.4 (c 3.5, C₂H₅OH)
286	3,6-O-Methyl-α-D-glucose	113–116	+61.5 (c 3, H₂O)
287	Methyl 4,6-di-O-methyl-α-D-glucopyranoside	Sirup	+157 (CHCl₃)
288	Methyl 4,6-di-O-methyl-β-D-glucopyranoside	50–52	-28 (c 3, CHCl₃)

Table (continued) — third group (No. 318–345):

No.	Compound	M.p.	Rotation
318	α-D-Glucosamine hydrochloride		+100 → +72.5
319	β-D-Glucose, 2-deoxy-2-amino- (C₆H₁₃NO₅)	110–111	+28 → +47.5
320	β-D-Glucosamine hydrochloride	205	+25 → +72.5
321	N-Acetyl-D-glucosamine	202–204	+64 → +40.9
322	N-(2,4-Dinitrophenyl)-D-glucosamine	202–203	+65 [5461] (c 1, C₂H₅OH)(H₂O)
323	N-(2-Hydroxy-1-naphthylidene)-D-glucosamine	162	+274 → +217 [5461] (CH₃OH)
324	D-Glucosamine diphenyl-hydrazone	143	+25.9 (CHCl₃)
325	Tetra-O-acetyl-α-D-glucosaminopyranoside		+29.7 (H₂O)
326	Tetra-O-acetyl-α-D-glucosaminopyranoside hydrochloride	230	+93.4 (CHCl₃)
327	Tetra-O-acetyl-N-acetyl-α-D-glucosaminopyranoside	139–140	+1.2 (CHCl₃)
328	Tetra-O-acetyl-N-acetyl-β-D-glucosaminopyranoside	187–189	+36 (c 0.1, CHCl₃)
329	Tetra-O-acetyl-N-acetyl-aldehydo-D-glucosaminofuranoside	156–157	-25 (c 0.8, H₂O)
330	Methyl N-acetyl-β-D-glucosaminide	Sirup	+127 (H₂O)
331	Methyl N-acetyl-α-D-glucosaminide hydrochloride	119	-24.2 (H₂O)
332	Methyl β-D-glucosaminide hydrochloride	190	+104 (H₂O)
333	Methyl N-acetyl-α-D-glucosaminide	188–189	-43 (H₂O)
334	Methyl N-acetyl-β-D-glucosaminide	195–196	+116 (H₂O)
335	Methyl 3-O-methyl-N-acetyl-α-D-glucosaminide	211	+123 → +91.3 (H₂O)
336	3-O-Methyl-α-D-glucosamine hydrochloride	215 d.	-21.5 [16°] (c 2.5, CH₃OH)
337	Methyl 4,6-di-O-methyl-N-acetyl-β-D-glucosaminide	187	+169.8 (c 0.8, CH₃OH)
338	Methyl 3,4,6-Tri-O-methyl-α-D-glucosaminide	Sirup	+129.6 (c 0.5, H₂O)
339	Methyl 3,4,6-Tri-O-methyl-α-D-glucosaminide hydrochloride	237 d.	+104.3 (c 0.9, H₂O)
340	Methyl 3,4,6-tri-O-methyl-N-acetyl-α-D-glucosaminide	150	+19.5 (c 0.3, CHCl₃)
341	Methyl 3,4,6-tri-O-methyl-N-acetyl-β-D-glucosaminide	195	+49.2 → +99.5 (c 1.2, H₂O)
342	3,4,6-Tri-O-methyl-D-glucosamine hydrochloride	210 d.	+75 → +44.8 (c 0.5, H₂O)
343	3,4,6-Tri-O-methyl-N-acetyl-D-glucosamine	234	+73.3 → +29.7 (c 8)
344	D-Glucose, 6-deoxy- (chinovose)(epirhamnose)(glucomethylose)(isorhamnose)(isorhodeose)(quinovose)(C₆H₁₂O₅)	139–140	+66.9 → +5.4 (H₂O)
345	D-Glucomethylonic acid lactone	151–152	

9. CARBOHYDRATES: PHYSICAL AND CHEMICAL CHARACTERISTICS (Continued)

Part I: NATURAL MONOSACCHARIDES: ALDOSES[1,2] (Concluded)

No.	Substance[3]	MP °C	[α]_D, degrees[4]
	D-Glucose, 6-deoxy- (chinovose)(epirhamnose)(glucomethylose)(isorhamnose)(isorhodeose)(quinovose)(C6H12O5) (concluded)		
346	Methyl α-D-glucomethyloside	98-99	
347	Methyl β-D-glucomethyloside	131-132	-55.1 (H2O)
348	α-D-Glucose, 6-deoxy-3-O-methyl- (D-thevetose) (C7H14O5)	116	+84 → +33
349	1,2,4-Tri-O-acetyl-3-O-methyl-β-D-glucomethyl-oside	121	+6 (CH3COCH3)
350	1,2,4-Tri-O-acetyl-3-O-methyl-α-D-glucomethyl-oside	105	+122 (CH3COCH3)
351	Methyl β-D-thevetoside	116-117	-44±2 (c 1, H2O)
352	Methyl α-D-thevetoside	86-87	+148±2 (c 1, H2O)
353	α-L-Glucose (C6H12O6)	141-143	-95.5 → -51.4
354	(See α- and β-D-glucose)		
355	L-Glucose, 2-deoxy-2-amino-N-methyl-(C7H15NO5)	130-132	-64
	N-Methyl-α-L-glucosamine hydrochloride	160-163	-103 → -88 (c 0.6, H2O)
356	N-Acetyl-N-methyl-L-glucosamine	165-166	-51 (c 0.5, H2O)
357	Tetra-O-acetyl-N-acetyl-N-methyl-α-L-glucosamine	160-161	-100 (c 0.7, CHCl3)
358	Tetra-O-acetyl-N-acetyl-N-methyl-β-L-glucosaminide	153	-16.5 (c 3, CHCl3)
359	L-Glucose, 6-deoxy-3-O-methyl- (thevetose)(C7H14O5)	126-129	-36.9±2
360	1,2,4-Tri-O-acetyl-3-O-methyl-β-L-glucomethyl-oside	118-119	-7.5±2 (c 1.1, CH3COCH3)
361	1,2,4-Tri-O-acetyl-3-O-methyl-α-L-glucomethyl-oside	103-104	-113 (CH3OH)
362	L-Glucose, 2,6-dideoxy-3-O-methyl- (L-oleandrose) (C7H14O4)	62-63	+11.9±2.5
363	Oleandrose 2,4-dinitro-phenylhydrazone	155-160	+20.3 (c 0.6, CH3OH)
364	Oleandronic acid phenylhydrazide	136	
365	D-Gulose, 2,6-dideoxy-3-O-methyl- (sarmentose)[10] (C7H14O4)	78-79	+12 → +15.8
366	S-Benzyl-thiouronium salt of sarmentonic acid	146	+6.5±2 (c 1.2, CH3OH)
367	α-D-Mannose (C6H12O6)	133	+29.3 → +14.2
368	(See β-D-mannose)		
	β-D-Mannose (C6H12O6)	132	-16.3 → +14.5
369	D-Mannose phenylhydrazone	199-200	+26.3 → +33.8[11] (C5H5N)
370	D-Mannose benzylphenyl-hydrazone	170-171	+29.8 (CH3OH)

No.	Substance[3]	MP °C	[α]_D, degrees[4]
	β-D-Mannose (C6H12O6) (continued)		
373	Penta-O-acetyl-α-D-manno-pyranoside	64	+55 (c 4, CHCl3)
374	Penta-O-acetyl-β-D-manno-pyranoside	117-118	-25.3 (c 3, CHCl3)
375	Methyl α-D-mannofuranoside	118-119	113 (c 1, H2O)
376	Methyl α-D-mannopyranoside	193-194	79.2 (c 1, H2O)
377	Methyl β-D-mannopyranoside isopropyl alcoholate (C7H14O5)	74-75	-53.3 (c 4, H2O)
378	Methyl 2-O-methyl-α-D-mannofuranoside	82	+129.5 (c 2.6, H2O)
379	2-O-Methyl-D-mannose	136-137	+7.0 → +4.5 (c 2.9, H2O)
380	Methyl 4-O-methyl-α-D-mannopyranoside	101-102	+84.4±0.5 (c 0.8, H2O)
381	4-O-Methyl-α-D-mannopyranoside	127-129	+32.4 → +22.3 (c 4, H2O)
382	6-O-Methyl-D-mannose	Sirup	+15.3 (c 1.1, CHCl3)
383	Methyl 2,3-di-O-methyl-D-mannoside	Sirup	+43.5 (c 2.4, CHCl3)
384	2,3-Di-O-methyl-D-mannose	Sirup	+16, +22 (c 0.7-1.2, H2O)
385	Methyl 3,4-di-O-methyl-α-D-mannopyranoside	80	+88.6 [17°] (CHCl3)
386	3,4-Di-O-methyl-α-D-mannose monohydrate	114	+22 → +4 (c 2, H2O)
387	Methyl 4,6-di-O-methyl-α-D-mannopyranoside	Sirup	+80.5 [5780]
388	4,6-Di-O-methyl-D-mannose	Glass	+25 [5780] (c 1.2, H2O)
389	4,6-Di-O-methyl-D-mannonic acid phenylhydrazide	151	+14 [5780] (c 4.3, H2O)
390	Methyl 2,3,4-tri-O-methyl-α-D-mannopyranoside	Sirup	+58 (c 1.3, H2O)
391	2,3,4-Tri-O-methyl-D-mannose	102-103	+18.2 [5780] +7 (c 20, H2O)
392	Methyl 2,3,5-tri-O-methyl-D-mannofuranoside	Sirup	+54 [18°] (c 1.3, H2O)
393	2,3,5-Tri-O-methyl-γ-D-mannonolactone	118	+67 (c 1, H2O)
394	Methyl-2,3,6-tri-O-methyl-D-mannoside	Sirup	+26 (c 1, H2O)
395	2,3,6-Tri-O-methyl-D-mannose	Sirup	-6.5 (c 0.6, H2O)
396	2,3,6-Tri-O-methyl-γ-D-mannonolactone	84-85	+65.5 [18°] (c 1, HCl in CH3OH)
397	Methyl 2,4,6-tri-O-methyl-α-D-mannopyranoside	Sirup	+70 (c 1, H2O)
398	2,4,6-Tri-O-methyl-D-mannose monohydrate	89-90	+23 → +16 (c 1, H2O)
399	2,4,6-Tri-O-methyl-β-D-mannose monohydrate	104-107	-5.7 → +19 (c 1, H2O)
400	3,4,6-Tri-O-methyl-D-mannopyranose	101-102	+21 → +8.2 (c 2.1, H2O)
401	Methyl tetra-O-methyl-α-D-mannopyranoside	39-40	+43.5 (c 5, H2O)

No.	Substance[3]	MP °C	[α]_D, degrees[4]
	β-D-Mannose (C6H12O6) (concluded)		
404	Methyl tetra-O-methyl-α-D-mannofuranoside	24	+98.6 [19°] (c 1, H2O)
405	Tetra-O-methyl-D-mannofuranoside (?)	Sirup	+39 → +43 (c 0.5, H2O)
406	Methyl tetra-O-methyl-β-D-mannofuranoside	Sirup	+24.7 (c 4, CH3OH)
407	Tetra-O-methyl-γ-D-mannonolactone	107-108	+64.8 [4°] (c 1.7, H2O)
408	α-L-Mannose, 6-deoxy-, monohydrate (L-rhamnose) (C6H14O6)	93-94	-8.6 → +8.2
409	(See β-L-mannose, 6-deoxy-) β-L-Mannose, 6-deoxy-(L-rhamnose) (C6H12O5)	123-125	+38.4 → +8.9
410	L-Rhamnose p-bromo-phenylhydrazone	169-170	
411	L-Rhamnose p-nitro-phenylhydrazone	190-191	-50 → -8.5 (C5H5N, C2H5OH)
412	L-Rhamnose benzyl-phenylhydrazone	121	-10.4 → -7.4 (CH3OH)
413	Tetra-O-acetyl-β-L-rhamnopyranoside	98-99	+13.9 (c 15, C2H2Cl4)
414	Methyl α-L-rhamnopyrano-side	108-109	-62.5 (c 10, H2O)
415	Methyl β-L-rhamnopyrano-side	138-140	+95.4 (c 10, H2O)
416	Methyl 2-O-methyl-L-rhamnopyranoside	139-140	+31 (H2O)
417	2-O-Methyl-L-rhamnose	113-114	-50.2 (c 1.5, H2O)
418	Methyl 4-O-methyl-α-L-rhamnoside	Sirup	+13 (c 1, CH3OH)
419	4-O-Methyl-L-rhamnose	125-126	-89.2 (c 1, H2O)
420	Methyl 5-O-methyl-L-rhamnofuranoside	59-60	-4.3 (c 3, H2O)
421	5-O-Methyl-L-rhamno-furanoside	102-103	-6, -14 (c 2, H2O)
422	Methyl 2,3-di-O-methyl-α-L-rhamnoside	Sirup	+47.6 (c 1, H2O)
423	2,3-Di-O-methyl-L-rhamnose	Sirup	
424	2,3-Di-O-methyl-L-rhamnose anilide	136-138	
425	3,4-Di-O-methyl-L-rhamnose	91-92	-10 → +18.6 (c 1.5, H2O)
426	3,4-Di-O-methyl-L-rhamnose	98-99	+24 → +18.5 (c 0.5, H2O)
427	Methyl 2,3,4-tri-O-methyl-L-rhamnopyranoside (α form?)	Sirup	
428	Methyl 2,3,4-tri-O-methyl-β-L-rhamnopyranoside	53-54	-15.5 (H2O)
429	2,3,4-Tri-O-methyl-L-rhamnose	Sirup	+106 (c 1, H2O)
430	2,3,4-Tri-O-methyl-L-rhamnose anilide	112	+26 (c 2.5, H2O)
431	L-Talose, 6-deoxy- (L-talomethylose)(C6H12O5)	116-118	+127 / -19.5±2 [18°]

No.	Substance	MP °C	[α]D, degrees
371	D-Mannose p-bromophenyl-hydrazone	208	
372	D-Mannose p-nitro phenyl-hydrazone	194-195, 202-203	+56 (C5H5N, C2H5OH)
402	Tetra-O-methyl-α-D-manno-pyranose	50-51	+7.4 → +2.4 (H2O)
403	Methyl tetra-O-methyl-β-D-mannopyranoside	37	-80 (c 1, H2O)
432	L-Talomethylose p-bromo-phenylhydrazone	145-147	-10 → +4±3 [16°](c 0.8, C2H5OH)
433	L-Talonic acid lactone	134-135	+36 → +33±2 (c 1, H2O)

1/ Includes substances not found free but found in the hydrolyzates of a natural material. Unless otherwise stated, all data are for crystalline substances. 2/ In preparing this table the literature has been covered through 1952. 3/ Aldoses are arranged alphabetically within groups formulated according to increasing carbon content in the parent sugar. Since the substances are listed by their accepted chemical nomenclature, or derivative thereof, the following list of common or trivial names or synonyms is given, with relationship to listing in the table, to facilitate location of a substance: apiose (see D-glyceraldehyde), chinovose (see D-glucose), chitosamine (see D-galactose), chondrosamine (see D-galactose), cymarose (see D-allose), diginose (see D-galactose), digitalose (see D-galactose), digitoxose (see D-allose), epirhamnose (see D-galactose), L-fucose (see L-galactose), D-fucose (see D-galactose), glucosamine (see D-galactose), hamamelose (see D-Ribose), isorhamnose (see D-glucose), isorhodeose (see L-glucose), oleandrose (see L-glucose), L-rhamnose, quinovose (see L-glucose), sarmentose (see L-mannose), streptose (see L-lyxose), thevetose (see D- and L-glucose), vaccinin (see D-glucose). 4/ Unless otherwise stated, the specific rotations are taken at 20-25°C. Other temperatures or wave lengths are shown in brackets. c = g solute per 100 ml solution. 5/ The rotation given is taken from inference to the enantiomorph or D isomer. 6/ The designations for the α and β pair of these compounds are unknown because of the speculations concerning it in biological processes. 7/ This substance is included because it is postulated at concentrations of 5 g or less per 100 ml of solution and at concentrations of 5 g or less per 100 ml of solution. 8/ Some question exists on the presence of this material in nature. 9/ The specific rotations are reversed from those of the original authors, in accordance with modern terminology and Hudson's rules of rotation. 10/ This structure for sarmentose is postulated but not proved in reference. 11/ Passes through a minimum in mutarotation.

Part II: NATURAL MONOSACCHARIDES: KETOSES[1,2]

No.	Substance[3]	MP °C	[α]D, degrees[4]
1	Triulose (dihydroxyacetone) (C3H6O3)	80 (dimer)	None
2	Dihydroxyacetone p-nitro phenylhydrazone	160	
3	Dihydroxyacetone oxime	84	
4	Dihydroxacetone bis(2,4-dinitrophenylhydrazone)		
5	Dihydroxyacetone diacetate	46-47	
6	L-Glycero-tetrulose[5] (L-erythrulose)(ketoerythritol) (C4H8O4)	Sirup	+12
7	L-Erythrulose, O-nitro-phenylhydrazone	152-153	+48 [18°](c 1, C2H5OH)
8	D-Erythro-pentulose (adonose) (D-ribulose) (C5H10O5)	Sirup	+16.6 [27°](c 1, C2H5OH)
9	1,3,4,5-Di-O-iso-propylidene-D-ribulose (diacetone ribulose)	5	+105.5 [27°](c 1, CH3COCH3)
10	L-Threo-pentulose (L-xylulose)(xyloketose) (C5H10O5)	Sirup	+33.1
11	L-Xylulose p-bromophenyl-hydrazone	128-129	-26 → +31.9 (C5H5N)
12	β-D-Arabo-hexulose (β-D-fructose)(levulose) (C6H12O6)	102-104	-133.5 → -92
13	D-Fructose p-nitro phenyl-hydrazone	176	
14	D-Fructose oxime	118	
15	1,3,4,5-Tetra-O-acetyl-β-D-fructopyranose	131-132	-91.6 (c 3, CHCl3)
16	1,3,4,5,6-Penta-O-acetyl-D-fructose	70	+34.7 (c 8, CHCl3)
17	Penta-O-acetyl-β-D-fructo-pyranose	108-109	-120.9 (c 5, CHCl3)
18	Methyl α-D-fructofuranoside	69, 81	+93 (c 2, H2O)
19	Methyl β-D-fructofuranoside	Sirup	-50 (c 1, H2O)
20	Methyl α-D-fructopyranoside	96-97	+44 (c 1, H2O)
21	Methyl β-D-fructopyranoside	119-120	-172.1 (c 10, H2O)
22	1-O-Methyl-D-fructose	Sirup	-49.8 (c 2.2, CH3OH)
23	Methyl 3-O-methyl-D-fructoside	143	-34.6 (c 1.1, C2H5OH)
24	3-O-Methyl-D-fructose	122-123	-70.5 → -53.1 (H2O)
25	β-D-Arabo-hexulose (β-D-fructose) (concluded) 4-O-Methyl-D-fructose	Sirup	-87.5 (c 0.4, H2O)
26	6-O-Methyl-D-fructose	Sirup	+6.4 (c 1.2, 0.06N HCl)
27	3,4-Di-O-methyl-D-fructose	Sirup	-60.7 (c 0.8, H2O)
28	Methyl 1,3,4-tri-O-methyl-D-fructoside	Sirup	+57.4 (c 1, H2O)
29	1,3,4-Tri-O-methyl-D-fructose	73	-23.8 → -51.8 (c 8, H2O)
30	1,4,6-Tri-O-methyl-D-fructose	Sirup	+30.3 (H2O)
31	3,4,5-Tri-O-methyl-D-fructose	Sirup	-115.9 (H2O)
32	3,4,6-Tri-O-methyl-D-fructose	Sirup	+20.4, +26.6 [15°](c 1, CHCl3)
33	Methyl 1,3,4,5-tetra-O-methyl-β-D-fructopyranoside	33-34	-149.8 (c 3, H2O)
34	1,3,4,5-Tetra-O-methyl-D-fructose	98-99	-124.7 →
35	Methyl 1,3,4,6-tetra-O-methyl-α-D-fructofuranoside	Sirup	-121.3 (c 5, H2O)
36	1,3,4,6-Tetra-O-methyl-D-fructose	Sirup	+129.4 (c 2.6, H2O)
37	1,3,4,5,6-Tetra-O-methyl-D-fructose	99-100	+31.3 [16°]
38	1,3,4,5,6-Tetra-O-methyl-D-"fructofuronamide"	131-132	-76 [16°]
39	D-Lyxo-hexulose (D-tagatose) (C6H12O6) "Tagaturonic" acid	106-108	+2.7 → -4, -5
40	Penta-O-acetyl-D-tagato-pyranose	132	-12.5 (c 1.6, H2O)
41	Methyl α-D-tagatopyranose	128	+30.2 [578](c 4, CHCl3)
42	Methyl tetra-O-methyl-α-D-tagato-pyranose	Sirup	+56.8 [578]
43	Methyl tetra-O-methyl-D-tagatoside	Sirup	+21.4 [578](c 2, CH3OH)
44	Tetra-O-methyl-D-tagato-pyranose	Sirup	+9.7 [578](c 2, C2H5OH); -3.4 [578](c 2, CH3OH)
45	D-Ribo-hexulose (D-psicose) (C6H12O6)	Amorp. 63-65	+4.7
46	Penta-O-acetyl-keto-D-psicose	Sirup	-21.5 [29°](c 3, CHCl3)
47	Methyl tetra-O-methyl-D-psicopyranoside	Sirup	+36 heated in (HCl, CH3OH)
48	Di-O-isopropylidene-D-psicose	57-58.5	-98.2 (c 2, CH3COCH3)
49	L-Xylo-hexulose (L-sorbose) (C6H12O6)	159-161	-43.1
50	Di-O-isopropylidene-L-sorbose	155-157	+44.9 (c 1, CH3COCH3)
51	Penta-O-acetyl-keto-L-sorbose	99	+2.4 [578](CHCl3)
52	Tetra-O-acetyl-L-sorbo-pyranose	100.8	-21.3 (c 1.3, CHCl3)
53	Penta-O-acetyl-α-L-sorbo-pyranose	97	-56.5 (c 1.3, CHCl3)
54	Penta-O-acetyl-β-L-sorbo-pyranose	113.8	+74.4 (c 1.3, CHCl3)
55	Methyl tetra-O-methyl-L-sorbofuranoside	Sirup	-39.4 (c 1, CHCl3)
56	Tetra-O-methyl-L-sorbo-furanose	Sirup	+29.7 (c 1, CHCl3)
57	Methyl α-L-sorbopyranoside	120-121	-88.9 (c 8, H2O)
58	Methyl β-L-sorbopyranoside	106.2	+39 (c 1.7, H2O)
59	1,4,6-Tri-O-methyl-L-sorbofuranose	Sirup	+3.8 (c 1.5, CHCl3)
60	Methyl tetra-O-methyl-α-L-sorbopyranoside	Sirup	-46.2 [578]
61	Methyl tetra-O-methyl-β-L-sorbopyranoside	Sirup	+69.8 (c 1, CHCl3)
62	1,3,4,5-Tetra-O-methyl-L-sorbose	Sirup	-15.1 [578](c 2, CHCl3)
63	4-O-Methyl-L-sorbose	133	-30.9 [12°]
64	D-Altro-heptulose (D-sedohep-tulose) (sedoheptose) (C7H14O7)	Amorph.	+2.5
65	α-Sedoheptitol (volemitol) (D-glycero-D-manno-heptitol)(D-manno-D-taloheptitol)(D-altro-D-mannoheptitol)	152	+2.3 (c 9, H2O)

9. CARBOHYDRATES: PHYSICAL AND CHEMICAL CHARACTERISTICS (Continued)

Part II: NATURAL MONOSACCHARIDES: KETOSES[1,2] (Concluded)

	Substance[3]	MP °C	$[\alpha]_D$, degrees[4]
66	D-Altro-heptulose (D-sedoheptulose)(sedoheptose)$(C_7H_{14}O_7)$ (concluded)		
67	Sedoheptulosan	127-128, 155	-146 (c 9, H_2O)
68	L-Gala-heptulose hemihydrate (L-perseulose)$(C_7H_{14}O_7 \cdot \tfrac{1}{2} H_2O)$	110-115	-90 → -80
69	D-Perseitol (D-manno-D-gala-heptitol, α-mannoheptitol, D-glycero-D-galaheptitol)(L-Gala-D-glucoheptitol)(L-glycero-D-glucoheptitol)(D-altro-D-glucoheptitol)	187	-1.2 (c 5.5, H_2O)
70	D-Perseitol and volemitol (See Lines 69 and 65 above)	141	-2.4 (c 4, H_2O)
71	Hexa-O-acetyl-keto-L-perseulose	105	+0.57 [578] (c 4, $CHCl_3$)
72	Hexa-O-acetyl-L-perseulose	112	-113 [578] (c 1, $CHCl_3$)
73	D-Manno-heptulose (mannoketoheptose)(D-manno-D-tagatoheptose)$(C_7H_{14}O_7)$	152	+29.4
74	D-Manno-heptulose p-bromophenylhydrazone	179	
75	D-Manno-heptulose hexaacetate	110	+39 (c 2, $CHCl_3$)

/1/ Includes substances not found free but found in the hydrolyzates of a natural material. Also included are some substances which are bacterial oxidation products of a natural material. Unless otherwise stated, all data are for crystalline substances. /2/ In preparing this table the literature has been covered through 1952. /3/ Ketoses are arranged alphabetically within groups formulated according to increasing carbon content in the parent sugar. Since the substances are listed under their systematic name in carbohydrate nomenclature the following list of common names and synonyms is given to facilitate the location: adonose (see D-erythro-pentulose), D-allulose (see D-ribo-hexulose), dihydroxyacetone (see triulose), L-erythrulose (see D-glycero-tetrulose), D-erythrulose (see L-glycero-tetrulose), keto-erythritol (see D-glycero-tetrulose), D-fructose (see D-arabo-hexulose), levulose (see D-arabo-hexulose), L-lyxulose (see L-threo-pentulose), perseulose (see L-gala-heptulose), D-psicose (see D-ribo-hexulose), D-ribulose (see D-erythro-pentulose), D-sedoheptulose (see D-altro-heptulose), L-sorbose (see L-xylo-hexulose), D-tagatose (see D-lyxo-hexulose), L-threose (see L-glycero-tetrulose), volemose (see D-altro-heptulose), L-xylulose (see L-threo-pentulose), xyloketose (see L-threo-pentulose). /4/ Unless otherwise stated, the specific rotations are taken in water at concentrations of 5 g or less per 100 ml of solution and at 20-25°C. Other temperatures or wave lengths are shown in brackets; c = g solute per 100 ml of solution. /5/ Some of the early literature names this substance D-erythrulose.

Part III: NATURAL OLIGOSACCHARIDES[1,2]

	Substance[3]	MP °C	$[\alpha]_D$, degrees[4]
1	O-α-D-Manno-pyranosyl-L-glyceric acid $(C_9H_{16}O_9)$	88-89	+105 [15°]
2	Sodium salt	270 d.	
3	2-O-α-D-Galactopyranosyl-glycerol $(C_9H_{18}O_8)$	86-87	+151
4	Galactinol dihydrate (1-O-α-D-galactopyranosyl-myo-inositol dihydrate) $(C_{12}H_{22}O_{11} \cdot 2H_2O)$	220-222	+135.6
5	Galactinol nonamethyl ether	96.5-98	+119 (c 2, H_2O)
6	Primverose (6-O-β-D-xylopyranosyl-D-glucose) $(C_{11}H_{20}O_{11})$	208	+24.1 → -3.3
7	Primverose heptaacetate	216	-23.5 $(CHCl_3)$
8	Vicianose (6-O-α-L-arabinopyranosyl-D-glucose) $(C_{11}H_{20}O_{10})$	210	+56.6 [14°] → +40.5 [14°]
9	Vicianose heptaacetate	158-160	+6.5 [14°] $(CHCl_3)$
10	D-Xylopyranosyl D-glucopyranoside[5] $(C_{11}H_{20}O_{10})$	Amorph.	-36.5
11	D-Xylopyranosyl D-glucopyranoside dibenzoate	147-148	-106.7 (c 2, CH_3OH)
12	D-Xylopyranosyl D-glucopyranoside pentaacetate dibenzoate	203	-6.3 (c 0.8, CH_3OH)
13	iso-D-Xylosyl-D-glucoside dibenzoate	173-174	
14	Allolactose (6-O-β-D-galactopyranosyl-D-glucose) $(C_{12}H_{22}O_{11})$	165	+25
15	Allolactose octaacetate	166	
16	Amylolyose (3-O-β-D-glucopyranosyl-D-glucose) $(C_{12}H_{22}O_{11} \cdot H_2O)$		+59.3 → +46.4 [15°] (c 8)
17	β-Cellobiose (4-O-β-D-glucopyranosyl-D-glucopyranose) $(C_{12}H_{22}O_{11})$	225	+14.2 → +34.6 (c 8)
37	β-Maltose monohydrate $(C_{12}H_{22}O_{11} \cdot H_2O)$	102-103	+112.5 → +130
38	β-Maltose octaacetate	159-160	+62.6 (c 5, $CHCl_3$)
39	4-O-β-D-Manno pyranosyl-β-D-mannopyranose $(C_{12}H_{22}O_{11})$	193-194	-7.7 → -2.2
40	β-Melibiose dihydrate (6-O-α-D-galactopyranosyl-β-D-glucopyranose) $(C_{12}H_{22}O_{11} \cdot 2H_2O)$	82-85	+111.7 → +129.5
41	β-Melibiose octaacetate	177	+102.5
42	Robinobiose (6-O-β-L-rhamnopyranosyl-D-galactopyranose) $(C_{12}H_{22}O_{10})$	Amorph.	+2.72 → 0
43	Robinobiose heptaacetate	113, 84-85 amorph.	-19.23, -9.9 $(CHCl_3)$
44	Methyl β-robinobioside hexaacetate	159-160	-39.6
45	Rutinose (6-O-β-L-rhamnopyranosyl-D-glucopyranose) $(C_{12}H_{22}O_{10})$	189-192 d., amorph.	+3.2 → -0.8 [10°]
46	Rutinose heptaacetate	168-169	-29.7 $(CHCl_3)$
47	Scillabiose (4-O-D-glucopyranosyl-L-rhamnopyranose) $(C_{12}H_{22}O_{10})$	Amorph.	-24.8
48	Scillabiose hexaacetate	97	
49	α-Sophorose monohydrate (2-O-β-D-glucopyranosyl-α-D-glucopyranose) $(C_{12}H_{22}O_{11} \cdot H_2O)$	195-196	+32
50	α-Sophorose octaacetate	111	+45 (c 1, $CHCl_3$)
51	β-Sophorose octaacetate	192	-2.8 (c 10, $CHCl_3$)
52	Sucrose (β-D-fructofuranosyl-α-D-glucopyranoside) $(C_{12}H_{22}O_{11})$	188, 170[6]	+66.5 (c 26)
69	O-D-Mannopyranosyl-(1→6)-O-D-mannopyranosyl-(1→6)-O-D-glucopyranose (levulinose ?) $(C_{18}H_{32}O_{16})$	217	-16, -15.3, -11.6
70	6-[6-(Mannopyranosyl)-mannopyranosyl]-glucopyranose hendecaacetate	95-110	+18
71	Melezitose dihydrate (O-α-D-glucopyranosyl-(1→3)-O-β-D-fructofuranosyl-(2→1)-α-D-glucopyranoside)$(C_{18}H_{32}O_{16} \cdot 2H_2O)$	153-154	+88.2
72	Melezitose hendecaacetate	117	+103.6 (c 1, $CHCl_3$)
73	Planteose dihydrate (O-α-D-galactopyranosyl-(1→6)-O-β-D-fructofuranosyl-(1→6)-O-α-D-glucopyranoside) $(C_{18}H_{32}O_{16} \cdot 2H_2O)$	123-124	+125.2
74	Planteose hendecaacetate	135	+97 (c 1, $CHCl_3$)
75	Raffinose pentahydrate (O-α-D-galactopyranosyl-(1→6)-O-α-D-glucopyranosyl-(1→2)-β-D-fructofuranoside)$(C_{18}H_{32}O_{16} \cdot 5H_2O)$	80, 118-120	+105, +123.1
76	Raffinose hendecaacetate	99-101	+92.2, +100.3 (c 8, C_2H_5OH)
77	Rhamninose $(C_{18}H_{32}O_{14})$ amorph.	135-140 d. amorph.	-41.0
78	Rhamninose octaacetate (?)	95-100	-30.9 (C_2H_5OH)
79	Robinose[7] $(C_{18}H_{32}O_{14})$ amorph.	amorph.	
80	Scorodose $(C_{24}H_{42}O_{21})$ amorph.	200	+5.2 → +1.9
81	Acetyl scorodose	85-90	-41.5, -28.5 (c 5.4, $CHCl_3$)

Oligosaccharides (continued)

No.	Substance	MP °C	$[\alpha]_D$, degrees
18	α-Cellobiose octaacetate	229	+41.0 (c 6, CHCl3)
19	β-Cellobiose octaacetate	202	-14.7 (c 5, CHCl3)
20	α-Gentiobiose (C12H22O11·2CH3OH)	85-86	+31 → +9.6
21	α-Gentiobiose octaacetate	189	+52.4 (c 4, CHCl3)
22	β-Gentiobiose (6-O-β-D-glucopyranosyl-β-D-glucopyranose) (C12H22O11)	190	-3.0 → +10.5
23	β-Gentiobiose octaacetate	193	-5.4 (c 6, CHCl3)
24	Gynolactose (C12H22O11)	205	-27
25	Isomaltose (6-O-α-Glucopyranosyl-β-D-glucopyranose) (C12H22O11)	Amorph.	+103.2, +122
26	β-Isomaltose octaacetate	144-145	+96.9 (c 2.7, CHCl3)
27	α-Lactose monohydrate (C12H22O11·H2O)	202	+83.5 → +52.6
28	α-Lactose octaacetate	152	+53.6 (c 10, CHCl3)
29	β-Lactose (4-O-β-D-galactopyranosyl-β-D-glucopyranose) (C12H22O11)	252	+34.2 → +53.6
30	β-Lactose octaacetate	90	-4.7 (c 10, CHCl3)
31	Laminaribiose (3-O-β-D-glucopyranosyl-D-glucopyranose) (C12H22O11)	160-163	+20.8 → +16.1, +23.4 → +19
32		188-192	+7.5 → +20.8
33	α-Laminaribiose octaacetate monoethanolate	77-78	+20 (c 3.6, CHCl3)
34	β-Laminaribiose octaacetate	160-161	-28.8 (c 2.5, CHCl3)
35	α-Maltose (4-O-α-D-glucopyranosyl-α-D-glucopyranose) (C12H22O11)	108	+173
36	α-Maltose octaacetate	125	+122.8 (c 5, CHCl3)
53	Sucrose octaacetate	69, 75[6]	+59.6 (CHCl3)
54	Trehalose dihydrate (C12H22O11·2H2O)	97	+178.3 (c 7)
55	Trehalose (α-D-glucopyranosyl-α-D-glucopyranoside) (C12H22O11)	203	
56	Trehalose octaacetate	98	+162.3 (c 10, CHCl3)
57	Turanose (3-O-α-D-glucopyranosyl-D-fructopyranose) (C12H22O11)	157	+22 → +75.3
58	Turanose octaacetate, I	216-217	+20.5 (c 4, CHCl3)
59	Turanose octaacetate, II	158	+107 (c 1, CHCl3)
60	Turanose octaacetate, III (keto form)	96	+126.2 (c 6, CHCl3)
61	Turanose octaacetate, IV	194-195	+103.2 (c 3, CHCl3)
62	Gentianose (O-β-D-glucopyranosyl-(1→6)-O-α-D-glucopyranosyl-(1→2)-β-D-fructofuranoside) (C18H32O16)	202	+33.4
63	Labiose trihydrate (C18H32O16·3H2O)	BP 205 (126 s.)	+136.7
64	Labiose hendecaacetate	88	+122.5 (CHCl3)
65	Maltotriose (O-α-D-glucopyranosyl-(1→4)-O-α-D-glucopyranosyl-(1→4)-O-β-D-glucopyranose) (C18H32O16)	150	+160
66	β-Maltotriose hendecaacetate	amorph.	+86 (c 1.6, CHCl3)
67	Manninotriose (O-α-D-galactopyranosyl-(1→6)-O-α-D-galactopyranosyl-(1→6)-α-D-glucopyranose) (C18H32O16)	134-136	+167
68	Manninotriose hendecaacetate	Amorph. (105 s.)	+135 (C2H5OH)
82	Stachyose (manneotetrose) (O-α-D-galactopyranosyl-(1→6)-O-α-D-galactopyranosyl-(1→6)-O-α-D-galactopyranosyl-(1→2)-O-β-D-fructofuranoside) (C24H42O21)	170 (140 s.)	+146.3
83	Stachyose tetradecaacetate	95-96 amorph.	+120.2 (C2H5OH)
84	Verbascose (O-α-D-galactopyranosyl-(1→6)-O-α-D-galactopyranosyl-(1→6)-O-α-D-galactopyranosyl-(1→6)-O-α-D-glucopyranosyl-(1→2)-β-D-fructofuranoside) (C30H52O26)	219-220, 253	+169.9
85	Verbascose heptadecaacetate	132	+130.4
86	Hexasaccharide (cyclic oligosaccharide) (C36H60O30·12H2O)	290-300	+151.8
87	Octadeca-O-Methyl-hexasaccharide (cyclic)	98-103	+160.5
88	Schardinger-α-dextrin (cyclohexaamylose) (C36H60O30)		+150.6
89	α-Dextrin acetate		+105.5 (c 1, CHCl3)
90	Schardinger-β-dextrin (cycloheptaamylose) (C42H68O34)		+162.5
91	β-Dextrin acetate	196-196.5	+125.5
92	Schardinger-γ-dextrin (cyclooctaamylose) (C48H76O38)		+177.4
93	γ-Dextrin acetate		+138.5 (c 1, CHCl3)

1/ This table is limited to those oligosaccharides which exist free, or as simple derivatives, in nature or which may be derived from a larger oligosaccharide or a polysaccharide by means of enzymic action. /2/ In preparing this table the literature has been covered through 1952, and partially through 1953. Unless otherwise noted, all data are for crystalline materials. /3/ The substances are arranged alphabetically within groups which are formulated according to increasing carbon content. /4/ Unless otherwise stated, the rotations are taken in water at concentrations less than 5 and at temperatures of 20-25°C. Other temperatures are shown in brackets; c = grams solute per 100 ml of solution. /5/ The free sugar does not exist in nature but the dibenzoyl derivatives do. /6/ The compound crystallizes in one of two forms, depending on the solvent used. /7/ This substance may be robinobiose.

Part IV: NATURAL ALDITOLS AND INOSITOLS[1]

No.	Substance[2]	MP °C	$[\alpha]_D$, degrees[3]
1	Glycerol (C3H8O3)	20	None
2	Glycerol tribenzoate	76	None
3	Glycerol, α-deoxy- (1, 2-propanediol)[4] (C3H8O2)	Oil, BP 188-189	(Racemic) none
4	1, 2-Propanediol distearate	72-73	none
5	Erythritol (C4H10O4)	118-120	(Meso), none
6	Erythritol tetraacetate	85	None
7	Erythritol, 1,4-dideoxy- (2,3-butyleneglycol) (C4H10O2)	25, 34	(Meso), none
8	1,4-Dideoxy-erythritol pentahydrate	16.8	
9	2,3-Butyleneglycol diphenylurethane	196	
10	2,3-Butyleneglycol dibenzoate	77	
11	D-Threitol, 1, 4-dideoxy- (C4H10O2)	19	-13.0
12	1, 4-Dideoxy-D-threitol diacetate	Sirup BP 192-194/745 mm	+1.4
13	L-Threitol, 1,4-dideoxy- (C4H10O2)		+10.2
14	D, L-Threitol, 1, 4-dideoxy- (C4H10O2)	7.6	None
15	1,4-Dideoxy-D,L-threitol diacetate	41-41.5	
16	1, 4-Dideoxy-D, L-threitol dibenzoate	53-54	
17	D-Arabitol (C5H12O5)	103	+7.82 (c 8, borax soln.)
18	D-Arabitol pentaacetate	76	+37.2 (CHCl3)
19	Ribitol (adonitol) (C5H12O5)	102	(Meso), none
20	Ribitol pentaacetate	51	(Meso), none
21	Galactitol (dulcitol) (C6H14O6)	186-188	
22	Galactitol hexaacetate	168-169	
23	L-Iditol (C6H14O6)	73.5	-3.5 (c 10)
24	L-Iditol hexaacetate	121.5	-25.7 (c 5, CHCl3)
25	D-Mannitol (C6H14O6)	166	-0.21
26	D-Mannitol hexaacetate	126	+18.8 (CH3COOH)
27	D-Mannitol, 1,5-anhydro- (styracitol) (C6H12O5)	157	-49.9
28	Styracitol tetraacetate	66-67	-20.9 (C2H5OH)

(The right-hand column of Part IV is headed: Substance[2] (concluded))

13

9. CARBOHYDRATES: PHYSICAL AND CHEMICAL CHARACTERISTICS (Continued)

Part IV: NATURAL ALDITOLS AND INOSITOLS (Concluded)

#	Substance[3]	MP °C	$[a]_D$, degrees[4]
29	Sorbitol (D-glucitol) (C6H14O6)	112	-1.8 [15°]
30	Sorbitol hexaacetate	99	+12.5 (c 0.8, CHCl3)
31	Sorbitol, 1,5-anhydro-(polygalitol) (C6H12O5)	140-141	+42.4
32	Polygalitol tetraacetate	73-74	+38.9 (c 2, CHCl3)
33	D-Perseitol (D-manno-D-gala-heptitol)(D-gala-D-glycero-heptitol) (C7H16O7)	188	-1.1
34	D-Perseitol heptaacetate	119	-13.3 (CHCl3)
35	D-Volemitol (D-manno-D-talo-heptitol)(D-talo-D-glycero-heptitol) (C7H16O7)	153	+2.65
36	D-Volemitol heptaacetate	62	+36.1 (c 2, CHCl3)
37	Betitol (a dideoxy inositol) (C6H12O4)	224	None
38	Bioinosose (scyllo-meso-inosose)(inosose)(C6H10O6)	198-200	
39	Inosose phenylhydrazone	220-222	
40	Inosose pentaacetate	106-108	
41	Bornesitol (meso-inositol monomethyl ether) (C7H14O6)	200	+31.6
42	Conduritol (2,3-dehydro-2,3-dideoxy-D-inositol) (C6H10O4)	142-143	None
43	Conduritol dibromide	176	
44	Conduritol tetraacetate	BP 165° at 0.6 mm	
45	Dihydroconduritol	204	
46	Dambonitol (meso-inositol di-methyl ether) (C8H16O6)	206	None
47	Dambonitol tetraacetate	195	
48	meso-Inositol (myo-inositol) (C6H12O6)	217-218	None
49	meso-Inositol hexaacetate	211-212	
50	meso-Inositol monophosphate	190-191 d.	
51	meso-Inositol monophosphate brucine salt[5]	236-238	
52	meso-Inositol hexaphosphate dodeca-sodium salt +38 H2O[6]	58-59	
53	meso-Inositol tetraphosphate[7]		
54	meso-Inositol tri-phosphate[7]		
55	meso-Inositol diphosphate[7]		
56	DL-Inositol (C6H12O6)	253	
57	DL-Inositol hexaacetate	111	
58	Mytilitol (c-methyl-scyllitol)(C7H14O6)	259	(Meso), none
59	Mytilitol pentaacetate	157-158	
60	Mytilitol hexaacetate	180-181	
61	Pinitol (D-inositol monomethyl ether) (C7H14O6)	186	+65.5 (c 2, C2H5OH)
62	Pinitol pentaacetate	98	+8.6 (c 2, C2H5OH)
63	Quebrachitol (L-inositol monomethyl ether) (C7H14O6)	190-191	-80.2 [28°]
64	Quebrachitol pentaacetate	96-97	-25.1 [29°] (c 4, CHCl3)
65	D-Quercitol (deoxy-D-inositol) (C6H12O5)	235	+24.2
66	D-Quercitol pentaacetate	174	-73.9
67	L-Quercitol (deoxy-L-inositol)[8] (C6H12O5)	124-125	-26.0 (c 2.7, CHCl3)
68	L-Quercitol pentaacetate		
69	D-Quinic acid (2,3,4-tri-deoxy-3-carboxy-D-inositol) (C7H12O6)	164	+44 (c 10)
70	L-Quinic acid (C7H12O6)	162	-42.1
71	L-Quinic acid lactone tri-acetate (form 1)	132	
72	L-Quinic acid lactone tri-acetate (form 2)	139	
73	L-Quinic acid tetraacetate	130-136	-22.5 (c 5, C2H5OH)
74	DL-Quinic acid		
75	Scyllitol (cocositol) (C6H12O6)	352-353	None
76	Scyllitol hexaacetate	299-300	None
77	Streptidine (1,3-dideoxy-1,3-diguanidino-scyllitol) (C8H18N6O4)		None
78	Di-N-acetyl-tetra-O-acetyl-streptamine	342-345	
79	N,N'-Diacetylstreptamine	383-384	
80	Streptamine hemihydrate (1,3-diamino-1,3-dideoxy scyllitol)	205 s.	
81	Streptidine dipicrate	284-285 d.	
82	Sequoyitol (meso-inositol monomethyl ether) (C7H14O6)	234-235	(Meso), none
83	Sequoyitol pentaacetate	198	
84	Shikimic acid (3,4-dehydro-quinic acid) (C7H10O5)	183-184	-200 [16°]
85	Methyl shikimate	113-114	
86	Shikimic acid triacetate	Sirup BP 0.1 200-210	

/1/ This table contains the alditols and inositols which occur in nature, free or as hydrolytic products from natural substances. Naturally occurring simple derivatives of these polyols are also included. The literature has been covered through 1952 and partially through 1953. Unless otherwise noted all data are for crystalline materials. The alditols are all listed first, arranged alphabetically as groups which are formulated according to increasing carbon content in the parent compound. The inositols are then listed similarly. /3/ Unless otherwise stated the rotations are taken in water at concentrations less than 5 and at temperatures of 20-25 °C. Other temperatures are shown in brackets; c = grams solute per 100 ml of solution. /4/ The 1-phosphate ester of this diol is said to occur in brain tissue and sea urchin eggs. /5/ Prepared from natural phytin, the calcium and magnesium salt of phytic acid or meso-inositol hexaphosphate. /6/ Found as a hydrolyzate product of liposital. /7/ This is not an enantiomorph of D-quercitol. Other isomeric relationship is involved. /8/ Obtained by enzyme action on meso-inositol hexaphosphate.

Part V: NATURAL ALDONIC, URONIC, AND ALDARIC ACIDS[1]

#	Substance[2]	MP °C	$[a]_D$, degrees[3]
1	D-Glyceric acid (C3H6O4)	Gum	Dextro
2	Methyl D-glycerate	Sirup BP 119/14 mm	-4.8
3	Methyl 2,3-di-O-methyl-D-glycerate	Sirup BP 77/15 mm	-69.7
4	D-Glyceronamide	99.5-100	-63.1 (c 2.4, CH3OH)
5	2,3-Di-O-methyl-D-glyceronamide	77-77.5	-54.5 (c 3.1, CH3OH)
6	L-Glyceric acid, brucine salt	222	-33.2
7	L-Glyceric acid (C3H6O4)	Gum	Levo
8	Calcium L-glycerate dihydrate	134-135	-12 [30°]
9	D-Arabonic acid (C5H10O6)	114-116	10.5 (c 6)
10	D-Arabono-γ-lactone (See also L-arabonic acid)	96	73.7
39	D-Gluconic acid, 2-deoxy-2-"keto"- (C6H10O7) (concluded) Methyl tetra-O-acetyl-2-deoxy-2-"keto"-D-gluconate	168-169	-133 (c 2, CHCl3)
40	D-Gluconic acid, 5-deoxy-5-"keto"- (C6H10O7)	110-130 variable	-14.5
41	5-Deoxy-5-"keto"-D-gluconic acid phenylosazone	190-212 variable	
42	5-Deoxy-5-"keto"-D-gluconic acid p-nitrophenylhydrazone	151	
43	D-Mannonic acid (C6H12O7)	119	15.6 → 47
44	D-Mannono-γ-lactone	172-173	51.8 → 47
45	D-Mannono-γ-lactone tetra-acetate	161-162	52 (80% CH3COCH3)
46	D-Mannonamide	214-216	-17.3
47	D-Mannono-6-lactone		111.9 → 39.9°
48	D-Mannonic phenylhydrazide		-8.1 [180°]
70	β-D-Glucuronic acid (C6H10O7) (concluded) Methyl (methyl 4-O-methyl-D-glucopyranosid)uronate	Sirup	95 (c 10, H2O)
71	Methyl 4-O-methyl-α-D-glucopyranosiduronamide	236	150
72	Methyl 4-O-methyl-β-D-glucopyranosiduronamide	232	-50
73	4-O-Methyl-D-glucuronic acid	Sirup	45 (c 5.8, H2O)
74	Methyl 2,3-di-O-methyl-D-glucopyranosiduronic acid	Sirup	68
75	Methyl 2,3-di-O-methyl-D-glucopyranosiduronic acid	Sirup	76 (c 0.7, H2O)
76	Methyl 2,3-di-O-methyl-D-glucopyranosiduronic phenylhydrazide	225-227	

No.	Compound	M.P. (°C)	$[\alpha]_D$
11	L-Arabonic acid ($C_5H_{10}O_6$)	118-119	-9.6 → -41.7[4]
12	L-Arabonamide	135-136	37.2
13	L-Arabonic acid phenylhydrazide	215	
14	L-Arabonic acid tetraacetate (See also D-arabonic acid above)	135-135.5	-32 (c 1.5, $CHCl_3$)
15	D-Ribonic acid ($C_5H_{10}O_6$)	112-113	-17.0
16	D-Ribono-γ-lactone	77	16.5
17	D-Ribonamide	136-137	
18	D-Ribonic acid tetraacetate	138-139	-24.4 (c 2.3, $CHCl_3$)
19	D-Xylonic acid ($C_5H_{10}O_6$)		-2.9 → 20.1[4]
20	D-Xylono-γ-lactone	99-103	85.5 → 24.2
21	D-Xylonic acid tetraacetate	86-88	-2 (c 2, $CHCl_3$)
22	Cadmium D-xylonate, cadmium bromide double salt dihydrate		8.8
23	D-Galactonic acid ($C_6H_{12}O_7$)	122	-11.2 → -57.6[4]
24	D-Galactono-γ-lactone	112	-73 → -63.7
25	D-Galactonamide	172-172.5	30.2
26	D-Galactonic phenylhydrazide	203	10.4
27	D-Galactonic acid pentaacetate	131-132	12 (c 3, $CHCl_3$)
28	D-Galactonic acid, 2-deoxy-2-"keto"- ($C_6H_{10}O_7$)	169	-5
29	2-Deoxy-2-"keto"-D-galactonic acid, brucine salt	172	-22.5 (50% C_2H_5OH)
30	D-Gluconic acid ($C_6H_{12}O_7$)	130-132 (110-112 s.)	-6.7 → 11.9[4] s.) 11.9[4]
31	D-Glucono-γ-lactone	134-136	67.5 → 17.7
32	D-Gluconamide	143-144	31.2
33	D-Gluconic phenylhydrazide	200	12
34	D-Glucono-δ-lactone	150-152	61.7 → 6.2
35	D-Gluconic acid pentaacetate	110-111	11.5 (c 2, $CHCl_3$)
36	D-Gluconic acid, 2-deoxy-2-"keto"- ($C_6H_{10}O_7$)		-81.7 (sodium salt)
37	Methyl 2-deoxy-2-"keto"-D-gluconate	173	-82.1
38	2-Deoxy-2-"keto"-D-glucono-γ-lactone triacetate	154	-60.4 (c 2.2, $CHCl_3$) → -77.4

No.	Compound	M.P. (°C)	$[\alpha]_D$
49	α-D-Galacturonic acid monohydrate ($C_6H_{12}O_8$)	159-160 (110-115 s.) 160	97.9 → 50.9
50	D-Bromophenylhydrazine salt of D-galacturonic acid p-bromophenylhydrazone	145-146	9±2[20°](c 0.7, CH_3OH)
51	β-D-Galacturonic acid ($C_6H_{10}O_7$)	160	27 → 55.6
52	D-Galacturonic acid p-bromophenylhydrazone	150-151	11.5±2[22°] (c 1.36, CH_3OH)
53	Methyl α-D-galacturono-pyranoside dihydrate	113	129.9
54	Methyl β-D-galacturono-pyranoside monohydrate	134	-39.2
55	Methyl (methyl-α-D-galacto-pyranoside) uronate monohydrate	142	125.4
56	Methyl (methyl-β-D-galacto-pyranoside) uronate	194	-45.6
57	2-O-Methyl-D-galacto-pyranuronamide	173	
58	Methyl (methyl 2-O-methyl-α-D-galactopyranoside)uronate	Sirup	80
59	Methyl 2-O-methyl-α-D-galactopyranosiduronamide	174	55 (c 0.05, CH_3OH)
60	Methyl 2,3-di-O-methyl-β-D-galactofuranosiduronamide	122	-146 [16°]
61	2,3-Di-O-methyl-D-galactopyranuronic acid	Sirup	62 [14°]
62	Methyl (methyl 2,3-di-O-methyl-D-galactopyranoside)uronate	170	
63	2,3,4-Tri-O-methyl-α-D-galacturonic acid monohydrate	98-99 70	120 → 104
64	Methyl (methyl 2,3,4-tri-O-methyl-D-galactopyranoside)uronate	100	149.0 (c 1.2, CH_3COCH_3)
65	β-D-Glucuronic acid ($C_6H_{10}O_7$)	156 180	11.7 → 36.3 / 18.6
66	D-Glucuronolactone	110-112	203.6 (c 0.9, $CHCl_3$)
67	α-D-Glucopyranurono-γ-lactone triacetate	194-195	84.1 (c 1.5, $CHCl_3$)
68	β-D-Glucopyranuronolactone triacetate		
69	Phenylhydrazide of D-glucuronic phenylhydrazone	182	

No.	Compound	M.P. (°C)	$[\alpha]_D$
77	Methyl (methyl 2,3,4-tri-O-methyl-D-glucopyranoside)uronate	Sirup	87
78	Methyl 2,3,4-tri-O-methyl-D-glucopyranosiduronamide	183	137.5 (c 0.7, H_2O)
79	α-D-Mannuronic acid monohydrate ($C_6H_{12}O_8$)	(110 s.) 120-130 d.	16.0 → -6.1 (c 6.8)
80	β-D-Mannuronic acid ($C_6H_{10}O_7$)	140-141	89.3
81	D-Mannopyranurono-γ-lactone ($C_6H_{10}O_7$)	165-167	-47.9 → -23.9 CH_3OH
82	D-Mannopyranuronohydrazone	160 d.	64.5±1 (c 2.3, CH_3OH)
83	D-Bromophenylhydrazine salt of D-mannuronic p-bromophenylhydrazone	143-144 d.	48.5±1 (c 1.4, CH_3OH)
84	D-Bromophenylhydrazide of D-mannuronic p-bromophenylhydrazone	174-175 d.	18.5±1 (c 0.75 C_5H_5N)
85	2,3,-Di-O-methyl-D-manno-pyranuronic acid	Sirup	30 (c 1.5, CH_3OH)
86	Methyl (methyl 2,3-di-O-methyl-D-mannopyranoside)uronate	Sirup	59
87	2,3,4-Tri-O-methyl-D-mannopyranuronic acid	Sirup	36.4
88	Methyl (methyl 2,3,4-tri-O-methyl-D-mannopyranoside)uronate	Sirup	60 (c 10, H_2O)
89	2,3,4-Tri-O-methyl-D-mannosaccharodiamide	228	-17 (c 0.5, CH_3OH)
90	D-Tartaric acid ($C_4H_6O_6$) See L-tartaric acid	170	-15
91	L-Tartaric acid ($C_4H_6O_6$)	170	15 [15°]
92	L-Tartaric acid diacetate trihydrate	58	-19.32
93	Dimethyl L-tartrate	48, 61.5	2.74
94	L-Tartaramide	195	106.5
95	L-Malic acid ($C_4H_6O_5$)	100	-2.3 (c 8.4)
96	Malic acid acetate	132	-6.84
97	Dimethyl malate	Sirup	-37.9
98	Malamide	BP11 129 156-157	

L-Malic acid structure:
$$\begin{array}{c} CO_2H \\ H-\triangle-OH \\ CH_2 \\ CO_2H \end{array}$$

/1/ This table contains those sugar acids which are found free, as components in hydrolyzates of natural products, or as oxidation products of bacterial action on some natural monosaccharide or alditol. The literature has been covered through 1952 and partially through 1953. Unless otherwise stated, all data are for crystalline substances. /2/ The aldonic acids are listed first, arranged alphabetically in groups which are formulated according to increasing carbon content in the parent sugar. Then uronic acids, and finally, glycaric acids are similarly listed. It is to be noted that while acetate derivatives are given for a few of the aldonic acids not all of such derivatives have been made directly from the parent free acid. Since some have, however, the acetates listed have been given as a matter of completeness. /3/ Unless otherwise stated, the rotations are taken in water at concentrations less than 5 and at 20-25°C. Other temperatures are shown in brackets; c = grams of solute per 100 ml of solution. /4/ Equilibrates with the lactone. /5/ There is some claim that bacterial action on calcium D-gluconate produces L-gulonic acid. This fact is yet to be firmly established since no definitive derivative of L-guluronic acid has been produced. L-Guluronic forms the same phenylosazone as 5-deoxy-5-"keto"-D-gluconic acid. /6/ Passes through a minimum point in mutarotating.

9. CARBOHYDRATES: PHYSICAL AND CHEMICAL CHARACTERISTICS (Concluded)
Part VI: NATURAL PHOSPHATE ESTERS[1,2]

#	Substance	Hydrolysis Constant k[3] 1st Ester[4] Group	Temp °C	Medium	[a] Degrees[5]	Wave Length[6]	Compound	Conc.
1	Dihydroxyacetone phosphate	33.7	100	N HCl				
2	D-Fructose 1-phosphate	70	100	N HCl	-64.2	5461	Free acid	11.3
3					-39	5461	Ba salt	6.1
4					-52.1	5461	Brucine salt	
5	D-Fructose 6-phosphate	4.4	100	N HCl	+3.6	D	Ba salt	10
6	D-Fructose 1,6-diphosphate	52[6]	100	N HCl	+4.1	D	Free acid	13.6
7	α-D-Galactose 1-phosphate	5.9	37	0.25 N HCl	+108	D	K salt	2.6
8					+148	D	Free acid	1.7 (0.2 N HCl)
9					+92	D	Ba salt	2.3
10					+113	5461	Ba salt	
11	β-D-Galactose 1-phosphate	5.6	37	0.25 N HCl	+31.3	D	Trihydrate Ba salt	1.2
12	D-Gluconic acid 6-phosphate	0.21	100	N HCl	+0.2	5461	Free acid	
13					+18	5461	Free acid lactone	
14	α-D-Glucose 1-phosphate	1.3	37	0.25 N HCl	+118	D	Free acid	1
15		5[7]	33	N HCl	+75.5	D	Ba salt	1.3
16					+78	D	K salt dihydrate	
17					+90	5461	K salt dihydrate	
18					+0.5[8]	D	Dibrucine salt octahydrate[9]	
19	β-D-Glucose 1-phosphate	15[7]	33	N HCl	-20[10]	D	Dibrucine salt decahydrate[11]	1.7
20	D-Glucose 6-phosphate	0.23	100	N HCl	+35.7	D	Free acid	0.7
21					+41.4	5461	Free acid	
22					+18	D	Ba salt	8.4
23					+21.2	5461	Ba salt	1.3
24					+21.2	D	K salt	
25	α-D-Glucose 1,6-diphosphate	0.78	30	N H_2SO_4	+83±4	D	Free acid	0.2
26	β-D-Glucose 1,6-diphosphate	3.15	30	N H_2SO_4	-19±2	D	Free acid	0.4
27	D-Glyceraldehyde 3-phosphate[12]	37.5	100	N HCl	+12	D	Free acid	
28	D-Glyceric acid 2-phosphate				+24.3	D	Free acid	
29					-68	D	Free acid	
30	D-Glyceric acid 3-phosphate	1.8[13]	125	N HCl	-14.5	D	Ba salt	
31					-725	D	Ba salt	
32	D-Glyceric acid 1,3-diphosphate	26	38	Water	Very small			
33	D-Glyceric acid 2,3-diphosphate				-4±0.5	D	Ba salt	15 (aq. HNO_3)
34					-4		Na salt	28

#	Substance	Hydrolysis Constant k[3] 1st Ester[4] Group	Temp °C	Medium	[a] Degrees[5]	Wave Length[6]	Compound	Conc.
35	D-Glyceric acid 2,3-diphosphate (concluded)				-2±0.3	D	Ba salt	6-17, (H_2O or 1 $NHNO_3$)
36					-5[12]	D	Na salt	6-14
37					+4.6±0.4[14]	D	Na salt	
38	α-L-Glycerophosphate (L-glycerol 1-phosphate)(L-glycerin 1-phosphate)	0.15	80	Water, pH 6.3	+1.0	D	Ag salt	6.5
39					-4.7	D	Dimethyl ether, dimethyl ester	
40					-5.3	D	Diethyl ether, diethyl ester	
41					-2.8±0.1	D	Glycerl-phosphorylcholine	
42	D-Mannose 6-phosphate	0.29	100	N HCl	+15.1	5461	Free acid	1.7
43					+3.5	5461	Ba salt	0.7
44	β-D-Ribose 1-phosphate	1200	25	0.5 N HCl	-12.9	D	Free acid	
45	D-Ribose 3-phosphate	4.5	100	0.25 N HCl	-9.7	D	Na salt	3.8
46	D-Ribose 5-phosphate	0.5	100	0.25 N HCl	+6.0	D	Ba salt	3.7
47					+16.5	D	Free acid	3 (1 N HCl)
48					+20	D	Free acid	(0.2 N HCl)
49	β-D-Ribose[15] 2-deoxy-, 1-phosphate	13-17[13]		Acetate buffer pH 4.5				
50	β-D-Ribose, 2-deoxy-, 5-phosphate							(Molybdate ion)
51	D-Ribulose 5-phosphate	50[13]	100	N HCl	-40	D	Free acid	
52	L-Sorbose 1-phosphate	60[13]	100	N HCl	-16.5	D	Mono K salt	2
53					-7.2	D	Ba salt dihydrate	2.5 (0.1 N HCl)
54	Trehalose monophosphate				+185	5461	Free acid	2.4
55					+132	5461	Ba salt	3.2
56					+31	5461	Brucine salt monohydrate	0.8
57	Unidentified keto-heptose monophosphate							(Molybdate ion)
58	D-Xylose 5-phosphate	4	100	N HCl	+8	5461	Ba salt	
59	D-Xylulose phosphate (D-xyloketose 1-phosphate)	4	100	N HCl	+3.2	D	Na salt	5
60		86	100	N HCl	+5	D	Ba salt	2

[1] In preparing this table the literature has been covered through 1952, and Chem. Abs. coverage has extended through Sept., 1953. [2] Unless otherwise noted all data are for crystalline material. Phosphate esters known only from strictly chemical syntheses are excluded. Included are some compounds which have not actually been isolated as such, but for which evidence for probable existence or structure is at hand. [3] Values are k x 10[3]. [4] The 1st ester group is that one that lies farthest in the sugar carbon chain structure from the primary hydroxyl carbon (or asymmetric center) which determines the parent sugar's D or L configuration. [5] Taken at 20-25°C in water unless otherwise noted. [6] D represents the sodium D line, 5896. [7] Constants were determined on the dibrucine salts. [8] Rotation taken at 29°C. [9] Brucine salt melts at 173-178°C. [10] Rotation taken at 27°C. [11] Brucine salt melts at 160-165°C. [12] The compound fuses above 75°C, Fischer, H. O. L., and Baer, E., Ber. 65:337, 1040, 1932. [13] Calculated by the contributors of this table from the data of the original investigator, using k = 0.30/time in min for 50% hydrolysis. [14] The signs of these rotations are actually opposite, as taken from the original journal articles. [15] Deoxy-β-D-ribose 1-phosphate cyclohexylamine salt sinters and decomposes at 152°C.

10. GLYCOSIDES: CHARACTERISTICS, OCCURRENCE, AND USES

#	Glycoside	Formula	M.P.[1] °C	Rotation [α]D	Solubility[1] g/100 ml — H₂O	Alc.	Eth., etc.	Occurrence	Uses	Aglycone	M.P.[1] °C	Rotation [α]D	Sugar
1	Absinthin	C₃₀H₄₀O₈	68		sl.s.	s.	s.,eth.,chl.,bz.,NaOH	Wormwood	Anemia; anorexia; achlorhydria; constipation.				Glucose
2	Aesculin	C₁₅H₁₆O₉	205 d.[2]	−38	0.175	5	sl.s.,eth.,s.h.chl.,NaOH	Horse chestnut tree[3,4]	Instead of quinine in intermittent fever; neuralgia; lupus vulgaris.	Aesculetin	270 d.		Glucose
3	Aloin	Mixture			s.	sl.s.	sl.s.,eth.,chl.	Aloe spp	Chronic constipation; amenorrhea.				Pentoses
4	Amygdalin	C₂₀H₂₇O₁₁N	220[2]	−42	8.3 h.	sl.s.	i.eth.	Almonds	Expectorant.	d-Mandelonitrile			Glucose
5	Apiin	C₂₆H₄₂O₁₀	228[2]		s.h.	sl.s.h.	i.eth.	Celery; parsley	Diuretic; insecticide; dropsy.	Apigenin	350		Glucose; apiose
6	Arbutin	C₁₂H₁₆O₇	195-200	−64	12.5	7.7	i.eth.,CS₂,chl	Cranberry, pear tree[3]	Diuretic.	Hydroquinone	170		Glucose
7	Barbaloin	C₂₀H₁₈O₈	148		s.	s.	sl.s.eth.	Aloe spp	Chronic constipation.	Aloe-emodin	224		Glucose
8	Bryonin	C₄₈H₆₆O₁₈	208		sl.s.	s.	i.eth.,chl.	Bryonia alba[5]	Dropsy; congested liver; pericarditis; rheumatism.[5]	Bryogenin			Glucose
9	Carminic acid	C₂₂H₂₀O₁₃	136 d.		s.	s.	s.eth.,NaOH,i.chl.	Cochineal	Indicator. Pigment in color photography, paints, bacteriology.	Carmine red			
10	Coniferin	C₁₆H₂₂O₈	185	−68	0.5	sl.s.	i.chl.	Conifers; sugar beet	Preparation of vanilla.	Coniferyl alcohol	73-74		Glucose
11	Convallatoxin	C₂₉H₄₂O₁₀	247	0	0.05	s.	sl.s.eth.,chl.	Lily of the valley	Cardiac glycoside.	Strophanthidin	235	+43.1	Rhamnose
12	Convolvulin	C₅₄H₉₆O₂₇	155-168		sl.s.	s.	i.eth.,s.acet.	Jalap resin, Canadian hemp	Purgative. Cardiotonic.	Methylethylacetic acid; tiglic acid			Glucose; rhodeose
13	Crocin	C₄₄H₆₄O₂₆	186 d.[2]		sl.s.	sl.s.	i.eth.,chl.	Saffron, crocus, gardenia	Plays role in sex process of algae.	Crocetin	285		Gentiobiose
14	Cymarin	C₃₀H₄₄O₉	139	+35	s.	s.	s.chl.,me.al.,i.eth.;s.	Daphne	Cardiac stimulant; tonic.	Strophanthidin	235 d.	+43.1	Cymarose
15	Daphnin	C₁₅H₁₆O₉	125 d.[2]	−115	sl.s.	sl.s.	i.eth.;s.NaOH	Digitalis purpurea[3]	Inflammation and vesication of skin; epispastic.	7,8-Dihydroxycoumarin	253 d.		Glucose
16	Diginin	C₂₈H₄₀O₇	155-183	−176	i.		sl.s.eth.;s.chl.,CCl₄	Digitalis purpurea[6]	Digitalis glycoside. Cardiotonic.	Diginigenin	115	−226	Diginose
17	Digitonin	C₅₅H₉₀O₂₉	235 d.[2]	−54	s.		i.eth.,chl.	Digitalis purpurea	Test for cholesterol and some other sterols.	Digitogenin	250	−81	Glucose; galactose
18	Digitoxin	C₄₁H₆₄O₁₃	256	+4.8	0.001	1.7	i.eth.	Digitalis purpurea	Congestive heart failure. Cardiotonic.	Digitoxigenin + digitose	253	+19.1	Digitose
19	Digoxin	C₄₁H₆₄O₁₄	265 d.	+13.3	0.001	0.45	i.eth.,chl.	Digitalis lanata	Digitalis glycoside. Cardiotonic.	Digoxigenin + digitoxose	222	+27	
20	Gaultherin	C₁₉H₂₆O₁₂	179-180	−58	s.	s.	i.eth.,s.acet.	Wintergreen plant	Source of methyl salicylate.	Methyl salicylate	−8.6	+1.2	Glucose; xylose
21	Gitonin	C₅₀H₈₂O₂₃	272	−51	sl.s.	0.98	s.eth.,i.chl.,s.acet.	Digitalis purpurea	Similar to digitonin.	Gitogenin	272	−61	Galactose; xylose
22	Gitoxin	C₄₁H₆₄O₁₄	285	+3.5	sl.s.		s.eth.,i.chl.;s.acet.	Digitalis lanata	Minor digitalis glycoside.	Gitoxigenin	235	+38.5	Digitoxose
23	Gratiolin	C₄₃H₇₀O₁₅	235-237		sl.s.	s.	sl.s.eth.;s.chl.	Gratiola glucoside	Cathartic; emetic; diuretic; dropsy.	Gratiogenin	198		Glucose
24	Hesperidin	C₂₈H₃₄O₁₅	260-262	−76	v.sl.s.	s.me.al	i.eth.,chl.;s.NaOH	Citrus plants	Purpura; vascular complications; hypertension; anti-hyaluronidase.	3′,5,7-Trihydroxy-flavanone	390 d.		Glucose
25	Indican	C₁₄H₁₇O₆N	176-178	−66	v.sl.s.	s.	sl.s.eth.,chl.	Indigofera spp	Jaundice; constipation; amenorrhea.	Indoxyl	390		Glucose
26	Iridin	C₂₄H₂₆O₁₃N	208		sl.s.	s.h.	i.eth.,chl.	Rhizome of iris	Chronic constipation.	Irigenin	186		Various
27	Jalapin	C₃₄H₅₆O₁₆	131-150		sl.s.	s.	s.eth.,chl.	Scammony resin	Angina pectoris; coronary thrombosis; bronchial asthma.	Jalapinolic	67-69		Glucose
28	Khellinin	C₁₉H₂₀O₁₀	175[2]	0		s.me.al.,i.eth.		Toothpick ammi[6]		2-Hydroxymethyl-5-methoxy-furanochrome	155		
29	Ouabain	C₂₉H₄₄O₁₂	185 d.	−32.5	1.2	1	sl.s.eth.,chl.	Strophanthus gratus[6]	As for digitalis.	Ouabagenin	255	+11.3	Rhamnose
30	Phloridzin	C₂₁H₂₄O₁₀	110[2]	−52	0.1	25	i.eth.,chl.	Fruit trees[4]	Additive to lubricating oils.	Phloretin	271		Glucose
31	Picrocrocin	C₁₆H₂₆O₇	154-156	−50			sl.s.eth.,chl.	Crocus	Coloring; flavoring.	Safranol			Glucose
32	Quercitrin	C₂₁H₂₀O₁₁	182-185[2]		i.c.	c.sl.s.	i.eth.,s.NaOH	Quercitron[4]	Astringent; tonic; textile dye.	Quercetin	314 d.		Glucose
33	Rutin	C₂₇H₃₀O₁₆	215 d.		sl.s.c.		i.eth.,chl.	Buckwheat plant	Vascular purpura; hypertension; diabetes; inc. capillary fragility.	Quercetin	313-4		Glucose; rhamnose
34	Salicin	C₁₃H₁₈O₇	199-201	−67	4	1	i.eth.,chl.	Poplar, willow[4]	Analgesic. Rheumatism; malaria; typhoid; chorea.	Saligenin	87		Glucose
35	Sarsasaponin	C₄₅H₇₄O₁₇	240	−66	s.	s.h.	sl.s.eth.		Production of progesterone, testosterone	Sarsasapogenin	200	−75	Glucose; rhamnose
36	Solanine	C₄₅H₇₃O₁₅N	285 d.	−60	i.	s.h.	i.eth.,chl.	Solanum	Vomiting of pregnancy; asthma; epilepsy; locomotor ataxia; tetanus.	Solanidine	219	−29	Glucose; galactose; rhamnose
37	Streptomycin·HCl	C₂₁H₃₉O₁₂N₇·3HCl	210-5 d.	−84	s.	v.sl.s.	i.eth.,chl.	Cultures of Streptomyces griseus[4]	Tuberculosis; susceptible gram-negative bacteria.	Streptidine			L-Streptose
38	Tannic acid	C₇₆H₅₂O₄₆			v.s.	sl.s.	v.sl.s.,eth.,chl.	Oak, sumac[4]	Tanning; mordant in dyeing and printing.	Gallic acid	235 d.		Glucose

/1/ Abbreviations: abs. = absolute; acet. = acetone; bz. = benzene; c. = cold; chl. = chloroform; d. = decomposes; eth. = ether; h. = hot; i. = insoluble; me. al.= methyl alcohol; s. = soluble; sl. = slightly; v. = very. /2/ Hydrated salt. /3/ Leaves. /4/ Bark. /5/ It has been reported that this compound is therapeutically inactive. /6/ Seeds.

17

11. FATTY ACIDS: PHYSICAL AND CHEMICAL CHARACTERISTICS

	Common Name	Systematic Name	Formula	Molecular Weight	M.P. or Fr.P.*[1] °C	Boiling Point[2] °C	Specific Gravity[3]	Refractive Index[4] n_D^x	Neutralization Value[5]	Iodine Value (Calculated)[6]	Solubility[7]	Source
						Saturated Fatty Acids						
1	Formic	Methanoic	HCOOH	46.0	8.6	100.8	1.220^{20}	1.3714^{20}	1219		s. w.	Red ant
2	Acetic	Ethanoic	CH₃COOH	60.1	16.7	118.2	1.049^{20}	1.3715^{23}	934.2		s. w.	Vinegar
3	Propionic	Propanoic	C₂H₅COOH	74.1	-22.0	141.1	0.992^{20}	1.3874^{20}	757.3		s. w., al., eth., chl.	Butter fat
4	Butyric	Butanoic	C₃H₇COOH	88.1	-7.9	162.7^{69}	0.958^{720}	1.3906^{20}	636.8		s. w., eth., al.	Butter fat
5	Valeric	Pentanoic	C₄H₉COOH	102.1	-34.5	187			549.3		sl. s. w.; s. al., eth.	
6	Caproic	Hexanoic	C₅H₁₁COOH	116.2	-3.9	205.3	0.9313^{615}	1.4163^{520}	483.0		sl. s. w.; s. eth., al.	Butter fat, palm oil
7	Enanthic	Heptanoic	C₆H₁₃COOH	130.2	-8.9	223.5	0.9221^{515}	1.4130^{20}	431.0		v. sl. s. w.; s. al., eth., bz	Violet leaf oil
8	Caprylic	Octanoic	C₇H₁₅COOH	144.2	16.5*	239.3	0.9088^{420}	1.4285^{20}	389.1		v. sl. s. w.; s. al., eth., chl.	Butter fat, coconut oil
9	Pelargonic	Nonanoic	C₈H₁₇COOH	158.2	12.2*	254			354.6		sl. s. w.; s. eth., al.	
10	Capric	Decanoic	C₉H₁₉COOH	172.3	31.3*	268.7	0.8858^{40}	1.4285^{540}	325.7		sl. s. al., eth., chl.	Butter fat, coconut oil
11	Undecylic	Undecanoic	C₁₀H₂₁COOH	186.3	28.3*	295			301.2		sl. s. h. w.; s. acet., al., eth.	
12	Lauric	Dodecanoic	C₁₁H₂₃COOH	200.3	43.9*	225^{100}	0.8690^{50}	1.4261^{60}	280.1		s. al., eth., chl.	Laurel kernel oil
13	Tridecylic	Tridecanoic	C₁₂H₂₅COOH	214.3	41.8*	236^{100}			261.8		s. al., eth.	
14	Myristic	Tetradecanoic	C₁₃H₂₇COOH	228.4	54.1*	250.5^{100}	0.862^{254}	1.4273^{70}	245.7		s. al., eth., acet., chl., glac. acet. a.	Nutmeg, butter fat
15	Palmitic	Hexadecanoic	C₁₅H₃₁COOH	256.4	62.7*	268^{100}	0.8527^{62}	1.4339^{60}	218.8		s. h. al., eth.	Palm oil
16	Stearic	Octadecanoic	C₁₇H₃₅COOH	284.5	69.6*	291^{100}	0.9408^{100}	1.4332^{70}	197.2		s. al., eth., acet., bz., CS₂.	Mutton tallow, cocoa butter
17	Arachidic	Eicosanoic	C₁₉H₃₉COOH	312.5	75.4	$203\text{-}205^{1}$	0.8240^{100}	1.4250^{100}	179.5		s. chl., eth.	Peanut oil
18	Behenic	Docosanoic	C₂₁H₄₃COOH	340.6	80.0	306^{60}	0.8221^{100}	1.4270^{100}	164.7		sl. s. eth., al.	Peanut oil, behen oil
19	Lignoceric	Tetracosanoic	C₂₃H₄₇COOH	368.6	84.2			1.4287^{100}	152.2		sl. s. al.; s. acet., bz., eth.	Beech-tar paraffin
20	Cerotic	Hexacosanoic	C₂₅H₅₁COOH	396.7	87.7			1.4287^{100}	141.4		s.h.me.al., h.al., h.bz., h.chl., h.acet.	Beeswax, wool wax
21	Montanic	Octacosanoic	C₂₇H₅₅COOH	424.7	90.9		0.8198^{100}	1.4301^{100}	132.1		s. pet. eth., h. al., glac. acet. a.	Beeswax, montan wax
22	Melissic	Triacontanoic	C₂₉H₅₉COOH	452.9	93.6		0.8191^{100}	1.4313^{100}	123.9		s. h. al., chl., CS₂.	Beeswax, mineral waxes
23	Lacceroic	Dotriacontanoic	C₃₁H₆₃COOH	480.8	96.2			1.4323^{100}	116.7		s. bz., acet., a., chl.	Stick-lac wax
24	Geddic	Tetratriacontanoic	C₃₃H₆₇COOH	508.9	98.3-0.5				110.2		s. bz., acet., chl.	Ghedda wax
25		Hexatriacontanoic	C₃₅H₇₁COOH	536.9	99.9				104.5			
						Unsaturated Fatty Acids (Monoethenoid)						
26		2-Hexenoic	C₆H₁₀O₂	114.1	32		0.9540	1.4464^{40}	491.5	222.5	s. eth., bz.	Japanese peppermint oil
27	Obtusilic	4-Decenoic	C₁₀H₁₈O₂	170.2		$148\text{-}150^{13}$	0.9197^{20}	1.4497^{20}	329.6	149.1	s. al., eth.	Tohaku oil
28	Caproleic	9-Decenoic	C₁₀H₁₈O₂	170.2		$143\text{-}8^{15}$	0.9238^{15}	1.4507^{15}	329.6	149.1	s. eth., chl., bz., pet. eth.	Butter fat, whale oil
29	Linderic	4-Dodecenoic	C₁₂H₂₂O₂	198.3	1.0-1.3	$170\text{-}172^{13}$	0.9081^{20}	1.4529^{20}	282.9	128.0	s. eth., chl., bz., pet. eth.	Tohaku oil
30	Lauroleic	5-Dodecenoic	C₁₂H₂₂O₂	198.3			0.9130^{15}	1.4535^{15}	282.9	128.0	s. eth., chl., bz., pet. eth.	Herring oil, whale oil
31		4-Tetradecenoic	C₁₄H₂₆O₂	226.4	18.0-0.5	$185\text{-}188^{13}$	0.9055^{15}	1.4575^{15}	247.9	112.2	s. eth., bz.	Butter fat, cochineal wax
32	Tsuzuic	5-Tetradecenoic	C₁₄H₂₆O₂	226.4			0.9046^{20}	1.4552^{20}	247.9	112.2	s. eth., bz.	Tsuzu seeds
33	Myristoleic	9-Tetradecenoic	C₁₄H₂₆O₂	226.4					247.9	112.1	s. eth., bz.	Whale oil
34		9-Hexadecenoic	C₁₆H₃₀O₂	254.4	-1		0.9018^{20}	1.4549^{20}	220.5	99.8	s. al., eth.	Butter fat, whale oil
35	Palmitoleic	9-Hexadecenoic	C₁₆H₃₀O₂	254.4					220.5	99.8	s. al., eth.	Marine oils, milk fat
36	Petroselenic	6-Octadecenoic	C₁₈H₃₄O₂	282.5	32-33	$237\text{-}238^{18}$	0.8824^{35}	1.4535^{47}	198.6	89.9	s. acet., me. al., eth.	Parsley seed oil
37	Oleic	9-Octadecenoic	C₁₈H₃₄O₂	282.5		200-201.2	0.8952^{0}	1.4582^{320}	198.6	89.9	s. acet., me. al., eth.	Olive oil, pork fat
38	Vaccenic	11-Octadecenoic	C₁₈H₃₄O₂	282.5	6-10				198.6	89.9	s. acet., me. al.	Butter fat, mutton fat
39	Gadoleic	9-Eicosenoic	C₂₀H₃₈O₂	310.5					180.7	81.8	s. al.	Sperm oil, cod-liver oil
40		11-Eicosenoic	C₂₀H₃₈O₂	310.5	50	267^{15}			180.7	81.8	s. al.	Jajoba oil
41	Cetoleic	11-Docosenoic	C₂₂H₄₂O₂	338.6					165.7	75	v. s. al., eth.	Marine oils
42	Erucic	13-Docosenoic	C₂₂H₄₂O₂	338.6	33.5	$241\text{-}243^{5}$			165.7	75.0	s. eth., al., acet.	Mustardseed oil
43	Selacholeic	15-Tetracosenoic	C₂₄H₄₆O₂	366.6	42.5-43				153.0	69.2	s. eth., chl., bz., pet. eth.	Shark liver oil
44	Ximenic	17-Hexacosenoic	C₂₆H₅₀O₂	394.7					142.2	64.3	s. eth., chl., bz., pet. eth.	Tallow wood
45	Lumequeic	21-Triacontenoic	C₃₀H₅₈O₂	450.8					124.5	56.3	s. eth., chl., bz., pet. eth.	Tallow wood
						Unsaturated Fatty Acids (Polyethenoid)						
46	Linoleic	9,12-Octadecadienoic	C₁₈H₃₂O₂	280.4	-5.0 to -5.2	$20.2^{1.4}$	0.9038^{18}	$1.4715^{11.5}$	200.1	181.0	s. acet., me. al., eth.	Soybean oil, linseed oil
47	Hiragonic	6,10,14-Hexadecatrienoic	C₁₆H₂₆O₂	250.4			0.9324^{15}	1.4876^{15}	224.1	304.2	s. acet., al., eth., pet. eth.	Sardine oil
48	Linolenic	9,12,15-Octadecatrienoic	C₁₈H₃₀O₂	278.4	-14.4 to -14.5	$157\text{-}158^{0.001}$	0.9046^{20}	1.4780^{20}	201.5	273.5	s. acet., al., eth., pet. eth.	Linseed oil, hempseed oil
49	Elaeostearic	9,11,13-Octadecatrienoic	C₁₈H₃₀O₂	278.4	48	235^{12}		1.5112^{50}	201.5	273.5	v. s. eth.; s. al., CS₂	Tung oil, esang seed oil
50	Moroctic	4,8,12,15-Octadecatetraenoic	C₁₈H₂₈O₂	276.4			0.9334^{15}	1.4930^{15}	203.0	372.6	s. acet., al., eth., pet. eth.	Sardine oil
51	Parinaric	9,11,13,15-Octadecatetraenoic	C₁₈H₂₈O₂	276.4	85-6			1.4930^{15}	203.0	367.3	s. pet. eth., eth.	"Akarittom" seed fat

Unsaturated Fatty Acids (Polyethenoid) (Concluded)

No.	Common name	Systematic name	Formula	Mol. wt.	M.p.	B.p.	d	n	Neut. val.	Iodine val.	Solubility	Source
52	Arachidonic	5,8,11,14-Eicosa-tetraenoic	$C_{20}H_{32}O_2$	304.5	-49.5			1.4824[20]	184.3	333.5	s. acet., me. al.	Glandular organs, liver lipids
53	Timnodonic	4,8,12,15,18-Eicosa-pentaenoic	$C_{20}H_{30}O_2$	302.4					185.5	419.7	s. eth., chl., bz., pet. eth.	Sardine oil
54	Clupanodonic	4,8,12,15,19-Docosa-pentaenoic	$C_{22}H_{34}O_2$	330.5	-78			1.5039[15]	169.8	384.0	s. acet., eth.	Herring oil, cod-liver oil
55	Nisinic	4,8,12,15,18,21-Tetracosahexaenoic	$C_{24}H_{36}O_2$	356.5			0.938[15]		157.4	427.2	s. eth., chl., bz., pet. eth.	Sardine oil, cod-liver oil

Hydroxy- and Keto-fatty Acids

No.	Common name	Systematic name	Formula	Mol. wt.	M.p.	B.p.	d	n	Neut. val.	Iodine val.	Solubility	Source
56	Sabinic	12-Hydroxy-dodecanoic	$C_{12}H_{24}O_3$	216.2	84				259.5		s. al., h. bz.	Juniper wax
57	Ipurolic	3,11-Dihydroxy-tetradecanoic	$C_{14}H_{28}O_4$	260.2	100-101				215.6		s. eth., chl.	Japanese morning glory seed
58	Convolvulinolic	11-Hydroxy-pentadecanoic	$C_{15}H_{30}O_3$	258.2	63.5-64				217.3		s. eth., pet. eth., chl., al.	Convolvulin resin
59	Jalapinolic	11-Hydroxy-hexadecanoic	$C_{16}H_{32}O_3$	272.3	68-69				206.0		s. eth., al., pet. eth.	Jalap-root wax
60	Juniperic	16-Hydroxy-hexadecanoic	$C_{16}H_{32}O_3$	272.3	95				206.0		s. bz., eth., al.	Conifer waxes
61	Dihydroxystearic	9,10-Dihydroxy-octadecanoic	$C_{18}H_{36}O_4$	316.5	cis 95 / trans 132				177.3		s. eth., h. w., al. (cis); pet. eth., h. al (trans)	Castor oil
62	Phellonic	2-Hydroxy-docosanoic	$C_{22}H_{44}O_3$	356.6	88-91				157.3		s. chl., eth., acet., pyr., glac. acet. a.	Cork, subein, brain lipids
63	Cerebronic	2-Hydroxy-tetracosanoic	$C_{24}H_{48}O_3$	384.6	99.5-100.5				145.9		s. eth., pyr., acet., h. al.	Brain lipids
64	Hydroxycerotic	2-Hydroxy-hexacosanoic	$C_{26}H_{52}O_3$	412.7	86.5				135.9		s. eth., acet., pyr., glac. acet. a.	Brain lipids
65	Lactarinic	6-Keto-octadecanoic	$C_{18}H_{34}O_3$	298.4	86				188.0		s. h. al, eth., chl.	Lactarius mushrooms
66	Ricinoleic	12-Hydroxy-9-octadecenoic	$C_{18}H_{34}O_3$	298.4	5.5		0.940[27.4]	1.4716[20]	188.0	170.1	s. acet., pet. eth.	Castor oil
67	Hydroxynervonic	2-Hydroxy-9-tetracosenoic	$C_{24}H_{46}O_3$	382.6					146.6	66.3	s. eth., chl., bz.	Brain lipids

Branched Chain and Cyclic Fatty Acids

No.	Common name	Systematic name	Formula	Mol. wt.	M.p.	B.p.	d	n	Neut. val.	Iodine val.	Solubility	Source
68	Isobutyric	2-Methyl propanoic	$C_4H_8O_2$	88.1	-46	155	0.9529[6.15]	1.3964[15]	636.8		s. al., pet. eth.	Dolphin oil
69	Isovaleric	3-Methyl butanoic	$C_5H_{10}O_2$	102.1	-51	176.7	0.937[15]	1.40178[22.4]	549.34		s. w., al., chl., eth.	Dolphin oil
70	Isopalmitic	14-Methyl penta-decanoic	$C_{16}H_{32}O_2$	256.4	62.4				218.79		s. acet., pet. eth.	
71	Isostearic	16-Methyl hepta-decanoic	$C_{18}H_{36}O_2$	284.5	69.5				197.22		s. eth., pet. eth.	
72	Tuberculostearic	10-Methyl octa-decanoic	$C_{19}H_{38}O_2$	298.5	10-11		0.8771[25]	1.4512[25]	187.95		s. eth., al., acet.	Wax of tubercle bacilli
73	Phytomonic		$C_{20}H_{40}O_2$	312.5	24				179.5		s. eth., al.	Crown gall bacilli
74	Phthioic		$C_{26}H_{52}O_2$	396.7	20-21		0.8763[25]	1.4628[25]	141.5		s. acet., eth.	Tubercle bacilli
75	Mycocerosic		$C_{30}H_{60}O_2$	452	27-28			1.4532[40]	124.1		s. eth., chl.	Tubercle wax
76	Mycolic		$C_{88}H_{172}O_4$	1294.2	54-56				43.35		s. eth.	Human tubercle bacilli
77	Hydnocarpic	11-(2-Cyclo-pentenyl)-undecanoic	$C_{16}H_{28}O_2$	252.4	59-60	247-248[20]			222.3	100.6	s. pet. eth., al., chl.	Chaulmoogra oil
78	Chaulmoogric	13-(2-Cyclo-pentenyl)-tridecanoic	$C_{18}H_{32}O_2$	280.4	68.0-.5				200.1	90.5	s. acet., chl., eth.	Chaulmoogra oil
79	Gorlic	13-(2-Cyclopentenyl)-6-tridecanoic	$C_{18}H_{30}O_2$	278.4	6(liq)	232.5	0.9436[25]	1.4782[25]	201.5	182.5	s. acet.	Chaulmoogra oil
80	Tariric	6-Octadecynoic	$C_{18}H_{32}O_2$	280.4	liquid				200.06	181.0	s. h. al.	

/1/ *=freezing point. /2/ At atmospheric pressure (760 mm of mercury) unless otherwise indicated by specific pressure in superscript. /3/ At temperature indicated in superscript. /4/ Refractive index (n) is given for the sodium D-line at temperature shown in superscript. /5/ mg KOH required to neutralize one g of acid. /6/ Grams of iodine absorbed by 100 g of acid. /7/ a. = acid; acet. = acetone; acet. a. = acetic acid; al. = alcohol; bz. = benzene; chl. = chloroform; eth. = ether; glac. = glacial; h. = hot; me. = methyl; pet. = petroleum; pyr. = pyridine; s. = soluble; sl. = slightly; v. = very; w. = water.

12. FATS AND OILS: PHYSICAL AND CHEMICAL CHARACTERISTICS

Values are considered typical rather than average, and frequently represent specific analyses for particular samples (especially in the case of the constituent fatty acids). Extreme variations may occur, depending on a number of variables, such as source, treatment, and age of a fat or oil.

Constituent Fatty Acids are given in g/100 g total fatty acids. Constants columns: Melting or *Solidification Point (°C); Specific Gravity or *Density 15°/15°C[1]; Refractive Index n 40°C[2]/d; Iodine Value; Saponification Value.

No.	Fat or Oil	M.P. (°C)	Sp. Gr.[1]	Refr. Index[2]	Iodine Value	Sapon. Value	Caproic	Caprylic	Capric	Lauric	Myristic	Palmitic	Stearic	Arachidic	Palmitoleic	Oleic	Linoleic	Linolenic	C20 Polyeth.	C22 Polyeth.	Others
	Vegetable Fats and Oils																				
1	Babassu oil (Attalea funifera)	22–26	*0.893^{60}	1.4436	15.5	247	0.2	4.8	6.6	44.1	15.4	8.5	2.7	0.2		16.1	1.4				
2	Castor oil (Ricinus communis)	*-18.0	0.961	1.4770	85.5	180.3										7.4	3.1				+3
3	Cocoa butter (Theobroma cacao)	34.1	0.964	1.4568	36.5	193.8						24.4	35.4			38.1	2.1				
4	Coconut oil (Cocos nucifera)	25.1	0.924	1.4493	10.4	268	0.8	5.4	8.4	45.4	18.0	10.5	2.3	0.4[4]	0.4	7.5	Trace				
5	Corn oil (Zea mays)	*-20.0	0.922	1.4734	122.6	192.0					1.4	10.2	1.1		1.5	49.6	34.3				
6	Cottonseed oil (Gossypium hirsutum)	*-1.0	$0.917^{25/25}$	1.4735	105.7	194.3					1.4	23.4	1.3		2.0	22.9	47.8				+5
7	Linseed oil (Linum usitatissimum)	*-24.0	0.938	1.4782^{25}	178.7	190.3						6.3	2.5			19.0	24.1	47.4			+8
8	Mustard oil (Brassica alba)		0.9145^{6}	1.4756	102.6	174.6					1.3[7]	14.1[7]	24.0[7]	0.8[7]		27.2[7]	16.6[7]	1.8[7]			
9	Neem oil (Azadirachta indica)	-3	0.9176	1.4615	71.6	194.5[6]					2.6[7]	8.2[7]	4.8[7]	0.5[7]		58.5[7]	30.3[7]				
10	Nigerseed oil (Guizotia abysinica)		0.9256	1.4716	128.5[6]	190.6					3.3[7]	11.3[9]					57.3[7]				
11	Oiticica oil (Licania rigida)		$0.974^{25/25}$		140–180											6.2					+10
12	Olive oil (Olea Europaea sativa)	*-6.0	0.918	1.4679	81.1	189.7					Trace	6.9	2.3	0.1		84.4	4.6				
13	Palm oil (Elaeis guineesis)	35.0	0.915	1.4578	54.2	199.1					1.4	40.1	5.5			42.7	10.3				
14	Palm kernel oil (E. guineesis)	24.1	0.923	1.4569	37.0	219.9		2.7	7.0	46.9	14.1	8.3	1.3			18.5	0.7				
15	Peanut oil (Arachis hypogaea)	*3.0	0.914	1.4691	93.4	192.1						8.3	3.1	2.4		56.0	26.0				+11
16	Perilla oil (Perilla ocimioides)	*-15	*0.935^{15}	1.4812^{25}	195	192						9.6				17.8		17.5			
17	Poppyseed oil (Papaver somniferum)		0.9255	1.4685	135.5	194.5						4.8[7]	2.9[7]			30.1[7]	62.2[7]	1			
18	Rapeseed oil (Brassica campestris)	*-10	0.915	1.4706	98.6	174.7										32	15	6.5			+12
19	Safflowerseed oil (Carthamus tintorius)		*0.900^{60}	1.4626	145	192						6.8[9]				18.6	70.1				
20	Sesame oil (Sesamum indicum)	*-6.0	$0.919^{25/25}$	1.4646	106.6	187.9						9.1	4.3	0.8	0.4	45.4	40.4				
21	Soybean oil (Soja hispida)	*-16.0	0.927	1.4729	130.0	190.6				0.2	0.1	9.8	2.4	0.9		28.9	50.7	3.4			+13
22	Sunflowerseed oil (Helianthus annuus)	*-17.0	0.923	1.4694	125.5	188.7						5.6	2.2			25.1	66.2				
23	Tung oil (Aleurites fordii)	*-2.5	0.934	1.5174^{25}	168.2	193.1						4.6[9]	16.0[9]			4.1	0.6				+14
24	Wheat germ oil (Triticum vulgare)				125											28.1	52.3	3.6			
	Land-animal Fats and Oils																				
25	Butter fat	32.2	$0.911^{40/15}$	1.4548	36.1	227	2.0	0.5	2.3	2.5	11.1	29.0	9.2		4.6	26.7	3.6				+15
26	Human depot fat	*15	0.918	1.4602	67.6	196.2					2.7	24.0	8.4		5	46.9	10.2				+16
27	Lard oil	*30.5	$0.910^{25/25}$	1.4615	58.6	194.6					1.3	28.3	11.9		2.7	47.5	6				+17
28	Neatsfoot oil			1.464^{25}	69–76	190–199						17–18	2–3			74–76					
29	Tallow, beef			1.4565	49.5	197					6.3	27.4	14.1			49.6	2.5				
30	Tallow, mutton	*42.0	0.945		40	194					4.6	24.6	30.5			36.0	4.3				
	Marine-animal Fats and Oils																				
31	Cod liver oil (Gadus morrhua)		0.925^{25}	1.481^{25}	165	186					5.8	8.4	0.6		20.0	29.1[8]		20.7	25.4	9.6	
32	Herring oil (Clupea harengus)		0.900^{60}	1.4610^{60}	140	192					7.3	13.0	Trace		4.9			29.6	30.1	23.2	
33	Menhaden oil (Brevoortia tyrannus)		0.903^{60}	1.4645^{60}	170	191					5.9	16.3	0.6		15.5				19.0	11.7	+19
34	Sardine oil (Sardinops caerulea)		0.905^{60}	1.4660^{60}	185	191					5.1	14.6	3.2	0.6	11.8				18.1	14.0	+20
35	Sperm oil, body (Physeter macrocephalus)				76–88	122–130				1	5	6.5			26.5	37	19				+21
36	Sperm oil, head (P. macrocephalus)				70	140–144				16	14	2			15	17	6.5			1	+22
37	Whale oil (Balaena mysticetus)		0.892^{60}	1.460^{60}	120	195			3.5	0.2	9.3	15.6	2.8		14.4	35.2			13.6	5.9	+23

/1/ Underlined superscripts indicate temperature at which density was determined, or, for specific gravity, the temperature of measurement referred to that of water at the indicated temperature; where no superscript appears, the sp. gr. is that calculated to 15°C referred to water at 15°C. /2/ Underlined superscripts indicate temperature of measurement, if other than 40°C. /3/ Contains 87% ricinoleic acid. /4/ Includes behenic and lignoceric acid. /5/ Behenic, 0.2. /6/ Calculated from reported range. /7/ % by weight. /8/ Behenic, 1.1; lignoceric, 1.0; erucic, 51.0. /9/ Includes behenic acid. /10/ Licanic, 82.5. /11/ Licanic, 3.1; lignoceric, 3.1; Behenic, 3.1. /12/ Eleostearic, 90.7. /13/ C_{14} monoethenoic, 0.1. /14/ Eleostearic, 50. /15/ Butyric, 3.6; decenoic, 0.1; C_{12} monoethenoic, 0.1; C_{14} monoethenoic, 0.9; gadoleic plus erucic, 1.4. /16/ Gadoleic plus erucic, 2.5. /17/ C_{14} monoethenoic, 0.2; gadoleic plus erucic, 2.1. /18/ Oleic plus linoleic, 2.5. /19/ Behenic, 0.8. /20/ C_{14} monoethenoic, trace; C_{14} polyethenoic, 15.4. /21/ C_{14} monoethenoic, 4; gadoleic, 19. /22/ C_{12} monoethenoic, 15.4. /23/ C_{24} polyethenoic, 2.5; C_{24} polyethenoic, 0.2.

13. WAXES: PHYSICAL AND CHEMICAL CHARACTERISTICS

	Wax	Melting Point °C	Refractive Index n_D^{+1}	Specific Gravity or Density* 15°/15°C[2]	Iodine Value	Acid Value	Saponification Number
1	Alcocer	67-79	1.455-1.463[85]	0.982-0.986*[15]	14.4-20.4	12.7-18.1	35-86
2	Bamboo leaf	79-80		0.961*[25]	7.8[3]	14.5	43.4
3	Bayberry (Myrtle)	41-53	1.436-1.446[80]	0.981-0.991*[15]	1.0-3.9	2.5-4.5	205-217
4	Beeswax, crude	62-67	1.439-1.453[80]	0.927-0.970	6.8-16.4[4]	16-25	85-100
5	Beeswax, white, U.S.P.	61-70	1.447-1.465[65]	0.959-0.975*[15.5]	7-11	17-24	85-109
6	Beeswax, yellow	62-65	1.442-1.449[65]	0.923-0.970	3.4-11	19-22	85-106
7	Candelilla	70-75	1.454-1.463[85]	0.945-0.996	5.2-32.8	15-25	46.7-59.7
8	Caranday	80-85		0.990[25]	8.0-8.9	5-9.5	64.5-78.5
9	Carnauba	82-85	1.467-1.472[40]	0.990-1.001	7.2-13	6-15	65-90
10	Castor oil, hydrogenated	83-88		0.980-0.990*[20]	2.5-8.5	1-5	83-88
11	Chinese insect	80.5-84	1.4566-1.4568[40]	0.932-0.970	1.4	0.2-1.5	70-93
12	Cotton	70-79		0.957-0.998[25]	11-24.5	21-32	109-180
13	Cranberry	194-218		0.970-1.010*[15]	44.2-57.4	42.1-69.3	85-134
14	Douglasfir	61-63		1.050[20]	27.8-62.5	58.6-80.1	160-210
15	Esparto	67.5-81		0.987-0.989	18-22	22.7-23.9	69.8-79.3
16	Fiber	61-80.5		0.968-0.988	11-23	10.6-34	61-79
17	Flax	65-75		0.908-0.985	25-35	12-25	65-85
18	Ghedda	60.4-66.4	1.440[80]	0.956-0.973	4.8-11.4[5]	3.5-10.5	86-130
19	Japan	48.5-54.5		0.975-0.993	4.5-12.8	6-20	206-237
20	Jojoba	11.2-11.8	1.465[25]	0.864-0.899	81.7-83.4[4]	0.23-0.57	99.2-95.0
21	Madagascar	88.0			3.2-5.9	17.7-28.0	140-159
22	Montan, crude	73-82		1.01-1.02*[25]	14-18	40-60	90-110
23	Montan, refined	80-86		1.01-1.03*[25]	10-14	40-60	90-110
24	Ouricury	81-86		0.998-1.069	6.2-23.8	12-20	80-100
25	Ozocerite, refined	73-75		0.907-0.920			
26	Palm	74-86		0.991-1.045*[15]	8.9-16.9[4]	5.0-10.6	64.5-104
27	Paraffin, American	49-63	1.422-1.448[80]	0.897-0.915*[14]			
28	Rice bran	75-83			8-19.4	15-17	57-104
29	Shellac	79-82		0.971-0.980	1.3-8.8[3]	0-2[6]	37-50[7]
30	Sisal hemp	74-81		1.007-1.010	22.3-33.3[4]	16-22.2	56-86.3
31	Sorghum	77-82			15.7-20.9	10-16	16-44
32	Spermaceti	42-50	1.440[70]	0.905-0.960	3.0-5.9	0-6.0	108-135
33	Sperm, body	3-46	1.462[30]	0.880-0.883	81-84	1.2	123-133
34	Sugarcane, crude	52-70		0.961-0.998[25]	10-40	8-45	50-120
35	Sugarcane, cuticle	74-81.5			8-15.6	7-24	24-57
36	Sugarcane, commercial	76-82	1.4435[90]	0.983[25]	8-20	8-23	55-106
37	Wool, refined	36-55	1.478-1.482[40]	0.904-0.945	15-47[3]	5-22	82-140

/1/ Superscripts indicate temperature at which measurement was made. /2/ For specific gravity, superscripts indicate temperature of measurement referred to that of water at the indicated temperature; where no superscript appears, the sp.gr. is that calculated to 15°C referred to water at 15°C. For density, superscripts indicate temperature at which determination was made. /3/ Wijs test. /4/ Hanus test. /5/ Hubl test. /6/ A range of 12-24.3 has been reported. /7/ A range of 64-126 has been reported.

14. PHOSPHATIDES, CEREBROSIDES, AND RELATED LIPIDS: PHYSICAL AND CHEMICAL CHARACTERISTICS

	Lipid	Formula	Melting Point °C	Specific Rotation[1] $[\alpha]_D$	Iodine Value	Solubility[1]
	Phosphatides					
1	Lecithins	$C_{10}H_{20}NPO_9RR'$		5.5-6.0 in chl.	33-127	v.s. al., eth., chl., bz., pet. eth., c. tet., c. disf.; i. actn., me. acet., par.
2	Lysolecithin	$C_9H_{21}NPO_8R$	100	-2.6 in chl.		v.s. al., eth., chl., pyr.; i. w., actn.
3	Cephalin (phosphatidyl-ethanolamine)	$C_7H_{12}NPO_8RR'$	174	13.6 in pet. eth.	40-80	v.s. chl., bz., pet. eth., c. disf., ac.a.; i. al., eth., acetn.
4	Phosphatidic acids	$C_5H_7PO_8RR'$				v.s. eth., actn., m. f. solv.; sl. s. w.
5	Cardiolipin	$C_5H_7PO_8RR'$(?)		5.8 in al.	99.8-126	v.s. al., actn., m. f. solv.; i. w.
6	Sphingomyelins	$C_{47}H_{97}N_2PO_7$	196-198	13.8 in pyr.	30.7	sl. s. al., pyr.; i. eth., actn.
7	Sphingosine	$C_{18}H_{37}NO_2$				v.s. al., actn.; sl. s. eth., pet. eth.; i. w.
8	Dihydrosphingosine	$C_{18}H_{39}NO_2$	60-61			
9	Lignocerylsphingosine	$C_{42}H_{83}NO_3$	156-157			v.s. eth., actn.
10	Plasmalogens	$C_5H_{12}NPO_6R$				v.s. chl., aq. KOH; sl. s. al., eth., pet. eth., actn.; i. w.
	Cerebrosides					
11	Cerasine	$C_{48}H_{93}NO_8$	180-187	-2.5 to -9 in pyr.	31.3	v.s. pyr.; sl. s. al., chl., bz., e. acet., ac. a., actn.; i. eth., pet. eth., w.
12	Phrenosine	$C_{49}H_{94}NO_9$	212	3.7 in pyr.	30.7	v.s. pyr.; sl. s. al., chl., bz., e. acet. ac. a., actn.; i. eth., pet. eth., w.
13	Nervone	$C_{48}H_{91}NO_8$	180	-4.3 in pyr.	62.7	v.s. chl., bz., e. acet., ac. a., actn., pyr.; sl. s. al., i. eth., pet. eth., w.
14	Cerebronyl-N-sphingosine	$C_{42}H_{83}NO_4$	83-84		38.8	v.s. al., eth., actn.; i.w.
15	Dihydropsychosine	$C_{24}H_{49}NO_7$				v.s. al., actn.; i. eth., pet. eth., w.
16	Ganglioside	$C_{64}H_{118}N_2O_{26}$		-2.8 in pyr.		v.s. mixt. of chl. or bz. with al.; sl. s. al.; i. eth., e. acet., actn.
17	Pyschosine	$C_{26}H_{47}NO_7$	215			v.s. al.; i. eth., pet. eth.

/1/ ac. a.=acetic acid; actn.=acetone; al.=alcohol; aq. KOH=aqueous KOH; bz.=benzene; c. disf.=carbon disulfide; c. tet.=carbon tetrachloride; chl.=chloroform; e. acet.=ethyl acetate; eth.=ether; i.=insoluble; me. acet.=methyl acetate; m. f. solv.=most fat solvents; par.=paraldehyde; pet.=petroleum; pyr.=pyridine; sl.=slightly; s.=soluble; v.=very; w.=water.

15. STEROLS: PHYSICAL AND CHEMICAL CHARACTERISTICS

Part I: ANIMAL STEROLS (ZOOSTEROLS)

	Common Name	Systematic Name[1]	Empirical Formula	Melting Point °C	Specific Rotation[2] $[a]_D$	Source
	Vertebrate Sterols					
1	Cholesterol[3]	Δ^{5}-Cholesten-3β-ol	$C_{27}H_{46}O$	149	-39	All animal cells; spinal cord; wool grease.
2	7-Dehydrocholesterol[4]	$\Delta^{5,7}$-Cholestadien-3β-ol	$C_{27}H_{44}O$	148	-114	Cholesterol; skin of swine; snail.
3	7α-Hydroxycholesterol	Δ^{5}-Cholestene-3β,7α-diol	$C_{27}H_{46}O_2$	157	-88	Sclerotic aorta; serum (pregnant mare).
4	7β-Hydroxycholesterol	Δ^{5}-Cholestene-3β,7β-diol	$C_{27}H_{46}O_2$	178	+7.2	Liver (cattle; swine); serum (pregnant mare).
5	7-Ketocholesterol	Δ^{5}-Cholesten-3β-ol-7-one	$C_{27}H_{44}O_2$	157	-104	Testes (cattle; swine).
6	Dicholesteryl ether		$C_{54}H_{90}O$	196	-38	Spinal cord.
7		$\Delta^{3,5}$-Cholestadien-7-one	$C_{27}H_{42}O$	112	-305	Testes (swine); sclerotic aorta; spleen (swine).
8		$\Delta^{4,6}$-Cholestadien-3-one	$C_{27}H_{42}O$	80	+35	Sclerotic aorta; spleen (swine).
9	Cholestanol[3]	Cholestan-3β-ol	$C_{27}H_{48}O$	142	+24	Cholesterol; sclerotic aorta.
10		Cholestane-3,6-dione	$C_{27}H_{44}O_2$	175		Testes (swine).
11		Cholestan-3β-ol-6-one	$C_{27}H_{46}O_2$	143		Spleen (swine).
12		Cholestane-3β,5α,6β-triol	$C_{27}H_{48}O_3$	239	+3.2	Liver (cattle); testes (swine); sclerotic aorta.
13		Cholestane-3β,5α-diol-6-one	$C_{27}H_{46}O_3$	225		Cholesterol; liver (swine).
14		Δ^{4}-Cholesten-3-one	$C_{27}H_{44}O$	81	+89	Feces; hypophysis, testes (swine).
15		Δ^{4}-Cholestene-3β,6β-diol	$C_{27}H_{46}O_2$	258	+9.0	Spleen (swine).
16	Coprostanol	Coprostan-3β-ol	$C_{27}H_{48}O$	101	+28	Feces.
17	Epicoprostanol	Coprostan-3α-ol	$C_{27}H_{48}O$	117	+32	Feces; ambergris.
18		Coprostan-3-one	$C_{27}H_{46}O$	63	+36	Ambergris.
19	Lathosterol[3]	Δ^{7}-Cholesten-3β-ol	$C_{27}H_{46}O$	122	+5.7	Skin; cholesterol.
	Invertebrate Sterols					
20	Aptostanol		$C_{28}H_{50}O$	135	+22	Sponge.
21	Chalinasterol[5]	$\Delta^{5,22}$-24-iso-Ergostadien-3β-ol	$C_{28}H_{46}O$	144	-42	Sponge; oyster.
22	Clionasterol	Δ^{5}-24-iso-Stigmasten-3β-ol(?)	$C_{29}H_{50}O$	138	-37	Sponge.
23	Corbisterol	$\Delta^{5,7,22}$-Stigmastadien-3β-ol	$C_{29}H_{46}O$	151	-106	Corbicula leana.
24	Haliclonasterol		$C_{28}H_{48}O$	141	-41.5	Sponge.
25	Neospongosterol	Δ^{22}-24-iso-Ergosten-3β-ol	$C_{28}H_{48}O$	153	+10	Sponge.
26	Palysterol		$C_{29}H_{50}O$	140	-47	Sea anemone.
27	Poriferasterol	$\Delta^{5,22}$-24-iso-Stigmastadien-3β-ol	$C_{29}H_{48}O$	156	-49	Sponge.

/1/ The numbers after the symbol Δ indicate the position of double bonds in the basic cyclopentenoperhydrophenanthrene ring. /2/ Chloroform solvent for most determinations. /3/ Also isolated from invertebrates. /4/ Provitamin D_3. /5/ Possibly identical with ostreasterol.

Part II: PLANT STEROLS (PHYTOSTEROLS)

	Common Name	Systematic Name[1]	Empirical Formula	Melting Point °C	Specific Rotation[2] $[a]_D$	Source
1	Δ^{5}-Avenasterol	$\Delta^{5,11}$(?)-Stigmastadien-3β-ol	$C_{29}H_{48}O$	137	-37.6	Oats.
2	Δ^{7}-Avenasterol	$\Delta^{7,11}$(?)-Stigmastadien-3β-ol	$C_{29}H_{48}O$	145	+8.8	Oats.
3	Brassicasterol	Δ^{5}-24-iso-Ergosten-3β-ol	$C_{28}H_{46}O$	148	-64	Rapeseed; mussel.
4	Campesterol	Δ^{5}-24-iso-stigmasten-3β-ol	$C_{28}H_{48}O$	158	-33	Rapeseed; soybean; wheat germ.
5	Ergostanol	Ergostan-3β-ol	$C_{28}H_{50}O$	143	+16	
6	β-Sitosterol	Δ^{5}-Stigmasten-3β-ol	$C_{29}H_{50}O$	140	-36	Cottonseed; calycanthus seed; cinchona bark; wheat germ; rubber.
7	γ-Sitosterol	Δ^{5}-24-iso-Stigmasten-3β-ol	$C_{29}H_{50}O$	148	-43	Soybean; wheat germ; rye germ.
8	Dihydrositosterol	Stigmastan-3β-ol	$C_{29}H_{52}O$	140	+25	Grains.
9	α-Spinasterol	$\Delta^{7,22}$-Stigmastadien-3β-ol	$C_{29}H_{48}O$	175	-2.7	Spinach; senega root; alfalfa; colocynth.
10		Δ^{7}-Stigmasten-3β-ol	$C_{29}H_{50}O$	145	+9	Wheat germ.
11	Stigmasterol	$\Delta^{5,22}$-Stigmastadien-3β-ol	$C_{29}H_{48}O$	170	-51	Calabar bean; soybean.
	Mycosterols					
12	Ascosterol	$\Delta^{8,23}$(?)-Ergostadien-3β-ol	$C_{28}H_{46}O$	147	+45	Yeast.
13	Cerevisterol	$\Delta^{7,22}$-Ergostadiene-3β,5α,6β-triol	$C_{28}H_{46}O_3$	254	-79	Yeast; ergot.
14	Chondrillasterol		$C_{29}H_{48}O$	168	-1.1	Green algae; sponge.
15	Episterol	$\Delta^{7,24(28}$?)-Ergostadien-3β-ol	$C_{28}H_{46}O$	151	-5	Yeast.
16	Ergosterol[3]	$\Delta^{5,7,22}$-Ergostatrien-3β-ol	$C_{28}H_{44}O$	165	-130	Ergot; yeast; Aspergillus niger.
17	Dehydroergosterol	$\Delta^{5,7,9(11),22}$-Ergostatetraen-3β-ol	$C_{28}H_{42}O$	146	+149	Yeast; ergot.
18	5-Dihydroergosterol	$\Delta^{7,22}$-Ergostadien-3β-ol	$C_{28}H_{46}O$	174	-20	Yeast.
19	Fecosterol	$\Delta^{8,24(28}$?)-Ergostadien-3β-ol	$C_{28}H_{46}O$	162	+42	Yeast.
20	Fucosterol	$\Delta^{5,24(28)}$-Stigmastadien-3β-ol	$C_{29}H_{48}O$	124	-38	Brown algae.
21	Fungisterol	Δ^{7}-Ergosten-3β-ol	$C_{28}H_{48}O$	148	-0.2	Ergot.
22	Zymosterol	$\Delta^{8,24}$-Cholestadien-3β-ol	$C_{27}H_{44}O$	108	+47	Yeast.

/1/ The numbers after the symbol Δ indicate the position of double bonds in the basic cyclopentenoperhydrophenanthrene ring. /2/ Chloroform solvent for most determinations. /3/ Provitamin D_2.

16. BILE ACIDS: PHYSICAL AND CHEMICAL CHARACTERISTICS

Part I: 24-CARBON ACIDS[1]

	Acid	Empirical Formula	Hydroxyl Groups	Melting Point °C	Specific Rotation $[\alpha]_D$	Sources
1	Bufodesoxycholic acid[2]	$C_{24}H_{40}O_4$				Toad.
2	Chenodesoxycholic acid	$C_{24}H_{40}O_4$	3α, 7α	140	+11	Man, coypu, guinea pig, ox, sheep, chicken, duck, goose, turkey, fish.
3	Cholic acid[3]	$C_{24}H_{40}O_5$	3α, 7α, 12α	196-198	+37	Man, antelope, bear, goat, ox, sheep, other mammals, duck, turkey, reptiles, salamander, fish.
4	Desoxycholic acid	$C_{24}H_{40}O_4$	3α, 12α	176-177	+53	Man, antelope, deer, dog, goat, ox, rabbit, other mammals, salamander.
5	3α,12α-Dihydroxy-7-keto-cholanic acid	$C_{24}H_{38}O_5$	3α, 12α	263-264		Ox, snake.
6	7α,12α-Dihydroxy-3-keto-cholanic acid	$C_{24}H_{38}O_5$	7α, 12α	181-182, ethyl ester		Ox.
7	3α-Hydroxy-$\Delta^{8(14)}$-cholenic acid	$C_{24}H_{38}O_3$	3α	160	+71	Chicken.
8	3α-Hydroxy-6-ketoallo-cholanic acid	$C_{24}H_{38}O_4$	3α	194		Swine.
9	3α-Hydroxy-7-ketocholanic acid ("nutriacholic acid")	$C_{24}H_{38}O_4$	3α	201-203	-27	Coypu, guinea pig.
10	3α-Hydroxy-12-ketocholanic acid	$C_{24}H_{38}O_4$	3α	164-165	+110	Ox.
11	"α"-Hyodesoxycholic acid	$C_{24}H_{40}O_4$	3α, 6α	196-197	+8	Boar, swine.
12	"β"-Hyodesoxycholic acid	$C_{24}H_{40}O_4$	3β, 6α	189-190	+5	Swine.
13	3-Keto-$\Delta^{4,6}$-choladienic acid	$C_{24}H_{34}O_3$		150-152		Chicken.
14	"α"-Lagodesoxycholic acid	$C_{24}H_{40}O_4$	3, 12(?)	156-157	+80	Rabbit.
15	"β"-Lagodesoxycholic acid	$C_{24}H_{40}O_4$		213	+37	Rabbit.
16	Lithocholic acid	$C_{24}H_{40}O_3$	3α	184-186	+32	Man, ox, rabbit.
17	"β"-Phocaecholic acid	$C_{24}H_{40}O_5$	3, 7, 23(?)	222-223	+27	Seal, walrus.
18	Pythocholic acid	$C_{24}H_{40}O_5$	3α, 12, 16 or 15(?)	186-187	+28, methyl ester	Snake (Boidae)
19	Ursodesoxycholic acid	$C_{24}H_{40}O_4$	3α, 7β	203	+57	Coypu, bear.

/1/ Derivatives of cholanic acid, possibly excluding Items 1 and 15 (unknown structure) and Item 8 (possible allomerization product). /2/ Not crystallized. /3/ Conjugates with glycine and taurine; glycocholic and taurocholic acids are bile acids most commonly found in man.

Part II: 27-AND 28-CARBON ACIDS[1]

	Acid	Empirical Formula	Hydroxyl Groups	Melting Point °C	Specific Rotation $[\alpha]_D$	Sources
1	Acid (unnamed)	$C_{27-28} \cdot H_{46-48}O_6$		255		Shark.
2	Sterocholic acid	$C_{28}H_{46}O_4$		256		Ox.
3	Tetrahydroxyisostero-cholanic acid	$C_{27-28} \cdot H_{46-48}O_6$		205		Turtle.
4	Tetrahydroxynorstero-cholanic acid	$C_{27}H_{46}O_6$	3α, 6α, 12, 24(?)	212-214	+27	Chicken, fish.
5	Tetrahydroxystero-cholanic acid	$C_{27-28} \cdot H_{46-48}O_6$	3α, 7α, 12α	150		Tortoise, turtle.
6	Trihydroxybufoisostero-cholenic acid	$C_{28}H_{40}O_5$	3α, 7α, 12α	227	+47	Toad.
7	Trihydroxybufostero-cholenic acid	$C_{28}H_{40}O_5$	3α, 7α, 12α	160	-13	Toad.
8	Trihydroxycoprostan-26-oic acid (originally "α"-trihydroxybisnorsterocholanic acid)	$C_{27}H_{46}O_5$	3α, 7α, 12α	172	+22	Crocodile, frog.
9	Trihydroxycoprostan-27-oic acid (originally "β"-trihydroxybisnorsterocholanic acid)	$C_{27}H_{46}O_5$	3α, 7α, 12α	195-196		Frog.
10	Varanic acid	$C_{27}H_{46}O_6$	3α, 7α, 12α	120		Lizard.

/1/ Only Items 8 and 9 are of completely determined structure.

#	Protein	Source	Unit Cell Dimensions (Å units), Space Group[1] (a b c β)	MW[2]	Method	Sedimentation Constant[3]	Partial Specific Volume[4]	Protein Crystal Density[5]	Isoelectric pH[6]
1	Actin, G-	Rabbit muscle		80,000	l	3.7			4.5
2	Adrenocorticotropic hormone	Sheep pituitary		20,000	sd	2.0	0.75[7]		4.6-4.7(0.1)
3	Aldolase	Rabbit muscle		147,000	sd(?)	7.9	0.740		8.5(0.0)
4	Amandin	Almond		208,000	e	11.4	0.746		
5	Amylase, α	Barley malt		60,000	o				6
6	Amylase, β	Sweetpotato		150,000	sd	8.9	0.749[7]		4.79(0.1)
7	Antitoxin, diphtheria	Horse plasma		180,000	sd	7.2	0.745[7]		6.0
8	Bence-Jones	Human urine[8]		36,000[9]	e;sd	3.55	0.749		4.3-4.7
9	Bushy stunt virus	Tomato[8]	386, I (cubic)	10,800,000	x	132	0.739		4.11(0.02)
10	Carbonic anhydrase	Beef blood		30,000	sd	2.8	0.749[7]		5.3(0.1)
11	Carboxypeptidase	Beef pancreas		33,000[10]	sd;vd	3.07	0.75[7]		6.0(0.2)
12	Cardiotoxin	Cobra venom		46,000	d		0.75[7]		
13	Casein (caseinogen)	Cow milk		33,600	o		0.728		4.6
14	Catalase	Human blood		220,000	s;a	11.2	0.73[7]		
15	Chorionic gonadotropin	Human urine[11]		100,000	sd	4.3	0.76		
16	Chymotrypsin, α	Beef pancreas	49.6 67.8 66.5 102°, P2_1	22,500	sd;sv	2.5	0.73		8.1(0.1)
17	Chymotrypsinogen, α	Beef pancreas		22,500	sd;sv	2.5	0.72		9.5(0.01)
18	Colostrum globulin, immune	Cow colostrum		175,000[12]	d	7			5.85(0.1)
19	Conalbumin	Chicken egg white		74,000	a				6.8(0.1)
20	Concanavalin A	Jack bean		96,000	sd	6.0	0.73		
21	Crotoxin	Rattlesnake venom		30,000	e;sd	3.1	0.704		4.7(0.1)
22	Cytochrome-c	Beef or horse heart		16,000	sd	1.9	0.707		10.65[13](0.1)
23	Edestin	Hemp seed		310,000	sd	12.8	0.745	1.29-1.32	5.5[14]
24	Excelsin	Brazil nut	86, 208.2[15], R3	295,000	sd	11.8	0.743	1.285	
25	Fetuin	Fetal calf blood		50,000		3.1-3.4	0.70		3.5(0.2)
26	Fibrinogen	Human blood		500,000[16]	o;sv	9			5.4(0.1)
27	Gelatin	Collagenous tissues		Variable[17]	o				4.9(0.01)
28	Gliadin	Wheat		27,000	e	2.1	0.71		6.5[14]
29	Globin	Horse blood		37,000	sd	2.5	0.749		7.5(0.1)[18]
30	Globulin, α	Barley		26,000	sd	2.5	0.72		5.0(0.1)
31	Globulin, γ	Barley		170,000	sd	8.3			5.7(0.1)
32	Gluten	Wheat		39,000[19]	e	2.5	0.700		7
33	Growth hormone	Beef pituitary		47,000[20]	a;sd	3.6	0.76		6.85(0.1)
34	Hemocyanin	Helix pomatia		8,900,000	sd	103	0.738		5.05(0.02)
35	Hemoglobin	Human blood	109 63.2 54.4 111°, C2[21]	66,700[22]	sd	4.5	0.749	1.16	6.87(0.1)
36	Hexokinase	Baker's yeast		97,000	sd	3.1	0.740[7]		4.5-4.8(0.02M)[23]
37	Insulin	Beef pancreas	83, 34, R3[24]	36,000	o;sd	3.5	0.749	1.28	5.2(0.033)
38	Lactalbumin, α	Cow milk		17,500	sd	1.9			
39	Lactogenic hormone	Beef, sheep pituitary		26,500	o				5.7(0.05)
40	Lactoglobulin, β	Cow milk	69.29 70.42 156.47, P2_1 2_1 2_1	35,400	x	3.12	0.751	1.146	5.1(0.1)
41	Lactoglobulin, immune	Cow milk		180,000	sd	7			5.8(0.1)
42	Lysozyme chloride	Chicken egg white	79.1, 37.9, P4_1 2_1	13,900	x	2.1	0.722	1.233	11.35(0.1)
43	Metakentrin	Sheep pituitary		40,000	o;a	3.6			4.6(0.1)
44	Myosin	Rabbit muscle		850,000	sd;o	7.1			5.4(0.1-0.5)
45	Ovalbumin	Chicken egg white		44,000	sd	3.55	0.749	1.24-1.27	4.58(0.1)
46	Pepsin	Hog gastric mucosa	67.9, 292, C6_1 2	36,000	x	3.3			2.75-3.0
47	Relaxin	Pregnant sow ovary		9,000	a;s				
48	Ribonuclease	Beef pancreas	30.90 38.80 54.06 106°, P2_1	13,400	x	1.85	0.709	1.220	7.8(0.055)
49	Ricin	Castor bean		80,000	sd	4.8	0.75[7]		5.2-5.5
50	Salmine	Salmon testes		7,000	a	<1			12
51	Serum albumin	Human blood	178[25] 54[25] 166[25] 91°, C2	65,600	x	4.6	0.733	1.145	4.9
52	Serum globulin, α_1	Human blood		200,000	sv	5.0	0.841		
53	Serum globulin, β_1	Human blood		90,000	sv	5.5	0.725		
54	Serum globulin, γ	Human blood		160,000	sv	7.2	0.739		5.7(0.1)[26]
55	Serum globulin, γ_1, anti-pneumococcus	Human blood		190,000	sd	7.4	0.745[7]		5.6(0.1)[27]
56	Thymus nucleohistone	Calf thymus		2,000,000	e;sd	31.0	0.658		
57	Thyroglobulin	Hog thyroid		700,000	sd	19.2	0.72		4.58(0.02)
58	Tobacco mosaic virus	Tobacco leaves[8]		40,000,000	x	185	0.72		3.49(0.02)
59	Toxin, botulinum, type A	Cl. botulinum		900,000	sd	17	0.75		
60	Toxin, botulinum, type B	Cl. botulinum		60,000	d				
61	Toxin, diphtheria	C. diphtheriae		74,000	sd	4.6	0.736		4.1(0.005)[23]
62	Toxin, tetanus	Cl. tetani		67,000	a;s	4.5			
63	Trypsin	Beef pancreas		20,700	a				10.8(0.03M)
64	Trypsin inhibitor	Beef pancreas	111, 122, C6_3 2	6,000	o				
65	Tuberculin protein	M. tuberculosis		32,000	sd	3.3			4.3(0.03)
66	Tyrosinase	Ps. campestris		100,000	sd	6.4	0.75[7]		<5
67	Urease	Jack bean		480,000	sd	18.6	0.73		5.0(0.012)[14]
68	Yellow enzyme, "old"	Brewer's yeast		80,000	sd;e	5.8	0.731		5.22(0.02)
69	Zein	Maize		40,000	sd	1.9	0.73[7]		

/1/ From X-ray data. Wet preparation, unless otherwise noted. /2/ The code describing the method used is: a=chemical analysis or combining ratio; d=diffusion constant; e=sedimentation equilibrium; l=light scattering; o=osmotic pressure; s=sedimentation velocity; v=intrinsic viscosity; x=X-ray diffraction. /3/ Specific sedimentation velocity in units of 10^{-13}. /4/ Cubic centimeters increase in volume of solution per gram of protein dissolved. /5/ Grams per cubic centimeter, wet. /6/ pH at which protein does not move in an electric field. The ionic strength is given in parentheses. /7/ Assumed value. /8/ Pathological. /9/ 35,000-37,000. /10/ 32,000-34,000. /11/ During pregnancy. /12/ 160,000-190,000. /13/ At 0°C for the oxidized (ferri) form. /14/ Based on solubility minimum. /15/ Dry. /16/ 400,000-580,000. /17/ 5,000-400,000. /18/ For human globin. /19/ To 4,600,000. /20/ 44,000-49,000. /21/ Met-co-oxyhemoglobin I (horse). /22/ Same value also for oxy-, met-, and carboxyhemoglobin. /23/ By cataphoresis. /24/ Crystalline modification of insulin (Scott-Zn) with molecular weight of 5734. /25/ Dimensions of a pseudo-orthogonal unit cell with all faces centered. /26/ Depends on fraction employed. /27/ Hyperimmune horse blood.

18. PLASMA PROTEINS, ELECTROPHORETIC ANALYSIS: MAMMALS AND BIRDS

Veronal-citrate buffer, pH 8.6; ionic strength 0.1. Values are mobilities (m = sq cm per sec per volt x 10^5) and percentages of total protein.

	Species	Fast[1] m	Fast[1] %	Albumin m	Albumin %	α1 m	α1 %	α2 m	α2 %	α3 m	α3 %	β m	β %	φ m	φ %	γ m	γ %
1	Man			6.6	59.6	5.4	6.7	4.3	8.8			3.1	11.0	2.3	4.8	1.3	9.1
2	Cat			7.7	41.4	6.3	8.1	5.2	20.2	4.1	4.7	3.4	8.7	2.6	5.2	1.6	12.5
3	Cow			7.0	40.6	5.5	10.7	4.7	8.3			3.7	13.7	2.6	16.3	1.4	11.0
4	Dog			6.8	39.6	5.7	16.9	4.4	8.0			3.3	13.0	2.4	13.3	1.2	9.3
5	Fox			7.5	47.1	6.4	10.2	5.2	7.8					3.2	31.2	1.3	3.9
6	Goat			7.3	49.2	5.6	13.7	4.1	12.7			3.1	3.9	2.5	7.6	1.5	12.9
7	Guinea pig			6.1	54.6	5.4	4.0	4.9	3.7	4.4	15.2	3.0	8.8	2.1	8.1	1.0	5.6
8	Horse	7.9	0.8	7.1	29.8	5.8	8.2	4.8	12.3			3.7	21.9	2.5	15.8	1.4	11.2
9	Mink			4.9	51.5	4.2	11.7	3.8	9.8			3.7	10.3	3.2	5.0	2.2	12.1
10	Monkey	7.4	0.5	6.6	50.0	5.4	8.9	4.8	5.2	4.2	4.7	3.3	16.1	2.2	8.4	1.4	9.0
11	Rabbit			6.8	63.3	5.1	11.5					3.5	13.0	2.4	7.9	1.4	4.3
12	Rat	7.1	1.3	6.1	59.1				15.4					2.7	19.4	1.6	4.8
13	Sheep			6.8	43.7	5.3	9.8	4.3	6.7			3.4	15.0	2.6	9.7	1.6	15.0
14	Swine	7.3	0.4	6.5	39.9	5.2	6.0	4.4	16.3			3.7	8.2	2.8	13.9	1.8	15.2
15	Chicken	7.5	0.6	6.8	40.4	5.4	14.9	4.1	11.3							2.5	32.8
16	Duck	7.6	2.6	6.7	47.8	5.8	21.9	4.9	6.1					3.7	15.5	2.5	6.0
17	Pheasant	6.1	0.4	5.2	58.5	4.2	14.0	3.6	6.5					2.9	16.3	1.7	4.3
18	Pigeon	7.8	3.1	6.4	64.1	5.2	7.2	4.5	4.5					3.3	17.4	1.7	7.7
19	Turkey	6.7	1.0	5.9	51.5	5.0	13.4	4.1	4.3					2.9	21.6	1.7	8.1

/1/ A component on the leading shoulder of the albumin peak.

19. SERUM PROTEINS, ELECTROPHORETIC ANALYSIS: REPTILES, AMPHIBIANS, FISH, AND INVERTEBRATES

Veronal buffer, pH 8.6; ionic strength 0.1. Values are mobilities (m = sq cm per sec per volt x 10^5) and percentages of total protein.

	Species	1 m	1 %	2 m	2 %	3 m	3 %	4 m	4 %	5 m	5 %	6 m	6 %	7 m	7 %	8 m	8 %	9 m	9 %	10 m	10 %
1	Rattlesnake, diamond back	1.7	4.4	2.6	5.9	3.2	6.0	3.7	21.0	4.3	8.7	4.7	3.9	5.3	8.7	5.8	4.0	6.3	4.6	7.3	32.8
2	Rattlesnake, timber	3.4	3.8	4.7	3.5	6.2	19.7	7.4	9.4	8.7	8.8	8.0	13.3	11.0	10.3	12.4	28.4	14.0	2.8		
3	Snake, milk	1.4	1.3	2.0	5.7	2.6	16.4	3.4	11.6	3.8	5.9	4.4	5.8	5.1	11.9	6.5	23.8	7.9	17.6		
4	Snake, water	3.8	16.6	4.1	17.9	5.7	30.7	6.9	6.9	7.6	10.3	8.8	3.5	10.0	6.1	11.7	9.4				
5	Snake, water moccasin	1.0	2.5	1.8	15.8	2.8	18.3	3.9	13.5	4.5	5.4	5.0	5.3	5.7	11.3	6.4	6.1	6.8	5.4	7.4	15.6
6	Turtle, snapping	1.1	5.3	1.8	20.5	3.8	31.5	3.6	16.6	4.5	7.5	5.3	16.2	6.1	2.4						
7	Turtle, soft-shelled	1.4	1.9	2.5	15.5	3.5	11.6	4.4	17.6	5.8	51.8	6.9	1.6								
8	Frog, bull	1.5	8.4	2.3	7.0	3.1	5.5	3.7	5.8	4.3	12.0	4.9	22.4	5.6	16.0	6.5	22.4	7.2	0.5		
9	Bass, rock	2.3	1.3	3.0	5.7	3.6	2.9	4.3	9.3	5.4	24.2	6.1	17.3	7.0	10.7	7.9	27.9	8.8	0.7		
10	Buffalo-fish	1.4	2.5	2.5	25.0	3.1	10.2	3.9	9.7	4.7	17.8	5.4	5.5	6.2	5.5	6.9	23.8				
11	Bullhead	1.8	0.6	3.0	4.7	4.0	8.5	5.4	15.8	6.8	7.3	7.6	9.3	8.7	30.6	10.0	23.2				
12	Carp	2.3	4.1	3.7	8.2	4.7	14.3	5.7	15.0	7.1	21.5	8.6	36.9								
13	Catfish, channel	1.3	2.9	1.8	3.8	2.3	3.2	3.0	6.6	3.9	6.6	4.7	11.2	5.7	20.6	6.5	45.1				
14	Catfish, eel, willow cat	1.7	6.2	2.3	7.8	3.1	4.3	3.7	5.1	4.4	14.1	5.6	32.4	6.7	4.2	7.7	25.9				
15	Perch, yellow	2.5	1.8	2.9	2.6	3.5	7.0	4.4	4.6	5.0	16.6	5.3	8.8	6.5	4.4	7.2	5.2	8.0	7.0	8.7	11.0[1]
16	Pike, northern	1.9	7.8	2.8	12.2	3.7	6.3	4.3	7.8	5.7	48.2	8.0	13.5	8.7	4.2						
17	Sucker	1.4	1.4	2.1	13.6	3.0	14.2	3.8	12.1	4.9	18.7	5.5	7.6	6.4	31.8	7.4	0.6				
18	Sturgeon, rock	1.7	22.6	2.3	8.5	3.0	10.4	3.6	5.6	4.3	5.3	5.0	18.3	5.6	11.5	6.2	8.9	6.9	7.4	7.4	1.5
19	Trout, lake	1.3	1.4	2.2	3.8	2.7	7.9	3.4	6.5	4.2	8.2	4.9	12.8	6.5	58.4	7.5	1.0				
20	Trout, rainbow	1.3	1.2	2.0	1.6	2.7	3.4	3.1	4.0	4.2	34.7	5.1	6.7	6.3	45.6	7.4	2.8				
21	Whitefish	1.3	0.5	2.7	5.5	3.0	11.5	3.5	12.7	4.1	8.1	4.8	14.6	5.7	12.1	5.9	17.6	7.0	14.7	7.7	0.5
22	Crab, horseshoe	2.0	4.0	4.5	7.5	5.1	10.7	6.1	24.5	6.7	53.3										
23	Snail, land	2.4	2.7	3.5	2.0	4.7	4.8	6.2	7.0	7.1	13.6	7.9	62.3	9.5	7.6						

/1/ Eleventh and twelfth components with m and % of 9.7, 29.8, and 10.8, 1.2, respectively, were also found.

20. PLASMA PROTEINS, PROPERTIES AND REACTIONS: MAN

	Protein Component	Electrophoretic Fraction	Interacts with:	General Properties
1	Albumin	Albumin	Fatty acids, bile salts, dyes	Osmotic regulation of blood volume.
2	α1-Lipoproteins	α1- globulin	Steroids	35% lipid.
3	Antibody euglobulin	γ1-globulin	Antigens	Typhoid "O" and other agglutinins.
4	Antibody γ-globulin	γ-globulins	Antigens	Antibodies for pathogenic organisms.
5	Antihemophilic globulin			Necessary for clotting of hemophilic blood.
6	β1-Lipoproteins	β1- globulin	Steroids	Carrier for vitamins, hormones, triglycerides.
7	Bradykininogen	α2- globulin	Tryptic enzymes	Bradykinin precursor.
8	Cholinesterase		Choline esters	
9	Complement components C'1, C'2	α- and β- globulins	Antigen-antibody complex	
10	Fibrinogen		Thrombin	Forms fibrin clot.
11	Hypertensinogen	α2- globulin	Renin	Hypertensin precursor.
12	Isoagglutinins	γ-globulins	Incompatible red blood cells	Anti-A, anti-B, anti-Rh agglutinins.
13	Peptidase		L-Leucylglycylglycine	
14	Phosphatase, alkaline		Phosphoric acid monoesters	
15	Plasmin		Proteins	Digests protein, fibrin clots.
16	Plasminogen		Streptokinase	Enzyme precursor.
17	Prothrombin		Thromboplastin	Enzyme precursor.
18	Siderophilin	β- globulin	Fe+++	Iron transport.
19	Thrombin		Fibrinogen	Catalyzes formation of fibrin clot.
20	Thyrotropic hormone	α- globulin		Influences thyroid activity.

21. ENZYMES: CHEMICAL COMPOSITION

Enzymes listed were either crystalline or electrophoretically homogeneous. Values are grams per 100 grams enzyme.

Enzyme	C	H	N	S	P	Other Elements	Alanine	Arginine	Aspartic Acid	Cysteine	Cystine ½	Glutamic Acid	Glycine	Histidine	Isoleucine	Leucine	Lysine	Methionine	Phenyl-alanine	Proline	Serine	Threonine	Tryptophan	Tyrosine	Valine
1 Alcohol dehydrogenase	52.8	6.96	16.54	1.21	Trace	Trace(Fe)	8.56	6.33	9.7		1.12	11.4	5.61	4.21	7.87	11.5	9.54	1.17	3.06	5.71	6.57	7.1	2.31	5.31	7.40
2 Aldolase																									
3 α-Amylase, human pancreas			16.8	0	0.01																				
4 α-Amylase, human saliva			15.8	0	0.01																				
5 α-Amylase, swine pancreas	49.46	7.18	15.52	1.33	0.05	0.035(Fe)																			
6 α-Amylase, barley malt			15.52		0.01													4.32							
7 β-Amylase, sweetpotato			13.4 / 15.1					6.0			0.79[1] / 1.3													7.0 / 4.1	
8 Carbonic anhydrase			15.9			0.33(Zn)																			
9 Carboxypeptidase, pancreatic	52.6	7.2	14.4	0.47	0	0.18(Zn)	5.16				1.40[2]		5.06		7.65	9.41		0.44	7.16	3.66	10.1	9.21	3.62		5.58
10 Catalase, horse blood			16.8			0.093(Fe)		5.06	11.7		1.65[2]	10.7		3.47			7.81							10.3	
11 Catalase, horse liver			16.8			0.093(Fe)		8.75	16.5		1.85[2]	10.9		4.17			7.50							6.0	
12 Catalase, human blood	50.0	7.06	16.7	0		0.077(Fe)		8.90	16.5			10.3		3.86			6.91							5.8	
13 α-Chymotrypsin			15.5	1.85	0	0.16(Cl)				1.22	3.66			1.26		9.1		1.25				11.2	5.81	2.83	
14 β-Chymotrypsin			16.24	1.56						1.29	3.51			1.22		9.4		1.29				10.6	6.40	2.87	
15 γ-Chymotrypsin			16.00	1.59						1.27	3.59			1.26		8.5		1.28				10.7	6.27	3.09	
16 Chymotrypsinogen	50.6	7.0	15.8	1.9	0	0.17(Cl)		2.82	11.3	1.29	3.30	9.0	5.3	1.23	5.7	10.4	8.0	1.22	3.6	5.9	11.4	11.4	1.4[3]	2.96	10.1
17 Cytochrome - c	52.52	7.76	15.36	1.47	0	0.43(Fe)		5.6[3]			1.43[2]			6.3[3]			30.8[3]							3.53	
18 Desoxyribonuclease	50.16	6.91	14.88	1.09	0																				
19 Enolase	53.62	7.55	17.34	0.38																					
20 D-Glyceraldehyde phosphate dehydrogenase[4]	52.54	7.51	16.41	1.08	Trace		6.72	5.23	12.4		1.09	6.8	6.03	5.01	9.1	6.78	9.42	2.70	5.55	3.67	7.7	7.2	2.05	4.57	12.0
21 Hexokinase	52.16	7.08	15.62	0.91	0.11																				
22 Lecithinase	50.77	6.41	15.88	4.0				4.7	6.2	0	0	10.4	6.3	3.6	8.1	11.4	7.8	1.8	4.9	5.1		8.9	0.41	6.2	7.8
23 Lipoxidase			18.6	2.53				12.9	18.2			4.3	5.7	1.05	5.3	8.4	5.9	2.0	3.1	1.4	7.0	5.4	10.6	3.7	4.7
24 Lysozyme			15.5	1.2			6.0	7.75	11.3		8.0[2]	12.4	8.41	0.85	6.05	6.10	5.67		3.16	5.11	5.91	3.89	4.68	14.7	8.43
25 Papain	51.7	6.86	14.6	0.94	0.09		5.63	1.0	16.0	0.5	4.58[2]	11.9	6.4	0.9	10.8	10.4	0.9	1.7	6.4	5.0	12.2	9.6	2.36	8.5	7.1
26 Pepsin, cattle	51.9	6.48	15.62	1.58	0.03						1.64														
27 Pepsin, salmon	52.8	6.88	15.9	0.09																					
28 Pepsinogen	48.1	8.07	16.65																						
29 Peptic inhibitor[5]	47.0	7.35	13.2	0.43																			0	0.4[3]	
30 Peroxidase	53.35	7.30	17.40			0.13(Fe)		31[3]																	
31 Phospho-enoltrans-phosphorylase, human				1.60	0.06			6.91						0.71			4.06								
32 Phosphorylase, rabbit muscle			16.5				4.79	11.6	9.3		0.45	13.4	3.8	3.3	6.5	10.5	7.2	2.7	6.2	4.7	3.05	4.24	2.0	5.9	7.3
33 Polypeptidase, yeast	54.46	7.36	13.5	0.14	0.3																				
34 Pyrophosphatase, yeast	51.4	7.19	14.51	1.46	0.04	0.0035(Cu)	4.9	3.3	12.1			9.7	2.9	2.2	8.9	6.0	10.9	1.3	6.2	6.4	3.1	4.8	3.6	6.0	4.1
35 Rennin	48.2	6.2	16.1	1.1	Trace	2.85(Cl)																			
36 Ribonuclease	50.2	6.6	16.13	1.1	0		7.67	4.94	15.0		7.0	12.4	1.64	4.22	2.67	2.02	10.5	4.0	3.51	3.94	11.4	8.90	3.65	7.60	7.49
37 Trypsin	50.1	6.9	15.3	1.1																				7.8	
38 Trypsinogen	51.95	7.16	16.74		0																				
39 Tryptic inhibitor[5], soybean			13.6	0.97																			2.2	4.0	
40 Tyrosinase	51.6	7.1	16.0		0	0.25(Cu)																			
41 Urease			17.15	1.2																					
42 Verdoperoxidase						0.1(Fe)																			
43 "Yellow enzyme, old"	51.4	7.07	16.27	0.48	0.043			8.25			0.34	7.1	7.1	2.75			13.7		5.75				4.86	7.75	

/1/ Cysteine plus cystine. /2/ Cystine. /3/ Per cent of total nitrogen. /4/ Element analysis refers to yeast enzyme; amino acid composition to rabbit muscle enzyme. /5/ Not an enzyme in the strict sense of the term.

26

22. ENZYMES: PHYSICAL PROPERTIES

#	Enzyme	Source	Molecular Weight	Isoelectric pH	Solubility[1] g/100 ml	Absorption Maximum mμ	Optical Rotation[2] $[\alpha]_D^{25}$	Substrate	Temp °C	pH	Turnover Number[3]	K_s[4] Molarity
1	Alcohol dehydrogenase	Yeast	70,000		s. w.			Ethanol, DPN	20	8.2	18,000	1.2×10^{-3}[5]
2	Aldolase	Rat muscle	147,000	5,7	0.3[2] at pH 8.5			Fructose-1,6-diphosphate	25	7.1	10,100	4.8×10^{-3}
4	α-Amylase	Human saliva		5.0-5.5	0.3[2] at pH 8.5			Starch				
5	α-Amylase	Human pancreas		4.6-5.2	6[2] at pH 8.5				25	4.7		0.078%
6	α-Amylase	Swine pancreas	45,000	5.7	10[2] at pH 8.5; s. al. 40%			Starch				
7	β-Amylase	Malt, barley	60,000	4.7-4.8								
		Sweetpotato	150,000	5.3								
8	Carbonic anhydrase	Red cells, mammalian	30,000	5.95	i. w.			CO_2	0	7.3		9×10^{-3}
9	Carboxypeptidase	Cattle pancreas	33,000					Benzenesulfonyl glycyl-phenylalanine	25	7.5		1.4×10^{-2}
10	Catalase	Cattle liver	225,000	5.7	s. w.	405		H_2O_2	25.5	7.0	120,000,000[6]	2[7]
11	Catalase	Horse liver	225,000	5.4		405		H_2O_2	23-25	6.7	210,000,000[6]	3[7]
12	Catalase	Human blood	220,000			405		H_2O_2	18	6.8	135,000,000[6]	
13	α-Chymotrypsin	Cattle pancreas	22,500	8.1-8.6	v. s. w.		-0.40°/mg N	Benzoyl-L-phenylalanine methyl ester	25	7.8	3,060	1.2×10^{-4}
14	α-Chymotrypsinogen	Cattle pancreas	22,500	9.5	sl. s. w.	280	-0.48°/mg N					
15	Desoxyribonuclease	Cattle pancreas	60,000	5.0	s. w.							
16	Diaphorase	Swine heart	70,000			274, 359, 451		2,6-Dichlorophenol-indophenol		8.5	2,700	
17	Enolase	Brewers' yeast	66,000[8]	5.0-5.4	i. w. (low pH)			2-Phosphoglycerate	20	7.34	6,500	1.37×10^{-3}
18	Fumarase	Swine heart	204,000	4-5		279		Fumarate	25	7.4	30,000	
19	Glutamic dehydrogenase	Cattle liver	1,000,000					Glutamic acid	Room	7.6		
20	α-Glycerophosphate dehydrogenase	Yeast	120,000	4-7	sl. s. w.	280		Dihydroxyacetone phosphate	22	7	26,500	
21	Hexokinase	Yeast	97,000	4.5-4.8	s. w.			Glucose	30	8.0	13,000[9]	1.6×10^{-4}
22	Lactic dehydrogenase	Rat liver	126,000	6.3	s. w.; dil. salt sol.	280, 412		Lactate, DPN	25	7.0	12,800	10^{-8}
23	Lactoperoxidase	Milk	82,000	8.05	s. dil. salt sol.			H_2O_2		7.0	1,500	
24	Lipase	Swine pancreas						Methyl butyrate	25-28	7.0		9×10^{-2}
25	Lipoxidase	Soybean	102,400	5.4	s. dil. salt sol.	280		Linoleate	20	9.0	21,600	1.35×10^{-3}
26	Lysozyme	Egg	13,900	11.35	sl. s. w.							
27	N₂ fixing system	Azotobacter						Nitrogen	32	7.0	18	2×10^{-2}[10]
28	Papain	Papaya latex	27,000[8]	9-9.5	s. w. al. 70%	280	-71°/gram	Carbobenzoxy-1-glutamyl-1-tyrosine ethyl ester	38	4.0	0.18	1.9×10^{-3}
29	Pepsin	Cattle	36,000	2.7	s. w.		-61°/gram					
30	Pepsinogen	Cattle	42,000[11]									
31	Peroxidase	Horseradish	44,100	7.2		278		H_2O_2	25	4.1	16,800	4.5×10^{-7}[12]
32	Phosphoglucomutase	Rabbit muscle		5.8	s. salt sol.			Glucose-1-phosphate	30	7.5	40,000	
33	Phosphorylase	Muscle	375,000[13]	4.75	s. w.			Glucose-1-phosphate	30	6.7		2.6×10^{-3}
34	Pyrophosphatase	Yeast	100,000									
35	Pyruvate kinase	Muscle						Phosphopyruvate	20	6.77	6,000	
36	Rennin	Calf gastric juice	40,000	4.5-4.65	sl. s. w.	280	-0.47°(5%)					
37	Ribonuclease	Cattle pancreas	13,400	7.8	s. w.		-0.27°/mg N					
38	Trypsin	Cattle pancreas	20,700	10.8	v. s. w.			Benzoyl-L-arginine ester	25	7.7	1,610	8×10^{-5}
39	Trypsinogen	Cattle pancreas	34,000	9.3								
40	Tyrosinase	Wild mushroom	100,000	5.0-5.1	i. dil. a., salt sol.			Tyrosine	25	6.0		8×10^{-4}[14]
41	Urease	Jack bean meal	480,000	5.22		273, 330		Urea	20	7.1	460,000	4×10^{-3}
42	"Yellow enzyme, old"	Yeast	80,000									

/1/ Abbreviations: a.=acid; al.=alcohol (ethyl, 95%); dil.=dilute; i.=insoluble; s.=soluble; sl.=slightly; v.=very; w.=water. Underlined superscripts represent temperature at which solubility was determined. /2/ In water at concentration shown at 25°C. /3/ Moles of substrate decomposed by one mole of enzyme per minute. /4/ Michaelis constant. /5/ K_s determined at pH 8.6 and 38°C. /6/ True only under the hypothetical condition that the concentrations of substrate and enzyme are the same and constant. /7/ Ratio of two consecutive reaction constants of enzyme with substrate. /8/ ±2000. /9/ For glucose. /10/ Expressed in atmospheres. /11/ ±3000. /12/ No true Michaelis-Menten constant exists. /13/ Estimated range 340,000-400,000. /14/ K_s is for tyrosinase from Neurospora sp.

23. ENZYMES: OCCURRENCE AND REACTIONS

	Enzyme	Co-factors[1]	Reactions Catalyzed[1]	Conditions Suitable for Enzyme Action[2]			Occurrence
				pH	Substrate Concentration	Temp °C	
1	Aconitase	Fe++	Citric acid→cis-aconitic acid→isocitric acid	7.4	0.03 M	25	Tissues; bacteria; yeasts; seeds; leaves.
2	Adenosinetriphosphatase	Ca++	ATP→ADP + PO4	7.5	1 mg P/ml	37	Brain; muscle; venoms; potatoes.
3	Aldolase	Co++, Fe++, or Zn++	Fructose-1,6-diphosphate→triosephosphates	9	0.01 M	38	Muscle; E. coli; yeasts; higher plants.
4	Amino tripeptidase	NaCl	Tripeptide→dipeptide + amino acid	8.0	0.05 M	39	Mucosa; muscle.
5	α-Amylase (animal)		Starch or glycogen→dextrins + maltose	7	1%	37	Liver; saliva; urine.
6	α-Amylase (plant)		Starch or glycogen→dextrins + maltose	4.5-5.5	12 mg/ml	30	Bacteria; yeasts; cereals.
7	β-Amylase (animal, plant)		Starch→dextrins + maltose	4-5	10 mg/ml		Cereals; soybeans; sweetpotatoes.
8	Amylosucrase		Sucrose→"glycogen" + fructose	5.6	10 mg/ml		Bacteria.
9	Apyrase	Ca++	ATP→AMP + 2 phosphate	6.5		30	Liver; muscle; yeasts; tubers.
10	Arginase	Co++, Mn++	L-Arginine→L-ornithine + urea	9.5	0.66%	38	Liver; bacteria; fungi; seeds; spleen.
11	Asparaginase		L-β-Asparagine→L-aspartic acid + NH3	8-7.5	0.5 M	40	Liver; mucosa; bacteria; fungi; seeds.
12	Aspartase		L-Aspartic acid→fumaric acid + NH3	5-9	0.1 M	37	Bacteria; yeasts; leaves.
13	Carbonic anhydrase		H2CO3→CO2 + H2O		0.08 M	15	Erythrocytes; gastric mucosa.
14	Carboxylase, amino acid	Pyridoxal phosphate	Amino acid→amines + CO2	4.5-5.5	0.001 M	30	Liver; kidney; pancreas; bacteria; higher plants.
15	Carboxylase, oxalacetic	Mn++	Oxalacetate→pyruvate + CO2	5.0	0.5 mg/L	30	Liver; bacteria; seeds; leaves.
16	Carboxylase, pyruvic	Thiamine pyrophosphate Mg++	Pyruvate→acetaldehyde + CO2	6.0	0.15 M	30	Fungi; bacteria; seeds.
17	Carboxylase, succinic		Succinic acid→propionic acid + CO2				Bacteria.
18	Carboxypeptidase		Peptide (free COOH)→amino acid + peptide	8.5	6% edestin	25	Pancreas (as zymogen).
19	Catalase		H2O2→H2O + O2	6.8	0.01 N	0	Erythrocytes; liver; kidney; bacteria; higher plants.
20	Cellulase		Cellulose→simple sugars				Snails; bacteria; fungi; malt.
21	Chlorophyllase	CaCl2, ATP	Chlorophyll→chlorophyllide + phytol	5.9	1 mg/ml	25	Bacteria; leaves; stems.
22	Choline acetylase	CoA, ATP	Choline + acetyl CoA→acetylcholine	7			Brain; muscle; bacteria.
23	Chymotrypsin	Ca++	Proteins→polypeptides + amino acids	7.6	5% casein	38	Pancreas.
24	Conjugase		Pteroylglutamate→pterine + glutamic acid	7-8		37	Pancreas; tissues; yeasts; tubers.
25	Dehydrogenase, alcohol	DPN	Ethanol→acetaldehyde	7.8	0.03%	20	Liver; kidney; brain; blood; yeasts; bacteria; higher plants.
26	Dehydrogenase, glucose	DPN or TPN	D-Glucose→D-gluconic acid	7.4	0.2 M	38	Liver.
27	Dehydrogenase, glucose-6-phosphate	TPN	Glucose-6-phosphate→phosphogluconate	7.5	0.02 M	38	Blood; yeasts.
28	Dehydrogenase, glutamic	DPN or TPN	Glutamate→α-ketoglutarate + NH3	8.2	0.0001 M	37	Liver; kidney; muscle; brain.
29	Dehydrogenase, β-hydroxybutyric	DPN	L-β-Hydroxybutyrate→acetoacetate	7	0.05 M	38	Widespread.
30	Dehydrogenase, isocitric	DPN, TPN, Mg++, Mn++	D-Isocitrate→α-ketoglutarate + CO2	7.0	0.0002M	25	Widespread.
31	Dehydrogenase, lactic	DPN	Lactate→pyruvate	9.3	0.02 M	20	Widespread.
32	Dehydrogenase, malic	DPN or TPN	L(-)Malate→oxalacetate	7.2	0.025 M	37	Brain; kidney; liver; muscle; widespread in plants.
33	Dehydrogenase, succinic	Cytochrome c (?)	Succinate→fumarate	7.4	0.01 M	37	Widespread.
34	Dehydrogenase, triosephosphate	DPN	D-Glyceraldehyde-3-phosphate→1, 3-diphosphoglycerate	8.6-9.0	0.0001 M	27	Widespread.
35	Dehydrogenase, yeast aldehyde	K+, DPN+, cysteine	Acetaldehyde→CH3COOH + DPNH + H+				Yeast.
36	Desoxyribonuclease	Mg++, Mn++	Thymonucleic acid→nucleotides	6-7	0.5%	37	Intestinal mucosa; pancreas; seeds.
37	Emulsin (β-glucosidase)		Salicin→saligenin + β-D-glucose				Small intestine; bacteria; fungi; almonds; plants.
38	Enolase	Mg++, Mn++, Zn++	2-Phosphoglycerate→(enol)phosphopyruvate	7	0.1 mg P/ml	20	Muscle; yeasts; leaves.
39	Esterase, acetylcholine		Acetylcholine→acetate + choline	7.4	3 mg/ml	37	Liver; pancreas; brain; blood; insects.
40	Esterase, acetylsalicylic acid		Acetylsalicylic acid→salicylic acid + acetic acid	5.3 or 7			Brain; kidney; liver.
41	Esterase, cholesterol		Cholesterol esters→cholesterol + acids				Liver; kidney; spleen; intestinal mucosa; blood; pancreas; bacteria.
42	Esterase, pectin		Pectin→pectate + methanol	6.2	1%	30	Leaves; fruits; bacteria.
43	Esterase, simple		Ethyl butyrate→ethanol + butyrate	8.0	Saturated	20	Widespread (animals); seeds; fungi.
44	Ficin	H2S, HCN, cysteine	Proteins→amino acids and peptides(?)	5		35	Fig tree sap.
45	Fumarase		Fumaric acid→L(-)malic acid	6.6	0.025 M	40	Liver; muscle; bacteria; fungi; higher plants.
46	β-Galactosidase (lactase)		Lactose→galactose + glucose	5.6	2.5%	38	Bacteria; seeds.
47	α-Glucosidase (maltase)		Maltose→glucose	7.2	50 mg/ml	30	Intestinal mucosa; fungi; malt.
48	β-Glucosidase		β-Glucosides→glucose + aglycon	4.4-5.0	1 mg/ml	30	Intestinal mucosa; liver; kidney; bacteria; higher plants.
49	β-Glucuronidase		β-Glucuronide→glucuronate + alcohol	4.5	0.001 M	38	Widespread (animals); bacteria; higher plants.

No.	Enzyme	Activators, coenzymes	Reaction	pH	Substrate conc.	Temp.	Source
50	Glyoxalase	Glutathione	Methylglyoxal→lactate	7	1 mg/ml	25	Liver; kidney; muscle; blood; bacteria; fungi; seeds.
51	Guanase		Guanine→xanthine + NH_3	8.7	Saturated	40	Liver; pancreas; spleen; kidney; seeds.
52	Hexokinase	Mg^{++}, Mn^{++}	Hexose + ATP→hexosemonophosphate + ADP	7.5	0.001 M	30	Liver; muscle; kidney; brain; bacteria; yeasts; higher plants.
53	Histaminase		Histamine→aldehyde + H_2O_2 + NH_3	6.8-7.6	0.01 M	37	Widespread (animals); bacteria; fungi.
54	Histidase		Histidine→glutamate + formate + NH_3	8	0.01 M	38	Spleen; testes; insects; venoms; bacteria.
55	Hyaluronidase		Hyaluronate→acetylglucosamine + glycuronate	7.0	0.1%	37	Intestinal mucosa; invertebrates; fungi; bacteria; higher plants.
56	Invertase (sucrase, saccharase)		Sucrose→glucose + fructose	4.5	4 g/25 ml	20	Liver; muscle; pancreas; venoms; mushrooms.
57	Lecithinase A		Lecithin→lysolecithin + fatty acid	7	Egg yolk	38	Liver; spleen; pancreas; brain; fungi; seeds; rice bran.
58	Lecithinase B		Lysolecithin→glycerylphosphorylcholine + fatty acid	4		41	Intestinal mucosa; leaves; malt; bacteria; fungi.
59	Leucyl peptidase	Mg^{++}, Mn^{++}	Leucyl peptides→leucine + other amino acids	8-9	0.05 M	40	Pancreas.
60	Lipase	$CaCl_2$	Fats→glycerol + fatty acids	9	2.5 g/15 ml	30	Bacteria; fungi; seeds.
61	Lipase		Fats→glycerol + fatty acids	4.7-5.0		25	Intestinal mucosa; muscle; seeds.
62	Lipoxidase		Linoleic acid, etc.→oxidized fatty acids	6.5	0.02%	23	Insects; ostracods; bacteria; fungi.
63	Luciferase	Mg^{++}, ATP	Luciferin + O_2→oxidized luciferin + light	7.2	10^{-6} M	38	Nasal mucosa; latex of fig.
64	Lysozyme		Bacterial cells→lysed bacterial cells	5.3		38	Widespread (animals); fungi.
65	Oxidase, D-amino acid		D-Amino acids + O_2→α-keto acids + H_2O_2 + NH_3	8.6	0.01 M	38	Liver; kidney; venoms; fungi; bacteria.
66	Oxidase, L-amino acid		L-Amino acids + O_2→α-keto acids + H_2O_2 + NH_3	8.8	0.015 M	26	Widespread (plants).
67	Oxidase, ascorbic acid		L-Ascorbic acid + O_2→dehydroascorbate + H_2O	6.0	0.01 N	37	Widespread (animals; plants).
68	Oxidase, cytochrome c		Ferro-cytochrome c + O_2→ferri-cytochrome c + H_2O	7.2	0.0001 M	39	Fungi.
69	Oxidase, glucose; (notatin)		D-Glucose + O_2→gluconate + H_2O_2	6.0	1%	20	Seeds, latex.
70	Oxidase, xanthine		Xanthine or aldehyde→uric or other acids	7.5	0.003 M	30	Gastric mucosa.
71	Papain	HCN, H_2S, cysteine	Proteins, proteoses, etc.→amino acids	4.0	0.5%	25	Widespread (animals; plants).
72	Pectinase		Pectin→galacturonide	7.5	0.5%	20	Widespread (animals; plants).
73	Pepsin		Proteins→proteoses, peptones, amino acids	1.5-2.0	2%	25	Gastric mucosa.
74	Phosphoglucomutase	Co^{++}, Mg^{++}, Mn^{++}	Glucose-1-phosphate→glucose-6-phosphate	7.5-9.2	10^{-6} M	30	Widespread (animals; plants).
75	Phosphoglyceromutase		3-Phosphoglycerate→2-phosphoglycerate	7	10^{-5} M	24	Widespread (animals; plants).
76	Phosphomonoesterase I (alkaline phosphatase)	Mg^{++}	β-Glycerophosphate→H_3PO_4 + glycerol	9.2	0.02 M	37	Widespread (animals); bacteria; fungi; none in higher plants.
77	Phosphomonoesterase II (acid phosphatase)		β-Glycerophosphate→H_3PO_4 + glycerol	5-6	0.05 M	37	Prostate; spleen; liver; bacteria; fungi; seeds; tubers.
78	Phosphomonoesterase III	Mg^{++}, Mn^{++}	Monoesters of phosphate→H_3PO_4 + alcohols	3.4-4.2			Liver; spleen; liver; seeds.
79	Phosphomonoesterase IV		α-Glycerophosphate→H_3PO_4 + glycerol	5.2-6.2			Blood; bacteria; yeasts.
80	Phosphorylase, amylo-	Starch or glycogen	Dextrin + glucose-1-phosphate→starch or glycogen + phosphate	6.8	0.001 M	30	Widespread (animals; plants).
81	Phytase	Mg^{++}	Phytate→inositol + phosphate	5.5-7.8	0.1%	37	Blood; intest. mucosa; fungi; seeds.
82	Pyrophosphatase I	Mg^{++}, Mn^{++}	Pyrophosphate→phosphate	7.2-7.8	0.001 M	38	Widespread (animals); fungi; seeds.
83	Pyruvic kinase	ADP, Mg^{++}, K^{+}	Phospho(enol)pyruvic acid→pyruvic acid + ATP	7.0		21	Yeasts; muscle; E. coli.
84	Q-enzyme		Amylose→amylopectin	7.3		25	Liver; muscle; seeds; tubers.
85	Reductase, cytochrome c	TPN	Ferri-cytochrome c→ferro-cytochrome c	5.8	2×10^{-5}M	40	Liver; yeasts.
86	Rennin		Casein→paracasein	4-5	Raw milk	25	Calf stomach.
87	Ribonuclease		Ribonucleic acid→ribonucleotides	7.5	0.25 mg P/ml	25	Liver; spleen; pancreas; lungs; bacteria; higher plants.
88	Transaminase	Mg^{++}	Glutamate + oxalacetate→α-ketoglutarate + aspartate	7.9	0.02 M	40 / 25	Widespread (animals, plants).
89	Transphosphorylase, phosphocarboxyl-		1,3-Diphosphoglycerate + ADP→3-phosphoglycerate + ATP	7.9	1 mg/ml	25	Muscle; yeasts.
90	Transphosphorylase, phospho(enol)-	Mg^{++}, K^{+}	Phosphopyruvate + AMP→pyruvate + ATP	8-9	1.5 mM	38	Muscle; yeasts; higher plants.
91	Trypsin		Proteins, esp. denatured→polypeptides and amino acids	5.5-7	2.2%	25	Pancreatic juice.
92	Tyrosinase		Catechol, etc. + O_2→o-quinone, etc. + H_2O	7.0	2 mg/ml	25	Melanomas; skin; plants.
93	Urease		Urea→CO_2 + NH_3		1.5%	20	Blood; gastric mucosa; insects; bacteria; fungi; seeds.
94	Xylokinase	ATP	Xylose→xylose-5-PO_4 + ADP				Liver.

1/ Abbreviations: ADP=adenosine diphosphate; AMP=adenylic acid, adenosine-monophosphate; ATP=adenosine triphosphate; CoA=coenzyme A; DPN=diphosphopyridine nucleotide, coenzyme I; DPNH=reduced DPN; TPN = triphosphopyridine nucleotide, coenzyme II.   2/ These conditions should be considered as indicative only, since the details vary widely with the method used and the source of the enzyme.

Amino Acids		Empirical Formula	Molecular Weight	Melting Point °C[1]	Solubility (g/100 ml)[2,3]		Specific Rotation				pH at Isoelectric Point[3]
Common Name	Synonyms				Water 25°C	Other Solvents	Solvent	g/100ml	Temp °C	$[\alpha]_D$	
1 L-Alanine	2-Aminopropanoic acid	$C_3H_7O_2N$	89.1	297	16.51	sl. s.;i. eth., acet.	HCl, 1.0N	5.79	15	+14.7	6.11(DL)
2 β-Alanine	3-Aminopropanoic acid	$C_3H_7O_2N$	89.1	196	v. s.	v.sl.s.al.;i.eth.					
3 α-Aminobutyric acid	2-Aminobutanoic acid	$C_4H_9O_2N$	103.12	285	28	0.18 al.; i. eth.	HCl, 20%		20	+14.1	5.98
4 L-Anserine	Methylcarnosine	$C_{10}H_{16}O_3N_4$	240.3				H_2O	5.0	20	+12.2	
5 L-Arginine	α-Amino-δ-guanidino-n-valeric acid	$C_6H_{14}O_2N_4$	174.21	238	v. s.	i. al., eth.	HCl, 6.0N	1.65	23	+26.9	10.76
6 L-Asparagine	α-Aminosuccinamic acid	$C_4H_8O_3N_2$	132.14	236	2.46	v.sl.s.al.;i. eth.;s. dil. NH_4OH	HCl, 3.4N	2.24	20	+34.3	5.41
7 L-Aspartic acid	α-Aminosuccinic acid	$C_4H_7O_4N$	133.11	269-71	0.50	v.sl.s.al.;i. eth.;s. dil. HCl	HCl, 6.0N	2.0	24	+24.6	2.98
8 L-Canaline	α-Amino-δ-(amino-oxyl)butyric acid	$C_4H_{10}O_3N_2$	134.14	214			H_2O	1.6	21	-8.1	
9 L-Canavanine	α-Amino-δ-guanidinoxy-n-butyric acid	$C_5H_{12}O_3N_4$	176.2	184			H_2O	3.2	20	+7.9	7.93
10 L-Carnosine	β-Alanylhistidine	$C_9H_{14}O_3N_4$	226.3				H_2O	2.0	20	+20.5	
11 L-Citrulline	α-Amino-δ-carbamido-n-valeric acid	$C_6H_{13}O_3N_3$	175.2	222	v. sl. s.	i. al.	HCl, 1.0N	2.0	27	+24.3	
12 L-Cystathionine		$C_7H_{14}O_4N_2S$	222.3				HCl, 1.0N	1.0	22	+23.7	
13 Cysteic acid		$C_3H_7O_5NS$	169.15		s.						
14 L-Cysteine	2-Amino-3-mercapto-propanoic acid	$C_3H_7O_2NS$	121.15	175-78	v. s.	s. a., alk.	H_2O	2.0	21	-10.1	5.07
15 L-Cystine	3,3'-Dithiobis(2-amino-propanoic acid)	$C_6H_{12}O_4N_2S_2$	240.29	258-61	0.011	i.al., eth.;s. a.	HCl, 1.0N	1.0	24	-214.4	5.02
16 L-Dibromotyrosine	3,5-Dibromotyrosine	$C_9H_9O_3NBr_2$	339.0	245[4]			HCl, dil.		20	+1.3	
17 L-Dihydroxyphenyl-alanine	α-Amino-β-3,4-dihydroxyphenylpropionic acid; dopa[5]	$C_9H_{11}O_4N$	197.2	280	0.50	i. al., eth.; s. a., alk.	HCl, 4%	1.0	25	-12.0	
18 L-Diiodotyrosine	3,5-Diiodotyrosine; iodogorgoic acid	$C_9H_9O_3NI_2$	433.0	194	0.062		HCl, 1.1N	5.1	20	+2.9	4.29(DL)
19 L-Djenkolic acid	3,3'-Methylenedithio-bis(2-aminopropionic acid)	$C_7H_{14}O_4N_2S_2$	254.3	300-50	0.10		HCl, 1%	2.0	26	-44.5	
20 L-Ergothioneine	Betaine of thiolhistidine	$C_9H_{15}O_2N_3S$	228.29				H_2O	5.0	21	+116.0	
21 L-Ethionine		$C_6H_{13}O_2NS$	163.2		s.		HCl, 0.2N	0.8	25	+23.5	
22 L-Glutamic acid	α-Aminoglutaric acid	$C_5H_9O_4N$	147.13	247	0.86		HCl, 6.0N	1.0	22	+31.2	3.22(DL)
23 L-Glutamine	α-Aminoglutaramic acid	$C_5H_{10}O_3N_2$	146.15	185-6	4.25	v.sl.s.al.;i.eth.					5.65
24 Glycine	Aminoethanoic acid, glycocoll	$C_2H_5O_2N$	75.0	233	24.99	0.043 al. 90%				0	6.20
25 L-Histidine	α-Amino-β-imidazole-propionic acid	$C_6H_9O_2N_3$	155.1	277	4.19	v. sl. s. al.; i. eth.	H_2O	1.1	25	-39.0	7.64
26 L-Homocysteine		$C_4H_9O_2NS$	135.18		s.						
27 L-Homocystine		$C_8H_{16}O_4N_2S_2$	268.3		v. sl. s		HCl, 1.0N	1.0	26	+77	
28 L-Hydroxylysine	α,ε-Diamino-δ-hydroxy-n-hexanoic acid	$C_6H_{14}O_3N_2$	162.2	220			HCl, 1.0N	0.4	22	+7.5	
29 L-Hydroxyproline	4-Hydroxy-2-pyrrol-idine-carboxylic acid	$C_5H_9O_3N$	131.1	238-41	36.11	v. sl. s. al.; i. eth.	H_2O	1.0	22	-75.2	5.82
30 L-Isoleucine	2-Amino-3-methyl-pentanoic acid	$C_6H_{13}O_2N$	131.17	283-4	4.12	0.09al.;i. eth. s.hot acet. a.	HCl, 6.1N	5.1	20	+40.6 (DL)	6.04(DL)
31 L-Lanthionine	β-Amino-β-carboxy-ethyl sulfide	$C_6H_{12}O_4N_2S$	208.3								
32 L-Leucine	2-Amino-4-methyl-pentanoic acid	$C_6H_{13}O_2N$	131.17	295	2.19	0.022 al.; i. eth.;s.acet.a.	HCl, 6.0N	2.0	26	+15.1	6.04(DL)
33 L-Lysine	2,6-Diaminohexanoic acid	$C_6H_{14}O_2N_2$	146.19	224	v. s.	v. sl. s. al.; i. eth.	HCl, 6.0N	2.0	23	+25.9	9.47
34 L-Methionine	α-Amino-γ-methylthio-n-butyric acid	$C_5H_{11}O_2NS$	149.21	283	5.75	i. al.	HCl, 0.2N	0.8	25	+21.2	5.74(DL)
35 L-Norleucine	α-Aminocaproic acid	$C_6H_{13}O_2N$	131.17	301	1.149(DL)	0.017(DL) al.	HCl, 6.0N	4.3	20	+21.3	6.08(DL)
36 L-Norvaline	2-Aminopentanoic acid	$C_5H_{11}O_2N$	117.1	291-2	10.7[6]	sl.s.al.;i.eth.	HCl, 20%	5	20	+22.8	
37 Octapine		$C_9H_{18}O_4N_4$	246.27								
38 L-Ornithine	2,5-Diaminopentanoic acid	$C_5H_{12}O_2N_2$	132.2	225	v. deliq.	v. s. al.;sl. s. eth.	H_2O	4.0	27	+16.5[7]	
39 L-Phenylalanine	α-Amino-β-phenyl-propionic acid	$C_9H_{11}O_2N$	165.2	283	2.96	sl. s. al.; i. eth.	H_2O	1.9	20	-35.1	5.91(DL)
40 L-Proline	2-Pyrrolidinecarboxylic acid	$C_5H_9O_2N$	115.1	220-2	162.3	1.55 al.; i. eth.	HCl, 0.5N	0.6	20	-52.6	6.3
41 Sarcosine	Methyl glycine	$C_3H_7O_2N$	89.1	210	v. s.					0	6.00
42 L-Serine	α-Amino-β-hydroxy-propionic acid	$C_3H_7O_3N$	105.1	228	5.023(DL)	i. al., eth.	HCl, 1.0N	9.3	25	+14.5	5.68(DL)
43 L-Thiolhistidine	α-Amino-β-2-thioimi-dazolepropionic acid	$C_6H_9O_2N_3S$	187.2				HCl, 1.0N	1.0	25	-9.5	
44 L-Threonine	α-Amino-β-hydroxy-n-butyric acid	$C_4H_9O_3N$	119.12	229-30	20.1(DL)	i. al., eth.	H_2O	1.0	26	-28.4	5.59
45 L-Thyroxine	α-Amino-β-[3,5-diiodo-4-(3',5'-diiodo-4'-hy-droxyphenoxy)phenyl]-propionic acid	$C_{15}H_{11}O_4NI_4$	776.9	235-6	0.001	i. al., eth.	NaOH, 0.13 N in 70% al.	3		-4.4	
46 L-Tryptophan	α-Amino-β-indole-propionic acid	$C_{11}H_{12}O_2N_2$	204.2	289	1.14	sl. s. al.; i. eth.	H_2O	1.0	20	-31.5	5.88
47 L-Tyrosine	α-Amino-β-(p-hydroxy-phenyl)propionic acid	$C_9H_{11}O_3N$	181.2	295	0.045	0.01 al.,i.eth., acet.s. alk.	HCl, 6.3N	4.4	20	-8.6	5.63
48 L-Valine	α-Aminoisovaleric acid	$C_5H_{11}O_2N$	117.15	293	8.85	0.019 al. (DL)	HCl, 6.0N	3.4	20	+28.8	6.00(DL)

/1/ Most amino acids decompose when they melt. /2/ a. =acid; acet. =acetone; acet. a. =acetic acid; al. =alcohol; alk. =alkali; deliq. =deliquescent; dil. =dilute; eth. =ether; i. =insoluble; s. =soluble; sl. =slightly; v. =very. /3/ DL=racemic mixture. /4/ Dihydrate. /5/ 3,4-Dihydroxyphenylalanine.
/6/ At 5°C. /7/ Dihydrochloride.

25. BIOLOGICAL SUBSTANCES: MOLECULAR SIZE AS DETERMINED BY IONIZING RADIATION

Values are "molecular weights" obtained at room temperature, except where noted, but do not have the accuracy and reliability of certain physical constants. Ionizing radiation can be used to determine approximate shape and structure of molecules as well as molecular weights.

	Material	Reported Molecular Size	Molecular Weight Determined by:[1]		Remarks
			Electrons	Heavy Particles	
1	ACTH	4566		2400	Entire molecule not needed for activity.
2	α-Amylase	100,000-200,000	145,000		Requires 3 simultaneous ionizations for inactivation.
3	Catalase	250,000		58,000 at 90°K 110,000 at 300°K 250,000 at 350°K 500,000 at 385°K	1/4, 1/2, 1, and 2 molecules (?).
4	Chymotrypsin	23,000	50,000	48,000 28,000	Casein digestion assay; polymer (?). Milk clotting assay.
5	Colicine K		60,000-90,000		
6	Cytochrome oxidase	75,000/mole hemin	160,000		Requires 3 simultaneous ionizations for inactivation.
7	Dehydrogenase, succinic	110,000-140,000	310,000		Requires 3 simultaneous ionizations for inactivation.
8	DNA (absorption spectrum unit)	1300 and 5500 found as digestion products.	2100	500 A^2	Breakup of larger DNA units increases absorption coefficient before digestion with DNA-ase.
9			700,000(X rays)		
10	DNA (pneumococcus transforming principle)		At least 2 components, one $<10^6$, another $>2\times10^6$.		Biologically active unit.
11			$(5-7)\times10^6$	Non-spherical	
12	DNA-ase	63,000	62,000	62,000	
13	Dysentery toxin		11,000	11,000	Toxic unit.
14	Gramicidin	8700	6400	6000	
15	Hemocyanin	$6.7-8 \times 10^6$		6,700,000	
16	Hemoglobin, pH5	67,000	46,000	46,000	
17	Hemoglobin, pH7	67,000	66,000		Requires 3 simultaneous ionizitations for inactivation; effect on solubility of molecule.
18	Hyaluronidase (HUA-ase)	65,000; 11,000 purified	75,000	75,000 (globular)	
19	Hyaluronic acid (HUA)		100,000	100,000 (long, thin)	Same at 90°K.
20	Hyaluronic acid-hyaluronidase complex			175,000	Assayed for enzyme activity.
21	Insulin	n x 6000	23,000	23,000 (spherical)	Assayed for biological activity.
22	Invertase	120,000	120,000	123,000	Varies with temperature.
23	Mucoprotein, sheep	87,000		82,000	Assumed long and thin.
24	Myosin	840,000	470,000		
25	Oxytocin	1007	1800		Dimer (?).
26	Penicillin	356		550	Cluster size comparable to molecular size.
27	Pepsin	36,000-39,000		39,000	
28	Peptides, di- and tri-	130-250		400-900	Assayed chromatographically; cluster size comparable to molecular size.
29	Ribonuclease	13,000	21,000 30,000 (X rays)		
30	Serum albumin, bovine, bulk	69,000	83,000		Requires 3 simultaneous ionizations for inactivation; effect on solubility of molecule.
31	Serum albumin, bovine, monolayer	69,000		7000	Serological unit.
32	Trypsin	15,000-24,000	34,000	31,000	Dimer (?); independent of substrate used for assay.
33	Trypsin (soybean) inhibitor	24,000 9,000	12,000	12,000	
34	Trypsin - STI complex	41,000 30,000	30,000	30,000	
35	Urease	100,000[2]	87,000	87,000	

/1/ For general description of method used to obtain molecular sizes from radiation data, and for references to original literature, see Pollard, E.C., et al, Progress in Biophysics 5:72, 1955. /2/ Recent value; old value 480,000.

26. PYRROLE PIGMENTS AND RELATED COMPOUNDS

Part I: PORPHYRINS

These pigments are derived from porphin (A) by substitution of the nuclear hydrogen atoms. There are four stereoisomers called "etioporphyrins" (I, II, III, IV) which are used as the basis for classifying naturally occurring porphyrins. The natural porphyrins correspond to etioporphyrins I and III; chlorophylls and hemoglobins are of type III only; free porphyrins are predominately of type III; small quantities of type I in physiological condition, great quantities in some pathological states.

A = (-CH₂:COOH); B = (-CHO); D = (-CO-CH₃); E = (-CH₂:CH₃); H = hydrogen; M = (-CH₃); P = (-CH₂:CH₂:COOH); V = (-CH:CH₂); X = (-CO-CH₂-)[1]; Y = [-CH(OH)-CH₃]; Z = [-CO-CH(COO-CH₃)-][1]

Porphin

(A)

Etioporphyrins

(I) (II) (III) (IV)

Porphyrin Precursor (Porphobilinogen)

HOOC-H₂C-C — C-CH₂CH₂COOH
H₂N-H₂C-C   CH
          N
          H

(See Line 11)

#	Porphyrin	Substituents in Positions[2] 1;2	3;4	5;6	7;8	Physical and Chemical Properties[3,4]	Form[6]	Solvent[4]	I	II	III	IV	Soret	Occurrence in Nature
1	Chlorocruro-porphyrin	M;B	M;V	M;P	P;M									Fe complex prosthetic group of chlorocruorin of Sabellid worms.
2	Coproporphyrin I (C₃₆H₃₈O₈N₄)	M;P	M;P	M;P	P;M	MP me.est. = 248-258°C; HCl No. me.est.1.5; s.eth.-ac.a.	Free, or me.est.	Neutral (eth.-ac.a.)	623.5	568	528.5	495	405	Free form in feces, urine, erythrocytes, bile, yeast, bacteria. Widespread in traces in animals, plants, microorganisms. Increased pathologically in porphyrinurias and porphyrias.
3	Coproporphyrin III (C₃₆H₃₈O₈N₄)	M;P	M;P	M;P	P;M	MP me.est.=137°C; remelts at 172°C; HCl No.me.est. = 1.5;s.eth.-ac.a.								
4	Deuteropor-phyrin IX (C₃₀H₃₀O₄N₄)	M;H	H;M	M;P	P;M	MP me.est. = 218-224°C; HCl No. me.est. 2.0; s. chl.			621.5	566	526	494		Free form in human feces.
5	Mesoporphyrin (C₃₄H₃₈O₄N₄)	M;E	E;M	M;P	P;M	MP me.est. = 216°C; HCl No. me. est. 2.5.		Neutral(eth.-ac.a) / Pyridine	623.5	567.5	528.5	494.5	391	Free form in human feces, ambergris.
6	Oxopheopor-phyrin-a₅	M;D	E;M	M;E	Z;P;M									Mg complex of 3,4,7,8-tetrahydroporphyrin, esterified with phytol (in side chain 7): bacteriochlorophyll. Another porphyrin with an acetyl side chain is probably the prosthetic group of milk peroxidase.
7	Pheoporphyrin-a₅	M;E	M;E	M;E	Z;P;M									
8	Pheoporphyrin-b₆	M;E	B;E	M;E	Z;P;M									
9	Vinylpheopor-phyrin-a₅	M;E	V;M	M;E	Z;P;M									Mg complex in chlorella mutant esterified with phytol in 7=protochlorophyll. Mg complex of 7,8-dihydroporphyrin esterified with phytol in 7=chlorophyll a,
10	Vinylpheopor-phyrin-b₆	M;E	B;V	M;E	Z;P;M									Mg complex of 7,8-dihydroporphyrin esterified with phytol in 7=chlorophyll b.
11	Phylloerythrin IX (C₃₃H₃₄O₃N₄)	M;E	M;E	M;X	P;M	MP me. est. = 213°C; HCl No.free porphyrin 7-9.	Free	Acetone	636.8	589.4	560.8	521.8		Free form in feces and bile of ruminants.
12	Porphobilinogen (C₁₀H₁₄O₄N₂) (monopyrrole)	A;P	-	-	-	MP hydrochloride = 165-170°C; i.c.w., org. solvents.								Obligatory precursor for biosynthesis of porphyrins and heme; in urine in hepatic porphyria, lead and sedormid poisoning; gives red compound with Ehrlich's reagent which is insoluble in CHCl₃.
13	Porphyrin a (cytoporphyrin)	Two or three M, 2 P, 1 B, one long alkyl, probably IV.												Fe complex prosthetic group of cytochrome oxidase (cytochrome-a₃) and cytochrome-a, a₁.

Spectral Characteristics λ-maximum in mμ[5]

(continued table: Porphyrins)

#	Substance	Substituents[1,2]	Physical Properties[4]	Spectral maxima[5] (Neutral (eth.-ac.a) / Pyridine)					Remarks
14	Protoporphyrin IX ($C_{34}H_{34}O_4N_4$)	M V M V M P P M	MP me. est. = 225–230°C; HCl No. me. est. 5.5; s. eth.-ac.a.	623.5	576	537	502	395	Free form in bone marrow, erythrocytes, feces, chloroma, Harderian glands (rodents), bird egg shells, earthworm. Fe complex (heme) prosthetic group of hemoglobins, myoglobins, catalase, peroxidase (horseradish), cytochrome-b, cytochrome-c (modified). Mg complex in chlorella mutant.
15	Uroporphyrin I ($C_{40}H_{38}O_{16}N_4$)	A P A P A P A P	MP me. est. = 293°C; HCl No. ?; i.eth.-ac.a; extr. from aq. sol. (pH 3.0–3.2) with eth. acetate.	Free, or me. est.					Very small amounts in normal human urine, larger amounts in some forms of porphyria and lead poisoning. Also present in mollusk shells and some plants. Normal in urine of Sciurus niger. Porphyrins with 5–7 carboxyl groups also occur.
16	Uroporphyrin III ($C_{40}H_{38}O_{16}N_4$)	A P A P P A	MP me. est. = 264°C; other properties same as Uroporphyrin I.	Chloroform 626	570.5	536	501	408	Very small amounts in urine, larger amounts in some forms of porphyria and sedormid poisoning. Cu complex: turacin in turaco feathers may serve as source of uroporphyrin III.

/1/ Substituent groups X and Z constitute bridges between C 6 and C_γ. /2/ Letters in the columns refer to substituents (abbreviated as per code) appearing in the position indicated by column number (numbers correspond to those in reference structural formula). /3 All porphyrins show a strongly red fluorescence in Wood's light both in acid and alkaline solutions and in many neutral solutions. /4/ Abbreviations: ac.a. = acetic acid; aq. = aqueous; c. = cold; est. = ester; eth. = ether; i = insoluble; me. = methyl; MP = melting point; s. = soluble. /5/ λ maximum in mμ = wave length of maximum absorption. /6/ Free porphyrin and its ester give the same bands in the same solvent.

Part II: IRON-PORPHYRIN PIGMENTS

#	Substance	General Nature	Physical and Chemical Properties[1]	Spectral Characteristics λ maximum in mμ[2]	Remarks
	Heme Compounds				
1	Hematin (hydroxyhemin) ($C_{34}H_{35}O_7N_4Fe$)	Fe^{+++} complex of protoporphyrin; moderately stable.	s. alk.	Alcohol HCl 400(131-151); Acetic acid 630-635 540 510 400(SOCH) $E^{1\%}$ 1960-2260; 10% NaOH 580(10.5); Alcoholic NaHCO$_3$ 590 402.5(79.5) $E^{1\%}_{1 cm}$ 1190; Ether 650; Reducing agent (Stoke's) produces hemochromogen bands.	Produced by atmospheric oxidation of heme; present in serum in hemolytic and pernicious anemia, malaria, congenital porphyria, certain poisonings, septicemia, severe liver damage; bound to serum albumin as methemalbumin; occasionally present in bile, feces, urine.
2	Heme (protoheme IX) ($C_{34}H_{32}O_4N_4Fe$)	Fe^{++} complex of protoporphyrin; extremely unstable, easily oxidized to hematin.	Fe removed by dilute HCl in glac. ac. a.	Phosphate buffer, pH 7 550 575 415(Soret) $E^{1\%}_{1cm}$ 895	Occurs as prosthetic group of hemoglobin; combines with many N-containing bases to form hemochromes.
3	Hemin (chlorohemin) ($C_{34}H_{32}O_4N_4FeCl$)	Crystalline chloride of hematin; stable.	Br. or blk. cryst.; s. dil. alk., strong organic bases; i.a.	0.1N KOH 645.2 591 539.7	Not found in nature. Crystals sinter at 240°C, melt at 300°C. Converted to hemochromogen by Na$_2$S$_2$O$_4$ +pyridine.
4	Methemalbumin (ferrihemalbumin)	Compound of hematin and serum albumin. Iron is in Fe^{+++} state.	Easily soluble in water as serum albumin.	(Best identified by conversion to hemochromogen) 623 540 500; Reduction to Fe^{++} analogue 570 530 (ferrohemalbumin)	Found in plasma in blackwater fever, severe anemias, severe liver damage, blood extravasates, etc.
5	Pyridine hemochromogen	Compound of heme + pyridine, 2 molecules of which are coordinately linked with the Fe atom. Term "hemochromogen" or "hemochrome" also used generically for coordination compounds of heme with nitrogenous bases.	(Spectrum unstable in presence of dithionite (cf HbS)) 558(31-35.3) 525(16.2)	Term "hemochromogen" also used generically for nitrogenous compounds combined with heme; all have similar spectra.
6	Spirographishemin (chlorocrurohemin) ($C_{33}H_{32}O_5N_4FeCl$)	Hemin of chlorocruoroporphyrin.	Same as hemin (above).	CO compound of chlorocruoroheme. 410(Soret)	Prosthetic group in chlorocruorins. No function per se, only as part of chlorocruorins.
	Hemoglobin Compounds				
7	Carboxyhemoglobin	Compound of 4 molecules CO per 4 Fe of Hb; iron in Fe^{++} state.	MW = 66,700. Solubility similar to that of Hb.	568-572(13.7-15) 538-540(14.1-15.3) 418(154)	Diluted solutions are pink (cf HbO$_2$); also distinguished from HbO$_2$ by stability of spectrum in presence of reducing agents.
8	Hemoglobin (Hb)	Four heme molecules + globin; iron in Fe^{++} state.	MW = 66,700; easily soluble in water, varying with pH and salt concentration; red-purple color.	Main band at 560 555[12.9-13.6] 430[Soret] (118-134) { Slight variation according to species of origin.	O$_2$ carrier in red corpuscles of all vertebrates. Combines reversibly with O$_2$ to form oxyhemoglobin, and with CO to form carboxyhemoglobin (affinity for CO 400 x that for O$_2$). Several varieties of human Hb known: A, F, S, C, D, E, G.

/1/ Abbreviations: a. = acid; ac.a. = acetic acid; alk. = alkali(ne); blk. = black; br. = brown; cryst. = crystal; dil. = dilute; i. = insoluble; MW = molecular weight; s. = soluble. /2/ λ maximum in mμ = wave length of maximum absorption; figures in parentheses are $E^{1\%}_{1cm}$, i.e., extinction coefficients of millimolar solutions of 1cm thickness; $E^{1\%}_{1cm}$ = extinction coefficients of 1% solutions of 1cm thickness.

26. PYRROLE PIGMENTS AND RELATED COMPOUNDS (Continued)

Part II: IRON PORPHYRIN PIGMENTS (Concluded)

	Substance	General Nature	Physical and Chemical Properties[1]	Spectral Characteristics maximum in $m\mu$[2]	Remarks
9	Methemoglobin (Met Hb)	Like Hb, except iron is in Fe^{+++} state.	MW = 66,700; solubility differs from Hb, depending on pH.	Acid solution 630(3.7-3.8) 500(9.5) 405-407(Soret)(134-154) Alk. solution 577(9.5) 540(9.7) 411 (Soret) (71-90) Addition of Stoke's reagent produces spectrum of Hb (cf hematin)	Small amounts normally present in red blood cells. Larger amounts formed by oxidation (K ferricyanide, nitrites, chlorates, phenacetin, sulfonamides).
10	Myohemoglobin (Mb or MHb)	Heme + globin (different from globin in Hb), Fe^{++} readily oxidized to Fe^{+++} (Met Hb).	MW = 16,900-19,000. More soluble than Hb in sat. $(NH_4)_2SO_4$; more alkali resistant than Hb.	Aqueous solution 555 435 Myooxyhemoglobin is differentiated from oxyhemoglobin by the position of its α-band at 582 mμ.	In all muscles of higher vertebrates, terrestrial and aquatic; also in nematodes, mollusks. Main function is to store O_2 in muscles (completely saturated with O_2 at low pressures).
11	Oxyhemoglobin (HbO_2)	Compound of Hb with 4 equivalents of oxygen, available physiologically; iron in Fe^{++} state.	MW = 66,700. Solubility similar to Hb. Bright red color.	577(15.1-16.2) 540-542(14.2-15.3) 412-415 (Soret)(125-128.3)	Present in fresh blood of all vertebrates; diluted solutions are yellow (cf HbCO); reduced to Hb by dithionite with color changes from rose to violet-red.
12	Sulfhemoglobin (HbS)	From treatment of Hb with H_2S; O_2 (chemical structure not definitely ascertained); not more than 10% HbS formed.	MW = 66,700. Solubility similar to that of Hb.	617 623 (11L) Band stable in presence of dithionite (cf methemalbumin) and in presence of $NaCN/Na_2CO_3$. 620 (CO) 612 618 (16)	No physiological function; pathological product; occurs in erythrocytes after administration of sulfur, sulfonamides, trinitrotoluene, aromatic amines, and in certain septicemias.
13	Chlorocruorin (Ch)	Globin + chlorocruroheme (molecule contains many such units).	MW about 3 x 10⁶. Solubility similar to Hb.	Reduced form 574 (broad band) Oxidized form 604 560 CO compound 600 507	Found in several species of annelids (Polychaeta), e.g., Spirographis, a marine worm.
14	Choleglobin	Native globin + prosthetic group (composition not clear). Formed by coupled oxidation of Hb with ascorbic acid.	Solubility similar to Hb. Degradation product yields biliverdin.	629 Fe^{++} compound (aqueous solution) 674 Fe^{++}CO compound (aqueous solution) 628	Formed in blood in certain septicemias and poisonings (phenylhydrazine). Is normal Hb degradation product intermediary in bile pigment formation.
15	Erythrocruorins (invertebrate hemoglobins)	Protoheme + globins (different from vertebrate globins).	Solubility similar to Hb. Combines similarly to Hb with O_2 and CO_2.	Absorption maxima similar to Hb with minor differences according to species.	Occurs in nematodes, annelids, crustaceans, insects, mollusks, echinoderms.
				Hematin Enzymes	
16	Catalase	Hematin-containing enzyme; catalyzes decomposition of H_2O_2, and peroxidation of certain substrates by H_2O_2.	MW about 220,000. 4 hematins per molecule. Iron is Fe^{+++}, not reducible by $Na_2S_2O_4$.	629-622(10.8) 544-536 506.5-500 409-400(145) 280-266	Present in aerobic cells, highly concentrated in a few animal tissues (liver, red cells); absent only in strict anaerobes, and a few facultative anaerobes. Catalytic activity inhibited by cyanide, H_2S, hydroxylamine, azide, o-aminophenol, 2,4-dichlorophenol and other compounds.
17	Cytochromes a, a₃; a₁, a₂	Heme of porphyrin a (Part I, No. 13) is prosthetic group of a, a₃ and probably a₁; heme of chlorin is prosthetic group of a₂.	MW unknown. a₃ probably in mitochondria, probably as lipoprotein complex. Soluble only as complex with cholate and similar compounds.	Reduced a₃ + a 605-600 (due to a₃ and a) 445 (due mainly to a₃) a₃CO 590-430 (a does not react with CO) Reduced a₁ 590 435-440 Reduced a₂ 635-630 (Soret band weak or absent)	Cytochromes a₃, probably also a₁ and a₂, react directly with oxygen (oxidases; cytochrome-a only electron carrier); a₃ + a widespread in animals, plants, and some bacteria; a₁ and a₂ in other bacteria.[4]
18	Cytochrome-c, c₁[3]	Prosthetic group based on hematoporphyrin modified by firm sulfur linkages to cysteine groups of protein.	MW = 13,500-16,000. Soluble, very stable protein; nonauto oxidizable, does not react with CO. E_0' (pH 7.0, 37°C) = 0.25 volts.	Cytochrome Fe++ 550(26-28) 522(15.5-16.9) 415(143) 345 316 Fe+++ 565 (indistinct) 530(9.4-9.7) 407(112) 346	Occurs in all animal and plant cells, and in cells of most microorganisms. Specific electron carrier reacting with cytochrome-a.
19	Cytochromes b	Prosthetic group protoheme; for b₂ = protoheme + flavin.	Only b₂ (lactic dehydrogenase of yeast) prepared as soluble cryst. enzyme; b in mitochondria. All members rendered autooxidizable, do not react with CO. E_0' of b (pH7.0, 37°C) = 0 (approx.)	Reduced band in region 565-555 Soret band about 430	Essential electron carriers below cytochrome-c in the respiratory chain. Occur in all living cells of animals, plants and microorganisms, except strict anerobes.

| 20 | Peroxidases | MW = 44,100, with one hema-tin group. Soluble enzyme. Iron Fe^{+++} reduced by dithionite. | In neutral solution 645(12) 583 548 498 / 558 594 (weak) Dithionite Iron Fe^{+++} reduced by dithionite. | | Prosthetic groups (1) for horse-radish and cytochrome-c per-oxidases = protohemin; (2) for lactic peroxidase = hemin (of a different porphyrin); (3) for myeloperoxidase = group similar to that of choleglobin. | Peroxidases occur in plants and animals; biological functions still inadequately known. Detection by treatment of material with H_2O_2 + benzidine: green color develops. |

/1/ Abbreviations: a. = acid; ac. a. = acetic acid; alk. = alkali(ne); blk. = black; br. = brown; cryst. = crystal; dil. = dilute; i. = insoluble; MW = molecular weight; s. = soluble. /2/ λ maximum in mμ = wave length of maximum absorption; figures in parentheses are E_{1cm}, i.e., extinction coefficients of millimolar solutions of 1 cm thickness; $E^{1\%}_{1cm}$ = extinction coefficients of 1% solutions of 1cm thickness. /3/ As usually used, "cytochrome oxidase" (cytochrome-c oxidase) equals a_3 + a, strictly only a_3 (atmungsferment); cytochromes a_1 and a_2 are also oxidases in microorganisms. /4/ Respiration inhibited by cyanide, azide, particularly CO (specific light reversion of inhibition).

Part III: THE BILIRUBINOIDS AND RELATED DIPYRRYL COMPOUNDS

These are derivatives of the tetrapyrrolic structure (A) formed by varying degrees of oxidation, and substitution of the nuclear H atoms 1, 2, 3, 4, 5, 6, 7, 8. While formula (A) describes the bilirubinoids as linear tetrapyrrolic chains with terminal hydroxyl groups, their structure is more correctly described as that of a tetrapyrrolic ring closed by a hydrogen bond between oxygen atoms (N>CO-HOC≦N). All natural members are derived from Fischer's protoporphyrin IX by fission at the α-methene link. They are therefore known as Bilirubinoids IX-a.

The main characteristics are as follows:
(Gm) Gmelin reaction: given by bilirubins; the later stages also by biliverdins and bilipurpurins.
(Di) Diazo reaction: depending on the splitting of the molecule at a central -CH_2- group.
(Eh) Ehrlich reaction: characteristic of bilanes.
(Pe) Pentdyopent reaction: given by most bile pigments, hematin compounds and dipyrryl methenes.
(Sc) Schlesinger reaction: given by dipyrryl methenes.
(Fe) Ferric chloride reaction: given by all except trienes and more highly oxidized pigments, and except tetrahydromesobilane and -bilene; - = negative reaction.

Substituent groups: E = (-CH_2CH_3); M = (-CH_3); OH = hydroxyl; H, H_2 = hydrogen; P = (-CH_2:CH_2:COOH); V = (-CH:CH_2). + = positive reaction; (+) = non-characteristic reaction; - = negative reaction.

Substance	Substituents in Positions 1 2 3 4 5 6 7 8 / 1' 2' 3' 4' 5' 6' 7' 8'	Physical and Chemical Properties[1]	Spectral Characteristics λ maximum in mμ[2]	Reactions Gm Di Eh Pe Sc Fe	Remarks
			Bilanes and Hydrobilanes		
1 Mesobilane (mesobili-rubinogen, uro-bilinogen IX-a) ($C_{33}H_{44}O_6N_4$)	M E M P P M M E / H H_2 H H_2 H H_2 H H +4H	Colorl. cryst.;MP = 199°C; s. al., am. al., chl., dil. alk.; sl. s. eth.; i.w.		- - + + - -	Hemoglobin degradation product. In feces; a little in normal, more in pathological urine and bile. Distinguish from 2 (below) by Fe reaction or by violet pigment (bands at 665, 600, 510 mμ) on warming with $NaOH$-$CuSO_4$.
2 Tetrahydromeso-bilane (sterco-bilinogen) ($C_{33}H_{42}O_6N_4$)	M E M P P M M E / H H_2 H H_2 H H_2 H H +4H	Colorl., non-cryst.;MP = 125-150°C; s.al., am.al., chl., dil. alk.; sl.s. eth.; i.w.	Red pigment (s. chl.) on treatment with Ehrlich reagent: about 560 mμ(64.5).	- + - + - -	Main excretory product of hemoglobin in most vertebrates. Distinguish from 1 (above) by negative Fe reaction, or $NaOH$-$CuSO_4$ reaction (only one band at 530-500 mμ).
			Bilenes and Hydrobilenes		
3 Mesobilene (urobilin IX-a) ($C_{33}H_{42}O_6N_4$)	M E M P P M M E / H H_2 H H_2 H H_2 H OH	Reddish yel. col.; MP free substance 190°C.; HCl = 199°C; s. al., chl., dil. alk.; sl.s.eth.; i.w.	Dioxane 452(25.1) 330(3.6) / Alcohol HCl 490(50.1) 375(7.4) / Zn complex in me. al. 509.5	- - - + - +	Oxidation product of 1 (above). Distinguish from 4 (below) by positive Fe and Pe reactions, optical inactivity and band position in alcohol HCl in reversion spectroscope.
4 Tetrahydromeso-bilene (stercobilin) ($C_{33}H_{46}O_6N_4$)	M E M P P M M E / H H_2 H H_2 H H_2 H OH +4H	Reddish yel.col.; MP free substance 236°C.; HCl = 165°C; s. al., chl., dil. alk.; sl. s. eth.; i.w.	Dioxane 456(33.0) 372(8.5) / Alcohol HCl 488(55) / E band (Na salt in H_2SO_4) 530 / Zn complex in alcohol 506.5 / Cu complex in alcohol 515 / $[\alpha]^{20}$ free 320 / D.HCl 3800	- - - + - -	Oxidation product of 2 (above). Distinguish from 3 (above) by stability in presence of $FeCl_3$, negative Pe reaction and optical activity (levorotatory).

/1/ Abbreviations: ac.a. = acetic acid; acet. = acetone; al. = alcohol; alk. = alkali(ne); am. = amyl; bz. = benzene; chl. = chloroform; col. = color; colorl. = colorless; cryst. = crystal(line); dil. = dilute; dimeth. = dimethyl; est. = ester; eth. = ether; eth. ac. = ethyl acetate; glac. = glacial; grn. = green; i. = insoluble; MP = melting point; me. = methyl; or. = orange; purp. = purple; pyr. = pyridine; sl. = slightly; s. = soluble; vlt. = violet; w. = water; yel. = yellow. /2/ λmaximum in mμ = wave length of maximum absorption; figures in parentheses are E_{1cm}, i.e., extinction coefficients of millimolar solution of 1cm thickness.

Part III: THE BILIRUBINOIDS AND RELATED DIPYRRYL COMPOUNDS (Concluded)

	Substance	Physical and Chemical Properties[1]	Spectral Characteristics λmaximum in mμ[2]	Reactions: Gm, Di, Eh, Pe, Sc, Fe	Remarks
			Biladienes		
5	Bilirubin ($C_{33}H_{36}O_6N_4$)	Or. col.; MP dimeth. ester 198-200°C; sol. hot pyr., hot chl., CCl_4; dil. alk.; sl.s. acet., eth. ac.; i.w., al., eth.	Chloroform 450(56), NaOH 420	+ − + + + +	Breakdown product of heme compounds in bile, feces of newborn, hemorrhagic infarcts (hematoidin), gallstones. Present in serum, urine, tissues during jaundice. Reduction with Na/Hg gives mesobilane. Sc reaction with iodine: 635 mμ band of bilipurpurin.
6	Mesobilierythrin (mesobilirhodin) ($C_{33}H_{40}O_6N_4$)	Red col.; s. bz., chl.; sl.s.eth.; i.w.	HCl/chloroform 605(weak) 557(weak) 497, 560 495; Zn complex in alcohol 630(weak) 509	− − + + Sc: grn.-yel. fluorescence +	Prosthetic group of phycoerythrin of red and some blue algae; efficient photo-sensitizer in algal photosynthesis. Related compound in Aplysia.
7	Mesobilirubin ($C_{33}H_{40}O_6N_4$)	Yel. or or.col.; MP free substance = 315°C, dimeth. ester = 190°C; s.pyr., chl., dil. alk.; sl. s. eth. ac., eth., i.w.	Chloroform 425(61.4)	+ − + + − +	Possibly present in small intestine. Reduction with Na/Hg gives mesobilane. Sc reaction with iodine: 625 mμ band of mesobilipurpurin.
8	Mesobiliviolin ($C_{33}H_{40}O_6N_4$)	Vlt. col.;MP·HCl = 165°C, s.bz., chl.; sl.s.eth.;i.w.	Chloroform 570-575, Aqueous HCl 598, Zn complex in alcohol 625-629 575(weak)	− − + + Sc: red fluorescence +	In human feces, probably derived from mesobilane. Prosthetic group of phyco-cyanins (chromoproteins of red and blue algae) which act as efficient photosensitizers in algal photosynthesis. Related compound in Aplysia.
			Bilatrienes		
9	Biliverdin[3] ($C_{33}H_{34}O_6N_4$)	Blue-grn.col.; MP dimeth. est. = 215°C; s. hot meth. al., hot glac. ac.a., dil. alk.; sl.s.eth., chl., dil.HCl; i.w.	Methyl alcohol 640(10.4) 392(25), 5% HCl/methyl alcohol 680(28) 377(48), Aqueous HCl/alcohol λmax 675 λmin 500	+ − + + − −	In gr. bile of some animals, egg shells of many birds (oocyan), placenta of some mammals (uteroverdin), hematomas. Green stage of Gmelin reaction. Biliverdin-iron present as prosthetic group of (inactive) liver catalase. Sc reaction with iodine same as for bilirubin.
10	Glaucobilin (mesobiliverdin) ($C_{33}H_{38}O_6N_4$)	Grn.-blue col.;MP free substance = 316-318°C, dimeth. est. = 214-223°C; s. hot me. al., dil. alk.; sl.s.eth., chl., dil.HCl; i.w.	5% HCl/methyl alcohol 670(30.9) 363(46.8) 309(17.8)	+ − + + + −	Glaucobilin or related bilatrienes present in hemolymph and integuments of insects (coelenterates, mollusks, annelids). Sc reaction with iodine same as for meso-bilirubin.
			Biladienones		
11	Bilichrysin ($C_{33}H_{34}O_7N_4$) and meso compound	Yel. col. MP;(mesobilichrysin) = 240°C.	Mesobilichrysin in NH_3/alcohol 416(40.5) 311(23)	(+) (+) − +(+) Sc: red fluorescence +	Isomerization product of bilipurpurin.
12	Bilipurpurin ($C_{33}H_{34}O_7N_4$) and related compounds	Red-purp. col.	Zn complex in alcohol 635-645, Meso compound 619-630	− − + + Sc: red fluorescence −	Purple stage of Gmelin reaction and other oxidations of bilirubins and biliverdin. Resembles biliviolins.
13	Choletelin ($C_{33}H_{34}O_8N_4$) and related compounds	Yel. col.	HCl/alcohol 490-495, Zn complex in alcohol 505-515	− − + + Sc: grn. fluorescence −	Yellow stage of Gmelin reaction and other oxidations of bilirubin, biliverdin, bilipurpurin. Resembles urobilins.
			Dipyrryl Compounds		
14	Probilifuscins, bilifuscins, propentdyopents ($C_{16}H_{18-20}O_{4-5}N_2$) their oxidation products.	Colorl. except bilifuscins, which are brown polymerization and oxidation products of probilifuscins. Propentdyopents are red in NaOH-$Na_2S_2O_4$ (pentdyopent).	Characteristic absorption bands in NaOH-$Na_2S_2O_4$ at about 525 (523-525) account for name "pent-dyopent."	No characteristic reaction.	Secondary products of oxidation of bile pigments and hematin compounds, excreted in urine and feces in jaundice and liver disease; present in gallstones.

/1/ Abbreviations: ac.a. = acetic acid; acet. = acetone; al. = alcohol; alk. = alkali(ne); am. = amyl; bz. = benzene; chl. = chloroform; col. = color; colorl. = colorless; cryst. = crystal(line); dil. = dilute; dimeth. = dimethyl; est. = ester; eth. = ether; eth. ac. = ethyl acetate; glac. = glacial; grn. = green; i. = insoluble; MP = melting point; me. = methyl; or. = orange; purp. = purple; pyr. = pyridine; sl. = slightly; s. = soluble; vlt. = violet; w. = water; yel. = yellow. /2/ λmaximum in mμ = wave length of maximum absorption; figures in parentheses are E_{1cm}, i.e., extinction coefficients of millimolar solutions of 1 cm thickness. /3/ Oxidation product of bilirubin.

Flavones · Flavonols · Isoflavones · Isoflavanones

Flavanones · Chalcones · Dihydrochalcones · Benzophenones

Xanthones · Chromones · Aurones · Flavanonols

Catechins · Anthocyanidins

	Pigment	Melting Point, °C [1]	Hydroxyl Position, C-	Methoxyl Position, C-	Source
				Flavones	
1	Acacetin	261 (203)	5, 7	4'	Robinia pseudoacacia (leaves).
2	Acrammerin	350 (232)	5, 7, 3', 4', 5'	8	Gleditsia triacanthos (pods).
3	Apigenin	348 (182)	5, 7, 4'		Parsley (leaves, stems, flowers), Dahlia spp (white flowers).
4	Baicalein	266 (192)	5, 6, 7		Scutellaria baicalensis (roots).
5	Chrysin	275 (192)	5, 7		Populus monilifera balsamifera (buds), Oroxylum indicum (bark).
6	Chrysoeriol	325 (215)	5, 7, 4'	3'	Eriodictyon glutinosum.
7	Diosmetin	255 (196)	5, 7, 3'	4'	Scrophularia nodosa, Dahlia variabilis.
8	Flavone	100			Primula spp.
9	Fukugetin	5, 7, 3', 4'	5, 7, 3', 4'	(6-epoxy-p-hydroxy-cinnamoyl)	Garcinia spicata (bark), Xanthocymus ovalifolia (bark).
10	Genkwanin	286 (198)	5, 4'	7	Daphne genkwa (flowers), Prunus puddum (bark).
11	5-Hydroxy-7, 4'-methoxyflavone	175 (199)	5	7, 4'	Betula spp (leaf buds).
12	Lotoflavin	300 (178)	5, 7, 2', 4'		Lotus arabicus.
13	Luteolin	331 (226)	5, 7, 3', 4'		Chrysanthemum indicum (flowers), Digitalis purpurea (leaves), celery (seeds).
14	Nobiletin	134		5, 6, 7, 8, 3', 4'	Citrus nobilis (fruit peel).
15	Oroxylin-A	232 (132)	5, 7	6	Oroxylum indicum (root bark).
16	Pectolinarigenin	216 (151)	5, 7	6, 4'	Linaria vulgaris (flowers).
17	Primetin	231 (189)	5, 8		Primula modesta (leaves).
18	Primuletin	157 (145)	5		Primula spp.
19	Scutellarein	350 (237)	5, 6, 7, 4'		Scutellaria altissima (flowers, leaves), Galeopsis tetrahit, Teucrium chamaedrys.
20	Tectochrysin	163 (149)	5	7	Populus pyramidalis, P. nigra (buds), Pinus strobus (heartwood).
21	Tricin	292 (254)	5, 7, 4'	3', 5'	Triticum dicoccum (leaves).
22	Wogonin	203 (153)	5, 7	8	Scutellaria baicalensis.
				Flavonols	
23	Auranetin	140		3, 6, 7, 8, 4'	Citrus aurantium (fruit peel).
24	Ayanin	173 (177)	5, 3'	3, 7, 4'	Disthemonanthus benthamianus (heartwood).
25	Datiscetin	276 (141)	3, 5, 7, 2'		Datisca cannabina (leaves), Paeonia albiflora var. hortensis.
26	Erianthin	154 (163)	5, 7	3, 6, 8, 3', 4'	Blumea eriantha (flowers).
27	Fisetin	330 (200)	3, 7, 3', 4'		Rhus spp, Quebracho colorado (wood).
28	Galangin	215 (144)	3, 5, 7		Alpinia officinarum (rhizome).
29	Galangin monomethyl ether	299 (176)	5, 7	3	A. officinarum (rhizome).
30	Gardenin	162 (136)	5	3, 6, 8, 3', 4', 5'	Gardenia lucida (gum).
31	Gossypetin	314 (230)	3, 5, 7, 8, 3', 4'		Gossypium spp, Hibiscus spp (flowers).
32	Herbacetin	283 (193)	3, 5, 7, 8, 4'		Gossypium indicum, G. herbaceum (flowers).
33	Hibiscetin	350 (244)	3, 5, 7, 8, 3', 4', 5'		Hibiscus sabdariffa (flowers).
34	Icaritin	240 (147)[2]	3, 5, 7	4'-(8-γ-hydroxy-isoamyl)	Epimedium macranthum.
35	Isorhamnetin	305 (205)	3, 5, 7, 4'	3'	Cheiranthus cheiri, Trifolium pratense, Cassia acutifolia, etc.
36	Izalpinin	195 (171)	3, 5	7	Alpinia spp (seeds).
37	Kanugin	205		3, 7, 3'-(4', 5'-methylenedioxy)	Pongamia glabra.

/1/ Values in parentheses are for the fully acetylated derivatives unless otherwise noted. /2/ Tetraacetate.

Part I: FLAVONES, CHALCONES, XANTHONES, AND RELATED COMPOUNDS (Continued)

	Pigment	Melting Point, °C[1]	Hydroxyl Position, C-	Methoxyl Position, C-	Source
			Flavonols (concluded)		
38	Karanjin	159		3 ([7,8:5",4"]-furano)	Pongamia glabra.
39	Kaempferide	229 (195)	3,5,7	4'	Alpinia officinarum (rhizomes)
40	Kaempferol	278 (181)	3,5,7,4'		Robinia pseudoacacia (flowers), Indigofera arrecta (leaves), Gossypium herbaceum, etc.
41	Melisimplexin	185		3,5,6,7 (3',4'-methylenedioxy)	Melicope simplex (bark).
42	Melisimplin	235 (202)	5	3,6,7 (3',4'-methylenedioxy)	Melicope simplex (bark).
43	Meliternatin	199		3,5 (6,7,3',4'-dimethylenedioxy)	Melicope ternata (bark).
44	Meliternin	186		3,5,7,8 (3',4'-methylenedioxy)	Melicope ternata (bark).
45	Morin	290 (145)[3]	3,5,7,2',4'		Chlorophora tinctoria (wood).
46	Myricetin	361 (216)	3,5,7,3',4',5'		Myrica magi, M. rubra (bark), Ampelopsis meliaefolia.
47	Nor-β-anhydroicaritin[4]	305 (212)	3,5,4'	(2",2"-dimethyl-[7,8 6",5"]-chromano)	Phellodendron amurense (leaves).
48	Ombuin	230 (212)	3,5,3'	7,4'	Phytolacca dioica (leaves).
49	Patuletin	264 (172)	3,5,7,3',4'	6	Tagetes patula (flowers).
50	Quercetagetin	320 (211)	3,5,6,7,3',4'		Tagetes patula, T. erecta (flowers).
51	Quercetin	317 (194)	3,5,7,3',4'		Quercus tinctoria (bark), Prunus serotina, Helianthus annus, etc.
52	Rhamnazin	216 (155)	3,5,4'	7,3'	Polygonum hydropiper, Rhamnus infectoria.
53	Rhamnetin	296 (192)	3,5,3',4'	7	Rhamnus cathartica.
54	Rhamnocitrin	222 (201)	3,5,4'	7	Rhamnus cathartica (fruit).
55	Robinetin	330 (224)	3,7,3',4',5'		Robinia pseudoacacia, Gleditsia monosperma (wood).
56	Tambuletin	271 (142)	3,5,7,4'	8	Zanthoxylum acanthopodium (seeds).
57	Tambulin	205 (165)	3,5	7,8,4'	Z. acanthopodium (seeds).
58	Tangeretin	154		3,5,6,7,4'	Citrus nobilis deliciosa (fruit peel).
59	Ternatin	211 (166)	5,4'	3,7,8,3'	Melicope ternata (bark).
60	Thapsin (Calycopterin)	226 (129)	5,4'	3,6,7,8	Digitalis thapsi, Calycopteris floribunda (leaves).
61	Biochanin-A (Olmelin)	212 (190)	5,7	4'	Cicer arietenum (seeds), Gleditsia triacanthos.
62	Daidzein	323 (187)	7,4'		Soja hispida (seeds).
63	Ferreirin	212	5,7,2'	4'	Ferreirea spectabilis (heartwood)
64	Formononetin	257 (170)	7	4'	Ononis spinosa.
65	Genistein	291 (202)	5,7,4'		Genista tinctoria (shoots), Soja hispida (seeds).
66	Homoferreirin	168 (137)	5,7	2',4'	Ferreirea spectabilis (heartwood).
67	Irigenin	185 (128)	5,7,3'	6,4',5'	Iris florentina (rhizome)
68	Muningin	285 (233)	6,4'	5,7	Pterocarpus angolensis (heartwood).
69	Orobol	271 (212)	5,7,3',4'		Orobus tuberosus.
70	Osajin	193 (152), 162)[5]	5,4'	(6-isopentenyl-2", 2"-dimethyl-[7,8:6",5"]-pyrano)	Maclura pomifera.
71	Pomiferin	201 (154)	5,3',4'	(6-isopentenyl-2", 2"-dimethyl-[7,8:6",5"]-pyrano)	M. pomifera.
72	Prunetin	242 (225)	5,4'	7	Prunus spp (bark), Pterocarpus angolensis.
73	Pseudobaptigenin	299 (173)	7	(3',4'methylenedioxy)	Baptisia spp (root).
74	Santal	223 (170)	5,3',4'	7	Santalum album (wood), Baphia nitida.
75	Tectorigenin	227 (190)	5,7,4'	6	Iris tectorum, Belamcanda chinensis (rhizomes).
			Flavanones		
76	Alpinetin	225	7	5	Alpinia chinensis.
77	Butin	215 (131)	7,3',4'		Butea frondosa (flowers).
78	Citronetin	225 (119)	5,7	2'	Citrus limonum (fruit peel).
79	Cryptostrobin	203	5,7	(6-methyl)	Pinus strobus (heartwood).
80	Desmethoxymatteucinol	203 (162)[6]	5,7	(6,8-dimethyl)	Matteucia orientalis.
81	Eriodictyol	267 (137)	5,7,3',4'		Eriodictyon spp (leaves).
82	Hesperetin	228 (82)	5,7,3'	4'	Citrus spp (fruit peel)
83	Homoeriodictyol	225 (163)	5,7,4'	3'	Eriodictyon glutinosum (leaves).
84	Isosakuranetin	194 (140)	5,7	4'	Citrus trifoliata (flowers).
85	Liquiritigenin	207 (186)	7,4'		Glycyrrhiza glabra var glandilufera.
86	Matteucinol	174 (170)	5,7	4' (6,8-dimethyl)	Matteucia orientalis
87	8-Methoxybutin	197 (124)	7,3'4'	8	Coreopsis grandiflora (flowers)
88	Naringenin	251 (127)	5,7,4'		Citrus decumana (fruit peel), Salix purpurea (bark), Prunus serotina (heartwood).
89	Pinocembrin	195	5,7		Pinus cembra, P. montana, P. banksiana (heartwood).
90	Pinostrobin	102	5		Pinus strobus (heartwood)
91	Plathymenin	229 (151)	6,7,3',4'		Plathymenia reticulata (wood).
92	Ponkanetin	152		5,6,7,8,4'	Citrus poonensis (unripe fruit peel).
93	Sakuranetin	154 (97)	5,4'		Prunus spp (bark).
94	Strobopinin	227	5,7	(8-methyl)	Pinus strobus (heartwood).
			Chalcones (C), Dihydrochalcones (D), Benzophenones (B)		
95	Butein (C)	215 (131)	3,4,2',4'		Coreopsis douglasii, Dahlia variabilis (flowers).
96	Isocarthamin (C)	228	4,2',3',4',6'	(3'-glucoside)[7]	Carthamus tinctorius (flowers).
97	Isosalipurposide (C)	173	4,2',4',6'	(2'-glucoside)[8]	Salix purpurea (old bark).
98	Lanceoletin (C)	(166)	3,4,2',4'	3'	Coreopsis lanceolata, C. saxicola (ray flowers).
99	Lonchocarpin (C)	108	2'	(2",2"-dimethyl-[5",6":3',4']-pyrano)	Lonchocarpus sericeus (seeds and roots).
100	Pedicellin (C)	98		2',3',4',5',6'	Didyomocarpus pedicellata (leaves).
101	Pedicin (C)	145 (183)[9]	2',5'	3',4',6'	D. pedicellata (leaves).

/1/ Values in parentheses are for the fully acetylated derivatives unless otherwise noted. /3/ 3,7,2',4-Tetraacetate. /4/ Aglucone of amurensin.
/5/ Acetate exists in two forms. /6/ Mono-(probably 7-)acetate. /7/ Forms isocarthamidin (5,6,7,4'-tetrahydroxyflavanone) when hydrolyzed.
/8/ Forms naringenin (5,7,4'-trihydroxyflavanone) when hydrolyzed. /9/ Dibenzoate.

Part I: FLAVONES, CHALCONES, XANTHONES, AND RELATED COMPOUNDS (Concluded)

	Pigment	Melting Point, °C[1]	Hydroxyl Position, C-	Methoxyl Position, C-	Source
			Chalcones (C), Dihydrochalcones (D), Benzophenones (B) (concluded)		
102	Stillopsidin (C)	232 (156)	3, 4, 2', 4', 5'		Plathymenia reticulata (wood), Coreopsis stillmanii (flowers).
103	Strobochrysin (C)	168 (77)	2', 4', 6'	(5-methyl)	Pinus strobus (heartwood).
104	Asebogenin (D)	168 (77)	4, 2', 6'	4'	Andromeda japonica (leaves).
105	Phloretin (D)	264 (165)	4, 2', 4', 6'		Micromelum teprocarpum, root bark of fruit trees
106	Cotoin (B)	131 (94)	2, 6	4	Coto spp (bark).
107	Hydrocotoin (B)	98	2	4, 6	Coto spp (bark).
108	p-Hydroxybenzophenone	134 (81)	4		Talauma mexicana (leaves).
109	Maclurin (B)	222	2, 4, 6, 3', 4'		Morus tinctoria (wood)
110	Methylhydrocotoin (B)	115		2, 4, 6	Paracoto spp (bark).
111	Methylprotocotoin (Hydroxyleucotin) (B)	135		2, 4, 6 (3', 4'-methylenedioxy)	Coto spp (bark).
112	Protocotoin (B)	142	2	4, 6 (3', 4'-methylenedioxy)	Coto spp (bark).
			Xanthones (X), Chromones (C), Aurones (A)		
113	Decussatin (X)	150 (167)	8	3, 4, 7	Swertia decussata (flowers).
114	Desmethylswertianol (X)	317	1, 3, 5, 8		Swertia tosaensis (roots).
115	Euxanthone (X)	240 (185)	1, 7		Platonia insignis (heartwood).
116	Gentisin (X)	267 (197)	1, 7	3	Gentiana lutea, Swertia japonica (roots).
117	Jacareubin (X)	257 (213)	1, 5, 6	(2', 2'-dimethyl-[5', 6':2, 3] -pyrano)	Calophyllum brasiliense (heartwood).
118	Lichexanthone (X)	187	1	3, 6 (8-methyl)	Parmelia formosana, P. quercina.
119	Ravenelin (X)	268 (205)	1, 4, 8	(3-methyl)	Metabolite of Helminthosporium ravenelii curtis and H. turcicum passerini.
120	Swertianol (X)	267 (240)	1, 3, 8	5	Swertia tosaensis, S. japonica (roots).
121	Swertinin (X)	217 (157)	1, 2	5, 6	Swertia decussata (stems)
122	Angustifolionol (C)	118	5	7(2, 6, 8-trimethyl)	Backhousia angustifolia (oil).
123	Chellol (C)	178		5 (2-hydroxymethyl-[2', 3':6, 7] -furano)	Ammi visnaga (seeds).
124	Eugenin (C)	120 (154)	5	7 (2-methyl)	Eugenia aromatica (flowers).
125	Eugenitin (C)	162 (177)	5	7 (2, 6-dimethyl)	E. caryophyllata (flowers).
126	Isoeugenitol (C)	230 (151)	5, 7	(2, 8-dimethyl)	E. caryophyllata (flowers).
127	Khellin (C)	155		5, 8 (2-methyl-[2', 3':6, 7] -furano)	Ammi visnaga (seeds).
128	Peucenin (C)	212	5, 7	(2-methyl-6-iso-propenyl-2)	Peucedanum ostruthium (wood).
129	Visnagin (C)	145		5 (2-methyl-[2', 3':6, 7] -furano)	Ammi visnaga (seeds).
130	Aureusidin (A)	295 (185)	4, 6, 3', 4'		Antirrhinum majus, Oxalis cernua (yellow flowers).
131	Leptosidin (A)	254 (166)	6, 3', 4'	7	Coreopsis grandiflora (flowers).
132	Sulfuretin (A)	312 (194)	6, 3', 4'		Cosmos sulfureus, Dahlia variabilis (yellow flowers).

	Pigment	Melting Point, °C[1]	Hydroxyl Position, C-	Optical Rotation[10]	Source
			Flavanonols		
133	Alpinone	178 (118)	3, 5 (7-methoxyl, 2-methyl)	+79 (pyridine)[11]	Nothofagus dombeyi, Prunus serotina (heartwood), Cercidiphyllum japonicum.
134	Ampelopsin	246 (175)	3, 5, 7, 3', 4', 5'		Ampelopsis meliaefolia kudo.
135	Dihydrorobinetin	228 (143)	3, 7, 3', 4', 5'	+13.8 (acetone)	Robinia pseudoacacia (wood).
136	Fustin	218 (151)	3, 7, 3', 4'		Rhus cotinus, Quebracho colorado (wood).
137	Katusuranin	241	3, 5, 7, 4'	+45 (acetone + water)	Cercidiphyllum japonicum, Nothofagus dombeyi, Prunus serotina.
138	Phellamuretin	220 (199)	3, 5, 4' (2", 2"-dimethyl-[7, 8: 6", 5"] -chromano)		Phellodendron amurense.
139	Pinobanksin	178	3, 5, 7	+14.4 (methanol)	Pinus spp (heartwood).
140	Taxifolin	242 (130)	3, 5, 7, 3', 4'	+46 (acetone + water); +13 (ethanol)	Pseudotsuga menziesii (heartwood), Larix decidua (heartwood).
141	Pinobanksin 7-methyl ether	181	3, 5 (7-methoxyl)	-20 (chloroform)	Pinus clausa (heartwood).

/1/ Values in parentheses are for the fully acetylated derivatives unless otherwise noted. /10/ Determined at 20°C unless otherwise specified. /11/ Determined at 29°C.

Part II: CHARACTERISTIC REACTIONS OF SOME FLAVONOID TYPES

	Type	Cold Alkali	Hot Alkali	Concentrated H_2SO_4	Ferric Chloride	Mg-HCl[1]	Lead Acetate
1	Flavones	Yellow to red-orange	Yellow to red-orange	Lemon or green yellow		Red-orange	Yellow ppt
2	Flavonols	Yellow	Yellow	Yellow to green and blue-green (some fluoresce)	Olive-green	Pink to red	Orange-yellow ppt
3	Chalcones	Red	Blue-red	Yellow to orange	Brown	No color change	Brick-red ppt
4	Aurones	Red[2]	Red[2]	Red[3]	No color change	No color change	
5	Flavanones	Colorless	Red	Red to yellow		Red-violet to blue-violet	Very light yellow to yellow ppt

/1/ Small piece of magnesium ribbon or turnings is placed in an alcoholic solution of the compound, and a few drops of concentrated hydrochloric acid are added. /2/ Deep purple if the 6-hydroxyl position is not free (as in a methyl ether, etc.). /3/ Yellow-orange if there is no 4'substituent.

Part III: ALGAL PIGMENTS: PHYSICAL CONSTANTS

	Pigment[1]	Absorption Maxima (mμ) and Specific Extinction Coefficients			Fluorescence Emission Maxima (mμ)	Molecular Weight	Isoelectric pH	Abs. max. (mμ) of Chromophore (in acid $CHCl_3$)	Source
1	R-Phycoerythrin	495 $(E_{sp}5.68)$	540 $(E_{sp}6.50)$	565 $(E_{sp}7.92)$	580	290,000	4.3	576	Ceramium rubrum; Porphyra spp
2	C-Phycoerythrin			563				576	Phormidium fragile; Nostoc sp
3	R-Phycocyanin	550 $(E_{sp}4.06)$		$(E_{sp}6.35)$	630-690	272,000	4.85		Ceramium rubrum; Porphyra perforata
4	C-Phycocyanin		615 $(E_{sp}9.74)$		637	208,000	4.7	630	Lyngbya lagerheimii; Arthrospira sp

/1/ All are soluble in dilute salt solutions and precipitated by 10-20% $(NH_4)_2SO_4$.

Part IV: SOME GENERAL TYPE CHARACTERISTICS

	Common Name and (Type Compound)	Chemical Constitution	Molecular Formula and (Weight)	Solubility[1]	Absorption Maxima[1] mμ	Source
			Carotenoids			
1	Beta-carotene	[1, 19-Di-(β-iono)-3, 7, 12, 16-tetra-methyl-octo-deca-noene-2, 4, 6, 8, 10, 12, 14, 16, 18]-polyene	$C_{40}H_{56}$ (536)	s.CS_2, chl., bz.	520, 485, 450 in CS_2; 497, 466 in chl.	Widely distributed in plants together with chlorophyll and xanthophyll.
2	Xanthophyll	[1-(3-Hydroxy-β-iono)-3, 7, 12, 16-tetramethyl-octo-deca-noene-2, 4, 6, 8, 10, 12, 14, 16, 18]-polyene	$C_{40}H_{56}O_2$ (568)	s.chl., acet., eth., bz.	508, 475, 445 in CS_2; 487, 456, 428 in chl.	See carotene above.
			Diaroyl Methane			
3	Curcumin[2]	1, 7-Di-(4-hydroxy-3-methoxy-phenyl)-heptadiene-1, 6-dione-3, 5	$C_{21}H_{20}O_6$ (368)	s.eth.	425[3] in al.[4]; 667, 625, 615, 385, 294 (solid state).	←Roots, shoots of Curcuma tinctoria.
			Carbocyclic Compounds			
4	Atromentin (Benzoquinone)	2, 5-Di-(p-hydroxyphenyl)-3, 6-di-hydroxy-1, 4-benzoquinone	$C_{18}H_{12}O_6$ (324)	s.al., amyl alc., eth.	No characteristic absorption spectrum.	←Fungus Paxillus atro-tomentosus.
5	Vitamin K, (Naphthoquinone)	2-Methyl-3-(3, 7, 11, 15-tetramethyl-hexadecene-2)-naphthoquinone-1, 4	$C_{31}H_{46}O_2$ (324)	s.eth., acet., hexane	325, 270, 260, 249, 243 in hexane.	←Leaves of plants; microorganisms.
6	Alizarin (Anthracene)	1, 2-Dihydroxyanthraquinone	$C_{14}H_8O_6$ (240)	s.al., eth., bz.	388, 250[3] in al.	←Roots of Olenlandia umbellata.
7	Thelephoric acid (Phenanthrene)	(3, 4'-Dihydroxy-3'-carboxyl-5, 6'-dione-4, 1'-diphenyl)-1-(2, 4-pentadienolic acid)	$C_{20}H_{12}O_9$ (396)	s.pyr.	495 in pyr.	←Various spp of Telephora.
			Heterocyclic Compounds Containing Heterocyclic Oxygen			
8	Usnic acid (five-membered ring)	([Phenyl-1-[ethanone-1]-2, 4-dihy-droxy-3-methyl]-[furyl-5, 6]-2-methyl-3-hydroxy-4-[ethanone-1]-5-carbonyl)-cyclohexadiene-3, 6	$C_{18}H_{16}O_7$ (344)	s.al., eth., bz.	Not available.	←Various spp of Usnea, Pamelia, Leganora.
9	Flavone (six-membered ring)	2-Phenyl-chromone	$C_{15}H_{10}O_2$	s.al., eth., w.	298, 250 in al.	←Leaves, flower stems, seed capsules of some Primulae spp.
10	Polargonidin[5] (six-membered ring)	3, 5, 7, 4'-Tetrahydroxy-flavone	$C_{15}H_{11}O_5$	s.ac.a., al., butanol	500, 420[3] in w.; 530, 420[3] in al.	←Asters and carnations.
			Compounds Containing Heterocyclic Nitrogen			
11	Indigo (Indole)	1, 2-Di-(3-carbonyl-2-indole)-ethene	$C_{16}H_{10}O_2N_2$ (262)	s.h.chl., h. aniline	591 in xylol.	Various spp of Indigofera; Polygonum tinctorium.
12	Chlorophyll a (Pyrrole)	Mg-complex of 1, 3, 5, 8-tetramethyl-4-ethyl-2-vinyl-9-oxo-10-carbmeth-oxy-phorbine-7-propionic acid-phytyl-ester	$C_{55}H_{72}O_5$ $N_4Mg·\frac{1}{2}H_2O$ (901)	s.eth., acet., me.alc.	See table below.	Chloroplasts of green plants.
13	Leghemoglobin (Pyrrole)	Iron complex of globin and 1, 3, 5, 8-tetramethyl-2, 4-divinyl-porphin-6, 7 7-dipropionic acid	$C_{34}H_{32}O_4·$ N_4Fe-globin (17000)	s.w.	555, 485 in w.	Root nodules of leguminous plants.

/1/ Abbreviations: ac. a. = acetic acid; acet. = acetone; al. = ethanol (95%); alc. = alcohol; bz. = benzene; chl. = chloroform; eth. = ether; h. = hot; me. = methyl; pyr. = pyridine; s. = soluble; w. = water. /2/ Indian saffron. /3/ Read crom absorption curve. /4/ Undergoes changes in solution. /5/ Occurs as the 3-galactoside.

Part V: CHLOROPHYLLS

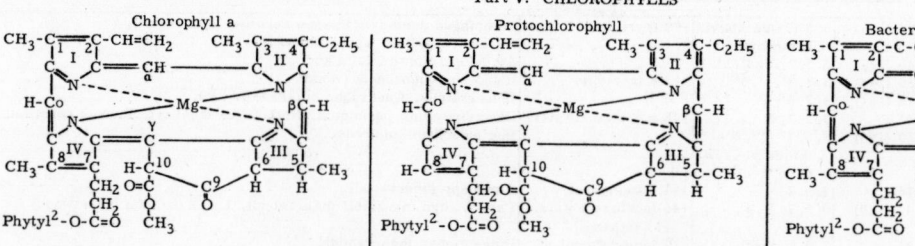

	Pigment	Absorption Maxima[3] In Ether mμ	Phaeophytin[4] in Ether mμ	Fluorescence Maxima[3] In Ether mμ	Phaeophytin[4] in Ether, mμ	Principal Source	Remarks
1	Chlorophyll a	660, 617, 575, 430, 410.	668, 612, 564, 543, 506, 412.	668, 723	672.5, 715	All photosynthetic tissues except photosynthetic bacteria.	
2	Chlorophyll b	640, 595, 535, 455.	655, 600, 545, 525, 436.	649, 708	657, 707	Photosynthetic tissues of higher plants, ferns, mosses, chloro-phyceae, (green algae) Euglenineae and some diatoms(?).	When present, represents about 20-40% of the total chlorophylls.
3	Chlorophyll c (Chlorofucin)	627, 579.5 545, 446.	640, 595, 565, 525, 420.	629, 690.	649, 719.	Diatoms, dinoflagellates, (Dino-phyceae) and brown algae (Phaeophyceae).	Probably phytyl-free.
4	Chlorophyll d	686, 645, 595, 545, 445, 390.	590, 636, 545, 520, 425, 380.	696, 752.	701.	Red algae especially (Rhodochorton nothii).	Contains phytyl residue and the cyclopentanone ring.
5	Chlorophyll e	654, 415 (in methanol).				Yellow-green algae (Tribonema bombycinum).	
6	Protochlorophyll	623, 571, 535, 432.		627, 685 (in acetone)		Etiolated seedlings.	Probable precursor of the chlorophylls.
7	Bacteriochlor-	770, 708, 574, 390, 365.	754, 686, 612, 528, 492, 385, 367.			All purple sulfur and non-sulfur photosynthetic bacteria.	
8	Chlorobium Chlorophyll (Chloroviridin)	764, 659, 624, 431, 408.	760, 660, 604, 549, 515, 412			Green sulfur photosynthetic bac-teria (Chlorobium spp).	Not identical with bac-terio-chlorophyll.

/1/ Structure is still tentative. /2/ Phytol = $(CH_3)_2$-$CH(CH_2)_3$-CH-$(CH_2)_3$-$CH(CH_2)_3$-C=CH-CH_2OH. /3/ Principal maxima underlined. /4/ The $\underset{CH_3}{\quad} \underset{CH_3}{\quad} \underset{CH_3}{\quad}$ magnesium-free pigment.

28. PLANT RESINS: SOURCE, PHYSICAL AND CHEMICAL CHARACTERISTICS
Data are approximations and may vary depending upon the history of the sample.

	Substance	Source	Specific Gravity	Softening Point, °C	Melting Point, °C	Acid Number	Saponification Number	Iodine Number	Solvent
1	Accra copal	Copaifera sp	1.033	75	120	98	140	58	Amyl alcohol, aniline
2	Accroides	Xanthorrhoea spp	1.34	75	110	64-106	65	200	Alcohol, esters, ketones
3	Amber	Fossils of Pinaceae	1.05-1.10	175	250-315	15-35	85-150	62	Turpentine oil, CS_2
4	Animé copal	Fossils	1.03		230	18-27	60-90	128-137	
5	Benguela copal	Copaifera demeusei	1.06	65	165	123	157	61-85	Amyl alcohol, aniline
6	Benzoin[1]	Storax (Styrax benzoin)	1.09		>100	75-100	190-207	57-76	Ethyl alcohol, acetone
7	Boea manila	Agathis alba'	1.07	79-80	130-132	118-141	143-175	110-137	Ethyl alcohol, ketones
8	Brazil copal	Hymenaea courbaril	1.053	50	100	123	133	123-134	Amyl alcohol, aniline
9	Cameron copal	Copaifera demeusei	1.052	100	150	160	70	65-70	Aniline, ether
10	Colombia copal	Hymenaea spp	1.054	90	<300	119	156		Amyl alcohol, aniline
11	Congo copal	Copaifera demeusei	1.06	90	128	100	124	115	Amyl alcohol, amyl acetate, aniline
12	Damar, Batavia	Shorea spp, Hopea spp	1.03-1.06	70-76	99-110	22-23	29-39	95-127	Chloroform, benzene
13	Demerara copal	Hymenaea courbaril	1.047	90	180	98	102		Ether[2], chloroform[2], aniline[2]
14	Dragon's blood	Daemonorhops draco	1.25		100	11	153	54-98	Alcohol, ether, benzene
15	Elemi, Manila	Canarium luzonicum	1.02-1.05		75	20-35	21-44	118	Esters
16	Guaiacum	Guaiacum officinale	1.2		85-90	20-53	74-84		Ether[3]
17	Jalap	Exogonium purga	1.14		150	12-27		132	Ethyl alcohol
18	Kauri, pale	Kauri-pine (Agathis australis)	1.05	90-130	127-134	57-81	67-117	82-154	Amyl alcohol, aniline
19	Kissel copal	Copaifera demeusei	1.066	65	110	70	118		Aniline
20	Madagascar copal	Trachylobium verrucosum	1.056	130	300	66	78	126	Amyl alcohol[2], aniline[2]
21	Manila hard	Agathis alba	1.07	79-80	130-132	118-141	143-175	110-137	Amyl alcohol, aniline
22	Manila soft	A. alba	1.06	77-88	121	127-134	158-190	121-126	Alcohol
23	Mastic	Pistacia lentiscus	1.04-1.07	55	76	50-70	62-90	64-124	Amyl alcohol, ether, benzene
24	Pontianak	Agathis alba	1.07-1.08	82-135	126-169	112-121	148-180	119-142	Alcohol, hydrocarbons
25	Red Angola copal	Copaifera demeusei	1.066	90	305	128	132	63-137	Amyl alcohol, acetone
26	Rosin	Pine, longleaf (Pinus palustris)	1.07-1.09	70-80	120-135	150-175	167-194	80	Organic solvents
27	Sandarac	Arara-tree (Callitris quadrivalvis)	1.05-1.09	100-130	135-150	117-155	145-157	112-141	Alcohol, ether
28	Sierra Leone copal	Copaifera copalifera	1.072	60	130	110	123	63-133	Amyl alcohol, aniline
29	White Angola copal	Copaifera demeusei	1.055	45	95	127	160	130	Amyl alcohol, acetone
30	Zanzibar copal	Trachylobium verrucosum	1.054	150	300	93	93	115-123	Amyl alcohol[2], amyl acetate[2]

/1/ A balsam. /2/ Partly soluble. /3/ 54-74% solubility.

29. PLANT TANNINS: SOURCE AND CHEMICAL CHARACTERISTICS

Plant tannins are polyphenols, within plant extracts, capable of converting the collagen in hides and skins into non-putrescible leather. Varying quantities of mono- and disaccharides, gums and various phenols are associated with the tannin in the extract, but are not alone capable of forming the conversion. There are two main categories of tannins, generally but not absolutely valid: HYDROLYZABLE, hydrolyzed by HCl or enzymes into sugars and phenolic carboxylic acids, and CONDENSED, converted by hot HCl into more highly condensed and insoluble red "phlobaphenes" or tanners' red," constitution unknown.

Part I: HYDROLYZABLE TANNINS

	Tannin[1]	Empirical Formula	Source	Present in Commercial Extract	Constitution and Hydrolysis Products
1	Acertannin	$C_{20}H_{20}O_{13} \cdot 2H_2O$	Acer ginnala (leaves)		Digalloylaceritol 2 gallic acid + aceritol
2	Brevilagin		Caesalpinia brevifolia (pods)	Algarobilla (brevifolin carbonic acid)	Glucose + ellagic acid + $C_{13}H_8O_8$
3	Chebulagic acid	$C_{41}H_{30}O_{27} \cdot 10H_2O$	Terminalia chebula (fruit) Caesalpinia coriana (pods)	Myrobalan and divi-divi	Glucose + gallic acid + ellagic acid + chebulic acid $(C_{14}H_{12}O_{11})$
4	Chebulinic acid	$C_{41}H_{32}O_{27} \cdot 2H_2O$	Terminalia chebula (fruit)	Myrobalan	Glucose + 3 gallic acid + chebulic acid $(C_{14}H_{12}O_{11})$
5	Corilagin	$C_{27}H_{22}O_{18}$	Terminalia chebula (fruit)	Myrobalan and divi-divi	Glucose + gallic acid + ellagic acid
6	Dehydrodigallic acid	$C_{14}H_{10}O_{10}$	Castanea vesca (leaves, shoots[2])		Gallic acid
7	Ellagic acid	$C_{14}H_6O_8$	Quercus sp[3] (galls)	Divi-divi, algarobilla, myrobalan, valonia, chestnut	4, 5, 6, 4', 5', 6', -Hexahydroxy-diphenic acid - δ,δ-dilactone
8	Hamameli tannin	$C_{20}H_{20}O_{14} \cdot 6H_2O$	Hamamelis virginiana (bark)		Digalloylhamamelose 2 gallic acid + hamamelose
9	Tannic acid[4]	$C_{76}H_{52}O_{46}$	Rhus chinensis (galls)	Chinese tannin	Glucose + 10 gallic acid
10	Valonia acid dilactone	$C_{21}H_{10}O_{13}$	Quercus aegilops[5] (acorn cups)	Valonia	Ellagic acid + gallic acid

/1/ Except where indicated, all tannins listed are crystalline. /2/ Young. /3/ Numerous other sources. /4/ Amorphous. /5/ And allied species.

Part II: CONDENSED TANNINS

Condensed tannins are composed of complex mixtures of highly condensed and probably closely related polyphenols, constitution unknown, and lower molecular polyphenolic fractions in which certain constituents are identified. These tannins comprise about 60% of solid commercial plant extracts, associated therein with varying admixtures of "non-tannins."

	Extract	Source	Alkali Fusion Products	Polyphenolic Constituents	Associated Non-tannin Constituents
1	Cube Gambier	Uncaria gambier (leaves)	Phloroglucinol, protocatechuic acid	d-Catechin, dl-epigallocatechin, d-epigallocatechin, quercitin	
2	Cutch	Acacia catechu (wood)	Phloroglucinol, protochechuic acid	l-Catechin, dl-catechin, l-epigallocatechin, dl-epigallocatechin, quercitin	
3	Green tea tannin	Thea sinensis (leaves)		l-Epigallocatechin, d-gallocatechin, d-catechin, l-epigallocatechin gallate, l-catechin gallate, theogallin, quercitin, kaempferol	Sucrose, glucose, fructose, maltose, arabinose, rhamnose, ribose, mesoinositol, gallic acid, anthoxanthins, theanine
4	Quebracho	Schinopsis lorentzii (heartwood)	Resorcinol, protocatechuic acid	Fisetin, ellagic acid	Glucose, arabinose, xylose, gallic acid
5	Wattle (Mimosa)	Acacia mollissima (bark)	Resorcinol, gallic acid; protocatechuic acid, β-resorcylic acid, pyrogallol, phloroglucinol, catechol	Catechin, gallocatechin, fisetin	Sucrose, glucose, fructose, gums

30. ESSENTIAL OILS, PLANT: SOURCE, PHYSICAL AND CHEMICAL CHARACTERISTICS

Essential Oil (Botanical Source) Geographical Source	Plant Part, Yield[1] g/100 g	Properties[2]	Chemical Constituents[3]	Essential Oil (Botanical Source) Geographical Source	Plant Part, Yield[1] g/100 g	Properties[2]	Chemical Constituents[3]
1 Almond, bitter (Prunus amygdalus) France, Italy, Spain	Dried, ripe, defatted seed (0.5-0.7)	Sp gr = 1.042-1.07; α_D = 0.0 to +0.17; n_D = 1.532 - 1.544	Benzaldehyde*, hydrocyanic acid, benzaldehyde cyanohydrin	112 Lemongrass, East Indian type (Cymbopogon flexuosus) India	Grass (0.2-0.4)	Sp gr = 0.899-0.911; α_D = +1.5 to -5; n_D = 1.483 - 1.4899	Citral*
4 Anise seed (Pimpinella anisum) Russia, Germany, France	Dried, ripe fruit (1.9-3.1)	Sp gr = 0.984-0.994; α_D = -2 to +1; n_D = 1.5530-1.5600	Acetaldehyde, p-methoxyphenyl-acetone, anethole*, methyl chavicol	115 Lemongrass, Java type (Cymbopogon citratus) W. Indies, Madagascar, Honduras;	Shoots (0.2-0.4)	Sp gr = 0.875-0.900; α_D = -3 to +1; n_D = 1.4830-1.4890	Myrcene*, geraniol, nerol, α- and β-citral*, methyl heptenone
7 Anise, star (Illicium verum) China	Fruit (2.5-3.0)	Sp gr = 0.98-0.995; α_D = +0.6 to -4.08; n_D = 1.553 - 1.5582	d-α-Pinene, anisaldehyde, p-methoxyphenylacetone, ane-thole*, methyl chavicol	118 Lime, acid, distilled (Citrus aurantifolia) E. and W. Indies, Florida, Mexico	Fruit (0.3-0.4)[4]	Sp gr = 0.855-0.8635; α_D = +34 to +47; n_D = 1.4745 - 1.4770	Bisabolene, d-limonene*, borneol, 1-α-terpineol, n-decylaldehyde, lauric aldehyde, n-octylaldehyde
10 Basil, sweet (Ocimum basilicum) France, Germany, Algeria, Spain	Flowering shoots (0.09-0.11)	Sp gr = 0.896-0.935; α_D = -7.0 to -13.87; n_D = 1.477-1.495	Linalool, methyl chavicol*, cineole	121 Linaloe (Bulsera delpechiana) Mexico	Wood (6-11)	Sp gr = 0.875-0.8981; α_D = -14 to +8.2; n_D = 1.460-1.466	1-Linalool*
13 Bergamot (Citrus aurantium bergamia) W. Africa, Italy	Fruit rind (0.5)[4]	Sp gr = 0.881-0.887; α_D = +8.0 to +24.27; n_D = 1.464-1.468	d-Limonene, 1-linalool, nerol, 1-linalyl acetate*, bergaptene, bergaptol	124 Mandarin (Citrus reticulata) Florida, W.Indies, Sicily	Fruit (0.75-0.85)	Sp gr = 0.854-0.859; α_D = +64 to +75; n_D = 1.4745-1.478	Limonene
16 Birch, sweet (Betula lenta) Canada, U.S.A.	Twigs (1.2-1.9)	Sp gr = 1.184-1.190; Inactive; n_D = 1.5350-1.5380	Triacontane (?)($C_{30}H_{62}$), methyl salicylate*, an ester ($C_{14}H_{24}O_2$)	127 Mint (Mentha aravensis) Japan, China, Brazil	Entire plant (1.3-1.6)	Sp gr = 0.895-0.909(?); α_D = -29 to -43 (?); n_D = 1.459-1.465(?)	1-Limonene, 1-menthol*, isomenthone, 1-menthone, 1-menthyl acetate
19 Bois de Rose (Aniba rosaeodora) French Guiana, Brazil	Wood (0.7-1.2)	Sp gr = 0.875-0.895; α_D = -4 to +5; n_D = 1.4620-1.4685	Linalool*, dipentene, terpineol, nerol, gerianol, p-methylaceto-phenone, cineole	130 Myrtle (Myrtus communis) Southern France, Algeria, Spain, Asia Minor	Leaves (0.18-0.25)	Sp gr = 0.881-0.929; α_D = +15 to +27.5; n_D = 1.464 - 1.4703	Cineole, 1-myrtenol, d-myrtenol (as ester)*
22 Cade (Juniperus oxycedrus) France, Spain	Wood (1.2-1.3)	Sp gr = 0.956-1.061; α_D = +4.3 to +4.7(?); n_D = 1.511-1.514(?)	d-Cadinene*, d-cadinol, creosol, guaiacol	133 Nutmeg (Myristica fragrans) E. and W. Indies, Ceylon, Indonesia	Dried, ripe seed (5-16)	Sp gr = 0.861-0.917; α_D = +8 to +45; n_D = 1.4690-1.4880	α-Pinene*, borneol, geraniol, d-linalool, myristicin, safrole, eugenol, d-camphene*
25 Calamus (Acorus calamus) Europe, Asia, North America	Rhizomes (1.5-4.8)	Sp gr = 0.950-1.083; α_D = -0.9 to +31; n_D = 1.50313-1.5522	Asarone*	136 Orange, bitter (Citrus aurantium amara)	Fruit rind (0.15-0.33)	Sp gr = 0.845-0.8525; α_D = -87 to +965; n_D = 1.4730-1.4770	Limonene*, linalool, d-α-terpineol, decylaldehyde, acetic acid, cinnamaldehyde
28 Camphor (Cinnamomum camphora) Formosa, China	Wood (1.0-3.0)	Sp gr = 0.954[5]; α_D = +32.4(?); n_D = 1.4806(?)	α-Pinene, β-pinene, 1-linalool, camphor*, 1,8-cineole, 1,4-cineole, safrole	139 Orange, sweet (Citrus sinensis) Portugal, Florida, California, Sicily	Fruit rind (0.1-0.7)[4]	Sp gr = 0.842-0.846[5]; α_D = +94 to +995; n_D = 1.4723-1.4737	d-Limonene*, linalool, citral
31 Caraway (Carum carvi) Holland, Asia	Dried, ripe seed (3-6)	Sp gr = 0.907-0.919; α_D = +70 to +81; n_D = 1.484-1.488	d-Limonene, carveol, carvone*, dihydrocarvone, d-dihydropinol	142 Origanum (Coridothymus capitatus) Spain	Fresh plant (0.9)	α_D = ± to +1(?); n_D = 1.499-1.508	p-Cymene, d-α-pinene, a sesquiterpene, carvacrol*, thymol
34 Cardamon (Elettaria cardamomum var. α-major) Southern India, Ceylon	Seeds (3-8.6)	Sp gr = 0.923-0.940; α_D = +20 to +41; n_D = 1.461-1.467	Cineole*, terpineol, terpinyl acetate, limonene, sabinene(?)	145 Palmrosa (Cymbopogon martini var. motia) India	Grass (1-1.25)	Sp gr = 0.887-0.900; α_D = +6 to -3; n_D = 1.4685-1.4790	Geraniol*, farnesol, citral, citronellal, formaldehyde, acetic acid
37 Cassia (Cinnamomum cassia) China	Leaves, twigs (0.3-0.8)	Sp gr = 1.051-1.069; α_D = -1 to +1; n_D = 1.6020-1.6135	Cinnamaldehyde*, o-methoxy-benzaldehyde, methyl-o-coumaral-dehyde, cinnamylacetate, coumarin	148 Patchouly (Pogostemon cablin) Java, Singapore	Dried leaves (3.0)	Sp gr = 0.950-0.991; α_D = -40 to -72; n_D = 1.5060-1.5160	Patchouly alcohol, azulene, benzaldehyde, cinnamaldehyde, eugenol
40 Catnip (Nepeta cataria) Sicily, U.S.A.	Entire plant (0.3)	Sp gr = 0.986-1.083; α_D = +1.3 to +13.3; n_D = 1.4872-1.4913	Nepatalic acid*	151 Pennyroyal (Mentha pulegium) Spain, Morocco	Entire plant (1.0)	Sp gr = 0.936-0.982(?); α_D = +15 to +24(?); n_D = 1.483-1.494(?)	1-α-Pinene, menthol, 1-menthone, d-pulegone*, piperitone, 3-octanyl acetate
43 Cedarwood (Juniperus virginiana) North America	Heartwood (2-3)	Sp gr = 0.945-0.960; α_D = -27 to -45; n_D = 1.5020-1.5070	Cedrene*, cedrenol, cedrol, pseudocedrol	154 Pepper (Piper nigrum) Jamaica	Berries (1-3.2)	Sp gr = 0.873-0.916; α_D = +3 to -16; n_D = 1.480-1.499	β-Caryophyllene, dl-limonene, 1-α-phellandrene, α-pinene, piperonal
46 Celery seed (Apium graveolens) Europe, India	Seed (1.9-2.5)	Sp gr = 0.878-0.916; α_D = +48 to +78; n_D = 1.4800-1.4900	d-Limonene*, sedanoic anhydride, sedanolide, selinene, palmitic acid, guaiacol(?)	157 Peppermint (Mentha piperita) North America, Europe	Entire plant (0.3-1.0)	Sp gr = 0.901-0.913; α_D = -18 to -32; n_D = 1.4590-1.4650	1-Menthol*, d-menthone, 1-menthone, menthofuran, dimethyl sulfide
49 Cinnamon (Cinnamomum zeylanicum) Ceylon	Dried bark (0.2)	Sp gr = 1.016-1.036; α_D = 0 to -2; n_D = 1.5730-1.5910	Cinnamaldehyde*, 1-α-pinene, 1-linalool, cinnamaldehyde*, eugenol	160 Perilla (Perilla frutescens) Japan	Blossoms, leaves (0.1-0.15)	Sp gr = 0.923-0.938; α_D = -73 to -96.5; n_D = 1.4971-1.5048	Perillaldehyde*
52 Citronella (Cymbopogon nardus) Ceylon	Dried grass (0.5)	Sp gr = 0.898-0.910; α_D = -9 to -18; n_D = 1.4790-1.4855	Geraniol*, citronellol, camphene, limonene, 1-borneol, farnesol, methyl eugenol	163 Pimenta berry (Pimenta officinalis) Jamaica	Fruit (3.3-4.3)	Sp gr = 1.025-1.055; α_D = 0 to -4; n_D = 1.5270-1.5400	Caryophyllene, eugenol*, eugenol methyl ether, cineole
55 Citronella (Cymbopogon winterianus) Java	Shoots (0.5-2.4)	Sp gr = 0.882-0.901; α_D = -0.47 to -5.75; n_D = 1.463-1.475	Geraniol*, citronellol, cadinol, d-citronellal, methyl eugenol, geranyl butyrate	166 Pine, dwarf (Pinus mugo) Austrian Tyrol	Twigs, leaves (0.3-0.6)	Sp gr = 0.859-0.877; α_D = -5 to -15.5; n_D = 1.4750-1.4800	Pinene, limonene, dipentene, borneol, ketones, phenols

No.	Plant[1]	Part (yield)[1]	Physical properties[2]	Constituents[3]
58-60	Clove (Eugenia caryophyllata) Madagascar, Zanzibar	Dried, un-opened buds (15.5-17)	Sp gr = 1.043-1.068; α_D = to -1.58; n_D = 1.5270-1.5350	Caryophyllene, furfural, eugenol*, vanillin, methyl salicylate, and benzoate
61-63	Coriander (Coriandrum sativum) Europe	Seeds (0.15-1.1)	Sp gr = 0.870-0.885; α_D = +4 to +13; n_D = 1.463-1.471	Linalool*, p-cymene, l-borneol, geraniol, n-decylaldehyde, acetic acid, decylic acid
64-66	Cubeb (Piper cubeba) Java, Singapore	Berries (10-20)	Sp gr = 0.909-0.930; α_D = -12.5 to -46; n_D = 1.4919-1.4981	Cubeb camphor, terpenes
67-69	Dill weed (Anethum graveolens) Europe, North America, Hungary	Entire plant (0.3-1.5)	Sp gr = 0.890-0.906; α_D = +84 to +95; n_D = 1.4800-1.4850	α-Pinene, terpinene, carvone, d-phellandrene*, limonene
70-72	Estragon (Artemisia dracunculus) U.S.A., Southern France	Shoots (0.35)	Sp gr = 0.900-0.966(?); α_D = +1.9 to +9(?); n_D = 1.504-1.520(?)	Phellandrene (?), p-methoxycin-namaldehyde, methyl chavicol*
73-75	Eucalyptus (Eucalyptus polybractea) Australia	Leaves (1.5-2.5)	Sp gr = 0.922-0.930; α_D = +0.5 to +2; n_D = 1.458-1.462	p-Cymene, 1,8-cineole*
76-78	Fennel, bitter (Foeniculum vulgare) France, Italy, India, Russia	Seeds (1-6)	Sp gr = 0.959-0.980; α_D = +12 to +24; n_D = 1.528-1.5380	Camphene, d-α-phellandrene, anisaldehyde, d-fenchone, anethole*, methyl chavicol
79-81	Geranium (Pelargonium spp) Algeria, Réunion, Norway	Shoots (0.15)	Sp gr = 0.882-0.904; α_D = -7 to -14; n_D = 1.4629-1.4720	l-α-Pinene, sesquiterpenes, citronellol*, sesquiterpene alcohols, l-isomenthone, formic esters
82-84	Ginger (Zingiber officinale) Asia, West Indies, Africa	Dried rhizomes (1.5-3.0)	Sp gr = 0.877-0.888; α_D = -28 to -45; n_D = 1.4880-1.4940	d-Camphene, d-β-phellandrene, d-borneol, zingeberol, citral, cineole, zingiberene
85-87	Gingergrass (Cymbopogon martini var. sofia) India	Grass (1-1.25)	Sp gr = 0.900-0.953; α_D = +54 to -30; n_D = 1.4780-1.4930	Geraniol*
88-90	Grapefruit (Citrus paradisi) U.S.A., Brazil	Peel (0.06)[4]	Sp gr = 0.855-0.860; α_D = +91 to +96[5]; n_D = 1.4750-1.4780	Limonene*, linalool, citral, decylaldehyde, octylaldehyde, umbelliferone
91-93	Guaiac wood (Guaiacum officinale) Argentina, Paraguay	Wood (2.7-5.4)	Sp gr = 0.973-0.985; α_D = -3 to -12.3; n_D = 1.502-1.508	Guaiol, bulnesol
94-96	Hyssop (Hyssopus officinalis) Mediterranean region, France (0.15-0.8)	Leaves, blossoms	Sp gr = 0.9237-0.956; α_D = -15.7 to -19.3; n_D = 1.4783-1.4829	l-Pinocamphone*
97-99	Jasmine (Jasminum officinale) India, Arabia, China	Flowers (0.17)	Sp gr = 0.993-1.047; α_D = +2.2 to +3.7; n_D = 1.4944-1.5015	Benzyl acetate*, l-linalool
100-102	Juniper berry (Juniperus communis) Central Europe	Fruit (0.8-1.6)	Sp gr = 0.860-0.879; α_D = 0 to -15; n_D = 1.4740-1.4840	α-Pinene, borneol(?), geraniol(?), l-terpinen-4-ol(?)
103-105	Lavender (Lavandula officinalis) France	Leaves, flowers (0.3-0.9)	Sp gr = 0.882-0.895; α_D = -3 to -10; n_D = 1.4590-1.4700	d-Pinene, d-borneol, geraniol, lavandulol, l-linalool, l-linalyl acetate*, coumarin
106-108	Lavandin (Lavandula hybrida) Southern France	Leaves, flowers (1-1.8)	Sp gr = 0.884-0.897; α_D = -2 to -6; n_D = 1.4610-1.4650	Linalool*, linalyl acetate*, d-borneol, d-camphor
109-111	Lemon (Citrus limon) Italy, Spain, U.S.A.	Fruit rind (0.3-0.6)[4]	Sp gr = 0.849-0.8555; α_D = +57 to +65.65; n_D = 1.4738-1.4755	d-Limonene*, geraniol, linalool, citral*, cadinene, bisabolene
169-171	Rose (Rosa damascena) Bulgaria, Turkey	Flowers (0.02)	Sp gr = 0.848-0.8636; α_D = -1 to -4; n_D = 1.4570-1.46306	Stearoptenes, l-citronellol*, geraniol, d-linalool, nerol, phenylethyl alcohol
172-174	Rosemary (Rosmarinus officinalis) Mediterranean	Entire plant (0.4-0.7)	Sp gr = 0.901-0.919; α_D = -5 to +10; n_D = 1.4640-1.4760	α-Pinene, borneol, camphor, bornyl acetate, cineole
175-177	Sage, Dalmatian (Salvia officinalis) Mediterranean	Leaves (0.7-2.0)	Sp gr = 0.909-0.931; α_D = +2 to +9; n_D = 1.4570-1.4690	d-α-Pinene, salvene ($C_{10}H_{18}$), borneol, d-camphor, d-β-thujone*, l-α-thujone*, cineole
178-180	Sandalwood (Eucarya spicata) Australia	Wood (1.4-2.6)	Den. = 0.969-0.976; α_D = -3 to -10; n_D = 1.498-1.508	α-Santalol*
181-183	Sandalwood (Santalum album) Southern India	Wood, roots (4.5-6.2)	Sp gr = 0.965-0.980; α_D = -15 to -20; n_D = 1.500-1.5100	Santene, α-santalol*, β-santalol*, santalone, santalic acid, α- and β-santalenes
184-186	Sassafras (Sassafras albidum) U.S.A.	Roots (1.8)	Sp gr = 1.072-1.084; α_D = +2 to +4; n_D = 1.5250-1.5350	Phellandrene, α-pinene, d-camphor, safrole*
187-189	Spearmint (Mentha spicata) North America	Entire plant (0.7)	Sp gr = 0.923-0.940; α_D = -48 to -59; n_D = 1.4840-1.4910	l-Phellandrene, dihydrocarveol, l-carvone* (l-linalool), cineole (in Russian variety)
190-192	Spruce (Picea excelsa) Norway	Leaves (0.2)	Sp gr = 0.874-0.888; α_D = -20.6 to -40; n_D = 1.474-1.478	α-Pinene, β-pinene, bornyl acetate, dipentene cadinene
193-195	Tangerine (Citrus reticulata) Java, W. Indies, Florida	Fruit (0.1)	Sp gr = 0.850-0.856; α_D = +90.7 to +93.5; n_D = 1.4732-1.4750	Limonene*
196-198	Tansy (Tanacetum vulgare) England, France, U.S.A.	Herbs (0.2-0.5)	Sp gr = 0.916-0.9409; α_D = -6.3 to +38.8; n_D = 1.4456-1.4707	β-Thujone*
199-201	Thyme (Thymus vulgaris) Spain	Flowering plant (0.7-2.6)	Sp gr = 0.916-0.941; α_D = -0.27 to -3.2; n_D = 1.495-1.505	Camphene, caryophyllene, β-pinene, l-borneol*, carvacrol, thymol*
202-204	Tuberosa (Polyanthes tuberosa) France	Flowers (0.08)	Sp gr = 1.009-1.035; α_D = -2.5; n_D = 1.5136-1.5352	Methyl salicylate and anthranilate, methyl and benzyl benzoates
205-207	Turpentine gum, American (Pinus palustris) U.S.A.	Oleoresin (20)	Sp gr = 0.860-0.874; α_D = +15(?); n_D = 1.4680-1.4780	d-α-Pinene*, l-β-pinene, terpinolene, pinocarveol, methyl chavicol
208-210	Vetiver (Vetiveria zizanioides) India, Burma	Roots (1.5-2.0)	Sp gr = 0.9852-1.058; α_D = +14 to +45; n_D = 1.510-1.5306	Vetivenols*, α- and β-vetivones, benzoic and palmitic acids
211-213	Wintergreen (Gaultheria procumbens) North America	Leaves (0.5-0.7)	Sp gr = 1.184-1.190; α_D = -0.4 to -1.5; n_D = 1.5350-1.5380	Methyl salicylate*, an ester ($C_{14}H_{24}O_2$), triacontane
214-216	Wormseed, American (Chenopodium ambrosioides) C.America, W.Indies, U.S.A.	Dried plant (1-2)	Den.=0.937-0.9908; α_D = -0.1 to -12.5; n_D = 1.4741-1.4778	Ascaridole*, p-cymene, l-limonene, α-terpinene, d-camphor, butyric acid
217-219	Wormwood (Artemisia absinthium) Europe, North America	Shoots (0.3-0.4)	Sp gr = 0.884-0.9545(?); α_D = (?); n_D = 1.460-1.483(?)	An azulene, phellandrene, thujyl alcohol, α-thujone*, β-thujone, thujyl acetate
220-222	Ylang ylang (Cananguim odoratum) Philippines, Java, and other areas	Flowers (1.8-2.6)	Sp gr = 0.956-0.991; α_D = -23 to +43; n_D = 1.4960-1.5050	d-Caryophyllene, d-α-pinene, benzyl alcohol, acetate and benzoate, methyl benzoate*

/1/ Plant from which oil is obtained, followed in parentheses by yield of oil, expressed as g per 100 g plant material. /2/ Sp gr = specific gravity; den. = density; α_D = optical rotation; n_D = refractive index. Values for specific gravity are calculated to 15°C; those for n_D are reported at 20°C. /3/ For most of the oils listed these constituents are only a few of those that have been identified. An asterisk immediately following a constituent indicates that constituent as present in the greatest amount organoleptically and/or most important for commercial uses. /4/ Method of production is by expression of specified material. /5/ Determined at 25°C. /6/ Determined at 30°C. /7/ Calculated to 15°C. /8/ Determined at 25°C and referred to water at the same temperature.

31. NATURAL TEXTILE·FIBERS: PHYSICAL AND CHEMICAL CHARACTERISTICS

Fiber	Specific Gravity	Fiber Length (cm)	Fiber Diameter (μ)	Tensile Strength (kg/sq mm)	Tenacity (g/Grex[1])	Ultimate Elongation (%)	Young's Modulus (dynes/sq cm[2])	Initial Young's Modulus (g/den[1])	Stiffness (g/Grex[1])	Density (g/cu cm)
1 Abaca (Musa textilis)	1.48-1.50	150-350	14-35	40.7	5.0	2.2-3.8			175	1.50
2 Banana (M. paradisiaca sapientum)										
3 Cotton, Egyptian (Gossypium peruvianum)	1.54	3.6	16.4	44	3.8	7		74		1.55
4 Cotton, Sea Island (G. barbadense)	1.54	2.8-3.6	9.5	68	5.3	7		33-36		1.55
5 Cotton, Upland (G. hirsutum)	1.54	0.6-6.25	18	37-76	2.0-5.0	7	5.9	49-54	57	1.55
6 Coir (Cocos nucifera)		21	18							
7 Flax (Linum usitatissimum)	1.50	15.2-92	15	76	5.5	1.6	36		270	1.50
8 Green hemp (Crotalaria tenuifolia)										
9 Hemp (Cannabis sativa)	1.49	92-183	18-23	84	4.0	3-5	5.1		200	1.50
10 Henequen (Agave fourcroydes)		75-112	17.6-17.9		3.0	3.5-4.5				
11 Jute (Chorchorus sp)	1.49	150-360	15.5	41	2.8	0.8	4.5-13.8		185	1.50
12 Kenaf (Hibiscus cannabinus)		165	24	22						
13 Mauritius hemp (Fourcroea gigantea)										
14 Musk-dana (Hibiscus abelmoschus)										
15 Ramie (Boehmeria nivea)	1.52	20-30	25.5	91-99	5.0	3.7			167	1.53
16 Roselle (Hibiscus sabdariffa)										
17 Sanseveria (Sanseveria sp)			20	23.3		2.7				
18 Sisal (Agave sisalana)		45-90	10-30	40	5.0	2.0-2.5			127	0.317
19 Sunn (Crotalaria juncea)			31							
20 Urena (Urena lobata)										
21 Silk, boiled	1.25	Continuous	5-21	45.5	3.4	13-20	6.9-8.8	1.6	15	1.35
22 Wool, scoured[5]	1.30	3.75-38	25	17.2	1.3	30-50	2.5-3.9	0.5	4	1.30

Fiber	Specific Heat	Moisture Regain[3] (%)	Cellulose (g/100g[4])	Holo-cellulose (g/100g[4])	α-Cellulose (g/100g[4])	Furfural Yield (g/100g[4])	Lignin (g/100g[4])	Fat and Wax (g/100g[4])	Water Extract-ables (g/100g[4])	Ash (g/100g[4])
1 Abaca (Musa textilis)	0.322		63-86			9	8.6	0.71	1.09	1.15
2 Banana (M. paradisiaca sapientum)				85	58	9.37	13.06			2.63
3 Cotton, Egyptian (Gossypium peruvianum)	0.319	7.0-8.5	90							
4 Cotton, Sea Island (G. barbadense)	0.319	7.0-8.5	90							
5 Cotton, Upland (G. hirsutum)	0.319	7.0-8.5	88-95					0.7	2.66	1.32
6 Coir (Cocos nucifera)			61				33			
7 Flax (Linum usitatissimum)	0.322	12	45-80	90	59	1.46	4.53	2.6	6.75	0.79
8 Green hemp (Crotalaria tenuifolia)				91	58	1.47	5.46			1.39
9 Hemp (Cannabis sativa)	0.323	12	59-85					0.62	3.82	0.90
10 Henequen (Agave fourcroydes)		4.6	48-88				5.4			1.1
11 Jute (Chorchorus sp)	0.324	13.8	51-88	83	61	6.64	11.78	0.82	1.14	0.50-1.56
12 Kenaf (Hibiscus cannabinus)		9.8	82		61-64		7.43-8.47			0.60-1.34
13 Mauritius hemp (Fourcroea gigantea)			81				18			2.0
14 Musk-dana (Hibiscus abelmoschus)				80	49	11.04	9.81			0.84
15 Ramie (Boehmeria nivea)		12	72-97	97	89	1.29	0.08		2.4	1.2
16 Roselle (Hisbiscus sabdariffa)				84	54	9.61	6.88			0.61
17 Sanseveria (Sanserveria sp)			88	85	60	10.94	7.30		2.3-2.5	0.7-0.8
18 Sisal (Agave sisalana)		6.2	53-80	92	65	12.20	6.27			0.62
19 Sunn (Crotalaria juncea)		9.2	88	91	66	1.76	3.86	0.61	2.12	0.82
20 Urena (Urena lobata)			80	79	54	11.19	10.03			0.25
21 Silk, boiled	0.331	10.3-12.4								
22 Wool, scoured[5]	0.326	14.7								

/1/ 1 Grex = 0.9 denier. 1 denier = wt in g per 9000 m fiber length. /2/ Values presented as dynes per sq cm x 10^{10}. /3/ Moisture regain at 65% relative humidity, 21°C. /4/ Dry weight. /5/ Contains keratin, 98 g/100g.

32. THE PROTOPLASMIC SURFACE: PHYSICAL, CHEMICAL, AND ELECTRICAL CHARACTERISTICS

This table describes certain characteristics of the protoplasmic surface of some representative animal and plant cells. Values in parentheses are ranges and conform with estimate "d" of the 95% range (cf Introduction).

Part I: SURFACE TENSION

	Organism	Cell	Dynes/cm
1	Sea urchin (Arbacia punctulata)	Egg, unfertilized[2]	0.2[1]
2	Sea urchin (A. punctulata)	Egg, fertilized[3]	0.09[2]
3	Marine worm (Chaetopterus pergamentaceus)	Egg, unfertilized	1.3[1]
4	Salamander (Triturus viridescens)	Egg, unfertilized	0.16[3]
5	Salamander (T. viridescens)	Egg, fertilized	0.10(0.06-0.17)[3]
6	Marine mollusk (Busycon canaliculatum)	Egg, fertilized	0.34(0.13-0.66)[3]
7	Clam (Cumingia tellenoides)	Egg, unfertilized	0.54[1]
8	Mollusk (Illyanassa obsoleta)	Egg, fertilized	1.1[1]
9	Newt (Triturus pyrrhogaster)	Egg, fertilized	1.4[1]
10	Frog (Rana pipiens)	Erythrocyte	1.3[1]
11	Rabbit (Oryctolagus cuniculus)	Leukocyte	2.1[1]
12	Protozoa (Amoeba dubia)		(1-3)[1]
13	Slime mold (Physarum polycephalum)		(0.1-0.6)[1]

/1/ Centrifugal fragmentation technique. /2/ Kinetic (Poisseuile's Law) technique. /3/ Sessile drop technique. /4/ Force to stretch cell with needle.

Part II: THICKNESS OF PLASMA MEMBRANE

	Organism	Cell	Microns
1	Man (Homo sapiens)	Erythrocyte	(0.015-0.026)[1]
2	Man (H. sapiens)	Erythrocyte	0.5[2]
3	Dog (Canis familiaris)	Erythrocyte	0.003[3]
4	Mouse (Mus musculus)	Mitochondria of cell of kidney tubule	0.016[1]
5	Rabbit (Oryctolagus cuniculus)	Erythrocyte	0.012[3]
6	Rabbit (O. cuniculus)	Erythrocyte	(0.021-0.023)[4]
7	Rabbit (O. cuniculus)	Erythrocyte	0.003[3]
8	Protozoa (Amoeba proteus)	Leukocyte	0.05[1]
9	Bacteria (Bacillus cereus)		(0.21-0.35)[5]
10	Yeast (Saccharomyces sp)		0.004[3]

/1/ Electron microscope. /2/ Diffraction method (wet membrane). /3/ Dielectric method. Assumed dielectric constant of 3. /4/ Leptoscopic method (dry membrane), pH 6.0. /5/ Microscopic stain technique.

Part III: ELECTROKINETIC PROPERTIES OF CELL MEMBRANES

	Organism	Cell[1]	Zeta Potential mV	Electrophoretic Mobility μ/sec/V/cm
1	Sea urchin (Arbacia punctulata)	Egg, unfertilized[2]	30(26-36)	16(13-17)
2	Sea urchin (A. punctulata)	Egg, unfertilized[3]	34(30-39)	18(15-20)
3	Sea urchin (Pseudocentrotus depressus)	Egg, unfertilized[2]	25	
4	Starfish (Asterias forbesi)	Egg, unfertilized[2]	20	
5	Starfish (A. forbesi)	Egg, unfertilized[3]	19	
6	Marine clam (Cumingia tellenoides)	Egg, unfertilized[2]	29	
7	Marine clam (C. tellenoides)	Egg, unfertilized[3]	34(31-37)	
8	Man (Homo sapiens)	Erythrocyte	16.8	1.31[4]
9	Man (H. sapiens)	Leukocyte[5]		0.38(0.33-0.44)
10	Man (H. sapiens)	Lymphocyte[5]		0.51(0.47-0.56)
11	Cat (Felis catus)	Erythrocyte	17.8	1.39
12	Dog (Canis familiaris)	Erythrocyte	21.1	1.68
13	Guinea pig (Cavia porcellus)	Erythrocyte	14.2	1.11
14	Guinea pig (Cavia porcellus)	Leukocyte[6]	26.0	1.20
15	Horse (Equus caballus)	Erythrocyte[7]	14.5	0.98(0.90-1.07)
16	Horse (E. caballus)	Leukocyte[7]	17.0	0.54(0.46-0.59)
17	Horse (E. caballus)	Lymphocyte[7]	17.0	0.60
18	Horse (E. caballus)	Platelets[7]	12.0	0.45(0.40-0.51)
19	Monkey (Macaca mulatta)	Erythrocyte	17.9	1.33
20	Mouse (Mus musculus)	Erythrocyte	17.9	1.4
21	Opossum (Didelphis azarae)	Erythrocyte	13.7	1.07
22	Rabbit (Oryctolagus sp)	Erythrocyte	7.0	1.03(1.01-1.08)[4]
23	Rat (Rattus rattus)	Erythrocyte	18.6	1.45
24	Sloth (Bradypus griseus)	Erythrocyte	12.4	0.97
25	Swine (Sus scrofa)	Erythrocyte	12.5	0.98
26	Bacteria (β-hemolytic streptococci)	Cell		1.06
27	Bacteria (Escherichia coli)	Cell	(34-42)[8]	0.64[9]

/1/ All blood cells suspended in M/15 phosphate buffer solution of pH 7.4, unless otherwise indicated. /2/ Jelly removed from cell. /3/ Jelly not removed from cell. /4/ Suspended in an isotonic phosphate-buffer-glucose solution, pH 7.2. /5/ Suspended in physiological salt solution, pH 7.4. /6/ Suspended in M/15 phosphate buffer, pH 7.0. /7/ Suspended in plasma or serum. /8/ Suspended in N/100 lactate buffer, pH 4.7. /9/ Suspended in M/15 phosphate buffer solution, pH 6.9.

Part IV: PERMEABILITY OF CELL SURFACES TO WATER

Values are cu μ per sq cm surface area per minute per atmosphere difference in osmotic pressure x 10^6, unless otherwise indicated. Experimental temperature, approximately 20° C.

	Animal	Value		Animal	Value			Value
	Protozoa		8	Sand dollar (Dendraster sp)	(10-40)	16	Rabbit (Oryctolagus cuniculus)	116[3,4]
1	Amoeba proteus	0.21[1]	9	Marine clam (Cumingia tellenoides)	41(40-42)	17	Rabbit (O. cuniculus) Skeletal muscle	2.9[4]
2	Gregarina sp	20	10	Marine worm (Chaetopterus pergamentaceus)	(46-47)	18	Frog (Rana pipiens)	(118-666)[5]
3	Zoothamnium sp	(12-25)	11	Marine worm (Urechis caupo)	27		Plant	
	Eggs[2]			Erythrocytes (except where indicated)		19	Algae (Halicystis osterhoutii)	230(220-250)
4	Sea urchin (Arbacia punctulata)	10(9-13)	12	Man (Homo sapiens)	360	20	Algae (Nitella flexilis)	463[5]
5	Sea urchin (A. punctualta)	14[3]	13	Man (H. sapiens)	135[4]	21	Algae (Spirogyra sp)	3900[5]
6	Sea urchin (Pseudocentrotus depressus)	21(18-24)	14	Cattle (Bos taurus)	250	22	Fern, water (Salvinia auriculata)	55
7	Starfish (Patiria miniata)	(10-40)	15	Rabbit (Oryctolagus cuniculus)	(35-1164)[5]	23	Onion (Allium cepa)	30

/1/ Unit is μ/sec. /2/ Unfertilized. /3/ Outward flow. /4/ Leukocytes. /5/ Unit is mol/sq cm surface area/min/g mol difference in concentration x 10^{-8}.

32. THE PROTOPLASMIC SURFACE: PHYSICAL, CHEMICAL, AND ELECTRICAL CHARACTERISTICS (Concluded)

Part V: PERMEABILITY OF CELL SURFACES TO IONS

Values are cm per hr x 10^-6, unless otherwise indicated. Experimental temperatures: approximately 20°C for egg and muscle data, 37° for erythrocytes, 15° for nerve and all plants except Valonia which was 25°C.

SODIUM

	Animal	Value
	Eggs[1]	
1	Marine worm (Urechis caupo)	600[2]
	Erythrocytes	
2	Man (Homo sapiens)	(0.6–1.6)
3	Man (H. sapiens)	13.8(11.3–15.8)[3]
4	Cat (Felis catus)	5
5	Dog (Canis familiaris)	14
6	Frog (Rana pipiens)	2
	Skeletal muscle	
7	Frog (Rana pipiens)	400
8	Frog (R. pipiens)	0.07(0.05–0.08)[3,4]
	Nerve	
9	Cuttlefish (Sepia officinalis)	10.3(5.3–15.0)[5]
10	Cuttlefish (S. officinalis)	6.6(4.5–9.6)[3,5]
11	Cuttlefish (S. officinalis)	0.36(0.10–0.92)[6]
12	Squid (Loligo forbesi)	3.5(2.3–4.1)[5]
13	Squid (L. pealei)	57,600
	Plant	
14	Algae (Nitella coronata)	28.8[2]
15	Algae (Tolypellopsis stelligera)	26(7–55)
16	Algae (Valonia macrophysa)	0.09[2]
17	Algae (Valonia ventricosa)	0.012
18	Water plant (Elodea sp)	28.82

POTASSIUM

	Animal	Value
	Eggs[1]	
19	Starfish (Pisaster ochraceus)	600[2]
	Erythrocytes	
20	Man (Homo sapiens)	4.8[4]
21	Cat (Felis catus)	2.44
22	Dog (Canis familiaris)	5.7
23	Frog (Rana pipiens)	8.8[4]
	Skeletal muscle	
24	Frog (Rana pipiens)	3200
25	Rabbit (Oryctolagus cuniculus)	3200
26	Rat (Rattus rattus)	16,000–50,000
	Nerve	
27	Crab (Carcinus maenas)	0.55
28	Crab (C. maenas)	2.9(2.7–3.6)[3,5]
29	Crab (C. maenas)	0.116
30	Crab (C. maenas)	0.13(0.10–0.20)[3,6]
31	Cuttlefish (Sepia officinalis)	0.39(0.32–0.47)[5]
32	Cuttlefish (S. officinalis)	4.7(3.9–5.5)[3,5]
33	Cuttlefish (S. officinalis)	0.10(0.06–0.22)[6]
34	Squid (Loligo pealii)	1250
	Plant	
35	Algae (Nitella clavata)	0.012[2]
36	Algae (N. coronata)	157.8[2]
37	Algae (N. flexilis)	0.012[2]
38	Algae (Tolypellopsis stelligera)	28(10–48)
39	Algae (Valonia macrophysa)	0.44[2]
40	Algae (V. ventricosa)	0.05[2]
41	Water plant (Elodea sp)	157.8[2]

BROMINE

		Value
42	Algae (Nitella coronata)	0.0002[2]

CHLORINE

		Value
43	Algae (Valonia ventricosa)	0.06[2]
44	Algae (Nitella coronata)	0.0072[2]

IODINE

		Value
45	Algae (Valonia macrophysa)	0.0018[2]

PO₄ (PHOSPHATE)

		Value
46	Algae (Nitella coronata)	25[2]

RUBIDIUM

		Value
47	Starfish (Patiria miniata)	600[2]
48	Algae (Nitella coronata)	510[2]
49	Algae (Valonia ventricosa)	1.12

[1] Unfertilized. [2] Unit is mol/sq cm surface area/min/g mol difference in concentration x 10^-8. [3] Outward flow. [4] Unit is mol/sq cm/min x 10^-12. [5] Unit is mol/sq cm/im-pulse x 10^-12. [6] Unit is mol/sq cm/min x 10^-8.

Part VI: PERMEABILITY OF CELL SURFACES TO NON-ELECTROLYTES

Values are in mol per sq cm surface area per minute per g mol difference in concentration x 10^-8, unless otherwise indicated. Temperature range, 20–25°C.

ETHYLENE GLYCOL

	Animal	Value
	Protozoa	
1	Gregarina sp	40.2
	Eggs[1]	
2	Sea urchin (Arbacia punctulata)	36(29–56)
3	Starfish (Asterias sp)	102(50–182)
4	Marine worm (Chaetopterus pergamentaceus)	143(140–153)
5	Marine clam (Cumingia tellenoides)	156(151–163)
	Erythrocytes	
6	Cattle (Bos taurus)	9.6
7	Hedgehog (Erinaceus europaeus)	246
8	Worm (Phascolosoma gouldi)	7.3
	Plant	
9	Algae (Ceramium diaphanum)	49.8
10	Algae (Chara ceratophylla)	71.6
11	Algae (Melosira sp)	22.5
12	Algae (Pylaiella litoralis)	5.8
13	Algae (Spirogyra sp)	6.6
14	Bacteria (Beggiatoa mirabilis)	83.4
15	Moss (Plagiothecium denticulatum)	2
16	Oyster plant (Rhoeo discolor)	10.4
17	Turmeric (Curcuma rubricaulis)	6.6

DIETHYLENE GLYCOL

	Animal	Value
	Eggs[1]	
18	Sea urchin (Arbacia punctulata)	26
	Erythrocytes	
19	Cattle (Bos taurus)	4.5
20	Worm (Phascolosoma gouldi)	3.7

[1] Unfertilized. [2] Unit is mol/min x 10^-4.

PROPYLENE GLYCOL

	Animal	Value
	Protozoa	
21	Gregarina sp	79.2
	Eggs[1]	
22	Sea urchin (Arbacia punctulata)	77
	Erythrocytes	
23	Cattle (Bos taurus)	19.8
24	Worm (Phascolosoma gouldi)	11.7
	Plant	
25	Algae (Chara ceratophylla)	145

GLYCEROL

	Animal	Value
	Protozoa	
26	Gregarina sp	1.1
	Eggs[1]	
27	Sea urchin (Arbacia punctulata)	5
28	Marine worm (Chaetopterus pergamentaceus)	62(58–69)
	Erythrocytes	
29	Man (Homo sapiens)	9
30	Cattle (Bos taurus)	0.11
31	Hedgehog (Erinaceus europaeus)	163
32	Worm (Phascolosoma gouldi)	<0.004
	Plant	
33	Algae (Ceramium diaphanum)	1.3
34	Algae (Chara ceratophylla)	1.2
35	Algae (Melosira sp)	2
36	Algae (Pylaiella litoralis)	0.1
37	Algae (Spirogyra sp)	0.2
38	Bacteria (Bacterium paracoli)	3.3
39	Bacteria (Beggiatoa mirabilis)	63.6
40	Moss (Plagiothecium denticulatum)	0.02
41	Maianthemum (Maianthemum sp)	9.8[2]
42	Oyster plant (Rhoeo discolor)	0.7
43	Turmeric (Curcuma rubricaulis)	0.1

ERYTHRITOL

	Animal	Value
	Erythrocytes	
44	Cattle (Bos taurus)	<0.003
45	Hedgehog (Marmota monax)	31.7
	Plant	
46	Algae (Ceramium diaphanum)	0.1
47	Algae (Chara ceratophylla)	0.08
48	Algae (Melosira sp)	0.8
49	Algae (Pylaiella litoralis)	0.007
50	Algae (Spirogyra sp)	0.02
51	Bacteria (Bacterium paracoli)	0.3
52	Bacteria (Beggiatoa mirabilis)	50.3
53	Moss (Plagiothecium denticulatum)	0.004
54	Oyster plant (Rhoeo discolor)	0.03
55	Turmeric (Curcuma rubricaulis)	0.02

SACCHAROSE

	Plant	Value
56	Algae (Chara ceratophylla)	0.05
57	Algae (Melosira sp)	0.4
58	Bacteria (Beggiatoa mirabilis)	8.1
59	Moss (Plagiothecium denticulatum)	0.0005
60	Turmeric (Curcuma rubricaulis)	0.0005

ACETAMIDE

	Animal	Value
	Eggs[1]	
61	Sea urchin (Arbacia punctulata)	(55–60)
	Erythrocytes	
62	Cattle (Bos taurus)	283
63	Worm (Phascolosoma gouldi)	15.8
	Plant	
64	Algae (Chara ceratophylla)	90

[1] Unfertilized.

Part VI: PERMEABILITY OF CELL SURFACES TO NON-ELECTROLYTES (Concluded)

Values are in mol per sq cm surface area per minute per g mol difference in concentration x 10^{-8}, unless otherwise indicated. Temperature range, 20-25°C.

#	ACETAMIDE (concluded) Plant (concluded)	Value
65	Algae (Melosira sp)	28.2
66	Algae (Pylaiella litoralis)	16.8
67	Moss (Plagiothecium denticulatum)	4
68	Turmeric (Curcuma rubricaulis)	4.8

#	PROPIONAMIDE Animal	Value
	Eggs[1]	
69	Sea urchin (Arbacia punctulata)	(134-150)
	Erythrocytes	
70	Cattle (Bos taurus)	114
71	Worm (Phascolosoma gouldi)	62.3
	Plant	
72	Algae (Ceramium diaphanum)	168
73	Algae (Chara ceratophylla)	216
74	Algae (Melosira sp)	180
75	Algae (Pylaiella litoralis)	84
76	Algae (Spirogyra sp)	27
77	Moss (Plagiothecium denticulatum)	12
78	Oyster plant (Rhoeo discolor)	9.6
79	Turmeric (Curcuma rubricaulis)	13.2

#	MALONAMIDE Animal	Value
80	Protozoa (Gregarina sp)	15
	Plant	
81	Algae (Ceramium diaphanum)	1.5
82	Algae (Chara ceratophylla)	0.2
83	Algae (Melosira sp)	1.1
84	Algae (Pylaiella litoralis)	0.1
85	Algae (Spirogyra sp)	0.1[1]
86	Bacteria (Bacterium paracoli)	1.7
87	Bacteria (Beggiatoa mirabilis)	94.8
88	Moss (Plagiothecium denticulatum)	0.05
89	Maianthemum (Maianthemum sp)	5.5[2]
90	Oyster plant (Rhoeo discolor)	0.01
91	Turmeric (Curcuma rubricaulis)	0.02

#	UREA Animal	Value
	Erythrocytes	
92	Man (Homo sapiens)	1166
93	Cattle (Bos taurus)	1080
94	Hedgehog (Erinaceus europaeus)	1666
95	Worm (Phascolosoma gouldi)[3]	1.6
	Plant	
96	Algae (Ceramium diaphanum)	5
97	Algae (Chara ceratophylla)	6.7
98	Algae (Melosira sp)	2.5
99	Algae (Pylaiella litoralis)	0.5
100	Algae (Spirogyra sp)	1.1
101	Bacteria (Bacterium paracoli)	5
102	Bacteria (Beggiatoa mirabilis)	70.2
103	Moss (Plagiothecium denticulatum)	0.2
104	Maianthemum (Maianthemum sp)	(23, 4-33.3)[2]
105	Oyster plant (Rhoeo discolor)	0.2
106	Turmeric (Curcuma rubricaulis)	0.09

#	METHYL UREA Plant	Value
107	Algae (Ceramium diaphanum)	5.8
108	Algae (Chara ceratophylla)	11.4
109	Algae (Melosira sp)	7.2
110	Algae (Pylaiella litoralis)	1.9
111	Algae (Spirogyra sp)	1.7
112	Moss (Plagiothecium denticulatum)	0.7
113	Maianthemum (Maianthemum sp)	75[2]
114	Oyster plant (Rhoeo discolor)	0.5
115	Turmeric (Curcuma rubricaulis)	0.5

#	THIOUREA Animal	Value
	Erythrocytes	
116	Cattle (Bos taurus)	1.2
117	Hedgehog (Erinaceus europaeus)	138
118	Worm (Phascolosoma gouldi)	2
	Plant	
119	Algae (Chara ceratophylla)	12.8

#	MANNITOL Animal	Value
120	Maianthemum (Maianthemum sp)	90[2]
121	Oyster plant (Rhoeo discolor)	21[2]
	Erythrocytes	
122	Man (Homo sapiens)	<0.33
123	Cattle (Bos taurus)	<0.003
124	Hedgehog (Erinaceus europaeus)[4]	2
	Plant	
125	Algae (Chara ceratophylla)	<0.05

#	BUTYRAMIDE Animal	Value
	Eggs[1]	
126	Sea urchin (Arbacia punctulata)	(338-394)
	Erythrocytes	
127	Cattle (Bos taurus)	163
128	Worm (Phascolosoma gouldi)[5]	410

#	MONACETIN Animal	Value
	Erythrocytes	
129	Cattle (Bos taurus)	6.8
130	Worm (Phascolosoma gouldi)	0.6
	Plant	
131	Algae (Chara ceratophylla)	26.6

#	DIACETIN Animal	Value
	Erythrocytes	
132	Cattle (Bos taurus)	62.5
133	Worm (Phascolosoma gouldi)	4.5
	Plant	
134	Algae (Chara ceratophylla)	133

#	TRIMETHYLENE GLYCOL Animal	Value
	Eggs[2]	
135	Sea urchin (Arbacia punctulata)	43
	Erythrocytes	
136	Cattle (Bos taurus)	6
	Plant	
137	Algae (Chara ceratophylla)	7.3

/1/ Unfertilized. /2/ Unit is mol/min x 10^{-4}. /3/ Triethylene glycol = 2; xylose = <0.003; formamide = 293; propyl alcohol=636. /4/ Xylose = 0.66. /5/ Formamide = 9.8; tetraethylene glycol = 0.4; triethylene glycol = 1.2

Part VII: COMPOSITION OF ERYTHROCYTE STROMA

#	Species	Protein	Lipid	Phospholipid	Cholesterol	Neutral Fat
		Per cent of Stroma				
1	Man (Homo sapiens)	49.5	11.2	7.3	2.6	1.8
2	Cattle (Bos taurus)	57	25.6	15.9	7.5	2.0
3	Chicken (Gallus domesticus)	91	3.9	2.5	1.1	0.2
4	Horse (Equus caballus)	53	20.4	12.7	7.4	0.3
5	Sheep (Ovis aries)	68.4	23.9	14.7	4.9	4.3

#	Species	Histidine	Arginine	Lysine	Tyrosine	Tryptophan	Cysteine	Methionine
		Molecular Ratio in Stroma						
6	Man (Homo sapiens)	7	15	14.5	8	3	2	3.5
7	Cattle (Bos taurus)	6.5	15	12	8	3	2	3
8	Horse (Equus caballus)	7	14.5	13.5	8	3	2	4
9	Sheep (Ovis aries)	8	14	11.5	7	2.5	2	4

#	Species	Glycine	Leucine	Tyrosine	Tryptophan	Total Nitrogen	Amino Nitrogen
		Per cent Anhydrous Ash-free Stroma Protein					
10	Man (Homo sapiens)	3.6	11.2	3.4		15.9	11.6
11	Cattle (Bos taurus)	3.7	10.1		1.4	13.7	10.4
12	Sheep (Ovis aries)	3.7	11.4			15.3	12.0

#	Species	Lipid	Cephalin	Lecithin	Cholesterol
		mg per sq μ Stroma Surface Area x 10^{-12}			
13	Man (Homo sapiens)	4.2			
14	Cat (Felis catus)	4.4			
15	Cattle (Bos taurus)	3.9	2.3	0.2	0.6
16	Dog (Canis familiaris)	4.9			
17	Monkey (Macaca mulatta)	4.7	2.0	1.3	1.3
18	Rabbit (Oryctolagus sp)	3.9	1.5	0.4	1.2
19	Rat (Rattus rattus)	4.3	2.4	0.4	0.8
20	Sheep (Ovis aries)	5.6			

33. VITAMINS AND PROVITAMINS: PHYSICAL AND CHEMICAL CHARACTERISTICS

#	Vitamin or Provitamin	Common Alternate Designations	Chemical Name	Molecular Formula	Units in Which Expressed	Physical State[1]	Melting or Boiling Point[1] °C	Stability[1]	Solubility[1,2] g/100 ml	Specific Rotation[1,3] $[\alpha]\tfrac{t}{D}$	Absorption Maximal
					Vitamins						
1	Vitamin A$_1$	Axerophthol; anti-xerophthalmia factor.	3,7-Dimethyl-9-(2,6,6-trimethyl-1-cyclohexen-1-yl)-2,4,6,8-nonatetraen-1-ol.	$C_{20}H_{30}O$	0.30 μg vitamin A alcohol, or 0.344 vitamin A acetate = one I.U. = one U.S.P. unit.	Pale yellow crystals.	62-64. Distills at 120-125 at 5×10^{-3} mm.	Inactivated by ultraviolet. Sensitive to air-oxidation.	s. most org. solv., fats, oils; i.w.	None.	325.5 in isopropanol.
2	Vitamin A$_2$			$C_{20}H_{28}O$		Yellow prisms.	59-60				351, 328
3	Vitamin A, neo-		5-cis-Vitamin A.	$C_{20}H_{30}O$		Yellow needles.					
4	Ascorbic acid	Vitamin C; anti-scorbutic factor.	L-Threo-2,3,4,5,6-pentahydroxy-2-hexeno-γ-lactone.	$C_6H_8O_6$	0.05 mg = one I.U. or one U.S.P. unit.	Crystals, plates or needles; monoclinic; colorless.	190-192 with some decomposition.	Stable to air when dry. Impure preparations and natural products oxidized by air and light.	33 w. 3.5 al. 2 abs. al. 1 glyc.	$+20.5\text{-}21.5^{25}$ in w. $+48^{23}$ in me. al.	243.5 in metaphosphoric acid.
5	Biotin	Vitamin H; coenzyme R; factor S, W, X; bios II G; anti-egg white injury factor.	cis-Hexahydro-2-oxo-1H-thieno[3,4]imidazole-4-valeric acid.	$C_{10}H_{16}N_2O_3S$	Gravimetric.	Fine, long needles or white crystalline powder.	232-233 (some decomposition).	Stable to air, temp. Moderately acid and neutral sol. stable several months; alk. sol. less stable.	0.022 w.^{25} 0.080 al.^{25} More s.h.w. or dil. alk.	$+91^{21}$ in 0.1 N NaOH.	
6	Choline		(β-Hydroxyethyl)trimethylammonium hydroxide.	$C_5H_{15}NO_2$	Gravimetric.	Colorless, viscous, hyg. alk. liquid.		Dil. aq. sol. stable to boiling; dec. hot alkali.	v.s.w., al.; i. eth.		
7	Cobalamin	Cyanocobalamin (vitamin B$_{12}$); hydroxycobalamin (vitamin B$_{12a}$' B$_{12b}$).	Not fully determined.	$C_{61\text{-}64}H_{86\text{-}92}N_{14}O_{13}PCo$	Gravimetric.	Hyg. dark red needles. Birefringent.	Darkens 210-220. Not melted 300.	Heat stable in aq. sol. Inactivated slowly by weak acid, alkali.	1.25 w.; i.chl. acet., eth.	$-59^{23}_{656}\ \pm9$ in dil. aq. sol.	548-550, 361, 278 in 0.1 N NaOH.
8	Vitamin D$_2$	Calciferol; activated ergosterol; anti-rachitic factor.	9,10-Secoergosta-5,7,10(19),22-tetraen-3-ol.	$C_{28}H_{44}O$	Crystals = 40 million I.U. or U.S.P. units per gram.	Prisms from acetone.	115-118 Sublimes in very high vacuum without decomposition.	Crystals stable 9 mo. in amber-evacuated ampuls at 4°C. Propylene glycol sol. stable in air for long periods of time.	6.95 acet. 7; s. most org. solv.; sl. s. vegetable oils; i. w.	$+103^{20}$ in al. $+82.6$ in acet. $+91.2$ in eth. $+52$ in chl.	264.5±0.5 in ethanol or hexane.
9	Vitamin D$_3$	Activated 7-dehydro-cholesterol.	22,23-Dihydro-24-demethylcalciferol.	$C_{27}H_{44}O$	Crystals = 40 million I.C.U.⁴ or I.U. per gram.		82-83	s. most fat solv.; i.w.	s. most fat solv.; i. w.	$+83.3^{20}$ in acet.	
10	Vitamin E	α-Tocopherol, anti-sterility factor.	5,7,8-Trimethyltocol.	$C_{29}H_{50}O_2$	One mg DL-α-tocopherol acetate = one I.U.	Slightly viscous pale-yellow oil.	Boils 200-220 at 0.1 mm.	Very stable to heat, a. Slowly oxidized by atmospheric O_2, rapidly by ferric and silver salts.	v.s. oils, fats, acet., chl., al., eth.;i.w.	$+0.32^{25}_{546.1}$ in al. -3.0 in bz.	292 in ethanol.
		β-Tocopherol⁵.	5,8-Dimethyltocol.	$C_{28}H_{48}O_2$		Yellow oil.		Same as α-	Same as α-	$+2.9^{25}_{546.1}$ in al.	295
		γ-Tocopherol⁵.	7,8-Dimethyltocol.	$C_{28}H_{48}O_2$		Crystals.		Same as α-	Same as α-	$+2.2^{25}_{546.1}$ in al.	295
		σ-Tocopherol⁵.	8-Methyltocol.	$C_{27}H_{46}O_2$		Yellow oil.		Same as α-	Same as α-	$+3.4^{25}_{546.1}$ in al.	298
11	Inositol	meso-Inositol; i-inositol; bios I.	Hexahydroxycyclohexane.	$C_6H_{12}O_6$	Gravimetric.	Efflorescent crystals (dihydrate).	218 (dihydrate) 250-253 anh.	Becomes anhydrous at 100°. Decomposes at 250°.	17.5 w. i.abs.al., eth.	Inactive.	
12	Vitamin K$_1$	Antihemorrhagic vitamin; vitamin K.	2-Methyl-3-phytyl-1,4-naphthoquinone.	$C_{31}H_{46}O_2$	Gravimetric in terms of menadione.	Yellow, viscous oil.	-20. Dec. above 100-120.	Stable to air, moisture. Dec. sunlight.	i.w.;sl.s.me. al.;s.al., chl.	-0.4^{20} (57.5% in bz.)	239,243,249, 260,270, 325 in hexane.
13	Vitamin K$_2$	vitamin K⁶.	2-Methyl-3-difarnesyl-1,4-naphthoquinone.	$C_{41}H_{56}O_2$		Yellow crystals.	53.5-54.5	Stable dil.a.; labile alk. hydroxides.	al.;acet., eth. bz.,		
14	Niacin	Nicotinic acid; P.P. factor.	Pyridine-3-carboxylic acid.	$C_6H_5NO_2$	Gravimetric.	Colorless needles.	236.5	Stable in air, and to light and pH. Non-hyg.	1.67 w.^{25} 0.73 al.^{25}; i. eth.	Inactive.	213,263,212, 261 in hexane.

No.	Name	Synonyms	Chemical name	Formula	Assay	Appearance	M.P.	Stability	Solubility	Sp. rotation	Absorption maxima
15	Niacinamide	Nicotinic acid amide.	Pyridine-3-carboxamide.	$C_6H_6N_2O$	Gravimetric.	White cryst. powder.	129–131		100 w.; 66.6 al.;sl.s.eth.	Inactive.	
16	Pantothenic acid	Chick anti-dermatitis factor; factor II.	D(+)-N-(α, γ-Dihydroxy-β, β-dimethylbutyryl)-β'-alanine.	$C_9H_{17}NO_5$	One "chick unit" = 0.14 μg D-pantothenic acid.	Colorless, viscous oil.	Unstable. Ca salt dec. 195–196.	Very hyg. Labile to a., alk., heat. Ca salt stable to air and light.	v.s.w., glac. acet.a.;sl.s eth.;i.bz., chl.	+37.5^{25} Ca salt: +28.2^{25}	
17	Para-amino-benzoic acid	PABA	p-Aminobenzoic acid.	$C_7H_7NO_2$	Gravimetric.	Mono-clinic prisms from dil. al.	187.0–187.5	Incompatible with ferric salts and oxidizing agents.	0.5 w.^{25};v.s. al., eth., glac. acet.a.;sl.s.bz.	Inactive.	264 in alk.; 225, 270 in a.
18	Pteroyl-glutamic acid	PGA; folic acid; folacin, vitamin M; L. casei factor; vitamin Bc.	N-[4-{[(2-Amino-4-hydroxy-6-pteridyl)-methyl]-amino}-benzoyl]-glutamic acid.	$C_{19}H_{19}N_7O_6$	Gravimetric.	Yellowish-orange crystals.	Darkens and chars from about 250°.	Very labile to heat in a. media. Sun-light causes deterioration.	sl.s.w., me. al.;i.acet., chl., eth., bz.;s.acet.a.		257, 282, 365 in 0.1 N NaOH.
19	Pyridoxine[7]	Vitamin B6-HCl; anti-acrodynia factor; adermine.	5-Hydroxy-6-methyl-3,4-pyridine dimethanol hydrochloride.	$C_8H_{11}NO_3 \cdot HCl$	Gravimetric.	White, odor-less powder.	205–212 dec. Sublimes; free base 160.	Fairly stable to light and air. Acid sol. stable; may be heated 120° for 30 minutes.	22 w.; l.l eth. al.;sl.s. acet.;i.eth.	Inactive.	291; 220, 254, 325; 245, 309.5[8]
20	Riboflavin	Vitamin B2; vitamin G; lactoflavin; ovoflavin; hepatoflavin.	6,7-Dimethyl-9-(1'-ribityl)-isoalloxazine.	$C_{17}H_{20}N_4O_6$	Gravimetric.	Yellow to orange-yellow poly-morphic crystals.	277–291 with decom-position.	When dry, stable to diffused light. Very labile in alk. sol. especially in light. Stable to mineral acids in dark.	0.01^{40} w.; 0.045$^{27.5}$ al.; i.eth., acet., chl., bz.	−112 to −122 in dil. alcoholic NaOH (50 mg in 2 ml).	223, 267, 375, 444 in 0.1 N HCl.
21	Thiamine	Vitamin B1; aneurin; anti-neuritic factor.	3-(4-Amino-2-methylpyr-imidyl-5-methyl)-4-methyl-5-β-hydroxy-ethylthiazolium chloride hydrochloride.[9]	$C_{12}H_{17}N_4OSCl \cdot HCl$	1 gram contains 330,000 I.U. pure thiamine·HCl.	Monoclinic plates in rosette clusters, or white powder.	246–250 dec.	When dry, stable at 100°. Very hyg. absorbing nearly one mole H_2O in air forming a hydrate.	100 w.; 1 al.; 0.3 abs.al.; 5 gly.;i.bz., eth., chl., hexane.	Inactive.	246; 263 in 0.1 N HCl.
					Provitamins						
22	β-Carotene[10]	Provitamin A.		$C_{40}H_{56}$	0.0006 mg = one I.U.	Red crystals.	180 corr.	Sensitive to O_2, autooxidation in light; stable to heat.	i.w.;sl.s.al., eth.;s.bz., pet.eth., CS_2		520, 485, 450 in CS_2.
23	Ergosterol	Provitamin D2.	Δ5, 7, 22-Ergostatrien-3β-ol.	$C_{28}H_{44}O$		Small white plates from al.	168	Destroyed by UV; dec. oxid. agents.	v.s.most fat solv.;i.w.	−130 in chl.	280 in eth.
24	7-Dehydro-cholesterol	Provitamin D3.	Δ5, 7-Cholestadien-3β-ol.	$C_{27}H_{44}O$		Crystals.	150		v.s.most fat solv.;i.w.	−113 in chl.	280 in eth.
25	22-Dihydro-ergosterol	Provitamin D4.		$C_{28}H_{46}O$		Crystals.	152–153		v.s.most fat solv.;i.w.	−109 in chl.	
26	7-Dehydro-sitosterol	Provitamin D5.		$C_{29}H_{49}O$		Crystals.	144–145		v.s.most fat solv.;i.w.	−116 in chl.	260
27	7-Dehydro-stigmasterol	Provitamin D.		$C_{29}H_{46}O$		Crystals.	154		v.s.most fat solv.;i.w.	−113.1 in bz.	
28	Epi-7-dehydro-cholesterol	Provitamin D.		$C_{27}H_{44}O$		Crystals.	124–126		v.s.most fat solv.;i.w.	−70.5 in chl.	
29	Kitol	Dimer of vitamin A.[10]		$C_{40}H_{60}O_2$		Prisms from al.	88–90		v.s.most fat solv.;i.w.	−1.35 in chl.	290
30	Lumisterol	Provitamin D[11].		$C_{28}H_{44}O$		Colorless, viscous oil.	118		v.s.most fat solv.;i.w.	+192 in acet.	
31	Panthenol	Provitamin(?) of pantothenic acid.	D(+)-3-(α, γ-dihydroxy-β-β-dimethyl buty-ryl)aminopropanol.	$C_9H_{19}NO_4$	Gravimetric.	Colorless, viscous oil.	Racemizes at boiling point.	Labile to a., alk.	v.s.w., al.; sl.s.eth.	+29.7^{20} (3% aq.)	
32	Tachysterol	Provitamin[11].		$C_{28}H_{44}O$					v.s.most fat solv.;i.w.	−70 in bz.	280

/1/ Abbreviations: a.=acid; abs.=absolute; acet.=acetone; glac. acet. a.=glacial acetic acid; al.=alcohol (95% ethyl); alk.=alkali; anh.=anhydrous; aq.=aqueous; bz.=benzene; chl.=chloroform; corr.=corrected; cryst.=crystals; crystalline; dec.=decomposes; dil.=dilute; eth.=ether; glyc.=glycerol; h.=hot; hyg.=hygroscopic; i.=insoluble; me.=methyl; org.=organic; oxid.=oxidizing; pet.=petroleum; s.=soluble; sl.=slightly; sol.=solution; solv.=solvents; UV=ultraviolet; v.=very; w.=water. /2/ Superscripts indicate temperature of measurement. /3/ Superscripts indicate concentration of solvent. /4/ International Chick Unit. /5/ Much less active than α-tocopherol. /6/ Synthetic vitamin K, menadione (2-methyl-1,4-naphthoquinone), has similar activity as natural K. /7/ The vitamin B6 group also includes pyridoxal and pyridoxamine, with different properties and biological activity. /8/ First value in 0.1 N HCl, next three in phosphate buffer at pH 7, and last two in 0.1 N NaOH. /9/ The mononitrate is a less hygroscopic form. /10/ Other carotenoids having vitamin A activity are α-carotene, γ-carotene, neo-β-carotene and cryptoxanthin. /11/ Intermediates between provitamin and vita-min.

34. MILK, CHEMICAL COMPOSITION: MAN, COW, GOAT

Ranges are given in parentheses, and represent estimate "c" of the 95% range (cf Introduction).

Constituent per 100 ml Whole Milk	Man			Cow	Goat
	Colostrum[1]	Transitional Milk[2]	Mature Milk	Mature Milk	
1 Water, g	87(83-90)	86(84-90)	88(83-90)	87(80-92)	87(81-90)
2 Calories, utilizable[3]	57	64	65	65	68
3 Total solids, g	12.8(10-17)	13.6(10-16)	12.4(10-17)	12.7(8-20)	13.4(10-19)
4 Ash, g	0.33(0.2-0.7)	0.24(0.1-0.4)	0.21(0.1-0.5)	0.72(0.3-1.2)	0.77(0.4-1.1)
5 Protein, g	2.7(1-21)	1.6(1-3)	1.2(1-6)	3.3(2-6)	3.3(2-5)
6 Amino acids, total[4], g	1.20(0.7-4.0)	0.94(0.4-1.3)	1.28(0.9-1.6)	3.3(2.7-4.1)	
7 Casein, g	1.2(0.3-5.2)	0.7(0.4-1.8)	0.4(0.04-0.7)	2.8(1.4-6.3)	2.5(1.7-3.9)
8 Lactalbumin, g		0.8	0.3(0.1-0.6)	0.4(0.2-0.6)	0.4(0.4-0.6)
9 Lactoglobulin, g	3.5(0.4-13)	0.5(0.2-1.4)	0.2	0.2(0.1-0.4)	0.3
10 Whey protein, g	1.7		0.6(<0.3-1.1)	0.6(0.2-1.4)	1.1(0.8-2.0)
11 Carbohydrate, g	5.3(1.1-7.9)	6.4(4.8-8.4)	7.0(4.2-9.2)	4.8(2.1-6.1)	4.7(3.3-6.3)
12 Fat, g	2.9(0.7-12.7)	3.6(0.4-9.6)	3.8(0.5-9.0)	3.7(0.9-9.8)	4.1(1.2-8.4)
13 "Essential" fatty acids[5], mg	246		346	96	168
14 Vitamin A, estimated total[6], mg	0.1(0.02-0.47)	0.1(0.06-0.2)	0.06(0.01-0.25)	0.04(0.015-0.95)	
15 Ascorbic acid, mg	4.4(0.4-10.4)	5.4(2.7-9.0)	4.3(0-11.2)	1.6(0.2-3.1)	1.4(Trace-3.2)
16 Biotin, µg	0.1(Trace-0.3)	0.4(Trace-1.8)	0.4(Trace-4.2)	3.5(0.2-11.0)	6.3(4.7-8.3)
17 Choline, mg			9(5-14)	13(4-28)	
18 Cobalamin[7], µg	0.04(0.01-0.15)	0.04(0-0.07)	Trace	0.56(0.07-1.15)	0.02(0-0.14)
19 Vitamin D, calc. as calciferol[8], µg			0.01(0-0.25)	0.06(0.01-0.1)	
20 Vitamin E, mg	1.3(0.1-4)	1.3(0.5-3)	0.6(0.1-1)	0.1	
21 Folic acid group[9], µg	0.05(0.01-0.15)	0.02(0.015-0.025)	0.2(0.1-0.36)	0.2(0.1-5)	0.03(0-0.16)
22 Inositol, mg			39(19-56)	13(3-39)	21(14-26)
23 Vitamin K, calc. as K_1[10], µg			2(0-17)	8(0-33)	
24 Niacin[11], µg	75(<10-145)	175(60-360)	172(66-690)	85(19-150)	273(200-320)
25 Pantothenic acid, µg	183(29-302)	288(135-412)	196(80-584)	350(155-568)	289(130-338)
26 Para-aminobenzoic acid	(?)	(?)	(?)	(?)	(?)
27 Pyridoxine group[12], µg			11(2-22)	48(3-95)	7(4-13)
28 Riboflavin, µg	29.6(12-50)	33.2(27-49)	42.6(13-100)	157(20-342)	114(76-650)
29 Thiamine, µg	15(0.5-82)	6(0-26)	16(<1-43)	42(27-90)	48(32-68)
30 Calcium, mg	31(13-66)	34(18-63)	33(15-61)	125(56-381)	130(103-176)
31 Chlorine, mg	91(20-233)	54(17-116)	43(9-355)	103(70-290)	159(56-260)
32 Cobalt, µg				0.06	
33 Copper, mg	0.05(0.02-0.6)	0.05(0.04-0.07)	0.04(0.01-0.07)	0.03(0.003-0.40)	0.04(0.02-0.05)[13]
34 Fluorine, µg				16(7-28)	
35 Iodine, µg	12(4.5-45)	2	7(4-9)	21(0.4-187)	
36 Iron, mg	0.09(0.02->0.13)	0.04(0.02-0.05)	0.15(0.02-0.45)	0.10(0.01-1.0)	0.05(0.01-0.07)
37 Magnesium, mg	4(1-8)	4(2-5)	4(2-6)	12(7-22)	16(10-24)
38 Manganese, µg	Trace		0.7	2(<1-4)	8(7-9)
39 Phosphorus, mg	14(6-25)	17(10-32)	15(7-35)	96(56-129)	106(84-161)
40 Potassium, mg	74(66-87)	64(53-77)	55(27-81)	138(38-287)	181(106-242)
41 Silicon				Trace	
42 Sodium, mg	48(26-136)	29(19-54)	15(2-44)	58(31-214)	41(19-60)
43 Sulfur, mg	22(20-26)	20(15-23)	14(5-30)	30(24-44)	16(2-29)
44 Zinc, mg	0.62(0.07-0.98)	0.77(0.04->1.15)	0.53(0.02->1.38)	0.38(0.17-0.66)	Trace

/1/ 1st-5th day of lactation. /2/ 6th-10th day of lactation. /3/ Kilocalories, calculated on basis of "physiological fuel values" of 8.80 calories per gram of fat; 3.85 calories per gram of carbohydrate (lactose); and 4.25 calories per gram of protein. /4/ Represents only the total of values that are available. /5/ Arachidonic, octadecadienoic acid. /6/ Milligrams of carotenoids x 0.75 ÷ (0.6 x 4.3), plus mg preformed vitamin A = estimated total vitamin A. /7/ Vitamin B_{12}, cyanocobalamin. /8/ 0.025 µg calciferol = one I. U. /9/ Pteroylglutamic acid (folacin), vitamin M, vitamin B_c, factor U, L. casei factor, Norite eluate factor. /10/ 0.083 µg vitamin K_1 = one Dam unit. /11/ Nicotinic acid (niacin) and nicotinic acid amide (nicotinamide). /12/ Includes pyridoxine, pyridoxal, pyridoxamine. /13/ Range of means.

35. MILK, CHEMICAL COMPOSITION: VARIOUS ANIMALS

Values are grams per 100 grams whole milk.

	Animal	Water	Protein	Fat	Lactose	Ash		Animal	Water	Protein	Fat	Lactose	Ash
1	Anteater	63	11	20	0.3	0.8	14	Horse	90.1	2.6	1.0	6.9	0.35
2	Bison	86.9	4.8	1.7	5.7	0.9	15	Llama	86.5	3.9	3.2	5.6	0.8
3	Buffalo	82.1	5.9	7.9	4.7	0.78	16	Monkey	88.4	2.2	2.7	6.4	0.18
4	Camel	87.7	3.5	3.4	4.8	0.71	17	Mule	90	2.0	1.8	5.5	0.47
5	Cat	81.6	10.1	6.3	4.4	0.75	18	Orangutan	88.5	1.4	3.5	6.0	0.24
6	Deer	65.9	10.4	19.7	2.6	1.4	19	Pig	82.8	7.1	5.1	3.7	1.1
7	Dog	76.3	9.3	9.5	3.0	1.2	20	Rabbit	71.3	12.3	13.1	1.9	2.3
8	Dolphin	44.9	10.6	34.9	0.9	0.53	21	Rat	72.5	9.2	12.6	3.3	1.4
9	Donkey	90.3	1.7	1.4	6.2	0.4	22	Reindeer	64.8	10.7	20.3	2.5	1.4
10	Elephant	70.7	3.6	17.6	5.6	0.63	23	Seal	46.4	9.7	42.0		0.85
11	Fox	81.6	6.6	5.9	4.9	0.93	24	Sheep	82.0	5.6	6.4	4.7	0.91
12	Guinea pig	81.9	7.4	7.2	2.7	0.85	25	Whale	64.8	11.1	21.2	1.6	1.7
13	Hippopotamus	90.4		4.5	4.4	0.1	26	Zebra	86.2	3.0	4.8	5.3	0.7

36. BLOOD: PHYSICAL PROPERTIES

Values in parentheses are estimate "b" or "c" of the 95% range when so designated by superscript (cf Introduction).

Part I: GENERAL

No.	Property	Animal	Blood[1]	Value	Temp[2] °C
		Vertebrates			
1	Specific gravity	Man	Whole	1.056(1.052-1.061)[b]	25/4
2			RBC	1.093(1.089-1.097)[b]	25/4
3			Plasma	1.024(1.022-1.026)[b]	25/4
4		Cat	Whole	1.051(1.045-1.057)[b]	25/4
5		Cattle	Whole	1.052(1.046-1.058)[b]	20/4
6			RBC	1.084(1.079-1.090)[b]	20/4
7			Plasma	1.029(1.026-1.033)[b]	20/4
8		Dog	Whole	1.052	
9		Goat	Whole	1.042(1.035-1.049)[b]	25/4
10			Plasma	1.022(1.019-1.025)[b]	25/4
11		Horse	Whole	1.053(1.046-1.059)[c]	20/4
12			Plasma	1.027(1.025-1.028)[c]	20/4
13		Mouse	Whole	1.057(1.052-1.062)[b]	25/4
14		Rabbit	Whole	1.050(1.048-1.052)[b]	25/4
15			RBC	1.098(1.093-1.104)[b]	
16			Plasma	1.025(1.018-1.031)[b]	
17		Rat	Whole	1.054(1.046-1.061)[b]	25/4
18			Plasma	1.023(1.018-1.028)[b]	25/4
19		Sheep	Whole	1.051(1.041-1.061)[b]	20/4
20			RBC	1.084(1.080-1.087)[c]	
21			Plasma	1.028(1.025-1.029)[c]	
22		Swine	Whole	1.046(1.039-1.054)[b]	25/4
23			Plasma	1.022(1.019-1.025)[b]	25/4
24		Chicken	Whole	1.056(1.050-1.064)[c]	
25			Plasma	1.019(1.017-1.021)[c]	
		Invertebrates			
26		Apis[3]	Whole	1.045	
27		Bombyx[3]	Whole	(1.032-1.041)	
28		Calliphora[3]	Whole	1.021	
29		Deilephila[3]	Whole	1.031	
30		Dytiscus[4]	Whole	1.026	
31		Gastrophilus[3]	Whole	1.062	
32		Hydrophilus[4]	Whole	1.012	
33		Periplaneta[4]	Whole	1.016	
34		Phormia[3]	Whole	1.018	
35		Prodenia[3]	Whole	1.032	
		Vertebrates			
36	Relative viscosity[5]	Man	Whole	4.7	38
37			Plasma	1.8	38
38			Serum	1.5	38
39		Cat	Whole	4.2	38
40		Cattle	Whole	4.6	20
41		Dog	Whole	4.7	38
42		Goat	Whole	4.0	20
43		Horse	Whole	4.1	20
44			Plasma	1.9	20
45			Serum	1.7	20
46		Rabbit	Whole	3.4	37
47			Serum	1.4	37
48		Sheep	Whole	4.3	20
49			Plasma	1.6	20
50			Serum	1.5	20
51		Swine	Whole	5.9	20
52			Serum	1.6	20
53		Chicken	Serum	1.4	
54		Duck	Whole	4.0	20
55			Plasma	1.5	10-14
56		Goose	Whole	4.6	20
57			Plasma	1.5	12-17
58		Turtle	Whole	2.2	20
59		Frog	Whole	2.8	15
60			Serum	1.5	15

No.	Property	Animal	Value (mm of water)
	Osmotic pressure, serum colloids	Mammals	
61		Man	330(280-480)[c]
62		Cat	300(240-330)[c]
63		Cattle	280(260-300)[c]
64		Dog	310(230-470)[c]
65		Goat	300(300-310)[c]
66		Guinea pig	250(230-280)[c]
67		Horse	280(230-350)[c]
68		Rabbit	290(230-350)[c]
69		Rat	260(220-290)[c]
70		Sheep	300(290-340)[c]
71		Swine	330(300-350)[c]
		Birds	
72		Chicken	150(140-160)[c]
73		Dove	110(80-120)[c]
		Reptiles	
74		Turtle (Malacoclemmys), spring	58(48-68)[c]
75		Turtle (Malacoclemmys), fall	96(80-110)[c]
		Amphibians	
76		Frog (Rana catesbiana)	103(95-115)[c]
77		Frog (R. temporaria)	70(to 140)[c]
78		Toad (Bufo vulgaris)	133(85-240)[c]
		Fish, fresh-water	
79		Carp, common (Cyprinus carpio)	(100-115)
80		Eel (Anguilla anguilla)	225
81		Pike (Esox lucius)	(110-145)
82		Tench (Tinca vulgaris)	101(95-110)
		Fish, salt-water	
83		Bass (Labrax lupus)	(175-250)
84		Cod (Gadus morrhua)	113(112-114)
85		Eel, conger (Conger conger)	(145-175)
86		Dogfish, spiny (Squalus acanthias)	(42-43)
87		Mackerel (Scomber scombrus)	(196-198)
88		Plaice (Pleuronectes platessa)	115(105-125)
89		Ray, electric (Torpedo marmorata)	(42-52)
90		Scorpion fish (Scorpaena scrofa)	(180-185)
91		Turbot (Rhombus maximus)	174
	Freezing point depression, serum	Vertebrates	Δf.p. °C
92		Man	0.562(0.555-0.570)[c]
93		Cattle	0.585
94		Dog	0.571
95		Horse	0.564
96		Rabbit	0.592
97		Sheep	0.619
98		Swine	0.615
99		Turtle	0.690
		Fish	
100		Pike	0.514
101		Plaice	0.732
102		Tench	0.523
	Freezing point depression, blood	Invertebrates	
103		Aedes aegypti[3]	0.4-0.5
104		Apis mellifera[3]	0.86
105		Bombyx mori[3]	0.48
106		Cancer spp	1.82
107		Culex pipiens[3]	0.4-0.5
108		Dytiscus circumcinctus[4]	0.56
109		Ephestia elutella[3]	1.12
110		Melolontha vulgaris[3]	0.81
111		Popillia japonica[3]	1.03
112		Ranatra linearis[4]	0.75
113		Saturnia pyri[3]	0.77
114		Venus spp	1.39

Part II: RED BLOOD CELLS

No.	Property	Animal	Value millivolts	No.	Property	Animal	Value $cm^2/volt \cdot sec \times 10^{-4}$	No.	Property	Animal	Value[7] mm/hr	No.	Property	Animal	Value[7] mm/hr
1	Electrical charge[6]	Man	-16.8	9	Electrophoretic mobility[6]	Man	1.31	17	Sedimentation rate	Man ♂	(0-9)	25	Sedimentation rate (concluded)	Rabbit	2(1.5-2.5)
2		Cat	-17.8	10		Cat	1.39	18		♀	(0-15)	26		Rat	(0.7-1.8)
3		Dog	-21.1	11		Dog	1.65	19		Cat	7.3(4-13)	27		Sheep	0.5(0.5-0.7)
4		Guinea pig	-14.2	12		Guinea pig	1.11	20		Cattle	1.2(1-1.8)	28		Swine	5.3(3-8)
5		Monkey, rhesus	-17.0	13		Monkey, rhesus	1.33	21		Dog	4(2.5-5)	29		Chicken	3.7(2-6)
6		Mouse	-17.9	14		Mouse	1.40	22		Goat	0.5	30		Goose	3.4(2.7-4)
7		Rabbit	-7.0	15		Rabbit	0.55	23		Guinea pig	1.1(0.7-1.7)	31	Sedimentation time	Man	(6-10 hours)
8		Rat	-18.6	16		Rat	1.45	24		Horse	125(120-135)	32		Rabbit	(17-42 hours)

/1/ RBC = red blood cells. /2/ For specific gravity, values are for the temperature of measurement referred to water at 4°C. /3/ Larva. /4/ Adult.
/5/ Relative to water at temperature of measurement. /6/ M/15 phosphate buffer at pH 7.4. /7/ Measured at end of first hour.

37. BLOOD, CHEMICAL COMPOSITION: MAN

Values are mg/100 ml (unless otherwise indicated) of blood or blood fraction shown in the column headings. Values in parentheses are ranges, and are estimate "d" of the 95% range unless followed by superscript (cf Introduction).

#	Constituent	Whole Blood mg/100ml blood	Red Blood Cells mg/100ml RBC	Plasma mg/100ml plasma	Serum mg/100ml serum
1	Water, g/100ml	83(81-86)[1]	72(70-75)[2]	94(93-95)	93(93-94)[c]
2	Aluminum, μg/100ml	15(7-40)	7(7-17)	46(?-88)	27(24-31)
3	Bicarbonate, mEq/L	20.9(19.1-22.7)[b]			
4	Calcium, mEq/L	4.8	(0.6-1.4)	4.8(4.3-5.2)	5.2(4.8-6.1)
5	Chloride, mEq/L	82(71-87)	78	102(93-110)	102(97-108)[b]
6	Copper, μg/100ml	98(72-125)	115(71-160)	109(75-145)	
7	Fluoride, μg/100ml	28(11-45)	27(11-44)	28(10-45)	
8	Iodide, μg/100ml	7.7(3-13)			7.1(4.8-8.6)
9	Iodine, protein-bound, μg/100ml	(4.0-8.5)			5.0(3.6-6.4)
10	Iron	48(43-52)		0.1(0.03-0.18)	(0.08-0.15)
11	Lead, μg/100ml	29(18-49)	57(29-86)	2.9(?-7.8)	
12	Lithium, μg/100ml	1.9			
13	Magnesium, mEq/L	3.2(3.0-3.7)	5.1(1.6-6.6)	8(?-19)	1.8(1.7-1.9)
14	Manganese, μg/100ml	13(0-25)	19(7-48)	23(19-29)	
15	Phosphorus, acid-soluble[3]	23.1(18.6-29)	50(39-59)	3.6	5.13
16	Potassium, mEq/L	48(39-62)	95(89-101)[b]	(140-155)	4.2(3.6-4.8)[b]
17	Silicon, μg/100ml	235(140-295)[4]		350(220-570)	
18	Sodium, mEq/L	83(72-91)	18.6(8.7-28.6)[b]	(140-155)	138(132-144)[b]
19	Sulfate, mEq/L			(1.0-1.5)	
20	Tin, μg/100ml	22(7-40)	26(7-64)	44(?-10)	
21	Zinc, μg/100ml	880(490-1270)	1440(910-1970)	300(0-615)	125
22	Protein, total, g/100ml	(19.8-23.8)	36.8	(6.5-7.4)	(5.9-7.2)
23	Albumin, g/100ml			4.4(4.0-4.8)[b]	4.3
24	Globulin, g/100ml			2.5(1.8-3.3)[b]	2.9
25	Albumin-globulin ratio			1.7(1.3-2.2)[b]	1.5
26	α-Globulin, g/100ml			0.29(0.2-0.4)[b]	
27	α_2-Globulin, g/100ml			0.56(0.4-0.7)[b]	
28	β-Globulin, g/100ml			0.84(0.6-1.1)[b]	1.01
29	γ-Globulin, g/100ml			0.90(0.6-1.2)[b]	0.93
30	Hemoglobin, g/100ml	(14.0-16.1)	33.5(30-40)[b]	Trace	
31	Fibrinogen, g/100ml	0.16		0.29	
32	Glycoprotein, acid			50	
33	Mucoprotein				(101-110)
34	Fructose	(0.5-5)	74(46-102)*	*	
35	Glucose	90(80-100)[b]*			97(61-130)[b]*
36	Glycogen	5.5(1.2-16.2)[5]	0		0
37	Glucosamine	(60-82)			
38	Mucopolysaccharides			200	
39	Lipid, total	560(400-720)	600(410-780)[b]	530(385-675)[b]	
40	Fat, neutral	135(85-235)[b]	93(11-150)[b]	140(24-260)[b]	67(61-78)
41	Fatty acids	245(185-310)		315(295-340)	245(175-325)
42	Phospholipid		350(280-420)[b]	165(110-220)[b]	211(180-255)
43	Cephalin	65	210	(7-9)	
44	Lecithin	115	70	(117-156)	107
45	Sphingomyelin	185	70	(41-56)	
46	Cholesterol, total	(120-210)	175	(195-230)	(130-225)
47	Cholesterol esters			146	(121-125)
48	Ammonia	0.18(0.12-0.24)			(0.2-1.1)
49	Bilirubin	0.18(0.1-0.25)			
50	Creatine	3.9(2.9-4.9)[b]	8.1(6.0-10.2)[b]	0.91(0.87-0.95)[b]	(2.5-3.0)
51	Creatinine	0.86	1.8(1.7-1.9)[b]	(4.6-10.6)	(0.7-1.1)
52	Glutamine	34			
53	Glutathione	(6.7-8.6)			
54	Histamine, μg/100ml	41(31-52)			
55	Nucleotides	10.5			
56	Purines, total	64(48-79)		4.9(3.9-5.9)[b]	(38-54)
57	Ribonucleic acid	(30-45)	135(100-170)	34(28-40)[b]	
58	Urea	3.2(2.2-4.2)[b]	30(25-39)[b]	3.8(2.0-5.6)[b]	(4.0-4.8)
59	Uric acid	50(38-53)	1.9(0.8-3.0)[b]		
60	Amino acids, total	4.0(2.8-5.2)[b]	4.0(2.5-5.6)[b]	(2.4-7.6)	
61	Alanine	1.0(0.6-1.7)[b]	0.3(0.1-0.6)[b]	(1.2-3.0)	
62	Arginine			(0-1.2)	
63	Aspartic acid	0.9(0.6-1.2)[b]	0.4(0.3-0.5)[b]	(1.8-5.0)	
64	Cystine			(0-1.3)	
65	Glutamic acid	(1.8-2.5)		(0.8-5.4)	
66	Glycine	1.3(0.9-1.7)	2.4(1.6-3.1)[b]	(1.0-3.8)	
67	Histidine	1.3(0.9-1.5)	1.1(0.8-1.6)	(1.2-4.2)	
68	Isoleucine	1.7(1.4-2.0)[b]	0.9(0.5-1.4)	(1.0-5.2)	
69	Leucine	2.2(1.3-3.0)[b]	1.5(1.0-1.8)[b]	(2.3-5.8)	
70	Lysine	0.5(0.4-0.6)[b]	1.4(0.9-1.8)[b]	(0.25-1.0)	
71	Methionine	1.0(0.8-1.2)[b]	0.5(0.3-0.8)[b]	(1.1-4.0)	
72	Phenylalanine		1.0(0.7-1.3)[b]	(1.5-5.7)	
73	Proline			(0.3-2.0)	
74	Serine				
75	Threonine	1.6(1.3-2.0)[b]	1.6(1.3-2.1)[b]	(0.9-3.6)	
76	Tryptophan	0.7(0.5-1.0)[b]	0.24(0.2-0.4)[b]	(0.9-3.0)	
77	Tyrosine	1.1(0.8-1.4)[b]	1.1(0.7-1.5)[b]	(0.9-2.4)	
78	Valine	2.4(2.0-2.9)[b]	2.0(1.6-2.5)[b]	(2.5-4.2)	
79	Ergothioneine	(7-20)	(5.9-7.7) mg P		
80	Adenosine triphosphate	(43-53)			
81	Phosphoric acid ester	17.3			
82	Lactic acid	19(0-41)	12	36	
83	Vitamin A[7], μg/100ml	120(20-300)		220(40-540)	
84	Ascorbic acid	0.62(0.2-0.7)	1.0(0.5-2.8)	0.7(0.1-2.5)	
85	Biotin, μg/100ml	1.2(0.8-1.7)		1.3(1.0-1.7)	
86	Cobalamin, μg/100ml	0.08(0.06-0.14)			
87	Choline, total			(26-35)	
88	Choline, free	2.5(1.0-4.0)		(0.05-2.5)	
89	Vitamin D[8], μg/100ml		(4.4-7.5)		2.8(1.7-4.1)
90	Vitamin E	3.5(2.3-5.3)		1.2(0.9-1.9)	
91	Folic acid, μg/100ml		1.7(1.5-5.0)	1.7(1.5-5.0)	
92	Inositol			0.50(0.4-0.8)	
93	Nicotinic acid	0.6(0.2-0.9)	1.3	0.07(0.02-0.15)	
94	Pantothenic acid				
95	Para-aminobenzoic acid, μg/100ml	30(15-45)	25(15-30)	15(6-35)	
96	Riboflavin, μg/100ml	3.4	22(18-26)	3.2(2.6-3.7)	
97	Thiamine, μg/100ml	8.0(4-11)	8(7-10)	7(1-9)	

/1/ A range of 80.5-80.8 has been reported. /2/ A value of 66 has been reported. /3/ Inorganic phosphorus. /4/ A value of 830 has been reported. /5/ All localized in granulocytes. /6/ A value of 315 has been reported. /7/ As β-carotene; 0.6 μg = one I. U. /8/ As calciferol; 0.025 μg = one I. U.

38. BLOOD, CHEMICAL COMPOSITION: VERTEBRATES OTHER THAN MAN

Values are mg/100 ml unless otherwise indicated, and are for plasma except where accompanied by the following code: Bl = blood; Ce = cells; S = serum. Values in parentheses are ranges and, unless followed by superscript, are estimate "d" of the 95% range (cf Introduction).

	Constituent	Cattle	Dog	Goat	Guinea Pig	Horse	Monkey	Rabbit
1	Water, g/100 ml	85 Bl	84 Bl	81 Bl		81 Bl		86 Bl
2	Calcium, mEq/L	5.4 (4.7-6.1)	5.3 (4.7-6.1)	(4.5-6) Bl	5.3 (3.7-6.8)	6.1 (5.6-6.7) S		7.0 (5.6-8.0)
3	Chloride, mEq/L	104 (97-111) S	106 (99-110)		105 (98-115)	102 (98-106)	110 (103-118)	105 (92-112)
4	Copper, μg/100 ml	(130-155) Bl				36 (34-37) Bl		85 (74-99) Bl
5	Iodide, μg/100 ml		29 (14-52) S		7.3 S			
6	Magnesium, mEq/L	2.3 (1.0-2.9) S	1.8 (1.3-2.0)		2.0 S	(1.5-2.1) S		2.0 (1.7-2.5)
7	Phosphate, inorg.	(5.6-6.5) S	5.6 (S)	(3-11) Bl	5.3 S	(3.1-5.6) S		5.9 S
8	Potassium, mEq/L	4.8 (3.9-5.8) S	4.4 (3.7-5.8)		7.4 (6.8-8.9) S	3.3 (2.7-3.5) S	3.3 (2.7-4.7) S	4.1 (2.7-5.1) S
9	Sodium, mEq/L	142 (132-152) S	150 (135-160)		145 (140-150) S	149 (146-152) S	145 (143-164) S	158 (155-165) S
10	Protein, total, g/100 ml	6.9 (5.7-8.3) S	(6.1-7.8)		5.4 (5.0-5.6) S	7.6 (6.6-8.3) S	6.8 (5.9-7.5) S	7.2 (6.0-8.3)
11	Albumin, g/100 ml	3.1 (2.3-3.7)	(3.1-4.0)		3.2 (2.8-3.9) S	3.1 (2.3-3.8) S		4.6 (4.1-5.1) S
12	Globulin, g/100 ml	3.8 (3.0-5.1) S	(2.0-3.3)		2.2 (1.7-2.6) S	4.5 (3.2-5.3) S		2.7 (1.9-3.6) S
13	α-Globulin, g/100 ml	1.1 S	1.2 S			1.4 S		
14	β-Globulin, g/100 ml	1.9 S	1.3 S			2.1 S		
15	γ-Globulin, g/100 ml	2.3 S	0.8 S			1.4 S		
16	Hemoglobin, g/100 ml	11.1 Bl	13.6 Bl	11.4 Bl		10.1 Bl		
17	Fibrinogen, g/100 ml	0.72	(0.42-0.64)		0.33	(0.29-0.43)	(0.25-0.40)	
18	Glucose	46 (36-57) Bl	60 (44-78) Bl	(43-65) Bl	96 (82-107) Bl	73 (54-95) Bl	148 S	85 (67-107) Bl
19	Lipids, total	350 (185-510)[b]	580 (47-725)		170 (94-245)			245 (69-415)[b]
20	Fat, neutral	105 (0-230)[b]			73 (0-145)[b]			105 (7-205)[b]
21	Phospholipid	84 (17-150)[b]			51 (25-77)[b]			78 (13-145)[b]
22	Cephalin	3 S	22					27
23	Lecithin	54 S	370 (300-470)					86 Ce
24	Sphingomyelin	22 S	55 S					38
25	Cholesterol	110 (8-210)[b]	173 (140-215)	(55-200) Bl	32 (21-43)[b]	77 S	118 S	45 (10-80)[b]
26	Non-protein N	(20-40) Bl	(17-38) Bl	(30-44) Bl	39 (30-51)	(20-40) Bl		
27	Amino acid N							
28	Creatinine	(1-2.1) Bl	(1-1.7) Bl	(0.9-1.8) Bl		(1.2-1.9) Bl		
29	Urea N	(6-27) Bl	(10-20) Bl	(13-28) Bl	19 (8-28) S	(10-20) Bl		15.9 (6.0-25) S
30	Uric acid	(0.05-2.1) Bl	0.33 (0-0.5) Bl	(0.33-1.0) Bl	2.5 (1.3-5.6) S	(0.9-1.1) Bl		2.6 (1.0-4.3) S
31	Adenosine triphosphate	27 Ce	53 Ce			18 Ce		112 Ce
32	Diphosphoglyceric acid		133 Ce			140 Ce		194 Ce
33	Phytic acid	0	0	0		0	0	0
34	Lactic acid	(5-20) Bl	(7-29) Bl			(10-16) Bl		

	Constituent	Rat	Sheep	Swine	Chicken	Reptile[1]	Frog[2]	Fish[3]
35	Water, g/100 ml	86 Bl	87 Bl	83 Bl	87 Bl			
36	Calcium, mEq/L	6.2 (5.4-7.2)[b]	5.7 S	(5.5-5.7) S	5.0 (4.6-5.3)	5.4	3.2	10.8
37	Chloride, mEq/L	110 (105-117) S	116	103 (100-105) S	122 (115-140)	122	70	
38	Copper, μg/100 ml	107[4]		206 (155-260)	14 S			
39	Iodide, μg/100 ml	3.4			7.2			
40	Magnesium, mEq/L	2.9 (2.0-3.7)	1.9 (1.7-2.1)	2.2 (1.9-3.2)	(1.4-2.0) S	3.4	7.6	1.3 S
41	Phosphate, inorg.	5.9 S	6.9 S	(5.3-9.6) S	(6.2-7.9) S	3.2 S	6.0 S[5]	9.0 S
42	Potassium, mEq/L	5.9 (5.4-6.4)	4.8	5.9 (4.9-7.1) S	6.0 (4.6-6.5)	4.6	4.8	
43	Sodium, mEq/L	151 (143-156) S	160	155 (140-160) S	154 (140-175)	140	105	
44	Protein, total, g/100 ml	6.3	5.7	8.7 (7.9-10.3)	(3.6-6.1) S			
45	Albumin, g/100 ml	(3.4-4.3)[b]	3.1	3.8 (2.1-4.6) S	(1.7-2.5) S			
46	Globulin, g/100 ml	(1.8-2.5)[b]	2.3	4.9 (3.9-5.6) S	(1.8-2.9) S			
47	α-Globulin, g/100 ml		0.96 S					
48	β-Globulin, g/100 ml		1.4 S					
49	γ-Globulin, g/100 ml		2.1 S					
50	Hemoglobin, g/100 ml		10.3 Bl	14 S				
51	Fibrinogen, g/100 ml	(0.16-0.34)[b]	0.36					
52	Glucose	(56-76) Bl	(30-57) Bl	(45-75) Bl	(125-205) Bl	(46-88) Bl	(36-49) Bl[5]	(100-255) Bl
53	Lipids, total	230 (70-415)[b]			520 (340-700)[b]			
54	Fat, neutral	85 (26-145)[b]	90 (24-125)[b]	96 (80-130)	225 (63-385)[b]			
55	Phospholipid	83 (36-130)[b]	90 (24-125)[b]	96 (80-130)	155 (84-225)[b]			
56	Cephalin			3 S				
57	Lecithin			72 S				
58	Sphingomyelin			21 S				
59	Cholesterol	52 (28-76)[b]	(20-38) Bl	150 Bl	100 (52-150)[b]			
60	Non-protein N		(20-38) Bl	(20-45) Bl	(20-36) Bl			
61	Amino acid N		(4.6-8) Bl	(8-8.5) Bl	(3.8-9.6) Bl			
62	Creatinine		(1.2-1.9) Bl	(1-2.7) Bl	(0.7-1.2) Bl			
63	Urea N	12.9 (9.6-16.3) S	(8-20) Bl	(8-24) Bl	5.7 Bl			
64	Uric acid	2.5 (1.8-3.0) S	(0.05-1.9) Bl	(0.05-1.9) Bl	4.5 (1.2-7.1) Bl			
65	Adenosine triphosphate	77 Ce	45 Ce	115 Ce	57 Ce	560 Ce[6]	23 Ce[5]	167 Ce[7]
66	Diphosphoglyceric acid	146	<3.5 Ce	190 Ce	0	0		0
67	Phytic acid	0	0	0	250 Ce	95 Ce		
68	Lactic acid	(5-21) Bl	(9-12) Bl					(13-19)[b] Bl

/1/ Turtle (Terrapene carolina) except where indicated. /2/ Rana catesbiana. /3/ Carp, except where indicated. /4/ A value of 320 has been reported. /5/ Species not specified. /6/ Snake. /7/ Catfish.

39. CHANGES IN STORED PRESERVED BLOOD

Values are for whole preserved human blood kept at 4°C and analyzed within 20 minutes after removal from storage. Blood (Bl), red blood cells (RBC); plasma (Pl). All values derived from Rapoport, S., J. Clin. Invest. 26:591, 1947.

Variable	Preservative[1]	Stored 0 da			Stored 10 da			Stored 20 da			Stored 30 da			Stored 40 da		
		Bl	RBC	Pl	Bl	RBC	Pl	Bl	RBC	Pl	Bl	RBC	Pl	Bl	RBC	Pl
pH[2]	C	7.4			7.1			7.1								
	CD	7.4			7.1			6.8			6.7			6.7		
	ACD	7.1			6.7			6.6			6.6			6.6		
Potassium, mEq/liter	C		100	5		75	23		63	32						
	CD		100	5		74	20		65	25		60	28		53	34
	ACD		90	5		75	12		68	19		60	23		53	27
Sodium, mEq/liter	C		25	166		45	149		55	142						
	CD		21	158		40	148		47	145		52	142		58	138
	ACD		18	160		25	152		30	148		37	142		42	137
Inorganic phosphorus, mg/100 ml	C		0	0		35	7		35	10						
	CD		0	2		10	3		28	6		29	10		31	12
	ACD		5	2		18	5		25	8		27	9		29	10
Lactic acid, mg/100 ml	C	20			80			80								
	CD	10			135			185			210					
	ACD	20			90			130			155			170		
Glucose, mg/100 ml	C	70			10[3]			10[3]			10					
	CD	720[4]			650?			575?			520					
	ACD	670[5]			600?			550?			470					

/1/ Preservative C: 3.2 g trisodium citrate-di-H_2O, in 100 ml aqueous solution, pH 7.5 (effective toxicity re blood = 141%). Ten ml added to 100 ml blood, increasing blood citrate by 10 mM/liter, and plasma citrate by 17 mM/liter. Preservative CD: 2.13 g trisodium citrate-di-H_2O, plus 5 g glucose anhydrous, in 100 ml aqueous solution, pH 7.5 (effective tonicity re blood = 94%). Fifteen ml added to 100 ml blood, increasing blood citrate by 11 mM/liter, and plasma citrate by 19 mM/liter; blood glucose by 650 mg/100 ml. Preservative ACD: 1.33 g trisodium citrate-di-H_2O, plus 470 mg citric acid, plus 3 g glucose anhydrous, in 100 ml aqueous solution, pH 5.03 (effective tonicity re blood = 66%). Twenty five ml added to 100 ml blood, increasing blood citrate by 13 mM/liter, plasma citrate by 21 mM/liter, blood glucose 600 mg/100 ml, citric acid by 16.5 mEq/liter. Blood changes: Blood preserved with C for 8 days shows changes equivalent to those in blood stored for 18 days with CD, and for 33 days with ACD. /2/ pH measured at 37.5°C. Blood and plasma, same pH. /3/ Residual non-fermentable reducing substances. /4/ Normal blood glucose plus glucose in CD. /5/ Normal blood glucose plus glucose in ACD.

40. BLOOD ENZYME ACTIVITY: VERTEBRATES

Values in parentheses are ranges, and, when accompanied by a literal superscript, are estimates of the 95% range (cf Introduction). B = blood, C = RBC; P = plasma; S = serum.

No.	Animal		Activity/100 ml
	Adenosine Deaminase[1]		
1	Rabbit	B	415
	Adenosine Polyphosphatase, Acid[2]		
2	Man	S	41(21-61)[b]
	Adenosine Polyphosphatase, Alkaline[2]		
3	Man	S	30(10-51)[b]
	Adenylic Acid Deaminase, Muscle[3]		
4	Rabbit	B	41
	Aldolase[4]		
5	Man	S	(350-800)[d]
6		C	+
7	Rat, albino	C	90,000
8		S	6000
	Amylase[5]		
9	Man	S	(60-150)[b]
	Arginase[6]		
10	Man	C	♂5100
11		C	♀4400
12		B	♀2000
13	Monkey	P	0
14	Mouse	P	0
15		C	0
16	Rat	P	+
17		C	0
	Carbonic Anhydrase[7]		
18	Man	C	73,000
19	Cat	C	128,000
20	Calf	C	44,000
21	Dog	C	84,000
22	Guinea pig	C	60,000
23	Swine	C	59,000
24	Rat	C	144,000
25	Chicken	C	22,000
	Catalase		
26	Man	C	0.18[8]
	Catalase (concluded)		
27	Man	S	6909
28	Cow	S	202,800[10]
	Cholinesterase		
29	Man	B	336[11]
30		C	547[11]
31		P	176[11]
32		S	(135-362)[12]
33	Cat	S	(92-140)[12]
34	Dog	S	(112-303)[12]
35	Guinea pig	S	(125-230)[12]
36	Horse	S	(248-310)[12]
37	Mouse	S	(430-685)[12]
38	Ox	S	45[12]
39	Swine	S	40[12]
40	Rabbit	S	(18-35)[12]
41	Rat	S	253[13]
42	Sheep	S	0[12]
43	Chicken	S	(28-78)[12]
	Cholinesterase[14,15,16]		
44	Man	C	261
45		P	5.8
46	Cat	C	12.1
47		P	16.2
48	Cow	C	211
49		P	Trace
50	Dog	C	61
51		P	14.8
52	Guinea pig	C	153
53		P	16.6
54	Horse	C	81
55		P	8.1
56	Rabbit	C	34
57		P	25.2
58	Rat	C	+
59		P	+
	Cholinesterase[14,15,16] (concluded)		
60	Sheep	C	76
61		P	13.0
62	Fowl	C	Trace
63		P	72
64	Labrus	C	0
65	(bony fish)	C	0.3
66	Scyllium	C	0
67	(elasmo-	P	7.6
68	branch)		
	Cholinesterase[15,17]		
68	Man	C	Trace
69		P	110
70	Cat	C	0
71		P	45
72	Cow	C	Trace
73		P	Trace
74	Dog	C	0
75		P	144
76	Guinea pig	C	Trace
77		P	60
78	Horse	C	Trace
79		P	243
80	Rabbit	C	0
81		P	19.8
82	Rat	C	0
83		P	5.8
84	Sheep	C	0
85		P	0
86	Fowl	C	Trace
87		P	4.5
88	Labrus	C	Trace
89	(bony fish)	P	Trace
90	Scyllium	C	0
91	(elasmo-branch)	P	Trace
	Dehydropeptidase[18]		
92	Man	S	359
	Glucose-6-phosphate Dehydrogenase		
93	Rat	C	+
	β-Glucuronidase[19]		
94	Man	S	♂(0-181)
95		S	♀(37-230)
	Glyoxalase[20]		
96	Man	C	1,398,000
97		B	611,700
98	Rat	C	2,040,000
99		B	861,000
	Hexokinase		
100	Rat	C	+
	Histaminase[21]		
101	Man	B	36(30-40)
102		B	18(0-36)
	Lactic Dehydrogenase		
103	Man	S	+
104		C	+
	Lipase[22]		
105	Man	S	(0-150)
	Methemoglobin Reductase		
106	Rabbit	C	+
	Phenosulfatase[23]		
107	Man	S	(30-1550)
	Phosphatase, Acid[24]		
108	Man	S	(1.0-4.0)
	Phosphatase, Alkaline[25]		
109	Man, adult	S	(10.5-13.0)[26]
110			(1.0-4.0)[27]
111	Child	S	(5.0-14.0)[28]
	Profibrinolysin[29]		
112	Man	P	(50-125)
	Vitamin B_c Conjugase[30]		
113	Man	P	(80-100)

/1/ μg N liberated/hr. /2/ μM P from ATP/hr at pH 4.8 for acid adenosine polyphosphatase, and at pH 8.9 for alkaline adenosine polyphosphatase. Corrected for inorganic P and non-enzymatic hydrolysis. /3/ μg N liberated/hr in presence of 0.05% adenylic acid. /4/ μl fructose diphosphate/hr at 38°C at pH 8.6. No change in pregnancy. /5/ mg dextrose or equivalent (by copper reduction) from starch under specified conditions. /6/ Units as described by Kochakian. Fall in malnutrition. /7/ Amount of RBC that will halve the time of uncatalyzed reaction at 3°C under specified conditions. Fall in newborn; parallels RBC Zn concentration in all conditions in adults. /8/ g/100g dry weight. /9/ Units described by Dille, et al. /10/ mg H_2O_2 split/10 min under conditions specified. /11/ μM acetylcholine hydrolyzed/min as measured by ml 0.01N NaOH required to neutralize acetic acid formed/min from 0.0025M acetylcholine at pH 7.65 at 25°C. /12/ μM acetylcholine hydrolized/min from 0.01M acetylcholine. /13/ μM acetylcholine hydrolyzed/min from 0.015M acetylcholine. /14/ μM acetyl-β-methylcholine hydrolyzed/min as measured by volume CO_2 evolved/min from 0.03M acetyl-β-methylcholine. /15/ Hematocrit values of 45 assumed. /16/ RBC cholinesterase activity high in reticulocytes and young cells; high in conditions accompanied by hyperactive hematopoiesis. /17/ μM benzoylcholine hydrolyzed/min as measured by volume CO_2 evolved/min from 0.006M benzoylcholine. /18/ μMNH_3/30 min from DL-alanyldehydroalanine at 37°C at pH 8.1. /19/ μg phenolphthalein/hr from phenolphthalein-glucuronide at 38°C at pH 4.5. Rise in pregnancy from 300 μg at 3 months to 1350 μg at term. /20/ μl CO_2/20 min from methylglyoxal at pH 7.2 at 26°C in presence of glutathione. /21/ μg histamine destroyed in 90 min at 37°C. Rise in pregnancy. /22/ ml N/20 NaOH/24 hr from standard olive oil emulsion. /23/ Amount of enzyme which produces color equivalent to 10 μg of p-nitrophenol from p-nitrophenyl sulfate. /24/ mg phenol/hr from disodium phenylphosphate at pH 5.0. /25/ Rise in osteoblastic activity and pregnancy. /26/ mg phenol/30 min from disodiumphenylphosphate at 37.5°C at pH 9.0. /27/ mg P/hr from β-glycerophosphate at 37°C at pH 8.6. /28/ mg P/hr from β-glycerophosphate at 37°C at pH 8.6. /29/ Units of fibrinolysin. A unit will completely lyse a 0.1% fibrin clot in 120 seconds at 28°C at pH 7.2 in isotonic saline buffered with imidazole. /30/ μg folic acid/90 min from yeast extract at 37°C at pH 4.5.

41. SEROUS FLUIDS, CHEMICAL CHARACTERISTICS: VERTEBRATES

The concentrations in transudates of constituents of blood will depend on the plasma concentration of the constituent, the membrane permeability of the constituent and, in the case of electrolytes, the charge of the ion and the concentrations of non-diffusible ions (proteins) in the plasma and in the transudate. For non-electrolytes readily passing through the membrane, the concentration in transudate water will equal that in plasma water provided a steady state is present. In the case of electrolytes, the concentrations in the transudate will differ from that in plasma according to the Gibbs-Donnan law for heterogeneous solutions. Values are mg/100 ml, unless otherwise indicated. Those in parentheses are ranges, and unless followed by a superscript, are estimate "d" range (cf Introduction).

	Constituent or Property	Animal	Plasma	Transudates	Pleural Fluid	Pericardial Fluid	Peritoneal Fluid
1	Water, %	Man	94 (93-95)	94 (90-99)	98 (96.4-99)		(95-99)
2		Dog	93 (91-95)	98.9 (98.3-99.3)			
3		Horse	91	(93.5-95.8)			
4	Ash, %	Man	(0.6-1.0)		0.76	0.67	0.98
5	pH	Man	7.39 (7.33-7.45)[b]	(7.45-7.68)	7.2 (6.8-7.6)		7.4 (6.8-9.8)
6		Turtle	7.72 (7.46-7.80)			8.25 (7.9-8.5)	8.12 (7.8-8.4)
7		Fish	7.36 (7.2-7.6)	7.45 (7.1-7.6)		6.12 (5.3-6.9)	5.80 (5.4-6.3)
8	Conductivity, mhos x 1000	Man	(10.5-12.4)	14.2 (11.3-15.5)			13.4 (13.2-13.5)
9	Calcium, mEq/L	Man	4.8 (4.3-5.2)	4.0 (2.6-4.9)			
10		Dog	5.3 (4.7-6.1)	3.5 (3.2-4.1)	4.3 (2.8-5.4)		4.0 (2.0-4.9)
11		Turtle	5.4 (3.1-6.5)	2.4		2.1 (0.6-4.5)	3.4 (2.4-5.2)
12		Fish	4.9 (2.9-6.0)	4.6 (3.0-6.9)		1.4 (0.5-3.5)	3.4 (1.7-6.6)
13	Carbon dioxide, mEq/L	Man	29.5 (23-33)	28.7 (22-37)	23.8 (21-31)		26.7 (24-29)
14		Dog	24 (17-27)	26.1 (21-31)			21.4 (10-30)
15		Turtle	40.4 (23-52)	44		88.5 (29-130)	68.9 (24-130)
16		Fish	8.2 (6-12)	7.3 (5-10)		0.4 (trace-0.5)	0.3 (trace-0.4)
17	Chloride, mEq/L	Man	102 (93-110)	105.8 (98-110)	100 (92-135)	124.8	109 (91-120)
18		Dog	106 (99-110)	126 (119-127)			124 (110-145)
19		Turtle	112	75.6		55.1 (15-130)	70.8 (33-125)
20		Fish	236 (225-265)	262 (245-280)		370 (365-375)	274 (190-330)
21	Magnesium, mEq/L	Man	1.8 (1.7-1.9)	2.0 (1.6-2.4)	1.7 (0.7-2.4)		0.5
22		Dog	1.8 (1.3-2.0)	1.7 (1.4-2.2)			
23		Turtle	3.4 (0.5-7.9)	0.8		1.1 (0.3-3.5)	2.1 (0.3-5.0)
24		Fish	2.8 (1.7-3.5)	1.0 (0.9-1.0)		2.6 (1.0-5.0)	17.8 (8.0-25.0)
25	Phosphorus, total	Man	23 (19-29)		11.4 (6-31)		
26		Dog	26	(12-18)			
27	Phosphorus, inorg.	Man	3.4 (2.4-4.4)	3.0 (1.2-4.4)	3.8 (2.1-5.1)		4.0 (1.2-5.3)
28		Fish	19.8 (9-40)	12	5.6 (0-11)	4.3 (0-8.7)	5.6 (0-11)
29	Potassium, mEq/L	Man	3.6	3.4 (2.8-6.0)	4.8 (2.5-6.6)		4.1 (2.0-5.6)
30		Dog	4.4 (3.7-5.8)	5.0 (4.2-6.1)			
31		Turtle	4.6 (2.4-6.7)	2.0		3.1 (1.1-6.1)	3.2 (2.4-4.3)
32		Fish	5.3 (4.5-6.8)	4.8 (3.8-6.0)		16.6 (8.5-22)	6.6 (5.2-8.9)
33	Sodium, mEq/L	Man	(140-155)	140 (120-155)	140 (135-150)		138 (125-155)
34		Dog	150 (135-160)	150 (145-155)			
35		Turtle	138 (120-165)	123		140 (130-150)	137 (120-150)
36		Fish	259 (235-275)	266 (260-270)		314	246 (145-305)
37	Nitrogen, total	Man	(3000-3700)	(320-835)	287 (260-340)		150 (45-555)
38		Dog					149 (26-295)
39	Protein, g/100 ml	Man	(6.5-7.4)	0.85 (0.4-1.3)	1.8 (0.3-4.1)	3.3 (0.8-4.9)	2.1 (0.02-4.5)
40		Cat	7.6 (6.1-9.0)			2.4 (2.2-2.7)	(0.6-2.5)
41		Dog	6.7 (6.1-7.8)	3.0 (0.2-4.8)		1.7 (0.8-2.9)	2.6 (1.6-3.7)
42		Monkey	6.8 (5.9-7.5)			1.7 (1.3-2.2)	
43		Rabbit	5.7			2.2 (1.5-3.6)	
44		Rat	6.3			2.1	
45		Chicken	3.6 (2.6-4.6)			3.5	
46	Albumin, g/100 ml	Man	4.4 (4.0-4.8)	2.2	0.97 (0.8-1.2)	2.2	0.88 (0.3-1.6)
47		Dog	(3.1-4.0)			1.0 (0.7-1.5)	
48	Globulin, g/100 ml	Man	2.5 (1.8-3.3)	0.6	0.79 (0.3-1.2)	0.6	0.81 (0.2-1.7)
49		Dog	(2.0-3.3)			0.75 (0.4-1.5)	
50	Albumin-globulin ratio	Man	1.7 (1.3-2.2)	(2.5-3.5)	1.5 (0.9-3.5)		1.1 (0.9-1.6)
51		Dog	1.4				1.6 (0.7-2.6)
52	Euglobulin, g/100 ml	Man	0.2		(0.7-1.1)		
53	Pseudoglobulin, g/100 ml	Man	1.8		(1.8-2.2)		
54	Fibrinogen	Man	0.29	0.03 (0-0.8)	0.1 (0-0.3)	0.03	0.1 (0-0.2)
55		Horse	(0.29-0.43)	(0.04-2.2)			
56	Non-protein nitrogen	Man		(27.5-30)	31 (20-42)		30.2 (20-43)
57		Dog		34 (20-45)			
58		Fish	1090 (1070-1125)	680			870 (760-1015)
59	Amino acid N	Man		6.4	5.6 (4.2-8.9)		
60		Fish	7.5 (5.6-9.4)				(0-2.6)
61	Ammonia	Man	0.18 (0.12-0.24)	1.2			
62	Creatine	Man	0.23 (0-0.8)	3.2	3.0 (2.1-4.9)		
63		Fish	2.9 (1.8-4.2)	2.4			3.9 (3.6-4.2)
64	Creatinine	Man	0.91 (0.87-0.95)	2.4	1.2 (0.7-2.1)		1.2 (1.0-2.0)
65		Fish	(0-0.5)			0	(0-0.7)
66	Purine N	Man		0.39			
67	Urea N	Man	14 (5-22)	14.4	13 (9.8-22)		16 (11.9-21)
68		Dog		11 (9.9-16.5)			
69		Fish	1180 (1045-1300)	970 (555-1240)		1065 (690-1345)	1015 (900-1100)
70	Uric acid	Man	3.2 (2.2-4.2)	4.0 (2.5-5.0)	4.0 (1.9-8.0)		4.2 (1.8-5.3)
71		Dog	0.33	Trace			
72	Lipid, total, g/100 ml	Man	(0.38-6.67)	1.5 (0.7-2.5)			
73	Fatty acids	Man	315 (295-340)		268 (130-430)		
74	Cholesterol	Man	(195-230)	40 (13-60)	147 (20-329)		60 (5-150)
75	17-OH-corticosteroids, μg/100 ml	Man	13 (2-34)	3 (0-11)	8 (0-16)	(5-16)	4.2 (0-9)
76	Phosphatides	Man	165 (110-220)	142			164
77	Lecithin	Man	117	(60-150)	50 (0-125)		40 (0-140)
78	Lactic acid	Man	36	(17-32)	17.8 (11-47)		
79	Bilirubin	Man	0.18 (0.1-0.25)	(0-0.2)	(0.1-0.7)		0.5

42. LYMPH, CHEMICAL COMPOSITION: MAMMALS

Values in this table are the result of a four-year search for data in the field of lymph composition. Numerous gaps point up lack of available information and/or need for research. Values are mg/100 ml, unless otherwise indicated.

	Constituent	Species	Thoracic Duct Plasma	Thoracic Duct Lymph	Skin Lymphatics Plasma	Skin Lymphatics Lymph	Cervical Lymphatics Plasma	Cervical Lymphatics Lymph	Right Lymph Duct Plasma	Right Lymph Duct Lymph	Intestinal Lymphatics Plasma	Intestinal Lymphatics Lymph	Liver Lymphatics Plasma	Liver Lymphatics Lymph	Leg Lymphatics Plasma	Leg Lymphatics Lymph
1	Calcium	Man	9.5	7.7												
2		Dog	10.4	9.2			11.7	9.8								
3	Chloride	Man	335	335												
4		Dog	390	415			410	430								
5	Phosphorus, inorganic	Man	4.0	3.9												
6		Dog	4.3	3.6			5.6	5.9								
7	Potassium	Man	19.1	18.3												
8		Dog		18.7			16.4			21.1						
9	Sodium	Man	290	290												
10		Dog		330			375	360								
11	Protein, g/100 ml	Man	6.0	2.8-3.6		0.7										
12		Cat	7.6	4.8				3.5	7.4	4.9	5.8		5.3	5.2		3.3
13		Dog	6.2	4.0			6.2	3.6			5.7	2.8	5.7	4.4	5.5	1.7
14		Rat	5.8	3.1				3.1								
15	Albumin, g/100 ml	Man	3.5	1.6-2.4												
16		Dog	3.6	2.4			3.6	2.4			3.5	1.9	3.4	2.7		
17		Rat	3.9	1.9												
18	Globulin, g/100 ml	Man	2.5	1.2												
19		Dog	2.6	1.5			2.6	1.3			1.6	0.6	1.8	1.3		
20		Rat	1.9	1.2												
21	Fibrinogen, g/100 ml	Man														
22		Dog	0.4	0.2												
23	Prothrombin, %[1]	Man														
24		Dog		51									93			7.6
25	Amino acids	Man														
26		Dog	2.4	2.4			4.9	4.8								
27	Non-protein N	Man	25.7	23.4												
28		Dog	40.0	39.0			37.5	37.4	30.0	31.0					27.2	26.7
29	Urea	Man														
30		Dog		23.5			21.7	23.5								
31	Creatinine	Man	1.1	1.0												
32		Dog					1.4	1.4								
33	Glucose	Man	135	136												
34		Dog	125	125			125	130			220	220	110	115		
35	Non-fermentable	Man														
36	reducing substances	Dog					5.5	5.8								
37	Total lipid, g/100 ml	Man														
38		Dog	0.3-0.6	0.2-7.3			0.6	0.3								
39	Fatty acids	Man														
40		Dog					440	240								
41	Cholesterol	Man	120	75												
42		Dog					135	55			72	48				
43	CO$_2$ Content	Man														
44		Dog					57[2]	59[2]								
45	pH	Man														
46		Dog					7.3	7.4								

/1/ Percentage of level in plasma. /2/ ml/100 ml.

43. SWEAT, CHEMICAL COMPOSITION: MAN

Values are mg/100 ml of sweat, unless otherwise indicated. Those in parentheses are averages of ranges reported in the literature.

	Constituent	Value		Constituent	Value
1	Water, %	(99.2-99.7)	25	Threonine	5.4(1.7-9.1)
2	Calcium	2.1(1-8)	26	Tryptophan	1.1(0.4-1.8)
3	Chloride	(30-300)	27	Tyrosine	3.2(1.2-5.0)
4	Iodine, µg	0.8(0.5-1.2)	28	Valine	3(1.5-4.5)
5	Iron, µg	27(22-45)	29	Reducing substances, as glucose	(2.8-40)
6	Magnesium	0.2(0.14-4.5)	30	Volatile acids, ml 0.1 N	(2.4-5.6)
7	Manganese, µg	6(3-7)	31	Lactic acid	225(45-452)
8	Nitrogen, ammonia	(2.5-35)	32	Ascorbic acid[1], µg	(0-200)
9	Nitrogen, total	31(27-64)	33	Biotin, µg	Trace
10	Phosphorus	0.5(0-2)	34	Choline, µg	(0.3-1.5)
11	Potassium	(21-126)	35	Folic acid group, µg	0.6(0.53-0.88)
12	Sodium	(29-294)	36	Inositol, µg	21(15-36)
13	Sulfur, total	(0.7-7.4)	37	Nicotinic acid, µg	(7-22)
14	Non-protein nitrogen	31(27-64)	38	Pantothenic acid, µg	3.8(2.2-4.4)
15	Amino acid N	2.8(1.6-4.8)	39	p-Aminobenzoic acid, µg	0.24(0.08-1.7)
16	Creatinine	(0.1-1.3)	40	Pyridoxine, µg	(0.08-0.18)
17	Urea	(12-57)	41	Pyridoxal, µg	3.2(0.4-8.25)
18	Uric acid	1.4(0.7-2.5)	42	Riboflavin, µg	(0-0.5)
19	Arginine	13.5(5.8-21.4)	43	Thiamine, µg	0.15(0-0.6)
20	Histidine	8.0(6-10)	44	Specific gravity	(1.001-1.006)
21	Isoleucine	2.3(1.0-3.6)	45	pH	(3.8-6.5)
22	Leucine	2.7(1.2-4.2)	46	Maximum rate of production, ml/min	(17.7-38.2)
23	Lysine	2.3(1.4-3.2)	47	Stimulus to sweating[2], °C	(39-45)
24	Phenylalanine	2.2(1.0-3.5)			

/1/ Includes dehydroascorbic acid. /2/ Thermally induced, average skin temperature at rest.

44. CEREBROSPINAL FLUID: PHYSICAL AND CHEMICAL CHARACTERISTICS

Values are mg/100 ml unless otherwise indicated; those in parentheses are ranges.

Part I: MAN

#	Constituent or Property	Value	#	Constituent or Property	Value	#	Constituent or Property	Value
1	Volume, ml	(90-150)	22	Protein, total	28(12-43)	43	Isoleucine N	0.01
2	Specific gravity	1.0071(1.0062-1.0082)	23	Cisternal	15	44	Leucine N	0.01
3	Solids, total	1000(850-1700)	24	Lumbar	25(20-40)	45	Lysine N	0.05
4	Freezing point, $^{\circ}$C	-0.570(-0.60 to -0.054)	25	Ventricular	10	46	Methionine N	0.004
5	pH	7.4(7.35-7.70)	26	Albumin, %[1]	55(40-70)	47	Phenylalanine N	0.02
6	Pressure, mm H_2O	150(70-180)	27	Fibrinogen	0	48	Threonine N	0.03
7	Aluminum	Trace	28	α-Globulin[1]	10(5-20)	49	Tyrosine N	0.01
8	Barium	Trace	29	β-Globulin[1]	12(15-20)	50	Valine N	0.02
9	Bicarbonate	48	30	γ-Globulin[1]	11(5-20)	51	Cholesterol	(0.24-0.50)
10	Boron	Trace	31	X-proteins[1,2]	7(2-15)	52	Fatty acids	(1-3)
11	Calcium	5(4.5-5.2)	32	Non-protein N	19(12-28)	53	Reducing substances[3]	70(44-110)
12	Chloride	440(420-450)	33	Creatinine	1.2(0.5-1.9)	54	Fructose	3.4(2.0-7.5)
13	Copper	0.013(0.006-0.02)	34	Urea	11.7(8-28)	55	Hexosamine	9(5-18)
14	Iodine	<0.001	35	Uric acid	(0.07-2.8)	56	Polysaccharides	3.4(2.3-6.8)
15	Magnesium	2.36(2.0-2.6)	36	Amino acid N	1.23	57	Ascorbic acid	0.6(1-8)
16	Phosphorus	1.5(1.2-2.1)	37	Alanine N	0.21	58	Citric acid	0.04
17	Potassium	9.8(8.5-13.2)	38	Arginine N	0.1	59	Lactic acid	17(11-27)
18	Sodium	525(500-545)	39	Cystine N	0.02	60	Pyruvic acid	(0.4-1.0)
19	Strontium	Trace	40	Glutamine N	0.73	61	Acetylcholine	0
20	Sulfur	0.6	41	Glycine N	0.03	62	Cholinesterase[4]	Present
21	CO_2, vol %	59(57-62)	42	Histidine N	0.05	63	Glucuronidase[5]	Present

/1/ Per cent of total protein. /2/ 2 components migrating in electrophoresis more rapidly than albumin at pH about 8; not lipoproteins. /3/ Includes glucose. /4/ About 1% of serum concentration. /5/ An unidentified esterase is also present.

Part II: VERTEBRATES

#	Constituent or Property	Value	#	Constituent or Property	Value	#	Constituent or Property	Value
	Cat			**Dog (concluded)**			**Monkey (concluded)**	
1	Calcium	6	27	Uric acid	0.24		Protein, total (concluded)	
2	Chloride	425	28	Allantoin	0.30(0.25-0.47)	52	Cisternal fluid	(8-15)
3	Protein, lumbar fluid	17	29	Glucose	63	53	Lumbar fluid	(20-30)
4	Glucose	58	30	Ascorbic acid	6.6	54	Globulin	(0.4-6.3)
5	Ascorbic acid	3.8		**Goat**		55	Glucose	54
	Cattle		31	Specific gravity	1.0049	56	Ascorbic acid	2.3
6	Specific gravity	1.0065(1.005-1.008)	32	Chloride	410		**Rabbit**	
7	pH	7.5(7.4-7.6)	33	Protein, lumbar fluid	12	57	Specific gravity	1.005
8	Pressure, mm H_2O	(80-150)	34	Glucose	56	58	Chloride	(600-730)
9	Calcium	6(5.2-6.1)		**Horse**		59	Protein, total	(15-19)
10	Chloride	410	35	Specific gravity	1.0065(1.004-1.008)	60	Non-protein N	(5.6-16.8)
11	Potassium	(11.2-13.8)	36	pH	7.25(7.13-7.36)	61	Glucose	(50-57)
12	Protein, total	(22-27)	37	Pressure, mm H_2O	380(270-490)		**Shark**	
13	Lumbar fluid	34	38	Calcium	6.3(5.5-7)	62	Specific gravity	(1.0233)
14	Albumin	(10-22)	39	Chloride	450	63	pH	7.2
15	Non-protein N	16	40	Magnesium	2.0(1.1-2.9)	64	Uric acid	0.14
16	Creatinine	1.4	41	Phosphorus, inorganic	1.4(0.9-2.2)		**Sheep**	
17	Urea	11	42	Potassium	12.7(10.6-14.2)	65	Calcium	5.8
18	Glucose	(48-68)	43	Protein, total	47.6(29-72)	66	Chloride	(750-870)
	Dog		44	Cisternal fluid	50(30-66)	67	Magnesium	2.9
19	Specific gravity	1.0065(1.006-1.009)	45	Albumin	38.6(22.6-68)	68	Protein, total	(8-70)
20	pH	7.37(7.35-7.39)	46	Globulin	9.3(3.4-18.4)	69	Non-protein N	29(9.6-42)
21	Pressure, mm H_2O	145(30-230)	47	Urea	(23-31)	70	Glucose	(48-110)
22	Chloride	410	48	Glucose	56(49-76)		**Swine**	
23	Protein, cisternal fluid	30	49	Ascorbic acid	1.7	71	Protein, total	(24-29)
24	Protein, lumbar fluid	12		**Monkey**		72	Albumin	(17-24)
25	Albumin	(10-25)	50	Chloride	420	73	Globulin	(5-10)
26	Globulin	9	51	Protein, total	(8-50)	74	Glucose	(45-85)

45. SEBUM, CHEMICAL COMPOSITION

Sebum denotes the lipid obtained by extracting the intact skin or hair or wool; in birds, the lipid is from the preen gland oil. Values are g/100 g; those in parentheses are ranges.

#	Constituent	Man[1]	Guinea Pig	Ox	Rabbit	Rat	Sheep	Duck	Goose
1	Fatty acids, free, total	28.3(22.0-32.2)	8.2	5.1	9.0	7.4	11.0		
2	Straight-chain	28.3							
3	Branched-chain	0							
4	Fatty acids, combined[2], total	34.6(27.5-41.0)	50.5	53.4	43.6	51.4	44.0	47.6	47.5
5	Straight-chain	34.6					3.5	14.8	9.5
6	Branched-chain	0					25.0	32.8	38.0
7	Hydroxy	0					15.0		
8	Triglycerides	32.5	0	0	0	0	0		
9	Unsaponifiable matter, total	30.1(25.1-35.9)	36.7	42.7	45.9	41.4	(40-50)		
10	Squalene	5.5(3.3-11.2)	0	0	0	0	0(?)		
11	Hydrocarbons	8.1(5.0-20.0)	1.5		3.4	1.5	<1		
12	Aliphatic alcohols, total	6.2(4.7-6.9)	2.6		30.3	16.9	9.0	48.0	48.0
13	Straight-chain	2.4					1.5	48.0	48.0
14	Branched-chain	3.8					7.5	0	0
15	Cholesterol	4.1(2.7-6.9)	15.0[3]	14.4	3.9	10.1[3]	10.0(4.6-12.5)	1.4	0.25
16	Dihydrocholesterol	0.1					2.5		
17	Isocholesterol[4]	0		0			12.5		
18	Aliphatic diols						2.5		

/1/ Adult forearm. /2/ As triglycerides, waxes and other esters. /3/ Cholesterol plus Δ^7-isomer. /4/ A mixture of lanosterol, dihydrolanosterol, agnosterol, and dihydroagnosterol. Also present in sebum of goat (2.5%), camel (2.2%) and llama (1.2%).

46. SYNOVIAL FLUID, PHYSICAL AND CHEMICAL CHARACTERISTICS: MAMMALS

Values in parentheses are estimate "d" of the 95% range (cf Introduction).

Constituent or Property	Man, Knee Joint	Cattle Astragalotibial Joint	Horse Astragalotibial Joint	Constituent or Property	Man, Knee Joint	Cattle Astragalotibial Joint	Horse Astragalotibial Joint
1 Volume, ml	1.1(0.13-3.5)	25(5-65)	(5-40)	16 CO_2, mm Hg		58.8(50-70)	
2 Solids, total, %	3.4(1.2-4.8)	2.1(1.7-3.9)		17 Base, total, mEq/L		165(150-180)	
3 pH	7.39(7.29-7.45)	7.31(7.27-7.43)		18 Protein, total, g/100 ml	2.8	0.9(0.4-1.4)	1.4(0.9-1.9)[4]
4 Viscosity, relative	235(5.7-1160)[1]	5(2-12)[2]	(3-29)[3,4]	19 Albumin, g/100 ml	1.9	0.71(0.5-0.9)	1.2
5 Specific gravity	(1.008-1.015)	(1.009-1.012)		20 Globulin, g/100 ml	0.9	0.2	
6 Freezing point, °C		(-0.51 to -0.55)		21 β-Globulin, g/100 ml			0.32
7 Osmotic pressure, mm H_2O		150(125-170)		22 a-Globulin, g/100 ml			0.37
8 Bicarbonate, mEq/L		28.5(25-32)		23 Fibrinogen	0	0	
9 Calcium, FI/Se[5]	0.87	0.83	0.97	24 Mucin, g/100 ml	0.85	0.14(0.03-0.25)	0.47(0.3-0.7)[4]
10 Chloride, Se/Fl ratio[6]	0.98	0.99	0.98	25 Mucin,N, g/100 ml	0.1(0.07-0.13)	0.07(0.05-0.13)	0.04(0.03-0.05)
11 Magnesium, mEq/L		1.4(1.3-1.7)		26 Mucin glucosamine, g/100 ml	0.07(0.05-0.13)	(0.02-0.05)[8]	
12 Phosphorus, mEq/L		2.2(1.5-3.0)		27 Non-protein N, Se/Fl ratio[6]	0.91	0.87	1.05
13 Potassium, mEq/L	4.0	4.0(3.6-4.4)	2.6(1.8-3.6)[7]	28 Uric acid, mg/100 g	3.9	1.5(1.2-2.1)	5.3(5-5.6)
14 Sodium, mEq/L	135	145(140-148)		29 Sugar, reducing, mg/100 g	Same as plasma	65(45-95)	(77-82)
15 Sulfate, mEq/L		5.0(4.5-5.4)		30 Hyaluronic acid, mg/100 g	155(4-295)	(20-25)	56

/1/ Hess and Ostwald viscosimeter, 25°C. /2/ Scott-Blair viscosimeter, 20°C. /3/ Hess viscosimeter, 20°C. /4/ Carpal joint. /5/ Square root of distribution ratio: synovial fluid/serum concentration.
/6/ Distribution ratio, serum concentration/synovial fluid concentration. /7/ mg/100 g. /8/ Joint not specified.

47. BODY FLUIDS, ELECTROLYTE AND NITROGEN BALANCE IN NORMAL PREGNANCY: MAN

Part I: BLOOD AND URINE

Values are mg/100 ml, unless otherwise indicated; those in parentheses are estimate "b" of the 95% range (cf Introduction).

Constituent or Property	Fluid	Value	Constituent or Property	Fluid	Value	Constituent or Property	Fluid	Value
1 pH	Blood	7.4	10 Protein, total, %	Serum	6.35	19 Creatinine	Urine	1-2
2 Calcium	Serum	9.58	11 Albumin, %	Serum	3.88	20 Ammonia N[2]	Urine	3-5
3 Chloride	Serum	580	12 Globulin, %	Serum	2.47	21 Glucose	Blood	80
4 Iodine, μg/100 ml	Plasma	11	13 Fibrinogen, %	Plasma	0.35	22 Lipids, %	Blood	0.9
5 Phosphorus	Serum	3.21	14 Nitrogen, total,[1] g	Urine	8-12	23 Fat, neutral	Plasma	355(200-500)
6 Potassium	Serum	16.0	15 Non-protein N	Blood	28.0	24 Phospholipid	Plasma	250(160-335)
7 Sodium	Serum	330	16 Urea N	Blood	12.5	25 Cholesterol, ester	Plasma	140(45-235)
8 CO_2, vol %	Serum	48	17 Urea N, % of total N	Urine	70-85	26 Cholesterol, free	Plasma	65(35-95)
9 Base, total, mM	Serum	147	18 Uric acid	Blood	3.0	27 Phosphatase, B.U.[3], %	Serum	6.6

/1/ Per 24 hours. /2/ % of total nitrogen. /3/ Bodansky units.

Part II: AMNIOTIC FLUID

Values are mg/100 ml, unless otherwise indicated.

Constituent or Property	Value
1 Volume, ml	700[1]
2 Water, %	98.5
3 Specific gravity	1.006-1.008
4 Calcium	5.5
5 Phosphorus	3.1
6 Sodium	280
7 Protein, total, %	0.53
8 Non-protein N	24-25
9 Uric acid	4.5
10 Sugar, reducing	19

/1/ At term.

Part III: FLUID BALANCE

Values are liters, unless otherwise indicated.

Constituent or Property	Value[1]	% of Body Weight
1 Body water,[2] total	40	55
2 Extracellular space[3]	16	22
3 Sodium space[4]	20	28
4 Amniotic fluid volume	0.7	
5 Blood volume	5.4	
6 Water content of blood, %	83	
7 Plasma volume[5]	3.3	4.8
8 Cell volume	1.9	
9 Hematocrit, %	38	

/1/ Average values at term. /2/ Antipyrine volume. /3/ Inulin volume. /4/ Na^{24} volume. /5/ Gregersen method.

Part IV: ELECTROLYTE AND NITROGEN BALANCE

Values are mg in 24 hr urine sample.

Constituent or Property	Value
1 Calcium	+280
2 Chloride	+0.88
3 Iron	+1-1.5
4 Nitrogen	+1360
5 Phosphorus	+210
6 Potassium	+0.51
7 Sodium	+1.26

48. PROSTATIC FLUID AND SEMEN, PHYSICAL AND CHEMICAL CHARACTERISTICS: MAMMALS

Values are mg/100 ml, unless otherwise indicated; those in parentheses are ranges and, unless accompanied by superscript, are estimate "d" of the 95% range (cf Introduction). Data for additional species are given in the footnotes. (SP) indicates that values are for seminal plasma.

Constituent or Property	Prostatic Fluid Man[1]	Prostatic Fluid Dog[2]	Semen Man	Semen Cattle	Semen Dog	Semen Horse	Semen Rabbit	Semen Sheep	Semen Swine
1 Volume of ejaculate[3], ml	13-32% of semen	97% of semen	3.5(2.0-6.0)	4.0(2.0-10.0)	6.0(2.0-15.0)	70(30-300)	1.0(0.4-6.0)	1.0(0.7-2.0)	250(150-500)
2 Spermatozoa[3], millions/ml	0	0	100(50-150)	1000(300-2000)	3000(1000-9000)	120(30-800)	700(100-2000)	3000(2000-5000)	100(25-300)
3 Spermatozoa, size[4], μ			55:5x4x3.5;45	65:5x4x1;13;44	60:7x4x1;10;44	58:7x4x2;10;42	56:9x1x1;9;39		57:8x4x1;11;38
4 Specific gravity	1.022(1.018-1.027)	(1.006-1.008)	1.035(1.031-1.039)	1.034(1.015-1.053)	1.011				
5 Freezing point depression, °C			(0.55-0.58)	0.61(0.54-0.73)	(0.58-0.60)	0.60(0.58-0.62)	(0.55-0.59)	0.64(0.55-0.70)	0.62(0.59-0.63)
6 Conductivity, mho $\times 10^{-4}$			(88-107)	105(90-115)	(129-138)	123(110-130)	94(85-100)	63(50-80)	129(125-135)
7 pH[3]	6.5(6.3-6.6)	6.1(5.8-6.5)b	7.4(7.1-7.5)	6.9(6.4-7.8)	(6.7-6.8)	7.4(7.2-7.8)	(6.6-7.5)	6.9(5.9-7.3)	7.5(7.3-7.9)
8 Water, g/100 ml	93.2(92.7-93.6)	98.1(97.5-98.7)b	91.8(89.1-94.4)	90(87-95)	97.6	97.6		85.2	95.4(94-98)
9 Calcium, mEq/L	60(57-65)	0.6	12(10-14) (SP)	17(12-23)		10		5	(1-3)
10 Chloride, mEq/L	38(35-46)	156(145-170)b	43(28-57) (SP)	50	(175-185)			24	92(42-120)
11 Magnesium, mEq/L			12	10	2	2		2	9(4-12)
12 Phosphorus, total			112(90-120)	82		19		355	66
13 Acid-soluble	(1-2)	Trace	57(28-94)	33				170	66
14 Inorganic	7(6-9)	(1-2)	11	9		17		12	24
15 Lipid[5]			6					29	2
16 Potassium, mEq/L	48(29-61)	5.1(4.7-5.5)b	23(17-27) (SP)	44(SP)		17		19	6
17 Sodium, mEq/L	153(150-160)	159(155-165)b	117(100-135) (SP)	112				45	66(22-105)
18 Carbon dioxide, ml/100 ml	9(7-12)	5(3-6)b	54(43-74)	16		24		16	285(125-370)
19 Trace metals	Zn+	Zn 14(15-22)	*	Fe 2				Fe 0.8; Cu 0.2; Zn 1.0	50
20 Nitrogen, total	415(295-510)	210	915(560-1225)	755		165		875	615(335-765)
21 Proteose	16(trace-48)	0-30	+		Trace			+	+
22 Fructose[6,7]	286(260-310)	(30-40)	224(90-520)	500(100-1100)	180	15(9-45)	(40-42)	500(275-?)	12(5-25)
23 Lipids, total	80(62-105)	166(130-210)							
24 Cholesterol									
25 Sex hormones	54(30-90)	22	σ +; ♀ +	σ +		σ +			
26 Non-protein nitrogen			80	48		55		57	22
27 Amino acids, free			90(53-130)	8					
28 Ammonia	+		2	2		1		2	1
29 Creatine				3		6			
30 Creatinine				12		4			0.3
31 Urea			72 (SP)	4		3		44	5
32 Uric acid			6					6	3
33 Ergothioneine			0-trace	0-trace	0-trace	0		0-trace	15-20
34 Spermine	++		(20-250)	+					
35 Citric acid	(480-2700)	30	480(0-2300)	720(200-1700)	Trace	50(30-110)	(110-550)	137(110-260)	140(40-325)
36 Lactic acid			35(20-50)	29(15-43)		15		36	27
37 Ascorbic acid[9]	(0.5-0.6)	0.8(0.6-0.9)b	12.8(11.2-14.4)b	6.1(3.0-9.0)				5.1(1.6-8.1)	+
38 "B-Vitamins"[10]	+		+	+	+	+		+	+
39 Nor-adrenalin	+	+	0.1-0.2	0.1					
40 Amylase			+	+	+				
41 Cholinesterase	+	++	+	+	+			++	++
42 Cytochrome[11]			+					+	+
43 β-Glucuronidase	++	+	++	+++	++	+	+		
44 Hyaluronidase[11]			++	+++	++	+++	+++		++
45 5-Nucleotidase			+					+	Low
46 Oxidases	Diamine		Diamine	Xanthine; L-amino-acid					
47 Phosphatase, acid, U/100ml[12]	219,000(54,000-420,000)	(3-285)		170(50-340)				+	
48 Phosphatase, alk., U/100ml[12]	Low	(0-107)	Low						
49 Proteases[13]	+	+	+	390(100-3500)	+			High	Low
50 Miscellaneous	Heptocosane		Sulfite 8.1						

/1/ Resting fluid. /2/ Pilocarpine stimulated. /3/ Buffalo semen: volume, 2.5(0.5-4.5); sperm no., 630(210-770); pH, 6.3(6.0-6.6)b. Fox semen: volume, 1.5(0.2-4.0); sperm no., 70(30-250); pH, (6.2-6.4). Goat semen: volume, 0.7(0.5-0.9)b; sperm no., 2600(650-7500); pH, 6.4(6.0-6.8)b. /4/ Values are respectively: total length; length of midpiece; length of tail. Other species: cat, 55; 5 x 3 x 1; 8; 43. Hamster, 155; 13 x 2 x 1; 50; 93. Monkey, 75; 6 x 4 x 2; 11; 59. Rat, 182; 18 x 2 x 1; (?); 164. /5/ Value x 25.8 = total phospholipid. Cephalin content of human prostatic fluid, 107(82-135); ether-insoluble content, 73(63-90). /6/ Prostatic fluid values are for total reducing sugar. Rabbit semen may contain up to 40 mg% glucose. Little, if any, glucose present in semen of other species. /7/ + in semen of goat, guinea pig, hamster, mouse, opossum, rat. /8/ Seminal plasma: alanine, 0.25; aspartic acid, 0.09; glutamic acid, 0.35; glycine, 0.09; histidine, 0.16; phenylalanine, 0.16; serine, 0.13. /9/ Guinea pig, prostatic fluid, 1.5(0.9-2.1)b, semen, 8.2(6.8-9.6)b. /10/ Man: choline, 70-2000; inositol, 100. Rat: choline, +. Swine: inositol, 450. Cattle: thiamine, 0.09 (0.03-0.15); riboflavin, 0.21(0.15-0.31); pantothenic acid, 0.37(0.23-0.47); niacin, 0.36(0.25-0.55); inositol, low. /11/ + in rat semen. /12/ U=units; one unit indicates activity for the liberation of one mg phenol from monophenylphosphate in one hr at 37°C; low in rat semen and prostatic fluid. /13/ Prostatic fluid and semen of man and dog contain fibrinogenase and fibrinolysin. Semen of man also contains aminopeptidase and pepsinogenase. Vesiculase is present in rat and guinea pig semen.

49. TEARS, PHYSICAL AND CHEMICAL CHARACTERISTICS: MAN

Values in parentheses are ranges.

Man

#	Constituent or Property	Value
1	Volume, g/16 hr	(0.5-0.67)
2	Volume, ♂ (15-29 yr), mg/5 min	20+
3	Volume, ♀ (12-29 yr), mg/5 min	13+
4	pH	7.47(7.3-7.7)
5	Conductivity, ⟺ % NaCl	0.9
6	Freezing point depression, °C	-0.551
7	Osmotic conc., ⟺ % NaCl	0.9
8	Osmotic pressure, Δ	0.551
9	Osmotic pressure, ⟺ mM NaCl	160(150-170)
10	Refractive index	1.3369
11	Surface tension, n	(0.695-0.749)
12	Vapor pressure, ⟺ % NaCl	0.93
13	Viscosity, }	(1.053-1.405)
14	Solids, total, %	1.8
15	Dialyzable[1], %	0.47
16	Non-dialyzable, %	0.91
17	Ash, %	1.05
18	Bicarbonate, mEq/L	26
19	Chloride, mEq/L	128(118-138)
20	Potassium, mEq/L	24.1(20-28)
21	Sodium, mEq/L	(142-147)
22	Protein, total, %	0.67
23	Albumin, %	0.39
24	Globulin, %	0.28
25	Nitrogen, total, %	0.16
26	Non-protein N, %	0.05
27	Urea, %	0.03
28	Ammonia (as NH_3), %	0.005
29	Glucose, true, mg/100 ml	2.5
30	Sugar, reducing, mg/100 ml	6.1
31	Lysozyme activity, units[2]	1440(800-2500)
32	Ascorbic acid, mg/100 ml	0.14

1/ Other than NaCl.   2/ Viscosimetric units.

50. SALIVA, PHYSICAL AND CHEMICAL CHARACTERISTICS: VERTEBRATES

Values are mg/100 ml of the unstimulated, mixed secretion of the salivary glands, unless otherwise indicated. Values in parentheses are estimate "d" of the 95% range (cf Introduction). S=paraffin stimulated.

#	Constituent or Property	Value
	Man	
1	pH	6.7(5.6-7.6)
2		7.4(7.2-7.6) S
3	Specific gravity	(1.010-1.020)
4	Freezing point, °C	(-0.7 to -0.34)
5	Rate of flow, ml/min	0.57(0.1-1.8)
6		1.9(0.4-4.8) S
7	Solids, total	580(385-860) S
8	Ash	(200-220)
9	Calcium, mEq/L	3.1(2.3-5.5)
10		2.8(1.8-4.6) S
11	Carbon dioxide, vol %	14.9(8.2-25.3)
12		37.1(19.2-46.0) S
13	Chloride, mEq/L	15.5(8.4-17.7)
14		11.8(8.7-17.7)
15	Cobalt, µg/100 ml	2.4(0-12.5) S
16	Copper, µg/100 ml	25.6(10-47) S
17	Fluoride, mEq/L	(0-0.005)
18	Iodine, µg/100 ml	(0-350)
19	Magnesium, mEq/L	0.6(0.16-1.06)
20	Phosphorus, total	19.3
21	Phosphorus, inorganic	14.9(7.4-21.1)
22	Phosphorus, lipid	(0.05-0.20)
23	Potassium, mEq/L	14.1(12.8-16.1)
24		18(14.6-23.8) S
25	Sodium, mEq/L	17.4(8.7-23.9)
26		23.9(7.8-38.3) S
27	Thiocyanate, mEq/L	(2.6-5.2)
28	Nitrogen, total	90(36-125) S
29	Nitrogen, protein	64(23-90) S
30	Mucin	270(80-600) S
31	Non-protein nitrogen	36.4(8.2-62) S
32	Ammonia, mM/L	3.5(0.8-7.1) S
33	Creatinine	(0.6-1.09)
34	Urea	8.8(0-14) S
35	Uric acid	1.5(0.5-2.9)
36	Alanine	1.2(0.5-2.9)
37	Arginine	(3.3-10) S
38	Aspartic acid	0.15(0.13-0.33)
39	Cystine	1.2(0.5-1.3)
40	Glutamic acid	

#	Constituent or Property	Value
	Man (continued)	
41	Glycine	1.4(0.5-3.6)
42	Histidine	(0.35-2.0) S
43	Isoleucine	(0.2-0.9) S
44	Leucine	0.77(0.15-1.5) S
45	Lysine	(0.005-0.01) S(?)
46	Methionine	(0.6-2.5) S
47	Phenylalanine	(0.35-1.5) S
48	Proline	0.66(0.33-1.2)
49	Serine	(0.4-4.5) S
50	Threonine	(0.2-1.0) S
51	Tyrosine	(0.2-0.9) S
52	Tryptophan	(0.7-2.2) S
53	Valine	19.6(11.3-28.1)
54	Glucose	1.0(0.2-3.1) S
55	Citric acid	0.17
56	Lactic acid, mEq/L	7.5(3-15)
57	Cholesterol	0.07(0-0.37) S(?)
58	Ascorbic acid	0.08
59	Biotin, µg/100 ml	1.6(0.6-3.6) S
60	Choline	0.33(0.15-0.5) S(?)
61	Cobalamin, µg/100 ml	2.4(0.3-7.5) S
62	Folic acid, µg/100 ml	1.5
63	Vitamin K, µg/100 ml	11.5(2.3-40.9) S
64	Nicotinic acid, µg/100 ml	8.1(1.2-19) S
65	Pantothenic acid, µg/100 ml	0.6(0.1-1.7) S
66	Pyridoxine, µg/100 ml	5.0
67	Riboflavin, µg/100 ml	(0.2-1.4) S
68	Thiamine, µg/100 ml	100(20-250)
69	Amylase, units/ml[1]	0.33(0.23-0.43) S
70	Cholinesterase, units/L[2,3]	0.34(0.12-0.65) S
71	Esterase, total, units/L[2,4]	1.42(0.25-2.58) S
72	Lipase, units/L[2,5]	670(250-1360) S
73	Lysozyme, units/L[2]	4.23(2.5-7.7) S
74	Phosphatase, acid, units/L[2,6]	
	Cattle	
75	pH	(8.1-8.2)
76	Specific gravity	(1.002-1.009)
77	Solids, total	880
78	Bicarbonate, mEq/L	91
79	Chloride, mEq/L	4.3

#	Constituent or Property	Value
	Dog	
80	pH	7.5
81	Solids, total	(440-1600)
82	Ash	(290-610)
83	Calcium, mEq/L	(2.9-9.6)
84	Chloride, mEq/L	(16.3-70)
85	Phosphorus, total	(1.2-3.0)
86	Potassium, mEq/L	(12.3-23.7)
	Goat[2]	
87	pH	(8.1-8.3)
88	Specific gravity	(1.002-1.063)
89	Solids, total	1300
90	Ash	520
91	Nitrogen, total	(5-22)
92	Chloride, mEq/L	(2.8-3.4)
	Horse	
93	pH	(7.3-8.6)
94	Specific gravity	(1.001-1.008)
95	Solids, total[2]	1000
96	Ash	(100-500)
97	Chloride, mEq/L[2]	(0.006-0.06)
	Sheep	
98	pH	(8.4-8.7)
99	Specific gravity[2]	(1.009-1.011)
100	Solids, total	1100
101	Ash	(700-900)
102	Nitrogen, total	(4-10)
103	Calcium, mEq/L	(7.0-12.1)
104	Chloride, mEq/L	(0.5-0.8)
105	Magnesium, mEq/L	(37-72)
106	Phosphorus, total, mM/L[2]	52
107	Phosphorus, inorg., mEq/L[2]	(4.1-11.8)
108	Potassium, mEq/L	
	Swine	
109	pH	(7.1-7.4)
110	Specific gravity[2]	(1.007-1.009)
111	Dry matter, g/100 ml[2]	(0.3-4.6)
112	Ash, g/100 ml[2]	(0.1-0.4)
113	Nitrogen, mM/L[2]	(0.04-0.1)
	Chicken	
114	pH	(6.7-6.9)

1/ One unit of amylase is considered as the amount required to digest 5 ml of 1% soluble starch to the achromic point under the conditions of the test.   2/ Parotid gland secretion.   3/ β-Carbo-naphthoxycholine substrate.   4/ β-Naphthyl acetate substrate.   5/ β-Naphthyl laurate substrate.   6/ Monosodium-β-naphthyl phosphate substrate.

Unless otherwise indicated values are mg/100 ml; those in parentheses are ranges.

Part I: GASTRIC JUICE

B=basal conditions (absence of all avoidable stimuli); C=caffeine stimulation; F=fasting normal value; FS=stimulated by food; H=histamine stimulation; HS=histamine and sham feeding stimulation; R=hunger juice; S=sham feeding, egg albumin and zein meals; U=fistulated.

#	Constituent or Property	Cond.	Value
	Man		
1	pH		(1.49-8.38)
2	Specific gravity		1.006(1.004-1.010)
3	Freezing point, °C	F	(-0.3 to -0.8)
4	Calcium, mEq/L	F	3.6(2.0-4.8)
5	Chloride, total, mEq/L	F	(78-159)
6		H	(131-170)
7	Potassium, mEq/L	F	11.6(6.4-16.6)
8	Sodium, mEq/L	F	49(18.7-70)
9	HCl, free, mEq/L	F	(0-115)
10		H	(78-135)
11	Acidity, total, mEq/L	F	(46-118)
12		H	(86-137)
13	Nitrogen, total, mg/ml	F	(0.91-2.18)
14		H	(0.73-1.34)
15	Nitrogen, α-amino acid	F	(5.6-8.4)
16		C	(7.2-14.4)
17	Protein	B	330
18	Alanine	F	(1.8-2.7)
19		C	(2.0-2.6)
20	Arginine	F	(3.3-3.6)
21		C	(3.5-5.0)
22	Aspartic acid	F	(1.7-2.3)
23		C	(1.6-2.5)
24	Cystine	F	(1.8-3.7)
25		C	(1.6-4.4)
26	Glycine	F	(1.3-1.6)
27		C	(1.2-2.1)
28	Glutamic acid	F	(2.0-3.2)
29		C	(2.6-4.7)
30	Histidine	F	(1.3-2.0)
31		C	(1.3-1.8)
32	Isoleucine	F	(0.7-1.4)
33		C	(2.3-2.5)
34	Leucine	F	(1.2-2.2)
35		C	(1.2-3.3)
36	Lysine	F	(1.4-1.8)
37		C	(1.3-1.6)
38	Methionine	F	(0.8-1.5)
39		C	(0.9-1.9)
40	Phenylalanine	F	(0.8-1.8)
41		C	(0.7-1.6)
42	Proline	F	(1.7-3.2)
43		C	(2.2-3.3)
44	Serine	F	(1.6-2.3)
45		C	(1.9-2.1)
46	Threonine	F	(1.5-2.5)
47		C	2.0
48	Tryptophan	F	(1.4-1.9)
49		C	(1.2-1.9)
50	Tyrosine	F	(1.0-1.1)
51		C	(0.9-1.3)
52	Histamine, μg/100 ml		(1.3-53.5)
53	Fucose		13.8
54	Glucose, mg/ml	F	(0.35-1.19)[1]
55		H	(0.33-1.12)[1]
56	Glucuronic acid		2.0
57	Hexoseamines		33
58	Hexoses, total		32
59	Sialic acid		7.31
60	Ascorbic acid		0.95(0.91-1.05)
61	Lysozyme, μg/ml		7.6(2.6-19.2)
62	Pepsin, hemoglobin units/hr	B	4100(0-8,300)[2]
63	Pepsin, units/ml		(9.7-63)[3]
	Cat[4]		
64	Solids, total	FS	(170-650)
65	Ash	FS	(120-380)
66	Organic matter	FS	(48-265)
67	Calcium, mEq/L	FS	(1.7-5.3)
68	Chloride, mEq/L	FS	(156-166)
69	Phosphorus	FS	(0.16-0.55)
70	Potassium, mEq/L	FS	(11.5-13.6)
71	Sodium, mEq/L	FS	(12.2-56)
72	HCl, total, mEq/L	HS	(128-155)
73	free, mEq/L	HS	(97-122)
74	Nitrogen	HS	(10-41)
75	Histamine, μg/100 ml		(2.5-4.5)
76	Reducing power		(4-37)[5]
77	Pepsin, Mett units		(0-400)
	Cattle		
78	pH[6]		(2-4.1)

#	Constituent or Property	Cond.	Value
	Cattle (concluded)		
79	Specific gravity[7]		(1.002-1.003)
80	Acidity[7], mEq/L		(36-98)
81	Nitrogen[6], mg/100 g dry matter		2400
	Dog		
82	Specific gravity		(1.002-1.004)
83	Freezing point, °C		-0.59(-0.64 to -0.49)
84	Solids, total		(430-650)
85	Ash		133
86	Organic matter		294
87	Calcium, mEq/L		(0.95-3.3)
88	Chloride, total, mEq/L		173
89		S	123(98-143)
90	Phosphorus	R	0.27
91	Potassium, mEq/L		7.2
92		S	15.2(10.3-22.0)
93	Sodium, mEq/L		22
94		S	64(46-79)
95	HCl, free, mEq/L		150
96	Acidity, mEq/L	S	32(0-50)
97	Nitrogen, total		(50-80)
98	protein	S	(18-19.9)
99	non-protein (NPN)		(9.8-10.9)
100	total base		(5.4-6.6)
101	volatile base		(1.8-2.6)
102	non-volatile base		(3.6-4)
103	creatine + creatinine		(0.09-0.11)
104	histidine-arginine		(1.56-1.77)
105	humin bodies		(3.3-3.7)
106	lysine fraction		(1.9-2.2)
107	mono-amino fraction[8]		(0.7-1.02)
108	purine fraction		(0.10-0.11)
109	urea		(0.11-0.16)
110	Ammonia, mM/L		(1.2-4.6)
111	Arginine, moles[9]	S	(0.08-0.26)
112	Aspartic acid, moles[9]	S	(0.30-0.68)
113	Glutamic acid, moles[9]	S	(0.81-2.36)
114	Histidine, moles[9]	S	(0.04-0.08)
115	Isoleucine, moles[9]	S	(1.11-1.93)
116	Leucine, moles[9]	S	(1.30-3.58)
117	Lysine, moles[9]	S	(0.15-0.26)
118	Methionine, moles[9]	S	(0.13-0.22)
119	Phenylalanine, moles[9]	S	(0.06-0.44)
120	Proline, moles[9]	S	(0.05-0.21)
121	Serine, moles[9]	S	(0.43-0.76)
122	Threonine, moles[9]	S	1.00
123	Tryptophan, moles[9]	S	(0.03-0.04)
124	Tyrosine, moles[9]	S	(0.3-0.36)
125	Valine, moles[9]	S	(1.07-1.30)
126	Histamine, μg/L	S	(4-22)
127	Ascorbic acid		0.69(0.33-1.51)
128	Pepsin, units/ml	S	81(41-164)
	Goat		
129	Specific gravity		1.006
130	Acidity, mEq/L		(4-84)
	Horse		
131	HCl, mEq/L		(3.8-5.8)
	Sheep[6]		
132	pH	U	(1.05-3.6)
133	Freezing point, °C		(-0.56 to -0.61)
134	Dry matter, g/100 ml		(3.7-8.2)
135	Calcium, soluble, mEq/L		(190-335)
136	Chloride, mEq/L		(141-177)
137	Magnesium, soluble, mEq/L		(9.9-18.9)
138	Phosphorus, inorganic		(34-100)
139	Acidity, normal, mEq/L		86
	Swine		
140	Ash		(400-800)
141	Dry matter		(900-2400)
142	Chloride, mEq/L		78
143	Sodium, mEq/L		80
144	Acidity, mEq/L		100
145	Pepsin units[10]		34(4-38)
	Chicken		
146	Acidity, total, mEq/L	H	(120-180)
147	free, mEq/L	H	(80-150)
	Pigeon		
148	Acidity, total, mEq/L		(60-148)
149		H	(120-195)
150	free, mEq/L		(40-136)
151		H	(70-160)
152	Pepsin, Mett units	H	(0-36)

/1/ After hydrolysis. /2/ Substrate: lyophilized bovine hemoglobin powder. /3/ After test meal; substrate: plasma protein. /4/ Determinations from one animal only. /5/ As glucose. /6/ Abomassal contents. /7/ Calf. /8/ Phosphotungstic acid filtrate. /9/ Avg. moles free amino acid per mole threonine. /10/ Method under investigation.

51. DIGESTIVE FLUIDS, PHYSICAL AND CHEMICAL CHARACTERISTICS: VERTEBRATES (Continued)

Unless otherwise indicated values are mg/100 ml; those in parentheses are ranges.

Part II: BILE

H = hepatic; G = gallbladder; ? = source uncertain.

#	Constituent or Property		Value
	Man		
1	pH	H	7.5(6.2-8.5)
2		G	6.0(5.6-8.0)
3	Specific gravity	?	(0.998-1.062)
4	Freezing point, °C	?	-0.56
5	Specific conductivity[1]	?	(99-137)
6	Surface tension, dynes/cm	?	(39-41)
7	Viscosity, centipoises	?	(0.843-2.342)
8	Solids, total	H	2660(1000-4000)
9		G	11,140(4,700-16,500)
10	Dry matter	H	(2300-3300)
11		G	18,000
12	Inorganic matter	H	(200-900)
13		G	(500-1100)
14	Calcium, mEq/L	H	(2.0-4.5)
15		G	(5.0-7.0)
16	Chloride, mEq/L	H	(75-110)
17		G	(15-30)
18	Copper	?	(0.063-1.07)
19	Iodine[2]	?	(0.004-0.014)
20	Iodine[3]	?	0.05
21	Iron	?	(0.03-7.0)
22	Phosphorus, total	H	(9-22.3)
23	Potassium, mEq/L	H	4.9
24	Nitrogen, total	H	(67-92)
25		G	490
26	amino acid	H	5.4
27		G	(6.0-21.6)
28	peptide	H	14.0
29		G	(3.9-27.0)
30	rest	H	45.5
31		G	(68-94.0)
32	Base, total, mEq/L	G	(150-180)
33	Protein, total	H	275
34		G	(315-540)
35	Urea	H	23.6
36		G	(20-45)
37	Bile acids	H	(200-1830)
38		G	(1,500-10,000)
39	Bile pigment	H	(50-170)
40		G	(200-1500)
41	Bile salts	H	(650-1400)
42		G	11,500
43	Bilirubin	H	(20-200)
44		G	1000
45	Coproporphyrin	G	0.01
46	Mucin and pigment	H	610(430-930)
47		G	3420(1800-4300)
48	Glucides, total	H	(35-91)
49		G	240
50	Sugars, reducing	H	(17-52)
51		G	80
52	Cholesterol	H	120(80-170)
53		G	630(350-930)
54	Fat, neutral	H	110(40-300)
55		G	370(150-560)
56	Fatty acids	H	110(40-300)
57		G	(150-1090)
58	Lecithins	H	(100-575)
59		G	3500
60	Phospholipids	H	60(50-60)
61		G	200(180-220)
62	Phosphatides	H	(50-80)
63		G	(200-500)
64	Choline, total	H	(35-89)
65		G	550
	Cat		
66	pH	H	5.33
67	Chloride, mEq/L	H	12(10-13)
68		G	5(0-20)
69	Base, fixed, mEq/L	H	17.2(15.7-19.4)
70		G	27.4(26.1-31.8)
71	Bile pigment	H	119(52-218)
72		G	(238-1190)
73	Coproporphyrin	G	0.096
74	Alkaline phosphatase, units/100 ml[4]	G	(190-415)
	Cattle[5]		
75	pH	G	(6.74-7.47)
76	Solids, total	G	(8900-9040)
77	Ash and alkali	G	(1250-1300)
78	Bile acids, g/100 ml	G	(1550-1700)
79	Mucin	G	500

#	Constituent or Property		Value
	Cattle[5] (concluded)		
80	Cholesterol	G	60
81	Lipids, total	G	(100-160)
	Dog		
82	pH	H	(7.4-8.5)
83	Specific gravity	H	(1.008-1.015)
84	Dry matter	H	(2300-4500)
85		G	(11,400-24,600)
86	Calcium, mEq/L	H	7.3
87		G	26.1
88	Chloride, mEq/L	H	64
89	Iodine	?	(0.013-0.113)
90	Iron, mEq/100ml	?	(4-8)
91	Magnesium, mEq/L	H	3.6
92	Phosphorus, total	H	(10-15)
93		G	(87-280)
94	Potassium, mEq/L	H	6.6
95	Sodium, mEq/L	H	174
96	Nitrogen, total	H	(65-105)
97		G	(255-635)
98	Proteins, total	H	(130-210)
99		G	(190-520)
100	Allantoin content	?	18.9
101	Ammonia	?	(0.4-0.6)
102	Uric acid°	H	(0.37-0.50)
103	Bile salts	H	(500-2400)
104		G	(7,900-15,000)
105	Bilirubin[7]	H	(42-55)
106		G	(92-170)
107	Coproporphyrin	G	147
108	Glucides, total	G	(736-938)
109	Sugars, reducing	G	(64-72)
110	Cholesterol	H	(4-15)[8]
111		G	(80-100)
112	Fatty acids, total, g/100 ml	H	(0.18-0.27)
113		G	(1.6-5.0)
114	Lecithins, g/100 ml	H	(250-400)
115		G	(2250-7000)
116	Choline	H	(39-58)
117		G	(340-1110)
118	Alkaline phosphatase, units/100 ml[4]	H	(0-900)
	Goat		
119	Specific gravity	H	(1.004-1.010)
120	Dry matter	H	(2880-4720)
121	Ash	H	(480-760)
122	Bile pigment	H	126
	Goose		
123	Solids, total	G	21,950
124	Ash and alkali	G	2100
125	Bile acids	G	19,000
126	Mucin and pigment	G	3100
	Guinea Pig		
127	Solids, total	G	2160
128	Ash and alkali	G	100
129	Bile acids	G	780
130	Mucin	G	510
131	Lipids, total	G	140
	Horse		
132	Specific gravity	H	1.01
133	Bile pigment	H	33(12-38)
	Rabbit		
134	pH[6]	G	(6.4-6.7)
135	Specific gravity	G	1.048
136	Bicarbonate, mEq/L	H	46
137	Calcium, mEq/L[6]	H	(4-9.5)
138	Chloride, mEq/L	H	82
139	Iodine[2]	H	(0.004-0.014)
140	Iodine[3]	H	(0.026-0.069)
141	Magnesium, mEq/L	H	0.5
142	Phosphate, mEq/L	H	2.5
143	Potassium, mEq/L	H	5.7
144	Sodium, mEq/L	H	151
145	Sulfate, mEq/L	H	4.4
146	Ammonia (fresh bile)	H	(0.22-0.07)
147	Bile pigment	H	21.8
148		G	(87-131)
149	Sugars, reducing	H	20
150	Alkaline phosphatase, units/100 ml[4]	G	(56-302)
	Rat		
151	pH[8]	H	8.3
152	Specific gravity[8]	H	1.011

/1/ 30°C; per ohm cm. /2/ Fasting. /3/ Fed. /4/ King-Armstrong units; phenyl phosphate substrate; modified Bodansky method. /5/ Ox.
/6/ Fistula bile. /7/ Values obtained by Van den Bergh method. /8/ Average.

51. DIGESTIVE FLUIDS, PHYSICAL AND CHEMICAL CHARACTERISTICS: VERTEBRATES (Continued)

Unless otherwise indicated values are mg/100 ml; those in parentheses are ranges.

Part II: BILE (Concluded)

H = hepatic; G = gallbladder; ? = source uncertain.

	Constituent or Property		Value		Constituent or Property		Value
	Rat (concluded)				**Swine** (concluded)		
153	Bilirubin, mg/100 ml/24 hr	H	8.3	169	Bile salts	G	7200
154	Cholesterol, mg/100 ml/24 hr	H	12.7	170	Bilirubin	?	(32-62)
	Sheep			171	Coproporphyrin	G	0.077
155	pH	H	(5.98-6.72)	172	Mucin, pigment, ash	G	1630
156	Bile pigment	H	108	173	Glucides, total	H	(120-300)
157		G	(50-110)	174	Sugars, reducing	H	(37-150)
158	Coproporphyrin	G	0.077	175	Cholesterol	H	(130-180)
	Swine			176		G	37
159	Solids, total	H	(11,500-18,900)	177	Fatty acids, total	H	(820-2000)
160		G	10,600	178		G	(370)
161	Phosphorus, total	H	(48-116)	179	Lecithins	H	(1200-2900)
162		G	20.5	180		G	520
163	Nitrogen, total	H	(370-480)	181	Lipids, total	G	1800
164		G	266	182	Choline, total	H	(180-450)
165	Protein	H	(280-410)	183		G	80
166		G	420		**Chicken**		
167	Bile acids	G	12,000	184	pH	H	(6.0-6.2)
168	Bile salts	H	(8,500-12,000)	185	Pigment	H	147

Part III: PANCREATIC JUICE

Unless otherwise indicated values are mg/100 ml secretion from pancreatic fistula; those in parentheses are ranges.

	Constituent or Property	Value		Constituent or Property	Value
	Man[1]			**Man[1]** (continued)	
1	pH	7-8	27	Lipase, units/100 ml	(300-2730)
2	Specific gravity	1.008	28	Phosphatase, Bodansky units/100 ml	(0.8-12.7)
3	Freezing point depression, °C	0.625		**Dog**	
4	Solids, total	(1240-1540)	29	pH	(7.1-8.2)
5	Solids, organic	(380-690)	30	Specific gravity	(1.007-1.014)
6	Ash	(520-860)	31	Freezing point depression, °C	(0.56-0.66)
7	Bicarbonate, mEq/L	(60-75)	32	Solids, total	(1400-6390)
8	Calcium, mEq/L	(2.2-3.2)	33	Solids, organic	480-2220
9	Chloride, MEq/L	(60-80)	34	Ash	840-970
10	Magnesium, mEq/L	0.3	35	Bicarbonate, mEq/L	(15-157)
11	Phosphorus[2], mEq/L	(0.026-1.22)	36	Calcium, mEq/L	(1.8-2.0)
12	Potassium, mEq/L	(4.1-5.6)	37	Chloride, mEq/L	(66-114)
13	Sodium, mEq/L	138	38	Magnesium, mEq/L	(0.2-1.4)
14	Sulfate, mEq/L	8.4	39	Phosphate, mM/L	(0.18-0.5)
15	Protein, total	(190-340)	40	Potassium, mEq/L	(3.0-7.0)
16	Albumin	60	41	Sodium, mEq/L	(151-162)
17	Globulin	40	42	Acid combining power, mEq/L	(58.8-80.4)[4]
18	Nitrogen	(590-1370)	43	Nitrogen, total	(280-936)
19	non-protein	(28-40)	44	protein	(75-84)
20	urea	(0.5-5.0)	45	non-protein	(18-84)
21	uric acid	0.2	46	Urea	(24-59)
22	Glucose	(8.5-18.0)	47	Glucose	25
23	Proteolytic enzymes, total[3]	(9.4-139)	48	Amylase, g maltose/ml juice	(23.9-47.5)[4]
24	Proteolytic enzymes, active[3]	(0.04-16.5)	49	Trypsin, mg tyrosine/ml juice	(407.5-2440)[4]
25	Trypsin, units/100 ml	(7.1-42.8)	50	Pseudocholinesterase, units/ml[5]	(420-1080)[4]
26	Amylase, units/100 ml	(6.4-31.1)			

/1/ Not listed are creatinine, uric acid, copper, SiO_2, and zinc (traces present); cobalt, iron, and nickel (absent). /2/ As $HPO_4^=$. /3/ Trypsin
/4/ Secretin stimulated. /5/ One unit cholinesterase = amount of enzyme liberating $1 \mu l$ CO_2/min (0.06M acetylcholine perchlorate substrate).

Part IV: DUODENAL SECRETION

	Constituent or Property	Value		Constituent or Property	Value
	Man			**Man** (concluded)	
1	pH[1]	(5.8-7.6)	30	Cholesterol[3], mg/100 g	36.1(0-315)
2	Volume[2], ml/hr	30	31	Cholic acid, mg/100 g	(130-460)
3	Specific gravity	1.010	32	Bilirubin[3]	22.4(0-129)
4	Inorganic matter, mg/g	8	33	Icteric index[3]	59(17-299)
5	Solids, total, mg/g	15	34	Amylase[4], glucose units/hr	637
6	Bicarbonate (total CO_2), mEq/L	(8.4-41)	35	Lipase[4], fatty acid units/hr	179
7	Chloride, mEq/L	(64.2-110.3)	36	Phosphatase[5], units/100 ml	(10-30)
8	Potassium, mEq/L	(1.0-11.0)	37	Proteolytic enzymes, total[6]	(35-78)
9	Sodium, mEq/L	(84.8-143.4)	38	Active (trypsin)[6]	(16.4-48)
10	Nitrogen, mEq/L	41		**Cat[7]**	
11	Nitrogen, α-amino-	9.2	39	pH	(8.7-8.9)
12	Alanine	3.1	40	Specific gravity	1.009
13	Arginine	2.9	41	Solids, total, mg/g	13.3[7]
14	Aspartic acid	3.0	42	Inorganic matter, mg/g	8.42
15	Cystine	4.5	43	Organic matter, mg/g	4.88
16	Glutamic acid	2.2		**Dog**	
17	Glycine	1.7	44	pH	(6.30-7.28)
18	Histidine	1.2	45	Specific gravity[7]	1.009
19	Isoleucine	1.1	46	Solids, total[7], mg/g	15.41
20	Leucine	1.2	47	Inorganic matter[7], mg/g	9.26
21	Lysine	2.2	48	Organic matter[7], mg/g	6.15
22	Methionine	2.0	49	Ash, mg/g	7.6-9.4
23	Phenylalanine	1.7		**Goat[7]**	
24	Proline	3.0	50	pH	(8.2-8.4)
25	Serine	2.0	51	Specific gravity	1.007, 1.008
26	Threonine	1.8	52	Solids, total, mg/g	14.6
27	Tryptophan	1.1	53	Inorganic matter, mg/g	7.73
28	Tyrosine	0.5	54	Organic matter, mg/g	6.83
29	Valine	1.9			

/1/ Duodenal contents. /2/ Spontaneous; after secretin ♂ = 181, ♀ = 126. /3/ Value for fasting adult. /4/ Duodenal contents, Lagerlöf method
(starch solution substrate for amylase, tributyrin for lipase). /5/ Bodansky units (alkaline) di-sodiumphenyl phosphate substrate; value rises to
200 after fatty meal. /6/ Casein substrate. /7/ Brunner's glands secretion.

51. DIGESTIVE FLUIDS, PHYSICAL AND CHEMICAL CHARACTERISTICS: VERTEBRATES (Concluded)
Unless otherwise indicated values are mg/100 ml; those in parentheses are ranges.

Part IV: DUODENAL SECRETION (Concluded)

	Constituent or Property	Value		Constituent or Property	Value
	Rabbit[8]			Sheep (concluded)	
55	pH[8]	(8.6-9.0)	64	Acidity, total, mEq/L	(39-62)
56	Specific gravity[7]	1.009	65	Acid, volatile, mEq/L	(5-19)
57	Solids, total, mg/g[7]	15.21	66	Chloride, mEq/L	(109-135)
58	Inorganic matter, mg/g[7]	10.23		Swine	
59	Organic matter, mg/g[7]	4.98	67	pH[8]	(8.4-8.9)
	Sheep		68	Specific gravity	(1.007-1.008)
60	pH[1]	(2.3-4.7)	69	Solids, total, mg/g[7]	11.80
61	Specific gravity	1.007	70	Inorganic matter, mg/g[7]	6.81
62	Dry matter, mg/g	(30-66)	71	Organic matter, mg/g[7]	4.99
63	Ash, mg/g	(3.9-6.5)			

/7/ Brunner's glands secretion.   /8/ From fistula.

Part V: DIGESTIVE ENZYMES

AM = amylase (diastase); CA = carbonic anhydrase; EK = enterokinase; EP = erepsin, peptidases; SU = sucrase; LP = lipase, esterases; MT = maltase; NC = nuclease; PE = pepsin; PH = phosphatase; RI = ribonuclease; RN = rennin (chymosin); TR = trypsin; UR = urease; + = present; - = absent; ± = doubtful.

	Animal	Enzyme	Salivary Glands T	Salivary Glands S	Esophagus T	Esophagus S	Stomach T	Stomach S	Pancreas T	Pancreas S	Small Intestine T	Small Intestine S	Cecum and Colon T	Cecum and Colon S
1	Man	AM		+						+	+	±		
2		EK										+		
3		EP		+					+	+	+	+		
4		SU										+		
5		LP	+	+	+		+	+	+	+	+	±		
6		MT									+			
7		PE					+	+						
8		PH		+			+				+		+	
9		RN						-[1]						
10		TR									+			
11		UR					+							
12	Cat	AM		-					+		+			
13		CA					+		+		+			
14		EK									+	+		
15		EP							+		±	±		
16		SU										±		
17		LP					+			+		-		
18		MT							+					
19		PE					+							
20		PH	+				+		±		+		+	
21		TR									+	+		
22		UR					+							
23	Cow	AM		±			+		+	+				
24		EK										+		
25		LP	+				+		+					
26		PE			-		+							
27		PH									-			
28		RI							+					
29		RN			+[2]	±[2]	+							
30		TR							+	+				
31		UR					+							
32	Dog	AM		-			±	+	+		+		±	
33		CA					+							
34		EK								+	+			
35		EP							+	+	+	+		
36		SU										±		
37		LP		+			+	+	+	+	+	±	+	
38		MT							+					
39		NC					+							
40		PE			-		+							
41		PH									+			
42		RI							+					
43		RN					±[2]	+						
44		TR							+	+		±		
45		UR					+							
46	Goat	AM		-							±			
47		EK									+			
48		EP									-			
49		SU									±			
50		LP					+[2]				±			
51		RN					+[2]							
52		TR									-			
53		UR			-									
54	Guinea pig	AM		+										
55		EP							+		+			
56		LP					+			+				
57	Horse	AM		±								+		
58		EK										+		

	Animal	Enzyme	Salivary Glands T	Salivary Glands S	Esophagus T	Esophagus S	Stomach T	Stomach S	Pancreas T	Pancreas S	Small Intestine T	Small Intestine S	Cecum and Colon T	Cecum and Colon S
59	Horse (concluded)	LP		+			+							
60		PE									-			
61	Monkey	AM		+										
62		EK										+		
63		EP		+										
64	Rabbit	AM		±					+		+	+		
65		CA					+		+		+			
66		EK										+		
67		ER							+		+	-		
68		LP					+	+	+		+	±		
69		PE		+							-			
70		PH		+							+			
71		TR							+		-			
72		UR					+							
73	Rat	AM		±							+	+		
74		CA					+				+			
75		EK									+			
76		EP									+			
77		LP					+		+					
78		MT									+			
79		PE					+							
80		PH									+			
81		TR							+					
82		UR					+							
83	Sheep	AM		-					+	+				
84		EK									+			
85		LP		+			+		+				-	
86		PE			-		+							
87		RN					+[2]							
88		TR							+	+				
89		UR					+							
90	Swine	AM		+			-		+		+			
91		EK									+	+		
92		EP					+				-			
93		SU										±		
94		LP					+		+		+	±		
95		PE			-		+	+			±			
96		PH					+							
97		RI							+					
98		RN					+[2]							
99		TR							+	+	-			
100		UR					+							
101	Chicken	AM		+					+		+			
102		LP					+							
103							+							
104	Frog	AM		+										
105		EP									+			
106		MT									+	-		
107		PE			+		+	+						
108		TR									+			
109		UR					+							
110	Fish (one or more varieties)	AM		±							+	±		
111		LP					+				+	+		
112		MT									+	-		
113		PE			+		+							
114		RN					-[1]							
115		TR									+			

/1/ In adult.   /2/ Young only.

52. VARIOUS CELLS AND CELL PARTS: CHEMICAL COMPOSITION

DNA = desoxyribonucleic acid; RNA = ribonucleic acid.

#	Tissue or Cell	Chemical Constituent	Value
	Man		
1	Liver, whole cell	DNA phosphorus, $\mu\mu$g/cell	1.0
2		RNA phosphorus, $\mu\mu$g/cell	4.3
3		Total nitrogen, $\mu\mu$g/cell	75.3
4	Nucleus	Nucleoprotein, %	42.59
5		Acidic protein, %	35.51
6		Total protein, "residual," %	4.7-7.5
7	Sperm	DNA phosphorus, $\mu\mu$g/sperm	0.31
8		RNA phosphorus, $\mu\mu$g/sperm	0.24
	Cattle		
	Liver, beef		
9	Whole cell	DNA phosphorus, $\mu\mu$g/cell	0.34
10		RNA phosphorus, $\mu\mu$g/cell	0.70
11	Nucleus	Total nucleic acid, % dry wt	27.5-30.7
12		DNA, $\mu\mu$g/nucleus	6.4
13		RNA, % dry wt	
	Heart, beef		
14	Nucleus	DNA, % dry wt	30.0
15		Total lipid, % dry wt	26.0
16		Phospholipid, % dry wt	15.7
17		Cholesterol, % dry wt	3.6
18		Fatty acid, % dry wt	6.5
	Sperm		
19	Whole cell	DNA, $\mu\mu$g/cell	2.82-3.4
20	Head	Total nucleic acid, % dry wt	48.0
21		DNA, $\mu\mu$g/head	3.3
22		Basic protein, % dry wt	28.7
23		Acidic protein, "lipo-," % dry wt	19.6
	Thymus, beef		
24	Nucleus	Total nucleic acid, % total N	31.0
25		Basic protein, % total N	35.0
26		Acidic protein, % total N	14.0
	Thymus, calf		
27	Whole cell	DNA phosphorus, mg/g fresh tissue	2.24-2.50
28		RNA phosphorus, mg/g fresh tissue	0.80-1.00
	Dog		
29	Liver, whole cell	Total lipid, % dry wt	17.2
30		Phospholipid, % dry wt	9.2
31		Cholesterol, % dry wt	1.07
32		Neutral fat, % dry wt	6.9
33	Nucleus	Total lipid, % dry wt	16.5
34		Phospholipid, % dry wt	10.7
35		Cholesterol, % dry wt	1.2
36		Fatty acid, % dry wt	4.6
37	Sperm, head	Total nucleic acid, % dry wt	55.3
38		Basic protein, % dry wt	25.0
39		Acidic protein, "lipo-," % dry wt	17.0
	Guinea Pig		
40	Liver, whole cell	Total protein, % dry wt	15.0
41	Mitochondria	Total N, % dry wt of fraction	10.0-12.0
42		Total lipid, % dry wt of fraction	25.0
43		Phospholipid, % dry wt of fraction	16.0
44	Microsome	Total N, % dry wt of fraction	9.15
45		Total lipid, % dry wt of fraction	40.0-51.0
46		Phospholipid, % dry wt of fraction	28.0-29.0
47		Phospholipid, % total lipid	58
	Mouse		
48	Liver, whole cell	DNA, mg/g fresh tissue	2.85
49		RNA, mg/g fresh tissue	9.0
50		RNA phosphorus, μ/mg N	28.0
51		Total protein, mg/g fresh tissue	126.3
52		Phospholipid, mg/g fresh tissue	30.1
53	Nucleus	DNA, %	27.0
54		RNA, %	3.4
55		Nucleoprotein, %	66.0
56		Phospholipid, %	3.4
57	Mitochondria	DNA, % total nucleic acid	5.6[1]
58		RNA, % total nucleic acid	16.8
59		RNA, % dry wt of fraction	3.7
60		Total N, %	23.5
61		Total N, % dry wt of fraction	12.1
62		Total lipid, % dry wt of fraction	27.4
63		Phospholipid, % of total lipid	56.6
64		Cholesterol[2], % of total lipid	12.6
65		Neutral fat, % of total lipid	30.8
66	Microsome	DNA, % total nucleic acid	14.2[1]
67		RNA, % total nucleic acid	52.4
68		RNA, % dry wt of fraction	9.1
69		Total N, %	23.1
70		Total N, % dry wt of fraction	10.3
71		Total lipid, % dry wt of fraction	35.1
72		Phospholipid, % of total lipid	62.7
73		Cholesterol[1], % of total lipid	14.5
74		Neutral fat, % of total lipid	22.8
	Rabbit		
75	Liver, whole cell	DNA phosphorus, mg/g fresh tissue	0.16-0.29
76		RNA phosphorus, mg/g fresh tissue	0.44-0.76
77	Mitochondria	Total nucleic acid, μ RNA P/mg N	70.0
	Rabbit (concluded)		
78	Mitochondria (concluded)	Total N, % dry wt of fraction	10.5
79		Total lipid, % dry wt of fraction	29.6
80		Phospholipid, % dry wt of fraction	17.5
81	Microsome	Total nucleic acid, μg RNA P/mg N	80.0
82		Total N, % dry wt of fraction	9.0
83		Total lipid, % dry wt of fraction	43.4
84		Phospholipid, % dry wt of fraction	31.2
	Rat		
85	Liver, whole cell	DNA, mg/g fresh tissue	1.92
86		DNA, % dry wt	0.7-0.9
87		DNA phosphorus, mg/g fresh tissue	0.21-0.25
88		RNA, mg/g fresh tissue	5.88
89		RNA phosphorus, mg/g fresh tissue	0.77-1.10
90		RNA phosphorus, μg/mg N	27.0
91		Total protein, mg/g fresh tissue	129.0
92		Total lipid, % dry wt	15.2
93		Phospholipid, % dry wt	8.3
94		Cholesterol, % dry wt	2.4
95		Neutral fat, % dry wt	4.1
96	Nucleus	Total nucleic acid, % dry wt	11.4-27.5
97		DNA, % dry wt	4.4-30.0
98		DNA, $\mu\mu$g	6.0-11.1
99		DNA, mg/g fresh tissue	1.84
100		DNA, %	13.0
101		RNA, % dry wt	2.9-7.6
102		RNA, mg/g fresh tissue	0.64
103		Nucleoprotein, mg/g fresh tissue	20.0
104		Total lipid, % dry wt	10.5-18.13
105	Mitochondria	Total lipid, % dry wt	3.2-10.0
106		DNA, % total nucleic acid	11.7[1]
107		RNA phosphorus, μg/mg N	11.0
108		RNA, % total nucleic acid	19.0-46.0
109		Total N, %	23.0-38.6
110		Total protein, %	30.0-33.0
111		Total protein, mg/g fresh tissue	35.0-40.0
112		Total lipid, % dry wt of fraction	25.0-30.0
113		Phospholipid, % dry wt of fraction	66.0
114	Microsome	RNA, % total nucleic acid	50.0
115		Total nitrogen, %	18.0-20.0
116		Total protein, mg/g fresh tissue	19.0-21.0
117		Total lipid, % dry wt of fraction	40.0
	Fowl		
118	Erythrocytes, nucleus	Total nucleic acid, % dry wt	33.9-38.1
119		DNA, $\mu\mu$g/cell	2.34-2.49
120		DNA, %	45.0
121		RNA, % dry wt	0.7-2.5
122		Nucleoprotein, %	50.0-60.0
123		Acidic protein, %	33-40
124	Liver, nucleus	Total nucleic acid, % dry wt	29.4-31.2
125		DNA, $\mu\mu$g/nucleus	2.39-2.54
126		RNA, % dry wt	2.0-2.2
127	Sperm, nucleus	DNA, $\mu\mu$g/nucleus	1.26
	Fish		
128	Cod sperm, head	Total nucleic acid, % dry wt	30.3
129		RNA, % dry wt	0.3
130	Herring sperm, head	Total nucleic acid, % dry wt	38.8-59.0
131		RNA, % dry wt	0-1.2
132	Salmon sperm Head	Total nucleic acid, % dry wt	60.5
133	Whole cell	RNA, % dry wt	0.1
	Sea Urchin		
134	Sperm	DNA, $\mu\mu$g/cell	1.0
135		DNA, % dry wt	15.0
136	Ovum	DNA, $\mu\mu$g/cell	28.0
137		DNA, % dry wt	0.01
	Bacteria		
138	Staphylococcus	Total nucleic acid, % dry wt	11.57
139		DNA, % dry wt	2.82
140		RNA, % dry wt	8.75
141		Total N, % dry wt	13.95
142		Total protein, % dry wt	75.5
143	Bacillus anthracis	Total nucleic acid, % dry wt	4.35
144		DNA, % dry wt	1.15
145		RNA, % dry wt	3.20
146		Total N, % dry wt	10.0
147		Total protein, % dry wt	58.1
148	Escherichia coli	Total nucleic acid, % dry wt	12.84
149		DNA, % dry wt	3.72
150		RNA, % dry wt	9.12
151		Total N, % dry wt	14.61
152		Total protein, % dry wt	78.5
153	Salmonella typhosa	Total nucleic acid, % dry wt	13.12
154		DNA, % dry wt	4.40
155		RNA, % dry wt	8.72
156		Total N, % dry wt	14.40
157		Total protein, % dry wt	76.8

/1/ Contamination with nuclear material cannot be excluded.   /2/ Unsaponifiable.

53. BODY FLUIDS, CHEMICAL COMPOSITION: INVERTEBRATES

Part I: INSECTS

Values are for hemolymph and are mg per 100 ml, unless otherwise indicated.

No.	Constituent	Organism	Stage	Value
1	Albumin	Bee, honey (Apis mellifera)	Larva	3400
2		Beetle, water (Hydrophilus piceus)	Adult	800
3	Allantoin	Silkworm, Chinese oak (Antheraea pernyi)	Larva	10
4	Ammonia	Beetle, water (Hydrophilus piceus)	Adult	0
5		Silkworm, Chinese oak (Antheraea pernyi)	Larva	7
6	Bicarbonate	Armyworm, southern (Prodenia eridania)	Larva	7.8[1]
7		Fly, horse bot (Gasterophilus intestinalis)	Larva	90
8		Armyworm, southern (Prodenia eridania)	Larva	37
9	Calcium	Bee, honey (Apis mellifera)	Larva	14
10		Beetle, Japanese (Popillia japonica)	Larva	32
11		Butterfly, European cabbage (Pieris brassicae)	Larva	23-36
12		Cricket, Mormon (Anabrus simplex)	Larva	62
13		Fly, horse bot (Gasterophilus intestinalis)	Larva	11.4
14		Moth, cynthia (Samia cynthia)	Pupa	36-38
15		Moth, pine hawk (Sphinx pinastri)	Pupa	30-33
16		Moth, spurge hawk (Deilephila euphorbiae)	Larva	41
17		Silkworm, Chinese oak (Antheraea pernyi)	Pupa	33
18	Carbon dioxide	Bee, honey (Apis mellifera)	Larva	26-35[1]
19		Beetle, diving (Dytiscus marginalis)	Adult	7-53[1]
20		Beetle, water (Hydrophilus piceus)	Adult	55-90[1]
21		Fly, horse bot (Gasterophilus intestinalis)	Larva	40-130[1]
22		Silkworm (Bombyx mori)	Larva	9-11[1]
23	Chlorine	Armyworm, southern (Prodenia eridania)	Larva	120
24		Bee, honey (Apis mellifera)	Larva	120
25		Beetle, diving (Dytiscus marginalis)	Adult	225
26		Beetle, Japanese (Popillia japonica)	Larva	60-70
27		Butterfly, European cabbage (Pieris brassicae)	Larva	70-95
28		Fly, horse bot (Gasterophilus intestinalis)	Larva	53
29		Mosquito, northern house (Culex pipiens)	Larva	170
30		Mosquito, yellow fever (Aëdes aegypti)	Larva	180
31		Moth, goat (Cossus cossus)	Adult	27
32		Moth, pine hawk (Sphinx pinastri)	Pupa	58-63
33		Moth, spurge hawk (Deilephila euphorbiae)	Larva	49
34		Silkworm (Bombyx mori)	Adult	52
35	Cholesterol	Armyworm, southern (Prodenia eridania)	Larva	13
36		Bee, honey (Apis mellifera)	Larva	33
37	Citric acid	Fly, horse bot (Gasterophilus intestinalis)	Larva	45
38	Copper	Armyworm, southern (Prodenia eridania)	Larva	0.5
39		Fly, horse bot (Gasterophilus intestinalis)	Larva	1.5
40	Creatine	Bee, honey (Apis mellifera)	Larva	280
41	Fructose	Fly, horse bot (Gasterophilus intestinalis)	Larva	0
42		Moth, wax (Galleria mellonella)	Larva	3.3
43	Glycogen	Armyworm, southern (Prodenia eridania)	Larva	2.8
44		Bee, honey (Apis mellifera)	Larva	85
45		Fly, horse bot (Gasterophilus intestinalis)	Larva	
46		Moth, wax (Galleria mellonella)	Larva	50
47		Silkworm (Bombyx mori)	Larva	5.8
48	Iron	Moth, spurge hawk (Deilephila euphorbiae)	Larva	Trace
49	Lactic acid	Armyworm, southern (Prodenia eridania)	Larva	12-44
50		Fly, horse bot (Gasterophilus intestinalis)	Larva	320
51	Lipids	Armyworm, southern (Prodenia eridania)	Larva	370-585
52		Bee, honey (Apis mellifera)	Larva	137
53		Fly, horse bot (Gasterophilus intestinalis)	Pupa	830
54		Moth, spurge hawk (Deilephila euphorbiae)	Larva	17
55	Magnesium	Armyworm, southern (Prodenia eridania)	Larva	19-22
56		Bee, honey (Apis mellifera)	Larva	47
57		Beetle, Japanese (Popillia japonica)	Larva	50-110
58		Butterfly, European cabbage (Pieris brassicae)	Larva	1.7[1]
59		Cricket, Mormon (Anabrus simplex)	Adult	56-72
60		Moth, pine hawk (Sphinx pinastri)	Larva	43
61		Moth, spurge hawk (Deilephila euphorbiae)	Larva	
86	Nitrogen, protein	Armyworm, southern (Prodenia eridania)	Larva	165
87		Bee, honey (Apis mellifera)	Adult	1100
88		Beetle, Japanese (Popillia japonica)	Larva	655-925
89		Beetle, water (Hydrophilus piceus)	Adult	500-720
90		Cricket, Mormon (Anabrus simplex)	Adult	695
91		Fly, horse bot (Gasterophilus intestinalis)	Larva	1720
92		Moth, spurge hawk (Deilephila euphorbiae)	Larva	825
93		Silkworm (Bombyx mori)	Pupa	415-940[1]
94	Oxygen	Armyworm, southern (Prodenia eridania)	Larva	1.6-2.5[1]
95		Bee, honey (Apis mellifera)	Larva	0.5-0.8[1]
96		Beetle, diving (Dytiscus marginalis)	Adult	Trace
97		Beetle, water (Hydrophilus piceus)	Adult	0.11[1]
98	Phospholipid	Armyworm, southern (Prodenia eridania)	Larva	99
99	Phosphorus, total	Armyworm, southern (Prodenia eridania)	Larva	125
100		Bee, honey (Apis mellifera)	Adult	180-190
101		Cricket, Mormon (Anabrus simplex)	Adult	180
102		Fly, horse bot (Gasterophilus intestinalis)	Larva	110
103		Moth, spurge hawk (Deilephila euphorbiae)	Larva	12.0
104	Phosphorus, inorganic	Armyworm, southern (Prodenia eridania)	Larva	17.6
105		Bee, honey (Apis mellifera)	Larva	32
106		Beetle, diving (Dytiscus marginalis)	Adult	10.5
107		Cricket, Mormon (Anabrus simplex)	Adult	110
108		Fly, horse bot (Gasterophilus intestinalis)	Larva	12.5
109		Moth, cynthia (Samia cynthia)	Pupa	11
110		Moth, goat (Cossus cossus)	Larva	11.5
111		Moth, pine hawk (Sphinx pinastri)	Pupa	66
112		Moth, spurge hawk (Deilephila euphorbiae)	Larva	30
113	Potassium	Armyworm, southern (Prodenia eridania)	Larva	155
114		Bee, honey (Apis mellifera)	Larva	95
115		Butterfly, European cabbage (Pieris brassicae)	Larva	60-120
116		Cockroach, American (Periplaneta americana)	Adult	70[2]
117		Cricket, Mormon (Anabrus simplex)	Adult	60[2]
118		Fly, flesh (Calliphora erythrocephala)	Larva	145-155
119		Fly, horse bot (Gasterophilus intestinalis)	Larva	45
120		Moth, cynthia (Samia cynthia)	Pupa	160-170
121		Moth, emperor (Eudia pavonia)	Pupa	155
122		Moth, pine hawk (Sphinx pinastri)	Pupa	110-175
123		Silkworm (Bombyx mori)	Larva	155[2]
124		Silkworm, Chinese oak (Antheraea pernyi)	Pupa	170
125		Worm, cabbage, imported (Pieris rapae)	Larva	290-310
126	Reducing substances, total, as glucose	Armyworm, southern (Prodenia eridania)	Larva	66
127		Bee, honey (Apis mellifera)	Larva	120-440
128		Beetle, Japanese (Popillia japonica)	Larva	225-285
129		Beetle, water (Hydrophilus piceus)	Adult	25-105
130		Cockroach, American (Periplaneta americana)	Adult	55-75
131		Fly, horse bot (Gasterophilus intestinalis)	Larva	355
132		Grasshopper, differential (Melanoplus differentialis)	Adult	36
133	Sodium	Moth, spurge hawk (Deilephila euphorbiae)	Adult	125
134		Silkworm (Bombyx mori)	Larva	90-230
135		Armyworm, southern (Prodenia eridania)	Larva	51
136		Bee, honey (Apis mellifera)	Larva	12-17
137		Beetle, Japanese (Popillia japonica)	Larva	35-50
138		Cockroach, American (Periplaneta americana)	Adult	245[2]
139		Cricket, Mormon (Anabrus simplex)	Adult	50[2]
140		Fly, flesh (Calliphora erythrocephala)	Larva	365
141		Fly, horse bot (Gasterophilus intestinalis)	Larva	400
142		Moth, cynthia (Samia cynthia)	Pupa	4.6-7.3
143		Moth, emperor (Eudia pavonia)	Pupa	7.0
144		Moth, Mediterranean flour (Ephestia kuehniella)	Larva	37-69

66

Part I (concluded) — INSECTS

No.	Constituent	Organism	Stage	Value
62	Nitrogen gas	Beetle, diving (Dytiscus marginalis)	Adult	1.8[1]
63		Beetle, water (Hydrophilus piceus)	Adult	1.9[1]
64	Nitrogen, total	Armyworm, southern (Prodenia eridania)	Larva	1450
65		Bee, honey (Apis mellifera)	Larva	570
66		Beetle, Japanese (Popillia japonica)	Adult	1300
67		Cricket, Mormon (Anabrus simplex)	Larva	1850
68		Fly, horse bot (Gasterophilus intestinalis)	Larva	1200
69		Moth, spurge hawk (Deilephila euphorbiae)	Adult	950–1250
70		Silkworm (Bombyx mori)	Larva	235
71	Nitrogen, amino	Armyworm, southern (Prodenia eridania)	Adult	135
72		Bee, honey (Apis mellifera)	Larva	250–310
73		Beetle, diving (Dytiscus marginalis)	Larva	230–245
74		Beetle, Japanese (Popillia japonica)	Adult	40–80
75		Beetle, water (Hydrophilus piceus)	Adult	260
76		Cricket, Mormon (Anabrus simplex)	Larva	95
77		Fly, horse bot (Gasterophilus intestinalis)	Larva	235
78		Moth, goat (Cossus cossus)	Larva	170
79		Moth, spurge hawk (Deilephila euphorbiae)	Larva	400
80	Nitrogen, non-protein	Armyworm, southern (Prodenia eridania)	Larva	305–385
81		Bee, honey (Apis mellifera)	Larva	470–555
82		Beetle, Japanese (Popillia japonica)	Adult	605
83		Cricket, Mormon (Anabrus simplex)	Larva	130
84		Fly, horse bot (Gasterophilus intestinalis)	Larva	355
85		Moth, spurge hawk (Deilephila euphorbiae)	Larva	
145	Sodium	Silkworm (Bombyx mori)	Larva	32[2]
146		Silkworm, Chinese oak (Antheraea pernyi)	Pupa	26
147		Worm, cabbage, imported (Pieris rapae)	Larva	21–30
148	Succinic acid	Fly, horse bot (Gasterophilus intestinalis)	Larva	240
149	Sulfur	Armyworm, southern (Prodenia eridania)	Larva	44
150		Fly, horse bot (Gasterophilus intestinalis)	Larva	9.7
151		Beetle (Dytiscus sp)	Whole	1.5–2.0
152		Beetle, hydrophilid	Whole	0.75
153		Beetle, potato	Whole	3.5
154	Thiocyanate	Beetle, stag (Lucanus cervies)	Whole	2.9
155	Urea	Armyworm, southern (Prodenia eridania)	Larva	6.2
156		Beetle, water (Hydrophilus piceus)	Adult	2.6
157		Fly, horse bot (Gasterophilus intestinalis)	Larva	20.4
158	Uric acid	Armyworm, southern (Prodenia eridania)	Larva	14.8
159		Bee, honey (Apis mellifera)	Larva	4–8
160		Beetle, diving (Dytiscus marginalis)	Larva	18.0
161		Beetle, water (Hydrophilus piceus)	Adult	11–15
162		Fly, horse bot (Gasterophilus intestinalis)	Larva	2.2
163		Moth, spurge hawk (Deilephila euphorbiae)	Larva	18–28
164	Zinc	Silkworm (B. mori)	Larva	5–15
165		Silkworm (B. mori)	Pupa	7–15
166		Silkworm (B. mori)	Adult	13–15
167		Fly, horse bot (Gasterophilus intestinalis)	Larva	0.9
168		Silkworm (Bombyx mori)	Larva	1.1–1.3

/1/ Volume per cent. /2/ Serum only.

Part II. MOLLUSKS

No.	Constituent	Organism	Fluid[1]	Value[2]
1	Ammonia	Clam, soft shell (Mya arenaria)	U	21.5% tot. N excr.
2		Sea hare (Aplysia limacina)	MF	5% tot. NPN
3			U	33.5% tot. NPN
4		Slug (Limax agrestis)	B	11.5% tot. NPN
5		Snail (Helix pomatia)	U	4.5% tot. NPN
6			B	13.7% tot. NPN
7			B	11–18% tot. NPN
8	Calcium	Clam, hard shell (Venus mercenaria)	MF	9.5 mM/liter
9		Mussel (Anodonta cygnea)	B	8.4 mM/liter
10		Octopus, lesser (Eledone cirrosa)	B	9.8 mM/liter
11		Sea hare (Aplysia punctata)	BF	13.3 mM/liter
12	Carbon dioxide	Shell (Busycon spp)	B	13.5 mm CO_2 tens.
13	Chlorine	Clam, hard shell (Venus mercenaria)	MF	515 mM/liter
14		Mussel (Anodonta cygnea)	B	11.7 mM/kg H_2O
15		Octopus, lesser (Eledone cirrosa)	B	460 mM/liter
16		Sea hare (Aplysia punctata)	BF	625 mM/liter
17	Cholesterol	Abalone, red (Haliotis refuscens)	BF	3.6 mg/100ml
18	Copper	Shell (Busycon canaliculatum)	B	9–16 mg/100ml
19		Snail (Helix pomatia)	B	6–12 mg/100ml
20	Iron	Oyster (Ostrea spp)	MF	25 mM/liter
21		Clam, hard shell (Venus mercenaria)	B	19–55 mg/kg meat
22	Magnesium	Mussel (Anodonta cygnea)	B	0.2 mM/kg H_2O
23		Octopus, lesser (Eledone cirrosa)	B	48.7 mM/liter
24		Sea hare (Aplysia punctata)	BF	53 mM/liter
25	Nitrogen	Octopus (Octopus vulgaris)	HC	16% comp.
26		Shell (Busycon canaliculatum)	HC	16% comp.
27		Snail (Helix pomatia)	HC	15% comp.
28	Oxygen	Octopus (Octopus spp)	HC	22% comp.
29	Phospholipid	Snail (Helix pomatia)	B	0.7 mg/100ml
30	Potassium	Clam, hard shell (Venus mercenaria)	MF	7.4 mM/liter
31		Mussel (Anodonta cygnea)	B	0.5 mM/kg H_2O
32		Octopus, lesser (Eledone cirrosa)	B	11.6 mM/liter
33		Sea hare (Aplysia punctata)	BF	12.0 mM/liter
34	Protein	Clam, soft shell (Mya arenaria)	B	0.09 g/100ml
35		Mussel (Anodonta spp)	B	0.07 g/100ml
36		Sea hare (Aplysia spp)	B	0.28 g/100ml
37		Snail (Helix spp)	B	2.8 g/100ml
38	Sodium	Clam, hard shell (Venus mercenaria)	MF	440 mM/liter
39		Mussel (Anodonta cygnea)	B	15 mM/kg H_2O
40		Octopus, lesser (Eledone cirrosa)	BF	390 mM/liter
41	Sulfur as SO_4	Sea hare (Aplysia punctata)	MF	25.6 mM/liter
42		Clam, hard shell (Venus mercenaria)	B	0.8 mM/kg H_2O
43		Mussel (Anodonta cygnea)	B	18.5 mM/liter
44		Octopus, lesser (Eledone cirrosa)	U	8–9% tot. NPN
45	Urea	Octopus (Octopus vulgaris)	B	5% tot. NPN
46		Oyster (Gryphoea angulata)	MF	3.2% tot. NPN
47		Sea hare (Aplysia limacina)	U	8.7% tot. NPN
48		Snail (Helix pomatia)	U	20% tot. NPN
49	Uric Acid	Octopus (Octopus vulgaris)	B	13–36% tot. NPN
50		Sea hare (Aplysia limacina)	U	1.4% tot. NPN
51		Octopus (Octopus vulgaris)	U	4.6% tot. NPN
52		Sea hare (Aplysia limacina)	U	2.6% tot. NPN
53		Snail (Helix pomatia)	U	10.7% tot. NPN
54	Zinc	Clams, various	W	77 mg/kg
55		Oyster (Ostrea spp)	W	26–2300 mg/kg

/1/ B = blood; BF = body fluid; HC = hemocyanin; MF = mantle fluid; U = urine; W = whole organism. /2/ Comp. = composition; excr. = excreted; mM = millimole; NPN = non-protein nitrogen; tens. = tension; tot. = total.

Part III: A PARASITIC NEMATODE

Perivisceral fluid of the roundworm of swine (Ascaris lumbricoides). Values are millimoles per liter, unless otherwise indicated; those in parentheses are ranges.

No.	Constituent	Value	No.	Constituent	Value	No.	Constituent	Value
1	Ammonia	0.75	7	Hematin	0.03 (0.01–0.04)	13	Phospholipid	123 (120–130) mg/100ml
2	Ascorbic acid	(0.04–0.07)	8	Iron	0.13 (0.08–0.21)	14	Phosphorus, total	(11.2–12.3)
3	Ash (sulfate)	0.96 (0.7–1.1)g/100ml	9	Magnesium	4.9 (4.5–5.8)	15	Potassium	24.6 (16.4–36.6)
4	Calcium	5.9 (4.7–9.0)	10	Nitrogen, protein	0.69 (0.65–0.73)g/100ml	16	Sodium	130 (120–140)
5	Chloride	52.7 (46–57)	11	Nitrogen, non-protein	50 (47–53)mg/100ml	17	Urea	0.17
6	Glucose	1.2 (1.1–1.4)	12	Nitrogen, amino	(10–20)	18	Zinc	0.14 (0.13–0.19)

54. CELLS, TISSUES, AND ORGANS: pH VALUES

Methods used in pH determinations are given in the footnotes. Values in parentheses are ranges of values and correspond to estimate "d" of the 95% range (cf Introduction).

No.	Organism and Part — Animals	pH
	PROTOZOA	
1	Actinosphaerium eichornii	(6.6-6.9)[1]
2	Digestive vacuole (before food)	4.3[1]
	During digestion	5.4[1]
3	After digestion	
	Amoeba dubia	
4	Cytoplasm	6.8(6.4-7.2)[1]
5	Vacuole	7.6[2]
	A. limax	
6	Exoplasm	7.2[2]
7	Pseudopodia, resting	(7.0-7.2)[2, 3]
8	After movement	6.8[4, 5]
	A. polypodia	
9	Hyaline cytoplasm	(7.2-7.3)[1]
	A. proteus	
10	Cytoplasm	6.9(6.8-7.0)[1]
11	Resting	(6.7-7.3)[6]
12	After movement	(6.5-7.0)[6]
	Entamoeba coli	
13	Cytoplasm	6.7(6.6-6.8)[6]
14	Endoplasm, resting	6.5[6]
15	After movement	(6.5-7.0)[6]
16	Exoplasm, resting	6.8[6]
17	After movement	(6.5-7.0)[6]
18	Nucleus	7.0[6]
	E. histolytica (Human)	
19	Cytoplasm	7.0[7]
20	Endoplasm, resting	6.5[6]
21	After movement	(5.8-6.3)[6]
	Leishmania donovani	
22	Cytoplasm	(6.4-6.8)[2]
	Nyctotherus cordiformis	
23	Cytoplasm	(6.8-7.0)[1]
24	Macronucleus	6.0[2]
25	Pulsating vacuole	7.2(7.0-7.4)[2]
	Paramecium caudatum	
26	Cytoplasm (aerobiosis)	6.8(6.7-6.9)[2]
27	Digestive vacuole	4.0(4.0-7.6)[2]
	Trichomonas vaginalis	
28	Cytoplasm	(5.5-6.8)[2]
	Vorticella spp	
29	Digestive vacuole	5.0[2]
30	Resting	4.5(4.5-7.0)[2]
31	After contracting	3.5[2]
	PORIFERA	
	Aplysinidae spp	
32	Body substance	<6.0[4, 8]
33	Cortex	8.0[4, 8]
34	Choanosome	<7.0[4, 8]
	Mellita sexiesperforata	
35	Integument	7.5[4, 8]
	COELENTERATA	
	Aglantha digitalis, medusa	
36	Umbrella epithelium	7.0[2]
	Clytia johnstoni, medusa	
37	Tissue	6.6[2]
	Hydra fusca	
38	Cortical protoplasm	(7.5-7.6)[6]
39	Inner protoplasm	6.8(6.7-7.0)[6]
40	Nucleus	<6.8[6]
41	Nematocyst cell, cytoplasm	7.1(7.0-7.2)[6]
42	Pigment cell, cytoplasm	(7.4-7.6)[6]

No.	Organism and Part — Animals (continued)	pH
	MOLLUSCA (concluded)	
81	Chromodoris zebra	>5.6(5.6-7.6)[8]
	Mactra solidissima	
82	Nucleus of integument	6.8(6.6-7.0)[1]
83	Cytoplasm	7.4(7.2-7.6)[1]
	Octopus vulgaris	
84	Liver cells	7.0[11]
	Patella picta	
85	Muscle tissue	(5.6-6.0)[10]
	Pecten yessoensis	
86	Ciliated cells	7.0[2]
	Sepia officinalis	
87	Liver cells	6.0[11]
	Trochocochlea lineata	
88	Cytoplasm	5.2[10]
	ARTHROPODA (Crustacea)	
	Astacus fluviatilis	
89	Hepatopancreas	(6.0-6.3)[11]
	Carcinus maenas	
90	Hepatopancreas	6.1[11]
91	Muscle fibers	6.8[11]
	Chondrocanthus lophii	
92	Egg, cytoplasm	5.0[10]
	Maja squinado	
93	Egg, cytoplasm	5.0[10]
	Platycarcinus pagurus	
94	Hepatopancreas	(5.9-6.8)[11]
	Portunus puber	
95	Hepatopancreas	6.1[11]
	ARTHROPODA (Insecta)	
	Chironomus plumosus, larva	
96	Salivary gland cell, cytoplasm	(7.1-7.2)[2, 6]
97	Vacuole	6.9(6.8-6.9)[2, 6]
	Dytiscus marginalis	
98	Striated muscle cells	6.7(6.7-6.8)[6]
	UROCHORDATA	
	Ascidia mentula	
99	Cytoplasm	5.0[10]
100	Nucleus	(7.2-7.5)[10]
101	Unfertilized egg, cytoplasm	6.6(6.5-6.7)[1]
102	Vacuole	5.0[2]
	Fragarum elegans	
103	Tissue	(5.6-6.0)[10]
	Styelopsis spp	
104	Cytoplasm	4.7[10]
	PISCES	
	Fundulus heteroclitus	
105	Cytoplasm	6.4(6.1-6.8)[11]
106	Striated muscle cells	(6.6-6.8)[11]
	AMPHIBIA	
	Rana esculenta	
107	Histiocytes, cytoplasm	(6.0-7.2)[2, 12]
	R. pipiens	
108	Muscle fibers (in NaCl)	6.0[1]
109	(in NaHCO₃)	8.4[1]
	R. temporaria	
110	Unfertilized egg, cytoplasm	6.0[10]
111	Ovarian egg cell tissue	7.2[11]
112	Fertilized egg, cytoplasm	8.5[11]
	Salamander spp	
113	Muscle fibers	6.6[11]

No.	Organism and Part — Animals (concluded)	pH
	Ovary, eggs (concluded)	
165	Stromal cells	6.8(6.7-6.9)[6]
166	Pancreas, parenchyma	(7.2-7.4)[6]
167	Islet cells	(6.6-6.9)[6]
168	Spleen	6.7(6.5-7.0)[2]
	Mouse (Mus musculus)	
169	Bone	6.8(6.5-7.2)[2]
170	Lymph node	<6.2[2]
171	Muscle, striated	6.0[1]
172	Spleen	6.7(6.5-7.0)[2]
	Rabbit (Oryctolagus cuniculus)	
	Alimentary canal	
173	Stomach, chief cells	6.8[1]
174	Parietal cells	6.7[1]
175	Duodenum	6.9[11]
176	Ileum	6.3[11]
177	Cecum	7.1[11]
178	Large intestine	7.0[11]
179	Liver, peripheral cells	(7.1-7.5)[6]
180	Central cells	(6.7-7.0)[6]
181	Kupfer cells	(6.4-6.5)[6]
182	Pancreas, parenchyma	(7.2-7.4)[6]
183	Islets	(6.6-6.9)[6]
184	Uterus, non-pregnant	6.8[14]
185	Involuting	6.6[14]
	Rat (Rattus rattus)	
	Alimentary canal	
186	Stomach, chief cells	6.8(6.6-7.0)[6]
187	Parietal cells	6.5(6.4-6.6)[6]
188	Duodenum	(6.8-7.0)[6]
189	Jejunum	7.3[6]
190	Ileum	(7.4-7.6)[6]
191	Large intestine	(7.4-7.6)[6]
192	Bone	6.8(6.5-7.3)[2]
193	Liver, total tissue	6.9(6.8-7.0)[15]
194	Peripheral cells	7.3(7.1-7.5)[6]
195	Central cells	(6.8-7.0)[6]
196	Kupfer cells	(6.4-6.5)[6]
197	Ovary, eggs	7.8(7.5-7.8)[6]
198	Follicular cells	7.1(7.0-7.3)[6]
199	Stromal cells	6.8(6.7-6.9)[6]
	Plants	
	MICROORGANISMS	
200	Brucella abortus	(7.2-7.6)[2]
201	Eberthella typhi	(7.2-7.6)[2]
202	Escherichia coli	(7.2-7.6)[2]
203	Klebsiella pneumoniae	(7.2-7.6)[2]
204	Saccharomyces cerevisiae	(6.1-6.3)[2]
205	Staphylococcus spp	(6.1-6.3)[2]
206	Streptococcus spp	(6.1-6.3)[2]
	THALLOPHYTA (Algae)	
	Laminaria digitata	
207	Stipe, outer cortex, mature / Young	(4.8-5.3)[16]
208	Stipe, inner cortex	5.9[16]
209	Medulla, mature	(6.4-6.8)[16]
210	Young	(4.8-5.2)[16]
211	Nitella clavata, Cytoplasm	(5.9-6.2)[16]
	THALLOPHYTA (Fungi)	
	Agaricus campestri	
212	Cytoplasm	(5.0-6.2)[2, 11]
213	Stipe, pileus and hymeneal layers	5.9[16]

No.	Organism / Tissue	pH
43	Digestive cell, 3 day fast	7.2[6]
44	After ingestion	<6.1[6]
	Sagartia parasitica	
45	Tissue	(5.6-6.0)[9]
	Serularia pumila	
46	Tissue	5.2[9]
	Tiara pileata, medusa	
47	Mantle canal and tentacle	(6.2-6.4)[2]
48	Umbrella	7.2[2]
	ROTIFERA	
	Roussette spp	
49	Cytoplasm	(5.6-6.0)[10]
	ECHINODERMATA	
	Arbacia equituberculata	
50	Cytoplasm	(5.0-5.2)[11]
	A. punctulata	
51	Unfertilized egg, cytoplasm	6.8(6.6-7.0)[1]
52	Pigment cells	5.3(5.0-5.6)[5]
	Asterias glacialis	
53	Unfertilized egg, cytoplasm	7.2[1]
54	Oocyte, cytoplasm	7.2(7.0-7.4)[1]
	A. rubens	
55	Unfertilized egg, cytoplasm	6.7(6.6-6.8)[1]
56	Nucleus	7.5(7.4-7.6)[1]
57	Fertilized egg, cytoplasm	6.7(6.5-6.9)[1]
58	Cortical protoplasm	5.0[2]
59	Inner protoplasm	7.6[2]
	Echinocardium cordatum	
60	Unfertilized egg, cytoplasm	6.6[1]
	Ophiura lacertosa	
61	Unfertilized egg, cytoplasm	6.7(6.6-6.8)[1]
	Paracentrotus lividus	
62	Unfertilized egg, cytoplasm	7.2(7.0-7.4)[1]
63	Nucleus	6.6[1]
64	Unfertilized egg, cytoplasm / Nucleus	7.2[1]
	Psammechinus miliaris	
65	Cytoplasm	5.2[10]
	ANNELIDA	
	Arenicola claparedii	
66	Nucleus	(7.2-7.5)[10]
	Lumbricus spp	
67	Ectoderm, central protoplasm	7.3[6]
68	Muscle cells	6.7[6]
	Nereis limbata	
69	Cytoplasm	(5.6-6.0)[10]
	Platydella soleae	
70	Salivary gland tissue	(5.6-6.0)[10]
71	Clitellum tissue	(5.6-6.0)[10]
	Sabellaria alveolata	
72	Cytoplasm	5.0[10]
73	Nucleus	5.0[10]
74	Unfertilized egg, cytoplasm	6.6(6.5-6.7)[1]
	Spirographis spp	
75	Cytoplasm	6.0[10]
76	Chordoid cells	7.2[2]
77	Cytoplasm, tentacles	7.2[2]
78	Vacuole	6.6[2]
	MOLLUSCA	
79	Anodonta cygnea — Liver cells	6.8[11]
	Aplysia limacina	
80	Cytoplasm	(7.0-7.8)[10]
114	Triton marmoratus — Unfertilized egg, cytoplasm	7.2(7.2-7.3)[2]
	T. taeniatus	
115	Outer cells, blastula	(7.6-7.8)[11]
116	Embryonic yolk	(6.9-7.0)[11]
	AVES	
	Pigeon (Columba spp)	
117	Flight muscle tissue	(5.5-5.9)[11]
118		(6.1-6.8)[13]
119	Leg muscle tissue	(5.5-6.1)[11]
120		(6.7-7.4)[13]
	MAMMALIA	
	Cat (Felis catus)	
	Alimentary canal	
121	Stomach, parietal cells	(6.9-7.0)[6]
122	Chief cells	(6.4-6.5)[6]
123	Duodenum	(6.8-7.0)[6]
124	Jejunum	(7.2-7.3)[6]
125	Ileum	(7.4-7.6)[6]
126	Large intestine	(7.4-7.6)[6]
127	Cartilage, bronchial	(6.6-6.9)[6]
128	Kidney tissue	7.0[11]
129	Tubules	(6.7-7.0)[6]
130	Reticular cells	6.5(6.4-6.6)[6]
131	Liver tissue	(6.8-7.0)[13]
132	Peripheral cells	(7.3-7.5)[6]
133	Central cells	(6.7-7.0)[6]
134	Kupffer cells	(6.4-6.5)[11]
135	Muscle, cardiac	(6.8-7.0)[11]
136	Ovary, eggs	(7.5-7.8)[6]
137	Follicular cells	7.1(7.0-7.3)[6]
138	Stromal cells	6.8(6.7-6.9)[6]
139	Pancreas, parenchyma	(7.2-7.4)[6]
140	Islet cells	(6.9-7.0)[6]
141	Skin, surface epithelium	(7.3-7.5)[6]
142	Basal epithelium	(6.8-6.9)[6]
143	Horny epithelium	6.2[6]
144	Uterus, horn	6.6[14]
	Dog (Canis familiaris)	
145	Cardiac muscle	6.9(6.8-7.0)[15]
146	Striated muscle	(6.4-6.7)[15]
	Hamster (Cricetus spp)	
147	Testes, cortical protoplasm	7.4[6]
148	Central protoplasm	6.8[6]
149	Spermatozoids	(6.4-7.4)[6]
150	Interstitial cells	6.7(6.6-6.8)[6]
	Guinea pig (Cavia porcellus)	
	Alimentary canal	
151	Cartilage, chondrocytes	(6.6-6.8)[6]
152	Stomach, parietal cells	(6.9-7.1)[6]
153	Chief cells	(6.5-6.6)[6]
154	Duodenum	(6.8-7.0)[6]
155	Jejunum	(7.2-7.3)[6]
156	Ileum	(7.4-7.6)[6]
157	Large intestine	(7.4-7.6)[6]
158	Kidney, tubules	(6.8-7.0)[6]
159	Liver, total tissue	6.9(6.8-7.0)[13]
160	Peripheral cells	7.3(7.1-7.5)[6]
161	Central cells	(6.8-6.9)[6]
162	Kupffer cells	6.4[6]
163	Ovary, eggs	(7.5-7.8)[6]
164	Follicular cells	7.1(7.0-7.3)[6]
	THALLOPHYTA (Fungi) (concluded)	
214	Amanita muscaris — Stipe, pileus and hymeneal layers	6.2[16]
215	Coprinus atramentarius — Stipe	6.2[16]
216	Hypholoma fasciculare — Stipe	(4.8-5.2)[16]
	BRYOPHYTA	
	Polytrichum commune	
217	Epidermal walls	<3.4[16]
218	Cortex	(4.0-4.4)[16]
	PTERIDOPHYTA	
219	Dryopteris filix mas — Rachis and rhizome	(4.8-5.2)[16]
	Equisetum maximum	
220	Rhizome, endodermis	(4.8-5.2)[16]
221	Phloem	5.9[16]
	SPERMATOPHYTA (Gymnosperma)	
	Pine, Austrian (Pinus nigra austriaca)	
222	Stem, epidermal and xylem walls	<3.4[16]
223	Mesophyll	(4.8-5.2)[16]
	SPERMATOPHYTA (Angiosperma)	
	Broad bean (Vicia faba)	
224	Stem, epidermis	5.6[16]
225	Cortex, outer	(4.8-5.9)[16]
226	Pericycle	(5.6-5.9)[16]
227	Pith	(5.6-5.9)[16]
228	Roots, exodermis	(4.8-5.2)[16]
229	Phloem	(4.0-5.2)[16]
230	Cambium	(4.8-5.2)[16]
231	Leaves, epidermis	(4.8-5.6)[16]
232	Chlorenchyma	(4.8-5.2)[16]
233	Flowers, epidermis	(5.6-5.9)[16]
234	Anthers	(4.8-5.6)[16]
235	Pollen	(4.8-5.2)[16]
236	Seeds, plumule	
	Potato (Solanum tuberosum)	
237	Stems, epidermis	(4.8-5.2)[16]
238	Cortex, outer	(4.8-5.9)[16]
239	Pericycle	5.6[16]
240	Roots, piliferous layer	5.6[16]
241	Phloem	5.6[16]
242	Cambium	5.9[16]
243	Tuber, sap	(4.8-5.2)[16]
244	Cytoplasm	5.9[16]
245	Leaves, epidermis	5.6[16]
246	Chlorenchyma	5.9[16]
	Sunflower (Helianthus annuus)	
247	Stems, epidermis	(4.0-4.4)[16]
248	Cortex, outer	(4.8-5.8)[16]
249	Pericycle	(4.8-5.8)[16]
250	Roots, exodermis	(4.0-5.2)[16]
251	Phloem	(4.8-5.2)[16]
252	Cambium	(4.8-5.2)[16]
253	Leaves, epidermis	(4.0-4.4)[16]
254	Chlorenchyma	(4.8-5.8)[16]
255	Flowers, epidermis	(<3.4-4.4)[16]
256	Anthers	(5.6-5.9)[16]
257	Pollen	(4.8-5.2)[16]
258	Seeds, plumule	(4.8-5.2)[16]

/1/ Microinjection of liquid indicators. /2/ Vital staining. /3/ Micropipette method. /4/ Natural indicators. /5/ Spectrophotometric determination. /6/ Microinjection of solid indicator particles. /7/ Tissue culture method. /8/ Gas cell apparatus. /9/ Data on method not available. /10/ Crushed cells in solution. /11/ Electrometric methods. /12/ Ameboid movement with phagocytosis of India ink. /13/ Haas colorimetric method. /14/ Perfusion of tissues, buffering capacity. /15/ Tissue brei. /16/ Range indicator method of Small.

55. VERTEBRATE TISSUES AND ORGANS: CHEMICAL COMPOSITION

The subject matter of this table is probably the most controversial, and the values therein the most widely variable, of any table in the Handbook. Data from many contributors and hundreds of literature references have gone into its make-up, and each value or range may represent a "reconciliation" of several divergent values obtained by almost as many divergent analytical methods from a number of domestic and foreign laboratories. Therefore, it has been almost impossible to devise a system for presenting an accurate mean value or "95% range" for any component listed. Some of the values are means, some single observations, others ranges of means, and still others ranges of extremes. Consequently the user of this table is warned that these values are to be considered only as "yardsticks," and are not subject to statistical manipulation or conclusive interpretation.

Part I: NERVE TISSUE

Section 1: Man, Cat, Cattle, Dog, Rabbit, Rat

Values are mg/100 g fresh tissue, unless otherwise indicated. * = dry weight; PN = peripheral nerve.

Component	Man Whole Brain	Man Spinal Cord	Man Gray Matter[1]	Man White Matter[1]	Cat Whole Brain	Cat Gray Matter[1]	Cat White Matter[1]	Cat PN	Cattle Whole Brain	Cattle Gray Matter[1]	Cattle White Matter[1]	Dog Whole Brain	Dog Gray Matter[1]	Dog White Matter[1]	Rabbit Whole Brain	Rabbit Spinal Cord	Rat Whole Brain	Rat Gray Brain[1]
1 Water, %	70-85	65-75	80-85	60-75	80				70-85			75	80	65-75	75-80	68	80	80
2 Ash, %	1.5	1.4	0.92	0.7-1.8	1.0		2.4		1.15 PN	1.5	2.4		1.5	2.7			1.4	
3 Calcium	7-15	18	10.4	14	4-17		16	215	12-18	13	16	2-26			8.6-12	5.2-16	4.7-55*	45*PN
4 Chlorine	110-160	150	115-215	130-160	140		175		110-185	125	175	125-130	155	125	130-165	145	160-220	120
5 Copper	0.04-0.53		2.4-4.9*[2]	1.8-8.2*[2]					0.18PN									
6 Iron	5.2-8.3								4.4-8.2									
7 Magnesium	19-40		30	21			7.4		65*	5	7.4	13.0-13.5			35		4-9	75*PN
8 Manganese			0.16	0.2														
9 Nitrogen, total, %	1.6-1.83	1.6	1.6-1.7	1.7-1.8	1.7		1.7	2.5	1.3-10 PN	1.7	1.7	1.9	1.5-1.7	1.4-1.81	1.7		1.4	1.8
10 Acid-soluble, %			0.26[2]	0.33	53			0.14	2.1 PN				0.14	0.13			2.1	
11 Amino								0.1					0.1	0.08	0.13-0.18		0.13-0.18	
12 Phosphorus, total	215-415	550	205-245	365-440	300		435	380-435	245-440	255	435	730[4]	250-260	440-470	330 PN		195-305	1090*PN
13 Inorganic	32-50[2]		40	45-64	14-46			25	16 PN			7-9	55	55			13-20	16 PN
14 Acid-soluble	115-165[2]		140	240	67			51				655	80	65-75			55-75	
15 Potassium	285-400	360	230-345	230-380	345				215-345			360-375	375	340	360-400	375-400	235-450	400
16 Sodium	110-300	200	120-205	160-225	120				75-165			115	150	120	120-145	145	115	115
17 Sulfur	207	85	55-75	90-150														
18 Zinc	0.7					10	8		0.22 PN	10	8	12	8	8-13	8-9		1.5	
19 Protein, total, %	10-11	0.6 PN	7.3-8.2	7.7-9.2	9-11			10.9-12.3	10.3	8							11	
20 Neurokeratin, %		0.31	1.12	1.12				18-20	0.48			11-13						
21 Lipid, total, %	13.3	22-30*	16.3-17.8	16.3-17.8	13.3			5.9-7.3	24-30*						10.2-12.4	10.6	23-45	
22 Phospholipid, total, %	25*	2.3-18.5PN	5.1-5.3	6.2-11.3	4.3-5.7	4.0-4.5		1.7-3.0	13-16*	3.9-4.2		4-5	3.9-4.2	8.3-8.5	5.0-5.6	5.4	4.7-5.8[6]	4.5
23 Cephalin, %	14.8-26.0*	0.4-1.2 PN	3.1-4.3	2.7-3.7	2.1-2.7	1.9		1.54	6.6-7.5*					2.8	2.8	1.8	1.5-2.4	
24 Lecithin, %	4.6-4.9*	0.3-0.6 PN	1.8-2.2	0.9-1.7	1.2-1.3	1.3			5*						1.4		0.9-1.8	
25 Sphingomyelin, %	4.5-6.8*	2.6-2.8*	0.6-1.2	1.8-2.6	0.9	0.7		3.14							0.9	3.7	0.7-1.6	
26 Sulfolipid, %				1.2								4						
27 Cerebroside, %	1.2-2.4	5-6*	0.6-1.2	1.4-4.8	1.9-2.5	1.1-1.9	5.3	1.5-2.9	11.6-12.5*	1.5	1.2	3 PN	1.5	6.9-7.4	2.4-2.9	5.9	1.1-1.2	1.2
28 Cholesterol, %	2.6-4.4	0.53	0.8-1.1	3.8-4.2	2.2-2.8	1.2-1.3		2.3-3.4	10-11*					5.9	2.2	5.9	0.2-0.6	0.9
29 Nucleic acid, DNA	80	3.1-1.5, 32, 7		4-9.87	5.87			4.3-5.87	80	57		80	57	67	95		140	
30 RNA	105-140			12-267	7.67			3.6-3.97	95	107		95	107	57	215		160	

/1/ Unspecified. /2/ Cortex. /3/ Infant. /4/ Spinal cord. /5/ % of total P. /6/ Plasmalogens 320-340 mg/100 g fresh tissue. /7/ As phosphorus.

Section 2: Other Animals.

* = dry weight; AX = axoplasm; GM = grey matter (unspecified); PN = peripheral nerve; SC = spinal cord.

Values are mg/100 g fresh WHOLE BRAIN tissue unless otherwise indicated.

Component	Beaver PN	Guinea Pig	Horse PN	Monkey	Mouse	Sheep	Chicken	Duck	Gull	Pigeon	Tortoise	Frog	Carp	Perch, Yellow	Shark, Sand	Invertebrates Value	Invertebrates Organism
1 Water, %		78	71	78	79	84GM 1.4GM	79	78	81	79	83	84[1]	81	82	81		
2 Ash, %												1.6	2.2				
3 Calcium		4-11	1.0			10.8						14PN				5	Crab
4 Chlorine			230				1.1-1.2	1.7			1.2	130PN				355AX	Squid
5 Nitrogen, total, %					2.2							1.5					
6 Phosphorus, total		300	250	390 PN	320							330PN	1.3	150			
7 Potassium			130-180		370							185PN				78AX	Squid
8 Sodium			450		100							145PN				420PN	Cockroach
9 Sulfur			40		260											140PN	Cockroach
10 Protein, total, %	5.9	8.7-9.2		9.5SC	10.4	10.7	7.2-7.6	10.7		45-50*	8	6.7-7.5PN	5.5PN			90-95*	Bee
11 Lipid, total, %		9.8-10.5					9.2-10.2	9.4		4.2-5.4	7.2		9.2			35-45*	Bee
12 Phospholipid		4.2-4.9		8.2PN	4.5		4.2	3.7		4.4	4.2[2]	3[1]	4	4.2	3.7		
13 Cephalin, %		2.8	2.8						4	2.4	2.2[2]	1.2[1]		1.7	2.8	16-18*	Bee
14 Lecithin, %		1.4							2.3		1.3[2]			1.5	1.3		
15 Sphingomyelin, %		0.9							1.3	0.7	0.42	0.3[1]		0.9	0.6	0.15[3]AX	Squid
16 Cerebroside, %	1.3	2.2-2.4				1.0	1.6-2	1.8	0.4	1.3	1.2	1.2[1]	0.7	0.3	1.2	1-2*	Bee
17 Cholesterol, %	3.2	1.7-1.9							1.4	1.4-2	1	0.8[1]		1.3	1.1	0.8-1.6*	Bee
18 Nucleic acid, DNA		110									120		205				
19 RNA		255									385		265				

/1/ Leopard frog. /2/ Turtle. /3/ Cephalin + lecithin, %.

Part II: LUNG

Values are mg/100 g fresh tissue, unless otherwise indicated. * = dry weight; FF = fat-free.

Component	Man	Cattle	Dog	Rabbit	Rat
1 Water, %	78-80	80	78	80-82	77-85
2 Ash, %	1.1			1	
3 Bromine	0.3-0.7	0.35			
4 Calcium	17				
5 Chlorine	260		195-255	230	215-430
6 Chromium, µg/100 g	13				
7 Copper	0.5-1.4*			12.4	
8 Iron	2-22				
9 Magnesium	7	62*			
10 Phosphorus, total	95-120				
11 Nucleic acid	250*		265*		375*
12 Potassium	150		155-250	165	1.9
13 Silicon[1]	20-40				
14 Sodium	240		155-210		
15 Zinc	4-15*				
16 Protein, %	14.9-16.7	11.5*FF	14.2*FF	1.3[2]	6.6
17 Phospholipid, %	3.4	3.7*			0.8
18 Cephalin, %	1.4-2.6*	3.3*			1.8
19 Lecithin, %	3.8-4*				
20 Sphingomyelin, %	0.9-1.5*	2.3*			0.45
21 Cholesterol, %	2.2*	2.2*FF			0.4
22 Carbohydrate, %	0.4*				

/1/ As total silica. /2/ Total lipid.

Part III: HEART

Values are mg/100 g fresh tissue, unless otherwise indicated. * = dry weight; FF = fat-free.

Component	Man Whole Heart	Man Left Ventricle	Man Right Ventricle	Man Auricles	Cat	Cattle	Dog	Guinea Pig	Rabbit	Rat	Swine	Chicken
							Whole Heart					
1 Water, %	71-80	76-85	78-83	80-84	79-81	70-77	76-81	76	76-80	76-83	80	70
2 Ash, %	1.1	3.5-5.6*				0.92			1.0	0.16	0.6	
3 Aluminum	0.1-0.3						0.17		0.07			
4 Bromine	0.07-0.3						0.18					
5 Calcium	125-185	105-170	125-185	120-170	120-145	10	9.3	6.8	67*	3-20		
6 Chlorine						100[1]	110-135		125-180	85-110		
7 Chromium	0.01											
8 Copper	0.34	0.2-0.5			1.4*	0.76	0.27[2]	2.1*	2.2*	0.2	1.5	1.5*
9 Fluorine	0.46											
10 Iron	35*	4-21	4.4-15.1			4.2-6.2			12.4	5-11		
11 Lead	0.05-0.08											
12 Magnesium	17.4	13-25	13-30			110-125	21-23[2]	9	51*	18-26	0.2	
13 Manganese	0.02-0.05					0.03	0.21	0.02	0.02	0.06		0.07*
14 Phosphorus	275	145-235	125-185	95-220	207	160-235	217	280	175-240	240	320	
15 Potassium	35-120*	245-355	190-240		300-365	255-355[2]	285-340		275	320-340		
16 Silicon									120-135	85-95	95	
17 Sodium	7-14	85-140	80-165	75-170	95-110	80-135[2]	88	135				
18 Zinc	16					16.5	2	0.7-1.2	1.1-6.1	0.8		
19 Protein, %					17.6		18[2]		2*[2]		2.2*[2]	
20 Collagen, %		0.6-1.4	1.2-2.0	3.4-4.0	1.2	1.9[2]	2.7[2]			0.14		
21 Elastin, %		0.2-0.9	0.5-2.4		0.15	0				0.14		
22 Lipid, %	8.3					3.1-19.5			4[3]	0.4-2.4		1.5[2]
23 Phospholipid, %	6.3-7.5*FF					7.4-11.8*	11.7*			5*		
24 Choline-, %	6*FF					4.9*	5.3*			2*		
25 Cephalin, %	1.4-2.8*					5.3*				0.84		
26 Lecithin, %	3.3-5.7*					4*				2		
27 Sphingomyelin, %	0.2-0.5*					0.5*				0.14		
28 Cerebroside, %						2*				1.4*		
29 Cholesterol, total, %					0.44*[2]	0.4*[4]	0.6*	0.2	0.6*	0.4-0.6*		0.27
30 Glycogen					475		440-495	240	335-640	240-680		
31 Creatine	115-265	140-265	100-195		220-335		210-325		210-245	160-260		180*

/1/ Auricle. /2/ Ventricle. /3/ Total fat. /4/ Free cholesterol.

71

55. VERTEBRATE TISSUES AND ORGANS: CHEMICAL COMPOSITION (Continued)

Part IV: MUSCLE

Section 1: Man, Cat, Cattle, Dog, Rabbit, Rat

Values are mg/100 g fresh muscle (type unspecified), unless otherwise indicated. * = dry weight; FF = fat-free.

Component	Man	Cat	Cattle	Dog	Rabbit	Rat
1 Water, %	74-84[1]	77	70	73-76	68-80	76
2 Ash, %	1.1		0.8-1		1.0-1.4	1.3
3 Bicarbonate	98[1]	70[1]				
4 Bromine	0.3-0.6					
5 Calcium	6.5-7.4	3.5	11	3.3	18	6.3[1]
6 Chlorine	45-110	55	55	50-75	50-100	40-140
7 Chromium, μg/100 g	0.2					
8 Copper	0.64-1.3*					
9 Iron	25.3		2.8-3.7		2.7	1.9
10 Magnesium	18.4-21.5	28.2[1]	32	44[1]	29	27[1]
11 Manganese, μg/100 g	8.2-10					
12 Nitrogen, %	3			3.5[2]	1.24[3]	
13 Phosphorus, total	150-200	205	210	185-205[1]	245	185-250
14 Acid-soluble	175	165[1]		115-140[1]	150-185[1]	160-185
15 as PO4	85-195[1]			75-120[1]	22-35[1]	75-105[1]
16 Potassium	300-435	350	260-525	320[1]	415	385-475
17 Sodium	65-105	55	45-165	74	40-55	40-60

Component	Man	Cattle	Cat	Dog	Rabbit	Rat
18 Zinc	12-30*	19.3, 2.1*FF	18.2	21[1]	0.9-1.4*	21[1]
19 Protein, %	18.5				19-25	
20 Collagen, %						0.65-2.0[4]
21 Elastin, %						0.07-0.37[4]
22 ATP[5]			90[1]	40-60[1]	270-420[1]	330[1]
23 Anserine			250[1]	105[1]	370[1]	505[1]
24 Carnosine				29[1]	100[1]	46[1]
25 Citric acid				1.16	2.5	
26 Lactate	80-120[1]	10-14*	15-20[1]	30-60[1]	39[1]	9-29[1]
27 Lipid, total, %	7.6	6-12*	2.5	14	1.2-7.6	3.7-10.6
28 Fat, neutral, %					7	0.75-1.8
29 Phospholipid, %		3.7*		5.8*		4.4-8.6*
30 Choline phospholipid, %		2.3*		2.9*		2.1*
31 Cholesterol, %	0.2*	0.24*	0.2*	0.3*	0.05	0.07
32 Hexose monophosphate			35-45[1]	35-55[1]		260[1]
33 Glycogen	1.3-2.2[1]		0.3-1	0.5-1.9[1]	140	270-320
34 Creatine	440[1]		380-440	370	380-440	440

/1/ Skeletal muscle. /2/ Sacrospinalis muscle. /3/ Collagen. /4/ Thigh muscle. /5/ Adenosine triphosphate. /6/ Abdominal muscle.

Section 2: Other Animals

Values are mg/100 g fresh muscle (type unspecified), unless otherwise indicated. * = dry weight; FF = fat-free.

Component	Guinea Pig	Sheep	Swine	Chicken	Pigeon	Snake!	Turtle	Frog	Cod	Eel	Salmon
1 Water, %	75	52-64	65		74[1]	75-78	79	79-82[1]	72-83	54-59	64-70
2 Ash, %		0.85					1			1.2	1.2[3]
3 Calcium		10-20	1			15-30		8-21[1]	25	9-16	17
4 Chlorine		70				35-125		40-65[1]	215	50-110	190
5 Magnesium		33	100*[4]	110*[4]		4.6-10.2		24-65[1]	22	14.4	32
6 Phosphorus		185-210			260[1,5]	175-215		105-185[1]	220-240	190-200	230
7 Potassium		205-295				85-140		305-350[1]	350	190-245	340
8 Sodium		80-140				110-145		55[1]	140	50-95	120
9 Protein, %	19-21[6]	17.1	19								
10 Lipid, total, %		17.5-32	8	7-12.7*[7]			14.5	2.1[1]	25	13.5-15.3	25
11 Phospholipid, %		4.7	3.1*	2.7-4.4*[7]	3-5*[8]		17.4*	7.1[1]	9.5*	26-30	18.3*
12 Cholesterol, %		0.26*	0.06	0.79	0.11		5.3*	0.04	4.3*		4.4*
13 Glycogen	290-910[6]						0.7		0.05	4-95[2]	0.06
14 Creatine	280-440			65[11]	36[11]	180-445		80[1]			24-65[3]

Invertebrates

Component	Organism	Value
1 Water, %	Lobster	78-84
2 Ash, %	Lobster	1.6
3 Calcium	Crayfish	107
4 Chlorine		
5 Magnesium	Crayfish	21
6 Phosphorus	Cockle	140-180
7 Potassium	Crayfish	400
8 Sodium	Crayfish	105
9 Protein, %	Lobster	14.2-20.1
10 Lipid, total, %	Shrimp	8.1*
11 Phospholipid, %	Shrimp	4*
12 Cholesterol, %	Shrimp	0.710
13 Glycogen	Oyster	2600-4200

/1/ Skeletal muscle. /2/ Flatfish. /3/ Shark. /4/ Gluteus muscle. /5/ Breast muscle. /6/ Gastrocnemius muscle. /7/ "Dark and white" meat. /8/ Pectoralis major muscle. /9/ Thigh muscle.
/10/ Free cholesterol. /11/ Breast muscle.

Part V: GONADS AND SEX ORGANS

Values are per cent fresh tissue, unless otherwise indicated. * = dry weight; FF = fat-free.

	Man	Man	Man	Man	Guinea Pig	Dog	Cattle	Rabbit	Rabbit	Rabbit	Rat	Rat	Swine
Component	Ovary	Uterus	Testis	Prostate	Mammary	Testis	Testis	Mammary	Ovary	Uterus	Testis	Prostate	Prostate
1 Water	80.5 FF		84	82.5	80	83-92 FF	86	38[1]	73-75	82-89 FF	87.3 FF	18-26[3]	15.6
2 Solids, total				16-20	10.3*		21.82	12.5 FF	23.5-25				
3 Ash				0.83				0.3					
4 Bromine, mg/100 g		0.3-0.8	0.26									0.85-1.2[3]	
5 Chlorine, mg/100 g		210		0.28		205-225 FF, 315-390 FF	0.27	135[5]	1.1-1.6	0.9-1.1	1-1.6		
6 Potassium, mg/100 g[4]		290				1.7				140-150, 240-260	330		
7 Uranium, μg/100 g	3.3												
8 Zinc, mg/100 g			6.8-16.3*	4.0, 9.4-25	9.7		4.12	1.4-16.7[6]	1.9-2.3	1.1-1.8	2.7-3.1	13-25[7]	3.8
9 Lipid, total				1.2			1.6	17-36[2]	1.1		1.1		
10 Fatty acids				0.12	76.5*[9]			12.3[8]					
11 Cholesterol, total				0.22-0.8				89.3[9,10]					
12 Citric acid					80-100		14.3-23.2[13]	52-6[2]	1.2[11]		0.8*[12]	70-120[3]	38

/1/ In lactation, 55-75% H2O. /2/ Prostate. /3/ Ventral. /4/ Of tissue water. /5/ Ovary. /6/ Testis. /7/ Posterior. /8/ Early lactation. /9/ Calcium salts. /10/ Per 100 g dry fat. /11/ Immature ovary. /12/ Free cholesterol. /13/ Mammary.

Part VI: TEETH

Section 1: Man

Values are per cent dry tissue, unless otherwise indicated. FW = fresh tissue; TA = tissue ashed.

Component	Whole Teeth	Enamel	Dentine	Pulp
1 Water	4-14.3 FW[1]	0.5-6.6 FW[1]	4.2-16.7 FW[1]	60-65 FW
2 Ash	68-80	95.4	71.1	21.2
3 Calcium	27-37TA	35-39	27.8	5.7
4 Chlorine		0.3	0	
5 Copper, mg/100 g	0.52 TA			
6 Fluorine, mg/100 g	4.5-28.7 FW	0-25	13.3-32 FW	
7 Lead, mg/100 g	5.1 TA			

Component	Whole Teeth	Enamel	Dentine	Pulp
8 Magnesium	0-1.8 FW	0.16-1.16 TA	0.8-1.6 TA	10.1
9 Nitrogen	16.5-19.0TA	16.8-18.5TA	16.5-19.0TA	3.5
10 Phosphorus		0.052	0.07	
11 Potassium	3.0			
12 Silicon, mg/100 g				
13 Sodium		0.25	0.2	
14 Zinc, mg/100 g	0.3 TA	15.2-25 TA	14.8-26 TA	

Component	Whole Teeth	Enamel	Dentine	Pulp	Swine Pulp
15 Carbonate[3]	3-5TA	2.6-3.7TA	4.3-5.1TA		3.8 FW
16 Protein, total	18 FW	0.2-0.5 FW	15.5 FW		0.23 FF
17 Insoluble					4.2 FW
18 Fat, total					0.07 FW
19 Phospholipid					0.23 FW
20 Cholesterol, mg/100 g	0.7	0.09	0.8		
21 Citric acid					

/1/ Deciduous. /2/ Or less. /3/ As CO2.

Section 2: Other Mammals

Values are per cent dry tissue, unless otherwise indicated. FW = fresh tissue; FF = fat-free tissue; TA = tissue ashed.

Component	Dog Dentine	Elephant Dentine[1]	Guinea Pig Whole Teeth[2]	Hamster Enamel[2]	Hamster Dentine[2]
1 Ash				85-92	74-76
2 Calcium	37.6 TA	32.9 TA	35-36 TA	25-34	19-24
3 Fluorine, mg/100 g	28-41 FW[3]	4.1 TA	1.7 1.9 TA	0.7-1.3	0.8-1.5
4 Magnesium				17-18	14-16
5 Phosphorus	19.6 TA	19.6 TA	20 TA		

Component	Hare Whole Teeth[2]	Horse Dentine	Monkey Dentine	Rabbit Whole Teeth[2]	Rabbit Enamel[2]	Rat Enamel[2]	Rat Dentine[2]
1 Ash	36 TA			35-36 TA	33-35 FF	27-28 FF	
2 Calcium	1.8-2.3 TA	37.1 TA	37 TA	1.5-2.5 TA	0.25-0.44 FF		0.37-1.5 FF
3 Phosphorus	19-20	1.9 TA	20 TA	20 TA	15.9-17.4 FF		15.9-17.4 FF
		19.2 TA					

/1/ Tusk. /2/ Incisors and molars. /3/ Whole teeth.

Part VII: BONE

Section 1: Man, Cattle, Dog, Horse, Rabbit, Rat

Values are per cent fresh tissue (compact bone) unless otherwise indicated. * = dry weight; FF = fat-free tissue; Unspec. = bone type not specified.

Component	Man Unspec.	Man Epiphysis	Man Femur	Man Rib	Cattle Bone Type	Cattle Value	Dog Bone Type	Dog Value	Horse Bone Type	Horse Value	Rabbit Bone Type	Rabbit Value	Rat Bone Type	Rat Value
1 Water	30-44			81	Femur	75*FF	Unspec.	40-59	Femur	70.2	Unspec.	39-58	Femur	34.6
2 Ash	22.1	84[1]	66.8*FF		Unspec.	25.8*	Unspec.	25-30	Femur	26.2	Femur	72*FF	Unspec.	34-40
3 Calcium			25.6*FF	25.6*FF	Unspec.	5.8*FF	Femur	25.5*FF	Femur	5.7	Femur & tibia	27-31*FF	Femur & tibia	27-29*FF
4 Carbonate, as CO3			4.0*FF				Femur	4.5*FF					Femur	5.2*FF
5 Chlorine	0.17								Femur	0.192				
6 Copper, mg/100 g	0.65*		0.2	0.37-4.8							Unspec.	0.18[2]		
7 Fluorine, mg/100 g	10.3-16.1[3]			61-310*FF	Rib	36-51*FF			Femur	100	Long bone	12-18*FF	Femur & tibia	10-29*FF
8 Iron, inorg., mg/100 g			0.015	11.2-16.7							Unspec.	8.1		
9 Magnesium			0.39*FF	0.02	Femur[5]	0.42-0.64*FF	Femur	0.44*FF	Femur	0.23	Femur	0.7*	Femur	0.54*
10 Manganese, mg/100 g	0.3			0.2	Femur	0.05	Femur	0.05	Femur	0.54*			Unspec.	2.2
11 Nitrogen			4.2-4.6*FF	5.1*FF	Rib	4.25*	Femur	5.27*FF	Unspec.	2.2	Femur & tibia	2.9-3.5*FF	Femur & tibia	3.0-3.7*FF
12 Phosphorus	11.5*FF		12.3*FF	0.3	Unspec.	11.9*	Femur	11.9*FF	Femur	3.0-3.7*FF	Unspec.	3.6-4.2	Femur & tibia	11.9-13.5*FF
13 Potassium	0.055								Femur	11.9-13.5*FF				
14 Sodium	0.44*FF						Unspec.	0.44*FF						
15 Strontium	0.06-0.226													
16 Fat					Femur	0.1*	Unspec.7	13.0	Unspec.	5-7	Femur	0.1*	Unspec.7	5-7
17 Citric acid	0.7-2.0*FF			1.4-1.9 FF	Leg bones	1.4-2.1*FF	Femur	1.0-1.3*FF	Tibia	0.3-0.42*	Tibia	0.72-0.83*	Tibia	0.3-0.42*

/1/ Cartilage. /2/ mg/100 g. /3/ Vertebrae. /4/ Compact and spongy (cancellous) bone. /5/ Femur head spongy bone. /6/ Tibia. /7/ Total lipid.

Section 2: Other Vertebrates

Values are per cent dry, fat-free tissue, unless otherwise indicated. FW = fresh tissue.

Component	Cat Bone Type	Cat Value	Ferret Bone Type	Ferret Value	Guinea Pig Bone Type	Guinea Pig Value
1 Ash	Femur	67-70			Femur & tibia	28-31
2 Calcium	Femur & tibia	26-29	Femur & tibia	26-31	Femur & tibia	26-31
3 Carbonate, as CO3						5.0[2]
4 Magnesium	Femur & tibia	3.4-4.6	Femur & tibia	3.3-4.5	Femur & tibia	3.3-4.5
5 Nitrogen	Femur & tibia	11.5-12.9	Femur & tibia	11.5-13.2	Femur & tibia	2.7-3.1
6 Phosphorus						11.5-13.2
7 Citric acid	Rib	0.4-0.6 FW				

Component	Sheep Bone Type	Sheep Value	Turkey Bone Type	Turkey Value	Turtle Bone Type	Turtle Value	Frog Bone Type	Frog Value
1 Ash	Rib[1]	61-64	Femur	69.5	Femur	62.7	Femur	67.6
2 Calcium	Rib[1]	22.2-23.0	Femur	26.5	Femur	24.3	Femur	26.2
3 Carbonate, as CO3	Femur	4.7	Femur	4.5	Femur	5.6[2]	Femur	4.7[2]
4 Magnesium	Femur	0.52-0.70	Femur	0.52	Femur	0.54		
5 Nitrogen	Femur & tibia	2.9-3.5	Femur	4.9	Femur	5.9	Femur	5.2
6 Phosphorus	Rib	10.8	Femur	12.6	Femur	10.5	Femur	12.3
7 Citric acid							Unspec.	0.29

/1/ Compact and spongy bone. /2/ Per cent of ash, calculated as CO2.

55. VERTEBRATE TISSUES AND ORGANS: CHEMICAL COMPOSITION (Continued)

Part VIII: BONE MARROW

Values are mg/100 g fresh tissue, unless otherwise indicated. * = dry weight.

Component	Man, Sternum	Man, Tibia	Unspec.[1]	Cat, Femur	Cattle, Femur	Dog, Femur	Guinea Pig, Femur	Rabbit, Femur	Rabbit, Rib	Rat, Femur	Combined[2]	Swine, Femur	Frog, Femur
1 Water, %	14.0			50	41.3	21.0	71	74	46-55	68	7-16	8.1	65
2 Ash, %	0.55												
3 Calcium	32.7	4.4-11.0											
4 Copper					0.35[3]			0.07-0.093			0.2-0.4[1]	2.2[4]	
5 Iron	30-55												
6 Phosphorus, %	18.3							7.6					
7 Protein, %				11.5	1.4	5.4	17.0			17.2	2.4-3.6	1.2	5.4
8 Fat, %			30-90	38.2			10.4	56		14.0			28.4
9 Sugar	65-275	11-55											

/1/ Unspecified origin of marrow. /2/ Radius + ulna + distal end of tibia. /3/ "Leg (long) bones." /4/ Rib.

Part IX: LIVER

Section 1: Man, Cattle, Rabbit, Rat

Values are mg/100 g fresh tissue, unless otherwise indicated. * = dry weight.

Component	Man	Cattle	Rabbit	Rat
1 Water, %	73-77	69-71	70-76	69-72
2 Ash, %	1.4	1.4	1.2-2.0	1.4-1.6
3 Arsenic	0.15			
4 Bromine	0.04-0.43	0.7		
5 Calcium	7.2-9.4	8.3	5-16	2.8-3.8
6 Chlorine	96-150		105-160	90-115
7 Chromium, µg/100 g	0.6			
8 Copper	1.5-13	8.5	3.0[1]	2.1-20.4*
9 Iron, total	13.4	12.1	18.5	3.0-22
10 Inorganic	3.0-16.2		8.2-10.3	7.0-18.2
11 Lead	0.2			
12 Magnesium	17			19
13 Manganese	0.08	60-75*	13.4	
14 Phosphorus, total	180-240	375	0.2	280-375
15 DNA[2]	19	34		20-37
16 RNA[3]	37	70		55-120
17 Potassium	170-250	225-395	190-260	365-395
18 Silicon	5-20	53-345	75-140	305
19 Sodium	120-150		22	3.0-3.2
20 Zinc		3.4-8.4		16.0-22
21 Protein, %	17.0	20.0		
22 Collagen, %	0.5-1.5			0.23
23 Elastin, %	0.1-0.5			
24 Lipid, total, %	7.0	6-7.4		5.0
25 Fat, total, %		7.0		1.1-29
26 Phospholipid, %	9-11*	17.3-25.1*	0.23	2.2-2.7
27 Cephalin, %	3.3-6.0*	5.0*		0.8-1.4
28 Lecithin, %	3.3-6.0*	8.0*		1.1-3.1
29 Sphingomyelin, %		0.8*		0.2-0.4
30 Cholesterol, total, %	0.3-0.43*	0.32	0.05	0.25-0.3
31 Carbohydrate, %	0.2-0.4	4.0		
32 Ascorbic acid	5.0			2.3

/1/ In the newborn. /2/ Desoxyribonucleic acid P. /3/ Ribonucleic acid P.

Section 2: Other Vertebrates

Values are mg/100 g fresh tissue, unless otherwise indicated. * = dry weight; FF = fat-free.

Component	Cat	Dog	Guinea Pig	Mouse	Sheep	Swine	Chicken	Eel
1 Water, %	70-72	73-75	70-75		67	78		80
2 Calcium		5.0-22	4.2					9.0
3 Chlorine	94-103	149						195
4 Copper	2.0[1]		5.1[1]	5.0		1.3-3.5*	0.4*[4]	
5 Iron, total	23.2[1]		4-5		10-135	6.4*	6-35	
6 Inorganic				1.1-3.1	9-45	2.6*		
7 Magnesium					73*			105
8 Phosphorus	280	80-140[2]	110-175[2]	350-385*				28-83
9 Potassium	290	115-275						245
10 Sodium	76	120						195
11 Zinc	15[1]		4.3	20		3.0		205
12 Protein, %	17.1			6.4				13.2
13 Fat, total, %	6.0	4.0[3]	2.0-3.2	3.2-4.2			2.0-3.4	6.5
14 Phospholipid, %			2.0-4.2					
15 Cholesterol, total, %		12.0	0.17-0.54	0.4-0.7		0.13*FF	0.3-0.6	

/1/ In the newborn. /2/ Nucleic acid P. /3/ Total lipid. /4/ In the young animal.

Part X: SPLEEN

Section 1: Man, Cattle, Rabbit, Rat.

Values are mg/100 g fresh tissue, unless otherwise indicated. * = dry weight; FF = fat-free.

Component	Man	Cattle	Rabbit	Rat
1 Water, %	76-81		78-79	77-78
2 Ash, %	1.5		1.0	
3 Bromine	0.23-0.6	0.5		
4 Calcium	9.3			
5 Chlorine	160		150	140-160
6 Chromium, µg/100 g	1.6			
7 Copper	0.12-1.3	0.65*	2.4[1]	
8 Iron, total	28			
9 Inorganic	8.5-17			35-40
10 Magnesium	14.2	70-85*		3.5
11 Phosphorus, total	375	90-205[2]		165-260[2]
12 DNA[3]	75	95	80-95	55-145
13 Phosphorus, RNA[4]	35	50	65-80	35-85
14 Silicon	5-20			
15 Zinc	6-9*		9.3-9.9[1]	
16 Protein, %	17.5			
17 Collagen, %	0.6-1.5	3.1*FF		3.5*FF
18 Elastin, %	0.13-0.5	4.6*FF		0.6*FF
19 Lipid, total, %	3		0.44	0.8-1.3
20 Phospholipid, %	5.5-11.3*			10.8*
21 Cephalin, %	1.6-6.9*			1.2
22 Lecithin, %	3-4*			1.1
23 Sphingomyelin, %	0.7-1			0.2
24 Cholesterol, %				0.3

1/ In the newborn. 2/ Nucleic acid P. 3/ Desoxyribonucleic acid P. 4/ Ribonucleic acid P.

Section 2: Other Mammals

Values are mg/100 g fresh tissue, unless otherwise indicated. * = dry weight; FF = fat-free.

Component	Cat	Guinea Pig	Mouse	Rat	Man	Cattle	Swine
1 Water, %				81			
2 Copper	2[1]	5.1	4-7[1]	5.4[1]			
3 Iodine, µg/100 g			16[1]	1.5			
4 Iron, inorganic	23.2[1]	4.1[1]	130	8.5[1]			
5 Phosphorus, DNA[2]	75-95						
6 Phosphorus, RNA[3]		15[1]	19.9[1]			4.3[1]	3[1]
7 Zinc						0.5-1.5	
8 Collagen, %							2.4*FF
9 Elastin, %							1.3[1]FF
10 Cholesterol, %			0.8			0.43	

1/ In the newborn. 2/ Desoxyribonucleic acid P. 3/ Ribonucleic acid P.

Part XI: KIDNEY

Section 1: Man, Cattle, Rabbit, Rat.

Values are mg/100 g fresh tissue, unless otherwise indicated. * = dry weight; FF = fat-free.

Component	Man	Cattle	Rabbit	Rat	Swine
1 Water, %	78-79	75	74-80	75-77	
2 Ash, %	0.8	1.1	1.3	1.3-1.5	
3 Calcium	19.2	14	5	6-11	
4 Chlorine	190-210		225	200-320	
5 Chromium, µg/100 g	8.5				
6 Copper	0.2-0.4	1.1	0.014*	0.018*	
7 Iodine, µg/100 g		2.3	5		
8 Iron	41	11-15	9		
9 Lead	0.14				
10 Magnesium	21	80-85*	13.4	18-25	
11 Manganese, µg/100 g	21-30				
12 Phosphorus	170	260		290[1]	
13 Potassium	170	225-240	340	300-330	
14 Silicon	5-20				
15 Sodium	165	145-170	150-250		
16 Uranium, µg/100 g	0.3-1.3				
17 Zinc	5.4			14.4-50*	
18 Protein, %	18	15		18	
19 Lipid, total, %	5.3	4.4	1.1	1.1-3	
20 Phospholipid, %	7.3-9.1*	7.7-9.1*		2.4	
21 Fatty acids, %	2				
22 Cephalin, %	2.3-4.3*	2.1*		0.95	
23 Lecithin, %	4.4-6.6*	5.5*		1.4	
24 Sphingomyelin, %	0.6-0.8*	1.6*		0.3	
25 Cholesterol, %	0.3-0.4	0.41		0.3	
26 Citric acid			6	4-8	

1/ Nucleic acid P.

Section 2: Other Mammals

Values are mg/100 g fresh tissue, unless otherwise indicated. * = dry weight; FF = fat-free.

Component	Dog	Guinea Pig	Sheep	Swine	Rat
1 Water, %	79	77-84	77-80		
2 Chlorine	230				
3 Copper, µg/100 g	14.2*	19.9*	17.8*		
4 Iodine, µg/100 g			1.4	2700*	
5 Magnesium			95*	1.5	
6 Phosphorus	50[1]	220-265	1100-1400*		
7 Potassium	230 FF				
8 Lipid, total, %	2	0.5	0.2-0.4	0.4	
9 Cholesterol	1.6	3.9			
10 Citric acid					

1/ Nucleic acid P.

55. VERTEBRATE TISSUES AND ORGANS: CHEMICAL COMPOSITION (Concluded)

Part XII: EYE

Section 1: Man, Cat, Dog, Horse, Rabbit, Whale, Frog, Perch, Trout

Values are mg/100 g fresh tissue, unless otherwise indicated. * = dry weight; TA = on basis of total ash.

Component	Man Lens	Man Aqueous Humor	Cat Aqueous Humor	Cat Lens	Dog Aqueous Humor	Dog Aqueous Humor	Horse Aqueous Humor[1]	Horse Vitreous Humor[1]	Rabbit Lens	Rabbit Aqueous Humor	Whale Lens	Frog Lens	Perch Lens	Trout Lens
1 Water, %	68			74			99.7	99.7[2]	69-71					
2 Calcium, %	0.45 TA						6.2	6.8						
3 Chlorine	2.1 TA	410-435[3]	460[3]		430-460		435	415		295-410				
4 Copper									0.05		0.42*	3.0*	0.09*	0.24
5 Magnesium							2.6	2.2						
6 Nitrogen, total					25-55		27	30						
7 Non-protein			23[4]	77	12-40		24	26	42-44	11-23				
8 Phosphorus, total	3.4 TA				3.5[5]		22-30[5]							
9 As phosphate	0.54*	13.0-24.5[7]			0.8-1.5[6]		3.3	3.1		5-8[3]				
10 Potassium	15 TA						19	19.2	450-480[3]	56				
11 Sodium	8 TA	400-415[3]	365[3]		540-675[8]		280	275	50-70[3]	335[3]				
12 Sulfate	1.2*				0.2-0.59		6.1	6.2			3.5*	7.8*	1.6*	0.7
13 Zinc									1.3-1.6	0.05-0.14				
14 Protein[10], total, %	3.2-6.5							21.5[11]						
15 Fat, total, %	0.9-2.3													
16 Glucose	25-60	55-110	57[3]		74		98	97	100-125	120-130[3]				
17 Urea			40-55				28	29	19-60	22-70				

/1/ Except for H₂O, values are mg/100 ml fluid. /2/ Lens has 66-69% H₂O. /3/ Mg/100 mg H₂O. /4/ Young animal. /5/ Lens. /6/ As P₂O₅. /7/ Vitreous humor. /8/ As NaCl. /9/ As S.
/10/ Amino acid composition is roughly the same as that for bovine total lens protein - see Section 2. /11/ Mucoprotein.

Section 2: Cattle.

Values are mg/100 g fresh tissue, unless otherwise indicated. Amino acids are mole % of total protein. * = dry weight.

Component	Choroid	Conjunctiva	Cornea	Aqueous Humor	Vitreous Humor	Iris	Lens	Retina	Sclera
1 Water, %	82-84	81-82	82-84	99		81-82	64	86	70-73
2 Ash, %	1.1-1.4	0.4-1	0.6-0.9	0.85-0.94	0.8-0.9	0.8-1.2	0.68-0.73	0.9-1.0	0.4-0.5
3 Calcium			0.14-0.23	0.01	0.02-0.34		0.12-0.24	0.12-0.4	0.14-0.25
4 Chlorine		6	280-285	360-515	410		60-69	145	225
5 Copper	0.3-0.4	0.13-0.21							
6 Iron	1.3-3.0	0.24-0.3	0.21-0.3	0.02	0.012	0.3-0.4	0.03	0.4	0.4
7 Magnesium			0.21-0.3						
8 Manganese, µg/100 g	17-30	7-11	9.4-12.5	3	2	21-30	8	11	8-13
9 Phosphorus			90-95	1.0-1.5	2-4.2		14-22	24-40	71
10 Potassium			265	27	17-30		90-95	50	185
11 Sodium					300		45	155	
12 Sulfate							470	0.3	0.18
13 Zinc	0.22	0.16	0.2	0.03	0.03	0.4	0.18-0.33	0.09	
14 Lipid, total,[1] %	29-35[2]	6	6.5-8.0		+	22-35	0.32	13.4-17	10.5-14
15 Phospholipid,[1] %	2.4-4.3[2]		1.1-1.5	0.9-1.2	0.9-1.2	1.3-1.7	0.19	1.0-1.6	1.1-1.5
16 Inositol	1.6-2.1	1.0	0.8-1.6	0.8-1.7	0.8-1.7	1.9-3.5	125-175	0.8-1.4	0.9-1.3
17 Citric acid							1.8-2.4		
18 Formic acid							1.0-1.2		
19 Lactic acid							55-65		
20 Malic acid	18.5-29	6.5	8.8-14.9	7.7-8.1	7.7-8.1	10.4-13.3	9.9-13.5	12.9-13.9	6.9-8.1
21 Hyaluronic acid				4.0	62				
22 Creatine	37-55		25-35	2.1-5.3	2.1-5.3	45-70	0.86-1.2	45-80	7.7-13.7
23 Creatinine	2.1-2.5	1.1-1.9	1-1.2	0.85-1.1	0.85-1.1	1.1-1.3	1.3-1.5	1.3-1.5	0.85-1.1
24 Spermine	3.1-4.2	2.1-2.9	4.9-8.8		0	35-40	2.9-5.8	25-35	0.1-0.3
25 Carnosine	16.1-17.8	9-11.3	4.4-4.7	0.16-0.29	0	3.2-4.1		2.6-3.0	1.7-2.6

Component	Choroid	Conjunctiva	Iris	Lens
26 Protein, H₂O-sol, %[3]	9.3-18.1	10.4-16.9	4.0-7.4	0.9-2.45
27 H₂O-insol, %	8.5	14	11.2	
28 Albumin, %[4]				
29 Collagen, %	4.8	11.2	7.2	
30 Elastin, %	1.6	1.1	0.7	
31 Mucoprotein, %	2.1	1.6	3.3	
32 Pigment protein	3.3		4	
33 Alanine				4.7
34 Arginine	14.2*[6]		9.2*[6]	8.2
35 Aspartic acid				7.9
36 Cystine	4.2*[6]		2.2*[6]	1.8
37 Glutamic acid				11.0
38 Glycine				9.3
39 Histidine	1.6*[6]		1.3*[6]	3.5
40 Isoleucine				5.7
41 Leucine				7.4
42 Lysine	1.3*[6]		5.2*[6]	4.8
43 Methionine				2.0
44 Phenylalanine				6.5
45 Proline				2.6
46 Serine				9.2
47 Threonine	0.75*[6]		0.73[6]	3.5
48 Tryptophan				1.5
49 Tyrosine	4.8*[6]		4.7*[6]	4.7
50 Valine				5.7

/1/ In the lens the following lipid components are also present (as mg/100 g tissue): fatty acids, 1.0; cephalin, 31; lecithin, 125; sphingomyelin, 38; cerebroside, 65; cholesterol, 4.2; unsaponifiable substances, 55. /2/ Choroid + pigmented epithelium. /3/ In lens, α-crystallin = 32%, and β-crystallin = 53% of total protein. /4/ Albumin + globulin: choroid, 2.4%; iris, 1.0%; sclera, 0.6% of total protein. /5/ % of total protein. /6/ % of mucoprotein.

Part XIII: SKIN
Section 1: Man

Values are mg/100 g fresh, non-fat-free whole skin, unless otherwise indicated. * = dry weight.

Component	Value	Component	Value	Component	Value
1 Water, %	70-75[1]	14 Nitrogen, combined amino acid	20-51	27 Collagen, %	35-40[1]
2 Ash, %	1.4-2.6*[1]	15 Free amino acid N	17-31	28 Lipid, total, %	0.3-10
3 Boron	1.7-17.2*[1]	16 Creatine N	0.4-0.6	29 Fats and fatty acids, %	1.0
4 Calcium	8.6-12.8[1]	17 Creatinine N	1.1-1.6	30 Cholesterol, total	370*[1]
5 Chlorine	265-300[1]	18 Urea N	6-11.5	31 Combined	160
6 Copper	3-19*[1]	19 Uric acid N	1.0-1.3	32 Free	85
7 Iodine	0.15-0.2*[1]	20 Ammonia N	17-46	33 7-Dehydrocholesterol	430[2]
8 Iron	0.9-5.9*[1]	21 Phosphorus	30-105*	34 Δ-7-Cholestanol	1500[2]
9 Lead	25-135*[1]	22 Potassium	51-77[1]	35 Ergosterol, % total sterols	0.42
10 Magnesium, total, %	4.5-5.9[1]	23 Silicon, %	0.64-2.1*[1]	36 Glucose	55-80
11 Nitrogen, total, %	16.1*[1]	24 Sodium	205-260[1]	37 Glycogen	45-115
12 Non-protein, %	3.0*[1]	25 Sulfur	290-340[1]	38 Sugar, non-fermentable	12
13 Collagen, %	11.3*[1]	26 Zinc	1.2-5.5[1]	39 Chondroitin H_2SO_4	20-30
				40 Histamine	0.1-0.24
				41 Hyaluronic acid	19-30
				42 Urea	330[2]
				43 Ascorbic acid	0.2-0.7*
				44 Biotin, μg/100 g	2.3-8.5*
				45 Choline	120
				46 Cobalamin, μg/100 g	1.6-2.4*
				47 Folic acid, μg/100 g	0.9-15*
				48 Inositol	23-79*
				49 Pantothenate	0.13-0.71
				50 Pyridoxine	18-66*
				51 Nicotinic acid	0.9-2.4*
				52 Riboflavin	1.2-3.4*
				53 Thiamine	20-40*

/1/ Fat-free tissue. /2/ Epidermis.

Section 2: Other Vertebrates

Values are mg/100 g fresh, non-fat-free whole skin, unless otherwise indicated. * = dry weight.

Component	Dog*[1]	Guinea Pig*[1]	Mouse[2]	Rabbit	Frog	Eel
1 Water, %	68-74		60	67-69[1]		66-68
2 Ash, %		32-100	44	0.72		670
4 Calcium	31-58	570-1815		50-85*	300	155
5 Chlorine	960-1185			250-265[1]	170	5.3
6 Magnesium	18-27	30-55	6.4	15-50*	4	19.4
7 Phosphorus			19	345*[3]	340	405

/1/ Fat-free tissue. /2/ Epidermis. /3/ Fresh tissue. /4/ Non-fat-free.

Component	Dog*[1]	Guinea Pig*[1]	Mouse[2]	Rabbit	Rat[1]	Frog	Eel
8 Potassium	275-390	215-245	345	100-190*	370-445*	130-145	150
9 Sodium	605-890	350-410	125	115-245*	210-245*	90	145
10 Protein, %	26-32[3]	34.4[3,4]			25-30		25-26
11 Collagen N, %	10.5-12[4]	23.4					
12 Lipid, total, %	25[3,4]			1.6	13-17[4]		5-6
13 Fat, total, %	16-48[3,4]			1	1.9-7.6		
14 Cholesterol			28.6	425-630*	305-465[4]		

/1/ Fat-free tissue. /2/ Epidermis. /3/ Fresh tissue. /4/ Non-fat-free.

Part XIV: KERATINOUS APPENDAGES OF THE SKIN
Section 1: Hair: Man

Values are mg/100 g fresh hair, unless otherwise indicated. Unspec. = type and color not specified.

Component	Unspec.	Brown	Black
8 Chromium	4.1	4.0	4.2
9 Cobalt	♂0.23-0.73[1]	0.92	0.53
10 Copper	♂3.2	♀2.6	♀2.6
11 Iron	♂0.22	0.24	0.22
12 Lead	♂0.2-0.7		
13 Manganese	♂20.8	♀21.2	♀18.8
14 Nickel	♂2.0	♀2.0	♀2.0

Component	Unspec.	Brown	Black
15 Phosphorus	♂80	♂65	♀95
16 Sulfur, %	♂3.8	♀3.8	
17 Uranium, μg/100 g	♀12.7		
18 Zinc	♂21.2	♀11.6	18.2
19 Sugars[3]	80		
20 Pentose	30		
21 Protein	91	85	85

/1/ Dry weight, fat-free. /2/ Red hair. /3/ Reducing substances determined as glucose.

Section 2: Hair and Other Appendages: Vertebrates Other Than Man

Values are mg/100 g fresh weight hair or other tissue, unless otherwise indicated.

Component	Cat	Cattle	Chimpanzee	Dog	Guinea Pig[1]	Hedgehog	Horse	Mouse	Rabbit[2]	Rat	Sheep	Swine	Man Nail	Cattle Horn	Horse Hoof	Chicken Feather
1 Water, %									10-13		9-28	11.4				
2 Chromium										1.4-3.2[3]						
3 Copper					0.1-4.7						1-3		0.07-0.72			
4 Lead		0.6			0.04-0.64								0.12			
5 Sulfur, %		3.6-3.9[4]	4.2-4.4[4]	17.2		2.9	4.9		0.9-4.1		3.2-3.9		3.3-3.5	12.9[5]	2.2	9.1
6 Zinc											16.4		10.8[5]			
7 Sugars[6]	250								230	130[3]	200					
8 Pentose									200	60[3]	50					
9 Protein, %		91-100[7]					98	95-135	450				73		90	
10 Cholesterol							27.7			640-830[8]						
11 Citric acid																

/1/ Black, brown, white. /2/ Various colors. /3/ White. /4/ Dry weight, ash-free. /5/ Dry weight. /6/ Reducing substances determined as glucose. /7/ Nitrogen x 6.25. /8/ Total sterols.

56. INSECT TISSUES: CHEMICAL COMPOSITION

No.	Constituent	Organism	Stage	Type[1]	Tissue Condition	Value[2]
1	Allantoin	Silkworm, Chinese oak (Antheraea pernyi)	Larva	FB	Wet	82 mg %
2	Aluminum	Bee, honey (Apis mellifera)	Adult	W	Dry	0.01%
3	Amino acids	Mosquito spp	Adult	W		+
4		Silkworm (Bombyx mori)	Adult	W		+
5	Ammonia	Blowfly, Australian sheep (Phaenicia cuprina)	Larva	FB	Wet	21 mg %
6		Blowfly, Australian sheep (P. cuprina)	Larva	RHG		540 mg %
7		Silkworm, Chinese oak (Antheraea pernyi)	Larva	FB	Wet	13 mg %
8	Ascorbic acid	Beetle, diving (Dytiscus marginalis)	Adult	G	Wet	0.031%
9	Barium	Many insects from various families	Adult	W		+
10	Boron	Mealworm, yellow (Tenebrio molitor)	Larva	W		+
11		Bee, honey (A. mellifera), drone	Pupa	W	Dry	1-1.6%
12	Chitin	Bee, honey (A. mellifera), worker	Pupa	W	Dry	4.8%
13		Fly, horse bot- (Gasterophilus intestinalis)	Larva	W	Dry	5-9%
14		Silkworm (Bombyx mori)	Larva	W	Wet	0.04-0.08 %
15	Cholesterol	Mealworm, yellow (Tenebrio molitor)	Larva	W	Wet	0.1-0.6%
16		Moth, privet hawk- (Sphinx ligustri)	Pupa	W	Wet	0.09%
17		Silkworm, Chinese oak (Antheraea pernyi)	Pupa	W	Wet	0.07%
18	Copper	Bee, honey (Apis mellifera)	Adult	W	Dry	0.006%
19		Beetle, confused flour- (Tribolium confusum)	Pupa	W	Wet	26 mg/kg
20		Cockroach, American (Periplaneta amer.)	Adult	W	Wet	31 mg/kg
21		Cockroach, oriental (Blatta orientalis)	Adult	W	Wet	14-24 mg/kg
22		Fly, horse bot- (Gasterophilus intestinalis)	Larva	W	Wet	13 mg/kg
23		Grasshopper, differential (Melanoplus diff.)	Egg	W	Wet	28 mg/kg
24		Silkworm (Bombyx mori)	Larva	W		0.002%
25		Silkworm, cecropia (Samia cecropia)	Pupa	W	Wet	10 mg/kg
26	Fatty acids	Beetle, potato (Leptinotarsa decemlineata)	Adult	W	Dry	1.5-15%
27		Locust, migratory (Melanoplus mexicanus mex.)	Larva	W	Dry	2.4%
28		Mealworm, yellow (Tenebrio molitor)	Larva	W	Wet	6.6-14.3%
29		Scale, white wax (Ceroplastes destructor)	Adult	Wax	Dry	22%
30		Silkworm (Bombyx mori)	Larva	W	Wet	0.5-4.8%
31	Flavins	Beetle, diving (Dytiscus marginalis)	Adult	MT	Wet	100 mg %
32		Cricket, house (Acheta domesticus)	Adult	MT	Wet	8 mg %
33		Fly, horse bot- (Gasterophilus intestinalis)	Larva	W	Wet	1.2 mg %
34		Locust, desert (Schistocerca gregaria)	Adult	MT	Wet	200 mg %
35		Mealworm, yellow (Tenebrio molitor)	Larva	MT	Wet	16 mg %
36		Moth, goat (Cossus cossus)	Larva	W	Wet	2.3 mg %
37		Moth, privet hawk- (Sphinx ligustri)	Pupa	MT	Wet	150 mg %
38		Roach, oriental (Blatta orientalis)	Adult	MT	Wet	10 mg %
39		Silkworm, Chinese oak (Antheraea pernyi)	Adult	W	Wet	0.8 mg %
40	Glycogen	Armyworm, southern (Prodenia eridania)	Adult	W	Dry	0.8-2.9 %
41		Bee, honey (Apis mellifera)	Larva	W	Dry	0-32.5%
42		Caterpillar, tent (Malacosoma armigera)	Larva	W	Dry	0.4-3%
43		Fly, horse bot- (Gasterophilus intestinalis)	Larva	W	Dry	14-31%
44		Moth, spurge hawk- (Deilephila euphorbiae)	Pupa	W	Dry	0.78%
45		Moth, wax (Galleria mellonella)	Pupa	W		0
46		Silkworm (Bombyx mori)	Larva	W	Dry	0.5-1.2%
47	Iodine	Bee, honey (Apis mellifera)	Adult	W	Dry	0.000009%
48		Beetle, forest may- (Melolontha melolontha)	Adult	W	Wet	0.1 %
49		Beetle, water (Hydrous piceus)	Adult	W	Wet	0.08%
50		Fly, house (Musca domestica)	Adult	W	Wet	0.03%
51	Iron	Bee, honey (Apis mellifera)	Adult	W	Dry	0.01%
52		Grasshopper, differential (Melanoplus spp)	Egg	W	Wet	0.12%
53	Lactic acid	Fly (Gasterophilus spp)	Larva	W	Wet	0.03-0.11%
54	Lipids	Bee, honey (Apis mellifera)	Larva	W	Dry	18.0%
55		Cockroach, American (Periplaneta amer.)	Adult	W	Dry	25.5-28.6%
56		Cockroach, German (Blattella germanica)	Adult	W	Dry	15.6-17%
57		Fly, horse bot- (Gasterophilus intestinalis)	Larva	W	Dry	12.7-26%
58		Fly, tsetse (Glossina morsitans)	Adult	W	Dry	16.2-35.3%
59		Grasshopper, differential (Melanoplus diff.)	Egg	W	Dry	17-22%
60	Lipids (concluded)	Mealworm, yellow (Tenebrio molitor)	Larva	FB	Wet	7.8-15.7%
61		Moth, codling (Carpocapsa pomonella)	Pupa	W	Dry	44%
62		Silkworm (Bombyx mori)	Adult	W	Dry	24%
63	Manganese	Ant, red (Formica rufa)	Adult	H	Dry	0.3%
64		Beetle, water (Gyrinus natator)	Adult	W	Wet	0.0007%
65		Butterfly, Eur. cabbage (Pieris brassicae)	Adult	W	Wet	0.00025%
66		Cricket, Eng. green (Tettigonia viridissima)	Adult	W	Wet	0.0004%
67		Hornet, bald-faced (Vespula maculata)	Larva	GW	Dry	0.13%
68		Locust, desert (Schistocerca gregaria)	Adult	W	Ash	0.16%
69	Nickel	Silkworm, desert (S. gregaria)	Adult	W	Ash	0.009%
70		Silkworm (Bombyx mori)	Pupa	W		?
71	Nitrogen, amino	Moth, cynthia (Samia cynthia)	Pupa	W	Wet	0.2%
72		Moth, pine hawk- (Sphinx pinastri)	Pupa	W	Wet	0.2%
73		Silkworm, Chinese oak (Antheraea pernyi)	Pupa	W	Wet	0.2%
74	Nitrogen, non-protein	Moth, emperor-(Eudia pavonia)	Adult	W	Wet	0.6%
75		Moth, pine hawk- (Sphinx pinastri)	Adult	W	Wet	0.5%
76		Silkworm, Chinese oak (Antheraea pernyi)	Adult	W	Wet	0.8%
77	Nitrogen, total	Bee, honey (Apis mellifera), drone	Adult	W	Dry	11.6%
78		Bee, honey (A. mellifera), worker	Adult	W	Dry	11.5-13.4%
79		Beetle, Japanese (Popilia japonica)	Pupa	W	Dry	1.9-2.9%
80		Caterpillar, east. tent- (Malacosoma amer.)	Adult	W	Dry	9.0%
81		Blowfly (Phaenicia sericata)	Larva	W	Dry	12.5%
82		Silkworm (Bombyx mori)	Egg	W	Wet	0.9-3.3%
83	Phospholipid	Mealworm, yellow (Tenebrio molitor)	Larva	W	Wet	0.6-2.2%
84	Phosphorus, inorganic	Moth, emperor (Eudia pavonia)	Adult	W	Wet	0.03-0.07%
85		Moth, hawk (Deilephila euphorbiae)	Adult	W	Wet	0.11-0.18%
86		Moth, privet hawk- (Sphinx ligustri)	Adult	W	Wet	0.03-0.06%
87		Silkworm, Chinese oak (Antheraea pernyi)	Adult	W	Wet	0.02-0.04%
88	Phosphorus, labile	Moth, hawk (Deilephila euphorbiae) ♂	Adult	W		9.2 mg %
89		Moth, hawk (D. euphorbiae) ♀	Adult	W		110 mg %
90	Phosphorus, total	Moth, emperor (Eudia pavonia)	Pupa	W		2 g/kg
91		Moth, hawk (Deilephila euphorbiae)	Adult	W	Wet	0.18-0.41%
92		Moth, privet hawk- (Sphinx ligustri)	Pupa	W		2.7 g/kg
93		Silkworm, Chinese oak (Antheraea pernyi)	Pupa	W		2.3 g/kg
94	Potassium	Mosquito (Aedes aegypti)	Larva	MG & MT	Dry	15.6 mg/g
95	Reducing substances	Beetle, Japanese (Popilia japonica)	Adult	W	Wet	1.0%
96		Fly, house (Musca domestica)	Adult	W	Wet	0.8-1.2%
97	as glucose[3]	Moth, wax (Galleria mellonella)	Larva	W	Wet	0.2-0.3%
98	Silicon[3]	Locust,migratory (Melanoplus mexicanus mex.)	Adult	W	Dry	11.9%[4]
99	Sodium	Mosquito (Aedes aegypti)	Larva	MG & MT	Dry	6.9 mg/g
100	Strontium	Many insects from various families	Adult	W		+
101	Sulfur	Locust,migratory (Melanoplus mexicanus mex.)	Adult	Fat	Dry	0.02%
102	Titanium[5]	Locust, desert (Schistocerca gregaria)	Adult	W	Dry	0.16%[4]
103	Urea	Silkworm (Bombyx mori)	Egg	W	Wet	24-29 mg %
104		Silkworm, Chinese oak (Antheraea pernyi)	Larva	FB	Wet	29 mg %
105		Blowfly (Phaenicia sericata)	Egg	W	Wet	18 mg %
106	Uric acid	Silkworm (Bombyx mori)	Egg	W	Dry	1.7-3.6 mg/g
107		Silkworm, Chinese oak (Antheraea pernyi)	Larva	FB	Dry	6.75 mg/g
108		Beetle, confused flour- (Tribolium conf.)	Pupa	W	Dry	59.8%
109		Blowfly (Phaenicia sericata)	Egg	W		79%
110	Water	Cockroach, oriental (Blatta orientalis)	Adult	W		61%
111		Cockroach, American (Periplaneta amer.)	Adult	W		70.6%
112		Fly, blue bottle- (Cynomyopsis cadaverina)	Larva	W		73.3%
113		Fly, horse bot- (Gasterophilus intestinalis)	Larva	O		64.7%
114		Silkworm (Bombyx mori)	Larva	W		75-94%
115		Silkworm, cecropia (Samia cecropia)	Pupa	W		71.8%
116		Weevil, bean (Acanthoscelides obtectus)	Adult	W		48.2%
117	Zinc	Beetle, ground (Carabus auratus)	Adult	W	Wet	0.18 g/kg
118		Fly, house (Musca domestica)	Egg	W	Dry	Trace

/1/ FB = fat body; G = gut; H = head; GW = gut wall; MG = midgut; MT = malpighian tubes; O = ovary; RHG = rear hindgut; W = whole. /2/ mg % = mg per 100 g tissue. /3/ As SiO_3. /4/ Per cent of total ash. /5/ As TiO_2.

Values for whole organisms are mg per 100g dry organism, and for human tissues are mg per 100g wet tissue. Ranges represent estimate "d" of the 95% range (cf. Introduction). Too much reliance should not be placed on the exact numerical values since incomplete extractions and other limitations are involved in the methods used.

	Organism or Tissue	Biotin	Folic Acid Group[1]	Inositol	Niacin[2]	Pantothenic Acid	Pyridoxine[3] Group	Riboflavin	Thiamine
	THALLOPHYTA								
	Bacteria								
1	Aerobacter aerogenes	0.24-0.39	0.10-0.28	140-160	20-24	14-34	0.7-1.8	4.3	1.1-1.5
2	Azotobacter chroococcum				59.0				3.3-9.6
3	A. vinelandii	0.26-0.42				15.2-18.4		30.5-35.0	
4	Clostridium acidiurici							1.4	
5	C. butyricum	0.17	0.05	86	25	9.2	0.62	5.5	0.93
6	Lactobacillus delbrueckii							11.5	
7	Mycobacterium smegmatis							860	
8	M. tuberculosis							15-20	
9	Phytomonas tumefaciens					4.1			1.2
10	Propionibact. pentosaceum								0.04-0.62
11	Proteus vulgaris	0.34	0.42	100	25	10	0.68		2.1
12	Pseudomonas fluorescens	0.71	0.18	170	21.0	9.0	0.57	6.8	2.6
13	Serratia marcescens	0.41	0.32	160	23.5	12.4	0.11	3.5	2.7
	Fungi								
14	Aspergillus oryzae								1.8
15	Fusarium graminarum								0.5
16	F. lini								2.0
17	Neurospora sitophila						0.91-1.37		
18	Penicillium chrysogenum	0.06-0.15	1.34-1.46		15.0-21.2	10.7-21.2	2.3	3.98-4.75	0.26
19	P. notatum		0.36-0.45		18.0				0.69
20	Mushrooms	0.14		135	54	13.8		2.6	0.88
	Yeasts								
21	Brewer's	0.007		28	12.6	4.2		1.52	0.8
22	Candida arborea	0.03-0.32	1.5-2.0		16.60			4.6-6.9	3.1-3.3
23	Hansenula suaveolens	0.17	0.17		60	18		5.4	0.8
24	Mycotorula lipolytica	0.18	0.31		60			5.9	0.5
25	Oospora lactis	0.1-0.2	0.6-1.5		19-25			4-5.5	2-2.9
26	Saccharomyces cerevisiae	0.05-0.18	1.9-3.6		19-295	11.8-19.8	1.6-6.5	3.6-7.5	2.9-9
27	Torulopsis utilis	0.11-0.19	0.4-3.1	340-360	21-53	8.6-18	3.5	2.6-6.2	0.6-5.3
	EMBRYOPHYTA								
28	Bean, lima	0.012		180	1.2	0.9		0.14	0.57
29	Peas, black-eyed	0.022		250	1.4	1.1		0.15	0.85
30	Wheat seed	0.006		190	4.5	1.3		0.18	0.55
31	PROTOZOA	0.075		330	9.0	10.5		1.7	3.8
	MOLLUSCA								
32	Oyster	0.053		270	7.3	3.0		1.3	1.1
	ANNELIDA								
33	Earthworm	0.025		52	4.8	1.0		2.5	0.78
	INSECTA								
34	Ant, red	0.037		220	4.7	2.9		1.4	0.73
35	Cockroach	0.048		134	12.0	6.5		2.6	1.62
36	Fly, fruit, larva	0.205		93	21.0	11.6		4.7	2.4
37	Termite	0.066		215	17.5	8.8		2.65	1.28
	VERTEBRATA								
38	Chick[4]	0.175		118	40.5	37.0		1.34	0.83
39	Fish	0.031		88	7.8	2.4		0.52	0.95
40	Frog	0.057		123	5.3	1.7		1.14	0.64
41	Rat	0.033		56	18.0	3.8		1.05	0.50
42	Snake	0.025		107	14.2	2.5		4.5	0.51
43	Toad, horned	0.07		210	17.0	3.6		2.1	1.1
	HUMAN TISSUES								
44	Adrenal	0.035		69	2.4	0.8		0.82	0.16
45	Brain	0.058		151	2.0	1.5		0.25	0.16
46	Colon	0.009		78	1.3	0.5		0.21	0.10
47	Heart	0.017		50	4.1	1.6		0.83	0.36
48	Ileum	0.006		75	1.9	0.53		0.42	0.055
49	Kidney	0.067		124	3.7	1.9		2.0	0.28
50	Liver	0.074		66	5.8	4.3		1.6	0.22
51	Lung	0.019		40	1.8	0.5		0.19	0.15
52	Mammary gland	0.004		27	1.0	0.39		0.24	0.043
53	Ovary	0.0025		58	1.8	0.39		0.43	0.061
54	Seminal ducts	0.0015		<10	0.92	0.20		0.10	0.069
55	Skeletal muscle	0.0035		45	4.7	1.2		0.20	0.12
56	Skin	0.0022		20	0.86	0.31		0.12	0.052
57	Smooth muscle	0.006		58	3.1	0.62		0.23	0.12
58	Spleen	0.006		103	2.3	0.54		0.36	0.11
59	Stomach	0.019		76	1.9	0.61		0.52	0.056
60	Testes	0.009		160	1.6	0.5		0.20	0.08

/1/ Pteroylglutamic acid (folacin), vitamin M, B_c, factor U, L. casei factor, Norite eluate factor. /2/ Nicotinic acid and nicotinamide. /3/ Includes pyridoxine, pyridoxal, pyridoxamine. /4/ Embryo.

58. VERTEBRATE TISSUES AND ORGANS: RELATIVE ENZYME CONTENT

Methods by which values have been derived, and units of measurement, are listed numerically at the end of the table and are assigned, by numbers in brackets, to the appropriate enzymes. Values in parentheses are ranges and, unless accompanied by superscript, represent estimate "d" of the 95% range (cf Introduction).

#	Animal	Tissue or Organ	Concentration
		Aconitase [1]	
1	Rat	Brain	10.0
2	Rat	Intest. mucosa	7.8
3	Rat	Kidney	80
4	Rat	Liver	61.5
5	Rat	Lung	14.5
6	Rat	Salivary gland	11.9
7	Rat	Testes	7.6
		Adenosinetriphosphatase [2]	
8	Rat	Brain	7.0
9	Rat	Cardiac muscle	27.3
10	Rat	Kidney	20.3
11	Rat	Liver	12.9
12	Rat	Lung	21.8
13	Rat	Pancreas	11.5
14	Rat	Submaxillary gl.	16.4
15	Rat	Skel. muscle	23.3
16	Rat	Spleen	13.0
		Aldolase [3]	
17	Rabbit	Blood	0.018
18	Rabbit	Cardiac muscle	0.62
19	Rabbit	Skel. muscle	7.5(3.44-8.5)
20	Rat	Brain	0.34(0.14-0.72)
21	Rat	Cardiac muscle	0.62
22	Rat	Kidney	0.35
23	Rat	Liver	0.33(0.18-0.56)
24	Rat	Skel. muscle	7.5(3.44-8.5)
25	Rat	Spleen	0.22(0.10-0.33)
		Arginase [4]	
26	Mouse	Bone marrow	4.0
27	Mouse	Brain	3.0
28	Mouse	Cardiac muscle	7.0
29	Mouse	Gastric mucosa	4.0
30	Mouse	Intest. mucosa	80
31	Mouse	Kidney	42
32	Mouse	Liver	246
33	Mouse	Lung	50
34	Mouse	Pancreas	8.0
35	Mouse	Skel. muscle	4.0
36	Mouse	Skin	27
37	Mouse	Spleen	6.0
38	Rat	Brain	3.0
39	Rat	Kidney	60
40	Rat	Liver	213
41	Rat	Pancreas	4.0
42	Rat	Skel. muscle	8.0
43	Rat	Spleen	10.0
		Asparaginase I [5]	
44	Rat	Brain	1.0
45	Rat	Kidney	4.0
46	Rat	Liver	3.0
47	Rat	Spleen	1.0
		Asparaginase II [5]	
48	Rat	Brain	0.0
49	Rat	Kidney	4.0
50	Rat	Liver	21.0
51	Rat	Spleen	22.0
		Carbonic Anhydrase [6]	
52	Cattle	Erythrocytes	0.9
		Carboxylase, Oxalosuccinic [7]	
53	Monkey	Brain	45
54	Ox	Brain	94
55	Swine	Cardiac muscle	840
56	Swine	Kidney	230
57	Swine	Liver	80
58	Pigeon	Breast muscle	740
59	Pigeon	Liver	60
		Carboxypeptidase [8]	
60	Dog	Duodenal fluid	(0.2-0.3)
61	Dog	Pancreas	(1.9-3.0)
62	G. pig	Duodenal fluid	(0.2-0.5)
63	G. pig	Pancreas	(2.0-4.5)
64	Man	Duodenal fluid	(0.2-0.5)
65	Man	Pancreas	(2.0-5.0)
66	Rat	Duodenal fluid	(0.2-0.6)
67	Rat	Pancreas	(2.5-6.0)
		Catalase [9]	
68	Horse	Erythrocytes	0.40
69	Horse	Liver	1.70
70	Man	Erythrocytes	0.50

#	Animal	Tissue or Organ	Concentration
		Choline Acetylase [10]	
71	G. pig	Cardiac muscle	19.5
72	G. pig	Kidney	0.0
73	G. pig	Liver	0.0
74	G. pig	Skel. muscle	16.2(10.5-22.2)
75	Pigeon	Breast muscle	32.8(30.4-34.4)
76	Rabbit	Cardiac muscle	63(58.6-67.3)
77	Rabbit	Sciatic nerve	60
		Dehydrogenase, Alcohol [6]	
78	Horse	Liver	1.0
		Dehydrogenase, Glutamic Acid [11]	
79	Rat	Brain	$10.3(6.2-15.5)^C$
80	Rat	Cardiac muscle	$4.9(0-8.0)^C$
81	Rat	Kidney	$24.7(19.3-29.1)^C$
82	Rat	Liver	$49.3(37.2-62.8)^C$
83	Rat	Spleen	$5.2(3.5-6.8)^C$
		Dehydrogenase, Isocitric [12]	
84	Mouse	Liver	2.64
		Dehydrogenase, Lactic Acid [13]	
85	Mouse	Brain	228
86	Mouse	Cardiac muscle	292
87	Mouse	Gastric mucosa	201
88	Mouse	Intest. mucosa	732
89	Mouse	Kidney	367
90	Mouse	Liver	428
91	Mouse	Lymph node	209
92	Mouse	Pancreas	155
93	Mouse	Skel. muscle	972
94	Mouse	Spleen	144
95	Mouse	Testes	206
		Dehydrogenase, Malic Acid [14]	
96	Mouse	Brain	42.2
97	Mouse	Liver	100(97-103)
98	Pigeon	Skel. muscle	107.0
99	Rat	Brain	27.5(27.2-27.8)
100	Rat	Kidney	81(70-90)
101	Rat	Liver	103(73-125)
		Dehydrogenase, Succinic Acid [15]	
102	Rat	Brain	19.2(13.3-25.1)
103	Rat	Cardiac muscle	97.9(78.1-117.7)
104	Rat	Kidney	138(99.7-176)
105	Rat	Liver	66.4(58.8-76.0)
106	Rat	Lung	16.2(12.7-19.7)
107	Rat	Skel. muscle	16.1(11.7-20.5)
		Desoxyribonuclease [16]	
108	Mouse	Bone marrow	7.0
109	Mouse	Brain	4.0
110	Mouse	Cardiac muscle	9.0
111	Mouse	Gastric mucosa	6.0
112	Mouse	Intest. mucosa	15.0
113	Mouse	Kidney	10.0
114	Mouse	Liver	14.0
115	Mouse	Lung	8.0
116	Mouse	Lymph nodes	25.0
117	Mouse	Pancreas	5.0
118	Mouse	Skel. muscle	12.0
119	Mouse	Spleen	16.0
120	Mouse	Thymus	3.0
		β-D-Glucosidase [17]	
121	Rat	Adrenal	1.5-3.0
122	Rat	Brain	2-4
123	Rat	Cardiac muscle	0.8-1.6
124	Rat	Intest. large	5.0
125	Rat	Intest. small	4-6
126	Rat	Kidney	4.8
127	Rat	Liver	1-3
128	Rat	Pancreas	(0.2-1.5)
129	Rat	Salivary gland	(0.6-2.5)
130	Rat	Spleen	3-5
131	Rat	Stomach	4.0
132	Rat	Testes	1-4
133	Rat	Thyroid	8-10
134	Rat	Uterus	1-3
		Esterase, Choline [18]	
135	Rat	Adrenal	2.5
136	Rat	Brain	5.5
137	Rat	Cardiac muscle	10.8
138	Rat	Gastric mucosa	1.5
139	Rat	Intest. mucosa	6.5
140	Rat	Liver	0.9

#	Animal	Tissue or Organ	Concentration
		Esterase, Choline [18] (concluded)	
141	Rat	Salivary gland	1.6
142	Rat	Skin	3.0
		Esterase, True (Acetylcholine) [19]	
143	Cat	Cer. symp. ga.	28.4
144	Cat	Sciatic nerve	0.7
145	Cat	Symp. fiber	3.7
146	Dog	Brain cortex	(2-3)
147	Dog	Cer. symp. ga.	14.0
148	Dog	Lenticular n.	70
149	Dog	Symp. fiber	5.0
150	Eel, elect.	Elect. org. ant.	(400-500)
151	elect.	Elect. org. post.	100
152	G. pig	Brain cortex	1.3
153	G. pig	Cer. symp. ga.	12.8
154	Ox	Brain cortex	1.5
155	Ox	Caudate nerve	5.9
		Fumarase [6]	
156	Swine	Cardiac muscle	0.02
		β-D-Galactosidase [20]	
157	G. pig	Liver	12.0
158	G. pig	Spleen	6.0
159	Mouse	Liver	6.5
160	Mouse	Spleen	13.0
161	Rat	Adrenal	20-33
162	Rat	Brain	1.5
163	Rat	Cardiac muscle	2.0
164	Rat	Kidney	36.0
165	Rat	Liver	18.0
166	Rat	Pancreas	6.0
167	Rat	Salivary gland	5-11
168	Rat	Spleen	14-20
169	Rat	Thyroid	31-36
170	Rat	Uterus	13-15
		β-Glucuronidase [21]	
171	Rat	Adrenal	4.6
172	Rat	Kidney	5.3
173	Rat	Liver	16.0
174	Rat	Lung	5.2
175	Rat	Prostate	3.0
176	Rat	Skel. muscle	0.1
177	Rat	Spleen	25.3
178	Rat	Testes	0.1
179	Rat	Uterus	6.8
		Hexokinase [22]	
180	Rat	Brain	$27.1(20.3-31.2)^C$
181	Rat	Cardiac muscle	$14.5(9.2-17.9)^C$
182	Rat	Kidney	$7.9(6.3-11.0)^C$
183	Rat	Liver	$1.4(0.2-2.6)^C$
184	Rat	Lung	$4.3(2.9-4.6)^C$
185	Rat	Pancreas	$5.6(4.0-7.4)^C$
186	Rat	Small intestine	$11.7(9.3-13.3)^C$
187	Rat	Spleen	$8.3(7.3-9.3)^C$
188	Rat	Testes	$13.7(11.4-18.8)^C$
189	Rat	Uterus	$8.5(6.0-10.9)^C$
		Histaminase [23]	
190	G. pig	Cardiac muscle	1.30
191	G. pig	Intest. mucosa	1.54
192	G. pig	Kidney cortex	0.73
193	G. pig	Liver	1.88
194	G. pig	Lung	0.60
195	G. pig	Spleen	0.44
196	Mouse	Brain	0.18
197	Mouse	Cardiac muscle	0.73
198	Mouse	Kidney cortex	1.30
199	Mouse	Liver	0.82
200	Mouse	Lung	1.17
201	Mouse	Spleen	0.74
202	Swine	Kidney cortex	5.00
203	Swine	Liver	2.30
204	Rabbit	Cardiac muscle	21.20
205	Rabbit	Kidney cortex	4.80
206	Rabbit	Liver	6.53
207	Rabbit	Lung	21.20
208	Rabbit	Spleen	1.34
209	Rat	Brain	0.72
210	Rat	Cardiac muscle	2.52
211	Rat	Kidney cortex	0.93
212	Rat	Liver	0.30
213	Rat	Lung	8.25

/1/ The pancreas values are for procarboxypeptidase.

58. VERTEBRATE TISSUES AND ORGANS: RELATIVE ENZYME CONTENT (Concluded)

Methods by which values have been derived, and units of measurement, are listed numerically at the end of the table and are assigned, by numbers in brackets, to the appropriate enzymes. Values in parentheses are ranges and, unless accompanied by superscript, represent estimate "d" of the 95% range (cf Introduction).

#	Animal	Tissue or Organ	Concentration
		Hyaluronidase [24]	
214	G. pig	Adrenal	1.3
215	G. pig	Brain	0.06(0.04-0.10)^C
216	G. pig	Kidney	0.32(0.2-0.55)^C
217	G. pig	Liver	0.11(0.06-0.15)^C
218	G. pig	Skel. muscle	0.12(0.08-0.15)^C
219	G. pig	Spleen	0.13(0.08-0.21)^C
220	G. pig	Testes	125(100-150)^C
221	Mouse	Brain	0.08(0.07-0.09)^C
222	Mouse	Kidney	0.12(0.09-0.16)^C
223	Mouse	Liver	0.14(0.08-0.20)^C
224	Mouse	Spleen	0.13(0.08-0.17)^C
225	Rabbit	Brain	0.03
226	Rabbit	Kidney	0.05
227	Rabbit	Liver	0.07
228	Rabbit	Lung	0.26
229	Rabbit	Spleen	0.25
230	Rabbit	Stomach	0.07
231	Rabbit	Testes	200
		Oxidase, D - Amino Acid [25]	
232	Cat	Kidney	645
233	Cat	Liver	122
234	Dog	Kidney	(680-1100)
235	Dog	Liver	(306-580)
236	G. pig	Kidney	32
237	G. pig	Liver	27
238	Horse	Kidney	23.0
239	Horse	Liver	22.0
240	Rat	Kidney	(108-132)
241	Rat	Liver	(15-31)
		Oxidase, L-Amino Acid [6]	
242	Rat	Kidney	0.20
		Oxidase, Cytochrome-c [26]	
243	Rat	Brain	53
244	Rat	Cardiac muscle	218.
245	Rat	Kidney	157.9
246	Rat	Liver	62
247	Rat	Lung	22.9
		Oxidase, Monamine [27]	
248	Man	Cardiac muscle	552
249	Man	Kidney cortex	567
250	Man	Kidney medulla	252
251	Man	Liver	1027
252	Man	Skel. muscle	155
253	Man	Uterus	111
254	Ox	Cardiac muscle	52
255	Ox	Intestine	278
256	Ox	Kidney	655
257	Ox	Liver	796
258	Ox	Spleen	97
		Oxidase, Monamine [27] (concluded)	
259	Swine	Cardiac muscle	33
260	Swine	Intestine	94
261	Swine	Kidney	435
262	Swine	Liver	257
263	Swine	Pancreas	75
264	Swine	Spleen	14.0
265	Swine	Thyroid	6.0
		Phosphoglucomutase [28]	
266	G. pig	Liver	7.0(5.9-9.6)
267	G. pig	Skel. muscle	32.1(26.4-41.9)
268	Rat	Liver	2.0(6.5-18.4)
269	Rat	Skel. muscle	34.0(30.7-58.0)
		Phosphomonoesterase I (Alk. Phosphatase) [29]	
270	Mouse	Bone marrow	23.0
271	Mouse	Brain	12.0
272	Mouse	Intest. mucosa	2789
273	Mouse	Kidney	1072
274	Mouse	Liver	4.0
275	Mouse	Lung	36
276	Mouse	Pancreas	1.0
277	Mouse	Skel. muscle	2.0
278	Mouse	Spleen	17.0
279	Mouse	Submaxillary gl.	23.0
280	Rat	Brain	4.0
281	Rat	Kidney	1500
282	Rat	Liver	4.0
283	Rat	Pancreas	3.0
284	Rat	Plasma	9.0
285	Rat	Skel. muscle	2.0
286	Rat	Spleen	21.0
		Phosphomonoesterase II (Acid Phosphatase) [30]	
287	Mouse	Bone marrow	22.0
288	Mouse	Brain	15.0
289	Mouse	Gastric mucosa	27
290	Mouse	Intest. mucosa	34
291	Mouse	Kidney	15.0
292	Mouse	Liver	12.0
293	Mouse	Pancreas	10.0
294	Mouse	Skel. muscle	19.0
295	Mouse	Skin	30
296	Mouse	Spleen	73
297	Mouse	Submaxillary gl.	22.0
298	Rat	Brain	16.0
299	Rat	Kidney	95
300	Rat	Liver	25.0
301	Rat	Pancreas	18.0
302	Rat	Plasma	0.4
303	Rat	Skel. muscle	16.0
304	Rat	Skin	8.0
		Phosphoprotein Phosphatase [31]	
305	Rat	Adrenals	1.95(1.12-3.08)^C
306	Rat	Bone marrow	0.90(0-1.62)^C
307	Rat	Cardiac muscle	1.28(0.71-1.70)^C
308	Rat	Gastric mucosa	1.74(1.28-2.28)^C
309	Rat	Kidney	2.43(1.33-4.21)^C
310	Rat	Liver	2.69(1.87-3.74)^C
311	Rat	Mammary gland	0.98(0.84-1.15)^C
312	Rat	Pancreas	0.76(0.72-0.82)^C
313	Rat	Salivary gland	1.35(0-3.86)^C
314	Rat	Spleen	3.35(0.93-5.48)^C
315	Rat	Testes	2.03(1.90-2.16)^C
316	Rat	Thymus	2.48(2.29-2.58)^C
		Ribonuclease [32]	
317	Rabbit	Blood cells	66
318	Rabbit	Blood, whole	78
319	Rabbit	Bone marrow	1.5
320	Rabbit	Pancreas	2.4
321	Rabbit	Plasma	16.0
322	Rabbit	Spleen	4.7
323	Rat	Blood cells	60
324	Rat	Blood, whole	126
325	Rat	Bone marrow	5.4
326	Rat	Cardiac muscle	0.33
327	Rat	Kidney	1.63
328	Rat	Liver	0.37
329	Rat	Pancreas	16.7
330	Rat	Plasma	42
331	Rat	Spleen	2.06
		Succinoxidase [33]	
332	Rat	Brain	49(41-64)^C
333	Rat	Cardiac muscle	219(197-250)^C
334	Rat	Kidney	195(174-226)^C
335	Rat	Liver	88(79-101)^C
336	Rat	Lung	17.9(15.0-21.6)^C
337	Rat	Skel. muscle	35.5(29.2-48.7)^C
338	Rat	Spleen	23.3(19.4-35.3)^C
		TPN-Cytochrome-c-Reductase [34]	
339	Mouse	Liver	0.77
		Transaminase [35]	
340	Rat	Brain	260
341	Rat	Cardiac muscle	425
342	Rat	Kidney	245
343	Rat	Liver	245
344	Rat	Lung	51
345	Rat	Skel. muscle	316
346	Rat	Spleen	16.0
347	Rat	Testes	150
		Tyrosinase [36]	
348	Mouse	Melanoma	1865

[1] Q citrate formed from cis-aconitate at pH 7.4 by rat tissue extract. [2] mg of inorganic phosphate split off ATP per mg fresh rat tissue per 15 min (Ca added). [3] mg phosphorus released per min per g of wet tissue(fructose-1,6-diphosphate substrate).[4] Ratio of % hydrolysis of arginine after 2 hr incubation at 38° to the cube root of total N per ml of tissue extract. [5] μM asparagine deaminated per ml of tissue extract at pH 8.4. [6] Grams of pure enzyme per kg whole tissue. [7] mm^3 CO_2 evolved from substrate per hr per mg of protein calculated from the first 5 min of reaction (oxalosuccinic acid substrate). [8] mg of carboxypeptidase per g or ml of fresh tissue homogenate or fluid. [9] Grams catalase per kg wet tissue (H_2O_2 substrate). [10] μg acetylcholine formed per hr per g wet tissue. [11] Q_{O_2} per hr per 100 mg of tissue at 38°. [12] μM TPN reduced per min per 100 mg of fresh tissue. [13] Moles x 10^{-8} pyruvate reduced per min per mg total homogenate nitrogen at 26°. [14] μl O_2 consumed per 10 min per 20 mg fresh tissue. [15] Δ log (ferricytochrome-c) per min per mg tissue protein. [16] In terms of the decrease in viscosity after $\frac{1}{2}$ hr incubation at 30° of a mixture containing 3 ml of 1% sodium thymonucleate and 3 ml of tissue extract (1.23 mg N per ml). [17] μg of 6-bromo-2-naphthol produced per hr at 37° with 0.6 ml of tissue homogenate supernatant. Determined by colorimetric method using 6-bromo-2-naphthyl-β-D-glucopyranoside as substrate. [18] ml CO_2 liberated during hydrolysis of acetylcholine per g fresh rat tissue per hr. [19] mg acetylcholine hydrolyzed by 100 mg tissue per hr at normal temperature and pressure. [20] μg of 6-bromo-2-naphthol produced per hr per 0.6 ml of tissue homogenate supernatant at 37°. Determined by colorimetric method using 6-bromo-2-naphthyl-β-D- galactopyranoside as substrate. [21] μg phenolphthalein liberated from phenolphthalein glucuronide per mg fresh rat tissue per hr. Determined by colorimetric method. [22] μl of glucose utilized per mg tissue (dry weight) per hr. [23] Expressed as units per g wet tissue; one unit of histaminase activity is defined as the quantity capable of catalysing the release of NH_3 at the rate of 1 μM per 24 hr at 10° C. [24] Schering units per g tissue. Activity determined by the "long-time viscosity test" using umbilical cord hyaluronidase as substrate. [25] μl O_2 consumed per hr per 100 mg dry acetone powdered tissue at 37.5^{o} C. [26] Δ log (ferricytochrome-c) per min per mg protein. [27] μl O_2 consumed per hr per g of wet tissue (tyramine substrate). [28] Decrease in acid labile phosphorus in mg phosphorus per hr per g of tissue (Mg activator, glucose-1-phosphate substrate). [29] Average ratio of % hydrolysis of phenyl phosphate after 1 hr incubation at 38° to the total N per ml of tissue extract at pH 9.5. [30] Average ratio of % hydrolysis of phenyl phosphate after 1 hr incubation at 38° to the total N per ml of tissue extract at pH 4.6. [31] Enzyme units per mg fresh tissue. An enzyme unit corresponds to the number of μM of phosphorus liberated from casein phosphate per min under experimental conditions. [32] mm^3 CO_2 per min per mg or ml wet tissue (yeast nucleic acid substrate). [33] Q_{O_2} = μl of O_2 taken up in the oxidation of succinate per hr per mg of dry tissue(cytochrome-c and succinate substrate). [34] μM cytochrome-c reduced per min per 100 mg fresh tissue. [35] μl substrate transaminated per hr per mg dry tissue (glutamic acid and oxalacetic acid substrate). [36] μl O_2 consumed per min per g tissue (1 mg tyrosine substrate).

59. CELL SAP: PHYSICAL PROPERTIES
Data applicable to sap of leaves except as otherwise specified.

	Species	Freezing Point Depression °C	Osmotic Pressure, atm	Conductivity mhos x 10^5		Species	Freezing Point Depression °C	Osmotic Pressure, atm	Conductivity mhos x 10^5
1	Aconite (Aconitum porrectum)	1.1-1.2	13.3-14.6	1560-1750	36	Oak, pin (Quercus palustris), 9 ft high	1.7	20.2	1060
2	Alfalfa (Medicago sativa)	1.4-2.0	16.3-24.1	2040-2940	37	Oak, pin (Q. palustris), 23 ft high	1.7	20.8	1000
3	Apple (Pyrus malus)	2-2.3	24-27	1100-1320	38	Oak, pin (Q. palustris), 33 ft high	1.9	23.2	900
4	Apple (P. malus), twig	1.5-1.7	18-20.6	860-950	39	Orange (Citrus sinensis)	1.4-2.4	15-22.2	1460-1690
5	Apple (P. malus), root	0.9-1.4	9.6-11.4	680-1270	40	Orange (C. sinensis), shoot	1.1-1.7	14.2-20.8	
6	Asparagus (Asparagus officinalis)	1.5-1.6	18.1-19.1	1800-2050	41	Peach (Prunus persica)	2.2-2.9	25-35	1140-1330
7	Barley (Hordeum vulgare)	1.4	17.3	2870	42	Peach (P. persica), twig	1.3-2.2	16.3-25	710-860
8	Bean (Phaseolus sp)	0.9-1.4	11.7	1310	43	Peach (P. persica), root	0.7-0.9	8.7-11.6	260-310
9	Beet (Beta vulgaris)	0.7-1.1	8-13.7	1630-1690		Poplar (Populus alba)			
10	Beet (B. vulgaris), root	1.5-1.8	17.7	555	44	Spring leaves	1.3	15.9	910
11	Burroweed (Allenrolfea occidentalis)	3-5.2	36-62	6260-7010	45	Summer leaves	1.5	17.8	650
12	Carrot (Daucus carota)	1.2-1.4	13.2-16.7	1940-2360	46	Stem bark	1.2	14.6	450
13	Coffee (Coffea arabica)	1.3	15.5		47	Stem tracheae	0.05	0.6	34
14	Columbine (Aquilegia caerulea)	1.2	14.3	1530	48	Root bark	1.1	13.2	380
15	Corn (Zea mays)	0.9-1.5	11-18.1	960-2210	49	Root tracheae	0.07	0.9	52
16	Corn (Z. mays), stem	1-1.4	11.8-16.3	960-2160	50	Potato (Solanum tuberosum)	0.4-0.8	5.2-9	
17	Corn (Z. mays), root	0.8-1.1	0.9-12.7	2180-2520	51	Potato (S. tuberosum), stem	0.6-0.9	7.5-11.3	
18	Cotton (Gossypium barbadense)	1.5-2.2	18.3-27	2950-3160	52	Potato (S. tuberosum), tuber	0.4-0.8	5.4-10.3	555
19	Cotton (G. herbaceum)	1.1-1.5	13.2-19	2880-3370	53	Sagebrush (Artemisia tridentata)	2.2-4.2	26-50	1000-2400
20	Cotton (G. hirsutum)	1.2	13.8	2020	54	Saltgrass (Distichlis spicata)	1.6-5	19.8-60	2840-9100
21	Fig (Ficus carica)	1.2	14.6		55	Sawgrass (Cladium effusum)	0.6-1.1	6.8-13.3	
22	Grape (Vitis labrusca)	0.1-1.1	10.7-13	670	56	Sorghum (Sorghum vulgare)	0.9-1.1	10.7-13.4	1500-1780
23	Grapefruit (Citrus paradisi)	1.5	17.9	1390	57	Sorghum (S. vulgare), stem	1.2-1.6	14.3-19.7	840-2220
24	Greasewood (Sarcobatus vermiculatus)	2-3	25-37	4700-6700	58	Sorghum (S. vulgare), root	1.1-1.8	12.5-21.9	1800-2600
25	Lemon (Citrus limonia)	1.2-2.0	14.4-23.9	1320-1720	59	Spanish moss (Tillandsia usneoides)	0.5-0.9	6-10.4	
26	Lemon (C. limonia), shoot	1.1-1.8	12.8-21.3		60	Strawberry (Fragaria sp)	2.2	26.8	1750
27	Lime (C. aurantifolia)	1.3-1.6	16.1-19	1480-1490	61	Sunflower (Helianthus annuus), in Arizona	1.4	16.4	2650
28	Mangrove (Rhizophora mangle)	2.5	30		62	Sunflower (H. annuus), in Florida	0.7	8.6	1690
29	Maple (Acer grandidentatum), in Utah	1.1-2.2	12.5-27	1030-1690	63	Sweetclover (Melilotus alba)	1.1-1.7	12.9-20.6	1310-1790
30	Maple (A. grandidentatum), in Florida		30	860	64	Sweetpotato (Ipomoea batatus)	0.9	9.5	1890
31	Maple, red (A. rubrum), 12 ft high	1.3	16	940	65	Tomato (Lycopersicon esculentum)	0.8	8.2	
32	Maple, red (A. rubrum), 27 ft high	1.4	16.4	910	66	Tomato (L. esculentum), root	0.4-1.3	5-15.9	
33	Maple, red (A. rubrum), 47 ft high	1.4	16.7	860	67	Wheat (Triticum aestivum), entire plant	0.8-2.4	9.6-28	1370-2950
34	Mistletoe (Phoradendron juniperinum)	2-2.5	25-30	1960-2370					
35	(Host: Juniper (Juniperus utahensis))	1.4-2.3	17.5-28	940-1490					

60. XYLEM AND PHLOEM EXUDATION: SQUASH, PUMPKIN

Part I: XYLEM EXUDATION: SQUASH

	Period	Total Sap ml	Rate of Flow ml/plant/min	Dry Matter g/100g	Temp[1] °C
1	9:15-9:30 A. M.	10.5	0.17	0.16	
2	9:30-9:45 A. M.	28.0	0.47	0.16	
3	9:45-10:00 A. M.	30.0	0.50	0.16	
4	10:00-10:10 A. M.	24.5	0.61	0.15	
5	10:10-10:15 A. M.	10.2	0.51	0.13	26.5
6	10:15-10:20 A. M.	12.5	0.62	0.16	
7	10:20-10:25 A. M.	12.0	0.60	0.18	
8	10:25-10:30 A. M.	12.5	0.62	0.18	
9	10:30-10:35 A. M.	12.5	0.62	0.19	
10	10:35-10:40 A. M.	11.5	0.57	0.22	
11	10:40-10:45 A. M.	10.5	0.52	0.18	
12	10:45-10:50 A. M.	11.0	0.55	0.19	
13	10:50-10:55 A. M.	10.0	0.50	0.20	30
14	10:55-11:00 A. M.	8.5	0.42	0.23	
15	11:00-11:05 A. M.	9.5	0.47	0.21	

/1/ Values applicable to greenhouse. Temp of culture solution, 25°C.

Part II: PHLOEM EXUDATION: SQUASH

	Period	Total Sap Fresh Weight g	Total Sap Dry Weight[1] g	Phloem Area sq cm	Rate of Flow[2] cm/hr	Temp[1] °C
1	2:00-3:00 P. M.	0.788	0.055 (6.9)	0.044	17.9	26.0
2	3:00-4:00 P. M.	0.852	0.042 (4.9)	0.059	14.4	27.0
3	4:00-5:00 P. M.	0.710	0.032 (4.5)	0.060	11.8	22.5
4	5:00-6:00 P. M.	0.596	0.026 (4.4)	0.060	9.9	30.0
5	6:00-7:00 P. M.	0.437	0.019 (4.3)	0.073	6.0	26.0
6	7:00-8:00 P. M.	0.321	0.016 (5.0)	0.077	4.2	21.0
7	8:00-9:00 P. M.	0.499	0.020 (4.1)	0.077	6.5	24.0
8	9:00-10:00 P. M.	0.671	0.024 (3.6)	0.077	8.7	23.5
9	10:00-11:00 P. M.	0.725	0.023 (3.1)	0.084	8.6	24.5
10	11:00-12:00 P. M.	0.584	0.019 (3.3)	0.087	6.7	23.0
11	12:00-1:00 A. M.	0.586	0.018 (3.2)	0.082	7.1	23.5
12	1:00-2:00 A. M.	0.689	0.021 (3.0)	0.082	8.4	25.0

/1/ Dry weight as percentage of fresh weight is enclosed in parentheses. /2/ Determinations based on cross-sectional area of total phloem. Because sieve tubes occupy approximately 25% of the phloem, values must be multiplied by 4 to obtain actual rates.

Part III: COMPOSITION OF PHLOEM EXUDATE FROM FRUITS: PUMPKIN

	Fruit Size[1]	Carbon g/100g	Nitrogen g/100g	Ash g/100g	C:N	Dry Matter g/100g		Fruit Size[1]	Carbon g/100g	Nitrogen g/100g	Ash g/100g	C:N	Dry Matter g/100g
				Phloem Exudate							Fruits		
1	A	45	13.2	9.7	3.4	9.4	4	A	43	3.5	10.9	12.2	6.9
2	B	44	13.1	8.7	3.4	9.7	5	B	38	2.5	10.1	15.7	5.5
3	C	44	13.2	9.1	3.4	10.5	6	C	37	2.6	10.1	14.1	5.1

/1/ Fruit A: length, 10 cm; greatest diameter, 2.7 cm; weight, 43 g. Fruit B: length, 21 cm; greatest diameter, 5.7 cm; weight, 344 g. Fruit C: length 27 cm; greatest diameter, 7.6 cm; weight, 894 g.

61. CELL SAP: pH VALUES
Data applicable to sap of leaves except as otherwise specified.

#	Species	pH	#	Species	pH
1	Aconite (Aconitum porrectum)	5	24	Oat (Avena sativa), entire plant	5.6-5.7
2	Alfalfa (Medicago sativa)	5.3	25	Olive (Olea europaea), shoot	5.2
3	Apple (Pyrus malus), twig	5.4-6	26	Onion (Allium cepa)	4.3
4	Apple (P. malus), fruit	3.4	27	Orange (Citrus sinensis)	5.8
5	Asparagus (Asparagus officinalis)	5.8	28	Orange (C. sinensis), shoot	5.3-6.2
6	Banana (Musa paradisiaca sapientum), midrib	4.7	29	Orange (C. sinensis), fruit	3.6
7	Barley (Hordeum vulgare)	6	30	Oxalis (Oxalis sp)	1.7-2.1
8	Bean (Phaseolus sp)	5.9-6.1	31	Pineapple (Ananas sativus)	4.7
9	Beet, sugar (Beta vulgaris)	6	32	Pineapple (A. sativus), fruit	4.4
10	Begonia (Begonia lucerna)	0.9-1.4	33	Potato (Solanum tuberosum), tuber	5.6
11	Boston fern (Nephrolepis exaltata bost.)	5.2	34	Rape (Brassica napus)	6-6.4
12	Buckwheat (Fagopyrum esculentum)	5.5-5.9	35	Rhubarb (B. campestris napo-brassica), petiole	3.6
13	Buckwheat (F. esculentum), stem	4.7-5	36	Sorghum (Sorghum vulgare), entire plant	5.4-5.7
14	Burroweed (Allenrolfea occidentalis)	5.9-6.6	37	Soybean (Glycine soja)	5.8-6.2
15	Columbine (Aquilegia caerulea)	4.6-5.3	38	Soybean (G. soja), stem	5.7-5.8
16	Corn (Zea mays)	5-5.6	39	Soybean (G. soja), root	6.3-6.6
17	Corn (Z. mays), stem	5.3-5.7[1]	40	Sugarcane (Saccharum officinarum)	5.5-5.7
18	Cotton (Gossypium herbaceum)	5.1-6.8	41	Sugarcane (S. officinarum), stem	5.5-6.6
19	Cranberry (Vaccinium sp), fruit	2.4	42	Sunflower (Helianthus annuus)	6.3-6.9
20	Garlic (Allium sativum), bulb	3.5	43	Tobacco (Nicotiana tabacum)	5.3-5.8
21	Grapefruit (Citrus paridisi), fruit	3	44	Tomato (Lycopersicon esculentum)	5.3-5.8
22	Lemon (C. limonia), shoot	5.1-6.1	45	Wheat (Triticum aestivum), entire plant	5.6-6.1
23	Milo (Sorghum vulgare durra)	4.7			

/1/ Exuded sap not expressed under pressure, 4.3-4.7.

62. CELL SAP: CHEMICAL COMPOSITION

#	Species	Plant Part	Growth Stage	Value mg/100g
	Calcium			
1	Bean, field (Phaseolus sp)	Leaf	Mature	515-690
2		Stem	Mature	137-283
3	Corn (Zea mays)	Stem		4.7-11.6
4	Peanut (Arachis hypogaea)	Lower leaf	Immature	500
5	Potato (Solanum tuberosum)	Lower stem	Mature	100
6	Rye (Secale cereale)	Entire plant		52-59
7	Tomato (Lycopersicon esculentum)	Stem	Immature	18
8	Wheat (Triticum aestivum)	Shoot	Mature	68-106
9		Entire plant	Immature	43
	Magnesium			
10	Bean, field (Phaseolus sp)	Leaf	Mature	42-109
11		Stem	Mature	76-105
12	Beet, sugar (Beta vulgaris)	Leaf	Mature	80-200
13		Stem	Mature	70-130
14	Cabbage (Brassica oleracea cap.)	Stem		6
15	Collard (B. oleracea acephala)	Stem		2.4-7.8
16	Pea, black (Pisum sp)	Petiole		19-42
17	Peanut (Arachis hypogaea)	Lower leaf		290
18	Rye (Secale cereale)	Entire plant	Immature	14-88
19	Tomato (Lycopersicon esculentum)	Stem		6-41
20	Wheat (Triticum aestivum)	Shoot		27-107
21		Entire plant	Immature	39
	Nitrogen as NO_3[1]			
22	Barley (Hordeum vulgare)	Leaf	Mature	20
23		Stem	Mature	23
24	Beet, garden (Beta vulgaris)	Leaf	44-79 da old	3-52
25	Buckwheat (Fagopyrum esculentum)	Shoot		12.6-17.2
26	Cabbage (Brassica oleracea cap.)	Lower leaf	Immature	13-55
27		Stem	Immature	54
28	Carrot (Daucus carota)	Root	2-3 mo old	3-32
29	Celery (Apium graveolons)	Leaf		18-52
30	Collard (Brassica oleracea aceph.)	Stem		13-64
31	Corn (Zea mays)	Lower stem	Mature	8-41
32		Entire plant	Immature	0.5-25
33	Fescue (Festuca elatior)	Entire plant	Immature	1.8
34	Lettuce (Lactuca sativa)	Leaf	Mature	6-45
35	Oat (Avena sativa)	Stem	Mature	41
36	Pea, black (Pisum sp)	Petiole		2-22
37	Potato (Solanum tuberosum)	Lower stem		16.1-18.4
38	Rye (Secale cereale)	Entire plant	Immature	3.8-12.4
39	Soybean (Glycine soja)	Entire plant	Fruiting	2.4-3.6
40	Sugar cane (Saccharum officinarum)	Stem	Mature	10-40[2]
41	Tomato (Lycopersicon esculentum)	Petiole	Fruiting	6.9
42		Stem	Immature	5.8-11.5
43	Wheat (Triticum aestivum)	Shoot	Mature	1-58
44		Entire plant	Immature	2.8
	Phosphorus			
45	Barley (Hordeum vulgare)	Leaf	Mature	6.4-56
46		Stem	Mature	8.9-78
47		Entire plant	36 da old	10
48	Bean, field (Phaseolus sp)	Leaf	Mature	3.5-17.7
49	Beet, sugar (Beta vulgaris)	Leaf	Mature	10.5-250
	Phosphorus (concluded)			
50	Beet, sugar (Beta vulgaris)	Stem	Mature	4.5-24.2
51	Buckwheat (Fagopyrum esculentum)	Leaf		22-105
52		Stem		24-145
53	Cabbage (Brassica oleracea cap.)	Lower leaf	Immature	0.02-1.7
54	Carrot (Daucus carota)	Root	2-3 mo old	0.04-1.0
55	Celery (Apium graveolens)	Leaf	Mature	8.8-17.9
56		Stem	Mature	6-22.8
57	Clover (Trifolium pratense)	Entire plant	82 da old	7.7-21.2
58	Collard (Brassica oleracea aceph.)	Stem		5.8-7.6
59	Corn (Zea mays)	Lower stem	Mature	2.7-3.8
60		Entire plant	Mature	1.6-12.2
61	Fescue (Festuca elatior)	Entire plant	Immature	0.5
62	Pea, black (Pisum sp)	Petiole		1.2-4.4
63	Peanut (Arachis hypogaea)	Lower leaf	Immature	2.3
64	Potato (Solanum tuberosum)	Lower stem	Mature	6
65	Rape (Brassica napus)	Leaf	Immature	15-86
66	Rye (Secale cereale)	Entire plant	Immature	82-112
67	Sorghum (Sorghum vulgare)	Entire plant		90-116
68	Soybean (Glycine soja)	Entire plant	Fruiting	2.6-9.0
69	Sugarcane (Saccharum officinarum)	Stem	Mature	11-19
70	Tomato (Lycopersicon esculentum)	Petiole	Fruiting	30
71		Stem	Immature	12.5-20
72		Shoot	Immature	9.7-19.2
73	Turnip (Brassica rapus)	Root		0-3.4
74	Wheat (Triticum aestivum)	Shoot	Immature	35-81
75		Entire plant	Immature	80
	Potassium			
76	Barley (Hordeum vulgare)	Leaf	Mature	310-860
77		Stem	Mature	260-800
78		Entire plant	36 da old	250
79	Bean, field (Phaseolus sp)	Leaf	Mature	28-200
80	Beet, sugar (Beta vulgaris)	Leaf	Mature	97-516
81		Stem	Mature	340-414
82	Cabbage (Brassica oleracea cap.)	Lower leaf	Immature	112-455
83	Celery (Apium graveolens)	Leaf	Mature	239-418
84		Stalk	Mature	255-408
85	Clover (Trifolium pratense)	Entire plant	82 da old	44-234
86	Collard (Brassica oleracea aceph.)	Stem		160-415
87	Corn (Zea mays)	Lower stem	Mature	166
88		Entire plant		390-650
89	Parsnip (Pastinaca sativa)	Root	3-4 mo old	142-353
90	Pea, black (Pisum sp)	Petiole		250-415
91	Peanut (Arachis hypogaea)	Lower leaf	Immature	500
92	Potato (Solanum tuberosum)	Lower stem	Mature	254-621
93	Rye (Secale cereale)	Entire plant	Immature	579
94	Soybean (Glycine soja)	Entire plant	Fruiting	96-885
95	Sugarcane (Saccharum officinarum)	Stem	Mature	128-266
96	Tomato (Lycopersicon esculentum)	Stem	Immature	200-300
97	Turnip (Brassica rapus)	Leaf		92-425
98		Root		199-343
99	Wheat (Triticum aestivum)	Entire plant	Immature	411

/1/ Values are NO_3-N except as otherwise specified. /2/ Total nitrogen.

63. SHOOTS, LEAVES, SEEDS: MINERAL COMPOSITION

Values àre g/100g or mg/kg of specified dry weight material.

Species	K	P	Ca	Mg	S	B	Cu	Fe	Mn	Zn
			g/100g					mg/kg		
Shoots										
Pandanales; Helobiae										
1 Cattail (Typha angustifolia)	2.0	0.16	1.5	0.1	0.10					
2 Elodea (Elodea canadensis)	1.5-3.0	0.28-0.74	2.9-8.2	0.5-1.2	0.15-0.97					
3 Plantain (Alisma plantago-aquatica)	1.8	0.24	1.0	0.3	0.39					
Glumiflorae										
4 Barley (Hordeum vulgare)	3.9	0.35	0.7	0.2	0.19	4-53	14	180-540		
5 Bentgrass (Agrostis tenuis)	1.1-3.8	0.15-0.17	0.2-0.9	0.1					296	
6 Bermudagrass (Cynodon dactylon)	1.1-3.0	0.18-0.27	0.4-0.5	0.1-0.3	0.36-0.50	4		150		
7 Bluegrass (Poa pratensis)	1.4-4.3	0.19-0.95	0.1-1.2	0.1-0.2	0.06-0.66	6-12		60-425	29-216	17-28
8 Broomsedge (Andropogon virginicus)	1.2	0.08-0.23	0.3	0.1	0.07					
9 Crabgrass (Digitaria sanguinalis)	3.7	0.30	0.3	0.5	0.17					
10 Fescue (Festuca elatior)	2.4-4.0	0.24-0.37	0.5-0.9	0.1-0.3	0.08-0.17					
11 Johnsongrass (Sorghum halepense)	1.6	0.22	0.4	0.2	0.06					
12 Orchardgrass (Dactylis glomerata)	1.6-4.5	0.19-0.58	0.3-0.8	0.1-0.3	0.06-0.27	5-18			120-370	
13 Redtop (Agrostis alba)	0.7-4.2	0.05-0.41	0.1-1.0	0.1-0.3	0.08-0.33		3-5	56-160	79-510	10-60
14 Rescuegrass (Bromus catharticus)	3.7	0.30	0.2	0.2	0.18		6			14
15 Rye (Secale cereale)		0.23	0.3			0.3-3	7-8			20-21
16 Ryegrass (Lolium perenne)	2.2-4.9	0.28-0.30	0.5-0.9	0.2	0.2	2.9		880		
17 Sedge (Carex acuta)	0.9-1.2	0.12	0.2-1.7	0.1-0.2	0.02-0.13	5[1]		350-680[1]		
18 Sudangrass (Sorghum vulgare sud.)	0.4-2.5	0.16-0.40	0.4-1.2	0.3-0.8	0.05		10	70-140		
19 Timothy (Phleum pratense)	0.8-3.8	0.08-0.60	0.04-1.2	0.03-0.04	0.07-0.32	10-16	2-7	30-287	11-165	30-60
20 Wheat (Triticum aestivum)	2.8	0.32	0.8	0.1	0.11	3-10	3-12	290-580		13-25
21 Velvetgrass (Holcus lanatus)	2.0	0.22	0.4	0.1	0.28	7		140		25
Spathiflorae; Liliiflorae										
22 Cuckoo-pint (Arum maculatum)	1.4	0.28	2.1	0.5	0.2	9		1620		
23 Asparagus (Asparagus officinalis)	1.4-3.4	0.14-0.78	0.2-1.4	0.1-0.2	0.13-0.26	9-244	7-17	60-979	12-29	52
24 Onion (Allium cepa)	2.6	0.19	2.6	0.3	0.18	4-44				
Polygonales; Centrospermae										
25 Buckwheat (Fagopyrum esculentum)	1.7-2.6	0.13-0.54	1.7-2.6	0.4-0.6	0.10-0.11	26[2]		100	14	15
26 Sorrell, sheep (Rumex acetosella)	1.4-1.9	0.40-0.49	1.2-2.9	0.5-0.7	0.12					
27 Chickweed (Stellaria media)	3.7	0.40	1.32	1.7	0.14					
28 Corn cockle (Agrostemma githago)	3.1	0.44	2.8	0.5	0.13					
29 Lamb's-quarters (Chenopodium album)	3.5	0.36	2.1	0.4	0.15			158[3]		
30 Purslane (Portulaca oleracea)	10.8	0.48	1.6	1.2	0.27					
31 Saltbush (Atriplex canescens)	0.8	0.05	0.7	0.4	0.28					
Rhoeadales; Rosales										
32 Celandine (Chelidonium majus)	2.0	0.48	1.5	0.2	0.06	17				
33 Mustard (Brassica hirta)	3.1	0.40	1.8	0.3	0.60	13-54		350		
34 Alfalfa (Medicago sativa)	0.7-4.0	0.15-0.71	0.6-3.5	0.1-1.0	0.19-0.40	12-128	4-61	110-675	10-124	13-112
35 Broadbean (Vicia faba)	2.1	0.27	0.9	0.2	0.14			280	36	
36 Clover (Trifolium incarnatum)	0.7-5.9	0.08-0.53	1.0-1.8	0.2-0.4	0.06-0.40	70		470-1400	24-387	
37 Lespedeza (Lespedeza spp)	1.2-1.4	0.13-0.30	1.0-1.2	0.2-0.3		18-20		126-1028	54-331	
38 Pea, garden (Pisum sativum)	1.7	0.34	1.5	0.5	0.33	17-22			15	
39 Soybean (Glycine soja)	0.5-2.3	0.09-0.74	0.5-2.2	0.2-0.9	0.12-0.52	1-13	4-12	100-570	45-280	28-80
40 Vetch (Vicia sativa)	2.1-2.3	0.33-0.44	1.6-2.0	0.3-0.5	0.27-0.28	10[1]			14-360[1]	
Malvales; Tubiflorae										
41 Carrot (Daucus carota)	2.4-3.4	0.20-0.29	1.3-3.3	0.2-0.4	0.07-0.48	20-45	5-10	355-765	23-199	26
42 Cotton (Gossypium spp)	0.9-2.1	0.23-0.43	1.0-2.2	0.1-0.7	0.26-0.33	60-795[3]		1754[3]	80-100[3]	
43 Bindweed (Convolvulus arvensis)	2.5	0.77	2.0	0.5	0.19					
44 Bugleweed (Ajuga reptans)	2.4-3.5	0.23-0.76	0.2-1.8	0.3-0.7	0.14-0.43	16		1000-2030		
45 Dodder (Cuscuta europaea)	3.7	0.54	0.2	0.1	1.0					
46 Horsenettle (Solanum carolinense)	1.9	0.98	1.3	1.0	0.48					
47 Mullein (Verbascum thapsus)	3.0	0.19	1.0	0.2	0.21					
48 Peppermint (Mentha piperita)	1.5-2.6	0.19-0.31	0.7-1.9				8-12			
49 Potato (Solanum tuberosum)	0.03-4.2	0.08-0.26	0.6-4.1	0.2-1.2	0.15-0.68	14-39	11		86-108	
Plantaginales; Campanulatae										
50 Plantain (Plantago lanceolata)	2.6	0.27	1.2	0.2	0.33					
51 Bellflower (Campanula patula)	2.4	0.25	0.8	0.3	0.16					
52 Dandelion (Taraxacum officinale)	4.4	0.49	1.0	0.3	0.22	14	13[3]	440	19[3]	98-101[3]
53 Ragweed (Abrosia artemisiifolia)	1.9	0.25	1.8	0.4	0.23			190		17-65
Leaves										
Glumiflorae; Principes										
54 Sugar cane (Saccharum officinarum)	0.4-2.5	0.07-0.98	0.1-0.6	0.04-0.6	0.06-0.23			370	30	
55 Date (Phoenix dactylifera)	0.2-1.6	0.06-0.19	0.3-1.1	0.1-0.2		73-172				
Salicales; Juglandales										
56 Aspen, European (Populus tremula)	1.4	0.34	3.1	0.2	0.10					
57 Pecan (Carya illinoensis)	0.3-0.9	0.10-0.15	1.1-1.6	0.4			21-28	144-185		4-202
58 Walnut, black (Juglans nigra)	2.0-2.4	0.32-0.54	1.1-3.2	0.4-0.5	0.01-0.23	40-67	11	280-780	60-190	26-49
Fagales; Urticales										
59 Hornbeam (Carpinus betulus)	0.5	0.2	2.3	0.1	0.04					
60 Oak, black (Quercus velutina)	1.0-1.2	0.15-0.20	0.9-2.2	0.3-0.4	0.04-0.25		7-9	250-280	490-1870	38-68
61 Elm, American (Ulmus americana)	0.6-2.0	0.13-0.59	1.4-2.4	0.4-0.6	0.02-0.35	277	7-16	245-810	39-130	10-22
62 Fig (Ficus carica)	1.0	0.21	2.2	0.7	0.08	245-1349				
63 Hackberry (Celtis occidentalis)	1.7-2.3	0.16-0.44	2.5-7.8	0.4-0.5	0.17-0.29		6-8	550-730	100-170	6-32
64 Mulberry, red (Morus rubra)	2.3	0.29	3.8	0.4	0.09		7	500	250	30
65 Nettle (Urtica dioica)	2.2	0.80	4.6	0.9	0.76					
66 Ramie (Boehmeria spp)	0.7	0.41	4.9	0.8	0.15					
Santalales; Ranales										
67 Mistletoe (Viscum album)	0.1-2.3	0.25-0.77	0.9-1.7	0.3-0.7	0.08-0.26					
68 Magnolia, bigleaf (Magnolia macrophylla)	1.2-3.3	0.18-0.48	0.1-2.4	0.3-0.4	0.02-0.29		6-8	150-230	29-30	19-62
69 Waterlily (Nymphaea alba)	1.1-1.6	0.15-0.22	1.8-2.2	0.2-0.3	0.06-0.07					
70 Yellow-poplar (Liriodendron tulipifera)	0.9-1.7	0.20-0.36	1.0-3.5	0.2-0.3	0.26-0.38		3-5	240-380	40-90	26-68

/1/ Applicable to various species.   /2/ Applicable to stems.   /3/ Applicable to leaves.

63. SHOOTS, LEAVES, SEEDS: MINERAL COMPOSITION (Concluded)

Values are g/100g or mg/kg of specified dry weight material.

No.	Species	K	P	Ca	Mg	S	B	Cu	Fe	Mn	Zn
		g/100g					mg/kg				
	Leaves (concluded)										
	Rosales										
71	Apple (Pyrus malus)	0.5-3.9	0.09-0.75	0.6-2.7	0.1-0.8		11-43	3-12	65-507	20-156	4-345
72	Blacklocust (Robinia pseudoacacia)	1.2-2.1	0.20-0.56	1.5-4.5	0.3-0.4	0.02-0.39	30-70	7	190-330	40-50	7-50
73	Cherry, black (Prunus serotina)	1.1-1.3	0.14-0.47	1.3-2.4	0.4-0.6	0.06-0.21	104[1]	6-8	210-290	170-230	27-72
74	Crabapple (Malus coronaria)	1.4-1.8	0.34-0.56	1.3-1.9	0.2-0.3	0.16-0.21		8-9	180-300	20-30	7-52
75	Peach (Prunus persica)	0.8-2.4	0.09-0.72	1.1-2.7	0.4-1.4		17-81			17-325	6-345
76	Peanut (Arachis hypogaea)	4.2	0.26	2.1	0.7						
77	Pear (Pyrus communis)	0.8-2.2	0.11-0.16	1.2-3.0	0.3-0.4			5-41	28-94		
78	Sweetgum (Liquidambar styraciflua)	0.6-1.6	0.17-0.37	0.8-2.0	0.4-0.5	0.01-0.26	19-29	9-15	200-740	310-700	2-27
79	Sycamore (Platanus occidentalis)	1.2-1.6	0.15-0.46	1.4-2.2	0.3	0.08-0.42		4-7	180-260	120-150	9-42
80	Yellow-wood (Cladrastris lutea)	1.8-2.4	0.42-0.78	1.8-3.7	0.2-0.3	0.11-0.25		7-12	180-360	30-70	11-40
	Geraniales; Sapindales; Rhamnales										
81	Flax (Linum usitatissimum)	1.3-2.3	0.34-0.45	0.9-1.2	0.3-0.6	0.15-0.38	7-24[4]	3-4[4]			20-28[4]
82	Holly, American (Ilex opaca)	0.7-2.0	0.07-0.40	0.5-1.1	0.3-0.5	0.21-0.33		6-14	200-270	260-540	130-240
83	Maple, sugar (Acer saccharum)	1.0-1.6	0.24-0.46	6.2-2.4	0.2-0.4	0.01-0.24		11-12	150-440	40-220	24-54
84	Tung (Aleurites fordii)	0.6-2.9	0.13-0.50	0.6-4.9	0.2-0.6		15-125	4-15	41-375	22-2884	16-229
85	Buckeye, Ohio (Aesculus glabra)	0.9-2.6	0.28-0.61	1.6-4.4	0.3-0.5	0.15-0.31		5-7	340-500	70-120	28-35
86	Grape, riverbank (Vitis vinifera)	0.6-1.0	0.08-0.20	1.8-2.8	0.2-0.4	0.10-0.11	16-2084[1]	3-47[1]	190-220[1]	180-220[1]	
	Malvales; Umbelliflorae; Ebenales										
87	Basswood, American (Tilia americana)	1.1-2.5	0.22-0.62	1.4-6.4	0.4-0.8	Tr-0.34		8-10	220-430	7-210	21-54
88	Dogwood, flowering (Cornus florida)	0.4-1.1	0.18-0.32	2.7-4.2	0.3-0.5	0.38-0.70	23	7-9	240-380	30-50	3-28
89	Ivy, English (Hedera helix)	1.0	0.26	3.6	0.2	0.28					
90	Persimmon (Diospyros virginiana)	2.0-2.4	0.14-0.46	0.6-1.8	0.3-0.5	0.27-0.28		5-8	210-250	90-220	36-48
	Oleales; Tubiflorae										
91	Ash, blue (Fraxinus quadrangulata)	1.3-2.0	0.35-0.61	0.6-2.0	0.3-0.4	0.11-0.39		11-16	250-330	60-80	12-34
92	Lilac (Syringa vulgaris)	0.9-1.0	0.20-0.54	0.5	0.2	0.01-0.05	4-8[1]		110-700[1]		
93	Olive (Olea europaea)	0.5-1.1	0.12-0.30	0.8-1.9	0.1-0.2	0.02-0.05	7-44		250-880		
94	Belladona (Atropa belladonna)	2.8	0.37	1.2	0.4	0.26					
95	Catalpa (Catalpa speciosa)	1.3-2.5	0.30-0.58	1.2-2.3	0.3-0.5	0.22-0.48		18-21	330-680	80-130	28-50
96	Sweetpotato (Ipomoea batatas)	1.6-2.4	0.19-0.28	0.7-1.2	0.4-0.5						
	Rubiales; Campanulatae										
97	Cinchona (Cinchona ledgeriana)	0.8-1.2	0.20-0.49	0.4-0.7	0.2-0.3						
98	Coffee (Coffea arabica)	2.7	0.16	0.9	0.2	0.08					
99	Aster (Aster amellus)	3.5	0.16	2.5	0.3	0.25					
100	Guayule (Parthenium argentatum)	4.0-7.7	0.30-0.36	2.4-5.1	0.8-1.4	1.46-1.65					
	Seeds										
	Glumiflorae; Fagales										
101	Barley (Hordeum vulgare)	0.3-0.9	0.15-0.62	0.01-0.2	0.02-0.3	0.02-0.37	0.6-13	1-70	14-350	7-38	21-132
102	Bluegrass, Kentucky (Poa pratensis)	0.7	0.85	0.3	0.2	0.20		60	350-460	85-110	360
103	Millet (Panicum miliaceum)	0.3	0.29	0.02	0.2	0.003					
104	Rice (Oryza sativa)	0.2-0.5	0.19-0.43	0.05-0.1	0.1-0.2	0.001-0.14	9.4	3-4	76-350	18-70	30
105	Rye (Secale cereale)	0.5-0.6	0.21-0.52	0.04-0.2	0.1-0.2	0.01-0.41	2-9	2-7	57-700	32-157	13-73
106	Ryegrass (Lolium italicum)	0.5	0.54	0.5	0.2	0.31					
107	Sorgo (Sorghum vulgare)	0.3	0.29-0.41	0.01-0.1	0.2	0.01					
108	Timothy (Phleum pratense)	0.5	0.35	0.2	0.1	0.03			61-410	72	
109	Wheat (Triticum aestivum)	0.2-1.0	0.15-0.54	0.01-0.30	0.1-0.3	0.003-0.29	1.11	3-24	3-420	5-260	19-105
110	Beech, European (Fagus sylvatica)	1.0-1.2	0.44-0.49	0.3-0.5	0.2-0.3	0.08-0.09					
111	Chestnut (Castanea sativa)	0.7	0.17	0.1	0.1	0.09					
	Centrospermae; Ranales; Rhoeadales										
112	Beet (Beta vulgaris)	1.0	0.44	0.9	0.5	0.10					
113	Waterlily (Nymphaea tetragona)	1.4	0.73	0.2	0.2						
114	Mustard (Brassica hirta)	0.6	0.73	0.6	0.2	0.08	12		290		
115	Poppy, opium (Papaver somniferum)	0.5-0.7	0.82-0.89	1.3-1.6	0.3-0.4	0.05-0.10					
116	Radish (Raphanus raphanistrum)	0.7	0.87	0.6	0.1	0.07					
117	Rape (Brassica napus)	0.9	0.82	0.4	0.3	0.04	11		85-480	38	
	Rosales; Geraniales										
118	Apple (Pyrus malus)	0.8	0.71	0.2	0.4	0.05					
119	Almond (Prunus amygdalus)	0.2-1.1	0.44-0.93	0.2-0.3	0.2-0.5	0.01-0.05	15-57	11-13	42-190	13	21
120	Bean (Phaseolus vulgaris)	1.2-1.9	0.41-0.50	0.1-0.2	0.15-0.20	0.05-0.23	17		120	20	
121	Bean, mung (P. aureus)	0.6-1.2	0.31-0.58	0.3-0.6	0.2	0.02			21	14-15	
122	Broadbean (Vicia faba)	1.2-1.3	0.58-0.62	0.1	0.1-0.2	0.05-0.09	11-223	10-11			
123	Chick pea (Cicer arietinum)	0.7	0.57	0.1	0.4	0.04	14	7	560	29	19
124	Cowpea (Vigna sinensis)	1.3-1.8	0.36-0.74	0.1-0.2	0.2-0.3	0.28		5-7	67-662	45	
125	Lupine (Lupinus spp)	0.8	0.48	0.2	0.2	0.12			210	678	
126	Pea, garden (Pisum sativum)	0.8-1.0	0.38-0.61	0.06-0.11	0.1-0.2	0.04-0.16	2-8	6-15	70-282	4-25	40-48
127	Plum (Prunus domestica)	0.9	0.62	0.2	0.4	0.12					
128	Soybean (Glycine soja)	0.8-2.4	0.50-1.80	0.1-0.3	0.2-0.3	0.002-0.45	6-41	12-23	57-161	14-41	18
129	Vetch (Vicia sativa)	0.8-1.1	0.50-0.53	0.1-0.2	0.2	0.04-0.14				14-72[1]	
130	Flax (Linum usitatissimum)	0.6-0.9	0.43-0.85	0.2-0.3	0.3-0.4	0.03-0.06	11-17		85-118	38-102	20
131	Orange (Citrus aurantium)	0.9-1.0	0.29-0.45	0.4-0.5	0.1-0.2	0.03-0.06					
	Rhamnales; Malvales; Opuntiales										
132	Grape, riverbank (Vitis vinifera)	0.6-0.7	0.33-0.34	0.4-0.7	0.1	0.04-0.07					
133	Cacoa (Theobroma cacao)	0.9	0.53	0.1	0.2	0.04					
134	Cotton (Gossypium hirsutum)	0.9-1.9	0.48-1.79	0.1-0.3	0.2-0.4	0.05-0.76	27-130[1]	54[1]	150-590[1]	13-31[1]	320[1]
135	Prickly pear (Opuntia compressa)	0.2	0.003	0.5	0.2	0.001					
	Oleales; Tubiflorae										
136	Olive (Olea europaea)	0.7	0.38	0.1	0.02	0.03	3				
137	Sesame (Sesamum indicum)	0.5	0.66	1.2	0.4	0.02					
138	Tobacco (Nicotiana tabacum)	1.3	0.62	0.2	0.3	0.02	6[1]		240[1]	70[1]	
	Rubiales; Cucurbitales										
139	Coffee (Coffea arabica)	1.7-1.9	0.22-0.38	0.1-0.2	0.2	0.05-0.06	8-17	8-20	150-280	14-32	
140	Watermelon (Citrullus vulgaris)	0.7	0.48	0.04	0.1	0.03					

/1/ Applicable to various species.   /4/ Applicable to shoots.

64. PLANT TISSUES AND ORGANS: MINERAL COMPOSITION

Values are g/100 g or mg/kg dry weight material, as specified in column headings.

	Species	Plant Part[1]	K	P	Ca	Mg	S	B	Cu	Fe	Mn	Zn
					g/100 g					mg/kg		
1	Carnation	Leaves	1.4	0.21	0.9	0.2	0.08					
2	(Dianthus	Stems	1.0	0.24	1.7	0.2	0.14					
3	caryophyllus)	Roots	1.1	0.28	1.8	0.2	0.06					
4		Petals	2.5	0.36	0.2	0.1	0.09					
5		Leaves	1.8-2.0	0.23-0.34	2.0-2.8	0.5-0.7	0.04-0.05	57			40-84	
6		Petioles	2.6	0.48	2.2	0.6	0.06					
7	Clover, red	Stems	1.7-2.0	0.12-0.32	1.1-1.3	0.4-0.5	0.04-0.06	28			15-20	
8	(Trifolium	Shoot, veg.	2.2-3.0	0.32-0.53	1.9-2.0	0.5-0.6	0.09	23-58	6-20[2]	100-1300[2]	25-542[2]	24-80[2]
9	pratense)	Shoot, fl.	1.1-3.4	0.21-0.29	1.1-2.1	0.4-0.7	0.09-0.19	19-109			287	
10		Shoot, fr.	1.0-1.8	0.23-0.39	1.3-2.0	0.5-0.6	0.06-0.16				465	
11		Flowers	1.5-2.1	0.38-0.50	1.2	0.4-0.5	0.06	40			30-66	
12		Seed	1.3	0.75	0.2	0.4	0.04		17	21-336	6-38	76
13		Leaves	0.2-1.6	0.05-0.26	0.1-0.9	0.2-0.3	0.23-0.25	27-72		41-810	230-440	
14		Stems	0.3-2.4	0.03-0.20	0.1-0.6	0.1-0.3	0.05-0.17			400-740	100-230	
15		Shoot, veg.	6.2-9.9	0.21-0.39	0.6-0.7	0.3	0.32-0.42	15-18[2]	2-9[3]	312-321[2]	52-200[2]	5-80[3]
16	Corn	Shoot, fl.	1.7-7.1	0.14-0.55	0.6-0.7	0.2-0.4	0.08-0.37					
17	(Zea mays)	Shoot, fr.	0.3-1.9	0.04-0.42	0.1-0.8	0.1-0.5	0.08-0.31					
18		Roots	0.3-1.3	0.03-0.14	0.1-0.7	0.1-0.2	0.03-0.28			500-760	450-880	
19		Flowers, ♂	1.3	0.15	0.57	0.27						
20		Flowers, ♀	1.5	0.15	0.63	0.34						
21		Cob	0.5	0.09	0.02	0.1	0.02			250	310	
22		Kernel	0.2-0.9	0.23-0.80	0.01-0.06	0.1-0.3	0.004-0.30	1.9	4-30	13-550	5-500	20
23		Leaves[4]						60-795		1754	80-100	
24		Stems[4]						6-186		610	40-50	
25	Cotton	Shoot, veg.	2.6-3.3	0.30-0.33	0.2-2.8	0.5-1.3						
26	(Gossypium	Shoot, fr.	1.0-1.5	0.17-0.20	1.4-1.5	0.4-0.6						
27	hirsutum)	Burs	1.4-5.7	0.07-0.21	0.4-1.0	0.2-0.3						
28		Lint	0.5-0.8	0.02-0.12	0.01-0.27	0.1	0.04-0.06			190	11-190	
29		Seed	0.9-1.9	0.48-1.79	0.1-0.3	0.2-0.4	0.05-0.76	27-130	54	150-590	13-31	320
30		Leaves	3.2	0.82	0.7	0.2	0.08					
31		Petioles	4.3	0.72	1.7	0.2	0.17					
32		Bark	0.5	0.13	2.7	0.05						
33		Wood	0.2	0.07	0.2	0.02						
34	Horsechestnut	Peduncle	5.0	0.70	0.6	0.07	0.13					
35	(Aesculus	Calyx & ovaries	2.7	0.38	0.5	0.2	0.08					
36	hippocastanum)	Stamen	2.6	0.44	0.5	0.1						
37		Petals	2.4	0.35	0.5	0.1						
38		Bracts	1.5	0.65	1.4	0.1	0.24					
39		Fruit						11		Trace		
40		Seed	1.1-1.2	0.22-0.31	0.06-0.1	0.1	0.02-0.03					
41		Shoot, veg.	2.8-2.9	0.24-0.36	0.4-0.5	0.1-0.2	0.14-0.17		4-12		79-90	18-40
42	Oat	Shoot, fl.	2.0-2.2	0.21-0.48	0.3-0.7	0.1-0.3	0.07-0.57	15-50	3-4	50-270	5-82	12-25
43	(Avena	Shoot, fr.	0.8-2.2	0.16-0.40	0.2-0.5	0.1-0.4	0.07-0.28	2-17	1-9	154	5-116	12-13
44	sativa)	Roots										19-550
45		Straw	0.6-3.5	0.02-0.36	0.2-0.7	0.1-0.5	0.08-0.51	8	2-54	61-860	4-1656	4-193
46		Seed	0.3-1.1	0.15-0.96	0.02-0.19	0.1-0.4	0.02-0.29	1-19	0.7-51	7-350	14-76	22-40
47		Young lvs.	1.6	0.18	4.3	0.1	0.23					
48		Old lvs.	0.1	0.11	8.2	0.1	0.26	17-386[2]	7-18	38-345	24-46	24-47[2]
49	Orange	Twig bark	0.6	0.28	5.2	0.1	0.27					
50	(Citrus	Twig wood	0.2	0.22	1.3	0.1	0.12					
51	sinensis)	Trunk bark	0.7	0.24	4.4	0.4	0.18					
52		Trunk wood	0.2	0.16	0.7	0.1	0.11					
53		Root bark	0.8	0.24	3.3	0.2	0.20					
54		Root wood	0.2	0.16	0.7	0.1	0.08					
55		Small roots	0.16-1.25	0.25	0.4-0.5	0.2-0.8	0.14	95[2]				240[2]
56		Leaves	1.6-1.9	0.24-0.35	6.3-7.6	1.1-3.2	0.43-0.66	43-728				
57		Petioles	0.8	0.12	1.5	0.6	0.09					
58		Upper stems	2.5	0.13	0.7	0.2	0.09					
59	Sunflower	Lower stems	1.4	0.09	0.5	0.2	0.17					
60	(Helianthus	Roots	1.4-3.8	0.10-0.34	0.4-2.2	0.1-1.3	0.34	30-77				
61	annuus)	Flowers	1.6	0.41	0.8	0.3	0.08					
62		Fruits	1.0-3.2	0.32-0.50	0.3-1.0	0.2-0.3	0.19			34	23	19
63		Fruit coats	0.9	0.07	0.4	0.2	0.05					
64		Head minus fr.	9.4	0.41	2.5	1.3	0.46					
65		Seed	1.0	1.01	0.1-0.2	0.4	0.02					
66		Leaves, veg.	4.9	1.06	4.2	0.8		21-150[2]	12-21[2]	106-840[2]	53-4930[2]	17-30[5]
67		Leaves, early fl.	5.8	1.07	4.1	0.8						
68		Leaves, fl.	3.3	0.63	3.4	0.5						
69		Leaves, early fr.	2.5	0.59	3.1	0.5						
70		Leaves, mid-fr.	1.8	0.46	4.2	0.6						
71		Stems, veg.	10.7	0.63	3.2	0.8		21-26[2]	6-13	110-230	14-45[2]	
72	Tomato,	Stems, early fl.	10.2	0.78	3.2	0.9						
73	Pan America	Stems, fl.	3.8	0.59	1.6	0.4						
74	(Lycopersicon)[6]	Stems, early fr.	2.2	0.55	1.7	0.3						
75		Stems, mid-fr.	1.3	0.43	1.8	0.4						
76		Roots, veg.	5.1	0.71	1.4	0.6						
77		Roots, early fl.	5.5	0.85	1.5	0.7						
78		Roots, fl.	2.1	0.98	1.7	0.5						
79		Roots, early fr.	2.2	1.08	1.9	0.7						
80		Roots, mid-fr.	1.4	1.18	2.8	0.5						
81		Fruits	4.0	0.74	0.4	0.4		13-36	4-34	32-800	2-410	2-67

/1/ Veg. = plants in vegetative condition; fl. = plants flowering; fr. = plants fruiting. Shoots are stems with terminal buds and leaves. /2/ Value from unspecified condition of growth. /3/ Value for stover (mature cured stalk, without ears). /4/ Values for Hirsutum sp. /5/ Value for leaflets. /6/ L. esculentum x L. pimpinellifolium.

65. SEEDS: CHEMICAL COMPOSITION

Values, except as otherwise indicated, are g or mg per 100g seeds.

	Species	Gross Composition					Amino Acids (g/100g)											Fatty Acids (g/100g fat[1])					Vitamins (mg/100g)			
		Water	Protein	Fat	Carbohydrate	Ash	Arginine	Histidine	Isoleucine	Leucine	Lysine	Methionine	Phenylalanine	Threonine	Tryptophan	Tyrosine	Valine	Palmitic	Stearic	Oleic	Linoleic	Linolenic	Niacin	Pantothenic Acid	Riboflavin	Thiamine
1	Barley (Hordeum vulgare)	11.1	8.2	1.0	78.8	0.9	0.61	0.26	0.51	0.84	0.42	0.19	0.62	0.48	0.19		0.61	9	3	33	54		3.1	0.66	0.08	0.12
2	Bean, lima (Phaseolus vulgaris mac.)	12.6	20.7	1.3	61.6	3.8																	2.0	0.84	0.18	0.48
3	Bean, mung (P. aureus)	9.8	23.9	1.1	62.0	3.9	0.30	0.21	0.12	3.2	0.74	0.25	1.2	0.60	0.17	0.66	1.9	28	8	18	40	3	1.6		0.21	0.68
4	Chick-pea (Cicer arietinum)	10.6	20.8	4.7	60.9	3.0																	1.6		0.18	0.49
5	Corn (Zea mays)	10.6	8.8	4.0	73.0	1.2	0.45	0.24	0.36	1.1	0.29	0.21	0.46	0.34	0.08		0.50	10.2	3.0	50	34		4.4	0.64	0.10	0.49
6	Cotton (Gossypium hirsutum)[2]	7.3	23.1	22.9	43.2	3.5	3.0	1.1	1.8	2.2	1.5	0.5	2.2	1.1	0.4	0.6	1.8	←27→		19	54				0.31	
7	Cowpea (Vigna sinensis)	10.6	24.0	1.4	61.6	3.5											2.2						2.2		0.16	0.92
8	Flax (Linum usitatissimum)[2]	7.3	24.0	35.9	30.3	3.6	3.6	0.65	1.8	2.3	1.4	0.35	2.2	1.3	0.63		2.2									
9	Gingko (Gingko biloba)	7.3	7.2	1.6	41.2	1.7																				
10	Hemp (Cannabis sativa)	7.0	28	37														←10.1→		16	46	28				
11	Lentil (Lens culinaris)	11.2	25.0	1.0	59.5	3.3																				
12	Lotus (Nelumbium nelumbo)	9.6	16.5	2.3	63.9	3.6																	2.2		0.24	0.56
13	Oat (Avena sativa)	9.8	12.0	4.6	69.6	4.0	0.99	0.23	0.80	0.87	0.51	0.23	0.72	0.54	0.20	0.50	0.99	10		59	31		1.0	0.63	0.13	
14	Pea (Pisum sativum)	11.6	23.8	1.4	60.2	3.2	2.6	0.4	1.2	1.9	1.5	0.1	1.4	1.2	0.2		1.2						3.1	1.01	0.28	0.92
15	Peanut (Arachis hypogaea)[2]	4.0	26.2	42.8	24.3	2.7	6.9	1.3	2.6	4.1	1.9	0.6	3.1	1.6	0.8		2.8	6.3	4.9	61	21.8		15.6	3.50	0.13	0.77
16	Pigeon-pea (Cajanus cajan)	13.1	21.9	4.7	59.9	1.5																	2.1		0.11	1.09
17	Popcorn (Zea mays praecox)	9.8	11.9		72.1	1.5																	1.5		0.10	0.39
18	Pumpkin (Cucurbita pepo)	2.4	22.9	31.9	13.2	3.6																			0.10	0.18
19	Rape (Brassica napus)	9.5	20.4	43.6	22.3	4.2												1		32	15					
20	Rice (Oryza sativa)	12.0	7.5	1.7	77.7	1.1	0.54	0.14	0.28	0.51	0.28	0.14	0.31	0.22	0.10		0.40	13.2	11.9	44	39		4.6	1.01	0.05	0.32
21	Rye (Secale cereale)	11.0	12.1	1.7	73.4	1.8	0.59	0.25	0.44	0.67	0.45	0.18	0.47	0.37	0.14		0.56	←21→		18	61		1.6	0.92	0.22	0.43
22	Safflower (Carthamus tinctorius)	6.0	12.7	30.8		3.0												←5.8→		16	78					
23	Sesame (Sesamum indicum)	5.8	19.3	51.1	18.1	5.7												8.5					4.5	1.04	0.22	0.93
24	Sorghum (Sorghum vulgare)	10.0	11.2	3.5	73.8	1.5																			0.13	
25	Soybean (Glycine soja)[2]	7.5	34.9	18.1	34.8	4.7	4.1	1.3	2.6	4.3	3.1	0.5	3.1	2.3	0.7		2.7	←15→		27	52	6	2.3	1.56	0.31	1.07
26	Sunflower (Helianthus annuus)[2]	5.0	18.5	27.8		3.3	5.46	1.43	2.78	3.71	1.45	1.61	2.39	1.64	1.14		2.70	←11.3→		30	60					
27	Wheat (Triticum esculentum)	12.5	12.3	1.8	71.7	1.7	0.63	0.31	0.58	0.91	0.35	0.22	0.70	0.38	0.19		0.64	13.8	1.0	30	49	6	4.3	1.39	0.12	0.52

/1/ Component fatty acids are expressed as per cent by weight of the total fatty acids of the seed. /2/ Values for amino acids are applicable to meal or flour.

66. POLLEN: PROXIMATE CHEMICAL COMPOSITION

	Species	Water	Protein	Fat	Starch	Reducing Sugar	Non-reducing Sugar	Ash
		g/100g pollen						
1	Almond (Prunus amygdalus)	9.8	28.7	3.2	0.7	24.4	3.1	2.6
2	Asparagus (Asparagus officinalis)	10.7	25.6	4.1	1.4	20.0	4.6	4.4
3	Bermuda grass (Cynodon dactylon)	13.3	20.4	2.4	0.4	25.5	3.4	3.1
4	Birch brush (Ceanothus integerrimus)	10.1	16.7	0.9	0	19.6	4.8	3.1
5	Buckthorn (C. crassifolius)	8.1	29.9	1.2	2.0	23.5	3.7	3.1
6	Cattail (Typha latifolia)*	6.4	18.8	4.3	13.0	27.7	18.9	3.8
7	Chamaebatia (Chamaebatia foliolosa)	15.7	23.4	4.2	2.8	41.2	0.04	2.6
8	Clover (Trifolium sp)	13.4	20.7	3.2	7.8	20.0	4.2	5.5
9	Clover, Ladino (T. repens)*	11.6	23.7	3.4	1.3	29.1	0.05	5.7
10	Corn (Zea mays)*	5.5	20.3	3.7	22.4	6.9	7.3	2.6
11	Dandelion (Taraxacum vulgare)*	10.9	11.1	14.4	2.0	32.4	0.6	0.9
12	Date (Phoenix dactylifera)	17.1	35.5	3.1	0	1.1	0.2	6.4
13	Eucalyptus (Eucalyptus globulus)*	9.1	26.2	1.4	2.0	21.5	6.5	2.7
14	Mustard, black (Brassica nigra)	13.2	21.7	8.6	2.7	22.0	1.2	2.5
15	Mustard, common (B. campestris)	9.9	25.3	9.6	1.1	21.7	1.8	2.8
16	Oak (Quercus kelloggii)	11.5	19.1	6.6	1.1	32.5	2.0	2.0
17	Olive (Olea europaea)	10.1	16.7	4.7	1.1	28.3	5.8	1.9
18	Peach (Prunus persica)	8.5	26.5	2.7	1.6	21.8	9.0	2.8
19	Pine, digger (Pinus sabiniana)*	14.1	7.5	2.0	3.5	7.5	3.5	2.6
20	Pine, lodgepole (P. contorta)	7.0	7.0	2.0	3.7	41.2	3.4	1.3
21	Pine, monterey (P. radiata)*	11.2	13.4	1.8	2.4	0.05	11.4	2.4
22	Red-maids (Calandrinia ciliata)	9.1	16.8	5.7	7.1	29.1	0.05	2.7
23	Thistle, milk (Silybum marianum)	5.5	19.9	7.6	1.2	26.4	0.2	1.9
24	Thistle (Centaurea solstitialis)	16.2	21.2	6.6	1.2	21.6	2.1	1.8
25	Walnut (Juglans hindsii)	3.9	23.2	17.6				3.1
26	Willow, black (Salix nigra)*	12.3	22.2	4.2	1.4	30.2	0.6	2.6

Data applicable to bee-collected pollen except for species indicated by an asterisk (*). Bees add reducing sugars, such as honey or nectar, when collecting pollen. Values are g per 100 g pollen.

67. LIGNIFIED CELL WALLS: CHEMICAL COMPOSITION
Values are grams per 100 grams, dry-weight tissue.

	Beech (Fagus)[1]		Fir (Abies)[2]		Spruce (Picea)[3]		Pine (Pinus sylvestris)				Poplar[4]		Rye[5]	Wheat[6]
Constituent	Sapwood	Heartwood	Sapwood	Heartwood	Sapwood	Heartwood	Sapwood	Heartwood	Wood Near Branches	Branch Wood	17 yr old	43 yr old		
1 Cellulose	49[7]				49[7]		49	50	51	47	47	44	52	48
2 Mannan	9.1[7]						12	9.8	7.7	7				
3 Galactan	0.3[7]						0.3	0.5	1.1	1.6				
4 Hexosans											16.1	16.7		
5 Pentosans	27[7]				6.7[7]		10	11.1	11.6	13.4	15.9	17.1	30	27
6 Polyuronides					2.5[7]									
7 Lignin	23[7]				28[7]		29	29	29	31	19.3	24.3	15.7	16.2
8 Liposoluble extract					1.8[7]		3.5	5.9	12.1	29	2	2.4	3	4.1
9 Water	97	65	189	45	170	34								
10 Protein	0.13	0.12	0.098	0.091	0.06	0.06								
11 Fat	0.32	0.27	0.07	0.35	0.53	1.25								
12 Starch	0.08	0.07												
13 Hexosan	↑		11.76	8.42	9.21	9.23								
14 Xylan	20.8	20.0	12.54	10.44	13.48	11.40								
15 Methylpentosan	↓		2.02	2.60	1.34	1.52								
16 Lignin	22.9	22.9	28.7	29.6	30.3	30.2								
17 Cellulose	49.3	49.3	40.1	41.8	39.1	40.3								
18 Water-soluble sugars	2.4	1.4	1.66	2.14	1.86	1.61								
19 Resin and wax	0.06	0.14	0.40	1.76	0.63	2.18								
20 Humin			5.79	5.51	5.76	5.80								
21 Ash	0.39	0.33	0.25	0.42	0.24	0.30					0.8	0.7	5.5	6.5
22 K_2O	0.12	0.09	0.05	0.16	0.04	0.04								
23 Na_2O	0.002	0.003												
24 CaO	0.12	0.12	0.11	0.09	0.12	0.13								
25 MgO	0.04	0.03	0.03	0.04	0.05	0.04								
26 MnO	0.004	0.003												
27 Fe_2O_3	0.02	0.03												
28 SiO_2	0.02	0.03												
29 P_2O_5	0.02	0.02	0.02											
30 SO_3	0.03	0.03			0.03	0.03								
31 Cl	0.007	0.005	0.004	0.005	0.001	0.002								

/1/ Fagus sylvatica. /2/ Abies alba. /3/ Picea abies. /4/ Populus canadensis. /5/ Secale cereale. /6/ Triticum esculentum. /7/ Type of wood unspecified.

68. CORN COLEOPTILE: CHEMICAL COMPOSITION

	Constituent	9 mm[1] mg[2]	9 mm[1] g/100g[3]	32 mm[1] mg[2]	32 mm[1] g/100g[3]	55 mm[1] mg[2]	55 mm[1] g/100g[3]		Constituent	9 mm[1] mg[2]	9 mm[1] g/100g[3]	32 mm[1] mg[2]	32 mm[1] g/100g[3]	55 mm[1] mg[2]	55 mm[1] g/100g[3]
	Cell wall								Cell content						
1	Cellulose	0.19	8.3	0.93	13.2	1.62	13.0	4	Water solubles	1.02	44	2.65	40	5.70	46
2	Hemicelluloses	0.23	9.0	0.97	14.5	1.37	11.0	5	Protein	0.51	22.2	1.02	15.2	1.63	13.1
3	Pectin	0.05	2.2	0.27	4.0	0.58	4.7	6	Ash	0.16	6.9	0.30	4.4	0.44	3.6

/1/ Refers to length of corn coleoptile. /2/ mg per coleoptile. /3/ Grams per 100 grams, dry-weight tissue.

69. NECTAR: SUGAR CONTENT
Unless otherwise specified, values are grams of indicated sugar per 100 grams or milliliters nectar.

	Species	Total Sugar mg/fl/24 hr[1]	Total Sugar g/100g[2]
1	Alfalfa (Medicago sativa)	0.1	33
2	Apple (Pyrus malus)	0.8	75
3	Banana (Musa paradisiaca sapientum)	74	27
4	Cherry, sour (Prunus cerasus)	1.2	15
5	Cherry, sweet (P. avium)	0.5	21
6	Cucumber (Cucumis sativus)	1.0	30
7	Horsechestnut (Aesculus hippocastanum)	1.1[2]	69
8	Hound's-tongue (Cynoglossum amabile)	0.3	36
9	Jasmine (Jasminum primulinum)	0.3	33
10	Locust (Robinia pseudoacacia)	1.0	55
11	Milkweed (Asclepias cornutii)	3.1	58
12	Morning glory (Ipomoea purpurea)	8.0	41
13	Nasturtium (Tropaeolum majus)	1.7	46
14	Nettle (Lamium album)	0.8[2]	42
15	Pear (Pyrus communis)	0.3	16
16	Pumpkin (Cucurbita pepo)	28	28
17	Rape (Brassica napus)	0.5	47
18	Raspberry (Rubus idaeus)	7.6	46
19	Snapdragon (Antirrhinum majus)	1.5	45
20	Storax (Styrax officinalis)	1.1	79
21	Sunflower (Helianthus annuus)	0.3	38
22	Sweetclover (Melilotus alba)	0.04	36

	Species	Total Sugar g/100ml	Fructose g/100ml	Glucose g/100ml
23	Basswood (Tilia vulgaris)	21-42	5.4-10	5.3-9.8
24	Blackberry (Rubus fruticosus)	15.4-45	5.2-14.2	5.3-13.5
25	Borage (Borago officinalis)	22-29	3.8-6.8	4.0-6.9
26	Clover (Trifolium pratense)	8.3-30	2.3-8.0	0.7-2.2
27	Clover (T. repens)	25-39	9.6-14.2	7.7-12.2
28	Fireweed (Epilobium angustifolium)	18.4-41	7.9-16.3	5.5-11.3
29	Ivy (Hedera helix)	10-11.5	2.5-2.6	7.6-8.7
30	Lavender (Lavandula spica)	24-32	2.8-4.4	2.0-3.2
31	Loganberry (Rubus loganobaccus)	17-51	8.3-26	8.3-25
32	Mint (Pycnanthemum pilosum)	14-26	4.6-9.4	0.2-0.6
33	Mustard (Brassica alba)	9.3-17.6	4.3-8.3	5.2-9.5

	Species	Total Sugar g/100g	Sucrose g/100g	Fructose g/100g	Glucose g/100g
34	Cotton, acala (Gossypium sp)	28	0.71	14.27	10.36
35	Cotton, pima (G. barbadense)	20	0.35	10.36	9.25
36	Eucalyptus (Eucalyptus globulus)	16.5	5.78	5.47	5.23
37	Prune, French (Prunus domestica)	20	1.83	←—18.20—→	
38	Prune, Italian (P. domestica)	9.9	0.76	←— 9.10 —→	
39	Poinsettia (Euphorbia pulcherrima)	48	9.69	17.48	21.01
40	Orange, navel (Citrus sinensis)	26	12.87	7.46	5.42
41	Orange, Valencia (C. sinensis)	23.4	12.38	6.08	5.06
42	Wax-plant (Hoya carnosa)	41	29	←—11.9—→	

/1/ mg of nectar sugar produced by each flower of the plant specified per 24 hr period. /2/ Value from small number of determinations.

Values, except those for "Water, Free," are grams per 100 grams dry weight of organism, whole virus complex, or related material. Those for "Water, Free," are grams per 100 grams wet weight, except where otherwise indicated.

Organism or Related Material	Protein	Carbo-hydrate[1]	Lipid, Total	DNA[2]	RNA[3]	Water, Free	Ash	C	H	N	P	S
Fungi												
1 Alternaria spp								46.0-51.0		4.0		
2 Aspergillus clavatus	22-35	57.6	7.6-16.6					48.8		3.6-5.6		
3 A. nidulans	13-26	54.5	16.8-19.9					49.4		2.1-4.1		
4 A. niger	28.1	69.3	0.3-26				1.5-7.5	41.0-49.4		4.7-7.6	0.1-0.3	0.08-0.13
5 A. oryzae	34-38	61.3	1.8-5.6				8.1	42.1-45.8		5.4-6.1	1.72	0.04
6 A. sydowi	21-35	68.1	5.0-12.0					39.8-52.2		3.3-5.7		
7 Cephalothecium roseum								52.5				
8 Cladosporium spp								52.5-53.5		2.6		
9 Dematium pullulans								44.1		2.8-4.7		
10 Fusarium javanicum								55.5				
11 Gliocladium spp								53.1		2.4		
12 Helminthosporium gramineum								51.3		3.2-3.7		
13 Mucor stolonifer			7.0				6.9			8.2		
14 Penicillium chrysogenum	15-44	54.0	2.3-7.1					45.4-48.2		2.4-7.0		
15 P. cyaneo-fulvum	22-36	60.5	3.2-8.2							5.8		
16 Rhizopus nigricans							6.1-12.2			5.8		
17 Rhodotorula gracilis			31.2-49									
18 Saccharomyces cerevisiae	61.3	25.4[4]	4.8				8.5			8.4		
19 Sordaria spp								49.8				
20 Sporotrichum carneolum								51.1				
21 Trichoderma lignorum								49.4		2.6-10.3		
22 Torulopsis lipofera			28.1							5.4	5.2	
23 T. utilis			6.4							7.3-9.2		
24 Ustilago avenae								52.0				
25 Yeast		790-830[5]	7			61-67	8.7			7.5		
26 Yeast cell wall	13	+	8.5			11.2	3.2			2.1	0.3	
Bacteria												
27 Agrobacterium tumefaciens		1.5	7-8.1			5.0-8.2[6]	6.8-27.8			5.3-10.3	2.0-4.3	0-0.3
28 Azotobacter chroöcoccum						85	4.2	22.4		2.9		
29 Bacillus anthracis						80	7.8			9.2		
30 B. anthracis, spores						85	1.2	52.1	6.8	12.4-16.2		
31 B. mycoides	52.4		0.4			88	5.6			10.3-11.3		
32 B. subtilis	10.1%[7]		4.4			0[8]	10.8			10.1	3.1	
33 B. subtilis, spores	63.7			1.5	4.4	69[8]				11.2	1.8	
34 Brucella abortus	13.3%[7]	1.1-1.5[9]	5-6			4-5[6]	4.8-5.1			13.2-13.4	1.2	0.5
35 Br. melitensis	12.8%[7]	1.8-2.7[9]				3.5-5.1[6]	4.5-5.3			12.7-13	1.3	0.4
36 Br. suis	13.8%[7]	2.6-3.4[9]				1.1-2.2[6]	4.3-5.1			13.7-14	1.4	0.6
37 Corynebact. diphtheriae	9.8%[7]		4.9	1.7	4.8	84		48.9	8.6	9.8-11.2	0.6	1.4
38 Diplococcus pneumoniae[10]	10.4%[7]						5.8[11]	50[11]		9.4		
39 Escherichia coli	72.4	4.0	4.0	5.2	19.1	73	8.6			11.9-13.2	2.7	0.1
40 Klebsiella pneumoniae	8.9%[7]	36.1				86	3.0-7.2	49		8.9		
41 Malleomyces mallei	12.6%[7]		39.3			76	5.2	41.8	5.9	12.6-14.0	1.1	1.0
42 Micrococcus pyogenes[12]	54.9		2.8				13.9			13.2	1.8	0.4
43 Mycobact. tuberculosis	53.6		39.0			85.9	9.6	47.4-63	7-9.2	7.3-9.4	0.6-2.7	0.2-1.4
44 Neisseria gonorrheae		5.1-5.3	10-10.3				7.2-8.9			12.4-13.3		7.2-8.9
45 Proteus vulgaris	47.0	14.2	11.5			80	10.9			8.8		
46 Pseudomonas aeruginosa				4.9	4.4	75	9.0			10.3		
47 Salmonella typhimurium	9.6%[7]		4.9			78				9.6		
48 S. typhosa	9.9%[7]					79	5.7			9.9		
49 Serratia marcescens						78	8.9-13.9			10.6		
50 Shigella dysenteriae	74.0[13]		5.4[13]			78	8.3			8.9		
51 Streptococcus pyogenes[14]										13.2-13.7	2.3	
52 Vibrio comma	73.1			2.1	1.6	73	1.3-3.7	50		9.8-12.3		
Viruses, Rickettsiae and Related Materials												
53 Equine encephalomyelitis[15]	49	4.0	54	0	4.4		2.8	62.2	9.2	7.7	2.2	
54 Influenza A, PR 8	65	4-8[4]	44	0	0.9	52.0	3.3	53.2-55.1	7.9	10.0-10.3	0.9-1.1	
55 Influenza B, Lee	64	13.1(?)	33	0	0.9	34.5		52.7		9.6-10.4	0.7-0.94	
56 Influenza, swine	68	10.0	24	+	?	43.3		51.4		9.0	0.87	
57 Japanese B encephalitis							4.8	54.4	7.5	11.9	1.5	
58 Newcastle disease[16]	67	7.1	27					51.8		9.9	0.85	
59 Rabbit papilloma, Shope	90	6.5	1.5[17]	8.7		58.0	2.5	49.6	7.2	14.5-15.0	0.94	2.2
60 Rous sarcoma							2.0-5.8			15.3		
61 Vaccinia, element. bodies	89	2.8	5.7	5.6	0	5.6[6]	0.72	33.7		15.3	0.57	
62 Alfalfa mosaic	85	9.0			15		3.0	53.8	6.7	15.2	1.4	0.65
63 Cucumber, 3, 4	94	2.3			6		2.3	50.0	7.0	15.4	0.54	0
64 Potato mosaic, latent	92				6			47.8	7.4±[18]	14.6-16.1	0.5-0.7	1.1
65 Ribgrass mosaic	94	2.3			6		2.3	50.3	7.0	15.7	0.6	0.64
66 Southern bean mosaic	79				21		5.7	45.6	6.5	17.0	1.9	1.3
67 Tobacco mosaic	94	2.5		0	6		1.5	51.0	7.6	16.6	0.56	0.2
68 Tobacco necrosis	82	6.5			18		5.8-7.0	45.0	6.5	16.3	1.6	1.6
69 Tobacco ringspot	60	18.0		0	40			50.5	7.6	14.6	3.6	0.39
70 Tomato mosaic, aucuba		2.5			6		1.5	50.0	7.0	16.7	0.52	0.2
71 Tomato bushy stunt	83	6.0		0	17		3.0	47.5	7.7±[19]	15.8-16.4	1.3-1.5	0.4-0.8
72 Tomato enation		2.5			6		1.0	50.0	7.0	16.7	0.54	0.3
73 Turnip mosaic, yellow	65					35				14.4-15.3	3.4	
74 Bacteriophage, staph.		1.5					13	40.6-41.8	5.3	14.1-14.6	4.6-5.0	
75 Bacteriophage, T[2]	51	13.6	2.6(?)	50	0			42.0		13.5	4.8	
76 Rickettsia prowazeki	35	4.1	47	1.5±[21]			3.0			12.2	0.93	
77 Chick embryo tissue[22]	41	7.0	35		10.6							

/1/ By difference (includes ash varying from 2.5-8.5%), unless otherwise indicated. /2/ Desoxyribonucleic acid. /3/ Ribonucleic acid. /4/ Actual analysis. /5/ As μg glucose. /6/ Loss in water. /7/ Percent nitrogen. /8/ Bound water. /9/ Crude C polysaccharide. /10/ Type I. /11/ Type not specified. /12/ Var. aureus. /13/ Paradysenteriae, Flexner. /14/ Mucoid. /15/ Eastern. /16/ California. /17/ Fatty acid. /18/ Range 7.3-7.6. /19/ Range 7.2-8.2. /20/ Range 33.4-40.3. /21/ Range 0.5-2.5. /22/ Normal component.

Values, unless otherwise indicated, are: for protein, grams per 100 grams of protein on a moisture-free, ash-free basis; for fungi and bacteria,

	Substance	Alanine	Arginine	Aspartic Acid	Cystine[1]	Glutamic Acid	Glycine	Histidine	Isoleucine	Leucine
					Animal Proteins					
1	Actin	6.3	6.6	10.9	0.9	14.8	5.2	2.9	7.5	8.2
2	Albumin, egg	7.6	6.0	9.3	2.8	16.5	3.6	2.9	7.0	9.9
3	Albumin, serum, human		6.2	10.4	5.6	17.4	1.6	3.5	1.7	11.0
4	Casein, α-, cow	3.8	4.3	8.4	0.4	22.5	2.3	2.9	6.4	7.9
5	Casein, human	2.0	3.4	4.7	0.6	20.9		2.0	6.3	12.2
6	Fibrin, beef	4.0	7.7	11.9	1.9	13.8	5.2	2.1	5.7	6.7
7	Fibrinogen, human	3.7	7.8	13.1	2.3	14.6	5.6	2.6	4.8	7.1
8	Fibroin, silk	25.8	1.1	2.6	0.0	2.2	43.6	0.4	1.2	0.9
9	Gelatin	10.0	8.0	7.5	0.1	10.8	26.0	0.8	1.3	2.9
10	Globulin, α-, serum[4]		7.7	9.0	1.5	21.6	3.1	2.8	1.7	14.2
11	Globulin, β-, serum[4]		6.8	9.8	3.4	14.5	5.6	2.8	5.0	8.2
12	Globulin, γ-, serum[4]		4.8	8.8	2.4	11.8	4.2	2.5	2.7	9.3
13	Hemoglobin, horse	9.8	3.7	10.6	0.5	8.2	5.6	7.8	1.6	16.6
14	Hemoglobin, human	10.2	3.3	11.0		7.2	4.8	8.4	0.2	15.1
15	Lactoglobulin, γ-	7.1	2.8	11.6	3.5	20.0	1.5	1.7	8.0	15.8
16	Myosin, rabbit	6.9	7.1	11.4	1.0	22.8	2.9	2.3	5.5	10.3
17	Wool	4.0	10.6	7.4	13.6	14.0	6.8	1.1	4.3	8.6
					Enzymes					
18	Pepsin		1.0	16.0	2.1	11.9	6.4	0.8	10.8	10.4
19	Phosphorylase	4.8	11.6	10.4	0.4	13.6	3.9	3.3	6.5	10.5
20	Ribonuclease		5.2	14.2	6.5	13.0	1.3	4.2	3.1	0
					Hormones					
21	Growth hormone, ox	.	9.0	10.4	2.3	12.9	3.7	2.6	4.1	12.1
22	Insulin	4.5	3.4	6.8	12.5	18.6	4.3	5.3	2.8	13.2
23	Lactogenic hormone, sheep		8.6	11.6	3.1	14.1	4.0	4.5	7.2	12.5
					Plant Proteins					
24	Arachin, peanut	4.0	13.5	4.9	1.4	17.0	3.2	2.4	7.7	8.0
25	Edestin	5.5	16.7	12.0	1.2	20.7	5.1	2.6	4.6	7.4
26	Gliadin	2.1	2.7	1.3	2.6	45.7	0.5	1.9	5.4	6.5
27	Globulin, pumpkin seed		16.3					2.2	4.6	8.0
28	Globulin, wheat bran		13.3					1.9	3.8	6.4
29	Gluten, corn		2.1		1.0	24.5	4.3	1.5	5.1	16.0
30	Gluten, wheat	2.8	3.3	9.6	1.9	27.0	7.0	1.9	4.2	7.0
31	Phaseolin, kidney bean		6.0					2.2	6.7	10.5
32	Zein	12.3	2.0	6.6	0.9	26.9	0.4	1.7	7.3	23.7
					Fungi[5]					
33	Aspergillus niger		1.0	+		+		0.9	0.9	1.5
34	A. niger, before sporulation		2.6					1.2	1.4	2.6
35	A. niger, after sporulation		1.4					1.5	0.7	1.3
36	A. niger, spores		1.2					0.5	1.0	1.7
37	A. oryzae		+		+			+		
38	A. sydowi		0.6	0.2		0.1		0.1	0.2	1.4
39	Penicillium notatum		1.4					1.7	1.2	2.1
40	Rhizopus nigricans		1.2					1.0	1.0	1.5
41	Rhodotorula rubra		3.7					2.0	2.1	3.3
42	Saccharomyces cerevisiae		2.4					2.7	2.5	3.8
43	Yeast, baker's[6]		5	8	1.2	11		7	3	5
44	Yeast, brewer's[6]		10	7	1.5	12		7	3	5
45	Yeast, commercial		4.3		1.0			2.8	5.9	7.4
					Bacteria[5]					
46	Aerobacter aerogenes[7]		10.4			5.6		3.4		
47	Agrobacter tumefaciens			2.8		1.6				
48	Azotobacter agile[8]		9.5		0.4			0.1		
49	A. vinelandii[8]		8.3–13.2	7.3	0.4	6.8		0.1–7.9		
50	Bacillus brevis[7]		9.9			7.3		2.5		
51	B. subtilis[7]		7.6			5.3		2.5		
52	Corynebacterium diphtheriae[8]		5.3	3.9		3.0		0.6	1.2	1.0
53	Escherichia coli[8]		6.6–7.8		–			1.9–6.4	6.3	7.4
54	E. coli, bacteriophage[9, 10], host[11]	8.4	8.2	9.6		9.6	7.9	3.3	4.6	8.7
55	Lactobacillus arabinosus[8]		3.3			10.5–12.0		1.7–1.9	5.5	5.9–6.2
56	L. casei[8]		3.6			9.7		1.9	6.2–6.7	6.8
57	Micrococcus pyogenes, S[12]		8.9					6.3		
58	M. pyogenes, R[13]		5.4					5.1		
59	Mycobacterium tuberculosis[8]		3.8–13.8		1.3–1.7	5.1		0.9–7.2		
60	Neisseria gonorrheae		4.3–6.0		0.6					
61	Proteus vulgaris[7]		7.7			4.9		4.4		
62	Streptococcus fecalis[7]		5.4			4.4		2.0		
63	Streptomyces griseus		2.9					0.8	1.6	3.8
					Viruses[5]					
64	Influenza A, PR 8	2.5	5.0	7.4		7.7	2.5	1.4	5.2	5.3
65	Papilloma, Shope	3.1	7.0	10.7	6.4[14]	11.4	3.1	1.8	4.1	7.5
66	Polyhedral, silk worm[7]	4.7	18.4	8.1	+	3.7	5.8	1.4	7.6[13]	+[13]
67	Cucumber 4	6.1	9.3	13.1	–	6.5	1.5	–	4.6	9.4
68	Rib-grass	6.4	9.9	12.6	–	15.5	1.3	0.7	5.9	9.0
69	Tobacco mosaic	5.1	9.8	13.5	–	11.3	1.9	–	6.6	9.3
70	Tomato aucuba[16]	5.1	11.1	13.7	–	11.5	1.9	–	5.7	9.2
71	Bacteriophage, E. coli[9, 10]	9.4	6.5	12.0		12.0	7.3	<2.6	3.9	6.5

/1/ Values are cystine 1/2, and do not include small quantities of cysteine reported for some proteins. /2/ Total nitrogen accounted for by amino proteins of unknown purity, in contrast with the animal and plant proteins which were mostly highly purified preparations. /6/ Expressed as grams bacterial cell infected with bacterial phage. /12/ Var. aureus, smooth. /13/ Var. aureus, rough. /14/ Cysteine plus cystine. /15/ Isoleucine, grams per 100 grams dry weight of organism; for viruses, grams per 100 grams of the whole virus complex.

Lysine	Methionine	Phenyl-alanine	Proline	Serine	Threonine	Tryptophan	Tyrosine	Valine	Nitrogen, Total, %	Nitrogen Recovered², %	Hydrolysate, Total³, %	
Animal Proteins													
7.6	4.5	4.8	5.1	5.9	7.0	2.0	5.8	4.9	16.7	96	111	1
6.5	5.3	7.2	3.8	8.2	4.0	1.2	4.1	8.8	15.8	97	115	2
12.3	1.3	7.8	5.1	3.7	5.0	0.2	4.7	7.7	16.0			3
8.9	2.5	4.6	7.5	6.3	4.9	1.6	8.1	6.3		102		4
5.5	2.2	5.8	8.9	5.4	4.5	1.5	5.4	5.0		79		5
9.0	2.2	7.6	5.3	15.3	9.9	3.6	5.6	5.6	16.8	101	123	6
9.2	2.5	4.6	5.7	6.9	6.2	3.3	5.4	4.1				7
0.8	0.1	1.6	1.0	13.9	1.3	0.4	10.8	3.6	10.0	89	111	8
4.1	0.9	2.6	16.5	3.4	2.2	0.0	0.4	2.3	17.6	95	123	9
8.9	1.4	4.6	4.7	5.0	4.9	1.9	4.5	5.2				10
6.6	1.7	4.7	7.1	7.1	6.1	2.0	6.0	7.0	15.2			11
8.1	1.1	4.6	8.1	11.4	8.4	2.9	6.8	9.7	16.0			12
8.6	1.0	6.5	8.5	5.8	4.4	1.2	2.9	9.0	16.8	97	112	13
9.6	1.4	7.6	4.4	5.0	5.8	1.5	3.0	10.6	16.9			14
11.3	3.2	4.8	5.0	4.4	5.5	1.9	3.7	5.8	15.5	96	118	15
12.4	3.3	4.5	2.5	4.3	4.9	0.8	3.2	4.9	16.7	98	111	16
3.3	0.7	4.0	8.0	9.8	6.5	1.5	5.5	5.4	16.2	88	115	17
Enzymes													
1.5	1.7	6.4	5.0	12.2	9.6	2.4	8.5	7.1	15.4	86	113	18
7.2	2.7	6.2	4.7	3.4	4.4	2.0	5.9	7.3	16.5			19
10.4	4.5	3.6	3.6	12.0	9.0	0	7.9	7.3		99		20
Hormones													
7.2	2.8	7.9			8.9	0.8	4.3	3.9		88		21
2.4	0.0	8.3	2.5	5.2	2.1	0.0	13.4	7.8	15.7	90	110	22
5.3	3.6	4.1	6.2	6.5	4.8	1.2	4.7	5.9	15.9			23
Plant Proteins													
3.5	0.7	6.4	6.0	5.3	2.7	0.7	5.9	4.5	18.3	72	98	24
3.2	2.4	5.9	4.3	6.3	3.9	1.5	4.3	5.7	18.6	102	113	25
0.8	1.7	6.1	13.4	4.9	2.1	0.6	3.2	2.7	17.7	91	105	26
2.8		7.2			2.6			6.5	16.3			27
4.2	1.0	4.2			3.5	0.9		6.6	13.3			28
1.2	2.5	4.6			4.0	0.3	3.8	5.7	10.9	83	82	29
1.7	1.5	4.1	8.0	4.0	2.5	1.2	1.3	4.1	13.5	70	94	30
7.2	1.1	8.0			4.2	0.5		6.0	16			31
0.0	2.2	6.2	10.5	7.7	2.5	0.1	5.3	3.5	16.0	99	120	32
Fungi⁵													
1.0	0.2	0.8			1.1	0.3	0.3	1.1				33
2.7	0.5	1.5			1.7	0.5		1.8				34
1.2	0.2	0.8			0.9	0.3		0.9				35
1.3	0.2	1.0			1.3	0.3		1.3				36
+						+	+					37
0.8			0.5	1.8	0.4	0.04	0.4	0.1				38
1.5	0.4	1.2			1.4	0.5		1.5				39
1.6	0.3	0.8			1.0	0.2		1.1				40
3.0	0.5	1.7			1.8	0.4		2.5				41
3.1	0.6	2.1			2.4	0.6		2.8				42
8	0.8	3	3	4	4	-	3	7				43
8	0.8	1	3	3	6	-	2	7				44
7.5	2.7	4.1			5.5	1.3	3.6	5.0				45
Bacteria⁵													
6.8							1.4					46
												47
5.8						0.5	2.1					48
2.5-4.1						0.2	2.5					49
7.9							2.2					50
7.5							1.5					51
4.1			3.8			+	3.0	3.9				52
4.8-10.5						0.6-1.9	1.8	6.1				53
8.3	2.9	4.8	3.0	4.9	5.3	1.3	4.3	5.0				54
5.2-5.9	1.1	2.8			3.8	0.5		5.2-5.4				55
7.7	1.1	3.5			4.7	0.4-0.6		5.8				56
9.9												57
												58
1.3-7.7		13.7	4.0			1.7-2.7	1.3-2.1	16.3				59
				2.4-3.0	2.9-3.3	1.1	2.3					60
6.4							2.1					61
7.6							0.8					62
2.2	0.6	1.6			2.4	0.7	3.5					63
Viruses⁵													
3.6	2.3	3.7	2.6	2.2	3.7	1.1	3.1	3.4				64
7.0	2.1	4.6	5.5	4.0	5.1	1.0	5.8	5.4				65
3.0	1.8	+¹⁵	2.3	6.7	6.8	?	2.4	2.4				66
2.4	-	9.8	5.7	9.4	7.0	0.5	3.7	8.9				67
1.5	2.2	5.4	5.5	5.7	8.2	1.4	6.8	6.2				68
1.5	-	8.4	5.8	7.2	9.9	2.1	3.8	9.2				69
1.4	-	8.3	5.8	7.0	10.4	2.1	3.7	8.8				70
8.5	<1.3	4.2	5.0	4.8	7.0		3.7	6.5				71

acids. /3/ A value greater than 100 is the result of water addition during hydrolysis. /4/ Human. /5/ These analyses were made on mixtures of amino acid N/100g of whole yeast. /7/ As % of total N. /8/ As % of protein. /9/ T₄ phage. /10/ As % of total amino acids. /11/ Represents the plus leucine plus phenylalanine. /16/ Strain green aucuba.

72. CHROMOSOME NUMBERS: ANIMALS

Phyla are separated by solid lines; other major systematic groupings are separated by broken lines. Changes in alphabetical sequence of sections between lines indicated transitions from one group to another within a class. s = spermatogonium; o = oogonium; m = somatic cell. Data adapted and revised by S. Makino from his "Atlas of Chromosome Numbers in Animals." Superscripts after species refer to sex types in footnotes.

Species	Chromosome Number (2n)	Species	Chromosome Number (2n)	Species	Chromosome Number (2n)
1 Rhopalura ophiocomae	6m	84 Armadillidium opacum	54 s	167 Xiphidion gladiatum[2]	33 s
2 Sycon ciliatum	26 m	85 Ligia exotica	72 s	168 X. maculatum[2]	21 s
3 Hydra circumcincta	30 m	86 Porcellio scaber	56 s	169 Mantis religiosa[2]	27 s
4 H. vulgaris attenuata	32 s,o,m	87 Proasellus meridianus	16 s	170 Creobroter laevicolis[2]	27 s
5 Pelmatohydra obligactis	30 m	88 Trichoniscus elisabethae	16 s (3n, 24s)	171 Iris oratoria[2]	25 s
6 Moniezia expansa	12-14(?) m	89 Gammarus chevreuxi	52 s	172 Toxomantis sinensis[2]	27 s
7 Fasciola hepatica	12 o,m	90 Cambaroides japonicus	196 s	173 Bostra sp[2]	35 s
8 Parorchis acanthus	22 s	91 Macrocheira kampferi	106 s	174 Isagoras sp[2]	47 s
9 Schistosoma japonicum	16 s,o	92 Eupagurus ochotensis	254 s	175 Oncotophasma sp[2]	41 s
10 Polystomum integerrimum	20 m	93 Telphusa fluviatillis	78 s	176 Pseudophasma menius[2]	23 s
11 Aphanostoma diversicolor	20-30	94 Pediculopsis graminum	6 m (parth.,3m)	177 Diestrammena marmorata[2]	57 s
12 Stenostomum grandi	20-40	95 Agalena opulenta[3]	44 s	178 Tridactylus japonicus[2]	13 s
13 Mesostomum ehrenbergii	10 m	96 Aranea dumetorum[3]	14 s	179 Labidura riparia[5]	14 s
14 Microstomum bispiralis	16 s	97 Tetragnatha japonica[3]	24 s	180 Isoperla grammatica[2]	26 s
15 Dalyellia spp	4 s	98 Clubiona japonicola[3]	20 s	181 Perla maxima[3]	19 s
16 Amphibollela virginiana	4 s	99 Drapetisca socialis[3]	24 s	182 Perlodes microcephala[4]	27 s
17 Castrada sp	6 s	100 Heptathela kimurai[3]	80 s	183 Zootermopsis angusticollis	52♀ m
18 Polycystis goettei	16 s	101 Schizocosa crassipes[3]	22 s	184 Cerastiposocus venosus[2]	17 s
19 Plagiostomum stellatum	10 s	102 Oxyopes ramosus[3]	21 s	185 Lipeurus baculus	12♀ m
20 Curtisia foremanii	12 s,o	103 Philodromus roseus[3]	28 s	186 Ameletus costalis[5]	18 s,o
21 Thysanozoon brocchi	18 s,m	104 Icius elongatus[3]	28 s	187 Ephemera danica	11 s
22 Micrura caeca	32 m	105 Heteropoda venatoria[4]	41 s	188 Aeschna coerulea[2]	25 s, 26 o
23 Asplanchna intermedia	24 s, o m	106 Ariamnes cylindrogaster[3]	22 s	189 Anax junius[2]	27 s, 28 o
24 Dinophilus apatris	20 m	107 Xysticus viaticus[2]	23	190 Ictinus rapax[2]	23 s
25 Allolobophora chlorotica	32 m	108 Gagrellopsis nodulifera	16 s	191 Diplacodes trivialis[2]	25 s
26 Dendrobaena subrubicunda	68 m	109 Buthus martensii	24 s	192 Orthetrum sabina[2]	25 s
27 Eiseniella tetraedra	72 m	110 Tityus bahiensis	20 s	193 Sympetrum pedemontanum[2]	25 s
28 Lanice conchylega	6 m	111 Tachypleus tridentatus	26 s	194 Trithemis pallidinervis[2]	25 s
29 Ophryotrocha gracilis	10 s,o,m	112 Porocephalus armillatus	20 o	195 Ceriagrion rubiae[2]	27 s
30 Sabellaria spinulosa	8 s,m	113 Macrobiotus lacustris	10 m	196 Lestes sponsa[2]	25 s
31 Glossosiphonia complanata	26 s	114 Thereunema hilgendorfi[5]	36 s	197 Phyllaphis coweni	5 s, 6 o
32 Protoctepsis tesselata	16 m	115 Otocryptops sexspinosus[6]	15 s, 14 o	198 Aphis oenothera	10 s,m
33 Phascolosoma gouldii	20 m	116 Anurida maritima	8 o	199 A. salicetti	5 s, o m
34 Sagitta spp	18 s,m	117 Lepisma domestica	34 s	200 Chermes pectinata	20 ♀m
35 Mactra sp	24 m	118 Acrida turrita[2]	23 s	201 Euceraphis betulae	8 s,o,m
36 Compeloma rufum	12 o	119 Atractomorpha ambigua[2]	19 s	202 Hyalopterus purni	9 s
37 Pterotrachea mutica	32 m	120 Chorthippus (Stenobothrus) lineatus[2]	17 s	203 Macrosiphum pisi[2]	7 s, 8 ♀m
38 Tulotoma magnifica	24	121 Chortophaga viridifasciata[2]	23 s	204 Melahaxoanthus salicicola	6 s, ♀m
39 Viviparus contectoides	26	122 Chrysochraon japonicus[2]	17 s	205 Myzus linderae[2]	11 s, 12 o
40 Limacina retroversa	24 s,m	123 Circotettix verruculatus[2]	21 s	206 Phylloxera fallax[3]	10 s,o, ♀m
41 Montagua gouldii	32 m	124 Hesperotettix pratensis[2]	22 s	207 Tetraneura ulmi[2]	13 s, 14 o
42 Lymnaea japonica	36 s	125 Dissosteira sp[2]	23 s	208 Aphrophora coctalis[5]	30 s
43 Arion empiricorum	32 m	126 Gomphocerus rufus[2]	17 s	209 Clastoptera obtusa[2]	15 s
44 Euhadra awaensis	58 s	127 Locusta migratoria[2]	23 s	210 Dactylopius sp	10 ♀m, ♂s
45 Cepaea hortensis	48 s	128 Mecostethus lineatus[2]	23 s	211 Icerya purchasi	4 s,o,m
46 Helicigona arbustorum	48 s	129 Melanoplus dawsonii[2]	23 s	212 Gossyparia spuria	28 s, ♂m, ♀m
47 Helix aspersa	54 s	130 Mermiria bivittata[2]	22 s,o,m	213 Lecanium hesperium	14 m
48 H. pomatia univalens	24 s	131 Miramella dairisama[2]	21 s	214 Llaveia bouvari[2]	5 s, 6 o
49 Limax cinereo-niger	16 s	132 Oxya intricata[2]	23 s	215 Nautococcus schraderae[2]	5 ♂m, 6 ♀m
50 Incillaria fruhstorferi	48 s	133 Paratylotropidia brunneri[2]	19 s, 20♀m	216 Pseudococcus acericola	12 s,o
51 Polygra appressa	60-62 s	134 Philocleon anomalus[2]	12 s	217 Amphiscepa bivittata[2]	25 s
52 Stenotrema hirsutum	58 s	135 Podisma mikado[2]	21 s	218 Phlepsius irroratus[2]	15 s
53 Succinea horticola	34 s	136 Romalea microptera[2]	23 s	219 Canpylenchia curvata[2]	19 s
54 S. ovalis	40 s	137 Schistocerca alutacea[2]	23 s	220 Enchenopa binotata[5]	20 s,o
55 Echinorhynchus gigas	8 m	138 Stauroderus bicolor[2]	17 s	221 Entilia sinuata[2]	21 s
56 Ascaris lumbricoides[1]	43-48 s	139 Syrbula sp[2]	23 s	222 Vanduzea arcuata[2]	17 s
57 A. megalocephala bivalens	4 s,o,m	140 Teratodes monticolis[2]	23 s	223 Belostoma flumineum[5]	24 s
58 A. m. univalens	2 s,o,m	141 Traulia ornata[2]	23 s	224 Adelphocoris lineolatus[2]	17 s
59 Spirina parasitifera	14 s	142 Trimerotropis sp[2]	23 s	225 Notostira erratuca[2]	17 s
60 Heterakis sp[2]	9 s	143 Zubovskya glacialis[2]	21 s	226 Cimex stadleri	31 s
61 Rhabditis monohystera	20 o,m	144 Blatta orientalis[2]	47 s	227 Alydus calcaratus[2]	13 s
62 Ophiostomum mucronatum	12 m	145 Periplaneta australasiae[2]	27 s	228 Anasa tristis[2]	21 s
63 Strongylus paradoxus[2]	11 s	146 Acheta campestris[2]	29 s	229 Archimerus alternatus[2]	15 s
64 Gordius spp	4 s,o,m	147 Apithes agitator[2]	13 s	230 Camptopus lateralis[2]	13 s
65 Pedicellina americana	22 s,o,m	148 Endocous cavernicola[2]	19 s	231 Metapodius femoratus[5]	22 s,o
66 Asterias amurensis	30 s	149 Gryllus assimilis[2]	29 s	232 Diactor bilineatus[2]	21 s
67 Strongylocentrotus lividus	36 m	150 Lebinthus sp[2]	11 s	233 Syromastes marginatus[5]	22 s,o
68 Toxopneustes variegatus	36 m	151 Lipholplus kanetataki[2]	19 s	234 Phthia picta[2]	21 s
69 Henricia nipponica	54 s	152 Madasumma hibinonis[2]	15 s	235 Protenor belfragei[2]	13 s, 14 o
70 Artemia salina	42 s (4n,84s)	153 Oecanthus longicauda[5]	20 s	236 Callicorixa caledonica[5]	24 s
71 Daphnia pulex	20 s	154 Scapsipedus sp[2]	17 s	237 Cymatia bonsdorffi[5]	26 s
72 Heterocypris incongruens	20 o,m	155 Galloisiana nipponensis[5]	30 s	238 Corixa punctata[5]	24 s
73 Calanus finmarchicus	34 s,o	156 Gryllotalpa africana[2]	23 s	239 Leptocoris haemotoloma[2]	13 s
74 Diaptomus castor	34 m	157 Amblycorypha oblongifolia[2]	33 s	240 Dysodius lunatus[7]	31 s
75 Heterocope weismanni	32 s	158 Conocephalus sp[2]	33 s	241 Gerris lateralis[2]	21 s
76 Copilia denticornis	16 s	159 Ephippigera vitium[2]	29 s	242 Lygaeus turcius[5]	14 s,o
77 Cyclops fuscus	14 m	160 Hexacentrus mundus[2]	31 s	243 Hygotrechus sp[2]	21 s
78 C. gracilis	6 m	161 Isotima japonica[2]	27 s	244 Aphanus japonicus[8]	17 s
79 C. insignis	22 m	162 Kuwayamaea sapporensis[2]	27 s	245 Eremocoris erraticus[5]	20 s
80 C. viridis	12 s,o,m	163 Mecopoda elongata[2]	27 s	246 Geocoris japonicus[5]	20 s,o
81 Hersilia apodiformis	24 s,o,m	164 Odontura maraccana[2]	27 s	247 Macrodema micropterum[5]	18 o
82 Mytilicola intestinalis	22 o,m	165 Saga pedo	68♀ m	248 Nysius jacobeae[5]	14 s,o
83 Scalpellum scalpellum	32 s,o	166 Scudderia sp[2]	31 s	249 Oncopeltus fasciatus[5]	16 s,o

/1/ X_1-X_5♂. /2/ X-O♂. /3/ X_1X_2-O♂. /4/ 3X-O♂. /5/ X-Y♂. /6/ 4X-5Y♂. /7/ X_1X_2-Y♂. /8/ 4X-Y♂.

72. CHROMOSOME NUMBERS: ANIMALS (Concluded)

Phyla are separated by solid lines; other major systematic groupings are separated by broken lines. Changes in alphabetical sequence of sections between lines indicated transitions from one group to another within a class. s = spermatogonium; o = oogonium; m = somatic cell. Data adapted and revised by S. Makino from his "Atlas of Chromosome Numbers in Animals." Superscripts after species refer to sex types in footnotes.

	Species	Chromosome Number (2n)		Species	Chromosome Number (2n)		Species	Chromosome Number (2n)
250	Rhyparochromus chiragra[5]	14 s	333	Coccinella bruchii[5]	18 s	417	Mollienisia sphenops	46 s
251	Stigonocoris rusticus[5]	18 o	334	Epilachna pustulosa[5]	20 s	418	Platypoecilus maculatus	48 s
252	Mesovelia furcata[8]	35 s	335	Harmonia axyridis[5]	16 s	419	Xiphophorus hellerii	48 s
253	Naucoris cimicoides[2]	51 s	336	Synonycha grandis[5]	20 s,o	420	Oncorhynchus keta	74 s
254	Ranatra linearis[9]	43 s	337	Acanthoscelides obtectus	20 ♀m	421	Osmerus eperlanus	58 m
255	Notonecta undulata[5]	26 s	338	Otiorhynchus arcticus	22 s	422	Salmo carpio	96 s
256	Aelia accuminata[5]	14 s	339	O. gemmatus	33 ♀m (3n)	423	Thymallus thymallus	102 m
257	Banasa calva[5]	26 s,o	340	O. scaber	44 ♀m (4n)	424	Ichthyophis glutinosus	42 s, ♂m
258	Coptosoma punctissimum[5]	12 s	341	Polydrosus mollis	22 o	425	Hynobius nebulosus	56 s
259	Dinidor rufocinctus[10]	21 s, 22 o	342	Hydrous acuminatus[5]	30 s	426	Amblystoma mexicanum	28 s
260	Dolycoris baccarum[5]	14 o	343	Paslidoremus inclinatus[2]	19 s	427	Salamandra salamandra	24 s
261	Eusacoris aeneus[5]	16 s	344	Meloe sp[5]	20 s	428	Triturus cristatus	24 s
262	Euschistus fissilis[5]	14 s	345	Anomala rufocuprea[5]	18 s	429	Cryptobranchus allegheniensis	62 s
263	Graphosoma rubrolineatum[5]	14 s	346	Popillia japonica[5]	18 s	430	Bufo arenarum	22 s
264	Halyomorpha picus[5]	14 s	347	Listrotrophus cingulatus[5]	26 s	431	B. calamita	22 s
265	Megymenum gracilicorne[5]	20 s	348	Blaps lusitanica[15]	19 s, 20 o	432	B. viridis	22 s, o
266	Nezara hilaris[5]	14 s,o	349	Biaperis boleti[5]	14 s	433	Alytes obstetricans	36 s
267	Palomena angulosa[5]	16 s,o	350	Tenebrio molitor[5]	20 s,o	434	Bombina orientalis	24 s
268	Pentatoma juniperina[5]	14 s	351	Acroschismus wheeleri	16 s,o,m	435	Hyla arborea	24 s
269	Rhytidolomia sancia[5]	14 o	352	Apis mellifica	16 s,o	436	Pelobates fuscus	26 s
270	Thyanta calceata[10]	27 s, 28 o	353	Habrobracon pectinophorae	20 s,o	437	Xenopus laevis	36 s
271	Largus cinctus[2]	11 s, 12 o	354	Trigonaspis megaptera	10 s	438	Rana japonica	26 s
272	Pyrrhocoris apterus[2]	23 s, 24 o	355	Diprion polystomum	6 s, 12 ♀m	439	R. pipiens	26 s
273	Polididus armatissimus[5]	12 s	356	Melittobia chalybii	5 ♂m, 10 ♀m	440	R. temporaria	26 s,m
274	Velinus nodipes[11]	28 s, 30 o	357	Lasius flava	24 ♀m	441	Rhacophorus schlegelii	26 s
275	Velia currens[2]	25 s	358	Aenoplex smithii	13 s, 26 o	442	Alligator mississippiensis	32 s
276	Rhaphidia xanthostigma[5]	26 s	359	Pteromalus puparum	5 ♂m, 10 ♀m	443	Chelonia japonica[13]	56 s, 55 o
277	Glyptobasis dentifera[5]	22 s	360	Thrinax macula	7 s, 14 o	444	Emys orbicularis	50 s
278	Chrysopa aspera[5]	12 s,o	361	Trichogramma chilonis	5 s, 10 o	445	Calotes versicolor[13]	34 s, 33 o
279	C. flava[5]	14 s	362	Polistes fadwigae	9 s, 18 o	446	Anguis fragilis	44 s,o
280	C. perla[5]	12 s,o	363	P. snelleni	13 s, 26 o	447	Chamaelon vulgaris	24 s,o
281	C. vulgaris	12 s,o,♀m	364	Fucellia marina	12 m	448	Eublepharis variegatus	32 s
282	Semidalis albata	18 o	365	Asilus lecythus[5]	14 s	449	Gymnodactylus milliusi	38 s
283	Hemerobius stigma[5]	14 s	366	Bibo bortulanus[5]	10 m	450	Heloderma suspectum	38 s
284	Myrmeleon europaeus[5]	14 s,o	367	Calliphora erythrocephala[5]	12 s,o,m	451	Anolis carolinensis	34 s
285	Palpares pardus asanai[5]	26 s	368	Miastor americana	48 s,o, 12 ♀m	452	Sceloporus spinosus	22 s
286	Panorpa japonica[2, 12]	46 o	369	Lasioptera asterspinosae	8 ♀m, 6 ♂m,	453	Lacerta viridis	38 s
287	Stenopsyche griseipennis[13]	26 s, 25 ♀m	370	Chironomus spp	8 s 50s,o	454	Takydromus tachydromoides	38 s
288	Chaetopteryx villosa	60 s	371	Scatophaga pallida[5]	12 s,o	455	Lacerta vivipara[13]	36 s, 35 o
289	Halesus tesselatus	42 s	372	Aedes spp[5]	6 s,o	456	Scincis officinalis	32 s
290	Limnophilus affinis	12 s	373	Anopheles punctipennis[5]	6 s,o	457	Ameiva surinamensis	50 s
291	Phragmatobia fuliginosa[14]	56 s, 58 o	374	Culex spp[5]	6 s,o,m	458	Naja naja atra	38 s
292	Abraxas grossulariata	26 s,o	375	Drosophila melanogaster[5]	8 s,o	459	Ancistrodon acutus	36 s
293	Biston hirtaria	28 s,o	376	D. willistoni[5]	6 s,o	460	Vipera aspis	42 s
294	Dendrolimus jezoensis	60 s	377	D. melanica[5]	10 s,o, ♂m	461	Pica pica sericea[13]	82 s, 81 o
295	Bombyx mori	56 s	378	D. aldrichi[5]	12 o	462	Cuculus canorus	72 s
296	Lymantria dispar	62 s,o	379	D. virilis[5]	12 s,o,m	463	Emberiza elegans	84 s
297	L. japonica	62 s,o	380	D. pseudoobscura[5]	10 s,m	464	Egretta garzetta	76 s
298	Orgyia thyellina	22 s	381	D. ananassae[5]	8 s,o,m	465	Aix sponsa	80 s
299	Dicranura erminea	56 s	382	D. obscura[5]	10 s,o, ♂m	466	Anas platyrhyncha[13]	80 s, 70 o
300	D. vinula fennica	42 m	383	Scatophila unicornis[5]	13 ♂m, 14 ♀m	467	Cygnus cygnus	80 s
301	D. vinula delavoiei	62 m	384	Melophagus ovinus[5]	18 s	468	Columba livia domestica[13]	80 s, 79 o
302	Pygaera curtula	48 m	385	Olfersia bisulcata[5]	8 s	469	Bambusicola thoracica	78 s
303	P. pigra	46 s,m	386	Dicranomyis trinotata	6 s	470	Gallus gallus domesticus[13]	78 s, 77 o
304	Papilio podalirius	54-58 s	387	Liponeura cinerasceus[5]	10 s	471	Meleagris gallopavo[13]	82 s, 81 o
305	P. rutulus	28 s	388	Musca domestica[5]	12 s,o	472	Numida meleagris[13]	76 s, 75 o
306	Pieris brassicae	30 s,o	389	Brachypeza radiata[5]	12 m	473	Phasianus colchicus karpowi[13]	82 s, 81 o
307	P. napi	50 s	390	Fungivora blanda	8 o, ♀m	474	Syrmaticus soemmerringii	82 s
308	Fumea casta	62 s, 61 o	391	Rhymosia fenestralis[5]	8 m	475	Didelphys virginiana[5]	22 s,m
309	Chiro simplex	58 s	392	Camptoneura picta	12 s	476	Myotis myotis	44 s
310	Callosamia promethea	38 s	393	Piophila casei	12	477	Erinaceus europaeus[5]	48 s
311	Philosamia cynthia	26 s,o, ♀m	394	Aphiocaeta sp	6 m	478	Talpa europaea[5]	34 s
312	P. cynthia walkeri	26 s	395	Physegenua vittata	12 s	479	Lepus cuniculus[5]	44 s
313	P. cynthia pryeri	28 s	396	Sarchophaga sp[5]	12 m	480	Cavia cobaya[5]	64 s
314	Telea polyphemus	60 s	397	Sciara ocellaris	8 m	481	Myocastor coypus[5]	42 s
315	Deilephila euphorbiae	28 s	398	Simulium sp[5]	6 m	482	Mesocricetus auratus[5]	44 s
316	Solenobia alpicolella	60-62	399	Precticus trivittatus[5]	16 s	483	Apodemus agrarius[5]	48 s
317	S. triquetrella	62 m	400	Eristalis bastardi[5]	12 s	484	Micromys minutus[5]	68 s
318	Talaeporia tubulosa	60 ♂m, 59♀m	401	Phorocera hamata[5]	12 ♂m	485	Peromyscus maniculatus[5]	48 s
319	Tischeria angusticolella	42 s,o	402	Chaetogus fulvifrons	8 s	486	Mus musculus[5]	40 s
320	Anthia sexguttata[2]	35 s	403	Ctenocephalus canis[5]	14 m	487	Rattus norvegicus[5]	42 s
321	Dytiscus circumcinctus[5]	38 s	404	Leptosylla musculi[5]	22 s	488	Cynomys ludovicianus[5]	52 s
322	Bruchus quadrimaculatus[2]	19 s, 20 m	405	Cionia intestinalis	18 m	489	Sciurus vulgaris[5]	40 s
323	Agrilus anxius[5]	22 s,o	406	Branchiostoma japonica[5]	32 s	490	Canis familiaris[5]	78 s
324	Julodis whithilli[2]	24 s	407	Bdellostoma burgeri	48 (?)s	491	Felis catus[5]	38 s
325	Sternocera laevigata[2]	26 s	408	Protopterus annectens	34 s	492	Phocoenoides dalli[5]	44 s
326	Pterolophia caudata[5]	20 s	409	Raja macrorhynchus	24 s	493	Bos taurus[5]	60 s
327	Agelastica caerulae[5]	24 s	410	Squalus suckleyi	62 s	494	Ovis aries[5]	54 s
328	Chrysomela exanthematica[2]	23 s	411	Betta splendens	42 s	495	Sus scrofa	40 s
329	Coptocycla clavata[5]	18 s	412	Misgurnus anguillicaudatus	52 s	496	Equus caballus[5]	66 s
330	Luperoides praeustus[2]	32 s,o	413	Acheilognathus lanceolatus	50 s	497	E. asinus[5]	66 s
331	Melasoma populi[5]	32 s	414	Carassius auratus	94 s	498	"Mule"[5]	66 s
332	Calvia 14-guttata[5]	20 s	415	Cyprinus carpio	104 s	499	Macaca mulatta[5]	48 s,m
			416	Lebistes reticulatus	48 s	500	Homo sapiens	48 s,o

/2/ X-O♂. /5/ X-Y♂. /9/ 5X-O♂. /10/ 2X-Y♂. /11/ 3X-Y♂. /12/ X-X♀. /13/ X-O♀. /14/ Z-2W♀. /15/ 2XX-Y♂.

93

73. CHROMOSOME NUMBERS: GYMNOSPERMS AND ANGIOSPERMS

Extra fragment chromosomes are indicated by "f". Values are diploid chromosome numbers. Data adapted from Darlington, C. D., and Janaki Ammal, E. K., "Chromosome Atlas of Cultivated Plants," G. Allen and Unwin, Ltd., London, 1945.

	Species	Number
	Gymnospermae	
	Cycadaceae	
1	Zamia (Zamia floridana)	16
	Ginkgoaceae	
2	Ginkgo (Gingko biloba)	24
	Taxaceae	
3	Yew (Taxus baccata, T. cuspidata)	24
4	Yew (T. canadensis)	24+f
	Pinaceae	
5	Arborvitae (Thuja orientalis)	22
6	Cedar (Cedrus libani)	24
7	Douglas-fir (Pseudotsuga menziesii)	26
8	Fir (Abies balsamea, A. cephalonica)	24
9	Fir (A.concolor, A.normanniana)	24
10	Hemlock (Tsuga canadensis)	24
11	Hemlock (T. caroliniana)	24
12	Juniper (Juniperus chinensis)	44
13	Juniper (J. communis, J. rigida)	22
14	Larch (Lardix decidua)	24
15	Pine (Pinus spp)[1]	24
16	Redcedar (Juniperus virginiana)	22
17	Redcedar (Thuja plicata)	22
18	Redwood (Sequoia giganteum)	22
19	Redwood (S. sempervirens)	44
20	Spruce (Picea spp)[2]	24
21	White-cedar (Thuja occidentalis)	22
	Angiospermae: Monocotyledoneae	
	Najadaceae	
22	Eelgrass (Zostera marina, Z. nana)	12
	Alismataceae	
23	Alisma (Sagittaria montevidensis)	20
24	Plantian (Alisma plantago-aquatica)	10
	Hydrocharitaceae	
25	Elodea (Elodea canadensis)	24
26	Elodea (E. densa)	48
27	Vallisneria (Vallisneria gigantea)	40
28	Vallisneria (V. spiralis)	20
	Gramineae	
29	Barley (Hordeum distichum)	14
30	Barley (H. jubatum)	28
31	Barley (H. nodosum)	42
32	Barley (H. vulgare)	14
33	Bluegrass (Poa compressa)	35,42,45,49,56
34	Bluegrass (P. pratensis)	28-124
35	Corn (Zea mays)	20
36	Crabgrass (Digitaria sanguinalis)	36
37	Dallis grass (Paspalum dilatatum)	40
38	Fescue (Festuca elatior)	14,28,42,70
39	Gammagrass (Tripsacum dactyloides)	36,72
40	Johnson grass (Sorghum halepense)	40
41	Oat (Avena barbata)	28
42	Oat (A. fatua, A. sativa)	42
43	Oat (A. strigosa)	14
44	Quackgrass (Agropyron repens)	28,42
45	Redtop (Agrostis alba)	28,42
46	Rice (Oryza sativa)	24
47	Rye (Secale cereale)	14
48	Ryegrass (Lolium multiflorum)	14
49	Ryegrass (L. perenne)	14
50	Teosinte (Euchlaena mexicana)	20
51	Timothy (Phleum pratense)	14,42
52	Wheat (Triticum aestivum)	42
53	Wheat (T. durum)	28
54	Wheatgrass (Agropyron cristatum)	14,28,42
	Cyperaceae	
55	Sedge (Carex hirta)	112
56	Sedge (C. panicea)	32
	Palmae	
57	Coconut (Cocos nucifera)	32
58	Date (Phoenix dactylifera)	36
59	Palmetto (Sabal palmetto)	36

	Species	Number
	Angiospermae: Monocotyledoneae (concluded)	
	Bromeliaceae	
60	Pineapple (Ananas sativus)	50,75,100
61	Spanish moss (Tillandsia usneoides)	32
	Commelinaceae	
62	Rhoea (Rhoea discolor)	12
63	Spiderwort (Tradescantia virginiana)	24+0-6f
64	Wandering-jew (T. fluminensis)	60
	Pontederiaceae	
65	Water-hyacinth (Eichhornia crassipes)	32
	Juncaceae	
66	Rush (Juncus effusus)	40
	Liliaceae	
67	Asparagus (Asparagus officinalis)	20
68	Autumn crocus (Colchicum autumnale)	38
69	Bluebell (Scilla non-scripta)	16
70	Garlic (Allium sativum)	16
71	Grape-hyacinth (Muscari racemosum)	54
72	Helleboro (Venatrum nigrum)	64
73	Hyacinth (Hyacinth orientalis)	16,19-30
74	Lily (Lilium spp)[3]	24
75	Lily, day (Hemerocallis flava)	22
76	Onion (Allium cepa)	16
77	Trillium (Trillium grandiflorum)	10
78	Tulip (Tulipa gesneriana)	24,36
	Amaryllidaceae	
79	Belladonna (Amaryllis belladonna)	22
80	Century plant (Agave americana)	60,120,180
81	Jonquil (Narcissus jonquilla)	14,28
82	Narcissus (N. poeticus)	14,21,28
83	Narcissus (N. pseudonarcissus)	14,15,20,22,28,30
84	Yucca (Yucca spp)	60
	Iridaceae	
85	Crocus (Crocus versicolor)	26
86	Gladiolus (Gladiolus spp)	30
87	Iris (Iris orientalis)	14
88	Iris (I. versicolor)	72,84,105
	Musaceae	
89	Banana (Musa paradisiaca sap.)	22,33
90	Plantain (M. paradisiaca)	44,55,77,88
	Zingiberaceae	
91	Ginger (Zingiber officinale)	22
	Cannaceae	
92	Canna (Canna discolor, C. flaccida)	18
	Orchidaceae	
93	Lady's slipper (Cypripdium acaule)	20
94	Lady's slipper (C. spectabile)	22
95	Orchid (Cattleya trianei)	40
96	Orchid (Cymbidium giganteum)	40
97	Orchid (Dendrobium nobile)	38
	Angiospermae: Dicotyledoneae	
	Piperaceae	
98	Peperomia (Peperomia sandersii)	24
99	Pepper (Piper nigrum)	128
	Salicaceae	
100	Poplar (Populus spp)[4]	38
101	Willow (Salix alba)	76
102	Willow (S. cordiophylla)	38
103	Willow (S. viminalis)	38
	Juglandaceae	
104	Hickory (Carya spp)[5]	32
105	Walnut (Juglans spp)[6]	32
106	Walnut (J. californica)	34

	Species	Number
	Angiospermae: Dicotyledoneae (continued)	
	Betulaceae	
107	Alder (Alnus cordata)	42
108	Alder (A. glutinosa, A. incana)	28
109	Alder (A. japonica)	56
110	Alder (A. maritima)	28
111	Alder (A. rubra, A. rugosa)	28
112	Alder (A. spaethii)	56
113	Alder (A. viridis)	14
114	Birch (Betula alba)	84
115	Birch (B. fontinalis)	28
116	Birch (B. grossa)	42
117	Birch (B. lenta)	28
118	Birch (B. nigra)	28
119	Birch (B. papyrifera)	28,42
120	Hornbeam (Carpinus spp)[7]	16
121	Hornbeam (C. betulus)	8,64
	Fagaceae	
122	Beech (Fagus sylvatica)	24
123	Chestnut (Castanea crenata)	24
124	Chestnut (C. dentata, C. mollisima)	24
125	Oak (Quercus spp)[8]	24
	Ulmaceae	
126	Elm (Ulmus spp)[9]	28
127	Elm (U. americana)	56
	Moraceae	
128	Fig (Ficus carica)	26
129	Hemp (Cannabis sativa)	20
130	Jack fruit (Artocarpus integra)	56
131	Mulberry (Morus alba, M. indica)	28
	Urticaceae	
132	Ramie (Boehmeria nivea)	28
	Loranthaceae	
133	Mistletoe (Viscum album)	20
134	Mistletoe (V. articulatum)	24
	Polygonaceae	
135	Buckwheat (Fagopyrum esculentum)	16
136	Dock (Rumex aquaticus)	200
137	Dock (R. crispus)	60
138	Rhubarb (Rheum officinale)	22
139	Rhubarb (R. rhaponticum)	44
	Chenopodiaceae	
140	Beet (Beta vulgaris)	18
141	Pigweed (Chenopodium album)	54
142	Saltbush (Atriplex littoralis)	18
143	Spinach (Spinacia oleracea)	12
	Portulacaceae	
144	Purslane (Portulaca oleraceae)	54
	Caryophyllaceae	
145	Carnation (Dianthus caryophyllus)	30,90
146	Chickweed (Stellaria media)	40,44
147	Pink (Dianthus deltoides)	30
148	Sweet william (D. barbatus)	30
	Nymphaeaceae	
149	Spatterdock (Nuphar advenum)	34
150	Waterlily (Nymphaea capensis)	28
151	Waterlily (N. lotus)	56
152	Waterlily (N. odorata)	84
	Ranunculaceae	
153	Anemone (Anemone caroliniana)	16
154	Anemone (A. hortensis)	16
155	Buttercup (Ranunculus bulbosus)	14,16
156	Buttercup (R. repens)	32
157	Christmas rose (Helleborus niger)	32
158	Clematis (Clematis hybrida)	16
159	Clematis (C. paniculata)	16,48,64
160	Columbine (Aquilegia canadensis)	14
161	Columbine (A. vulgaris)	14
162	Larkspur (Delphinium ajacus)	16
163	Marsh marigold (Caltha palustris)	32,48,56

/1/ Spp: banksiana, bungeana, echinata, flexilis, jeffreyi, longifolia, murrayana, nigra, palustris, parivlora, peuce, pinaster, ponderosa, resinosa, rigida, sylvestris, strobus, tabulaeformis, thunbergii, virginiana. /2/ Spp: abies, glauca, mariana, pungens, sitchensis. /3/ Spp: candidum, elegans, giganteum, longiflorum, pardalinum, regale, speciosum. /4/ Spp: acuminata, adenopoda, alba, angulata, angustifolia, balsamifera, canadensis, candicans, canescens, cathayana, deltoides, grandidentata, jacki, koreana, lasiocarpa, laurifolia, maximowiczii, nigra, sieboldi, tomentosa, tremula, tremuloides. /5/ Spp: alba, glabra, laneyi, ovata, ovalis. /6/ Spp: cinerea, intermedia, mandschurica, nigra, regia, rupestris, sieboldiana. /7/ Spp: caroliniana, cordata, japonica, laxifolia, orientalis, tschnoskii, turczanionovii. /8/ Spp: acutissima, alba, agrifolia, bicolor, borealis, cerris, chrysolepis, coccinea, douglasii, dumosa, engelmanii, garrayana, glandulifera, ilicifera, imbricaria, incana, lobata, macrocarpa, marylandica, michauxii, montana, nigra, palustris, pontica, prinoides, prinus, robur, stellata, tomentosa, velutina. /9/ Spp: campestris, carpinifolia, glabta, fulva, japonica, laciniata, laevis, procera, pumila, racemosa.

Extra fragment chromosomes are indicated by "f". Values are diploid chromosome numbers. Data adapted from Darlington, C. D., and Janaki Ammal, E. K., "Chromosome Atlas of Cultivated Plants," G. Allen and Unwin, Ltd., London, 1945.

	Species	Number
	Angiospermae: Dicotyledoneae (continued)	
164	Monkshood (Aconitum napellus)	32
165	Peony (Paeonia albiflora, P. moutan)	10
	Berberidaceae	
166	Barberry (Berberis canadensis)	28
167	Barberry (B. vulgaris)	28
168	Mahonia (Mahonia aquifolium)	28
169	Nandina (Nandina domestica)	20
	Magnoliaceae	
170	Cucumber-tree (Magnolia acuminata)	76
171	Magnolia (M. denudata, M. grandiflora)	114
172	Magnolia (M. soulangeana)	76
173	Sweet bay (M. virginiana)	38
174	Yellow-poplar (Liriodendron tulipifera)	38
	Calycanthaceae	
175	Allspice (Chimonanthus fragrans)	22
176	Sweet-shrub (Calycanthus floridus)	22
	Annonaceae	
177	Cherimoya (Annona cherimola)	14
178	Custard-apple (A. reticulata)	14
179	Papaw (Asimina triloba)	18
	Lauraceae	
180	Avocado (Persea americana)	24
181	Camphor-tree (Cinnamomum camphora)	24
182	Cinnamon (C. zeylanicum)	24
183	Sweet-bay (Laurus nobilis)	42
	Papaveraceae	
184	Poppy (Eschscholtzia californica)	12
185	Poppy (Papaver orientale)	42
186	Poppy (P. rhoeas)	14
187	Poppy (P. somniferum)	22
	Capparidaceae	
188	Caperbush (Capparis spinosa)	38
189	Spider flower (Cleome spinosa)	20
	Cruciferae	
190	Cabbage (Brassica oleracea var.)	18
191	Candytuft (Iberis amara)	14, 16
192	Candytuft (I. sempervirens)	22, 44
193	Radish (Raphanus sativus)	18
194	Shepherd's purse (Capsella bursa-pastoris)	16, 32
195	Turnip (Brassica rapus)	20
196	Wallflower (Cheiranthus cheiri)	14
197	Watercress (Nasturtium officinale)	32, 48, 64
	Droseraceae	
198	Sundew (Drosera anglica)	40
199	Sundew (D. intermedia)	20
200	Venus' fly-trap (Dionaea muscipula)	30
	Crassulaceae	
201	Kalanchoe (Kalanchoe aromatica)	34
202	Kalanchoe (Kalanchoe spp)	500
203	Sedum (Sedum pusillum)	8
	Saxifragaceae	
204	Currant (Ribes americanum, R. nigrum)	16
205	Deutzia (Deutzia crenata)	130
206	Deutzia (D. gracilis)	26
207	Gooseberry (Ribes grossularia)	16
208	Hydrangea (Hydrangea paniculata floribunda)	72
209	Hydrangea (H. quercifolia)	36
	Hamamelidaceae	
210	Sweetgum (Liquidambar styraciflua)	30
211	Witch-hazel (Hamamelis virginiana)	24
	Platanaceae	
212	Aspen (Platanus acerifolia)	42
213	Sycamore (P. occidentalis)	42
	Rosaceae	
214	Almond (Prunus amygdalus)	16
215	Apple (Pyrus malus)	34
	Angiospermae: Dicotyledoneae (continued)	
216	Blackberry (Rubus occidentalis)	14
217	Cherry (Prunus avium)	16, 24, 32
218	Cherry (P. cerasus)	32
219	Cherry-laurel (P. laurocerasus)	176
220	Chokeberry (P. virginiana)	32
221	Crabapple (Malus asiatic, M. baccata)	34
222	Flowering almond (Prunus triloba)	64
223	Hawthorn (Crataegus crus-galli)	68
224	Hawthorn (C. cordata)	72
225	Hawthorn (C. oxyacantha)	34
226	Loquat (Eriobotrya japonica)	34
227	Mt. ash (Sorbus americana)	34
228	Peach (Prunus persica)	16
229	Pear (Pyrus communis)	34, 51
230	Plum (Prunus domestica)	48
231	Quince (Cydonia oblonga)	34
232	Raspberry (Rubus idaeus)	14, 21, 28
233	Raspberry (R. strigosus)	14
234	Rose (Rosa multiflora)	14
235	Spiraea (Spiraea japonica)	18
236	Strawberry (Fragaria virginiana)	56
237	Strawberry (F. vesca)	14
	Leguminosae	
238	Alfalfa (Medicago sativa)	32
239	Bean (Phaseolus lunatus, P. vulgaris)	22
240	Broadbean (Vicia faba)	12
241	Clover (Trifolium aureum)	14
242	Clover (T. incarnatum, T. pratense)	14
243	Clover (T. repens)	32
244	Lentil (Lens esculenta)	14
245	Lespedeza (Lespedeza striata)	22
246	Locust (Robinia pseudoacacia)	20
247	Lupine (Lupinus angustifolus)	40
248	Lupine (L. luteus)	46
249	Pea (Pisum sativum)	14
250	Peanut (Arachis hypogaea)	40
251	Redbud (Cercis canadensis)	12
252	Silktree (Albizzia julibrissin)	26
253	Soybean (Glycine soja)	40
254	Sweetclover (Melilotus officinalis)	16
255	Sweetpea (Lathyrus odoratus)	14
	Oxalidaceae	
256	Sorrel (Oxalis acetosella)	22
	Tropaeolaceae	
257	Nasturtium (Tropaeolum majus)	28
	Linaceae	
258	Flax (Linum usitatissimum)	30
	Rutaceae	
259	Grapefruit (Citrus paradisi)	18, 27, 36
260	Lemon (C. limonia)	18, 36
261	Lime (C. aurantifolia)	27
262	Orange (C. aurantium)	18
263	Orange (C. sinensis)	45
	Euphorbiaceae	
264	Castor-bean (Ricinus communis)	20
265	Euphorbia (Euphorbia splendens)	36
266	Poinsettia (E. pulcherrima)	28
267	Tung oil tree (Aleurites fordii)	22
	Callitrichaceae	
268	Callitriche (Callitriche autumnalis)	6
	Buxaceae	
269	Boxwood (Buxus sempervirens)	28
	Aquifoliaceae	
270	Holly (Ilex aquifolium)	40
271	Holly (I. opaca)	36
272	Winterberry (I. verticillata)	36
273	Yapon (I. vomitoria)	40
	Angiospermae: Dicotyledoneae (continued)	
	Aceraceae	
274	Maple (Acer campestre)	26
275	Maple (A. carpinifolium)	52
276	Maple (A. circinatum)	26
277	Maple (A. griseum, A. negundo)	26
278	Maple (A. platanoides)	26, 78
279	Maple (A. pseudoplatanus)	52
280	Maple (A. rubrum)	78, 104
281	Maple (A. saccharinum)	52
	Hippocastanaceae	
282	Horsechestnut (Aesculus hippocastanum)	40
	Balsaminaceae	
283	Balsam (Impatiens balsamina)	14
284	Jewelweed (I. biflora)	20
	Vitaceae	
285	Grape (Vitis labrusca)	38
286	Grape (V. rotundifolia)	40
287	Grape (V. vinifera)	38, 57, 76
	Tiliaceae	
288	Basswood (Tilia spp)[10]	82
289	Basswood (T. amurensis)	164
	Malvaceae	
290	Cotton (Gossypium barbadense)	52
291	Cotton (G. hirsutum)	52
292	Hollyhock (Althaea rosea)	42, 56
293	Mallow (Malva sylvestris)	42
294	Okra (Hibiscus esculentus)	72, 130
	Theaceae	
295	Camellia (Camellia japonica)	30
296	Tea (Thea sinensis)	30
	Violaceae	
297	Pansy (Viola tricolor)	26
298	Violet (V. arvensis)	34
299	Violet (V. odorata)	20
	Passifloraceae	
300	Granadilla (Passiflora quadrangularis)	18
301	Map pop (P. incarnata)	18
302	Passion fruit (P. edulis)	18
	Begoniaceae	
303	Begonia (Begonia carminata)	42
304	Begonia (B. margaritae)	52
	Cactaceae	
305	Cactus (Echinocereus angusticeps)	22
306	Cactus (E. engelmannii)	44
307	Cactus (Zygocactus truncatus)	24
	Nyssaceae	
308	Tupelo (Nyssa sylvatica)	44
	Myrtaceae	
309	Eucalyptus (Eucalyptus globulus)	20
310	Guava (Psidium guajava)	22
311	Myrtle (Myrtus communis)	22
	Oenotheraceae	
312	Fuchsia (Fuchsia rosea)	44
313	Fuchsia (F. splendens)	22
314	Primrose (Oenothera biennis)	14
315	Primrose (O. pumila)	28
	Umbelliferae	
316	Caraway (Carum carvi)	20
317	Carrot (Daucus carota)	18
318	Celery (Apium graveolens)	22
319	Dill (Anethum graveolens)	22
320	Parsnip (Pastinaca sativa)	22
321	Parsley (Petroselinum sativum)	23
	Cornaceae	
322	Dogwood (Cornus controversia)	20
323	Dogwood (C. florida)	22
324	Dogwood (C. mas)	18
	Ericaceae	
325	Blueberry (Vaccinium atrococcum)	48
326	Blueberry (V. angustifolium)	48
327	Rhododendron (Rhododendron spp)[11]	26

/10/ Spp: cordata, europaea, glabra, neglecta, oliveri, platyphyllos. /11/ Spp: arborescens, carolinianum, catawbiense, maximum, ponticu, roseum, vesey, viscosum.

73. CHROMOSOME NUMBERS: GYMNOSPERMS AND ANGIOSPERMS (Concluded)

Extra fragment chromosomes are indicated by "f". Values are diploid chromosome numbers. Data adapted from Darlington, C. D., and Janaki Ammal, E. K., "Chromosome Atlas of Cultivated Plants." G. Allen and Unwin, Ltd., London, 1945.

	Species	Number		Species	Number		Species	Number
	Angiospermae: Dicotyledoneae (continued)			**Angiospermae: Dicotyledoneae (continued)**			**Angiospermae: Dictoyledoneae (concluded)**	
328	Rhododendron (Rhododendron calendulaceum)	52	357	Labiatae			Caprifoliaceae	
			357	Coleus (Coleus blumei)	24	382	Cranberry (Viburnum trilobum)	18
	Primulaceae		358	Lavender (Lavandula officinalis)	54	383	Elder (Sambucus canadensis)	36
329	Cyclamen (Cyclamen persicum)	48,84	359	Peppermint (Mentha piperita officinalis)	72,84	384	Honeysuckle (Lonicera sempervirens)	36
330	Primrose (Primula vulgaris)	22	360	Peppermint (M. piperita vulgaris)	68,72		Cucurbitaceae	
	Plumbaginaceae		361	Rosemary (Rosmarinus officinalis)	24	385	Cucumber (Cucumis sativus)	14
331	Plumbago (Plumbago europaea)	14	362	Thyme (Thymus serpyllum)	24	386	Gourd, bottle (Lagenaria vulgaris)	22
	Ebenaceae			Solanaceae		387	Muskmelon (Cucumis melo)	24
332	Persimmon (Diospyros kaki)	90	363	Eggplant (Solanum melongena)	24	388	Pumpkin (Cucurbita pepo)	40
333	Persimmon (D. virginiana)	60,90	364	Pepper (Capsicum annuum)	24	389	Squash (C. maxima, C. moschata,	40
	Oleaceae		365	Petunia (Petunia violacea)	14	390	Watermelon (Citrullus vulgaris)	22
334	Ash (Fraxinus americana)	46	366	Nightshade (Atropa belladonna)	72		Campanulaceae	
335	Ash (F. chinensis)	138	367	Potato (Solanum tuberosum)	48	391	Canterberry bell (Campanula medium)	34
336	Ash (F. pennsylvanica)	46	368	Tobacco (Nicotiana tabacum)	48	392	Cardinal flower (Lobelia cardinalis)	14
337	Forsythia (Forsythia suspensa)	28	369	Tomato (Lycopersicon esculentum)	24		Compositae	
338	Forsythia (F. viridissima)	28		Scrophulariaceae		393	Aster (Aster laevis)	54
339	Fringe-tree (Chionanthus virginica)	46	370	Foxglove (Digitalis purpurea)	56	394	Aster (A. multiflorus)	10
340	Jasmine (Jasminum nudiflorum)	52	371	Mullein (Verbascum thapus)	32	395	Chrysanthemum (Chrysanthemum frutescens)	27
341	Lilac (Syringa vulgaris)	46-48	372	Snapdragon (Antirrhinum majus)	16	396	Chrysanthemum (C. leucanthemum)	36
342	Olive (Olea europaea)	46		Bignoniaceae		397	Chrysanthemum (C. maximum)	90
343	Osmanthus (Osmanthus fortunei)	44	373	Catalpa (Catalpa bignonioides)	40	398	Cosmos (Cosmos bipinnatus)	24
344	Privet (Ligustrum vulgare)	46	374	Trumpet vine (Campsis radicans)	40	399	Dahlia (Dahlia variabilis)	64
	Asclepiadaceae			Gesneriaceae		400	Dandelion (Taraxacum officinale)	24
345	Milkweed (Asclepias incarnata)	22	375	African violet (Saintpaulia ionantha)	28	401	Guayule (Parthenium argentatum)	35,38,54 72,108-111
346	Wax plant (Hoya carnosa)	22		Plantaginaceae		402	Lettuce (Lactuca sativa)	18
	Convolvulaceae		376	Plantain (Plantago lanceolata)	24,96	403	Marigold (Tagetes erecta)	24
347	Cypress vine (Ipomoea sloteri)	58	377	Plantain (P. major)	12	404	Sunflower (Helianthus annuus)	34
348	Moonflower (I. speciosum)	30		Rubiaceae		405	Yarrow (Achillea millifolium)	36,54
349	Morning glory (I. purpurea)	30	378	Button bush (Cephalanthus occidentalis)	44	406	Zinnia (Zinnia elegans)	24
350	Sweetpotato (I. batatas)	90	379	Cinchona (Cinchona ledgeriana)	40			
	Polemoniaceae		380	Coffee (Coffea arabica)	22			
351	Phlox (Phlox divaricata)	14+0-1f	381	Gardenia (Gardenia intermedia)	22			
352	Phlox (P. drummondii)	14,28						
353	Phlox (P. maculata)	14						
	Borraginaceae							
354	Borage (Borago officinalis)	16						
355	Myosotis (Myosotis alpestris)	24,48,72						
356	Myosotis (M. palustris)	22,64						

74. CHROMOSOME NUMBERS: FUNGI

Values are haploid numbers taken from the 1940-1952 literature. Because of the difficulty in obtaining accurate counts (mainly at meiosis) of the typically small fungi chromosomes, values in many cases should be considered estimates. Reports of two chromosomes for haploid numbers have been questioned and, therefore, are not listed.

	Species	Number		Species	Number		Species	Number
1	Absidia apinosa	12	29	Gymnosporangium nidus-avis	8	57	Peziza micropus	8
2	Achlya bisexualis	3	30	G. transformans	8	58	P. ochracea	6
3	A. megasperma	5	31	Helotium citrinum	6	59	P. saniosa	8
4	A. recurva	4	32	Helvella atra	6	60	P. succosa	8
5	Albugo evolvuli	8	33	H. crispa	6	61	P. venosa	6
6	A. portulacae	8	34	H. lacunosa	6	62	P. vesiculosa	8
7	Allomyces arbuscula[1]	16	35	Humarina leucoloma	8	63	Phaeobulgaria inquinans	6
8	A. cystogenus	14	36	Hypomyces solani	6	64	Phyllactinia corylea	8
9	A. javanicus javanicus	13-21	37	Isoachlya intermedia	6	65	Phytophthora himalayensis	3
10	A. javanicus macrogynus[2]	28	38	Lamprospora constellatio	6	66	Plasmopara viticola	14-16
11	Amanita caesaria	4	39	L. haemastigma	6	67	Pyronema omphalodes	6, 12
12	Ascobolus magnificus	8	40	Leotia lubrica	8	68	Rhizophydium coronum	6, 8
13	A. sterocarius	16	41	Lepiota lenticularis	4	69	Saprolegnia litoralis	7
14	Aspergillus nidulans	4	42	Melastiza charteri	4	70	Schizophyllum commune	3
15	Calonectria rigidiuscula	7	43	Nectria episphaeria	7	71	Sclerotinia trifoliorum	6, 8
16	Ciliaria hirta	4	44	N. flava	4	72	Scodellina leporina	8
17	Coleosporium helianthi	8	45	Neurospora crassa	7	73	Septobasidium spp	5
18	C. sidae	8	46	N. sitophila	7	74	Sepultaria arenicola	8
19	C. vernoniae	8	47	N. tetrasperma	6, 7	75	Sordaria fimicola	8
20	Cudonia circinans	6	48	N. sp (8-spored)	7	76	Spathularia clavata	6
21	Dermatocarpon aquaticum	8	49	Olpidiopsis achlyae	6	77	Stigmatea geranii	4
22	Dictyostelium discoideum	7	50	Otidea vitellina	8	78	Taphrina deformans	4
23	Eremascus albus	6	51	Patella albida	8	79	Thekopsora hydrangeae	4
24	Giberella lateritium	6	52	P. melaloma	4, 6	80	Thraustotheca primoachlya	5
25	G. roseum	6	53	P. scutellata	6	81	Torula utilis	4
26	Glomerella cingulata	4	54	Paxina acetabulum	6	82	Tremellodon gelatinosum	4
27	Gymnosporangium clavipes	8	55	P. hispida	8	83	Uromyces aloes	6
28	G. juniperi-virginianae	8	56	Penicillium cyclopium	6-7	84	Venturia inaequalis	4, 6

/1/ N = 8-32 in various isolates. /2/ N = 50 or more in certain polyploid isolates.

Part I: BACTERIA AND VIRUSES

Generation time for bacteria is the average interval between cell divisions.

	Organism	Culture Medium	Temperature °C	Generation Time min		Organism	Culture Medium	Temperature °C	Generation Time min
1	Aerobacter aerogenes	Broth or milk	37	16-18	52	Phytomonas tabacum	Broth	25	81
2		Glucose + peptone	37	17.3	53	Proteus vulgaris	Broth	37	21.5
3		Peptone	37	22-30	54		Peptone + phosphate	37	40
4		Synthetic	37	29-44	55	Pseudomonas fluorescens	Broth	30	40
5	Azotobacter spp	Mineral salts + sugar	25-30	240-348	56		Glucose broth	37	34-34.5
6	A. chroococcum	Glucose broth		27-39	57	P. pyocyanea	Broth	37	34
7		Sugar + urea	28	74	58		Glucose broth	37	31
8	Bacillus cereus	Broth	37	18.8	59		Lactose broth	37	34
9		Glucose broth	37	17-24.5	60	Rhizobium japonicum	Mineral salts + yeast + mannitol	25	344-461
10	B. megatherium	Broth	30	31	61	R. leguminosarum	Mineral salts + mannitol	25	79-187
11	B. mycoides	Broth	37	28	62	R. meliloti	Mineral salts + yeast + mannitol	25	107
12	B. subtilis	Glucose broth		26-32	63	R. trifolii	Mineral salts + yeast + mannitol	25	101
13	B. thermophilus	Broth	55	18.3	64	Salmonella enteritidis	Broth	42	21.5
14		Tryptophan + broth	54.5	16	65	S. paratyphi	Broth	37	23
15	Clostridium amylobacter	Corn mash	37	51	66		Peptone	37	28
16	C. botulinum	Glucose broth	37	35	67	S. suipestifer	Broth	37	26
17	C. welchii	Milk	37	35	68	S. typhi	Bile + pus	37	24.5
18	Corynebacterium diphtheriae	Serum + glucose broth	37	34	69		Broth	37	23.5
19	C. pseudodiphtheriae	Broth	37	37	70		Glucose broth	37	29
20	Diplococcus mucosus	Milk	37	32	71		Glucose + peptone	37	33
21	D. pneumoniae I	Broth	37	24.5	72	Serratia marcescens	Milk	37	37
22		Serum	37	29	73	Shigella dysenteriae	Milk	37	23
23		Serum + broth	37	20.5	74		Peptone + phosphate	37	37
24	D. pneumoniae II	Broth	37	33	75	Spirochaeta spp	Modified thioglycolate	37	528
25		Glucose broth	37	30	76	Staphylococcus albus	Glucose broth	37	24-25
26		Serum + broth	37	23	77	S. aureus	Broth	37	27-30
27	Erwinia carotovora	Broth	37	57	78		Glucose broth	37	32
28		Glucose broth	37	42	79	Streptococcus fecalis	Glucose-citrate broth	37	27
29	E. amylovora	Broth	30	71-94	80		Milk	37	26.5
30	Escherichia coli	Broth	37	17	81	S. hemolyticus	Beef heart broth	37	32
31		Lactose broth	37	16	82		Glucose broth	37	26
32		Milk	37	12.5	83		Glucose serum broth	37	34
33	E. coli communior	Broth	37	16	84	S. lactis	Glucose milk	37	26
34	Lactobacillus acidophilus	Milk	37	66-87	85		Lactose broth	30	48
35	L. bulgaricus	Glucose milk	37	41-75	86		Milk	37	26
36		Milk	37	39-74	87		Peptone milk	37	37
37		Peptone milk	37	50	88	S. liquefaciens	Milk	37	27
38		Tomato juice + milk	37	38-40	89	S. mastitidis	Glucose milk	37	35-37
39		Yeast extract	37	37	90	S. thermophilus	Milk	37	27
40	L. casei	Milk	25	38	91	Treponema pallidum	Rabbit skin	37	1800
41	L. delbruckii	Wort	45	83	92		Rabbit testes	37	1980
42	L. pentoaceticus	Yeast extract	28	67	93	Vibrio comma	Broth	37	21.2-38
43	Mycobacterium tuberculosis[1]	Synthetic	37	792-932	94	V. costatus	Broth	27	42
44	Pasteurella lepiseptica	Broth + blood		24.4		Viruses			
45	Phytomonas campestris	Broth	23-25	165	95	Influenza A (PR-8)	Allantoic membrane[2]	37	330-510[3]
46	P. campsetre	Broth	25	98	96	A (5 strains)	Allantoic membrane[2]	37	300-360[3]
47	P. glycineum	Broth	23-25	95	97	B (3 strains)	Allantoic membrane[2]	37	480-600[3]
48	P. phaseoli	Bean broth	25	160	98	Swine	Allantoic membrane[2]	37	360[3]
49		Broth	25	150					
50		Glucose broth	25	138					
51	P. sojae	Broth	23-25	82					

/1/ Human strain H-37. /2/ Chick embryo. /3/ For viral agents generation time is the time required for infected cells to release new virus.

Part II: PROTOZOA

	Organism	Substrate	Temperature °C	Cell Division per da		Organism	Substrate	Temperature °C	Cell Division per da
1	Astasia	Tryptophan + Ac[1]	25	3.1	11	Paramecium aurelia	Lettuce + bacteria	20±	0.72[4]
2	Chilomonas paramecium	NaAc[1] + mineral salts	24	3.5	12	P. caudatum	Mineral salts + bacteria[5]	25-28	1.8
3	Didinium nasutum	Hopkin's + paramecium	21	3.6	13		Oat medium + bacteria	26	2.3
4	Euglena gracilis	In dark, no Ac[1]	10	0.03	14	Polytomella uvella	Aerated peptone	22	4.4
5		In dark + Ac[1]	23	0.47	15		Non-aerated peptone	22	1.8
6		Wheat infusion	25	3.5	16	Stentor coeruleus	Peter's + ciliates	19	0.6-0.9
7	Glaucoma pyriformis	Yeast extract	25	6.1[2]	17		Modified Peter's[6]	18-20	0.7-2.1
8		Yeast extract	24.2	6.9	18		Hetherington's[6]	22	0.65
9		Yeast + yeast extract[3]	25.2	7.6-8	19	Stylonychia pustulata		25?	4.5-5
10	Leucophrys patula	Glaucoma	25	3.7	20	Tetrahymena geleii		24	5.7-10.9

/1/ Acetate. /2/ Phelp's strain. Hetherington's strain, 6.4 div./da. /3/ Or peptone. /4/ At 28°C, 2 div./da. /5/ B. subtilis. /6/ Plus ciliates.

76. GENETICS OF PARAMECIUM

Part I: PARAMECIUM AURELIA (After Beale.)

Nine varieties with 17 mating types have been found. Only one mating type has been found in Variety 7. Values in the table are maximum percentages of conjugating pairs formed in mixtures of two types of paramecia. "Inc." means incomplete mating reaction, not leading to conjugation; when Inc. is enclosed in parentheses (Inc.) it indicates a weak, tentative reaction involving only a small proportion of the animals. Intervarietal conjugation gives rise to hybrid nonviability or low viability, or low viability of F_2 or back-cross generations.

Group	Variety	Mating Type	I	II	V	VI	IX	X	XIII	XVII	XVIII	III	IV	VII	VIII	XI	XII	XV	XVI
A	1	I	0	95	0	0	0	40	0	0	0	0	0	0	0	0	0	0	(Inc.)
		II		0	1	0	40	0	10	0	0	0	0	0	0	0	0	(Inc.)	0
	3	V			0	95	0	0	0	0	0	0	0	0	0	0	0	0	40 Inc.
		VI				0	0	0	(Inc.)	0	0	0	0	0	0	0	0	0	0
	5	IX					0	95	0	0	0	0	0	0	0	0	0	0	0
		X						0	(Inc.)	0	0	0	0	0	0	0	0	0	0
	7	XIII							0	0	0	0	0	0	0	0	0	0	(Inc.)
	9	XVII								0	95	0	0	0	0	0	0	0	0
		XVIII									0	0	0	0	0	0	0	0	0
B	2	III										0	95	0	0	0	0	0	0
		IV											0	0	0	0	0	0	0
	4	VII												0	95	0	0	0	95 Inc.
		VIII													0	0	0	95	0
	6	XI														0	95	0	0
		XII															0	0	0
	8	XV																0	95
		XVI																	0

Part II: PARAMECIUM BURSARIA (After Sonneborn.)

Six varieties with 23 mating types have been found. Only one mating type has been found in Variety V. In mixtures of the two mating types represented on the corresponding row and column, + = occurence of conjugation, - = no conjugation. Intervarietal conjugation between varieties II and IV is lethal.

Variety	Mating Type	A	B	C	D	E	F	G	H	J	K	L	M	N	O	P	Q	R	S	T	U	V	W	X
I	A	-	+	+	+	-	-	-	-	-	-	-	-	-	-	-	-	-	-	-	-	-	-	-
	B	+	-	+	+	-	-	-	-	-	-	-	-	-	-	-	-	-	-	-	-	-	-	-
	C	+	+	-	+	-	-	-	-	-	-	-	-	-	-	-	-	-	-	-	-	-	-	-
	D	+	+	+	-	-	-	-	-	-	-	-	-	-	-	-	-	-	-	-	-	-	-	-
II	E					-	+	+	+	+	+	+	+	-	-	-	-	+	-	-	-	-	-	-
	F					+	-	+	+	+	+	+	+	-	-	-	-	-	-	-	-	-	-	-
	G					+	+	-	+	+	+	+	+	-	-	-	-	-	-	-	-	-	-	-
	H					+	+	+	-	+	+	+	+	-	-	-	-	-	-	-	-	-	-	-
	J					+	+	+	+	-	+	+	+	-	-	-	-	-	-	-	-	-	-	-
	K					+	+	+	+	+	-	+	+	-	-	-	-	-	-	-	-	-	-	-
	L					+	+	+	+	+	+	-	+	-	-	-	-	+	-	-	-	-	-	-
	M					+	+	+	+	+	+	+	-	-	-	-	-	+	-	-	-	-	-	-
III	N													-	+	+	+	-	-	-	-	-	-	-
	O													+	-	+	+	-	-	-	-	-	-	-
	P													+	+	-	+	-	-	-	-	-	-	-
	Q													+	+	+	-	-	-	-	-	-	-	-
IV	R																	-	+	-	-	-	-	-
	S																	+	-	-	-	-	-	-
V	T																			-	-	-	-	-
VI	U																				-	+	+	+
	V																				+	-	+	+
	W																				+	+	-	+
	X																				+	+	+	-

Part III: PARAMECIUM CAUDATUM (After Gilman.)

Sixteen varieties with 31 mating types, but only one in Variety 10, have been found. In mixtures of the two mating types represented on the corresponding row and column, + = strong mating reaction and conjugation, ± = mating reaction but no conjugation, - = no mating reaction or conjugation.

Variety	Mating Type	I	II	III	IV	V	VI	VII	VIII	IX	X	XI	XII	XIII	XIV	XV	XVI	XVII	XVIII	XX[1]	XXI	XXII	XXIII	XXIV	XXV	XXVI	XXVII	XXVIII	XXIX	XXX	XXXI	XXXII
1	I	-	+	-	-	-	-	-	-	-	-	-	-	-	-	-	-	-	-	-	-	-	-	-	-	-	-	-	-	-	-	-
	II	+	-	-	-	-	-	-	-	-	-	-	-	-	-	-	-	-	-	-	-	-	-	-	-	-	-	-	-	-	-	-
2	III	-	-	-	+	-	-	-	-	-	-	-	-	-	-	-	±	-	±	±	-	-	-	-	-	-	+	-	-	-	-	-
	IV	-	-	+	-	-	-	-	-	-	-	-	-	-	-	+	-	±	-	-	-	-	-	-	-	-	+	-	+	-	+	-
3	V	-	-	-	-	-	+	-	±	-	-	-	-	-	-	-	-	-	-	-	-	-	-	-	-	-	-	-	-	-	-	-
	VI	-	-	-	-	+	-	-	-	-	±	-	-	-	-	-	-	-	-	-	-	-	-	-	-	-	-	-	-	-	-	-
4	VII	-	-	-	-	-	-	-	+	-	-	-	-	-	-	-	-	-	-	-	-	-	-	-	-	-	-	-	-	-	-	-
	VIII	-	-	-	-	±	-	+	-	-	-	-	-	-	-	-	-	-	-	-	-	-	-	-	-	-	-	-	-	-	-	-
5	IX	-	-	-	-	-	-	-	-	-	+	-	-	-	-	-	-	-	-	-	-	-	-	-	-	-	-	-	-	-	-	-
	X	-	-	-	-	-	±	-	-	+	-	-	-	-	-	-	-	-	-	-	-	-	-	-	-	-	-	-	-	-	-	-
6	XI	-	-	-	±	-	-	-	-	-	-	-	+	-	-	-	-	-	-	-	-	-	-	-	-	-	-	-	-	-	-	-
	XII	-	-	-	-	-	-	-	-	-	-	+	-	-	-	-	-	-	-	-	-	-	-	-	-	-	-	-	-	-	-	-
7	XIII	-	-	-	-	-	-	-	-	-	-	-	-	-	+	-	-	-	-	-	-	-	-	-	-	-	-	-	-	-	-	-
	XIV	-	-	-	-	-	-	-	-	-	-	-	-	+	-	-	-	-	-	-	-	-	-	-	-	-	-	-	-	-	-	-
8	XV	-	-	-	+	-	-	-	-	-	-	-	-	-	-	-	+	-	-	+	-	-	-	-	-	-	+	-	-	-	-	-
	XVI	-	-	±	-	-	-	-	-	-	-	-	-	-	-	+	-	-	+	-	-	-	-	-	-	-	+	-	-	-	-	-
9	XVII	-	-	-	±	-	-	-	-	-	-	-	-	-	-	-	±	-	+	+	-	-	-	-	-	-	-	-	-	-	-	-
	XVIII	-	-	±	-	-	-	-	-	-	-	-	-	-	-	-	-	+	-	-	-	-	-	-	-	-	-	-	-	-	-	-
10	XX[1]	-	-	±	-	-	-	-	-	-	-	-	-	-	-	+	-	+	-	-	-	-	-	-	-	-	-	-	-	-	-	-
11	XXI	-	-	-	-	-	-	-	-	-	-	-	-	-	-	-	-	-	-	-	-	+	-	-	-	-	-	-	-	-	-	-
	XXII	-	-	-	-	-	-	-	-	-	-	-	-	-	-	-	-	-	-	-	+	-	-	-	-	-	-	-	-	-	-	-
12	XXIII	-	-	-	-	-	-	-	-	-	-	-	-	-	-	-	-	-	-	-	-	-	-	+	-	-	-	-	-	-	-	-
	XXIV	-	-	-	-	-	-	-	-	-	-	-	-	-	-	-	-	-	-	-	-	-	+	-	-	-	-	-	-	-	-	-
13	XXV	-	-	-	-	-	-	-	-	-	-	-	-	-	-	-	-	-	-	-	-	-	-	-	-	+	-	-	-	-	-	-
	XXVI	-	-	-	-	-	-	-	-	-	-	-	-	-	-	-	-	-	-	-	-	-	-	-	+	-	-	-	-	-	-	-
14	XXVII	-	-	-	+	-	-	-	-	-	-	-	-	-	-	-	+	-	-	-	-	-	-	-	-	-	-	+	-	+	-	+
	XXVIII	-	-	+	-	-	-	-	-	-	-	-	-	-	-	-	-	-	-	-	-	-	-	-	-	-	+	-	+	-	+	-
15	XXIX	-	-	-	+	-	-	-	-	-	-	-	-	-	-	-	-	-	-	-	-	-	-	-	-	-	+	-	+	-	+	-
	XXX	-	-	-	-	-	-	-	-	-	-	-	-	-	-	-	-	-	-	-	-	-	-	-	-	-	-	+	-	+	-	±
16	XXXI	-	-	-	+	-	-	-	-	-	-	-	-	-	-	-	-	-	-	-	-	-	-	-	-	-	+	-	+	-	-	+
	XXXII	-	-	-	-	-	-	-	-	-	-	-	-	-	-	-	-	-	-	-	-	-	-	-	-	-	-	+	-	±	+	-

[1] One mating type XIX has been found.

76. GENETICS OF PARAMECIUM (Concluded)

Part IV: PARAMECIUM CALKINSI

+ = mating reaction and conjugation; – = none in mixtures of two mating types represented in the corresponding row and column.

Variety	Mating Type	I	II	III	IV
1	I	–	+	–	–
1	II	+	–	–	–
2	III	–	–	–	+
2	IV	–	–	+	–

Part V: PARAMECIUM MULTIMICRONUCLEATUM

(Parts IV, V and VI after Wichterman.)

+ = mating reaction and conjugation; – = none in mixtures of two mating types represented in the corresponding row and column.

Mating Type	I	II	III	IV
I	–	+	+	+
II	+	–	+	+
III	+	+	–	+
IV	+	+	+	–

Part VI: PARAMECIUM TRICHIUM

+ = mating reation and conjugation; – = none in mixtures of two mating types represented in the corresponding row and column.

Mating Type	I	II	III
I	–	+	+
II	+	–	+
III	+	+	–

Part VII: INHERITANCE OF MATING TYPES

Section 1: Paramecium aurelia (After Sonneborn.)

a. Analysis of 4 caryonides from individual pairs of conjugants.

No. of Pairs	Number of Caryonides I	Number of Caryonides II
1	4	0
18	3	1
21	2	2
13	1	3
3	0	4

b. Analysis of the two sister caryonides from each ex-conjugant.

Number of Ex-conjugants[1]	Number of Caryonides I	Number of Caryonides II
35	2	0
70	1	1
34	0	2

/1/ Each ex-conjugant contains two macronuclei derived from a single fusion nucleus. When the ex-conjugant divides into two daughter cells, each cell contains one of the two marconuclei. All descendants of each daughter cell constitute a caryonide.

Section 2: Paramecium bursaria (After Jennings.)

Parental Types (Mating Types of the Conjugants)	Number of Pairs Yielding Clones of the Parental Mating Types	Numbers Yielding Clones of Non-Parental Mating Types
A X B	103	6
A X C	39	22
A X D	66	14
B X C	89	1
B X D	64	38
C X D	120	4
L X M	44	43
Total:	525	128

Part VIII: DIFFERENCES BETWEEN VARIETIES: PARAMECIUM BURSARIA

	Differences	Variety I	Variety II	Variety III
1	Time of day or night when animals can undergo mating reaction.	Daytime.	Daytime.	Any time of day or night.
2	Length of time of conjugation (at 26.5°C).	20–22 hours.	36 or more hours.	
3	Chromosomes	Intermediate between varieties II and III.	Thin and short.	Generally thick and long.

Part IX: GEOGRAPHICAL DISTRIBUTION OF VARIETIES

Section 1: Paramecium aurelia[1]

Variety	North America	South America	Western Europe	Japan	India
1	X	X	X	X	.
2	X	X	X	.	.
3	X	.	.	.	.
4	X	X	.	X	.
5	X	.	.	.	.
6	X	.	.	.	X
7	X	.	.	.	.
8	X	.	.	.	.
9			X		

Section 2: Paramecium bursaria[2]

Variety	U.S.A.	China	Japan	Russia	Central, Western Europe
I	X	X	X	.	.
II	X	.	.	.	.
III	X	.	.	.	.
IV	.	.	.	X	.
V	.	.	.	X	.
VI	.	.	.	.	X

Section 3: Paramecium caudatum[3]

Variety	U.S.A.	Japan	France	Variety	U.S.A.	Japan	France
1	X	X	.	9	X	.	.
2	X	.	.	10	X	.	.
3	X	X	.	11	X	.	.
4	X	.	.	12	.	X	.
5	X	.	.	13	.	X	.
6	X	.	.	14	X	.	.
7	X	.	.	15	.	.	X
8	X	.	.	16	.	.	X

/1/ After Sonneborn, Beale, and Schneller.   /2/ After Jennings, Opitz, and Chen.   /3/ After Gilman.

77. THE ANTIGENIC TYPES: PARAMECIUM AURELIA (RACE 51)
(After Sonneborn.)

Serum taken from a rabbit repeatedly injected with paramecia paralyzes paramecia of the same strain. The serum may or may not have a paralyzing effect on other strains. If a second rabbit is injected with a resistant strain, the serum obtained will paralyze paramecia of the second strain but not the first. This indicates interaction between paramecia antigens of rabbit antibodies. Each antigenically distinct strain is called a serotype. A culture of one serotype, derived from a single ancestral cell, may give rise to cells of different hereditary serotypes. The accompanying diagram illustrates a single cell of race 51 (serotype A) giving rise to the original A and seven distinctly different serotypes, B, C, D, E, G, H and J.

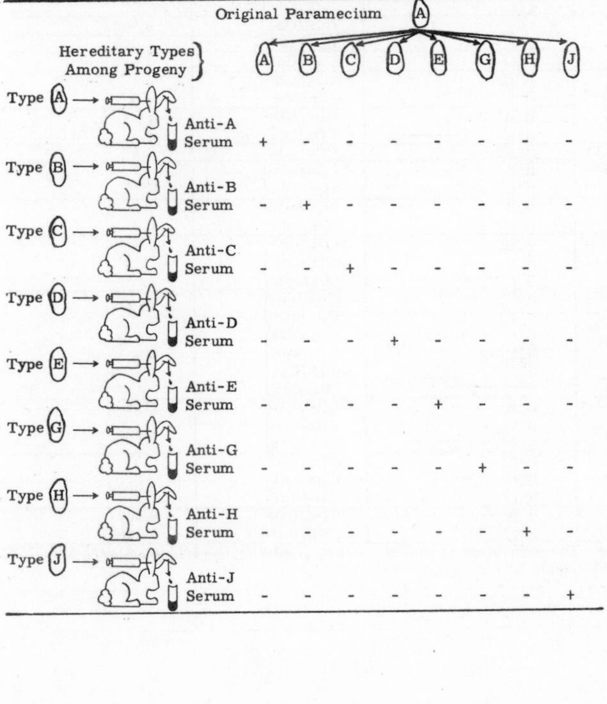

Original Paramecium (A)

Hereditary Types Among Progeny: A B C D E G H J

	Anti-A Serum	Anti-B Serum	Anti-C Serum	Anti-D Serum	Anti-E Serum	Anti-G Serum	Anti-H Serum	Anti-J Serum
Type A	+	–	–	–	–	–	–	–
Type B	–	+	–	–	–	–	–	–
Type C	–	–	+	–	–	–	–	–
Type D	–	–	–	+	–	–	–	–
Type E	–	–	–	–	+	–	–	–
Type G	–	–	–	–	–	+	–	–
Type H	–	–	–	–	–	–	+	–
Type J	–	–	–	–	–	–	–	+

78. GENETIC SYSTEM INVOLVED IN CONTROL OF ANTIGENIC TRAITS: PARAMECIUM AURELIA (RACE 51) (After Beale.)

In Figure 1, the two conjugants do not exchange cytoplasm. This is normal. The 51A parent gives rise to 51A animals, whereas 51B parent gives rise to 51B animals. Inheritance therefore appears to be cytoplasmically determined. If a substantial amount of cytoplasm is exchanged between two mates, both would produce either type 51A or type 51B. In Figure 2, small amounts of cytoplasm are exchanged. One mate produces type 51A, while the other produces mostly type 51B and some type 51A. Evidence indicates that antigenic types differ only in cytoplasmic factors.

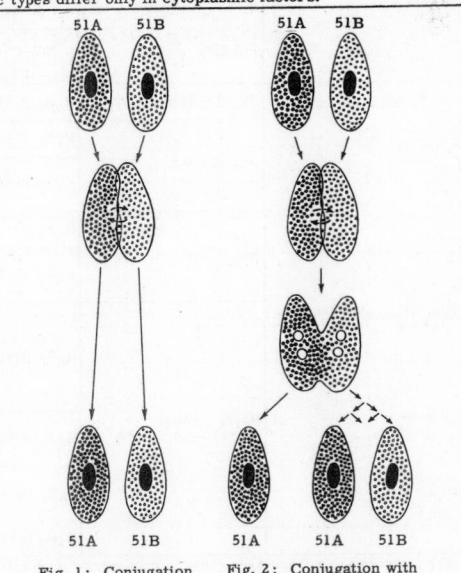

Fig. 1: Conjugation without Cytoplasmic Exchange

Fig. 2: Conjugation with Cytoplasmic Exchange

79. BLOOD GROUPS AND FACTORS: DISTRIBUTION IN VARIOUS POPULATIONS
Values are per cent of the population.

General	Differentiated	American Indian[1]	Arabian, Baghdad	Australian, Aborigine	Chinese	Egyptian, Cairo	English	Eskimo, S.W. Greenland	German, Berlin	Hawaiian	Hindu	Italian	Japanese	Norwegian	Russian	Swedish	U.S.A. Negro	U.S.A. White
						Blood Groups[2]												
1 O		23.5-98.5	34.1	53.1	30.0	26.6	46.7	36.3	36.5	36.5	31.3	41.2	31.2		33.7	37.9	49.3	45.0
2 A	A_1	1.5-76.5	30.8	44.7	25.0	35.7	41.7	54.6	42.5	60.8	19.0	39.4	38.4		38.4	46.7	26.0	31.4
3	A_2																	9.6
4 B		0-1.6	28.9	2.1	35.0	27.1	8.6	5.3	14.5	2.2	41.2	14.0	21.8		20.8	10.3	21.0	10.0
5 AB	A_1B	0	6.2	0	10.0	10.5	3.0	3.7	6.5	0.5	8.5	5.4	8.6		7.1	5.1	3.7	2.9
6	A_2B																	1.1
						Rh Positive												
7 Rh_o		1.1		4.0	0.9	11.5	2.5	1.0	2.0		2.9	1.3	0	1.5			45.9	2.2
8 Rh_1	Rh_1Rh_1	40.7		39.0	60.6	25.5	19.7	34.9	19.5		35.2	23.3	37.4	15.9			0.9	20.9
9	Rh_1rh	7.4		14.0		39.7	35.2		35.6		32.4	37.3		35.6			22.8	33.8
10 Rh_2		9.5		21.0	3.0	9.2	12.2	19.7	12.9		3.8	9.6	13.3	13.8			16.3	14.9
11 Rh_2	Rh_1Rh_2	38.1		15.0	34.1	8.2	13.6	44.4	13.9		16.2	11.8	47.3	14.7			4.4	13.9
12	Rh_2Rh_1	3.1		6.0		0.1			0.4		0	0.6					0	0.1
						Rh Negative												
13 rh		0		0	1.5	5.9	14.8	0	14.4		7.6	14.8	1.3	16.2			7.4	12.5
14 rh'		0		1.0			0.7	0	0.5		1.9	0.5	0	0.7			1.5	0.9
15 rh''		0		0			1.3	0	0.8			0.5	1.2				0.7	0.5
16 rhy		0		0			0		0			0.3	0.7				0	0
						Blood Factors (M-N Blood Groups)[3]												
17 M		60.0		3.0	33.2	28.3	30.5	67.6	30.2		42.7	28.9	29.0		32.2	36.1	28.4	29.2
18 N		4.9		67.4	18.2	23.1	21.4	2.4	19.7		10.7	17.1	21.1		21.2	16.9	21.9	21.3
19 MN		35.1		29.6	48.6	48.6	48.2	30.0	50.0		46.7	53.9	49.9		46.5	47.0	49.6	49.6

/1/ Blood group data from Toba Indians (Argentina), Blackfeet (Montana), and Pueblo (New Mexico); Rh data from Mexican Indians; M-N data from U.S.A., tribe not specified. /2/ Equivalents in obsolete terminologies of Moss and Jansky are: O=Moss IV, Jansky I; A=Moss and Jansky II; B=Moss and Jansky III; AB=Moss I, Jansky IV. /3/ Other blood group systems are the P, Lutheran (Lu^a), Kell-Cellano (K, k), Lewis (Le^a, Le^b), Duffy (Fy^a, Fy^b), and Kidd (Jk^a, Jk^b). The approximate frequencies for U.S.A. whites are: P 49%; Lu^a 4%, Lu^b 96%; K 5%, k 95%; Le^a 47%, Le^b 48%; Fy^a 41%, Fy^b 59%; Jk^a 52%, Jk^b 48%.

80. HEREDITY OF BLOOD GROUPS AND FACTORS: APPLICATION IN DISPUTED PATERNITY

Children's Groups		OxO	OxA	OxB	AxA	AxB	BxB	OxAB	AxAB	BxAB	ABxAB	MNxMN	MNxM	MNxN	MxM	MxN	NxN
							If Parents' Groups Are:										
1	Can be:	O	A, O	B, O	A, O[1]	AB, O[2], A[3], B[1]	B, O[3]	A, B	A, AB, B[1]	B, AB, A[3]	A, B, AB	M, N, MN	M, MN	N, MN	M	MN	N
2	Cannot be:	A, B, AB	B, AB	A, AB	B, AB	None	A, AB	O, AB	O	O	O	None	N	M	N, MN	M, N	M, MN

/1/ This type not possible if either parent is genetically A/A. /2/ If one parent was genetically A/O and the other B/O, an O can result. /3/ This type not possible if one parent is genetically B/B.

81. THE Rh-Hr (CDE-cde) SYSTEM OF BLOOD FACTORS

Plus (+) indicates agglutination by antiserum; thus C+ = agglutination of red cells by anti-C (anti-rh') and presence of agglutinogen C, i.e., in the red cells. Minus (-) = no reaction with antiserum and absence of agglutinogen. In CDE notation, diagonal (/) separates genes contributed by one parent from those contributed by the other parent.

	Phenotypes and their Frequencies[1]; Classified by Agglutination Reactions with Antisera			Genotypes		
	1 Antiserum (Anti-D)	3 Antisera (Anti-C, D, E)	5 Antisera (Anti-C, D, E, c, e)	Wiener Terminology	Fisher-Race Terminology	Calculated Frequencies %
1	Rh_o (D-), negative 14.9%	rh (C-D-E-), 13.4%	rr (C-D-E-c+e+)	rr	cde/cde	13.4
2		rh' (C+D-E-), 1.1%	r'r' (C+D-E-c-e+)	r'r'	Cde/Cde	0.02
3			r'r (C+D-E-c+e+)	r'r	Cde/cde	1.1
4		rh'' (C-D-E+), 0.4%	r''r'' (C-D-E+c-e-)	r''r''	cdE/cdE	0.003
5			r''r (C-D-E+c+e+)	r''r	cdE/cde	0.4
6		rh'rh'' (rhy) (C+D-E+), 0.02%	r_yr (C+D-E+c+e+)	r'r''	Cde/cdE	0.02
7				r_yr	Cde/cde	
8			r_yr' (C+D-E+c-e+)	r_yr'	CdE/Cde	0.0003
9			r_yr'' (C+D-E+c+e-)	r_yr''	CdE/cdE	0.0001
10			$r_y r_y$ (C+D-E+c-e-)	$r_y r_y$	CdE/CdE	0.000001
11	Rh_o (D+), positive 85.1%	Rh_o (C-D+E-), 2.5%	R_oR_o (C-D+E-c+e+)	R^oR^o	cDe/cDe	0.1
12				R^or	cDe/cde	2.4
13		Rh_1 (C+D+E-), 51.2%	R_1R_1 (C+D+E-c-e+)	R^1R^1	CDe/CDe	16.9
14				R^1r'	CDe/Cde	1.1
15			R_1R_o (C+D+E-c+e+)	R^1R^o	CDe/cDe	2.6
16				R^1r	CDe/cde	30.6
17				R^or'	cDe/Cde	
18		Rh_2 (C-D+E+), 16.5%	R_2R_2 (C-D+E+c-e-)	R^2R^2	cDE/cDE	2.7
19				R^2r''	cDE/cdE	0.2
20			R_2R_o (C-D+E+c+e+)	R^2R^o	cDE/cDe	1.1
21				R^2r	cDE/cde	12.5
22				R^or''	cDe/cdE	
23		Rh_1Rh_2 (Rh_z) (C+D+E+), 14.9%	R_zR_o (C+D+E+c+e+)	R^zR^o	CDE/cDe	13.9
24				R^1R^2	CDe/cDE	
25				R^zr	CDE/cde	0.9
26				R^zr'	CDe/cdE	
27				R^2r'	cDE/Cde	
28				R^or_y	cDe/CdE	
29			R_zR_1 (C+D+E+c-e+)	R^zR^1	CDE/CDe	0.08
30				R^zr'	CDe/CdE	0.001
31				R^1r_y	CDe/CdE	
32			R_zR_2 (C+D+E+c+e-)	R^zR^2	CDE/cDE	0.03
33				R^zr''	CDe/CdE	0.0004
34				R^2r_y	cDE/CdE	
35			R_zR_z (C+D+E+c-e-)	R^zR^z	CDE/CDE	0.0001
36				R^zr_y	CDE/CdE	0.00002

/1/ Frequencies are percentages showing occurrence in American whites. The percentage of whites reacting positively to various antisera are: 70%, anti-C (anti-rh'); 85%, anti-D (anti-Rh_o); 30%, anti-E (anti-rh''); 80%, anti-c (anti-hr'); 97%, anti-e (anti-hr'').

82. GENETIC LINKAGE: MAN
Part I: COMPLETELY SEX-LINKED GENES (X-CHROMOSOME TRANSMISSION)

	Mutation	Gene Symbol	Phenotypic Expression		
			Hemizygote $X\overline{Y}$	Heterozygote $X\overline{X}$	Homozygote XX
1	Classical hemophilia	h	Severe bleeder.	Normal.	Severe bleeder.
2	Mild hemophilia	h^m	Mild bleeder.	Occasionally slightly affected.	Unknown.
3	Plasma thromboplastin component deficiency		Severe bleeder.	Slightly affected.	Unknown.
4	Retinitis pigmentosa		Choroidoretinal degeneration.	Tapetal reflex.	Unknown.
5	Ocular albinism		Lack of pigment in globe.	Fundal changes.	Unknown.
6	Red-green color blindness	b	Color blindness.	Mildly affected.	Color blindness.
7	Hemeralopia		Night blindness with myopia.	Normal.	Unknown.
8	Megalocornea		Large cornea.	Occasionally affected.	Unknown.
9	Microphthalmia		Microphthalmia and blindness.	Normal.	Normal.
10	Choroidemia		Night blindness, constricted visual fields, blindness.	Depigmented retina.	Unknown.
11	Nystagmus		Severe nystagmus.	Slight nystagmus.	Unknown.
12	Optic atrophy		Blindness.	Occasionally blind.	Unknown.
13	Congenital retinal detachment		Retinal detachment and blindness.	Normal.	Blindness(?).
14	External ophthalmoplegia		Ophthalmoplegia, myopia, absent knee jerks.	Absent knee jerks.	Unknown.
15	Macular dystrophy		Loss of central vision.	Normal.	Unknown.
16	Childhood progressive muscular dystrophy		Muscular dystrophy.	Normal.	Unknown.
17	Peroneal atrophy		Peroneal atrophy.	Occasionally affected.	Unknown.
18	Idiocy		Idiocy with microcephaly.	Normal.	Unknown.
19	Alopecia congenita		Hairlessness.	Normal.	Unknown.
20	Anhidrotic ectodermal dysplasia		Widespread ectodermal defects.	Normal.	Unknown.
21	Icthyosis simplex		Scaly skin.	Normal.	Scaly skin.
22	Keratosis follicularis (Lameris)		Multiple skin keratoses.	Normal.	Unknown.
23	White occipital lock of hair		White lock of hair at occiput.	Normal.	Unknown.

Part II: HOLANDRIC GENES (Y-CHROMOSOME TRANSMISSION)

	Mutation	Phenotypic Expression $X\overline{Y}$		Mutation	Phenotypic Expression $X\overline{Y}$
1	Ichthyosis hystrix gravior	Bark-like skin.	4	Keratoma dissipatum	Horny papules on hands and feet.
2	Hypertrichosis of the ears.	Hiary ears.	5	Color vision anomaly	Poor color discrimination.
3	Webbed toes	Webbed toes.			

Part III: INCOMPLETELY SEX-LINKED GENES (X- and Y-CHROMOSOME TRANSMISSION)

The concept of homologous segments of the X- and Y-chromosomes has become widely disseminated throughout the literature on human genetics. However, the accuracy of the original observations on which the concept is based has been questioned; therefore, data should be considered with great caution.

	Mutation	Gene Symbol	Phenotypic Expression				
			Heterozygotes			Homozygotes	
			$\overline{X}\overline{Y}$	$X\overline{Y}$	$X\overline{X}$	$X\overline{Y}$	XX
1	Interstitial nephritis		Severe, usually fatal.	Unknown	Mild or no disease observed	Unknown	
2	Total color blindness	ac	← Normal. →			← Day blind. →	
3	Xeroderma pigmentosa	xe	← Freckled. →			← X. pigmentosa. →	
4	Oguchi's disease	og	← Normal. →			← Night blindness without myopia. →	
5	Recessive epidermolysis bullosa	ep	← Normal. →			← Skin blisters with scarring. →	
6	Dominant retinitis pigmentosa	Re	← Pigmented retina with blindness. →			Unknown.	
7	Recessive retinitis pigmentosa	re	← Normal. →			← Pigmented retina with blindness. →	
8	Recessive spastic paraplegia		← Normal. →			← Spasticity, exaggerated tendon. →	

83. MUTATION RATES: MAN

Knowledge of mutation rates in man as in other organisms is still considered provisional, and the traits for which estimates are available are a highly selected fraction of all genes. Estimates for chondrodystrophy, aniridia and neurofibromatosis may be more reliable than those for epiloia and Waardenburg's syndrome. In some cases, significant figures have been reduced although two digits do not imply greater accuracy than one. Reported estimates for autosomal recessive traits are probably not reliable. The error in these estimates is unknown but may be appreciable.

	Character	Method of Estimation[1]	Mutations per Gene in One Generation	Remarks
			Dominant Genes	
1	Epiloia	Direct	$0.4-0.8 \times 10^{-5}$	
2	Chondrodystrophy	Direct	4.9×10^{-5}	Estimates may be spuriously high because of some evidence of phenocopies.
3		Direct	4.2×10^{-5}	
4		Direct	7×10^{-5}	
5		Indirect	4.3×10^{-5}	
6	Pelger's nuclear anomaly	Direct	2.7×10^{-5}	
7	Aniridia	Direct	0.5×10^{-5}	
8	Retinoblastoma	Direct	4.3×10^{-6}	Estimate based on proposition that 75% of all sporadic cases of retinoblastoma are phenocopies.
9	Retinoblastoma	Direct	1.4×10^{-5}	Estimates by treating all cases as caused by mutation.
10		Direct	2.3×10^{-5}	
11	Waardenburg's syndrome	Direct	3.7×10^{-6}	
12	Neurofibromatosis	Direct	$1.3-2.5 \times 10^{-4}$	
13		Indirect	$0.8-1.0 \times 10^{-4}$	
14	Facio-scapulo-humeral progressive muscular dystrophy	Direct	4.7×10^{-6}	
15		Indirect	4.7×10^{-6}	
16	Multiple polyposis of the colon	Indirect	$1.0-3.0 \times 10^{-5}$	
			Sex-linked Recessive Genes	
17	Hemophilia	Indirect	3.2×10^{-5}	Estimate may include three types of hemophilia: (a) classical sex-linked hemophilia caused by a deficiency of anti-hemophilic globulin, (b) a sex-linked clotting defect caused by a lack of "plasma thromboplastin component," and (c) an autosomally inherited clotting defect caused by a lack of "plasma thromboplastin antecedent."
18	Childhood progressive muscular dystrophy	Direct[2]	1×10^{-4}	
19		Indirect	1×10^{-4}	
20		Indirect	$4.5-6.5 \times 10^{-5}$	
21		Direct	3.2×10^{-5}	
22		Indirect	3.8×10^{-5}	

/1/ All indirect estimations make use of estimates of the relative fitness, and frequency at birth, of the trait, and assume that the population is in equilibrium. /2/ Not a true direct estimate but an approximation which overestimates the mutation rate.

84. LINKAGE GROUPS: VARIOUS ANIMALS

Size or length of linkage maps reflects the intensity of genetics investigation on an organism rather than the number of genes possessed by the organism. Symbols for genes are capitalized only when characterized by dominance. Numbers in brackets are footnote references.

Mouse, house (Mus musculus) [1]

#	Locus	Symbol	Mutation and Phenotype
			Linkage Group I
1	16	fr	Frizzle. Decreased proportion of coarser types of hair; vibrissae curled.
2	4, 3	sh-1	Shaker-1. Deaf; choreic head movements.
3	16, 12	c[2]	Albinism. Absence of pigmentation.
4		p	Pink-eye. Pink eyes; reduction of black or brown pigment in coat.
5		o	Oligodactyly. Homozygotes lack 5th (or 4th and 5th) toe on front and/or hind feet.
			Linkage Group II
6	0.16	d	Dilution. Clumping of pigment in coat color.
7		se	Short ear. Reduction of pinna.
			Linkage Group III
8	8	s	Spotting. Unpigmented areas on fur.
9	33	hr	Hairless. Shedding of hair at 10-14 days.
10	7	pi	Pirouette. Whirling movements, resembles waltzing.
11	18	W	Dominant spotting. Homozygous lethal.
12	16	lx	Hemimelia tibiae. Reduction of tibia generally associated with bent fibula.
13		rl	Reeler. Impaired locomotion through disturbed balance.
			Linkage Group IV
14	12	r	Rodless retina. Outer nuclear layer of retina rodless.
15		si	Silver. Absence or reduction of pigment granules.
			Linkage Group V
16		Ra[3]	Ragged. Affects coat texture.
17	3	kr	Kreisler. Deaf, prolonged running in circles.
18	5	a	Non-agouti. Determines pigment distribution of black, brown and yellow in individual hair.
19	10	un	Undulated. Tail undulations; sometimes hunchback; animals often runts.
20	3	we	Wellhaarig. Shortened whiskers at birth, later curved.
21	19	pa	Pallid. Pink eyes, agouti coat color.
22	8	fi	Fidget. Head shaking side to side, some circling.
23	17	hy-1	Hydrocephalus-1. Dome-shaped, or increased head size from ventricular distension.
24		Sd	Danforth's short tail. Affects urogenital system. Homozygotes lethal. Heterozygotes short-tailed or tailless.
			Linkage Group VI
25	11.6	bt	Belted. Dorsal white spotting in belt area.
26	0, 3	Ca	Caracul. Hair lies in fluffy waves, straightens later. Whiskers curved.
27		N	Naked. Hair breaks off at 10-14 days.
			Linkage Group VII
28	29	wa-2	Waved-2. Wavy coat.
29	20	sh-2	Shaker-2. Deaf, choreic head movements, whirling in circles.
30		Re	Rex. Curly whiskers in juvenile. Curly vibrissal and short curly guard hairs.
31		vt	Vestigial.
32		Tr	Trembler. Spastic paralysis in legs; more marked in hind pair.
			Linkage Group VIII
33	7	b[4]	Brown. Coat color brownish hue.
34		m	Misty. Dilutes fur color, produces white tail tip in heterozygotes.
35		an	Anemia. Small, pale, sterile.
			Linkage Group IX
36	4.3	T[5]	Brachyury. Short tail. Homozygotes inviable.
37	2(?)	Ki	Kinky tail. Possibly an allele of Fu. Homozygotes inviable.
38	3.9	Fu	Fused. Resembles short tail. Expression variable.
39		H-2	Histocompatibility-2. Determines susceptibility and resistance to tissue transplants.
			Linkage Group X
40	20	v	Waltzing. Deaf, moves in circles.
41		ji	Jittery. Muscular incoordination in righting after being placed on back.

Mouse, house (Mus musculus) [1] (concluded)

#	Locus	Symbol	Mutation and Phenotype
			Linkage Group XI
42	9	wa-1	Waved. Short whiskers, waved hair.
43		Wh	White. Snow-white fur; eyes pink, reduced in size.
			Linkage Group XII
44	45	je	Jerker. Deaf; resembles waltzing.
45		ru	Ruby-eye. Eyes vary between ruby and pink.
			Linkage Group XIII
46		Lp[6]	Loop-tail. Twisted tail, wobbling head.
47	40, 23	py	Polydactyly.
48	6	ln	Leaden. Resembles maltese dilution (blue).
49		Sp	Splotch. White spotting on belly, occasionally on back.
50	32	fz	Fuzzy. Thin and faintly wavy hair.
			Linkage Group XIV
51	28	cr	Crinkled. Modified hair structure.
52	15	f	Flexed-tail. Causes anemia and belly-spot.
53		ch	Congenital hydrocephalus. Lethal at birth.
			Linkage Group XX (Sex Chromosome)
54	12	Bn	Bent-tail. Viability of homozygous females and bent-tail males much reduced.
55	5	Ta	Tabby. Coat of heterozygous females transversely striped. Homozygous females and tabby males with coat resembling crinkled (cr).
56	0(?)	Br	Brindled. Coat fleeked with patches of light hair. Brindled males die prior to 3 weeks.
57	21	Mo	Mottled. Similar to brindled except that males die in utero; perhaps an allele of Br.
58	(?)	jp	Jumpy. Behavior disorder manifest in hemizygous males at about 11 days and lethal at 25-32 days.
59		To	Tortoise shell. Similar to mottled but probably not allelic. Position not determined.

Rabbit (Lepus cuniculus)

#	Locus	Symbol	Mutation and Phenotype
			Linkage Group I
60	0	c	Albinism. Coat color alleles vary from chinchilla to complete albinism.
61	14.4	y	Yellow fat.
62	42.8	b	Brown. Brown coat color.
			Linkage Group II
63	0	du	Dutch pattern. White belt on colored background.
64	1.2	En	English. Colored spots on white background.
65	14.3	l	Angora hair. Increased hair fiber length.
			Linkage Group III
66	0	r_1	Rex-1. Short plush-like coat.
67	17.2	r_2	Rex-2. Short plush-like coat.
			Linkage Group IV
68	0	a	Non-agouti. Coat color black.
69	14.7	dw	Dwarf. Small size, lethal shortly after birth.
70	29.9	w	Wide-banded agouti. Wide banding of agouti hairs.
			Linkage Group V
71	0	br	Brachydactyly. Abnormality of toes.
72	28.3	f	Furless. Fur restricted to extremities.
73	36.8	an	Erythrocyte agglutinogen.
			Linkage Group VI
74	0	E	Extension. Extension of dark pigment.
75	26.2	At	Production of atropinesterase.

Guinea pig (Cavia porcellus) [1]

#	Locus	Symbol	Mutation and Phenotype
			Linkage Group I
76	42.4±	R	Rough fur at least on hind toes.
77		Px	Pollex. Tendency to return of thumb, little toe and rarely big toe.
			Linkage Group II
78	24.4±	si	Silvered (stationary from birth). Incomplete recessive.
79		m	Modifier. Modifies rough fur effect. Homozygote high grade roughness.

Rat, common (Rattus norvegicus) [7]

#	Locus	Symbol	Mutation and Phenotype
			Linkage Group I
80	0	p	Pink-eye. Coat yellow, eyes pink.
81	20.5	r	Red-eyed yellow. Coat yellow, eyes red.
82	21	c	Albino. Absence of pigment from coat and eyes.
83	24.3	l	Lethal. Skeleton imperfect.
84	66.3	w	Waltzing. Runs in circles.

/1/ Locus values for house mouse, guinea pig, fowl and parasitic wasp are recombination percentages between successive genes listed. Where two values appear, the first represents data from heterozygous females and the second from heterozygous males. /2/ c-o = 15, 20. /3/ Ra-a = 24. /4/ b-an = 7. /5/ T-Fu = 4.3. /6/ Lp-ln = 35. /7/ Jaundice (j), curly coat (Cu_2), cataract (Ca), blue dilution of coat (d), hooded coat pattern (h), cowlick (cw), and shaker (sr) have been found to be independent of linkage groups I-V and of each other and are provisionally regarded as markers of seven additional chromosome pairs.

Size or length of linkage maps reflects the intensity of genetics investigation on an organism rather than the number of genes possessed by the organism. Symbols for genes are capitalized only when characterized by dominance. Numbers in brackets are footnote references.

Locus		Symbol	Mutation and Phenotype
			Rat, common (Rattus norvegicus) [7] (concluded)
			Linkage Group II
85	0	Sh	Shaggy. Hair and vibrissae curved.
86	4	Cu	Curly. Hairs of coat and vibrissae curved.
87	14.3	an	Anemia. Lack of red blood cells. Young anemic.
88	28	in	Incisorless. Incisors lacking.
89	47	s	Silvered coat.
90	52	b	Brown. Chocolate pigmentation.
			Linkage Group III
91	0	n	Naked, except for short fuzzy coat.
92	45	hr	Hairless. Hair lost at about 4 weeks of age.
93	88	wo	Wobbly. Ataxic locomotion.
			Linkage Group IV
94	0	k	Kinky. Hairs of coat and vibrissae kinky.
95	34.1	st	Stub. Short stubby tail.
			Linkage Group V
96	0	A	Agouti. Fur color wild type, agouti.
97	44.6	f	Fawn. Tawny blue to fawn coat color.
			Silkworm (Bombyx mori)
			Linkage Group I (Z Chromosome)
98	0	os	Low degree of translucency of larva.
99	14	Ge	Giant egg. Length and width 1.26 and 1.11, respectively, times the normal egg.
100	36.4	e	Elongate. First and second abdominal segments of larva unusually elongated.
101	38.7	Vg	Vestigial. Wings poorly developed.
102	49.6	od	Translucent. Skin of larva shows high degree of translucency.
			Linkage Group II
103	0	P	Plain. Full grown larva white. $+p$, p^B, p^M, p^S, p^{Sa} multiple or pseudo-alleles of p.
104	6.1	S	New striped. Dark stripe on larva. Heterozygote almost as dark as homozygote.
105	6.9	Gr	Gray egg. Milky white shell, dark serosa pigment.
106	25.6	Y	Yellow blood. Deep yellow hemolymph in larva.
107	26.7	oa	Mottled translucent. Mottled translucency on larval skin.
108	31.8	Rc	Rusty. Yellowish-brown cocoon, lighter inner layer.
			Linkage Group III
109	0	Ze	Zebra. Black band on anterior end of each segment. Pair of black spots on ventral side of each larval segment.
110	0	ap	Apodal. All thoracic legs rudimentary.
111	22.8	lem	Lemon. Greenish-yellow coloring over skin visible from second instar.
			Linkage Group IV
112	0	L	Multilunar. Pairs of large brownish or yellowish round spots on thoracic and abdominal segments.
113	25.8	sk	Stick. Larva body slender and hard.
114	33.1	Spc	Speckle. Many dark spots on larval skin. Female sterile.
			Linkage Group V
115	0	pe	Pink-eyed. White egg. Pigment absent from serosa.
116	4.7	ok	Kinshiryu. High degree translucency of larva.
117	31.7	re	Red egg. Reddish-brown serosa.
118	40.8	oc	Chinese. High degree translucency of larva.
			Linkage Group VI
119	0	E	Plain supernumerary legs. Supernumerary legs in 1st and 2nd abdominal segments of larva. E^{Ca}, E^D, E^H, E^{Kp}, E^N multiple of pseudo-alleles of E.
120	1.4	Nc	No crescent supernumerary legs. Supernumerary leg in the 2nd abdominal segment.
121	3.0	+M	Tetra molting. Standard type, larva pupates after 4th molt. M^3, M^5 multiple or pseudoalleles of $+M$.
122	8	b2	Brown egg 2. Grayish-brown pigment in serosa.
123	13.6	F	Flesh. Cocoon color reddish-yellow or salmon.
124	17.7	l-k	Lethal-k. Embryo killed few days before hatching.
			Linkage Group VII
125	0	q	Quail. Larval body tinted reddish-purple and covered with shredlike lines.
126	7.0	Gb	Green b. Greenish cocoon color.
127	21	obt	B_8-mottled. Moderate degree translucency of larva. Not lethal.
			Silkworm (Bombyx mori) (concluded)
			Linkage Group VIII
128	0	ae	Amylase negative. Amylase in digestive fluid weak.
129	1.1	be	Amylase negative. Amylase in body fluid (hemolymph) weak.
			Linkage Group IX
130	0	I	Yellow inhibitor. Suppression of yellow blood and yellow cocoon.
131	5.9	I-a	Dominant chocolate. Like chocolate, head black.
132	6.7	bd	Dilute black. Whole larval body dilute black.
133	7.4	og	Giallo Ascoli. High degree translucency. Female almost sterile.
			Linkage Group X
134	0	w_1 (w-1)	White egg 1. No pigment in serosa, white eyes in moth.
135	0.0+	fl	Wingless. Fore and hind wings absent in pupa and moth.
136	3.4	w_2 (w-2)	White egg 2. Egg gradually changes from white to light reddish color. White eyes in moth.
137	6.9	w_3 (w-3)	White egg 3. Light purplish-brown egg. Black eyes in moth.
			Linkage Group XI
138	0	K	Knobbed. Dermal protuberances appear on dorsal sides of several segments of larva, pupa and moth.
139	5.5	Bu	Burnt. Larva skin from 2nd to 5th segments shows burn-like scar.
140	17.1	bp	Black pupa.
141	24.0	mp	Micropterous. Small wings.
			Linkage Group XII
142	0	Ng	No glue. Eggs easily separated from papers because of poor development of mucous glands in females.
143	14.0	C	Golden egg. Cocoon golden yellow outside, nearly white inside.
144	52.1	rd	Clumpy. Irregular egg shape and highly variable.
			Linkage Group XIII
145	0	ch	Chocolate. Newly hatched larva reddish-brown.
146	11.3	cf	Crayfish. Fore and hind wings swollen and protrude laterally from body in pupa.
			Linkage Group XIV
147	0	Di	Dirty. Irregular black lines and dots cover dorsal surface of larva.
148	2.7	U	Ursa. Dark brown pigments cover dorsal and lateral sides of larva.
149	10.7	odk	Mottled. Low degree translucency.
			Linkage Group XV
150	0	Se	White side egg. Egg surface irregular and with many furrows.
151	7, 8	Gc	Green c. Green cocoon.
			Parasitic wasp (Habrobracon juglandis) [1]
			Linkage Group I
152	12	Sk	Speckled. Bright red flecks of pigment in white eye.
153	13	r	Reduced. Small wings. Reduced, irregular venation.
154	30	gl	Glass. Small eyes, lacks facet outlines.
155		x	Sex gene. Nine factors known. Determine sex differences.
	10		
156	22	fu	Fused. Antennal segments fused. Tarsal segments lacking or fused.
157	42	sb	Stubby. Males with antennae 7-9 segments long. Females with antennae 5-7 segments long.
158	30	bl	Black. Body color.
159	12	le	Lemon. Body color pale lemon-yellow.
160	14	c	Cantaloup. Eyes light pink, darken to deep red.
161	3	l	Long. Antennal segments elongated. Leg segments longer and thinner than wild type.
162	7	n	Narrow. Narrow wings, cuts off irregular slices of costal and inner wing margins.
163	8	ho	Honey. Body lacks black pigment entirely.
164	15	vl	Veinless. Wing veins missing, except along costal margin.
165	12	ro	Rough. Fourth radius vein absent and adjacent veins roughened.
166	37	bu	Bulged. Eyes abnormally bulged transversely.
167	41	cr	Crescent. Eyes small. Pigment in ocelli reduced, crescent-shaped.
168		sl/co	Semilong. Antennal and leg segments lengthened.

/1/ Locus values for house mouse, guinea pig, fowl and parasitic wasp are recombination percentages between successive genes listed. Where two values appear, the first represents data from heterozygous females and the second from heterozygous males. /7/ Jaundice (j), curly coat (Cu2), cataract (Ca), blue dilution of coat (d), hooded coat pattern (h), cowlick (cw), and shaker (sr) have been found to be independent of linkage groups I-V and of each other and are provisionally regarded as markers of seven additional chromosome pairs.

Size or length of linkage maps reflects the intensity of genetics investigation on an organism rather than the number of genes possessed by the organism. Symbols for genes are capitalized only when characterized by dominance. Numbers in brackets are footnote references.

Parasitic wasp (Habrobracon juglandis) [1] (concluded)

Locus		Symbol	Mutation and Phenotype
Linkage Group I (concluded)			
169	33	sl/co	Coalescent. Antennal segments coalescent.
170	32	ct	Cut. Outer wing margin indented or straightened, giving cut appearance.
171	37	rd	Red. Color varies from light red to dark red or almost black with temperature.
172	7	gy	Gynoid. Short antennae in male, resembling female. Abdominal sclerites resemble female.
173		ac/el	Aciform. Terminal half of antennae very slender, needle-like.
174			Eyeless. Heads malformed. Eye rudiments present.
Linkage Group II			
175	28	k	Kidney. Kidney eye shape.
176	5	dw	Dwindling. Irregularity and fusion of antennal segments.
177	11	m	Miniature. Reduced body size. Semi-lethal, may die as pupa.
178		o	Orange. Eyes orange varying to pink and red.
Linkage Group III			
179	25	bk	Broken. Outer margin of primary wing broken and wings fragile.
180		wh/pl	White. White eye. Ocelli colorless.
181	9		Pellucid. Compound eyes semi-transparent.
182		st	Stumpy. Extreme reduction of tarsal segments.
Linkage Group IV			
183	23	sv	Shot-veins. Wing veins broken and distorted.
184	27	td	Truncated. Wings extremely reduced, irregular in shape, (not truncate, tr).
185		ma	Maroon. Light ocelli. Compound eyes deep reddish brown.
Linkage Group V			
186	22	wa	Wavy. Wings shortened. Costal margin wavy.
187		br	Broad. Thorax abnormally broadened.
Linkage Group VI			
188	40	ta	Tapering. Antennae deficient with much fusion and irregularity of segments distally.
189		un^2	Undulating-2. Surface of wings in undulating waves.
Linkage Group VII			
190		pk/ew^3	Pink. Compound eyes pink.
191			Extended wings. Wings extended in active wasps.
Linkage Group VIII			
192	18	wt	Wet. Wing microchaetae very long and irregular giving wet appearance.
193		bf	Black feet. Tarsi abnormally black.

Domestic fowl (Gallus gallus) [1]

Locus		Symbol	Mutation and Phenotype
Linkage Group I (Sex Chromosome)			
194	13	ko	Head streak in down.
195	10	B	Barring.
196	27	Id	Inhibitor. Inhibits melanin in dermis.
197	10	br	Brown eyes.
198	16	Li	Light down. In chicks not black.
199	11	S	Silver. Plumage color.
200		K	Slow feathering.
201		sd	Dilution to blue.
202		n	Naked.
203		al	Albinism. Incomplete.
204		dw	Dwarf.
205		xl	Lethal, after three weeks.
206		sh	Shaker. Lethal nervous disorder.
207		j	Jittery. Lethal nervous disorder.
Linkage Group II			
208	0.4	Cp	Creeper. Achondroplasia.
209	30	R	Rose comb.
210		U	Uropygial. Bifurcation of uropygial papilla.
Linkage Group III			
211	46	fr	Fray. Defective wing and tail feathers.
212	12.5	Cr	Crest. Top-knot and cerebral hernia.
213	17	I	Dominant white. Plumage.
214		F	Frizzling. Recurved feathers.
Linkage Group IV			
215	5	O	Blue eggshell color.
216	33	P	Pea comb.
217	46	ma	Marbling. Pattern in down of chick.
218		Na	Naked neck. Pterylae reduced.

Domestic fowl (Gallus gallus) [1] (concluded)

Locus		Symbol	Mutation and Phenotype
Linkage Group V			
219	43	Na	Naked neck. Pterylae reduced.
220	11	h	Silkie. Barbules lack hooklets.
221		Fl	Flightless. Remiges break off.
Linkage Group VI			
222	26	D	Duplex comb. Bifurcation of comb.
223	33	M	Multiple spurs.
224		Po	Polydatyly.

Fruit fly (Drosophila melanogaster)

Locus		Symbol	Mutation and Phenotype
X Chromosome (Element A)			
225	0	1(1)J1	Lethal (1) Jacobs-Muller. Almost complete lethal.
226	0	y	Yellow. Body yellow, bristles and larval mouth parts brown.
227	0+	ac	Achaete. Postdorsal centrals missing, fewer intra-ocellar hairs.
228	0±	Hw	Hairy-wing. Extra bristles and hairs along wing veins.
229	0+	sc	Scute. Scutellars missing and other bristles fewer.
230	0±	svr	Silver. Body, legs pale, bristles dark.
231	0+	su-s	Suppressor of sable.
232	0+	1(1)7e	Lethal (1)7e. Kills 1(1)7 early.
233	0+	saw	Sawtooth. Serrated hair along wing edges.
234	0.1	su-b	Suppressor of black.
235	0.1±	om	Ommatidia. Eyes slightly rough.
236	0.1+	M(1)Bld	Minute (1) blond. Extreme Minute. Deficiency.
237	0.3	1(1)7	Lethal (1)7. Melanotic tumors in larva; lethal.
238	0.3±	sta	Stubarista. Aristae stubby, bristles short.
239	0.4±	tw	Twisted. Abdomen twisted counterclockwise.
240	0.6	br	Broad. Wings broad, short.
241	0.7	kz	Kurz. Bristles short, slender.
242	0.7±	rey	Rough eye. Small rough eye.
243	0.8	pn	Prune. Eye color dark brownish red, often mottled.
244	0.9	gt	Giant. Giant larvae, pupae, flies.
245	1.5	w	White. White eyes, testes, larval Malpighian tubules.
246	1.7	rst	Roughest. Eyes large, very rough.
247	3±	Co	Confluens. Veins thick, deltoid.
248	3±	spl	Split. Eyes rough, small. Bristles split.
249	3±	fa	Facet. Eyes rough, wings nicked.
250	3±	Ax	Abruptex. Wings arched, veins short.
251	3	N	Notch.
252	4.6	dm	Diminutive. Body, bristles small.
253	5±	M(1)3E	Minute (1) at 3E. Slight Minute.
254	5±	su^x-dx	Suppressor of deltex.
255	5.5	ec	Echinus. Eyes and facets large, rough.
256	6.9	bi	Bifid. Veins fused at wing base.
257	7+	M(1)4BC	Minute (1) at 4BC. Strong Minute.
258	7.3±	peb	Pebbled. Eyes slightly rough.
259	7.5	rb	Ruby. Eye color clear ruby.
260	8	dow	Downy. Bristles fuzzy. Female sterile.
261	11	rg	Rugose. Wings thin, frayed.
262	12.5	bo	Bordeaux. Eye color wine.
263	13.6	cx	Curlex. Wings curled upward.
264	13.7	cv	Crossveinless. Crossveins absent or traces.
265	15	rux	Roughex. Eyes small, rough. Male sterile.
266	15.2±	Ext	Extras. Veins augmented. Lethal in male.
267	16.3	vs	Vesiculated. Wings warped, inflated, divergent.
268	17	dx	Deltex. Veins thickened, delta-like.
269	17.5	ov	Oval. Eyes oval rough.
270	17.9	shf	Shifted. Vein L3 fails to reach wing margin.
271	18.9	cm	Carmine. Eye color dark ruby.
272	19.3	scp	Scooped. Wings upturned, warped.
273	20	ct	Cut. Wing scalloped at edges.
274	21	sn	Singed. Bristles and hairs curled. Female sterile.
275	23.1	oc	Ocelliless. Ocelli absent. Female sterile.
276	23.1±	gg	Goggle. Eyes bulging, head bristles fewer.
277	23.2	ptg	Pentagon. Dark trident and thoracic spot.
278	23.8	ch-b	Chilblained-b. Tarsi conglutinated.
279	24.3	dd	Displaced. Antennae and eyes deformed.
280	25±	tbd	Tiny-bristleoid. Bristles Minute type.
281	27.1±	con	Condensed. Body, wings short, eyes rough.
282	27.5	t	Tan. Body and antennae yellowish.
283	27.7	amx	Almondex. Eyes reduced, narrow. Female sterile.
284	27.7±	lz	Lozenge. Eyes narrow, ovoid. Female usually sterile.
285	28.1	dvr	Divers. With y, wings strongly curled.
286	31±	flp	Flap wings. Wings concave, eyes slightly rough.

/1/ Locus values for house mouse, guinea pig, fowl and the parasitic wasp are recombination percentages between successive genes listed. Where two values appear, the first represents data from heterozygous females and the second from heterozygous males.

Size or length of linkage maps reflects the intensity of genetics investigation on an organism rather than the number of genes possessed by the organism. Symbols for genes are capitalized only when characterized by dominance. Numbers in brackets are footnote references.

Locus	Symbol	Mutation and Phenotype	Locus	Symbol	Mutation and Phenotype
		Fruit fly (Drosophila melanogaster) (continued)			Fruit fly (Drosophila melanogaster) (continued)
		X Chromosome (Element A) (concluded)			Chromosome II (Elements B and C) (continued)
287	32±	ny	Notchy. Wing tips nicked.	357	16.5	cl	Clot. Eye color maroon, close to sepia.
288	32.8	ras	Raspberry. Eye color dark ruby.	358	17±	pi	Pied. Facets jumbled.
289	33	v	Vermilion. Eye color bright vermilion, ocelli colorless.	359	22	Sp	Sternopleural. Extra sternopleural bristles. Homozygous lethal.
290	33.2	dwx	Dwarfex. Body small, wings coarse.	360	22.3±	spd	Spade. Wings shortened. broad.
291	33.4	sbr	Small bristle. Bristles small, some missing.	361	24	gt-4	Giant-4. Giant flies.
292	36.1	m	Miniature. Wings small, dark.	362	31	d	Dachs. Tarsi 4-jointed, venation shifted.
293	36.2	dy	Dusky. Wings small, dusky.	363	33±	fy	Fuzzy. Thoracic hairs fuzzy.
294	36.4	ty-1	Tiny-like. Bristles short, fine.	364	39±	fol	Folded wings.
295	38.3	fw	Furrowed. Eyes furrowed, scutellum shortened, bristles gnarled.	365	39.3±	da	Daughterless. Homozygous females produce no daughters.
296	41.9	wy	Wavy. Wings waved, curled.	366	41	J	Jammed. Wing narrow strip.
297	42±	kk	Kinky. Bristles bent or forked.	367	43±	M(2)Sll	Minute(2)Schultz'11. Slight Minute.
298	43	s	Sable. Body black.	368	44	ab	Abrupt. Shortened L5 vein, scutellars few.
299	44.4	g	Garnet. Eye color garnet pink.	369	45±	oph	Ophthalmopedia. Eyes kidney-shaped or with appendage.
300	44.5	ty	Tiny. Bristles, body small. Female sterile.	370	46±	rk	Rickets. Segments of legs flattened and bent.
301	45.2	na	Narrow abdomen. Abdomen cylindrical. Female sterile.	371	46±	1(2)bs³-d	Lethal(2) with bs³-d. Lethal.
302	47.9	pl	Pleated. Wings pleated.	372	46±	M(2)e	Minute(2)e. Medium Minute.
303	49.3±	vb	Vibrissae. Vibrissae in tuft.	373	48.5	b	Black. Body, legs, veins black.
304	51.5	sd	Scalloped. Wing margins excised.	374	48.7	j	Jaunty. Wings upturned.
305	51.6	Bg	Bag. Wings short, blunt, inflated.	375	50	el	Elbow. Wings bent, alulae and balancers small.
306	53.5	sl	Small-wing. Wings short, oblong. Eyes large.	376	50±	lm	Limited. Sternites small. Female sterile.
307	54	mc	Microchaete. Hairs, bristles few and small.	377	50±	M(2)S13	Minute(2)Schultz'13. Strong Minute.
308	54.4	un	Uneven. Eyes rough, small.	378	50±	1(2)H	Lethal(2)Humphrey. Pupal semilethal.
309	54.5	r	Rudimentary. Wings short, oblique. Female sterile.	379	50.5	Su-H	Suppressor of hairless. Homozygous lethal.
310	55±	if	Inflated. Wings inflated, veins thickened.	380	51	rd	Reduced. Bristles small, irregular. Female sterile.
311	56±	cs	Creased. Wings longitudinally creased.	381	51±	pu	Pupal. Wings unexpanded.
312	56.6	M(1)o	Minute(1)o. Minute type.	382	52±	pys	Polychaetous. Extra and double bristles.
313	56.7	f	Forked. Bristles, hairs gnarled.	383	52.5±	cr-u	Cream-underscored. Specific dilutor of w^e and Pale. Male sterile.
314	57	B	Bar. Eyes narrow.	384	53	nub	Nubbin. Wings very small and thin with tendency to curve up or down.
315	59.2	od	Outstretched. Wings divergent.				
316	59.2	sy	Small-eye. Eyes small, rounded.	385	53±	ck	Crinkled. Wings flimsy.
317	59.4	Bx	Beadex. Wings excised.	386	53±	rdo	Reduced ocelli. Ocelli reduced in size, color moved to region between ocelli.
318	59.5	fu	Fused. Wing veins fused at base.	387	53.1	1(2)Bld	Lethal(2) opposite T(1;2)Bld. Lethal.
319	62±	M(1)36f	Minute(1)36f. Slight Minute.	388	53.5	M(2)S5	Minute(2)Schultz'5. Medium Minute.
320	62.5	car	Carnation. Eye color dark ruby.	389	53.9	hk	Hook. Bristles bent or barbed.
321	62.7	M(1)n	Minute(1)n. Extreme Minute.	390	54.3±	bri	Bright. Eye color bright red.
322	63±	fo	Folded. Wings unexpanded.	391	54.5	pr	Purple. Eye color purplish ruby.
323	64	sw	Short-wing. Wings trimmed, eyes small, rough.	392	54.5±	rn	Rotund. Wings round, tarsi 3-jointed. Sterile.
324	64±	su-f	Suppressor of forked.	393	54.7±	rn	Roughish. Eyes moderately rough.
325	65.6	cf	Cleft. Wing venation increased.	394	54.8	Bl	Bristle. Bristles short, beaded. Homozygous semilethal.
326	66	bb	Bobbed. Bristles small, sclerites irregular.				
		Chromosome II (Elements B and C)	395	54.9	Alu	Alula. Alula fused to wing. Wing warped.
327	0	net	Net. Extreme plexus venation.	396	54.9	Jag	Jagged. Wings nicked, eyes rough.
328	0	al	Aristaless. Aristae reduced, scutellars divergent.	397	55	lt	Light. Eye color yellowish pink.
329	0±	1(2)gl	Lethal(2) giant larva. Larval lethal.	398	55±	tri	Trident. Thorax darkened.
330	0	ocr	Ochracea. Eye color light, darkening with age.	399	55±	M(2)D	Minute(2)D. Body color and bristles pale.
331	0.1	ex	Expanded. Wings broad, spread. Eyes rough.	400	55.1-	rl	Rolled. Wing edges rolled, frayed.
332	0.3	ds	Dachsous. Wings shorter, crossveins closer.	401	55.1	M(2)S2	Minute(2)Schultz'2. Minute type. Deficiency.
333	1.3	S	Star. Eyes small, rough. Homozygous lethal.	402	55.1	M(2)S4	Medium Minute. Deficiency.
334	1.3±	Su-S	Suppressor of Star.	403	55.1	M(2)S8	Slight Minute. Deficiency.
335	1.3±	ast	Asteroid. Eyes small, rough.	404	55.1	M(2)S10	Minute(2)Schultz'10. Slight Minute. Deficiency.
336	2.3±	shr	Shrunken. Body small, wizened.	405	55.1	stw	Straw. Body, wings, bristles yellow.
337	3.8±	shv	Short vein. Constant terminal gaps in veins L2 and L4.	406	55.2±	blt	Blot. Wings inflated, blackened.
338	4	ho	Heldout. Wings extended.	407	55.2±	Cu	Curl. Lateral compression and indentation-fold of unfolded imaginal wing.
339	5±	fes	Female-sterile. Eggs do not develop.				
340	6±	E-S	Enhancer of Star. Increases expression of Star.	408	55.3	tk	Thick. Legs, tarsi, thickened, wings short.
341	7	Cy	Curly. Wings curled upward. Homozygous lethal.	409	55.3	pk	Prickle. Bristles, hairs irregular.
342	8.3	1(2)ay	Lethal(2)ay. Lethal.	410	55.4	ap	Apterous. Wings, balancers missing.
343	10±	Dt	Detached. Vein L2 does not reach margin.	411	55.6-	msf	Misformed. Eyes misformed, wings crumpled.
344	10.5	ang	Angle wing. Wings held up from dorsal surface.	412	55.7±	bur	Burgundy. Dull, darkish-brown eye color.
345	11	ed	Echinoid. Eyes large, rough.	413	55.9	ti	Tarsi irregular. Tarsal segments fused, eyes rough.
346	11-12	M(2)C	Minute(2) Curry. Fairly strong Minute. Deficiency.	414	56±	ltd	Lightoid. Eye color clear, translucent yellowish pink. Ocelli colorless.
347	12	ft	Fat. Body short, fat. Scutellar bristles far apart.				
348	12	G	Gull. Wings large, spread. Homozygous lethal.	415	56±	M(2)S12	Minute(2) Schultz'12. Slight Minute.
349	12.9±	M(2)z	Minute(2)z. Medium Minute.	416	56.5±	std	Staroid. Eyes small, very rough.
350	13	M(2)B	Minute(2) Bridges. Medium Minute. Deficiency.	417	56.6±	ta	Tapered. Wings narrow and pointed. Veins close. Male sterile.
351	13	dp	Dumpy. Wings truncated. Vortices on thorax.				
352	13±	dw-24F	Dwarf in 24F. Eyes dull, body dwarf.	418	57±	dil	Specific dilutor. Dilutor of bw and w alleles.
353	15	M(2)Sl	Minute(2) Schultz'l. Strong Minute.	419	57.1	buo	Burnt orange. Eye color orange-brown.
354	15±	1(2)cg	Lethal(2)comb-gap. Lethal from cg stock.	420	57±	M(2)38b	Minute(2)38b. Extreme Minute.
355	16	Sk	Streak. Central streak on thorax. Homozygous lethal.	421	57.5	cn	Cinnabar. Eye color bright scarlet. Ocelli colorless.
				422	58±	puf	Puff. Wings blistered.
356	16±	tkv	Thick-veins. Veins thick, irregular.	423	58.5	blo	Bloated. Wings ballooned, extra veins.

Size or length of linkage maps reflects the intensity of genetics investigation on an organism rather than the number of genes possessed by the organism. Symbols for genes are capitalized only when characterized by dominance. Numbers in brackets are footnote references.

Locus		Symbol	Mutation and Phenotype	Locus		Symbol	Mutation and Phenotype
			Fruit fly (Drosophila melanogaster) (continued)				Fruit fly (Drosophila melanogaster) (continued)
			Chromosome II (Elements B and C) (continued)				Chromosome II (Elements B and C) (concluded)
424	58.6±	sm	Smoky. Body color dark.	485	107.2	or	Orange. Bright orange eye color.
425	58.7– 60.2	Np	Notopleural. Bristles short, wings broad. Homozygous lethal. Deficiency.	486	107– 107.4	Px	Plexate. Venation like bs. Veins thickened, broken. Homozygous lethal. Deficiency.
426	60.1±	at	Arctus oculus. Number of facets reduced.	487	107.3	bs	Blistered. Wings blistered, small. Extra veins.
427	60.5±	arch	Arch. Wings downcurved in both axes.	488	107.3±	Pin	Pin. Thoracic bristles pin-like.
428	60.7	ad	Arcoid. Wings arched, broad, short. Crossveins close.	489	107.4	ba	Balloon. Wings inflated, extra veins.
429	60.8	chl	Chaetelle. Bristles very small. Slight plexus.	490	108±	M(2)33a	Minute(2)33a. Strong Minute. Deficiency.
430	61±	whd	Withered. Wings warped or shrunken.				Chromosome III (Elements D and E)
431	61.5±	tom	Tomboy. Homozygous females with male-like pigmentation of posterior tergites.	491	0	ru	Roughoid. Eyes small, rough. Erupted facets.
432	62	en	Engrailed. Scutellar notch, broken veins, extra sex comb.	492	0	mp	Microptera. Wings small, ballooned. Tarsi 4-jointed.
433	62±	upw	Upward. Wings upturned.	493	0±	aa	Anarista. Aristae small, without branches.
434	63±	l(2)rn	Lethal(2) with rotund. Lethal.	494	0.2	ve	Veinlet. Longitudinal wing veins interrupted.
435	65±	Bkd	Blackoid. Dark body color.	495	1.4	R	Roughened. Eyes rough. Homozygous semilethal.
436	65±	M(2)40c	Minute(2)40c. Minute type.	496	17±	rai	Raisin. Deep brown eye color.
437	65.2	po	Pale-ocelli. Ocelli nearly colorless.	497	19.2	jv	Javelin. Bristles and hairs cylindrical.
438	66.7	sca	Scabrous. Eyes rough, some bristles missing.	498	20	dv	Divergent. Wings spread.
439	67	vg	Vestigial. Wings, balancers vestigial.	499	20±	Me	Moire. Eye color brownish, 7 flecks. Homozygous lethal.
440	67	l(2)C	Lethal(2) Curry. Lethal before pupal stage.	500	23	Hn	Henna. Eye color dull, dark. Homozygous lethal.
441	69.7	wx	Waxy. Wings heavy, waxy. Male sterile.	501	25±	be-3	Benign tumor in 3. Non-lethal melanotic tumors.
442	70±	U^{H20}	Upturned U^{H20}. Wings curled.	502	26	se	Sepia. Eye color brownish red, darkening to black.
443	70±	l(2)mr^2	Lethal(2) with morula^2. Lethal.	503	26±	su-t	Suppressor of tan.
444	70.8	Pfd	Pufdi. Wings puffed, divergent. Homozygous lethal.	504	26.5	h	Hairy. Extra hairs on scutellars, veins, pleurae, head.
445	71	bat	Bat. Wings extended, bent back.	505	27±	abd	Abdominal. Abdominal bands broken, etched.
446	71.1	cg	Comb-gap. Sex combs large. Gap in wing vein L4. Female sterile.	506	35	rs	Rose. Eye color translucent pink.
				507	35.5	eyg	Eye-gone. Eyes and head reduced.
447	71.2±	dr	Droopy. Wings spread wide apart and drooping.	508	36.2	gv	Grooved. Longitudinal medial groove in thorax.
448	71.5±	sf	Safranin. Eye color dark chocolate.	509	36.5±	cr-3	Cream in 3. Specific dilutor of w^e eye color.
449	72	L	Lobe. Eyes small, nicked at anterior edge.	510	37±	rt	Rotated. Abdomen twisted counterclockwise.
450	72.3	kn	Knot. Veins L3 and L4 close. Eyes oblique.	511	37.5	app	Approximated. Crossveins close. Tarsi 4-jointed.
451	72.5	ch	Chubby. Larva, pupa, adult short.	512	39±	pyd	Polychaetoid. Extra bristles.
452	73±	dke	Dark eye. Eye color soft, dark, dull, with tiny fleck.	513	39.7±	M(3)S37	Minute(3)S37. Extreme Minute.
				514	40	tt	Tilt. Wings spread, warped, with gap in L3.
453	74±	gp	Gap. Vein L4 broken.	515	40.2	M(3)33j	Minute(3)33j. Medium Minute. Deficiency.
454	75.5	c	Curved. Wings thin, spread, lifted, curved.	516	40.2	M(3)h	Minute(3)h. Medium Minute. Allele of M(3)33j.
455	76±	Wr	Wrinkled. Wings wrinkled. Suppresses Lobe.	517	40.2	M(3)y	Minute(3)y. Medium Minute. Allele of M(3)33j.
456	77.5	M(2)S7	Minute(2)S7. Strong Minute.	518	40.4±	vo-3	Vortex in 3. Intensifier of dp^v.
457	79±	pw-c	Pink-wing-c. Eye color dilute, wings short, blunt.	519	40.4±	D	Dichaete. Wings spread. Homozygous lethal.
				520	40.5	Ly	Lyra. Wings cut, narrow. Homozygous lethal.
458	80±	fr	Fringed. Wing margins ragged.	521	41.4	Gl	Glued. Eyes small, facets rounded. Homozygous lethal.
459	81±	fj	Four-jointed. Tarsi 4-jointed. Wings short.				
460	81±	rf	Roof wings. Wings drooped at sides.	522	41.7±	fz	Frizzled. Thoracic hairs, bristles turn toward mid-line.
461	82±	wt	Welt. Eyes seamed, reduced.				
462	83±	abr	Abero. Abdominal bands irregular. Wings frayed, eyes rough. Female sterile.	523	41.7±	rp	Rotated-penis. Male genitalia rotated. Male sterile.
				524	42±	wk	Weak. Bristles weak, irregular. Body small.
463	83±	nw	Narrow. Wings narrow.	525	43	Wi	Washed eye. Modifies w. Homozygous lethal.
464	86.5	I-f	Intensifier or forked.	526	43.2	th	Thread. Aristae threadlike, without branches.
465	91.5	sm	Smooth. Abdomen hairless.	527	43.4±	mb	Minusbar. Modifies B to larger eye.
466	92.3	M(2)173	Minute(2)173. Moderate Minute.	528	43.5±	Cm	Crimp. Posterior wing edge crimped. Homozygous lethal.
467	93.3	hy	Humpy. Thorax ridged, wings truncated.				
468	99±	l(2)Su-H	Lethal(2) from suppressor of hairless. Lethal.	529	43.6	bul	Bulge. Eyes bulging, wings squared off.
469	99.2	a	Arc. Wings broad, bent down, crossveins closer.	530	44±	M(3)S38	Minute(3)Schultz'38. Strong Minute.
470	99– 101.2	M(2)1	Minute(2)1. Extreme Minute. Deficiency.	531	44	st	Scarlet. Eye color scarlet, ocelli white.
				532	45±	tra	Transformed. Transforms females to normal-appearing males.
471	100.5	px	Plexus. Network of extra veins.				
472	101±	pa	Patulous. Wings spread wide apart.	533	45.3	cp	Clipped. Wing margins clipped.
473	101.2	M(2)1^2	Minute(2)1^2. Slight Minute.	534	46	mot-28	Mottled-28. Eyes mottled with brown.
474	104	hv	Heavy vein. Veins thick, posterior crossveins oblique.	535	46	W	Wrinkled. Wings incompletely unfolded, pebbled.
				536	46±	as	Ascute. Wings held downward.
475	104±	l(2)bw	Lethal(2)brown. Probable deficiency. Lethal.	537	46±	je	Jelly. Eye color dark pinkish.
476	104.5	bw	Brown. Eye color brownish to garnet.	538	46±	Pdr	Purpleoider. Intensifier of pd.
477	104.7	mi	Minus. Bristles hairlike. Body small.	539	47	in	Inturned. Thoracic bristles directed toward mid-line.
478	105.5	abb	Abbreviated. Bristles slightly reduced. Female sterile.				
				540	47±	M(3)S39	Minute(3)Schultz'39. Strong Minute.
479	106.3	slt	Slight. Body small, bristles reduced.	541	47±	dn	Doughnut. Eye of se dn with light central spot. Male sterile.
480	106.4	pd	Purpleoid. Eye color dark pink, like purple.				
481	106.7±	ll	Lanceolate. Wings narrow, pointed.	542	47.1	ri	Radius incompletus. Vein L2 shows gap.
482	106.7	mr	Morula. Eyes rough, bristles small.	543	47.3	eg	Eagle. Wings spread, raised.
483	106.9	l(2)ax	Lethal(2)ax. Very early larval lethal.	544	47.5	Dfd	Deformed. Eyes small. Homozygous lethal.
484	107	sp	Speck. Black speck in wing axil. Body color olive.	545	47.5	wp	Warped. Wings spread, doubly warped.

Size or length of linkage maps reflects the intensity of genetics investigation on an organism rather than the number of genes possessed by the organism. Symbols for genes are capitalized only when characterized by dominance. Numbers in brackets are footnote references.

Locus		Symbol	Mutation and Phenotype	Locus		Symbol	Mutation and Phenotype
			Fruit fly (Drosophila melanogaster) (continued)				Fruit fly (Drosophila melanogaster) (concluded)
			Chromosome III (Elements D and E) (continued)				Chromosome III (Elements D and E) (concluded)
546	47.7	pb	Proboscipedia. Mouth parts footlike. Adult lethal.	586	79.7	M(3)124	Minute(3)124. Strong Minute. Allele of M(3)w.
547	48	p	Pink. Eye color dull ruby.	587	79.7	M(3)B	Minute(3)Burkart. Moderate Minute. Allele of M(3)w.
548	48±	Bb	Bubble. Wings small, inflated. Male sterile. Homozygous female lethal.	588	79.7	M(3)B^2	Minute(3)Bridges. Strong Minute. Allele of M(3)w.
549	48.3	bod	Bowed. Wings arched.	589	79.7	M(3)w	Minute(3)w. Strong Minute.
550	48.5	tet	Tetraltera. Wings haltere-like.	590	79.7	l(3)a	Lethal(3)first found. Lethal. Allele of M(3)w.
551	48.7	by	Blistery. Wings blistered distally.	591	80±	M(3)Fla	Minute(3)Florida. Strong Minute. Allele of M(3)w.
552	49±	M(3)S34	Minute(3)Schultz'34. Slight Minute.	592	84.5	M(3)36e	Minute(3)36e. Medium Minute.
553	49.7	ma	Maroon. Eye color dull ruby.	593	87±	M(3)be	Minute(3)beta. Medium Minute.
554	50	cu	Curled. Wings upcurved, body dark, post-scutellars crossed.	594	88±	mah	Mahogany. Eye color brownish, darkening.
555	50	M(3)S31	Minute(3)Schultz'31. Medium Minute. Deficiency.	595	90	Pr	Prickly. Bristles vestiges. Homozygous semilethal.
556	50±	mu	Mussed. Wings thin, crumpled.	596	90.2	m(3)j	Minute(3)j. Extreme Minute.
557	51±	ry	Rosy. Eye color deep ruby.	597	90.2	l(3)PR	Lethal with In(3R)P. Lethal. Allele of M(3)j.
558	52	kar	Karmoisin. Eye color like st but duller. Ocelli colorless.	598	91±	tx	Taxi. Wings divergent.
				599	91.1	ro	Rough. Eyes rough, small.
559	55±	C3G	Crossover suppressor in 3 of Gowen. Eliminates crossing over.	600	91.8	l(3)XaR	Lethal(3)XaR. Balancer of T(2;3)Xa.
560	55.5±	red	Red. Red malpighian tubules.	601	93±	cmp	Crumpled. Wings smaller, crumpled.
561	56.7	jvl	Javelin-like. Bristles cylindrical, crooked.	602	93.8	Bd	Beaded. Wing margins excised. Homozygous lethal.
562	57.9	cv-c	Crossveinless-c. Posterior crossvein absent or reduced.	603	94.1	Pw	Pointed-wing. Wings pointed at tip. Homozygous lethal.
563	58.2	Sb	Stubble. Bristles short, thick. Homozygous lethal.	604	95±	bf	Brief. Body small, bristles Minute-like. Male sterile.
564	58.5	ss	Spineless. Bristles very small.	605	95.4	rsd	Raised. Wings rise straight up.
565	58.8	bx	Bithorax. Balancers wing-like. Metathorax resembles mesothorax.	606	95.5	su^B-pr	Suppressor of purple. Male sterile.
566	59.5±	cal	Coal. Black body color, similar to e^4.	607	97.3	ra	Rase. Bristles, hairs smaller, fewer.
567	59±	Rf	Roof. Wings drooping at sides.	608	99.3±	Dp	Duplication. Similar to Ultra Bar.
568	59.9	fl	Fluted. Wings creased, darkish.	609	100±	ld	Loboid. Eyes lobe-like.
569	62	sr	Stripe. Dark dorsal stripe.	610	100.7	ca	Claret. Eye color clear ruby.
570	62.4	M(3)f	Minute(3)f. Minute type.	611	101	M(3)l	Minute(3)l. Medium Minute.
571	63.1	gl	Glass. Eye color dilute. Facets fused.	612	104.3	bv	Brevis. Bristles short, stubby.
572	64±	gl-1	Glass-like. Eye color orange, eyes rough, small.	613	106.2	M(3)g	Minute(3)g. Slight Minute. Requires E-M(3)g.
573	64±	k	Kidney. Eyes kidney shaped.				Chromosome IV (Element F)
574	64±	M(3)S35	Minute(3)Schultz'35. Extreme Minute.	614	0	ci	Cubitus-interruptus. Vein L4 interrupted.
575	64.5±	sed	Sepiaoid. Eye color chocolate.	615	0- 0.2±	M-4	Minute-4. Medium Minute. Deficiency for ci, ar, gvl and Scn.
576	65±	cv-d	Crossveinless-d. Posterior crossvein absent or reduced.	616	0- 0.2	ar	Abdomen rotatum. Abdomen twisted clockwise.
577	66±	Cur	Curl. Curly wings. Homozygous lethal.	617	0.2	gvl	Grooveless. Scutellar groove diminished.
578	66.2	Dl	Delta. Veins thick at margin. Homozygous lethal.	618	1.4	bt	Bent. Wings bent, legs knobby.
579	69.5	H	Hairless. Some bristles and hair. Homozygous lethal.	619	2	ey	Eyeless. Eye small or absent.
580	70.7	e	Ebony. Body color black.	620	3	sv	Shaven. Abdominal bristles fewer.
581	72.5	det	Detached. Crossveins broken, wings folded under.				
582	75.7	cd	Cardinal. Eye color dull scarlet, ocelli white.				
583	76.2	wo	White ocelli. Ocelli colorless.				
584	77.5±	obt	Obtuse. Wings short, blunt.				
585	79.1	bar-3	Bar-3. Phenotype like B/B.				

85. LINKAGE GROUPS: CORN AND TOMATO

Symbols for genes are capitalized only when characterized by dominance. Numbers in brackets are footnote references.

Locus		Symbol	Phenotype [1]	Locus		Symbol	Phenotype [1]
			Corn (Zea mays)				Corn (Zea mays) (continued)
			Chromosome I				Chromosome I (continued)
1	0	sr	Striate leaves.	4	25	ms$_{17}$	Male sterile.
2	15	ga$_6$	Gametophyte viability factor.	5	27	ts$_2$	Tassel seed. Terminal inflorescence with pistillate flowers.
3	21	zb$_4$	Zebra striping. Leaves with alternating transverse bands of green and whitish sectors.	6	28	P	Pericarp color.

/1/ Certain of the phenotypes, e.g., virescent and tassel seed, occur more than once. Descriptions are given only for the first listing.

(continued, page 108)

85. LINKAGE GROUPS: CORN AND TOMATO (Concluded)

Symbols for genes are capitalized only when characterized by dominance. Numbers in brackets are footnote references.

Corn (Zea mays) (continued)

Chromosome I (continued)

	Locus	Symbol	Phenotype [1]
7	30	zl	Zygotic lethal.
8	53	as	Asynaptic. Chromosomes unpaired at meiosis.
9	66	hm	Helminthosporium susceptibility.
10	80	br	Brachytic. Stalk has short internodes.
11	84	Vg	Vestigial glumes.
12	85	f_1	Fine striped (green-white) leaves.
13	107	an_1	Anther ear. Stamens develop in pistillate inflorescence.
14	128	Kn	Knotted leaves. Wart-like growths on leaves and stalk.
15	134	gs_1	Green striped. Leaves with light green stripes between vascular bundles.
16	157	Ts_6	Tassel seed.
17	161	bm_2	Brown midrib. Brown pigment in midrib.

Chromosome II

	Locus	Symbol	Phenotype [1]
18	0	ws_3	White sheath. Leaf sheaths and stalk deficient in chlorophyll.
19	4	al	Albescent. Seedlings become whitish.
20	11	lg_1	Liguleless. Absence of ligule on leaves.
21	30	gl_2	Glossy seedling.
22	49	B	Anthocyanin booster.
23	56	sk	Silkless. Ears without silks.
24	68	fl_1	Floury endosperm.
25	74	ts_1	Tassel seed.
26	83	v_4	Virescent. Young seedlings deficient in chlorophyll.
27	128	Ch	Chocolate pericarp.

Chromosome III

	Locus	Symbol	Phenotype [1]
28	0	cr_1	Crinkly leaves.
29	18	d_1	Dwarf.
30	32	rt	Rootless.
31	38	Lg_3	Liguleless.
32	40	Rg	Ragged leaves. Leaves appear split and torn from development of necrotic areas.
33	47	ts_4	Tassel seed.
34	64	ba_1	Barren stalk. No ear produced.
35	75	na_1	Nana (dwarf).
36	103	a_1	Anthocyanin.
37	103-	sh_2	Shrunken endosperm.
38	115	et	Etched endosperm.
39	121	ga_7	Gametophyte factor.

Chromosome IV

	Locus	Symbol	Phenotype [1]
40	0	de_1	Defective endosperm.
41	35	Ga_1	Gametophyte factor.
42	56	Ts_5	Tassel seed.
43	66	sp_1	Small pollen.
44	71	su_1	Sugary endosperm.
45	74	de_{16}	Defective endosperm.
46	84	zb_6	Zebra striping.
47	.100	Tu	Tunicate (pod corn). Enlarged glumes in male and female inflorescences.
48	105	j_2	Japonica striping. Leaves green-white striped.
49	111	gl_3	Glossy seedling.

Chromosome V

	Locus	Symbol	Phenotype [1]
50	0	gl_{17}	Glossy seedling.
51	1	a_2	Anthocyanin.
52	7	bm_1	Brown midrib.
53	8	bt_1	Brittle endosperm.
54	11	v_3	Virescent seedling.
55	13	bv	Brevis (dwarf) plant.
56	32	pr	Red aleurone color.
57	41	ys	Yellow stripe. Leaves green-yellow striped.
58	73	v_2	Virescent seedling.

Chromosome VI

	Locus	Symbol	Phenotype [1]
59	0	po	Polymitotic. Spores undergo extra meiotic-like divisions. Plants are male sterile.
60	13	Y	Yellow endosperm color.
61	33	pg_{11}	Pale green. Light green seedlings and plants.
62	44	Pl	Purple plant.
63	45	Bh	Blotched aleurone.
64	54	sm	Salmon silk.
65	64	py	Pigmy. Dwarf plant.

Chromosome VII

	Locus	Symbol	Phenotype [1]
66	0	o_2	Opaque endosperm.
67	4	in	Intensifier of aleurone color.
68	8	v_5	Virescent seedling.
69	22	ra_1	Ramosa. Branching of ear and tassel.
70	26	gl_1	Glossy seedling.
71	36	Tp	Toepod. Plant with many tillers and narrow leaves. Ears and tassels have enlarged bracts.
72	40	sl	Slashed leaves.
73	42	ij	Iojap. Leaves green-white striped.

Corn (Zea mays) (continued)

Chromosome VII (concluded)

	Locus	Symbol	Phenotype [1]
74	60	Bn	Brown endosperm color.
75	96	bd	Branched silkless. Ears branched without silks.

Chromosome VIII

	Locus	Symbol	Phenotype [1]
76	0	v_{16}	Virescent seedling.
77	14	ms_8	Male sterile.
78	28	j_1	Japonica striping.

Chromosome IX

	Locus	Symbol	Phenotype [1]
79	0	Dt	Dotted (controller of a_1 mutability).
80	7	yg_2	Yellow-green. Seedlings and plants of yellow-green color.
81	26	C	Aleurone color.
82	29	sh_1	Shrunken endosperm.
83	31	bz	Bronze aleurone and plant color.
84	44	bp	Brown pericarp color.
85	59	wx	Waxy endosperm.
86	66	pg_{12}	Pale green.
87	71	v_1	Virescent seedling.
88	74	bk_2	Brittle stalk.
89	106	Wc	White cap of endosperm.

Chromosome X

	Locus	Symbol	Phenotype [1]
90	0	Rp	Resistance to Puccinia.
91	16	Og	Old gold striping. Leaves green-yellow striped.
92	28	li	Lineate. Leaves with fine longitudinal striations.
93	38	l_8	Luteus seedling. Yellow seedlings.

Tomato (Lycopersicon esculentum) [2]

Chromosome 1 (Linkage Group III)

	Locus	Symbol	Phenotype [1]
94	0	br	Brachytic.
95	30	y	Colorless fruit skin.
96	65	Cf_1	Resistance to Cladosporium.

Chromosome 2 (Linkage Group I)

	Locus	Symbol	Phenotype [1]
97	0	dv	Dwarf virescent.
98	6	m	Mottled leaves.
99	11	d	Dwarf plant.
100	14	p	Peach
101	22	ro	Rosette.
102	25	ps	Positional sterile.
103	30	O	Oval fruit.
104	32	aw	Without anthocyanin.
105	48	Wo	Wooly plant.
106	53	s	Compound inflorescence.
107	60	ne	Necrotic leaves.
108	61	bk	Beaked fruits.
109	77	lc	Few fruit loculi.

Chromosome 7 (Linkage Groups X and XII)

	Locus	Symbol	Phenotype [1]
110	0	wt	Wilty foliage.
111	30	n	Nipple-tipped fruit.

Chromosome 8 (Linkage Groups VI and VIII)

	Locus	Symbol	Phenotype [1]
112	0	al	Anthocyanin loser.
113	40	dl	Dialytic stamens.
114	49	bu	Bushy.
115	76	l	Lutescent foliage.

Chromosome 9

	Locus	Symbol	Phenotype [1]
116	0	wd	Wilty dwarf.

Chromosome 10 (Linkage Group VII)

	Locus	Symbol	Phenotype [1]
117	0±	pe	Sticky fruit epidermis.
118	8	lg	Light green foliage.
119	36	u	Uniform-ripening fruit.
120	60	H	Hairs absent.
121	75	t	Tangerine fruit color.
122	98	Xa	Xantha seedling.

Linkage Group II

	Locus	Symbol	Phenotype [1]
123	0	r	Yellow fruit flesh.
124	15	wf	White flower.

Linkage Group IV

	Locus	Symbol	Phenotype [1]
125	0	c	Potato leaf.
126	17	sp	Self-pruning (determinate habit).
127	43	Cf_2	Cladosporium resistance.

Linkage Group V

	Locus	Symbol	Phenotype [1]
128	0	bi	Bifurcate inflorescence.
129	4	f	Fasciated fruit.
130	29	a	Anthocyanin absent.
131	49	hl	Hairless.
132	69	j	Jointless (also leafy inflorescence).
133	86	Cf_3	Cladosporium resistance.

Linkage Group XI

	Locus	Symbol	Phenotype [1]
134	0	e	Entire leaves.
135	28	w_1	Wiry foliage.

Linkage Group IX

	Locus	Symbol	Phenotype [1]
136	0	dm	Dwarf modifier.

Unnumbered Linkage Group

	Locus	Symbol	Phenotype [1]
137	0	tf	Trifoliate.
138	11	Fw	Furrowed cotyledons.

/1/ Certain of the phenotypes, e.g., virescent and tassel seed, occur more than once. Descriptions are given only for the first listing. /2/ Chromosome numbers are based on the identification of pachytene chromosomes according to length and, for this reason, certain chromosomes embrace more than one linkage group and do not always correspond to the linkage group numbers.

Part I: HYBRIDS REPORTED: PLANT AND ANIMAL KINGDOM

	Plants	Number		Animals	Number		Animals (concluded)	Number
1	Thallophytes	55	5	Echinoderms	30	9	Amphibia	52
2	Bryophytes	6	6	Mollusca	2	10	Reptiles	37
3	Pteridophytes	158	7	Arthropoda	240	11	Birds	400
4	Spermatophytes	8946[1]	8	Fish	154	12	Mammals	300

/1/ Exclusive of the orchids.

Part II: MAMMALS AND BIRDS

	Parental Species		Sex Ratio	Hybrid Fertility	
	Female	Male	% Males[1]	Male	Female
		Mammals			
1	Bison, American (Bison bison)	Cattle, bull (Bos taurus)	31	Infertile	Fertile
2	Cattle, Brahma [Zebu] (B. taurus [indicus])	Gayal, Indian (Bibos frontalis)		Infertile	Fertile
3	Cattle, cow (B. taurus)	Bison, American (Bos americanus)	15.7	Infertile[2]	Fertile
4	Cattle, cow (B. taurus)	Yak (B. grunniens)	36	Infertile[2]	Fertile
5	Guinea pig (Cavia porcellus)	Guinea pig, Peruvian (Cavia cutleri)		Fertile	Fertile
6	Horse (Equus caballus)	Ass [donkey] (Equus asinus)	44.4	Infertile	Fertile[3]
7	Horse (E. caballus)	Zebra (E. grevyi)		Infertile	Infertile
8	Mouse, Asiatic (Mus bactrianus)	Mouse, house (Mus musculus)	48.3	Fertile	Fertile
9	Mouse, house (M. musculus)	Mouse, Asiatic (M. bactrianus)	50.7	Fertile	Fertile
10	Yak (Bos grunniens)	Cattle, bull (Bos taurus)		Infertile[2]	Fertile
		Birds			
11	Chicken (Gallus domesticus)	Guinea fowl (Numida meleagris)		Infertile	
12	Chicken (G. domesticus)	Pheasant, common (Phasianus colchicus)	99.1	Infertile	
13	Chicken (G. domesticus)	Pheasant, ring-neck (P. torquatus)	88.5	Infertile	Infertile
14	Dove, dwarf turtle (Streptopelia humilis)	Dove, ring (Streptopelia risoria)	50	Fertile	Fertile
15	Dove, European turtle (S. turtur)	Dove, oriental turtle (S. orientalis)		Fertile	?
16	Dove, Oriental turtle (S. orientalis)	Dove, European turtle (S. turtur)		Fertile	Fertile
17	Dove, Oriental turtle (S. orientalis)	Dove, ring (S. risoria)	58.1	Fertile[4]	Fertile[4]
18	Dove, Oriental turtle (S. orientalis)	Pigeon, common (Columba livia)		Fertile[3]	?
19	Dove, ring (S. risoria)	Dove, dwarf turtle (Streptopelia humilis)	45.4	Fertile	Fertile
20	Dove, ring (S. risoria)	Dove, European turtle (S. turtur)	48.8	Fertile[4]	Fertile[4]
21	Dove, ring (S. risoria)	Dove, mourning (Zenaidura carolinensis)	100	Infertile	
22	Dove, ring (S. risoria)	Dove, pearl neck (Streptopelia chinensis)	57.8	Fertile	Fertile[4]
23	Dove, ring (S. risoria)	Dove, Senegal (S. senegalensis)	50	Fertile[4]	Fertile[4]
24	Dove, ring (S. risoria)	Pigeon, common (Columba livia)	97.2	Fertile[3]	Infertile
25	Dove, ring (S. risoria)	Pigeon, passenger (Ectopistes migratorius)		Infertile	
26	Duck, mallard (Anas platyrhynchos)	Duck, dusky (Anas fulvigula)	54.8	Fertile	Fertile
27	Duck, mallard (A. platyrhynchos)	Duck, muscovy (Cairina moschata)	56.1	Infertile	Infertile
28	Duck, muscovy (Cairina moschata)	Duck, mallard (Anas platyrhynchos)	54.6	Infertile	Infertile
29	Grouse, European wood (Tetrao urogallus)	Grouse, European black (Lyrurus tetrix)	83.3	Fertile[5]	Fertile[5]
30	Pheasant, golden (Chrysolophus pictus)	Pheasant, Lady Amherst's (Chrysolophus amherstiae)	43.9	Fertile	Fertile
31	Pheasant, Reeves (Phasianus reevesi)	Pheasant, ring-neck (Phasianus torquatus)	91.7	Infertile	Infertile
32	Pheasant, ring-neck (P. torquatus)	Chicken (Gallus domesticus)	49.7	Infertile	Infertile
33	Pigeon, common (Columba livia)	Pigeon, European stock (Columba oenas)		Fertile	Fertile
34	Pigeon, common (C. livia)	Pigeon, triangular spotted (C. guinea)		Fertile[5]	Fertile[5]

/1/ Sex ratios are given only where the total number of hybrid offspring is a minimum of 25. Hybrid sex determined after hatching. /2/ Usually. /3/ Rarely. /4/ Partially. /5/ Low.

Part III: INSECTS

	Parental Species		Sex Ratio	Hybrid Fertility			Parental Species		Sex Ratio	Hybrid Fertility	
	Female	Male	% Males[1]	Male	Female		Female	Male	% Males[1]	Male	Female
		Moths and Butterflies						Fruitflies			
1	Amorpha austauti	Smerinthus atlanticus	90			22	Drosophila aldrichi	Drosophila arizonensis			Infertile
2	A. austauti	S. ocellata	93			23	D. algonquin	D. athabasca		Infertile	Fertile
3	A. populi	S. ocellata	98			24	D. arizonensis	D. mojavensis		Infertile	Fertile
4	Clostera curtula	Clostera anachoreta		Fertile	Sterile	25	D. azteca	D. athabasca		Infertile	Infertile
5	Deilephila galii	Chaerocampa elpenor	>71			26	D. melanogaster	D. simulans			Infertile
6	Lycia hirtaria	Nyssia zonaria	39.3	Fertile	Infertile	27	D. melanopalpa	D. neorepleta		Fertile	Fertile
7	L. hirtaria	Poecilopsis pomonaria	75.6	Fertile	Infertile	28	D. miranda	D. persimilis	50	Infertile	Fertile[2]
8	Nyssia graecaria	Lycia hirtaria	100	Infertile		29	D. miranda	D. pseudoobscura	50	Infertile	Fertile[2]
9	N. zonaria	L. hirtaria	100	Infertile		30	D. mojavensis	D. arizonensis		Fertile	Fertile
10	N. zonaria	Poecilopsis lapponaria	98.1			31	D. montana	D. texana	90.9	Fertile	Fertile
11	N. zonaria	P. pomonaria	95.8			32	D. mulleri	D. aldrichi		Infertile	Infertile
12	Oporabia autumnata	Oporabia dilutata	52.5	Fertile	Infertile	33	D. mulleri	D. arizonensis	100	Infertile	
13	Poecilopsis isabellae	Lycia hirtaria	54.3	Fertile	Infertile	34	D. mulleri	D. mojavensis		Infertile	Fertile
14	P. lapponaria	Poecilopsis pomonaria	49.3	Fertile	Infertile	35	D. munda	D. occidentalis	55.5	Fertile	Fertile
15	P. pomonaria	Lycia hirtaria	51.5	Fertile	Fertile	36	D. munda	D. subquinaria	49.6	Infertile	Infertile
16	P. pomonaria	Nyssia zonaria	30.1			37	D. pseudoobscura	D. miranda		Infertile	Fertile[2]
17	Saturnia pyri	Saturnia pavonia	51.4	Fertile	Infertile	38	D. pseudoobscura	D. persimilis	48.2	Infertile	Fertile[2]
18	S. spini	S. pavonia	53	Fertile	Infertile	39	D. simulans	D. melanogaster		Infertile	Infertile
19	Smerinthus ocellata	Calasymbolus astylus	100			40	D. texana	D. montana	50.5	Fertile	Fertile
20	Tephrosia bistortata	Tephrosia crepuscularia	96.9	Fertile	Fertile	41	D. virilis	D. americana		Fertile	Fertile
21	T. crepuscularia	T. bistortata	48.9	Fertile	Fertile	42	D. virilis	D. montana	49.8	Fertile	Fertile

/1/ Sex ratios are given only where the total number of hybrid offspring is a minimum of 25. Hybrid sex determined after hatching. /2/ Rarely.

Part IV: PLANTS

SP = self pollination; CP = cross pollination; S = sterile; F = fertile; P = partially fertile; M = moderate.

	Parental Species	Compatibility			Parental Species	Compatibility	
		Parents	Hybrid			Parents	Hybrid
			Tomato (Lycopersicon species)				
1	L. esculentum x L. esculentum	SP-F; CP-F	SP-F; CP-F	9	L. glandulosum x L. peruvianum	CP-F	CP-S; CP-F
2	L. esculentum x L. glandulosum[1]	CP-S	SP-S; CP-P	10	L. glandulosum x L. pimpinellifolium[3]	CP-S	
3	L. esculentum x L. hirsutum	CP-F	SP-S; CP-P	11	L. hirsutum x L. hirsutum	SP-S	CP-S; CP-F
4	L. esculentum x L. h. glabratum	CP-F	SP-F; CP-F	12	L. hirsutum x L. pimpinellifolium	SP-F	SP-P; CP-F
5	L. esculentum x L. peruvianum[1,2]	CP-F	SP-S; CP-P	13	L. h. glabratum x L. h. glabratum	SP-F; CP-F	SP-F; CP-F
6	L. esculentum x L. pimpinellifolium	CP-F	SP-F; CP-F	14	L. peruvianum x L. peruvianum	SP-S; CP-F	SP-S; CP-F
7	L. esculentum x L. pissisi	CP-S	SP-S; CP-P	15	L. peruvianum x L. pissisi	CP-S	
8	L. glandulosum x L. glandulosum	SP-S; CP-F	SP-S; CP-F	16	L. pimpinellifolium x L. pimpinellifolium	SP-F; CP-F	SP-F; CP-F

/1/ Hybrids obtainable from embryo culture, occasionally without. /2/ L. peruvianum var. dentatum (L. chilense) will cross with L. esculentum without embryo culture and the F_1 will backcross more readily than other varieties of L. peruvianum. /3/ Hybrids probably obtainable with embryo culture.

86. FERTILITY AND INFERTILITY: HYBRIDS (Concluded)
Part IV: PLANTS (Concluded)

SP = self pollination; CP = cross pollination; S = sterile; F = fertile; P = partially fertile; M = moderate.

	Parental Species	Compatibility Parents	Compatibility Hybrid		Parental Species	Compatibility Parents	Compatibility Hybrid
	Pepper (Capsicum species)						
17	C. annum x C. annum	SP-F; CP-F	SP-F; CP-F	27	C. frutescens x C. pubescens	SP-S	
18	C. annum x C. pubescens	CP-S		28	C. frutescens x C. pendulum	SP-F	SP-S; CP-MS
19	C. annum x C. frutescens	CP-F[4]	SP-MS; CP-MS	29	C. pendulum x C. pendulum	SP-F; CP-F	SP-F; CP-F
20	C. annum x C. pendulum	CP-F[5]	SP-S; CP-S	30	C. pendulum x C. pubescens	SP-F	
21	C. annum x C. chacoense	CP-F	SP-S; CP-S	31	C. pubescens x C. pubescens	SP-F; CP-F	SP-F; CP-F
22	C. chacoense x C. chacoense	SP-F; CP-F	SP-F; CP-F	32	C. sinensis x C. annum	CP-F	SP-MS; CP-MS
23	C. chacoense x C. pubescens	CP-S		33	C. sinensis x C. frutescens	CP-F	SP-MS; CP-MS
24	C. chacoense x C. frutescens	CP-F	SP-S; CP-S	34	C. sinensis x C. pendulum	CP-F	SP-S; CP-S
25	C. chaoense x C. pendulum	CP-S[4]	SP-MS; CP-MS	35	C. sinensis x C. pubescens	CP-F[5]	SP-S; CP-S
26	C. frutescens x C. frutescens	SP-F; CP-F	SP-F; CP-F	36	C. sinensis x C. chacoense	CP-F[4]	SP-S; CP-MS
	Citrus Species[6]						
37	C. aurantifolia x C. aurantifolia	SP-P; CP-P		51	C. limonia x C. reticulata	CP-F	
38	C. aurantifolia x C. limonia	CP-F		52	C. limonia x P. trifoliata	CP-F	
39	C. aurantifolia x Fortunella japonica	CP-F	CP-P	53	C. limonia x C. paradisi	CP-F	
40	C. aurantium x C. aurantium	SP-P; CP-P		54	C. paradisi x C. paradisi	SP-P; CP-P	
41	C. aurantium x Poncirus trifoliata	CP-F		55	C. paradisi x C. reticulata	CP-F	SP-S; CP-F
42	C. grandis x C. grandis	SP-P; CP-P		56	C. paradisi x C. sinensis	CP-F	
43	C. grandis x C. aurantium	CP-F		57	C. reticulata x C. reticulata	CP-F[7]	CP-F
44	C. grandis x C. reticulata	CP-F		58	C. reticulata x F. japonica	CP-F	
45	C. grandis x C. medica	CP-F		59	C. reticulata x P. trifoliata	CP-F	CP-F
46	C. grandis x C. sinensis	CP-F		60	C. reticulata x C. sinensis	CP-F	CP-F
47	C. grandis x C. paradisi	CP-F		61	C. reticulata x C. ichangensis	CP-F	
48	C. ichangensis x Poncirus trifoliata	CP-F		62	C. sinensis x C. sinensis	SP-P; CP-P	
49	C. limonia x C. limonia	SP-P; CP-P		63	C. sinensis x P. trifoliata	CP-F	SP-P[8]; CP-P
50	C. limonia x C. sinensis	CP-F		64	F. japonica x P. trifoliata	CP-F	

/4/ Slightly. /5/ With embryo culture. /6/ Lime (Citrus aurantifolia), orange (C. aurantium), grapefruit (C. grandis), Citrus sp (C. ichangensis), lemon (C. limonia), citron (C. medica), grapefruit (C. paradisi), orange (C. reticulata), orange (C. sinensis), kumquat (Fortunella japonica), trifoliate orange (Poncirus trifoliata). /7/ A few varieties are self and cross incompatible. /8/ Some.

87. HYBRID VIGOR: CORN
Values in parentheses are estimates "b" of the 95% range (cf Introduction).

Part I: COMPARATIVE GROWTH RATES IN RECIPROCAL CROSS: ENDOSPERM AND EMBRYO

	Days after Pollination	Dent[1] Endosperm	Dent[1] Embryo	Dent x Pop Endosperm	Dent x Pop Embryo	Pop x Dent Endosperm	Pop x Dent Embryo	Pop Endosperm	Pop Embryo
1	12	0.2878	0.004	0.3684	0.006	0.245	0.001	0.215	0.001
2	16	1.0449	0.043	1.0668	0.049	0.585	0.020	0.556	0.012
3	20	2.0829	0.457	2.639	0.240	1.375	0.105	1.323	0.084
4	24	3.7549	0.493	3.938	0.556	1.915	0.221	1.904	0.153
5	28	5.1712	0.938	5.536	0.915	2.427	0.333	2.451	0.250
6	32	5.3761	1.081	5.997	1.074	3.089	0.449	2.894	0.315
7	36	5.6709	1.124	6.243	1.214	3.617	0.531	2.963	0.326
8	40	6.5997	1.541	7.438	1.409	3.662	0.566	3.343	0.395
9	44	7.0252	1.646	8.408	1.734	3.888	0.613	3.674	0.459
10	48	6.7793	1.702	8.541	1.724	4.341	0.705	3.398	0.483
11	52	7.3842	2.016	9.580	2.114	4.117	0.684	3.594	0.452
12	Harvest[2]	0.1805	0.0543	0.2171	0.0533	0.1059	0.0195	0.0925	0.0132

/1/ Individual harvest weights based on 50 kernel samples. /2/ Date and weight, linear component.

Part II: EFFECT OF CONTINUED INBREEDING ON REDUCTIONS IN HEIGHT AND YIELD: THREE INBRED LINES

	Generations, Number Inbred	Line 1-6 Height in.	Line 1-6 Yield/Acre, bushels	Line 1-7 Height in.	Line 1-7 Yield/Acre, bushels	Line 1-9 Height in.	Line 1-9 Yield/Acre, bushels
1	0	117	81(74-88)	117	81(74-88)	117	81(74-88)
2	1-5	87	64(53-75)	81	51(44-58)	77	41(36-46)
3	6-10	97(96-98)	45(33-57)	84(83-85)	36(31-41)	82(80-84)	34(30-38)
4	11-15	97(94-100)	38(34-42)	84(82-86)	34(31-37)	83(81-85)	26(24-28)
5	16-20	88(84-92)	22(18-26)	85(82-88)	24(21-27)	75(71-79)	14(11-17)
6	21-25	81(79-83)	20(14-26)	75(72-78)	21(18-24)	71(68-74)	13(11-15)
7	26-30	92(89-95)	24(15-33)	80(78-82)	18(14-22)	77(74-80)	9(5-13)

Part III: RELATIVE AVERAGE YIELDS: INBRED LINES AND DIALLEL F₁ CROSSES[1]

	Varieties	F₁ Hybrids[2]	Inbred		Varieties	F₁ Hybrids[2]	Inbred		Varieties	F₁ Hybrids[2]	Inbred
1	B2	87.4(81.4-93.4)	39.0(35.8-42.2)	4	OhO7	83.9(77.9-89.9)	28.5(25.3-31.7)	8	Hy	75.5(69.7-81.7)	31.9(28.7-35.1)
2	38-11	86.5(80.5-92.5)	26.5(23.3-29.7)	5	WF9	81.6(75.6-87.6)	28.5(25.3-31.7)	9	WV7	73.5(67.5-79.5)	20.1(16.9-23.3)
3	K159	86.3(80.3-92.3)	49.8(46.6-53.0)	6	R46	80.3(74.3-86.3)	39.8(36.6-43.0)	10	C.I.14	68.1(62.1-74.1)	2.7(0-5.9)
				7	OhO4	75.7(69.7-81.7)	15.1(11.9-18.3)				

/1/ Values, bushels/acre. /2/ All possible.

Part IV: DECREASE IN YIELDING CAPACITY, ADVANCED HYBRID GENERATIONS

	Specification	Average Yield, bushels/acre F_1	Average Yield, bushels/acre P_1	Average Difference, F_1-P_1	Yield F_2 bushels/acre Actual	Yield F_2 bushels/acre Expected	Loss of Vigor, Grain Yield Actual bushels	Loss of Vigor, Grain Yield Actual %	Loss of Vigor, Grain Yield Expected bushels	Loss of Vigor, Grain Yield Expected %
1	10 single hybrids	62.8	23.74	39.06	44.2	43.3	18.6	47.6	19.5	50.0
2	4 three-way hybrids	64.2	23.75	40.45	49.3	50.7	14.9	36.8	13.5	33.3
3	10 double hybrids	64.1	25.00	39.10	54.0	54.3	10.1	25.8	9.8	25.0

Part V: EFFECT ON YIELD AND PLANT HEIGHT: VARIOUS LEVELS OF HETEROZYGOSITY

	Degree of Heterozygosity, %	Type of Combination	Number of Entries	Grain Yield, bushels/acre Actual	Grain Yield, bushels/acre Predicted	Ear Node, Height, in. Actual	Ear Node, Height, in. Predicted
1	0	Inbred lines sibbed	4	41.5(40.57-42.43)		25.5(24.86-26.14)	
2	50	F₂ single crosses	6	62.2(60.18-64.22)	63.2(61.94-64.46)	32.8(32.08-33.52)	33.0(32.59-33.41)
3		Backcrosses	12	67.9(65.42-70.38)	63.2(61.94-64.46)	32.5(31.90-33.10)	33.0(32.59-33.41)
4	75	(A x B) (A x C)	12	75.2(73.14-77.26)	74.1(72.61-75.59)	38.4(37.62-39.18)	36.1(35.71-36.49)[1]
5	100	Single crosses	6	84.9(82.55-87.25)		39.6(39.06-40.14)	
6		Three-way crosses	12	84.9(82.46-87.34)	84.9(82.55-87.25)	40.5(39.90-41.10)	39.6(39.06-40.14)[1]
7		Double crosses	3	81.9(80.37-83.43)	84.9(82.55-87.25)[1]	40.9(40.01-41.79)	39.6(39.06-40.14)[1]

/1/ Differs significantly from actual.

88. HERITABILITY ESTIMATES: FARM ANIMALS

Values are from the best available information; however, the inadequacies of heritability estimates should be remembered in using this table. Values in parentheses, unless otherwise noted, are estimate "d" of the 95% range (cf Introduction).

Part I: CHICKENS AND TURKEYS

Characteristic	h^2S	h^2D	h^2DS	h^2o.d.		Characteristic	h^2S	h^2D	h^2DS	h^2o.d.
	Chickens[2]						**Chickens (concluded)[2]**			
1 Body weight, 8 wk (NH)	(16-39)		(32-50)	45		48 Albumin weight (WL)			110	
2 Body weight, 8 wk (BPR)	(31-32)		(33-60)	39		49 Albumin weight (Composite)			22	
3 Body weight, 8 wk (Composite)			46	40		50 Yolk weight (NH)			0	
4 Body weight, 10 wk (W. Wyan.)		(20-63)				51 Yolk weight (BPR)			2	
5 Body weight, 10 wk (Composite)			46	33		52 Yolk weight (WL)			20	
6 Body weight, 12 wk (SCWL)	20					53 Shell texture (Composite)			27	
7 Body weight, 12 wk (NH)	42	60	51			54 Shell thickness (Composite)			27	
8 Body weight, 22 wk (WL)	27					55 Blood spots (WL)			67	46
9 Body depth (NH)	11		43				**Turkeys[2]**			
10 Keel length (NH)	(27-50)	17	(34-37)			56 Body weight, 2 wk (MW)	♂28♀13		♂69♀73	
11 Breast width (NH)	13	29	21			57 Body weight, 4 wk (MW)	♂4	♂37♀76	♂20♀38	
12 Shank length (NH)	50	48	(33-49)			58 Body weight, 4 wk (BBB)	♂49♀38		♂40♀44	
13 Shank length (WL)			(33-54)			59 Body weight, 4 wk (BSW)			♂26♀19	
14 Thyroid weight (NH)			48			60 Body weight, 8 wk (MW)	♂19♀32	♂21♀72	♂20♀38	
15 Testes weight (NH)			29			61 Body weight, 8 wk (BBB)	♂56♀28		♂45♀45	
16 Feathering, 8 wk (NH)			33			62 Body weight, 8 wk (BSW)	♂11♀8		♂33♀16	
17 Feathering, 8 wk (BPR)			42			63 Body weight, 14 wk (BBB)	♂72♀39		♂62♀29	
18 Egg production[3] (WL)	21	22	(15-22)	(9-16)		64 Body weight, 14 wk (BSW)	♂6♀18		♂19♀16	
19 Egg production[3] (BPR)		41	25	30		65 Body weight 16 wk (MW)	♂46♀21	♂27♀67	♂36♀44	
20 Rate, Dec. to Mar. (Composite)			41	11		66 Body weight, 16 wk (WH)	♂23♀59	♂62♀42	♂42♀50	♂62♀41
21 Rate, Mar. to June (Composite)			38	0		67 Body weight, 24 wk (MW)	♂38♀29	♂12♀2	♂25♀16	
22 Rate, Dec. to June (Composite)			51	0		68 Body weight, 24 wk (WH)	♂33♀61	♂68♀70	♂51♀60	♂68♀59
23 Production Index (WL)	23	10	16	57		69 Body weight, 25 wk (BBB)	♂34♀29	♂2♀71	♂18♀50	
24 Sexual maturity (WL)	(24-27)	17	(31-33)	(31-35)		70 Body weight, 25 wk (WH)	♂29♀24	♂71♀71	♂50♀47	
25 Sexual maturity (Composite)			20	(7-26)		71 Body weight, 26 wk (BBB)	♂52♀29		♂52♀25	
26 Pause, 6 da (Composite)			(16-20)	(21-23)		72 Body weight, 26 wk (BSW)	♂13♀19		♂20♀24	
27 Pause, winter (WL)	8[4]					73 Breast width, 26 wk (BBB)	♂4♀4		♂23♀13	
28 Persistency (Composite)			10			74 Breast width, 26 wk (BSW)			♂37♀40	
29 Persistency (WL)	5[4]					75 Breast depth, 26 wk (BBB)	♂22♀21		♂30♀40	
30 Total mortality[5] (Composite)			12			76 Breast depth, 26 wk (BSW)			♂41♀21	
31 Total mortality[6] (WL)	8	11	8			77 Keel length, 26 wk (BBB)	♂32♀15		♂22♀18	
32 Leukosis mortality (WL)	5	3	8			78 Keel length, 26 wk (BSW)			♂-5♀14	
33 Reproductive disorders (WL)	2	6				79 Shank length, 26 wk (BBB)	♂25		♂34	
34 Hatchability (Composite)				16		80 Shank length, 26 wk (BSW)			♂52	
Egg weight[7]						81 Egg production, Feb-June (B)				♀2
35 Sexual maturity[8] (WL)	60		50	(44-61)		82 Egg production, Feb-June (BSW)				♀11
36 Nov. (10 eggs) (WL)	48		36	61		83 Egg production, Feb-June (BBB)	♀9		♀14	♀16
37 March (1 egg) (Composite)			52	52		84 Egg production, Feb-June (WH)	♀29	♀27	♀28	
38 April (10 eggs) (WL)			47	39		85 Egg weight, Feb. (10 eggs) (BBB)	♀53		♀50	♀64
39 April (10 eggs) (Composite)				61		86 Egg weight, May (10 eggs) (WH)	♀22	♀62	♀42	
40 Jan. to May[9] (WL)	37[4]			55		87 Fertility, 1-7 da[11] (BBB)		♀53	♀26	
41 Dec. to May[10] (NH)			67			88 Fertility, 8-14 da[11] (BBB)		♀26	♀12	
42 Dec. to May[10] (BPR)			40			89 Fertility (BBB)			♀30	
43 Dec. to May[10] (WL)			93			90 Hatchability, 1-7 da (BBB)	♀3		♀13	♀40
44 Dec. to May[10] (Composite)				50		91 Hatchability, 8-14 da (BBB)	♀14		♀21	♀26
45 Shell color (BPR; RIR)	30	91	58	78		92 Hatchability, Feb-June (B)				♀33
46 Albumin weight (NH)			83			93 Hatchability, Feb-June (BSW)				♀1
47 Albumin weight (BPR)			14							

/1/ h²S = paternal half sib correlation; h²D = maternal half sib correlation; h²DS = full sib correlation; h²o. d. = offspring-dam regression. /2/ Breeds and varieties are denoted in parentheses. For chickens: NH = New Hampshire, BPR = Barred Plymouth Rock, WL = White Leghorn, SCWL = Single Comb White Leghorn, W. Wyan. = White Wyandotte, RIR = Rhode Island Red, Composite = composite of several breeds. For turkeys: MW = Medium White, BBB = Broad Breasted Bronze, B = Bronze, BSW = Beltsville Small White, WH = White Holland. /3/ Annual egg production of survivors. /4/ Method of determining estimate not specified. /5/ 319 da after housing. /6/ 1st laying year. /7/ Estimates based on cited number of eggs at specified periods. /8/ 10 eggs. /9/ All eggs. /10/ Representative egg sample. /11/ Stored eggs.

Part II: BEEF AND DAIRY CATTLE

Characteristic	P	DO	SO	S		Characteristic	h^4
	Beef Cattle[2]						**Dairy Cattle**
1 Birth weight	48	42	35			13 Birth weight	60[5]
2 Gain, birth to weaning	21	7	17			14 Mature weight	60[5]
3 Weaning weight	28	10	26			15 Milk production	(25-38)
4 Yearling weight, off pasture	45	39				16 Butterfat production	(17-32)
5 Gain, off pasture	39	18		30		17 Butterfat per cent	(33-57)
6 Final feedlot weight	84		92			18 Type classification rating (overall)	(14-31)
7 Gain in feedlot	64		97	43		19 Amount of spotting (Holsteins)	(93-99)
8 Grade or score at weaning	27	22	11			20 Mastitis resistance	(14-38)
9 Grade or score as yearlings[3]	27	14				21 Gestation length	32[5]
10 Grade or score at slaughter	46					22 Services per conception	(3-7)
11 Carcass grade	32						
12 Economy of gain	29		48				

/1/ P = paternal half sibs, DO = dam offspring regression, SO = sire offspring regression, S = selection experiments. /2/ Values prepresent weighted averages (based on volume of data) of published estimates. Not listed are area of eye muscle, 70P, and thickness of fat, 38 P. /3/ Off pasture. /4/ Estimates based on intrasire regression unless otherwise noted. /5/ Average of several methods and/or breeds.

Values are from the best available information; however, the inadequacies of heritability estimates should be remembered in using this table. Values in parentheses, unless otherwise noted, are estimate "d" of the 95% range (cf Introduction).

Part III: SHEEP

	Characteristic	p	b	Average[2]		Characteristic	p	b	Average[2]
		\multicolumn{3}{c}{Method of Estimation[1]}			\multicolumn{3}{c}{Method of Estimation[1]}		
1	Birth weight	30			9	Type score at weaning	15	7	(7-13)
2	Yearling staple length		36		10	Condition score at weaning	2.4	14	(4-21)
3	Yearling weight clean wool		(28-38)		11	Skin folds			(45-51)
4	Yearling body weight		40		12	Neck folds	36	45	(8-39)
5	Yearling body score		12		13	Face covering	51	60	(46-56)
6	Body folds		37		14	Number of nipples		14.4[3]	
7	Weaning weight	27			15	Number of functional nipples		22	
8	Staple length at weaning	41	(34-39)	(17-43)					

/1/ p = paternal half sibs, b = intrasire regression. /2/ Average of several methods and/or breeds. /3/ Intrasire correlation.

Part IV: SWINE

	Characteristic	Breed	Estimate of Heritability[1]			Characteristic	Breed	Estimate of Heritability[1]	
1	Birth weight	Composite	2	A	66	56-168 da	Not stated	45	A
2	Birth weight	Duroc	0	A	67	84-112 da	Not stated	10	D
3	Birth weight	Duroc	-23	E	68	84-112 da	Duroc	31	A
4	Birth weight	Hampshire	5	A	69	112-140 da	Duroc	4	A
5	Birth weight	Hampshire	6	D	70	112-140 da	Not stated	10	D
6	Birth weight	Hampshire	8	E	71	112-154 da	Duroc	25	A
7	Birth weight	Not stated	14	D	72	112-154 da	Crosses	34	A
8	Body weight, 21 da	Duroc	4	A	73	112-168 da	Duroc	17	A
9	Body weight, 21 da	Hampshire	24	A	74	140-168 da	Duroc	13	A
10	Body weight, 21 da	Hampshire	14	D	75	140-168	Not stated	10	D
11	Body weight, 21 da	Hampshire	-4	E		Daily weight gain			
12	Body weight, 21 da	Not stated	-6	D	76	Birth-200 lb	Not stated	21	A
13	Body weight, 56 da	Duroc	15	A	77	Birth-200 lb	Not stated	3	D
14	Body weight, 56 da	Hampshire	17	A	78	56 da - 200 lb	P.C. and Minn. No. 1	31	D
15	Body weight, 56 da	Hampshire	8	D	79	56 da - 200 lb	Not stated	40	A
16	Body weight, 56 da	Hampshire	-2	E	80	56 da - 200 lb	Not stated	21	D
17	Body weight, 56 da	P.C. and Landrace	3	D	81	56 da - 200 lb	Danish Landrace	41	A
18	Body weight, 56 da	P.C. and Minn. No. 1	-20	D	82	56 da - 200 lb	Danish Landrace	46	B
19	Body weight, 60 da	Poland China	7	A	83	56 da - 200 lb	Danish Landrace	-19	F
20	Body weight, 63 da	Duroc	14	D	84	56 da - 200 lb	Danish Landrace	24	O
21	Body weight, 72 da	Duroc	9	E	85	56 da - 225 lb	Duroc	18	A
22	Body weight, 84 da	Duroc	26	A	86	56 da - 225 lb	P.C. and Landrace	31	A
23	Body weight, 112 da	Duroc	28	A	87	56 da - 112 da	Duroc	18	A
24	Body weight, 112 da	Not stated	0	A	88	72 da - 225 lb	Duroc	43	E
25	Body weight, 140 da	Duroc	19	A	89	112 da - 225 lb	Duroc	14	A
26	Body weight, 140 da	Not stated	21	A	90	50 lb - 200 lb	P.C. and Minn. No. 1	26	D
27	Body weight, 150 da	Hampshire	14	A		Sow Productivity			
28	Body weight, 150 da	Hampshire	16	J	91	Litter size at birth	Composite	17	K
29	Body weight, 154 da	Not stated	10	D	92	Litter size at birth	Poland China	17	H
30	Body weight, 154 da	P.C. and Landrace	7	D	93	Litter size at birth	Poland China	18	H
31	Body weight, 154 da	Hampshire	23	D	94	Litter size at birth	Yorkshire	10	H
32	Body weight, 154 da	Hampshire	17	J	95	Litter size at birth	Tamworth	34	H
33	Body weight, 154 da	Hampshire	9	E	96	Litter size at birth	Berkshire	44	H
34	Body weight, 154 da	Composite	19	P	97	Litter size at birth	Chester White	13	K
35	Body weight, 168 da	Duroc	25	A	98	Litter size at birth	P.C. and Landrace	-11	D
36	Body weight, 168 da	Not stated	27	A	99	Litter size at birth	Duroc	25	D
37	Body weight, 180 da	Poland China	20	A	100	Litter size at birth	Duroc	24	K
38	Body weight, 180 da	Poland China	62	D	101	Litter size at birth	German Landrace	14	A
39	Body weight, 180 da	Poland China	30	M	102	Litter size at birth	German grazing hog	12	A
40	Body weight, 180 da	Poland China	40	I	103	Litter size at birth	Duroc	3	D
41	Body weight, 180 da	Poland China	30	D	104	Litter size at birth	Composite	16	A
42	Body weight, 180 da	P.C. and Minn. No. 1	14	D	105	Litter size at birth	Composite	14	D
43	Body weight, 180 da	Duroc	22	D	106	Litter size at birth	Composite	15	I
44	Body weight, 180 da	Duroc	23	N	107	Litter size at birth	Not stated	7	D
45	Body weight, 180 da	Hampshire	24	A	108	Litter size at birth	Duroc	22	K
46	Body weight, 180 da	Hampshire	65	D	109	Litter size at birth	Duroc	28	K
47	Body weight, 180 da	Hampshire	19	J	110	Litter size at birth	Swiss Land. and York.	12	K
48	Body weight, 180 da	Hampshire	5	D	111	Live pigs farrowed	Composite	18	A
49	Body weight, 180 da	Hampshire	22	E	112	Live pigs farrowed	Composite	16	D
50	Body weight, 180 da	Hampshire	16	J	113	Live pigs farrowed	Composite	9	I
51	Body weight, 180 da	P.C. and Landrace	34	A	114	Live pigs farrowed	Duroc	24	D
52	Body weight, 200 da	Yorkshire	27	G	115	Live pigs farrowed	Duroc	21	K
	Body weight gain				116	Live pigs farrowed	Composite	22	D
53	Birth-21 da	Duroc	7	A	117	Litter size, 21 da	Duroc	20	D
54	Birth-56 da	Duroc	22	A	118	Litter size, 21 da	Duroc	34	K
55	Birth-56 da	Duroc	15	A	119	Litter size, 21 da	Swiss Land. and York.	7	K
56	Birth-56 da	Crosses	2	A	120	Litter size, 28 da	Chester White	16	K
57	21-56 da	Duroc	15	A	121	Litter size, 56 da	Not stated	6	D
58	21-56 da	Not stated	-2	D	122	Litter size, 56 da	Duroc	19	D
59	56-84 da	Duroc	20	A	123	Litter size, 56 da	Duroc	25	K
60	56-84 da	Not stated	18	A	124	Litter size, 56 da	P.C. and Landrace	-9	D
61	56-84 da	Not stated	6	D	125	Litter size, 56 da	Duroc	13	K
62	56-112 da	Duroc	51	A	126	Litter size, 56 da	Duroc	18	K
63	56-112 da	Duroc	28	A	127	Litter size, 56 da	Composite	32	D
64	56-112 da	Crosses	35	A	128	Percent live pigs, 56 da	Composite	40	D
65	56-112 da	Not stated	28	A	129	Litter size, 56-70 da	Composite	17	K

/1/ Estimates of heritability are based on the indicated methods: A = paternal half sib correlation, B = maternal half sib correlation, C = paternal and maternal half sib correlations, D = intra-sire regression of progeny on dam, E = regression of progeny on mean of parents, F = correlation between progeny averages of sire and of son, G = regression of progeny on mean of parental full sibs, H = daughter-dam correlation, I = correlation between full sibs, J = line differences due to selection, K = repeatability of sow's own performance, L = variance between strains, M = regression of variance on genetic relationship between pigs, N = average of two methods, O = average of three methods, P = method not specified.

88. HERITABILITY ESTIMATES: FARM ANIMALS (Concluded)

Values are from the best available information; however, the inadequacies of heritability estimates should be remembered in using this table. Values in parentheses, unless otherwise noted, are estimate "d" of the 95% range (cf Introduction).

Part IV: SWINE (Concluded)

	Characteristic	Breed	Estimate of Heritability[1]			Characteristic	Breed	Estimate of Heritability[1]	
130	Litter size, 63 da	Duroc	-3	D	180	Thickness of shoulder fat	Yorkshire	42	A
131	Litter size, 70 da	Chester White	20	K	181	Thickness of shoulder fat	Yorkshire	49	C
132	Litter size, 154 da	Not stated	9	D	182	Thickness of loin fat	Yorkshire	48	A
133	Litter size, 154 da	P.C. and Landrace	-15	D	183	Thickness of loin fat	Yorkshire	59	C
134	Litter size, 168 da	Duroc	42	D	184	Thickness of belly	Swedish Landrace	39	A
135	Litter size, 168 da	Duroc	32	K	185	Thickness of belly	Danish Landrace	62	A
136	Litter size, 180 da	Duroc	-12	D	186	Thickness of belly	Danish Landrace	44	B
137	Litter weight at birth	Composite	36	D	187	Thickness of belly	Danish Landrace	47	F
138	Litter weight, 21 da	Swiss Land. and York.	12	K	188	Thickness of belly	Danish Landrace	46	O
139	Litter weight, 56 da	Composite	7	D	189	Length of carcass	Yorkshire	40	A
140	Litter weight, 56 da	Duroc	21	D	190	Length of carcass	Yorkshire	60	C
141	Litter weight, 56 da	Duroc	53	K	191	Length of carcass	Yorkshire	42	G
142	Litter weight, 56 da	Not stated	2	D	192	Length of carcass	Composite	48	P
143	Litter weight at weaning	Duroc	14	K	193	Length of carcass	P.C. and Landrace	73	A
144	Litter weight at weaning	Duroc	0	K	194	Length of carcass	Swedish Landrace	61	A
145	Litter weight, 60 da	Composite	18	K	195	Length of carcass	Danish Landrace	78	A
146	Litter weight, 154 da	Not stated	11	D	196	Length of carcass	Danish Landrace	81	B
147	Litter weight, 168 da	Duroc	2	D	197	Length of carcass	Danish Landrace	35	F
148	Litter weight, 168 da	Duroc	34	K	198	Length of carcass	Danish Landrace	54	O
149	Productivity index	Poland China	16	D	199	Length of hind leg	Duroc	23	A
150	Length of gestation	P.C. and Landrace	21	I	200	Length of hind leg	Composite	73	P
151	Feed economy	P.C. and Landrace	57	A	201	Length of hind leg	P.C. and Landrace	58	A
152	Feed economy	Duroc	26	E	202	Per cent lean cuts	P.C. and Landrace	29	A
153	Feed economy	Duroc	24	J	203	Per cent lean cuts	Composite	15	P
154	Feed economy	Yorkshire	30	A	204	Per cent fat cuts	P.C. and Landrace	52	A
155	Feed economy	Yorkshire	57	C	205	Per cent fat cuts	Composite	69	P
156	Feed economy	Composite	26	P	206	Per cent ham	Yorkshire	51	A
157	Feed economy	Danish Landrace	29	A^2	207	Per cent ham	Yorkshire	65	C
158	Feed economy	Danish Landrace	12	B^2	208	Per cent shoulder	Yorkshire	38	A
159	Feed economy	Danish Landrace	-10	F^2	209	Per cent shoulder	Yorkshire	56	C
160	Feed economy	Danish Landrace	8	O^2	210	Per cent Wiltshire sides	Danish Landrace	40	A
161	Feed economy	Swedish Landrace	12	A	211	Per cent Wiltshire sides	Danish Landrace	32	B
162	Feed economy	Swedish Landrace	23	A	212	Per cent Wiltshire sides	Danish Landrace	0	F
163	Market score	Duroc	33	N	213	Per cent Wiltshire sides	Danish Landrace	20	O
164	Market score	Poland China	10	D	214	Size of ham	Swedish Landrace	61	A
165	Age at slaughter	Swedish Landrace	57	A	215	Ham circumference	Duroc	17	A
166	Age at 200 lb weight	Yorkshire	55	A	216	Loin area	Yorkshire	66	A
167	Age at 200 lb weight	Yorkshire	85	C	217	Loin area	Yorkshire	79	C
	Carcass				218	Loin area	Yorkshire	16	G
168	Dressing per cent	P.C. and Landrace	38	A	219	Carcass score	Yorkshire	35	G
169	Thickness of backfat	P.C. and Landrace	54	A	220	Carcass score	Yorkshire	35	A
170	Thickness of backfat	Duroc	12	A	221	Carcass score	Yorkshire	49	C
171	Thickness of backfat	Composite	40	P	222	Belly score	Yorkshire	14	C
172	Thickness of backfat	Landrace Danish	80	A	223	Firmness of fat score	Swedish Landrace	35	A
173	Thickness of backfat	Danish Landrace	55	B	224	Conformation score	Poland China	20	D
174	Thickness of backfat	Danish Landrace	37	F	225	Type score within strains	Poland China	38	A
175	Thickness of backfat	Danish Landrace	47	O	226	Type score between strains	Poland China	92	L
176	Thickness of backfat	Swedish Landrace	54	A	227	Number of vertebrae	Composite	74	E
177	Thickness of backfat	Yorkshire	37	G	228	Scrotal hernia	P.C. and Landrace	15	A
178	Thickness of backfat	Yorkshire	38	A	229	Amount of spotting	Beltsville No. 1	76	O
179	Thickness of backfat	Yorkshire	53	C					

/1/ Estimates of heritability are based on the indicated methods: A = paternal half sib correlation, B = maternal half sib correlation, C = paternal and maternal half sib correlations, D = intra-sire regression of progeny on dam, E = regression of progeny on mean of parents, F = correlation between progeny averages of sire and of son, G = regression of progeny on mean of parental full sibs, H = daughter-dam correlation, I = correlation between full sibs, J = line differences due to selection, K = repeatability of sow's own performance, L = variance between strains, M = regression of variance on genetic relationship between pigs, N = average of two methods, O = average of three methods, P = method not specified.
/2/ To be multiplied by $(1 + 3r_{oo})$ where r_{oo} is the correlation between litter mates.

113

89. GENETIC SEGREGATIONS AT 1% AND 5% PROBABILITY LEVELS

Values are given for the number of offspring required in order to obtain at least one desired individual among different genetic segregations at 1% and 5% probablility levels. Numbers underlined indicate that corresponding calculated numbers are between 0.01 and 0.49 greater than the number entered.

	Ratio of Undesired to Desired Type	Type of Segregation	Number[1] of Required Offspring Probability Level 1%	5%	Remarks
		F$_2$ Segregation			General method for calculating number (n) of required individuals at desired probability levels for all Mendelian ratios:
1	2:1	Monohybrid, homozygous lethal	12	7	
2	3:1	Any (normal) monohybrid	16	10	$$p = \left(\tfrac{e}{f}\right)^n$$
3	15:1	Any dihybrid	71	46	p = probability level desired
4	63:1	Any trihybrid	292	190	e = the multiple dominant term of the numerator of a Mendelian fraction
5	255:1	Any tetrahybrid	1177	765	f = the common denominator of all the terms of the Mendelian fraction
		Backcross (Testcross) Segregations			n = the number of required individuals needed to assure the desired probability level
6	1:1	Any monohybrid	7	4	Example: How many individuals in a 15:1 Mendelian ratio are required to show at 5% probability that no double recessive is expected?
7	3:1	Any dihybrid	16	10	
8	7:1	Any trihybrid	35	22	p = 0.05 e = 15 f = 16 n = ?
9	15:1	Any tetrahybrid	71	46	Solving by logarithms:
10	31:1	Any pentahybrid	145	94	n(log 15 − log 16) = log 0.05
		Genotypic Segregations			Answer: n = 46.4
11	2:1	Any class of 3, e.g., 9:3:3:1	12	7	Note: Rule of thumb method for estimating any value
12	5:1	Any class of 6, e.g., 9:6:1	25	16	of n is: at 5% probability use three times the Men-
13	6:1	Any class of 7, e.g., 9:7 or 7:1	30	19	delian denominator; at 1% probability use five times
14	8:1	Any class of 9, e.g., 9:3:3:1	39	25	the Mendelian denominator.
15	11:1	Any class of 12, e.g., 12:3:1	53	34	
16	14:1	Any class of 15, e.g., 15:1	67	43	
17	26:1	Any class of 27, e.g., 27:37	122	79	
18	36:1	Any class of 37, e.g., 27:37	168	109	
19	62:1	Any class of 63, e.g., 63:1	288	187	
20	80:1	Any class of 81, e.g., 81:175	371	241	

/1/ Values are calculated from formula, $n = k(r + \tfrac{1}{2})$, where k equals 4.61 and 3.00 for the 1% and 5% probability levels, respectively; r equals the ratio between the undesired and desired types.

90. SIGNIFICANT LEVELS OF t, F, AND χ^2
In each cell upper value represents 5% level, lower value 1% level.

Degrees of freedom for lesser mean square		t	**Degrees of freedom for greater mean square[1]** 1	2	3	4	5	6	8	10	12	15	20	50
			F											
	1	12.7 / 63.7	161 / 4052	200 / 4999	216 / 5403	225 / 5625	230 / 5764	234 / 5859	239 / 5981	242 / 6056	244 / 6106	246 / 6156	248 / 6208	252 / 6302
	2	4.3 / 9.9	18.5 / 98.5	19.0 / 99.0	19.2 / 99.2	19.2 / 99.2	19.3 / 99.3	19.3 / 99.3	19.4 / 99.4	19.4 / 99.4	19.4 / 99.4	19.4 / 99.4	19.4 / 99.4	19.5 / 99.5
	3	3.2 / 5.8	10.1 / 34.1	9.6 / 30.8	9.3 / 29.5	9.1 / 28.7	9.0 / 28.2	8.9 / 27.9	8.8 / 27.5	8.8 / 27.2	8.7 / 27.0	8.7 / 26.9	8.7 / 26.7	8.6 / 26.4
	4	2.8 / 4.6	7.7 / 21.2	6.9 / 18.0	6.6 / 16.7	6.4 / 16.0	6.3 / 15.5	6.2 / 15.2	6.0 / 14.8	6.0 / 14.5	5.9 / 14.4	5.9 / 14.2	5.8 / 14.0	5.7 / 13.7
	5	2.6 / 4.0	6.6 / 16.3	5.8 / 13.3	5.4 / 12.1	5.2 / 11.4	5.0 / 11.0	5.0 / 10.7	4.8 / 10.3	4.7 / 10.0	4.7 / 9.9	4.6 / 9.7	4.6 / 9.6	4.4 / 9.2
	6	2.4 / 3.7	6.0 / 13.7	5.1 / 10.9	4.8 / 9.8	4.5 / 9.2	4.4 / 8.8	4.3 / 8.5	4.2 / 8.1	4.1 / 7.9	4.0 / 7.7	3.9 / 7.6	3.9 / 7.4	3.8 / 7.1
	8	2.3 / 3.4	5.3 / 11.3	4.5 / 8.6	4.1 / 7.6	3.8 / 7.0	3.7 / 6.6	3.6 / 6.4	3.4 / 6.0	3.3 / 5.8	3.3 / 5.7	3.2 / 5.5	3.2 / 5.4	3.0 / 5.1
	10	2.2 / 3.2	5.0 / 10.0	4.1 / 7.6	3.7 / 6.6	3.5 / 6.0	3.3 / 5.6	3.2 / 5.4	3.1 / 5.1	3.0 / 4.8	2.9 / 4.7	2.8 / 4.6	2.8 / 4.4	2.6 / 4.1
	12	2.2 / 3.1	4.8 / 9.3	3.9 / 6.9	3.5 / 6.0	3.3 / 5.4	3.1 / 5.1	3.0 / 4.8	2.8 / 4.5	2.8 / 4.3	2.7 / 4.2	2.6 / 4.0	2.5 / 3.9	2.4 / 3.6
	15	2.1 / 2.9	4.5 / 8.7	3.7 / 6.4	3.3 / 5.4	3.1 / 4.9	2.9 / 4.6	2.8 / 4.3	2.6 / 4.0	2.6 / 3.8	2.5 / 3.7	2.4 / 3.5	2.3 / 3.4	2.2 / 3.1
	20	2.1 / 2.8	4.4 / 8.1	3.5 / 5.8	3.1 / 4.9	2.9 / 4.4	2.7 / 4.1	2.6 / 3.9	2.4 / 3.6	2.4 / 3.4	2.3 / 3.2	2.2 / 3.1	2.1 / 2.9	2.0 / 2.6
	50	2.0 / 2.7	4.0 / 7.2	3.2 / 5.1	2.8 / 4.2	2.6 / 3.7	2.4 / 3.4	2.3 / 3.2	2.1 / 2.9	2.0 / 2.7	2.0 / 2.6	1.9 / 2.4	1.8 / 2.3	1.6 / 1.9
	100	2.0 / 2.6	3.9 / 6.9	3.1 / 4.8	2.7 / 4.0	2.5 / 3.5	2.3 / 3.2	2.2 / 3.0	2.0 / 2.7	1.9 / 2.5	1.8 / 2.4	1.8 / 2.2	1.7 / 2.1	1.5 / 1.7
	∞	1.96 / 2.58	3.8 / 6.6	3.0 / 4.6	2.6 / 3.8	2.4 / 3.3	2.2 / 3.0	2.1 / 2.8	1.9 / 2.5	1.8 / 2.3	1.8 / 2.2	1.7 / 2.0	1.6 / 1.9	1.4 / 1.5
	χ^2 =		3.8 / 6.6	6.0 / 9.2	7.8 / 11.3	9.5 / 13.3	11.1 / 15.1	12.6 / 16.8	15.5 / 20.1	18.3 / 23.2	21.0 / 26.2	25.0 / 30.6	31.4 / 37.6	67.5 / 76.0

/1/ With only one degree of freedom for greater mean square, $F = t^2$; and chi-square for n d.f. is equal to n x F, for n and ∞ d.f.

91. BREEDING HABITS: MAMMALS

If the estrous cycle occurs typically in a species as an isolated event during the breeding season, the species is monestrous, (Me). If the cycles occur in series, continuously, or seasonally, the species is polyestrous, (Pe). If a female mates with only one male during its lifetime, the female is monogamous, (Mo); if it mates with a different male each breeding season it is polygamous, (Po); and if it mates with 2 or more different males during any one breeding season it is promiscuous, (Pr). Values in parentheses are ranges, estimate "d" of the 95% range (cf Introduction).

	Species	Age at Puberty	Breeding Season	Sexual Cycle Type	Sexual Cycle Duration, da	Gestation Period, da	Litter Size	Litter No./yr	Mating Habits
1	Man (Homo sapiens)	(12-15.4) yr	All yr	Pe	(27-28)	267[1]	1[2,3]		
2	Antelope (Hippotragus niger)		All yr			(270-281)			
3	Ape (Macaca sylvanus)			Pe	(27-33)	210			
4	Armadillo (Dasypus novemcinctus)	1 yr	Summer	Me		(150-240)	4	1	
5	Ass (Equus asinus)	1 yr	Mar-Aug	Pe	22	365(340-385)	1		
6	Baboon (Papio porcarius)	4 yr	All yr	Pe	(29-42)	210	1		
7	Badger (Taxidea taxus)		Aug-Sept	Me		(183-265)	3(1-7)		
8	Bat (Eptesicus fuscus)		Fall	Me[4]	150	35	2(1-4)	1-3	Pr
9	Bat, vampire (Desmodus rotundus)		All yr	Pe	5+ mo		1	1+	Po
10	Bear (Ursus horribilis)	(2-3) yr	June-July	Me		208(180-225)	2(1-4)		Mo
11	Beaver (Castor canadensis)	2 yr	Jan-Feb			120(65-128)	4(1-6)		
12	Bobcat (Lynx rufus)		Late Feb			50	3(1-4)		
13	Buffalo (Bison bison)	3 yr	All yr[5]	Pe	21	275(270-285)	1(1-2)	1	Po
14	Camel (Camelus spp)		All yr	Pe	(10-20)	(315-410)	1		
15	Cat (Felis catus)	(6-15) mo	Feb-July	Pe[6,7]	(15-28)	63(52-69)	4		Pr
16	Cattle (Bos taurus)	(6-14) mo	All yr	Pe	(14-23)	281(210-335)	1	1	Po, Pr
17	Chinchilla (Chinchilla laniger)	4 mo	All yr[8]	Pe	28	(105-115)		(1-8)	
18	Chimpanzee (Pan troglodytes)	(8-9) yr	All yr	Pe	(34-35)	237(216-261)	1[3]		
19	Chipmunk (Tamias striatus)	(2.5-3) mo	Mar-July	Pe		31	(3-6)	2	
20	Deer (Cervus elaphus)	♂ 3.5; ♀ 2.5 yr	Sept-Oct	Pe		234(225-246)	1[3]		Po, Pr
21	Dog (Canis familiaris)	(6-8) mo	Spring-fall	Me	9	63(53-71)	7(1-22)[9]		Pr
22	Eland (Taurotragus oryx)		All yr	Pe	21	260(255-270)	1		
23	Elephant (Elephas maximus)	(8-16) yr		Pe	3-4[10]	624(510-720)	1		
24	Elk (Alces alces)		Sept-Oct	Me	14	(240-250)	1[3]		Po
25	Ferret (Mustela putorius)		Mar-Aug	Pe[6]		(42-45)	8.5	(5-13)	
26	Fox (Vulpes fulva)	10 mo	Dec-Mar[11]	Me	(2-4)[12]	52(49-56)	(4-9)		Po
27	Gibbon (Hylobates lar)	8-10 yr	All yr	Pe	(29-30)	210	1		
28	Giraffe (Giraffa camelopardalis)		July-Sept	Pe		(400-480)	1		
29	Gnu (Connochaetes taurinus)	♀ 2 yr	June	Pe		(240-270)	1		
30	Goat (Capra hircus)	8 mo	Sept-winter	Pe[7]	21	148(135-160)	(1-5)		Pr
31	Gopher (Geomys breviceps)	3 mo	Feb-Aug	Pe		(40-50)	3(1-9)	1-3	
32	Guinea pig (Cavia porcellus)	(55-70) da	All yr	Pe	16	68(58-75)	3(1-8)		
33	Hamster (Mesocricetus auratus)	(5-8) wk	All yr	Pe	4	16(15-18)	(1-12)	3	
34	Hare (Lepus americanus)	1 yr	Mar-Aug	Pe		30(30-38)	3(1-7)	1	Pr
35	Hedgehog (Erinaceus europaeus)	2nd yr	Mar-Sept	Me		(35-49)	5(3-7)	1	
36	Hippopotamus (Hippopotamus amphibius)		All yr	Pe	30	231(210-250)	1		
37	Horse (Equus caballus)	1 yr	All yr[13]	Pe[7]	(10-37)	336(264-420)	1		
38	Hyena (Crocuta crocuta)		All yr	Pe	14	(91-110)	1		
39	Jaguar (Panthera onca)		Sept-Oct			(93-110)	(2-4)		
40	Kangaroo (Macropus rufus)		Once a yr			(38-40)	1		
41	Leopard (Panthera pardus)		All yr			(92-105)	3(1-4)		
42	Lion (P. leo)	2 yr	All yr	Pe	21	(105-113)	(1-6)		
43	Lynx (Lynx canadensis)		Early Mar			60	(1-5)		
44	Marmoset (Hapale jacchus)	♀ 14 mo				146(140-150)	2(1-3)		
45	Marten (Martes foina)	2 yr	July-Aug	Me		(255-285)	(3-5)		
46	Monkey (Macaca mulatta)	3 yr	All yr[14]	Pe	28	164(155-180)	1		
47	Mouse (Mus musculus)	35 da	All yr	Pe	4	19(19-31)	6(1-12)	(4-6)	
48	Muskrat (Ondatra zibethica)	1 yr	Apr-Oct	Pe		30(30-42)	7(1-11)	2	Mo, Pr
49	Nutria (Myocaster coypus)	8 mo	All yr	Pe	(24-29)	(120-150)	10		
50	Otter (Lutra canadensis)	1 yr	Feb	Me		60	(1-4)		
51	Panther (Felis concolor)		All yr[15]			(90-93)	3	(1-2)	
52	Swine (Sus scrofa)	7(5-8) mo	All yr	Pe	21	114(101-130)	9(6-15)[9]		Po
53	Platypus (Ornithorhynchus paradoxus)	(1-2) yr	July-Oct	Me	60		2		
54	Porcupine (Erethizon dorsatus)	3rd yr	Nov-Dec	Me		112	1(1-4)		
55	Rabbit (Oryctolagus cuniculus)	(5.5-8.5) mo	All yr	Pe[6]		31(30-35)	8(1-13)[9]		
56	Raccoon (Procyon lotor)	1 yr	Jan-June			63(60-73)	4(1-6)		
57	Rat (Rattus norvegicus)	(37-67) da	All yr[16]	Pe	4-5	21(21-30)	12(4-20)	2	Pr
58	Reindeer (Rangifer tarandus)	1.5 yr	Sept-Oct			230(210-246)	1[3]		
59	Rhinoceros (Didermocerus sumatrensis)	20 yr	July-Oct	Me		210	1		
60	Sable (Martes zibellina)	2 yr	June-Aug	Pe	(9-12)	(270-285)	(1-4)		
61	Sea lion (Zalophus californianus)		June-July	Me		(348-365)	1		
62	Seal (Arctocephalus pusillus)	2 yr	Oct-Dec			(330-360)	2(1-2)		
63	Sheep (Ovis aries)	(7-8) mo	Fall[17]	Pe	(16-21)	151(144-152)	(1-4)[9]		Pr
64	Shrew (Sorex araneus)	2nd yr	Mar-Sept	Me		(35-49)	5(3-7)	1	
65	Skunk (Mephitis mephitis)		Mar		(9-10)	62	3-8		
66	Squirrel (Sciurus carolinensis)	(1-2) yr	Dec-Aug			44	4(1-6)	(1-2)	Pr
67	Tapir (Tapirus terrestris)		Seasonal[18]			397(392-405)			
68	Tiger (Panthera tigris)	1.5 yr	All yr			(105-112)	3(1-6)		
69	Vole (Microtus agrestis)	♂ 6-8; ♀ 3 wk	Feb-Oct	Pe		21(21-29)	4		Pr
70	Walrus (Odobenus rosmarus)	4-5 yr	Apr-July			365(330-370)			
71	Wapiti (Cervus canadensis)	3 yr	All yr[19]	Pe	21	255(249-262)	1[3]	1	Po
72	Waterbuck (Kobus ellipsiprymnus)		May-July	Pe	21	240	1		
73	Whale (Balaenoptera borealis)	2 yr	May-Aug	Pe		360	1		
74	Wolf (Canis lupus)	2 yr	Dec-Apr			63	(3-9)	2	
75	Woodchuck (Marmota monax)	? yr	Mar-Apr			28	4		
76	Woodrat (Neotoma micropus)		Apr-Dec	Pe		33	2(2-3)		
77	Zebra (Equus quagga)		Mar-Nov			(340-365)			

/1/ 274-280 days from 1st day of last menses, 267 days from ovulation. /2/ Twins in 83 births; triplets in 6,889 births; quadruplets in 571,787 births, etc. /3/ Usually. /4/ Ovulation in spring. /5/ Peak, July-Sept. /6/ Induced ovulation. /7/ Seasonally. /8/ Peak, late fall-winter. /9/ Differs with strain or breed. /10/ In captivity. /11/ Peak, late Jan-Feb. /12/ Period of sexual receptivity. /13/ Mainly spring-summer. /14/ Except summer; Oct-Jan, fertile months. /15/ Peak, Jan. /16/ Except winter. /17/ Few breeds all year. /18/ Prior to rainy season. /19/ Peak, Sept-Oct.

92. INCUBATION, NESTLING, AND PARENTAL ATTENTIVENESS: BIRDS

The amount of time or activity engaged in by each sex (as indicated in column headings) in nest building, incubation, or feeding and care, is represented by symbols ranging from 0 (no time or activity) to ++++ (100% of activity).

	Order, Family	Common Name	Nest Building Male	Nest Building Female	Incubation Duration da	Incubation Male	Incubation Female	Attentive Periods [1]	Male Feeds Female	Nestling Period [2] da	Male	Female	Trips per Hour [3]
	Struthioniformes												
1	Struthionidae	Ostriches	++++	0	42	+++	+	9-15 hr	0	0	++	++	
	Rheiformes												
2	Rheidae	Rheas			35-42	++++	0		0	0	++++	0	
	Casuariiformes												
3	Dromiceiidae	Emus, cassowaries			58-61	++++	0	Continuous	0	0	++++	0	
	Apterygiformes												
4	Apterygidae	Kiwis	++	++	75	++++	0	Up to 7 da	0	6	++++	0	
	Tinamiformes												
5	Tinamidae	Tinamous			21	++++	0		0	0	++++	0	
	Sphenisciformes												
6	Spheniscidae	Penguins	++	++	38-56	++	++	1-5+ da	0	56-112	++	++	1-2/da
	Gaviiformes												
7	Gaviidae	Loons			28-30	++	++		0	0	++	++	
	Colymbiformes												
8	Colymbidae	Grebes	++	++	21-27	++	++	0.5-5 hr	0	0	++	++	
	Procellariiformes												
9	Diomedeidae	Albatrosses	++	++	63-80	++	++	5.3-21.8 da	0	150-251	++	++	2-5/wk
10	Procellariidae	Fulmars, shearwaters	++	++	51-58	++	++	1-7 da	0	49-95	++	++	0.5-2/da
11	Hydrobatidae	Storm petrels	++	++	38-50	++	++	1-5 da	0	56	++	++	1/da
12	Pelecanoididae	Diving petrels	++	++	56	++	++	1 da	0	54	++	++	1-2/da
	Pelecaniformes												
13	Phaethontidae	Tropic-birds			28	++	++		+	62	++	++	2-3/da
14	Pelecanidae	Pelicans			28-42	++	++		0	14-35	++	++	3+/da
15	Sulidae	Boobies	++	++	42-45	++	++	1 da	0	45+	++	++	1+/da
16	Phalacrocoracidae	Cormorants	++	++	24-25	++	++	1-3 hr	0	35-42	++	++	1
17	Anhingidae	Anhingas				++	++				++	++	
18	Fregatidae	Man-o'war birds	++	++		++	++				++	++	
	Ciconiiformes												
19	Ardeidae	Herons, bitterns	++	++	18-28	++	++	1-6 hr	0	10-52	++	++	0.5-3
20	Scopidae	Hammerheads	++	++	21	++	++			42	++	++	
21	Ciconiidae	Storks	++	++	30-38	++	++	1-4.5 hr	0	63	++	++	5-11/da
22	Threskiornithidae	Ibises	++	++	21-24	++	++	6-18 hr	0	42+	++	++	12-20/da
23	Phoenicopteridae	Flamingos			30-32	++	++	12 hr		3-4	++	++	
	Anseriformes												
24	Anhimidae	Screamers	++	++	42	++	++	7-17 hr	0	0			
25	Anatidae	Swans, geese, ducks	+	+++	21-35	+	+++	4-23.7 hr	0	0	+	+++	
	Falconiformes												
26	Cathartidae	Vultures			39-56	++	++		0	56-70	++	++	
27	Accipitridae	Hawks	+	+++	28-56	+	+++	1-20 hr	+++	28-133	++	++	0.1-4
28	Falconidae	Falcons	+	+++	28-29	+	+++	3 hr	+++	25-35	++	++	0.3-5.8
	Galliformes												
29	Megapodiidae	Megapodes	++++	0	57-70	0	0		0	0			
30	Cracidae	Chachalacas	++	++	22-24	0	++++			0			
31	Tetraonidae	Grouse, ptarmigans	0	++++	21-27	0	++++	6-11.5 hr	0	0	+	+++	
32	Phasianidae	Quail, pheasants	++	++	21-28	+	+++	7-23+ hr	0	0	++	++	
33	Meleagrididae	Turkeys	0	++++	28	0	++++	23-24 hr	0	0	0	++++	
34	Opisthocomidae	Hoatzins	++	++									
	Gruiformes												
35	Mesoenatidae	Monias				+++	+		0		+++	+	
36	Turnicidae	Bustard-quail	++	++	12-13	++++	0		0	0	++++	0	
37	Pedionomidae					++++	0		0	0	++++	0	
38	Gruidae	Cranes	++	++	29-32	++	++	44-165 min	0	0	++	++	
39	Rallidae	Rails	++	++	19-24	++	++	38 min	++	0-2	++	++	
40	Rhynochetidae	Kagus	++	++	36	++	++						
41	Eurypygidae	Sun-bitterns	++	++	27	++	++		0	21	++	++	
42	Otididae	Bustards			20-25	0	++++			0	0	++++	
	Charadriiformes												
43	Jacanidae	Jacanas			23	++++	0				++++	0	
44	Rostratulidae	Painted snipes				+++	(?)						
45	Haematopodidae	Oyster-catchers			24-27	++	++	12 hr	0	0	++	++	
46	Charadriidae	Plovers	++	++	23-28	++	++	0.5-2.3 hr	0	0	++	++	
47	Scolopacidae	Sandpipers			18-29	++	++	11-15 hr	0	0	++	++	
48	Recurvirostridae	Avocets	++	++	23	++	++	10-66 min	0	0			
49	Phalaropodidae	Phalaropes	++++	0	20-21	+++	+		0	0	+++	+	
50	Burhinidae	Thick-knees			26-27	++	++		0	0			
51	Glareolidae	Pratincoles				+	+++						
52	Stercorariidae	Skuas, jaegers			23-26	++	++			0	++	++	
53	Laridae	Gulls, terns	++	++	20-34	++	++	0.5-24 hr	+	0-several	++	++	0.2-7
54	Rhynchopidae	Skimmers				0	++++		0	0	++	++	
55	Alcidae	Murres, puffins, guillemots	++	++	24-42	++	++	12 hr	+	2-49	++	++	
	Columbiformes												
56	Pteroclididae	Sand grouse			22-28	++	++	12 hr	0				
57	Raphidae	Solitaires			49	++	++						
58	Columbidae	Pigeons, doves	++	++	12-19	++	++	4-20 hr	0	10-35	++	++	0.2-1

/1/ Time bird sits on eggs at one sitting before leaving to feed and rest. /2/ Time from hatching until the birds leave the nest. /3/ Unless otherwise indicated.

92. INCUBATION, NESTLING, AND PARENTAL ATTENTIVENESS: BIRDS (Concluded)

The amount of time or activity engaged in by each sex (as indicated in column headings) in nest building, incubation, or feeding and care, is represented by symbols ranging from 0 (no time or activity) to ++++ (100% of activity).

	Order, Family	Common Name	Nest Building		Incubation					Feeding and Care of Young			
			Male	Female	Duration da	Male	Female	Attentive Periods[1]	Male Feeds Female	Nestling Period[2] da	Male	Female	Trips per Hour[3]
	Psittaciformes												
59	Psittacidae	Parrots	+	+++	17-31	+	+++	Continuous	++++	28-36	++	++	
	Cuculiformes												
60	Cuculidae	Cuckoos	++	++	11-18	++	++	0.5-1.5 hr	0	6-22	++	++	2-12
	Strigiformes												
61	Tytonidae	Barn owls			30-34	+	+++		+++	56-64+	++	++	1.4-2.0
62	Strigidae	Owls	++	++	27-35	+	+++	23.5 hr	+++	21-35	++	++	1-8
	Caprimulgiformes												
63	Caprimulgidae	Goatsuckers	0	0	16-20	+	+++	1.4-14 hr	+	0	++	++	3.7
	Apodiformes												
64	Apodidae	Swifts	++	++	17-21	++	++	32-75 min	+	20-42	++	++	0.7-2.5
65	Trochilidae	Hummingbirds	0	++++	16-17	0	++++	5-99 min	+	19-25	0	++++	1.1-3.3
	Trogoniformes												
66	Trogonidae	Trogons	++	++	18-19	++	++	2-16 hr	0	16-30	++	++	2.0-2.4
	Coraciiformes												
67	Alcedinidae	Kingfishers	++	++	21-23	++	++	1.7-24 hr	+	24-35	++	++	1.9-3.8
68	Momotidae	Motmots	+	+++	17-21	++	++	1-5 hr	0	28-30	++	++	4.0-4.8
69	Meropidae	Bee-eaters	++	++	22	++	++	15-30 min		30	++	++	
70	Coraciidae	Rollers			18-19	++	++			26-28	++	++	
71	Upupidae	Hoopoes			16	0	++++	11.5 hr	++++	29	++	++	1.9
72	Phoeniculidae	Wood hoopoes									++	++	3
73	Bucerotidae	Hornbills	++	++	28-40	0	++++	Continuous	++++	75	+++	+	1.6-2+
	Piciformes												
74	Galbulidae	Jacamars	+	+++	19-22	++	++	145 min	+	20-26	++	++	
75	Bucconidae	Puffbirds	++	++		++	++	58 min	0				
76	Capitonidae	Barbets	++	++	13-15	++	++	37 min	+		++	++	
77	Ramphastidae	Toucans			16	++	++	38 min	0	43-45	++	++	3.4
78	Picidae	Woodpeckers	+++	+	11-18	+++	+	22-147 min	0	19-35	+++	+	1-30
	Passeriformes												
79	Dendrocolaptidae	Wood hewers	++	++	15±	++	++	27 min	0	19	++	++	9.7
80	Furnariidae	Oven birds	++	++	15-20	++	++	22-97 min	0	13-29	++	++	2-4
81	Formicariidae	Antbirds	++	++	14-17	++	++	79-180 min	0	9-13	++	++	1.3-5.3
82	Cotingidae	Cotingas	+	+++	18-19	0	++++	12-37 min	0	19-25	++	++	
83	Pipridae	Manakins	0	++++	19-21	0	++++	111 min	0	13-15	0	++++	1.2
84	Tyrannidae	Tyrant flycatchers	+	+++	14-21	0	++++	9-57 min	+	12-24	+	+++	3.7-35.0
85	Menuridae	Lyrebirds	0	++++	28	0	++++			42	0	++++	
86	Alaudidae	Larks	0	++++	11-12	+	+++		+	9-12	++	++	5.9-8
87	Hirundinidae	Swallows	++	++	14-18	+	+++	6-33 min	+	18-28	++	++	4-40
88	Oriolidae	Old world orioles	+	+++	14-15	+	+++			14-15	++	++	
89	Corvidae	Crows	++	++	16-20	+	+++	35-94 min	+++	15-38	+	+++	1.7-4
90	Paradiseidae	Birds of paradise	0	++++	14-18	+	+++	16-36+ min	0	18-31	+	+++	12.9
91	Paridae	Titmice	++	++	13-15	+	+++	10-38 min	++	14-21	++	++	3.6-34.5
92	Sittidae	Nuthatches	++	++	15	0	++++	31 min	++	22-24	++	++	11.9-18.4
93	Certhiidae	Creepers	+	+++	15	+	+++		+	15-20	++	++	
94	Chamaeidae	Wren-tits	++	++	15-16	++	++	47 min	0	15-16	++	++	8.8
95	Timaliidae	Babbling thrushes	+	+++	21±	+	+++		+		+	+++	
96	Cinclidae	Dippers	+	+++	16	+	+++	31 min	+	19-24	+	+++	8.8-25.9
97	Troglodytidae	Wrens	++	++	14-19	0	++++	12-86 min	+	13-22	++	++	5.6-19.2
98	Mimidae	Thrashers, catbirds	+	+++	12-13	+	+++	20.8-22.7 min	0	11-14	++	++	3.6-14.2
99	Turdidae	Thrushes	+	+++	12-14	+	+++	12-120 min	+	12-18	++	++	5.5-38.5
100	Sylviidae	Old world warblers	+	+++	12-15	+	+++	11-80 min		9-14	++	++	10-33
101	Regulidae	Kinglets	++	++	14-17	0	++++		0	18-20	++	++	17.5
102	Muscicapidae	Old world flycatchers	++	++	12-20	+	+++	15-87 min	++	10-20	++	++	6.2-33.6
103	Prunellidae	Accentors, hedge sparrows	+	+++	12-15	+	+++	19-30 min	+	13	++	++	5.1
104	Motacillidae	Pipits	+	+++	13-14	+	+++	19-48 min	+	10-15	+	+++	3.6-25
105	Bombycillidae	Waxwings	++	++	12	+	+++	37 min	+++	16	++	++	3.0
106	Ptilogonatidae	Silky flycatchers	+++	+	15	++	++	9 min	+	18-19	+++	+	2.5-5.3
107	Artamidae	Wood-swallows	+++	+		+++	+		0		++	++	
108	Laniidae	Shrikes	++	++	16	+	+++	23 min	+++	15-21	++	++	
109	Prionopidae	Wood-shrikes	++	++		++	++	17-30 min			++	++	7-10.9
110	Sturnidae	Starlings	++	++	12	++	++	20 min	0	20-21	++	++	19-22
111	Meliphagidae	Honey-eaters	+	+++	13-18	+	+++		0	14-18	++	++	9
112	Nectariniidae	Sun birds	+	+++	12-13	+	+++				+	+++	20
113	Dicaeidae	Flower-peckers	+	+++		+	+++				++	++	
114	Zosteropidae	White-eyes	++	++	11-12	++	++		0	9-11	++	++	7
115	Vireonidae	Vireos	+	+++	13-14	+	+++	10-38 min	0	11-13	++	++	3.9-13.5
116	Coerebidae	Honey creepers	+	+++	12-14	0	++++	19-61 min	0	14-19	++	++	4.7-13.2
117	Parulidae	Wood warblers	+	+++	11-17	0	++++	23-110 min	+	8-14	++	++	1.6-27.4
118	Ploceidae	Weaver finches	+++	+	12-16	+	+++	14 min	0	13-19	+	+++	4-20
119	Icteridae	Blackbirds	0	++++	11-14	0	++++	9-30 min	+	9-34	+	+++	6.2-17.7
120	Thraupidae	Tanagers	+	+++	12-16	0	++++		++	10-24	++	++	
121	Fringillidae	Finches, sparrows	+	+++	11-14	+	+++	14.6-continuous	++	8-17	++	++	1.3-21.3

/1/ Time bird sits on eggs at one sitting before leaving to feed and rest. /2/ Time from hatching until the birds leave the nest. /3/ Unless otherwise indicated.

93. NESTING SUCCESS: SOME PRECOCIAL AND ALTRICIAL BIRDS

Precocial young are hatched covered with down and ready to leave the nest in a few hours. Altricial young are born blind and naked, and need parental brooding and feeding for some time; when they leave the nest they are covered with feathers and can walk or hop and are soon able to fly. In some respects fledging of altricials corresponds to hatching of precocials.

Part I: SUCCESS OF OPEN NESTS: ALTRICIAL SPECIES

Data adapted by Nice, M. M.

	Species	Nests			Eggs				
		Total	Successful		Total	Hatched		Fledged	
			Number	%		Number	%	Number	%
1	Mourning dove (Zenaidura macroura)	249	130	52.8	500			213	42.6
2		592	309	52.2					
3		4273	2043	47.9	8018	4379	54.6	3734	46.6
4		235	122	52.0					
5		204	142	69.6	398	310	77.8	274	68.8
6	Horned lark (Otocoris alpestris)	30	18	60.0	102	79	77.4	46	45.1
7	American robin (Turdus migratorius)	136	78	57.3	259	157	60.6	131	54.4
8		64	49	76.6					
9		176	86	48.8	548	316	57.8	246	44.9
10	Whinchat (Saxicola rubetra)	129	57	44.4					
11	Cedar waxwing (Bombycilla cedrorum)	60	46	76.7	245	189	77.1	171	69.8
12	Redwing (Agelaius phoeniceus)	67			214	156	72.9	105	49.1
13		356			1140	823	72.2	675	59.2
14	Yellow-headed blackbird (Xanthocephalus xanthocephalus)	128			443	314	70.9	99	22.4
15	Brewer's blackbird (Euphagus cyanocephalus)	107	53	49.5	521	327	62.7	205	39.3
16	Bronzed grackle (Quiscalus versicolor)	62	34	54.8	288	209	72.6	135	46.9
17	Goldfinch (Spinus tristis)	35	21	60.0	161	113	70.2	80	49.7
18		239			696	455	65.3	338	48.6
19	McCown's longspur (Rhynophanus mccowni)	45	27	60.0	153	92	60.1	71	46.4
20	Corn bunting (Emberiza calandra)	54			207			126	60.9
21		53	40	76.7	204			144	70.6
22	Chipping sparrow (Spizella passerina)	88	55	62.5	277	185	66.8	170	61.4
23	Field sparrow (S. pusilla)	593	226	38.1	1738	888	51.1	620	35.7
24	Song sparrow (Melospiza melodia)	147	77	52.4	585	389	66.5	243	41.5
25		76	30	39.5	321	147	45.8	80	24.9
26	Seven species	43	18	41.9					
27	Eight species	240	99	41.2					
28	Twenty-five species	246	101	41.0					
29	Ten species	30	20	66.6	145	93	64.1	70	48.3
30	Species (number not specified)	156			687	420	61.1	300	43.7
31	Eleven species	71			265	160	60.4	124	46.7
32	Six species	113			428	295	68.9	248	55.6
33	Eleven species				2151	1299	60.4	1010	46.9
34	Six species	121	57	47.0	421	257	61.0	170	40.4
	Summary[1]								
35	25 Studies, nest success	8034	3938	49.0					
36	24 Studies, hatching success of eggs laid				20,204	12,052	59.7		
37	22 Studies, hatching success of passerine eggs				11,788	7,363	62.5		
38	27 Studies, fledging success of eggs laid				21,115			9,728	46.1

/1/ The frequency of the percentages of hatching success in the 24 studies is: 1, 40-49; 3, 50-59; 12, 60-69; 8, 70-79. The median is 64.7%, in contrast to the 59.7% average of the 20,204 eggs. It is clear that this figure is biased by the low success (54.6%) of the 8,018 mourning dove eggs. Mourning doves build notoriously frail nests. Omitting the two mourning dove studies, the hatching success of the 11,788 passerine (song birds) eggs is 62.5%. The frequency of the percentages of fledging success in the 27 studies is: 2, 20-29; 2, 30-39; 14, 40-49; 4, 50-59; 3, 60-69; 2, 70-79. The median is 46.9%, which corresponds closely to the 46.1% average for the 21,115 eggs.

Part II: HATCHING SUCCESS OF SOME PRECOCIAL SPECIES: GALLINACEOUS BIRDS

Data adapted from Hickey, J. J., "Recent Studies in Avian Biology," edited by Albert Wolfson, University of Illinois Press: Urbana, 1955.

	Species	Place	Number of Nests	Per Cent Successful
1	Ring-necked pheasant (Phasianus colchicus)	Iowa	445	23
2		Pennsylvania	310	20
3		Ohio	563	58
4		Utah	149	36
5		Iowa	527	26
6	California quail (Lophortyx californica)	California	96	18
7	Bobwhite quail (Colinus virginianus)	Georgia, Florida	602	36
8		Texas	189	46
9	European partridge (Perdix perdix)	Michigan	143	32
10		Wisconsin	435	32
11	Summary: 10 studies on Phasianinae		3299	35.5
12	Willow ptarmigan (Lagopus lagopus)	Norway	125	63
13		Norway	107	80
14	Ruffed grouse (Bonasa umbellus)	New York	1431	61.4
15	Prairie chicken (Tympanuchus cupido)	Wisconsin	100	50
16	Sage grouse (Centrocercus urophasianus)	Utah	161	60
17		Colorado	238	35
18		Wyoming	134	34
19	Summary: 7 studies on Tetraoninae		2296	57.5
20	Total summary: 17 studies		5595	44.5

93. NESTING SUCCESS: SOME PRECOCIAL AND ALTRICIAL BIRDS (Concluded)

Precocial young are hatched covered wtih down and ready to leave the nest in a few hours. Altricial young are born blind and naked, and need parental brooding and feeding for some time; when they leave the nest they are covered with feathers and can walk or hop and are soon able to fly. In some respects fledging of altricials corresponds to hatching of precocials.

Part III: SUCCESS OF SOME HOLE-NESTING ALTRICIAL SPECIES
Data adapted from Allen, R. W., and Nice, M. M., American Midland Naturalist, 47:606-665, 1952.

	Species	Years Observed	Nests	Eggs	Hatched Number	Hatched %	Fledged Number	Fledged %
1	Tree swallow (Iridoprocne bicolor)	9	219	1123	928	83.4	679	61.0
2		3	352	1759	1424	81.0	857	48.7
3		3	80	430	310	72.1	303	70.5
4		2	37	184	163	88.6	123	66.8
5		8	60	363	358	98.6	340	93.7
6	Pied flycatcher (Muscicapa hypoleuca)	8	221	1074			789	73.5
7	Black-capped chickadee (Parus atricapillus)	2	11	74			53	71.6
8	Great tit (P. major)	5	202	1936	1653	85.4	1416	75.1
9		19	5011	45,466			29,529	64.9
10		2	66	460	425	92.4	340	72.4
11		2	623	6012	4579	76.2	3938	65.5
12	Blue tit (P. caeruleus)	5	183	1887	1548	82.0	1453	77.0
13		2		247	185	75.0	168	68.0
14		4	37	286	187	65.0	128	44.7
15		2	46	413	366	88.6	327	79.2
16	Coal tit (P. ater)	1	18	161	153	95.0	131	81.4
17	House wren (Troglodytes aedon)	19	1056	6673	5576	82.3	5351	79.0
18		3	34	211	135	64.0	118	55.2
19		6		469			339	83.7
20		21	64	333	199	59.7	161	48.3
21	Bewick wren (Thryomanes bewicki)	15	21	129			79	56.8
22	Bluebird (Sialia sialis)	11	1401	6260	3943	63.0	2786	44.5
23		2	86	377	302	80.1	274	72.7
24		3	301	1290			839	65.0
25		9	67	272	213	78.3	172	63.2
26		20	50	203	131	64.5	127	62.5
27	Starling (Sturnus vulgaris)			10,557			7923	75.1
28		6		472			410	84.5
29	Prothonotary warbler (Protonotaria citrea)	11	121	413	159	38.5	106	25.7
30		2	36	163	100	61.3	100	61.3
31	House sparrow (Passer domesticus)	6		114			97	78.5
32	Five species	2		755			500	66.2
	Summary							
33	22 Studies (7 species) on hatching success			30,276	23,537	77.7		
34	32 Studies (14 species) on fledging success			90,676			60,016	66.2

94. BREEDING HABITS: REPTILES

In many of the ovoviviparous forms there exists a type of placentation, verging in some cases on viviparity; however, to avoid confusion, the term viviparous is not used. All reptiles have internal fertilization. Values in parentheses are ranges, estimate "d" of the 95% range (cf Introduction).

	Species	Sexual Maturity[1] yr	Breeding Season[2]	Manner of Birth	Gestation or Incubation Time[3]	Broods[4] Size[5]	Broods[4] No./yr
	Crocodila						
1	Alligator, American (Alligator mississipiensis)	5-10	Jan-Sept	Oviparous	56-66	29-88	1
	Sauria						
2	Chameleon, false (Anolis carolinensis)	♂ 2; ♀ 1	Apr-Aug	Oviparous	6-7 wk	1	8-10
3	Gila monster (Heloderma suspectum)			Oviparous	30	5-13	1
4	Lizard, alligator (Gerrhonotus multicarinatus)		May	Oviparous	51-60	8-20	1
5	Lizard, collared-, western (Crotaphytus collaris)	<1-<3	May-June	Oviparous	8-13 wk	4-24	1
6	Lizard, night desert (Xantusia vigilis)	♀ 3	May-June	Ovoviviparous	3 mo	2(1-3)	1
7	Lizard, Pacific fence (Sceloporus occidentalis)	2	Mar-Apr	Oviparous	2 mo	9(6-13)	1
8	Lizard, sagebrush (Sceloporus graciosus)		Apr-May	Oviparous	62	2-7	1
9	Lizard, Texas horned (Phrynosoma cornutum)		Apr-May	Oviparous	39-47	23-37	1
10	Racerunner, common tessellated (Cnemidophorus tigris)		May-June	Oviparous	80	2-4	1-2
11	Skink, common five-lined (Eumeces fasciatus)	<2	May-June	Oviparous	4-9 wk	2-18	1
12	Slowworm (Anguis fragilis)	3-4	May-June	Ovoviviparous	3 mo	7-19	1
13	Uta, northern ground (Uta stansburiana)		Apr-May	Oviparous	61-67	2-4	1
	Serpentes						
14	Bullsnake (Pituophis catenifer)	<3	Apr-May	Oviparous	70(64-71)	3-19	1
15	Copperhead (Ancistrodon contortrix)	3-4	Apr-May	Ovoviviparous		142	2-10
16	Cottonmouth (A. piscivorus)		Mar-Apr; fall	Ovoviviparous	5 mo	3-15	1
17	Racer, western blue (Coluber constrictor)		May-June	Oviparous	1-2 mo	15-25	1
18	Racer, western striped (Masticophis taeniatus)	3	Apr-May	Oviparous			
19	Rattlesnake, Gt. Basin (Crotalus viridis)	3-4	Apr-June	Ovoviviparous	4-5 mo	3-13	0.5
20	Snake, brown (Storeria dekayi)		Mar-Apr	Ovoviviparous	4 mo	14(13-24)	1
21	Snake, common garter (Thamnophis sirtalis)	2-3	Mar-May; fall	Ovoviviparous	87-116	28(6-51)	1-2
22	Snake, hog-nosed (Heterodon platyrhinos)		Apr-May	Oviparous		8-40	1
23	Snake, mud (Farancia abacura)		July	Oviparous	110[6]	22-104	1
24	Snake, Pacific rubber (Charina bottae)	2-3	June	Ovoviviparous		3-5	1
25	Snake, water (Natrix erythrogaster)		Apr-May	Ovoviviparous	120-150	8-27	1
	Testudinata						
26	Terrapin, diamondback (Malaclemys terrapin)	5-6	Spring	Oviparous	3 mo	4-9	1-3
27	Tortoise, desert (Gopherus agassizii)	15-20	May	Oviparous	80-120	2-13	1
28	Turtle, Atlantic loggerhead (Caretta caretta)		Mar-July	Oviparous	31-65	120-130	2-3
29	Turtle, common box (Terrapene carolina)	3-5	Apr-May	Oviparous	88(70-114)	2-7	1
30	Turtle, common musk (Sternotherus odoratus)	♂ 2-3; ♀ 9-11	Apr-Oct	Oviparous	60-75	1-6	1-2
31	Turtle, common snapping (Chelydra serpentina)		Apr-Nov	Oviparous	81-90	25(8-80)	1-2

/1/ Males in some species mature before females. /2/ Varies with geographical distribution. /3/ Accepted average expressed in da; other values in wk or mo are approximations. /4/ Broods or clutch. Brood = young produced at one time; clutch = eggs laid at one time. /5/ Number of eggs or young. /6/ From one observation only.

95. BREEDING HABITS: AMPHIBIANS

Data should be considered with caution. Growth, particularly, may be modified greatly by changes in temperature, moisture, and light. Breeding data may vary when mating and egg laying are not concurrent but take place at the extremes of the cited season as, for example, with some salamanders.

Species	Breeding Season	Eggs or Young per Clutch	Fertilization	Place of Egg Development	Form at Hatching or Birth	Period of Growth to Sexual Maturity (da)		
						Egg	Larva	Adult
Urodela								
1 Eel, congo (Amphiuma tridactylum)[1]	May-Nov	42-150	Internal[2]	Terrestrial[3]	Larva			2-3 yr
2 Eel, mud (Siren intermedia)[1]		224-706		Aquatic	Larva			2 yr
3 Hellbender (Cryptobranchus alleganiensis)[1]	Aug-Sept	300-450	External	Aquatic[4]	Larva	64-84	540	5-6 yr
4 Mudpuppy (Necturus maculosus)[1]	Sept-June	18-180	Internal[2]	Aquatic[3]	Larva	38-63		5 yr
5 Newt; eastern (Diemictylus viridescens)[1]	Apr-June	200-375	Internal[5]	Aquatic[6]	Larva	20-35	80	2 yr
6 Salamander, Eschscholtz (Ensatina eschscholtzi)[1]	Oct-Apr	12-14	Internal[5]	Terrestrial[3]	Adult			
7 Salamander, European (Salamandra salamandra)[7]	July	12-72	Internal	-[8]	Larva[9]		90-150	4-5 yr
8 Salamander, four-toed (Hemidactylium scutatum)[1]	Apr-Oct	22-64	Internal[5]	Terrestrial[3]	Larva	38-60	48	2½ yr
9 Salamander, green (Aneides aeneus)[1]	May-June	10-26	Internal[5]	Terrestrial[3]	Adult	84-91		
10 Salamander, marbled (Ambystoma opacum)[1]	Sept-Jan	50-200	Internal[5]	Terrestrial[3]	Larva	30-180	180-240	410-510
11 Salamander, slimy (Plethodon cinereus)[1]	Oct-Dec	3-13	Internal[5]	Terrestrial[3]	Adult[10]			2 yr
12 Salamander, spotted (Ambystoma maculatum)[1]	Mar-Apr	To 250				31-54	61-110	2 yr
13 Salamander, tiger (A. tigrinum)[1]	Jan-Mar	23-110	Internal[5]	Aquatic[6]	Larva	24-30	75-118	360
14 Salamander, two-toed (Eurycea bislineata)[1]	Jan-Apr	12-41	Internal[5]	Aquatic[6]	Larva	60-70	2-3 yr	
15 (Hynobius chinensis)[11]	May	35-70	External	Aquatic[4]	Larva		60	
Anura								
16 Bullfrog (Rana catesbeiana)[1]	Feb-Aug	10,000-25,000	External	Aquatic[6]	Embryo	4-5	2 yr	2-3 yr
17 Frog (Zachaenus parvulus)[12]	July	30	External	Terrestrial[3]	Adv. tadpole		17	
18 Frog, Chilean (Rhinoderma darwini)[12]			External	Internal[13]	Adult			
19 Frog, chirping (Arthroleptella hewitti)[14]	October	36		Terrestrial	Adv. tadpole		10	
20 Frog, common (Rana temporaria)[7]	Feb-Apr	1500-4000	External	Aquatic[6]	Embryo	14-21	90-180	4-5 yr
21 Frog, cricket (Acris gryllus)[1]	All year	250	External	Aquatic[6]	Embryo	4	50-90	2 yr
22 Frog, leopard (Rana pipiens)[1]	Feb-Dec	1200-1500	External	Aquatic[6]	Embryo		60-90	1-2 yr
23 Frog, New Zealand (Leiopelma hochstetteri)[15]	December	6-18	External	Terrestrial[16]	Adult		30	
24 Toad, bell (Ascaphus truei)[1]	May-Sept	28-50	Internal	Aquatic[6]	Embryo	30	365	
25 Toad, common tree (Hyla versicolor)[1]	Apr-July	1000-2000	External	Aquatic[6]	Embryo	4-5	45-65	1-3 yr
26 Toad, Fowler's (Bufo woodhousei)[1]	Apr-Aug	8000	External	Aquatic[6]	Embryo	2-4	40-60	
27 Toad, narrow mouth (Microhyla carolinensis)[1]	May-Sept	850	External	Aquatic[6]	Embryo	2	20-70	2 yr
28 Toad, spadefoot (Scaphiopus holbrooki)[1]	Jan-Dec	100+	External	Aquatic[6]	Embryo	0.5+	18-28	
29 Toad, Surinam (Pipa pipa)[12]			External	Aquatic[17]	Adult			
30 (Discoglossus pictus)[7]	Jan-Oct	300-1000	External	Aquatic[6]	Embryo	2-4	30-60	
31 (Xenopus laevis)[14]	Sep-Oct	<100-1000	External	Aquatic[6]	Embryo	3	35-300	♂ ½, ♀ 2 yr
Apoda								
32 Caecilian (Typhlonectes compressicauda)[12]		6	Internal	Internal[3,18]	Adult			

/1/ North America. /2/ From spermatophore deposited by male in female cloaca. /3/ Protected by female. /4/ Protected by male. /5/ From spermatophore laid by male and picked up by female. /6/ No parental protection. /7/ Europe. /8/ Carried by female. Viviparous form. /9/ Or adult. /10/ Gills at hatching or disappear before hatching. /11/ China. /12/ South America. /13/ In female vocal sac. /14/ Africa. /15/ New Zealand. /16/ Sex of protector not determined. /17/ On back of female. /18/ Viviparous form.

96. BREEDING HABITS: FISH

Data should be considered with caution because spawning activities vary widely with such factors as the species, area, and temperature of the water. Number of eggs may vary with size of female. A = salt water; B = pelagic or buoyant eggs; C = demersal eggs; D = fresh water; E = fluviatile; F = lacustrine; G = anadromous; H = brackish water.

Species	Spawning Season	Locale and Type	Egg or Young	Number of Eggs	Type of Fertilization
1 Bass, largemouth (Micropterus salmoides)	Spring, summer	C D E F	Oviparous[1]	2,000-26,000	External
2 Bowfin (Amia calva)	Spring	C D E F	Oviparous[2]	23,000-64,000	External
3 Bullhead, brown (Ameiurus nebulosa)	Spring	C D E F	Oviparous[3]	2,000-10,000	External
4 Carp (Cyprinus carpio)	Spring, summer	C D F	Oviparous[2]	500,000-2,000,000	External
5 Cod, Atlantic (Gadus callarias)	Winter, spring	A B	Oviparous[2]	3,000,000-9,000,000	External
6 Dogfish, Atlantic spiny (Squalus acanthias)	All year	A	Ovoviviparous[2]	2-11	Internal
7 Eel, American (Anguilla rostrata)	Winter	A B	Oviparous	5,000,000-20,000,000	External
8 Eel, Conger (Conger oceanica)	Summer	A B	Oviparous[2]	3,000,000-7,900,000	External
9 Flounder, winter (Pseudopleuronectes americanus)	Winter, spring	A C	Oviparous	500,000-1,500,000	External
10 Gar, longnose (Lepisosteus osseus)	Spring	C D E F	Oviparous	36,500	External
11 Haddock (Melanogrammus aeglefinus)	Winter, spring	A B	Oviparous[2]	169,000-1,840,000	External
12 Hagfish, Atlantic (Myxine glutinosa)	All year	A C	Oviparous[2]	19-30	
13 Halibut, Atlantic (Hippoglossus hippoglossus)	Spring, summer	A B	Oviparous	2,183,000	External
14 Herring, Atlantic (Clupea harengus)	Spr., sum., aut.,	A C	Oviparous[2]	20,000-40,000	External
15 Lamprey, sea (Petromyzon marinus)	Spring	C D E G[4]	Oviparous[2]	236,000	External
16 Mackerel, Spanish (Scomberomorus maculatus)	Spring, summer	A B	Oviparous[2]	20,000	External
17 Mummichog (Fundulus heteroclitus)	Spring, summer	C D E H	Oviparous[2]	460	External
18 Pike, northern (Esox lucius)	Spring	C D E H	Oviparous[2]	10,000-100,000	External
19 Pumpkinseed (Lepomis gibbosus)	Spring, summer	C D E F	Oviparous[1]	Several thousand	External
20 Ray, southern sting (Dasyatis americana)		A	Ovoviviparous[2]	3-5	Internal
21 Salmon, Atlantic (Salmo salar)	Spring	C D E G[5]	Oviparous[6]	7000	External
22 Sea horse, northern (Hippocampus hudsonius)	Spring	A	Oviparous[1]	150	External
23 Shad (Alosa sapidissima)	Spring	C D E G	Oviparous[2]	100,000-156,000	External
24 Shark, hammerhead (Sphyrna zygaena)	Summer	A	Viviparous[2]	29-37	Internal
25 Shark, man-eater (Carcharodon carcharias)	Summer	A	Vivip. or Ovovi.[2]	9	Internal
26 Skate, little (Raja erinacea)	All year	A C	Oviparous[2]	6	Internal
27 Stickleback, three spine (Gasterosteus aculeatus)	Spring	D H	Oviparous[1]	100-150	External
28 Sturgeon, Atlantic (Acipenser sturio)	Spring, summer	C D E G	Oviparous[2]	1,000,000-2,500,000	External
29 Trout, brown (Salmo trutta)	Autumn, winter	C D E[5]	Oviparous[2]	200-6000	External
30 Trout, rainbow (S. gairdnerii)	Spr., sum., aut.,	C D E G[5]	Oviparous[6]	400-3000	External

/1/ Male guards nest or eggs. /2/ No parental care. /3/ Both parents guard nest or eggs. /4/ Dig shallow pits for nests on gravelly riffles. /5/ Clear, shallow, moving water on gravel nests or reeds. /6/ Eggs covered by gravel or sand.

97. BREEDING HABITS: AQUATIC INVERTEBRATES

Breeding habits of invertebrates vary with changes in location, temperature, light, and for marine forms, salinity. Asterisks indicate where data apply to specific locations providing the most complete information.

Species and Location	Sexual Maturity Age[1]	Sexual Maturity Size[2] mm	Eggs or Young per Brood	Type Sexuality	Breeding Season	Ovum Type
Xiphosura						
1 Crab, horseshoe (Limulus polyhemus), Delaware Bay area*	9-11 yr	♂ 178-258[3]	Few-1000	Dioecious[4]	Apr-July	Oviparous
Crustacea						
2 Crab, blue (Callinectes sapidus), Chesapeake Bay area*	♂♀ 13 mo	♂ 135-215[5]	1,750,000	Dioecious[4]	July-Aug	Ovigerous
3 Crayfish (Orconectes immunis), New York State area*	♂♀ 15 mo	♂ 40-60[6]	102(84-195)	Dioecious[4]	June-Oct	Ovigerous
4 Cyclops (Cyclops viridis), Germany*	♂ 41-132 da[7]	♀ 1.5-5[8]	75(20-160)[9]	Dioecious[4]	All year	Ovigerous
5 Lobster (Homarus americanus), Delaware-Newfoundland*	4-5 yr	♂ 17-60[10]	8500[11]	Dioecious[4]	July-Sept	Ovigerous
6 Waterflea (Daphnia longispina), northeastern U.S.A.*	♀ 75-86 hr	♂ 1.2; ♀ 1.9	28(4-35)	Dioecious[4, 12]	All year[13]	Ovigerous
Mollusca						
7 Chiton, gray (Ischnochiton magdalenensis), Calif.-Mexico	2 yr	35-36	57,970	Dioecious		Oviparous
8 Clam, hard shell (Venus mercenaria), Baja California*	1-2 yr	5-7		Monoecious[14, 15]	July-Aug	Oviparous
9 Clam, pismo (Tivela stultorum), Pacific area	5 yr	10-12	750,000	Monoecious[14, 15]		Oviparous
10 Clam, razor (Siliqua patula), eastern Pacific area*	2-4.2 yr	10-14		Dioecious[14]		Oviparous
11 Clam, soft shell (Mya arenaria), Arctic-N. Carolina; Pacific	1-2 yr			Dioecious[14]	May-Aug	Oviparous
12 Drill, oyster (Urosalpinx cinerea), Delaware Bay area*	15-25 mo	15-24	300-960	Dioecious[14]	Apr-Nov	Oviparous
13 Limpet (Acmaea digitalis), Alaska-Mexico				Dioecious[14]		Oviparous
14 Mussel (Mytilus edulis), cosmopolitan	1-2 yr			Dioecious	May-Sept	Oviparous
15 Nudibranch, red (Rostanga pulchra), California			9-156	Monoecious[14, 16]	Dec-Feb	Oviparous
16 Ormer (Haliotis tuberculata), Channel Islands-Europe	3 yr	5	10,000	Dioecious[14]	July-Sept	Oviparous
17 Oyster (Crassostrea virginica), Delaware Bay area	1 yr	25-50	½-1 million	Monoecious[14, 15]	June-Aug	Oviparous
18 Periwinkle (Litorina littorea), North Atlantic-Florida			1-3	Dioecious[14]		Oviparous
19 Scallop, bay (Aequipecten irradians), western Atlantic	12 mo	78		Monoecious[14]		Oviparous
20 Scallop, giant (Placopecten magellanicus), North Atlantic*	3-4 yr	50-70		Dioecious[14]	June-Oct	Oviparous
21 Snail, burrowing (Polynices duplicatus), northern U.S.A.-Mexico	2 yr	>12		Dioecious[4]	June-Aug	Oviparous
22 Snail, edible (Helix pomatia), Europe	33-39 mo		40-200	Monoecious[14, 16]	May-July	Oviparous
23 Snail, pond (Lymnaea stagnalis), Wisconsin	4-14 mo	50-60	6,000	Monoecious[14, 16]	July-Oct	Oviparous
24 Top-shell, great (Trochus niloticus), Indo-Pacific	2 yr	6-7		Dioecious[4]		Oviparous
25 Whelk, channelled (Busycon canaliculatum), Cape Cod-Mexico			360-6240	Dioecious[4]		Oviparous
26 Yoldia, file (Yoldia limatula), North Atlantic; Pacific				Dioecious[14]		Oviparous
Echinodermata						
27 Starfish (Asterias forbesi), Long Island Sound*	1-2 yr	60-210[17]	Thousands	Dioecious[14, 15]	June-Aug	Oviparous

/1/ At onset. /2/ Greatest dimension. /3/ ♀ 243-351; prosomal width. /4/ Sexual dimorphism. /5/ ♀ 134-185. /6/ ♀ 44-90. /7/ ♀ 36-128. /8/ ♂ smaller. /9/ In early summer. /10/ ♀ 18-48. /11/ Average difficult to obtain because females are disposed of before reaching maximum egg-laying age under present fisheries conditions. /12/ Parthenogenetic reproduction most of season and illustrated by remaining data. /13/ Except winter. /14/ No sexual dimorphism. /15/ Protandrous hermaphrodite: male organs appear first, later replaced by female organs. /16/ Cross fertilization. /17/ Dependent on food supply.

98. REPRODUCTION: INVERTEBRATES

Fertilization of the egg can be internal (Int) or external (Ext). Sex is indicated as monoecious (Mo) or dioecious (Di).

Phylum (Class) [Genus]	Fertilization	Reproduction Zygote	Reproduction Development	Adult Sex	Adult Form
1 Porifera (Calcarea) [Sycon][1]	Int	In mesenchyme of sponge.	Amphiblastula.	Mo	Sponge.
2 Coelenterata (Hydrozoa) [Obelia][1]	Ext	Free.	Planula-colony-medusa buds.	Di	Hydroid colony.
3 Coelenterata (Scyphozoa) [Aurelia]	Int	In folds of oral lobes.	Planula-scyphistoma-ephyra.	Di	Medusa.
4 Coelenterata (Anthozoa) [Metridium][1]	Ext	Free.	Planula.	Di	Polyp.
5 Platyhelminthes (Turbellaria) [Dugesia][1]	Int	In capsule.	Development direct.	Mo[2]	Planaria.
6 Platyhelminthes (Trematoda) [Fasciola]	Int	In capsule.	Miracidium-rediae-cercariae[3].	Mo[2]	Liver fluke.
7 Platyhelminthes (Cestoda) [Taenia]	Int	In capsule.	Oncosphere-hexacanth-cysticercus.	Mo[4]	Tapeworm.
8 Rhynchocoela [Cerebratulus][1]	Ext	Free.	Coeloblastula-pilidium	Di	Nemertine worm.
9 Rotifera [Philodina]	None	None.	Development direct.	Pf[5]	Rotifera.
10 Nematoda [Ascaris]	Int	In shell.	To juvenile stage in open; completion in host.	Di	Intestinal worm.
11 Bryozoa (Gymnolaemata) [Bugula][1]	Int	In body of parent.	Trochophore larva.	Mo[4]	Colony.
12 Bryozoa (Phylactolaemata) [Pectinatella][1]	Int	In body of parent.	Ciliated hollow larva gemmates.	Mo[4]	Colony.
13 Brachiopoda [Lingula]	Ext	Free.	Trochophore larva.	Di	Brachiopod.
14 Mollusca (Pelecypoda) [Venus]	Ext	Free.	Trochophore larva-veliger larva.	Di	Quahog.
15 Mollusca (Pelecypoda) [Anodonta]	Int	Develops in gills of parent.	Glochidium parasitic on fish gill.	Mo	Mussel.
16 Mollusca (Gastropoda) [Buccinum]	Int	In capsule.	Trochophore larva-veliger larva.	Di	Whelk.
17 Mollusca (Gastropoda) [Helix]	Int	In ground.	Development direct.	Mo[2]	Snail.
18 Mollusca (Cephalopoda) [Loligo]	Int	Encased in sticky secretion.	Development direct.	Di	Squid.
19 Annelida (Polychaeta) [Nereis]	Ext	Free.	Trochophore larva.	Di	Sandworm.
20 Annelida (Oligochaeta) [Lumbricus]	Int	In capsule.	Development direct.	Mo[2]	Earthworm.
21 Arthropoda (Crustacea) [Cambarus]	Int	Fastened to swimmerets.	Development direct.	Di	Crayfish.
22 Arthropoda (Insecta) [Romalea]	Int	Laid in ground.	Nymph stages.	Di	Grasshopper.
23 Arthropoda (Insecta) [Ephemera]	Int	Laid in water.	Aquatic nymph.	Di	May fly.
24 Arthropoda (Insecta) [Pieris]	Int	Laid on plants.	Caterpillar-pupa.	Di	Butterfly.
25 Arthropoda (Insecta) [Melolontha]	Int	Laid in ground.	Grub-pupa.	Di	Beetle.
26 Arthropoda (Insecta) [Apis]	Int	Laid in hive.	Larva-pupa.	Di	Honeybee.
27 Echinodermata (Asteroidea) [Asterias]	Ext	Free.	Dipleurula-bipinnaria-brachiolaria	Di	Starfish.
28 Echinodermata (Ophiuroidea) [Ophioderma]	Ext	Free.	Dipleurula-ophiopluteus.	Di	Brittle star.
29 Echinodermata (Echinoidea) [Arbacia]	Ext	Free.	Dipleurula-echinopluteus.	Di	Sea urchin.
30 Echinodermata (Holothuroidea) [Cucumaria][1]	Ext	Free.	Dipleurula-modified auricularia.	Di	Sea cucumber.
31 Echinodermata (Crinoidea) [Antedon]	Ext	Attached to pinnules.	Dipleurula-ciliated larva-stalked crinoid.	Di	Feather star.
32 Hemichordata [Saccoglossus]	Ext	Free.	Free larva, gradual change to adult.	Di	Tongue worm.
33 Chordata (Cephalochordata) [Branchiostoma]	Ext	Free.	Development direct.	Di	Amphioxus.

/1/ Also reproduce asexually. /2/ Cross fertilization. /3/ Miracidium free, sporocysts and rediae in snails, cercariae in water or on grass where they are picked up by ruminant. /4/ Self-fertilization. /5/ Parthenogenetic female.

Data are to be considered with caution because duration of stages varies seasonally, geographically and climatically; in some cases duration of pupal and larval stages applies only under summer conditions. Where insects breed all year regardless of season, the cycle is continuous.

E = egg; L = larva; N = nymph; P = pupa; A = adult; Cont. = continuous.

Species and Type Metamorphosis[1]	Eggs per Female	Duration, days				Over-wintering Stages	Generations per Season	Host[2]; Stage
		E	L or N	P	A			
		Anoplura						
1 Louse, cattle (4 species) [I]	30-50	10-30	9-15		10-30	Cont.	7-10	Cattle; A, N
2 Louse, human (3 species) [I]	50-300	5-21	7-10		10-30	Cont.	10-12	Man; A, N
		Coleoptera						
Beetle								
3 Black carpet (Attagenus piceus) [C]	42-114	6-11	238-638	6-24	32-72	L	<1	Fabric; L
4 Carpet (Anthrenus scrophulariae) [C]	32	10-18	66	14		Cont.	1-3	Fabric; L
5 Cigarette (Lasioderma serricorne) [C]	30	>6	>30	14-21	21	L	5-6	Dry food; A, L
6 Colorado potato (Leptinotarsa decem-lineata) [C]	>500	4-9	10-21	5-10		A	1-3	Potato, etc.; A, L
7 Confused flour (Tribolium confusum) [C]	300-400	4-14	>22	5-18	1000	A	5-6	Grain, flour; A, L
8 Dried-fruit (Carpophilus hemipterus [C]	>80	>3	28-120	>14	15		>8	Fruit; L
9 Drug-store (Stegobium paniceum) [C]			20-150	12-18		L	3-6	Dry food; A, L
10 Flea (Systena spp) [C]	500-900	5-8	14-21	10-14		A	2-3	Potato; A, L
11 May (Phyllophaga fisca) [C]		21	>730	30	21-28	A, L	³/₄	Crops, trees; A, L
12 Mexican bean (Epilachna varivestis) [C]	250-1200	5-14	20-35	10		A	3-4	Bean, cowpea; A, L
13 Red-legged ham (Necrobia rufipes) [C]	400-1000	>3	>17	>13	420	L	6-10	Meat, fish; A, L
14 Saw-toothed grain (Oryzaephilus suri-namensis) [C]	45-285	>8	>30	>6	180-1100	Cont.	6-7	Grain, fruit; A, L
15 Striped cucumber (Acalymma vittata) [C]			14-40	7		A[3]	1-4	Cucurbits; A, L
16 Borer, lesser grain (Rhyzopertha dominica) [C]	300-500						8-12	Wood, books; A, L
17 Cadelle (Tenebroides mauritanicus) [C]	436-1000	7-10	39-414	8-25	365	A, L	3	Grain, cereal; A, L
18 Curculio, plum (Conotrachelus nenuphar) [C]	41-175	4-10	17-48	8-30	‡365	A	1 to >1	Peach, apple, etc.; A, L
19 Mealworm, yellow (Tenebrio molitor) [C]	276	12-16	>600	18-20	60-90	L	>1	Grain; L
Weevil								
20 Alfalfa (Hypera postica) [C]	200-800	13-17	17-21	7-14	14-21	A, E	1	Alfalfa; L
21 Bean (Acanthoscelides obtectus) [C]	200	5-20	11-40	5-18	14-63	A	2-5	Bean; L
22 Cotton boll (Anthonomus grandis) [C]	80-200	3-5	7-12	3-5	30-300	A	4-10	Cotton; A, L
23 Cowpea (Callosobruchus maculatus) [C]	82-196	4-6	9-240	5-18	15	A, L	8-10	Dried pea; L
24 Granary (Sitophilus granarius) [C]	50-250	4-8	19-34	5-16	210-250	Cont.	8-12	Grain; A, L
25 Sweetpotato (Cylas formicarius elegan-tulus) [C]	7		14-21	7		Cont.	6-8	Sweetpotato; A, L
		Diptera						
Fly								
26 Horn (Siphona irritans) [C]	50-400	1-4	4-8	4-8	5-20	P	4-10	Cattle; A
27 Horse (Tabanus atratus) [C]	100-400	2-5	100-600	5-20	5-20	L	1-2	Animal; A
28 House (Musca domesticus) [C]	75-200	1-3	4-10	4-18	10-50	Cont.	4-18	Garbage, manure; A
29 Stable (Stomoxys calcitrans) [C]	20-100	2-5	11-30	5-20	5-30	P	4-10	Animals; A
30 Vinegar (Drosophila spp) [C]		<1	3-11	2-8	14	A, L	5-6	Fruit, vegetables; A, L
31 Grub, cattle (Hypoderma spp) [C]	100-500	3-10	250-280	1-25		L	1	Cattle; A, L
32 Maggot, seed-corn (Hylemya cilicrura) [C]	100	1-8	10-16	10-20	30-35	Cont.	2-5	Corn, bean, etc.; L
33 Mosquito (hundreds of species) [C]	100-1036	2-1800	5-15	2-5	5-300	A, L, E	1-17	Animals; A
34 Yellow fever (Aedes aegypti)		2-365	6	2-3	15-60	Cont.		
35 Screwworm (Callitroga americana) [C]	100-300	1-2	4-5	5-40	5-30	None[4]	2-12	Animals; L
		Hemiptera						
36 Bug, harlequin (Murgantia histrionica) [I]	75-100	4-15	40-60			A, N	3-4	Cabbage, etc.; A, N
37 Bug, squash (Anasa tristis) [I]	200-300	7-14	28-42		15-110	A	1	Squash, etc.; A, N
		Homoptera						
38 Aphid, melon (Aphis gossypii) [I] [5]		90-120	3-7		7-28	A, E	20	Cotton, melon; A, N
39 Aphid, pea (Macrosiphum pisi) [I] [5]		90-120	10			E or Cont.	7-20	Pea, clover, etc.; A, N
40 Cicada, periodical (Magicicada septendecim) [I]		42-49	13-17 yr		30-40	N		
41 Greenbug (Toxoptera graminum) [I] [5]	3-7	90-120	6-30		26-60	A, N, E	5-20	Small grains; A, N
42 Leafhopper, beet (Circulifer tenellus) [I]	300-400	5-40	25-52		120-150	A	3-5	Beet, bean, etc.; A, N
43 Leafhopper, potato (Empoasca fabae) [I]	60-90	10	14		30	Cont.	2-4	Potato, bean; A, N
		Hymenoptera						
44 Bee, honey (Apis mellifera) [C] [5,6]		3	8	9	35-40	A	1	
45 Sawfly, wheat stem (Cephus cinctus) [C]	50	7-10	300	7-10	7	L	1	Wheat, grass; L
46 Wasp, digger (Tiphia vernalis) [C]	50-75	8-9	120-180	180-240	30-42	P	1	Japanese beetle; L
		Lepidoptera						
47 Bollworm, pink (Pectinophora gossypiella) [C]	200	4-10	14-21	12-18	14	L	3-6	Cotton; L
Borer								
48 European corn (Pyrausta nubilalis) [C]	400	4-9	30-40	10-14	10-24	L	1-3	Corn, etc.; L
49 Peach tree (Sanninoidea exitiosa) [C]	200-600	7-48	270-380	16-25	4-16	L	1-2	Peach, etc.; L
50 Squash vine (Melittia cucurbitae) [C]	150-200	7-14	30	Winter		L, P	1-2	Squash, etc.; L
51 Sugarcane (Diatraea saccharalis) [C]	200	4-9	20-30	6-7	7-14	L	4-5	Sugarcane; L
52 Cabbageworm, imported (Pieris rapae) [C]	200-500	7	14	7-14		P	3-6	Cabbage, etc.; L
53 Earworm, corn (Heliothis armigera) [C]	1000	2-8	13-28	14	12	P	1-7	Corn, tomato; L
54 Hornworm, tobacco (Protoparce sexta) [C]	200-300	7	21-28	14-28		P	1-3	Tobacco, etc.; L
55 Leafworm, cotton (Alabama argillacea) [C]	400-600	3-20	7-21	7-21	10-24	None in U.S.[4]	3-8	Cotton; L
Moth								
56 Casemaking clothes (Tinea pellionella) [C]	>40	>6	30-100	10-90	7-28		1-2	Fabric, fur; L
57 Codling (Carpocapsa pomonella) [C]	6-100	4-14	15-72	7-40	3-20	L	>1 to >3	Apple, pear, etc.; L
58 Indian-meal (Plodia interpunctella) [C]	200-400	1-2	13-288	>8	18	L	3-6	Grain; L
59 Mediterranean flour (Ephestria kuehniella) [C]	116-700	>3	40	5-7	3-4		>6	Mill products; L
60 Oriental fruit (Grapholitha molesta) [C]	100-200	3-28	10-26	5-35	2-34	L	4-7	Peach, apple; L
		Mallophaga						
61 Louse, cattle biting (Bovicola bovis) [I]	20-50	7-30	15-25		10-30	Cont.	7-10	Cattle; A, N
		Orthoptera						
62 Cockroach, American (Periplaneta americana) [I]	200-1000	35-100	200-400		212-303	Cont.		
63 Grasshopper (many species) [I]	300-400	90-120	40-60		>30	E	1	Crops, grass; A, N
		Siphonaptera						
64 Flea (many species) [C]	50-400	2-13	7-30	7-35	8-150	Cont.	3-5	Animals; A
		Thysanoptera						
65 Thrips, gladiolus (Taeniothrips simplex) [I]	150	4-12	4-12	3-8	26-32	A	6	Gladiolus; A, N

/1/ [I] = incomplete metamorphosis (having external development of wings); [C] = complete metamorphosis (having internal development of wings until pupal stage). /2/ Host and/or food preference. /3/ Unmated. /4/ Migrates from warmer regions in spring. /5/ Parthenogenesis. /6/ Worker bees only.

100. OVUM MORPHOLOGY: VERTEBRATES
Part I: DIMENSIONS AND GENERAL CHARACTERISTICS
Ranges, where given, are estimate "d" of the 95% range (cf Introduction).
I = isolecithal; T = telolecithal; (+) = present; (-) = absent; NR = not recognizable.

	Species	Type	Polarity[1]	Diameter mm	Volume cu mm	Vitelline Membrane	Zona Pellucida[2] mm	Corona Radiata	Tertiary Membranes	Transport Time[3] da	Viability hr
1	Man	I	NR	0.089-0.091[4]		+[5]	0.019-0.035[6]	+	-	3[7]	24[8]
2	Armadillo	I		0.080		+	+				
3	Bat	I	+	0.095-0.140		+	0.090-0.110	+	-	>21	
4	Cat	I	+	0.120-0.130		+	0.012-0.115	+	-	4-8	
5	Cat, marsupial	I	+	0.240	0.001	+	+	-	+[9]		12-24
6	Cow	I	NR	0.135-0.157		±[10]	0.012-0.015	-	-	3-4	12-24
7	Dog	I	+	0.135-0.145		+	0.135	+	-	6-8	96-192
8	Ferret	I	+	0.116-0.132		±[10]	0.004-0.006[11]	+	-	5-6	30
9	Fish	T[12]		0.4-150	0.033-1.766						
10	Frog	T		0.7-10[13]	0.18-524[13]						
11	Goat	I	NR	0.140-0.145			0.0125	-	-	2.5-4	
12	Guinea pig	I	+	0.075-0.107		±[10]	0.012	+	-	3.5	<26
13	Horse	I	NR	0.099-0.141		+[14]	0.0135[11]	+	+[15]	4	24
14	Hummingbird	T[12]		(Shell 14 x 9.5)	113						
15	Lizard (Draco spp)	T[12]		5	65						
16	Monkey, rhesus	I	+	0.109-0.173		±[10]	0.0115-0.034[16]	+	-	3	<24
17	Mouse	I	+	0.070-0.087	0.00036	+	+	+	-	1.45	12
18	Opossum	I	+[17]	0.130-0.160[18]	0.001	+	0.004-0.008[11]	-	+[19]	2	
19	Ostrich	T[12]		(Shell 155 x 130)							
20	Platypus	I	+	2.5-4.5[20]	8.2	+	+[11]	-	+[21]		
21	Rabbit	I	NR	0.110-0.146		±[10]	0.011-0.023	+	-	2.5-4	6
22	Rat	I	NR	0.070-0.076		±[10]	+	+	-	3	<12-33
23	Sheep	I	NR	0.120-0.180	0.0018	±[14]	0.011-0.016	-	-	2-4	12-24
24	Snake (Python)	T[12]		120 x 60	195-226						
25	Swine	I	NR	0.120-0.140		±[10]	0.015			3-4	12-48

/1/ Of uncleaved egg. /2/ Values are mm membrane thickness. /3/ Time for ova to reach site of implantation or attachment. /4/ Unfertilized tubal egg with vitelline membrane only. With zona pellucida, 0.133; with corona radiata, 0.178-0.202. /5/ Very slight membrane, consists merely of cytoplasmic membrane of vitellus. /6/ Unfertilized tubal ova. /7/ Probably maximum time for non-segmenting ovum to reach uterine cavity. Time between fertilization and implantation, 6-7 da. /8/ Probably fertilizable for not more than 12 hr. /9/ Laminated albuminous layer and very thin shell membrane formed in the tube. /10/ Perivitelline space present. /11/ Homogenous and gelatinous. /12/ With meroblastic cleavage. /13/ Lower value for green frog, upper value for marsupial frog. /14/ Perivitelline space filled with finely granular material. /15/ In the tubal egg there is a thin albuminous coat. /16/ Clear, highly refractile membrane, sharply defined; inner third is pale iridescent blue. /17/ Determined by position of polar body. /18/ With shell membrane dimensions increase to 0.40-0.50 mm. /19/ Produced by secretory activity of oviduct, an albuminous coat 0.05 mm thick and a shell membrane 0.0012 mm thick. /20/ Shell up to 6.5. /21/ Well developed membrane, consisting of an albuminous coat (more than 2 mm thick), a shell membrane, and a parchment-like shell.

Part II: CYTOPLASM AND NUCLEUS

	Species	Cytoplasm	Nucleus
1	Man	Transparent, colorless, finely granular, vitellus completely fills the space within zona.	Central. 1st polar body extruded and maturation spindle formed before ovulation. Nucleolus with chromatin.
2	Armadillo	Deutoplasmic granules.	One or two may be formed with maturation spindle. 1st spindle formed in ovary. Four young develop from one egg.
3	Bat	Fat droplets, yolk vesicles. Mitochondria concentrated in cortex.	1st polar body formed before ovulation. Polynuclear ova.
4	Cat	Deutoplasm with fat globules. Mitochondria concentrated in cortex. Polyovular follicles.	1st polar body extruded before, and 2nd maturation spindle established at ovulation. Polynuclear ova.
5	Cat, marsupial	Yolk accumulated at animal pole.	Pronuclei in granular formative cytoplasm. 1st polar body extruded in ovary.
6	Cow	Scattered fat granules (0.001-0.004 mm).	1st polar body formed before ovulation. Polynuclear ova may occur.
7	Dog	Highly refractile fat globules, so dense that vitellus is dark. Mitochondria concentrated in cortex.	Membrane, nucleolus, and/or chromatin visible; ovum discharged from ovary while nuclear material in germinative vesicle form. Polyovular follicles, polynuclear ova.
8	Ferret	Highly refractile fat granules, so dense that vitellus is dark.	1st polar body formed before ovulation. Ovulation only after coitus.
9	Goat	Fine fat granules, evenly distributed.	1st polar body formed before ovulation.
10	Guinea pig	Small fat globules at vegetal pole. Mitochondria scattered. Golgi apparatus as fenestrated membrane at periphery.	1st polar body formed before ovulation. Polynuclear ova.
11	Horse	Highly refractile fat globules, so dense that vitellus is dark.	1st polar body extruded before ovulation.
12	Monkey, rhesus	Yellowish, fine yolk granules. Vitellus fills zona. Polyovular follicles.	1st polar body extruded before ovulation. Polynuclear ova.
13	Mouse	Yellowish granular material and scattered non-fat yolk globules. Vitellus fills zona. Mitochondria first appear concentrated in periphery. Golgi bodies more numerous toward one pole.	Clear non-granular nucleus in center. 1st polar body formed in ovary. Polynuclear ova.
14	Opossum	Usually elliptical. Yolk differentiated in 3 zones. Fat chiefly in middle or submarginal zone. In some, large fat vacuole occurs at one pole, usually opposite polar body. Polyovular follicles.	1st polar body given off in ovary. Chromosomes, as with all mammals, are short rods in the form of open ring. Polynuclear ova.
15	Platypus	Bulk is formed of yellowish yolk spheres, up to 0.036 mm, dispersed in peripheral and central zone. Latebra in center of yolk.	0.014-0.20 mm in diameter. Diffusely staining, vesicular in character, has faint reticulum, dark-staining vacuolated nucleolus. 1st polar body given off in ovary. Egg normally monospermic.
16	Rabbit	Transparent. Mitochondria first appear concentrated in periphery. Golgi material is loose network of thick threads at periphery.	1st polar body extruded before ovulation. Polynuclear ova.
17	Rat	Optically heterogeneous, not transparent. 2 or 3 vacuoles detectable near center.	1st polar body formed before ovulation.
18	Sheep	Yellowish granular material, dense, numerous non-fat yolk globules. Mitochondria first appear concentrated in periphery. Polyovular follicles may occur.	1st polar body extruded before ovulation. Polynuclear ova may occur.
19	Swine	Yolk heavy with fat. Polyovular follicles may occur.	1st polar body formed before ovulation. Polynuclear ova may occur.

101. OVUM CHARACTERISTICS: MAMMALS

Part I: SEQUENCE AFTER SPERM PENETRATION

Values are hours unless otherwise specified.

Animal	Starting Time[1]	Sperm Penetration	Second Polar Body Formation	Male Pronucleus Formation	Animal	Starting Time[1]	Sperm Penetration	Second Polar Body Formation	Male Pronucleus Formation
1 Man	O	<1 da		48 (?)	7 Hamster[2]	C	6-8[3]	>6	12-24[3]
2 Cat	C	2-3 da	Not < 22		8 Mouse	C	1/4-2	5-7	6-24[3]
3 Cattle	O		11-39		9 Rabbit	C	10-13	13-14½	14-18[3]
4 Ferret	C	6-30	<41	41-52	10 Rat	O	2-4	10-14+ (C)	14-35 (C)
5 Fox, silver	1st C	2-3 da	>3-4 da		11 Sheep	C			<36
6 Guinea pig	C	10	13½	12-31	12 Weasel[4]	1st C	<53-80	>74	53-80[3]

/1/ O = ovulation; C = coitus. /2/ Golden. /3/ Approximately. /4/ Long-tailed.

Part II: ZYGOTE CLEAVAGE RATES

Values are hours unless otherwise specified; those indicated with an asterisk (*) are approximate.

Animal	Starting Time	1st Cleavage Spindle	2-cell	4-cell	8-cell	16-cell	32-cell	Blastocoele Formation
1 Man	Ovulation							<5-8 da*
2 Cattle	Ovulation	27-32	27-42	31-54	50-83	4 da*	59-131*	8-9 da*
3 Ferret	Coitus	53-70	51-71	64-74	64-116	95-120*		4½-6 da*
4 Goat	Coitus	30*	30-48*	48-60*	85*	120*		5 da*
5 Guinea pig	Coitus	27-38	23-48	30-75	80-82*	107*		115*
6 Hamster, golden	Coitus		24-36*	48-60*	72*	66-72*		78*
7 Horse			24	30-36		98-100*		
8 Mink	1st coitus		3 da*	3-4 da	4-7 da	5-6 da*	7 da*	
9 Monkey	Ovulation		26-49*	24-52*		4-6 da*		
10 Mouse	Coitus	21-28	21-43	38-50	50-64	60-70*	68-80*	66-82*
11 Pony	Ovulation		24*	33*	53*	98*		
12 Rabbit	Coitus	24	21-25	25-32	32-40	40-47*	48*	75-96*
13 Rat	Coitus	24-35	1-2 da	2-3 da	3-4 da	4 da*		4½ da*
14 Sheep	Coitus		38-39*	42*	42-44*	3 da	4-5 da*	6-7 da*
15 Shrew	1st coitus		60-64	81				
16 Swine	Coitus	51*	25-51*	25-74*	90			5-6 da*
17 Weasel, long-tailed	1st coitus		70-85*	70-99*	99 hr- 8 da	8 da*	11 da*	11-15 da*

Part III. TRANSPORTATION OF ZYGOTE TO UTERUS AND TIME OF IMPLANTATION

Animal	Starting Time	Age or Stage at Entry	Implantation Time	Animal	Starting Time	Age or Stage at Entry	Implantation Time
1 Man	Ovulation		8-13 da	13 Hedgehog		8 cell	
2 Armadillo, 9-banded		Blastocyst	4 mo	14 Mink	1st coitus	8 da; blastocyst	25 da
3 Badger, American			2 mo	15 Monkey	Ovulation	By 16 cell	9-11 da
4 Badger, European			6 mo	16 Mouse	Coitus	66-72 hr[1]	4-5 da
5 Cat		Early blastocyst		17 Opossum	Coitus	Pronuclear stage;	24 hr
6 Cattle	Ovulation	3-4 da; 8-16 cell	25-35 da	18 Platypus		1 cell	None
7 Deer, European roe			4 mo	19 Rabbit	Coitus	72-96 hr[1]	7-8 da
8 Echidna		1 cell	None	20 Rat	Coitus	3½-5 da[1]	5-6 da
9 Ferret	Coitus	117-144 hr[1]		21 Sheep	Coitus	72-96 hr	9-11 da
10 Goat	Coitus	32 hr		22 Squirrel, ground	Coitus	4 da; 4 cell	4-5 da
11 Guinea pig	Coitus	3½-4½ da; 4-8 cell	6 da	23 Swine	Coitus	4-5 da; 3-4 cell	11 da or less
12 Hamster, golden	Coitus	2½ da; 4-8 cell		24 Weasel, long-tailed	1st coitus	11-15 da[1]	8 mo

/1/ Late morula early blastocyst.

Part IV: INTRA- AND INTERSPECIFIC ZYGOTE TRANSFER

Data are for zygotes of pre-implantation stages transferred to host genital tracts.

Donor	Host	Degree of Development	Donor	Host	Degree of Development
1 Cow	Cow	To term	10 Rabbit	Rabbit	To term
2 Cow	Rabbit	One cleavage	11 Rabbit	Mouse	One cleavage
3 Goat	Goat	To term	12 Rabbit	Rat	One cleavage; blastocoele
4 Goat	Sheep	Dead embryo at 45 da	13 Rabbit	Guinea pig	One cleavage ¦formation
5 Guinea pig	Mouse	None	14 Rat	Rat	To term
6 Mouse	Mouse	To term	15 Rat	Rabbit	None
7 Mouse	Rabbit	One cleavage	16 Rat	Mouse	None
8 Mouse	Guinea pig	Development in blastocyst shape	17 Sheep	Sheep	To term
9 Mouse	Rat	One cleavage	18 Sheep	Goat	Stillborn
			19 Swine	Swine	To term

Part V: POLYPLOID AND PARTHENOGENETIC ROUTES OF DEVELOPMENT

Type of Development	Possible Origin of Development Route[1]			Maximum State of Development Reported		
	2nd Polar Body	1st Cleavage	Sperm[3]	Age[2] — Mouse	Rabbit	Other Mammals
1 Diploidy, normal	Normal	Normal	Present	Normal development		
2 Triploidy	Suppressed	Normal	Present	9½ da embryo	Adult[4]	Pig: adult[4]
3 Tetraploidy	Normal	Suppressed	Present	3½ da blastula	4-cell	
4 Hexaploidy	Suppressed	Suppressed	Present	12-cell[5]	4-cell	
5 Polyploidy (evolutionary origin)				Adults[6]	Adults[6]	Man[4]; hamster (tetraploid); rat[4] (± triploid)
Parthenogenesis[7]						
6 Haploidy	Normal	Normal	Absent	3½ da blastula	8-cell	Ferret; 4-cell; guinea pig: 1-cell; sheep: 1-cell
7 Diploidy	Suppressed	Normal	Absent		Adult	Sheep: 1-cell
8 Tetraploidy	Suppressed	Suppressed	Absent		1-cell	

/1/ Suppression of 2nd polar body (= suppression of 2nd maturation division) can double maternal chromosomes. Suppression of 1st cleavage division can double maternal and paternal chromosomes combined. Presence or absence of sperm determines presence or absence of paternal chromosomes.
/2/ Embryonic age from coition. /3/ Gynogenesis (fertilization with genetically inactivated sperm) is classified as parthenogenesis (cf Fn 7).
/4/ Controversial results. /5/ Development route probable. /6/ Indirect evidence. /7/ Parthenogenesis = development of unfertilized ovum.

Because of space limitations, certain symbols are used to indicate the condition typical for the organism or class to which an organism belongs. In instances where there are exceptions to type within a class the symbol is followed by an asterisk (*). Symbols apply to the columns in the table as indicated in the following key:

EGG TYPE		CLEAVAGE		BLASTULATION		GASTRULATION		MESODERM	
Homolecithal	Ho	Holoblastic	HO	Coeloblastula		Emboly	EM	Ectomesoderm	EC
Telolecithal	Te	Radial	Ra	Equal	EC	Epiboly	EP	Endomesoderm	
Centrolecithal	Ce	Biradial or disym-		Unequal	UC	Polar ingression	Pl	Teloblastic bands	Te
		metrical	Bi	Placula	Pl	Unipolar	Un	Secondary bands	Se
MEMBRANE		Bilateral	Bl	Stereoblastula	St	Many-celled	Mc	Enterocoele	En
Viteline membrane	Vi	Spiral	Sp	Morula	Mo	Multipolar	Mp	Solid ingrowth	So
Zonal radiata	Zr	Meroblastic	ME	Stomoblastula	So	Delamination	DE	Mesenchyme	Me
Chorion	Ch	Superficial	Su	Superficial	Su	Simple	Si	COELOM	
Tertiary membrane	Te	Discoidal	Di	Discoblastula	Di	Coeloblastic	Co	Acoelomate	Ac
		Irregular	Ir			Morula	Mo	Pseudocoelomate	Ps
						Syncytial	Sy	Coelomate	Co
								Schizocoele	Sc
								Enterocoele	En

	Phylum (Class)[1] [Genus]	Egg Type	Membrane	Cleavage	Blastulation	Gastrulation	Mesoderm	Coelom
1	Porifera (Calcispongiae) [Scypha]	Ho		HO	EC, UC, Pl, So	EM, Sy		
2	Coelenterata[2] (Hydrozoa) [Tubularia]	Ho, Ce*	Te	HO, Sp*	St, Mo, Su*	All[3]		
3	Coelenterata[2] (Scyphozoa) [Aurelia]	Ho	Vi, Te	HO	St, Mo	EM, Mo		
4	Coelenterata[2] (Anthozoa) [Urticina, Actinia]	Ho, Ce*	Ch, Te	HO	EC, Mo	EM, Mp, Co		
5	Ctenophora (Nuda) [Beroe]	Ho		Bi	UC	EP	EC	
6	Platyhelminthes (Turbellaria) [Planocera, Yungia]	Te	Vi, Te	Sp	UC, Mo	EP		Ac
7	Platyhelminthes (Trematoda) [Polystomum]	Ho	Vi	HO, Di, Ir	UC, St		EC	Ac
8	Platyhelminthes (Cestoidea) [Taenia]	Ho	Vi	Ir		EP		Ac
9	Nemertea[4]	Te	Vi, Zr	HO, Sp	UC, St			Ac
10	Nemertea[4] (Heteronemertea)[5] [Cerebratulus]	Te	Vi, Zr	HO, Sp	UC	EM, Un	EC, Te	Ac
11	Nemertea[4] (Hoplonemertea)[5] [Tetrastemma, Prostoma]				UC*	Mc*		Ac
12	Acanthocephala (Archioacanthocephala)[5] [Macracanthorhynchus]	Te	Vi	HO, Sp	St	Un		Ps
13	Rotatoria (Rotifera) [Asplanchna]	Te	Te	HO, Sp*		Un*	EC*	Ps
14	Gastrotricha[6] [Neogossea]	Te		HO, Ir, Sp*	UC	Un		Ps
15	Nematomorpha[6] [Gordius, Paragordius]	Ho		HO, Bl		EM, Co*	EC, Me*	Ps
16	Nematoidea[6] [Ascaris, Parascaris]	Ho	Vi, Te	HO, Bl	EC, Pl	EP	EC, Se	Ps
17	Tardigrada [Macrobiotus]				EC	EM	En	Co, En
18	Chaetognatha [Sagitta]	Te		Ra	UC	EP	En	Co, En
19	Bryozoa (Entoprocta) [Loxosoma, Pedicellina]	Ho		HO, Sp	UC	EM	EC, Te*	Ps
20	Bryozoa (Ectoprocta) [Bugula]	Ho	Zr*	HO, Ra	UC, Pl	Pl, Un	Me	Co
21	Brachiopoda [Terebratulina]			HO, Sp*, Ir	EC	EM	En	Co, En
22	Phoronidea [Phoronus]				EC	EM, Un	EC, Me	Co, En
23	Enteropneusta [Saccoglossus]		Vi, Ch	HO, Bl, Ir*		EP	En	
24	Echinodermata (Crinoidea) [Antedon]	Te	Ch	Ra	UC	EM	Me, En	Co, En
25	Echinodermata (Asteroidea) [Asterias]	Ho	Ch	Ra	EC	EM	En	Co, En
26	Echinodermata (Ophiuroidea) [Amphiura]	Ho	Ch	Ra	EC	EM	En	Co, En
27	Echinodermata (Echinoidea) [Echinus]	Ho	Ch	Ra	EC	EM	En	Co, En
28	Echinodermata (Holothuroidea) [Synapta]	Ho	Ch	Ra, Su*	EC	EM	En	Co, En
29	Priapuloidea[6] [Priapulus]	Ho		HO, Ir				Ps
30	Annelida (Archiannelida) [Polygordius]	Te	Vi	HO, Sp	UC, Pl	EP	EC, Te	Co, Sc
31	Annelida (Polychaeta) [Nereis, Eupomotus]	Te	Vi, Zr[7]	HO, Sp	UC, St	EM*, EP	EC, Te	Co, Sc
32	Annelida (Oligochaeta) [Criodrilus]	Te	Vi	HO, Sp	UC, Mo	EM*, EP	EC, Te	Co, Sc
33	Annelida (Hirudinea) [Clepsine, Nephelis]	Te	Vi	HO, Sp	UC	EP	EC, Te	Co, Sc
34	Echiuroidea (Echiurida) [Echiurus, Urechis]	Te		HO, Sp	UC	EP	Te	Co, Sc
35	Sipunculoidea [Phascolosoma]		Vi, Zr	HO, Sp	UC, St*	Pl, Un	EC, Te	Co, Sc
36	Onychophora [Peripatus]	Te		ME, Su	St, Su	EM, EP	Se	Co, Sc
37	Arthropoda (Pycnogonida) [Pycnogonum]			ME				Co, Sc
38	Arthropoda (Scorpiones)[5] [Euscorpius]	Te		ME, Di	Di	EM, Si	Se	Co, Sc
39	Arthropoda (Acari)[5] [Trombidium]	Ce		ME, Su	Su			Co, Sc
40	Arthropoda (Araneae)[5] [Aglena, Argiope]			ME, Su	Su	Mp	Se	Co, Sc
41	Arthropoda (Branchiopoda)[8] [Branchypus, Artemia]	Ce	Vi, Te	ME, Su	Su	Mp	Se	Co, Sc
42	Arthropoda (Cladocera)[5] [Daphnia]	Ce	Vi, Te	Su	Su	Mc	Se	Co, Sc
43	Arthropoda (Ostracoda)[8] [Cypris]	Ce	Vi, Te	ME, Su	Su	Mp	Se	Co, Sc
44	Arthropoda (Copepoda)[8] [Cyclops]	Ce	Vi, Te	ME, Su	Su	Un	Se	Co, Sc
45	Arthropoda (Cirripedia)[8] [Balanus, Lepas]	Ce	Vi, Te	ME, Su	Su	Un	Se	Co, Sc
46	Arthropoda (Mysidacea)[5] [Mysis]	Ce	Vi, Te	ME, Su	Su	Mp, Si	Se	Co, Sc
47	Arthropoda (Amphipoda)[9] [Gammarus]	Ce	Vi, Te	ME, Su	Su	Si		Co, Sc
48	Arthropoda (Decapoda)[5] [Gallinectes, Astacus]	Ce	Vi, Te	ME, Su	Su	Si	So	Co, Sc
49	Arthropoda[9] (Symphyla) [Scolopendra]	Ce	Ch	ME, Su	Su	Si	So	Co, Sc
50	Arthropoda [Musca, Dytiscus]	Ce	Vi, Zr, Ch, Te[10]	ME, Su	Su			Co, Sc
51	Arthropoda (Hymenoptera)[5] [Platygaster]		Vi, Zr	HO, Ir				Co, Sc
52	Mollusca (Crepipoda) [Chiton, Ischnochiton]	Te	Vi, Zr, Ch	HO, Sp	UC, St	EM, Un	EC, Te	Co, Sc
53	Mollusca (Gastropoda) [Patella, Crepidula]	Te	Te, Ch	HO, Sp	UC, St	EP, Un, Mc	EC, Te	Co, Sc
54	Mollusca (Scaphopoda) [Dentalium]	Te	Ch	HO, Sp	UC	Pl, EP, Un	EC, Te	Co, Sc
55	Mollusca (Pelecypoda) [Unio, Dreissensia]	Te	Vi	HO, Sp	UC	EM, Un, Mc	EC, Te	Co, Sc
56	Mollusca (Cephalopoda) [Loligo, Sepia]	Te	Vi, Ch, Te[11]	ME, Di	Di	EM	Se	Co, Sc

/1/ Unless otherwise noted. /2/ Also called Cnidaria. /3/ Except EP. /4/ Also called Rhynchocoela. /5/ Order. /6/ Currently included in phylum Aschelminthes by many investigators. /7/ Identified by some observerers as zona radiata, by others as cortical cytoplasm. /8/ Subclass. /9/ Also called Myriapoda. /10/ Chorion present in parasitic forms. /11/ Fertilization membrane is formed as sperm enters egg.

103. CORPUS LUTEUM OF PREGNANCY: VERTEBRATES

(A)=time of maximum development; (B)=time of appearance of retrogressive changes; (C)=period during which ovariectomy is followed by abortion. Comparable data for corpus luteum during "normal" cycles are to be found under the appropriate designations in the footnotes.

	Animal	Corpus Luteum During Pregnancy	Fate of Theca Interna Cells
		Mammals	
1	Man (Homo sapiens)	(A) 7th-10th wk. (B) Gradually from 7th to 12th wk. (C) Up to 8th wk but also performed at end of 4th wk without abortion.[1]	Form paralutein cells. "K" cells may invade gland. Form 8% of pregnancy corpus.
2	Armadillo, nine-banded (Dasypus novemcinctus)	Large during period of delayed implantation. (A) At implantation. (B) Middle of pregnancy. (C) At time of implantation.[2]	
3	Baboon, Chacma (Papio porcarius)	(A) 3rd wk. (B) Falls after 4-5 wk, then constant for 26 wk. Disappears rapidly after parturition.[3]	Form the vascular reticular system.
4	Bat, big-eared (Corynorhinus rafinesquei)	(A) Shortly after attachment of blastocyst. (B) Early in pregnancy.	
5	Bat, little brown (Myotis lucifugus)	Pre-ovulatory luteinization of granulosa cells. (A) 4th-5th da.	No true differentiation of theca interna occurs.
6	Bat, vampire (Desmodus rotundus murinus)	(A) When blastocyst is present in oviduct. (B) After mid-pregnancy.	Do not participate in gland formation.
7	Cat (Felis catus)	(A) 10th-16th da. (B) 20th da. Rejuvenated during lactation and may persist for 6-8 mo from mating. (C) Up to 50th da.	Migrate into gland on 2nd da. Resume fibroblastic appearance after 3rd da. Some remain at periphery.
8	Cat, marsupial (Dasyurus viverrinus)	(A) 3rd da. (B) Persists for 7-8 wk (lactation) then declines. No trace after 4th mo.	May contribute connective tissues.
9	Cow (Bos taurus)	(A) 90th da. (B) 150th da. Central cavity present in gland; marked color changes occur. (C) Always.[4]	Invade luteal tissue from 6th da. May become connective tissue.
10	Deer, fallow (Dama dama)	(A) 30th da onwards. (B) Still active at 150 da.	Invade luteal tissue.
11	Dog (Canis familiaris)	(A) 18th da. (B) After 30th da. (C) During 1st half of pregnancy, at least. Remains throughout anestrus.	
12	Elephant, African (Loxodonta africana)	(A) Accessory corpora formed early or at ovulation. All retrogress at mid-term. (B) Replacement corpora persist until term, then decline rapidly.	Form an investing layer which retains its character after parturition.
13	Ferret (Mustela furo)	(A) 3rd-5th wk. (B) 3-4 da before parturition.	
14	Goat (Capra hircus)	(A) 30th da. (B) Slowly from 60th da. (C) Always.[5]	Invade luteal tissue but can be distinguished for several wk.
15	Guinea pig (Cavia porcellus)	(A) 20 da. (B) After parturition. (C) After mid-pregnancy.[6]	Hypertrophy and rapidly become indistinguishable from luteal cells.
16	Hamster, golden (Cricetus auratus)	(A) 2-3 da. (B) Rapidly after parturition. (C) Between 11th and 12th da.[7]	
17	Hedgehog (Erinaceus europaeus)	(B) During lactation.[8]	
18	Horse (Equus caballus)	(A) 14th da. (B) 35th-40th da followed by large crop of accessory corpora lutea which degenerate from 150th da. (C) Before 200th da.[9]	Incorporated in luteal tissue. May hypertrophy markedly in pregnancy.
19	Mink (Mustela vison)	(A) 10th-12th da. Inactive phase during delayed implantation. Persists through pregnancy and 4-5 wk post-partum.	Migrate into gland 10-18 hr after ovulation.
20	Monkey (Macaca mulatta)	(A) Up to 19th da as on 12th da. "Transition" stage 19th-24th da. (B) 25 da. (C) Up to 25th da.[10]	Retained until 4th da (not distinguishable 4th-6th da). As paralutein cells in pregnancy corpus.
21	Mouse (Mus musculus)	(A) 9th-11th da. (B) Present but active at parturition. (C) Throughout pregnancy.[11]	Proliferate actively during 1st da. Invade luteal tissue in relation to capillaries but may become connective tissue. No trace after 36-60 hr.
22	Opossum, Virginian (Didelphis virginiana)	(A) 3rd da. (B) 12-13 da; disappears by 3rd mo. (C) Always.[12]	Do not contribute any glandular elements.
23	Platypus (Ornithorhynchus paradoxus)	(A) Time of formation of blastocyst. (B) Shortly before egg is laid.	Invade luteal tissue and also remain in groups at periphery of gland.
24	Rabbit (Oryctolagus cuniculus)	(A) 8th da; maximum diameter at mid-pregnancy. (B) Resorbed slowly after parturition. (C) Always followed by abortion or resorption.	Invade corpus and said to form vascular and connective tissue.
25	Rat (Rattus rattus)	(A) 9th-11th da. (B) Slowly after parturition. (C) Throughout pregnancy but not always after 14th da.[13]	Early proliferation. May form luteal cells.
26	Seal, common (Phoca vitulina)	(B) Heavily vacuolated at parturition but persists for several weeks.	Remain as paralutein cells in early pregnancy.
27	Seal, northern fur (Callorhinus ursinus)	Luteal cells heavily vacuolated during delayed implantation. (A) Larger at 1 yr of age than at 2-3 mo. (B) Heavily vacuolated at parturition but persists for 2 mo more.	Remain as paralutein cells in early pregnancy but do not appear active during period of delayed implantation or from a few wk after.
28	Sheep (Ovis aries)	(A) Remains large from 14th da. (B) 120th-140th da. (C) May not be after 55th da.[14]	Invade luteal tissue but atrophy rapidly.
29	Shrew, elephant (Elephantulus myurus)	(A) At 10 mm embryo stage but continues to increase in size. (B) At 30 mm embryo stage.[15]	Form a core to everted corpus and may give rise to connective tissue.
30	Shrew, mole (Blarina brevicauda)	(A) At 3 mm embryo stage. (B) Rapid after 7 mm embryo stage; vanished at parturition.	
31	Shrew, water (Neomys fodiens bicolor)	Corpora merge with interstitial tissue at 4-8 cell ovum stage.	Enlarge in early pregnancy.
32	Swine (Sus scrofa)	(A) 75th da. (B) 110th da.[16]	Some invade luteal tissue early. Some remain at periphery of gland.
33	Whale, blue (Balaenoptera musculus)	Appears active during pregnancy. Degenerates after parturition but corpus albicans persists for many years.	Invade gland in radial strands. May become connective tissue after parturition.
34	Whale, caaing (Globiocephala melaena)	(A) Young corpus has heavily vacuolated cells. (B) Persists in degenerate form after parturition.	Some remain at periphery of gland.
		Birds	
35	Fowl (Gallus domesticus)[17]	Postovulatory follicle retrogresses rapidly with no lutealization of granulosa after 2 da.	Deposit collagenous fibers and later disappear.

/1/ (A) 6th da stage of maturity. (B) 10th da onwards. /2/ Breeds in July with implantation in November. /3/ (A) 7th-8th da. (B) 13th da. /4/ (A) 9th-10th da. (B) 14th-16th da. /5/ (A) 9th da. (B) 12th da. No trace by 6 wk. /6/ (A) 9th-10th da. (B) 11th da. /7/ (A) 2nd da. (B) Rapidly after 3rd da. /8/ Granulosa cells not luteinized; gland shrinks steadily to time of next ovulation. /9/ (A) 12th-14th da. (B) 14th da. /10/ (A) 8th da. (B) 13th da. Corpora aberrantia persist 23 wk. Accessory corpora in 17% of cycles. /11/ (A) 2nd-3rd da. (B) 3rd da. /12/ (A) 3rd da. (B) 7-8 da; almost disappeared by 20th da. /13/ (A) 2nd-3rd da. (B) After 3rd da. /14/ (A) 6th-8th da. (B) 14th da; trace by 24th da. /15/ (A) At mid-dense stroma stage of uterus. (B) At same time as pre-menstrual change in uterus. /16/ (A) 6th-9th da. (B) 13th-16th da. /17/ Also, cowbird (Molothrus bonariensis). Removal of ruptured follicle causes holding of oviduct egg beyond time of lay 1-7 da.

103. CORPUS LUTEUM OF PREGNANCY: VERTEBRATES (Concluded)

(A)=time of maximum development; (B)=time of appearance of retrogressive changes; (C)=period during which ovariectomy is followed by abortion. Comparable data for corpus luteum during "normal" cycles are to be found under the appropriate designations in the footnotes.

	Animal	Corpus Luteum During Pregnancy	Fate of Theca Interna Cells
		Reptiles	
36	(Amphibolurus muricatus)	(A) 1st-2nd wk. (B) 3rd wk; disappears 2 wk after laying.	May grow into gland to provide blood vessels and connective tissue.
37	Gecko (Hoplodactylus maculatus)	(A) At 30 somite stage. (B) At 33 mm embryo stage.	Play no part in gland formation.
38	Lizard (Lygosoma quoyi)	(A) About 2nd wk. (B) End of 2nd mo.	No ingrowth among luteal cells.
39	Lizard (Xantusia vigilis)	(A) 4th wk. (B) 8th-9th wk. Disappears 4th wk post-partum.	Surround corpus. May contribute vascular and connective tissue elements.
40	Lizard, blindworm (Anguis fragilis)	Persists during development of embryo.	Remain at periphery of corpus.
41	Lizard, green (Lacerta viridis)	Present during gestation.	May give rise to connective tissue.
42	Lizard, viviparous (L. vivipara)	(A) 1 mo after ovulation. (B) End of 2nd mo.	Form peripheral cellular layer at first. Later may give rise to supporting connective tissue of corpus.
43	Snake, brown (Storeria dekayi)	Maintained throughout gestation. (B) Degenerates slowly after parturition. (C) Resorption or abortion if performed in middle of gestation.	
44	Snake, garter (Thamnophis sirtalis and T. radix)	Maintained throughout gestation. (B) Degenerates slowly after parturition. (C) Normal delivery if performed late in gestation.	Contribute to supporting tissue of corpus. Luteinization of thecal cells.
45	Snake, N. American garter (Natrix cyclopion)	Maintained throughout gestation. (B) Degenerates slowly after parturition. (C) Normal delivery if performed in late pregnancy; resorption or abortion if in early or in middle of pregnancy.	
46	Snake, sea (Enhydrina schistosa)	Starts to retrogress slowly from 44 mm embryo stage.	Hypertrophy after ovulation and contribute connective tissue ingrowths to the gland.
47	Snake, sea (Hydrophis cyanocinctus)	(A) 195 mm embryo stage. (B) Degenerates after parturition.	Little distinction between theca interna and theca externa.
48	Turtle, box (Terrapene carolina)	Persists until egg laying. (B) Degenerated by 6-9 wk later.	Hypertrophy and form part of gland on inner aspect of theca interna and theca externa.
		Fish	
49	Dogfish, spiny (Squalus acanthias)	(A) Reduced to half-size when embryo 3.5-7.5 cm. (B) Advanced at 1 yr (fetus 12-20 cm); much reduced at birth.	Form mechanical support to gland cells; not glandular.
50	Ray, fiddler (Rhinobatus granulatus)	Each ovary can contain over 20 corpora in varying stages of development.	Hypertrophy and contribute to luteal tissue.
51	Shark, basking (Cetorhinus maximus)	Corpora lutea of ovulation probably formed (4-5 mm in diameter) which gradually diminish in size. Many smaller corpora formed by atresia which persist for long time.	Form thin sheath of flattened cells.

104. CHORIO-ALLANTOIC PLACENTATION: EUTHERIAN MAMMALS

Placentation of only a small percentage of total genera in each major zoological group has been studied, hence there may be many exceptions to the data in this table. Transitional types of placentation are placed with the closest major type. Developmental stages and accessory placental areas are not considered here. Data are based solely on the most prominent overall condition of the definitive chorio-allantoic placenta. Examples of main zoological groups (with common names in brackets) for each placental type are presented in Part II.

Part I: PLACENTAL TYPE AND TISSUES

	Placental Type	Maternal Tissues			Fetal Tissues	
		Endothelium	Reticulum	Epithelium	Trophoblast	Endothelium[1]
1	Epitheliochorial[2]	Present	Present	Present	Present	Present
2	Endotheliochorial	Present	Present	Absent	Present	Present
3	Hemochorial[3]	Absent	Absent	Absent	Present	Present
4	Hemoendothelial[4]	Absent	Absent[4]	Absent	Absent[4]	Present

/1/ Maternal endothelium is probably covered by a more or less delicate net of reticulum fibers functioning as a support rather than as a transmitting layer. This presumably forms the thick hyalin-like layer seen in some carnivores (raccoon). Thin and delicate reticulum probably likewise surrounds all fetal capillaries, but is infrequently stained and therefore remains unnoticed. /2/ Syndesmochorial type is eliminated, and the forms (antelope, cattle, sheep) usually included are presented with the epitheliochorial group. The definitive functional portions of the so-called syndesmochorial placentas are actually epitheliochorial in nature. However, evidence has indicated that the epithelium lining the maternal crypts of some artiodactyls is of trophoblastic origin. If this is finally substantiated, then these forms may be in a sense syndesmochorial or endotheliochorial in type. /3/ Hemochorial placentas may be either villous or labyrinthine in type or transitional between these two (trabecular). /4/ Studies by cytological and histochemical methods and the electron microscope have indicated the persistence of an extremely thin layer of plasmoditrophoblast and reticulum.

Part II: PLACENTAL TYPE AND ZOOLOGICAL GROUPS

	Epitheliochorial	Endotheliochorial	Hemochorial	Hemoendothelial
1	Insectivora (Scalopus[1]) [prairie mole]	Insectivora (Sorex[2], Blarina[2], Talpa[3]) [long-, short-tailed shrew, European mole]	Insectivora (most) [shrew, mole, hedgehog]	Lagomorpha [rabbit, pika]
2	Prosimii (except Tupaioidea and Tarsiiformes) [lemur[4]]	Chiroptera (Rhinolophus, Desmodus, Noctilio, Myotis, Rhinopoma, Pteropus, etc.) [bat]	Molossidae (in later stages) [free-tailed bat]	Rodentia (Geomyoidea) [pocket gopher, kangaroo rat]
3	Pholidota [pangolin]	Prosimii (Tupaia) [tree shrew]	Prosimii (Tarsius) [tarsier]	
4	Cetacea [whale, dolphin, porpoise]	Edentata (Bradypus) [sloth]	Anthropoidea [man, ape, gibbon, monkey]	
5	Perissodactyla [horse]	Rodentia (Pedetes[5], Castor) [S. African jumping hare, beaver]	Edentata (Myrmecophagidae, Dasypodidae) [anteater, armadillo]	
6	Artiodactyla[6] [ox, sheep, goat, antelope, swine, giraffe, camel, hippopotamus, cattle, deer]	Carnivora[7] [raccoon, dog, cat, ferret, bear, sea lion, seal]	Rodentia (most) [mouse[8], rat[8], squirrel, guinea pig, N. American porcupine]	
7		Tubulidentata [aardvark]	Hyracoidea [hyrax]	
8		Proboscidea [elephant]	Sirenia [manatee]	

/1/ Moles of the genera Parascalops, Scapanus and Neurotrichus appear similar but may be nearer the endotheliochorial condition. /2/ European and American shrews have been considered hemochorial. /3/ European mole passes through an endotheliochorial stage but reaches a hemochorial condition later. /4/ A small portion of the definitive placenta of Galago demidoffi (bush baby) is endotheliochorial. /5/ Only examples of this type thus far known among rodents. /6/ See Fn 2, Part I. /7/ See Fn 1, Part I. /8/ The late placentas of Myomorpha are apparently partly hemoendothelial.

127

105. SUMMARY: VALUES IN MAMMALIAN REPRODUCTION

Values in parentheses are estimates "d" of the 95% range (cf Introduction).

Part I: TIME INTERVALS BETWEEN VARIOUS PHASES

Species	Age of Puberty	Sexual Cycle Type[1]	Sexual Cycle Duration da	Duration of Estrus	Ovulation Time[2]	Ovulation Type[3]	Number of Eggs Released[4]	Copulation Time	Copulation Length	Sperm Transit, Vagina to Tube	Fertilization Time	Ovum Transport, Tube to Uterus da	Segmentation to Formation of Blastocoele da	Implantation or Attachment da	Gestation Period da
1 Man (Homo sapiens)	12-15.4 yr	Pe	27-28	2-8 da	15 da[5] (10-13)	S	1(BA)	Any-time[4]	15-30 min	3 hr		3[6]	5-8[7]	8-13	267[8]
2 Armadillo, 9-banded (Dasypus novemcinctus)	1 yr	Me				S		July-Sept				In stage of monodermic blastocyst		120	120[9]
3 Bat, greater horseshoe (Rhinolophus ferrumequinum)	15 mo	Me			April	S	1(right)	Fall, spring[10]							
4 Cat (Felis catus)	6-15 mo	Pe[11]	15-28	4 da[12] 9-10 da[13]	24-56 hr[14]	I	4-6(B)	3rd da[15]	1-2 hr		2 da[14]	4-8		13-14?	63(52-69)
5 Cattle (Bos taurus)	6-14 mo	Pe	14-23	14-18 hr	10-15.5 hr[16]	S	1(BA)[17]	Estrus	Seconds	6 hr	Few hr[18]	3-4	8-9	40-50	281(210-335)
6 Chimpanzee (Pan satyrus)	9 yr	Pe	34-35	2-3 da	20 (16-24) da	S		Any-time[19]						<10.5	(216-261)
7 Dog (Canis familiaris)	6-8 mo	Me	9	9 da[20]	1-3 da[21]	S	8-10(B)	Estrus	1-2 hr	20 min[22]	Several da[17]	6-8		13-14?	63(53-71)
8 Ferret (Mustela furo)		Me		Continuous[23]	30-36 hr[14]	I	8-9(B)	Estrus	1-3 hr	6 hr		5-6	4.5-6[7]	9-12	42
9 Fox, red, silver (Vulpes fulva)	10 mo	Me	2-4[24]	Continuous[25]	1-2 da[14]	S	3-4?(B)	Feb	15-20 min	8 min[14]	1-2 da[18]	2.5-4			52(49-56)
10 Goat (Capra hircus)	8 mo	Pe[11]	21	40 hr	End of estrus[7]	S	2-4(BA)	Estrus	Seconds	8 min[14]		2.5-4	7		148(135-160)
11 Guinea pig (Cavia porcellus)	55-70 da	Pe	16-19	6-11 hr	10 hr[21] Early estrus	S	2-4(B)	Estrus		15 min	Few hr[18]	3.5	5-6	6	68(58-75)
12 Hamster, golden (Mesocricetus auratus)	5-8 wk	Pe	4		Early estrus	S	?(B)	Estrus[26]				3[27]	3.25	5 or +	16(15-18)
13 Horse (Equus caballus)	1 yr	Pe[11]	10-37	4.5-9 da	24-48 hr[28]	S	1(BA)	Estrus	10-30 min	30 min	4	6-7		25	336(264-420)
14 Mink (Mustela vison)	8-9 mo	Pe[11]	8-9	2 da	36-50 hr[14]	I	7(B)	Estrus	0.5-2.5 hr		6-7	3	6-8	9[14]	45-60
15 Monkey, rhesus (Macaca rhesus)	3 yr	Pe	28	4-6 da	(9-20) da	S	1(BA)	Any-time[29]			3		6-8		(146-180)
16 Mouse (Mus musculus)	35 da	Pe	4	9-20 hr[30]	2-3 hr[21]	S	6(B)	Onset of estrus		0.25-1 hr	2 hr[14]	1.45	2.5-4	4-5	19(19-21)
17 Opossum (Didelphus virginiana)	8 mo	Pe[11]	28	1-2 da	Early estrus	I	10(B)	Estrus							12.5
18 Rabbit (Oryctolagus cuniculus)	5.5-8.5 mo	Pe	None[31]	1 mo or +	10 hr[14]	I	10(B)	Any-time[32]	Seconds	3-4 hr	2 hr[18]	2 2.5-4	3-4	7-8	31(30-35)
19 Rat (Rattus rattus)	6-11 wk	Pe	4-6	9-20 hr[33]	8-11 hr[21]	S	10(B)	1-4 hr[21]		0.5-1 hr		2.5-4	4.5	5-6	22
20 Sheep (Ovis aries)	7-8 mo	Pe[11]	16-21	24-48 hr	18-40 hr[21]	S	1-2(BA)[17]	Estrus	Seconds	5-6 hr	7-10 hr[14]	2-4	6-7	9-11	151(144-152)
21 Swine (Sus scrofa)	7(5-8) mo	Pe	21	2-3	30-48[21]	S	6-12(B)	Estrus	1-2 hr	4-6 hr	Few hr[18]	3-4	5-6	11 or -	114(101-130)

/1/ Pe = polyestrus; Me = monestrous. /2/ Values are, unless otherwise specified, time from start of sexual (estrous) cycle. /3/ I = induced ovulation; S = spontaneous ovulation. /4/ Ovaries involved in parentheses. B = both but alternately; BA = both; B = both. /5/ Before menstruation. /6/ Probably maximum time for non-segmenting ovum to reach uterine cavity. Time between fertilization and implantation, 6-7 da. /7/ Approximately. /8/ 274-280 da from first da of last menses, 267 da from ovulation. /9/ From implantation. /10/ Sperm stored in female from October to April. /11/ Seasonally. /12/ Presence of male. /13/ Absence of male. /14/ After mating. /15/ Of estrus; most receptive at this time. /16/ From end of estrus. /17/ Right ovary predominates. /18/ From ovulation. /19/ Most receptive, 15-18 da of sexual cycle. /20/ 9 da proestrus, 9 da estrus. /21/ From onset of estrus. /22/ From beginning of copulation. /23/ March to August. /24/ Period of receptivity. /25/ December to March. /26/ 8-10 P.M. /27/ Morula or blastocyst. /28/ Before end of estrus. /29/ Most receptive 2 da before ovulation. /30/ Begins 10 P.M.-1 A.M. /31/ Cycle indefinite; growth of follicles in waves of 16 da. /32/ Most receptive in estrus. /33/ Begins 4-10 PM.

Part II: MISCELLANEOUS OTHER DATA

	Species	Chromosome Number 2n	Age at First Breeding mo	Return to Estrous Cycle, Post-partum	Reproduction Interval	Optimum Breeding Period	Sperm Deposit Site	Sperm: Time of Transit[1] min	Sperm: Fertility in vivo[2] hr	Fertilization Site[3]	Placenta: Morphologic Type	Placenta: Histologic Type	Uterine Mucosa	Follicle Size, Ovulation	Ovum Viability, Unfertilized hr
1	Man	48								Oviduct[8]	Discoid	Hemochorial	Deciduate		
2	Cat	38	10[4]	2-3 wk[5]	Varies[6]	Varies[7]	Anterior vagina	100			Zonary to discoid	Endochorial	Deciduate		12
3	Cattle	60	15-24[4]	7-105 da	13-15 mo[4]	Mid-late estrus	Anterior vagina or cervix	2.5-140	to 28	Fallopian tube	Cotyledonary	Mesochorial	Semiplacenta	10-20 mm[9]	
4	Dog	78	6-8[10]	30-90 da[4]	5-12 mo	Estrus, every 2nd da[11]	Anterior vagina or cervix	20		Fallopian tube[12]	Zonary	Endochorial	Central band or zone	10 mm[9]	96-192
5	Goat	60	5-18[4]	Next season	Annual	Mid-late estrus	Anterior vagina			Fallopian tube	Cotyledonary	Mesochorial	Semiplacenta		to 30
6	Guinea pig	33	1.5-2	6-8 hr	Varies[13]	Late estrus	Uterus	15	22	Fallopian tube	Discoid	Hemochorial	Semiplacenta	0.8 mm	
7	Horse	60	24-36	9-11 da	12-24 mo	Varies[15]	Uterus				Diffuse	Epichorial	Nondeciduate	3.5-5.5 cm	
8	Mouse	40	2.5-3.5	2-4 da[14]	Varies[13]	Varies[15]	Uterus	to 15		Fallopian tube[16]	Discoid	Hemochorial	True	0.5 mm[9]	6
9	Rabbit	22	3.5-4.5[17]	Immediate	Varies[6]	May-July[18]	Anterior vagina or cervix	5-240	to 30	Fallopian tube[19]	Discoid	Hemochorial	True	1.8 mm[9]	
10	Rat	42	1.5-2.5	2-4 da[14]	Varies[13]	Varies[15]	Uterus	to 15	14	Fallopian tube[16]	Discoid	Hemochorial	True	0.9 mm	16-17[20]
11	Sheep	54	6-18[4]	Next season	Annual	Mid-late estrus	Anterior vagina	10-30		Fallopian tube	Cotyledonary	Mesochorial	Semiplacenta	15-19 mm	12-24
12	Swine	40	5-10[4]	3-4 da[4,5]	5-12 mo[4]	Late mid-estrus	Cervix			Fallopian tube	Diffuse	Epichorial	Nondeciduate	7-10 mm	to 12

/1/ From cervix to ovarian end of oviduct (Fallopian tube). /2/ In female genital tract. /3/ Implantation site: uterine horn. /4/ Variable. /5/ After weaning. /6/ May reproduce continually. /7/ Geographically influenced. /8/ Upper third. /9/ Diameter. /10/ Or first estrus. /11/ Also anytime after 4th da of estrus. /12/ Probably middle half. /13/ With strain or management. /14/ After removal of litter. /15/ With strain. /16/ Ovarian end. /17/ Fall born; spring born, 6.5-7.5 mo. /18/ In USA. /19/ Upper half. /20/ In oviduct.

Part III: SURVIVAL IN VITRO: SPERM

	Species	Method of Collecting Semen[1]	Diluent: Ratio	Diluent: Substance	Cooling °C/min	Storage Temperature °C	Storage Time[2]	Sperm-Extender Ratio	Insemination: Site	Insemination: Time	Volume cc
1	Cattle	A	1:1	2.9% Na citrate dihydrate: egg yolk[3] + 0.3% sulfanilamide + 500 μg/ml dihydrostreptomycin.	1	5	<48	<1:200 (>11,000,000 sperm/ml)	Cervix or uterus	End of estrus	1-2
2	Dog	A or M		None.			0	1:1	Cervix[4]	11-13 da[5]	1-10
3	Horse	A	5:1	5% glucose in H$_2$O: egg yolk.	1	5	<40	1:4	Uterus[7]	12-20 hr[6]	10-50
4	Mouse	A		Locke's solution[9]			0		Anterior of vagina	After mating[10]	0.02-0.10
5	Rabbit	S		Krebs' solution[9]			0		Cervix[12]	Estrus	0.25-1.0
6	Rat	S		Locke's solution[11]	1	5	<48		Cervix	Last half of estrus	0.1-0.2[13]
7	Sheep, goat	A		As cattle[14]			0	<1:11 (>11,000,000 sperm/ml) 1:2.5[15]; 1:5[16]	Cervix or uterus[4]	12-23 hr[6]	0.1-0.2
8	Swine	A		Krebs' solution.							50[15], 250[16]

/1/ A=artificial vagina; M=manual manipulation; S=stripping sperm from vas deferens. /2/ 0=use immediately without storage. /3/ Fresh. /4/ Place cotton plug in vagina after insemination. /5/ After first bleeding. /6/ After onset of estrus. /7/ By laparotomy, female under ether anesthesia. /8/ After mating with vasectomized male. /9/ Modified. /10/ With vasectomized buck. /11/ Dilution must produce thick, viscid suspension. /12/ Female anesthetized; plug vagina with cotton dipped into secretions from seminal vesicles and coagulating fluid. /13/ Into each cervical canal. /14/ Necessity of bacterial antigens unknown. /15/ Gilts. /16/ Sows.

106. PREGNANCY TESTS: MAN

	Test[1]	Test Animals	Duration of Test	Source of Test Material	Substance Tested For:	Earliest Positive Indications	Positive Diagnostic Findings	Accuracy[2] False % +	Accuracy[2] False % -	Remarks
1	Aschheim-Zondek	3-4 female mice, 3-4 wk old; 6-8 g	96-100 hr	1st morning urine.	Chorionic gonadotropin.	10 da-2 wk after 1st missed menses.	Hemorrhagic follicles on ovary; corpora lutea containing entrapped ovum.	6	3.5	Sensitive; accurate; reliable; expensive(?); time consuming; occasional false positives caused by maturation of mouse ovaries[3].
2	Ovarian hyperemia[4]	2-3 immature female rats; 45-60 g	1-24 hr	1st morning urine.	Chorionic gonadotropin.	1-2 wk after 1st missed menses.	Ovary usually enlarged; diffuse reddening or many distinct red spots.	1-2	10	Difficult end point; false negatives are common; very rapid test[4].
3	Friedman	Mature female rabbits, 3-4 lb; previously isolated 4 wk	18-24 hr	1st morning urine.	Chorionic gonadotropin.	1-2 wk after 1st missed menses.	Early corpora lutea; ova can be washed from tubes; hemorrhagic follicles.	1	2-3	Animals need not be sacrificed; rapid but expensive test.
4	Galli-Mainini	Male frog (Rana pipiens) or male toad (Bufo arenarum)	10-120 min	1st morning urine, or blood serum.	Chorionic gonadotropin.	2 wk after 1st missed menses.	Spermatozoa in urine collected from cloacal region; examined microscopically pre- and post-injection.	0(?)[5]	25	Less sensitive in summer months, in early pregnancy, presence of jaundice; inexpensive; animals need not be sacrificed.
5	Hogben	Segregated female S. African clawed "toad" (Xenopus laevis)	5-18 hr	1st morning urine.	Chorionic gonadotropin.	1-2 wk after 1st missed menses.	Presence of egg mass on floor of container housing toad.	0.6	0.26	Simple end point; animals need not be sacrificed and may be used repeatedly; rapid, accurate test.
6	Delfs	Immature female rats, 21-23 da old; 34-42 g	72-96 hr	Blood serum; pooled urine.	Total chorionic gonadotropin.	After 1st missed menses.	Uterine weight increase (vs controls) determined at 72 hr post-injection.	17	24	Used primarily as quantitative assay (in trained hands) of chorionic gonadotropin levels.
7	Guterman		3 hr	1st morning urine.	Pregnanediol.	At time of 1st missed menses.	Development of color complex; orange to deep orange-brown with sulfuric acid.	7-8	8-9	Valuable(?) in abortion and hydatidiform mole; false positives: (a) late in menstrual cycle; (b) progesterone treatment; (c) luteal cysts; (d) pseudocyesis.
8	Kapeller-Adler		½ hr	1st morning urine.	Histidine.	1st wk after missed menses.	Colorimetric qualitative and quantitative.	10	11	Simple; inexpensive; urine constituents alter color reaction as do catabolic products in urine. Non-specific(?).
9	Visscher-Bowman		½ hr	1st morning urine.	Chorionic gonadotropin(?).	After 1st missed menses.	Russet color reaction with flocculation.	8	11	Simple; inexpensive; false positives: (a) in fever; (b) excess of catabolic products in urine. Non-specific(?).
10	Gilfillen-Gregg		½-1 hr	Injection of chorionic gonadotropin.		After 1st missed menses.	No skin reaction in pregnancy, i.e., hypoallergy to chorionic gonadotropin.	22	13	Simple, but interpretation difficult; limited in Negroes.
11	Basal temperature deviations			Temperature, rectal or oral.		Ante- and post-conception observation.	Luteal phase temperature sustained for more than 16 da (preceded by a characteristic biphasic curve)[7].	0(?)		Early diagnosis of pregnancy; false positives: (a) mild febrile illness; (b) changes in climate; (c) pseudocyesis; (d) persistent corpus luteum.
12	Schwartz		3-7 da	Estrone and progesterone injections daily, or oral estrogen and progesterone.		At time of 1st missed menses.	Continued amenorrhea with otherwise normal menstrual cycles and no demonstrable pelvic disease.	High degree of accuracy		Simple; inexpensive(?); false positives: (a) ectopic pregnancy when patient is spotting; (b) amenorrhea of more than 6 mo duration; (c) pseudocyesis; (d) persistent corpus luteum.
13	Richardson		½ hr	1st morning urine; blood serum or saliva.	Estrogens.	At time of 1st missed menses.	Development of color complex with phenylhydrazone, phenylsulfone.	2	2	False positives in hyperestronism; ovarian tumor; of value in diagnosis of hydatidiform mole. Non-specificity(?) can cause false reactions.
14	Colostrum "Q"		1 hr	Colostrum.	Immune reaction to protein of colostrum.	2 wk after 1st missed menses.	Pregnancy: disappearance of original wheal in 30 min. Non-pregnant: enlargement of wheal 2-3 times with red areola.	5	2	Unreliable in hyperallergic individuals and Negroes; false positives in menopause and during menstrual period.

1/ Tests 1-6, 9(?) depend on physiological reactions of test animal to chorionic gonadotropin present in pregnancy urine. 2/ Claimed. 3/ False positives may also occur during depression of ovarian function (e.g., menopause). 4/ A recent modification of this test involves the addition of a pituitary synergist; the duration of the test is reduced to 1-3 hr, false positives to 0.1%, false negatives to 2%, and the end point is much more definite. 5/ False positives have been reported, and a percentage of false negatives as high as 16. 6/ False positives of 1%, and false negatives up to 4% have been reported. 7/ The luteal phase is partially biphasic.

Terms followed by an asterisk (*) are defined in the Glossary Part VI.

Part I: LIFE CYCLE, SEXUALITY, AND SEXUAL MECHANISM: ALGAE

Data in columns B and D refer to the corresponding patterns presented in Parts III and V. In column C, M = monoecious*; D = dioecious*.

#	Species (A)	Life Cycle Type (B)	Pattern of Sexuality (C)	Sexual Mechanism and Development (D)	#	Species (A)	Life Cycle Type (B)	Pattern of Sexuality (C)	Sexual Mechanism and Development (D)
	Chlorophyta					Chrysophyta			
1	Chlamydomonas paupera	B	M	3-5-10	32	Xanthophyceae, most spp	A		
2	C. eugametos	B	D	3-5-10	33	Botrydium granulatum	B	M & D^4	3-7-9-10
3	Volvox aureus	B	D^1	3-7-9-10	34	Vaucheria sessilis	B	M	3-8-9-10
4	V. globator	B	M	3-7-9-10	35	V. dichotoma	B	D	3-8-9-10
5	Tetraspora lubrica	B	D	3-7-9-10	36	Chrysophyceae, most spp	A		
6	Sphaerocystis schroeterii	A			37	Ochrosphaera neopolitana	B	M	3-7-9-10
7	Chlorella vulgaris	A			38	Centrales, most spp	A		
8	Chlorococcum humicolor	B	M	3-7-9-10	39	Cyclotella meneghiniana	G	M	1-10
9	Dictyosphaerium indicum	B	D	3-7-9-10	40	Amphora normani	G	M	1-10
10	Hydrodictyon reticulatum	B	M	3-7-9-10	41	Rhopalodia gibba	G	D	1-10
11	Protosiphon botryoides	B	M	3-7-9-10		Pyrrophyta			
12	Chlorochytridium lemnae	G	?	1-10	42	Peridinium wisconsinensis	A		
13	Ulothrix rorida	B	M	3-7-9-10		Phaeophyta			
14	U. zonata	B	D	3-7-9-10	43	Pylaiella rupincola	A		
15	Ulva lactuca	F	D	3-7-9-10	44	Ectocarpus siliculosus	F	D	3-8-9-10
16	Cladophora suhrina	F	D	3-7-9-10	45	Sphacelaria bipinnata	F	M	3-8-9-10
17	C. glomerata	G	M	1-10	46	Lamanaria saccharina	F	D	3-8-9-10
18	Protococcus viridis	A	.		47	Pelvetia fastigiata	G^5	M	1-10
19	Draparnaldiopsis indica	F	D	3-7-9-10	48	Fucus vesiculosus	G^5	D	1-10
20	Coleochaete pulvinata	B	M	3-8-9-10		Rhodophyta			
21	C. scutata	B	D	3-8-9-10	49	Rhodospora	A		
22	Oedogonium kurzii	B	M	3-7-9-10	50	Porphyra elongata	B	M	3-7-9-11
23	O. grande	B	D	3-7-9-10	51	P. dentata	B	D	3-7-9-11
24	O. crassiusculum	B	M	See Fn 2	52	Batrachospermum moniliforme	B	M	3-8-9-11
25	O. spirale	B	D	See Fn 2	53	B. elegans	B	D	3-8-9-11
26	Spirogyra setiformis	B	D	$(3)-7-12^3$	54	Polysiphonia violacea	F	D	3-8-9-11
27	S. granulata	B	M	(3)-7-12	55	Griffithsia barbata	F	M	3-8-9-11
28	Dasycladus clavaeformis	G	D^4	1-10		Cyanophyta			
29	Bryopsis pulvinata	G	M	1-10	56	All species	A		
30	Chara fragilis	B	M	3-8-9-10					
31	Nitella capitata	B							

/1/ Dioecism is not absolute; colonies with both eggs and sperm have been reported. /2/ Species produces, in lieu of antheridia, specialized swarmers (androspores) which come to rest upon or near the oögonium and develop into dwarf male plants, each of which bears 1 to 4 antheridia. /3/ The fusing elements of the species are commonly termed gametes but are here considered gametangia because of the low degree of morphological differentiation. The copulatory process in these forms approaches somatic copulation, the sexual fusion of vegetative cells common in higher fungi. /4/ Species includes monoecious and dioecious varieties. /5/ Species commonly with 2 haploid nuclear generations in the oögonium and 4 in the antheridium.

Part II: LIFE CYCLE, SEXUALITY, AND SEXUAL MECHANISM: FUNGI

Data in columns B, C, D refer to the corresponding patterns presented in Parts III, IV, V.

#	Species (A)	Life Cycle Type (B)	Pattern of Sexuality (C)	Sexual Mechanism and Development (D)	#	Species (A)	Life Cycle Type (B)	Pattern of Sexuality (C)	Sexual Mechanism and Development (D)
	Myxomycetes					Ascomycetes (concluded)			
1	Labyrinthula macrocystis	A			34	Penicillium luteum	C^6	O	3-8-12-13
2	Dictyostelium discoideum	B	O	3-5-10	35	Sphaerotheca fuliginea	C^6	O	3-8-12-13
3	Physarum polycephalum	G^1	?	2-10	36	Erysiphe cichoracearum	C	I/III^3	3-8-12-13
4	Plasmodiophora brassica	F	?	3-7-9-10	37	Neurospora sitophila	C	III	3-8-9-11-13
	Phycomycetes				38	Pleurage anserina	C	III^7	3-8-9-11-13
5	Olpidium viciae	B	?	3-7-9-10	39	Sordaria fimicola	C	O	3-8-12-13
6	Polyphagus euglenae	B	I	3-7-12	40	Venturia inequalis	C	I/III	3-8-12-13
7	Allomyces javanicus	F^2	O	3-8-9-10	41	Glomerella cingulata	C	O^8	3-8-9-11-13
8	A. cystogenus	G^2	?	1-10	42	Mycosphaerella tulipifera	C	?	3-8-9-11-13
9	A. anomalus	A			43	Hypomyces solani f. cucurbitae	C	IV	3-8-9-11-13
10	Blastocladiella variabilis	F	I	3-7-9-10	44	Claviceps purpurea	C	?	3-8-12-13
11	Monoblepharis sphaerica	B	O	3-8-9-10	45	Stigmatomyces baeri	C	O	3-8-9-11-13
12	Myzochytium vermicola	B	O	3-7-12	46	Amorphomyces falagriae	C	I	3-8-9-11-13
13	Lagenidium rabenhorstii	B	I^3	3-7-12	47	Pyronema confluens	C	O	3-8-12-13
14	Achlya ambisexualis	B	II	3-8-9-11	48	Sclerotinia gladiolii	C	III	3-8-9-11-13
15	A. americana	B	O	3-8-9-11	49	Ascobolus magnificus	C	III	3-8-12-13
16	Sapromyces reinschii	B	II	3-8-9-11		Basidiomycetes			
17	S. androgynous	B	O	3-8-9-11	50	Stereum hirsutum	D	O	3-6-13
18	Phytophthora omnivora	B	II	3-8-9-11	51	Fomes pinicola	D	V^9	3-6-13
19	P. erythroseptica	B	O	3-8-9-11	52	Aleurodiscus polygonius	D	VI^9	3-6-13
20	Phycomyces blakesleeanus	B	I	3-8-12	53	A. canadensis	E	$O^{7,10}$	(4)-13
21	Sporodinia grandis	B	O	3-8-12	54	Coprinus stercorarius	D	O	3-6-13
22	Basidiobolus ranarum	B	O	3-7-12	55	C. comatus	D	V^9	3-6-13
23	Entomophthora sepulchralis	B	O	3-8-12	56	Schizophyllum commune	D	VI^9	3-6-13
	Ascomycetes				57	Galera pubescens f. bispora	E	$O^{7,11}$	(4)-13
24	Eremascus fertilis	B	O	3-8-12	58	Cyathus striatus	D	VI^9	3-6-13
25	Schizosaccharomyces octosporus	B	O	3-5-10	59	Exidia glandulosa	D	V^9	3-6-13
26	Zygosaccharomyces lactis	B	V	3-5-10	60	Calocera cornea	E	$O^{7,11}$	(4)-13
27	Saccharomycodes ludwigii	G	V	2-10	61	Auricularia auricula-judae	D	V^9	3-6-13
28	Saccharomyces ellipsoideus	G^4	V^5	2-10	62	Phleogena fagina	D	O	3-6-13
29	S. fragilis	G	O	2-10	63	Puccinia graminis	D	III	3-8-9-11-13 or 3-6-13
30	Candida albicans	A							
31	Taphrina epiphylla	D-E	V	3-5-10-13	64	P. xanthi	D	O	3-6-13
32	Aspergillus niger	A			65	Graphiola phonicis	C	O	3-6-13
33	A. repens	C	O	3-8-12-13	66	Ustilago violacea	E	V	4-13 or 3-6-13

/1/ Haploid phase may consist of one to few nuclear generation. /2/ One mitotic division of haploid nucleus interposed between meiosis and gametic fusion. /3/ Type of heterothallism unknown. /4/ Haploid phase may vary in duration from a single nuclear generation, i.e., in the fusion of ascospores, to many generations involving an extended haploid vegetative stage. /5/ Genetic (compatibility) factors governing mating type may be relatively unstable, a condition termed "partial heterothallism." /6/ Dicaryon may be limited to a single cell, the ascal initial. /7/ Two nuclei of opposed compatibilities regularly included in the ascospore, which germinates to produce a self-fertile, heterokaryotic mycelium, a condition termed "secondary homothallism." /8/ Basically homothallic but may be "partial heterothallism." /9/ Mating behavior is determined by multiple allelemorphs (incompatibility factors at one locus, V (bipolar sexuality), or at two loci, VI (tetrapolar sexuality). /10/ Genetically bipolar and secondarily homothallic. /11/ Secondarily homothallic.

Part III: TYPES OF LIFE CYCLES: NUCLEAR PHASE
Schematic representation of the occurrence and relative duration of the 3 nuclear phases in algae and fungi.

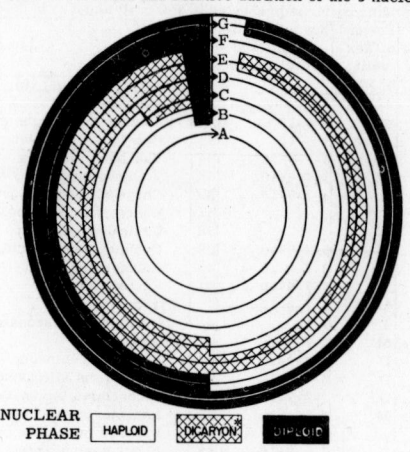

NUCLEAR PHASE   HAPLOID   DICARYON*   DIPLOID

Part IV: PATTERNS OF SEXUALITY: FUNGI

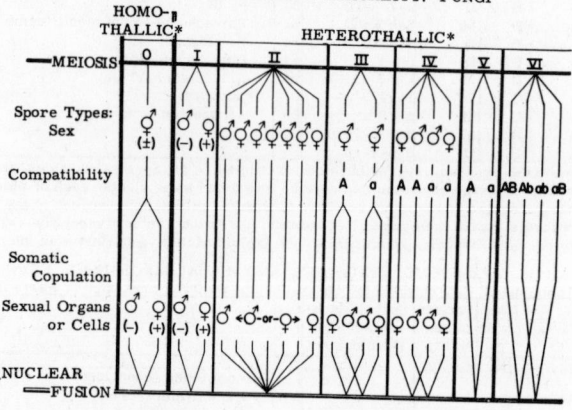

Part V: SEXUAL MECHANISMS AND DEVELOPMENT PATTERNS: ALGAE AND FUNGI

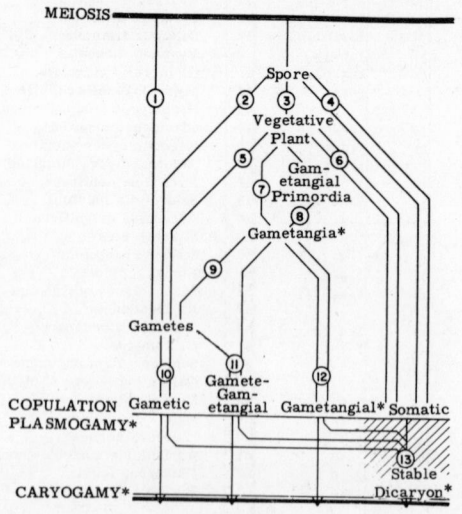

Part VI: GLOSSARY

Caryogamy: Sexual fusion of 2 nuclei. Dicaryon: Condition of cells, containing 2 nuclei brought together usually by a sexual process and which divide in unison. Dioecious: Individual plants are unisexual. Gametangium: A cell or organ in which gametes are formed. Sometimes gamete formation is suppressed and a gametangium itself may function in copulation. Heterothallism: Condition in which 2 self-sterile strains are necessary to form the sexual stage. Homothallism: Condition in which the organism is sexually self-fertile. Monoecious: Individual plants produce both kinds of gametes or sex organs. Plasmogamy: Sexual fusion of 2 cells without fusion of nuclei.

MH=morphological heterothallism; PH=physiological heterothallism; multiple factors: b=bipolar, t=tetrapolar, m=evidence for multiple factors; H=homothallism; H2=secondary homothallism. Relative degree of maleness and femaleness, as well as detectable but not absolute heterothallism, is indicated by (rel). Available evidence implies that organisms 1-83, indicated as PH, have only 2 mating types in a population; the Basidiomycetes, excluding most rusts and smuts, have multiple mating types. Morphological heterothallism and secondary homothallism are categories as defined by Whitehouse, H. L. K., in Biol. Rev., 24: 411, 1949.

	Species	Type		Species	Type		Species	Type
	Phycomycetes: general			Basidiomycetes: Tremellales		144	Hebeloma circinans,	
1	Achlya ambisexualis	H(rel)	71	Auricularia auricula-judae	PHbm		H. truncatum	PHt
2	A. regularis	MH	72	Dacryomyces deliquescens	Phb	145	Hydnum auriscalpium	PHt
3	Blastocladiella cystogena,		73	Exidia glandulasa	PHbm	146	Hypholoma spp	PHt
	B. stubenii	PH	74	E. nucleata	PH	147	Inocybe tricholoma	PHt
4	Dictyuchus spp	MH	75	E. recesa, E. saccharina	PHbm	148	Irpex fuscoviolaceus,	
5	Peronospora parasitica	H(rel)	76	Femsjonia luteo-alba	PHb		I. pendulus	PHt
6	Phytophthora parasitica	MH(rel)	77	Pilacre faginea	PHb	149	Lentinus ursinus	PHt
7	Sapromyces reinschii	MH(rel)		Basidiomycetes: Ustilaginales		150	Lenzites betulina	PHtm
8	Zoophagus insidians	MH	78	Sphacelotheca spp	PH	151	L. malaecensis	PH
	Phycomycetes: Mucorales		79	Tilletia caries, T. foetida	PH	152	L. saepiaria	PHb
9	Absidia spp	PH	80	Ustilago spp	PH	153	L. tigurius	PHt
10	Blakeslea trispora	PH		Basidiomycetes: Uredinales		154	Leptoporus adustus	PHb
11	Chaetocladium brefeldii	PH	81	Cronartium ribicola	PH	155	L. imberbis, L. ostreiformis	PHb
12	Choanephora conjuncta	PH	82	Gymnosporagium globosum	PH	156	Leucoporus arcularius,	
13	C. cucurbitarum	PH	83	G. haraeanum	PH		L. brumalis	PHt
14	Circinella spinosa, C. umbellata	PH	84	G. juniperi-virginianae	PHb	157	Marasmius cohaereus	PHb
15	Cunninghamella bertholletiae	PH	85	Melampsora lini	PHb	158	M. elongatipes	PHt
16	C. echinata, C. elegans	PH	86	Phragmidium speciosum	PHb	159	M. oreades	PH
17	Helicostylum piriforme	PH	87	Puccinia spp	PHb	160	M. personatus	PHt
18	Mucor spp	PH	88	Uromyces appendiculatus	PHb	161	Marasmus spp	PHt
19	Parasitella simplex	PH	89	U. vignae	PHb	162	Merulius rufus	PHb
20	Phycomyces blakesleeanus,			Basidiomycetes: Agaricales		163	Mycena spp	H
	P. nitens	PH	90	Agaricus campestris	H	164	Mycena spp	PHt
21	Rhizopus nigricans	PH	91	Agrocybe dura	PHt	165	Odontia bicolor, O. separans	PH
22	Syncephalastrum racemosum	PH	92	A. pediales,		166	O. setigera	PHb
	Ascomycetes: general			A. semiorbicularis	PHb	167	O. sudans	PHt
23	Ascobolus spp	PH	93	A. sphaleromorpha	PH	168	Omphalia mairei	PH
24	Ascophanus granulatus	PH	94	Armillaria mucida	PHt	169	O. maura	PHt
25	Aspergillus fischeri	H	95	Clitocybe aurantiaca	PHt	170	O. maura alba	PHb
26	A. glaucus, A. repens	H	96	C. cyathiformis	PHb	171	Panaeolina foenisecii	PH
27	Bombardia lunata	PH	97	C. dicolor, C. gallinacea,		172	Panaeolus acuminatus	PHb
28	Ceratostomella spp	PH		C. gigantea	PHt	173	P. campanulatus	PHt
29	Cercospora caudae-suis	H	98	C. radicellata	PH	174	P. fimicola	PH
30	Chaetomium spp	H	99	Collybia spp	PHt	175	Panellus mitis	PHt
31	Diaporthe phaseolorum	PH	100	Conocybe pubescens	PHt, H2	176	Panus stipticus	PHtm
32	Endoconidiophora fagaearum	PH	101	C. spicula	PHt	177	Peniophora spp	PHb
33	Erysiphe cichoraceorum	PH	102	Coprinus spp	PHb	178	P. candida	PHt
34	Fimetaria fimicola	H	103	Coprinus spp	PHt	179	P. ciliata	PH
35	Gelasinospora tetrasperma	H	104	C. amphithallus	PHt[1]	180	P. cinerea, P. farinosa	PHt
36	Gibberella moniliformis	PH	105	C. angulatus, C. callinus	PHtm	181	Phlebia aurantiaca	
37	Monascus spp	H	106	C. bisporus	H	182	Pholiota adiposa, P. aurivella	PHb
38	Neurospora crassa	PH	107	C. comatus	PHbm	183	P. cylindracea, P. mutabilis	PHt
39	N. tetrasperma	H2	108	C. hiascens, C. meveus	PHtm	184	Pieurotus spp	PHt
40	Patella melaloma	PH	109	C. pellucidus	H	185	Polyporus anceps	PHbm
41	Penicillium spp	H	110	C. sasii	PHb[1]	186	P. borealis	PHt
42	Pleurage spp	H	111	C. sclerocystidiosus	PHtm	187	P. tuckahoe	PH
43	P. anserina	H2	112	C. silvaticus	PH	188	Poria microspora	PHbm
44	Podospora minuta	PH, H2	113	C. stellatus	H	189	P. mucida	PHt
45	Sclerotinia sclerotiorum	H	114	Coriolus abietinus	PHtm	190	Psathyrella spp	PHt
46	Stromatinia gladioli	PH	115	C. hirsutus	PHb	191	Pseudocoprinus disseminatus	PHbm
47	S. narcissi	MH	116	C. versicolor	PHt	192	P. impatiens	PHtm
48	Taphrina deformans	H	117	Corinellus shutake	PHb	193	Psilocybe foenisecii	PHt
49	T. epiphylla, T. klebahni	PH	118	Corticium bombycinum	PHt	194	P. subviscida	PH
50	Venturia inaequalis, V. pirina	PH	119	C. calceum	PH	195	Radulum orbiculare	PHbm
	Ascomycetes: Laboulbeniaceae		120	C. conigenum	PHb	196	Rhodopaxillus nudus	PH
51	Amorphomyces spp	MH	121	C. coronilla	PHbt, H	197	Schizophyllum commune	PHtm
52	Apatomyces laboulbenioides	MH	122	C. effuscatum	PHtm	198	Solenia anomala	PHb
53	Aporomyces subulatus	MH	123	C. evolvens	PHt	199	Sprassis crispa	PHb
54	A. trinitatis, A. uniflagellatus	MH	124	C. hydnans	PH	200	Stereum chilletii	PHt
55	Chitonomyces, all species	MH	125	C. incrustans	PHb	201	S. murrayi	PH
56	Dicrandromyces terminalis	MH	126	C. laeve	PH	202	S. rufum	PHt
57	Dimeromyces, all species	MH	127	C. polygonium	PHt	203	S. spadiceum	PHb
58	Dimorphomyces denticatus,		128	C. porosum, C. radiosum	PH	204	S. sanguinolentum	H
	D. muticus	MH	129	C. serum	PHt	205	Stropharia semiglobata	PHbm
59	Dioicomyces spp	MH	130	Cortinellus berkeleyana	PHt	206	Trametes cinnabarina	PHt
60	Eudimeromyces, all species	MH	131	Crinipellis stipitarius	PHt	207	T. suavaeolens	PHtm
61	Herpomyces spp	MH	132	Cytidia flocculenta, C. salicina	PHt	208	Typhula erythropus	PHt
62	Nanomyces appendiculatus	MH	133	Deconica atrorufal,		209	T. gyrans, T. trifolii	PH
63	N. fijianus,			D. iniquilina	PHt	210	Xeromphalina campanella	PHt
	N. perpendicularis	MH	134	D. coprophila, D. crobula	PHb		Gasteromycetes	
64	Rhizopodomyces merragatae	MH	135	Drosophila spp	PHt	211	Crucibulum vulgare	PHtm
65	Tetrandromyces brachidae	MH	136	D. semivestita	PHb	212	Cyathus olla, C. stercoreus	PHt
66	Triandromyces bottegoi	MH	137	Flammula carbonaria	PHt	213	C. striatus	PHtm
	Ascomycetes: Yeasts		138	F. conissans, F. lenta	PHt	214	C. vernicosus	PH
67	Dematium chodati	PH	139	Fomes fraxineus	PHb	215	Nidula candida	PH
68	Endomycopsis ohmeri	PH	140	F. igniarius	PHtm	216	Nidularia farcta	PHt
69	Saccharomyces cerevisiae,		141	F. pinicola, F. roseus	PHbm	217	N. pisiformis	PHt
	S. ludwigii	PH	142	Galera sphagnorum	PHt	218	Scleroderma aurantium	PH
70	Zygosaccharomyces lactis	PH	143	Gloeocystidium roseo-cremum	PHb	219	Sphaerobolus stellatus	PHt

/1/ Amphithallic, i.e. both hetero- and homothallic spores occur in the same fruit.

109. BREEDING SYSTEMS: PLANTS

Systems listed below indicate the usual classification of breeding. Where variability exists within a species, the predominating system is enclosed in parentheses.

SC-S = species predominately self-compatible, no imbreeding degeneration; SC = self-compatible, intermediate, with perhaps a predominance of outcrossing; SC-M = self-compatible, monoecious, therefore rarely selfed under open pollination; SI = self-incompatible; D = dioecious; A = apomictic.

Monocotyledones

	Species	System[1]
	Pandanaceae	
1	Screw-pine (Pandanus tectorius)	D
2	Screw-pine (P. utilis)	D
	Gramineae	
3	Barley (Hordeum sativum)	SC-S
4	Buffalo grass (Buchloe dactyloides)	D
5	Corn (Zea mays)	SC-M
6	Fescue (Festuca pratensis)	SI
7	Millet (Panicum miliaceum)	SC-S
8	Oat (Avena sativa)	SC-S
9	Orchardgrass (Dactylis glomerata)	SI
10	Rice (Oryza sativa)	SC-S
11	Rye (Secale cereale)	SI
12	Ryegrass (Lolium perenne)	SI
13	Sorghum (Sorghum vulgare)	SC-S
14	Sugar cane (Saccharum officinarum)	SI
15	Teosinte (Euchlaena mexicana)	SC-M
16	Timothy (Phleum pratense)	SI
17	Wheat (Triticum spp)	SC-S
18	Wildrice (Zizania aquatica)	SC-M
	Cyperaceae	
19	Sedge (Cyperus papyrus)	SC
20	Sedge (C. tegetiformis)	SC
	Palmaceae	
21	Date (Phoenix dactylifera)	D
22	Oil palm (Elaeis guineensis)	SC
23	Palmetto (Sabal palmetto)	SC
24	Palmyra palm (Borassus flabellifer)	D
25	Wine palm (Caryota urens)	SC
	Cyclanthaceae	
26	Carludovica (Carludovica palmata)	SI
	Araceae	
27	Sweet flag (Acorus calamus)	SI
	Bromeliaceae	
28	Pineapple (Ananas sativus)	SI
	Juncaceae	
29	Rush (Juncus effusus)	SC
	Liliaceae	
30	Aloe (Aloe spp)	SI
31	Asparagus (Asparagus officinalis)	D
32	Chives (Allium schoenoprasum)	SI
33	Garlic (A. sativum)	A
34	Hyacinth (Hyacinthus orientalis)	SC
35	Lily (Lilium candidum)	
36	Lily (L. regale)	(SC)
37	Onion (Allium cepa)	SC[2]
38	Shallot (A. ascalonicum)	SC
39	Smilax (Smilax officinalis)	D
40	Tulip (Tulipa spp)	SC
41	Yucca (Yucca spp)	SI
	Amaryllidaceae	
42	Agave (Agave spp)	SI
43	Narcissus (Narcissus spp)	SI
	Iridaceae	
44	Crocus (Crocus spp)	SC
45	Iris (Iris spp)	SC
	Dioscoreaceae	
46	Yam (Dioscorea alata)	SC
	Musaceae	
47	Abaca (Musa textilis)	SC
48	Plantain (M. paradisiaca)	SC
	Zingiberaceae	
49	Ginger (Zingiber officinale)	SI
	Cannaceae	
50	Canna (Canna edulis)	SC
	Marantaceae	
51	Arrowroot (Maranta arundinacea)	SC
	Dicotyledones	
	Piperaceae	
52	Pepper (Piper spp)	D
	Salicaceae	
53	Poplar (Populus spp)	D
54	Willow (Salix spp)	D
	Myricaceae	
55	Wax myrtle (Myrica cerifera)	D
	Juglandaceae	
56	Hickory (Carya spp)	SC-M
57	Walnut (Juglans spp)	SC-M
	Betulaceae	
58	Alder (Alnus spp)	SC-M
59	Birch (Betula spp)	SC-M

Dicotyledones (continued)

	Species	System[1]
	Betulaceae (concluded)	
60	Filbert (Corylus spp)	SC-M
61	Hophornbeam (Ostrya virginiana)	SC-M
62	Hornbeam (Carpinus spp)	SC-M
	Fagaceae	
63	Beech (Fagus spp)	SC-M
64	Chestnut (Castanea spp)	SC-M
65	Oak (Quercus spp)	SC-M
	Ulmaceae	
66	Elm (Ulmus spp)	SC-M
67	Hackberry (Celtis occidentalis)	SC
	Moraceae	
68	Breadfruit (Artocarpus incisa)	SC
69	Broussonetia (Broussonetia papyrifera)	D
70	Castillo (Castilloa elastica)	SC
71	Chlorophora (Chlorophora tinctoria)	D
72	Ficus (Ficus, most spp)	SC
73	Fig (F. carica)	D
74	Hemp (Cannabis sativa)	D
75	Hop (Humulus lupulus)	D
76	Mulberry (Morus alba)	D
77	Mulberry (M. nigra)	D
78	Osage-orange (Maclura pomifera)	D
	Proteaceae	
79	Silk oak (Grevillea robusta)	SC
	Polygonaceae	
80	Buckwheat (Fagopyrum esculentum)	SI[3]
81	Sea-grape (Coccoloba uvifera)	D
	Chenopodiaceae	
82	Beet (Beta vulgaris)	SI
83	Spinach (Spinacia oleracea)	D
	Caryophyllaceae	
84	Bouncing-bet (Saponaria officinalis)	SC
85	Carnation (Dianthus caryophyllus)	SC
	Berberidaceae	
86	May apple (Podophyllum peltatum)	SC
	Annonaceae	
87	Custard-apple (Annona spp)	SC
	Myristicaceae	
88	Nutmeg (Myristica fragrans)	D
	Lauraceae	
89	Avocado (Persea gratissima)	SC
90	Beberru wood (Nectandra rodioei)	SC
91	Cinnamon (Cinnamomum spp)	SC
92	Sassafras (Sassafras albidum)	D
93	Sweet bay (Laurus nobilis)	D
	Papaveraceae	
94	Poppy (Papaver somniferum)	SC
95	Poppy, prickly (Argemone mexicana)	SC
	Capparidaceae	
96	Caper-bush (Capparis spinosa)	SC
	Cruciferae	
97	Cabbage (Brassica oleracea)	(SI)
98	Horse-radish (Radicula armoracia)	SI
99	Mustard (Brassica nigra)	SI
100	Mustard (B. juncea)	SC
101	Pepper-grass (Lepidium sativum)	SC-S
102	Radish (Raphanus sativus)	SI
103	Rape (Brassica napus)	SC
104	Roquette (Eruca sativa)	SI
105	Rutabaga (Brassica campestris)	SI
106	Sea-kale (Cakile maritima)	SI
107	Stock (Matthiola incana)	SC
108	Wallflower (Cheiranthus cheiri)	SI
109	Water-cress (Radicula nasturtium-aquaticum)	SC
	Resedaceae	
110	Dyer's-weed (Reseda luteola)	SC
111	Mignonette (R. odorata)	SI
	Saxifragaceae	
112	Currant; gooseberry (Ribes spp)	SC
	Hamamelidaceae	
113	Witch-hazel (Hamamelis virginiana)	SC
	Platanaceae	
114	Sycamore (Platanus occidentalis)	SC-M
115	Sycamore (P. orientalis)	SC-M
	Rosaceae	
116	Almond (Prunus communis)	(SI)
117	Apple (Pyrus malus)	SI
118	Apricot (Prunus armeniaca)	SC

Dicotyledones (continued)

	Species	System[1]
	Rosaceae (concluded)	
119	Cherry (Prunus avium)	SI
120	Cherry (P. cerasus)	SC
121	Loquat (Eriobotrya japonica)	SC
122	Medlar (Mespilus germanica)	SC
123	Peach (Prunus persica)	SC
124	Pear (Pyrus communis)	SI
125	Plum (Prunus americana)	SI
126	Plum (P. salicina)	SI
127	Quince (Cydonia oblonga)	SC
128	Rose (Rosa, most spp)	SC
129	Rose (R. rugosa)	SI
130	Rubus (Rubus, most spp)	SC
131	Rubus (R. calvatus)	A
132	Rubus (R. nitidioides)	A
133	Rubus (R. thyrsiger)	A
134	Strawberry (Fragaria chiloensis)	D
135	Strawberry (F. vesca)	D
136	Strawberry (F. virginiana)	D
137	Strawberry (F. viridis)	SI
	Leguminosae	
138	Acacia (Acacia spp)	SC
139	Alfalfa (Medicago sativa)	SI
140	Bean (Phaseolus aureus)	SC
141	Bean (P. lunatus)	SC-S
142	Bean (P. multiflorus)	SC
143	Bean (P. vulgaris)	(SC-S)
144	Broadbean (Vicia faba)	SC
145	Cassia (Cassia spp)	SC
146	Clover (Trifolium hybridum)	SI
147	Clover (T. incarnatum)	SI
148	Clover (T. pratense)	SI
149	Clover (T. repens)	SI
150	Crotalaria (Crotalaria juncea)	SC
151	Honeylocust (Gleditsia triacanthos)	SC
152	Hyacinth-bean (Dolichos lablab)	SC
153	Ky. coffeetree (Gymnocladus dioica)	
154	Lentil (Lens esculenta)	SC-S
155	Lespedeza (Lespedeza striata)	SC
156	Locust (Robinia pseudoacacia)	SC
157	Pea (Pisum sativum)	(SC-S)
158	Peanut (Arachis hypogaea)	(SC-S)
159	Pigeon-pea (Cajanus indicus)	SC
160	Soybean (Glycine soja)	(SC-S)
161	Sweetpea (Lathyrus odoratus)	(SC-S)
	Geraniaceae	
162	Geranium (Pelargonium graveolens)	SC
163	Geranium (P. odoratissimum)	SC
	Linaceae	
164	Flax (Linum usitatissimum)	SC-S
	Erythroxylaceae	
165	Coca (Erythroxylum coca)	SI[3]
	Zygophyllaceae	
166	Guaiacum (Guaiacum officinale)	SC
	Rutaceae	
167	Citrus (Citrus spp)	SC[2]
168	Torch-wood (Amyris elemifera)	SC
	Meliaceae	
169	Mahogany (Swietenia mahogani)	SC
	Euphorbiaceae	
170	Castor bean (Ricinus communis)	SC-M
	Buxaceae	
171	Boxwood (Buxus sempervirens)	SC-M
	Anacardiaceae	
172	Pistachio (Pistacia cabulica)	D
173	Pistachio (P. lentisous)	D
174	Pistachio (P. vera)	D
	Aquifoliaceae	
175	Holly (Ilex spp)	D
	Aceraceae	
176	Maple (Acer spp)	SC
	Rhamnaceae	
177	Buckthorn (Rhamnus cathartica)	D
178	Buckthorn (R. frangula)	SC
179	Buckthorn (R. infectoria)	D
180	Buckthorn (R. purshiana)	SC
	Vitaceae	
181	Grape (Vitis vinifera)	SC
	Tiliaceae	
182	Basswood (Tilia spp)	SC

/1/ Self-compatible, fertile by means of its own pollen; self-incompatible, sterile to its own pollen; monoecious, staminate and pistillate flowers borne on same plant; dioecious, staminate and pistillate flowers born on separate plants; apomictic, reproduction without fertilization. /2/ Some plants apomictic. /3/ Heterostyled, i.e., stigma and stamens inserted at different levels.

109. BREEDING SYSTEMS: PLANTS (Concluded)

Systems listed below indicate the usual classification of breeding. Where variability exists within a species, the predominating system is enclosed in parentheses.

SC-S = species predominately self-compatible, no imbreeding degeneration; SC = self-compatible, intermediate, with perhaps a predominance of outcrossing; SC-M = self-compatible, monoecious, therefore rarely selfed under open pollination; SI = self-incompatible; D = dioecious; A=apomictic.

	Species	System[1]		Species	System[1]		Species	System[1]
	Dicotyledones (continued)			Dicotyledones (continued)			Dicotyledones (concluded)	
	Malvaceae (concluded)			Myrtaceae (concluded)			Labiatae	
183	Cotton (Gossypium spp)	SC-S	206	Guava (Psidium guajava)	SC	230	Catnip (Nepeta cataria)	SC
184	Hibiscus (Hibiscus cannabinus)	SC	207	Pimento (Pimenta officinalis)	SC	231	Lavender (Lavandula officinalis)	SC
	Bombacaceae		208	Rose-apple (Eugenia jambos)	SI	232	Marjoram (Origanum majoram)	SC
185	Baobab (Adansonia digitata)	SC		Umbelliferae		233	Mint (Mentha spp)	SC
186	Durian (Durio zibethinus)	SC	209	Angelica (Angelica archangelica)	SC	234	Sage (Salvia officinalis)	SC
187	Silk-cotton tree (Bombax ceiba)	SI	210	Caraway (Carum carvi)	SC	235	Thyme (Thymus vulgaris)	SC
188	Silk-cotton tree (Ceiba casearia)	SC	211	Carrot (Daucus carota)	SC		Solanaceae	
	Sterculiaceae		212	Celery (Apium graveolens)	SC	236	Belladonna (Atropa belladonna)	SC
189	Cacao (Theobroma cacao)	SI	213	Parsley (Petroselinum hortense)	SC	237	Eggplant (Solanum melongena)	SC
190	Sterculia (Sterculia urens)	SC	214	Parsnip (Pastinaca sativa)	SC	238	Pepper (Capsicum frutescens)	SC
	Dilleniaceae			Ericaceae		239	Potato (Solanum tuberosum)	SC
191	Actinidia (Actinidia chinensis)	D	215	Vaccinium (Vaccinium spp)	SC	240	Thorn-apple (Datura stramonium)	SC
	Theaceae			Sapotaceae		241	Tobacco (Nicotiana rustica)	SC
192	Camellia (Camellia sasanqua)	SC	216	Mimusops (Mimusops balata)	SC	242	Tobacco (N. tabacum)	SC
193	Tea (Thea sinensis)	SC	217	Sapodilla (Achras zapota)	SC	243	Tomato (Lycopersicon esculentum)	SC
	Guttiferae			Ebenaceae			Scrophulariaceae	
194	Mangosteen (Garcinia mangostana)	A	218	Persimmon (Diospyros ebenum)	D	244	Foxglove (Digitalis purpurea)	SC
	Bixaceae		219	Persimmon (D. kaki)	D		Bignoniaceae	
195	Annatto-tree (Bixa orellana)	SC	220	Persimmon (D. virginiana)	D	245	Catalpa (Catalpa speciosa)	SC
196	Cochlospermum (Cochlospermum			Oleaceae			Rubiaceae	
	gossypium)	SC	221	Ash (Fraxinus spp)	SC	246	Cinchona (Cinchona spp)	SI
	Violaceae		222	Olive (Olea europaea)	SC	247	Coffee (Coffea liberica)	SI
197	Violet (Viola odorata)	SC		Loganiaceae			Valerianaceae	
	Passifloraceae		223	Strychnos (Strychnos nux-vomica)	SC	248	Valeriana (Valeriana officinalis)	SC
198	Passion-flower (Passiflora edulis)	SC		Gentianaceae			Cucurbitaceae	
199	Passion-flower (P. ligularis)	SI	224	Gentian (Gentiana lutea)	SC	249	Cultivated spp	SC-M
200	Passion-flower (P. quadrangularis)	SI		Apocynaceae			Compositae	
	Caricaceae		225	Funtumia (Funtumia elastica)	SC	250	Artichoke (Helianthus tuberosus)	SI
201	Papaya (Carica papaya)	D	226	Strophanthus (Strophanthus spp)	SC	251	Chicory (Cichorium intybus)	SI
	Punicaceae			Convolvulaceae		252	Dahlia (Dahlia pinnata)	SI
202	Pomegranate (Punica granatum)	SC	227	Sweetpotato (Ipomoea batatas)	SI	253	Dandelion (Taraxacum, some spp)	A
	Lecythidaceae			Boraginaceae		254	Dandelion (T. kok-saghyz)	SC
203	Brazil-nut (Bertholletia excelsa)	SC	228	Borage (Borago officinalis)	SI	255	Endive (Cichorium endivia)	SC
204	Lecythis (Lecythis zabucajo)	SC		Verbenaceae		256	Guayule (Parthenium arentatum)	SI[2]
	Myrtaceae		229	Teak (Tectona grandis)	SC	257	Sunflower (Helianthus annuus)	SI
205	Eucalyptus spp	SC						

/1/ Self-compatible, fertile by means of its own pollen; self-incompatible, sterile to its own pollen; monoecious, staminate and pistillate flowers borne on same plant; dioecious, staminate and pistillate flowers born on separate plants; apomictic, reproduction without fertilization. /2/ Some plants apomictic.

110. EJECTION OF SPORES: FUNGI

Part I: SPORE DISPERSAL: DISTANCE EJECTED

	Species	Distance Ejected	
		Horizontal mm	Vertical mm
1	Aleuria vesiculosa	10-25	10-20
2	Ascobolus immersus	300	350
3	Auricularia mesenterica	0.4-0.5	
4	Basidiobolus ranarum	10-20	
5	Coleosporium campanulae, C. petasiditis	0.6-0.9	0.3
6	Conidiobolus villosus	40	
7	Coprinus atramentarius	0.05	
8	C. curtus, C. niveus	0.1-0.2	
9	Cyathus pallidus		900-1200
10	Dacryomyces delinquescens	0.5-0.7	
11	Empusa muscae	20-30	
12	Endophyllum euphorbiae-sylvaticae[1]	0.4-0.5	
13	Endothia parasitica	90	22
14	Exidia alba	0.4	
15	Geoglossum hirsutum	5	
16	Gymnosporangium juniperi-virginianae[1]		0.3-0.4
17	Hypomyces lactifluorum		10
18	Pilobolus kleinii	2450	1840
19	P. longipes	2630	1840
20	Podospora curvicolla		>260-450
21	Puccinia spp, basidiospores[2]	0.6	0.3
22	P. graminis, aeciospores		7-8
23	P. pulverulenta, aeciospores		4-5
24	Sclerospora philippinensis, S. spontanea	1-2	
25	Sordaria fimicola		60-150
26	Sphaerobolus iowensis	5050	4000
27	S. stellatus	5660	4500
28	Tilletia tritici	1.4	0.5-1
29	Urnula geaster		20-30
30	Uromyces poae, aeciospores		9
31	U. pisi, aeciospores	15-20	15-20

/1/ Data applicable to basidiospores. /2/ Species include: P. annularis, P. arenariae, P. glechomatis, P. malvacearum.

Part II: SPORE DISPERSAL: SPECIAL FEATURES

	Species	Projectile Size	Initial Velocity m/sec	Mechanism Analogue	Spore-fall Period	Principal Mechanism of Dispersal
1	Ascobolus immersus	35-45μ x 55-65μ	10	Squirt-gun	Diurnal	Osmotic pressure in epiplasm of ascus plus elastic contractility of ascus wall.
2	Coprinus atramentarius	5.5μ x 10μ	0.04	Ballon-gun	Con-tinuous[1]	Excretion of small drop of water at spore hilum.
3	Pilobolus longipes	0.5 mm (dia)	14	Squirt-gun	Diurnal	Osmotic pressure in subsporangial swelling, plus elastic contractility of sporangium wall.
4	Sphaerobolus stellatus	1-1.3 mm (dia)	9	Sling-shot	Diurnal	Eversion of peridial layer by increase in osmotic pressure.

	Species	Special Feature of Projectile	Accessory Features in Dispersal	Tropistic Responses
1	Ascobolus immersus	Gelatinous envelope covers 8-ascospore cluster.	Asci protrude from paraphyses which hold bases of asci in position.	Positive heliotropism of apothecium and asci.
2	Coprinus atramentarius	Spores describe a curved trajectory in falling, known as a "sporabola."	Cystidia hold gills apart; autodigestion clears cystidia and gills before spore-fall.	Negative geotropism of stipe.
3	Pilobolus longipes	Non-wettable sporangial wall basally ringed with wettable gelatin.	Ocellus-like subsporangial swelling; light orients sporangiophore.	Positive heliotropism of sporangiophore and subsporangial swelling.
4	Sphaerobolus stellatus	Glebal mass adhesive because of high fat content.	Air spaces between tooth-sinuses prevent formation of vacuum.	Positive heliotropism of fruit-body.

/1/ For 24-48 hr.

135

Methods listed, accompanied by preferred calendar periods, represent those widely used for the genera, but are not intended to indicate that all species of the genera can be propagated satisfactorily by each method. Horticultural varieties are not propagated by seeds, as the new plants (from seed) may vary considerably from the parent plants.

Species	Method[1]	Time
Fruit and Nut Crops		
1 Almond (Prunus communis)	Shield bud	Summer
2 Apple (Pyrus malus	Whip graft	Winter
	Shield bud	Spring-summer
3 Avocado (Persea americana)	Patch bud	Spring
	Whip graft	Winter
4 Blackberry (Rubus spp)	Shoot	Spring
	Root cutting	Late winter
5 Blueberry (Vaccinium corymbosum)	Hardwood cutting	Early spring
	Softwood cutting	Early summer
6 Cherry (Prunus spp)	Shield bud	Summer
7 Citrus crops (Citrus spp)	Inverted-T bud	Spring-summer
8 Cranberry (Vaccinium macrocarpum)	Hardwood cutting	Fall
9 Dewberry (Rubus spp)	Tip layering	Summer-fall
10 Fig (Ficus carica)	Hardwood cutting	Winter-spring
	Simple layering	Winter
11 Grape (Vitis spp)	Hardwood cutting	Winter
	Whip graft	Late winter
	Chip bud	Spring
12 Hickory (Carya spp)	Veneer graft	Winter-spring
13 Peach (Prunus persica)	Shield bud	June-summer
14 Pear (Pyrus communis)	Whip graft	Winter
	Shield bud	Summer
15 Pecan (Carya illinoensis)	Patch bud	Spring
16 Plum (Prunus spp)	Top graft	Winter
	Shield bud	Spring-summer
17 Raspberry (Rubus occidentalis)	Tip layering	Late summer
18 Raspberry (R. strigosus)	Shoots	Fall-spring
	Root cutting	Fall
19 Strawberry (Fragaria spp)	Runners	Summer-fall
20 Walnut (Juglans spp)	Veneer graft	Late winter
	Patch bud	Spring-summer
Herbaceous Perennials		
21 Begonia (Begonia spp)	Softwood cutting	Year-round
	Leaf cutting	Year-round
22 Caladium (Caladium spp)	Tuber division	Spring
23 Carnation (Dianthus caryophyllus)	Softwood cutting	Spring-summer
24 Chrysanthemum (Chrysanthemum spp)	Softwood cutting	Year-round
	Division	Fall
25 Coleus (Coleus blumei)	Softwood cutting	Year-round
26 Dahlia (Dahlia spp)	Softwood cutting	Spring
	Leaf-bed cutting	Spring
	Root division	Spring
27 Gladiolus (Gladiolus hortulanus)	Cormels	Fall
	Corm division	Spring
28 Hyacinth (Hyacinthus orientalis)	Scooping bulb	Summer
	Notching bulb	Summer
29 Iris (Iris germanica)	Rhizome division	Fall
30 Peony (Paeonia spp)	Division	Fall
Trees and Shrubs: Broadleaf		
31 Abelia (Abelia grandiflora)	Softwood cutting	Summer
	Hardwood cutting	Fall
	Simple layering	Spring-summer
	Mound layering	Spring
32 Alder (Alnus spp)	Seed	Fall
	Hardwood cutting	Winter
	Whip graft	Winter
33 Barberry (Berberis spp)	Seed	Fall or spring
	Semi-hardwood cutting	Summer
	Hardwood cutting	Fall-winter
34 Basswood (Tilia spp)	Seed	Fall or spring
	Whip graft	Early spring
	Simple layering	Spring
	Air layering	Early spring
35 Birch (Betula spp)	Seed	Fall
	Cleft graft	Early spring
	Air layering	Spring
36 Boxwood (Buxus spp)	Semi-hardwood cutting	Summer
	Hardwood cutting	Fall-winter
	Simple layering	Spring-summer
37 Camellia (Camellia spp)	Semi-hardwood cutting	Spring-summer
	Air layering	Spring
38 Cotoneaster (Cotoneaster spp)	Seed	Fall or spring
	Semi-hardwood cutting	Summer
	Root graft	Early winter
39 Dogwood (Cornus spp)	Seed	Fall or spring
	Semi-hardwood cutting	Early summer
	Hardwood cutting	Summer
	Simple layering	Spring
	Air layering	

Species	Method[1]	Time
Trees and Shrubs: Broadleaf (concluded)		
40 Elaeagnus (Elaeagnus spp)	Seed	Fall or spring
	Semi-hardwood cutting	Late summer
	Hardwood cutting	Fall-winter
	Simple layering	Spring-summer
	Mound layering	Spring
41 Hawthorn (Crataegus spp)	Seed	Fall or winter
	Whip graft	Spring
	Shield bud	Summer
	Simple layering	Spring
	Air layering	Spring
42 Holly (Ilex spp)	Semi-hardwood cutting	Summer
	Side graft	Spring
	Shield bud	Spring
	Simple layering	Spring-summer
	Air-layering	Spring
43 Lilac (Syringa spp)	Softwood cutting	Early summer
	Wedge graft	Winter
	Simple layering	Early spring
	Air layering	Early spring
44 Magnolia (Magnolia spp)	Seed	Fall
	Softwood cutting	Late spring
	Semi-hardwood cutting	Fall
	Side graft	Summer
	Air layering	Spring
45 Maple (Acer spp)	Seed	Fall
	Hardwood cutting	Winter
	Side graft	Winter
	Air layering	Spring
	Shield bud	Summer
46 Mockorange (Philadelphus spp)	Softwood cutting	Late spring
	Hardwood cutting	Winter
47 Oak (Quercus spp)	Seed	Fall or spring
	Side graft	Early spring
48 Poplar (Populus spp)	Seed[2]	
	Hardwood cutting	Fall
	Root graft	Early winter
	Air layering	Early spring
49 Privet (Ligustrum spp)	Softwood cutting	Late spring
	Hardwood cutting	Late summer
	Simple layering	Spring-summer
50 Rhododendron (Rhododendron spp)	Seed	Spring
	Semi-hardwood cutting	Mid-summer
	Saddle graft	Winter
	Veneer graft	Winter
	Simple layering	Spring
	Air layering	Spring
51 Rose (Rosa spp)	Semi-hardwood cutting	Late spring
	Splice graft	Spring
	Shield bud	Spring-summer
	Air layering	Spring-summer
52 Viburnum (Viburnum spp)	Seed	Spring
	Softwood cutting	Late spring
	Semi-hardwood cutting	Summer
	Side graft	Summer
	Simple layering	Spring-summer
Trees and Shrubs: Conifers		
53 Arborvitae (Thuja spp)	Seed	Fall or spring
	Semi-hardwood cutting	Summer
	Hardwood cutting	Fall-winter
	Side or veneer graft	Fall-winter
54 Cypress (Cupressus spp)	Seed	Fall or spring
	Semi-hardwood cutting	Summer
	Veneer graft	Summer
55 Douglas fir (Pseudotsuga spp)	Seed	Fall or spring
	Veneer graft	Summer
56 Fir (Abies spp)	Seed	Fall or spring
	Veneer graft	Winter
57 Hemlock (Tsuga spp)	Seed	Fall or spring
	Side or veneer graft	Spring
	Semi-hardwood cutting	Summer
	Air layering	Early spring
58 Juniper (Juniperus spp)	Seed	Fall or spring
	Side graft	Winter
	Hardwood cutting	Winter
59 Pine (Pinus spp)	Seed	Fall or spring
	Veneer graft	Winter-spring
	Air layering	Spring-fall
60 Spruce (Picea spp)	Seed	Fall or spring
	Semi-hardwood cutting	Summer
	Veneer graft	Fall-winter
61 Yew (Taxus spp)	Seed	Fall or spring
	Hardwood cutting	Fall-winter
	Air layering	Spring

/1/ Propagation by seed may involve pretreatment. Seeds of those species having no apparent rest period may be sown in spring, those having a definite rest period should be artificially stratified or sown in fall. /2/ To be sown as soon as mature.

Species	Seed-Bearing Age[1] yr	Good-Crop Frequency yr	Weight of 1000 Seeds[2] g	Dormancy Type[3]	Germination Duration, da Untreated	Germination Duration, da Pretreated	Sprouting, %[4] In Lab	Sprouting, %[4] In Field
			Broadleaf Trees					
1 Alder (Alnus rubra)	10-100	3-5	0.7(0.4-1.2)	Embryo?	60	30-40	27	14
2 Ash (Fraxinus americana)	20-175	3-5	45(25-82)	Embryo	>60	40-60	38	20
3 Ash (F. pennsylvanica)	20-	1-3	26(18-41)	Embryo	60->90	40-60	42	20
4 Aspen (Populus tremuloides)	20->70	4-5	0.1	None	7		59	50
5 Basswood (Tilia americana)	15->100	1-3	91(57-151)	Embryo + seed coat	200-1000	30-60	34	20
6 Beech (Fagus grandifolia)	40-100	2-3	284(197-349)	Embryo	150-160	60	85	40
7 Birch (Betula lenta)	40-	1-2	0.7(0.5-0.9)	Embryo?	90	30	43	15
8 Birch (B. alleghaniensis)		1-2	1(0.5-1.6)	Embryo?	>120	30-40	27	15
9 Birch (B. papyrifera)	15->70	1-3	0.3(0.1-0.7)	Embryo?	>100	30-40	34	15
10 Butternut (Juglans cinerea)	20-80	2-3	15,120(11,340-30,240)	Embryo + seed coat?	>110	45-60	65	50
11 Catalpa (Catalpa speciosa)	20-	2-4	22(15-28)	None?	60		75	70
12 Cherry (Prunus serotina)	10-125	1-3	94(56-146)	Embryo + seed coat?	>190	30	63	30
13 Chestnut (Castanea dentata)	20->150	2-3	3489(2835-4536)	Embryo	100	30-45	72	55
14 Coffeetree (Gymnocladus dioica)	20->100	1-2	1649(1243-2160)	Seed coat	200	60-90	75	50
15 Cottonwood (Populus deltoides)	10-death	1-3	1(0.8-2.3)	None	2-6		88	80
16 Elm (Ulmus americana)	15-300	1-3	6.7(4.8-9.4)	Embryo (variable)	90	15-60	63	15
17 Elm (U. rubra)	15-200	2-4	11.1(8.4-13)	Embryo[5]	90->120	50-70	17	10
18 Hackberry (Celtis occidentalis)		1-3	105(84-130)	Embryo + seed coat?	60-100	60	41	20
19 Hickory (Carya glabra)	30-300	1-2	2268(2016-2592)	Embryo	250-300	30-45	85	40
20 Hickory (C. ovata)	40-300	1-3	4536(3024-5670)	Embryo	300-350	45-60	80	55
21 Hickory (C. tomentosa)	25-200	2-3	5040(4,014-13,341)	Embryo	300-350	45-60	66	65
22 Honeylocust (Gleditsia triacanthos)	10-100	1-2	162(112-259)	Seed coat	120-180	15-40	50	50
23 Locust (Robinia pseudoacacia)	6-60	1-2	19(13-28)	Seed coat	40-70	10-25	68	25
24 Maple (Acer rubrum)		1-3	20(12-36)	Embryo (variable)	>90	30-40	46	58
25 Maple (A. saccharinum)	35-	1-3	324(239-504)	None	20-30		76	18
26 Maple (A. saccharum)	to >200	3-7	74(50-142)	Embryo	>150	30	39	15
27 Oak (Quercus alba)	20-300	4-10	3024(2160-6480)	None	30-50		78	66
28 Oak (Q. coccinea)	20-150	Irregular	1620(1120-2926)	Embryo	>240	60	62	60
29 Oak (Q. falcata)	25-125	1-2	762(578-1163)	Embryo	>240	30-40	<90	65
30 Oak (Q. rubra)	25-200	2-3	3240(1779-5670)	Embryo	>300	40-60	58	70
31 Oak (Q. velutina)	20-100	2-3	1814(1134-3629)	Embryo	>240	30-50	47	>50
32 Pecan (Carya illinoensis)	20-300	1-2	4536(2835-8247)	Embryo	200-300	45-60	50	50
33 Sweetgum (Liquidambar styraciflua)	20-150	1-3	6(5-7)	Embryo?	120-200	20-60	70	50
34 Sycamore (Platanus occidentalis)	25-250	1-2	2.2(2-3)	Embryo?	30-60	15-20	35	20
35 Tupelo (Nyssa sylvatica)			137(113-245)	Embryo	>150	30-60	30	20
36 Walnut (Juglans nigra)	12-	Irregular	11,340(4,536-22,680)	Embryo + seed coat	100-300	15-40	75	55
37 Yellow-poplar (Liriodendron tulipifera)	15->200	Irregular	32(19-45)	Embryo + seed coat?	90-180	50-70	5	3
			Conifers					
38 Alaska-cedar (Chamaecyparis nootkatensis)	15-300	Occasional	4.2(2.5-6.9)	Embryo?	>300	60	10	5
39 Baldcypress (Taxodium distichum)		3-5	95(50-349)	Embryo, + seed coat?	60-110	30-50	12	8
40 Cypress (Cupressus arizonica)		1-3	11.3(6.7-16.8)	Embryo?	75	30	26	15
41 Douglas-fir (Pseudotsuga menziesii)	15-600	3-5	10.8(6.7-22.7)	Embryo + seed coat?[6]	60-90	15-30	85	55
42 Fir (Abies amabilis)	30-300	2-3	40(30-55)	Embryo (variable)	100	30	22	15
43 Fir (A. balsamea)	20->60	2-4	7.6(4.8-15.1)	Embryo (variable)	210	60-120	22	15
44 Fir (A. concolor)	40-200	3-5	30(17-55)	Embryo (variable)	>100	30	34	15
45 Fir (A. grandis)	20-300	2-3	20(10-36)	Embryo? (variable)	100	30	28	15
46 Fir (A. magnifica)	50->200	2-3	69(41-113)	Embryo (variable)	>100	30-45	25	15
47 Fir (A. procera)	30-300	Infrequent	31(24-40)	Embryo (variable)	100	30	24	15
48 Hemlock (Tsuga canadensis)	30->400	2-3	2.4(1.3-3.4)	Embryo (variable)	200	60	38	20
49 Hemlock (T. heterophylla)	25-300	2-5	1.5(0.9-2.1)	Embryo (variable)	>90	30	56	30
50 Incense-cedar (Libocedrus decurrens)	20->200	3	30(16-71)	Embryo? (variable)	>60	20-30	50	25
51 Juniper (Juniperus scopulorum)	10-300	2-5	16(11-25)	Embryo + seed coat	>200	20-30	22	20
52 Larch (Larix occidentalis)	40->60	5-6	3.2(2.3-4.6)	Embryo? (variable)	60	20-30	27	20
53 Pine (Pinus banksiana)	5->80	3-4	3.4(1.8-6.4)	Embryo (occasional)	15-60		68	45
54 Pine (P. echinata)	16->280	5-10	9.4(7.3-12.4)	Embryo?	60-120	35-45	68	35
55 Pine (P. elliottii)	12->150	1-10	31(28-35)	Embryo? (occasional)	45	20-40	61	30
56 Pine (P. jeffreyi)	8->150	2-4	113(84-146)	Embryo (occasional)	60-90		68	50
57 Pine (P. lambertiana)	40-300	3-5	216(142-302)	Embryo? (variable)	120	40	56	35
58 Pine (P. monticola)	15-300	4-6	17(14-32)	Embryo?+ seed coat[6]	200	60-90	48	30
59 Pine (P. palustris)	20->350	3-7	108(76-119)	Embryo? (rare)	30-40	35	54	35
60 Pine (P. ponderosa)	20-300	2-5	38(20-66)	Embryo? (occasional)	60	30	59	45
61 Pine (P. resinosa)	25->200	3-7	8.7(6.4-15.1)	None	30		75	55
62 Pine (P. strobus)	15-250	3-5	16.8(8.6-22.7)	Embryo	60-100	30-40	64	50
63 Pine (P. taeda)	12->60	3-10	25(18-28)	Embryo?	70	35-45	60	30
64 Port-Orford-cedar (Chamaecyparis lawsoniana)	8-200	4-5	2.2(0.8-5.7)	Embryo?	60-110	60	52	25
65 Redcedar (Juniperus virginiana)	10-175	2-3	10(8-26)	Embryo + seed coat	>180	20-30	42	30
66 Redcedar (Thuja plicata)	16->200	2-5	1.1(0.9-2.2)	Embryo (variable)	40	20	51	35
67 Redwood (Sequoia sempervirens)	20->300	1-3	3.7(1.5-7.7)	Embryo? (variable)	40-60		10	5
68 Sequoia (S. gigantea)	125->300	1-3	5(3.4-8.4)	Embryo? (variable)	40-60		25	15
69 Spruce (Picea engelmannii)	16->200	2-3	3.4(2.3-6.6)	Embryo (occasional)	50		69	45
70 Spruce (P. glauca)	30-	2-6	1.9(1.1-3.2)	Embryo	50-140	30-45	50	35
71 Spruce (P. mariana)	30-250	4-5	1.1(0.9-1.4)	Embryo	30-80	20-30	64	40
72 Spruce (P. rubens)	30-	3-8	3.2(1.6-4.5)	Embryo	30-50	20-30	60	40
73 Spruce (P. sitchensis)	25-300	3-4	2.2(1.1-2.9)	Embryo (variable)	60	50	60	40
74 White-cedar (Chamaecyparis thyoides)	4->100	1-3	1.0(0.9-1.1)	Embryo?	60-110		84	40
75 White-cedar (Thuja occidentalis)	30->100	1-3	1.3(0.8-2.5)	Embryo (variable)	50	30	46	30

/1/ Age of most abundant production. /2/ Cleaned. /3/ Dormancy may be general, variable (dormant and non-dormant seeds in same sample), occasional, or rare. Type is general unless otherwise indicated. /4/ Great variation reported. /5/ Northern sources only. /6/ Variable.

113. PHENOLOGICAL VALUES: FOREST TREES, U. S. A.

Within a species there is variation in time of growth expressions, depending upon such factors as latitude, altitude, slope, distribution of rainfall, and earliness or lateness of growing season. Many species have a broad distribution. Growth-period values are averages. Dates of stages where the growing season is short are enclosed in parentheses; dates of stages not so enclosed are for the long growing season. When the month is followed by I, growth stage occurs during first 10 days of the month; by II, during second 10 days; by III, during last 10 days. When no number appears after the month, growth stage occurs during the entire month. Species indicated by an asterisk (*) are evergreen; all other species are deciduous.

Species	Leafing	Leaf Falling	Flowering[1]	Seed Maturing	Seed Falling	Height Growth	Diameter Growth
Eastern United States							
1 Ash, black							
(Fraxinus nigra)	May III-June III	Sept III-Oct I	May III	July II-Aug III	July III-Oct III+	May III-July II	May III-Sept I
2 Ash, green	Apr		Apr II-Apr III				
3 (F. pennsylvanica)	(Apr III-June I)	(Sept III-Oct I)	(Apr III-May I)			(Apr III-July II)	(Apr II-July III)
4 Ash, white	Apr II-Apr III	Oct I-Nov I	Apr I-May I				
5 (F. americana)	(May III-June I)	(Sept III-Oct I)	(May I-May II)	(To Aug III)	(Sept I-Oct III)	(May III-June III)	(May II-July III)
6 Aspen, bigtooth	Apr II-May I	Oct I-Oct II	Apr I-Apr II	Apr III	May I-May II		
7 (Populus grandidentata)	(May III-June II)	(Oct I-Oct II)	(Apr III-May I)	(May II)	(May III-June I)		
8 Baldcypress							
(Taxodium distichum)	Mar II-Apr II	Oct III-Nov III	Mar I-Apr II	Oct 1-Oct II	Oct III-Dec III[2]		
9 Basswood, American	Apr II-May I	Oct I-Nov I	June	Aug	Sept I-Oct II+	Apr III-June II	June II-Sept II
10 (Tilia americana)	(May III-)	(Sept III-Oct I)	(July III)	(Aug III)	(Sept)		
11 Beech, American	Mar	Nov I-Dec II	Apr I-Apr II	To Sept II	Sept III-Nov I		
12 (Fagus grandifolia)	(May III-June I)	(Oct)	(June)	(To Sept I)	(Oct II-)		(Apr II-July I)
13 Birch, gray							
(Betula populifolia)	Apr III-May II	Oct	Apr III-May II	Sept III	Oct I-Nov III+		May III-Aug I
14 Birch, paper	Apr III-May I	Oct	Apr III-May I	To July III	Aug I -		
15 (B. papyrifera)	(May III-June I)	(Sept III-Oct II)	(June I)	(Sept II-Sept III)	(Oct)		
16 Birch, sweet (B. lenta)	Apr II-May III	Oct	Apr I-May I	Aug III-Sept I	Sept II-Oct III+		
17 Birch, yellow	Apr II-May I	Oct II-Oct III	Apr III	Aug I	Aug II-Oct III+		
18 (B. alleghediensis)	(May II-June I)	(Sept III-Oct II)	(May II)	(Aug II)	(Sept III-)	(May III-Aug I)	(June II-Aug I)
19 Buckeye, Ohio							
(Aesculus glabra)	Mar III-May I	Oct	Mar III-May II	To Sept II	Sept III-Oct II		
20 Butternut							
(Juglans cinerea)	Apr II-May II	Sept II-Oct II	Apr II-May II	Sept III	Oct I-Nov II		
21 Cherry, black	Mar III-Apr II	Oct II-Nov I	Apr	To June III	July I-Aug III+	Mar II-June III	May III-Sept III
22 (Prunus serotina)	(May II-June I)	(Sept III-Oct I)	(June I)	(Aug II)	(Sept I-)		
23 Chestnut (Castanea dentata)	Apr II-May II	Oct II-Nov III	June II-July I	Sept II-Oct I	Oct II-Nov III		
24 Cottonwood, eastern	Mar II-Apr I	Oct II-Nov I	Mar I-Mar II	Apr I	Apr II-Apr III		
25 (Populus deltoides)	(May I-May II)	(Sept III-Oct II)	(Apr III-May II)	(May II-May III)	(May III-June III)		
26 Dogwood, flowering	Mar III-Apr II	Oct I-Nov I	Mar III-Apr II	To Oct III	Nov		
27 (Cornus florida)	(May I-May II)	(Oct I-Oct II)	(May I-May II)	(Sept III)	(Oct II-Nov III)		Apr II-July I
28 Elm, American	Mar III-Apr I	Oct I-Nov I	Feb II-Mar I	Mar II-Mar III	Apr		
29 (Ulmus americana)	(May III-June I)	(Oct I-Oct II)	(May II-May III)	(June II)	(July III-)		
30 Elm, rock (U. thomasii)	Apr II-May I	Sept III-Oct II	Apr	May II	May III-July I		(May II-Aug I)
31 Elm slippery	Mar III-Apr I	Oct	Feb II-Mar I	Apr I	Apr II-Apr III		
32 (U. rubra)	(Apr III-May II)	(Sept III-Oct II)	(Apr II-Apr III)	(May II)	(May III-June I)		(Apr III-Aug III)
33 Elm, winged (U. alata)	Mar III-Apr II		Feb I-Mar I	Apr I-Apr II	Apr III-		Apr III-July II
34 Fir, balsam							
(Abies balsamea)*	May III-June I	Sept III-Oct II	May II-May III	Aug III-Sept I	Sept II-Nov III	May III-Aug II	May III-Sept I
35 Hemlock, eastern							
(Tsuga canadensis)*	May III-June II	Sept II-Oct III	May II-June I	Sept I-Oct II	Oct III-Apr III[2]	May III-Aug II	
36 Hickory, mockernut							
(Carya tomentosa)	Apr	Oct	Apr II-May I	To Sept III	Oct+		
37 Hickory, pignut	Apr	Oct I-Nov I	Apr II-May I	To Oct I	Oct I-Nov I+		Apr I-July II
38 (C. glabra)	(May I-May II)	Oct	(May I-May III)	(To Sept III)			
39 Hickory, shagbark							
(C. ovata)	Apr I-May I	Oct	Apr II-May II	Sept II-Sept III	Oct I-Nov I+		
40 Holly, American							
(Ilex opaca)*	Apr I-May I	Mar	Apr II-June I	Sept II-Oct II	Mar		
41 Locust, black							
(Robinia pseudoacacia)	Apr I-May I	Sept III-Oct III	Apr III-May III	Sept II-Oct I	Oct II-Dec III[2]		
42 Maple, red	Mar I-Apr II	Oct III-Nov III	Jan II-Jan III	To Mar II	Mar III-Apr II		
43 (Acer rubrum)	(May II-June I)	(Sept III-Oct I)	(May)	(To June III)	(July I)		May I-July II
44 Maple, silver	Feb III-May II	Oct III-Nov I	Feb I-Mar I	To Mar III	Apr	(May I-July III)	
45 (A. saccharinum)	(Apr II-May I)	(Oct II-Oct III)	(Mar III-Apr I)	(May I-May II)	(May III-June I)	(Apr II-July III)	(Apr III-Aug II)
46 Maple, sugar	Apr III-May I	Oct I-Nov I	Apr II-May I	to Sept II	Sept III-Oct III+	Apr II-May III	June II-Aug III
47 (A. saccharum)	(May III-June I)	(Sept III-Oct I)	(May II-May III)	(Aug I)	(Sept I-)	(May II-Aug III)	(June I-Sept I)
48 Mulberry, red							
(Morus rubra)	Apr	Oct	Apr II-May II	June	July 1-Aug III		
49 Oak, black							
(Quercus velutina)	Apr III-May III	Oct III-Nov III	Apr III-May II	Sept	Oct I-Nov I		
50 Oak, bur	Apr	Oct III-Nov II	Apr-III-May I				
51 (Q. macrocarpa)	(May I-May III)	(Sept III-Oct II)	(June I-June II)	(Sept II-Sept III)	(Oct)		
52 Oak, northern red	Apr II-May I	Oct I-Nov I	Apr II-May I	Sept I-Sept II	Sept II-Nov I		
53 (Q. rubra)	(May III-June I)	(Oct I-Oct II)	(May III-June I)	(Sept I)	(Sept II)	(May III-June II)	Apr II-July III
54 Oak, post	Apr	Oct II-Nov I	Apr II	Sept III-Oct I	Oct II-Nov I		
55 (Q. stellata)	(May I-May II)	(Oct I-)	(May II)		(Oct I)		Apr I-July I
56 Oak, scarlet (Q. coccinea)	Apr III-May II	Oct II-	Apr III-May I	Sept	Oct		
57 Oak, southern red							
(Q. falcata)	Apr		Apr I-May I	Sept	Oct		Apr I-July I
58 Oak, white	Mar III-Apr II	Oct III-May I	Apr I-Apr II	Sept III-Oct I	Oct II-Nov I		Mar III-July III
59 (Q. alba)	(May II-June I)	(Oct I-Oct III)	(May)	(Sept I-Sept III)	(Sept III-)		
60 Pine, eastern white	May I-Aug I	Sept I-Oct II	May II-June I	Aug I-Sept III	Oct	Apr III-June III	Apr III-Sept III
61 (Pinus strobus)*	(May III-Aug II)	(Sept II-Sept III)	(June III)	(Sept I-Sept II)	(Sept II-Oct III)	(May III-Aug I)	(May I-Sept III)
62 Pine, jack (P. banksiana)*	May III-	Oct II-	May II-June I	Sept I-Sept II	Sept III-3	May I-July I	
63 Pine, loblolly	Feb II-		Feb III-Mar I	Oct	Nov I-Dec III[2]		
64 (P. taeda)*	(Mar III-)	(Sept I-Dec III[4])	(Apr I-Apr II)	(Sept III-Oct I)	(Oct II-Dec III[2])	(Mar III-Aug I)	(Mar III-Aug II)

/1/ For conifers, dates of pollination are given. /2/ Seed fall continues through the winter, in smaller quantities. /3/ Seed fall continues for several years. /4/ Leaf fall continues throughout the year.

Within a species there is variation in time of growth expressions, depending upon such factors as latitude, altitude, slope, distribution of rainfall, and earliness or lateness of growing season. Many species have a broad distribution. Growth-period values are averages. Dates of stages where the growing season is short are enclosed in parentheses; dates of stages not so enclosed are for the long growing season. When the month is followed by I, growth stage occurs during first 10 days of the month; by II, during second 10 days; by III, during last 10 days. When no number appears after the month, growth stage occurs during the entire month. Species indicated by an asterisk (*) are evergreen; all other species are deciduous.

Species	Leafing	Leaf Falling	Flowering[1]	Seed Maturing	Seed Falling	Height Growth	Diameter Growth
Eastern United States (concluded)							
65 Pine, longleaf							
66 (Pinus palustris)*	Mar I-	Sept I-Dec III[4]	Feb I-Mar III	Sept I-Oct II	Oct II-Nov III[+]		Mar I-Aug III
67 Pine, pitch (P. rigida)*	May III-July III		Apr III-May II	To Oct III	Nov I-Apr III	Apr III-July I	Apr III-
68 Pine, red (P. resinosa)*	May III-Aug III	Oct I-	June I-June II	Sept II-Sept III	Oct I-Dec III[2]	May I-Aug I	May I-Sept III
69 Pine, shortleaf	Feb III-		Feb III-				
70 (P. echinata)*	(May III-July III)	Sept I-Dec III[4]	(May)	(Oct I-Oct II)	(Oct III-Dec III[2])	(May I-July III)	(Mar III-Aug III)
71 Pine, slash (P. elliottii)*	Feb III-		June III-Feb II	Sept I-Sept II	Sept III-Nov I		
72 Redcedar							
(Juniperus virginiana)*	Mar II-May II	Oct	Mar II-May II	Sept III-Nov III	Feb I-Mar III		
73 Spruce, black							
(Picea mariana)*	June I-		June I	Aug III-Sept II	Sept III-[5]	June I-Aug II	
74 Spruce, red (P. rubens)*			June I	To Sept I	Sept II-	June I-July III	May I-Sept I
75 Spruce, white (P. glauca)*	May II-May III		May	Aug III-Sept I	Sept II-Nov III	May II July III	
76 Sweetgum							
(Liquidambar styraciflua)	Mar II-Apr III		Mar II-May I	Sept II-Sept III	Oct		May III-Aug II
77 Sycamore, American							
(Platanus occidentalis)	Apr I-May I	Oct I-Nov I	Apr I-May I	Sept III	Oct I-Mar I[+]	Apr I-July II	May III-July I
78 Tamarack (Larix laricina)	May	Sept III-Oct III	Apr II-May I	To Sept I	Sept II-Oct II		
79 (Nyssa sylvatica)	(May)	(Sept III-Nov I)	(May III-June I)	(To Sept II)	(Sept III-Oct II)		
80 Walnut, black	Apr		Apr I-May I	Sept	Oct I-Nov I		
81 (Juglans nigra)	(May II-May III)	(Oct I-Oct II)	(May)	(Sept)			
82 White-cedar, northern							
(Thuja occidentalis)*	May II-		May III	Aug III-Sept III	Oct	May II-Aug III	May III-Sept I
83 Willow, black	Mar III-Apr II	Oct II-Nov I	Mar II-Mar III	Apr I-Apr II	Apr III-May II		
84 (Salix nigra)	(Apr III-May II)	(Oct)	(Apr III-May I)	(May II-May III)	(June)		
85 Yellow-poplar	Mar III-Apr II	Oct I-Nov I	Apr	Sept II-Sept III	Oct I-Jan I		
86 (Liriodendron tulipifera)	(Apr III-May II)	(Sept I-Oct III)	(May I-June I)			(Apr II-July III)	(May I-Aug I)
Western United States							
87 Alder, red	Mar III-Apr II	To Nov I	Mar II-Apr I	Sept I			
88 (Alnus rubra)	(Apr II-May I)	(To Oct II)	(Apr III-May I)	(Oct II)	(Nov I-Dec III[2])		
89 Aspen, quaking	Apr III	Oct I-Nov II	Apr I-Apr II	May I	May II	Apr II-	
90 (Populus tremuloides)	(June I)	(Sept)	(June II)	(June III)	(July I)	(May III-Aug I)	(May III-Aug III)
91 Cottonwood, black	Apr	To Nov I	Apr II-Apr III	May III			
92 (P. trichocarpa)	(Apr III-May II)	(Sept III-Oct I)	(May II-May III)	(June II)			
93 Dogwood, Pacific	Mar III-Apr II	To Nov I	Apr III-May II	Aug II			
94 (Cornus nuttallii)	(Apr III-May I)	(To Oct III)	(May I-June I)	(Sept I)			
95 Douglas fir	May I-May II	Oct I-Nov I	Apr II-Apr III	Aug III-Sept II	Sept II-Oct II	May I-July III	May I-Aug II
96 (Pseudotsuga menziesii)*	(June III)	(Sept II-Sept III)	(July I)	(Aug II)	(Aug III-Sept II)	(June I-July III)	(May III-Aug I)
97 Fir, alpine	June I	Aug II-Sept III	June I	Sept II	Sept III-Oct I	May III-July II	May III-Aug I
98 (Abies lasiocarpa)*	(June III)	(Sept I-Oct III)	(June III-July I)	(Aug III-Sept I)	(Sept II-Sept III)	(June I-July III)	
99 Fir, grand	May I-		May I		Sept II-Oct III		Apr III-Aug II
100 (A. grandis)*	(June I-)		(June II)	(Aug)	(Sept I-Oct III)		(May II-Sept II)
101 Fir, white	May II	Sept I-	June I			May I	
102 (A. concolor)*	(July I)	(Oct)	(May I-May II)	Aug II-Sept I	(Oct)	(June III-Aug I)	(May I-Aug I)
103 Hemlock, western	May I-		May I		Sept II-	Sept II -	
104 (Tsuga heterophylla)*	(June I)	(Sept I-Dec III)	(May II)	(Sept II-Sept III)	(Oct I-Dec III[2])	(May III-Aug I)	(May I-Sept I)
105 Incense-cedar							
(Libocedrus decurrens)*	May III		May III		Oct I-Nov III	May III-Aug III	Apr II-Aug III
106 Juniper, Rocky Mt.	May III		May III	Sept III	Oct I-	May I-	
107 (Juniperus scopulorum)*	(June I)		(June II)	(Oct I-Oct II)		(May III-)	
108 Larch, western	Apr II-		Apr II	Sept I	Oct I-		Apr III-July II
109 (Larix occidentalis)	(May II-)		(June I-June II)	(Aug I)	(Sept I-)		(May III-July II)
110 Maple, bigleaf	Mar I-Apr I	Oct III-Nov III	Mar II-Apr I	To Sept III	Oct I-Dec III[2]		May I-July III
111 (Acer macrophyllum)	(Apr II-May I)	(Sept III-Oct III)	(Apr III-May I)	(To Aug III)			
112 Oak, Calif. live							
(Quercus agrifolia)*	Mar I-Apr III		Apr		Dec I-Dec III[2]		Mar III-July III
113 Oak, canyon live							
(Q. chrysolepis)*	Apr III-June II		June I		Oct	Apr II-July II	Apr III-Aug III
114 Oak, Gambel	May III	Sept III-Oct I	May II-May III			May II	
115 (Q. gambelii)	(June I)	(Sept III)				(June I)	
116 Pine, Jeffrey							
(Pinus jeffreyi)*	June II-June III	Oct II-Nov I	June II-June III		Sept II-Oct II	May II-Aug I	Apr II-Sept II
117 Pine, limber	May III-June II	Sept III-Oct III	June I	Sept	Oct	May III-July III	
118 (P. flexilis)*	(June I-June II)	(Oct)	(June III-July I)	(Aug III-Sept I)	(Sept II-Oct III)		
119 Pine, lodgepole	May	Oct I-Nov I	May II-May III	Sept I-Sept II	Sept II-Oct I[6]	May I-July II	
120 (P. contorta)*	(June III)	(Sept II-Oct II)	(July I-July II)	(Aug)	(Sept[6])	(June III-)	
121 Pine, ponderosa	May III-June I	Oct I-Nov I	May III-June I	Aug I-Sept III	Sept I-Nov III	May I-Aug I	Apr II-Sept II
122 (P. ponderosa)*	(June II-July III)	(Sept I-Oct I)	(June II-June III)	(Aug)	(Sept)	(June I-July III)	(May III-Aug III)
123 Pine, sugar							
(P. lambertiana)*	July I-July II	Oct II-Nov II	June II-June III		Oct	May III-July II	Apr II-Aug III
124 Pine, western white	May II-		May III		Sept III-	May II-	May I-July II
125 (P. monticola)*	(June I-)		(June III-July I)	(Aug)	(Sept I-)		
126 Pinyon	May III-June I	Sept III-Oct III	May II-May III	Sept	Oct	May I-	(June I-Sept I)
127 (P. edulis)*	(June II-Aug I)	(May III-June II)	(May II-June III)	(Aug I-Sept I)	(Sept III-Oct II)	(May III-July I)	
128 Redcedar, western	May III		Apr III	Sept III	Sept III-Dec III[2]	May II-Sept I	Apr III-Oct I
129 (Thuja plicata)*		(Sept I-Oct III)	(May III)	(Aug III-Sept I)	(Sept I-)		(May II-Sept I)
130 Spruce, Engelmann	May III	Sept I-Sept II	May III-June I	Aug I-Sept I	Sept I-Oct I	May III-	May I-July II
131 (P. engelmannii)*	(June III)	(Sept I-Oct III)	(June III)	(Sept)	(Sept III-Oct II)	(June III-July III)	
132 Spruce, Sitka	Apr III-		May I		Sept III-		Apr III-Aug II
133 (P. sitchensis)*			(May III)	(Sept II-Sept III)	(Oct I-Dec III[2])	(May III-July II)	(May III-Sept I)

/1/ For conifers, dates of pollination are given. /2/ Seed fall continues through the winter, in smaller quantities. /4/ Leaf fall continues throughout the year. /5/ Cones are retained for 2-3 years during which seed fall continues. /6/ Most seeds are retained several years until cones are opened by a fire.

114. SIZE AND GROWTH RATE: FOREST TREES, U. S. A.

Values are approximate. Great variation exists within species.

#	Species	Height[1] ft	Crown Spread[2] ft	Trunk Diameter[3] ft	Relative Growth Rate
1	Alaska-cedar (Chamaecyparis nootkatensis)	60-90(130)	15-20	2-3(7)	Slow
2	Alder, red (Alnus rubra)	80-100(130)	20-40	1-3(5)	Rapid
3	Ash, black (Fraxinus nigra)	40-60(90)	20-30	1-2(5)	Slow
4	Ash, blue F. quadrangulata)	40-50(120)	30-40	1-2(4)	Rapid
5	Ash, green (F. pennsylvanica)	35-50(85)	30-40	1-2(2.5)	Rapid
6	Ash, Oregon (F. latifolia)	60-80(130)	30-40	2-3(5)	Moderate
7	Ash, white (F. americana)	60-80(125)	50-70	2-3(6)	Rapid
8	Aspen, bigtooth (Populus grandidentata)	60-70(80)	20-30	1-2(3)	Rapid
9	Aspen, quaking (P. tremuloides)	40-60(120)	20-40	1-2(4.5)	Very rapid
10	Baldcypress (Taxodium distichum)	80-120(150)	20-30	2-5(12)	Slow
11	Basswood, American (Tilia americana)	60-80(125)	40-50	2-3(5)	Rapid
12	Basswood, white T. heterophylla	60-80(125)	40-50	1.5-2.5(3)	Moderate
13	Beech, American (Fagus grandifolia)	70-100(120)	60-80	1-3(4)	Slow
14	Birch, gray (Betula populifolia)	20-30(60)	15-25	0.6-1(1.5)	Rapid
15	Birch, paper (B. papyrifera)	50-70(120)	20-30	1-2(5)	Rapid
16	Birch, river (B. nigra)	70-80(100)	40-50	2-3(5)	Rapid
17	Birch, sweet (B. lenta)	50-60(80)	20-30	1-2(5)	Moderate
18	Birch, yellow (B. alleghaniensis)	60-80(100)	30-40	1-2(4)	Rapid
19	Boxelder (Acer negundo)	40-50(75)	30-40	1.5-3(6)	Very rapid
20	Buckeye, Ohio (Aesculus glabra)	30-60(90)	30-40	1-2(2.5)	Moderate
21	Buckeye, yellow (A. octandra)	70-90(100)	30-50	2-3(4)	Rapid
22	Buckthorn (Rhamnus purshiana)	30-40(60)	15-25	0.5-1(3)	Rapid
23	Butternut (Juglans cinerea)	40-60(110)	20-30	1-2(3)	Rapid
24	California-laurel (Umbellularia californica)	60-100(175)	30-50	1-3(6)	Moderate
25	Catalpa, northern (Catalpa speciosa)	30-60(120	40-50	1-3(5)	Rapid
26	Cherry, black (Prunus serotina)	50-60(100)	20-40	1.5-3(5)	Rapid
27	Chestnut, American (Castanea dentata)	70-90(120)	50-70	2-4(10)	Rapid
28	Chinkapin, golden (Castanopsis chrysophylla)	60-80(150)	40-60	1-2.5(8)	Rapid
29	Cottonwood, black (Populus trichocarpa)	80-120(225)	30-50	3-4(8)	Rapid
30	Cottonwood, eastern (P. deltoides)	80-100(175)	40-60	3-4(11)	Very rapid
31	Cottonwood, plains (P. sargentii)	50-80(110)	20-40	2-3(5)	Rapid
32	Cucumbertree (Magnolia acuminata)	70-90(100)	50-60	2-3(5)	Rapid
33	Cypress, Arizona (Cupressus arizonica)	50-60(90)	15-25	1-2.5(5)	Slow
34	Dogwood, flowering (Cornus florida)	20-40(50)	25-35	0.5-1(1.5)	Slow
35	Dogwood, Pacific (C. nuttallii)	30-50(70)	20-30	0.5-1.5(2)	Slow
36	Douglas-fir (Pseudotsuga menziesii)	180-250(385)	15-40	4-6(15)	Rapid
37	Elm, American (Ulmus americana)	80-100(120)	80-110	2-4(11)	Rapid
38	Elm, rock (U. thomasii)	50-70(100)	20-30	1-2.5(5)	Rapid
39	Elm, slippery (Ulmus rubra)	50-70(90)	40-60	1-2(4)	Rapid
40	Fir, alpine (Abies lasiocarpa)	60-100(160)	15-25	1.5-2(3)	Moderate
41	Fir, balsam (A. balsamea)	40-60(85)	20-25	1-1.5(3)	Rapid
42	Fir, California red (A. magnifica)	150-180(230)	20-40	4-5(10)	Moderate
43	Fir, Fraser (A. fraseri)	30-50(65)	20-25	1-2(2.5)	Moderate
44	Fir, grand (A. grandis)	120-160(250)	20-30	2-4(6)	Moderate
45	Fir, noble (A. procera)	140-200(260)	20-40	2.5-5(8)	Rapid
46	Fir, Pacific silver (A. amabilis)	140-160(250)	20-40	2-4(6)	Moderate
47	Fir, white (A. concolor)	120-150(200)	20-30	3-4(6)	Moderate
48	Hackberry (Celtis occidentalis)	40-80(130)	40-50	1-2(5)	Rapid
49	Hemlock, eastern (Tsuga canadensis)	60-80(160)	20-30	2-3(6)	Slow
50	Hemlock, mountain (T. mertensiana)	70-100(130)	20-30	2.5-3.5(5)	Moderate
51	Hemlock, western (T. heterophylla)	100-170(260)	15-25	2-5(9)	Moderate
52	Hickory, bitternut (Carya cordiformis)	50-60(170)	20-30	1-2(4)	Moderate
53	Hickory, mockernut (C. tomentosa)	50-70(100)	20-30	1-2.5(3.5)	Slow
54	Hickory, pignut (C. glabra)	50-60(85)	25-35	1-2(4)	Slow
55	Hickory, shagbark (C. ovata)	60-80(120)	20-30	1-2(4)	Slow
56	Hickory shellbark (C. laciniosa)	60-80(120)	20-30	1-2(4)	Slow
57	Holly, American (Ilex opaca)	40-50(100)	20-25	1-2(4)	Slow
58	Honeylocust (Gleditsia triacanthos)	70-80(140)	40-50	2-3(6)	Rapid
59	Hophornbeam, eastern (Ostrya virginiana)	30-40(55)	20-25	1-1.5(1.5)	Slow
60	Incense-cedar (Libocedrus decurrens)	80-110(190)	15-25	2.5-4(11)	Slow
61	Juniper, alligator (Juniperus deppeana)	30-50(60)	10-15	1.5-3(6)	Very slow
62	Juniper, Rocky Mt. (J. scopulorum)	20-40(55)	10-15	1-2(3)	Slow
63	Juniper, Utah (J. osteosperma)	15-20(30)	10-15	1-1.5(2.5)	Very slow
64	Juniper, western (J. occidentalis)	20-30(40)	10-20	1-2.5(3)	Slow
65	Larch, western (Larix occidentalis)	140-180(210)	20-40	3-4(8)	Slow
66	Locust, black (Robinia pseudoacacia)	40-60(100)	20-40	1-2(5)	Rapid
67	Madrone, Pacific (Arbutus menziesii)	40-80(125)	20-40	1-2(4)	Slow
68	Magnolia, southern (Magnolia grandiflora)	60-80(135)	30-35	2-3(4.5)	Moderate
69	Mahogany, West Indies (Swietenia mahagoni)[4]	30-40(60)	15-30	0.5-1(1.5)	Slow
70	Maple, bigleaf (Acer macrophyllum)	50-80(120)	30-60	1-3(8)	Rapid
71	Maple, red (A. rubrum)	50-70(120)	40-60	1-2.5(5)	Rapid
72	Maple, silver (A. saccharinum)	60-80(120)	40-50	2-3(7)	Rapid
73	Maple, sugar (A. saccharum)	60-80(135)	40-50	2-3(5)	Slow
74	Mulberry, red (Morus rubra)	20-40(50)	20-30	0.5-1(1.5)	Moderate
75	Oak, black (Quercus velutina)	50-80(130)	40-50	2-3(7)	Moderate
76	Oak, blackjack (Q. marilandica)	20-30(55)	20-30	0.5-1.5(2)	Slow

/1/ Average range at maturity. Values for maximum height are enclosed in parentheses. /2/ Maximum crown spread of open-grown trees. Data primarily adapted and modified from Robinson, F. B., "Useful Trees and Shrubs." These values are not usually measured by foresters and may be more variable than the other data. They are presented here to show a general growth habit. /3/ Average range at maturity. Values for maximum diameter are enclosed in parentheses. Measurements at breast height (4.5 ft). /4/ Attains greater size in tropics.

114. SIZE AND GROWTH RATE: FOREST TREES, U. S. A. (Concluded)

Values are approximate. Great variation exists within species.

#	Species	Height[1] ft	Crown Spread[2] ft	Trunk Diameter[3] ft	Relative Growth Rate	#	Species	Height[1] ft	Crown Spread[2] ft	Trunk Diameter[3] ft	Relative Growth Rate
77	Oak, blue (Quercus douglasii)	50–80(130)	20–40	1–2(3)	Slow	116	Pine, pitch (Pinus rigida)	50–60(100)	30–40	1–2(3)	Rapid
78	Oak, bur (Q. macrocarpa)	70–80(170)	40–50	2–3(7)	Slow	117	Pine, ponderosa (P. ponderosa)	100–180(235)	25–35	3–4(9)	Moderate
79	Oak, California black (Q. kelloggii)	50–80(100)	30–50	1.5–2.5(11)	Slow	118	Pine, red (P. resinosa)	50–80(120)	20–40	2–3(5)	Rapid
80	Oak, California live (Q. agrifolia)	30–60(110)	30–50	1–3(6)	Slow	119	Pine, shortleaf (P. echinata)	80–100(150)	25–35	2–2.5(4)	Rapid
81	Oak, California white (Q. lobata)	50–90(130)	40–60	305(10)	Rapid	120	Pine, slash (P. elliottii)	80–90(130)	30–40	1–2(3)	Rapid
82	Oak, canyon live (Q. chrysolepis)	60–80(100)	50–120	2–4(11)	Slow	121	Pine, spruce (P. glabra)	80–90(120)	20–30	2–2.5(4)	Rapid
83	Oak, chestnut (Q. prinus)	50–60(100)	30–40	2–3(6)	Moderate	122	Pine, sugar (P. lambertiana)	160–180(250)	20–40	2–4(10)	Rapid
84	Oak, chinkapin (Q. muehlenbergii)	60–80(160)	30–40	2–3(4)	Rapid	123	Pine, Virginia (P. virginiana)	30–40(100)	15–25	1–1.5(3)	Moderate
85	Oak, emory (Q. emoryi)	30–50(65)	20–40	1–2(3)	Slow	124	Pine, western white (P. monticola)	150–180(210)	25–35	2.5–3.5(8)	Rapid
86	Oak, Gambel (Q. gambelii)	20–30(50)	20–30	0.5–1(1.5)	Slow	125	Pinyon (P. edulis)	15–30(50)	10–25	1–2(3)	Very slow
87	Oak, laurel (Q. laurifolia)	60–70(100)	20–40	2–3(7)	Moderate	126	Pinyon, singleleaf (P. monophylla)	20–30(50)	10–25	1–2(3)	Very slow
88	Oak, live (Q. virginiana)	40–50(100)	40–75	3–4(11)	Moderate	127	Popular, balsam (Populus balsamifera)	60–80(100)	40–60	1–2(5)	Rapid
89	Oak, northern red (Q. rubra)	60–70(150)	30–50	2–3(11)	Rapid	128	Port-Orford-cedar (Chamaecyparis lawsoniana)	140–180(225)	20–40	3.5–6(16)	Moderate
90	Oak, Nuttall (Q. nuttallii)	50–70(120)	20–40	1–2(3.5)	Moderate	129	Redcedar, eastern (Juniperus virginiana)	40–50(100)	10–15	1–2(4)	Slow
91	Oak, Oregon, white (Q. garryana)	50–70(120)	50–80	2–3(8)	Slow	130	Redcedar, western (Thuja plicata)	150–200(250)	20–30	4–8(20)	Rapid
92	Oak, overcup (Q. lyrata)	40–70(110)	30–40	1.5–2.5(4.5)	Slow	131	Redwood (Sequoia sempervirens)	150–275(365)	30–40	6–12(20)	Rapid
93	Oak, pin (Q. palustris)	60–80(120)	40–50	2–3(5)	Rapid	132	Sassafras (Sassafras albidum)	40–70(110)	35–45	1–2.5(6)	Rapid
94	Oak, post (Q. stellata)	40–50(100)	25–35	1–2(4)	Slow	133	Sequoia, giant (Sequoia gigantea)	250–280(350)	30–60	10–15(38)	Rapid
95	Oak, scarlet (Q. coccinea)	70–80(110)	40–50	2–3(4)	Moderate	134	Spruce, black (Picea mariana)	30–40(100)	20–30	0.5–1(3)	Slow
96	Oak, Shumard (Q. shumardii)	80–100(180)	40–60	4–5(8)	Rapid	135	Spruce, blue (P. pungens)	70–100(150)	15–25	1–2(3)	Slow
97	Oak, southern red (Q. falcata)	60–80(110)	40–50	2–3(7)	Moderate	136	Spruce, Engelmann (P. engelmannii)	100–120(165)	15–25	1–3(6)	Slow
98	Oak, swamp chestnut (Q. michauxii)	60–80(120)	30–40	2–3(9)	Slow	137	Spruce, red (P. rubens)	60–70(120)	20–25	1–2(4)	Slow
99	Oak, swamp white (Q. bicolor)	60–70(100)	40–50	2–3(7)	Slow	138	Spruce, Sitka (P. sitchensis)	180–200(300)	25–35	2–5(16)	Rapid
100	Oak, water (Q. nigra)	60–70(125)	40–60	1.5–3(5)	Rapid	139	Spruce, white (P. glauca)	60–70(120)	15–20	1.5–2(4)	Slow
101	Oak, white (Q. alba)	80–100(150)	60–90	2.5–4(8)	Slow	140	Sugarberry (Celtis laevigata)	60–80(130)	30–40	1.5–2.5(5)	Moderate
102	Oak, willow (Q. phellos)	80–100(130)	30–50	1.5–3(6)	Moderate	141	Sweetgum (Liquidambar styraciflua)	80–140(200)	60–70	2–5(6)	Rapid
103	Osage-orange (Maclura pomifera)	20–50(70)	30–40	1–2(5)	Moderate	142	Sycamore (Platanus occidentalis)	80–120(175)	60–80	2–5(14)	Rapid
104	Palmetto, cabbage (Sabal palmetto)	30–50(90)	10–20	1–1.5(2)	Slow	143	Tamarack (Larix laricina)	40–80(100)	20–30	1–2(3)	Moderate
105	Pecan (Carya illinoensis)	90–120(180)	30–50	2–4(6)	Moderate	144	Tanoak (Lithocarpus densiflora)	70–90(150)	30–50	1–3(7)	Moderate
106	Persimmon (Diospyros virginiana)	30–50(130)	20–30	1–1.5(7)	Slow	145	Tupelo, black (Nyssa sylvatica)	50–80(100)	20–30	2–3(4)	Rapid
107	Pine, Digger (Pinus sabiniana)	40–50(90)	15–25	1–2(4)	Moderate	146	Tupelo, water (N. aquatica)	80–100(120)	20–30	3–4(5)	Rapid
108	Pine, eastern white (P. strobus)	80–120(220)	40–50	2–4(6)	Rapid	147	Walnut, black (Juglans nigra)	50–90(150)	60–80	2–3(7)	Rapid
109	Pine, jack (P. banksiana)	30–60(90)	10–20	1–1.5(2)	Rapid	148	White-cedar, Atlantic (Chamaecyparis thyoides)	50–80(120)	10–20	1–2.5(5)	Slow
110	Pine, Jeffery (P. jefferyi)	90–100(130)	25–35	3–4(9)	Moderate	149	White-cedar, northern (Thuja occidentalis)	30–50(125)	5–10	2–3(6)	Slow
111	Pine, knobcone (P. attenuata)	60–80(100)	25–35	1–2(3)	Rapid	150	Willow, black (Salix nigra)	30–40(120)	20–30	1–2(6)	Rapid
112	Pine, limber (P. flexilis)	30–50(85)	15–25	1.5–2.5(7)	Slow	151	Willow, peachleaf (S. amygdaloides)	20–40(60)	15–25	1–1.5(3)	Rapid
113	Pine, loblolly (P. taeda)	90–110(190)	30–40	2–2.5(5)	Rapid	152	Yellow-poplar (Liriodendron tulipifera)	80–120(200)	30–40	2–5(12)	Rapid
114	Pine, lodgepole (P. contorta)	30–70(150)	15–25	1–2.5(3)	Slow	153	Yew, Pacific (Taxus brevifolia)	20–40(65)	15–25	1–1.5(2)	Slow
115	Pine, longleaf (P. palustris)	80–120(150)	20–30	2–3(4)	Rapid						

/1/ Average range at maturity. Values for maximum height are enclosed in parentheses. /2/ Maximum crown spread of open-grown trees. Data primarily adapted and modified from Robinson, F. B., "Useful Trees and Shrubs." These values are not usually measured by foresters and may be more variable than the other data. They are presented here to show a general growth habit. /3/ Average range at maturity. Values for maximum diameter are enclosed in parentheses. Measurements at breast height (4.5 ft).

115. SIZE AND GROWTH RATE: TREES, SHRUBS

Data adapted from Robinson, F.B., "Useful Trees and Shrubs." Values are approximate because variations in soil, moisture, air circulation, and light conditions have marked effect on growth; data should be used with caution.

	Species	Height[1] ft	Spread[2] ft	Relative Growth Rate		Species	Height[1] ft	Spread[2] ft	Relative Growth Rate
1	Ailanthus (Ailanthus altissima)	50-60	35-45	Rapid	83	Katsura tree (Cercidiphyllum japonicum)	20-40	30-40	Moderate
2	Alder (Alnus glutinosa)	35-50	25-30	Moderate	84	Larch (Larix decidua)	70-90	20-30	Rapid
3	Alder (A. incana)	10-15	10-15	Rapid	85	Lead plant (Amorpha canescens)	2-4	3-4	Moderate
4	Alder (A. rugosa)	15-25	15-20	Moderate	86	Leucothoe (Leucothoe catesbaei)	5-8	4-8	Slow
5	Aralia (Acanthopanax siedoldianus)	5-10	4-8	Moderate	87	Magnolia (Magnolia soulangeana)	20-25	20-30	Moderate
6	Arborvitae (Thuja koraiensis)	8-15	3-5	Slow	88	Magnolia (M. stellata)	15-25	15-20	Slow
7	Arborvitae (T. orientalis)	20-35	10-15	Rapid	89	Magnolia (M. tripetala)	20-25	25-30	Moderate
8	Ash (Fraxinus excelsior)	80-100	65-90	Rapid	90	Magnolia (M. virginiana)	20-30	10-15	Moderate
9	Barberry (Berberis thunbergi)	3-6	4-5	Slow	91	Maple (Acer ginnala)	12-20	8-12	Rapid
10	Basswood (Tilia cordata)	70-90	40-50	Slow	92	Maple (A. japonicum)	20-25	15-20	Slow
11	Beautyberry (Callicarpa japonica)	3-5	3-5	Moderate	93	Maple (A. palmatum)	15-20	15-20	Slow
12	Beautybush (Kolkwitzia amabilis)	5-10	8-10	Moderate	94	Maple (A. platanoides)	50-60	60-70	Rapid
13	Beech (Fagus sylvatica)	80-100	50-70	Slow	95	Maple (A. pseudoplatanus)	60-70	50-60	Rapid
14	Blackhaw (Viburnum prunifolium)	10-15	8-10	Moderate	96	Maple (A. spicatum)	25-30	20-25	Moderate
15	Birch (Betula alba)	40-50	20-30	Rapid	97	Mountain-ash (Sorbus americana)	25-30	20-25	Rapid
16	Birch (B. nana)	3-5	3-5	Slow	98	Mountain-ash (S. aucuparia)	25-40	20-30	Moderate
17	Birch (B. pumila)	3-8	2-5	Slow	99	Mountain-laurel (Kalmia latifolia)	8-15	8-10	Slow
18	Buckeye (Aesculus parviflora)	5-10	8-12	Moderate	100	Mulberry (Morus alba)	20-30	30-40	Rapid
19	Buckthorn (Rhamnus cathartica)	8-12	10-12	Moderate	101	Ninebark (Physocarpus opulifolius)	10-12	10-12	Rapid
20	Buckthorn (R. frangula)	8-15	6-8	Moderate	102	Oak (Quercus robur)	60-90	60-80	Slow
21	Buttonbush (Cephalanthus occidentalis)	5-15	5-10	Moderate	103	Oregon grape (Mahonia aquifolium)	3-8	3-5	Moderate
22	Catalpa (Catalpa bignonioides)	30-50	20-40	Rapid	104	Papaw (Asimina triloba)	15-30	15-25	Slow
23	Catalpa (C. ovata)	15-25	12-18	Rapid	105	Paulownia (Paulownia tomentosa)	40-50	30-40	Moderate
24	Cedar (Cedrus atlantica)	90-120	80-100	Moderate	106	Peashrub (Caragana arborescens)	10-20	8-18	Rapid
25	Cedar (C. deodara)	140-170	100-120	Rapid	107	Photinia (Photinia villosa)	8-20	5-15	Moderate
26	Cedar (C. libani)	75-120	80-100	Slow	108	Pine (Pinus bungeana)	70-90	45-55	Slow
27	Cedrela (Cedrela sinensis)	40-50	30-40	Rapid	109	Pine (P. cembra)	25-40	15-30	Very slow
28	Chaste-tree (Vitex agnus-castus)	15-20	8-12	Moderate	110	Pine (P. nigra)	60-100	30-40	Rapid
29	Cherry (Prunus avium)	35-50	20-30	Rapid	111	Pine (P. sylvestris)	70-90	40-50	Rapid
30	Cherry (P. cerasus)	20-30	15-20	Rapid	112	Poplar (Populus alba)	80-100	40-70	Very rapid
31	Chinquapin (Castanea pumila)	8-30	10-30	Rapid	113	Poplar (P. nigra)	50-60	60-70	Very rapid
32	Cherry-laurel (Prunus caroliniana)	20-40	15-20	Rapid	114	Poplar (P. nigra italica)	35-50	5-10	Very rapid
33	Chokeberry (Aronia arbutifolia)	6-10	4-6	Moderate	115	Privet (Ligustrum amurense)	10-15	10-12	Rapid
34	Chokeberry (A. melanocarpa)	4-6	2-3	Moderate	116	Privet (L. ovalifolium)	15-25	10-15	Rapid
35	Chokecherry (Prunus virginiana)	15-25	10-20	Rapid	117	Privet (L. quihoui)	5-8	6-8	Moderate
36	Clethra (Clethra alnifolia)	5-10	4-8	Moderate	118	Privet (L. vulgare)	15-20	15-20	Rapid
37	Coralberry (Symphoricarpus vulgaris)	3-6	4-8	Rapid	119	Quince (Cydonia oblonga)	4-8	6-10	Moderate
38	Cork tree (Phellodendron amurense)	40-50	30-40	Moderate	120	Redbud (Cercis canadensis)	25-40	25-35	Slow
39	Cork tree (P. sachalinense)	30-50	20-30	Rapid	121	Rhododendron (Rhododendron carolinianum)	4-6	4-5	Moderate
40	Crab apple (Malus arnoldiana)	15-20	15-20	Rapid	122	Rhododendron (R. catawbiense)	8-10	8-10	Moderate
41	Crab apple (M. baccata)	25-35	15-20	Rapid	123	Rhododendron (R. maximum)	10-15	10-15	Slow
42	Crab apple (M. coronaria)	20-25	20-25	Moderate	124	Rhododendron (R. nudiflora)	5-10	3-6	Slow
43	Crab apple (M. sargenti)	8-10	10-12	Moderate	125	Rhododendron (R. vaseyi)	5-10	4-10	Moderate
44	Cryptomeria (Cryptomeria japonica)	70-100	30-35	Slow	126	Rhododendron (R. viscosa)	3-8	3-8	Moderate
45	Cypress (Cupressus macrocarpa)	45-65	30-40	Moderate	127	Russian-olive (Elaeagnus angustifolia)	15-25	30-35	Moderate
46	Cypress (C. sempervirens)	70-90	8-12	Slow	128	Saltbush (Baccharis halimifolia)	4-10	8-10	Rapid
47	Devil's-walkingstick (Aralia spinosa)	20-30	10-15	Rapid	129	Scholartree (Sophora japonica)	30-60	30-50	Rapid
48	Dogwood (Cornus alba)	5-10	5-12	Slow	130	Serviceberry (Amelanchier arborea)	20-40	10-15	Rapid
49	Dogwood (C. alternifolia)	15-25	20-40	Moderate	131	Serviceberry (A. laevis)	20-30	15-20	Rapid
50	Dogwood (C. mas)	10-20	8-12	Moderate	132	Serviceberry (A. rotundifolia)	10-20	10-20	Rapid
51	Dogwood (C. sanguinea)	10-15	10-15	Moderate	133	Sheeplaurel (Kalmia angustifolia)	2-4	2-5	Slow
52	Dogwood (C. stolonifera)	8-12	8-10	Slow	134	Silktree (Albizzia julibrissen)	25-35	30-40	Rapid
53	Elder (Sambucus canadensis)	5-15	5-12	Rapid	135	Smoke tree (Cotinus coggygria)	15-20	15-20	Slow
54	Elder (S. nigra)	10-15	10-15	Rapid	136	Snowberry (Symphoricarpus racemosus)	4-6	4-6	Rapid
55	Elder (S. racemosa)	6-12	6-12	Rapid	137	Spicebush (Benzoin aestivale)	8-12	4-8	Slow
56	Elm (Ulmus campestris)	90-120	50-90	Rapid	138	Spruce (Picea abies)	80-120	20-30	Rapid
57	Elm (U. glabra)	80-100	50-65	Rapid	139	Spruce (P. omorika)	70-90	20-25	Slow
58	Elm (U. pumila)	30-60	20-40	Very rapid	140	Spruce (P. orientalis)	70-100	20-30	Slow
59	Filbert (Corylus americana)	3-8	5-10	Rapid	141	Sumac (Rhus aromatic)	6-10	6-10	Moderate
60	Filbert (C. avellana)	15-25	15-20	Rapid	142	Sumac (R. copallina)	10-30	20-25	Rapid
61	Fir (Abies homolepis)	40-50	20-25	Moderate	143	Sumac (R. glabra)	10-15	10-15	Rapid
62	Fir (A. nordmanniana)	90-120	20-30	Moderate	144	Sumac (R. typhina)	10-20	5-15	Rapid
63	Fir (A. veitchi)	70-80	25-35	Moderate	145	Sweetshrub (Calycanthus floridus)	5-8	6-10	Moderate
64	Fringetree (Chionanthus virginicus)	10-30	8-25	Slow	146	Sycamore (Platanus orientalis)	60-70	50-60	Rapid
65	Ginkgo (Ginkgo biloba)	50-80	30-40	Slow	147	Viburnum (Viburnum rhytidophyllum)	5-12	8-12	Rapid
66	Goldenchaintree (Laburnum anagyroides)	20-25	15-20	Slow	148	Viburnum (V. tomentosum)	8-10	8-10	Moderate
67	Goldenraintree (Koelreuteria paniculata)	25-35	30-40	Slow	149	Wax myrtle (Myrica pensylvanica)	6-12	2-8	Slow
68	Hawthorn (Crataegus crus-galli)	25-35	20-30	Slow	150	Wayfaring-tree (Viburnum lantana)	12-15	6-12	Moderate
69	Hawthorn (C. oxyacantha)	15-20	10-20	Moderate	151	White-cedar (Chamaecyparis obtusa)	70-80	20-30	Slow
70	Hawthorn (C. pedicellata)	10-20	10-20	Slow	152	White-cedar (C. pisifera)	100-120	10-20	Moderate
71	Hawthorn (C. phaenopyrum)	15-25	20-25	Moderate	153	Willow (Salix alba vitellina)	40-70	30-40	Very rapid
72	Hemlock (Tsuga caroliniana)	35-45	20-25	Moderate	154	Willow (S. babylonica)	30-40	30-40	Very rapid
73	Holly (Ilex aquifolium)	30-40	20-25	Slow	155	Willow (S. Caprea)	15-20	10-15	Very rapid
74	Holly (I. crenata)	5-12	8-12	Slow	156	Winterberry (Ilex verticillata)	5-10	3-5	Slow
75	Honeysuckle (Lonicera morrowi)	6-8	6-10	Rapid	157	Witch-hazel (Hamamelis japonica)	20-25	15-20	Slow
76	Honeysuckle (L. tatarica)	10-12	10-12	Very rapid	158	Witch-hazel (H. virginiana)	15-25	15-20	Slow
77	Horsechestnut (Aesculus hippocastanum)	40-65	30-40	Moderate	159	Yaupon (Ilex vomitoria)	10-15	5-8	Slow
78	Horsechestnut (A. pavia)	10-15	8-15	Rapid	160	Yellowroot (Zanthorhiza apiifolia)	2-4	3-5	Moderate
79	Indigobush (Amorpha fruticosa)	5-10	6-12	Rapid	161	Yellowwood (Cladrastis lutea)	35-45	35-40	Moderate
80	Inkberry (Ilex glabra)	8-12	10-12	Slow	162	Yew (Taxus baccata)	20-30	15-25	Very slow
81	Juniper (Juniperus chinensis)	15-20	2-4	Moderate					
82	Juniper (J. sabina)	4-10	5-8	Slow					

/1/ Average height at maturity. /2/ Spread of crown when grown in open habitat.

#	Species	Material and Dimension	Growth Rate[1]	Time and Specification[2]	Maximum Size	Time and Specification[2]	Location	Special Factor
1, 2	Nitella sp	Internodal cell, length	A: 1.7 mm/da R-E: 1.1/da[3]	0-1 da after 0.4 mm long	13 mm	10 da after 0.4 mm long	Laboratory	Mineral nutrient, 23-26°C, fluorescent light.
3, 4	Phycomyces blakesleeanus	Sporangiophore, length	A: 3.0 mm/hr R: 1/8 hr	Stage 4[4] Stage 4[4], 0.8 mm fr tip			Laboratory	Moist chamber, 22-25°C.
5	Daedalea quercina	Mycelial pellets, oven-dry weight	A: 45 mg/da	0-8 da	482 mg	14 da	Laboratory	70-ml shake culture, optimal synthetic medium, 28°C, inoculum 0.03 mg.
6	Fromes geotropus		A: 193 mg/da	0-7 da	1350 mg	7 da		
7	F. subroseus		A: 30 mg/da	1-8 da	298 mg	14 da		
8	Lentinus tingrinus		A: 140 mg/da	1-7 da	924 mg	7 da		
9	L. trabea		A: 93 mg/da	0-7 da	652 mg	7 da		
10	Polyporus palustris		A: 60 mg/da	0-6 da	402 mg	14 da		
11	P. tulipiferus		A: 75 mg/da	1-6 da	552 mg	14 da		
12	Trametes serialis		A: 112 mg/da	0-7 da	789 mg	7 da		
13	Bamboo (Dendrocalamus sp)	Stem, length	A: 26.7 cm/da	1-2 mo after bud opening	14 m	2.5 mo after bud opening	Field	Daily fluctuating temp 23-32°C, daily rain.
14	Bamboo (Sinocalamus oldhami)	Stem, length	A: 31.4 cm/da[5] Sample average: night, 0.97 cm/hr; day, 0.71 cm/hr	18 da after buds appeared above ground, height of 7 shoots of 1 plant, 3.2-7.7 m	Not reached at end of observations		Field	Sept 27-Oct 15, 1953; Cuba.
15	Barley (Hordeum sativum)	Kernel, length	A: 1.8 mm/da	3 da after pollination	9 mm	20 da after pollination	Field	Mean temp 26°C.
16		Kernel, length	R: 0.35/da	2 da after pollination	9 mm	20 da after pollination		
17		Kernel, fresh weight	A: 4.8 mg/da	6 da after pollination	57 mg	24 da after pollination		
18		Kernel, fresh weight	R: 0.5/da	2 da after pollination	57 mg	24 da after pollination		
19		Kernel, dry weight	A: 2.2 mg/da	12 da after pollination	32 mg	24 da after pollination		
20		Kernel, dry weight	R: 0.58/da	2 da after pollination	32 mg	24 da after pollination		
21, 22	Corn (Zea mays)	Plant, dry weight	A: 19.8 g/wk R: 1.37/wk	13 wk after planting 5 wk after planting	122 g	16 wk after planting	Field	
23, 24		Primary root, length	A: 2.0 mm/hr E: 0.4/hr	2 da after soaking seed 2 da, 4mm from tip			Laboratory	On moist filter paper, 25°C, in darkness.
25	Lily (Lilium longiflorum Floridii)	Flower bud, length	A: 11.5 mm/da	2 da before anthesis	155 mm	At anthesis	Greenhouse	Daily fluctuating temp between means, 16-27°C.
26		Flower bud, length	R: 0.077/da	2-30 da before anthesis	155 mm	At anthesis		
27		Anther, length	R: 0.088/da	20-30 da before anthesis	29 mm	At anthesis		
28		Anther, fresh weight	R: 0.18/da	20-30 da before anthesis	160 mm	At anthesis		
29		Anther, dry weight	R: 0.18/da	20-30 da before anthesis	35 mg	9 da before anthesis		
30	Tobacco (Nicotiana tabacum)	Leaf, area	E: 0.85/da[6]	Leaf 8.6 cm long, 3 cm from base, 0.5 cm from midrib				
31	Tomato (Lycopersicon esculentum)	Stem, length	A: 29.3 mm/da	6 wk after planting			Laboratory	Daily alternation of 8 hr light, 26.5°C, and 16 hr dark, 17°C.

/1/ The growth curve of a plant or organ is frequently sigmoid in form with (1) an acceleration phase, (2) a short, or sometimes prolonged, linear phase, and (3) a final phase of deceleration. Absolute rates (A) pertain to phase 2 and are maximum rates. They are estimates of the instantaneous rate dX/dt, where X is the dimension measured and t is time. Relative rates (R) are estimated maximum values of $(1/X)(dX/dt)$, where X is the dimension measured and t is time. Relative elemental rate (E) pertains to an infinitesimal portion, or element, of length (dX), area (dA), et al., of the organ under consideration. The maximum relative elemental rate of growth of an organ therefore is the relative rate of growth of that infinitesimal portion which is growing most rapidly. For increase in a linear dimension, the relative elemental rate has the form $d(dX/dt)/dX$, and for increase in area $\partial(\partial X/\partial t)/\partial X + \partial(\partial Y/\partial t)/\partial Y$. /2/ Time growth rate and/or maximum size attained. For relative elemental rates (E), location within organ is specified. /3/ Growth is uniform over length of internodal cell; hence relative rate of elongation of cell as a whole equals relative elemental rate for each point. /4/ Stage of growth following formation of the sporangium. /5/ Average rate: 24.9 cm/da. /6/ Assuming that drawings of leaf (Avery, G.S., 1933) were made at weekly intervals.

117. GROWTH RATES: PLANT TISSUE CULTURES

#	Tissue	Growth Period da	Initial Weight mg	Relative Increase W_1/W_0[1]	Relative Growth Rate (100 r)[1]	Culture Medium[2]
	Artichoke (Helianthus tuberosus)					
1	Tuber	60	100	2.0	1.1	G
2	Tuber	60	100	5.4	2.8	G+0.3 mg/L IAA
3	Crown gall	60	100	5.1	2.7	G
4	Crown gall	60	100	4.5	2.5	G+0.3 mg/L IAA
5	Tuber	35	283	1.1	0.2	G
6	Tuber	35	247	1.9	1.8	G+0.3 mg/L IAA
7	Tuber	35	245	3.0	3.2	G+25% coconut milk
8	Tuber	35	237	4.4	4.2	G+100% coconut milk
	Carrot (Daucus carota)					
9	Root cambium	67	170	20.3	4.5	G+0.1 mg/L IAA
10		0-7	170	2.0	9.9	
11		7-15	340	1.6	6.0	
12		15-21	548	1.7	9.0	
13		21-41	941	2.0	3.3	
14		41-67	1852	2.1	2.7	
15		24	4.0	59	17	
16	Root phloem	0-2	4.0	1.2	7.0	W+15% coconut milk
17		2-4	4.6	1.2	9.1	
18		4-6	5.6	1.6	22.9	
19		6-8	8.8	1.7	27	
20		8-10	15.1	2.0	34	
21		10-12	30	1.9	32	
22		12-14	57	1.6	22.4	
23		14-16	92	1.6	22.4	
24		16-20	139	1.4	8.6	
25		20-24	197	1.6	4.3	

#	Tissue	Growth Period da	Initial Weight mg	Relative Increase W_1/W_0[1]	Relative Growth Rate (100 r)[1]	Culture Medium[2]
	Endive (Chicorium intybus)					
26	Tuber	60	100	3.7	2.2	G
27	Tuber	60	100	5.9	3.0	G+0.3 mg/L IAA
	Marigold (Tagetes erecta)					
28	Tumor	42	35	25	7.6	H
29	Tumor	42	35	29	8.0	H+0.5% dulcitol
30	Tumor	42	35	31	8.1	H+0.5% methanol
	Periwinkle (Vinca rosea)					
31	Tumor	35		12.7	6.1	H
	Potato (Solanum tuberosum)					
32	Tuber	35	3	55	11.1	W+6% coconut milk[3]
	Rutabaga (Brassica campestris)					
33	Root	60	100	4.1	2.4	G
34	Root	60	100	5.6	2.9	G+0.3 mg/L IAA
	Salsify (Scorzonera hispanica)					
35	Root	60	100	6.4	3.1	G
36	Root	60	100	9.4	3.7	G+1.0 mg/L IAA
37	Crown gall	42	100	8.8	3.6	G
38	Crown gall	35	100	9.2	3.7	G+1.0 mg/L IAA
	Snake palm (Amorphophallus rivieri)					
39	Tuber	42	250	6	4.3	G+15% coconut milk
	Sunflower (Helianthus annuus)					
40	Crown gall	42	25	5.2	3.9	W_1
41	Crown gall	42	25	13.6	6.2	W_2
	Tobacco (Nicotiana, hybrid)[4]					
42	Stem	42	25	4.8	3.8	W_1
43	Stem	42	25	7.8	4.9	W_3

/1/ $W_1/W_0 = e^{rt}$, where W_0 is initial weight, W_1 is final weight, e is the base of natural log, r is the instantaneous growth rate expressed as per cent increase per day, and t is growth period in days. /2/ Abbreviations: G=Gautheret's agar; H=Hildebrandt et al.; W=White's liquid medium; W_1=White's agar; W_2= modified White's agar for sunflower tissue; W_3=modified White's agar for tobacco tissue; IAA = indoleacetic acid. /3/ Plus 2,4-dichlorophenoxyacetic acid, 18 mg/L. /4/ N. glauca x N. langsdorffii.

Part I: NUMBER, SIZE

#	Species	Roots: Number[1]				Roots: Total Length, cm[1,2]				Root Hairs: Diameter, μ[1]			Root Hairs: Length, μ[1]		
		I	II	III	IV	I	II	III	IV	I	II	III	I	II	III
1	Equisetaceae: Equisetum (Equisetum arvense)									15	15		1200	1200	
2	Equisetum (E. kansanum)									13	13		1500	1500	
3	Pinaceae: Douglas-fir (Pseudotsuga menziesii)[3,4]	1	6.3	5.0	0.3	10.1	11.5	1.9	0.03	21.8	22.9	22.0	240	125	155
4	Juniper (Juniperus monosperma)[3,5]	1	3.4	2.0		4.8	6.4	0.8		14.9	15.3	14.0	70	84	56
5	Pine (Pinus ponderosa)[3,6]	1	15	70	12	100	505	465	23	24	26	22	140	155	240
6	Spruce (Picea englemanni)[3,7]	1	12	43	4.7	75	140	70	0.5	18	18	18	140	125	110
7	Typhaceae: Cattail (Typha latifolia)		25[8]								12			1200	
8	Gramineae: Bentgrass (Agrostis astoriana)									13	12	12	600	600	50
9	Bentgrass (A. tenuis)									10	10	10	400	400	300
10	Bermudagrass (Cynodon dactylon)	4	660	22		60	1980	9		12	8	8	770	270	260
11	Bluegrass (Poa pratensis)[9]	900	39700	43900		5490	26520	6100		11	9	7	1120	935	510
12	Fescue (Festuca commutata)									13	13	12	400	400	350
13	Foxtail grass (Setaria viridis)	12	3360			170	405			8	8		100	100	
14	Love grass (Eragrostis curvula)									8	8	8	270	270	200
15	Oat (Avena sativa)[10]	110	2190	2400		915	2440	1220		14	13	13	1400	1100	860
16	Rye (Secale cereale)[11]	130	3670	2600		1220	3960	1220		15	12	12	1720	940	590
17	Wheat (Triticum aestivum)[12]					2000	1230								
18	Wheatgrass (Agropyron elongatum)									12	12	12	800	750	750
19	Wheatgrass (A. palustris)									11	11	10	900	800	800
20	Amarantaceae: Amaranth (Amaranthus torreyi)	1	40	325	255	8	730	280	25	9	9		230	220	
21	Leguminosae: Clover (Trifolium repens)	35	980	135		245	685	27		8	8	7	250	250	200
22	Honeylocust (Gleditsia triacanthos)									13	13		200	180	
23	Kudzu vine (Pueraria hirsuta)	1	54	755		9	380	225		12	12	11	150	140	140
24	Parosela (Parosela dalea)	1	52	1560	1560	13	520	1560	310	15	15	150	110	110	90
25	Soybean (Glycine soja)	1	51	470	260	11	255	375	105	17	17	14	240	80	80
26	Ulmaceae: Elm (Ulmus pumila)	1	55	1100	88000	55	2200	8800	176000	10			200		
27	Hackberry (Celtis occidentalis)									8	8		170	170	
28	Chenopodiaceae: Russian thistle (Salsola pestifer)	1	105	3150	630	35	1050	630	63	8	7		160	140	
29	Caryophyllaceae: Grasswort (Cerastium arvense)	1	14	105		7	35	16		12	12	10	750	600	600
30	Cruciferae: Descurainia (Descurainia pinnata)	1	10	520	1560	5	130	1040	470	7	7	6	350	300	210
31	Capparidaceae: Cleome (Cleome serrulata)											6			150
32	Zygophyllaceae: Tribulus (Tribulus terrestris)	1	200	160		25	160	32			7	7		140	130
33	Euphorbiaceae: Euphorbia (Euphorbia albomarginata)	1	22	220		11	220	155		9	8	8	300	240	240
34	Umbelliferae: Sium (Sium suave)									8	8		150	150	
35	Oleaceae: Ash (Fraxinus lanceolata)									5	5		370	370	
36	Convolvulaceae: Bindweed (Convolvulus arvensis)	1	28	170		14	335	32		14	14		80	80	
37	Labiatae: Catnip (Nepeta cataria)	1	100	1200	200	10	300	600	20	8	8	8	410	390	340
38	Solanaceae: Nightshade (Solanum eleagnifolium)	1	130	650		65	650	325			7	7		120	110
39	Bignoniaceae: Catalpa (Catalpa bignonioides)										10	10		250	250
40	Plantaginaceae: Plantain (Plantago major)	26	635	1450		275	1150	435		12	10	10	220	210	200
41	Compositae: Dandelion (Taraxacum officinale)	1	180	900		30	720	360			7	7		130	130
42	Marigold (Tageces patula)	1	72	430		12	110	130		14	14	14	180	160	140

/1/ I = main roots, i.e., roots arising directly from base of plant, may be seminal or adventitious; II = secondary roots, i.e., roots arising directly from main roots; III = tertiary roots, i.e., roots arising directly from secondary roots; IV = quaternary roots, i.e., roots arising directly from tertiary roots. /2/ Total length of roots in the specified categories refers to their combined lengths. /3/ Data applicable to seedlings, 6 months old. /4/ Total surface area of roots, 300 sq mm; total surface area of root hairs, 54 sq mm. /5/ Total surface area of roots, 1830 sq mm; total surface area of root hairs, 27 sq mm. /6/ Total surface area of roots, 1350 sq mm; total surface area of root hairs, 180 sq mm. /7/ Total surface area of roots, 260 sq mm; total surface area of root hairs, 110 sq mm. /8/ Per cm of main roots. /9/ Total surface area of roots, 2140 sq cm; total volume, 13900 cu mm; total surface area of root hairs, 15780 sq cm; number of root hairs in a core of soil 3 inches in diameter and 6 inches deep, 51.5 million. /10/ Surface area of roots, 320 sq cm; total volume, 2610 cu mm; surface area of root hairs, 3440 sq cm; number of root hairs in a core of soil (cf Fn 9), 6.3 million. /11/ Surface area of roots, 505 sq cm; total volume, 4580 cu mm; surface area of root hairs, 7680 sq cm; number of root hairs in a core of soil (cf Fn 9), 12.5 million. /12/ Surface area of roots, 310 sq cm.

Part II: EXTENT

#	Species	Location and Soil Type	Age	Condition of Growth	Extent of Roots Depth cm	Depth ft	Spread cm	Spread ft
1	Alfalfa (Medicago sativa)	Nebr.; alluvial silt loam.	2 yr		366	12	<30	<1
2	Apple (Pyrus malus)	N.Y.; heavy clay.	25 yr		>152	>5	>396	>13
3	Apple (P. malus)	Nebr.; porous loess.	3 yr		14-16		7-10	
4			17 yr		30-35		≧15	
5	Apricot (Prunus armeniaca)[1]	Okla.; silt loam over clay.			244	8	975	32
6	Asparagus (Asparagus officinalis)	Nebr.; silt loam over clay.	6 yr		305	10	122	4
7	Bean, kidney (Phaseolus vulgaris)	Nebr.; silt loam over clay.	2.5 mo	Mature pods.	137	4.5	61	2
8	Beet, garden (Beta vulgaris)	Nebr.; silt loam over clay.	3.5 mo	Edible roots.	305	10	122	4
9	Cabbage (Brassica oleracea capitata)	Nebr.; silt loam over clay.	4 mo	Mature heads.	238	7.8	107	3.5
10	Corn (Zea mays)	Nebr.; silt loam underlain by loess.	4 mo	Mature.	250	8.2	122	4
11	Lettuce (Lactuca sativa)	Nebr.; silt loam over clay.	3 mo	Flowering.	183	6	46	1.5
12	Oak, bur (Quercus macrocarpa)	Nebr.; silt loam.	65 yr[2]		>305	>10	1829	60
13	Oat (Avena sativa)	Nebr.; silt loam underlain by loess.	3 mo	Grain maturing.	207	6.8	40	1.3
14	Peach (Prunus persica)	Ga.; sandy top soil, clay subsoil.	2 yr		91	3	183	6
15	Pecan (Carya illinoensis)	Ga.; sandy top soil, clay subsoil.	6 yr		183	6	732	24
16	Pine, pitch (Pinus rigida)	N.Y.; sandy soil	30 yr		274	>9	975	32[3]
17	Potato (Solanum tuberosum)	Nebr.; silt loam underlain by loess.	3 mo	Mature tubers.	143	4.7	64	2.1
18	Squash (Cucurbita maxima)	Nebr.; silt loam over clay.	2.6 mo	Fruiting.	183	6	579	19
19	Tomato (Lycopersicon esculentum)	Nebr.; silt loam over clay.	4 mo	Fruiting.	137	4.5	168	5.5
20	Wheat (Triticum aestivum)	Nebr.; silt loam underlain by loess.	3 mo	Mature grain.	204	6.7	40	1.3

/1/ Seedling. /2/ Height of tree, 37.5 ft. /3/ Range, 30-35 ft.

119. INTERCELLULAR SPACE: LEAVES

Between the upper and lower epidermis of a leaf are numerous intercellular spaces or air chambers constituting a connected system throughout the leaf. Values are volume of intercellular space expressed as per cent of total volume of leaf and, unless otherwise specified, are applicable to mature leaves of plants grown out-of-doors in full sunlight. Values for leaves in shade are enclosed in parentheses.

#	Species	Volume, %	Method[1]	#	Species	Volume, %	Method[1]
1	Alfalfa (Medicago sativa), early spring leaf	29	C	79	Grapefruit (Citrus grandis)	23	C
2	Alfalfa (M. sativa), late spring leaf	27	C	80	Greenbrier (Smilax mauritanica)	23	W
3	Alfalfa (M. sativa), secondary leaf	26	C	81	Guevina (Guevina avellana), dried leaf[2]	45	W
4	Alfalfa (M. sativa), tertiary leaf	23	C	82	Guevina (G. avellana), in greenhouse[3]	50	W
5	Alfalfa (M. sativa), quaternary leaf	19	C	83	Hepatica (Hepatica angulosa)	25	T
6	Amaryllis (Amaryllis curvifolia)	36	W	84	Honeysuckle (Lonicera tartarica)	10	T
7	Anthropodium (Anthropodium paniculatum)	14	W	85	Hopseedbush (Dodonaea viscosa), in greenhouse	14	W
8	Anthurium (Anthurium digitatum)	12	W	86	Horsechestnut (Aesculus rubicunda), mature leaf	26(23)	T
9	Apple, delicious (Pyrus malus)	35	C	87	Horsechestnut (A. rubicunda), immature leaf	6(6)	T
10	Apple, liveland (P. malus)	34	C	88	Horsechestnut (A. rubicunda), inner leaf	(38)	T
11	Arctocalyx (Arctocalyx endlicherianus)	8.4	W	89	Horsechestnut (A. rubicunda), peripheral leaf	(33)	T
12	Ardisia (Ardisia crenulata)	22	W	90	Ivy, English (Hedera helix)	30;24	W;T
13	Aristolochia (Aristolochia labiosa)	30	W	91	Jewelweed (Impatiens sp), in dry habitat	34	T
14	Arum (Arum maculatum)	57	W	92	Jewelweed (I. sp), in moist habitat	49	T
15	Ash (Fraxinus excelsior), inner leaf	(28)	T	93	Katsura tree (Cercidiphyllum japonicum), mature leaf	18(26)	T
16	Ash (F. excelsior), peripheral leaf	19(21)	T	94	Katsura tree (C. japonicum), immature leaf	6(6)	T
17	Aster (Aster scaber)	(41)	W	95	Laurelcherry (Prunus laurocerasus)	29	W
18	Aucuba (Aucuba japonica)	27	W	96	Leopardbane (Doronicum sp), dried leaf[2]	22	W
19	Banana (Musa paridisiaca sapientum)	25-48	W	97	Leopardbane (Doronicum sp), in greenhouse[3]	59	W
20	Barberry (Berberis nervosa)	(36)	C	98	Leopardbane (Doronicum sp), in field	71	W
21	Basswood (Tilia cordata), mature leaf	20(26)	T	99	Life-plant (Bryophyllum calycinum), in greenhouse	17	C
22	Basswood (T. cordata), immature leaf	3.5(4)	T	100	Ligularia (Ligularia tibetica)	54	W
23	Bean (Phaseolus sp), dry habitat	19	T	101	Ligularia (L. tussilaginea)	(43)	W
24	Bean (Phaseolus sp), moist habitat	27	T	102	Lilac (Syringa vulgaris), mature leaf	20(28)[4]	T
25	Beech (Fagus sylvatica), mature leaf	22(28)	T	103	Lilac (S. vulgaris), immature leaf	9(10)	T
26	Beech (F. sylvatica), immature leaf	5(6)	T	104	Lily (Lilium candidum)	20	T
27	Beech (F. sylvatica), inner leaf	(32)	T	105	Loosestrife (Lysimachia ciliata), dried leaf[2]	24	W
28	Beech (F. sylvatica), peripheral leaf	(29)	T	106	Loosestrife (L. ciliata), in greenhouse[3]	31	W
29	Begonia (Begonia hydrocotylifolia)	3.5	W	107	Loosestrife (L. ciliata), in field	59	W
30	Begonia (B. incarnata)	19	W	108	Loosestrife (L. clethroides)	(33)	W
31	Bergenia (Bergenia cordifolia), dried leaf[2]	26	W	109	Mahonia (Mahonia aquifolium)	18	W
32	Bergenia (B. cordifolia), greenhouse[3]	26	W	110	Maple (Acer pseudoplatanus)	25	T
33	Bloodlily (Haemanthus coccineus)	21	W	111	Marlea (Marlea plantanifolia)	(25)	W
34	Bocconia (Bocconia frutescens)	27	W	112	Nasturtium (Tropaeolum sp), dry habitat	17	T
35	Bougainvillea (Bougainvillea glabra)[3]	19	T	113	Nasturtium (Tropaeolum sp), moist habitat	35	T
36	Boxwood (Buxus sempervirens)	19	T	114	New Zealand spinach (Tetragonia expansa)	22;18	W;C
37	Cacalia (Cacalia definifolia)	(35)	W	115	Oak (Quercus coccinea), mature leaf	24(33)	T
38	Camellia (Camellia japonica)	22;29	W;C	116	Oak (Q. coccinea), immature leaf	8(8)	T
39	Camphortree (Camphora officinalis)	7.7	W	117	Oleander (Nerium oleander), top leaf[5]	30	C
40	Canna (Canna tubiflora)	15	W	118	Oleander (N. oleander), bottom leaf[6]	34	C
41	Cassine (Cassine maurocenia), dried leaf[2]	17	W	119	Oleander (N. oleander), top leaf[5]	27	C
42	Cassine (C. maurocenia), greenhouse[3]	17	W	120	Oleander (N. oleander), bottom leaf[6]	42	C
43	Catalpa (Catalpa speciosa), large leaf	32	C	121	Orange (Citrus sinensis)[3]	29	W
44	Catalpa (C. speciosa), medium leaf	43	C	122	Paspalum (Paspalum setaceum)	6.8	W
45	Catalpa (C. speciosa), small leaf	(31)	C	123	Pear (Pyrus communis)	13(22)	T
46	Cestrum (Cestrum laurifolium)	40	W	124	Pentstemon (Pentstemon barbatus)	20	T
47	Chirita (Chirita sinensis)	14	W	125	Periwinkle (Vinca minor)	23	W
48	Chrysanthemum (Chrysanthemum morifolium)	28	W	126	Petteria (Petteria ramentacea)	20	T
49	Coprosma (Coprosma baueri)[3]	20	W	127	Photinia (Photinia glabra), old leaf	22(26)	W
50	Corn (Zea mays)	28	C	128	Photinia (P. glabra), young leaf	24(27)	W
51	Dahlia (Dahlia variabilis)	23	W	129	Pistia (Pistia texensis)	71	W
52	Dipteracanthus (Dipteracanthus schauerianus)	29	W	130	Plantain-lily (Hosta japonica)	28	W
53	Drimys (Drimys sp), dried leaf[2]	19	W	131	Plectranthus (Plectranthus fruticosus)	18	W
54	Drimys (Drimys sp), in greenhouse[3]	25	W	132	Psidium (Psidium cuneatum)	16	W
55	Dogwood (Cornus sanguinea), mature leaf	21(29)	T	133	Redbud (Cercis canadensis)	32	C
56	Dogwood (C. sanguinea), immature leaf	9(12)	T	134	Rhododendron (Rhododendron oreodoxum)	23	T
57	Elder (Sambucus nigra)	20	T	135	Sagittaria (Sagittaria trifolia)	36;39	W;C
58	Elder (S. sieboldiana)	(24)	W	136	Sarcococca (Sarcococca pruniformis)	17	W
59	English-daisy (Bellis perennis)	23	T	137	Saxifraga (Saxifraga stolonifera)	39	W
60	Epimedium (Epimedium pubigerum)	19	T	138	Sedum (Sedum sieboldii)	(28)	W
61	Eucalyptus (Eucalyptus globulus)	30	C	139	Sedum, stone crop (S. viride)	(43)	W
62	Euonymus (Euonymus americanus)	24	T	140	Senecio (Senecio doria)	58	W
63	Euonymus (E. japonicus)	23	W	141	Senecio (S. nemorensis)	64	W
64	Ficus (Ficus oppositifolia)	20	W	142	Solanum (Solanum serpentinum)	25	W
65	Filbert (Corylus tubulosa), mature leaf	17(33)	T	143	Sorrel (Rumex acetosa)	27(30)	W
66	Filbert (C. tubulosa), immature leaf	7(11)	T	144	Sowthistle (Sonchus oleraceus)	27	W
67	Flowering-maple (Abutilon theophrasti)	33	C	145	Sycamore (Platanus occidentalis), inner leaf	(27)	T
68	Garlic (Allium ursinum), dried leaf[2]	20	W	146	Sycamore (P. occidentalis), peripheral leaf	(33)	T
69	Garlic (A. ursinum), in greenhouse[3]	52	W	147	Tobacco (Nicotiana tabacum)	26	W
70	Garlic (A. ursinum), in field	66	W	148	Tovara (Tovara filiformis)	28(34)[7]	W
71	Gentian (Gentiana tibetica)	41	W	149	Turnip (Brassica rapa)	18	W
72	Ginkgo (Ginkgo biloba)	41	C	150	Valerian (Valeriana officinalis)	(30)	W
73	Globedaisy (Globularia incanescens)	25	T	151	Violet (Viola mandschurica)	23(20)	W
74	Glorybird (Calystegia soldanella)	37	W	152	Violet (V. rossii)	27	W
75	Goldenrod (Solidago sempervirens)	53	W	153	Walnut (Juglans regia), inner leaf	(25)	T
76	Granadilla (Passiflora quadrangularis)	21	W	154	Walnut (J. regia), peripheral leaf	18(21)	T
77	Grape, European (Vitis vinifera)	13	T	155	Waterchestnut (Trapa natans)	20	T
78	Grape, riverbank (V. vulpina)	25	C	156	Wax-plant (Hoya carnoso)	14	W

/1/ Methods of determination: W = measurement made by infiltrating intercellular space with water; C = measurement made on camera lucida drawings of leaf sections; T = measurement by infiltrating intercellular space with turpentine. /2/ Leaf dried 30 min prior to measurement. /3/ In greenhouse, plants growing in well-watered and well-lighted conditons. /4/ Measurements made on camera lucida drawings: in sun, 21%; in shade, 24%. /5/ Plants under artificial light of 175 ft-candles. /6/ Plant under artificial light of 77 ft-candles. /7/ Measurements made on camera lucida drawings: in sun, 33%; in shade, 39%.

Stomata are pores through which occur gaseous diffusion. Values for upper leaf surface are followed by those for lower surface. Number of stomata are per sq cm of leaf surface.

	Species	No. /sq cm	Pore Size μ[1]		Species	No. /sq cm	Pore Size μ[1]
1	Abronia (Abronia villosa)[2]	20,000;20,000		36	Mulberry (Morus alba)	0;48,000	
2	Acacia (Acacia aneura)	11,200;11,200		37	Nasturtium (Tropaeolum majus)	0;13,000	; 12x6
3	Ailanthus (Ailanthus altissima)	0;38,600		38	Nightshade (Solanum dulcamara)	6,000;26,300	
4	Alfalfa (Medicago sativa)	16,900;13,800		39	Oat (Avena sativa)	2,500;2,300	31x7;38x8
5	Apple, delicious (Pyrus malus)	0;29,400		40	Oak, English (Quercus robur)	0;45,000[5]	
6	Apple, Grimes golden (P. malus)	0;41,200		41	Oak, scarlet (Q. coccinea)	0;103,800	
7	Avens (Geum parviflora)	7,500;23,000		42	Oak, Spanish (Q. triloba)	0;119,200	;5x1
8	Barberry (Berberis vulgaris)	0;40,000		43	Parafoxia (Parafoxia linearis)[2]	22,000;23,600	
9	Barley (Hordeum vulgare)	5,500;5,400		44	Pea, garden (Pisum sativum)	10,100;21,600	
10	Basswood (Tilia vulgaris)	0;13,000		45	Peach (Prunus persica)	0;22,500	
11	Bean (Phaseolus vulgaris)	4,000;28,100	8x3;7x3	46	Plantain (Alisma plantago-aquatica)	5,000;3,600	
12	Begonia (Begonia coccinea)	0;4,000	;21x8	47	Plantain (Plantago triandra)	15,500;20,000	
13	Brachycome (Brachycome sinclairii)	22,000;15,000		48	Poplar, black (Populus nigra)	2,000;11,500	
14	Cabbage (Brassica oleracea cap.)	14,100;22,600		49	Potato (Solanum tuberosum)	5,100;16,100	
15	Castor bean (Ricinus communis)	6,400;17,600	8x4;10x4	50	Primrose (Oenothera deltoides)[2]	17,300;17,300	
16	Cherry (Prunus cerasus)	0;24,900		51	Rye (Secale cereale)	5,100;46,000	
17	Coleus (Coleus blumei)	0;14,100	;10x5	52	Salt-bush (Atriplex vesicarium)	12,000;12,000	
18	Corn (Zea mays)	5,200;6,800	19x4;19x5	53	Scilla (Scilla nutans) dry atmos.	5,500;4,950[6]	
19	Coach-whip (Fouquieria splendens)[2]	7,100;7,100		54	Scilla (S. nutans), moist atmos.	2,750;2,400[7]	
20	Cucumber (Cucumis sativus)	22,100;44,200		55	Sorrel, wood (Oxalis acetosella)	0;5,600	
21	Elder (Sambucus nigra), in sun	0;4,000-26,000		56	Soybean (Glycine soja)	14,700;16,600	
22	Elder (S. nigra), in shade	0;1,200-14,000		57	Spearwort (Ranunculus lingua)	1,300;2,700	
23	Ficaria (Ficaria verna), in sun	1,850;4,250[3]		58	Speedwell (Veronica fruticulosa)	22,400;18,600	
24	Ficaria (F. verna), in shade	2,700;4,900[4]		59	Stitchwort (Malachium aquatica)	3,100;5,400	
25	Forget-me-not (Myosotis scorpioides)	700;9,100		60	Sunflower (Helianthus annuus)	8,500;15,600	18x8;22x8
26	Frogbit (Hydrocharis morsus-ranae)	8,900;0		61	Sun-rose (Helianthemum alpestre)	28,600;20,400	
27	Geranium (Pelargonium domesticum)	1,900;5,900	23x8;24x9	62	Sycamore (Platanus occidentalis)	0;27,800	
28	Globedaisy (Globularia nudicaulis)	8,800;35,700		63	Tomato (Lycopersicon esculentum)	1,200;13,000	10x5;13x6
29	Groundsel (Senecio cottonii)	0;51,200		64	Walnut, black (Juglans nigra)	0;46,100	
30	Holly, American (Ilex opaca)	0;17,000	;12x6	65	Wandering-jew (Zebrina pendula)	0;1,400	;31x12
31	Ivy, English (Hedera helix)	0;15,800	;11x4	66	Water-soldier (Stratiotes aloides)	3,800;4,900	
32	Jimson weed (Datura stramonium)	11,400;18,900		67	Water lily (Nymphaea alba)	46,000;0	
33	Lilac (Syringa vulgaris)	0;33,000		68	Water lily (N. thermalis)	62,500;0	
34	Lychnis (Lychnis alpina)	15,600;14,600		69	Wheat (Triticum aestivum)	3,300;1,400	40x7;38x7
35	Marsh marigold (Caltha palustris)	0;4,000		70	Yew, English (Taxus baccata)	0;11,500	

/1/ Pore fully open.   /2/ In desert.   /3/ Average of 900-2800 (upper); 2800-5700 (lower).   /4/ Average of 1000-4400 (upper); 2800-7000 (lower).
/5/ Additional species not listed in table: black oak (Q. velutina), 58,000; northern red oak (Q. rubra), 68,000; willow oak (Q. phellos), 72,000.
(Upper surface for all, O.)   /6/ Average of 1100-9900 (upper); 900-9000 (lower).   /7/ Average of 1100-4400 (upper); 1300-3500 (lower).

121. RATIO OF INTERNAL TO EXTERNAL SURFACE: LEAVES

Between the upper and lower epidermis of a leaf are layers of mesophyll cells surrounded by intercellular spaces. The internal suface (I), of the leaf consisting of all the mesophyll surfaces in contact with intercellular spaces, is much larger than the external surface (E), formed by the two epidermal layers. The ratio presented is that of total internal surface to total external (both upper and lower surfaces). Values are applicable to leaves of plants grown in full sunlight; those for leaves in shade are enclosed in parentheses.

	Species	Surface Ratio I:E		Species	Surface Ratio I:E
1	Alfalfa (Medicago sativa), early spring leaf	15	16	Coleus (Coleus blumei)	4.6
2	Alfalfa (M. sativa), late spring leaf	14	17	Eucalyptus (Eucalyptus globulus)	31
3	Alfalfa (M. sativa), secondary leaf	11	18	Flowering-maple (Abutilon theophrasti)	11
4	Alfalfa (M. sativa), tertiary leaf	10	19	Gaultheria (Gaultheria shallon)	(8.2)
5	Alfalfa (M. sativa), quaternary leaf	9.9	20	Grape, riverbank (Vitis vulpina)	12
6	Apple, delicious (Pyrus malus)[1]	24	21	Grapefruit (Citrus grandis)	17
7	Apple, liveland (P. malus)[1]	23	22	Holly, American (Ilex opaca)	(13)
8	Apple, Jonathan (P. malus)[2]	14	23	Lemon (Citrus limonia)	22
9	Apple, wealthy (P. malus)[2]	15	24	Life-plant (Bryophyllum calicynum)	7.9
10	Apple, York (P. malus)[2]	12	25	Lilac (Syringa vulgaris)	13(6.8)
11	Barberry (Berberis nervosa)	(9.9)	26	Oleander (Nerium oleander)	20
12	Castor bean (Ricinus communis)	(13)	27	Redbud (Cercis canadensis)	16
13	Catalpa (Catalpa speciosa), leaf large	19	28	Sumac (Rhus glabra)	16
14	Catalpa (C. speciosa), leaf medium	14	29	Tobacco (Nicotiana tabacum)	7.1
15	Catalpa (C. speciosa), leaf small	(9.3)			

/1/ Twenty-year-old tree.   /2/ Two-year-old tree.

Values for needle leaves, indicated by an asterisk (*), represent the entire surface; values for flat leaves must be multiplied by 2 to obtain the entire externally exposed leaf surface (both upper and lower).

Part I: SURFACE AREA PER LEAF

	Species	Leaf Surface sq cm/leaf[1]		Species	Leaf Surface sq cm/leaf[1]
1	Alfalfa (Medicago sativa), early spring leaf	2	43	Lemon (Citrus limonia)	37-40
2	Alfalfa (M. sativa), late spring leaf	2	44	Lime (C. aurantifolia)	13-14.5
3	Alfalfa (M. sativa), secondary leaf	1.2	45	Kumquat (Fortunella margarita)	9
4	Alfalfa (M. sativa), tertiary leaf	0.6	46	Maple (Acer saccharum)	73
5	Alfalfa (M. sativa), quaternary leaf	0.4	47	Milkweed (Asclepias arenaria)	48
6	Apple, laxton (Pyrus malus)	18	48	Musa (Musa acuminata)	0.7-2 sq m
7	Atalantia (Atalantia citroides)	9	49	Morning glory (Ipomoea purpurea), 1st leaf	35
8	Atalantia (A. disticha)	3	50	Morning glory (I. purpurea), 3rd leaf	50
9	Balsamocitrus (Balsamocitrus gabonensis)	12	51	Morning glory (I. purpurea), 5th leaf	80
10	Banana (Musa paradisiaca sapientum)	2700-5200	52	Morning glory (I. purpurea), 7th leaf	100
11	Basswood (Tilia americana)	73	53	Oleander (Nerium oleander), 300 ft-c	10.5
12	Bean (Phaseolus vulgaris), 15 da old	49	54	Oleander (N. oleander), 86 ft-c	11
13	Beech (Fagus sp)	22[2]	55	Orange (Citrus sinensis), 3 yr old	3-130
14	Box-orange (Severinia buxifolia)	3.5	56	Orange (C. sinensis), 29 yr old	2-48
15	Catalpa (Catalpa speciosa), small leaf	29-71	57	Pepperweed (Lepidium alyssoides)	5
16	Catalpa (C. speciosa), medium leaf	135	58	Periwinkle (Vinca rosea), 300 ft-c	4.5
17	Catalpa (C. speciosa), large leaf	240-380	59	Periwinkle (V. rosea), 86 ft-c	4
18	Cherry-orange (Citropsis schweinfurthi)	10		Pine (Pinus banksiana), 36 yr old	
19	Citron (Citrus medica)	20-33	60	Unthinned forest	52.4 sq mm*
20	Clappia (Clappia suaedifolia)	0.7	61	Heavily thinned	51.6 sq mm*
21	Coldenia (Coldenia hispidissima)	0.2	62	Moderately thinned	49.7 sq mm*
22	Corn (Zea mays)	600-1320	63	Pine (P. contorta), dry habitat	128 sq mm*
23	Cottonwood (Populus fremontii wislizenii)	50	64	Pine (P. contorta), moist habitat	232 sq mm*
24	Crownbeard (Verbesina encelioides)	12	65	Pine (P. resinosa), 27 yr old	401 sq mm*
25	Cucumber (Cucumis sativus), cotyledons	15	66	Pine (P. strobus), 27 yr old	122 sq mm*
26	Cucumber (C. sativus), 1st leaf	18	67	Pummelo (Citrus grandis)	40
27	Cucumber (C. sativus), 2nd leaf	29	68	Ragweed (Ambrosia trifida)	100
28	Cucumber (C. sativus), 3rd leaf	33	69	Redbud (Cercis canadensis)	65
29	Date (Phoenix dactylifera), 12 yr old	43,700	70	Saltbush (Atriplex canescens)	1
30	Desert-lime (Eremocitrus glauca)	60 sq mm	71	Seepweed (Suaeda suffrutescens)	59 sq mm
31	Elm (Ulmus americana)	54	72	Spruce (Picea engelmannii), dry habitat	44 sq mm*
32	Fingerlime (Microcitrus australasica)	40 sq mm	73	Spruce (P. engelmannii), moist habitat	69 sq mm*
33	Fir (Abies lasiocarpa), moist habitat	80 sq mm*	74	Sumac (Rhus trilobata)	21
34	Fir (A. lasiocarpa), dry habitat	55 sq mm*	75	Sunflower (Helianthus annuus)	38
35	Frankenia (Frankenia jamesii)	0.2	76	Tabog (Chaetospermum glutinosum)	8.6
36	Gooseberry (Ribes rotundifolium)	2-16.5	77	Taro (Colocasia antiquorum)	9100
37	Gourd (Cucurbita foetidissima)	560	78	Trifoliate-orange (Poncirus trifoliata)	5
38	Grape, malaga (Vitis vinifera)	125-150	79	Wheat (Triticum aestivum), 1st leaf[3]	5
39	Grape, muscat (V. vinifera)	88	80	Wheat (T. aestivum), 3rd leaf[3]	13
40	Grapefruit (Citrus paradisi)	40-45	81	Wheat (T. aestivum), 5th leaf[3]	15
41	Greggia (Greggia camporum)	2	82	Yellow-poplar (Liriodendron tulipifera)	130
42	Groundsel (Senecio spartioides)	5	83	Zinnia (Zinnia grandiflora)	0.8

/1/ Values are sq cm unless otherwise specified. /2/ Calculated. /3/ Plants under artificial light, 600 ft-c.

Part II: NUMBER OF LEAVES AND TOTAL LEAF SURFACE AREA PER PLANT

	Species	Leaves no./plant	Leaves sq cm/plant		Species	Leaves no./plant	Leaves sq cm/plant
1	Alfalfa (Medicago sativa)	88[1]	16,000	32	Orange (Citrus sinensis), 29 yr old	172,613	2,000,000
2	Apple (Pyrus malus), 2 yr old		11,000	33	Peach (Prunus persica), 5 yr old[3]		922,000
3	Apple (P. malus), 5 yr old		294,000	34	Peach (P. persica), 5 yr old[4]		750,000
4	Apple (P. malus), 9 yr old	20,000	318,000	35	Pepperweed (Lepidium alyssoides)	1318[2]	6700
5	Barley (Hordeum vulgare), 49 da old		900	36	Periwinkle (Vinca rosea), 86 ft-c	163	630
6	Bean (Phaseolus vulgaris), 15 da old	2	98	37	Periwinkle (V. rosea), 300 ft-c	257	1150
7	Beech (Fagus sp), in forest	35,000	780,500[2]		Pine (Pinus banksiana), 36 yr old		
8	Beech (Fagus sp), in open field	200,000	4,460,000[2]	38	Unthinned forest	744,924	390,000*[5]
9	Beet, mangold (Beta vulgaris)		3050	39	Heavily thinned	1,628,022	840,000*[5]
10	Beet, sugar (B. vulgaris)		4080	40	Moderately thinned	891,211	443,000*[5]
11	Catalpa (Catalpa speciosa)	26,024	1,952,000	41	Pine (P. ponderosa), 2 yr old		72*
12	Coldenia (Coldenia hispidissima)	11,560[2]	2300	42	Pine (P. resinosa), 27 yr old, 2x2[6]	19,439	77,900*
13	Corn (Zea mays)		7900	43	Pine (P. resinosa), 27 yr old, 4x4[7]	51,060	205,000*
14	Cotton (Gossypium sp)		535-1200	44	Pine (P. strobus), 27 yr old, 2x2[6]	121,805	149,000*
15	Crownbeard (Verbesina encelioides)		560	45	Pine (P. strobus), 27 yr old, 4x4[7]	186,644	228,000*
16	Cucumber (Cucumis sativus), 135 ft-c		16	46	Potato (Solanum tuberosum)		17,800
17	Cucumber (C. sativus), 270 ft-c		18	47	Raspberry (Rubus occidentalis), shoot		13,100
18	Cucumber (C. sativus), full sun		180-1100	48	Raspberry (R. occidentalis), fruiting cane		16,300
19	Date (Phoenix dactylifera), 12 yr old	120	525 sq m	49	Saltbush (Atriplex canescens)		47,000
20	Fir (Abies alba), trunk diameter 40 cm	15,000,000		50	Seepweed (Suaeda suffrutescens)		3210
21	Fir (A. pectinata)		12,000*	51	Sorghum, red amber (Sorghum vulgare)		4840
22	Frankenia (Frankenia jamesii)	9487[2]	2182	52	Spruce (Picea sp), 4 yr old	6577	550*
23	Gourd (Cucurbita foetidissima)	1617[2]	911,976		Strawberry (Fragaria chiloensis)		
24	Grape, malaga (Vitis vinifera)	32	4000-4900	53	Dunlap, with runners		1440
25	Grape, muscat (V. vinifera)	26	2300-2400	54	Dunlap, without runners		896
26	Milkweed (Asclepias arenaria)	36	1700	55	Strawberry (F. virginiana)		350
27	Morning glory (Ipomoea purpurea)	9[2]	750	56	Sumac (Rhus trilobata)	3000[2]	63,240
28	Oleander (Nerium oleander), 86 ft-c	24	268	57	Sunflower (Helianthus annuus)	59[2]	2260
29	Oleander (N. oleander), 300 ft-c	23	241	58	Taro (Colocasia antiquorum)	10	90,730
30	Orange (Citrus sinensis), 3 yr old	16,419	344,000	59	Wheat (Triticum aestivum), 600 ft-c	5	46-65
31	Orange (C. sinensis), 6 yr old	37,257	590,000				

/1/ Per stem. /2/ Calculated. /3/ Variety Crawford. /4/ Variety Elberta. /5/ Plants under artificial light, 600 ft-c. /6/ Plants, in experimental plots, spaced 2 ft x 2 ft. /7/ Plants spaced 4 ft x 4 ft.

This table is a summary of the salient topographic, ontogenetic, morphologic and functional characteristics of the most common types of cells in tical or experimental demonstration. Only approximate boundaries can be drawn between certain types of cells, and the occurrence of intergra- differentiation when appropriately stimulated. Spores, gametes and many specialized cells (e. g., endodermal cells, secretory cells of glands,

	Cell Type	Origin	Site
1	Apical meristem	Lineal descendents of cells of embryo except in adventitious shoots* and roots*.	Apices of vegetative shoots, developing inflorescences and flowers; in root beneath inner edge of root cap*.
2	Vascular cambial cells	From procambium* and from parenchyma in interfascicular areas, cortex*, and phloem*.	Lateral in stem and root, between secondary xylem* and secondary phloem*.
3	Phellogen (cork cambium)	In stems, first phellogen cells arise from cortex* (most commonly from outermost layer), or from epidermis or phloem* parenchyma cells; in roots from the pericycle*.	Lateral in stem and root, between phellem (cork) and subjacent phelloderm*, cortical or phloem* tissue; also beneath surfaces exposed by abscission of organs (e. g., leaf scars) or beneath wounds.
4	Epidermal cell	From the protoderm*.	The prevalent cell type in the surface layer (epidermis) of foliar and floral organs, young stems and roots.
5	Guard cells	Typically originate in pairs by the division of specific "mother cells" of the protoderm*. A pair of guard cells to- gether with the intercellular space or pore between them is termed a stoma; in many plants, the paired guard cells are flanked or surrounded by distinctive subsidiary cells.	An extremely consistent cell type in the epidermis of foliage leaves and young stems; occurs also rather commonly in the epidermis of various types of floral organs; absent from the epidermis of roots.
6	Phellem (cork)	From phellogen; in stems of some monocotyledons tangen- tially dividing cortical parenchyma cells produce irregular bands of suberized cells termed storied cork.	Peripheral regions of stem, root and certain types of fruits; occurs in some bud scales and petioles; often produced as a result of wounding.
7	Parenchyma	From ground meristem*, procambium*, vascular cambium and phellogen.	Widely distributed throughout plant body; commonly the dom- inant cell type in cortex*, pith*, mesophyll*, fleshy fruits and the endosperm* of seeds; occurs in phloem* and xylem* as the component of vertical parenchyma strands and vascu- lar rays*.
8	Collenchyma	From ground meristem*.	The sole component of cylinders or strands of tissue in the subepidermal portions of stems, petioles and the larger veins of leaves; may occur in cortex* of roots.
9	Sclereid	From protoderm* (e. g., in developing seed coats), ground meristem*, phellogen, vascular cambium and procambium*; frequently arises by sclerosis* of a fully developed paren- chyma cell. some dicotyledonous	Common in seed coats and fruits; diffusely arranged in cor- tex*, functioning phloem*, outer bark, pith* and mesophyll* as idioblast* or as component of cell clusters; in leaves of genera restricted to vein endings (terminal sclereids).
10	Fiber	From protoderm*, ground meristem*, procambium* and vascular cambium.	Cortex*, primary and secondary vascular tissues of stem and root; epidermis of certain leaves; a component of the hypodermal strands or layers and the sclerenchymatous* sheaths of vascular bundles* in many kinds of leaves; may occur as an idioblast*.
11	Tracheid	From procambium* and vascular cambium. mous leaves; tracheid-like cells occuring as idioblasts* or components of cell layers or groups in angio- spermous leaves are termed "storage tracheids";	Primary and secondary xylem*; in a modified form, the dis- tinctive cell type in the transfusion tissue* of gymnosper- commonly formed in masses in cultures of callus* tissue.
12	Vessel member	From procambium* and vascular cambium.	Primary and secondary xylem* of most dicotyledons; absent from xylem* of all gymnosperms except members of the Gnetales; in certain monocotyledons, restricted to the pri- mary xylem* of the root.
13	Sieve cell	From procambium* and vascular cambium.	Primary and secondary phloem* of gymnosperms.
14	Sieve-tube member	From procambium* and vascular cambium.	Primary and secondary phloem* of angiosperms.
15	Laticifers	Non-articulated type from a single initial cell which develops into a continuous tube often ramifying throughout the plant; articulated type from an interconnected and progressively developed series of cells in which occurs a complete or partial resorption of certain cell walls.	Cortex*, phloem*, xylem rays*, pith*, mesophyll*.

GLOSSARY: ADVENTITIOUS SHOOT: A shoot arising from internodal regions of the stem, from roots, leaves, or from callus. ADVENTITIOUS wound-surfaces of stems, petioles, and roots. CORTEX: The zone of primary tissues situated between the epidermis and the vascular cylinder meristems or to different cell types. ENDOSPERM: Food-storing parenchymatous tissue in seeds, sometimes with massively-thickened cell dual cell which differs markedly in form, size, wall structure or contents from neighboring tissue-elements. LENTICEL: A small restricted MESOPHYLL: The photosynthetic parenchyma tissue of the leaf enclosed by the epidermis. PERICYCLE: The uniseriate or multiseriate zone suberized walls produced inwardly by the phellogen. PHLOEM: One of the tissues of the conductive or vascular system of the plant body; the cell, usually paired with a similar cavity in the adjacent cell; such pit-pairs are separated from each other by a common pit membrane. pressions in the primary walls of plant cells traversed by groups of protoplasmic strands or plasmodesmata; one or more pits may develop over primary vascular system (primary phloem and primary xylem) originates. PROSENCHYMATOUS: A term designating a cell which is conspic- arises; in some cases, cells internal to the epidermis may also originate from the protoderm. ROOT CAP: A thimble-shaped or conical mass of because of the presence of thick, usually lignified cell walls. SCLEROSIS: The process whereby a parenchyma cell acquires a thick lignified sec- TISSUE: A tissue composed of relatively short, broad tracheids which flanks or surrounds the vascular bundles in gymnospermous leaves; in ening tissue composed primarily of phloem and xylem. VASCULAR RAY: A radial band or sheet of parenchyma cells produced by the division phloem is a phloem ray; the two are continuous. XYLEM: One of the tissues of the conductive or vascular system of the plant body; the definitive

seed plants.   The typology adopted for the table reflects individual interpretation of morphologic data and hence is not subject to rigorous statis-
dations is indicated at several points in the table.   Moreover, many types of living cells are capable of growth, division and further structural
epithelial cells of resin ducts, cells of hairs) have not been included. Terms followed by an asterisk (*) are defined in the Glossary below.

Morphology	Functions	
Polyhedral; primary wall thin or irregularly thickened; primary pit fields* may be present; nucleus large, ovoid; cytoplasm vacuolated to varying degrees; mitochondria, plastid primordia and storage products may be present.	Point of origin of primary meristematic tissues, e.g., protoderm*, ground meristem* and procambium* from which primary body of shoot and root develops; in shoot apex, gives rise to the tissue of a leaf primordium.	1
Two types of cambial cells, viz.: elongate fusiform initials, from which tracheary elements, sieve elements, fibers and vertical parenchyma are derived, and ray initials, from which vascular rays* originate; cytoplasm of both kinds of initials highly vacuolated; primary walls with conspicuous pit fields.	Produce secondary phloem* and secondary xylem* cells. Growth in diameter of woody stems and roots results from tissue-formation by cambial cells.	2
Rectangular and radially flattened in transectional view, polygonal or nearly isodiametric in longisection; walls thin; cytoplasm vacuolated; may contain tannins and chloroplasts.	Produces phellem cells outwardly and in many cases, phelloderm cells* inwardly; forms complementary cells of lenticels*.	3
Polygonal, elongated or with undulate contour in surface view, variable in radial dimensions; walls thin or thick, the outer wall often the thickest; primary pit fields* present; walls typically cutinized (may be lignified or silicified), the outer wall covered by a cuticle except in roots; plastids, anthocyanin pigments and ergastic substances may occur.	Mechanical protection; restriction of transpiration; storage of H_2O and metabolic products; photosynthesis; H_2O absorption in roots; by division and dedifferentiation* may contribute to origin of adventitious shoots* and roots*.	4
Usually crescentic or kidney-shaped in surface view; walls unevenly thickened, cutinized and overlaid by a cuticle; often with ridge-like extensions above and below the pore; conspicuous starch-forming chloroplasts present; protoplast physiologically active in mature cells but rarely divides in response to wound or other stimuli.	Stomata are the important points of diffusion of gases through the epidermis. Reversible changes in turgor of guard cells result in the opening or closure of the pore.	5
Rectangular in transection and more or less radially flattened; irregular or rectangular in longisection; secondary wall typically suberized and occasionally lignified; pits absent; devoid of protoplasm at maturity.	Mechanical protection; restriction of transpiration. may contain resin and tannins.	6
Varies widely in shape from approximately tetrakaidecahedral to elongated or stellately branched; primary walls thin or thick, often with conspicuous pit fields; thick lignified secondary walls with pits* common in parenchyma cells of secondary xylem*; plastids and a wide range of ergastic substances present.	Photosynthesis; food and H_2O storage; secretion and excretion; commonly the protoplast retains marked capacity for growth, division and dedifferentiation* and hence prominently concerned in wound healing, formation of callus* tissue, and the origin of adventitious shoots* and roots*.	7
Relatively short and prismatic or elongated with tapering ends; primary walls unevenly thickened, composed of cellulose and pectin and with high percentage of H_2O; primary pit fields present; chloroplasts common; collenchyma and cortical parenchyma cells frequently intergrade in form and structure.	Mechanical support for growing stems and leaves; protoplast retains capacity for growth, division and dedifferentiation*.	8
Form extremely variable: polyhedral, columnar, fusiform, filiform, irregularly lobed or profusely branched; in some cases intergrades in form with fibers; secondary wall thick and lignified (sometimes with embedded crystals); pits* usually simple, often ramiform; protoplast may be retained at maturity.	Produces hard incompressible texture of many tissues.	9
Typical example of a prosenchymatous* cell, often reaching considerable length; secondary wall usually thick, often highly lignified; pits* abundant or sparse, simple or with greatly reduced borders; protoplast usually absent at maturity; a living protoplast and various ergastic materials occur in septate fibers; in secondary xylem* of dicotyledons, fibers and tracheids frequently intergrade in form and structure.	Mechanical support.	10
Typically elongated, with blunt, tapering or inclined ends; imperforate at maturity; secondary wall lignified, deposited in a wide variety of frequently intergrading patterns, i.e., as rings, one or several helical bands, transverse or oblique bars, a network, or as a continuous layer interrupted only by bordered pits*; devoid of protoplast at maturity.	Conduction of H_2O and mineral solutes; mechanical support.	11
Elongated to drum-shaped, with inclined or transverse perforated end walls; developed as a component member of an extensive series of superposed cells termed collectively a vessel; perforations usually restricted to end walls and are either single (simple perforation plate) or multiple (scalariform, reticulate and foraminate types of perforation plates); secondary wall lignified, with same range of patterns as in tracheid; devoid of protoplast at maturity.	Conduction of H_2O and mineral solutes; and possibly mechanical support.	12
Elongate in form with overlapping inclined or tapering ends; sieve areas numerous, all similar and relatively unspecialized in structure; each sieve area is a portion of the primary wall traversed by connecting strands of cytoplasm enclosed by cylinders of callose; protoplast at maturity enucleate, devoid of stainable contents and starch; usually connected with modified parenchyma cells termed albuminous cells.	Conduction of organic solutes.	13
Elongated in form with inclined or transverse end walls; developed as a component member of a series of superposed cells termed collectively a sieve tube; end walls with highly specialized sieve areas termed sieve plates; sieve plates simple (one sieve area) or compound (many sieve areas); lateral walls usually bear less specialized sieve areas; protoplast at maturity enucleate and devoid of stainable contents and starch; usually connected with one or more nucleated parenchyma cells termed companion cells, the latter ontogenetically developed as sister cells of the sieve-tube member.	Conduction of organic solutes.	14
Contain latex and are multi-nucleate; primary walls often relatively thick in mature tubes; non-articulated type an unbranched or very often a profusely branched tube; vertical series of articulated laticifers may become joined by lateral anastomoses into a complex network.	Probably excretory because of storage of such apparently non-functional metabolic products as rubber and resin; role of laticifers as food conducting and food storing structures doubtful.	15

ROOTS: Roots arising from stems, leaves, or from callus.   CALLUS: Tissue composed of parenchyma which originates by proliferation from in roots and stems.   DEDIFFERENTIATION: The process by which living physiologically mature cells resume growth and division, giving rise to walls.   GROUND MERISTEM: The undifferentiated tissue of a young organ exclusive of the protoderm and procambium.   IDIOBLAST: An individ-area of loosely-arranged cells situated in the periderm; the latter consists of the phellem (or cork), the phellogen, and the phelloderm. of parenchymatous tissue at the periphery of the primary vascular cylinder in roots.   PHELLODERM CELLS: Parenchymatous cells with un-definitive conductive cell types in the phloem are the sieve cell and the sieve-tube member.   PIT: A cavity or recess in the secondary wall of a PITH: A central column of tissue in the stem and in certain roots, bounded externally by the vascular cylinder.   PRIMARY PIT FIELDS: De-each pit field if a secondary wall is formed.   PROCAMBIUM: Undifferentiated tissue composed of more or less elongated cells from which the uously elongated in form with tapering ends.   PROTODERM: The undifferentiated surface cell layer of young organs from which the epidermis parenchymatous tissue occupying the true apex of the root.   SCLERENCHYMATOUS: A term designating cells or tissues which are hard or tough ondary wall; may occur late in the functional life of the parenchyma element and sometimes coincides with a change in its form.   TRANSFUSION Pinus, living parenchyma cells as well as tracheids occur in the transfusion tissue.   VASCULAR BUNDLE: A strand of conducting and strength-of ray initials in the vascular cambium.   That portion of a vascular ray found in the secondary xylem is a xylem ray; that portion in the secondary conductive cell types are the tracheid and vessel member.   XYLEM RAY: See Vascular Ray.

Part I:

	Tissue	Cell Division in Postnatal Life	Mode of Postnatal Growth
1	Adrenal	Mitosis adult rat: zona capsula, 0.13%; zona glomerulosa, 0.17%; zona fasciculata, 0.13%; zona reticularis, 0.06%; total gland, 0.12%. Considerably higher figures in young rat.	Principally by cell division. Capsule may contribute.
2	Alimentary canal	Dividing cells in crypts of duodenum and ileum. In rat, make up 3% of all cells; cycle, 1.13 hr. In stomach, dividing cells at base of foveolae.	Cell division and differentiation in mucous membrane. Muscle, by combination of cell division and increase in cell size.
3	Blood erythrocytes	Confined largely to erythroblasts in bone marrow; dividing cells in man, 1.17-1.83%.	In precursors, growth phase sharply separated from phase of hemoglobin formation.
4	Blood granulocytes	Confined largely to myeloblasts (2.7%) and myelocytes (0.46%) in bone marrow.	Growth stages sharply demarcated from the stages of granule formation.
5	Blood lymphocytes	In tissues of origin. Dividing cells in 3 mo rat: thymus, 0.22%; lymph nodes, 0.058%; lymph follicles in spleen, 0.058%.	Derived from reticulum cells and may be converted to other forms, but this is disputed. In dog, 25 times 10^6/kg/hr enter circulation; in cat, 35 times 10^6.
6	Blood platelets	Division of circulating platelets not described.	Evidence favors formation in marrow from cytoplasmic fragmentation of megakaryocytes.
7	Brain and spinal cord	Very rare but has been recorded.	Growth of axones; myelization of fiber tracts; may not be completed until 18th yr in man.
8	Heart	Negligible in cardiac muscle.	Increase in size of muscle fibers. In rabbit, from birth to maturity, diameter of fibers increases times 2.6 (to 19μ); in man, times 2.6 (to 14μ).
9	Kidney	Rare after early postnatal life except for regeneration in rodents. [1]	Increase in size of cells and structures. In man, from birth to maturity, diameter of glomerulus increases from 118-240μ; of proximal collecting tubules, from 18-34μ to 40-64μ. In rat, early postnatal growth partially caused by peripheral undifferentiated nephrogenic zone; number of nephrons doubled in first two weeks of postnatal life.
10	Liver	In rat, dividing cells rise from low values to 3.3% on 23rd da, then return to low values; mitotic percentage in adult albino rat, 0.005%.	In early life, considerable contribution from cell division; later, from increase in cell size.
11	Muscle, striped	Very scant and confined to nuclei. Some amitotic divisions.	Enlargement of fibers, possible splitting of fibers. In newborn, some continued formation from mesenchyme cells. Hypertrophy caused by increase of sarcoplasm in pre-existing cells.
12	Ovary	Mitosis demonstrated in germinal epithelium and, during early pregnancy, granulosa and theca interna cells.	In rabbit, follicles increase in size exponentially with time; completed in 18 da; total number of oocytes in gland related to age: log(number)=4.561-0.476 log(age in da).
13	Pancreas; submaxillary		Decrease of relative amount of connective tissue after birth; adult proportions reached at 11th-16th yr.
14	Parathyroid	Dividing cells in mice: 8 da, 0.07%; 18 da, 0.71%; 28 da, 0.1%.	Multiplication of clear or stem cells which differentiate into "dark" cells.
15	Prostate	In rat, mitosis numerous to 20th da; scant at 100 da. cell size and diameter of acini. From 11-55 da height of cells increases from 18-34μ, and diameter acini from 43-170μ. Growth affected by hormonal activity. In man, some squamous metaplasia in newborn.	In rat, by cell proliferation to 20th da, then by increase of cell size and diameter of acini.
16	Skin	Occurs in varying proportions in stratum basalis and spinosum. In adult mice, 2-8 dividing cells/cm length of 7μ ear section; duration of mitotic cycle, 2.5 hr. Number of divisions varies with time of da, carbohydrate metabolism, hormonal stimuli, etc. In newborn mice, 2-4% of nucleated cells in mitosis. Mitotic percentage in the planta of the rat (250g) averages 5.24% for 24 hr at 27°C.	Division of cells in deeper layers followed by differentiation.
17	Testis	In albino rat, cycle of spermatogonial division, 48 min. Spermatogenic wave lasts 4 da; spermatogenic cycle takes 16 da.	
18	Thymus	Mitosis: adult rabbit, 0.52%; 3 mo rat, 0.22%.	Weight in man: birth, 12g; puberty, 40g; 60 yr, 15g.
19	Thyroid	100-125 dividing cells recorded in whole gland of guinea pig; proliferation of undifferentiated interfollicular cells.	Following possibilities described: new follicles by budding; proliferation of cells derived from follicles.
20	Uterus	glands and muscle fibers; cell division of epithelial and muscle elements in addition; new muscle fibers may form from indifferent cells. Menstruation: in proliferative phase mitosis in endometrium rises 0.56% and nuclei of muscle fibers increase in size; regression of secretory phase: denuded surface covered in 7 da by cells from remaining glands.	Pregnancy: enlargement of pre-existing epithelial cells,

[1] In peripheral nerves.

Part II: INCREMENTS OF WEIGHT

Each value is derived from the weight at the end of a time period

Tissue	Prenatal Period[1]			Birth to Adult	Tissue	Prenatal Period[1]			Birth to Adult
	8-12 wk	12-16 wk	20-24 wk			8-12 wk	12-16 wk	20-24 wk	
1 Brain	15	4.5	1.7	3.7	4 Liver	17	3.6	1.8	18
2 Heart	6.5	4.3	1.9	15	5 Muscle,striped				30-40
3 Kidney	75	6.7	1.6	10	6 Ovary				37

[1] 280 da.

GENERAL

Life Span of Cells	Mechanism of Cell Replacement	Regenerative Capacity	
In cortex, uncertain but phagocytosis occurs in zona reticularis.	In cortex, cell division and migration of cells from superficial to deeper layers.	In cortex, after damage, repair by cell division but limited in adult. Active regeneration follows postnatal degeneration. Mitosis very scanty in medulla; postnatal growth from cell enlargement.	1
In small intestine, rat: 60-70% superficial epithelium shed/da; cell lives 1.57 da in duodenum, 1.35 da in ileum. Oral mucosa, rabbit, 5.1(4.5-5.7)/1000 cells [diurnal variation 3.8(3.6-4.0) and 7.2(6.6-7.8)]. Mitotic duration calculated as 64 min. Intermitotic period calculated as 208 hr.	Cells multiply in crypts in base of foveolae, move toward lumen and differentiate.	After removal of mucous membrane in dog's stomach, denuded area covered by growth of undifferentiated epithelium at rate of 2 mm/wk. Healing in 10 da if muscularis mucosae intact, 130 da if muscle destroyed. Brunner's glands can undergo limited regeneration. Cat's stomach: movement at 0.2-0.4 mm/hr; sudden loss of epithelium made good in a few hr.	2
120 da most generally accepted.	See Mode. In man, 0.83% red cells replaced each da.	In rabbit, recovery from 30% blood loss, 3 wk; in rat, 7 da. In man, recovery from loss of 600 ml, 50 da.	3
Neutrophils estimated at 7-80 hr; disappear from blood of cat at rate of 881/cu mm/hr.	Esinophilis, 10-14 da.	Replaced 1.5 times/da in cat.	4
Approximately 24 hr. Removed from blood by lungs, spleen, lymph glands, skin, intestine.	See Mode. Replacement in blood stream about twice a day.	Limited regeneration of lymph nodes after removal in young rabbits; mesenchyme cells form complete gland in 3-4 wks.	5
In cat, 2-4 da; utilization at rate of 2500/cu mm blood/hr.	After loss, new formation begins in a few hr. Normal regained 3-4 da.		6
Coextensive with normal function.	Confined to neuroglia.	Very largely confined to neuroglia; some axone formation. Regeneration of motor axones occurs at 4 mm/da after latent period of 7± da. A large number of factors affect rate. Preganglionic fibers[1] of cat regenerate in 36-61 da; function restored in 44 da.	7
Coextensive with normal function.	None.	Negligible. Hypertrophy caused by increase in size of fibers. Rabbit: normal diameter, 19.2μ; hypertrophied, 22.2μ; man, normal, 14μ; hypertrophied, 25μ.	8
Very largely coextensive with normal function.	By cell division in tubules.	True regeneration observed in rats. Hypertrophy caused by enlargement of existing elements, but increased cell division has been demonstrated after unilateral nephrectomy in the rat.	9
No figure quotable.	Dividing cells persist in small numbers in adult presumably to replace cell loss. Division also occurs in smaller extent in duct cells.	In rat, extirpation of 2/3 regenerated in 21 da, caused by cell division in the parenchymal cells, and to a Kupffer cells and connective tissue cells.	10
Coextensive with normal function.	Normally none.	Protoplasmic outgrowth from pre-existing fibers in which nuclei may divide by amitosis. Outgrowth begins 3rd da after injury, progresses at 1 - 1.5 mm/da. New fibers 30% normal diameter in 21 da; normal diameter in 4 mo. No new formation from indifferent cells.	11
Fertility of shed ova lost: rabbit, 12 hr; guinea pig, 26 hr; ferret, 30 hr.		No regeneration of ova but marked regeneration activity of germinal epithelium after hormonal stimulation.	12
		Limited amount after resection or duct ligation. Mitosis in acinar cells and duct epithelium, the latter giving rise to acinar cells and islet cells. In rat, submaxillary gland regeneration by division of acinar cells in 1st week, followed by proliferation of ducts with acini formed with terminal portions.	13
		Negligible. Hypertrophy and hyperplasia in chronic nephritis.	14
	Regeneration after surgical removal very rare in man.		15
Variable and dependent on rate of shedding of keratinized cells. Plantar epidermis cells of rat 19.1 da, of which 16.9 da are spent in basal layer and 2.2 da in stratum granulosum. Mitotic index: in corneal epithelium, rat (80-150g), 0.4%. arm, 1.5; face, 2.1-3.5.	See Mode. Adjustment between cell loss and cell formation. from hair follicles. Rate of healing greater in larger wounds. Growth of granulation tissue checked by epithelial overgrowth. Nails (man): growth 95μ/da (thumb). Fingernail growth 4 times toenail. Hair: length of cycle depends on thickness. Man: head, 3 yr; eyebrow, 120 da. Body of rat, 35 da. Rate of growth (man) varies with site (mm/wk): head, 2.7; Replacement by multiplication and differentiation of cells at bottom of hair follicles.	Re-epithelization of wounds by proliferation and migration of adjacent cells. Regeneration possible	16
Sperm survival time: in man, 48-72 hr; horse, 12 hr; mouse, 13.5 hr; rabbit, 96 hr; some bats may overwinter.		Possible after slight injury. In rabbit, 1 da in abdominal cavity causes loss of spermatogenic elements, with restoration in 2 wk.	17
			18
		After partial removal, hypertrophy of remainder preventable by iodine administration.	19
	scar. Smooth muscle fibers retain some power of division; new formation possible from undifferentiated connective tissue cells. Regeneration (smooth muscle) after injury limited, and fibrous scar usual.	Experimental incision in mouse heals in 48 hr without	20

INCREASE: MAN

divided by the weight at the beginning of the same time period.

Tissue	Prenatal Period[1]			Birth to Adult	Tissue	Prenatal Period[1]			Birth to Adult
	8-12 wk	12-16 wk	20-24 wk			8-12 wk	12-16 wk	20-24 wk	
7 Pancreas	Av 16	Av 16	1.6	20-40	10 Thymus	400	3.7	1.9	
8 Pituitary	2.5	3	1.7	3-6	11 Thyroid		6.6	2.2	14
9 Adrenal cortex	25	5	1.7		12 Uterus				27

125. EMBRYONIC GERM LAYERS AND DERIVATIVES: MAMMALS (EUTHERIA)

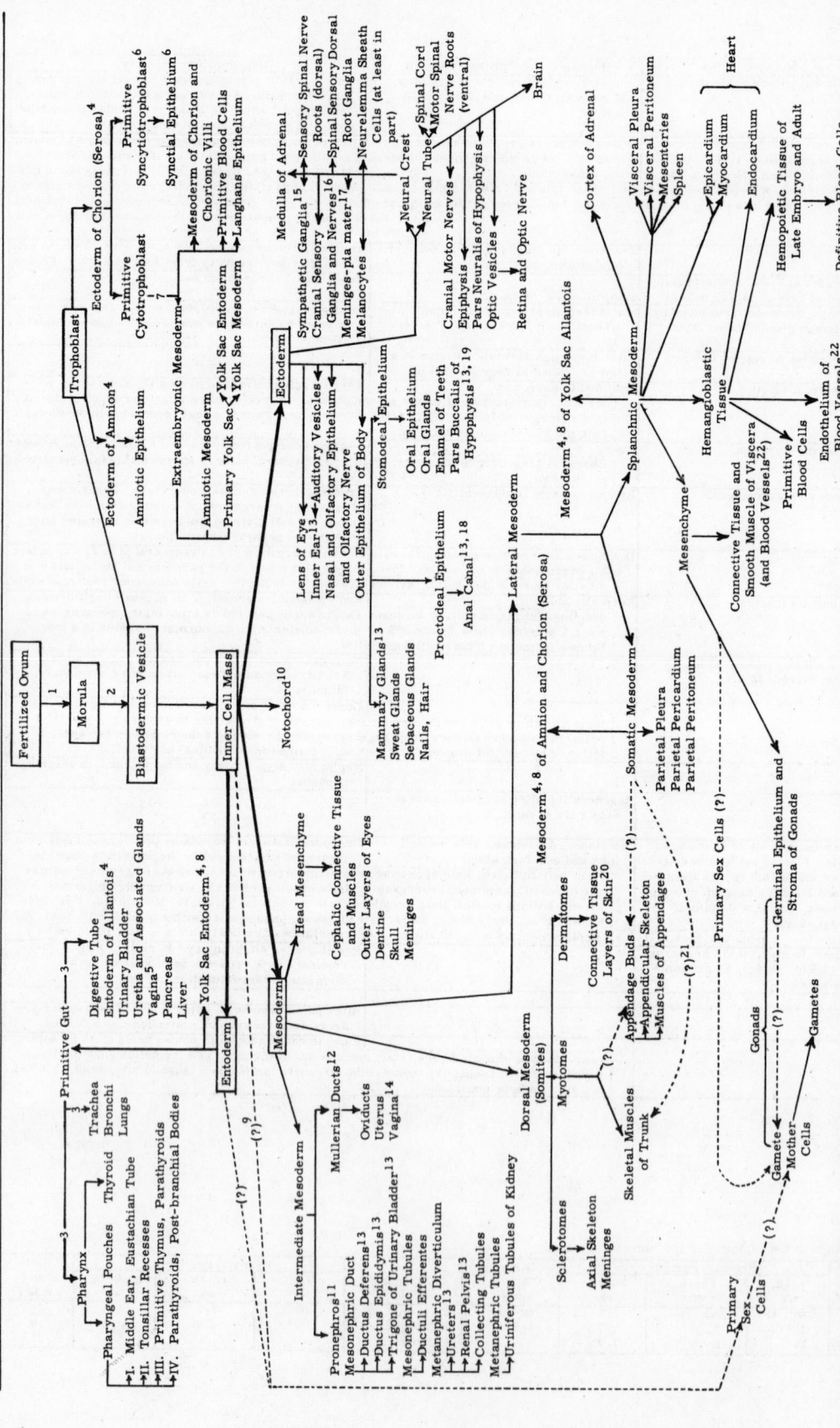

/1/ By cleavage divisions. /2/ By hollowing out and expansion. /3/ Epithelial portion of the structure from entoderm, remainder from mesoderm. /4/ Extraembryonic, i.e., part of the placenta or other extraembryonic membranes. /5/ Lower part. /6/ Variable; not present in all mammals. /7/ In primates only. /8/ Probably not in primates. /9/ In man. /10/ Embryonic structure. May form nucleus pulposus of intervertebral discs. /11/ Embryonic structure; disappears. /12/ Or from splanchnic mesoderm of peritoneum. /13/ Epithelial portion of the structure from ectoderm remainder from mesoderm. /14/ Upper part. /15/ Absolute derivation of neural crest on disputed grounds. /16/ Evidence from lower vertebrates that a portion of these may be derived from ectodermal placodes. /17/ Probably only part of pia mater, not dura or arachnoid. /18/ In part only. /19/ Anterior lobe and pars intermedia of the pituitary. /20/ In region of somites only. /21/ Ventral and lateral part, evidence from chick only. /22/ Not all from splanchnic mesoderm; some from somatic mesoderm or head mesenchyme.

152

126. PRENATAL DEVELOPMENT, REFLEX AND SPONTANEOUS MOTOR ACTIVITIES: MAMMALS

This table gives no clue to the combination of activities constituting a single response, except that activities reported as observed at the same gestation age may, in some instances, form a response pattern. Unless otherwise indicated (as "spontaneous"), each response is to be considered an induced exteroceptive reflex.

Motor Activity	Gestation Period, %[1]				
	Man[2]	Cat[3]	Guinea Pig[4]	Rat[5]	Sheep[6]
1 Earliest spontaneous[7] activity[8]	22.5	36	40		22.3
2 Earliest proprioceptive activity[8]	18.7-23.8				21.6-28[9]
3 Appearance of earliest and latest exteroceptive reflexes[10]	18.7-80	26-74	38-76	75-90	26-57[11]
Head					
4 Extension	26	42	48	76-79	26
5 Lateral flexion at neck	18.7	37-38	48	76	23-29[12]
6 Ventral flexion	32	36-42	52		35
7 Rotation	28	36-42	51	76	24.8-26[12]
Face					
8 Forehead movements	28		60		
9 Palpebral muscle movements	28		54		
10 Eyes, movement globus oculi	31		58		32[7]
11 Oronasal muscle movements	31	39	58	90	32
12 Lip movements	31		54		
13 Mouth closing	31		54	90	26
14 Mouth opening	23.8		52	77	26-32[12]
15 Mouth pursing	55				
16 Tongue movements	35	44-56	55	77	
17 Sucking	72[13]	74	55		31
18 Swallowing	30				51
19 Phonation	59[13]	74			
Neck					
20 Extension	26		39		24.2-35[12]
21 Lateral flexion	18.7	39-41	39	76	29
22 Ventral flexion		50	38		26
Trunk					
23 Rotation or twisting	35	67	54	81	24.2-31[14]
24 Chest contractions, respiratory	30-32				24.27
25 Diaphragmatic contractions, resp.	55				
26 Effective respiration	59[13]				
27 Abdominal muscle contractions	38	42-50	46-58[12]	81	
28 Cremasteric reflex	80	42-47	76	86	50
Upper trunk[15]					
30 Extension	26	42	45	76	
31 Lateral flexion	20	36-39	40-46[7]	75-76[16]	23-26[12]
32 Ventral flexion		38	43	77	24.27
Lower trunk[15]					
34 Extension	26	42	45	76	
35 Lateral flexion	21.2	39	40-46[7]	75	24.27

Motor Activity	Gestation Period, %[1]				
	Man[2]	Cat[3]	Guinea Pig[4]	Rat[5]	Sheep[6]
Rump					
36 Extension	26	52	55	81	
37 Lateral flexion		41	49	76	
38 Ventral flexion	21.2	39-48[17]		77	
39 Rotation		47		81	
Upper extremity					
40 Movement with trunk	21.2	37		76	
41 Adduction at shoulder		50	48		
42 Abduction at shoulder	29	33	39	75[16]	23-26[12]
43 Extension at shoulder	21.2	39	39		26
44 Flexion at shoulder		35-39			26
45 Rotation, medial					
46 Elbow extension	30	38			24.87
47 Elbow flexion	28	39	48		24.8-28[12]
48 Forearm pronation					
49 Wrist extension		58[16]		86	
50 Wrist flexion	28	38-48	48	75-81[17]	
51 Pollex flexion	26				
52 Pollex opposition	32				
53 Finger flexion	26				
54 Finger closure, maintained	38		54		
55 Grasp	46				
Lower extremity					
56 Movement with trunk	26			77	57
57 Scratch reflex		54	54		
58 Abduction at hip		67	67		
59 Adduction at hip					
60 Extension at hip	29	24.2-47[12]	51	81	
61 Flexion at hip	28	42-45	48	86	26
62 Rotation, lateral	28				
63 Rotation, medial					
64 Knee extension	32	44-58[17]			24.87
65 Knee flexion	29	68[16]			24.87
66 Ankle adduction					
67 Ankle dorsiflexion	29				
68 Ankle plantar flexion		61			24.87
69 Ankle rotation		68[16]			24.87
70 Hallux dorsiflexion	34				
71 Hallux plantar flexion	28				
72 Toe fanning	34				
73 Toe dorsiflexion	34	73[16]			
74 Toe plantar flexion	28	73[16]			

/1/ Per cent of gestation period = per cent of total gestation period elapsed at the time the motor activity appears. The gestation period is measured from the time of insemination except for man, in which case measurement is from the first day of the last menstrual period. To convert, in the case of man, to per cent of gestation period on insemination age, the following equation may be employed:

$$\text{Corrected per cent} = \frac{(\text{given per cent} \times 40) - 200}{38}$$

/2/ Gestation period = 280 da measured from the beginning of the last menstrual period; corrected = 266 da from ovulation. /3/ Gestation period = 66 da (see Fn 1). /4/ Gestation period = 67 da (see Fn 1). /5/ Gestation period = 21 da (see Fn 1). /6/ Gestation period = 157 da (see Fn 1). /7/ Spontaneous activity; believed to be essentially reflex in mammals. /8/ Unspecified. /9/ Doubtful reflex at the lower limit of this range. /10/ Complex patterns of behavior; behavior released by the head exteroceptors not included. /11/ Doubtful reflex at 22.3% of gestation period. /12/ See Fn 7; the qualification applies only to the lower limit of this range. /13/ Human fetus viable at 68% of gestation period (27 wk). /14/ Spontaneous activity at 26% of gestation period. /15/ Data for guinea pig do not distinguish between movements of the upper and lower segments of the trunk. /16/ Movement is reported without specific data as to direction of movement. /17/ See Fn 16; the qualification applies only to the lower limit of this range.

127. PRENATAL DEVELOPMENT, VARIOUS ORGANS AND TISSUES: CHICK

Time of origin is expressed in three ways, depending on available information: (1) days or hours of incubation, (2) number of pairs of somites, or (3) normal "stages" as described by Hamburger, V., and Hamilton, H. L. J. Morphology 88:49, 1951. Data adapted from Lillie's "Development of the Chick," Henry Holt & Co., 1952. Footnotes refer to onset of function only.

#	Organ or Structure	Time of Origin	Site of Origin
1	Abducens nerve	3rd da	Floor of myelencephalon beneath nerve VII.
2	Acrochordal cartilage	4½ da	At anterior tip of notochord.
3	Acoustico-facialis ganglion		Anterior edge of auditory pit.
4	Facial component	By stage of 15 s	From neural crest and posterodorsal epibranchial placode of 1st visceral furrow.
5	Acoustic component	21 s	From wall of auditory vesicle.
	Adrenal gland		
6	Cortical component[1]	78 hr	Coelomic epithelium at level of somites 17-22.
7	Medullary component[1]	4-7 da	From migratory cells of neural crest and sympathetic ganglia.
	Air sacs of lung[2]		
8	Primary bronchi and mesobronchi	4 da	Posterior end of trachea.
9	Entobronchi (secondary bronchi)	6th da	Mesial wall of anterior part of mesobronchus.
10	Ectobronchi (secondary bronchi)	6th da	Dorsal surface of middle part of mesobronchus.
11	Parabronchi (tertiary bronchi)	8-11 da	From secondary bronchus.
12	Allantois	28 s	Floor of hindgut just anterior to anal plate.
13	Amnion (and Chorion)[3]	8-9 s	Anterior edge of proamnion (in front of head).
14	Posterior amniotic fold	27 s	From somatopleure posterior to tail.
15	Aorta, dorsal[4]	5 s	From hemangioblasts at ventrolateral margin of somites.
16	Aorta, ventral	3-5 s	From hemangioblasts continuous anteriorly with primordia of heart.
17	Aortic arch 1[4]	9-10 s	Anterior to hyomandibular cleft.
18	Aortic arch 2	19-24 s	Posterior to hyomandibular cleft.
19	Aortic arch 3	26 s	Between visceral clefts 2 and 3.
20	Aortic arch 4[5]	36 s	Between visceral clefts 3 and 4.
21	Aortic arch 5[5]	4th da	Just anterior to aortic arch 6 and attached to the base and summit of arch 6.
22	Aortic arch 6	4th da	Behind 4th visceral cleft.
23	Auditory ossicles	5-6 da	From mesoderm above dorsal extremity of tubo-tympanic cavity.
24	Basioccipital bone	After 13 da	Skull.
25	Beak	5 da (Stage 27)	
	Blood cells		
26	Granulocytes	3 da	
27	Neutrophils	5 da	
28	Eosinophils	7 da	Spleen (?).
29	Basophils	14 da	Spleen (?).
30	Lymphocytes	17 da	Spleen and other lymphatic areas.
31	Macrophages	12 s	From endothelium or mesenchyme.
32	Thrombocytes	3-4 da	
33	Bursa of Fabricius[6]	5-6 da	Posterodorsal wall of cloaca.
34	Cecal processes	7th da	Junction of small and large intestine.
35	Canal of Schlemm	8th da	Margin of anterior chamber of eye.
36	Cardinal vein, anterior	12 s	From intersegmental capillary sprouts of the dorsal aorta.
37	Cerebellar fissures	10-11 da	External surface of cerebellum.
	Chorion (see Amnion)		
	Chromaffin cells (see Adrenal, medullary component)		
38	Ciliary processes[7]	8th da	From ciliary region of lenticular zone of optic cup.
39	Circulation of blood[7]	8-9 da	
	Clavicle ossification		

#	Organ or Structure	Time of Origin	Site of Origin
78	Hindgut	21 s	In splanchnopleure, with appearance of tail fold.
79	Hypoglossus (Cranial nerve XII)	78 hr	From ventral part of neural tube opposite somites 3-4.
80	Hypothalamus	97 hr	Ventral wall of diencephalon.
81	Interatrial septum	50-55 hr	From vault of atrium between openings of sinus venosus and pulmonary vein.
82	Interstitial cells	13th da	In stroma of testis.
83	Interventricular septum	4th da	Along sulcus from bulbo-atrial angle towards apex of heart.
84	Islets of Langerhans[11]	8-9 da	Within pancreatic diverticula.
85	Jaw, upper	4-5 da	Fusion of fronto-nasal and maxillary processes.
86	Jugal bone	9th da	Skull.
87	Jugular lymph sac	7 da	Fusion of lymphatic vessels near anterior cardinal vein.
88	Labial groove	Stage 36 (10 da)	In periderm of tip of jaws.
89	Laryngotracheal groove	23 s	Postbranchial floor of pharynx.
90	Leg bud	50-60 hr (Stages 16-17)	Somatopleure lateral to posterior-most somites and segmental plate.
91	Lens invagination	20-21 s	Ectoderm overlying optic vesicle.
92	Lingual glands	11 da	From oral epithelium beneath lateral margin of tongue.
93	Liver[12]	22 s	Diverticula of the entoderm of the anterior intestinal portal.
94	Lungs[2]	23 s	Postbranchial floor of pharynx.
95	Mandible, ossification	9th da	
96	Mandibular glands	8th da	Solid ingrowths of mucosa from base of tongue forward to near mandibular symphysis.
97	Mantle layer of spinal cord	3rd da	From middle zone of neural tube.
98	Maxilla (bone)	9th da	
99	Mesenteric vein	5th da	
100	Mesenteries, accessory	60 hr	In dorsal mesentery, near level of dorsal pancreas. Mesenchymatous outgrowths of splanchnic mesodermal covering of lateral wall of esophagus.
101	Mesocardia, lateral	10 s	At point of contact of somatopleure with proximal part of vitelline veins.
102	Mesonephric tubules[13]	29-30 s	From nephrotome between somites 13-14 and 30.
103	Mesothalamus	97 hr	Lateral wall of diencephalon.
104	Metanephric tubules[14]	7-8 da	Metanephrogenous blastema just behind level of umbilical arteries.
105	Nares, external and internal	4-5 da	By fusion of median and lateral frontonasal processes with maxillary processes of visceral arch I.
106	Nasal bone	9th da	
107	Nasal (olfactory) pits	Stage 17	Ectoderm of ventrolateral sides of head opposite telencephalon.
108	Neostriatum	8-12 da	Telencephalic cortex.
109	Neural crest	6-7 s	In head.
110	Neural folds	Stages 6-7	Anterior end of medullary plate.
111	Neural tube	Stage 8	Level of future mid-brain.
112	Neuroblasts, retinal	4th da	Fundus of retina.
113	Nictitating membrane	7th da	From semilunar fold of integument within eyelid on side next to beak.
	Notochord (see Head-process)		
114	Oculomotor nerve	28-30 s	Ventral zone of mid-brain, near median line.
115	Olfactory epithelium	28 s	Ectoderm of head, in front of eyes.
116	Olfactory nerve	4-6 da	Olfactory epithelium.
117	Oocytes	Shortly after hatching	Ovarian cortex.

No.	Structure	Time/Stage	Origin
40	Claws	10 da (Stage 36)	
41	Coelom	1-3 s	Within lateral plate mesoderm.
42	Comb	10 da (Stage 36)	Dorsal midline of beak.
43	Conjunctival sac	7th da	Within folds of eyelids.
44	Coracoid, chondrification	End of 6th da	Near union of coracoid with scapula.
45	Cornea propria	4th da	Beneath the corneal epithelium.
46	Cornea, inner epithelium (Bowman's membrane)	100th hr	From mesenchyme on inner face of cornea propria.
47	Cornea, Descemet's membrane	13-15 da	Beneath Bowman's membrane.
48	Costal processes (ribs)	5th da	
49	Crop	6th da	Dilation of esophagus at base of neck.
50	Cushions, endocardial, of atrioventricular canal	3-4 da	Floor and roof of the atrioventricular canal.
51	Dermis differentiation of fibers	Stage 38 (12 da)	Within mesenchyme next to ectoderm.
52	Diencephalon delimitation	18-20 s	From primitive fore-brain.
53	Duct of Cuvier (common cardinal vein)	15 s	From capillary plexus between root of anterior cardinal vein and omphalomesenteric vein at level of somite 4.
54	Ductus choledochus	68 hr	From depression of ventral wall of duodenum.
55	Egg-tooth[2]	Stage 30 (6½-7 da)	Dorsal tip of beak.
56	Embryonic shield	Stage 1	Posterior half of blastoderm.
57	Epimyocardium[8]	3-5 s	From thickening of splanchnopleure of amnio-cardiac vesicles.
58	Epiphysis	Stage 17 (30-35 s)	Roof of diencephalon.
59	Epithalamus	97 hr	Dorsolateral wall of diencephalon.
60	Esophagus	About 36 s	Gut immediately behind pharynx.
61	Esophagus, glands[9]	16 da	From entodermal epithelial lining of esophagus.
62	Eye pigment	Stage 20	
63	Eyelids	7th da	Circular fold of integument around the eyeball.
64	Facial nerve	3-4 da	From anteroventral portion of acoustico-facialis complex.
65	Femur, ossification	8th da	
66	Funiculi proecervicales	6th da	From ectoderm connecting 3rd and 4th visceral pouches with cervical sinus.
67	Gallbladder	68 hr	Hindmost part of posterior liver bud.
68	Germ wall	During cleavage (prior to laying)	From marginal periblast.
69	Germinal epithelium (primordium of gonad)	38 s	Coelomic epithelium at level of somites 20-27.
70	Gizzard	5th da	Posterior part of stomach.
71	Gizzard glands[10]	13-14 da	Lining epithelium of gizzard.
72	Glossopharyngeal ganglion	17 s	From neural crest and epibranchial placode of 2nd visceral furrow.
73	Glycogenic body of spinal cord	7½ da	Roof plate of spinal cord at level of spinal nerves 26-29.
74	Harderian gland	8th da	From conjunctival sac at innermost angle of nictitating membrane.
75	Head fold	Stage 6	At anterior end of medullary plate.
76	Head-process (notochord)	Stage 5	Anterior edge of Hensen's node.
	Heart (see Epimyocardium)		
77	Hepatic portal vein, definitive vessel	5th da	From the mesenteric vein in the dorsal mesentery.

No.	Structure	Time/Stage	Origin
118	Oogonia	7-8 da	From germ cells in secondary sexual cords of ovarian cortex.
119	Optic vesicles	Stages 8-9	From lateral wall of fore-brain.
120	Oral plate, rupture	30 s	
121	Ostium tubae abdominale	5th da	Anterior end of tubal ridge (primordium of oviduct).
122	Otocyst	12 s	Thickened ectoderm on dorsal surface of head opposite posterior-most neuromeres of hind-brain.
123	Otocyst closure	28-30 s	
124	Ovary, cortex	9-11 da	Proliferation from germinal epithelium.
125	Oviduct	4th da	Thickened peritoneum on dorsolateral surface of anterior end of mesonephros.
126	Oviduct, junction with cloaca	7th da	
127	Palatine glands	After 11th	From oral epithelium near choanae.
128	Pancreas[15], dorsal diverticulum	35 s	Dorsal wall of intestine, immediately above posterior liver bud.
129	Pancreas[15], ventral diverticulum	4 da	From common hepatic diverticulum near its junction with duodenum.
130	Paraphysis	4½ da	Roof of telencephalon, just in front of the velum transversum.
131	Parasphenoid bone	12th da	Skull.
132	Parathyroid	6-8 da	Ventral portion of visceral pouches 3 and 4.
133	Parencephalon	18-20 s	Anterior portion of diencephalon.
134	Parietal bone	13th da	Skull, behind squamosal bone.
135	Patella	13th da	Anterior face of knee joint.
136	Pecten	5th da	Growth of lips of optic cup over mesodermal keel of choroid fissure.
137	Pelvic lymph sac	5 da	Hemangioblasts from intersegmental veins of pelvic region.
138	Perilymph of ear	6th da	Mesenchyme surrounding otocyst.
139	Pharynx (foregut)	Stage 6	From entoderm of head fold.
140	Pigment of choroidea of eye	End of 7th da	From neural crest cells which invade at early stage.
141	Pigment of retina	Middle of 4th da	In situ in outer wall of retina.
	Pleuroperitoneal septum (see Mesenteries, accessory)		
142	Preganglionic column (visceral motor nucleus)	4½-8 da	From neuroblasts of ventrolateral motor column, which migrate to dorsolateral angle of central canal, spinal cord.
143	Premandibular head cavities	23 s	Within prechordal mesoderm.
144	Premaxilla (bone)	End of 9th da	Skull.
145	Primitive streak	Stage 2	Posterior edge of pellucid area.
146	Proventricular glands	5th da	Evaginations of entoderm of stomach.
147	Pterygoid bone	End of 9th da	Skull.
148	Pulmonary artery	35 s	From network of hemangioblasts extending caudally from ventral aorta.
149	Pulmonary diaphragm, muscles	10th da	From proliferation of hemangioblasts from dorsal wall of sinus venosus at level of lung buds.
150	Pulmonary vein	20 s	
151	Quadrate bone, otic process	End of 9th da	Skull.
152	Quadratojugal bone	End of 9th da	Skull.
153	Rathke's pouch[16]	20 s	From ectoderm of roof of stomodeum, immediately anterior to oral plate.
154	Renal portal system[17]	5th da	Through substance of mesonephros.

/1/ 8th da (180 hr). /2/ 19-21 da (time of hatching). /3/ From time of fusion of component folds, shortly after stage of 31 somites. /4/ With beginning of circulation at stage of 16 somites. /5/ Vestigial. /6/ Shortly prior to hatching. /7/ Stage of 16 somites. /8/ Contractions begin at stage of 9 somites. /9/ 19 da. /10/ 17½ da. /11/ 11-12 da. /12/ 7th da. /13/ Beginning of 4th da. /14/ 11th da. /15/ Islets, 11-12 da; acini, after hatching. /16/ Cellular types differentiate during 10th da. /17/ 5th da.

127. PRENATAL DEVELOPMENT, VARIOUS ORGANS AND TISSUES: CHICK (Concluded)

Time of origin is expressed in three ways, depending on available information: (1) days or hours of incubation, (2) number of pairs of somites, or (3) normal "stages" as described by Hamburger, V., and Hamilton, H. L., J. Morphology, 88:49, 1951. Data adapted from Lillie's "Development of the Chick," Henry Holt & Co., 1952. Footnotes refer to onset of function only.

	Organ or Structure	Time of Origin	Site of Origin
155	Rete cords of gonad	5th da	In stroma between genital primordium and mesonephros.
156	Sacculus	6-7 da	Protuberance on median surface of uppermost part of the pars inferior of the otocyst.
157	Scales of leg	Stage 37 (11 da)	Anterior surfaces of lower leg and toes.
158	Scapula	4-5 da	Base of wing bud.
159	Scleral papillae of eye	Stage 30 (7th da)	On conjunctiva surrounding iris, at some distance peripheral to its margin.
160	Sclerotic cartilage	8 da	In sclerotic (outer) coat of eye.
161	Semicircular canals of inner ear	5th da onward to 12th da	From pars superior of otocyst.
162	Septal gland of nose	8th da	Solid cord of cells from inner wall of vestibulum, opposite base of the vestibular turbinal.
163	Septum aortico-pulmonale	5th-6th da	Within truncus and bulbus arteriosus.
164	Shell of egg	4½-24 hr after ovulation	Uterus.
165	Shell membrane of egg	3½-4½ hr after ovulation	Isthmus of oviduct.
166	Spermatogonia	13th da onward	From primordial germ cells within sexual cords of testis.
167	Spinal nerves, motor component	3rd da	From medullary neuroblasts of ventral horn, spinal cord.
168	Spleen	2nd half, 4th da	Proliferation of peritoneum of left side of dorsal mesentery, just above the dorsal pancreas.
169	Spur	Stage 36	Medial surface of leg, just proximal to base of first toe.
170	Squamosal bone	End of 9th da	Skull.
171	Stapes	7-8 da	From mesenchyme adjacent to the bottom of the external auditory meatus.
172	Stomodeum	12 s	From expansion of embryonic parts surrounding the oral plate.
173	Subcardinal vein	70 hr	From series of venous islands on median surface of mesonephros.
174	Subclavian artery	4th da	From the segmental artery of the 18th intersomitic space.
175	Subintestinal vein	3rd da	From a plexus of capillaries around the gut.
176	Sympathetic nervous system	End of 3rd or beginning of 4th da	Aggregation of neural crest cells at dorso-lateral angle of dorsal aorta.
177	Synencephalon	18-20 s	Hindmost third of the diencephalon.
178	Tail bud	20-21 s	From primitive knot and remnant of primitive streak consolidated with it.
179	Teeth (vestige of dental ridge)[5]	6 da	Thickened ridge of ectoderm just inside margin of jaw.
180	Thoracic duct of lymphatic system	6-7 da	From intramesenchymal spaces along ventro-lateral side of dorsal aorta.
181	Thymus	6-8 da	From dorsal part of visceral pouches 3, 4, and possibly 5.
182	Thyroid[18]	12 s	Thickened epithelium of median floor of pharynx between levels of visceral arches II and III.
183	Toe	Stage 25	Toe plate of leg bud.
184	Trachea	4 da	Hinder portion of laryngotracheal groove.
185	Trigeminus, neural crest component	13-14 s	Neural crest of level of metencephalon.
186	Trigeminus, component from epibranchial placode	25-27 s	From ectodermal placode in front of and above first visceral cleft.
187	Trochlear nerve	End of 3rd da	Dorsal surface of brain in region of isthmus.
188	Trunk flexure	Stage 14	Behind level of somites 7-9.
189	Tuberculum impar of tongue	4th da	Slight rounded swelling between lower ends of first and second visceral arches.
190	Turbinals, nasal	4-8 da	From folds of lateral wall of nasal cavity.
191	Middle[19]	Beginning of 5th da	From ventral part of lateral nasal wall.
192	Superior[19]	5-6 da	Immediately above the middle turbinal.
193	Vestibular[19]	6-8 da	
194	Umbilical vein	3-4 da	From capillary plexus in the somatopleure extending back from duct of Cuvier.
195	Uncinate processes	Da before hatching[20]	Membranous ossifications along sternal ends of ribs (?).
196	Ureter[14]	End of 4th da	Broad diverticulum of mesonephric duct at the convexity of its terminal bend to the cloaca.
197	Uropygial gland[21]	10th da	From a pair of ectodermal invaginations at the dorsal midline of the base of the uropygium.
198	Uterus (shell-gland)[21]	12th da	Posterior end of left oviduct.
199	Vagus nerve, neural crest component	20 s	Indistinct aggregation of neural crest immediately in front of level of duct of Cuvier.
200	Vascular system	3-5 s and onward in later stages	Initiated in blood islands at posterior margin of area opaca.
201	Velum transversum	18-20 s	Indentation in roof of fore-brain.
202	Vertebrae, chondrification	7-8 da	Within membranous parts of vertebrae.
203	Vertebral artery	6-7 da	From the first 5 or 6 segmental arteries, and the plexus they form around the secondary sympathetic ganglia.
204	Visceral cleft 1	26 s	In pharyngeal region.
205	Visceral cleft 2	35 s	In pharyngeal region.
206	Visceral cleft 3	40 s	In pharyngeal region.
207	Visceral pouch 4, contact with ectoderm	35 s	Branchial region. No cleft develops.
208	Wattles	Stage 37	Throat.
209	Wing bud	50-60 hr (Stage 16)	Somatopleure lateral to somites 14-20.
210	Wing feathers	7 1/4 da	Along outer margin of wing.

/5/ Vestigial. /14/ /18/ 10th da. /19/ Non-sensory. /20/ Calcification starts at least one day prior to hatching. /21/ After hatching.

128. PRENATAL DEVELOPMENT, VARIOUS ORGANS AND TISSUES: PIG

No.	Stage of Appearance	Embryo Size mm[1]	Age da[2]	Organ, Tissue or Characterization
1	1	0.11-0.14		One cell
2	2		25-41 hr	Two cells
3	3		25 hr	Four cells
4	4		3	Eight to twelve cells
5	5		3.5	Sixteen cells (morula)
6	6		4.75	Blastocyst
7	7		5-7	Late blastocyst (still free in uterus)
8	8	0.49-1.36[3]	7-8	Bilaminar disc (beginning elongation)
9	9	2.5-3.0[3]	8-9	Proliferation of mesoderm
10	10		8-9	Primitive streak beginning
11	11		9	Medium primitive streak
12	12	10-65[3]	11-12	Completed primitive streak; notochord
13	13		13	Presomite neurula; neural plate and groove; hindgut
14	14	2.5-3.0	14-15	Pericardial cavity; endocardium; epimyocardium; anlagen of blood vessels; foregut; preoral gut; oral plate; allantois; occipital somites 1-4[4]
15	15	3.2-5.2	15-16	Cervical somites 5-12; visceral pouches 1-2; pharynx; mesonephros; neural tube; fusion of neural crest primordia; auditory placode; optic vesicle; fusion of paired cardiac tubes; blood in yolk sac, heart and vessels; ventral aorta
16	16	4.0-6.5	15-17	Thoracic somites 13-20; spiral torsion; truncus and bulbus arteriosus; ventricle; atrium; sinus venosus; glomeruli in mesonephros; dorsal aortae; first pair aortic arches; 3rd and 4th visceral pouches; liver diverticula; prosencephalon; mesencephalon; rhombencephalon; auditory pit
17	17	4.9-6.5	17	Thoracic somites 21-24; telencephalon; diencephalon; metencephalon; myelencephalon; closure of anterior neuropore; longitudinal neural artery; lateral cardinal vein
18	18	3.8-4.5[5]	16.5-18	Thoracic somites 25-26; head and tail meet; anterior limb bud; 2nd aortic arch; endocardial cushions; esophagus; stomach; post-cloacal gut; proctodaeum; anal plate; intestine; auditory vesicle; thyroid; hypophysis
19	19	3.6-4.6	16.5-17.5	Lumbar somites 27-29; hind limb bud; pancreas; lung buds; 3rd aortic arch; Gasserian and acoustico-facialis ganglia; interventricular septum
20	20	4.5-7.0	17.5	Lumbar somites 30-31; spiraling completed; 4th aortic arch; mesial cardinal vein; venous valves; oral plate ruptures; gallbladder; trachea
21	21	5.0-5.2	17.5	Lumbar somites 32-33; uncoiling; mandibular and maxillary processes; elongation of nuclei of mesenchyme cells in region of circular muscle layer of esophagus at level of laryngotracheal groove
22	22	5.8-8.0	19	Sacral somites 34-35; cranial ganglia IX and X; cranial nerves 3-12; optic cup and lens; 6th aortic arch; epiglottis; notochordal sheath; tongue primordia
23	23		20	Sacral somites 36-37; metanephric duct; foramen II in septum I
24	24	6.4	20	Caudal somites 38-40
25	25	8.0-8.6	20	Caudal somites 41-43; olfactory pits; lateral and median nasal processes; septum II; external carotid; adrenal cortex; myoblasts elongate; dermomyotome differentiates
26	26	9.0-10.0	20-21	Caudal somites 44-46; beginning umbilical hernia; pelvis; bronchi branching; myofibrillae in myoblasts of esophagus; neuroblasts; retinal differentiation; cerebral hemispheres; sacculus; utriculus; inferior vena cava; spleen; anlagen of external genitalia; ependymal mantle and marginal layers of neural tube; neurotrunks; bulbus dividing into aortic and pulmonary
27	27	11	21-22	Caudal somites 47-49; thymus
28	28	11.6-15	22	Caudal somites 50-52 (end of somite formation); cervical sinus closing; handplate; pulmonary, subclavian, basilar and vertebral arteries; Jacobson's organ; milk line; Müllerian ducts; parathyroids; neurohypophysis; olfactory lobe and nerve; vitreous body
29	29	16.4-18.6	22	Cervical sinus closed; lateral palatine processes; pentadactyle rudiments; semicircular canals; cochlea; pia mater and arachnoid layer; sympathetic ganglia and ramus anastomoticus; chondrification of vertebrae; appearance of sternum; cecum; milk hillocks; calyces
30	30	19.4-24	28	Median (premaxillary) palatine processes; sex differentiation; eyelids and plica semilunaris; testis differentiated; glomeruli and convoluted tubules in metanephros; appearance of presternum; brachiocephalic and left common carotid arteries; epiphysis; hair follicles; mammary gland primordia; dental lamina; enamel organs; coils of small intestine; anus open
31	31	25.0	30	Facial clefts closing; palate developing; heart myoblasts become spindle-shaped
32	32	26.6-30	32.5	Phalanges (3rd and 4th most prominent); fusion of palatine processes; mandible ossifies; elongation of nuclei in longitudinal muscle layer of esophagus and stomach
33	33	30-38	34.5	Facial clefts closed; palate completed; femur ossifies; coils of large intestine; humerus ossifies; ribs start to ossify; adrenal medulla; nasal chamber and nasal septum complete; cerebellum; muscle bundles
34	34	40.0	36.5	Growth of eyelids; gut withdrawn from umbilical cord; muscularis mucosae; bodies and arches of vertebrae start to ossify
35	35	44.5	39	Sealed eyelids
36	35			Penis raphé
37	35			Prepuce, scrotum in male; labia majora, clitoris in female
38	35	60.0	44	Neuroglia present
39	35	70.0	46	Odontoid process ossifies
40	35	75.0	48	Intercalated discs appear
41	35	76.0	48	Seminal vesicles, prostate, Cowper's glands in male; oviducts, uteri and vagina in female
42	35	85.0	51	Intercalated discs extend across cardiac muscle fibers
43	35	89.0	52	Tonsil
44	35	90.0	52	Corpora quadrigemina
45	35	100.0	54.5	Nymphae (labia minora)
46	35	113.0	58.5	Ameloblasts and odontoblasts
47	35	120.0	61	Sternebrae start to ossify
48	35	125.0	62	Testis descending
49	35	128.0	62.5	Petrous portion of temporal last to ossify, dentine and enamel
50	35	130.0	63	Sulci and gyri in cerebrum
51	35	200.0	92	Testis entering inguinal canal
52	35	210.0	95	Eyelids separate
53	36	250-300	98-140	Birth

/1/ Greatest length, neck length (spine length) or crown-rump length of embryo. /2/ Unless otherwise noted. /3/ Extra-embryonic length. /4/ 1st somite not delimited anteriorly. /5/ Apparent decrease in size may be attributed to torsion of embryo.

129. PRENATAL DEVELOPMENT, VARIOUS ORGANS AND TISSUES: FROG

Data for embryo stages adapted from Shumway, W., Anat. Rec., 78:139–144, 1940. Larval stage data adapted from Taylor, A. C., and Kollros, J. J., Anat. Rec. 94:7–23, 1946. Values are principally for Rana pipiens, but may vary widely with different geographic strains and culture conditions.

Embryo

Stage	Organ, Tissue or Characteristic	Size mm	Age[1]
1	Unfertilized egg	1.5-2	0
2	Fertilized egg; gray crescent	1.5-2	1
3	Two cells		3.5
4	Four cells		4.5
5	Eight cells		5.7
6	Sixteen cells		6.5
7	Thirty-two cells		7.5
8	Middle blastula		16
9	Late blastula		21
10	Early gastrula; dorsal lip stage		26
11	Middle gastrula; blastopore C- or U-shaped		34
12	Late gastrula; yolk plug; primitive gut		42
13	Early neurula; medullary plate defined		50
14	Mid-neurula; well-defined neural folds approaching each other; oral plate; anal pit; postanal gut		62
15	Late neurula; neural folds touch each other over most of their length; neurenteric canal; embryo rotates in jelly		67
16	Neural tube; ectoderm fused over it; oral sucker	3	72
17	Tail bud; nasal pit; dorsal aorta	3.5	84
18	Muscular response to stimulation of myotome; lens placode	4	96
19	Heart beats; pronephros functional; Rohon-Beard cells; thyroid evagination	5	118
20	Embryo hatched; gill circulation; lens vesicle	6	140
21	Mouth open; free swimming; cornea becoming transparent; olfactory nerve; two rudiments of ventral pancreas; lung rudiments	7	162
22	Circulation in tail fin; cartilaginous trabeculae; two gill slits are perforate; trabeculae carnae	8	192
23	Opercular folds and labial teeth appear; spontaneous respiratory activity of mouth begins; basal plate	8-9	216
24	Operculum closed on right side; adrenal cortex rudiment; respiratory rhythm begins	9-10	240
25	Operculum closed except for spiracle; rods and cones; germinal ridge; sucker regressed; rudiments of mesonephric tubules	10-11	284

Larva

Stage	Organ, Tissue or Characteristic	Stage[1]	Size mm	Age[1]
26	Feeding begins; rudiments of adrenal medulla and of hind limb appear	I	13	3
27	Lagena; neural lobe of hypophysis	II	17	6
28	Limb bud of equal length and diameter; lateral motor column			
29	Ovarial sac; cartilage in synotic tectum	III	23	11
30	Limb bud twice as long as it is broad; bent ventrad distally	IV	33	19
31	Flattened paddle at distal end of limb bud; scapular cartilage; ovary-testis distinguishable	V	39	23
32	Foot paddle indented between toes 4 and 5	VI	43	26
33	Urinary bladder rudiment; measurable thyroid hormone output	VII	50	31
34	Separation of fat body from gonad; spontaneous limb twitches	VIII	53	34
35	All toes marked by indentation of the foot margin between them; rudiments of fungiform papillae of tongue	IX	56	36
36	Margin of fifth toe web directed toward toe 2	X	58	40
37	Margin of fifth toe web directed toward toe 1	XI	61	43
38	Margin of fifth toe web directed toward the prehallux	XII	64	47
39	Rudiments of Harderian glands, and of skin glands	XIII	67	52
40	First toe pads; hind limbs take part in swimming	XIV	70	58
41	Nictitating membrane a low fold anterior to eyeball	XV	72	62
42	Some skin glands patent; peritoneal thickening presages oviduct	XVI	73	64
43	Cloacal tail piece resorbed; corneal reflex	XVII	73	67
44	Tail regression begins; skin windows form	XVIII	74[2]	70
45	Skin windows perforate; forelimbs emerge; oral beaks lost	XIX	73	72
46	Upper lid forms; first molt	XX	70	74
47	Conjunctival sac complete; lateral lines regressing	XXI	63	76
48	Labial fringes completely lost; vasa efferentia	XXII	44	79
49	Tympanic membrane outlined; tail stub of 1-2 mm	XXIII	33	81
50	Tail stub fully resorbed; oviduct extends nearly to cloaca	XXIV	26	84
51	Fully metamorphosed; gonads immature; urostyle	XXV	25[3]	88
52	Sexually mature	Juvenile	25-70	90-
		Adult	60-110	1-3 yr

/1/ Age is expressed in hours (at 18°C) for embryo stages 1-25, in days (at 20°C) for succeeding stages. Ages for embryo stages 2 through 20 in hours at 20°C are: 0.5, 2.3, 3.2, 4.0, 4.8, 5.6, 7.0, 17.0, 22, 28, 30, 38, 43, 49, 52, 61, 76, 88 and 96, respectively. /2/ Maximum size highly variable. Tadpoles over 100 mm length reported. /3/ Size at end of metamorphosis variable. Range 16-30 mm.

130. SUMMARY, DEVELOPMENT CHARACTERISTICS: MAMMALS AND BIRDS

Stage	Hawk	Chick	Sparrow	Opossum	Rabbit	Hamster	Rat	Swine	Sheep	Rhesus Monkey	Man
1	2 cells, hr		3 1/4		40	8	16	24	30	30	24	38
2	4 cells, hr				56	11	40	50	34	34	36	48
3	Implantation begins, da				6	6 1/2-7	4 1/2	6	7	10	9	6 1/2
4	Primitive streak, da	1 1/2-2	1 1/2-2	7-7 1/2	6 1/2-7	9	6 1/2-7	8 1/2-9	11-12	13	18-20	17-21
5	13-20 somite embryo, da	4 1/2	2 1/2	2 1/2	9	9 1/2	8 1/2	10 1/2	16	17	25	27
6	Tailbud forms, da		3 1/4	3 1/4	9 1/2	10	9	11 1/2	17	18	26	29
7	End of embryonic period, da	9	5	5	10	14	13 1/2	13	20	21	28	36
8	End of metamorphosis, da	13	8	7 1/2	12		13	16	24	32	40	60
9	Sex differentiation, da	12	6 1/2	6 1/2	15	13 1/2	13	13 1/2	21	28	36	45
10	Eyelids closed, da	23	13	11	12 1/4	19		17	32	42	48	70
11	Eyelids open, da		20	19				38		84		180
	Hatching or birth											
12	Age, da	35	21	13	12 1/2	32	35	22	112	150	164	267
13	Stage	35/36	36	35	35	35+		35	36	36	36	36
14	Weight, absolute, kg	0.012	.034	0.0017	0.131	0.057	0.0022	0.0045	2.5	5	450	3.2
15	Relative to mother, %	6	3	6	0.01	3	2.3	2.25	2.5	8	7.5	5.5

Hours and days are counted from the time of fertilization. In birds one day was added to observed incubation times; in mammals observed mating ages were reduced by the estimated number of hours necessary for the establishment of contact between egg and sperm (opossum 8, rabbit 14, hamster 8, rat 9, pig 8, sheep 6). In the monkey the ovulation age (Lewis-Hartman) was reduced by 2 hours. Values adapted from E. Witschi's "Development of Vertebrates." W. B. Saunders Co., 1956.

/1/ Grams.

158

Cattle:[1]	Ayrshire[1]		Brown Swiss[1]		Guernsey[1]		Holstein[1,2]		Jersey[1,2]	
Age and Sex	kg	lb	kg	lb	kg	lb	kg	lb	kg	lb
1 Birth ♂	33-40	73-89	43-50	95-110	29-41	65-90	42-47	92-104	22-29	49-64
2 1 wk ♂	34-43	76-94	45-53	100-117	34-41	75-90	46-49	101-109	25-29	56-65
3 2 wk ♂	39-49	86-108	53-59	116-130	41-47	90-103	48-54	106-120	28-35	62-77
4 3 wk ♂	42-57	92-127	60-68	133-150	45-51	99-113	53-65	116-144	33-38	73-83
5 4 wk ♂	52-65	114-143	68-83	151-183	49-57	108-125	57-73	125-162	36-43	79-96
6 5 wk ♂	58-77	128-169	78-92	173-204	59-65	130-143	64-79	141-174	41-48	90-106
7 6 wk ♂	68-88	150-195	86-99	190-218	66-70	145-155	66-86	145-190	49-56	107-123
8 7 wk ♂	75-97	165-213	96-106	211-234	74-76	164-168	75-96	165-213	57-64	126-142
9 8 wk ♂	82-102	180-225	102-117	227-259	84-86	186-190	92-107	202-236	63-77	140-169
10 3 mo ♀							96	211	64	141
11 6 mo ♀							176	389	127	281
12 9 mo ♀							254	561	193	426
13 1 yr ♀							315	697	233	514
14 2.5 yr ♀							525	1158	400	883
15 6-7 yr ♀							649	1433	477	1052

Dog:	Basenjis		Beagle		Cocker spaniel		German shepherd[3]	
Age and Sex	kg	lb	kg	lb	kg	lb	kg	lb
16 Birth ♂	0.23-0.34	0.50-0.75	0.40	0.88	0.20-0.30	0.44-0.66	0.39-0.52	0.87-1.14
17 ♀	0.26-0.30	0.57-0.66	0.30	0.66	0.20-0.31	0.44-0.68		
18 1 wk ♂	0.34-0.48	0.75-1.06	0.69	1.52	0.32-0.54	0.71-1.19	0.71-0.92	1.56-2.02
19 ♀	0.34-0.51	0.75-1.12	0.56	1.23	0.32-0.57	0.71-1.26		
20 2 wk ♂	0.52-0.68	1.15-1.50	1.01	2.23	0.50-0.77	1.10-1.70	1.31-1.56	2.90-3.45
21 ♀	0.52-0.71	1.15-1.56	0.80	1.76	0.50-0.77	1.10-1.70		
22 4 wk ♂	0.80-1.11	1.76-2.45	1.61	3.55	0.82-1.33	1.81-2.93	2.86-3.04	6.32-6.70
23 ♀	0.70-1.14	1.54-2.51	1.26	2.78	0.86-1.25	1.90-2.76		
24 6 wk ♂	1.22-1.66	2.69-3.66	2.48	5.47	1.46-2.30	3.22-5.07	4.45-5.04	9.82-11.13
25 ♀	1.06-1.64	2.34-3.61	1.79	3.95	1.54-2.14	3.39-4.72		
26 8 wk ♂	1.93-2.64	4.25-5.82	3.54	7.80	2.66-3.69	5.86-8.13	15.4-35.2	7.0-16.0
27 ♀	1.76-2.92	3.88-6.44	2.53	5.58	2.30-3.26	5.07-7.19	17.6-39.6	8.0-18.0
28 10 wk ♂	2.72-3.90	5.99-8.60	4.59	10.12	3.52-4.62	7.76-10.18	20.9-47.5	9.5-22.5
29 ♀	2.52-3.86	5.55-8.51	3.26	7.19	3.02-4.24	6.66-9.34	20.9-53.9	9.5-24.5
30 12 wk ♂	3.40-4.96	7.49-10.93	5.81	12.81	4.54-6.27	10.01-13.82	23.1-64.9	10.5-29.5
31 ♀	3.52-4.88	7.76-10.76	4.22	9.31	3.98-5.36	8.77-11.81	34.1-61.6	15.5-28.0
32 14 wk ♂	4.64-6.41	10.23-14.13	6.98	15.38	5.39-7.63	11.88-16.82	26.4-81.4	12.0-37.0
33 ♀	4.24-5.96	9.34-13.14	4.84	10.67	4.76-6.54	10.49-14.41	36.3-69.3	16.5-31.5
34 16 wk ♂	5.52-7.36	12.17-16.22	7.89	17.39	6.42-8.96	14.15-19.75	29.7-94.6	13.5-43.0
35 ♀	5.07-6.88	11.17-15.16	5.45	12.01	5.32-7.28	11.73-16.05	36.3-83.6	16.5-38.0

Goat:	Saanen, ♂		Saanen, ♀		Toggenburg, ♂		Toggenburg, ♀	
Age	kg	lb	kg	lb	kg	lb	kg	lb
36 Birth	3.6(3.0-4.2)	7.9(6.6-9.3)	3.1(2.4-3.9)	6.9(5.3-8.6)	3.5(2.9-4.1)	7.7(6.4-9.0)	3.1(2.5-3.6)	6.8(5.6-8.0)
37 1 mo	7.2(6.0-8.4)	15.8(13.1-18.5)	6.7(5.4-8.0)	14.8(11.9-17.17)	6.8(5.6-7.9)	14.9(12.4-17.4)	6.4(5.4-7.3)	14.0(11.9-16.1)
38 2 mo	11.3(9.4-13.2)	25(21-29)	11.0(9.2-13.0)	24(20-28)	11.2(9.6-12.8)	25(21-28)	10.2(8.8-11.6)	23(20-26)
39 3 mo	15.0(12.1-17.8)	33(27-39)	14.6(11.8-17.3)	32(26-38)	15.0(12.5-17.4)	33(28-38)	13.7(12.0-15.5)	30(26-34)
40 6 mo	25(20-30)	54(43-65)	25(20-27)	54(44-59)	23(20-27)	51(44-59)	21(18-24)	46(39-53)
41 9 mo	31(26-35)	67(57-78)	30(24-35)	66(54-78)	27(23-32)	60(51-69)	25(22-29)	56(48-64)
42 1 yr	41(34-47)	90(76-104)	35(28-42)	78(63-93)	35(30-39)	77(67-87)	29(25-33)	64(55-73)
43 2 yr	58(44-72)	128(97-160)	54(44-64)	118(97-140)	48(39-57)	106(87-125)	45(37-53)	99(81-117)
44 3 yr	68(51-85)	149(112-187)	58(46-71)	129(101-157)	58(49-68)	128(108-149)	52(41-62)	114(91-136)
45 4 yr	82	180	60(49-72)	133(107-159)	71(62-80)	156(136-177)	52(43-61)	114(94-133)
46 5 yr	77	169	70(54-86)	155(119-190)	67(49-84)	147(108-185)	54(47-61)	120(104-135)

Guinea Pig:	Cavia cutleri ♂		Cavia cutleri ♀		Race B ♂		Race B ♀		Age da	Inbred Line ♂		Random Breed ♂	
Age da	g	oz	g	oz	g	oz	g	oz		g	oz	g	oz
47 Birth	50	1.8	50	1.8	80	2.8	80	2.8	Birth	80(56-99)	2.8(2.0-3.5)	95(57-130)	3.3(2.0-4.6)
48 10	70	2.5	70	2.5	90	3.2	90	3.2	13	130(88-165)	4.6(3.1-5.8)	170(105-230)	6.0(3.7-8.1)
49 20	110	3.9	110	3.9	130	4.6	130	4.6	23	165(110-220)	5.8(3.9-7.8)	225(145-310)	7.9(5.1-10.9)
50 40	160	5.6	160	5.6	200	7.0	200	7.0	53	265(170-360)	9.3(6.0-12.7)	345(215-475)	12.2(7.6-16.7)
51 60	210	7.4	200	7.0	280	9.9	250	8.8	113	475(340-610)	16.7(12.0-21.5)	570(395-750)	20.1(13.9-26.4)
52 80	260	9.2	230	8.1	360	12.7	330	11.6	173	585(440-710)	20.6(16.2-25.0)	720(530-910)	25.4(18.7-32.1)
53 100	300	10.6	260	9.2	440	15.5	400	14.1	233	650(520-775)	22.9(18.3-27.3)	815(605-1025)	28.7(21.3-36.1)
54 120	330	11.6	280	9.9	500	17.6	450	15.9	293	690(560-840)	24.3(19.8-28.9)	875(670-1070)	30.9(23.6-37.7)
55 160	360	12.7	300	10.6	590	20.8	530	18.7	353	710(585-835)	25.0(20.6-29.5)	910(790-1030)	32.1(27.9-36.3)
56 200	380	13.4	320	11.3	660	23.3	610	21.5	413	730(600-860)	25.7(21.1-30.3)	940(720-1160)	33.2(25.4-40.9)
57 240	390	13.8	340	12.0	710	25.0	670	23.6	473	745(615-855)	26.3(21.7-30.9)	950(660-1245)	33.5(23.3-43.9)
58 280	400	14.1	360	12.7	750	26.4	700	24.7	533	760(635-885)	26.8(22.4-31.2)	985(780-1190)	34.7(27.5-42.0)
59 320	410	14.5	380	13.4	790	27.8	720	25.4	593	765(645-885)	27.0(22.7-31.2)	990(780-1205)	34.9(27.5-42.5)
60 360	420	14.8	400	14.1	800	28.2	740	26.1	653	775(650-900)	27.3(22.8-31.7)	1000(810-1195)	35.3(28.6-42.1)
61 400	420	14.8	400	14.1	800	28.2	740	26.1	713	780(660-900)	27.5(23.3-31.7)	1020(785-1260)	36.0(27.7-44.4)

Monkey:	Macaque		Marmoset, squirrel		Black-howler		Spider		White-faced	
Age and Sex	kg	lb	kg	lb	kg	lb	kg	lb	kg	lb
62 Birth ♂	0.49(0.39-0.67)	1.08(0.85-1.47)			1.59	3.5	0.91	2	0.02	0.5
63 ♀	0.47(0.33-0.64)	1.02(0.72-1.41)			(0.91-1.13)	(2-2.5)	(0.68-1.13)	(1.5-2.5)	(0.45-0.67)	(1-1.5)
64 Juvenile ♂	1.45(1.07-1.88)	3.19(2.34-41.4)			2.72	6	(2.27-2.72)	(5-6)	1.81	4
65 ♀	1.42(0.89-1.80)	3.10(1.96-3.96)			2.27	5	1.81		(1.36-1.59)	(3-3.5)
66 "Young"- ♂	2.20(1.48-2.98)	4.83(3.25-6.56)	0.453	1			(3.62-5.44)	(8-12)	(2.72-3.17)	(6-7)
67 adult ♀	2.19(1.45-2.68)	4.81(3.19-5.90)			4.08(3.62-6.34)	(8-14)	(4.08-5.89)	(9-13)	1.59(1.59-2.27)	(3-5)
68 "Old"- ♂	11.0(8.8-12.1)	24.1(19.4-26.7)	(0.57-0.79)	(1.25-1.75)	(6.34-8.15)	(14-18)	(6.8-8.6)	(15-19)	3.9(3.4-5.4)	8.5(7.5-12)
69 adult ♀	8.01(6.31-12.2)	17.6(13.9-26.8)	0.68(0.45-0.91)	1.5(1-2)	(4.98-7.47)	(11-16.5)	(6.34-8.61)	(14-19)		

/1/ Data for first 8 weeks obtained by one investigator under conditions of ad libitum feeding of milk alone. /2/ Data for 3 months to 7 years obtained by another investigator under practical feeding conditions, hence show slower gains. /3/ Values in Lines 16-25 and 26-35 are from different sources.

Mouse:	Black, piebald, ♂		Black, piebald, ♀		White, ♂	
Age	g	oz	g	oz	g	oz
70 Birth	1.4(1.1-1.7)	0.05(0.04-0.06)	1.4(1.1-1.7)	0.05(0.04-0.06)		
71 2 da	6.1(4.4-7.7)	0.22(0.16-0.27)	6.1(4.5-7.7)	0.21(0.16-0.27)		
72 3 wk	8.0(5.6-10.4)	0.28(0.20-0.37)	8.3(6.3-10.4)	0.29(0.22-0.37)	8.2(7.3-8.9)	0.29(0.26-0.32)
73 4 wk	12.3(9.8-14.7)	0.43(0.35-0.52)	12.1(9.7-14.5)	0.43(0.34-0.51)	12.4(11.6-13.3)	0.44(0.41-0.47)
74 6 wk	19.1(15.3-22.9)	0.67(0.54-0.81)	18.3(16.0-20.6)	0.65(0.57-0.73)	19.6(18.7-20.5)	0.69(0.66-0.72)
75 8 wk	22.6(18.8-26.4)	0.80(0.66-0.93)	19.7(16.5-22.8)	0.70(0.58-0.80)	22.2(20.9-23.5)	0.78(0.74-0.83)
76 12 wk	25.9(22.2-29.5)	0.91(0.79-1.04)	23.6(19.0-28.2)	0.83(0.67-0.99)	25.3(24.2-26.4)	0.89(0.85-0.93)
77 16 wk	28.6(21.1-36.0)	1.01(0.74-1.27)	26.5(20.1-33.0)	0.94(0.71-1.16)	27.2(25.7-28.7)	0.96(0.91-1.01)
78 20 wk	30.0(21.8-38.3)	1.06(0.77-1.35)	29.0(21.8-36.1)	1.02(0.77-1.27)	27.8(26.4-29.2)	0.98(0.93-1.03)
79 24 wk	33.1(25.7-40.5)	1.17(0.91-1.43)	32.3(25.5-39.1)	1.14(0.90-1.38)	27.6(26.3-28.8)	0.97(0.93-1.02)
80 28 wk					28.0(26.3-29.7)	0.99(0.93-1.05)
81 32 wk					29.4(28.2-30.5)	1.04(0.99-1.08)

Rat:	Sherman, albino, small, ♂		Sherman, albino, small, ♀		Sherman, albino, large, ♂		Sherman, albino, large, ♀	
Age	g	oz	g	oz	g	oz	g	oz
82 Birth	5.5(4.9-6.1)	0.19(0.17-0.22)	5.5(4.8-6.2)	0.19(0.17-0.22)	6.1(4.9-7.7)	0.21(0.17-0.27)	5.8(4.9-6.6)	0.20(0.17-0.23)
83 1 wk	13.4(10-17)	0.47(0.35-0.60)	13.1(10.5-16)	0.46(0.37-0.56)	17.5(12.5-23)	0.6(0.4-0.8)	16.2(13-19)	0.57(0.45-0.67)
84 2 wk	25(21-30)	0.88(0.74-1.06)	25(20-30)	0.88(0.71-1.06)	37(29-45)	1.3(1.0-1.6)	34(28-40)	1.2(1.0-1.4)
85 4 wk	61(51-71)	2.2(1.8-2.5)	56(48-63)	2.0(1.7-2.2)	93(78-108)	3.3(2.8-3.8)	80(68-91)	2.8(2.4-3.2)
86 6 wk	121(106-136)	4.3(3.7-4.8)	100(89-111)	3.5(3.1-3.9)	188(157-218)	6.6(5.6-7.7)	147(128-166)	5.2(4.5-5.9)
87 8 wk	177(149-205)	6.2(5.3-7.2)	130(122-137)	4.6(4.3-4.8)	274(231-317)	9.7(8.1-11.2)	196(169-222)	6.9(6.0-7.8)
88 10 wk	222(191-254)	7.8(6.7-9.0)	154(145-163)	5.4(5.1-5.8)	339(291-386)	12.0(10.3-13.6)	227(199-256)	8.0(7.0-9.0)
89 12 wk	252(213-291)	8.9(7.5-10.3)	169(159-179)	6.0(5.6-6.3)	393(328-458)	13.9(11.6-16.2)	251(232-280)	8.9(8.2-9.9)
90 15 wk	285(241-329)	10.0(8.5-11.6)	185(165-205)	6.5(5.8-7.2)	440(379-501)	15.5(13.4-17.7)	274(238-310)	9.6(8.4-10.9)
91 20 wk	326(278-373)	11.5(9.8-13.2)	202(178-225)	7.1(6.3-7.9)	490(423-556)	17.3(14.9-19.6)	303(270-335)	10.7(9.5-11.8)
92 30 wk	376(335-417)	13.3(11.8-14.7)	230(205-255)	8.1(7.2-9.0)			335(298-373)	11.8(10.5-13.2)
93 40 wk			240(215-265)	8.5(7.6-9.3)			358(311-404)	12.6(11.0-14.3)

Rat:	Wistar, albino, ♂		Wistar, albino, ♀		Wild Norway, ♂		Wild Norway, ♀	
Age	g	oz	g	oz	g	oz	g	oz
94 Birth	5.6(4.5-6.7)	0.2(0.16-0.23)	5.3(4.5-6.1)	0.18(0.16-0.22)				
95 3 wk	43(38-49)	1.5(1.3-1.7)	41(34-48)	1.4(1.2-1.7)				
96 4 wk	52	1.8	55	1.9				
97 6 wk	110	3.9	97	3.4	85(67-112)	3.0(2.4-3.9)	104(79-142)	3.7(2.8-5.0)
98 8 wk	170	6.0	128	4.5	170(127-218)	6.0(4.5-7.7)	152(120-200)	5.4(4.2-7.1)
99 10 wk	200	7.1	147	5.2				
100 12 wk	225(182-286)	7.9(6.4-10.1)	165(143-187)	5.8(5.0-6.6)	237(176-299)	8.4(6.2-10.6)	194(149-249)	6.8(5.2-8.8)
101 15 wk	251	8.8	180	6.3	289(217-361)	10.2(7.7-12.7)	230(178-291)	8.1(6.3-10.3)
102 17 wk					330(251-408)	11.6(8.9-14.4)	260(203-327)	9.2(7.2-11.5)
103 20 wk	280	9.9	200	7.1				
104 23 wk					388(302-472)	13.7(10.7-16.7)	311(245-383)	11.0(8.6-13.5)
105 28 wk					424(335-509)	15.0(11.8-18.0)	348(276-423)	12.3(9.7-14.9)
106 35 wk					446(358-531)	15.7(12.6-18.7)	376(300-452)	13.3(10.6-15.9)
107 40 wk	342	12.1	245	8.6	460(374-545)	16.2(13.2-19.2)	397(319-473)	14.0(11.3-16.7)
108 45 wk					468(385-551)	16.5(13.6-19.4)	413(333-488)	14.6(11.8-17.2)
109 50 wk					474(392-556)	16.7(13.8-19.6)	424(344-497)	15.0(12.1-17.5)
110 52 wk	364(263-465)	12.8(9.3-16.4)	243(196-290)	8.6(6.9-10.2)				
111 57 wk					477(397-558)	16.8(14.0-19.7)	433(352-507)	15.3(12.4-17.9)

Swine:	Berkshire		Duroc-Jersey		Yorkshire	
Age	kg	lb	kg	lb	kg	lb
112 Birth	1.84(1.34-2.17)	4.06(2.95-4.78)	2.74(2.73-2.76)	6.04(6.02-6.08)		
113 1 wk	2.58(2.17-3.10)	5.69(4.78-6.83)	3.30(2.96-3.64)	7.27(6.52-8.02)		
114 2 wk	4.32(3.47-4.91)	9.52(7.65-10.82)	5.25(4.75-5.74)	11.57(10.47-12.65)		
115 3 wk	7.02(5.78-8.14)	15.47(12.74-17.94)	7.43(6.84-8.03)	16.38(15.07-17.70)		
116 4 wk	9.85(8.43-12.60)	21.70(18.58-27.8)	8.84(8.55-9.12)	19.48(18.84-20.10)		
117 5 wk	14.02(12.30-17.00)	30.9(27.1-37.5)	13.13(12.80-13.45)	28.9(28.2-29.6)		
118 6 wk	18.31(16.14-21.36)	40.4(35.6-47.1)	16.96(16.50-17.45)	37.4(36.4-38.5)		
119 7 wk	23.16(21.02-27.04)	51.0(46.3-59.6)	20.94(20.43-21.45)	46.2(45.0-47.3)		
120 8 wk	27.45(24.32-31.36)	60.5(53.6-69.1)	24.21(23.86-24.55)	53.4(52.6-54.1)	11.8	26
121 10 wk			37.4(36.8-38.0)	82.4(81.1-83.8)	16.3	36
122 12 wk			50.8(50.0-51.5)	111.9(110.2-113.5)	20.4	45
123 14 wk					27.2	60
124 16 wk					35.8	79
125 18 wk					46.2	102
126 20 wk					47.6	105
127 22 wk					65.2	144
128 24 wk					78.8	174
129 26 wk					79.3	175
130 28 wk					87.9	194

Chicken:	Cornish, ♂		Cornish, ♀		White Leghorn, ♂		White Leghorn, ♀		New Hampshire, ♂		New Hampshire, ♀	
Age	kg	lb	kg	lb	kg	lb	kg	lb	kg	lb	kg	lb
131 Birth	0.032	0.07	0.032	0.07	0.036	0.08	0.036	0.08	0.041	0.09	0.036	0.08
132 1 wk	0.059	0.13	0.059	0.13	0.059	0.13	0.073	0.16	0.086	0.19	0.082	0.18
133 2 wk	0.109	0.24	0.105	0.23	0.123	0.27	0.118	0.26	0.154	0.34	0.154	0.34
134 3 wk	0.182	0.4	0.172	0.38	0.191	0.42	0.195	0.43	0.272	0.60	0.250	0.55
135 4 wk	0.268	0.59	0.256	0.56	0.268	0.59	0.272	0.60	0.404	0.89	0.363	0.80
136 5 wk					0.354	0.78	0.367	0.81	0.563	1.24	0.504	1.11
137 6 wk					0.449	0.99	0.436	0.96	0.735	1.62	0.640	1.41
138 7 wk					0.603	1.33	0.549	1.21	0.934	2.06	0.807	1.78
139 8 wk	0.727	1.6	0.636	1.4	0.689	1.52	0.640	1.41	1.152	2.54	0.948	2.09
140 9 wk					0.875	1.93	0.721	1.59	1.325	2.92	1.107	2.44
141 10 wk					0.944	2.08	0.776	1.71	1.628	3.59	1.284	2.83
142 12 wk	1.272	2.8	1.045	2.3	1.243	2.74	0.934	2.06	1.849	4.45	1.551	3.42
143 14 wk							1.107	2.44	2.554	5.63	1.828	4.03
144 16 wk	1.727	3.8	1.318	2.9			1.270	2.80	2.994	6.60	2.019	4.45
145 18 wk							1.402	3.09	3.293	7.26	2.254	4.97
146 20 wk	2.09	4.6	1.545	3.4			1.551	3.42	3.375	7.44	2.309	5.09

Turkey:	Broad-breasted bronze, ♂		Broad-breasted bronze, ♀		Beltsville, small white, ♂		Beltsville, small white, ♀	
Age	kg	lb	kg	lb	kg	lb	kg	lb
147 Birth	0.054	0.12	0.050	0.11	0.045	0.10	0.045	0.10
148 1 wk	0.113	0.25	0.109	0.24	0.095	0.21	0.086	0.19
149 2 wk	0.204	0.45	0.195	0.43	0.181	0.40	0.163	0.36
150 4 wk	0.585	1.29	0.517	1.14	0.472	1.04	0.404	0.89
151 6 wk	1.252	2.76	0.998	2.20	0.921	2.03	0.721	1.59
152 8 wk	2.028	4.47	1.651	3.64	1.483	3.27	1.148	2.53
153 10 wk	2.939	6.48	2.354	5.19	2.205	4.86	1.674	3.69
154 12 wk	4.037	8.90	3.166	6.98	2.726	6.01	2.087	4.60
155 14 wk	4.922	10.85	3.715	8.19	3.357	7.40	2.608	5.75
156 16 wk	6.214	13.70	4.604	10.15	4.264	9.40	3.062	6.75
157 18 wk	6.985	15.40	5.121	11.29	4.704	10.37	3.357	7.40
158 20 wk	8.328	18.36	5.851	12.90	5.643	12.44	3.742	8.25
159 22 wk	8.850	19.51	6.083	13.41				
160 24 wk	10.614	23.40	6.836	15.07	7.438	16.20	4.382	9.66
161 26 wk	11.508	25.37	7.307	16.11	8.038	17.72	4.631	10.21
162 28 wk	12.633	27.85	7.625	16.81	9.008	19.86	4.740	10.45
163 30 wk					9.113	20.09	5.085	11.21
164 35 wk	14.610	32.21	7.793	17.18				
165 40 wk	14.814	32.66	8.437	18.60				

Age	Duck, white pekin		Goose, pilgrim				Quail, bob-white	
	kg	lb	♂ kg	♂ lb	♀ kg	♀ lb	kg	lb
166 Birth	0.059	0.13			0.07	0.17	0.004	0.01
167 1 wk	0.150	0.33	0.227	0.5	0.227	0.5	0.018	0.04
168 2 wk	0.458	1.01	0.635	1.4	0.589	1.3	0.027	0.06
169 3 wk	0.744	1.64	1.270	2.8	1.270	2.8	0.045	0.10
170 4 wk	1.148	2.53	1.905	4.2	1.769	3.9	0.063	0.14
171 5 wk	1.506	3.32	2.404	5.3	1.814	4.0	0.082	0.18
172 6 wk	2.005	4.42	3.039	6.7	2.585	5.7	0.095	0.21
173 8 wk	2.758	6.08	3.946	8.7	3.447	7.6	0.132	0.29
174 10 wk			4.264	9.4	3.719	8.2		
175 12 wk			5.035	11.1	4.218	9.3	0.159	0.35
176 16 wk			5.352	11.8	4.672	10.3	0.172	0.38

	Lizard[4]						Snake[5]					
	Black footless		Desert night		Skink, western		Blacksnake, pilot		Cottonmouth		Greensnake, smooth	
	Sex & Age	mm	Sex & Age	mm	Sex & Age	mm	Sex & Age	mm	Sex & Age	mm	Sex & Age	mm
177	♂♀<1 yr	(46-82)	♂♀ Birth	23(22-24)	♂♀ Birth	26(25-26)	♂♀ Birth	307(267-331)	♂♀ 8 mo	228	♂♀ 9 mo	152
178	2 yr	(82-120)	1 yr	29	4 mo	40(37-43)	46 da	330	5 yr 8 mo	1115	♂ 21 mo	356
179	3 yr	(120-160)	2 yr	36	6 mo	45(41-49)	77 da	356	8 yr 3 mo	1282	♀ 21 mo	406
180	Adult	(>160)	♂ 3 yr	(38-39)	10 mo	45	108 da	403(343-545)	9 yr 1 mo	1308	♀ 33 mo	559
181			♀ 3 yr	(42-43)	11 mo	50			10 yr 2 mo	1320		
182					20 mo	62			11 yr 2 mo	1371		
183					24 mo	65			12 yr 2 mo	1397		

	Snake[5] (continued)								Turtle			
	Massasauga, eastern		Racer, western striped		Rattlesnake, great basin		Water snake, queen		Terrapin, diamondback[6]		Turtle, common box[7]	
	Sex & Age	mm	Sex & Age	mm	Sex & Age	mm	Sex & Age	mm	Sex & Age	mm	Sex & Age	mm
184	♂♀ Birth	233	♂ 1 yr	627(579-655)	♂ 1 yr	457	♂♀ Birth	183(166-225)	♂♀ Birth	(18-36)	♀ Birth	29-30
185	1 yr	375	♀ 1 yr	587(538-622)	♀ 1 yr	450(419-503)	3 mo	231(196-255)	1st season	(30-61)	♀ 30 yr	93
186	3 yr	541	♂ 2 yr	790	♂ 2 yr	557(492-627)	1 yr	325(256-375)	2nd season	(54-87)	41 yr	127
187	Adult	637(541-731)	♂ 3 yr	864(807-919)	♀ 2 yr	554(530-574)	♂ > 2 yr	529(375-692)	3rd season	(91-115)	64 yr	138
188			♂ 4 yr	833	♂ 3 yr	655(609-711)	♀ > 2 yr	584(375-787)	4th season	(103-118)		
189			♀ 4 yr	894(883-904)	♂ 4 yr	732			5th season	(110-115)		
190			♂ 5 yr	859	♀ 4 yr	663(642-681)			6th season	(110-115)		
191					♂ 6 yr	770(724-815)						
192					♀ 6 yr	666						

Fish:	Bass, rock		Carp		Catfish, channel		Crappie, black		Drum, fresh-water		Herring, lake		Paddlefish	
Age	kg	lb	kg	lb	kg	lb	kg	lb	kg	lb	kg	lb	kg	lb
193 1 yr	0.006	0.013	0.09	0.198	0.045	0.099	0.006	0.013	0.036	0.079	0.023	0.051	0.077	0.170
194 2 yr	0.028	0.062	0.45	0.992	0.135	0.298	0.045	0.099	0.135	0.298	0.04	0.088	1.35	2.975
195 4 yr	0.065	0.143	1.8	3.967	0.23	0.507	0.255	0.562	0.60	1.324	0.17	0.375	2.27	5.0
196 6 yr	0.165	0.364	2.5	5.510	0.68	1.50	0.37	0.816	1.18	2.601	0.23	0.507	3.40	7.494
197 8 yr	0.255	0.562	3.2	7.053	1.63	3.593	0.57	1.256	2.04	4.496	0.53	1.169	5.0	11.0
198 10 yr	0.38	0.838	5.1	11.240	4.3	9.477	0.68	1.499	5.10	11.24	0.71	1.565	6.8	14.99
199 Maximum	0.595	1.311	38	84	24	53	1.35	2.975	6.97	15.36	1.25	2.755	74	163

Fish: (continued)	Perch, yellow		Pike		Salmon, Atlantic		Sturgeon, lake		Sunfish, bluegill		Trout, lake		Whitefish, Lake Erie	
Age	kg	lb	kg	lb	kg	lb	kg	lb	kg	lb	kg	lb	kg	lb
200 1 yr	0.003	0.007	0.09	0.198	0.011	0.024	0.068	0.150	0.005	0.011	0.03	0.070	0.03	0.070
201 2 yr	0.03	0.070	0.27	0.595	0.033	0.073	0.136	0.299	0.026	0.057	0.14	0.309	0.085	0.187
202 4 yr	0.11	0.242	1.10	2.42	4.54	10.01	0.39	0.859	0.07	0.154	0.45	0.992	0.70	1.543
203 6 yr	0.23	0.507	2.10	4.63	16.0	35	0.72	1.587	0.17	0.375	1.13	2.49	1.36	2.997
204 8 yr	0.29	0.639	2.95	6.50			1.0	2.204	0.34	0.749	1.95	4.30	2.27	5.003
205 10 yr	0.37	0.815	4.50	9.92			1.4	3.09	0.34	0.749	3.82	8.42	2.78	6.127
206 Maximum	1.91	4.21	28	62	47	104	50	110	1.96	4.320	36	79	4.88	10.76

/4/ Snout-vemt measurement. /5/ Total length measurement. /6/ Plastron measurement. /7/ Carapace measurement.

132. BODY AND ORGAN WEIGHTS: MAN

Values for organs are averages of fresh weight, in grams, determined as quickly as possible after removal. Body weight values, in kilograms, are averages, and are included only to show a relationship between average organ weights and average total body weights. When a single value for an organ weight is reported, it is an average for both sexes. When a value is a weight averaged over a period of two or more years, it is given at the earliest age of the period covered.

#	Age	Body Weight kg	Adrenals g	Brain g	Heart g	Hypophysis g	Intestines[1] g	Kidneys g	Liver g	Lungs g	Pancreas g	Pineal Body g	Spleen g	Stomach[1] g	Thymus g	Thyroid[2] g	Epididymis g	Prostate g	Seminal Vesicles g	Testes g	Ovaries g	Uterus g	Uterine Tubes g
1	Birth ♂	3.54	9.01	353	20	0.121	142	24	134	52	2.77	0.008	9.4	6.5	11.2	2.09(6.6)	0.24	0.82	0.050	0.67			
2	♀	3.43	9.03	347	19		149	22	137	51			9.4								0.29	4.70	0.29
3	0-3 mo ♂	5.92	4.66	435	19	0.161		30	143	69	3.54	0.044	14.6	10.9	19.3	1.71(3.18)	0.42	0.9	0.052	0.91			
4	♀	5.62	4.60	411	17			27	133	64			11.4								0.63	2.88	0.26
5	3-6 mo ♂	8.4	3.61	600	25			43	184	94	5.38		18.9	14.1	22.9	2.11(4.4)				1.12			
6	♀	7.9	4.37	534	27			37	178	93			15.9								0.45	3.00	
7	6-12 mo ♂	10.8	4.97	877	37		409	61	261	135	9.24		24	18.3	22.1	2.04(3.44)				1.39			
8	♀	10.6	4.60	726	33		375	55	250	128			21								0.74	4.83	
9	1-2 yr ♂	12.2	3.68	971	47			74	343	170	13.54	0.053	32	27.1	26.0	2.53(5.24)	0.34	1.2	0.08	1.48			
10	♀	11.9	3.19	894	42			69	322	175			29								0.98	4.01	0.29
11	2-3 yr ♂	14.4	5.62	1076	59	0.232		94	459	246	19	0.081	44	37.9[3]	25.9	3.40(9.13)				1.93			
12	♀	13.8	3.97	1012	55			91	429	244			41								1.12	2.30	
13	3-4 yr ♂	16.3		1179	71		648	101	531	305			49		26.4	4.9(11.22)	0.41	1.1		1.64			
14	♀	16.2		1076	66		383	105	491	266			47										
15	4-5 yr ♂	18.5		1290	78	0.224		111	567	314	22	0.098	48	51.8[4]	24.4	5.24(15.15)							
16	♀	18.0		1156	75			116	559	312			45								1.90	3.29[5]	0.49
17	5-6 yr ♂	20.6	4.92	1275	89			108	592	261			57		23.3		0.50	1.3	0.099	1.67			
18	♀	20.0	5.02	1206	83			116	591	320			50										
19	6-7 yr ♂	22.7		1313	98	0.299	691	155	661	400	29	0.131	67		26.0	7.05(14.4)							
20	♀	22.2		1225	89			122	604	358			47										
21	7-8 yr ♂	25.1		1338	102			147	691	366			63		33.6								
22	♀	24.6		1265	96			134	683	404			56										
23	8-9 yr ♂	28		1294	128	0.366	559	141	808	405	27		74		27.7	9.3(18.34)							
24	♀	27		1208	104			139	733	382			69								3.30	7.59[6]	
25	9-10 yr ♂	31		1360	118			167	804	376			70		28.1					1.83[6]			
26	♀	30		1226	125			157	863	358			66										
27	10-11 yr ♂	33	6.86	1378	137	0.378		184	931	475	29	0.156	90	90[7]	28.9	8.69(23.2)	0.73	1.9	0.120	2.0			
28	♀	34	7.40	1247	144			189	905	571			112										
29	11-12 yr ♂	37		1348	149			178	902	466	35		80		30.8								
30	♀	38		1259	127			143	840	535			83										
31	12-13 yr ♂	41		1383	154	0.460	1000	185	987	682			85		23.6	14.8(24.7)	0.84	3.3		6.96			
32	♀	43		1256	131			193	1048	459			101										
33	13-14 yr ♂	46		1382	172			215	1103	505			107		34.0					7.17[8]			
34	♀	46		1243	164			188	998	602			94								4.12[8]	11.60[8]	
35	14-15 yr ♂	52	9.47	1356	203			250	1166	693	68		109		26.5	14.5(26)	1.64	4.3	0.90	15.56			
36	♀	50	11.38	1318	184			226	1209	517			127								6.03	32	1.05
37	15-16 yr ♂	58		1407	215	0.520	1460	251	1228	692			145		28.8	16.6(28)		8.8		23.5			
38	♀	52		1271	203			245	1349	709			131										
39	16-17 yr ♂	62		1300	234			253	1448	747	85	0.137	166	129[9]									
40	♀	53		1409	243			261	1414	627			172										
41	17-18 yr ♂	65		1254	252			297	1515	695			148			18.3(29)							
42	♀	55		1426	228			270	1417	777			123										
43	18-19 yr ♂	67		1312	260		1527	303	1702	848			169										
44	♀	55		1360	242			276	1541	655			151										
45	19-20 yr ♂	67		1430	283			295	1570	1036			153										
46	♀	69		1294	257			272	1433	785			138								7.87[10]	47.0[10]	2.13
47	20-30 yr ♂	71	13.75	1355	312	0.625	1600	313	1838	953		0.171	204		19.9	25(38)	4.0	16.6		28.3			
48	♀	56	13.80	1220	273			257	1437	793			168								10.16	77.5	
49	30-40 yr ♂	72	11.41	1365			1570	323	1872	1169			164		19.7					27.2			
50	♀	60	11.57	1228			1550	250	1462	886			179								9.25	78.0	
51	40-50 yr ♂	65	11.52	1357			1800	316	1888				172		18.7					27.0			
52	♀		10.17	1227				258	1570				127								6.15	100.5	
53	50-60 yr ♂	65	12.48	1360				294	1848				133		13.4					27.4			
54	♀		12.01	1212			1600	254	1464				132								5.73	95.8	
55	60-70 yr ♂	67	13.93	1319				293	1728				129							24.3			
56	♀	65	12.95	1194			1500	218	1400				123								2.87	63.3	
57	70-80 yr ♂	61	11.85	1290				253	1426				121							21.6			
58	♀	61	10.42	1145			1400	236	1263												3.99	59.0	

1/ Body weights of the individuals whose organ weights are given in this column were considerably lower than those shown in the body weight column for the various age groups. /2/ Normal thyroid values followed, in parentheses, by values for thyroid weight in geographical goiter areas. /3/ 2-4 yr. /4/ 4-7 yr. /5/ 3-5 yr. /6/ 6-10 yr. /7/ 7-14 yr. /8/ 11-14 yr. /9/ 14-20 yr. /10/ 15-20 yr.

133. BODY AND ORGAN WEIGHTS: VERTEBRATES

Values are based on fresh weight for adult organs, determined immediately after death of the organism, and are grams/100 grams body weight.

Species	Sex and Number	Body wt. kg	Adrenals g/100g	Brain g/100g	Eyes g/100g	Heart g/100g	Kidneys g/100g	Liver g/100g	Lungs g/100g	Spleen g/100g	Stomach & Intestines g/100g	Thyroid g/100g
Mammalia												
Man (Homo sapiens)												
1 Australian aborigine	♂1	76	0.005	1.77								0.005
2 Chinese	♂1	84	0.009	1.76		0.66	0.37	2.43		0.21		0.02
3 Filipino	♂1	43		2.57		0.46						0.06
4 Indian, Maya Quiche	♂1	42	0.03	3.02		0.52	0.44	2.48	3.13	0.14		0.08
5 Indian, Maya Quiche	♀1	46	0.02	2.18		0.49						0.02
6 Negro	♂7	47	0.03	2.73		0.81	0.51	2.81				0.06
7 White, American	♂7	67	0.02	1.96		0.42	0.41	2.30	0.73	0.25		0.04
8 White, European	♂4	49	0.03	2.53		0.64						0.03
9 Agouti, brown (Dasyprocta punctata)	♂♀5	2.6	0.03	0.58	0.50	0.51	0.59	2.84	0.22			
10 Antbear (Cyclops didactylus)	?1	0.09	0.84	4.77								
11 Anteater (Tamanduas tetradactyla)	♂♀4	2.2		1.09		0.03	0.82	2.64	1.05	0.14		0.009
12 Armadillo (Dasypus novemcinctus)	♂♀12	3.3	0.03	0.25		0.28	0.48		0.70	0.22		0.006
13 Ass (Equus asinus)	♀1	150	0.01	0.27		0.55	1.04	0.84	0.83	0.39		0.04
14 Bat, vampire (Desmodus rotundus)	♂♀5	0.028	0.04	3.34								0.004
15 Bear, brown (Ursus americanus)	♂1	550	0.001				0.03					0.04
16 Bear, grizzly (U. horribilis)	♀1	140	0.04	0.16		0.79	0.38			0.21		
17 Beaver (Castor canadensis)	♂1;♀1	5	0.009	0.45		0.43	1.08	3.03	0.97			0.09
18 Bison, American (Bison bison)	♀1	55	0.01	0.61	0.08	0.66	0.47	1.27	2.17	0.27		0.005
19 Buffalo, African (Syncerus caffer)	♂3;♀1	700	0.005	0.09	0.008	0.47	0.24	0.98	0.94	0.33	20.90	
20 Bushbok (Tragelaphus scriptus)	♂1;♀1	44	0.01	0.37	0.11	0.76	0.40	1.95	1.64	0.26	12.62	0.01
21 Camel, bactrian (Camelus bactrianus)	♂1	450	0.005	0.12	0.02					0.08		
22 Caribou, ground (Rangifer arcticus)	♂3;♀1	98	0.004	0.30	0.04	0.90	0.13	1.83	2.10	0.26	10.37	0.01
23 Cat, domestic (Felis catus)	♂7;♀3	3.3	0.02	0.77	0.32	0.45	1.07	3.59	1.04	0.29	3.14	0.010
24 Cattle, Holstein (Bos taurus)	♂5	900	0.005	0.05		0.37	0.20	0.92	0.69	0.15	4.83	0.006
25 Cattle, Holstein (B. taurus)	♀198	600	0.006	0.07		0.37	0.24	1.20	0.72	0.16		0.02
26 Cheetah (Acinonyx jubatus)	♂2	21	0.009	0.39	0.16	0.51	0.47	3.22	1.16	0.15		0.009
27 Chimpanzee (Pan troglodytes)	♂1	52	0.02	0.84		0.48						0.01
28 Chimpanzee (P. troglodytes)	♀1	44	0.02	0.74		0.50	0.48	2.75	1.36		14.09	0.04
29 Chipmunk (Tamias striatus)	♂2	0.07	0.04	2.96	0.74	7.96	0.10	7.4	0.96	0.29	6.2	0.03
30 Coati (Nasua nasua)	♂2	5.1	0.009	0.66	0.04	0.38	0.08	1.63	0.47	0.07		
31 Coyote (Canis latrans)	♀2	8.5				0.85	0.94	3.44	0.72	0.17		
32 Deer, white-tailed (Odocoileus virginianus)	♂1	65		0.32		0.97		1.57				0.02
33 Dog (Canis familiaris)	♂2;♀2	13	0.01	0.59	0.10	0.85	0.30	2.94	0.94		4.83	0.01
34 Elephant (Loxodonta africana)	♂1	6600	0.01	0.08	0.001	0.39	0.27	1.62	2.08		13.88	
35 Fox, gray (Urocyon cineroargenteus)	♂1	3.8	0.01	0.99	0.11	0.58	0.46	1.35	0.51		11.31	
36 Fox, red (Vulpes fulva)	♀1	4.6	0.01	1.15	0.09	0.90						0.003
37 Gazelle (Gazella thomsoni)	♂2	24	0.008	0.38	0.11	1.00	0.43	2.15	1.15			0.007
38 Giraffe (Giraffa camelopardalis)	♂1	1200	0.006	0.06	0.01	0.41	0.18	1.56	0.99	0.18	10.65	0.005
39 Goat (Capra hircus)	♂1	28		0.41	0.11			1.90				0.003
40 Gorilla (Gorilla gorilla)	♂1	180	0.02									
41 Guinea pig (Cavia porcellus)	♂58	0.26	0.07	1.33		0.53	1.17	5.14	1.18			0.02
42 Guinea pig (C. porcellus)	♀10	0.43	0.08	0.92	0.24	0.39	0.86	3.86	1.07	0.21		0.006
43 Hamster, golden (Mesocricetus auratus)	♂2;♀2	0.12	0.02	0.88	0.18	0.47	0.53	5.16	0.46			0.006
44 Hare, African (Lepus capensis)	♀1	2.9	0.02	0.35	0.25	1.02	0.42	1.77	0.61		10.07	0.008
45 Hippopotamus (Hippopotamus amphibius)	♀1	1350	0.004	0.05	0.003	0.34	0.23	1.75	0.84	0.23	27.70	0.008
46 Horse, Percheron (Equus caballus)	♂1	635	0.006	0.10	0.02	0.88	0.27	1.34	0.90	0.54		0.006
47 Horse, Percheron (E. caballus)	♀1	770	0.004	0.08	0.02	0.61	0.23	0.87	0.70	0.20		0.007
48 Hyena, spotted (Crocuta crocuta)	♂2	62	0.02	0.28	0.06	0.72	0.64	5.12	10.92		10.91	0.01
49 Hyrax (Heterohyrax brucei)	♂1	0.75	0.02	1.64		0.48	0.86	4.20	0.74		34	0.01
50 Jackal (Canis mesomelas)	♂2	2.8	0.02	1.61	0.24	0.75	0.81	4.30	1.05		10.81	0.03
51 Jaguar (Felis onca)	♀1	34	0.02	0.43	0.05	0.54	0.48	2.59	1.67	0.18		0.004
52 Kinkajou (Potos flavus)	♀1	2.6	0.007	1.18	0.07	0.54		3.76	2.99			0.02
53 Lemming, rock (Dicrostonyx rubricatus)	♂4	0.05	0.03	0.17	0.28	0.59	1.48	5.05	1.59	0.40		0.008
54 Leopard (Panthera pardus)	♂1	48	0.01	0.28	0.06	0.42		1.87	1.04	0.22		0.10
55 Lion (P. leo)	♂4	125	0.01	0.19		0.85			2.12			
56 Lion (P. leo)	♀3	97	0.01	0.20	0.04	0.54	0.53	3.24	2.06	0.22		0.004
57 Lynx (Lynx baileyi)	♂1	7.4	0.08				0.33					0.01
58 Manatee (Trichechus manatus)	♂1	425		0.08	0.001	0.29		1.30	0.72			0.01
59 Manatee (T. manatus)	♀1	560	0.002		0.01	0.22	0.24	1.12	0.67			0.02
60 Mole (Scalopus aquaticus)	♂1	0.04	0.04	2.93		0.69	1.59	3.91	1.86			0.004
61 Mongoose (Ichneumia albicauda)	♂1	4.4	0.01	0.64	0.09	0.64	0.79	1.39	1.32		6.25	
62 Monkey, black howler (Alouatta palliata)	♂♀28	6.2	0.01	0.81		0.33	0.58	3.25	0.63	0.74		0.02
63 Monkey, rhesus (Macaca mulatta)	♂4	3.3	0.02	2.78	1.06	0.38		2.09				0.01
64 Monkey, rhesus (M. mulatta)	♀7	3.6	0.03	2.57		0.34			1.89			0.01
65 Mouse, jumping (Zapus hudsonicus)	♂1;♀3	0.018	0.04	3.57	0.14	1.03	1.26	5.63	1.34			0.01
66 Mouse, meadow (Microtus drummondi)	♂♀67	0.023	0.03	0.29	0.10	0.68	1.53	4.56	1.70			0.01
67 Muskrat (Ondatra zibethica)	♂1	0.90	0.01	0.59	0.21	0.36	0.83	2.44	0.48		1.95	0.001
68 Opossum, woolly (Philander laniger)	♂1;♀1	190	0.53			1.58	2.10	4.74	1.58	0.79		
69 Porcupine (Erethizon dorsatum)	♂1;♀3	2.9	0.01	0.78	0.09	0.55	0.96	4				0.02
70 Porpoise (Phocaena phocaena)	♂1	140	0.007	1.22	0.04	0.52		2.08	3.69	0.04	9.28	0.01
71 Rabbit, giant Flemish (Lepus spp)	♂2	3.7	0.01	0.29		0.29	0.61	2.66				0.02
72 Rabbit, giant Flemish (Lepus spp)	♀22	2.5	0.02	0.40		0.35	0.70	3.19	0.53			
73 Raccoon (Procyon lotor)	♂1	5.2	0.02	0.82		0.81	0.68	3.58	3.58	0.28		0.008
74 Raccoon (P. lotor)	♀1	2.2	0.07	1.51	0.15	0.89	1.61	6.29	0.87		10.11	0.001
75 Rat, Norway (Rattus norvegicus)	♂2;♀1	0.25	0.05	1.22	0.10	0.52	1.09	3.35	0.79	0.29	2.52	0.004
76 Reedbuck (Redunca redunca)	♂2	31	0.006	0.34	0.10	0.76	0.32	1.65	1.34			0.008
77 Seal, ringed (Phoca hispida)	♂3;♀2	39	0.007	0.63	0.18	0.73	0.70	2.81	1.85	0.32		0.01
78 Shrew (Blarina brevicauda)	♂29	0.02	0.02	1.87	0.009	1.02	1.08	5.81	2.24			0.01
79 Shrew (B. brevicauda)	♀39	0.017	0.02	2.11	0.006	1.05	1.25	5.45	2.19			0.004
80 Skunk (Mephitis mephitis)	♂1;♀2	2.1	0.01	0.33		0.58	0.28	2.69	1.59			

Values are based on fresh weight for adult organs, determined immediately after death of the organism, and are grams/100 grams body weight.

Species	Sex and Number	Body wt. kg	Adrenals g/100g	Brain g/100g	Eyes g/100g	Heart g/100g	Kidneys g/100g	Liver g/100g	Lungs g/100g	Spleen g/100g	Stomach & Intestines g/100g	Thyroid g/100g
						Mammalia (concluded)						
81 Sloth, three-toed (Bradypus tridactylus)	♂♀6	1.8	0.01	0.75								
82 Squirrel, red (Sciurus hudsonicus)	♂4	0.18	0.03	2.57	0.27	0.86	0.62	2.18	1.45			0.01
83 Squirrel, red (S. hudsonicus)	♀4	0.25	0.03	2.02	0.21	0.73	0.53	2.68	1.28			0.01
84 Steinbok (Raphicerus campestris)	♂2	8.6	0.01	0.57	0.17	0.84	0.45	2.03	1.74		6.38	0.01
85 Swine (Sus scrofa)	♀36	102	0.004			0.32	0.26	1.51		0.13	1.95	0.007
86 Tapir (Tapirella bairdii)	♂1;♀1	11.4	0.02			0.85	1.30	3.07	2.10	1.12		
87 Tiger (Panthera tigris)	♀1	160	0.01	0.14		0.27		1.14	0.64	0.57		
88 Walrus (Odobenus rosmarus)	♂1;♀3	600	0.002	0.17	0.003	0.68	0.68	2.92	1.36		4.42	0.01
89 Warthog (Phacochoerus aethiopicus)	♂1	65	0.01	0.19	0.03	0.50	0.46	2.30	0.84		15.23	0.005
90 Weasel, arctic (Mustela arctica)	♂3;♀1	0.18	0.01	2.80	0.08	1.71	0.99	4.74	2.08			0.05
91 Whale, white (Delphinapterus leucas)	♂4	447	0.006	0.52	0.007	0.55	0.49	1.52	2.70	0.04	2.70	0.02
92 Whale, white (D. leucas)	♀2	300	0.009	0.78	0.007	0.57	0.61	1.59	2.62	0.05	3.06	0.02
93 Wildebeest (Connochaetes taurinus)	♂2	210	0.003	0.21		0.62	0.23	1.07	1.34		17.54	0.005
94 Wolf (Canis lupus)	♂1	22	0.01	0.52	0.08	1.08	0.82	2.76	3.56			
95 Zebra (Equus quagga)	♂3;♀1	280	0.008	0.20	0.03	1.42	0.35	1.67	0.80	0.41		0.007
						Aves						
96 Blackbird (Quiscalus quiscala)	♀1	0.08	0.02	3.56	0.23	0.14	0.16	3.21	0.21	0.06	7.78	0.01
97 Bluebird (Sialia sialis)	♂1;♀1	0.03	0.55	4.24		1.39						0.02
98 Buzzard, steppe (Buteo vulpinus)	♂1	0.56	0.05	1.41		0.82	0.60	1.94	0.83			0.03
99 Catbird (Dumatella carolinensis)	♀1	0.03	0.01	0.43		0.99			1.84			0.01
100 Canary (Serinus canarius)	♂1;♀1	0.016	0.04	4.72	1.75	1.29	0.16	5.39	0.15	0.11	14.17	0.008
101 Cowbird (Molothrus ater)	♀1	0.07	0.02	4.08		1.61						0.02
102 Crane, gray (Grus canadensis)	♂1	1.6	0.01	0.52	0.66	1.15	0.71	1.78	0.93	0.04	4.76	0.008
103 Crow (Corvus brachyrhyncos)	♂1	0.33	0.02	2.76		0.95			2.96			0.01
104 Duck, pintail (Anas acuta)	♀1	0.67	0.01	0.74	0.25	1.24	1.21	4.53	2.56	0.13	14.84	0.008
105 Eagle, tawny (Aguila rapax)	♂2;♀3	2.4	0.45	0.59	1.34	0.63	0.50	1.82	1.04		6.36	0.01
106 Egret, great white (Casmerodius albus)	♀1	10	0.02	0.59		0.90	0.79	3.20	3.21		13.11	0.01
107 Flamingo (Phoeniconaias minor)	♂3;♀2	15	0.02	0.49	0.22	0.94	1.18	2.68	1.47			0.03
108 Fowl, domestic (Gallus domesticus)	♂8	0.73	0.009	0.40	0.58	0.57	0.62	2.21	0.60	0.13		0.01
109 Fowl, domestic (G. domesticus)	♀16	0.61	0.01	0.44	0.58	0.63	0.68	2.36	0.61	0.15		0.01
110 Fowl, white leghorn, "germ-free"[1]	?	0.9-1.2	0.009			0.35		1.53	0.51			
111 Goose, Egyptian (Alopochen aegypticus)	♀1	1.9	0.02	0.39		0.96	0.50	1.77	1.80			0.02
112 Guineafowl (Numida meleagris)	♂1	1.6	0.02	0.26		0.88	0.45	1.76	1.79			0.02
113 Gull, herring (Larus argentatus)	♀2	0.53	0.02	0.95	1.45	0.98		5.12				0.007
114 Hawk, red-tailed (Buteo borealis)	♀3	1.0	0.01	0.97	2.06	0.67	0.30	1.37	0.9		1.79	0.09
115 Hummingbird (Amazilia tzacatl)	♀1	0.005	0.007	4.16	2.50	2.37	0.81	5.23	0.20			0.009
116 Ostrich, masai (Struthio camelus)	♂1	125	0.02	0.03	0.08	0.98		1.66	2.36			
117 Owl, horned (Buteo virginianus)	♂1	1.2	0.01	1.16		0.73			0.91			0.007
118 Partridge (Francolinus sephaena)	♂1	0.21	0.02	0.72		0.70	1.30	4.16				0.009
119 Pelican (Pelecanus occidentalis)	♀2	3.3	0.03	0.54	0.38	0.67		2.22	0.91		7.75	0.005
120 Pheasant (Phasianus colchicus)	♂1	0.62	0.02	0.53	0.85	0.90	0.77	1.46			9.04	0.008
121 Pigeon (Columba livia)	♂3;♀1	0.27	0.16	0.95		1.75		1.76				0.11
122 Raven (Corvus corax)	♀1	1.25		2.81		0.85	0.71					0.009
123 Robin (Turdus migratorius)	♂2	0.07	0.03	3.01		1.46			2.42			0.01
124 Sparrow (Passer domesticus)	♂75	0.024	0.03	4.36	1.95	1.73	1.46	5.12	1.56	0.18	11.45	0.02
125 Sparrow (P. domesticus)	♀11	0.023	0.03	4.38	2.23	1.69	1.53	4.67	1.72	0.18	11.53	0.02
126 Starling (Sturnus vulgaris)	♂15	0.06	0.02	3.26	1.46	1.62	1.71	3.46	1.87	0.11	9.15	0.01
127 Starling (S. vulgaris)	♀10	0.06	0.02	3.13	1.80	1.49	1.85	3.74	1.87	0.07	9.69	0.01
128 Stork, European (Ciconia ciconia)	♂2;♀1	3.3	0.01	0.47	0.51	0.92	0.65	1.92	1.11			0.01
						Reptilia						
129 Alligator (Alligator mississipiensis)	♂2	190	0.004	0.007	0.01	0.15		0.38	0.54	0.07	2.95	0.006
130 Crocodile (Crocodylus acutus)	♂1;♀1	110	0.004	0.01		0.12		1.02	1.00			0.004
131 Iguana lizard (Iguana iguana)	♀1	1.3	0.02			0.19		2.49	0.28		3.18	0.009
132 Lizard (Lacerta viridis)	♂♀15	0.05	0.04	0.24		0.12	0.12	5		0.16		0.02
133 Snake, black (Coluber constrictor)	♂1;♀2	0.43	0.03	0.07	0.05	0.22	0.60	0.60	0.80	0.18	2.79	0.02
134 Snake, boa (Boa imperator)	♀1	1.8	0.008	0.02	0.03	0.31	0.52	1.66	0.76			0.008
135 Snake, green (Zamenis viridis)	♂3;♀3	0.022	0.36	0.95			8.77	2.19		0.57		0.20
136 Snake, python (Python molurus)	♂1	6.1	0.04	0.02	0.02	0.30						0.02
137 Snake, watermoccasin (Ancistrodon pisci)	♀1	0.73	0.14	0.09	0.08	0.65	1.85	8.85	3.12	0.76	41.24	0.07
138 Toad, horned (Phrynosoma cornutum)	♂2;♀3	0.025	0.03	0.52	1.28	0.44						
139 Turtle (Aromochelys tristycha)	♂1	0.12				0.43	0.43	2.8	0.85	0.18	2.729	
140 Turtle (A. tristycha)	♀2	0.09				0.48	0.47	2.9	0.76	0.17		
141 Turtle (Testudo graeca)	♂♀30	0.32	0.009	0.09		0.48		2.66		0.06		0.01
142 Turtle, cumberland (Chrysemys elegans)	♂21	0.84				0.32	0.32	5.43	1.07	0.22	6.23	
143 Turtle, cumberland (C. elegans)	♀1	0.86				0.31	0.36	5.92	0.84	0.47	7.32	
						Amphibia						
144 Frog, bull (Rana catesbiana)	♂7	0.49	0.02	0.93	0.48	0.32	0.29	2.75	0.53	0.07	4.72	0.007
145 Frog, leopard (R. pipiens)	♂10	0.036				0.43	0.43	2.81	0.85	0.18	3.50	
146 Frog, leopard (R. pipiens)	♀19	0.038				0.48	0.47	2.88	0.76	0.17	3.77	
						Pisces						
147 Barracuda (Sphyraena barracuda)	♂3;♀3	8.8		0.04	0.44	0.24	1.82	0.69		0.15	4.17	0.002
148 Carp (Cyprinus carpio)	♂2;♀4	1.05		0.12	0.28	0.15	0.55			0.23	7.92	0.0008
149 Codfish (Gadus morrhua)	♀1	10.6		0.05	0.6	0.15	0.19	1.52		0.95	5.47	0.006
150 Haddock (G. aeglefinus)	♀6	3.3		0.06	0.2	0.17	0.34	4.05		0.08	8.90	0.002
151 Mackerel (Scomber vernalis)	♂1	0.76		0.08								
152 Mackerel (S. vernalis)	♀2	1.5		0.11	0.54	0.20		0.43		0.12	0.20	0.002
153 Perch (Perca flavescens)	♂6	0.17		0.15	0.55	0.23	0.27	0.88		0.09	2.90	0.002
154 Perch (P. flavescens)	♀1	0.19		0.17	0.73	0.77		1.54			4.12	0.001
155 Pike (Esox lucius)	♂4;♀3	0.42		0.12	1.15	0.15	0.42	0.86		0.09	5.10	0.002
156 Salmon (Salmo salar)	♂3	3.4		0.03	0.23	0.36	1.05	2.02		0.32	6.29	0.005
157 Salmon (S. salar)	♀5	5.4		0.02	0.15	0.19	0.74	1.73		0.22	4.30	0.0007
158 Trout, rainbow (Salmo irideus)	♂2	0.26		0.17	0.69	0.17	0.55	0.99		0.21	9.58	0.003
159 Trout, rainbow (S. irideus)	♀4	0.22		0.19	0.70	0.13	0.50	0.99		0.27	8.89	0.002

/1/ A discussion of the meaning of "germ-free" is given in the Lobund report of the University of Notre Dame.

134. FISH: WORLD RECORDS

No.	Species	Caught by Rod and Reel: Weight lb	Weight oz	Length in.	Girth in.	Location	Date	Caught by Any Method: Weight lb	Weight oz	Location
	Fresh-water Records[1]									
1	Black bass, largemouth (Micropterus salmoides)	22	4	32½	28½	Montgomery Lake, Ga.	1932	Same →		
2	Black bass, smallmouth (M. dolomieu)	10	8	22½	21¼	Wheeler Dam, Ala.	1950	Same →		
3	Bluegill sunfish (Lepomis macrochirus)	4	12	15	18¼	Ketona Lake, Ala.	1950	Same →		
4	Bullhead, black (Ameiurus melas)	8		24	17¾	Lake Waccabuc, N. Y.	1951	Same →		
5	Carp (Cyprinus carpio)	55	5	42	31	Clearwater Lake, Minn.	1952	83	8	Pretoria, S. Africa
6	Catfish, blue (Ictalurus furcatus)	94	8	56	35	James River, S. D.	1949	Same →		
7	Catfish, channel (I. lacustris)	55		50	27	James River, S. D.	1949	Same →		
8	Charr, arctic (Salvelinus alpinus)	11	8	30	17	Richmond Gulf, Hud. Bay	1950	Same →		
9	Gar, alligator (Lepisosteus spatula)	279		93		Rio Grande River, Tex.	1951	Same →		
10	Muskellunge (Esox masquinongy)	69	11	63½	31¼	Chippewa Flowage, Wis.	1949	102		Minocqua Lake, Wis.
11	Perch, white (Morone americana)	4	12	19½	13	Messalonskee Lake, Me.	1949	Same →		
12	Perch, yellow (Perca flavescens)	4	3½			Bordentown, N. J.	1865	Same →		
13	Pickerel, eastern chain (Esox niger)	9		30	15	Green Pond, N. J.	1948	9	5	Pontoosuc Lake, Mass.
14	Pike, northern (E. lucius)	46	2	52½	25	Sacandaga Res., N. Y.	1940	Same →		
15	Pike, walleyed (Stizostedion vitreum)	22	4	36¼	21	Fort Erie, Ontario	1943	Same →		
16	Salmon, Atlantic (Salmo salar)	79	2			Tanaelv, Norway	1928	103	2	River Devon, Scotland
17	Salmon, chinook (Oncorhynchus tschawytscha)	83				Umpqua River, Ore.	1910	126	8	Petersburg, Alaska
18	Salmon, landlocked (Salmo sebago)	22	8	36		Sebago Lake, Me.	1907	35		Crooked River, Me.
19	Salmon, silver (Oncorhynchus kisutch)	31				Cowichan Bay, B. C.	1947	Same →		
20	Trout, brook (Salvelinus fontinalis)	14	8			Nipigon River, Ontario	1916	Same →		
21	Trout, brown (Salmo trutta)	39	8			Loch Awe, Scotland	1866	40		Great Lake, Tasmania
22	Trout, cut-throat (S. clarkii)	41		39		Pyramid Lake, Nev.	1925	Same →		
23	Trout, Dolly Varden (Salvelinus malma)	32		40½	29¾	L. Pend Oreille, Id.	1949	Same →		
24	Trout, golden (Salmo agua-bonita)	11		28	16	Cook's Lake, Wyo.	1948	Same →		
25	Trout, lake (Cristivomer namaycush)	63	2	51½	32¾	Lake Superior	1952	80		Mackinaw, Mich.
26	Trout, rainbow[2] (Salmo gairdneri)	37		40½	28	Lake Pend Oreille, Id.	1947	42		Corbett, Ore.
27	Trout, Sunapee (Salvelinus aureolus)	11	8	33	17¼	Lake Sunapee, N. H.	1954	Same →		
	Salt-water Records[3]									
28	Albacore (Thunnus germo)	66	4			Catalina, Calif.	1912	Same →		
29	Amberjack (Seriola lalandi)	119	8	63½	46½	Rio de Janeiro, Brazil	1952	146		Flatts Inlet, Bermuda
30	Barracuda (Sphyraena barracuda)	103	4	66	31¼	West End, Bahamas	1932	Same →		
31	Bass, Calif. white sea (Cynoscion nobilis)	83	12	65½	34	Baja, Mexico	1953	Same →		
32	Bass, channel (Sciaenops ocellata)	83		52	29	Cape Charles, Va.	1949	Same →		
33	Bass, giant black sea (Stereolepis gigas)	483		87	73	Coronado Is., Mexico	1951	800		Avalon, Calif.
34	Bass, giant sea (Promicrops itaiara)	551		100		Galveston Bay, Tex.	1937	Same →		
35	Bass, sea (Centropristes striatus)	8		22	19	Nantucket Sound, Mass.	1951	Same →		
36	Bass, striped (Roccus saxatilis)	73		60	30½	Vineyard Sound, Mass.	1913	125		Edenton, N. C.
37	Blackfish (Tautoga onitis)	21	6	31½	23½	Cape May, N. J.	1954	22	8	Near New York
38	Bluefish (Pomatomus saltatrix)	24	3	41	22	San Miguel, Azores	1953	27		Nantucket, Mass.
39	Bonefish (Albula vulpes)	18	2	41½	18	Mana, Kauai, T. H.	1954	Same →		
40	Bonito, oceanic (Katsuwonus pelamis)	39	15	39	28	Walker Cay, Bahamas	1952	Same →		
41	Cobia (Rachycentron canadus)	102		70	34	Cape Charles, Va.	1938	Same →		
42	Cod (Gadus callarias)	57	8	56		Ambrose Lightship, N. Y.	1949	Same →		
43	Dolphin (Coryphaena hippurus)	75	8	50	21	Mafia Channel, E. Africa	1950	Same →		
44	Drum, black (Pogonias cromis)	88		48		Delaware Bay, N. J.	1954	146		St. Augustine, Fla.
45	Flounder, summer[4] (Paralichthys dentatus)	20		37	32	Oak Beach, N. Y.	1948	26		Noank, Conn.
46	Kingfish[5] (Scomberomorus cavalla)	76	8	63	31	Bimini, Bahamas	1952	100		
47	Marlin, blue (Makaira nigricans ampla)	742		154½	68	Bimini, Bahamas	1949	1200		Havana, Cuba
48	Marlin, Pacific black (M. nigricans marlina)	1560		174	81	Cabo Blanco, Peru	1953	Same →		
49	Marlin, silver (M. nigricans tahitiensis)	755		163¾	65¼	Pinas Bay, Panama	1953	Same →		
50	Marlin, striped (M. mitsukurii)	692		161		Balboa, Calif.	1931	Same →		
51	Marlin, white (M. albida)	161		104	33	Miami Beach, Fla.	1938	Same →		
52	Permit (Trachinotus goodei)	42	4	43	33½	Boca Grange, Fla.	1953	Same →		
53	Pollack (Pollachius virens)	32	4	44	26¾	Belmar, N. J.	1953	Same →		
54	Roosterfish (Nematistius pectoralis)	100		54	32	Cabo Blanco, Peru	1954	Same →		
55	Sailfish, Atlantic (Istiophorus americanus)	123		124	32¾	Walker Cay, Bahamas	1950	Same →		
56	Sailfish, Pacific (I. greyi)	221		129		Galapagos Islands	1947	Same →		
57	Sawfish (Pristis pectinatus)	736		175		Galveston, Tex.	1938	1500		Aransas Pass, Tex.
58	Shark, mako, Atlantic (Isurus oxyrhynchus)	1000		144		Mayor Island, N. Z.	1943	Same →		
59	Shark, man-eater[6] (Carcharodon carcharias)	2372		181	117	Streaky Bay, Australia	1953	Same →		
60	Shark, porbeagle (Lamna nasus)	260		136	68¾	Durban, S. Africa	1949	Same →		
61	Shark, thresher (Alopias vulpinus)	922				Bay of Islands, N. Z.	1937	Same →		
62	Shark, tiger (Galeocerdo cuvier)	1382		166	93	Sydney Heads, Australia	1939	Same →		
63	Snook[7] (Centropomus undecimalis)	50	8	55		Gatun Spillway, C. Z.	1944	Same →		
64	Swordfish (Xiphias gladius)	1182		179	78	Iquique, Chile	1953	Same →		
65	Tarpon (Tarpon atlanticus)	247		89½		Panuco River, Mexico	1938	350		Hillsboro River, Fla.
66	Tuna, Allison[8] (Thunnus albacares)	265		73	53	Makua, T. H.	1937	Same →		
67	Tuna, big-eyed (Parathunnus sibi)	368		89	63½	Cabo Blanco, Peru	1953	Same →		
68	Tuna, bluefin (Thunnus thynnus)	977		116	94½	St. Ann Bay, N. S.	1950	1800		Wedgeport, Nova Sco.
69	Tuna, dog-toothed (Gymnosarda nuda)	151	8			Tahiti	1936	Same →		
70	Wahoo (Acanthocybium solandri)	133	8	83	31	Green Cay, Bahamas	1943	Same →		
71	Weakfish (Cynoscion regalis)	17	8	46	19	Mullica River, N. J.	1944	30		New Jersey
72	Weakfish, spotted (C. nebulosus)	15	3	34½	20½	Fort Pierce, Fla.	1949	15	4	Indian River, Fla.
73	Yellowtail (Seriola dorsalis)	90		59	35½	La Paz, Mexico	1948	Same →		

/1/ Compiled by Field and Stream magazine. /2/ Or steelhead. /3/ Compiled by International Game Fish Association. /4/ Northern fluke. /5/ Or king mackerel. /6/ Or white shark. /7/ Robalo. /8/ Or yellowfin.

135. BODY WEIGHTS: INSECTS

Except where otherwise indicated, values are as follows: those for larvae are for the last instar; averages for both sexes are in milligrams; and ranges in parenthesis conform with estimate "c" of the 95% range (cf Introduction).

#	Species	Fresh Weight Larva mg	Fresh Weight Pupa mg	Fresh Weight Adult mg	Dry Weight Larva mg	Dry Weight Pupa mg	Dry Weight Adult mg
	ORTHOPTERA						
1	Cockroach, American (Periplaneta americana)			♂890(550-1470); ♀1050(650-1720)			
2	Cockroach, giant (Micropanesthia rhinoceris)			19.3g (18.4-19.5g)			
3	Cockroach, German (Blattella germanica)			♂(39-45); ♀(70-73)			
4	Cockroach, Hawaiian (Nyctobora noctivaga)			(1290-2190)			
5	Cockroach, Oriental (Blatta orientalis)			♂400(323-515); ♀750(540-870)[1,2]			♂100(81-126)[1]; ♀205(147-237)[1]
6	Grasshopper, differential (Melanoplus differentialis)			♂854(436-1232); ♀1428(812-2607)			
7	Grasshopper, Rocky Mt. (M. mexicanus mexicanus)			♂(153-161)[3], ♀(156-165)[3]			
8	Locust, migratory (Locusta migratoria)	(372-578)[4]		♂1350(1200-1400); ♀2500(2250-2900)[5]	119-1836		♂565[7]; ♀1212[8,9]
9	Walking stick (Dixippus morosus)			1050(900-1100)			
10	Walking stick (Sphodromantis bioculata)			2079			
	ODONATA						
11	Fly, big green dragon (Anax junius)	(1200-1500)		(500-900)			
	ANOPLURA						
12	Louse, bloodsucking (Enderleinellus zonatus)			♂0.005[10]			
	HEMIPTERA						
13	Bug, boxelder (Leptocoris trivittatus)			(32-39)[3]			
14	Bug, milkweed, large (Oncopeltus fasciatus)			♂47(31-75); ♀66(40-95)			(10.5-10.6)[3]
	LEPIDOPTERA						
15	Cabbageworm, imported (Pieris rapae)	156(110-165)					
16	Hornworm, tomato (Protoparce quinquemaculata)	8.3g (6.2-10.5g)			64(30-110)		
17	Moth, bee (Galleria mellonella)	175(85-310)					
18	Moth, codling (Carpocapsa pomonella)	47(42-63)					
19	Moth, raisin (Ephestia figulilella)	19.4					
20	Moth, striped sphinx (Deilephila euphorbiae)	4038	2609	1263	848	652	401
21	Moth, webbing clothes (Tineola biselliella)	(4.9-9.2)[11]	(3.0-5.5)[11]	♂(2.1-4.3); ♀(4.1-9.4)[11]			
22	Silkworm (Bombyx mori)	1770[12]	1170		374	339	
	DIPTERA						
23	Fly, black blow (Phormia regina)	44(22-63)	28(24-35)	♂(38-40)[3], ♀(42-50)[3]	9(5-13)		
24	Fly, black cherry fruit (Rhagoletis fausta)			♂3.0(1.8-3.9)[13], ♀4.1(1.5-6.8)[b]			
25	Fly, bluebottle (Calliphora erythrocephala)		(22-27)[14]	♂(50-69)[3], ♀(60-77)[3]			
26	Fly, giant crane (Tipula abdominalis)	1200(800-1600)		♂27; ♀40			
27	Fly, greenbottle (Lucilia sericata)	0.05[13]		♂(12-17); ♀(16-21)			
28	Fly, house (Musca domestica)			♂4.6(2.6-7.5)[13], ♀6.9(1.7-11)[b]			
29	Maggot, apple (Rhagoletis pomonella)			♂3.8(2.4-5.2)[13], ♀5.1(3.2-7.0)[b]			
30	Maggot, cherry (R. cingulata)						
31	Mosquito (Culex tarsalis)		2.2	♂1.37; ♀1.66[15]			
32	Mosquito, malaria (Anopheles quadrimaculatus)	1.91			0.61		
33	Mosquito, yellow-fever (Aedes aegypti)		♂2.99; ♀3.45	(3.6-3.9)[16]		♂0.60; ♀0.69	♂0.39; ♀0.47
	COLEOPTERA						
34	Beetle, Colorado potato (Leptinotarsa decemlineata)	98(83-110)[17]		♂160(146-176); ♀173			53
35	Beetle, confused-flour (Tribolium confusum)	2.0(1.5-2.4)		2.1(1.4-3.5)[18]			0.7(0.6-0.8)[19]
36	Beetle, convergent lady (Hippodamia convergens)			21.3			10.4
37	Beetle, diving (Dysticus marginalis)	1366(1305-1498)	1950	1356(1186-1466)			
38	Beetle, goliath (Goliathus goliathus)[20]			(40-100g)[21]			(15-35g)
39	Beetle, Japanese (Popillia japonica)	(196-276)	(176-222)[3]	♂114; ♀146	(44-60)[3]	(42-52)[3]	♂38; ♀49
40	Beetle, lady (Ceratomegilla fuscilabrus)			13.1			5.4
41	Mealworm, yellow (Tenebrio molitor)	(83-180)[22]					33(22-46)
42	Weevil, bean (Acanthoscelides obtectus)			♂(2.9-6.8); ♀(2.8-8.3)			
	HYMENOPTERA						
43	Ant, giant (Camponotus gigas)			(75-347)			
44	Bee, honey, worker (Apis mellifera)	137(158-171)	150(147-176)	120(87-134)[23]	35(34-41)		(16-18.6)[3]
45	Wasp, paper-nest (Polistes variatus), queen			149			59
46	Wasp, parasitic (Caraphractus cinctus)			0.005[10,24]			

/1/ Five da adult. /2/ 60-70 da, ♀1036(833-1165); 120 da, ♀914(781-1200). /3/ Averages from different experiments. /4/ At fifth instar; first instar, 14.3; second, 33.2-37.6; third, 66.4-77.4; fourth, 164-221. /5/ One da, ♀960-1900. /6/ At fifth instar; first instar, 3.12; second, 6.2-7.3; third, 16.2-26.6; fourth, 41.5-83.4. /7/ One da, ♂202-233. /8/ One da, ♀284-346. Values in Footnotes 4-8 are averages from different phases and rearing conditions. /9/ Weight prior to laying eggs. /10/ Smallest known insects; weights are approximate calculations from published measurements. /11/ Smaller if reared at 30°C; larger at 20°C. /12/ Other values, 3500; Italian strain, 4100; Japanese strain, 8417. /13/ Value for one hr larvae; 24 hr, 1.5(1-2); 48 hr, 17.8(16-20); 72 hr, 52(45-57); 96 hr, 52(43-56); 144 hr, 42(39-44). /14/ Also reported as (16-24.3); densely crowded cultures give pupae as small as 4 mg. /15/ Unfed ♀. /16/ Unfed, 1.5-1.75. /17/ Age not stated; probably only partly grown. /18/ One da adult, fresh weight 1.75(1.5-2.0). /19/ One da adult. /20/ Heaviest known insect. /21/ Calculated from dry weight of museum specimens corrected for recorded measurements. /22/ From hatching to largest fully grown larvae, 1-200. /23/ Queen, 262. /24/ Egg, 0.0002.

136. TOOTH DEVELOPMENT: MAMMALS

Part I: AGES OF TOOTH DEVELOPMENT AND ERUPTION: MAN

Values are approximate averages for whites without regard to sex. F = fetal age; P = postnatal age.

Teeth	Appearance of Tooth Bud		Beginning of Calcification	
	Deciduous mo	Permanent mo	Deciduous mo	Permanent mo
1 Incisors, first	F 3	F 6	F 5	P 3.5
2 second	F 3	F 6	F 5	P 3.5, 12[1]
3 Canines	F 3	F 6	F 6	P 4.5
4 Premolars, first		P 10		P 21
5 second		P 18		P 30
6 Molars, first	F 3	F 5	F 5	Birth
7 second		P 6	F 6	P 33
8 third		P 60		P 7-10 yr

Teeth	Emergence into Oral Cavity		Root Completion	
	Deciduous mo	Permanent yr	Deciduous yr	Permanent yr
9 Incisors, first	P 7,7.9.4[1,2]	P 6,7[1]	P 1.5-2	P 9-10
10 second	P 12	P 8	P 1.5-2	P 10-11
11 Canines	P 20	P 10,11[1]	P 2.5-3	P 12-15
12 Premolars, first		P 10		P 12-13
13 second		P 11		P 12-14
14 Molars, first	P 16	P 6	P 2-2.5	P 9-10
15 second	P 27[3]	P 12	P 3	P 14-16
16 third		P 20.5		P 18-25

/1/ First value mandibular, second value maxillary tooth. /2/ 4-12 mo = 98% range; 0-16 mo = extreme range. Prenatal emergence occurs rarely. /3/ 18-36 mo = 98% range; 10-38 mo = extreme range.

Part II: AGES OF DECIDUOUS TOOTH ERUPTION: MAMMALS

Values are days. Ranges in parentheses, conforming to estimate "b" or "c" of the 95% range (cf Introduction), are noted by superscript. MX = maxillary; MD = mandibular.

Animals		Incisors First	Incisors Second	Incisors Third	Canines	Molars First	Molars Second	Molars Third
1 Man ♂	MX	277(187-367)[b]	316(173-459)[b]		575(414-736)[b]	486(349-623)[b]	839(576-1102)[b]	
2	MD	222(126-318)[b]	395(228-562)[b]		587(415-759)[b]	492(378-606)[b]	787(560-1014)[b]	
3 ♀	MX	292(172-412)[b]	362(201-523)[b]		611(421-801)[b]	477(340-614)[b]	863(606-1120)[b]	
4	MD	237(112-362)[b]	420(206-634)[b]		614(412-816)[b]	474(343-605)[b]	824(573-1075)[b]	
5 Cattle[1]	MX	(0-7)[2]	(0-14)[2]	(0-21)[2]	(14-42)[3]	(0-14)[2]	(0-10)[2]	(0-10)[2]
6	MD	(0-7)[2]	(0-14)[2]			(0-14)[2]	(0-10)[2]	(0-10)[2]
7 Chimpanzee[4] ♂	MX	111(77-161)[c]	122(83-177)[c]		355(266-411)[c]	126(77-180)[c]	308(226-446)[c]	
8	MD	95(55-126)[c]	124(68-188)[c]		376(293-459)[c]	150(79-210)[c]	247(183-338)[c]	
9 ♀	MX	76(40-108)[c]	94(74-112)[c]		327(226-445)[c]	111(74-152)[c]	290(243-379)[c]	
10	MD	70(53-83)[c]	88(65-112)[c]		351(265-492)[c]	135(106-176)	225(154-291)[c]	
11 Dog[1]	MX	(21-42)	(21-42)	(28-42)	(21-28)	(28-35)	(21-35)	(21-28)
12	MD	(21-42)	(21-42)	(28-42)	(21-28)	(28-35)	(21-35)	(21-28)
13 Horse[1]	MX	(0-14)[2]	(14-42)	(150-270)	Vestigial[5]	(0-14)[2]	(0-14)[2]	(0-14)[2]
14	MD	(0-14)[2]	(14-42)	(150-270)	Vestigial[5]	(0-14)[2]	(0-14)[2]	(0-14)[2]
15 Monkey, rhesus ♂	MX	19.1(0.36-39)[b]	39(15-63)[b]		68(41-95)[b]	73(49-97)[b]	164(117-211)[b]	
16	MD	15.2(3.26-34)[b]	23(1-45)[b]		71(44-98)[b]	78(54-102)[b]	152(115-189)[b]	
17 ♀	MX	19.5(0.7-38)[b]	38(14-62)[b]		71(44-98)[b]	71(44-98)[b]	155(110-200)[b]	
18	MD	16(0.5-32)[b]	23(3-43)[b]		73(42-104)[b]	73(48-98)[b]	139(102-176)[b]	
19 Orangutan[7] ♂	MX	147	229		343	169	303	
20	MD	134	204		349	162	283	
21 Pig[1]	MX	(14-28)	(60-90)	Prenatal	Prenatal	(35-49)	(4-8)	(21-28)
22	MD	(14-28)	(45-60)	Prenatal	Prenatal	(35-49)	(4-8)	(14-28)

/1/ Values vary with breed. /2/ Lower limit of range prenatal in many animals. /3/ Fourth incisor. /4/ Similar values for lowland gorilla (Gorilla gorilla) with possible exception that canines may precede second molars. /5/ Vestigial teeth; do not erupt. /6/ Prenatal eruption. /7/ Values from single animal.

Part III: AGES OF PERMANENT TOOTH ERUPTION: MAMMALS

Values are years unless otherwise indicated. Ranges in parentheses unless otherwise indicated. MX = maxillary; MD = mandibular.

Animals	Incisors First	Incisors Second	Incisors Third	Canines	Premolars First	Premolars Second	Premolars Third	Premolars Fourth	Molars First	Molars Second	Molars Third
1 Man, white, male MX	7.47(5.88-9.06)	8.67(6.75-10.59)		11.69(9.0-14.38)	10.40(7.52-13.28)	11.18(8.1-14.26)			6.40(4.83-7.97)	12.68(9.99-15.37)	20.5(16-27)[1]
2 MD	6.54(5.01-8.07)	7.70(5.98-9.42)		10.79(8.3-13.28)	10.82(7.94-13.7)	11.47(8.18-14.76)			6.21(4.64-4.78)	12.12(9.45-14.79)	20.5(16-27)[1]
3 female MX	7.20(5.61-8.79)	8.20(6.28-10.12)		10.98(8.29-13.67)	10.03(7.15-12.91)	10.88(7.8-13.96)			6.22(4.65-7.79)	12.27(9.58-14.96)	20.5(16-27)[1]
4 MD	6.26(4.73-7.79)	7.34(5.62-9.06)		9.86(7.37-12.35)	10.18(7.3-13.06)	10.89(7.6-14.18)			5.94(4.37-7.51)	11.66(8.99-14.33)	20.5(16-27)[1]
5 Negro[2] MX	6.0(<5.0-8.0)	7.5(5.0-8.0)		10.3(8.0-13.0)	10.0(8.0-12.0)	10.3(8.0-13.0)			6.0(<5.0-8.0)	11.5(9.0-13.0)	19.0(12-?)
6 MD	5.5(<5-7.0)	6.5(5.0-8.0)		10.0(6.0-13.0)	10.0(8.0-13.0)	10.3(8.0-13.0)			5.5(<5.0-8.0)	11.5(9.0-14.0)	18.0(12-?)
7 Cattle[3] MX			(2.8-3.3)	(3.5-4.0)[4]					(0.4-0.7)	(1.0-1.5)	(2.0-2.5)
8 MD	(1.5-2.0)	(2.0-2.5)	(2.8-3.3)	(3.5-4.0)[4]					(0.4-0.7)	(1.0-1.5)	(2.0-2.5)
9 Chimpanzee[5] MX	5.4(4.8-6.0)	5.8(5.3-6.2)		7.2(6.8-7.5)	6.2(5.8-6.6)	6.6(6.0-7.2)			2.9(2.8-3.0)	6.4(6.1-6.8)	10.3(9.8-11.2)
10 MD	5.2(4.8-5.8)	5.5(5.4-6.1)		7.5(7.0-8.3)	6.0(4.8-6.7)	6.5(6.1-7.0)			2.9(2.8-3.0)	6.3(6.1-6.6)	9.3(8.7-10.1)
11 Dog[3] MX	(0.2-0.4)	(0.2-0.4)	(0.3-0.5)	(0.3-0.5)	(0.3-0.5)	(0.4-0.5)	(0.4-0.5)	(0.4-0.5)	(0.4-0.5)	(0.5-0.6)	
12 MD	(0.2-0.4)	(0.2-0.4)	(0.3-0.5)	(0.3-0.5)	(0.3-0.5)	(0.4-0.5)	(0.4-0.5)	(0.4-0.5)	(0.3-0.4)	(0.8-0.9)	(0.8-0.9)
13 Goat MX			(1.7-1.8)	(3.5-4.0)[4]			(1.7-1.8)	(1.7-1.8)	20 da	45 da	(0.8-0.9)
14 MD	(1.0-1.3)	(1.7-1.8)	(2.7-3.0)	(3.5-4.0)[4]	(1.0-1.3)	(1.0-1.3)	(1.7-1.8)	(1.7-1.8)	20 da	45 da	
15 Hamster, golden MX	(0-2) da							(7-9) da	(13-14) da	(32-36) da	
16 MD	(0-2) da							(7-8) da	(12-13) da	(29-32) da	
17 Horse[3] MX	2.2(2.0-3.0)	3.5(3.5-4.0)	(4.2-5.0)	(3.5-5.5)[6]	(0.4-0.5)[7]	(2.0-2.5)	(3.0-3.5)	(4.0-4.5)	2.9(2.8-3.0)	6.4(1-6.8)	3.5(3.5-4.5)
18 MD	2.5(2.4-8.5.8)	5.0(5.4-6.1)	(4.2-5.0)	(3.5-5.5)	(0.4-0.5)[7]	(2.0-2.5)	(2.5-3.0)	(3.5-4.0)	2.9(2.8-3.0)	6.3(6.1-6.6)	9.3(8.7-10.1)
19 Monkey, rhesus MX	2.7(2.1-3.0)	3.2(3.1-3.4)		4.3(3.5-5.4)	3.9(3.5-4.8)	4.0(3.6-4.7)		1.5(1.2-1.9)	1.5(1.2-1.9)	3.6(3.2-4.0)	6.1(4.9-10.9)
20 MD	2.8(2.2-3.0)	3.0(2.7-3.4)		4.2(3.7-5.1)	4.2(3.7-5.1)	4.1(3.6-4.9)		1.3(1.0-1.9)	1.3(1.0-1.9)	3.5(3.2-4.2)	5.7(4.7-7.6)
21 Mouse, albino MX	10 da						15 da	15 da	(15-20) da	28 da	
22 MD	10 da						15 da	15 da	(15-20) da	28 da	
23 Pig[3] MX	1.0		(0.7-0.8)	(0.7-0.8)	0.4	(1.0-1.3)	(1.0-1.3)	(0.3-0.5)	(0.3-0.5)	(0.7-1.0)	(1.5-1.7)
24 MD	1.0		(0.7-0.8)	(0.7-0.8)	0.4	(1.0-1.3)	(1.0-1.3)	(0.3-0.5)	(0.3-0.5)	(0.7-1.0)	(1.5-1.7)
25 Rat, albino MX	(8-10) da						20 da	20 da	(22-23) da	(31-36) da	
26 MD	(8-10) da						19 da	19 da	(21-22) da	(29-35) da	
27 cotton MX	(Prenatal-1.0) da						(5-7) da	(5-7) da	(9-13) da	(26-33) da	
28 MD	Prenatal						(4-7) da	(4-7) da	(7-12) da	(26-30) da	
29 Sheep MX			(1.5-2.0)	(3.5-4.0)[4]			(1.5-2.0)	0.4	0.4	(0.7-1.0)	(1.5-2.0)
30 MD	(1.0-1.5)	(1.5-2.0)	(2.5-3.0)[4]			(1.5-2.0)	(1.5-2.0)	0.3	0.3	(0.7-1.0)	(1.5-2.0)

/1/ Eruption at 13 years rare; somewhat less exceptional at ages 14 and 15. /2/ African Zulus. /3/ Values vary with breed. /4/ Fourth incisor. /5/ Usually absent in mares. /6/ Values derived from 3-6 animals of closely estimated ages. Gorilla data available only for individuals captured at very early age; values are approximately the same as for the chimpanzee. /7/ Rarely erupts.

Dist. = distally; extr. = extremities; f. = fused; innom. = innominate; pn. = prenasal;

#	Bone	Monotremata Platypus, duckbilled (Platypus ornitho-rhynchus)	Monotremata Anteater, spiny (Tachyglossus spp)	Marsupialia Opossum, Virginia (Didelphis virginiana)	Insectivora Shrew, common (Sorex personatus)	Chiroptera Bat, big brown (Eptesicus fuscus)	Primates Lemur (Lemur macaco)	Primates Monkey, New World "Howler" (Alouatta balzebul)	Primates Monkey, Old World "Guereza" (Colobus polykomos)	Primates Chimpanzee (Pan troglodytes)	Primates Man (Homo sapiens)
	Skull										
1	Occipital (chondral)	1	1	1	1	1	1	1	1		1
2	Parietal (dermal)	1 pr., f.	1 pr., f.	1 pr.	1 pr., f.	1 pr., f.	1 pr.	1 pr., f.	1 pr., f.	1 pr.	1 pr.
3	Sphenoid[2]										1
4	Ethmoid (chondral)	1	1	1	1	1	1	1	1		1
5	Turbinal (chondral)	2 pr.	2 pr.	2 pr.	2 pr.	2 pr.	2 pr.	2 pr.	2 pr.	2 pr.	1 pr.
6	Interparietal (dermal)	0	0	0	0	0	0	0	0	0	0
7	Frontal (dermal)	1 pr., f.	1 pr., f.	1 pr., f.	1 pr.	1 pr.	1 pr.	1 pr., f.	1 pr., f.	1 pr., f.	1 pr., f.
8	Nasal (dermal)	1 pr., 1 pn.	1 pr., f.	1 pr.	1 pr.	1 pr.	1 pr.	1 pr.	1 pr., f.	1 pr., f.	1 pr.
9	Lacrimal (dermal)[3]	1 pr.	1 pr.	1 pr.	1 pr.	1 pr.	1 pr.	1 pr.	1 pr.	1 pr.	1 pr.
10	Temporal, periotic[3] (petrosal)	1 pr.	1 pr.	1 pr.	1 pr.	1 pr.					
11	Temporal, tympanic	1 pr.	1 pr.	1 pr.	1 pr.	1 pr.	f.	f.	f.	f.	f.
12	Temporal, squamosal (dermal)	1 pr.	1 pr.	1 pr.	1 pr.	1 pr.					
13	Premaxilla (dermal)	1 pr.	1 pr.	1 pr.	1 pr.	0	1 pr.	1 pr.	1 pr., f.	1 pr., f.	1 pr., f.
14	Maxilla (dermal)	1 pr.	1 pr.	1 pr.	1 pr.	1 pr.	1 pr.	1 pr.	1 pr.	1 pr.	
15	Jugal (zygomatic, or malar; dermal)	1 pr.	1 pr.	1 pr.	0	1 pr.	1 pr.	1 pr.	1 pr.	1 pr.	1 pr.
16	Vomer (chondral)	1	1	1	1	1	1	1	1	1	1
17	Palatine (dermal)	1 pr., f.	1 pr.	1 pr.	1 pr.	1 pr.	1 pr.	1 pr.	1 pr.	1 pr.	1 pr.
18	Mandible (dermal)	1 pr.	1 pr.	1 pr.	1 pr.	1 pr.	1 pr., f.	1 pr., f.	1 pr., f.	1 pr., f.	1 pr., f.
19	Hyoid, basi- (splanchnic)	1	1	1	1	1	1	1	1	1	1
20	Hyoid, stylo- (splanchnic)	0	0	0	1 pr.	1 pr.	1 pr.	0	0	0	0
21	Hyoid, epi- (splanchnic)	1 pr.	1 pr.	0	1 pr.	1 pr.	1 pr.	0	0	0	0
22	Hyoid, cerato- (splanchnic)	1 pr.	1 pr.	1 pr.	1 pr.	1 pr.	1 pr.	1 pr.	0	0	1 pr.
23	Hyoid, thyro- (splanchnic)	1 pr.	1 pr.	1 pr.	1 pr.	1 pr.	1 pr.	1 pr.	1 pr.	1 pr.	1 pr.
	Vertebrae										
24	Cervical	7	7	7	7	7	7	7	7	7	7
25	Thoracic	17	16	13	13	11-12	12	12-13	12-13	13	12
26	Lumbar	2	3	6	6	5-6	6	6	6	4	5
27	Sacral	2	3-4	2		3	3	3	3	4-5	5, f.
28	Caudal	20-23	12-13	19-35		9±	25-29	27±	23±	4-5	4
	Vertebral Ribs										
29	Ribs, "true"	6 pr.	6 pr.	7 pr.	13 pr.	7 pr.	7 pr.	5 pr.	7 pr.	7 pr.	7 pr.
30	Ribs, "false"	11 pr.	10 pr.	6 pr.		4 pr.	5 pr.	7-8 pr.	5-6 pr.	6 pr.	5 pr.
	Sternum										
31	Manubrium	1	1	1	1	1	1	1	1	1	1
32	Sternebrae	3	3, f.	4	5	1	4	4	4	1	1
33	Xiphisternum	0	1	1	1	1	1	1	1	1	1
34	Ribs, sternal	6 pr.	6 pr.	7 pr.		7 pr.					
	Pectoral Girdle										
35	Interclavicle	1	1	0	0	0	0	0	0	0	0
36	Coracoid	1 pr.	1 pr.	*	*	*	*	*	*	*	*
37	Coracoid, anterior	1 pr.	1 pr.	0	0	0	0	0	0	0	0
38	Clavicle	1 pr.	1 pr.	1 pr.	1 pr.	1 pr.	1 pr.	1 pr.	1 pr.	1 pr.	1 pr.
39	Scapula	1 pr.	1 pr.	1 pr.	1 pr.	1 pr.	1 pr.	1 pr.	1 pr.	1 pr.	1 pr.
	Upper Extremity										
40	Humerus	1	1	1	1	1	1	1	1	1	1
41	Radius	1	1	1	1	1	1	1	1	1	1
42	Ulna	1	1	1	1	* or 0	1	1	1	1	1
43	Carpus										
44	Scaphoid	1	1	1	1	1	1	1	1	1	1
45	Lunate			1	1		1	1	1	1	1
46	Cuneiform[3] (triquetral)	1	1	1	1	1	1	1	1	1	1
47	Pisiform	1	1	1	1	1	1	1	1	1	1
48	Centrale	0	0	0	0	0	0	1	1	0	0
49	Trapezium	1	1	1	1	1	1	1	1	1	1
50	Trapezoid	1	1	1	1	1	1	1	1	1	1
51	Magnum[3] (capitate)	1	1	1	1	1	1	1	1	1	1
52	Unciform[3] (hamate)	1	1	1	1	1	1	1	1	1	1
53	Metacarpus	5	5	5	5	5	5	5	5	5	5
54	First										
55	Second										
56	Third										
57	Fourth										
58	Fifth										
	Phalanges										
59	First digit	2	2	2	2	2	2	2	2	2	2
60	Second digit	3	3	3	3	2	3	3	3	3	3
61	Third digit	3	3	3	3	3	3	3	3	3	3
62	Fourth digit	3	3	3	3	2	3	3	3	3	3
63	Fifth digit	3	3	3	3	2	3	3	3	3	3

/1/ The order Edentata is so diversified that all skeletal modifications cannot be included. /2/ In most mammals the sphenoid element is formed
anatomy; alternate name, used in human anatomy (Nomina Anatomica, 1955), is in parentheses. /4/ Fused with sphenoid. /5/ Ossified

MAMMALS

pr. = pair; prox. = proximally; sph. = sphenoid; var. = variable; * = rudimentary bone.

	Carnivora			Ungulata			Proboscidea	Sirenia	Cetacea		Edentata[1]	Rodentia		Lagomorpha
No.	Cat, domestic (Felis domesticus)	Dog (Canis familiaris)	Seal, harbor (Phoca vitulina)	Horse (Equus caballus)	Cattle, domestic (Bos taurus)	Swine (Sus scrofa)	Elephant, Asiatic (Elephas maximus)	Manatee (Trichechus spp)	Porpoise, harbor (Phocaena phocaena)	Whale, finback (Balaenoptera physalus)	Armadillo, nine-banded (Dasypus novemcinctus)	Guinea pig (Cavia tschudii pallidior)	Rat, Norway (Rattus norvegicus)	Hare, varying (Lepus americanus virginianus)
Skull														
1	1	1	1	1	1	1	1	1	1	1	1	1	1	1
2	1 pr.	1 pr.	1 pr.	1 pr.	1 pr., f.	1 pr., f.	1 pr.	1 pr.	1 pr.	1 pr.	1 pr.	1 pr.	1 pr.	1 pr.
3														
4	1	1	1	1	1	1	1	1	1	*	1	1	1	1
5	2 pr.	2 pr.	2 pr.	2 pr.	2 pr.	2 pr.	1+ pr.*	1 pr	0	*	2 pr.	2 pr.	2 pr.	2 pr.
6	1	1	1	0	0	0	0	0			1	0	1	0
7	1 pr.	1 pr.	1 pr.	1 pr.	1 pr.	1 pr.	1 pr.	1 pr.	1 pr.	1 pr.	1 pr.	1 pr.	1 pr.	1 pr.
8	1 pr.	1 pr.	1 pr.	1 pr.	1 pr.	1 pr.	1 pr.	0 or *	0	1 pr.	1 pr.	1 pr.	1 pr.	1 pr.
9	1 pr.	1 pr.	1 pr.	1 pr.	1 pr.	1 pr.	1 pr.	*	0	1 pr.	1 pr.	1 pr.	1 pr.	1 pr.
10	f.	f.	f.	f.		1 pr.	1 pr.				f.			
11					f.	1 pr.	1 pr.	1 pr.	1 pr.	1 pr.		1 pr.	1 pr.	1 pr.
12						1 pr.		1 pr.	1 pr.	1 pr.		1 pr.	1 pr.	1 pr.
13				1 pr.		1 pr.	1 pr.	1 pr.	1 pr.	1 pr.		1 pr.	1 pr.	1 pr.
14	1 pr.	1 pr.	1 pr.	1 pr.	1 pr.	1 pr.	1 pr.	1 pr.	1 pr.	1 pr.	1 pr.	1 pr.	1 pr.	1 pr.
15	1 pr.	1 pr.	1 pr.	1 pr.	1 pr.	1 pr.	1 pr.	1 pr.	1 pr.	1 pr.	1 pr.	1 pr.	1 pr.	1 pr.
16	1	1	1	1	1	1	1	1	1	1	1	1	1	1
17	1	1	1	1	1	1 pr.	1 pr.	0[4]	1 pr.	1 pr.	1	1	1	1
18	1 pr.	1 pr.	1 pr.	1 pr., f.	1 pr.	1 pr., f.	1 pr., f.		1 pr., f.	1 pr.	1 pr.	1 pr.	1 pr.	1 pr.
19	1 pr.	1 pr.	1 pr.	1 pr.	1 pr.	1	1	1	1		1	1	1	1
20	1	1	1	1	1	1	1	1 pr.	1 pr.	1 pr.	1 pr.	0	0	0
21	1 pr.	1 pr.	1 pr.	1 pr.	1 pr.	0	0	0	0	0	1 pr.	0	0	0
22	1 pr.	1 pr.	1 pr.	1 pr.	0	0	0	0	0	0	1 pr.	0	0	0
23	1 pr.	1 pr.	1 pr.	1 pr.	1 pr.	1 pr.	1 pr.	1 pr.	1 pr.	1 pr.	1 pr.	1 pr.	1 pr.	1 pr.
Vertebrae														
24	7	7	7	7	7	7	7	6	7, f.	7, f.	7, 2 & 3 f.	7	7	7
25	13	13	14-15	18-19	13-14	14-15	19-20	17-18	13	14	10	13	13	12
26	7	7	5	6	6	5-7	3-4	2	17	15	4-5	5-6	6-7	7
27	3	3	4-5	5	5	4	4	1*	0	0	7	2	3-4	2-3
28	18±	var.	9-14	15-21	16-21	20-26	31±	25±	25±	24±	27±	8±	27±	var.
Vertebral Ribs														
29	9 pr.	9 pr.	10 pr.	8 pr.	7-8 pr.	7 pr.	19-20 pr.	0 or 1 pr.	4-6 pr.[5]	1 pr.	5 pr.	6 pr.	7 pr.	7 pr.
30	4 pr.	4 pr.	5 pr.	10-11 pr.	5-7 pr.	7-8 pr.		16-18 pr.	7-9 pr.	13 pr.	5 pr.	7 pr.	6 pr.	5 pr.
Sternum														
31	1	1	1	1	1	1	1				1	1	1	1
32	6	8	6	5	5	4		1	1	1	4	3-4	3-5	3-4
33	1	1	1	1	1	1	1				1	1	1	1
34											4 pr.			
Pectoral Girdle														
35	0	0	0	0	0	0	0	0	0	0	0	0	0	0
36	*	*	*	*	*	*	*	*	*	*	*	*	*	*
37	0	0	0	0	0	0	0	0	0	0	0	0	0	0
38	*	*	0	0	0	0	0	0	0	0	1 pr.	1 pr.	1 pr.	1 pr.
39	1 pr.	1 pr.	1 pr.	1 pr.	1 pr.	1 pr.	1 pr.	1 pr.	1 pr.	1 pr.				
Upper Extremity														
40	1	1	1	1	1	1	1	1	1	1	1	1	1	1
41	1	1	1	1	1	1	1	1 f. at	1	1	1	1	1	1
42	1	1	1	*	*	1	1	1 extr.	1	1	1	1	1	1
43										5	5			
44				1	1	1	1	1	1		1			
45	1	1	1	1	1	1	1	1	1		1	1	1	1
46	1	1	1	1	1	1	1	1	1	Homologies difficult	1	1	1	1
47	1	1	1	1	1	1	1	1	1		1	1	1	1
48	1	1	1	1	1	1	0	0	0		0	0	0	1
49	0	0	0	0	0	0	0	0	0		1	0	0	1
50	1	1	1	0 or 1	0	0	1	1	1		1	1	1	1
51	1	1	1	1	1	1	1	1	0 or 1		1	1	1	1
52	1	1	1	1		1	1	1	1		1	1	1	1
53	1	1	5	1		1	5	5	5		5	5	1	5
54	*	*		0	0	0					0		*	
55	1	1		*	*	1					1		1	
56	1	1		1	1	1					1		1	
57	1	1		*		1					1			
58	1	1		0	*	1								
59									*[2]					
60	2	2	2	0	0	0	2	2			2	2	2	2
61	3	3	3	0	0	3	3	3			3	3	3	3
62	3	3	3	3	3	3	3	3			5	3	3	3
63	3	3	3	0	3	3	3	3			3	3	3	3

by union of basisphenoid, presphenoid, alisphenoids, orbitosphenoids, pterygoids, and possibly other skull bones. /3/ Name used in mammalian
intermediate ribs are present at the ventral ends of each of the first 6 pairs of vertebral ribs.

Dist. = distally; extr. = extremities; f. = fused; innom. = innominate; pn. = prenasal;

	Bone	Monotremata Platypus, duckbilled (Platypus ornithorhynchus)	Monotremata Anteater, spiny (Tachyglossus spp)	Marsupialia Opossum, Virginia (Didelphis virginiana)	Insectivora Shrew, common (Sorex personatus)	Chiroptera Bat, big brown (Eptesicus fuscus)	Primates Lemur (Lemur macaco)	Primates Monkey, New World "Howler" (Alouatta balzebul)	Primates Monkey, Old World "Guereza" (Colobus polykomos)	Primates Chimpanzee (Pan troglodytes)	Primates Man (Homo sapiens)
	Pelvic Girdle										
64	Epipubic	1 pr.	1 pr.	1 pr.	0	0	0	0	0	0	0
65	Ilium										
66	Ischium	1 pr., innom.	1 pr., innom.	1 pr., innom.	1 pr., innom.	1 pr., innom.	1 pr., innom.	1 pr., innom.	1 pr., innom.	1 pr., innom.	1 pr., innom.
67	Pubis										
	Lower Extremity										
68	Femur	1	1	1	1	1	1	1	1	1	1
69	Patella	1	1	0	1	1	1	1	1	1	1
70	Tibia	1	1	1	1	1	1	1	1	1	1
71	Fibula	1	1	1	1	1	1	1	1	1	1
	Tarsus										
72	Astragalus[3] (talus)	1	1	1	1	1	1	1	1	1	1
73	Calcaneus	1	1	1	1	1	1	1	1	1	1
74	Navicular	1	1	1	1	1	1	1	1	1	1
75	Cuneiform, medial	1	1	1	1	1	1	1	1	1	1
76	Cuneiform, intermediate	1	1	1	1	1	1	1	1	1	1
77	Cuneiform, lateral	1	1	1	1	1	1	1	1	1	1
78	Cuboid	1	1	1	1	1	1	1	1	1	1
79	Metatarsus	5	5	5	5	5	5	5	5	5	5
80	First										
81	Second										
82	Third										
83	Fourth										
84	Fifth										
	Phalanges										
85	First digit	2	2	2	2	2	2	2	2	2	2
86	Second digit	3	3	3	3	3	3	3	3	3	3
87	Third digit	3	3	3	3	3	3	3	3	3	3
88	Fourth digit	3	3	3	3	3	3	3	3	3	3
89	Fifth digit	3	3	3	3	3	3	3	3	3	3

/1/ The order Edentata is so diversified that all skeletal modifications cannot be included. /2/ P. phocaena has 5 digits: the first is rudimentary name, used in human anatomy(Nomina Anatomica, 1955), is in parentheses.

Values in parentheses are estimates "b" and "c" of the 95% range

Compressive Strength: a measure of the load or force per unit area required to crush a body. Tensile Strength: a measure of the load or force per on the immediately adjacent part. Torsion Strength: a measure of the load or force per unit area required to produce torsion or twisting of a body. This is also called Young's modulus. Specific Gravity: a ratio of the weight of a volume of material to the weight of the same volume of water.

Part I: MAN

	Specimen Type, Condition and Loading [1] Modulus of Elasticity	Value kg/sq mm (x 1000)		Specimen Type, Condition and Loading [1] Tensile Strength	Value kg/sq mm[c]
	Tension		18	Compact, fresh	9.97(5.74-11.00)[c]
1	Compact, fresh	2.31(1.82-2.71)[c]	19	Compact, dry	11.48(10.02-15.27)[c]
2	Compact, embalmed wet	1.60(0.79-2.15)[c]	20	Compact, embalmed wet	8.32(4.81-10.90)[c]
3	Compact, embalmed dry	1.88(1.20-2.58)[c]	21	Compact, embalmed dry	10.78(6.14-15.12)[c]
	Compression			**Shearing Strength**	
4	Compact, embalmed dry	1.94(1.42-2.27)[c]	22	Compact, fresh, parallel	5.03(4.25-6.50)[c]
	Bending		23	Compact, fresh, perpendicular	11.85(10.50-12.99)[c]
5	Compact, fresh	2.21(1.89-2.47)[c]	24	Compact, embalmed wet, perpendicular	6.89(4.23-10.76)[c]
6	Compact, dry	2.29(1.96-2.45)[c]	25	Compact, embalmed dry, perpendicular	5.62(2.52-8.87)[c]
	Compressive Strength	kg/sq mm	26	Spongy, fresh, parallel[2]	0.20(0.14-0.29)[c]
7	Compact, fresh, parallel	14.74(11.37-19.37)[c]	27	Spongy, fresh, perpendicular[2]	0.56(0.45-0.62)[c]
8	Compact, dry, parallel	17.37(11.25-23.19)[c]		**Torsion Strength**	
9	Compact, embalmed wet, parallel	13.36(9.00-17.72)[b]	28	Compact, fresh	7.9(7.097-9.31)[c]
10	Compact, embalmed wet, perpendicular	14.35(9.996-18.39)[c]	29	Compact, embalmed dry	7.47(5.87-9.27)[b]
11	Compact, embalmed wet, radially	11.94(5.48-19.40)[b]		**Other Properties**	
12	Compact, embalmed wet, tangentially	10.78(6.84-14.72)[b]	30	Density, compact, dry, g/cu mm	1.87(1.56-2.07)[c]
13	Compact, embalmed dry, parallel	20.52(16.90-24.14)[b]	31	Hardness[3], compact, wet	-4.2(-59 to 21)[c]
14	Compact, embalmed dry, perpendicular	16.84(14.63-30.11)[c]	32	Hardness[3], compact, embalmed wet	16.33(-25 to 38)[c]
15	Compact, embalmed dry, radially	13.50(9.08-17.92)[c]	33	Hardness[3], compact, embalmed dry	25.20(-24 to 47)[c]
16	Compact, embalmed dry, tangentially	13.11(8.81-17.41)[b]	34	Specific gravity, compact, fresh	1.93(1.80-1.997)[c]
17	Spongy, fresh parallel[2]	2.81(1.48-5.09)[c]			

/1/ Specimens loaded as indicated with long axis of bone or fiber. /2/ Specimens punched out from head and neck of femur. /3/ Rockwell factor, 1/8 inch steel ball penetrance, 45 kg load for 10 seconds.

Part II: OTHER ANIMALS

	Specimen Type, Condition and Loading[1] Modulus of Elasticity: Bending	Value kg/sq mm (x 1000)		Specimen Type, Condition and Loading[1] Modulus of Elasticity: Bending (concluded)	Value kg/sq mm (x 1000)
1	Calf, compact, fresh	1.80(1.71-1.89)[c]	5	Swine, domestic, compact, fresh	2.09(1.76-2.41)[c]
2	Fox, compact, fresh	2.24(2.08-2.37)[c]	6	Wolf, compact, fresh	2.24(1.90-2.71)[c]
3	Ox, compact, fresh	2.44(2.13-2.47)[c]	7	Goose, domestic, compact, fresh	1.80(1.68-1.96)[c]
4	Pig, wild, compact, fresh	1.75(1.60-1.90)[c]			

/1/ Specimens loaded as indicated with long axis of bone or fiber.

170

MAMMALS (Concluded)
pr. = pair; prox. = proximally; sph. = sphenoid; var. = variable; * = rudimentary bone.

	Carnivora			Ungulata			Proboscidea	Sirenia	Cetacea		Edentata[1]	Rodentia		Lago-morpha	
	Cat, domestic (Felis domesticus)	Dog (Canis familiaris)	Seal, harbor (Phoca vitulina)	Horse (Equus caballus)	Cattle, domestic (Bos taurus)	Swine (Sus scrofa)	Elephant, Asiatic (Elephas maximus)	Manatee (Trichechus spp)	Porpoise, harbor (Phocaena phocaena)	Whale, finback (Balaenoptera physalus)	Armadillo, nine-banded (Dasypus novemcinctus)	Guinea pig (Cavia tschudii pallidior)	Rat, Norway (Rattus norvegicus)	Hare, varying (Lepus americanus virginianus)	
Pelvic Girdle															
	0	0	0	0	0	0	0	*	0	0	0	0	0	0	64
	1 pr., innom.	1 pr., innom.	1 pr., innom.	1 pr., innom.	1 pr., innom.	1 pr., innom.	1 pr., innom.	0	0	0	Innom. f. with sacrum	1 pr., innom.	1 pr., innom.	1 pr., innom.	65
								*	*	*					66
								0	0	0					67
Lower Extremity															
	1	1	1	1	1	1	1	0	0	0	1	1	1	1	68
	1	1	1	1	1	1	1	0	0	0	1	1	1	1	69
	1	1 may be f. dist.	1 f. prox.	1	1	1	1	0	0	0	1 f. at extr.	1	1	1	70
	1			*	*	1	1	0	0	0		1	1	1	71
	1	1	1			1	1	0	0	0	1	1	1	1	72
	1	1	1			1	1	0	0	0	1	1	1	1	73
	1	1	1			1	1	0	0	0	1	1	1	1	74
	1	1	1	{1		1	1	0	0	0	1	1	1	1	75
	1	1	1		{1 1	1	1	0	0	0	1	1	1	1	76
	1	1	1			1	1	0	0	0	1	1	1	1 or 0	77
	1	1	1			1	1	0	0	0	1	1	1	1	78
			5				5	0	0	0	5	5	5		79
	*	*		0		0								0	80
	1	1		*	0									1	81
	1	1	1		{1	1								1	82
	1	1	1	*		1								1	83
	1	1	1	0	0	1								1	84
	*	*	2	0	0	0	1	0	0	0	2	2	2	0	85
	3	3	3	0	3	3	0	0	0	0	3	3	3	3	86
	3	3	3	3	3	3	0	0	0	0	3	3	3	3	87
	3	3	3	0	3	3	0	0	0	0	3	3	3	3	88
	3	3	3	0	3	3	1	0	0	0	3	3	3	3	89

and cartilaginous, and in the remaining four, varying numbers of phalanges become ossified. /3/ Name used in mammalian anatomy; alternate

PHYSICAL CHARACTERISTICS
(cf Introduction). Data in Part III are presented for purposes of comparison.
unit area required to pull a body apart. Shearing Strength: a measure of the load or force per unit area required to cause one part of a body to slide
Modulus of Elasticity: a number representing the degree of stiffness of a material; obtained by dividing the unit stress by the unit deformation.
Density: the weight of a unit volume of material at a specific temperature.

Part II. OTHER ANIMALS (Concluded)

	Specimen Type, Condition and Loading[1]	Value		Specimen Type, Condition and Loading[1]	Value
	Compressive Strength	kg/sq mm		Specific Gravity	
8	Calf, compact, fresh, parallel	12.31(10.92-13.44)[c]	22	Calf, compact, fresh	2.101
9	Ox, compact, fresh, parallel	17.19(12.17-23.42)[c]	23	Cow, compact, fresh	1.980
10	Ox, compact, dry, parallel	15.46(12.87-17.74)[c]	24	Fox, compact, fresh	1.995(1.985-2.006)[c]
11	Ox, compact, fresh, perpendicular	19.81(14.53-23.50)[c]	25	Horse, compact, fresh	1.961(1.924-1.998)[c]
12	Pig. wild, compact, fresh, parallel	13.78(12.92-14.21)[c]	26	Ox, compact, fresh	2.024(1.953-2.024)[c]
13	Swine, domestic, compact, fresh, parallel	13.95(9.996-14.79)[c]	27	Pig, wild, compact, fresh	2.060
14	Wolf, compact, fresh, parallel	19.96(18.69-20.81)[c]	28	Swine, domestic, compact, fresh	1.883(1.802-1.965)[c]
	Tensile Strength		29	Swine, suckling, compact, fresh	1.707
15	Calf, compact, fresh, parallel	8.61(5.996-13.32)[c]	30	Wolf, compact, fresh	1.970(1.951-1.984)[c]
16	Ox, compact, fresh, parallel	10.998(9.996-14.99)[c]	31	Chicken, compact, fresh	1.786
17	Ox, compact, dry, parallel	12.43(6.38-16.87)[c]	32	Duck, domestic, compact, fresh	1.840
18	Ox, compact, fresh, perpendicular	9.12(7.77-10.65)[c]	33	Frog, compact, fresh	1.507
19	Pig, wild, compact, fresh, parallel	10.29		Density	g/cu cm
20	Swine, domestic, compact, fresh, parallel	7.30	34	Dog, compact, embalmed dry	1.85(1.59-2.04)[c]
21	Wolf, compact, fresh, parallel	10.77(9.16-12.35)[c]			

/1/ Specimens loaded as indicated with long axis of bone or fiber.

Part III: WOOD AND STEEL

	Specimen Type and Loading[1]	Value		Specimen Type and Loading[1]	Value		Specimen Type and Loading[1]	Value
	Tensile Strength[2]	kg/sq mm		Compressive Strength[3] (concluded)	kg/sq mm		Shearing Strength[3] (concluded)	kg/sq mm
1	Conifers, perpendicular	0.2	10	Pine, shortleaf, parallel	4.5	17	Pine, shortleaf	0.8
2	Elm, parallel	20.4				18	Redwood	0.5
3	Fir, Douglas, parallel	8.2	11	Pine, shortleaf, perpendicular	0.6		Tensile Strength	
4	Hardwood, perpendicular	0.6	12	Redwood, parallel	3.6	19	Cast iron, gray iron	10.5-12.7
5	Hickory, parallel	22.5	13	Redwood, perpendicular	0.4	20	Steel, extra soft	31.6-38.7
6	Pine, longleaf, parallel	12.2		Shearing Strength[3]		21	Wrought iron	29.5-36.6
	Compressive Strength[3]		14	Fir, Douglas	0.6		Modulus of Elasticity	kg/sq mm (x 1000)
7	Fir, Douglas, parallel	3.5	15	Pine, longleaf	0.7	22	Cast iron, gray iron	8.4-9.8
8	Pine, Norway, parallel	5.3	16	Pine, Norway	0.8	23	Steel, extra soft	21.1
9	Pine, Norway, perpendicular	0.6				24	Wrought iron	18.3-20.4

/1/ Wood specimens loaded as indicated with fibers. /2/ 15% moisture content. /3/ Small size, air-seasoned.

139. BONE MARROW DIFFERENTIAL CELL COUNT: MAN AND DOG

Values for man based on sternal aspirations, 750 adults, male and female. Values for dog based on rib extrusions, 187 adult dogs. All values are percents and are the grand mean of results of several laboratories using different techniques. Ranges of investigators' means are in parentheses.

	Cell Type	Man	Dog		Cell Type	Man	Dog
1	Red	19.1	43.6		White, granulocytic(concluded)		
2	Early forms	2.9	5.4	14	Band cells	17.9(6.1-36.0)	24.6(11.7-42.0)
3	Proerythroblasts	0.5(0.2-4.0)	0.5(0.3-0.6)	15	Segmented cells	15.6(8.7-27.0)	9.6(3.9-30.0)[1]
4	Early normoblasts	2.4(1.5-5.8)	4.9(1.5-7.8)	16	Eosinophils		3.1(2.0-4.7)
5	Late forms	16.2	38.2	17	Other	12.6	2.7
6	Intermediate normoblasts	11.7(5.0-26.4)	22.3(11.0-26.0)	18	Lymphocytes	9.8(2.7-24.0)	0.9(0.7-1.9)
7	Late normoblasts	4.5(1.6-21.5)	15.9(4.6-17.4)	19	Monocytes	1.4(0.7-2.8)	0.2(0.0-0.2)
8	White	70.0	54.9	20	Megakaryocytes	0.2(0.03-0.4)	0.4(0.1-0.6)
9	Granulocytic	57.4	52.2	21	Plasmacytes	0.6(0.1-1.5)	0.3(0.0-0.4)
10	Myeloblasts	1.2(0.3-3.1)	1.2(0.6-2.4)	22	Reticulum cells	0.6(0.03-1.6)	0.9(0.0-1.0)
11	Progranulocytes	3.0(0.5-4.5)	1.4(0.7-2.8)	23	Non-identifiable	10.9	1.5
12	Myelocytes	8.7(0.9-20.3)	4.8(2.7-8.9)	24	Unclassified cells	1.7(0.02-3.3)	1.5(0.0-3.0)
13	Metamyelocytes	11.0(5.6-22.0)	7.4(3.4-15.3)	25	Disintegrated cells	9.2(1.1-20.8)	

/1/ Includes basophils (0.05-0.2).

140. BONE MARROW DIFFERENTIAL CELL COUNT, PREGNANCY: MAN

Values based on 10 ml sternal marrow aspirated from each of 40 pregnant and 28 non-pregnant females. Values and ranges are numbers of cells per cu mm. Because of extreme variability in the "normal" range, averages should be considered with caution. Data adapted from Pitts, H. H., and Packham, E. A., Arch. Int. Med., 64:471-482, 1939.

	Cell Type[1]	1st Trimester	2nd Trimester	3rd Trimester	Non-pregnant
			cells/cu mm		
1	Proerythroblasts	56(0-136)	73(0.203)	61(0-210)	28(0-122)
2	Early normoblasts	749(86-1314)	797(251-1875)	1050(51-3937)	616(62-1396)
3	Intermediate normoblasts	1139(259-2628)	1803(314-7000)	1865(51-8636)	1199(134-2904)
4	Late normoblasts	944(28-2700)	835(250-2000)	836(119-2730)	453(43-1089)
5	Myeloblasts	63(0-328)	173(0-1250)	96(0-635)	89(0-279)
6	Progranulocytes	378(38-900)	462(69-2500)	341(0-1460)	251(11-736)
7	Early neutrophilic myelocytes	262(0-675)	446(0-3500)	362(51-1050)	147(0-630)
8	Myelocytes, eosinophilic[2]	218(28-494)	251(0-1400)	167(0-700)	147(0-544)
9	Myelocytes, neutrophilic	2267(172-4336)	3229(659-13,125)	2138(391-7937)	1568(168-4140)
10	Metamyelocytes, neutrophilic	2165(259-5913)	2623(251-10,250)	1879(340-4900)	1437(168-4324)
11	Band neutrophils	11,659(2,189-28,251)	15,415(3,077-46,250)	11,819(4,901-29,400)	6,048(1,091-14,490)
12	Segmented neutrophils	5445(4050-8835)	5,441(1,575-11,750)	4613(394-8680)	3565(1132-7084)
13	Segmented eosinophils[3]	371(48-1140)	299(18-990)	228(0-700)	246(60-642)
14	Segmented basophils	78(0-197)	47(0-125)	49(0-191)	53(0-184)
15	Lymphocytes	3975(2894-6300)	4,467(1,686-10,000)	3719(1318-5400)	3428(1721-6520)
16	Monocytes	333(40-965)	245(0-642)	194(0-732)	312(32-717)
17	Disintegrated cells	4684(1382-8100)	4,675(1,037-11,500)	4,480(1,329-11,900)	3578(1081-6534)
18	Total nucleated cells	34,580(14,400-65,700)	41,510(15,700-125,000)	33,930(16,900-70,000)	23,100(7,500-46,000)

/1/ Proplasmacytes, plasmacytes, basophilic myelocytes, early myelocytes (eosinophilic and basophilic) not tabulated but present in less than 0.1 per cent. /2/ Includes eosinophilic metamyelocytes. /3/ Includes band eosinophils.

141. HISTOCHEMICAL PROPERTIES, BLOOD AND BONE MARROW CELLS: MAN

C = cytoplasm proper; G = specific granules; J = juxtanuclear bodies; M = mitochondria; N = nucleoli.

	Cell Type	Lipid[1]	Phospho-lipid[2]	Acid Phosphatase[3]	Alkaline Phosphatase[3]	Ribonucleo-protein[4]	Carbohydrate[5]	Peroxidase[6]
	Nuclei							
1	All types	Neg	Neg	Pos	Pos[7]	Pos N	Neg	
	Cytoplasm							
2	Myeloblasts	Pos M	Pos M	Neg		Pos C[8]	Neg	Neg
3	Progranulocytes	Pos GM	Pos G[7]M	Pos G	Neg	Pos C[8]	Neg	Pos G
4	Myelocytes	Pos GM	Pos G[7]M	Pos CG	Neg[9]	Neg	Pos[7,10]	Pos G
5	Metamyelocytes	Pos G[11]	Pos G[7]	Pos G	Pos C[8,10]	Neg	Pos[7,10]	Pos
6	Segmented neutrophils	Pos G[11]	Pos G[7]	Pos G	Pos C[8,10]	Neg	Pos[7,10]	Pos
7	Segmented eosinophils	Pos G	Pos G	Pos G	Neg	Neg	Pos G	Pos
8	Segmented basophils	Pos G	Pos G[7]				Pos G[10]	Neg
9	Tissue eosinophils	Pos G	Pos GM	Neg	Neg	Neg	Pos[7]	Pos
10	Lymphoblasts	Pos M	Pos M			Pos C[8]		Neg
11	Lymphocytes	Neg	Neg	Pos JG	Neg[12]	Pos C[8]	Neg[13]	Neg
12	Monocytes	Pos GM	Pos G				Pos C	Pos[14]
13	Megakaryocytes	Pos GM	Pos G[7]M	Pos[8]	Pos C[8]	Pos C[8,9]	Pos[10]	
14	Thrombocytes	Neg	Pos C[8]G			Neg	Pos[10]	
15	Proerythroblasts ("rubriblasts")	Pos M	Pos M	Pos J	Neg	Pos C[8]	Neg	Neg
16	Early normoblasts ("prorubricytes")	Pos M	Pos M	Pos J	Neg	Pos C[8]	Neg	Neg
17	Intermediate normoblasts ("rubricytes")	Pos M	Pos M		Neg	Pos C[8]	Neg	Neg
18	Late normoblasts ("metarubricytes")	Neg	Neg		Neg	Pos C[8]	Neg	Neg
19	Erythrocytes	Neg	Neg[8]	Neg[15]	Neg	Neg	Neg	Pos
20	Plasmacytes			Pos JG	Pos C[8]	Pos C	Pos[7]	Neg
21	Reticulum cells	Pos G	Pos G[6]	Pos G	Neg	Neg	Pos G[16]	Neg
22	Mast cells	Pos G[17]	Pos G	Pos G	Pos G	Pos CG	Pos CG[17]	Pos

/1/ Stained with Sudan black B unless otherwise specified. /2/ Detected by acid-hematein method; negatively evaluated by pyridine extraction method. /3/ Detected by modified Gomori method using glycerophosphate substrate. /4/ Detected by Feulgen reaction; negatively evaluated by digestion with ribonuclease. /5/ Detected by either periodic acid-Schiff, or by Gomori silver-methenamine methods. /6/ Detected by benzidine-peroxide. /7/ Controversial. /8/ Diffuse staining. /9/ May be positive (Rabinovitch and Andreucci). /10/ As glycogen. /11/ Stable sudanophilia. /12/ May be positive. /13/ Positive according to Stowell; Wachstein. /14/ Trace. /15/ Positive when substrate is ATP. /16/ Probably is phago-cytosed material (Lillie). /17/ Granules positive in many cells, negative in others.

142. COMPARATIVE ANATOMY OF THE HEART: CHORDATES

	Chordate	Location in Body	Chambers Forming Heart	Atrioventricular Valves	Semilunar Valves	Septum Atriorum	Septum Ventriculorum
1	Amphioxus	Heart lacking; aortic arches are contractile.					
2	Fishes Cyclostomes	Cervical.	One atrium, one ventricle.	Present, two or more cusps.	Numerous, in series, in conus arteriosus.	None.	None.
3	Selachii						
4	Ganoidii						
5	Teleostei[1]				One set (not in series) in conus arteriosus.		
6	Dipnoi		Two atria, one ventricle.	Lacking but function performed by a fibrocartilaginous swelling.	Numerous in conus; now beginning to divide.	Present.	
7	Amphibia Urodela, with lungs	High in thorax.	Two atria, one ventricle.		Present in bulbis cordis.	Perforated.	Incomplete.
8	Urodela, lungless		One atrium, one ventricle.	Present, right and left cusps.			
9	Anura		Two atria, one ventricle.	Present, dorsal and ventral cusps.			
10	Reptilia	High or low in thorax[2].	Two atria, two ventricles.	Two atrioventricular valves.	Present in pulmonary and aortic trunks.	Solid.	Incomplete or complete[3].
11	Aves	Low in thorax.					Complete.
12	Mammalia[4]						

	Chordate	Wall Structure of Chambers	Conus and Truncus Arteriosus	Sinus Venosus Size and Valves	Chambers Containing:		
					Arterial Blood	Mixed Blood	Venous Blood
1	Amphioxus	Heart lacking; aortic arches are contractile.					
2	Fishes Cyclostomes	Atrium generally smooth; ventricles with inner surface netlike or width larger trabeculae.	Conus long and well-developed; truncus represented by ventral aorta.	Sinus venosus large; sino-atrial valve generally well-developed.	None in heart.		Atria and ventricle.
3	Selachii		Conus long and well-developed; truncus short and little developed.				
4	Ganoidii		Conus moderately long; truncus long, thin-walled.				
5	Teleostei[1]		Conus very much reduced; truncus thick-walled and well-developed.				
6	Dipnoi		Conus and truncus shortened; bent somewhat spirally; partly or completely separated into two halves.	Opens into right atrium.	Left atrium.	Ventricle.	Right atrium.
7	Amphibia Urodela, with lungs	Atria smooth; ventricle with many muscle bands transversing cavity, giving it a spongy structure.	Conus incorporating into wall of heart; truncus divided into pulmonary and aortic portions.	Reduced in size by partial incorporation in right atrial wall; valve persists.	Left atrium.	Ventricle.	Right atrium.
8	Urodela, lungless		Truncus lacks septum.		None	None	Atrium, ventricle
9	Anura		Conus incorporating into wall of heart; truncus divided into pulmonary and aortic portions.	Sinus generally not recognizable as such on external aspect of heart; valve persists.	Left atrium.	Ventricle.	Right atrium.
10	Reptilia	Atria generally smooth; ventricles with trabeculae cordis but ventricular cavities not divided by muscle bands.	Conus entirely incorporated in ventricular mass; truncus directly from ventricles; truncus divided.	Sinus further reduced and valve vestigial.	Left atrium.	Ventricle.	Right atrium.
11	Aves[5]				Left atrium and left ventricle.	None.	Right atrium and right ventricle.
12	Mammalia[4]	Atria with moderate ridging (musculi pectinata); ventricles with trabeculae.	No conus; truncus completely divided.	Sinus lacking; vestiges of valve are "valvae of the inferior vena cava," "valve of the coronary sinus."			

/1/ Teleostei in general. /2/ High in lizards and turtles; low in snakes and crocodiles. /3/ Incomplete in some lizards and snakes; complete in others, e.g., crocodiles. /4/ Mammals in general, including man. /5/ Includes also crocodiles.

143. MALE GENITALIA, DIMENSIONS AND WEIGHT: MAMMALS

Values in parentheses are averages of ranges reported in the literature. L = Length; T = Thickness; W = Width; Wt = Weight.

Species	Testes L, cm	Testes W, cm	Testes T, cm	Testes Wt, g	Epididymis L, m	Ductus Deferens L, cm	Seminal Vesicles L, cm	Seminal Vesicles W, cm	Prostate Gland L, cm	Prostate Gland W, cm	Prostate Gland T, cm	Bulbourethral Gland L, cm	Bulbourethral Gland W, cm	Penis L, cm
1 Man (Homo sapiens)	4.2[2]	3.8[2]	2.52	(20-35)	8[3]	(38-61)	4.3	1.7[4]	4.0	2.8	1.9	Size of pea	Small[6]	13[5]
2 Cat (Felis catus)	1.5	1		2,016						1		Very small		
3 Cattle (Bos taurus)	11.5	7	6-7	300(284-340)		(25-38)	11.5	5	3.8	1.3	1.3	Absent		91
4 Dog (Canis familiaris)	Relatively small				(40-60)		Absent		Large (variable)			Absent		10
5 Goat (Capra hircus)	10			(255-284)					Disseminate					40
6 Guinea pig (Cavia porcellus)		5		2.8										
7 Horse (Equus caballus)	11	5	7	(225-300)	(72-86)	(15-20)	17.5	5		2[7]		5	2.5	51
8 Mouse (Mus musculus)	Ellipsoidal			2.6			Long, narrow Single, unpaired		3 pairs					
9 Rabbit (Oryctolagus cuniculus)							Long, narrow		2-lobed with isthmus			Paired, small		4
10 Rat (Rattus rattus)									2 pairs					
11 Sheep (Ovis aries)	10			(255-284)	(40-60)		5.7	2.5	Disseminate			Relatively large		40
12 Swine (Sus scrofa)				(591-871)	(62-64)[3]	(25-30)	14	4.4	2.5			12	3[9]	(46-51)

/1/ Non-erect. /2/ Age, 20-60 yr. /3/ Extended. /4/ T = 0.9 cm. /5/ Age, 20-25 yr. /6/ Wt = 0.4-0.5 g. /7/ Diameter at isthmus. /8/ Wt = 15-26 g. /9/ Wt = 146-209 g.

144. FEMALE GENITALIA, DIMENSIONS AND WEIGHT: MAMMALS

The size and weight of the ovaries depend on the stage of the ovarian cycle as well as age of the animal, size of breed, and virgin or parous condition of the uterus. Values in parentheses are averages of ranges reported in the literature. L = Length; T = Thickness; W = Width; Wt = Weight.

Species	Ovaries L, cm	Ovaries W, cm	Ovaries T, cm	Ovaries Wt, g	Uterine Tubes L, cm	Uterus Total Organ Wt, g	Horns L, cm	Body L, cm	Cervix L, cm	Cervix W, cm	Vagina L, cm	Vulva L, cm
1 Man (Homo sapiens)	3.5	1.8	1.2	7[1]	(7-14)	(33-41)[2,3]		8	(2.9-3.4)[2]		9[4]	
2 Cat (Felis catus)	1				5			2			2	2
3 Cattle (Bos taurus)	3.8	2.5		19	(20-23)	700	10	3.8	10	2.5	(25-30)	10
4 Dog (Canis familiaris)		2			(5-7.6)		38	(2-3)	1		(7.5-15)	
5 Ferret (Mustela putorius)					(10-15)	0.4[5]						
6 Goat (Capra hircus)		1.5			(10-15)		(11-15)					
7 Guinea pig (Cavia porcellus)					0.3		(10-12)(5-6)	2	4		(10-12)(2.5-4)	
8 Horse (Equus caballus)	7.5		3.5	(70-80)	(20-30)		25	(18-20)(L);10(W)			(15-20)(3.5-6)	(2.5-3)
9 Rabbit (Oryctolagus cuniculus)	1.5	0.7	0.6	0.55	10	8	(10-12)[6]		(5-8)	3.8		(10-13)4[7]
10 Sheep (Ovis aries)	1.5		1	(4-8)[8]	(10-15)		(10-12)	2.5	0.7[6]	0.76	(7.5-10)	(2.5-3)
11 Swine (Sus scrofa)				(3.5-10)	(15-30)		(120-150)	5	10		(10-13)	7.5

/1/ After pregnancy. /2/ Virgin uterus. /3/ Parous uterus approximately 35 g heavier. /4/ For posterior wall; anterior wall 7 cm. /5/ Anestrus; estrus, 1 g; pseudopregnant, 5 g. /6/ Duplex uterus with two cervices opening into vagina. /7/ At vestibule. /8/ In breeding season, depending on number of ovulations; otherwise smaller.

145. KIDNEY MEASUREMENTS: VERTEBRATES

Species	Body Weight kg	Kidney Weight of One Kidney g	Kidney % body wt	Glomerulus Radius μ	Glomerulus Thousands per Kidney[1]	Glomerulus Vol/Kidney cu mm	Glomerulus Vol/g Kidney cu mm
1 Man	70	156	0.22	100	1095	4599	29
2 Cat	2.8	8	0.29	66	184	227	28
3 Dog	9.1	31	0.34	90	408	1247	40
4 Elephant	4545	3650	0.08	169	7510	151,900	42
5 Ground hog	1.2	1.8	0.15	70	96	135	75
6 Guinea pig	0.56	1.9	0.34	63	76	79	42
7 Monkey	3.9	9	0.23	83	187	447	50
8 Mouse	0.02	0.12	0.61	37	12.4	2.6	21
9 Opossum	2	5.2	0.26	88	91	256	49

Species	Body Weight kg	Kidney Weight of One Kidney g	Kidney % body wt	Glomerulus Radius μ	Glomerulus Thousands per Kidney[1]	Glomerulus Vol/Kidney cu mm	Glomerulus Vol/g Kidney cu mm
10 Ox	410	640	0.16	122	3992	29,860	47
11 Rabbit	1.9	6.5	0.34	71	199	300	46
12 Rat, albino	0.24	0.75	0.31	61	31	30	40
13 Rat, kangaroo	0.07	0.30	0.43	48	18.8	8.9	30
14 Swine	47	77	0.16	83	1193	2859	37
15 Chicken	2.5				420		
16 Duck	3.67				994.5		
17 Goose	5.4				829.5		
18 Pigeon	0.232-0.420				137-176.5		

/1/ The number of glomeruli per kidney undergoes slow decrease after maturity and as the animal approaches senility.

146. SURFACE AREA RELATIONSHIPS: MAMMALS
Part I: SURFACE AREA FOR KNOWN HEIGHT AND WEIGHT: MAN

Note (shown in box within table, rows for body weight 80–100 kg): All values are square meters of body surface area derived according to the method of Sendroy and Cecchini, 1954. (Sendroy, J., Jr., and Cecchini, L. P., 1954. J. Applied Physiology 7:1-12)

#	Body Weight kg	20	30	40	50	60	70	80	90	100	110	120	130	140	150	160	170	180	190	200	210	220	230	240	250	260
1	5	.18	.20	.23	.26	.29	.33	.37	.42	.48	.55	.62														
2	10		.35	.36	.38	.41	.44	.48	.52	.57	.64	.69	.76													
3	15				.54	.57	.60	.63	.67	.72	.77	.83	.89													
4	20						.68	.72	.76	.80	.85	.91	.97	1.03												
5	25								.80	.84	.88	.93	.98	1.03	1.09	1.15										
6	30									.92	.96	1.01	1.05	1.10	1.16	1.22	1.28									
7	35										1.04	1.08	1.12	1.17	1.23	1.29	1.35	1.42								
8	40										1.11	1.15	1.20	1.25	1.30	1.36	1.42	1.48	1.55							
9	45											1.23	1.27	1.32	1.37	1.43	1.48	1.54	1.61							
10	50											1.30	1.34	1.39	1.44	1.49	1.54	1.60	1.67	1.74						
11	55											1.37	1.42	1.46	1.50	1.55	1.61	1.67	1.73	1.80						
12	60											1.44	1.48	1.52	1.57	1.62	1.67	1.73	1.79	1.85	1.92					
13	65												1.54	1.58	1.63	1.68	1.73	1.79	1.85	1.91	1.97					
14	70												1.61	1.65	1.70	1.75	1.80	1.85	1.91	1.96	2.02	2.08				
15	75												1.68	1.72	1.76	1.81	1.86	1.91	1.96	2.02	2.07	2.13				
16	80												1.74	1.78	1.82	1.86	1.91	1.96	2.02	2.07	2.13	2.18	2.25			
17	85												1.81	1.84	1.88	1.92	1.97	2.02	2.07	2.13	2.18	2.24	2.31			
18	90												1.87	1.90	1.94	1.98	2.03	2.08	2.13	2.18	2.24	2.30	2.36			
19	95													1.97	2.01	2.05	2.09	2.14	2.18	2.24	2.30	2.36	2.42	2.48		
20	100													2.03	2.07	2.12	2.16	2.20	2.24	2.30	2.35	2.41	2.47	2.54		
21	105													2.10	2.14	2.18	2.22	2.26	2.31	2.35	2.41	2.47	2.53	2.60		
22	110													2.17	2.21	2.24	2.28	2.32	2.36	2.41	2.47	2.53	2.58	2.65	2.73	
23	115													2.23	2.27	2.30	2.33	2.38	2.42	2.47	2.53	2.58	2.64	2.71	2.78	
24	120														2.33	2.36	2.39	2.43	2.48	2.53	2.58	2.63	2.70	2.77	2.84	2.93
25	125														2.39	2.42	2.45	2.49	2.53	2.58	2.63	2.69	2.76	2.83	2.90	2.97
26	130														2.44	2.47	2.51	2.54	2.59	2.63	2.68	2.75	2.82	2.88	2.95	3.02
27	135														2.50	2.53	2.56	2.60	2.64	2.69	2.74	2.81	2.87	2.93	3.00	3.08
28	140														2.55	2.58	2.62	2.66	2.70	2.74	2.80	2.87	2.93	2.98	3.06	
29	145														2.61	2.63	2.67	2.71	2.75	2.80	2.86	2.92	2.98	3.04		
30	150														2.66	2.69	2.72	2.77	2.81	2.86	2.92	2.97	3.03	3.09		
31	155														2.72	2.74	2.78	2.83	2.87	2.92	2.97	3.03	3.08			
32	160														2.77	2.80	2.83	2.88	2.92	2.97	3.02	3.08				
33	165															2.86	2.89	2.93	2.97	3.02	3.07					
34	170															2.91	2.94	2.98	3.03	3.07						
35	175															2.96	2.99	3.03	3.08							
36	180															3.01	3.04	3.08								
37	185															3.06	3.09									

Part II: CONSTANTS FOR ESTIMATING SURFACE AREA: MAMMALS

Ranges in parentheses are estimates "c" and "d" of the 95% range (cf Introduction) for body weight and K-values, respectively. K-values are derived from surface area values taken from extensive literature sources, using the formula $K = A(sq\ cm)/W^{2/3}(g)$.

#	Animal	Method[1]	Body Weight g	K-value (Constant)		#	Animal	Method[1]	Body Weight g	K-value (Constant)
1	Antelope	T	6300	14.1		37	Mouse	S	16.4(10.4-22.0)	11.4(9.7-13.3)
2	Bat	S	64.6(12.7-36.4)	57.5(54.0-59.8)		38	Mouse	S	20.2	6.3
3	Bat	S	83(5-116)	44.5(44.0-45.0)		39	Mouse	M	(16.0-24.8)	9.0(8.4-9.4)
4	Cat[2]	T	1550(1500-1600)	8.7(8.6-8.9)		40	Mouse, deer	S	22.0	8.5
5	Cat[2]	S	100(84-116)	10.0(9.9-10.0)		41	Mouse, field	S	29.0(26.0-31.0)	6.9(6.5-7.2)
6	Cat[2]	S	708(219-1389)	10.7(9.5-11.9)		42	Mouse, red back	S	22.0	7.1
7	Cattle[2]	S	375,000(163,000-641,000)	11.0(9.0-13.8)		43	Opossum	S	1200(1000-1300)	11.3(10.5-11.8)
8	Cattle	S	476,000(208,000-762,000)	9.3(8.1-10.8)		44	Rabbit[4]	S	32(26-40)	8.5
9	Hereford, thin[2]	S	241,000(89,000-407,000)	9.9(9.3-10.5)		45	Rabbit[4]	S	560(70-925)	9.7
10	Hereford, med[2]	S	315,000(78,000-493,000)	9.4(8.8-10.0)		46	Rabbit	T	1130(1120-1140)	10.0(9.0-11.0)
11	Hereford, fat[2]	S	314,000(171,000-549,000)	8.6(8.3-9.0)		47	Rabbit	T	2600	5.7
12	Cattle[2]	S	695,000(476,000-815,000)	7.6(7.3-7.9)		48	Rat, white	S	25(23-28)	9.5(9.4-9.6)
13	Dog	S	1070(130-3650)	10.1(9.3-11.0)		49	Rat	S	42(35-53)	10.5(10.1-10.8)
14	Dog	S	1080	11.0		50	Rat	S	80(50-129)	9.9(9.6-10.4)
15	Dog	T	9,500(8,900-10,100)	9.9(9.85-9.9)		51	Rat[3]	M	95(22-164)	7.6(7.3-8.8)
16	Dog	S & P	12,700(3,200-29,800)	11.6(10.2-12.5)		52	Rat	M	125(24-366)	7.5(6.6-8.3)
17	Dog	M	14,310(3,390-32,640)	11.2(10.3-12.1)		53	Rat	S	133(70-310)	11.6(10.9-12.1)
18	Dog	C	27,000	12.3		54	Rat	S	137(47-295)	9.0
19	Fox	T	6200(6100-6300)	13.0(12.9-13.2)		55	Rat	T	170(164-177)	7.15
20	Goat	T	15,100	10.5		56	Rat	S	176(25-461)	11.4(9.6-13.0)
21	Guinea pig	S	157(123-191)	10.4(10.1-10.8)		57	Rat	M	(19-418)	9.0
22	Guinea pig	S	206(123-269)	9.5(8.4-10.8)		58	Rat	S	(65-335)	10.5
23	Guinea pig	S	256(235-269)	8.6(8.4-8.9)		59	Sheep	T	17,680	11.0
24	Guinea pig[3]	S	323(160-810)	8.9(7.9-9.6)		60	Sheep	S	(21,800-29,100)	10.7
25	Guinea pig	S	373(148-650)	9.6(9.0-9.9)		61	Sheep	I	(2,200-68,000)	8.3
26	Guinea pig	T	400(380-420)	7.1		62	Sheep	S	(23,600-37,700)	8.5
27	Hedgehog	S	200	7.5		63	Sheep	S	(3,780-50,400)	9.1
28	Horse	C		9.0		64	Shrew, long-tailed	S	3.5	8.0
29	Horse	S	(47,000-555,000)	10.5		65	Shrew, short-tailed	S	20	7.0
30	Horse	I	(70,000-750,000)	(8.2-10.3)		66	Swine	S		8.8
31	Lion	T	64,200	12.3		67	Swine	T	40,110	15.3
32	Marten, pine	T	1400	8.8		68	Swine	I	(25,000-330,000)	9.0
33	Monkey	M	2670(800-6600)	11.8(10.8-13.2)		69	Swine	S	48,300(1,100-123,000)	9.9(8.6-12.4)
34	Mouse[3]	S	12.9	6.9		70	Whale, fin	P	160,000(115,000-220,000)	8.3(7.5-8.9)
35	Mouse	S	14.7(6.0-26.5)	7.9		71	Whale	P	43,000,000	11.1
36	Mouse	S	15.9(10.7-19.7)	10.5(10.4-10.5)		72	Woodchuck	M	1236	9.3

/1/ Method of determining surface area. C = paper cover; I = surface integrator; M = mold method; P = perimeter method; S = skinning; T = triangulation. /2/ "Empty" weight. /3/ Starved animals. /4/ With surface area of one side of ear only.

147. STATURE, WEIGHT, AND SURFACE AREA: MAN, VARIOUS NATIONALITIES AND TYPES

Values in parentheses are ranges and conform with the "b" estimate of the 95% range (cf Introduction).

	Race or Nationality	Stature cm	Stature in	Weight kg	Weight lb	Surface Area sq m[1]
1	Aeta, Pygmoids (Bataan) ♂	148(138-158)	58(54-62)	42(31-52)	91(69-114)	1.29(1.11-1.47)
2	Aeta, Pygmoids (Bataan) ♀	138(131-145)	54(51-57)	37(29-44)	80(65-96)	1.17(1.05-1.29)
3	Aeta, Pygmoids (Zambales) ♂	148(139-157)	58(55-62)	40(32-49)	89(70-108)	1.28(1.14-1.42)
4	Aeta, Pygmoids (Zambales) ♀	138(129-148)	54(51-58)	34(26-42)	75(57-92)	1.14(0.98-1.30)
5	African, Gobauoin (Somaliland) ♂	168(154-183)	66(61-72)	58(44-71)	127(96-157)	1.63(1.39-1.87)
6	African, Gobauoin (Somaliland) ♀	157(148-166)	62(58-65)	60(52-67)	131(114-148)	1.57(1.41-1.73)
7	Kung, Bushmen (Kalahari) ♀	157(143-170)	62(56-67)	40(31-50)	89(68-110)	1.33(1.13-1.53)
8	Morocco, natives ♂	169(158-182)	66(62-72)	64(50-78)	140(111-170)	1.71(1.47-1.95)
9	Negroes (West Africa) ♂	167(149-186)	66(58-73)	57(42-72)	125(93-158)	1.61(1.34-1.88)
10	Tunisia, natives ♂	173(163-183)	68(64-72)	62(53-71)	137(117-156)	1.70(1.56-1.84)
11	Albanians (South Italy) ♂	164(153-175)	64(60-69)	61(49-73)	135(108-160)	1.64(1.40-1.88)
12	Americans, white ♂	177(164-191)	70(64-75)	70(55-86)	155(121-189)	1.85(1.61-2.09)
13	Americans, white ♀	163(153-173)	64(60-68)	56(40-72)	123(88-158)	1.61(1.34-1.88)
14	Andamanese (Indian Ocean) ♂	148(135-161)	58(53-63)	45(36-54)	98(79-118)	1.35(1.17-1.53)
15	Andamanese (Indian Ocean) ♀	138(131-146)	54(51-57)	43(31-55)	94(67-120)	1.24(1.08-1.40)
16	Arabs (Yemen) ♂	163(150-175)	64(59-69)	59(48-69)	129(105-153)	1.57(1.41-1.73)
17	Chinese (Canton) ♀	148(138-158)	58(54-62)	54(37-71)	119(82-156)	1.43(1.19-1.67)
18	English, students (Oxford) ♂	178(166-190)	70(65-75)	69(55-83)	151(120-182)	1.82(1.60-2.04)
19	English, convicts ♂	167(153-181)	66(60-71)	65(50-80)	143(110-177)	1.70(1.45-1.95)
20	French, workers ♂	169(157-181)	66(62-71)	67(51-83)	147(112-182)	1.73(1.51-1.95)
21	French, workers ♀	159(150-168)	62(59-66)	56(42-70)	123(92-155)	1.54(1.34-1.74)
22	Indochinese (Cambodja) ♀	149(140-159)	59(55-62)	53(37-68)	116(82-150)	1.44(1.20-1.68)
23	Indochinese (Hué) ♂	146(136-156)	57(53-61)	43(31-54)	94(69-119)	1.28(1.10-1.46)
24	Indochinese (Tonkin) ♂	160(150-170)	63(59-67)	57(49-65)	126(108-144)	1.55(1.35-1.75)
25	Irish (North) ♂	172(160-184)	68(63-72)	68(51-84)	149(112-186)	1.77(1.53-2.01)
26	Italians ♂	168(155-181)	66(61-71)	63(44-82)	138(97-180)	1.81(1.50-2.12)[2]
27	Italians ♀	156(143-170)	61(56-67)	52(34-70)	114(75-154)	1.64(1.31-1.97)[2]
28	Japanese ♂	159(149-170)	63(59-67)	53(38-68)	116(83-150)	1.55(1.31-1.79)[3]
29	Otomi (Mexican Indian) ♂	158(148-167)	62(58-66)	55(43-64)	117(94-140)	1.52(1.34-1.70)
30	Semang (Malaya) ♂	154(141-167)	60(55-66)	41(29-54)	91(64-118)	1.31(1.13-1.49)
31	Semang (Malaya) ♂	144(134-154)	57(53-61)	33(24-42)	72(53-91)	1.14(0.96-1.32)
32	Spaniards ♂	169(157-181)	66(62-71)	67(50-84)	147(111-184)	1.74(1.50-1.98)

/1/ Body surface area calculated according to the formula $S = 71.84 \times \text{weight}^{0.425} \times \text{height}^{0.725}$, except where otherwise indicated. /2/ Measured by surface integrator. /3/ Measured by coating method.

148. BODY WEIGHTS WITH ORDINARY CLOTHING: MAN, NORTH AMERICA

	Height cm	Height in	Average Body Weights 20-24 yr kg	lb	25-29 yr kg	lb	30-34 yr kg	lb	35-39 yr kg	lb	40-44 yr kg	lb	45-49 yr kg	lb	50-54 yr kg	lb	55-59 yr kg	lb	Desirable Body Weights, >25 yr Small Framed kg	lb	Medium Framed kg	lb	Large Framed kg	lb
									Male															
1	149.9	59	53	117	55	122	57	125	58	127	59	130	60	132	60	133	61	134						
2	152.4	60	54	119	56	124	58	127	58	129	60	132	61	134	61	135	62	136						
3	154.9	61	55	121	57	126	59	129	59	131	61	134	62	136	62	137	63	138						
4	157.5	62	56	124	58	128	60	131	60	133	62	136	63	138	63	139	64	140	53-57	116-125	56-60	124-133	59-64	131-142
5	160.0	63	58	127	59	131	61	134	62	136	63	139	64	141	64	142	65	143	54-58	119-128	58-62	127-136	60-65	133-144
6	162.6	64	59	131	61	134	62	137	63	140	64	142	65	144	66	145	66	146	55-60	122-136	59-63	130-140	62-68	137-149
7	165.1	65	61	135	63	138	64	141	65	144	66	146	67	148	68	149	68	150	57-62	126-136	61-65	134-144	64-69	141-153
8	167.6	66	63	139	64	142	66	145	67	148	68	150	69	152	69	153	70	154	58-63	129-139	62-67	137-147	66-71	145-157
9	170.2	67	64	142	66	146	68	149	69	152	70	154	71	156	71	157	72	158	60-65	133-143	64-68	141-151	68-73	149-162
10	172.7	68	66	146	68	150	70	154	71	157	72	159	73	161	73	162	74	163	62-67	136-147	66-71	145-156	69-75	153-166
11	175.3	69	68	150	70	154	72	158	73	162	74	164	75	166	75	167	77	168	63-68	140-151	68-73	149-160	71-77	157-170
12	177.8	70	70	154	72	158	74	163	75	167	77	169	78	171	78	172	79	173	65-70	144-155	69-74	153-164	73-79	161-175
13	180.3	71	72	158	74	163	76	168	78	172	79	175	80	177	81	178	81	179	67-72	148-159	71-76	157-168	75-82	165-180
14	182.9	72	74	163	77	169	79	174	81	178	82	181	83	183	83	184	83	185	69-74	152-164	73-78	161-173	77-84	169-185
15	185.4	73	76	168	79	175	82	180	83	184	85	187	86	190	86	191	86	192	71-77	157-169	75-81	166-178	79-86	174-190
16	188.0	74	78	173	82	181	84	186	86	191	88	194	89	197	89	198	89	199	73-78	163-175	78-83	171-184	81-89	179-196
17	190.5	75	81	178	85	187	87	192	89	197	91	201	92	204	92	205	93	206	76-82	168-180	80-86	176-189	83-92	184-202
									Female															
18	149.9	59	51	113	53	116	54	119	55	122	57	126	58	129	59	131	60	132	47-50	104-111	50-53	110-118	53-58	117-127
19	152.4	60	52	115	54	118	55	121	56	124	58	128	59	131	60	133	61	134	48-51	105-113	51-54	114-122	54-59	119-129
20	154.9	61	53	117	55	120	56	123	57	126	59	130	60	133	61	135	62	137	49-52	107-115	52-55	117-125	55-60	121-131
21	157.5	62	54	120	56	122	57	125	58	129	60	133	62	136	63	138	63	140	50-54	110-118	53-57	117-125	56-61	124-135
22	160.2	63	55	122	57	125	58	128	60	132	62	136	63	139	64	141	64	143	51-55	113-125	54-58	124-132	57-62	127-138
23	162.6	64	57	126	58	129	60	132	62	136	63	139	64	142	65	144	66	146	53-57	116-125	56-60	127-138	59-64	131-142
24	165.1	65	58	129	60	132	62	136	64	140	65	143	66	146	67	148	68	150	54-58	119-128	57-61	130-140	60-65	133-145
25	167.6	66	60	133	62	136	63	140	65	144	67	147	68	151	69	152	70	153	55-60	123-132	58-63	134-144	62-68	138-150
26	170.2	67	62	137	63	140	65	144	67	148	68	151	70	155	71	157	72	158	57-62	126-136	60-65	137-147	64-69	142-154
27	172.7	68	64	141	65	144	67	148	69	152	70	155	72	159	73	162	74	163	58-63	129-139	61-65	142-154	66-71	145-158
28	175.3	69	66	145	67	148	69	152	71	156	72	159	74	163	74	166	76	173	60-65	133-143	62-67	145-158	68-73	149-162
29	177.8	70	68	149	69	152	70	155	72	159	73	162	75	166	77	170	81	177	62-67	136-147	64-68	149-162	69-75	152-166
30	180.3	71	70	153	70	155	72	158	73	162	75	166	77	170	79	174	83	182	63-68	139-150	67-71	152-166	70-77	155-169
31	182.9	72	72	157	72	159	73	162	75	165	77	169	79	173	81	177								

North Americans of different racial backgrounds, socio-economic conditions, geographical areas, and different periods in American history. Data for the Negro were collected about 1925; White, Cleveland, Ohio, 1920-35; Japanese, 1920-40; Japanese reared in Japan, 1951; Dutch, Finnish, Italian, 1930-40; American Indian, Mexican, 1920-40. Lower economic groups: children of unskilled and semiskilled workers, 16 states in U.S.A., 1937-39; upper economic groups: all occupational groups other than unskilled and semiskilled, 16 states U.S.A., 1937-39. Unskilled, semiskilled, and managerial, professional: Oregon boys of northwest European ancestry, studied in 1950. Roughly 25% in unskilled and semiskilled category, 49% in the excluded (middle) category, and 26% in the managerial and professional category. Poorest and best residential districts: white girls of Minneapolis, Minn., and Ottawa, Canada, 1930-45. Period 1860-1900 and period 1930-1950: investigations at each age were selected to approximate similar ethnic and socio-economic sampling in the 2 periods. Geographical sections of U.S.A.: about 1935. Values at age 7 are averages of means of ages 6 and 8.

No.	Specifications	Height ♂ cm	in.	Height ♀ cm	in.	Weight ♂ kg	lb	Weight ♀ kg	lb
1	Birth: Negro	49.6	19.5			3.2	7.1	3.1	6.8
2	White	50.8	20.0			3.5	7.8	3.4	7.6
3	Period 1860-1900	50.4	19.8						
4	Period 1930-1950	50.7	19.9						
5	2 yr: Japanese	83.8	33.0	82.4	32.4	13.4	29.6	12.5	27.5
6	White	89.6	35.2	85.4	33.6				
7	Period 1860-1900	81.6	32.1						
8	Period 1930-1950	86.9	34.2						
9	7 yr: Dutch	123.3	48.5			22.9	50.4		
10	Finnish	121.2	47.7			23.5	51.7		
11	Indian, American	120.8	47.6	117.0	46.0	21.6	47.5	20.3	44.7
12	Italian	119.3	47.0			22.7	49.9		
13	Japanese			114.1	44.9			20.7	45.6
14	Japanese, reared in Japan	113.9	44.8	112.7	44.4	20.4	44.9	19.7	43.3
15	Mexican			117.0	46.0			21.0	46.2
16	Negro	120.9	47.5	120.4	47.3	24.0	52.8	22.1	48.6
17	White	122.5	48.2	121.6	47.9			23.4	51.6
18	Lower economic groups	♂♀119.3	47.0			♂♀22.1	48.6		
19	Upper economic groups	♂♀120.8	47.6			♂♀22.9	50.4		
20	Unskilled, semiskilled	121.4	47.8			23.3	51.3		
21	Managerial, professional	123.6	48.7			24.5	53.9		
22	Poorest residential dist.	118.9	46.8			21.4	47.1		
23	Best residential dist.	122.0	48.0			22.8	50.2		
24	Period 1860-1900	114.3	45.0						
25	Period 1930-1950	122.4	48.2						
26	Northeastern USA	119.6	47.1			22.9	50.4	22.5	49.5
27	Southcentral USA	120.0	47.2			22.7	49.9	22.2	48.8
28	Northcentral USA	118.9	46.8			22.2	48.8	21.4	47.1
29	Western USA	118.6	46.7			21.9	48.2	21.4	47.1
30	10 yr: Indian, American			131.7	51.8			27.3	60.1
31	Japanese	129.6	51.0			27.8	61.2		
32	Japanese, reared in Japan	127.6	50.2	127.3	50.1	26.4	58.1	26.1	57.4
33	Mexican			132.2	52.0			28.2	62.0
34	Negro	135.3	53.3	135.2	53.2			30.7	67.5
35	White	137.9	54.3	137.7	54.2	32.0	70.7	31.8	70.3
36	Lower economic groups	♂♀135.0	53.1			♂♀29.7	65.3		
37	Upper economic groups	♂♀136.6	53.8			♂♀31.1	68.4		
38	Unskilled, semiskilled	137.8	54.3						
39	Managerial, professional	140.7	55.4						
40	Poorest residential dist.	134.3	52.9			32.3	71.1	29.0	63.8
41	Best residential dist.	138.7	54.6			34.3	75.5	31.8	70.0
42	Period 1860-1900	129.6	51.0						
43	Period 1930-1950	139.2	54.8						
44	Northeastern USA	135.1	53.2	135.1	53.2	30.5	67.1	30.3	66.7
45	Northcentral USA	135.4	53.3	134.4	52.9	30.5	67.1	30.1	66.2
46	Southcentral USA	134.9	53.1	134.1	52.8	30.2	66.4	29.3	64.5
47	Western USA	134.9	53.1	134.6	53.0	29.6	65.1	28.6	62.9
48	11 yr: Dutch	144.3	56.8			33.8	74.4		
49	Finnish	141.6	55.7			33.4	73.5		
50	Indian, American	138.9	54.7			30.3	66.7		
51	Italian	139.1	54.8			32.1	70.6		
52	Japanese, reared in Japan	132.1	52.0	132.5	52.2	28.8	63.4	29.2	64.2
53	Mexican	138.2	54.8						
54	Negro	140.9	55.4	141.2	55.5	35.2	77.6	35.8	79.0
55	White	142.7	56.2	143.5	56.5				
56	14 yr: Japanese	148.4	58.4	150.8	59.4			42.8	94.2
57	Japanese, reared in Japan			150.6	59.3			43.3	95.3
58	Mexican	156.5	61.5	146.7	57.8	40.5	89.1	41.2	90.6
59	Negro	160.0	63.0	152.0	59.8	48.0	105.8	44.5	97.9
60	White	163.7	64.4	154.7	60.8	48.9	107.9	47.7	105.2
61	Period 1860-1900	151.8	59.8					49.1	108.5
62	Period 1930-1950	158.2	62.3						
63	Northeastern USA	155.4	61.2			45.2	99.4	48.1	105.8
64	Northcentral USA	155.2	61.1			45.8	100.8	46.5	102.3
65	Southcentral USA	155.7	61.3			44.6	98.1	45.2	99.4
66	Western USA	153.9	60.6			41.2?	90.6?	45.7	100.5
67	15 yr: Dutch	168.6	66.4			50.5	111.1		
68	Finnish	164.4	64.7			52.1	114.6		
69	Indian, American	160.5	63.2			45.2	99.4		
70	Italian	161.4	63.5			50.9	112.0		
71	16 yr: Indian, American	157.7	62.1	150.3	59.2				
72	Japanese	161.0	63.3			49.1	108.0	47.2	103.8
73	Japanese, reared in Japan			158.1	62.1				
74	Negro	166.6	65.6	160.5	63.2	53.0	116.9	53.0	116.9
75	White	161.1	63.4	150.7	59.2	55.1	121.7	52.1	115.0
76	19 yr: Negro	172.9	67.9	159.9	62.8	68.1	150.2		
77	White	173.8	68.3	164.6	64.7	68.5	151.2	58.2	128.6
78	Period 1860-1900	172.1	67.7						
79	Period 1930-1950	175.6	69.1						
80	25 yr: Japanese, reared in Japan	161.8	63.7	150.4	59.2				
81	Period 1860-1900	171.8	67.6						
82	Period 1930-1950	173.5	68.3						

150. HEIGHT AND WEIGHT: MAN, VARIOUS NATIONALITIES

Data are from surveys conducted over the past 25 or more years. Values in parentheses are ranges and correspond to estimate "b" of the 95% range (cf Introduction).

#	Specifications	Height, Male cm	Height, Male in	Height, Female cm	Height, Female in	Weight, Male kg	Weight, Male lb	Weight, Female kg	Weight, Female lb
	Birth:								
1	USA White	50.8(46.8-54.8)	19.9(18.4-21.5)	50.2(46.4-54.1)	19.7(18.2-21.2)	3.5(2.2-4.9)	7.8(4.9-10.7)	3.4(2.5-4.4)	7.6(5.5-9.6)
2	USA Negro	49.6	19.5	48.7	19.1	3.2(3.0-3.4)	7.1(6.6-7.4)	3.1(2.9-3.3)	6.8(6.4-7.3)
3	African Pygmy	45.9	18.0	46.4	18.2	3.6	7.9	3.7	8.2
4	British	51.2	20.1	50.8	20.0	3.4	7.4	3.3	7.3
5	Chinese	48.2	18.9	48.2	18.9	3.1	6.8	3.0	6.6
6	Danish					3.4	7.5	3.3	7.3
7	French	49.9	19.6	49.2	19.3	3.1	6.8	3.1	6.8
8	German	51.0	20.0	50.5	19.8	3.5	7.7	3.3	7.3
9	Japanese	50.2	19.7	49.3	19.4	3.05	6.72	2.97	6.54
10	Russian	48.6	19.1	48.6	19.1	3.4	7.5	3.3	7.3
11	Swiss	50.8	20.0	50.2	19.7	3.3	7.3	3.1	6.8
	1 yr:								
12	USA White	75.2(67.3-83.1)	29.6(26.5-32.7)	75.4(66.5-84.3)	29.6(26.1-33.1)	10.9(7.0-14.8)	24.0(15.4-32.6)	10.3(7.9-12.6)	22.6(17.4-27.8)
13	USA Negro	74.9(62.1-87.7)	29.4(24.4-34.5)	83.7	32.9	8.6(6.5-10.6)	19.0(14.3-23.4)	8.6(6.1-11.0)	19.0(13.4-24.2)
14	African Pygmy	71.0	27.9	65.0	25.5			7.0	15.4
15	Austrian	76	29.9	75	29.5	10.2	22.5	9.8	21.6
16	British	70.8	27.8	69.8	27.4	9.3	20.5	8.8	19.4
17	Chinese	73.5	28.9	71.4	28.1				
18	German	75.0	29.5	74.5	29.3	9.7	21.4	9.5	20.9
19	Japanese	76.4	30.1	75.6	29.7	9.7	21.4	9.3	20.5
	2 yr:								
20	USA White	89.6(82.4-96.8)	35.2(32.4-38.0)	85.4(78.8-91.9)	33.6(31.0-36.1)	13.4(10.6-16.3)	29.6(23.4-35.8)	12.5(10.3-14.7)	27.5(22.6-32.4)
21	USA Negro	89.1(77.6-100.6)	35.0(30.5-39.5)	85.9(77.8-94.0)	33.8(20.6-36.9)	13.6		12.7	
22	Canadian	88.1	34.7	85.3	33.6	13.6	30.0	12.7	28.0
	3 yr:								
23	USA White	96.8(89.3-104.4)	38.0(35.1-41.0)	96.8(87.5-104.3)	37.7(34.4-41.0)	15.3(12.7-17.8)	33.7(28.1-39.3)	15.1(11.1-19.2)	33.4(24.4-42.3)
24	USA Negro	95.2(83.4-107.0)	37.4(32.8-42.1)	95.8(86.6-105.0)	37.7(34.0-41.3)				
25	African Pygmy	88.6	34.8						
26	Austrian	95	36.9	94	36.2	14.5	32.0	14.0	30.9
27	British	96.3	37.8	96.0	37.7	13.7	30.2	13.2	29.1
28	Canadian	93.0	36.6	91.4	36.0	14.5	32	14.0	31
29	Chinese	92.0	36.2	89.7	35.1				
30	Czechoslovakian	89.7	35.3	87.7	34.5				
31	German	93.0	36.5	92.5	36.4	14.1	31.1	13.7	30.2
32	Japanese	91.5	36.0	90.8	35.7	13.6	30.0	13.2	29.1
	4 yr:								
33	USA White	103.9(94.5-113.3)	40.9(37.2-44.6)	103.9(94.5-113.3)	40.9(37.2-44.6)	17.3(13.3-21.3)	38.2(29.4-47.0)	16.9(12.6-21.2)	37.3(27.9-46.7)
34	USA Negro	102.0(90.9-113.1)	40.1(35.7-44.4)	100.6(88.3-112.9)	39.5(34.7-44.4)	16.8	37	16.3	36
35	Canadian	99.6	39.2	99.6	39.2	15.3	33.7	14.7	32.4
36	Japanese	98.3	38.7	97.1	38.2				
	5 yr:								
37	USA White	111.5(101.6-121.4)	43.9(40.0-47.8)	110.7(100.8-120.7)	43.6(39.7-47.5)	19.6(14.7-24.5)	43.2(32.4-54.0)	19.0(13.8-24.3)	42.0(30.4-53.6)
38	USA Negro	110.0(98.9-121.1)	43.2(38.9-47.6)	109.9(98.7-121.1)	43.2(38.8-47.6)				
39	African Pygmy	100.4	39.5	98.1	38.6	13.5	29.7	13.5	29.7
40	Austrian	108	42.4	107	42.1	18.5	40.8	18.0	39.7
41	British	108.2	42.5	107.9	42.4	15.5	34.2	15.9	35.0
42	Canadian	106.4	41.9	106.2	41.8	18.1	40	18.6	41
43	Chinese	104.4	41.0	108.0	42.4	14.9	32.8	14.0	30.9
44	Czechoslovakian	103.5	40.7	102.7	40.4	20.5	45.2	19.1	42.1
45	French	107.9	42.4	106.9	42.0	18.4	40.6	17.8	39.2
46	German	107.0	42.1	106.5	41.9	18.6	41.0	17.8	39.2
47	Japanese	104.0	41.0	103.3	40.7	16.7	36.8	16.2	35.7
	6 yr:								
48	USA White	117.1(106.7-127.5)	46.1(42.0-50.2)	116.3(105.9-126.7)	45.8(41.7-49.9)	21.6(15.9-27.2)	47.6(35.2-60.0)	21.0(15.0-27.0)	46.4(33.1-59.7)
49	USA Negro	116.0(103.8-128.2)	45.6(40.8-50.4)	116.2(103.5-128.9)	45.7(40.7-50.7)	20.8	46	19.9	44
50	Canadian	113.3	44.6	112.3	44.2	18.4	40.6	17.5	38.6
51	Japanese	109.3	43.0	108.3	42.6				
	7 yr:								
52	USA White	122.4(111.5-133.4)	48.2(43.9-52.5)	121.7(110.7-132.6)	47.9(43.6-52.2)	23.8(17.5-30.1)	52.5(38.6-66.4)	23.2(16.5-29.9)	51.2(36.5-65.9)
53	USA Negro	120.3(108.9-131.7)	47.3(42.8-51.8)	120.8(105.7-135.9)	47.5(41.5-53.4)				
54	African Pygmy	103.9	40.8	102.8	40.4	17.6	38.8		
55	Austrian	119	46.8	118	46.4	22.5	49.6	22.0	48.5
56	British	118.1	46.4	117.9	46.3	19.8	43.6	19.3	42.5
57	Canadian	119.4	47.0	118.1	46.5	22.7	50	22.2	49
58	Chinese	114.6	45.0	117.2	46.1	18.4	40.6	20.1	44.3
59	Czechoslovakian	115.6	45.4	115.0	45.2	24.3	53.6	23.3	51.4
60	Danish	118.5	46.5	117.9	46.3	21.8	48.0	21.5	47.4

178

#	Group								
61	French	117.7	46.3	116.4	45.7	22.2	48.9	21.2	46.7
62	German	119.5	47.0	118.5	46.6	22.2	48.9	21.6	47.6
63	Japanese	114.4	45.0	113.5	44.7	20.3	44.7	19.5	43.0
64	Spanish	117	46.0	116	45.6	21.6	47.6	21.5	47.4
65	Swiss	120	47.2	119.0	46.8	22.2	48.9	21.6	47.6
66	8 yr: USA White	128.0(116.6-139.4)	50.4(45.9-54.9)	127.0(115.6-138.4)	50.0(45.5-54.5)	26.4(18.6-34.1)	58.2(41.1-75.3)	25.8(17.4-34.1)	56.9(38.5-75.3)
67	USA Negro	125.8(113.3-138.3)	49.4(44.5-54.4)	124.6(111.0-138.2)	49.0(43.6-54.3)	25.8	57	25.8	57
68	Canadian	124.7	49.1	124.2	48.9	22.3	49.1	21.9	48.2
69	Japanese	118.5	46.7	118.6	46.7				
70	9 yr: USA White	133.1(121.2-144.8)	52.4(47.7-57.1)	132.1(120.1-144.0)	52.0(47.3-56.7)	29.2(20.5-37.9)	54.4(45.2-83.6)	28.5(18.7-38.4)	63.0(41.2-84.8)
71	USA Negro	130.8(118.5-143.1)	51.4(46.6-56.2)	131.3(118.7-143.9)	51.6(46.7-56.6)				
72	African Pygmy	113.3	44.5	113.0	44.0	28.1	61.9	27.6	60.8
73	Argentinian	123	48.3	122	47.9	26.7	58.8	26.0	57.3
74	Austrian	128	50.3	127	49.9	23.4	51.6	22.0	48.4
75	British	128.0	51.3	127.8	50.2	28.5	63	28.1	62
76	Canadian	130.3	51.3	129.5	51.0	22.2	48.9	23.4	51.6
77	Chinese	123.7	48.6	126.6	49.8	28.1	61.9	27.8	61.3
78	Czechoslovakian	126.6	49.5	125.9	49.1	26.2	57.7	26.2	57.7
79	Danish	127.9	50.3	127.5	50.1	27.0	59.5	26.8	59.1
80	French	127.9	50.3	127.7	50.2	26.7	58.8	25.9	57.1
81	German	129.0	50.7	128.5	50.5	24.7	54.4	23.8	52.5
82	Japanese	124.1	48.9	123.6	48.7	24.7	54.4	26.0	57.3
83	Russian	125.3	49.2	124.5	49.0	26.3	58.0	26.2	57.7
84	Spanish	123	48.3	124.6	49.0				
85	Swiss	129	50.7	129.1	50.7				
86	10 yr: USA White	137.9(125.5-150.4)	54.3(49.4-59.2)	137.7(124.7-150.6)	54.2(49.1-59.3)	32.0(21.8-42.2)	70.7(48.2-93.2)	31.8(20.1-43.6)	70.3(44.4-96.2)
87	USA Negro	135.3(121.6-149.0)	53.2(47.8-58.6)	135.2(120.4-150.0)	53.1(47.3-58.9)	31.7	70	31.3	69
88	Canadian	135.9	53.5	135.4	53.3	26.9	59.2	26.5	58.3
89	Japanese	128.9	50.2	128.6	50.6				
90	11 yr: USA White	142.7(129.8-155.7)	56.2(51.1-61.3)	143.5(129.5-157.5)	56.5(51.0-62.0)	35.2(23.5-46.8)	77.6(51.9-103.3)	35.8(22.0-49.6)	79.0(48.6-109.4)
91	USA Negro	140.9(129.0-152.8)	55.4(50.7-60.1)	141.2(124.1-158.3)	55.5(48.8-62.2)				
92	African Pygmy	132	51.9	132	51.9	23.0	50.7	18.5	40.8
93	Argentinian	137	53.8	138	54.2	33.1	73.0	33.9	74.7
94	Austrian	136.7	53.7	137.9	54.2	31.8	70.1	31.5	69.4
95	British	140.7	55.4	140.5	55.3	34.9	59.1	34.9	59.9
96	Canadian	131.3	51.6	135.4	53.2	26.5	77	28.7	77
97	Chinese	133.4	52.4	133.4	52.4	32.0	58.4	33.6	63.3
98	Czechoslovakian	137.5	54.0	137.5	54.0	31.8	70.5	32.3	74.1
99	Danish	137.5	54.2	138.6	54.5	32.6	70.1	33.9	71.2
100	French	137.5	54.0	139.0	54.6	31.5	71.9	31.4	74.7
101	German	137.5	54.2	134.0	52.8	29.3	69.4	29.8	69.2
102	Japanese	132.9	52.2	134	52.7	29.0	64.6	31.5	65.7
103	Spanish	132.7	52.2	137.3	54.0	30.8	63.9	30.9	69.4
104	Swiss	138	54.2				67.9		68.1
105	12 yr: USA White	147.8(133.4-162.3)	58.2(52.5-63.9)	149.9(135.8-164.3)	59.0(53.3-64.7)	38.8(24.7-52.8)	85.6(54.6-116.6)	40.6(24.8-56.4)	89.1(54.8-124.6)
106	USA Negro	144.8(129.2-160.4)	56.9(50.8-63.0)	149.0(136.3-161.7)	58.6(53.6-63.5)	37.0(26.8-47.2)	81.6(59.1-104.0)	39.9(34.8-45.0)	88.1(76.7-99.2)
107	Canadian	145.8	57.4	147.8	58.2	38.1	84	41.7	92
108	Japanese	137.7	54.2	139.5	54.0	32.0	70.6	33.6	74.1
109	13 yr: USA White	153.7(137.7-169.7)	60.5(54.2-66.8)	153.9(141.0-166.9)	60.6(55.5-65.7)	43.3(27.1-59.5)	95.6(59.9-131.3)	45.4(29.4-61.4)	100.3(65.0-135.6)
110	USA Negro	150.1(133.0-166.3)	59.0(52.6-65.4)	153.7(137.5-169.9)	60.4(54.0-66.8)	43.9(34.5-53.3)	96.7(76.0-117.5)	43.8(23.2-64.4)	96.7(51.1-142.0)
111	African Pygmy	115.1	45.2	145	57.0	40.6	89.5	41.9	92.3
112	Argentinian	142	55.8	149	58.6	38.5	84.9	38.5	84.9
113	Austrian	148	58.2	154.4(141.0-167.6)	60.8(55.5-68.0)	42.7(26.8-58.7)	94.3(59.1-129.5)	45.1(31.1-59.1)	99.6(68.7-130.5)
114	British	155.1(136.9-173.5)	61.1(53.9-68.3)	153.4	60.4	42.6	94	46.3	102
115	Canadian	150.6	59.3	153.4	57.3	32.3	75.6	35.0	81.5
116	Chinese	141.1	55.4	145.7	56.9	34.3	84.0	37.0	77.1
117	Czechoslovakian	142.9	56.2	144.7	56.9	38.1	82.7	40.2	89.9
118	Danish	146.5	57.6	148.6	58.4	37.5	78.5	38.2	88.6
119	German	147.0	57.8	151.0	59.3	35.6	78.7	38.0	84.2
120	Japanese	142.6	56.1	143.7	56.5	35.7			83.8
121	Spanish	139.6	54.9	147.5					
122	14 yr: USA White	160.0(143.0-177.0)	63.0(56.3-69.7)	158.2(146.3-170.2)	62.3(57.6-67.0)	48.9(31.0-66.7)	107.9(68.5-147.3)	49.1(33.9-64.4)	108.5(74.8-142.2)
123	USA Negro	155.1(140.0-172.9)	61.5(55.1-67.9)	157.0(140.5-168.9)	60.8(55.2-66.4)	48.0(38.6-57.4)	105.8(85.1-126.5)	47.7(27.1-68.3)	105.2(59.7-150.5)
124	British	155.1(136.9-173.5)	61.1(53.9-68.3)	154.4(141.0-167.6)	60.8(55.5-66.0)	42.7(26.8-58.7)	94.3(59.1-129.5)	45.1(31.1-59.1)	99.6(68.7-130.5)
125	Canadian	158.0	62.2	155.7	61.3	48.9	108	48.5	107
126	Japanese	149.7	58.9	147.5	58.1	41.1	90.6	41.5	91.4

Data are from surveys conducted over the past 25 or more years. Values in parentheses are ranges and correspond to estimate "b" of the 95% range (cf Introduction).

150. HEIGHT AND WEIGHT: MAN, VARIOUS NATIONALITIES (Concluded)

		Height, Male		Height, Female		Weight, Male		Weight, Female	
	Specifications	cm	in	cm	in	kg	lb	kg	lb
127	15 yr: USA White	166.6(151.1-182.1)	65.6(59.5-71.7)	160.5(149.1-172.0)	63.2(58.7-67.7)	55.1(36.8-73.4)	121.7(81.3-162.1)	52.1(37.7-66.5)	115.0(83.2-146.8)
128	USA Negro	161.0(145.8-176.2)	63.4(57.3-69.2)	158.1(146.6-169.6)	62.2(157.6-66.6)	53.0(41.6-64.4)	116.9(91.7-141.9)	53.0(28.3-77.7)	116.9(62.4-171.3)
129	British	158.6(140.2-177.0)	62.4(55.2-69.7)	155.8(144.0-167.9)	61.4(56.7-66.1)	45.8(28.6-63.0)	101.1(63.2-139.0)	47.7(32.6-62.7)	105.2(72.0-138.4)
130	Canadian	164.3	64.7	158.0	62.2	53.9	119	50.7	112
131	Czechoslovakian	156	61.3			52.1	114.8		
132	Danish	160.1	62.9	158.0	62.1	49.2	108.4	49.6	109.3
133	German	160.5	63.1	160.0	62.9	48.1	106.0	49.5	109.1
134	16 yr: USA White	170.9(157.0-184.9)	67.3(61.8-72.8)	161.3(150.4-172.2)	63.5(59.2-67.8)	59.8(43.0-76.5)	131.9(94.9-168.9)	53.3(39.1-67.4)	117.6(86.4-148.8)
135	USA Negro	163.6(149.0-178.2)	64.3(58.6-70.0)	157.8(146.4-169.2)	62.2(157.5-66.5)	57.0(45.8-68.2)	125.7(100.9-150.3)	56.9(32.6-81.2)	125.7(71.9-179.0)
136	British	163.9(146.1-181.6)	64.5(57.5-71.5)	157.6(145.0-170.0)	62.0(157.1-66.9)	50.6(33.3-67.9)	111.7(73.5-149.9)	49.8(35.7-64.0)	110.0(78.7-141.3)
137	Canadian[1]	169.4	66.7	158.7	62.5	61.6	136	54.4	120
138	Japanese	158.9	62.6	150.7	59.3	49.9	110.0	47.7	105.1
139	17 yr: USA White	172.1(159.5-184.7)	67.6(62.7-72.6)	161.5(150.6-172.5)	63.6(59.3-67.9)	63.6(49.2-78.0)	140.4(108.6-172.3)	53.9(40.1-67.7)	119.0(88.6-149.4)
140	USA Negro	167.2(157.3-183.0)	66.9(61.8-71.9)	158.5(145.8-171.2)	62.3(157.3-67.3)	63.8(48.6-79.1)	140.9(107.2-174.6)	51.1(37.3-64.9)	112.8(82.4-143.2)
141	British	167.4(152.1-182.6)	65.9(59.9-71.9)	157.8(146.0-169.7)	62.1(157.5-66.8)	54.4(39.3-69.4)	120.0(86.7-153.3)	47.5	104.7
142	Chinese	162.4	63.8	154.3	60.6	48.3	106.5		
143	Czechoslovakian	159	62.5			61.3	135.1		
144	German	170.5	67.0	164.0	64.5	59.8	131.8	56.3	124.1
145	18 yr: USA White	173.5(161.1-185.8)	68.2(63.3-73.0)	163.7(156.0-171.4)	64.3(61.3-67.4)	67.0(50.3-83.6)	147.8(111.1-184.6)	57.4(46.0-68.8)	125.6(101.3-151.5)
146	USA Negro	173.4(158.5-188.2)	68.1(62.3-74.0)	159.2(148.1-170.3)	62.6(58.2-66.9)	67.0(53.0-81.0)	147.8(116.9-178.7)	51.8(37.5-66.1)	114.4(82.8-146.0)
147	British	168.4(153.7-183.1)	66.3(60.5-72.1)	157.9(145.5-170.4)	62.2(57.3-67.1)	56.4(41.5-71.3)	124.5(91.7-157.3)	56.2	124
148	Canadian[2]	172.7	68.0	159.0	62.6	65.2	144	56.2	124
149	Japanese	161.2	63.5	151.7	59.7	53.5	117.9	49.6	109.3
150	19 yr: USA White	173.8(161.4-186.3)	68.3(63.4-73.2)	164.6(155.5-173.7)	64.7(61.1-68.3)	68.5(51.4-85.5)	151.2(113.6-188.8)	58.2(48.9-67.4)	128.3(107.8-148.6)
151	USA Negro	172.9(160.1-185.6)	67.9(62.9-73.0)	159.9(147.2-172.6)	62.8(57.8-67.8)	68.1(53.0-83.1)	150.2(117.0-183.4)	52.5(38.3-66.8)	116.0(84.6-147.4)
152	British	169.5(155.5-183.6)	66.7(61.1-72.3)	158.2(147.1-169.4)	62.3(57.9-66.7)	57.9(43.2-72.6)	127.8(95.4-160.2)	44.4	97.9
153	Chinese	165.0	65.0	152.0	59.7	52.6	115.9	59.0	130.0
154	German	174.0	68.4	165.0	64.8	64.5	142.2		
155	20-24 yr: USA White	174.2(161.6-186.5)	68.4(63.5-73.3)	161.5	63.6	70.0(52.2-88.0)	154.7(115.2-194.2)	55.7	123.0
156	USA Negro	173.1(160.4-185.8)	68.1(63.0-73.1)	159.4(145.0-173.8)	62.6(57.0-68.3)	69.7(53.4-85.9)	153.8(118.0-189.7)	53.0(38.2-68.0)	117.1(84.2-150.0)
157	British	170.2(156.7-183.7)	67.0(61.7-72.3)	158.3(146.7-170.0)	62.3(57.8-66.9)	60.6(45.8-75.4)	133.8(101.1-166.6)	56.2	124
158	Canadian[3]	172.5	67.9	159.5	62.8	69.8	154	49.0	108.0
159	Chinese[4]	166.0	65.2	156.0	61.3	53.8	118.6	53.2	117.3
160	German[4]	167.0	65.6	157.4	61.9	59.5	131.1		
161	Japanese[5]	162.4	63.9	150.8	59.3	56.2	123.9	49.0	108.0
162	25-29 yr: USA White	173.9(161.7-186.1)	68.3(63.6-73.1)	161.0	63.4	71.5(53.4-89.5)	157.8(117.9-197.6)	56.5	124.7
163	USA Negro	173.0(160.7-185.4)	68.0(63.1-72.8)	158.7(142.1-175.3)	62.4(55.8-68.9)	70.7(52.8-88.5)	156.0(116.5-195.4)	53.1(37.3-69.0)	117.3(82.3-152.3)
164	British	169.6(156.5-182.6)	66.8(61.6-71.9)	157.8(145.0-170.7)	62.1(57.1-67.2)	61.7(46.4-77.1)	136.3(102.4-170.2)	57.1	126
165	Canadian	173.5	68.3	159.2	62.7	72.5	160	54.8	120.8
166	German[5]	168.2	66.1	159.0	62.2	66.2	145.9	48.3	106.5
167	Japanese	162.1	63.8	150.4	59.2	55.1	121.4		
168	30-34 yr: USA White	173.3(161.1-185.6)	68.1(63.3-73.3)	161.0	63.4	71.6(53.4-89.9)	158.1(117.8-198.4)	58.7	129.5
169	British	169.5(156.5-182.6)	66.7(61.6-71.9)	157.5(145.3-169.6)	62.0(57.2-66.8)	62.6(46.2-79.2)	138.4(102.0-174.8)	54.2(36.6-71.8)	119.6(80.8-158.4)
170	Canadian	172.7	68.0	159.5	62.8	75.7	167	58.9	130
171	German[6]	168.6	66.3	158.0	62.1	66.1	145.7	55.3	121.9
172	30-39 yr: USA Negro	170.0(157.9-182.1)	66.8(62.1-71.6)	158.8(146.2-171.4)	62.4(57.5-67.4)	71.9(52.4-91.3)[7]	158.6(115.7-201.5)[7]	48.2	106.2
173	31-40 yr: Japanese	160.4	63.1	149.3	58.8	54.7	120.6		
174	35-44 yr: USA White			160.3	63.1			62.5	138.0
175	USA Negro	168.6(154.8-182.4)	66.4(61.0-71.8)	156.8(144.2-169.6)	61.7(56.8-66.7)	62.6(45.5-79.6)	138.1(100.4-175.8)	56.2(36.0-76.4)	124.0(79.5-168.7)
176	Canadian	171.5	67.5	158.5	62.4	75.7	167	61.2	135
177	40 yr: German	168.6	66.3	158.0	62.1				
178	40-49 yr: USA Negro	170.6(157.9-183.3)	67.0(62.1-72.0)	158.7(147.3-170.1)	62.3(57.9-66.8)				
179	41-50 yr: Japanese	159.2	62.7	147.8	58.2	54.6	120.5	48.0	105.8
180	45-54 yr: USA White			159.4	62.8			67.0	147.8
181	British	167.2(154.0-180.2)	65.8(60.6-71.0)	155.8(143.3-168.5)	61.4(56.4-66.4)	62.2(43.9-80.5)	137.2(96.8-177.7)	58.6(35.8-81.4)	129.2(78.9-179.6)
182	Canadian	169.9	66.9	157.0	61.8	74.3	164		144
183	55-64 yr: USA White			158.0	62.2			65.2	144
184	British	166.5(152.8-178.9)	65.3(60.2-70.5)	154.5(141.5-167.6)	60.8(55.7-66.0)	62.2(43.0-81.2)	137.2(94.8-179.5)	58.2(34.8-82.0)	128.5(76.9-180.0)
185	Canadian	167.6	66.0	155.7	61.3	72.9	161	66.6	147
186	>64 yr: USA White			156.6	61.7			62.7	138.5
187	British	163.5(147.1-179.9)	64.4(57.9-70.8)	152.7(140.6-164.9)	60.1(55.3-64.9)	60.1(40.8-79.3)	132.6(90.2-175.0)	54.3(34.7-73.9)	119.9(76.7-163.2)
188	Canadian	166.4	65.5	153.9	60.6	70.2	155	62.5	138

/1/ 16 and 17 yr. /2/ 18 and 19 yr. /3/ 21 yr. /4/ 20 yr. /5/ 25 yr. /6/ 30 yr. /7/ 30-34 yr.

151. REGRESSION OF SITTING AND STANDING HEIGHTS ON BODY WEIGHT: MAN

These graphs are based on five large groups of measurements on males from infancy to old age. The five groups as listed in the upper left corner of the chart, contain 6,704, 16,510, 469, 3,097, and 2,638 values, respectively. The standing height curve is based on a total of 17,523 values; that for sitting height, on 14,992 values. In each of the five groups care was taken to exclude persons not in good health. Curves representing ordinary range limits (95% range) are not available, but would be expected to lie above and below each of these curves and parallel to it. The upper of such curves for standing height would represent the ordinarily encountered limit in the direction of slenderness, the lower the ordinarily encountered limit in the direction of heaviness of build. Evidence indicates that curves for females (not represented) are identical in slope and position with these for males. The means for males simply lie farther to the right along the curve than do the means for females of the same age. The line slopes for the standing height curve are 0.34, 0.63, and 0.35, with the breaks at 10 kg and 22 kg. For sitting height the comparable slopes are 0.34, 0.41, and 0.30. The relationships between standing height and weight for the three weight ranges are expressed by the formulae, $H/W^{0.34}$, $H/W^{0.63}$, and $H/W^{0.35}$.

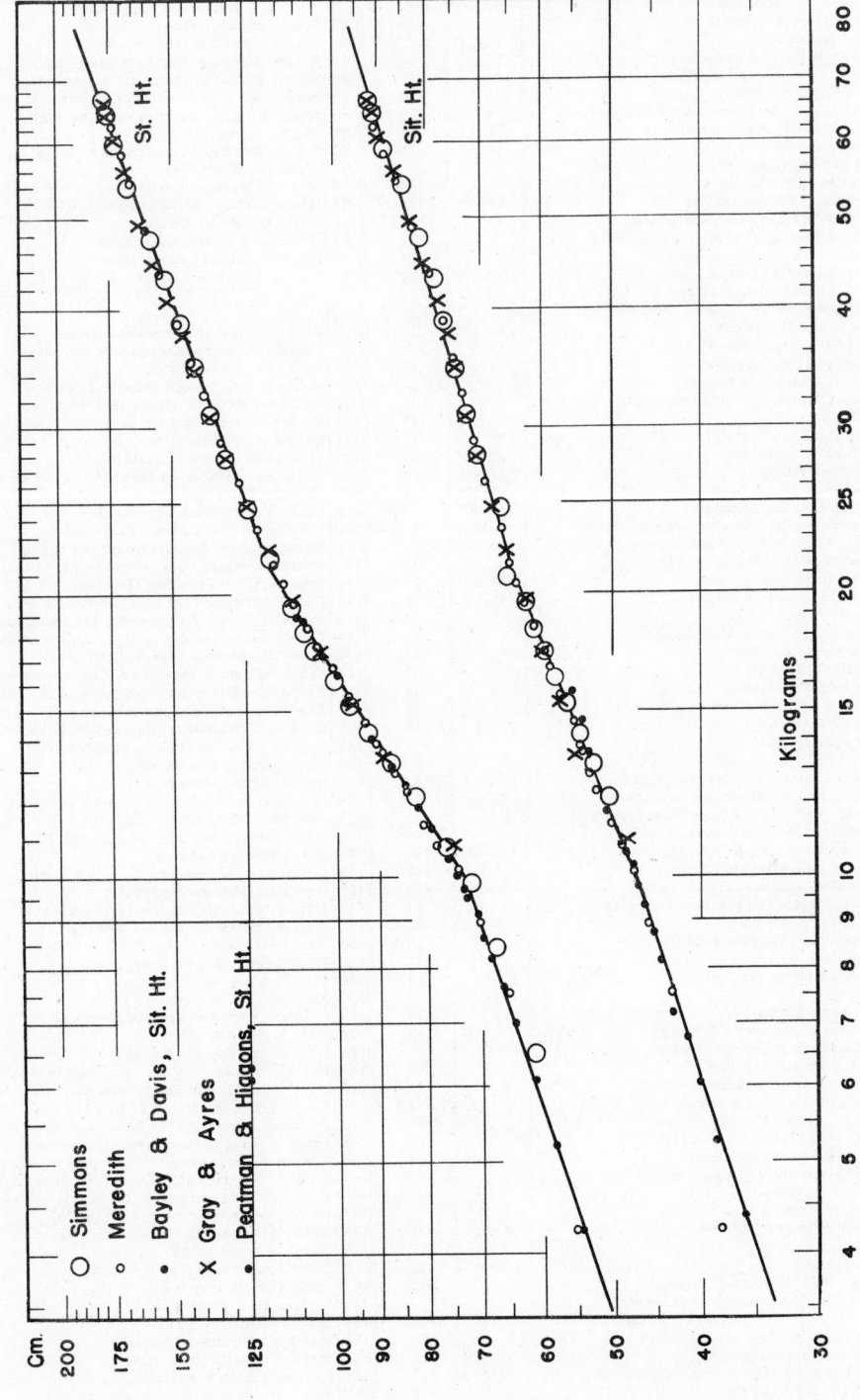

Cm.

○ Simmons

○ Meredith

• Bayley & Davis, Sit. Ht.

X Gray & Ayres

• Peatman & Higgons, St. Ht.

St. Ht.

Sit. Ht.

Kilograms

Animals in wild state are indicated by an asterisk (*). When no symbol ($\male$, $\female$) precedes value, sex of animal is unspecified.

#	Species	Av yr	Max yr	#	Species	Av yr	Max yr
	Vertebrata				**Vertebrata (continued)**		
	Mammalia				**Mammalia (concluded)**		
1	Agouti (Dasyprocta aguti)	6	>10	83	Seal, common (Phoca vitulina)		>14
2	Alpaca (Lama pacos)	12	>17	84	Sheep, domestic (Ovis aries)	10-15	20
3	Anteater, spiny (Tachyglossus aculeatus)		50[1]	85	Shrew, jumping (Elephantulus rozeti)		3.4
4	Antelope, pronghorned (Antilocapra americana)	8	15	86	Skunk, Canadian (Mephitis mephitis)		6
5	Ape, black (Cynopithecus niger)*	2	18	87	Sloth, two-toed (Choloepus didactylus)		>11
6	Ass, African wild (Equus asinus taeniopus)	14.6	19.3	88	Squirrel, gray (Sciurus carolinensis)	9	14-15
7	Baboon, sacred (Papio hamadryas)	15	$\female$24	89	Swine (Sus scrofa)	16	27
8	Badger, American (Taxidea taxus)	11	>13	90	Tapir, Brazilian (Tapirus terrestris)	<6	9
9	Bat, American brown (Eptesicus fuscus)		2	91	Tiger (Panthera tigris)	11	19
10	Bear, brown (Ursus arctos)		34	92	Weasel (Mustela nivalis)		>7
11	Bear, grizzly (U. horribilis)	20	>31	93	Whale, arctic (Balaena mysticetus)	24-37[1]	
12	Bear, polar (Thalarctos maritimus)	16	33	94	Wolf, European (Canis lupus)	12	14
13	Beaver, American (Castor canadensis)		$\female$19	95	Woodchuck (Marmota monax)		>9
14	Blackbuck (Antilope cervicapra)	7	$\male$15	96	Yak (Peophagus gruuniensis)		22
15	Buffalo, American (Bison bison)	10	$\female$>22	97	Zebra, mountain (Equus zebra)	22	>25
16	Buffalo, African (Syncerus caffer)	10	>15			Maximum	yr
17	Camel, dromedary (Camelus dromedarius)		>25		**Aves**		
18	Cat, domestic (Felis catus)	13-17	21	98	Bird of paradise (Paradisea apoda)	>12	
19	Cheetah (Acinonyx jubatus)	6	>15	99	Blackbird, European (Turdus merula)	18	
20	Chimpanzee (Pan troglodytes)	15-20	37	100	Bluebird (Sialia sialis)	4.5	
21	Chinchilla (Chinchilla laniger)	4	7	101	Bunting, red-headed (Emberiza luteola)	>13	
22	Chipmunk, eastern (Tamias striatus)	2.5	>7	102	Buzzard, African (Buteo desertorum)	>18	
23	Civet (Viverra spp)		>15	103	Canary, house (Serinus canarius)	24	
24	Coyote (Canis latrans)	9	14	104	Cardinal (Richmondena cardinalis)	22	
25	Deer, fallow (Dama dama)	10	$\female$15	105	Chickadee (Parus atricapillus)	>7	
26	Dingo (Canis dingo)	3	$\female$>12	106	Cockatoo, slender-billed (Kakatoe tenuirostris)	85[1]	
27	Dog, domestic (C. familiaris)	13-17	34	107	Condor (Vultur gryphus)	52	
28	Dolphin (Delphinus delphis)	25-30		108	Coot, slaty (Fulica ardesiaca)	3	
29	Dormouse, garden (Eliomys quercinus)	2-3	>5	109	Cormorant (Phalacrocorax carbo)	23	
30	Elephant, African (Loxodonta africana)	24	36	110	Cowbird, bay-winged (Molothrus badius)	>12	
31	Elephant, Indian (Elephas maximus)		57	111	Crane, common (Grus communis)	>42	
32	Elk, European (Alces alces)	15-20	25	112	Dove, collared (Turtur risorius)	30-40	
33	Fox, arctic (Alopex lagopus)	8	14	113	Duck, domestic (Anas platyrhynchus domesticus)	19[2]	
34	Fox, red (Vulpes fulva)		12	114	Eagle, Chilean (Geranoaetus melanoleucus)	>42	
35	Gazelle, Korin (Gazella rufifrons)		$\male$11	115	Egret, American snowy (Leucophoyx thula)	>16	
36	Genet (Genetta pardina)	>7	12.5	116	Emu (Dromiceius novaehollandiae)	40[1]	
37	Gibbon (Hylobates spp)		>23	117	Finch, chestnut-eared (Amadina castanotis)	>8	
38	Giraffe (Giraffa camelopardalis)	14	>28	118	Flamingo, European (Phoenicopterus roseus)	>22	
39	Gnu, brindled (Connochaetes taurinus)		16	119	Fowl, domestic (Gallus domesticus)	30	
40	Goat (Capra hircus)	8-10	18	120	Goldfinch, European (Carduelis carduelis)	27	
41	Gorilla (Gorilla gorilla)		>7	121	Goose, Canadian (Branta canadensis)	32	
42	Guinea pig (Cavia porcellus)	>2	>6	122	Gull, herring (Larus argentatus)	44	
43	Hamster, common (Cricetus cricetus)	2	2.5	123	Heron (Ardea cinerea)	>24	
44	Hamster, golden (Mesocricetus auratus)	1	1.8	124	Hornbill, Indian great (Buceros bicornis)	33	
45	Hedgehog, European (Erinaceus europaeus)		2	125	Jay, blue (Cyanocitta cristata)	>4	
46	Hippopotamus (Hippopotamus amphibius)	40	49[2]	126	Kingfisher, laughing (Halcyon sp)	11	
47	Horse, domestic (Equus caballus)	20-30	62	127	Kiwi (Apteryx australis)	20[2]	
48	Hyena, spotted (Crocuta crocuta)	12	$\female$25	128	Lovebird, gray-headed (Agapornis cana)	>8	
49	Ibex, Nubian (Capra nubiana)	8.5	>10	129	Lyrebird (Menura superba)	>8	
50	Jackal, black-backed (Canis mesomelas)	8	13	130	Macaw, blue-and-yellow (Ara ararauna)	43	
51	Jaguar (Panthera onca)	14	>22	131	Macaw, red-and-blue (A. macao)	64	
52	Kangaroo, red (Macropus rufus)		16.3	132	Magpie (Pica pica)	12	
53	Lemur, black (Lemur macaco)	10	$\male$21	133	Mockingbird (Mimus polyglottos)	>6	
54	Leopard (Panthera pardus)	14	23	134	Nightingale (Luscinia luscinia)	3.8	
55	Lion (P. leo)	20-25	29	135	Nuthatch, white-breasted (Sitta carolinensis)	>8	
56	Llama (Lama glama)	15	20	136	Ostrich, African (Struthio camelus)	50	
57	Loris, slow (Nycticebus coucang)		10	137	Owl, barn (Tyto alba)	>13	
58	Lynx, Canadian (Lynx canadensis)	6	>11	138	Owl, snowy (Nyctea nyctea)	24.5	
59	Marmoset (Hapale jacchus)	11	16	139	Parrot, Maximilian's (Pionus maximiliani)	9	
60	Marmot, alpine (Marmota marmota)	7	>13	140	Parakeet, ring-necked (Psittacula torquatus)	>20	
61	Marten, pine (Martes martes)	10	>13.5	141	Partridge, European (Perdix perdix)	>5	
62	Mongoose, zebra (Mungos mungo)	5	$\female$>8	142	Pelican, Australian (Pelecanus conspicillatus)	52	
63	Monkey, bonnet (Macaca radiata)	12	13	143	Penguin, king (Aptenodytes patagonica)	26	
64	Monkey, rhesus (M. mulatta)	15	29	144	Pheasant, ring-necked (Phasianus colchicus)	>27	
65	Mouse, harvest (Micromys minutus)	2	2.5	145	Pigeon, domestic (Columba livia domestica)	35	
66	Mouse, house (Mus musculus)	1-2	>3	146	Plover, old-world golden (Pluvialis apricaria)	>1	
67	Opossum (Didelphis spp)		>7	147	Puffin, Atlantic (Fratercula arctica)	8[2]	
68	Orangutan (Pongo pygmaeus)	8	$\male$26	148	Quail, European (Coturnix coturnix)	10	
69	Otter (Lutra spp)		>15	149	Raven (Corvus corax)	69	
70	Ox (Bos taurus)	20-25	30	150	Robin, American (Turdus migratorius)	>12	
71	Peccary, collared (Pecari tajucu)		>15	151	Rook (Corvus frugilegus)	>14	
72	Platypus (Ornithorhynchus paradoxus)	5		152	Skylark (Alauda arvensis)	24	
73	Porcupine, African (Hystrix cristata)	8-12	>20	153	Sparrow, Italian (Passer italiae)	20	
74	Prairie dog (Cynomys ludovicianus)	4	>8	154	Starling (Sturnus vulgaris)	>15	
75	Puma (Felis concolor)	9	16	155	Stork, black (Ciconia nigra)	30	
76	Rabbit, European (Oryctolagus cuniculus)	5-6	>13	156	Swallow (Hirundo rustica)	<1	
77	Raccoon (Procyon lotor)	4	>13	157	Swan, trumpeter (Cygnus buccinator)	>29	
78	Rat, house (Rattus rattus)	2-3	4	158	Thrush, song (Turdus musicus)	>11	
79	Reindeer (Rangifer tarandus)		12	159	Titmouse, great (Parus major)	9	
80	Rhinoceros, Indian great (Rhinoceros unicornis)	40-45	47	160	Turkey (Meleagris gallopavo)	>12	
81	Sea lion, California (Zalophus californianus)	13	19	161	Vulture, griffon (Gyps fulvus)	41	
82	Seal, cape fur (Arctocephalus pusillus)	13	$\female$>20	162	Waxbill, Amandava (Estrilda amandava)	>10	

/1/ Reported as not authenticated. /2/ Still alive at time of report.

Animals in wild state are indicated by an asterisk (*). When no symbol (♂, ♀) precedes value, sex of animal is unspecified.

Species	Recorded Life Span Maximum yr	Species	Recorded Life Span Av yr	Recorded Life Span Max yr
Vertebrata (continued)		**Vertebrata (concluded)**		
Reptilia		**Pisces (concluded)**		
163 Alligator, American (Alligator mississipiensis)	56	242 Cod, Atlantic (Gadus morhua)*		13
164 Anaconda (Eunectes murinus)	28	243 Dogfish (Scyllidae sp)		>2
165 Black snake (Coluber constrictor)	5.3[2]	244 Eel, electric (Electrophorus electricus)		11.5
166 Boa constrictor (Constrictor constrictor)	>23	245 Eel, N. American (Anguilla rostrata)		6
167 Caiman, black (Caiman niger)	28	246 Flounder (Pleuronectes flesus)		10
168 Chameleon (Chameleon sp)	>3.5	247 Flounder, starry (Platichthys stellatus)		>8
169 Cobra, African black (Naja melanoleuca)	>26[2]	248 Flounder, winter (Pleuronectes americanus)		1
170 Cooter (Pseudemys scripta)	7	249 Gar, longnose (Lepisosteus osseus)*		30
171 Copperhead, N. Am. (Ancistrodon contortrix)	18.5[2]	250 Goldfish (Cyprinus carassius auratus)		25
172 Cottonmouth, N. American (A. piscivorus)	21	251 Grayling, American (Thymallus signifer)*	4	11
173 Crocodile, American (Crocodylus acutus)	13.5	252 Grunion (Leuresthes tenuis)		4
174 Garter snake (Thamnophis sirtalis)	6	253 Haddock (Melanogrammus aeglefinus)*	1.9	15
175 Gecko, Moorish wall (Tarentola mauritanica)	7.4	254 Halibut, Atlantic (Hippoglossus hippoglossus)		40
176 Gila monster (Heloderma suspectum)	20	255 Herring, Pacific (Clupea pallasi)*	5.9	19
177 Iguana, Galapagos (Conolophus suberistatus)	15.1	256 Lamprey, American brook (Lampetra lamottei)		5
178 King snake (Lampropeltis getulus californiae)	14.8	257 Lungfish, African (Protopterus annectens)		>17
179 Lizard, European glass (Ophisaurus apus)	24	258 Lungfish, S. American (Lepidosiren paradoxa)		8.3
180 Lizard, long-tailed (Latastia longicaudata)	2.3	259 Mackerel, jack (Trachurus symmetricus)		>20
181 Lizard, monitor (Varanus salvator)	10.8[1]	260 Mackerel, Pacific (Pneumatophorus diego)		11
182 Matamata (Chelys fimbriata)	10.3	261 Minnow, European (Phoxinus phoxinus)		13
183 Puff adder (Bitis arietans)	13.9	262 Paddlefish (Polyodon spathula)		14
184 Python, African rock (Python sebae)	15.5	263 Perch (Perca fluviatilis)		>10.8
185 Rattlesnake, N. American (Crotalus atrox)	18.6	264 Perch, yellow (P. flavescens)*	3.4	13
186 Skink, sand (Chalcides ocellatus)	>9.5	265 Pickerel, chain (Esox niger)*	3.3	8
187 Terrapin, Reeve's (Geoclemys reevesii)	24.3	266 Pike (E. lucius)*	4.6	24
188 Tortoise, European pond (Emys orbicularis)	66	267 Roach (Rutilus rutilus)		12
189 Tortoise, Galapagos (Testudo elephantopus)[3]	177	268 Salmon, Atlantic (Salmo salar)*		13
190 Tuatara (Sphenodon punctatus)	>28	269 Salmon, pink (Oncorhynchus gorbuscha)*		1.8
191 Turtle, common box (Terrapene carolina)	123	270 Sardine, California (Sardinops caerulea)*	3.3	13
192 Turtle, green (Chelonia mydas)	21.0[2]	271 Seahorse (Hippocampus guttulatus)		6
193 Turtle, musk (Sternotherus odoratus)	53.1[2]	272 Shark (Scyliorhinus stellaris)*		18
194 Turtle, snapping (Chelydra serpentina)	20[2]	273 Shiner, common (Notropis cornutus)*		6
195 Water mocassin (Ancistrodon piscivorus)	21	274 Smelt, American (Osmerus mordax)*	2.3	5
196 Water snake (Natrix sipedon)	7	275 Smelt, jack (Atherinopsis californiensis)		9-10
197 Whip snake (Masticophis flagellum)	13.4	276 Sole, Dover (Microstomus pacificus)		15
198 Viper, cape (Causus rhombeatus)	>6.5	277 Squawfish, Sacramento (Ptychocheilus grandis)		9
Amphibia		278 Sturgeon, white (Acipenser transmontanus)		50
199 Coecilian, S. American (Siphonops annulatus)	9.5	279 Sunfish, green (Lepomis cyanellus)*	2.2	9
200 Congo "eel" (Amphiuma means)	26.8	280 Tautog (Tautoga onitis)		8
201 Frog, African speckled (Rana adspersa)	5.4[1]	281 Trout, brown (Salmo trutta)*	3.2	18
202 Frog, bull (R. catesbeiana)	>15.6	282 Trout, lake (Salvelinus namaycush)*	7.6	41
203 Frog, clawed (Xenopus laevis)	15	283 Trout, rainbow (Salmo irideus)*		>3.9
204 Frog, green (Rana clamitans)	>10.1	284 Tuna, bluefin (Thunnus thynnus)*		7
205 Frog, leopard (R. pipiens)	>5.9	285 Walleye, yellow (Stizostedion vitreum)*	4.8	18
206 Frog, palaearctic grass (R. temporaria)	>4.3	286 Whitefish, lake (Coregonus clupeaformis)*	5.3	26
207 Frog, palaearctic water (R. esculenta)	>5.1	**Invertebrata**		
208 Frog, red-spotted (Leptidactylus pentadactylus)	15.7			Maximum yr
209 Frog, S. African (Phrynomerus bifasciata)	>0.4	**Echinodermata**		
210 Hellbender (Cryptobranchus alleganiensis)	>28.5	**Asteroidea**		
211 Mudpuppy, N. American (Necturus maculosus)	>8.8	287 Starfish (Asterias rubens)		>5
212 Newt, California (Taricha torosus)	21	**Holothuroidea**		
213 Newt, common (Triturus viridescens)	2.9	288 Sea cucumber (Cucumaria planei)		>10
214 Newt, European crested (T. cristatus)	17	**Mollusca**		
215 Newt, Pyrenean (Euproctus asper)	>7	**Pelecypoda**		
216 Proteus, European (Proteus anguinus)	15	289 Clam, giant (Tridacna gigas)		60-100[1]
217 Salamander, Asiatic (Megalobratrachus maximus)	55	290 Mussel, edible (Mytilus edulis)		<1
218 Salamander, European (Salamandra atra)	3	291 Mussel, fresh-water (Margaritana margaritifera)		100[1]
219 Salamander, long-tailed (Eurycea lucifuga)	>1	292 Mussel, fresh-water (Pisidium spp)		2-4
220 Salamander, spotted (Ambystoma maculatum)	25	293 Mussel, fresh-water (Unio crassus)		12
221 Salamander, tiger (A. tigrinum)	11	294 Mussel, pearl (Pinctada spp)		8
222 Siren, N. American (Siren lacertina)	25.5	295 Mussel, pond (Anodonta fluviatilis)		10
223 Toad, American (Bufo americanus)	12-23	296 Oyster (Ostrea edulis)		10
224 Toad, Cuban (B. peltacephalus)	13	297 Scallop (Pecten jessoensis)		7
225 Toad, Degen's (B. vittatus)	2.4	298 Shell, fingernail (Musculium spp)		2-4
226 Toad, giant (B. alvarius)	2	299 Shell, fingernail (Sphaerium spp)		2-4
227 Toad, northwestern (B. boreas)	6	300 Shipworm (Teredo spp)		<1
228 Toad, Surinam (Pipa pipa)	>7.8[2]	**Gastropoda**		
229 Tree-frog, Florida (Hyla gratiosa)	5.9	301 Opisthobranch (Gasteropteron meckelii)		1
230 Tree-frog, giant (H. septentrionalis)	6.75	302 Periwinkle (Littorina littorea)		20
231 Tree-frog, palaearctic (H. arborea)	14	303 Prosobranch, freshwater (Neritina spp)		5
232 Tree-frog, rain (H. versicolor)	6.7	304 Sea hare (Aplysia spp)		1
233 Tree-frog, S. American (H. raddiana)	2.3	305 Shell, moon (Lunatia heros)		30

Species	Av yr	Max yr	Species		Maximum yr
Pisces			306 Slug (Milax marginatus)		2-3
234 Anchovy, northern (Engraulis mordax)		7	307 Slug (Limax spp)		1-3
235 Bass, large-mouth (Micropterus salmoides)		11[2]	308 Slug, marine (Doris spp)		1
236 Bass, small-mouth (M. dolomieu)		11[2]	309 Slug, marine nudibranch (Aeolidia spp)		1
237 Bass, striped (Roccus saxatilis)*		24	310 Slug, marine nudibranch (Janolus instatus)		1
238 Bullhead, black (Ameiurus melas)*		9	311 Snail, edible (Helix pomatia)		18[2]
239 Carp, mirror (Cyprinus carpio var.)		47[2]	312 Snail, fresh-water (Ancylus spp)		4-5
240 Carp, Prussian (C. carpis)		<6.5	313 Snail, fresh-water (Lymnaea spp)		4-5
241 Catfish, flathead (Pilodictis olivaris)*		15	314 Snail, fresh-water (Planorbis spp)		4-5
			315 Snail, land (Campylaea cingulata)		4-5

/1/ Reported as not authenticated. /2/ Still alive at time of report. /3/ May be Testudo radiata from Madagascar.

	Species	Maximum yr
	Invertebrata (continued)	
	Gastropoda (concluded)	
316	Snail, land (Helicigona, Arianta arbustorum)	4-5
317	Snail, pond (Viviparus contectus)	5
318	Snail, pulmonate (Paludina spp)	8-10
	Decapoda	
319	Squid (Loligo pealei)	>2
320	Squid (L. vulgaris)	>2
321	Squid, giant (Architeuthis spp)	10
	Amphineura	
322	Chiton, coat-of-mail shell (Chaetopleura apiculata)	4
	Arthropoda	
	Insecta	
323	Ant (Lasius sp)	10-15
324	Ant (Formica fusca)[4]	13
325	Ant, red (F. sanguinea)[5]	5
326	Aphid (Aphis evonymi)	0.08
327	Bedbug (Cimex lectularius)[6]	0.5
328	Bee, honey (Apis mellifera)[7]	<0.5
329	Bee, honey (A. mellifera)[4]	5
330	Bee, honey (A. mellifera)[5]	0.8
331	Beetle (Cybister roeselii)	0.02
332	Beetle, buprestid (Eurythrea spp)	27[1]
333	Beetle, capricorn (Hylotrupes bajulus)	98
334	Beetle, chrysomelid (Timarsha spp)	5
335	Beetle, darkling (Akis lusitanica)	7
336	Beetle, darkling (Blaps spp)	6
337	Beetle, flour (Tribolium sp)	3
338	Beetle, ground (Carabidae)[8,9]	7-11
339	Beetle, June (Melolontha vulgaris)[10]	4-5
340	Beetle, long-horned (Cerambycidae)[9]	45
341	Beetle, stag (Lucanus cervus)	6
342	Beetle, stag (L. cervus)[10]	0.02
343	Beetle, wood-boring (Buprestis splendens)	30
344	Booklouse (Liposcelis sp)	1.04
345	Cerambycid (Cerambyx sp)[10]	45
346	Cerambycid (Hesperophanes mixtus)[10]	9-10
347	Cerambycid (Stromatium fulvum)	11
348	Chafer, rose (Cetonia aurata)	6
349	Cicada, periodical (Magicicada septendecim)	17
350	Cricket (Gryllotalpa sp)	1
351	Earwig (Forficula auricularia)	5
352	Fly, fruit (Drosophila melanogaster)[11]	0.1
353	Fly, fruit (D. melanogaster)[12]	0.05
354	Fly, house (Musca domestica)	0.2
355	Fly, syrphid (Eristalis tenax)	0.09
356	Grasshopper (Melanoplus differentialis)	0.2
357	Grasshopper, short-horned (Acrididae)[9]	<1
358	Maggot, apple (Rhagoleteis pomonella)	0.3
359	Mantis, praying (Mantis religiosa)	8
360	Mosquito (Aedes geniculatus)	1.5
361	Roach, American (Periplaneta americana)	4.6
362	Roach, German (Blatella germanica)	1.3
363	Silverfish (Lepisma saccharina)	2
	Chilopoda	
364	Centipede, garden (Scutigerella immaculata)	0.9-1
365	Stone-crawler (Lithobius forficatus)	3
	Arachnida	
366	Spider, bird- (Avicularis avicularis)	15
367	Spider, house (Tegenaria civilis)	0.01
368	Spider, purse-web (Atypus piceus)	7[13]
369	Spider, British trapdoor (A. sp)	0.02
370	Spider, American tarantula (Mygali hentzii)	0.02
371	Tick, Rocky Mt. wood (Dermacentor andersoni)	3-4
	Crustacea	
372	Crab, fresh-water (Astacus fluviatilis)	30
373	Crustacea, fresh-water (spp)	1-1.5
374	Flea, water (Daphnia sp)[14]	7
375	Flea, water (D. magna)	0.2
376	Flea, water cladocera (D. longispina)	0.1
377	Lobster, European (Homarus gammarus)	33
378	Ostracod (Cyprinotus incongruens)	0.2-0.3
379	Ostracod (Herpetocypris strigata)	1.1
	Annelida	
	Polychaeta	
380	Sandworm (Platynereis dumerilii)	<1
	Oligocharta	
381	Earthworm (Lumbricus terrestris)	10
	Hirudinea	
382	Leech (Hirudo medicinalis)	27
	Nemathelminthes	
	Nematoda	
383	Eyeworm (Loa loa)	15
384	Filaria (Wuchereria bancrofti)	17
385	Hookworm (Ancylostoma duodenale)	7
386	Hookworm (A. caninum)[15]	2
	Invertebrata (concluded)	
	Nematoda (concluded)	
387	Hookworm (Necator americanus)	12
388	Immitis (Dirofilaria spp)[15]	7
389	Kidneyworm, giant, dog (Dioctophyme renale)	2
390	Lungworm, dog (Oslerus osleri)	0.4
391	Oxyurid, mice (Heterakis spumosa)	0.8
392	Nematode (Enterobius vermicularis)	0.1
393	Nematode (Haemonchus contortus)	1
394	Nematode (Trichostrongylus sp)	8.5
395	Nematode (Anguina tritica)[16]	27
396	Nematode (Ditylenchus dipsaci)[16]	9
397	Nematode (Pratylenchus pratensis)[17]	11
398	Nematode (Tylenchus polyhypnus)	39
399	Nematode, free-living (Cephalobus dubias)	0.4
400	Nematode, free-living (Diplogaster robustus)	0.04
401	Nematode, free-living (Pristionchus aerivora)	0.1
402	Nematode, free-living (Rhabditis elegans)	0.03
403	Nematode, trichinella (Trichinella spiralis)[18]	0.4
404	Nematode, trichinella cysts (T. spiralis)	30
	Acanthocephala	
405	Acanthocephalan, pig (Macracanthorhynchus hirudineceus)	1
	Gastrotricha	
406	Gastrotrich (Lepidodermella squamatum)	0.05
	Rotifera	
407	(Adinota barbata)	0.06
408	(A. vaga)	0.06
409	(Asplanchna sieboldii)	0.05
410	(Brachionus pala)	0.05
411	(Cupelopagis vorax)	0.1
412	(Ephines brachionus)	0.04
413	(E. senta)	0.02
414	(Euchlanis dilatata)	0.06
415	(E. triquetra)	0.06
416	(Floscularia conifera)	0.05
417	(Habrotrocha constricta)	0.09
418	(Keratella aculeata)	0.08
419	(Lecane inermis)	0.03
420	(Macrotrachela quadricornifera)	0.1
421	(Mniobia russeola)	0.08
422	(Philodina citrina)	0.06
423	(P. magalotrocha)	0.04
424	(P. roseola)	0.02
425	(Prales sordida)	0.02
426	(Proales decipiens)	0.03
427	(Rotaria macrura)	0.1
428	(R. rotatoria)	0.1
	Platyhelminthes	
	Turbellaria	
429	Flatworm (Planaria torva)	1.1
430	Worm, polyclad (Yungia aurantiaca)	1
	Cestoda	
431	Tapeworm, beef (Taenia saginata)[19]	0.09
432	Tapeworm, fish (Diphyllobothrium latum)[19]	0.09
433	Tapeworm, sheep (Moniezia expansa)	0.1
	Coelenterata	
	Hydrozoa	
434	Hydra, fresh-water (Hydra grisea)	1-2
	Scyphozoa	
435	Jelly-fish (Cotylorhiza tuberculata)	0.5-0.6
	Anthozoa	
436	Coral (Favites spp)	>22-28
437	Coral (Goniastrea spp)	>22-28
438	Coral (Montastrea spp)	>22-28
439	Coral (Pocillopora spp)	>22-28
440	Coral, solitary (Flabellum sp)	24
441	Sea-anemone (Actinia equina)	67
442	Sea-anemone (Cerianthus membranaceus)	40
443	Sea-anemone (Heliactis bellis)	20
444	Sea-anemone (Sagartia troglodytes)	50
	Porifera	
	Demospongiae	
445	Sponge, commercial (Hippospongia sp)	50
446	Sponge, siliceous (Axinella sp)	4
	Calcispongiae	
447	Sponge, calcareous (Scypha capillasa)	0.2
	Protozoa	
	Sarcodina	
448	(Elphidium crispum)	2-4
	Flagellata	
449	(Mastigamoeba sp)[20]	20
450	(Oikomonas sp)[20]	20
	Ciliata	
451	(Didnium nastum)[20]	10

/1/ Reported as not authenticated. /4/ Queen. /5/ Worker. /6/ Unfed female. /7/ Drone. /8/ Including developmental period. /9/ Family name. /10/ Larva. /11/ Normal strain. /12/ Vestigial strain. /13/ Three years as adult. /14/ Winter eggs. /15/ In dog. /16/ Desiccated in dry wheat gall. /17/ Desiccated in fig roots. /18/ Adults in guinea pigs. /19/ In man. /20/ Cysts.

Life span refers to age at natural death. There is great variation from the approximate ages given in table, and some individuals of each species live much longer than indicated.

Species	Life Span yr	Species	Life Span yr
Forest Trees, U.S.A.		**Forest Trees, U.S.A. (concluded)**	
1 Alaska-cedar (Chamaecyparis nootkatensis)	300-600	86 Persimmon (Diospyros virginiana)	60-80
2 Alder, red (Alnus rubra)	60-100	87 Pine, digger (Pinus sabiniana)	80-150
3 Ash, blue (Fraxinus quadrangulata)	200-300	88 Pine, eastern white (P. strobus)	300-500
4 Ash, Oregon (F. latifolia)	150-250	89 Pine, jack (P. banksiana)	80-150
5 Ash, white (F. americana)	260-300	90 Pine, jeffrey (P. jeffreyi)	300-500
6 Aspen, bigtooth (Populus grandidentata)	70-100	91 Pine, knobcone (P. attenuata)	100-150
7 Aspen, quaking (P. tremuloides)	70-100	92 Pine, limber (P. flexilis)	200-400
8 Baldcypress (Taxodium distichum)	600-1200	93 Pine, loblolly (P. taeda)	150-250
9 Basswood, American (Tilia americana)	100-140	94 Pine, lodgepole (P. contorta)	120-300
10 Beech, American (Fagus grandifolia)	300-400	95 Pine, longleaf (P. palustris)	300-400
11 Birch, gray (Betula populifolia)	50	96 Pine, pitch (P. rigida)	100-200
12 Birch, paper (B. papyrifera)	80-100	97 Pine, ponderosa (P. ponderosa)	300-500
13 Birch, sweet (B. lenta)	150-250	98 Pine, red (P. resinosa)	200-350
14 Birch, yellow (B. alleghaniensis)	150-300	99 Pine, shortleaf (P. echinata)	200-300
15 Buckeye, yellow (Aesculus octandra)	60-80	100 Pine, slash (P. elliottii)	150-250
16 Buckthorn, cascara (Rhamnus purshiana)	40-50	101 Pine, spruce (P. glabra)	75-150
17 Butternut (Juglans cinerea)	80	102 Pine, sugar (P. lambertiana)	300-600
18 California-laurel (Umbellularia californica)	200	103 Pine, Virginia (P. virginiana)	100-200
19 Catalpa, northern (Catalpa speciosa)	100	104 Pine, western white (P. monticola)	200-500
20 Cherry, black (Prunus serotina)	100-200	105 Pinyon (P. edulis)	150-400
21 Chestnut, American (Castanea dentata)	100-300	106 Pinyon, singleleaf (P. monophylla)	150-225
22 Chinkapin, golden (Castanopsis chrysophylla)	200-400	107 Poplar, balsam (Populus balsamifera)	100-150
23 Cottonwood, black (Populus trichocarpa)	150-200	108 Port-Orford-cedar (Chamaecyparis lawsoniana)	300-500
24 Cottonwood, eastern (P. deltoides)	60-100	109 Redcedar, eastern (Juniperus virginiana)	150-300
25 Cottonwood, plains (P. sargentii)	50-90	110 Redcedar, western (Thuja plicata)	500-800
26 Cucumbertree (Magnolia acuminata)	80-250	111 Redwood (Sequoia sempervirens)	800-1500
27 Cypress, Arizona (Cupressus arizonica)	100-300	112 Sassafras (Sassafras albidum)	100-500
28 Dogwood, Pacific (Cornus nuttallii)	125	113 Sequoia, giant (Sequoia gigantea)	2000-3000
29 Douglas-fir (Pseudotsuga menziesii)	300-700	114 Spruce, black (Picea mariana)	150-250
30 Elm, American (Ulmus americana)	150-300	115 Spruce, blue (P. pungens)	150-350
31 Elm, rock (U. thomasii)	250	116 Spruce, Engelmann (P. engelmannii)	200-500
32 Elm, slippery (U. rubra)	300	117 Spruce, red (P. rubens)	200-300
33 Fir, alpine (Abies lasiocarpa)	150-200	118 Spruce, Sitka (P. sitchensis)	400-750
34 Fir, balsam (A. balsamea)	100-150	119 Spruce, white (P. glauca)	150-350
35 Fir, California red (A. magnifica)	250-400	120 Sweetgum (Liquidambar styraciflua)	200-300
36 Fir, grand (A. grandis)	200-400	121 Sycamore, American (Platanus occidentalis)	250-500
37 Fir, noble (A. procera)	300-500	122 Tamarack (Larix laricina)	100-200
38 Fir, Pacific silver (A. amabilis)	250-300	123 Tanoak (Lithocarpus densiflora)	150-300
39 Fir, white (A. concolor)	150-400	124 Walnut, black (Juglans nigra)	150-250
40 Hackberry (Celtis occidentalis)	75-150	125 White-cedar, Atlantic (Chamaecyparis thyoides)	100-200
41 Hemlock, eastern (Tsuga canadensis)	300-600	126 White-cedar, northern (Thuja occidentalis)	300-400
42 Hemlock, mountain (T. mertensiana)	200-500	127 Willow, black (Salix nigra)	50-125
43 Hemlock, western (T. heterophylla)	300-600	128 Willow, peachleaf (S. amygdaloides)	50-100
44 Hickory, bitternut (Carya cordiformis)	175	129 Yellow-poplar (Liriodendron tulipifera)	200-250
45 Hickory, mockernut (C. tomentosa)	200-300	130 Yew, Pacific (Taxus brevifolia)	250-350
46 Hickory, pignut (C. glabra)	200-300	**Various Trees and Shrubs**	
47 Hickory, shagbark (C. ovata)	250-300	131 Alder, European (Alnus glutinosa)	100
48 Hickory, shellbark (C. laciniosa)	350	132 Barberry, European (Berberis vulgaris)	25
49 Hickory, water (C. aquatica)	125	133 Beech, European (Fagus sylvatica)	600
50 Holly, American (Ilex opaca)	100-150	134 Birch, European (Betula pubescens)	125
51 Honeylocust (Gleditsia triacanthos)	120	135 Buckthorn, European (Rhamnus cathartica)	100
52 Incense-cedar (Libocedrus decurrens)	300-400	136 Catalpa, southern (Catalpa bignonioides)	60
53 Juniper, alligator (Juniperus deppeana)	300-500	137 Cedar-of-Lebanon (Cedrus libanensis)	1200
54 Juniper, Rocky Mt. (J. scopulorum)	100-300	138 Cotoneaster, European (Cotoneaster integerrima)	15
55 Juniper, Utah (J. osteosperma)	150-300	139 Cypress, Italian (Cupressus sempervirens)	2000
56 Juniper, western (J. occidentalis)	300	140 Dogwood, bloodtwig (Cornus sanguinea)	50
57 Larch, western (Larix occidentalis)	300-600	141 Dogwood, Cornelian (C. mas)	300
58 Locust, black (Robinia pseudoacacia)	60-100	142 Elder, European (Sambucus nigra)	100
59 Magnolia, southern (Magnolia grandiflora)	80-120	143 Elder, European red (S. racemosa)	20
60 Maple, bigleaf (Acer macrophyllum)	150-300	144 Fig, religious (Ficus religiosa)	2000
61 Maple, red (A. rubrum)	80-250	145 Filbert, European (Corylus avellana)	150
62 Maple, silver (A. saccharinum)	50-125	146 Filbert, Turkish (C. colurna)	100
63 Maple, sugar (A. saccharum)	200-300	147 Hawthorn, English (Crataegus oxyacantha)	400
64 Mulberry, red (Morus rubra)	125	148 Honeysuckle, woodbine (Lonicera periclymenum)	40
65 Oak, black (Quercus velutina)	150-200	149 Hophornbeam, European (Ostrya carpinifolia)	100
66 Oak, blackjack (Q. marilandica)	100	150 Hornbeam, American (Carpinus caroliniana)	100
67 Oak, bur (Q. macrocarpa)	200-400	151 Hornbeam, European (C. betulus)	250
68 Oak, Calif. black (Q. kelloggii)	175-300	152 Juniper, common (Juniperus communis)	2000
69 Oak, Calif. live (Q. agrifolia)	150	153 Maple, Norway (Acer platanoides)	400
70 Oak, Calif. white (Q. lobata)	200-300	154 Mountain-ash, European (Sorbus aucuparia)	80
71 Oak, canyon live (Q. chrysolepis)	200-300	155 Pine, Austrian (Pinus nigra)	600
72 Oak, chestnut (Q. prinus)	300-400	156 Pine, Scotch (P. sylvestris)	500
73 Oak, live (Q. virginiana)	200-300	157 Pine, Swiss stone (P. cembra)	1200
74 Oak, northern red (Q. rubra)	200-400	158 Poplar, white (Populus alba)	300
75 Oak, overcup (Q. lyrata)	300-400	159 Rhododendron, garland (Rhododendron hirsutum)	50
76 Oak, pin (Q. palustris)	125-150	160 Rhododendron, rock (R. ferrugineum)	40
77 Oak, post (Q. stellata)	250	161 Service-tree (Sorbus domestica)	140
78 Oak, scarlet (Q. coccinea)	150	162 Service-tree (S. torminalis)	230
79 Oak, southern red (Q. falcata)	200-275	163 Spruce, Norway (Picea abies)	400
80 Oak, swamp chestnut (Q. michauxii)	100-200	164 Walnut, English (Juglans regia)	300
81 Oak, swamp white (Q. bicolor)	300	165 Willow, myrtle (Salix myrsinites)	100
82 Oak, water (Q. nigra)	175	166 Willow, white (S. alba)	150
83 Oak, white (Q. alba)	300-600	167 Wisteria, Chinese (Wisteria sinensis)	60
84 Osage-orange (Maclura pomifera)	75-100	168 Yew, English (Taxus baccata)	900
85 Pecan (Carya illinoensis)	300		

154. LIFE SPAN: POLLEN

#	Species	Temp. °C	Rel. Hum. %	Life Span[1] da	Germi-nation[2] %	#	Species	Temp. °C	Rel. Hum. %	Life Span[1] da	Germi-nation[2] %
	Field and Forage Crops						**Ornamental Plants (concluded)**				
1	Barley (Hordeum vulgare)	2.2[3]		19	41	36	Day lily (Hemerocallis flava)	17.5-21[4]	0[7]	29	
2	Bluegrass (Poa compressa)	17.5-21[4]		1		37	Deutzia (Deutzia scabra)	24[5]	Air dry	20	
3	Clover (Trifolium hybridum)	24[5]	Air dry	12		38	Gladiolus (Gladiolus hybrida)	10	50	100	30[13]
4	Corn (Zea mays)	5-10	50-70	3	70[6]	39	Iris (Iris pseudocorus)	24[5]	Air dry	28	
5	Cotton (Gossypium pima var.)	4.4-10		4[3]	64[6]	40	Lily (Lilium spp)	10	35-50	425	>45
6	Foxtail-grass (Alopecurus pratensis)	17.5-21[4]		2		41	Mockorange (Philadelphus floribundus)	24[5]	Air dry	32	
7	Hemp (Cannabis sativa)	17.5-21[4]	0[7]	8		42	Narcissus (Narcissus poeticus)	24[5]	Air dry	72	
8	Orchardgrass (Dactylis glomerata)	17.5-21[4]	30	3		43	Narcissus (N. pseudonarcissus)	24[5]	Air dry	80	
9	Rye (Secale cereale)	17.5-21[4]		0.5		44	Nasturtium (Tropaeolum majus)	17.5-21[4]	0[7]	88	
10	Ryegrass (Lolium perenne)	17.5-21[4]		1		45	Nicotiana (Nicotiana sylvestris)			205[14]	
11	Sweetclover (Melilotus alba)	17.5-21[4]	30	96		46	Poppy (Eschscholtzia californica)	17-22	0[9]	19	
	Fruit and Nut Crops					47	Poppy (Papaver rhoeos)	17.5-21[4]	0[7]	97	
12	Almond (Prunus amygdalus)	-18		1130	24	48	Primrose (Oenothera biennis)	17.5-21[4]	Air dry	8	
13	Apple (Pyrus malus)	2-8	50	1460	20	49	Primrose (Primula elatior)	17.5-21[4]	0[7]	180	
14	Apricot (Prunus armeniaca)	2-8	50	915	25	50	Rhododendron (Rhododendron spp)	24[5]	Air dry	42	
15	Avocada (Persea americana)[8]	15	0[9]	155		51	Snapdragon (Antirrhinum majus)	10-22		670	50[15]
16	Cherry, sour (Prunus cerasus)	2-8	50	1460	20	52	Stock (Matthiola spp)	5-10	0[7]	64	20
17	Cherry, sweet (P. avium)	-18		745	26	53	Sweetpea (Lathyrus odoratus)	24[4]	Air dry	23[6]	
18	Date (Phoenix dactylifera)	1.1[10]		275	87[6,11]	54	Tulip (Tulipa gesneriana)	17.5-21[4]	30	110	
19	Filbert (Corylus avellana)	17.5-21[4]	0[7]	65		55	Violet (Viola odorata)	17.5-21[4]	0[7]	235	
20	Grape (Vitis spp)[8]	-12	28	1460	6-21	56	Waterlily (Nymphaea alba)	17.5-21[4]	0[7]	35	
21	Grapefruit (Citrus paradisi)	10[12]		42	50		**Trees**				
22	Papaya (Carica papaya)	1.1	10	150	45	57	Basswood (Tilia platyphyllos)	17.5-21[4]	0[7]	16	
23	Peach (Prunus persica)	2-8	50	1100	1-20	58	Beech (Fagus sylvatica)	24[5]	Air dry	41	
24	Pear (Pyrus communis)	2-8	50	1280	20	59	Birch (Betula verrucosa)	24[5]		16	20
25	Pecan (Carya illinoensis)	5		4	40	60	Cinchona (Cinchona hybrida)	10	38	145	23[16]
26	Pistachio (Pistacia atlantica)	2.2	25	550	30	61	Ginkgo (Ginkgo biloba)	7	0[9]	365[6]	
27	Plum (Prunus domestica)	2-8	50	1280	20	62	Goldenchaintree (Laburnum anagyroides)	17.5-21[4]	30	260	
28	Quince (Cydonia oblonga)	2.2	25	550	54	63	Locust (Robinia pseudoacacia)	24[5]	Air dry	30	
29	Strawberry (Fragaria spp)	24[5]	Air dry	>16		64	Maple (Acer sp)	17-22	Air dry	18	
30	Walnut (Juglans sieboldiana)	0	40-60	255	12	65	Oak (Quercus coccinea)	2	25-35	365	46
	Ornamental Plants					66	Pine, red (Pinus resinosa)[17]	0-4	50	415	92[18]
31	Azalea (Rhododendron molle)	17.5-21[4]	30	175		67	Pine, Scotch (P. sylvestris)	17.5-21[4]	0[7]	280	
32	Bellflower (Campanula persicifolia)	24[5]	Air dry	21		68	Rubber-tree (Hevea sp)	6	67-80	19	
33	Buttercup (Ranunculus acris)	17.5-21[4]	0[7]	49		69	Spruce (Picea glauca)	2[19]	10-75	365	60
34	Camellia (Camellia japonica)	24[5]	Air dry	60		70	Tung oil tree (Aleurites fordii)	5[3]		24	>40
35	Cyclamen (Cyclamen persicum)	17-22	0[9]	185		71	Willow (Salix spp)	-3 to 3		50	2-10

/1/ Demonstrated viability in storage. /2/ Values are number of pollen grains germinating, expressed as percentages of total pollen grains tested at age specified under life span, unless otherwise indicated. Where no value is given data are not available. /3/ Flower spike or flower cut in early morning and kept under refrigeration. /4/ Average temperature for tests conducted during winter was 17.5°C; during summer, 21°C. /5/ Storage at room temperature. /6/ Data recorded on basis of seed or fruit set. /7/ Storage over concentrated sulfuric acid in desiccator. /8/ Horticultural varieties. /9/ Storage over calcium chloride in desiccator. /10/ Pollen stored in sealed or stoppered vial. /11/ At end of 365 days, 69%. /12/ Pollen stored under reduced pressure in evacuated and sealed tubes. /13/ Data recorded on basis of seed set per capsule. /14/ Sealed in ampules in vacuum or CO_2. /15/ Germination weak; no fruit set after storage of 161 days of 0°C. /16/ At end of 371 days, 6%. /17/ Data also applicable to white pine (P. strobus). /18/ Humidified at 75% relative humidity and 4°C for 12 hours after storage. /19/ Stored in darkness.

155. TEMPERATURE EFFECT ON LIFE SPAN: SEEDS
Seeds stored in sealed containers.

#	Species	Moisture Content[1] %	Median Life Span[2] yr at 24°C[4]	Maximum Life Span[3] yr at 24°C[4]	Median Life Span[2] yr at 5°C	Maximum Life Span[3] yr at 5°C	Median Life Span[2] yr at -4°C	Maximum Life Span[3] yr at -4°C
1	Ash (Fraxinus excelsior)	7	1	<2	7	<8		
2	Ash (F. pennsylvanica)	7	2	5	8	<9		
3	Aster (Callistephus chinensis)	7	2	3	10	12	>15	>15
4	Carrot (Daucus carota)	5	16	>20			>20	>20
5	Cauliflower (Brassica oleracea botrytis)	Air dry	>3	8				
6	Cinchona (Cinchona ledgeriana)	6	2	4	7	8	>9	>9
7	Cotton (Gossypium spp)	5	1	8	>13	>13	>13	>13
8	Dandelion (Taraxacum officinale)	6	6	>11	>14	>14	>14	>14
9	Eggplant (Solanum melongena)	5	18	>20			>20	>20
10	Elm (Ulmus americana)	7	2	4	8	10	15	>15
11	Fir (Abies grandis)	11	<1	<1	1	>10		>16
12	Fir (A. procera)	11	<1	1	1	>10		>16
13	Gladiolus (Gladiolus spp)	8	6	10	7	8	>10	>10
14	Grapefruit (Citrus paradisi)	60	<1	1	1	>1	<1	<1
15	Larkspur (Delphinium spp) Annual	Air dry	5	9	16	19	>18	>18
16	Perennial	Air dry	2	3	7	13	>18	>18
17	Lemon (Citrus limonia)	56	<1	<1	>1	>1	<1	<1
18	Lettuce (Lactuca sativa)	4	13	15			>20	>20
19	Lily (Lilium regale)	5	8	11	13	14	>17	>17
20	Onion (Allium cepa)	6	11	14			>20	>20
21	Pansy (Viola spp)	4	2	>3	3	4	>2	>2
22	Peony (Paeonia suffruticosa)	Air dry	<1	<1	3	8	5	7
23	Pepper (Capsicum frutescens)	5	8	12			>20	>20
24	Pine (Pinus caribaea)	Air dry	4	8	8	>8	>10	>10
25	Pine (P. echinata)	Air dry	1	2	11	>11	>12	>12
26	Pine (P. palustris)	Air dry	<1	<1	1	5	4	>6
27	Pine (P. taeda)	Air dry	1	2	10	>11	>12	>12
28	Spruce (Picea abies)	5					17	>17
29	Sweetpea (Lathyrus spp)	10	2	4	>3	>3		
30	Tomato (Lycopersicon esculentum)	5	17	>20			>20	>20
31	Venidium (Venidium spp)	5	>4	>4	>4	>4	>4	>4
32	Verbena (Verbena teucrioides)	6	3	6	9	13	>15	>15

/1/ At time of storage. /2/ Years for 50% seed survival. /3/ Maximum life span for a single seed. /4/ Temperature of laboratory, approximately 24°C.

Values are per 100 g of edible portion of fresh, uncooked food, unless otherwise specified. Values based on inadequate evidence are enclosed in parentheses.

Food	Water	Food Energy	Protein	Fat	Carbohydrate Total	Carbohydrate Fiber	Ash	Ca	Fe	P	Vitamin A	Ascorbic Acid	Niacin	Riboflavin	Thiamine
	g	Cal	g	g	g	g	g	mg	mg	mg	I. U.	mg	mg	mg	mg
1 Apple (Pyrus malus)	84.1	58	0.3	0.4	14.9	1.0	0.3	6	0.3	10	90	5	0.2	0.03	0.04
2 Apricot (Prunus armeniaca)	85.4	51	1.0	0.1	12.9	0.6	0.6	16	0.5	23	2790	7	0.8	0.05	0.03
3 Asparagus (Asparagus officinalis)	93.0	21	2.2	0.2	3.9	0.7	0.7	21	0.9	62	1000	33	1.4	0.19	0.16
4 Avocado (Persea gratissima)	65.4	245	1.7	26.4	5.1	1.8	1.4	10	0.6	38	290	16	1.1	0.13	0.06
5 Banana (Musa paradisiaca sapientum)	74.8	88	1.2	0.2	23.0	0.6	0.8	28	8	0.6	430	10	0.7	0.05	0.04
6 Barley, pearled, dry (Hordeum vulgare)	11.1	349	8.2	1.0	78.8	0.5	0.9	189	16	(2.0)	(0)	0	3.1	0.08	0.12
7 Bean, common, dried (Phaseolus vulgaris)	12.2	336	22.3	1.7	59.4	3.5	3.6	163	6.9	437	(0)	2	2.5	0.22	0.57
8 Bean, lima, immature (P. lunatus mac.)	66.5	128	7.5	0.8	23.5	1.5	1.7	63	2.3	158	280	32	1.4	0.11	0.21
9 Bean, lima, mature (P. lunatus macrocarpus)	12.6	333	20.7	1.3	61.6	4.3	3.8	68	7.5	381	0	2	2.0	0.18	0.48
10 Bean, snap, green and yellow (P. vulgaris)	88.9	35	2.4	0.2	7.7	1.4	0.8	65	1.1	44	630[1]	19	0.5	0.11	0.08
11 Beet, garden (Beta vulgaris)	87.6	42	1.6	0.1	9.6	0.9	1.1	27	1.0	43	20	10	0.4	0.05	0.02
12 Blackberry (Rubus spp)	84.8	57	1.2	1.0	12.5	4.2	0.5	32	0.9	32	200	21	0.4	0.04	0.04
13 Blueberry (Vaccinium corymbosum)	83.4	61	0.6	0.6	15.1	1.2	0.3	16	0.8	13	280	16	(0.3)	(0.02)	(0.02)
14 Brazil nut (Bertholletia excelsa)	5.3	646	14.4	65.9	11.0	2.1	3.4	186	3.4	693	Trace				0.86
15 Broccoli (Brassica oleracea botrytis)	89.9	29	3.3	0.2	5.5	1.3	1.1	130	1.3	76	3500	118	1.1	0.2	0.10
16 Brussels sprouts (B. oleracea gemmifera)	84.9	47	4.4	0.5	8.9	1.3	1.3	34	1.3	78	400	94	0.7	0.16	0.08
17 Cabbage (B. oleracea capitata)	92.4	24	1.4	0.2	5.3	1.0	0.8	46	0.5	31	80	50	0.3	0.05	0.06
18 Cantaloupe (Cucumis melo cantalupensis)	94.0	20	0.6	0.2	4.6	0.6	0.6	17	0.4	16	3420	33	0.5	0.04	0.05
19 Carrot (Daucus carota)	88.2	42	1.2	0.3	9.3	1.1	1.0	39	0.8	37	12000		0.5	0.06	0.06
20 Cauliflower (Brassica oleracea botrytis)	91.7	25	2.4	0.2	4.9	0.9	0.8	22	1.1	72	90	69	0.6	0.10	0.11
21 Celery (Apium graveolens)	93.7	18	1.3	0.2	3.7	0.7	1.1	50	0.5	40	0	7	0.4	0.04	0.05
22 Cherry, sour and sweet (Prunus spp)	83.0	61	1.1	0.5	14.8	0.3	0.6	18	0.4	20	620	8	0.4	0.06	0.05
23 Coconut (Cocos nucifera)	46.9	359	3.4	34.7	14.0	3.2	1.0	21	2.0	98	0	2	0.2	0.01	0.10
24 Collard (Brassica acephala)	86.6	40	3.9	0.6	7.2	1.2	1.7	249	1.6	58	6870	100	(2.0)	0.27	0.11
25 Corn, sweet, white and yellow (Zea mays)	73.9	92	3.7	1.2	20.5	0.8	0.7	9	0.5	120	390	12	1.7	0.12	0.15
26 Cranberry (Vaccinium macrocarpon)	87.4	48	0.4	0.7	11.3	1.4	0.2	14	0.6	11	40	12	0.1	(0.02)	(0.03)
27 Cucumber (Cucumis sativus)	96.1	12	0.7	0.1	2.7	0.5	0.4	10	0.3[2]	21	0[2]	8	0.2	0.04	0.03
28 Currant, red (Ribes rubrum)	84.4	55	1.2		13.6	4.0	0.6	36	0.9	33	120	36			0.04
29 Date, dried (Phoenix dactylifera)	20.0	284	2.2	0.6	75.4	2.4	1.8	72	2.1	60	60	(0)	2.2	0.10	0.09
30 Eggplant (Solanum melongena)	92.7	24	1.1	0.2	5.5	0.9	0.5	15	0.4	37	30	5	0.6	0.05	0.04
31 Fig, dried (Ficus carica)	24.0	270	4.0	1.2	68.4	5.8	2.4	186	3.0	111	80	(0)	1.7	0.12	0.16
32 Grape, American (Vitis spp)[3]	81.9	70	1.4	1.4	14.9	0.5	0.4	17	0.6	21	80	4	0.2	0.04	0.06
33 Grapefruit (Citrus paradisi)	88.8	40	0.5	0.2	10.1	0.2	0.4	22	0.2	18	Trace	40	0.2	0.02	0.04
34 Guava (Psidium guajava)	80.6	70	1.0	0.6	17.1	5.5	0.7	30	0.7	29	250	302	1.2	0.04	0.07
35 Kale (Brassica oleracea acephala)	86.6	40	3.9	0.6	7.2	1.2	1.7	225	2.2	62	7540	115	2.0	0.26	0.10
36 Lemon (Citrus limonia)	89.3	32	0.9	0.6	8.7	0.9	0.5	40	0.6	22	0	50	0.1	Trace	0.04
37 Lettuce (Lactuca sativa)	94.8	15	1.2	0.2	2.9	0.4	0.9	22	0.5	25	540	4	0.2	0.08	0.04
38 Mango (Mangifera indica)	81.4	66	0.7	0.2	17.2	1.0	0.5	9	0.3	13	6350	41	0.9	0.06	0.06
39 Mushroom (Agaricus campestris)	91.1	16	2.4	0.3	4.0	0.9	1.1	9	1.0	115	0	5	4.9	0.44	0.10
40 Mustard greens (Brassica japonica)	92.2	22	2.3	0.3	4.0	0.8	1.2	220	2.9	38	6460	102	0.8	0.20	0.09
41 Oats, rolled (Avena sativa)	8.3	390	14.2	7.4	68.2	1.2	1.9	53	4.5	405	(0)	(0)	1.0	0.14	0.60
42 Okra (Hibiscus esculentus)	89.8	32	1.8	0.2	7.4	1.0	0.8	82	0.7	62	740	30	1.1	0.07	0.08
43 Onion, immature, green (Allium cepa)	87.6	35	1.0	0.2	10.6	1.8	0.6	135	0.9	24	(50)	24	(0.2)	(0.04)	(0.03)
44 Onion, mature (A. cepa)	87.5	45	1.4	0.2	10.3	0.8	0.6	32	0.5	44	50	9	0.2	0.04	0.03
45 Orange (Citrus spp)	87.2	45	0.9	0.2	11.2	0.6	0.5	33	0.4	23	(190)	49	0.2	0.03	0.08
46 Papaya (Carica papaya)	88.7	39	0.6	0.1	10.0	0.9	0.6	20	0.3	16	1750	56	0.3	0.04	0.03
47 Parsnip (Pastinaca sativa)	78.6	78	1.5	0.5	18.2	2.2	1.2	57	0.7	80	0	18	0.2	0.12	0.08
48 Pea, garden, immature (Pisum sativum)	74.3	98	6.7	0.4	17.7	2.2	0.9	22	1.9	122	680	26	2.7	0.16	0.34
49 Pea, garden, mature, dried (P. sativum)	11.6	339	23.8	1.4	60.2	5.4	3.0	57	4.7	388	370	2	3.1	0.28	0.77
50 Peach (Prunus persica)	86.9	46	0.5	0.1	12.0	0.6	0.5	8	0.6	22	880	8	0.9	0.05	0.02
51 Peanut, roasted (Arachis hypogaea)	2.6	559	26.9	44.2	23.6	2.4	2.7	74	1.9	393	0	(0)	16.2	0.13	0.30
52 Pear (Pyrus communis)	82.7	63	0.7	0.4	15.8	1.4	0.4	13	0.3	16	20	4	0.1	0.04	0.02
53 Pecan (Carya illinoensis)	3.0	696	9.4	73.0	13.0	2.3	1.6	74	2.4	324	50	2	0.9	0.11	0.72
54 Pepper, green (Capsicum annuum)	92.4	25	1.2	0.2	5.7	1.4	0.5	11	0.4	25	630	120	0.4	0.07	0.04
55 Pineapple (Ananas sativus)	85.3	52	0.4	0.2	13.7	0.4	0.4	16	0.3	11	130	24	0.2	0.02	0.08
56 Plantain (Musa paradisiaca)	66.4	119	1.1	0.4	31.2	0.4	0.9	7	0.7	30	10[4]	14	0.6	0.04	0.06
57 Plum (Prunus spp)	85.7	50	0.7	0.2	12.9	0.5	0.5	17	0.5	20	350	5	0.5	0.04	0.06
58 Potato (Solanum tuberosum)	77.8	83	2.0	0.1	19.1	0.4	1.0	11	0.7	56	20	17[5]	1.2	0.04	0.11
59 Prune (Prunus spp)	24.0	268	2.3	0.6	71.0	1.6	2.1	54	3.9	85	1890	3	1.7	0.16	0.10
60 Pumpkin (Cucurbita pepo)	90.5	31	1.2	0.2	7.3	1.3	0.8	21	0.8	44	(3400)	9	(0.6)	(0.08)	(0.05)
61 Radish (Raphanus sativus)	93.6	20	1.2	0.1	4.2	0.7	1.0	37	1.0	31	30	24	0.3	0.02	0.03
62 Raisin (Vitis vinifera)	24.0	268	2.3	0.5	71.2	0.9	2.0	78	3.3	129	50	Trace	0.5	0.08	0.15
63 Rice, brown (Oryza sativa)	12.0	360	7.5	1.7	77.7	0.6	1.1	39	2.0	303	(0)	(0)	4.6	0.05	0.32
64 Rice, white (O. sativa)	12.3	362	7.6	0.3	79.4	0.2	0.4	24	0.8	136	(0)	(0)	1.6	0.03	0.07
65 Rutabaga (Brassica campestris)	89.1	38	1.1	0.1	8.9	1.3	0.8	55	0.4	41	330	36	0.9	0.08	0.07
66 Rye (Secale cereale)	11.0	321	12.1	1.7	73.4	2.0	1.8	(38)	3.7	376	(0)	(0)	1.6	0.22	0.43
67 Soybean, mature, dried (Glycine soja)	7.5	331	34.9	18.1	34.8	5.0	4.7	227	8.0	586	110	Trace	2.3	0.31	1.07
68 Soybean, sprouts (G. soja)	86.3	46	6.2	1.4	5.3	0.8	0.8	48	1.0	67	180	13	0.8	0.20	0.23
69 Spinach (Spinacia oleracea)	92.7	20	2.3	0.3	3.2	0.6	1.5	81	3.0	55	9420	59	0.6	0.20	0.11
70 Squash, summer (Cucurbita pepo)	95.0	16	0.6	0.1	3.9	0.5	0.5	15	0.4	15	260	17	0.8	0.09	0.05
71 Squash, winter (C. maxima)	88.6	38	1.5	0.3	8.8	1.4	0.8	19	0.6	28	4950	8	0.5	0.12	0.05
72 Strawberry (Fragaria spp)	89.9	37	0.8	0.5	8.3	1.4	0.5	28	0.8	27	60	60	0.3	0.07	0.03
73 Sweetpotato (Ipomoea batatas)	68.5	123	1.8	0.7	27.9	1.0	1.1	30	0.7	49	7700	22	0.6	0.05	0.09
74 Tangerine (Citrus reticulata)	87.3	44	0.8	0.3	10.9	1.0	0.7	(33)	(0.4)	(23)	(420)	31	(0.2)	(0.03)	0.07
75 Tomato (Lycopersicon esculentum)	94.1	20	1.0	0.3	4.0	0.6	0.6	11	0.4	27	1100	23	0.5	0.04	0.06
76 Turnip (Brassica rapa)	90.9	32	1.1	0.2	7.1	1.1	0.7	40	0.5	34	Trace	28	0.5	0.07	0.05
77 Turnip greens (B. rapa)	89.5	30	2.9	0.4	5.4	1.2	1.8	259	2.4	50	9540	136	0.8	0.46	0.09
78 Walnut, English (Juglans regia)	3.3	654	15.0	64.4	15.6	2.1	1.7	83	2.1	380	30	3	1.2	0.13	0.48
79 Watermelon (Citrullus vulgaris)	92.1	28	0.5	0.2	6.9	0.3	0.3	7	0.2	12	590	6	0.2	0.05	0.05
80 Wheat (Triticum aestivum)	12.5	330	12.3	1.8	71.7	2.3	1.7	46	3.4	354	(0)	(0)	4.3	0.12	0.52

/1/ For yellow varieties, 150 I. U. /2/ Applicable to pared cucumber; for unpared, 1.2 mg iron and 260 I.U. vitamin A. /3/ Data also applicable to European grapes with the following modifications; food energy, 66 cal.; protein, 0.8 g; fat, 0.4 g; ash, 0.5 g. /4/ Applicable to white varieties; for yellow varieties, 1200 I.U. /5/ Year-round average. Recently harvested potatoes, 24 mg; after storage of 3 mo, 12 mg; after storage of 6 mo, 8 mg.

157. FEEDS OF ANIMAL AND PLANT ORIGIN: COMPOSITION

Table adapted from "Composition of Concentrate By-product Feeding Stuffs." Preliminary Report, Agricultural Board, National Research Council, 1956.

Feeding Stuff	Dry Matter %	Crude Protein %	Ether Extract %	Crude Fiber %	Ash %	N-Free Extract %	Calcium %	Cobalt mg/lb	Copper mg/lb	Iron %	Magnesium %	Manganese mg/lb	Phosphorus %	Sulfur %	Carotene mg/lb	Niacin mg/lb	Pantothenic Acid mg/lb	Riboflavin mg/lb	Thiamine mg/lb
Concentrates: Animal Origin																			
1 Blood, dried	91.8	80.1	1.6	0.6	5.4	4.1	1.10	0.04	3.7	0.28	0.04	2.9	0.68	0.60		11.4	2.2	1.3	0.1
2 Blood flour	90.8	82.2	1.0	0.6	4.8	2.2	0.45		4.5	0.38	0.22	2.4	0.37	0.38		13.0	2.4	1.9	0.2
3 Blood meal	90.5	79.9	1.6	0.8	5.6	2.6	0.28	0.05	8.5		0.35	3.9	0.22	0.12		14.3	0.5	0.7	0.1
4 Bone meal, raw	93.2	26.2	4.6	1.4	57.8	3.2	22.14	0.03	7.4	0.08	0.61	13.8	10.35	0.22		1.9	1.0	0.6	0.2
5 Bone meal, steamed	95.2	12.1	3.2	1.7	71.8	6.4	28.98				0.73		13.59						
6 Bone meal, sterilized	96.6	6.5	0.6	0.6	82.8	6.1	35.20				0.49		14.81						
7 Bone meal, unspecified	97.2	13.0	2.7	2.1	76.3	3.1	30.10	0.03	8.9	0.06	0.48	5.4	13.89	0.49		1.9	1.1	0.3	0.1
8 Buttermilk, dried	92.5	32.0	5.8	0.4	9.6	44.7	1.34				0.02	1.6	0.94	0.08		2.0	1.4	14.1	1.6
9 Cheese rind	74.5	31.3	27.4	0.1	4.0	11.7	0.86				0.88		0.49						
10 Crab meal	92.7	31.1	1.8	10.8	40.7	8.3	15.32		14.9	0.44		60.8	1.59	0.32		3.9	13.7	2.7	
11 Cracklings, dried	92.5	56.9	10.9	1.4	22.8	0.5	7.40					6.5	4.13				3.0	1.8	
12 Fish liver oil meal, cod	91.3	51.3	26.5	0.4	4.1	9.0	0.17					2.7	0.75				20.9	15.1	8.2
13 Fish meal, cod	94.0	58.9	1.6	0.7	29.9	2.9	2.94		1.3	0.017		4.5	2.20			59.9		4.1	
14 Fish meal, herring	92.3	70.6	7.5	0.4	10.8	3.0	5.49	0.09	3.8	0.06		11.7	2.81			40.4	5.2	4.1	0.3
15 Fish meal, menhaden	92.2	61.3	7.7	0.7	19.6	2.9	5.44	0.03	5.4	0.02		3.6	3.26			25.4	3.1	2.2	0.4
16 Fish meal, salmon	93.0	58.0	9.6	0.8	16.7	8.4	4.90		9.2	0.03		10.1	2.77			11.3	4.2	2.6	0.2
17 Fish meal, sardine	93.2	65.5	4.3	1.1	15.4	6.9	6.06	0.05	6.9	0.04		10.8	3.52	0.25		28.2	4.1	2.7	0.6
18 Fish meal, unspecified	92.3	61.2	6.4	1.1	19.3	4.3	7.87				0.10	6.5	3.61			28.8	4.0	3.1	0.8
19 Fish meal, whitefish	91.6	63.2	4.4	0.7	21.7	1.6	2.17				0.22		1.77			31.7	26.1	4.1	
20 Fish solubles product, dried	91.1	51.9	5.9	3.4	10.5	19.4	0.50									100.4	20.5	2.0	0.1
21 Liver meal	92.6	66.5	15.1	1.6	6.0	3.7	0.66	0.06	40.5	0.06		4.0	1.25			92.9	48.2	21.0	1.2
22 Liver and glandular meal	93.4	65.1	16.0	1.6	5.8	4.9		0.09	44.1	0.05		3.3	1.14			73.4	2.2	18.5	0.1
23 Meat meal (meat scraps)	93.5	53.4	9.9	2.4	25.2	2.6	7.94	0.06	0.7	0.04	0.27	4.3	4.03	0.50		25.8	1.7	2.4	0.5
24 Meat meal, with bone	94.0	50.6	9.5	2.2	29.1	2.6	10.57	0.08		0.05	1.13	5.6	5.07			21.7	3.3	2.0	0.3
25 Milk albumin, dried	92.3	47.3	1.1	0.2	30.4	12.8	11.72		5.2	0.005	0.11	1.0	4.53			0.9	15.3	4.0	1.6
26 Milk, skimmed, dried	93.9	33.5	0.9	0.2	7.6	51.7	1.26	0.05	0.4	0.02		0.2	1.03	0.32		5.2	10.3	9.1	1.7
27 Milk, whole, dried	93.7	25.2	26.4	0.2	5.4	36.5	0.89			0.01		13.7	0.68		3.2	3.8		8.9	
28 Shrimp meal	90.2	47.4	3.1	11.2	26.6	1.9	7.35			0.01	0.54	3.9	1.59					1.8	
29 Tankage, digester, unspecified	92.5	52.9	9.1	1.9	26.8	1.8	7.34						3.73			17.8	1.1	1.1	0.2
30 Tankage, digester, with bone	94.1	49.6	11.9	2.5	26.3	3.3	10.97		10.6	0.04			5.14						
31 Whale meat meal	92.1	78.9	6.8	0.5	4.0	1.9	0.25						0.56			47.6	1.2	3.8	0.6
32 Whale meal, with bone	92.4	54.0	9.8	1.4	25.8	1.4	8.29						4.16						
33 Whey, whole, dried	93.5	13.1	0.8	0.2	9.7	69.7	0.89	0.05	23.9	0.02		2.4	0.73	1.04		5.5	22.2	13.1	1.6
34 Whey, dried, cheese	94.7	13.1	0.5	0.3	8.3	72.5												8.1	
Concentrates: Plant Origin																			
35 Apple pomace, dried	91.1	5.4	4.7	16.6	1.9	62.5	0.13			0.03	0.06	3.3	0.12	0.02					
36 Barley feed	90.3	12.6	3.0	8.2	3.6	62.9	0.06	0.00	4.3	0.01	0.16	13.9	0.43	0.05	0.2	28.9	3.5	1.0	2.7
37 Barley meal	90.8	14.7	1.0	2.4	5.5	67.2	0.05	0.05	5.7	0.01		7.7	0.70		0.1	16.6	6.6	1.8	2.1
38 Beet pulp, dried	90.8	9.1	0.6	19.4	3.6	58.1	0.68	0.03	9.7	0.03	0.27	15.9	0.10	0.20		7.4	0.7	0.7	0.2
39 Brewers grains, dried	92.4	25.9	6.2	14.5	3.6	42.2	0.27	0.08	15.0	0.01	0.14	17.1	0.50	0.31	0.0	19.7	3.9	0.7	0.3
40 Brewers yeast, dried	93.4	44.6	1.1	1.4	7.7	38.6	0.13		5.7	0.01	0.23	2.6	1.43	0.38		203.4	49.9	15.9	41.7
41 Buckwheat feed	94.4	16.7	4.0	14.3	4.5	54.9				0.02		37.1	0.48						
42 Citrus pulp, dried	90.1	6.6	4.6	13.0	6.0	59.9	1.96	0.08	2.6	0.02	0.16	3.1	0.12		0.1	9.8	5.9	1.1	0.7
43 Citrus seed meal	87.8	35.3	6.6	9.8	6.5	29.6	1.20		3.0	0.03	0.60	3.4	0.69						
44 Coconut oil meal, unspecified	91.2	20.6	7.5	11.7	6.4	45.0	0.18		4.3	0.68	0.36	34.3	0.61	0.34		17.5	2.4	1.9	0.5
45 Corn bran, unspecified	89.3	7.5	4.4	9.7	2.1	65.6	0.03				0.26	7.3	0.19	0.07				0.7	2.0
46 Corn distillers grains, dried	92.3	27.1	9.3	11.9	2.6	41.4	0.09	0.04	20.3	0.02	0.06	8.6	0.37	0.39	1.4	19.2	2.6	1.4	0.8
47 Corn meal, unspecified	87.8	9.0	3.6	1.6	1.2	72.4	0.02		1.4	0.004	0.11	2.8	0.24	0.08					
48 Corn oil meal, unspecified	90.9	21.5	3.7	11.2	1.9	52.6	0.09		5.0	0.02	0.28	4.1	0.56		0.2	24.1	1.6	2.5	3.2
49 Corn screenings	89.5	14.1	3.9	10.1	3.6	57.8													
50 Cottonseed feed	90.8	39.2	6.1	11.6	6.1	27.8	0.13				0.39		0.64	0.12				2.1	
51 Cottonseed flour	94.2	56.4	6.9	2.3	6.3	22.3	0.22									35.0			
52 Cottonseed hull bran	90.7	3.1	0.8	38.7	2.3	45.8	0.09	0.02	1.9	0.005		7.6	0.10			3.5		4.2	4.3
53 Cottonseed oil meal, unspecified	92.5	40.6	6.1	10.1	6.1	29.6	0.20	0.07	8.9	0.03	0.56	9.3	1.09	0.41	0.1	17.0	5.7	0.2	0.1
54 Distillers grains, dried	91.6	29.1	8.9	11.5	3.1	39.0	0.20	0.04	21.5	0.03	0.12	15.7	0.55	0.45	3.5	21.0	5.2	2.9	3.7
55 Flaxseed screenings	91.4	15.8	9.4	12.4	6.7	47.1	0.37						0.43					1.7	1.1

188

#	Feed	Dry matter	Protein	Fat	Fiber	Ash	N-free extract	Ca	P
56	Grapefruit pulp, dried	87.6	7.6	4.8	13.4	4.9	56.9	1.30	0.16
57	Linseed feed	90.5	33.8	4.8	9.5	6.0	36.4	0.43	0.65
58	Linseed oil meal, unspecified	90.0	35.2	5.5	7.8	5.5	36.7	0.35	0.85
59	Mustard seed oil meal	94.4	31.1	6.2	11.1	6.4	39.6	0.08	0.22
60	Oat feed	92.1	4.5	1.8	30.4	5.1	50.3	0.07	0.45
61	Oatmeal	90.7	16.1	1.8	3.0	2.2	63.1		0.10
62	Orange pulp, dried	89.3	7.0	8.3	9.6	4.4	66.5	0.63	0.56
63	Peanut oil meal, unspecified	93.5	42.6	5.2	11.0	5.2	26.4	0.16	0.11
64	Pineapple pulp, dried	89.1	4.2	1.5	17.0	3.1	63.3	0.21	
65	Potato meal, dehydrated	90.3	5.9	0.5	1.4	11.9	70.8		
66	Potato pomace, dried	88.6	7.7	0.4	6.1	4.2	70.2		
67	Rice bran, unspecified	90.6	13.5	15.1	10.9	10.9	40.2	0.06	1.82
68	Rice meal	91.5	8.3	1.0	4.6	0.6	76.5		0.26
69	Rice screenings	88.2	8.0	0.5	0.4	2.8	78.7	0.03	
70	Rice bran	90.0	16.5	2.0	3.3	2.6	65.4		
71	Rye distillers grains, dried	93.0	22.4	6.4	13.8	3.8	47.8	0.13	0.41
72	Rye feed	89.7	17.2	3.4	4.6	3.4	60.7	0.07	0.59
73	Rye middlings	89.8	17.1	3.1	5.8	4.7	60.4	0.06	0.63
74	Safflower oil meal, unspecified	91.8	21.4	3.9	32.3	11.8	29.5	0.37	0.92
75	Sesame oil meal, unspecified	93.3	41.3	8.4	6.1	3.0	25.7	2.07	1.38
76	Sorghum bagasse	92.5	3.5	1.3	28.5	1.3	56.2	0.04	0.31
77	Sorghum gluten meal, unspecified	90.1	41.7	4.3	3.0	2.2	39.8	0.04	0.27
78	Sorghum meal, milo sorghum	88.1	11.2	2.7	2.7	5.9	69.3	0.26	0.61
79	Soybean oil meal, unspecified	90.1	44.7	3.2	5.5	6.6	30.8	0.39	0.99
80	Sunflower oil meal, unspecified	91.6	43.9	2.3	13.6	4.2	25.2		
81	Tomato pomace, dried	92.0	21.7	13.0	29.0	6.1	24.1	0.28	0.57
82	Wheat bran, unspecified	89.1	16.0	4.1	9.9	2.1	53.0	0.14	1.17
83	Wheat flour	89.1	15.8	2.9	2.6	4.8	65.7	0.03	0.28
84	Wheat germ oil meal	89.7	27.3	9.1	2.6	5.2	45.9	0.07	1.06
85	Wheat mill feed (mixed feed)	89.9	15.3	4.0	8.2	3.2	57.2	0.09	1.02
86	Wheat screenings	89.3	15.0	3.0	6.5	4.4	61.6	0.08	0.36
87	Wheat standard middlings, unspecified	89.7	17.2	4.6	7.6	2.4	55.9	0.15	0.91
88	Wheat distillers grains, dried	93.0	33.8	5.8	12.4	2.4	38.6		0.50
89	Yeast distillers molasses, dried	94.5	24.0	0.6	7.4	14.0	48.5	0.10	
	Dry Roughages								
90	Alfalfa hay	90.5	14.8	2.0	28.9	8.2	36.6	1.47	0.24
91	Bluegrass hay, Kentucky	84.3	9.5	2.4	25.2	7.1	40.1	0.46	0.32
92	Brome hay, smooth	86.8	5.7	4.4	28.5	8.2	40.0	0.20	0.28
93	Brome grass hay	88.1	9.9	2.1	28.4	8.2	39.5		0.23
94	Clover hay, alsike	88.9	12.1	2.2	27.0	7.7	39.9	1.15	0.24
95	Clover hay, crimson	89.5	14.2	2.2	27.4	8.7	37.0	1.23	0.29
96	Clover hay, Ladino	88.0	19.4	3.2	20.7	9.8	34.9	1.32	0.29
97	Clover hay, red	88.1	11.8	2.6	27.2	6.4	40.1	1.35	0.19
98	Corn cobs	90.4	2.3	0.4	32.1	1.6	54.0	0.21	0.02
99	Corn fodder	82.6	6.8	2.1	21.8	5.2	46.7		0.14
100	Cowpea hay	90.4	18.6	2.6	23.3	11.3	34.6	1.37	0.29
101	Grass hay	89.9	6.7	1.8	28.9	7.6	44.9	0.48	0.21
102	Lespedeza hay, annual	89.2	12.7	2.4	26.7	5.2	42.2	0.98	0.18
103	Oat hay	88.1	8.2	2.7	28.1	6.9	42.2	0.21	0.19
104	Orchard grass hay	85.8	6.9	2.6	30.9	6.8	38.6	0.19	0.17
105	Prairie hay	90.7	5.7	2.3	30.4	7.4	44.9	0.36	0.18
106	Redtop hay	90.7	8.5	3.4	26.8	4.3	47.7	0.38	0.23
107	Sorghum fodder, sweet	88.8	6.2	3.3	25.0	6.2	48.1	0.34	0.12
108	Soybean hay	88.0	14.4	1.6	27.5	8.7	35.8	1.35	0.25
109	Sudan grass hay	89.3	8.8	1.6	27.9	8.1	42.9	0.36	0.26
110	Sweet clover hay	92.2	15.8	1.6	24.7	10.8	39.3	1.25	0.23
111	Timothy hay	89.0	6.5	2.4	30.2	4.9	45.0	0.23	0.20
112	Vetch hay, common	85.2	18.7	1.8	22.2	7.8	34.7	1.13	0.32
113	Wheat hay	90.4	6.1	1.8	26.1	6.4	50.0	0.14	0.18
	Silages								
114	Alfalfa	25.3	4.6	0.9	8.2	2.3	9.3	0.35	0.08
115	Corn	23.8	1.8	0.7	6.4	1.5	13.4	0.10	0.06
116	Grass	24.3	3.1	0.8	7.3	2.6	10.5		

Values are per 100 grams of edible portion of fresh, uncooked food, unless otherwise specified. Values based on inadequate evidence are enclosed in parentheses.

Food	Water g	Food Energy Cal	Protein g	Fat g	Carbohydrate Total g	Carbohydrate Fiber g	Ash g	Ca mg	Fe mg	P mg	Vitamin A I.U.	Ascorbic acid mg	Niacin mg	Riboflavin mg	Thiamine mg
Dairy Products															
1 Butter	15.5	716	0.6	81	0.4	0	2.5	20	0	16	3300[1]	0	0.1	0.01	Trace
2 Buttermilk	90.5	36	3.5	0.1	5.1	0	0.8	(118)	0.1	93	Trace	1	0.1	0.18	0.04
3 Cheese: Cheddar	37	398	25.0	32.2	2.1	0	3.7	725	1.0	495	1400	(0)	Trace	0.42	0.02
4 Cottage	76.5	95	19.5	0.5	2.0	0	1.5	96	0.3	189	(20)	(0)	(0.1)	0.31	0.02
5 Cream	51	371	9.0	37.0	2.0	0	1.0	68	0.2	97	(1450)	(0)	0.1	0.22	(0.01)
6 Swiss	39	370	27.5	28.0	1.7	0	3.8	925	0.9	563	1450	(0)	(0.1)	0.40	0.01
7 Cream, light	72.5	204	2.9	20.0	4.0	0	0.6	97	0.1	77	830	1	0.1	0.14	0.03
8 Milk, cow: whole	87	68	3.5	3.9	4.9	0	0.7	118	0.1	93	(160)	1	0.1	0.17	0.04
9 Skimmed	90.5	36	3.5	0.1	5.1	0	0.8	123	0.1	97	Trace	1	0.1	0.18	0.04
10 Milk, goat	87.4	67	3.3	4.0	4.6	0	0.7	129	0.1	106	(160)	1	0.3	0.11	0.04
Meats															
11 Beef: chuck	65	224	18.6	16	0	0	0.9	11	2.8	167	(0)	0	4.5	0.17	0.08
12 Flank	61	247	19.9	18	0	0	0.9	12	3.0	186	(0)	0	4.8	0.18	0.09
13 Hamburger	55	321	16.0	28	0	0	0.8	9	2.4	128	(0)	0	3.8	0.14	0.07
14 Heart	77.6	108	16.9	3.7	0.7	0	1.1	9	4.6	203	30	6	7.8	0.89	0.58
15 Kidney	74.9	141	15.0	8.1	0.9	0	1.1	9	7.9	221	1150	13	6.4	2.55	0.37
16 Liver	69.7	136	19.7	3.2	6.0	0	1.4	7	6.6	358	43,900	31	13.7	3.33	0.26
17 Porterhouse	58	296	16.4	25	0	0	0.8	10	2.5	134	(0)	0	3.9	0.15	0.07
18 Rib roast	59	282	17.4	23	0	0	0.8	10	2.6	149	(0)	0	4.2	0.15	0.07
19 Round	69	182	19.5	11	0	0	1.0	11	2.9	180	(0)	0	4.7	0.17	0.08
20 Rump	55	322	16.2	28	0	0	0.8	9	2.4	131	(0)	0	3.9	0.14	0.07
21 Sirloin	62	254	17.3	20	0	0	0.9	10	2.6	147	(0)	0	4.2	0.15	0.07
22 Tongue	68	207	16.4	15.0	0.4	(0)	0.9	9	2.8	187	(0)	(0)	5.0	0.29	0.12
23 Brains	78.9	125	10.4	8.6	0.8	0	1.4	16	3.6	330	0	18	4.4	0.26	0.23
24 Lamb: leg roast	63.7	235	18.0	17.5	0	0	0.9	10	2.7	213	(0)	0	5.2	0.22	0.16
25 Liver	70.8	136	21.0	3.9	2.9	0	1.4	8	12.6	364	50,500	33	16.9	3.28	0.40
26 Kidney	77.8	105	16.6	3.3	1.0	0	1.3	13	9.2	237	(1150)	13	7.4	2.42	0.51
27 Shoulder roast	58.3	295	15.6	25.3	0	0	0.8	9	2.3	155	(0)	0	4.5	0.19	0.14
28 Pork: bacon	20	630	9.1	65	1.1	0	4.3	13	0.8	108	(0)	0	1.9	0.12	0.38
29 Ham, fresh	53	344	15.2	31.0	0	0	0.8	9	2.3	168	(0)	0	4.0	0.18	0.74
30 Ham, smoked	42	389	16.9	35.0	(0.3)	0	5.4	10	2.5	136	(0)	0	4.0	0.19	0.70
31 Heart	76.8	117	16.9	4.8	0.4	0	1.1	35	2.7	132	30	6	6.0	1.24	0.43
32 Kidney	77.1	114	16.3	4.6	0.8	0	1.2	11	8.0	246	130	13	9.8	1.74	0.58
33 Liver	72.3	134	19.7	4.8	1.7	0	1.5	10	18.0	362	14,200	23	16.7	2.98	0.40
34 Loin or chops	58	296	16.4	25	0	0	0.9	10	2.5	186	(0)	0	4.3	0.19	0.80
35 Salt pork, fat	8	783	3.9	85	0	(0)	3.5	Trace	0.6	Trace	(0)	0	(0.9)	(0.04)	(0.18)
36 Sausage	41.9	450	10.8	44.8	0	0	2.1	6	1.6	100	(0)	0	2.3	0.17	0.43
37 Spare rib, medium	53	351	14.6	32	0	0	0.8	8	2.2	158	(0)	0	3.8	0.17	0.71
38 Rabbit, domesticated	54	122	16	6	0	0	0.8	15	1.0	271			9.9	0.04	0.06
39 Seal, canned	66	183	19.1	10.6	1.4				11.4				4.9	0.09	0.04
40 Veal: cutlet	70	164	19.5	9.0	0	0	1.0	11	2.9	200	(0)	0	6.5	0.26	0.14
41 Leg roast	68	186	19.1	12.2	0	0	1.0	11	2.9	206	0	0	6.3	0.27	0.17
42 Liver	71	141	19.0	4.9	4	0	1.3	6	10.6	343	22,500	36	16.1	3.12	0.21
43 Shoulder roast	70	173	19.4	10.0	0	0	1.0	11	2.9	199	(0)	0	6.5	0.26	0.14
44 Stew meat	64	231	18.3	17.0	0	0	0.9	11	2.7	182	(0)	0	6.1	0.24	0.13
45 Venison	73	140	20	6.0	0	0	1.0	12	3.0	216					0.14
Poultry and Eggs															
46 Chicken: broiler	71.2	151	20.2	7.2	0	0	1.1	14	1.5	200	(0)	(0)	10.2	0.16	0.08
47 Heart	69.6	157	20.5	7.0	1.6	0	1.3	23	1.7	142	30	6	5.2	0.91	0.12
48 Liver	69.6	141	22.1	4.0	2.6	0	1.7	16	7.4	240	32,200	20	11.8	2.46	0.20
49 Roaster	66.0	200	20.2	12.6	0	0	1.0	14	1.5	200	(0)	(0)	8.0	0.16	0.08
50 Egg, whole	74.0	162	12.8	11.5	0.7	0	1.0	54	2.7	210	1140	0	0.1	0.29	0.10
51 Egg white	87.8	50	10.8	0	0.8	0	0.6	6	0.2	17	(0)	0	0.1	0.26	0
52 Egg yolk	49.4	361	16.3	31.9	0.7	0	1.7	147	7.2	586	3210	0	Trace	0.35	0.27
53 Duck	54	326	16.1	29	0	0	1.3	9	2.4	172	0	0	6.0	0.23	0.16
54 Goose	50	354	16.4	32	0	0	0.9	9	2.4	176		9	5.6		0.15
55 Squab	58	279	18.6	22.1	0	0	1.5	12	3.0	217					
56 Turkey	58.3	268	20.1	20.2	0	0	1.0	23	3.8	320	Trace	(0)	8.0	0.14	0.09
Fish and Shellfish															
57 Bluefish	74.6	124	20.5	4.0	0	0	1.2	23	0.6	243			1.9	(0.09)	(0.12)
58 Clam	80.3	81	12.8	1.4	3.4		2.1	(96)	(7.0)	(139)	110		(1.6)	0.18	0.10
59 Cod	82.6	74	16.5	0.4	0	0	1.2	10	0.4	194	0	2	2.2	0.09	0.06
60 Crab	80.0	86	16.1	1.6	0.6		1.7	(39)	(0.8)	(160)			2.7	0.06	0.14
61 Eel	71.6	162	18.6	9.1	0	0	1.0	18	0.7	202	1800		1.4	0.37	0.28
62 Flounder	82.7	68	14.9	0.5	0	0	1.3	61	0.8	195			1.7	0.05	0.06
63 Haddock	80.7	79	18.2	0.1	0	0	1.4	23	0.7	197			2.4	0.08	0.05
64 Halibut	75.4	126	18.6	5.2	0	0	1.0	13	0.7	211	440		9.2	0.06	0.07
65 Herring, Atlantic	67.2	191	18.3	12.5	0	0	2.7		1.1	256	110		3.4	0.15	0.02
66 Herring, Pacific	79.6	94	16.6	2.6	0	0	1.3				100		(2.2)	0.22	0.02
67 Lobster	79.2	88	16.2	1.9	0.5	0	2.2	61	0.6	184			(1.9)	0.06	(0.13)
68 Mackerel	68.1	188	18.7	12.0	0	0	1.2	5	1.0	239	(450)		8.4	0.35	0.15
69 Oyster	80.5	84	9.8	2.1	5.6	0	2.0	94	5.6	143	320		1.2	0.20	0.15
70 Perch, yellow	80	88	18.7	0.9	0	0	1.2	20	1.0	215			1.7	0.07	0.09
71 Salmon	63.4	223	17.4	16.5	0	0	1.0		(0.9)	(289)	310	9	7.2	0.23	0.10
72 Sardine, canned	57.4	214	25.7	11.0	1.2	0	(4.7)	386	2.7	586	220	(0)	4.8	0.17	0.02
73 Scallop	80.3	78	14.8	0.1	3.4	0	1.4	26	1.8	208	0		1.4	0.10	(0.04)
74 Shad	70.2	168	18.7	9.8	0	0	1.4		0.5	260			(8.4)	0.24	(0.15)
75 Shrimp, canned	66.2	127	26.8	1.4	0	0	5.8	115	3.1	263	60	(0)	2.2	0.03	0.01
76 Swordfish	75.8	118	19.2	4.0	0	0	1.3	19	0.9	195	1580		9.1	0.05	0.05
77 Tuna, canned	60.0	198	29.0	8.2	0	0	2.7	(8)	1.4	(351)	80	(0)	12.8	0.12	0.05
78 Whitefish	70	156	22.9	6.5	0	0	1.6	25	1.3	263			(4.2)	(0.09)	(0.09)

/1/ Year-round average.

159. FERTILIZERS: CHEMICAL ELEMENT COMPOSITION AND NEUTRALIZING ACTION

Values are g per 100 g of fertilizers, and where composition of fertilizer material is variable, they are averages of several determinations for total element present (cf Fn 2 for exceptions in case of phosphorus and potassium).

Fertilizer Materials	Ca	Mg	N	P[2]	K[2]	S	Action
Inorganic Fertilizers							
N Materials							
1 Ammonia, anhydrous			82				Acidic
2 Ammonia solution[3]			21-25				Acidic
3 Ammonium chloride			24				Acidic
4 Ammonium nitrate			32-34				Acidic
5 Ammonium sulfate			20			24	Acidic
6 Calcium ammonium nitrate (A.N.L.)	7.1-14	0-4.5	20				Neut.
7 Calcium cyanamide[4]	39		21			0.4	Basic
8 Calcium nitrate	20		16				Basic
9 Calcium nitrate-urea[5]	9.3		34				Acidic
10 Sodium nitrate			16				Basic
11 Urea (Uramon)			42-46				Acidic
12 Urea-ammonia liquor			46				Acidic
P Materials							
13 Basic slag, Bessemer	34	2.4		7		0.2	Basic
14 Basic slag, open-hearth	32	3		2.2-6.5		0.2	Basic
15 Phosphate rock, defluorinated	20-30			7.9-10			Basic
16 Phosphoric acid, liquid				24		1.4[6]	Acidic
17 Superphosphate, double	12-14	0.3		19-21		1	Neut.
18 Superphosphate, ordinary	18-21	0.3		6.1-8.7		11-12	Neut.
K Materials							
19 Alunite, calcined	2.9	0.3			4.6	2	
20 Kainite	0.4-3.6	0-9			10-18	0.4-10	Neut.
21 Manure salts	0-0.7	0-3.6			21-33	0-5.2	Neut.
22 Potassium carbonate					54	0.2	Basic
23 Potassium chloride	0-2.1	0-1.8			40-51	0-2.8	Neut.
24 Potassium magnesium sulfate	0-4.6	3.6-12			17-25	13-22	Neut.
25 Potassium sulfate	0-1.8	0-1.2			40-43	16-19	Neut.
N-P, N-K Materials							
26 Ammoniated superphosphate, double	12-14	0.3	4-6	18-21		1	Acidic
27 Ammoniated superphosphate, ordinary	17-21	0.3	2-5	5.9-8.5		11-12	Acidic
28 Monoammonium phosphate[7,8]	1.1	0.3	11	21		2.4	Acidic
29 Monoammonium phosphate-ammonium sulfate[7,9]	0.4		16	8.7		15	Acidic
30 Urea-superphosphate			7	6.5			Acidic
31 Potassium ammonium chloride[10]			13		18		Acidic
32 Potassium nitrate	0.4	0.3	13		37		Basic
33 Sodium potassium nitrate			15		12		Basic
N-P-K, P-K Materials							
34 Ammonium potassium phosphate			5.5	24	15		Acidic
35 Monopotassium phosphate				23	29		Neut.
36 Potassium metaphosphate	0.4			24	32		Neut.
Organic Fertilizers							
Animal By-products							
37 Blood, dried	0.4		13	0.9	0.8		Acidic
38 Bone meal, raw	22	0.6	4	9.8		0.2	Basic
39 Bone meal, steamed	24	0.3	2.5	11		0.2	Basic
40 Fish scrap or meal, dried	6.1	0.3	9.5	3.1		0.2	Acidic
41 Hoof and horn meal	1.8		14	0.4		0.8	Acidic
42 Tankage, animal	11	0.3	7	4.4	0.4	0.4	Basic
43 Tankage, process	0.4		9	0.2		0.4	Acidic
44 Whale guano or tankage	6.4	0.3	9.5	2.8			Acidic
45 Wool waste	0.4		3.5	0.2	1.7		
Animal Excreta							
46 Guano, bat	5.4	0.3	8.5	2.2	1.2	0.8	Acidic
47 Guano, Peruvian	7.9	0.6	13	5.2	2.1	1.4	Acidic
48 Manure, cattle	2.9	0.6	2	0.7	1.7	0.2	Basic
49 Manure, horse	1.1	0.6	2	0.7	1.2	0.2	Basic
50 Manure, poultry	2.9	0.6	5	1.3	1.2	0.8	Acidic
51 Manure, sheep	3.6	1.2	2	0.7	2.5	0.6	Basic
52 Sewage sludge, activated	1.8	0.9	6	1.3	0.4	0.4	Acidic
53 Sewage sludge, dried	1.8	0.3	2	0.9		0.2	Acidic
Plant Residues							
54 Castor pomace	0.4	0.3	5.5	0.7	1.2		Acidic
55 Cocoa shell meal	1.1	0.3	2.5	0.4	1.7		Basic
56 Cottonseed hull, ash	6.8	3		2.4	22	1	Basic
57 Cottonseed meal	0.4	0.3	7	1.3	1.7	0.2	Acidic
58 Garbage tankage	3.2	0.3	2.5	1.3	0.8	0.4	Basic
59 Kelp, Pacific	1.1	0.6	2.5	0.7	12	1	
60 Linseed meal	0.4	0.6	5.5	0.9	1.2	0.4	
61 Peat, moisture-free	0.7	0.3	2			0.2	Acidic[11]
62 Seaweed	2.1	0.6	1.5	0.2	1.7	1.4	
63 Soybean meal	0.4	0.3	7	0.7	2.1	0.2	Acidic
64 Tobacco, ash	16	3.6		1.3	19		Basic
65 Tobacco stems	3.6	0.3	2	0.2	5	0.4	Basic
66 Wood ash, commercial	23	2.1		0.9	4.2	0.4	Basic

/1/ For conversion of values for elements to those for commonly used oxides of the elements, the following factors are employed: Ca x 1.399 = CaO, Mg x 1.658 = MgO, P x 2.291 = P_2O_5, K x 1.205 = K_2O; S x 2.497 = SO_3. /2/ Values for phosphorus (from inorganic fertilizers) are applicable to available phosphorus, i.e., amount of phosphorus soluble in water or in solutions of salts or acids. Values for potassium (from inorganic fertilizers) are applicable to water-soluble potassium. /3/ Includes ammonium hydroxide, aqua ammonia, ammonia liquor, "B" liquor. /4/ Also known as Cyanamid, Nitrolime. /5/ Also known as Calurea. /6/ Sulfate content arises from H_2SO_4 process used in production of P_2O_5. /7/ Data applicable to material prepared with P_2O_5 manufactured by the H_2SO_4 process. Material made with electric furnace P_2O_5 has higher purity. /8/ Also known as Ammo-Phos A. /9/ Also known as Ammo-Phos B. /10/ Also known as Potazote. /11/ Some peats may be basic.

Nutrients are especially sensitive to the reaction (pH) of the solvent, and to exposure to air, light and heat. Unless otherwise specified, reference is made to the properties of the nutrient in aqueous solution. Where no footnote is given, the stability of the nutrient is estimated on the basis of its chemical composition, or other well-known properties.

S = stable, i.e., nutrient exhibits no appreciable breakdown under the conditions specified. L = labile, i.e., nutrient exhibits appreciable decomposition under the conditions specified. +++ = appreciable loss; + = slight loss.

	Nutrient	pH7	<pH7	>pH7	Oxygen	Light	Heat	% Loss in Cooking[1]		Nutrient	pH7	<pH7	>pH7	Oxygen	Light	Heat	% Loss in Cooking[1]
	Vitamins									Vitamins (concluded)							
1	A	S[2]			L[2]	L	S[2]	10-30	15	Riboflavin	S[20]	S[21]	L	S[21]	L[22]	S[20]	0-48
2	Ascorbic acid	L[3]	S[3]	L[3]	L[3]	L[3]	L[3]	20-80	16	Thiamine	L[23]	S[24]	L[25]	L[26]	S[24]	L[23,25]	25-45
3	Biotin	S	S	S	S	S	S	0-72	17	Unsaturated fatty acids	S	S	L	L[27]	L[27]	S	<10
4	Choline	S	S	S	L	S	S			Amino acids[28]							
5	Cobalamin	S[4]	S[4]	S[4]	L	L	S[4]		18	Isoleucine	S	S	S	S	S	S	+
6	D2[5]	S		L	L[6]	L[6]	L	+++	19	Leucine	S	S	S	S	S	S	+
7	E	S	S	L	L[7]	L[8]	S[7]	50[9]	20	Lysine	S	S	S	S	S	S	+
8	Folic acid group	L	L[10]	S[10,11]	L[11]	L[12]	S[10]	0-97	21	Methionine	S	S	S	S	S	S	+
9	Inositol	S	S[13]	S	S	S	S[13]	0-95	22	Phenylalanine	S	S	S	S	L[29]	S	+
10	K	S	S	L[14]	S	L	S		23	Threonine	S	S	L	S	S	S	+
11	Niacin[15]	S	S	S	S	S	S	0-72	24	Tryptophan	S	L	S	S	L[29]	S	+
12	Pantothenic acid	S	L	L	S	S	L	0-44	25	Valine	S	S	S	S	S	S	+
13	p-Aminobenzoic acid	S	S[16]	S[17]	L	S	S		26	Inorganic salts	S	S	S	L[30]	S	S	+
14	Pyridoxine group	S[18]	S[18]	S[18]	S[19]	L	S[18]										

/1/ Nutrient loss expressed as percentage of quantity of nutrient present before cooking. /2/ Loses biological activity if heated in presence of oxygen for 5.5 hours. /3/ Decomposes in light; decomposition accelerated by oxygen, metal ions. /4/ Stable in boiling water at pH 7 for 2 hours. /5/ Stable in dry propylene glycol more than three years when stored in amber bottles. /6/ Activity lost in mixed feeds, also under prolonged irradiation in presence of oxygen. /7/ In absence of oxygen, stable to heat up to 200°C. /8/ Tocopherols stable to visible light, but readily destroyed by UV. /9/ Deep fat frying and baking result in appreciable destruction. /10/ No destruction at pH 6.8 and 100°C for 30 minutes. /11/ Aeration at pH 10 causes partial inactivation. /12/ Rapidly inactivated by light. /13/ Stable to refluxing with 10% HCl for 6 hours, to alkali and to a variety of chemical agents. /14/ Sensitive to alkali. /15/ Nicotinamide is partially hydrolyzed by alkali and acid, but the product, nicotinic acid, having the same vitamin activity as nicotinamide retains its biological activity. /16/ Only 15% destruction on autoclaving solutions in 6N H_2SO_4 for 60 minutes. /17/ Long treatment with alkali results in destruction. /18/ Pyridoxine not destroyed by heating with 5N acid or alkali at 100°C, or autoclaving in acid or alkali; pyridoxal and pyridoxamine stable in hot acid, but pyridoxal partially decomposed by hot alkali. /19/ Oxidized only by such strong agents as hot HNO_3, H_2O_2. /20/ Stable in neutral or acid solutions. /21/ 1/2% decomposed per month at pH 5.0 at 27°C. /22/ 50% of the riboflavin of milk destroyed when exposed to sunlight for 2 hours. /23/ 96.4% destroyed at 100°C at pH 7 in 3 hours. /24/ No destruction in 1% HCl in 7 hours at 100°C. /25/ 100% destroyed in 15 minutes at pH 9 at 100°C. /26/ Unstable in presence of air. /27/ Sensitive to light and air oxidation. /28/ Most amino acids undergo racemization in alkaline solutions, but they are otherwise stable. /29/ Modified by UV. /30/ Oxidation of some inorganic salts of lower valence to higher valence states (e.g., ferrous to ferric iron) when exposed to atmospheric oxygens.

161. NUTRIENT LOSSES IN COOKING

Values are rough appoximations of the percentage of nutrients lost in various types of cooking. I = baking; II = boiling; III = braising; IV = broiling; V = double boiler; VI = pressure saucepan; VII = roasting; VIII = steaming; IX = stewing; X = discarding water or drippings; XI = retaining water or drippings; XII = mashed; XIII = frying.

	Food Type	Cooking Method	Ca	Fe	P	A	C	Niacin	Riboflavin	Thiamine		Food Type	Cooking Method	Ca	Fe	P	A	C	Niacin	Riboflavin	Thiamine
1	Cabbage[2,3]	II;XI					10	25	1		22	Potatoes[2] (concluded)	II;XI						15		
2		II;X					40	25	15		23		II;X	15	10	0		20	20	25	20
3		VI					30				24		XII					50			
4		VIII					50		20		15	25		VI					30	0	5	5
5	Cereals[4]	V;15 min						0	0	0	26		VIII					15			
6		V;30 min						0	0	2	27	Roots and bulbs[2,9]	II;XI				5	10	15	15	
7		V;120 min						0	0	8	28		II;X	1	5	0		65	35		
8	Corn[2]	II					35	15	10	20	29		VI	25	5	15					
9	Flowers and shoots[2,5]	II;XI				0	10	15		1	30		VIII				5	50	40	0	25
10		II;X	20	5	15	0	30	25	35	40	31	Squash[2]	VIII					55			50
11		VI					30				32	Meats[10]	III;XI						10	5	40
12		VIII				0	25	15	15	15	33		III;X						35	25	55
13	Leafy[2,6]	II;XI					25	20	10	5	34		IV;XI						5	10	25
14		II;X	20	5	15		50	25	30	30	35		IV;X						20	20	30
15		VI					50				36		VII;XI						5	10	30
16		VIII					60	10	15	15	37		VII;X						20	15	40
17	Legumes, fresh[2,7]	II;XI					5	5	0	10	38		IX;XI						0	0	50
18		II;X	0	1	5	15	40	20	20	20	39		IX;X						50	30	75
19		VIII				10	15	0	5	5	40	Fish[10]	XIII						5	10	
20	Potatoes[2]	I					25				41		VIII						5	0	
21		II[8]					0														

/1/ Loss of water soluble vitamins increases in proportion to amount of cooking water used. /2/ Cooked immediately, without standing after preparation. /3/ Also Brussels sprouts. /4/ Rolled oats. /5/ Asparagus, broccoli, cauliflower. /6/ Kale, spinach, Swiss chard. /7/ Beans, peas. /8/ Boiled in jackets. /9/ Beets, carrots, onions, parsnips, turnips. /10/ Unspecified.

Item	Food Energy Cal	Protein g	Fat g	Carbo-hydrate g	Calcium mg	Iron mg	Vitamin A I.U.	Thiamine mg	Ribo-flavin mg	Niacin mg	Ascorbic Acid mg
1 Meat, poultry, fish	920	63	70.9	0.3	60	9.1	1600	0.99	0.83	18.9	3
2 Meat	1050	64	84.0	0.4	40	10.8	1900	1.30	0.97	17.7	5
3 Poultry, fish	600	59	38.3	0.1	100	4.9	800	0.24	0.48	21.8	0
4 Eggs	655	52	46.5	2.8	220	10.9	4600	0.39	1.17	0.3	0
5 Leafy, green, and yellow vegetables	130	8	1.0	26.5	180	3.9	9200	0.31	0.34	2.4	101
6 Leafy vegetables	60	6	0.9	11.5	220	3.6	8900	0.17	0.38	1.6	91
7 Other green and yellow vegetables	150	9	1.0	30.9	170	4.0	9300	0.34	0.33	2.7	104
8 Citrus fruit, tomatoes	150	4	1.1	35.4	70	1.9	2400	0.24	0.13	1.8	128
9 Citrus fruit	170	3	0.8	42.8	80	1.2	400	0.23	0.08	0.8	160
10 Tomatoes	120	5	1.6	25.5	50	2.7	5000	0.24	0.19	3.2	86
11 Other vegetables and fruit	210	4	1.6	50.9	70	2.0	1200	0.15	0.16	1.6	33
12 Fruit, fresh, canned and frozen	215	2	1.6	54.4	40	1.6	1600	0.13	0.13	1.3	28
13 Fruit, dried	1145	11	2.6	301.8	320	14.5	3800	0.51	0.50	5.7	9
14 Vegetables	155	6	1.6	33.9	90	2.1	500	0.17	0.19	1.9	41
15 Potatoes, sweetpotatoes	330	8	0.5	75.2	50	2.7	2200	0.40	0.15	4.3	65
16 Dry beans and peas, nuts	1920	104	85.7	211.7	600	24.7	100	2.56	0.93	26.2	5
17 Dairy products excluding butter (milk equivalent)	300	16	16.8	20.8	530	0.4	700	0.14	0.74	0.4	5
18 Non-fat solids (skim)	1645	162	4.5	236.1	5900	2.6	200	1.60	8.88	5.2	32
19 Milk, fluid whole	310	16	17.7	22.2	540	0.3	700	0.16	0.78	0.5	6
20 Cheese, all kinds	1350	105	98.7	9.4	2350	3.5	4300	0.10	1.74	0.2	0
21 Flour and cereal products, including enrichment	1650	47	5.7	346.7	80	10.2	100	1.41	0.79	11.5	0
22 Bread, white enriched (4% non-fat milk solids)	1245	39	14.5	235.2	360	8.0	0	1.10	0.70	10.0	0
23 Fats and oils, including bacon and salt pork	3540	11	391.0	1.6	35	1.0	3700	0.45	0.13	2.2	0
24 Butter and margarine	3260	3	367.7	1.6	90	0	15,000	0	0	0	0
25 Other, excluding bacon and salt pork	4045	0	454.0	0	0	0	0	0	0	0	0
26 Sugars and sirups	1695	Trace	0	437.7	35	2.1	0*	Trace	0.01	0.1	Trace

/1/ Nutritive values used in basic computations are from Watt, B. K., and Merrill, A. L., U. S. Dept. Agr. Handbook 8, 1950. Except for eggs, non-fat milk solids (skim), fluid whole milk and white bread, enriched, these average nutritive values per pound are weighted by the relative quantities of foods within each of the groups estimated by the Agricultural Economics Division, Agricultural Marketing Service, as disappearing during 1952 into retail channels for civilian consumption. No deductions have been made for losses during cooking except those taken into account in Handbook 8, as, for example, in canned vegetables.

163. NUTRIENTS: SELECTED SOURCES

Foods listed are important sources of nutrients indicated. Values are per 100 grams of edible portion of fresh uncooked food, unless otherwise specified.

Nutrient	Sources and Nutritive Value	Nutrient	Sources and Nutritive Value
1 Food energy, Cal	Cheese (except cottage): 300-400; cooking and table fats, salad oils: 700-900; grain products, dry: 330-390; treenuts and peanut: 560-700; salt pork, bacon, and other fat meats: 600-800; sugars: 370-385.	10 Tocopherol, mg	Bean, navy, dry: 3.6; butter: 2.4; margarine: 54; egg, whole: 2; corn oil: 87; peanut oil: 22; soybean oil: 140.
2 Protein, g	Egg: 13; grains: 8-14; legumes, dry, mature: 21-35; meat, poultry, fish: 16-20; milk: 3-4.	11 Folic acid, μg	Asparagus: 89-142; broccoli: 34; bean, navy, dry: 129; corn, sweet: 9-70; cheese, cottage: 21-46; date, dry: 25; greens: collards, kale, mustard: 20-115; liver: 220-290; nuts: 27-77.
3 Carbohydrate, g	Fruit, dried: 67-73; grains: 70-80; legumes, dry, mature (except soybean): 60-64; potato, sweetpotato: 19-28; sugars: 90-100.	12 Vitamin K, μg	Cabbage, cauliflower: 250-275; liver, pork: 115-230; oats: 75; soybean: 190; spinach: 334; wheat bran: 80.
4 Fat, g	Cheese (except cottage): 25-37; cooking and table fats, salad oils: 81-100; cream: 20-35; nuts: 54-75; salt pork, bacon, other fat meats: 55-85.	13 Niacin, mg	Beef, lamb, pork: 2.6-5.2; fish[3], poultry, veal: 5.6-10.5; liver, all kinds: 13.7-16.9; peanut: 16.2; wheat, other grain products, whole or enriched: 2-5.
5 Vitamin A, I.U.	Butter, margarine: 3300; carrot: 12,000; greens, all kinds: 3000-9500; liver, all kinds: 14,200-50,500; sweetpotato: 7700.	14 Pantothenic acid, mg	Bean, lima, dry: 0.8; kidney, lamb: 4.3; broccoli: 1.4; mushroom: 1.7; brains, beef: 2.1-2.9; egg: 2.7; liver, beef and pork: 5.7-8.2; peanut, roasted: 2.5; wheat bran: 2.4.
6 Ascorbic acid, mg	Various berries: 16-60; citrus fruit: 40-50; cantaloupe, honeydew: 23-33; green pepper: 120; broccoli, cabbage, cauliflower: 50-118; greens: collards, kale, mustard, turnip: 100-136; spinach: 59; potato, sweetpotato: 17-22; tomato: 23.	15 Pyridoxine, mg	Banana; cabbage; peanut, roasted; sweetpotato: 0.3; bean, lima, dry: 0.5; halibut: 0.1; liver, beef: 0.8; pork loin: 0.1-0.3; wheat, whole: 0.2; wheat germ: 0.6.
7 Choline, mg	Bean, snap: 340; pea: 260; egg yolk: 1130-1700; liver: 470-700; peanut: 160-170; soybean: 300-340; spinach: 240; wheat germ: 400.	16 Riboflavin, mg	Egg: 0.29; greens: collards, kale, turnip: 0.26-0.46; liver, all kinds: 2.46-3.96; meat, poultry: 0.12-0.26; milk: 0.17.
8 Vitamin B$_{12}$	Liver and kidney: high; milk, muscle meats, fish: medium; corn, soybean, wheat, yeast: low.	17 Thiamine, mg	Legumes, dry, mature: 0.48-1.07; treenuts and peanut: 0.25-0.86; pork: 0.48-0.80; brown rice, rye, corn: 0.32-0.43; whole wheat, oatmeal: 0.40-0.60.
9 Vitamin D, I.U.	Egg yolk, dried: 265; fish[1]: pilchard: 745; salmon: 314; sardine: 1379; fish[2]: herring: 315; mackerel: 1100; shrimp: 150; liver, all kinds: 8-58.	18 Calcium, mg	Cheese: cheddar type: 670-925; fish, canned with edible bone: 150-400; greens: collard, kale, mustard: 220-259; milk: 118; soybean, and soyflours: 195-265.
		19 Iron, mg	Egg yolk: 7.2; greens: collards, kale, mustard, spinach, turnip: 1.6-3.0; legumes, dry: 4.7-8.0; liver, all kinds: 6.6-18.0; wheat: 3.0-4.3.

/1/ Canned. /2/ Raw, fresh. /3/ Includes Atlantic mackerel, halibut, salmon, swordfish.

164. DAILY DIETARY ALLOWANCES: MAN, U.S.A.

Allowances are designed for the maintenance of good nutrition of healthy persons normally vigorous and active, living in a temperate climate.[1]

	Group	Age yr	Weight kg (lb)	Height cm (in.)	Calories[2]	Protein[3] g	Vitamin A I.U.	Ascorbic Acid mg	Vitamin D[4] I.U.	Niacin[5] mg	Ribo-flavin[6] mg	Thia-mine[7] mg	Calcium g	Iron mg	Other Nutrients[8]
1	Men	25	65(143)	170(67)	3200	65	5000	75		16	1.6	1.6	0.8	12	+
2		45	65(143)	170(67)	2900	65	5000	75		15	1.6	1.5	0.8	12	+
3		65	65(143)	170(67)	2600	65	5000	75		13	1.6	1.3	0.8	12	+
4	Women	25	55(121)	157(62)	2300	55	5000	70		12	1.4	1.2	0.8	12	+
5		45	55(121)	157(62)	2100	55	5000	70		11	1.4	1.1	0.8		+
6		65	55(121)	157(62)	1800	55	5000	70		10	1.4	1.0	0.8	12	+
7		Pregnant (3rd trimester)			Add 400	80	6000	100	400	15	2.0	1.5	1.5	15	+
8		Lactating (850 ml daily)			Add 1000	100	8000	150	400	15	2.4	1.5	2.0	15	+
9	Infants[9]	1/12 to 3/12	6(13)	60(24)	kg x 120	kg x 3.5	1500	30	400	3	0.4	0.3	0.6	6	+
10		4/12 to 9/12	9(20)	70(28)	kg x 110	kg x 3.5	1500	30	400	4	0.7	0.4	0.8	6	+
11		10/12 to 1	10(22)	75(30)	kg x 100	kg x 100	1500	30	400	5	0.9	0.5	1.0	6	+
12	Children	1-3	12(27)	87(34)	1200	40	2000	35	400	6	1.0	0.6	1.0	7	+
13		4-6	18(40)	109(43)	1600	50	2500	50	400	8	1.2	0.8	1.0	8	+
14		7-9	27(59)	129(51)	2000	60	3500	60	400	10	1.5	1.0	1.0	10	+
15	Boys	10-12	35(78)	144(57)	2500	70	4500	75	400	13	1.8	1.3	1.2	12	+
16		13-15	49(108)	163(64)	3200	85	5000	90	400	16	2.1	1.6	1.4	15	+
17		16-20	63(139)	175(69)	3800	100	5000	100	400	19	2.5	1.9	1.4	15	+
18	Girls	10-12	36(79)	144(57)	2300	70	4500	75	400	12	1.8	1.2	1.2	12	+
19		13-15	49(108)	160(63)	2500	80	5000	80	400	13	2.0	1.3	1.3	15	+
20		16-20	54(120)	162(64)	2400	75	5000	80	400	12	1.9	1.2	1.3	15	+

/1/ Recommended by the Food and Nutrition Board, National Research Council, 1953. These allowances can be attained with a variety of common foods, which also provide nutrient requirements less well known. The allowances should cover individual variations among normal persons as they live in the U.S.A. subjected to ordinary environmental stresses. /2/ Allowance must be adjusted to meet specific needs; the proper allowance is that which over an extended period will maintain body weight or rate of growth at the "healthy" level. Adjustment for weight: For men and women differing from the standard body sizes of 65 and 55 kilograms (143 and 121 lb), the following formulas are applicable: Cal. for men = 152 $(W^{.073})$, Cal. for women = 123.4 $(W^{.073})$, where W = body weight in kilograms. For example, allowances for 25-year-old men weighing 50, 60, 70, and 80 kilograms, respectively, would be 2600, 3000, 3400, and 3700 Calories. Women of the same age and weighing 40, 50, 60, and 70 kilograms would receive, respectively, 1800, 2100, 2400, and 2700 Calories. These calorie allowances are based on proper, not actual, body weight for a given height. Adjustment for activity: For normally vigorous daily activity, make no correction; for sedentary life, reduce Calories by 22%; for heavy work, add 20-25%; for heaviest work add 50%. Adjustment for climate: A 5 per cent increase or decrease in calorie allowance for every 10° C difference (decrease or increase) in mean external temperature from the reference base of 10° C is proposed. For example, add 2% to Calories for extreme northern U.S.A.; subtract 5% for southern U.S.A. /3/ Allowance of 1 gram per day per kilogram of body weight should be adjusted according to body weight. /4/ Little evidence for need for supplemental Vitamin D by vigorous adults leading a normal life; however, for night workers and others whose habits shield them from sunlight, the ingestion of small amounts of the vitamin is desirable. /5/ Calorie-correlated; allowance is ten times that for thiamine. /6/ Computed from protein allowance, using a factor of 0.025. /7/ Calorie-correlated; allowance provides 0.5 milligrams for each 1000 Calories for adults, but the thiamine intake should not fall below 1 milligram daily. /8/ Carbohydrates and fats are essential for energy, but recommended allowances cannot be formulated as yet. Water: the standard is one ml per Calorie of food; much of this is in prepared foods. Sodium, potassium, and chlorine: indispensable dietary constituents. Potassium is widespread and does not need consideration as a dietary adjunct. The average normal adult intake of NaCl, 7-15 g, more than meets the normal requirement; additional quantities may be required with increased sweating. Phosphorus: allowance should equal that for calcium in diets of children and of women during latter part of pregnancy and lactation; for other adults allowance should be approximately 1½ times that for calcium. Copper: 1-2 mg daily for adults; for infants and children 0.05 mg/kg body weight. Iodine: 0.002-0.004 mg/kg body weight. There is presumptive evidence that cobalt, magnesium, manganese, molybdenum and zinc may be essential. Vitamin B₆ (pyridoxine group): approximate allowance is 1-2 mg daily. Vitamin B₁₂ (cobalamin; cyanocobalamin): probably essential, but no requirement formulated. Folacin (folic acid group): less than 1 mg daily should be sufficient for any nutritional need. Vitamin K: requirement for maintance of normal blood prothrombin level is provided by the average diet. However, if supplementary K was not given mother antepartum (daily dose of 1 mg orally during last month of pregnancy), the newborn infant should receive a single dose of 1 mg. /9/ During the first month of life, allowances for many nutrients are dependent upon maturation of excretory and endocrine functions; therefore, no specific recommendations are given. From one month to one year the recommendations pertain to nutrients primarily from cow's milk.

165. DAILY DIETARY ALLOWANCES: MAN (CANADA, U.K., U.S.A.)[1]

Dietary standards of the three countries differ considerably in philosophy and objective. The Canadian standard represents "a nutritional floor beneath which maintenance of the health of the people cannot be assumed." The British standards "are believed to be sufficient to establish and maintain a good nutritional state in representative individuals of population groups." The American allowances[2] "represent not merely minimal needs of average persons, but nutrient levels selected to cover individual variations in a substantial majority of the population." All the allowances must be adjusted to the actual needs of the individual, particularly with respect to body weight, degree of activity, age and environment. The adult allowances are for normally healthy young adults living in a temperate climate and engaged in work requiring moderate activity. Canadian standards for children neither combine allowances for girls and boys, nor place children in age groups, nor treat children (age 16-20) differently from adults; however, for comparisons with U.K. and U.S.A. standards, rough averages have been made to arrive at the values shown in this table.

Group	Age yr	Weight kg	Calories[3]	Protein[4] g	Vit. A[5] I.U.	Vit. C[6] mg	Vit. D I.U.	Niacin mg	Riboflavin mg	Thiamine mg	Calcium g	Iodine mg	Iron mg	Phosphorus g
Adult Male														
1 Can.		64	2900[7]	60	4600	30		8.5	1.4	0.9	0.65	0.15-0.30	6	0.65
2 U.K.		65	3000	82	5000	20		12	1.8	1.2	0.8	0.1	12	
3 U.S.A.	25	65	3200	65	5000	75		16	1.6	1.6	0.8	0.15-0.30	12	1.2
Adult Female														
4 Can.		55	2400[7]	55	4000	30		7.5	1.1	0.8	0.55	0.15-0.30	12	0.55
5 U.K.		56	2500	69	5000	20		10	1.5	1.0	0.8	0.1	12	
6 U.S.A.	25	55	2300	55	5000	70		12	1.4	1.2	0.8	0.15-0.30	12	1.2
Pregnancy														
7 Can.			2900	80	6000	30	400	9	1.3	1.0	1.55	0.15-0.30	15	1.55
8 U.K.			2750	96	6000	40	400-600	11	1.6	1.1	1.5	0.15	15	
9 U.S.A.			2700	80	6000	100	400	15	2.0	1.5	1.5	0.15-0.30	15	1.5
Lactation														
10 Can.			3400	80	6000	30	400	10.5	1.6	1.1	1.55	0.15-0.30	15	1.55
11 U.K.			3000	111	8000	50	800	14	2.1	1.4	2.0	0.15	15	
12 U.S.A.			3300	100	8000	150	400	15	2.5	1.5	2.0	0.15-0.30	15	2.0
Children														
13 U.K.	<1	8	800	28	1500	10	800	3	0.5	0.3	1		6	
14 U.S.A.	4/12-9/12	8	kg x 110	kg x 3.5	1500	30	400	4	0.7	0.4	0.8	kg x 0.003	6	0.8
15 Can.	1-3	12	1250	37	860	30	400-800	3.7	0.6	0.4	1		6	
16 U.K.	1-3	12	1300	46	1500	15	400	5	0.8	0.5	1	0.15	7	
17 U.S.A.	1-3	12	1200	40	2000	35	400	6	1.0	0.6	1.0	kg x 0.003	7	1.0
18 Can.	4-6	19	1625	38	1400	30	400	5	0.8	0.5	1		6	
19 U.K.	4-6	18	1600	56	1500	15	400	6	1	0.6	1	0.15	8	
20 U.S.A.	4-6	18	1600	50	2500	50	400	8	1.2	0.8	1.0	kg x 0.003	8	1.0
21 Can.	7-9	26	2025	49	1900	30	400	6	1.1	0.6	1		6	
22 U.K.	7-9	27	1950	68	1500	20	400	8	1.2	0.8	1	0.15	10	
23 U.S.A.	7-9	27	2000	60	3500	60	400	10	1.5	1.0	1.0	kg x 0.003	10	1.0

Children 10-20 yr (values given as ♂ / ♀):

Group	Age yr	Weight kg	Calories[3]	Protein[4] g	Vit. A[5] I.U.	Vit. C[6] mg	Vit. D I.U.	Niacin mg	Riboflavin mg	Thiamine mg	Calcium g	Iodine mg	Iron mg	Phosphorus g
24 Can.	10-12	34 / 37	2400 / 2500	60 / 62.5	2400 / 2700	30 / 30	400	7.2 / 7.2	1.5 / 1.5	0.7 / 0.7	1 / 1		6	
25 U.K.	10-12	35 / 35	2450 / 2450	86 / 86	1500 / 1500	25 / 25	400	10 / 10	1.5 / 1.5	1 / 1	1.2 / 1.2	0.15	12	
26 U.S.A.	10-12	35 / 36	2500 / 2300	70 / 70	4500 / 4500	75 / 75	400	13 / 12	1.8 / 1.8	1.3 / 1.2	1.2 / 1.2	kg x 0.003	12	1.2 / 1.2
27 Can.	13-15	49 / 49	2950 / 2500	75 / 75	3500 / 3500	30 / 30	400	9 / 7.5	1.5 / 1.2	0.9 / 0.7	1.5 / 1.5		12	
28 U.K.	13-15	49 / 49	3150 / 2750	110 / 96	1500 / 1500	30 / 30	400	13 / 11	1.9 / 1.6	1.3 / 1.1	1.4 / 1.3	0.15	15	
29 U.S.A.	13-15	49 / 49	3200 / 2500	85 / 80	5000 / 5000	90 / 80	400	16 / 13	2.1 / 2.0	1.6 / 1.3	1.4 / 1.3	kg x 0.003	15	1.4 / 1.3
30 Can.	16-20	63 / 54	3500 / 2400	60 / 55	4300 / 3800	30 / 30	400	8.5 / 7.5	1.7 / 1.1	1.0 / 0.7	1.5 / 1.5		12	
31 U.K.	16-20	63 / 54	3400 / 2500	119 / 88	2500 / 2500	30 / 30	400	14 / 10	2.1 / 1.5	1.4 / 1.0	1.4 / 1.0	0.15	15	
32 U.S.A.	16-20	63 / 54	3800 / 2400	100 / 75	5000 / 5000	100 / 80	400	19 / 12	2.5 / 1.9	1.9 / 1.2	1.4 / 1.3	kg x 0.003	15	1.4 / 1.3

/1/ Canadian values were adapted from "Nutrition," a bulletin of the Canadian Council on Nutrition, Ottawa: King's Printer and Controller of Stationery, 1950, and from the Canadian Bulletin on Nutrition 3:No. 2, 1953. Values for U.K. were adapted from "Report of the Committee on Nutrition," London: British Medical Association, 1950, and "Report of the National Food Survey Committee," London: Her Majesty's Stationery Office, 1952. Values for U.S.A. were derived from "Recommended Dietary Allowances," Food and Nutrition Board, Washington: National Research Council, 1953. /2/ For further details see Table 164. /3/ Allowance must be adjusted for variations in body weight, activity, and climate. See Footnote 2, Table 164 /4/ Allowance should be adjusted for variations in body weight; the general standard is one gram of protein per kilogram of body weight. /5/ Canadian allowance is expressed as I.U. of carotene; one I.U. is equivalent to 0.0006 mg β-carotene. The British and American allowances are expressed as I.U. in a diet containing both carotene and preformed A (one I.U. preformed A alcohol = 0.0003 mg). /6/ Ascorbic acid. /7/ The work allowance for "moderate activity" included in the total calorie allowance is 800 Calories for men and 500 Calories for women. Deducting these figures from the total allowance will give the maintenance requirement.

166. SUMMARY OF DAILY NUTRIENT ALLOWANCES: VERTEBRATES

Values are for maintenance and normally vigorous activity of male, adult animals, and are per kg body weight per day, unless otherwise indicated.

Required (R); Not Required (R̶)

Nutrients	Man U.S.A.[1] 25 yr; 65 kg	Beef Cattle[2] 800 kg	Dairy Cattle[2] 900 kg	Dog[3]	Fox[3] 5.7 kg	Hamster[4] 0.025 kg	Horse[2] 635 kg	Monkey, Rhesus	Mouse[4] 0.025 kg	Rat, White 0.30 kg	Sheep[2] 79 kg	Swine[3] 227 kg	Chicken[3,5] 1.82 kg	Fish, Rainbow Trout
1 Water, ml	49	R	R	R	R	R	R	R	180	R	70	R	110	
2 Calories[6], metabolizable	49	47	28	75	122	645	43	160	500	115	51	45	150	50-60
3 Total food or feed, g	10.8	32	14	20-35	25	150	19	40	120	50	31	15	51	
4 Residue[7], g	1	15				4.8				R			R	
5 Protein[7], g	8.5			3-4	5	32	0.8	7.2	40	R	1.1	2.1	7.7	7-8
6 Carbohydrate, g	1.1-1.4	0.8	0.7		R	105	0.4	28.4	70	R	12		25	1-5
7 Fat, g				1.3		11.2			20	R	0.33	R	1.2	1-3
8 Vitamin A, I.U.[8]	77	150	150	100	50	1800	150	60	1000	17	150	135	215	R
9 Ascorbic acid, mg	1.1									R		R	R	20-40
10 Biotin, µg	R			R(?)	4	20	R	4	30	10			(?)	15-26
11 Choline, mg				33		640		8	200	40			56	4-8
12 Cobalamin, µg	R(?)			0.55		R(?)		40	4	R(?)		R		R(?)
13 Vitamin D, I.U.[9]	R		R	6.6	R	270	6.6	(?)	100	R	1.7	R	25.6[10]	R(?)
14 Vitamin E, mg	R(?)	R	R			4.0		12.8	5	1.2	8	3		R(?)
15 Folic acid group, µg				8	5	320		2.0	500	R(?)	0.3	R	15	100-200
16 Inositol, mg	R			R		400		80	1000	R				20-40
17 Vitamin K, µg	0.25			R		4800		40	R(?)	R				R(?)
18 Niacin, mg				0.24	0.26	8.0	0.1	40	5	R		0.17		3-4
19 Pantothenic acid, mg	15-31			0.05	0.20	1.6	R(?)	1.0	10	0.36		0.15	0.28	1-1.3
20 Para-aminobenzoic acid, mg				R		160		0.8		R				R(?)
21 Pyridoxine group, µg	25			25	30	1900		12(?)	1000	40			150	200-300
22 Riboflavin, µg	25			45	50	2600	R	140	2000	100	45	40	130	400-700
23 Thiamine, µg				18	30	1300	R	140	1000	50		17		100-200
24 Calcium, mg	12	22	18	260	160		28	140	900	160-200	45	90	1150	R
25 Chlorine, mg	93	30	R	225	R		R	155	800	20	150	45	160	
26 Cobalt, µg	R(?)	2000	R	6			(?)	230	400	R	2000			
27 Copper, µg	18	R	R	165			(?)	19	700	1000	R	R		
28 Fluorine, mg								480	0.6	R(?)				
29 Iodine, µg	2-4	R	R	33			R	0.04	1300			<4		
30 Iron, mg	0.18	R	R	1.3				600	30	8	R	R	20	R
31 Magnesium, mg	R(?)	R	R	11			R	5	60	5		R		
32 Manganese, mg	R(?)	R	R	0.11				10	5	2		R	1.7	
33 Molybdenum	R(?)	0.3	0.3					1.6			R	R		
34 Phosphorus, mg	18	22	18	220	160		31	170	900	140-180	40	60	385	
35 Potassium, mg	R	R	R	220				135	600	60		55-110		
36 Sodium, mg	60	20	R	150	R			130	500	200	100	30	100	
37 Sulfur, mg	R	R	R				R	14		R11		R		
38 Zinc, mg	R(?)	R	0.11	0.11				0.9	0.3	R	R	R		

1/ Values are daily dietary allowances calculated from those recommended by the Food and Nutrition Board, National Research Council, 1953. 2/ Values are daily nutrient allowances calculated from those recommended by the Committee on Animal Nutrition, Agricultural Board, National Research Council, 1949-50; a few values have been changed in accordance with revisions recommended by the Committee. 3/ Values are daily nutrient allowances calculated from those recommended by the Committee on Animal Nutrition, 1953-54; a few values have been changed in accordance with revisions recommended by the Committee. 4/ Young animal, sex not specified. 5/ Single comb white leghorn, laying. 6/ Kilocalories. 7/ Digestible. 8/ One I.U. = 0.0006 mg β-carotene. 9/ One I.U. = 0.025 µg D$_3$ (7-dehydrocholesterol). 10/ International Chick Units; one unit = 0.025 µg calciferol. 11/ Except as sulfur-containing amino acids.

167. VITAMINS, SUMMARY OF ESTIMATED DAILY ALLOWANCES: VERTEBRATES

Values are per kg body weight per day, unless otherwise indicated.
Required (R); Not Required (R̄).

#	Animal	Condition[1]	Vitamin A I.U.[2]	Ascorbic Acid mg	Biotin μg	Choline mg	Cobalamin μg	Vitamin D I.U.[3]	Vitamin E mg	Folic Acid Group μg	Inositol mg	Vitamin K μg	Niacin mg	Pantothenic Acid mg	Para-aminobenzoic Acid mg	Pyridoxin μg	Riboflavin μg	Thiamine μg
1	Cat[4]	Growth ♂♀	135					19					2.3				320	50
2		Maintenance ♂♀	85					12					1.4				190	30
3	Cattle, beef	Growth ♂♀	215		R5	R	R5	7	R			R(?)	R	R5		R5	275	R5
4		Maintenance ♂♀	150					R	R									
5		Pregnancy	215					R	R									
6		Lactation	1000					R	R									
7	Cattle, dairy	Growth ♂♀	150		R5	R	R5	6.6	R			R(?)	R	R5		R5	30[5]	R5
8		Maintenance ♂♀	260					R	R									
9		Pregnancy	260					R	R									
10		Lactation	200					R	R									
11	Dog	Growth ♂♀	200	R		55	1.1	21		15	R	R	0.4	0.1		55	90	33
12		Maintenance ♂♀	100	R(?)	R(?)	33	0.55	6.6		8	R	R	0.24	0.05		25	45	18
13	Fox	Growth ♂	135					R		14			0.74	0.56		80	140	80
14		♀	100					R		12			0.63	0.50		70	120	70
15		Maintenance ♂♀	50					R		5			0.26	0.20		30	50	30
16	Guinea pig	Growth ♂♀	R	100-200[6]	R(?)	1000-1500[6]		R(?)	60-120[6]	3000-6000[6]	R(?)	2000	10-20[6]	15-20[6]	R	R	3000[6]	6000-8000[6]
17		Reproduction	1800	100-200[6]	20	640	R(?)	270	4.0	320	400	4800	8.0	1.6	160	1900	2600	1300
18	Hamster	Growth ♂♀	185		R					R			0.1	R(?)	R	R	R	R
19	Horse	Maintenance ♂♀	150		R			6.6		R			0.1	R(?)		R	R	R
20		Pregnancy	215		R			6.6		R			0.13	R(?)		R	R	R
21		Lactation	215		R			6.6		R			0.13	R(?)		R	R	R
22	Mink	Growth ♂	165					R		20			0.98	0.80		100	200	100
23		♀	180					R		22			1.11	0.89		130	220	130
24		Maintenance ♂	135					R		15			0.78	0.63		90	150	90
25		♀	165					R		21			1.0	0.79		120	210	120
27	Monkey	Growth and maintenance ♂♀	60	4	8	40	(?)	13	2	80	40	40	1	0.8	12(?)	140	140	140
28	Mouse	Growth ♂♀	1000	R	30	200	4	100	5	500	R(?)	1000	5	10	R	1000	2000	1000
29	Rabbit	Growth ♂♀		R									225[6](?)				R	
30		Maintenance ♂♀		R				200	0.32				56					
31	Rat, cotton	Growth ♂♀	1500	R	20	160		R	4.0	320	160		4.0	3.2	48	400	480	400
32	Rat, white	Growth ♂♀	17	R	10	80	0.4	R	3.0(?)	8.0	R	R(?)	R(?)	1.0	R	300	300	200
33		Maintenance ♂♀	17	R	10	40	R(?)	R	1.2	R(?)	R	R	R	0.36	R	40	100	50
34		Pregnancy	R	R	10	50	R(?)	R	1.5	R(?)	R	R(?)	R(?)	0.45	R	90	40	50
35		Lactation		R	12	60	R	R	1.5	R(?)	R	R(?)	R(?)	0.45		70	20	50
36	Sheep	Growth ♂♀	215				1.7	8	0.3					R5		R5	R5	R5
37		Maintenance ♂♀	150				1.7	8	0.3									
38		Pregnancy	215				1.7	8	0.3									
39		Lactation	235					8	0.3									
40	Swine	Growth ♂♀	75	R			0.5	9.2		R			0.5	0.45		<110	100	50
41		Breeding ♂	135	R		R	R	3	R				0.17	0.15			40	17
42		Lactation	250				R	5.6					0.31	0.27			70	30
43	Chicken[7]	Growth ♂♀	350	R	12	175	1.2	26	2.6	70		52	3.5	1.23		380	380	240
44		Laying	265	R	8	56		30		15				0.28		170	130	
45		Breeding ♀	265	R	7	56	0.2	30		21			0.45	0.55		170	230	
46	Duck[8]	Growth ♂♀	400	R		125		220[6]		70		100	55[6]	116		36	4[6]	
47	Turkey[8]	Growth ♂♀	165	R				68		70			3.7	0.83		260	280	
48		Breeding ♀		R				28		200				0.42			110	
49	Trout[9]	Maintenance	R	20-40	15-26	4-8	R(?)	R(?)	R(?)	100-200	20-40	R(?)	3-4	1-1.3	R(?)	200-300	400-700	100-200

/1/ Values for growth are for very young animals (i.e., about 1/4 grown). Maintenance values are for adults. /2/ One I.U. = 0.0006 mg β-carotene. /3/ One I.U. = 0.025 μg calciferol. Requirements for poultry expressed in International Chick Units. /4/ Diet of raw, unprocessed feed. Values are rough approximations, and may be inadequate for proper maintenance. /5/ Required only until vitamin is synthesized in the rumen. /6/ Per kilogram of feed. /7/ Single comb white leghorn. /8/ Broad-breasted bronze turkey. /9/ Rainbow trout.

168. DAILY NUTRIENT ALLOWANCES: BEEF AND DAIRY CATTLE

Data are from Reports no. III and IV, Committee on Animal Nutrition, National Research Council, 1950. Based on air-dry feed containing 90% dry matter. Allowances are probably higher than minimum requirements. Bf = beef cattle; Dr = dairy cattle.

Specifications		Heifers and Steers								Bulls				Cows					
		Growth								Maintenance[1]				Maintenance				Lactating	
		Bf	Dr[2]	Bf	Dr[2]	Bf	Dr[2]	Bf	Dr[2]	Bf	Dr	Bf	Dr	Bf[3]	Dr	Bf[3]	Dr	Bf[4]	Dr[5]
		400		600		800		1000		1200		1800	2000	800		1200		1000	
1	Weight, lb													1.5					
2	Expected daily gain, lb	1.6	1.8	1.4	1.4	1.2	1.2	1.0	1.3	1.4										
3	Total feed, lb	12	11	16	15	19	19	21	22	22	18	26	27	22	14	18	18	28	
4	Digestible protein, lb	0.9	0.8	0.9	0.85	0.9	0.9	0.9	0.95	1.4	1.0	1.4	1.45	1.0	0.5	0.8	0.7	1.4	2.4
5	TDN[6], lb	7.0	6.5	8.5	8.5	9.5	10.0	10.5	11.0	13.0	10.3	14.0	15.6	11.0	6.8	9.0	9.2	14.0	20.8
6	Calcium[7], g	20	20	18	18	16	16	15	15	21	12	18	20	22	8	16	12	30	50
7	Phosphorus[7], g	15	15	15	15	15	15	15	15	18	12	18	20	18	8	15	12	24	38
8	Carotene[8], mg	24	24	36	36	48	48	60	60	72	72	108	120	48	48	72	72	300	90
9	Vitamin D[9], I.U.	+	+	+	+	+	+	+	+	+	+	+	+	+	+	+	+	+	+

/1/ Moderate activity; breeding. /2/ Large breeds. /3/ Pregnant. /4/ Nursing calves, 3-4 months after parturition. /5/ Assuming 40 lb milk daily with 4% fat. /6/ Total digestible nutrients. /7/ Fe, Cu, I, Mg, Mn, Co, K, S, Na and Cl are probably essential, but quantitative requirements have not been defined. /8/ 0.0006 mg β-carotene = one I. U. /9/ Usually obtained in sufficient quantities from sunlight or sun-cured roughages. Young animals should be given 400 I. U. per 100 lb body weight.

169. DAILY NUTRIENT REQUIREMENTS: SWINE

Data are from Report no. II, Committee on Animal Nutrition, National Research Council, 1953.

	Specifications	Market Stock						Pregnant ♀ and Breeding ♂		Lactating ♀	
								Young	Adult	Gilts	Adult
1	Weight, lb	25	50	100	150	200	250	300	500	350	450
2	Expected daily gain, lb	0.8	1.2	1.6	1.8	1.8	1.8	0.75	0.5		
3	Total feed[1], lb	2.0	3.2	5.3	6.8	7.5	8.3	6.0	7.5	11.0	12.5
4	TDN[2], lb	1.6[3]	2.4	4.0	5.1	5.6	6.2	4.5	5.6	8.3	9.4
5	Crude protein, lb	0.36	0.51	0.74	0.88	0.9	1.0	0.90	1.05	1.65	1.75
6	Calcium[4], g	7.3	9.4	15.6	17.0	18.7	20.7	16.3	20.4	30.0	34.0
7	Phosphorus[4], g	5.4	6.5	10.8	10.2	11.2	12.4	10.9	13.6	20.0	22.7
8	Sodium, as NaCl, g	4.5	7.3	12.0	15.4	17.0	18.8	13.6	17.0	25.0	28.4
9	Vitamin B12[5], μg	20.0	16.0	26.5							
10	Carotene[6], mg	0.5	1.0	2.0	3.0	4.0	5.0	15.0	18.7	27.5	31.2
11	Choline, mg	800.0									
12	Vitamin D, I.U.	180.0	288.0	477.0	612.0	675.0	747.0	540.0	675.0	990.0	1125.0
13	Niacin, mg	16.0	19.2	26.5	34.0	37.5	41.5	30.0	37.5	55.0	62.5
14	Pantothenic acid, mg	10.0	16.0	23.8	30.6	33.8	37.4	27.0	33.8	49.5	56.2
15	Pyridoxine, mg	1.2	1.9								
16	Riboflavin, mg	2.4	3.2	5.3	6.8	7.5	8.3	7.2	9.0	13.2	15.0
17	Thiamine, mg	1.0	1.6	2.6	3.4	3.8	4.2	3.0	3.8	5.5	6.2

/1/ Air-dried. /2/ Total digestible nutrients (75% TDN). /3/ For young pigs a high energy diet (80% TDN) is recommended. /4/ Fe, Cu, I, Mg, Co, K and Zn are probably essential, but quantitative requirements have not been defined. /5/ Cobalamin; cyanocobalamin. /6/ 0.0006 mg β-carotene = one I. U.

170. DAILY NUTRIENT REQUIREMENTS: CHICKEN

Data are from Report no. I, Committee on Animal Nutrition, National Research Council, 1954. Wh = single-comb white leghorn or similar breeds; Hb = heavy breeds.

	Specifications	Growth														Laying[1]		Breeding[1]	
		Wh	Hb	Wh	Hb	Wh	Hb	Wh	Hb	Wh	Hb	Wh	Hb	Wh	Hb	Wh	Hb	Wh	Hb
1	Age, wk	3-4	3	5-6	5	7.5-8.5	7	10-11	8-9	11-14	10-11	14-18	12	36-52		36-52			
2	Weight, lb	0.5	0.5	1.0	1.0	1.5	1.5	2.0	2.0	2.5	3.0	3.0	4.5	4.0	5.5	4.0	5.5		
3	Total feed, lb	0.067	0.062	0.097	0.103	0.117	0.131	0.156	0.181	0.175	0.240	0.168	0.192	0.241[2]	0.276[3]	0.241	0.276		
4	Crude protein, lb	0.013	0.012	0.019	0.021	0.019	0.026	0.025	0.029	0.028	0.038	0.027	0.031	0.036	0.041	0.036	0.041		
5	Calcium, g	0.30	0.281	0.44	0.468	0.53	0.595	0.71	0.822	0.80	1.09	0.76	0.872	2.46	2.82	2.46	2.82		
6	Iodine, mg	0.033	0.031	0.049	0.051	0.023	0.065	0.031	0.036	0.035	0.048	0.034	0.038	0.048	0.055	0.121	0.138		
7	Magnesium, mg	14.7	13.6	21.3	22.7	?	28.8	?	?	?	?	?	?	?	?	?	?		
8	Manganese, mg	1.68	1.55	2.43	2.58	?	3.28	?	?	?	?	?	?	?	?	3.62	4.14		
9	Phosphorus, g	0.18	0.169	0.26	0.281	0.32	0.357	0.43	0.493	0.48	0.654	0.46	0.523	0.66	0.75	0.66	0.75		
10	Potassium, mg	61	56	88	94	85	119	113	131	127	174	122	139	?	?	?	?		
11	Vitamin A, I.U.[4]	80.0	74.0	116.0	124.0	140.0	157.0	187.0	217.0	210.0	288.0	202.0	230.0	482.0	552.0	482.0	552.0		
12	Biotin, μg	2.7	2.5	3.9	4.1	?	5.2	?	?	?	?	?	?	?	?	?	?		
13	Choline, mg	40.0	37.0	58.0	62.0	?	78.6	?	?	?	?	?	?	?	?	?	?		
14	Vitamin D, I.C.U.[5]	6.0	5.6	8.7	9.3	10.5	11.8	14.0	16.3	15.8	21.6	15.1	17.3	54.2	62.1	54.2	62.1		
15	Folacin, μg	16.8	15.5	24.3	25.8	?	33	?	?	?	?	?	?	27	30	39	44		
16	Niacin, mg	0.80	0.74	1.16	1.24	?	1.57	?	?	?	?	?	?	?	?	?	?		
17	Pantothenic acid, mg	0.28	0.26	0.41	0.43	0.49	0.55	0.66	0.76	0.74	1.01	0.71	0.81	0.51	0.58	1.01	1.16		
18	Pyridoxine, mg	0.087	0.081	0.126	0.134	?	0.170	?	?	?	?	?	?	0.31	0.36	0.31	0.36		
19	Riboflavin, mg	0.087	0.081	0.126	0.134	0.094	0.170	0.125	0.145	0.140	0.192	0.134	0.154	0.241	0.276	0.410	0.469		
20	Thiamine, mg	0.054	0.050	0.078	0.082	?	0.105	?	?	?	?	?	?	?	?	?	?		

/1/ 60% production. /2/ Value for maintenance is 0.156. /3/ Value for maintenance is 0.192. /4/ One I. U. = 0.3 μg A alcohol, or 0.6 μg β-carotene = one U. S. P. unit. /5/ Vitamin D3 (7-dehydrocholesterol). 0.025 μg crystalline D3 = one I. C. U. (International Chick Unit). Chickens and turkeys utilize D2 (from irradiated ergosterol) poorly.

171. AMINO ACID REQUIREMENTS, AND COMPOSITION IN VARIOUS FOODS

Ranges, in parentheses, are estimate "c" of the 95% range (cf Introduction).

Essential (R); utilized (U).

Amino Acid	Requirements[1]					Composition						Milk, Mature		
	Man[2] Adult 70 kg	Rat[3] Adult 0.15 kg	Chicken[4] Young 0.25 kg	Dog[5] Adult 7 kg	Swine[6] Young 45 kg	Beef Muscle[7]	Casein[7]	Egg Albumin[7]	Egg Powder[7]	Peanut Flour[7]	Wheat Gluten[7]	Man	Cow	Sow
	grams per animal per day					grams per 100 grams protein						mg per 100 ml milk		
1 Alanine	U	U										35	75	
2 Arginine	U	U	R 0.47	R 0.49	R 6.1	6.42	3.72	5.31	5.43	7.41	3.30	51(28-67)	124(90-173)	316
3 Aspartic acid	U	U				9.33	6.93	9.76	9.40	8.52	3.38			
4 Citrulline	U													
5 Cystine[8]	U	U	R? 0.13			1.34	0.38	2.64	2.00	0.95	2.12	29(20-41)	29(23-34)	75
6 Glutamic acid	U	U				14.61	21.31	11.45	10.96	12.03	31.36	230	680	
7 Glycine	U	U	R 0.39			5.62	1.89	3.34	3.45	3.53	2.97	0	11	
8 Histidine	U	R 0.005	R 0.06	R 0.17	R 11.7	3.24	2.89	2.15	1.84	1.46	1.78	23(12-38)	80(51-130)	120
9 Hydroxyproline	U													
10 Isoleucine	R 0.70	R 0.03	R 0.23	R 0.56	R 14.4	5.16	4.63	5.73	5.39	2.72	4.07	86(46-114)	212(159-290)	234
11 Leucine	R 1.08	R 0.02	R 0.54	R 0.77	R 23.4	7.79	9.53	7.79	7.87	4.65	6.45	161(72-228)	356(240-400)	443
12 Lysine	R 0.80	R 0.009	R 0.35	R 0.42	R 29.2	8.58	7.71	6.39	5.35	2.29	1.81	79(50-111)	257(184-382)	408
13 Methionine	R 1.08	R 0.01	R 0.17	R 0.49	R 17.6	2.70	3.09	5.27	2.81	0.55	1.49	23(6-40)	173(111-228)	192
14 Phenylalanine	R 1.08	R 0.007	R 0.35	R 0.46	R 26.1	3.88	5.15	5.27	4.93	3.23	4.52	64(30-77)	173(111-228)	
15 Proline	U					5.13	12.72	3.81	3.91	3.26	12.66	80	250	
16 Serine	U											69	160	
17 Threonine	R 0.49	R 0.01	R 0.23	R 0.38	R 11.7	4.44	4.28	4.33	4.31	1.83	2.51	62(40-76)	152(115-220)	750
18 Tryptophan	R 0.24	R 0.005	R 0.08	R 0.10	R 5.8	1.01	0.91	1.02	0.99	0.51	0.69	22(13-31)	50(36-80)	200
19 Tyrosine[9]	U		R? 0.27			2.95	4.90	2.96	3.09	1.90	2.50	62(47-78)	190(158-251)	
20 Valine	R 0.80	R 0.02	R 0.31	R 0.59	R 11.7	5.13	7.01	6.62	6.10	3.00	3.81	90(48-133)	228(171-321)	1150

/1/ Values are essentially minimum requirements; for man they probably should be doubled to represent a "safe" allowance for normal, healthy adults, and this may be true for the other species listed. /2/ Values for man represent the L-forms of the amino acids, except glycine. /3/ White rat. /4/ New Hampshire. /5/ Cocker spaniel. The amino acids for which values are given probably are required, although the data available do not show this clearly. /6/ Synthetic diet with amino acids and diammonium citrate as nitrogen sources. /7/ Ash and moisture-free basis for partially purified proteins. /8/ Will replace about 1/2 of the methionine requirement. /9/ Will replace a portion of the phenylalanine requirement.

172. AMINO ACID REQUIREMENTS: INSECTS, BACTERIA

Required (R); not required (R̶).

Amino Acid	Insects[1]						Bacteria[2]													
	Cockroach, German; nymph[3]	Beetle, carpet; larva[4]	Beetle, confused flour; larva[5]	Fly, fruit, vinegar; larva[6]	Mosquito, yellow-fever; larva[7]	Parasite, spruce budworm; larva[8]	Aerobacter aerogenes	Bacillus anthracis	B. licheniformis	B. megatherium	B. subtilis	Brucella suis	Erwinia amylovora	Escherichia coli	Lactobacillus arabinosus	Leuconostoc mesenteroides	Pasteurella tularensis	Salmonella typhosa	Serratia marcescens	Shigella sonnei
1 Alanine	R[9]	R̶	R̶	R̶	R̶	R̶	R̶		R̶	R̶	R̶	R̶		R̶	R̶	R			R̶	R̶
2 Arginine	R[9]	R	R	R	R	R	R̶		R̶	R̶	R̶	R̶		R̶	R̶	R			R̶	R̶
3 Aspartic acid	R[9]	R̶	R̶	R̶	R̶	R̶			R̶	R̶	R̶	R̶		R̶	R̶	R			R̶	R̶
4 Citrulline																				
5 Cystine	R[9]	R̶	R̶	R̶	R?	R̶	R̶		R̶	R̶	R̶	R̶	R̶	R̶	R̶	R	R		R̶	R̶
6 Glutamic acid	R̶	R̶	R̶	R̶	R̶	R̶	R̶		R̶	R̶	R̶	R̶	R̶	R̶	R̶	R			R̶	R̶
7 Glycine	R̶	R̶	R̶	R̶	R̶	R̶	R̶		R̶	R̶	R̶	R̶	R̶	R̶	R̶	R			R̶	R̶
8 Histidine	R	R	R	R	R	R	R̶		R̶	R̶	R̶	R̶	R̶	R̶	R	R			R̶	R̶
9 Hydroxyproline	R̶	R̶	R̶	R̶	R̶	R̶	R̶		R̶	R̶	R̶	R̶	R̶	R̶	R	R			R̶	R̶
10 Isoleucine	R	R	R	R	R	R	R̶		R̶	R̶	R̶	R̶	R̶	R̶	R	R			R̶	R̶
11 Leucine	R	R	R	R	R	R	R̶		R̶	R̶	R̶	R̶	R̶	R̶	R	R			R̶	R̶
12 Lysine	R	R	R	R	R	R	R̶		R̶	R̶	R̶	R̶	R̶	R̶	R?	R			R̶	R̶
13 Methionine	R[9]	R	R	R	R	R	R̶		R̶	R̶	R̶	R̶	R̶	R̶	R̶	R			R̶	R̶
14 Norleucine	R̶	R̶					R̶													
15 Phenylalanine	R̶	R	R	R	R?	R	R̶		R̶	R̶	R̶	R̶	R̶	R̶	R	R			R̶	R̶
16 Proline	R[9,10]	R̶	R̶	R	R̶	R̶	R̶		R̶	R̶	R̶	R̶	R̶	R̶	R	R			R̶	R̶
17 Serine	R[9,10]	R̶	R̶	R	R̶	R	R̶		R̶	R̶	R̶	R̶	R̶	R̶	R	R			R̶	R̶
18 Threonine	R̶	R	R	R	R	R	R̶		R̶	R̶	R̶	R̶	R̶	R	R	R		R	R̶	R̶
19 Tryptophan	R?	R	R	R	R	R	R̶		R̶	R̶	R̶	R̶	R̶	R	R	R			R̶	R̶
20 Tyrosine	R[9]	R̶	R̶	R̶	R?	R̶	R̶		R̶	R̶	R̶	R̶	R̶	R̶	R	R			R̶	R̶
21 Valine	R[9]	R	R	R		R	R̶		R̶	R̶	R̶	R̶	R̶	R̶	R	R	R	R		R
22 Other am. acids[11]								R												
23 Other N source[12]							R		R	R	R	R	R	R					R	R

/1/ Diets containing all amino acids produce slightly better growth than mixtures of "required" acids alone. L-forms are biologically active, but the D-forms may be active for some species. See Table 173 for amino acid requirements of some additional species. /2/ There is wide variation in requirements among strains of a given species. /3/ Blattella germanica (L.). /4/ Attagenus (sp). /5/ Tribolium confusum Duv. /6/ Drosophila melanogaster Meig. /7/ Aedes aegypti (L.). /8/ Pseudosarcophaga affinis (Fall.). /9/ Synthesized under aseptic conditions but at a rate insufficient for normal growth and/or development. /10/ Required by males only. /11/ Unspecified. /12/ NH3, etc.

All insect tissues, and diets, contain nitrogen, carbon, oxygen and hydrogen. In addition, phosphorus, sulfur, iron, copper, magnesium, manganese, potassium, calcium and chlorine are probably universally required by insects. A number of other minerals, some only in traces, are consumed and found in the composition of the insect.

R = required; R̸ = not required; U = utilized; Ʉ = not utilized; u = poorly utilized.

Bee, honey, adult (Apis mellifera)

No.	Nutrient	Value
1	Carbohydrates	U
2	Arabinose	u
3	Cellobiose	u
4	Dextrin	Ʉ
5	Fructose	U
6	Galactose	u
7	Glucose	U
8	Inulin	Ʉ
9	Lactose	R̸
10	Maltose	U
11	Mannitol	U
12	Mannose	Ʉ
13	Raffinose	U(?)
14	Sorbitol	U
15	Sorbose	Ʉ
16	Starch	u
17	Sucrose	U
18	Xylose	U(?)

Beetle, carpet, larva (Attagenus sp)

No.	Nutrient	Value
19	Casein	U
20	Protein, total	6-12%[1]
21	Alanine	R̸
22	Arginine	R
23	Aspartic acid	R̸
24	Cystine	R̸
25	Glutamic acid	R̸
26	Glycine	R̸
27	Histidine	R
28	Hydroxyproline	R̸
29	Isoleucine	R
30	Leucine	R
31	Lysine	R
32	Methionine	R
33	Norleucine	R̸
34	Phenylalanine	R
35	Proline	R̸
36	Serine	R̸
37	Threonine	R
38	Tryptophan	R
39	Tyrosine	R̸
40	Valine	R
41	Carbohydrates	R̸
42	Fatty acids	R̸
43	Sterols, derivatives	R
44	Cholestanol	Ʉ
45	Cholesterol	U
46	Ergosterol	u
47	Biotin	R
48	Choline	R
49	Folic acid group	R
50	Inositol	R
51	Niacin	R
52	Pantothenic acid	R
53	Para-aminobenzoic acid	R̸
54	Pyridoxine group	R
55	Riboflavin	R
56	Thiamine	R

Beetle, cigarette, larva (Lasioderma serricorne)

No.	Nutrient	Value
57	Casein	U
58	Lactalbumin	U
59	Protein, total	45%[1]
60	Carbohydrates	U-R̸
61	Glucose	U
62	Starch	U
63	Sucrose	u(?)
64	Lipids, general	U
65	Fatty acids	R̸
66	Sterols, derivatives	R
67	Calciferol	Ʉ
68	Cholestanol	u
69	Cholesterol	U
70	Ergosterol	U
71	Sitosterol	U
72	Zymosterol	U
73	Biotin	R(?)
74	Choline	R(?)
75	Folic acid group	R̸
76	Inositol	R̸
77	Niacin	R̸
78	Pantothenic acid	R̸(?)
79	Para-aminobenzoic acid	R̸(?)

Beetle, cigarette, larva (Lasioderma serricorne) (concluded)

No.	Nutrient	Value
80	Pyridoxine group	R̸(?)
81	Riboflavin	R̸
82	Thiamine	R̸

Beetle, confused flour-, larva (Tribolium confusum)

No.	Nutrient	Value
83	Casein	U
84	Gelatin	U
85	Lactalbumin	U
86	Zein	U
87	Protein, total	15-45%[1]
88	Alanine	R̸
89	Arginine	R
90	Aspartic acid	R̸
91	Cystine	R̸
92	Glutamic acid	R̸
93	Glycine	R̸
94	Histidine	R
95	Hydroxyproline	R̸
96	Isoleucine	R
97	Leucine	R
98	Lysine	R
99	Methionine	R
100	Phenylalanine	R
101	Proline	R̸
102	Serine	R̸
103	Threonine	R
104	Tryptophan	R
105	Tyrosine	R̸
106	Valine	R
107	Carbohydrates	R̸(?)
108	Arabinose	Ʉ
109	Cellobiose	U(?)
110	Dextrin	U(?)
111	Fructose	Ʉ
112	Galactose	Ʉ
113	Glucose	U
114	Inulin	U(?)
115	Lactose	Ʉ
116	Maltose	U
117	Mannitol	U
118	Mannose	Ʉ
119	Raffinose	U
120	Sorbitol	U
121	Sorbose	Ʉ
122	Sucrose	Ʉ
123	Xylose	Ʉ
124	Lipids, general	U
125	Fatty acids	R̸
126	Sterols, derivatives	R
127	Calciferol	Ʉ
128	Cholestanol	u(?)
129	Cholesterol	U
130	Ergosterol	U
131	Sitosterol	U
132	Zymosterol	Ʉ
133	Biotin	R
134	Choline	R
135	Folic acid group	R
136	Inositol	R̸
137	Niacin	R
138	Pantothenic acid	R
139	Para-aminobenzoic acid	R̸
140	Pyridoxine group	R
141	Riboflavin	R
142	Thiamine	R

Beetle, drug-store, larva[2] (Stegobium paniceum)

No.	Nutrient	Value
143	Casein	U
144	Protein, total	45%[1]
145	Carbohydrates	50%[3]
146	Arabinose	Ʉ
147	Fructose	Ʉ
148	Galactose	Ʉ
149	Glucose	U
150	Inulin	Ʉ
151	Lactose	Ʉ
152	Maltose	U
153	Mannitol	U
154	Mannose	Ʉ
155	Raffinose	U
156	Sorbitol	Ʉ

Beetle, drug-store, larva[2] (Stegobium paniceum) (concluded)

No.	Nutrient	Value
157	Sorbose	Ʉ
158	Starch	U
159	Sucrose	Ʉ
160	Xylose	Ʉ
161	Lipids, general	U
162	Fatty acids	R
163	Sterols, derivatives	R
164	Calciferol	Ʉ
165	Cholestanol	U(?)
166	Cholesterol	U
167	Ergosterol	U
168	Sitosterol	U
169	Zymosterol	Ʉ
170	Biotin	R
171	Choline	R(?)
172	Folic acid group	R
173	Inositol	R̸(?)
174	Niacin	R
175	Pantothenic acid	R
176	Para-aminobenzoic acid	R̸
177	Pyridoxine group	R
178	Riboflavin	R
179	Thiamine	R

Beetle, drug-store, adult (Stegobium paniceum)

No.	Nutrient	Value
180	Biotin	R(?)
181	Choline	R̸(?)
182	Folic acid group	R̸(?)
183	Inositol	R̸
184	Niacin	R̸
185	Pantothenic acid	R̸
186	Para-aminobenzoic acid	R̸
187	Pyridoxine group	R̸
188	Riboflavin	Ʉ
189	Thiamine	R

Beetle, saw-toothed grain-, larva (Oryzaephilus surinamensis)

No.	Nutrient	Value
190	Gelatin	U
191	Protein, total	45%[1]
192	Carbohydrates	U
193	Arabinose	Ʉ
194	Dextrin	U
195	Fructose	U
196	Galactose	Ʉ
197	Glucose	U
198	Inulin	Ʉ
199	Lactose	U
200	Maltose	U
201	Mannitol	U
202	Mannose	u
203	Raffinose	Ʉ
204	Sorbitol	U
205	Sorbose	Ʉ
206	Starch	U
207	Sucrose	Ʉ
208	Xylose	Ʉ
209	Lipids, general	U
210	Fatty acids	R̸
211	Sterols, derivatives	R̸
212	Calciferol	Ʉ(?)
213	Cholestanol	U
214	Cholesterol	U
215	Ergosterol	U
216	Sitosterol	U
217	Zymosterol	U
218	Biotin	Ʉ
219	Choline	Ʉ
220	Inositol	Ʉ
221	Niacin	R
222	Pantothenic acid	R
223	Para-aminobenzoic acid	Ʉ
224	Pyridoxine group	Ʉ
225	Riboflavin	R
226	Thiamine	Ʉ

Beetle, spider, larva (Ptinus tectus)

No.	Nutrient	Value
227	Casein	U
228	Protein, total	45%[1]
229	Carbohydrates	U-R̸
230	Glucose	u
231	Starch	U

Beetle, spider, larva (Ptinus tectus) (concluded)

No.	Nutrient	Value
232	Lipids, general	u
233	Fatty acids	R̸
234	Sterols, derivatives	R
235	Calciferol	Ʉ
236	Cholestanol	u
237	Cholesterol	U
238	Ergosterol	U
239	Sitosterol	U
240	Zymosterol	u
241	Biotin	R
242	Choline	R
243	Inositol	R̸(?)
244	Niacin	R
245	Pantothenic acid	R
246	Para-aminobenzoic acid	R̸(?)
247	Pyridoxine group	R
248	Riboflavin	R
249	Thiamine	R

Blowfly, adult (Calliphora erythrocephala)

No.	Nutrient	Value
250	Carbohydrates	U
251	Arabinose	Ʉ
252	Cellobiose	Ʉ
253	Dextrin	u
254	Fructose	U
255	Galactose	U
256	Glucose	U
257	Inulin	Ʉ(?)
258	Lactose	u
259	Maltose	U
260	Mannitol	U
261	Mannose	U
262	Raffinose	U
263	Sorbitol	U
264	Sorbose	Ʉ
265	Starch	u
266	Sucrose	U
267	Xylose	u

Cockroach, German, nymph (Blattella germanica)[4]

No.	Nutrient	Value
268	Gelatin	U
269	Lactalbumin	U
270	Zein	U
271	Protein, total	15-30%
272	Alanine	R
273	Arginine	R
274	Aspartic acid	R̸
275	Cystine	R(?)
276	Glutamic acid	R̸
277	Glycine	R̸
278	Histidine	R̸
279	Hydroxyproline	R̸
280	Isoleucine	R
281	Leucine	R
282	Lysine	R
283	Methionine	R(?)
284	Phenylalanine	R̸
285	Proline	R̸
286	Serine	R
287	Threonine	R̸
288	Tryptophan	R(?)
289	Tyrosine	R̸
290	Valine	R
291	Carbohydrates	32%[3]
292	Dextrin	U
293	Glucose	U
294	Lactose	U
295	Starch	U
296	Sucrose	U
297	Lipids, general	U
298	Fatty acids	R̸
299	Sterols, derivatives	R
300	Cholesterol	U
301	Biotin	R̸(?)
302	Choline	R̸
303	Folic acid group	R̸
304	Inositol	R̸
305	Niacin	R
306	Pantothenic acid	R
307	Para-aminobenzoic acid	R̸
308	Pyridoxine group	R
309	Riboflavin	R
310	Thiamine	R

/1/ Per cent of protein in diet required to maintain growth and development. /2/ Deprived of normally present intracellular symbionts. /3/ Approximate percentage of carbohydrates required in optimum diet. /4/ Also aseptically reared on synthetic diet.

All insect tissues, and diets, contain nitrogen, carbon, oxygen and hydrogen. In addition, phosphorus, sulfur, iron, copper, magnesium, manganese, potassium, calcium and chlorine are probably universally required by insects. A number of other minerals, some only in traces, are consumed and found in the composition of the insect.

R = required; R̸ = not required; U = utilized; U̸ = not utilized; u = poorly utilized.

Fly, vinegar fruit-, larva (Drosophila melanogaster)[4]

No.	Nutrient	Value
311	Casein	U
312	Gelatin	U
313	Protein, total	2-3%[1]
314	Alanine	R̸
315	Arginine	R
316	Aspartic acid	R̸
317	Cystine	R̸
318	Glutamic acid	R̸
319	Glycine	R̸
320	Histidine	R
321	Hydroxyproline	R̸
322	Isoleucine	R
323	Leucine	R
324	Lysine	R
325	Methionine	R
326	Phenylalanine	R
327	Proline	R
328	Serine	R
329	Threonine	R
330	Tryptophan	R
331	Tyrosine	R̸
332	Valine	R
333	Carbohydrates	U
334	Arabinose	u
335	Cellobiose	U̸
336	Dextrin	u
337	Fructose	U
338	Galactose	u
339	Glucose	U
340	Inulin	U̸
341	Maltose	U
342	Mannitol	u
343	Mannose	U
344	Raffinose	U
345	Sorbitol	u
346	Sorbose	U
347	Starch	u(?)
348	Sucrose	U
349	Xylose	u
350	Lipids, general	U
351	Fatty acids	R̸
352	Sterols, derivatives	R
353	Calciferol	U̸
354	Cholestanol	u
355	Cholesterol	U
356	Ergosterol	U
357	Sitosterol	u
358	Biotin	R
359	Choline	R
360	Folic acid group	R̸
361	Inositol	R̸
362	Niacin	R
363	Pantothenic acid	R
364	Para-aminobenzoic acid	R̸
365	Pyridoxine group	R
366	Riboflavin	R
367	Thiamine	R

Mealworm, yellow, larva (Tenebrio molitor)

No.	Nutrient	Value
368	Casein	U
369	Gelatin	U
370	Lactalbumin	U
371	Zein	U
372	Protein, total	15-45%[1]
373	Lysine	R
374	Tryptophan	R
375	Carbohydrates	80-85%[3]
376	Arabinose	U
377	Cellobiose	u
378	Dextrin	U
379	Fructose	U
380	Galactose	U̸
381	Glucose	U
382	Inulin	U̸
383	Lactose	u
384	Maltose	U
385	Mannitol	U
386	Mannose	U̸
387	Raffinose	U
388	Sorbitol	U
389	Sorbose	U̸
390	Starch	U
391	Sucrose	U
392	Xylose	u
393	Lipids, general	U
394	Fatty acids	R̸
395	Sterols, derivatives	R
396	Calciferol	U̸
397	Cholesterol	U
398	Ergosterol	U
399	Sitosterol	U
400	Biotin	R
401	Choline	R̸(?)
402	Folic acid group	R
403	Inositol	R̸
404	Niacin	R
405	Pantothenic acid	R
406	Para-aminobenzoic acid	R̸
407	Pyridoxine group	R
408	Riboflavin	R
409	Thiamine	R

Mosquito, larva (Aedes aegypti)[4]

No.	Nutrient	Value
410	Casein	U
411	Alanine	R̸
412	Arginine	R
413	Aspartic acid	R̸
414	Cystine	R(?)
415	Glutamic acid	R̸
416	Glycine	R
417	Histidine	R
418	Hydroxyproline	R̸
419	Isoleucine	R
420	Leucine	R
421	Lysine	R
422	Methionine	R
423	Phenylalanine	R(?)
424	Proline	R̸
425	Serine	R
426	Threonine	R
427	Tryptophan	R
428	Tyrosine	R̸(?)
429	Valine	R(?)
430	Carbohydrates	U
431	Arabinose	U̸
432	Cellobiose	U̸(?)
433	Fructose	U(?)
434	Galactose	U(?)
435	Glucose	U(?)
436	Lactose	U(?)
437	Maltose	U(?)
438	Mannitol	U(?)
439	Mannose	U(?)
440	Raffinose	U̸
441	Sorbitol	U(?)
442	Sorbose	U̸
443	Starch	U
444	Sucrose	U
445	Xylose	u(?)
446	Lipids, general	U
447	Fatty acids	R̸
448	Sterols, derivatives	R
449	Calciferol	U̸
450	Cholestanol	u
451	Cholesterol	U
452	Ergosterol	u
453	Sitosterol	U
454	Zymosterol	u
455	Biotin	R
456	Choline	R
457	Folic acid group	R
458	Inositol	R̸(?)
459	Niacin	R
460	Panthothenic acid	R
461	Para-aminobenzoic acid	R̸(?)
462	Pyridoxine group	R
463	Riboflavin	R
464	Thiamine	R

Moth, Mediterranean flour-, larva (Ephestia kuehniella)

No.	Nutrient	Value
465	Casein	U
466	Protein, total	45%[1]
467	Carbohydrates	80%[3]
468	Dextrin	U
469	Fructose	U
470	Galactose	U̸
471	Glucose	U
472	Inulin	U̸
473	Lactose	U̸
474	Maltose	U
475	Mannitol	U̸
476	Raffinose	U̸
477	Sorbitol	U
478	Sorbose	U̸
479	Starch	U
480	Sucrose	U̸
481	Xylose	U̸
482	Lipids, general	U
483	Fatty acids	R
484	Sterols, derivatives	R
485	Calciferol	U̸
486	Cholestanol	u(?)
487	Cholesterol	U
488	Ergosterol	u(?)
489	Sitosterol	U
490	Zymosterol	U̸
491	Biotin	R
492	Choline	R
493	Folic acid group	R
494	Inositol	R
495	Niacin	R
496	Pantothenic acid	R
497	Para-aminobenzoic acid	R̸
498	Pyridoxine group	R
499	Riboflavin	R
500	Thiamine	R

Moth, webbing clothes- (Timeola bisseliella)

No.	Nutrient	Value
501	Casein	U
502	Protein, total	20-80%[1]
503	Carbohydrates	U-R̸(?)
504	Glucose	U
505	Starch	U
506	Lipids, general	U
507	Fatty acids	R
508	Sterols, derivatives	R
509	Cholesterol	U
510	Biotin	R(?)
511	Choline	R
512	Inositol	R̸
513	Niacin	R
514	Pantothenic acid	R
515	Para-aminobenzoic acid	R̸
516	Pyridoxine group	R
517	Riboflavin	R
518	Thiamine	R

Parasite of spruce budworm larva (Pseudosarcophaga affinis)[4]

No.	Nutrient	Value
519	Amino acids, total	2%[5]
520	Alanine	R
521	Arginine	R
522	Aspartic acid	R̸
523	Cysteine	R̸
524	Glutamic acid	R̸
525	Glycine	R
526	Histidine	R
527	Hydroxyproline	R̸
528	Isoleucine	R
529	Leucine	R
530	Lysine	R
531	Methionine	R
532	Phenylalanine	R
533	Proline	R̸
534	Serine	R
535	Threonine	R
536	Tryptophan	R
537	Tyrosine	R
538	Valine	R
539	Glutathione	R̸
540	Carbohydrates	U
541	Arabinose	u
542	Dextrin	U
543	Galactose	u
544	Glucose	0.5%[5]
545	Glycogen	U
546	Lactose	U
547	Levulose	U
548	Maltose	U
549	Mannitol	u
550	Mannose	u
551	Melezitose	U
552	Raffinose	u
553	Rhamnose	u
554	Sorbose	u
555	Starch	U
556	Sucrose	U
557	Sorbitol	u
558	Trebalose	u
559	Xylose	U
560	Cholesterol	0.1%[5]
561	Fatty acids	0.4%[5]
562	Ribonucleic acid	0.15%[5]
563	Biotin	R
564	Choline	2.0mg[6]
565	Folic acid group	R̸
566	Inositol	U
567	Niacin	0.3mg[6]
568	Pantothenic acid	0.43mg[6]
569	Para-aminobenzoic acid	R̸
570	Pyridoxine	R̸
571	Riboflavin	0.14mg[6]
572	Thiamine	0.1mg[6]
573	Vitamin B_{12}	R̸
574	Galactose	u
575	Glucose	U
576	Lactose	u
577	Levulose	U
578	Maltose	u
579	Mannitol	u
580	Raffinose	u
581	Sucrose	U
582	Xylose	u

/1/ Per cent of protein in diet required to maintain growth and development. /3/ Approximate percentage of carbohydrates required in optimum diet. /4/ Also aseptically reared on synthetic diet. /5/ Per cent in diet required to maintain optimum growth and development. /6/ mg/100 ml in diet required to maintain optimum growth and development.

174. NUTRIENT UTILIZATION: LOWER ALGAE AND RELATED COLORLESS ORGANISMS

Oxygen is essential for all organisms listed. Carbon dioxide is required by all species in this table for which data are available. Certain green forms, e.g., Chlamydomonas moewusii and Anabaena cylindrica, appear unable to grow in darkness. Colorless and green forms grown in darkness require an additional carbon source.

U = utilized; u = poorly utilized; Ʉ = not utilized; R = required; Ɍ = not required.

	Photosynthetic Forms																Colorless Forms									
Nutrient	Chlamydomonas agloeformis	C. moewusii	Chlorogonium elongatum	C. euchlorum	Chlorella vulgaris[1]	Euglena anabaena minor	E. deses	E. gracilis typica	E. gracilis bacillaris	E. gracilis urophora	E. klebsii	E. pisciformis	E. stellata	Haematococcus pluvialis	Nitzschia closterium	Anabaena cylindrica[2]	Astasia longa	A. quartana	Chilomonas paramecium	Hyalogonium klebsii	Polytoma caudatum	P. obtusum	P. ocellatum	P. uvella	Polytomella caeca	Prototheca zopfii
Vitamins																										
1 Cobalamin	Ɍ	Ɍ	Ɍ	Ɍ	Ɍ	Ɍ[3]		R[4]	R[4]	Ɍ[3]?		R[3]?	Ɍ	Ɍ	Ɍ	Ɍ			Ɍ							Ɍ
2 Thiamine	Ɍ	Ɍ	Ɍ	Ɍ	Ɍ	Ɍ[3]		R	R	R	R	R[3]?	Ɍ	Ɍ	Ɍ	Ɍ	R		R			R	Ɍ	R	Ɍ	R
3 Other	Ɍ	Ɍ	Ɍ	Ɍ	Ɍ	Ɍ[3]				?		Ɍ[3]?	Ɍ	Ɍ	Ɍ	Ɍ			Ɍ				Ɍ		Ɍ	
Carbon Source: Sugars																										
4 Arabinose		Ʉ?	Ʉ?	u															Ʉ?					Ʉ		Ʉ
5 Glucose		Ʉ?	Ʉ?	U	Ʉ	Ʉ	Ʉ	U	Ʉ	Ʉ	U				Ʉ	Ʉ		Ʉ?				Ʉ	Ʉ	Ʉ	U
6 Maltose		Ʉ?	Ʉ?	u						Ʉ	U							Ʉ?				Ʉ	Ʉ	Ʉ	U
7 Sucrose		Ʉ?	Ʉ?	u	Ʉ	Ʉ	Ʉ			Ʉ	Ʉ				U			Ʉ?						Ʉ	Ʉ
8 Xylose		Ʉ?	Ʉ?	u														Ʉ?						Ʉ	Ʉ
Carbon Source: Organic Acids (Other than Fatty Acids)[5]																										
9 Citric	Ʉ	Ʉ			u	Ʉ		Ʉ	U		Ʉ										Ʉ					Ʉ U[6]
10 Fumaric		Ʉ			u		Ʉ[6]	U																		Ʉ U[6]
11 Lactic	Ʉ	Ʉ		Ʉ	U	Ʉ	U	Ʉ	U		Ʉ		Ʉ				U?	U	U	U	Ʉ	U	U?	Ʉ?	Ʉ?	Ʉ U[6]
12 Malic	Ʉ	Ʉ		Ʉ	u	Ʉ	Ʉ[6]	U	U[6]		Ʉ		Ʉ				U?	Ʉ	Ʉ	Ʉ	Ʉ	U	U?	Ʉ?	Ʉ?	Ʉ
13 Phosphoglyceric	Ʉ	Ʉ				Ʉ	U	U	U[6]		Ʉ		Ʉ								Ʉ					Ʉ
14 Pyruvic	Ʉ	Ʉ		u	Ʉ	U	Ʉ	U			Ʉ		Ʉ				Ʉ?	u	Ʉ	U	U	u	u	u	u	Ʉ
15 Succinic	Ʉ	Ʉ		U	u	Ʉ	U	U	U[6]	Ʉ?			Ʉ				U?	U	u	U	Ʉ	U?	U?	U?	u	Ʉ U[6]
Carbon Source: Alcohols[7]																										
16 i-Butanol								U		U							u		U		Ʉ	Ʉ	Ʉ	Ʉ	Ʉ	Ʉ
17 n-Butanol		Ʉ						U		U							U	Ʉ	U		Ʉ	Ʉ	Ʉ	Ʉ	Ʉ	U
18 Ethanol		Ʉ	Ʉ	Ʉ				U		U							U	Ʉ	U		Ʉ	Ʉ	Ʉ	Ʉ	Ʉ	U
19 Glycerol		Ʉ			Ʉ	Ʉ		U		Ʉ							U	Ʉ	U		U	U	U	U	U	Ʉ
20 n-Hexanol								U		U							u		U		Ʉ	Ʉ	Ʉ	Ʉ	U	Ʉ
21 Methanol								U		Ʉ							U	Ʉ	U		Ʉ	Ʉ	Ʉ	Ʉ	U	
22 i-Pentanol								Ʉ		Ʉ							U	Ʉ	U		Ʉ	Ʉ	Ʉ	Ʉ	Ʉ	U
23 n-Pentanol								U		Ʉ							U	Ʉ	U		U	U	U	Ʉ	Ʉ	u
24 i-Propanol								Ʉ		Ʉ							Ʉ		u[8]		Ʉ	Ʉ	u	Ʉ	Ʉ	U
25 n-Propanol								U		Ʉ							U	Ʉ	u[8]		Ʉ	Ʉ	U	Ʉ	Ʉ	U
Carbon Source: Fatty Acids[9]																										
26 Acetic	U	Ʉ	U	U	u	Ʉ	U	U	U		U		U		U		U		Ʉ		U	U	U	Ʉ	U	U
27 i-Butyric	Ʉ		Ʉ	Ʉ		Ʉ	Ʉ	U		U		U		U			u	u	Ʉ	U	U	U	U	U	U	U
28 n-Butyric	U	Ʉ	U	Ʉ		Ʉ	Ʉ	U		Ʉ	U	Ʉ		U			U	U	U	U	U	U	U	U	U	U
29 i-Caproic								u		U							u	U	U		U	U	U	U	U	U
30 n-Caproic	Ʉ		Ʉ		Ʉ	Ʉ[10]		U		Ʉ[10]		Ʉ					u	U	U		U	U	U	U	U	U
31 n-Decylic								u									U		U		Ʉ	Ʉ	Ʉ	Ʉ	Ʉ	Ʉ
32 n-Heptylic					Ʉ[10]	Ʉ[10]		U		Ʉ[10]							U		U		Ʉ	Ʉ	Ʉ	Ʉ	Ʉ	Ʉ
33 n-Nonylic					Ʉ[10]	Ʉ[10]		u		u							u		u		Ʉ	Ʉ	Ʉ	Ʉ	Ʉ	Ʉ
34 n-Octylic					Ʉ[10]	Ʉ[10]		U		Ʉ[10]							U		U		Ʉ	Ʉ	Ʉ	Ʉ	Ʉ	Ʉ
35 Propionic	U	Ʉ	U	U	u	Ʉ		U		U		Ʉ	Ʉ	Ʉ			Ʉ	U	U		Ʉ	Ʉ	Ʉ	u	u	U
36 i-Valeric								U		Ʉ							U?	u	u		Ʉ	Ʉ	Ʉ	Ʉ	Ʉ	U
37 n-Valeric	Ʉ	Ʉ	Ʉ	Ʉ				U		Ʉ							U	u	u		Ʉ	Ʉ	Ʉ	Ʉ	u	U
Nitrogen Sources[11]																										
38 D-Alanine					U	Ʉ		U[12]	U[12]		U	Ʉ[13]														
39 Ammonium	U	U	U	U	U	Ʉ		U[12]	U[12]	U[12]	U	Ʉ[13]	U	U	U	U	U	U	U			u	U	Ʉ	U	U
40 D-Arginine					Ʉ	Ʉ		U[12]			U	Ʉ[13]	U		U			U			U	U	U	U	U	U
41 L-Asparagine	U[12]	U		U[12]	U	Ʉ		U[12]			U	Ʉ[14]	U	U[12]					u		U					
42 D-Glutamic acid[15]			Ʉ		Ʉ	Ʉ		U[12]	U[6,12]	U[6,12]	U	Ʉ[13]	U						U		U		U			
43 Glycine	U[12]			U	U	Ʉ		U[12]			Ʉ	Ʉ[13]	U	U[12]								U	U		U	
44 Histidine					Ʉ	Ʉ		Ʉ[12]			U	Ʉ[13]	U									U	u		u	
45 L-Leucine					Ʉ	Ʉ		U[12]			U	Ʉ[13]	U									U	u		u	
46 D-Lysine					Ʉ	Ʉ		Ʉ			U	Ʉ[13]	U									U	u		Ʉ	
47 Nitrate	U	U	U	U	Ʉ	Ʉ		Ʉ			u	Ʉ[13]	U									Ʉ	Ʉ			
48 Peptone	U[12]	U	U[12]	U[12]	U	U		U[12]	U[12]	U[12]	u	Ʉ[13]	U	u	U	U	U		?		Ʉ	Ʉ	U	Ʉ	Ʉ	
49 DL-Phenylalanine					U	U		U[12]			U	Ʉ[13]	U									u	u		Ʉ	U
50 DL-Proline					U	U		U[12]			U	Ʉ[13]	U									u	u		U	
51 DL-Serine					Ʉ	u		U[12]			U	Ʉ[13]	U									u	u		u	
52 L-Tryptophan					Ʉ	Ʉ		Ʉ			U	Ʉ[13]	Ʉ									u	u		u	
53 L-Tyrosine					Ʉ	Ʉ		Ʉ			U	Ʉ[13]	Ʉ									u				
54 DL-Valine					Ʉ	Ʉ		U[12]			U	Ʉ[13]	U												u	

/1/ Additional components not listed: fructose, U; galactose, u; lactose, U; mannose, u; inulin, u; methyl-γ-D-glucoside, u; methyl-β-D-glucoside, U; starch, u; cis-aconitic, u; inositol, u; dulcitol, u; mannitol, u; sorbitol, u; L-aspartic acid, u. /2/ Additional components not listed: mannitol, Ʉ; elementary nitrogen, U. /3/ The organism has been reported not to require vitamins; it is possible that this condition, as in other species of Euglena, exists only after adaptation to vitamin-less media. /4/ Pseudo-cobalamin also utilized. /5/ It has been shown that Prototheca zopfii and Euglena gracilis utilize most of these acids only at pH 3.5-5.5; the majority of the negative results tabulated may not be significant because they were obtained in media having a pH near neutrality. /6/ Utilized only at pH 3.0-5.5. /7/ Optimal concentrations are similar to those of the corresponding fatty acid (cf Fn 9). /8/ Inadequate for growth in mineral media. /9/ The following are average ranges of concentration (g per 100 ml media) at which fatty acids are utilized and non-toxic: acetic, propionic, butyric and isobutyric acids, 0.1-0.2; valeric and isovaleric acids 0.05-0.1; caproic, iso-caproic, heptylic and octylic acids, 0.01-0.03; nonylic acid, 0.01; decyclic acid, 0.005-0.008. Some negative results tabulated may be incorrect if toxic concentrations were employed. Toxicity usually increases with length of carbon chain and with decrease in pH of medium. /10/ Employed at toxic concentrations. /11/ For photosynthetic species data pertain to utilization in light. Some amino acids may serve also as carbon sources. /12/ Also utilized in darkness. /13/ Negative results may not be valid because tests were conducted in media lacking thiamine. /14/ Growth is obtained only if thiamine is present. /15/ When utilized, a good carbon source.

175. SUGAR UTILIZATION FOR GROWTH: FILAMENTOUS FUNGI

Interpretation of the amount of growth obtained on different sugars is often subject to error. Low yields may be attributed to slow utilization of the sugar involved, but are frequently caused by other factors. It is possible that some organisms listed as not utilizing a certain sugar, or utilizing it poorly will be found to utilize it well under different nutritional conditions. U = utilized; u = utilized slowly; Ʉ = utilization slight or none.

	Species	D-Glucose	D-Fructose	D-Mannose	D-Galactose	L-Sorbose	L-Arabinose	D-Xylose	Maltose	Sucrose	Lactose	Cellobiose	Raffinose
1	Achlya flagellata	U	Ʉ	Ʉ	Ʉ		Ʉ	Ʉ	U	U	Ʉ		Ʉ
2	Allomyces sp	U	Ʉ	U	Ʉ	Ʉ	Ʉ	Ʉ	U	Ʉ	Ʉ	Ʉ	
3	Alternaria solani	U	U	U	U	u	U	U	U	U	u	u	u
4	Aspergillus clavatus	U	U	U	U	Ʉ	U	U	U	U	u	U	U
5	A. elegans	U	U	U	u	u	U	U	U	U	u	u	U
6	A. niger	U	U	U	u	U	u	U	U	U	u	U	U
7	A. oryzae	U	U	U	U		u	u	U		Ʉ		u
8	A. rugulosus	U	U	U	U	u	U	U	U	U	u	u	U
9	Blakeslea trispora	U	U	U	U				U	u	u		
10	Blastocladia pringsheimii	U	U	U	Ʉ	Ʉ	Ʉ	Ʉ	U	U	Ʉ		
11	Botrytis cinerea	U	U	U	U	U	U	U	U	U	U	U	U
12	Ceratostomella fimbriata	U	u	U	u	Ʉ	u	u	U	U	Ʉ	u	Ʉ
13	Chaetomium convolutum	U	u	U	U	Ʉ	U	U	U	U	u	U	Ʉ
14	C. globosum	U	U	U	U	u	u	u	U	U	u	u	u
15	Choanephora cucurbitarum	U	U	U	U	Ʉ	u	u	U	Ʉ	Ʉ	U	Ʉ
16	Chytridium sp	U	U	U	U	Ʉ	Ʉ	Ʉ	Ʉ	Ʉ	Ʉ	Ʉ	Ʉ
17	Claviceps purpurea	U	U				U		U	U	U		U
18	Coccidioides immitis	U	U	U	U		Ʉ	u	U	Ʉ	Ʉ	U	u
19	Colletotrichum lindemuthianum	U	U	U	U	Ʉ	u	u	U	U	U	U	U
20	Collybia velutipes	U	U	U	u	Ʉ	u	u	U	U	u	U	u
21	Cordyceps militaris	U	U	U	U	Ʉ	u	U	U	u	Ʉ	U	u
22	Dendrophoma obscurans	U	U		U	Ʉ	u	U	U	U	Ʉ	U	u
23	Diaporthe phaseolorum batat.	U	U						U	U	U		
24	Dictyuchus monosporus	U	Ʉ	Ʉ	Ʉ		Ʉ	Ʉ	Ʉ	Ʉ	Ʉ		Ʉ
25	Diplodia macrospora	U	U	U	U				U	U	u		
26	D. natalensis	U	U	U	u				U	U	u		
27	Endoconidiophora fagacearum	U	u	U	u	Ʉ	u	u	Ʉ	U	Ʉ	U	u
28	Endothia parasitica	U	U	U	u	u	u	u	U	U	Ʉ	U	U
29	Entomophthora apiculata	U	u	U	u	u	Ʉ	Ʉ	Ʉ	Ʉ	Ʉ	Ʉ	Ʉ
30	E. coronata	U	U	U	u	Ʉ	Ʉ	Ʉ	Ʉ	Ʉ	Ʉ	Ʉ	Ʉ
31	Fusarium conglutinans	U	U	U	U	u	U	U	U	U	u	u	u
32	F. culmorum	U	U	U	U	u	u	u	u	u	u	U	U
33	F. lycopersici	U	U	U	U	U	U	U	U	U	u	u	u
34	F. medicaginis	U	U	U	U	u	U	U	U	U	u	u	U
35	F. nivale	U	U	U	U	u	U	U	U	U	u	U	U
36	F. niveum	U	U	U	U	U	U	U	U	U	U	U	U
37	F. tracheiphilum	U	U	U	U	u	U	U	U	u	U	u	U
38	Glomerella cingulata	U	U	U	U	u	U	U	U	U	u	U	U
39	Helicostylum pyriforme	U	U	U	U				U	u	u		
40	Helminthosporium sativum	U	U	U	u	u	u	u	U	U	u	u	u
41	Lenzites saepiaria	U	U	U	u	u	Ʉ	u	U	u	u	Ʉ	Ʉ
42	L. trabaea	U	u	U	u	u	u	u	U	u	U	U	u
43	Leptomitus lacteus	Ʉ	Ʉ		Ʉ				Ʉ	Ʉ			
44	Macrochytrium sp	U	Ʉ	U	Ʉ	Ʉ	Ʉ	U	U	Ʉ	Ʉ	U	Ʉ
45	Melanconium fuligineum	U	U	U	U	u	u	u	U	U	Ʉ	U	u
46	Memnoniella echinata	U	U	U	U		U	U	U	U	U	U	U
47	Monilinia fructicola	U	U	U	U	U	u	U	U	U	Ʉ	U	u
48	Monosporium apiospermum	U	U	U	U	Ʉ	u	U	u	U	u	u	u
49	Morchella esculenta	U	U	U	U		U	U	U	U	Ʉ	U	U
50	Mucor ramannianus	U	U	U	U	u	u	U	U	Ʉ	U	U	Ʉ
51	Neocosmospora vasinfecta	U	U	U	U	Ʉ	U	U	U	U	u	u	u
52	Ophiobolus graminis	U	u	U	U	Ʉ	u	u	U	U	u	u	u
53	Penicillium chrysogenum	U	U	U	U	u	U	U	U	U	u	u	U
54	P. digitatum	U	U	U	U		U	U	u	U	U	U	
55	P. expansum	U	U	U	U	u	u	U	U	U	Ʉ	U	U
56	P. spiculosporum	U	U	U	U	u	U	U	U	U	Ʉ	U	u
57	Phoma betae	U	U	U	U	u	U	U	U	U	u	U	U
58	Phycomyces blakesleeanus	U	U	U	u	Ʉ	u	U	U	U	Ʉ	u	Ʉ
59	Phymatotrichum omnivorum	U	U	U	Ʉ			Ʉ	U	U	u		u
60	Phytophthora cactorum	U	u	u	Ʉ				U	U	Ʉ		
61	P. erythroseptica	U	u	U	Ʉ				U	U	Ʉ		
62	P. fagopyri	U	u	u	Ʉ				u	U	Ʉ		
63	P. infestans	U	U	u	Ʉ	Ʉ	Ʉ	Ʉ	u	u	Ʉ	Ʉ	Ʉ
64	Pilaira moreaui	U	U	U	U				U	u	U		
65	Polyporus albellus	U	u	U	u	Ʉ	u	U	U	Ʉ	Ʉ	u	Ʉ
66	P. versicolor	U	U	U	u	u	U	u	U	U	u	U	u
67	Pythiogeton uniforme	U	U		Ʉ		Ʉ	U	U	U	u	U	
68	Pythiomorpha gonapodyoides	U	U	u	Ʉ				u	U	Ʉ		
69	Pythium ascophallon	U	u	U	Ʉ				U	U	Ʉ		
70	Rhizophlyctis rosea	U	Ʉ	Ʉ	Ʉ	Ʉ	Ʉ	Ʉ	Ʉ	Ʉ	Ʉ	U	
71	Rhizopus nigricans	U	U	U	U				U	Ʉ	Ʉ		
72	R. suinus	U	U	U	U				u	Ʉ	Ʉ		
73	Rosellinia arcuata	U	U	U	u				U	u	u		
74	Saprolegnia delica	U	U	Ʉ	Ʉ		Ʉ	Ʉ	U	Ʉ	Ʉ		Ʉ
75	S. ferax	U	Ʉ	Ʉ	Ʉ		Ʉ	Ʉ	U	Ʉ	Ʉ		Ʉ
76	Schizophyllum commune	U	U	U	u	Ʉ	u	u	u	u	u	u	u
77	Schizothecium longicolle	U	U	U	Ʉ	Ʉ	Ʉ	U	U	Ʉ	Ʉ	U	Ʉ
78	Sclerotium delphinii	U	U				U	U	U	U			
79	Septoria nodorum	U			u	Ʉ			u	u	u		
80	Sordaria fimicola	U	U	U	u	Ʉ	u	u	U	Ʉ	u	U	Ʉ
81	Sphaeropsis malorum	U	U	U	U	u	u	u	U	U	u	U	u
82	Stysanus stemonitis	U	u	U	U	Ʉ	U	u	U	U	U	U	U
83	Syncephalastrum racemosum	U	U	U	U	Ʉ	u	u	U	Ʉ	Ʉ	u	u
84	Thielavia basicola	U	U	U	U				U	U	Ʉ		
85	Thraustotheca clavata	U	Ʉ	Ʉ	Ʉ		Ʉ	Ʉ	U	U	Ʉ		Ʉ
86	Typhula variabilis	U	U	U	u				U	U	Ʉ		
87	Ustilago violacea	U	U	U	U		Ʉ	Ʉ	U	U	Ʉ	U	Ʉ

176. ORGANIC COMPLEXES REQUIREMENTS: BACTERIA

R = required; Ɍ = not required.

	Species	Vitamin A	Ascorbic Acid	Biotin	Choline	Cobalamin	Vitamin D	Vitamin E	Folic Acid	Inositol	Vitamin K	Niacin	Pantothenic Acid	Para-aminobenzoic Acid	Pyridoxine Group[1]	Riboflavin	Thiamine
1	Aerobacter aerogenes	Ɍ	Ɍ	Ɍ	Ɍ	Ɍ	Ɍ	Ɍ	Ɍ	Ɍ	Ɍ	Ɍ	Ɍ	Ɍ	Ɍ	Ɍ	Ɍ
2	Bacillus alvei			Ɍ								Ɍ					R
3	B. anthracis			Ɍ								Ɍ					R
4	B. brevis			Ɍ								Ɍ					Ɍ
5	B. cereus			Ɍ								Ɍ					Ɍ
6	B. cereus mycoides			Ɍ								Ɍ					Ɍ
7	B. circulans			R								Ɍ					R
8	B. coagulans			R								R[2]					R
9	B. licheniformis			Ɍ								Ɍ					Ɍ
10	B. macerans			R								Ɍ					R
11	B. megaterium			Ɍ								Ɍ					Ɍ
12	B. pasteurii			R?								R ?					R
13	B. polymyxa			R								Ɍ					Ɍ
14	B. pumilis			R								Ɍ					Ɍ
15	B. sphaericus			R?								Ɍ					R
16	B. subtilis			Ɍ								Ɍ					Ɍ
17	B. subtilis niger			Ɍ								Ɍ					Ɍ
18	Brucella abortus	Ɍ	Ɍ	R	Ɍ	Ɍ	Ɍ	Ɍ	Ɍ	Ɍ	Ɍ	R	R	Ɍ	Ɍ	Ɍ	R
19	B. melitensis	Ɍ	Ɍ	R	Ɍ	Ɍ	Ɍ	Ɍ	Ɍ	Ɍ	Ɍ	R	R	Ɍ	Ɍ	Ɍ	R
20	B. suis	Ɍ	Ɍ	R	Ɍ	Ɍ	Ɍ	Ɍ	Ɍ	Ɍ	Ɍ	R	R	Ɍ	Ɍ	Ɍ	R
21	Erwinia amylovora	Ɍ	Ɍ	Ɍ	Ɍ	Ɍ	Ɍ	Ɍ	Ɍ	Ɍ	Ɍ	R	Ɍ	Ɍ	Ɍ	Ɍ	Ɍ
22	E. tracheiphila	Ɍ	Ɍ	Ɍ	Ɍ	Ɍ	Ɍ	Ɍ	Ɍ	Ɍ	Ɍ	R[3]	Ɍ	Ɍ	Ɍ	Ɍ	Ɍ
23	Escherichia coli	Ɍ	Ɍ	Ɍ	Ɍ	Ɍ	Ɍ	Ɍ	Ɍ	Ɍ	Ɍ	Ɍ	Ɍ	Ɍ	Ɍ	Ɍ	Ɍ
24	Hemophilus influenzae[4]	Ɍ	Ɍ	Ɍ	Ɍ	Ɍ	Ɍ	Ɍ	Ɍ	Ɍ	Ɍ	Ɍ	Ɍ	Ɍ	Ɍ	Ɍ	Ɍ
	Lactobacillus																
25	Hetero-fermentative[5]			R		R[3,6]			R[3,7]			R	R	R[3,7]	R[3,7]	Ɍ	R
26	Homo-fermentative[5]			R		R[3,6]			R[3,7]			R	R	R[3,7]	R[3,7]	R	Ɍ
27	Leuconostoc citrovorum			R					R			R[8]	R		R[7,9]	R[7,9]	R[7,9]
28	L. dextranicum			R					R			R[8]	R		R[7,9]	R[7,9]	R[7,9]
29	L. mesenteroides			R					R			R[8]	R		R[7,9]	R[7,9]	R[7,9]
30	Pasteurella multocida[10]			R[3]								R[11]	R				
31	P. pseudotuberculosis	Ɍ	Ɍ	Ɍ	Ɍ	Ɍ	Ɍ	Ɍ	Ɍ	Ɍ	Ɍ	Ɍ	Ɍ	Ɍ	Ɍ	Ɍ	Ɍ
32	P. tularense																R[12]
33	Proteus morgani											R	R				
34	P. vulgaris											R					
35	Salmonella cholerae-sius	Ɍ	Ɍ	Ɍ	Ɍ	Ɍ	Ɍ	Ɍ	Ɍ	Ɍ	Ɍ	Ɍ	Ɍ	Ɍ	Ɍ	Ɍ	Ɍ
36	S. enteritidis	Ɍ	Ɍ	Ɍ	Ɍ	Ɍ	Ɍ	Ɍ	Ɍ	Ɍ	Ɍ	Ɍ	Ɍ	Ɍ	Ɍ	Ɍ	Ɍ
37	S. gallinarum																R
38	S. pullorum	Ɍ	Ɍ	Ɍ	Ɍ	Ɍ	Ɍ	Ɍ	Ɍ	Ɍ	Ɍ	R[3]	Ɍ	Ɍ	Ɍ	Ɍ	Ɍ
39	S. schottmuelleri	Ɍ	Ɍ	Ɍ	Ɍ	Ɍ	Ɍ	Ɍ	Ɍ	Ɍ	Ɍ	Ɍ	Ɍ	Ɍ	Ɍ	Ɍ	Ɍ
40	S. typhosa	Ɍ	Ɍ	Ɍ	Ɍ	Ɍ	Ɍ	Ɍ	Ɍ	Ɍ	Ɍ	Ɍ	Ɍ	Ɍ	Ɍ	Ɍ	Ɍ
41	Serratia marcescens	Ɍ	Ɍ	Ɍ	Ɍ	Ɍ	Ɍ	Ɍ	Ɍ	Ɍ	Ɍ	Ɍ	Ɍ	Ɍ	Ɍ	Ɍ	Ɍ
42	Shigella alkalescens	Ɍ	Ɍ	Ɍ	Ɍ	[illegible]	Ɍ	Ɍ	Ɍ	Ɍ	Ɍ	Ɍ	Ɍ	Ɍ	Ɍ	Ɍ	Ɍ
43	S. paradysenteriae											R[13]	R[3]				
44	S. sonnei											R[13]	R[3]				
45	Staphylococcus albus			R								R	R[9]		R[9]		R
46	S. aureus			R								R	R[9]		R[9]		R

/1/ Includes pyridoxine, pyridoxal, pyridoxamine. /2/ One strain only. /3/ Various strains. /4/ Requires hemin, diphosphopyridine. H. parainfluenzae requires diphosphopyridine nucleotide, putrescine. /5/ Some strains also require pyridoxal phosphate, pantethine. /6/ Or nucleotides. /7/ Occasional requirement as growth stimulant. /8/ Nicotinic acid for some strains only. /9/ Occasional requirement for growth. /10/ For P. pestis: only hemin required for aerobic types; no known requirements for anaerobic types. /11/ Nicotinamide. /12/ Thiamine diphosphate; adenosine also required. /13/ Usually required.

177. ORGANIC COMPLEXES REQUIREMENTS: FUNGI

Data are applicable to organic complexes (vitamins) which must be supplied to each organism in its substrate. In each case, the organism synthesizes all other vitamins needed in its metabolism. Different isolates of the same species may have different requirements.

B = biotin; I = inositol; N = nicotinic acid; Pn = pantothenic acid; Pa = para-aminobenzoic acid; Px = pyridoxine; T = thiamine; O = none.

Species	Vitamins Required	Species	Vitamins Required	Species	Vitamins Required	Species	Vitamins Required
1 Absidia spp[1]	O	63 Dematium chodati & pullulans	O	124 Mortierella spp[6]	O	188 Saccharomyces chodati	B, Pn, Px
2 A. ramosa	T[2]	64 D. nigrum	T[2]	125 Mucor spp[27]	O	189 Saccharomycodes ludwigii	B, I, N, Pn, Px, T
3 Achlya conspicua	O	65 Dendrophoma obscurans	T	126 M. mucedo	T	190 S. oviformis	B, Pn, Px
4 Allescheria boydii	B	66 Dermatea balsamea	T	127 Mycoderma lipolytica	T	191 S. tubiformis	B, Pn
5 Allomyces arbusculus	T[3]	67 Diaporthe strumella	O	128 M. valida	B	192 S. uvarum	B, I
6 Alternaria solani	O	68 Diplodia macrospora	B	129 Mycosphaerella confusa	O	193 Saprolegnia delica & mixta	O
7 Amanita pantherina	T[4]	69 Dipodascus uninucleatus	B, T	130 M. grossulariae	O	194 Schizophyllum commune	T[2]
8 Aphanomyces campto-stylus	O	70 Dothidella quercus	O	131 M. sentina	T	195 Schizosaccharomyces pombe	B, I, N, Pn
9 A. phycophilus	T	71 Endothia parasitica	B, T	132 Mycotorula lactis	N	196 Schwanniomyces occidentalis	B
10 Armillaria mellea	O	72 Entyloma arnoseridis	O	133 Nectria coccinea	T[17]	197 Sclerotinia camelliae	B, I, T
11 Ascobolus spp[5]	O	73 Epichloë typhina	I[17], T	134 Nematospora coryli	T	198 S. minor	B[17], T[17]
12 Ascochyta pisi	O	74 Epidermophyton floc-cosum	O	135 N. gossypii	B, I, T	199 S. sclerotiorum	O
13 Ascoidea rubescens	Px, T	75 Eremascus fertilis	O	136 Neocosmospora vasinfecta	O	200 Sclerotium delphinii	T[2]
14 Ashbya gossypii	B, I, T	76 Eremothecium ashbyi	B, I, T	137 Neurospora spp[28]	B	201 Septoria spp[35]	O
15 Aspergillus spp[6]	O	77 Exobasidium vaccinii	O	138 Nyctalis asterophora	O	202 S. apii	T[2]
16 Basidiobolus ranarum	O	78 Flammula carbonaria & penetrans	T	139 Ophiobolus graminis	B, T	203 Sistotrema confluens	T
17 Blakeslea trispora	T[2]	79 Fomes spp[18]	T	140 O. miyabeanus	O	204 Sordaria fimicola	B
18 Blastocladia pring-sheimii	B, N, T	80 F. fraxineus	O	141 O. oryzinus	B	205 Spathularia flavida	B, Px, T
19 Blastomyces brasiliensis	T	81 Fusarium spp[19]	T	142 Ophiostoma catonianum	Px, T[17]	206 Spermophthora gossypii	O
20 B. dermatitidis	T	82 F. avenaceum[20]	B	143 O. caeruleum	T	207 Sphaerobolus stellatus	O
21 Boletus spp[7]	T	83 Ganoderma lucidum	T	144 O. fagi	B[17], Px	208 Sphaeropsis malorum	O
22 Botrytis allii & cinerea	O	84 Glenosporella loboi	O	145 Panaeolus campanulatus	T	209 Sphaerulina trifolii	T
23 Brettanomyces bruxel-lensis	Px	85 Gliocladium fimbriatum	O	146 Panus stipticus & torulosus	T	210 Sporotrichum spp[36]	T
24 Bulgaria inquinans	O	86 Gloeocystidium roseo-cremeum	O	147 Parasitella simplex	T	211 S. schenckii	T
25 Calocera viscosa	T	87 Glomerella cingulata	O	148 Penicillium digitatum	B, Pn, Px, T	212 Stachybotrys atra	B
26 Candida chevalieri	O	88 Grossmannia serpens	B	149 Penicillium spp[29]	O	213 Stereum frustulosum	T[37]
27 C. pseudotropicalis	B, N, Pn, T	89 Gymnoascus setosus	O	150 Peniophora spp[30]	T	214 Stromatinia smilacinae	T[17]
28 Cephalosporium recifei	O	90 Hansenula anomala	O	151 Phacidium infestans	T[17]	215 Syncephalastrum cinereum	O
29 Ceratostomella spp[8]	B, Px, T	91 Haplosporangium parvum	O	152 Phialophora spp[31]	T	216 Thamnidium elegans	O
30 Ceratostomella spp[9]	Px, T	92 Helminthosporium spp[21]	O	153 Pholiota adiposa	T[17]	217 Thielaviopsis basicola	O
31 C. adiposum	I	93 Helvella infula	O	154 P. mutabilis & squarrosa	T	218 Telletia horrida	T[4]
32 C. rostrocylindrica	O	94 Hemispora stellata	O	155 Phoma apiicola & betae	O	219 T. levis	O
33 C. stenoceras	T	95 Histoplasma capsulatum	O	156 Phycomyces blakeslee-anus	T	220 T. tritici	O
34 Cercospora appi & beticola	O	96 Hormiscium dermatitidis	T	157 P. nitens	T	221 Torulaspora delbruckii	B
35 Chaetocladium brefeldii	T	97 Hormodendrum algeri-ensis	T	158 Phymatotrichum omnivorum	O	222 T. fermentati	B
36 Chaetomium spp[10]	T	98 H. langeroni	T	159 Phytophthora spp[6]	O	223 Torulopsis candida	B
37 C. convolutum	B, T	99 Hydnum spp[22]	T	160 Pichia alcoholophila	B	224 T. dattila	B, Px, T
38 Chaetostylum freseni	O	100 H. coralloides	O	161 P. belgica	B, I, Px, T	225 T. kefyr	N
39 Chalaropsis thielavioides	T	101 Hypholoma fasciculare	T	162 P. dombrowski	T	226 T. laurentii & neoformans	T
40 Choanephora cucurbitarum	T	102 Hypoxylon pruinatum	B, T	163 P. kluyveri	B, T	227 Trametes spp[38]	T
41 Circinella aspera & spinosa	O	103 Kloeckera brevis	B, I, N, Pn, Px, T	164 Piedraia hortai	T	228 Tricholoma spp[39]	T
42 Cladosporium herbarum & wernecki	O	104 Lachnum pygmaeum	B, T	165 Piptocephalis freseniana	O	229 Trichophyton spp[40]	O
43 Clavaria ligula	T	105 Lactarius deliciosus	O	166 Piricularia oryzae	B, T	230 Trichophyton spp[41]	T
44 Clitocybe spp[11]	T	106 Lambertella spp[23]	B[17], T	167 Pityrosporum ovale	B, T	231 T. faviforme	I, T
45 Clitopilus prunulus	T[4]	107 Lentinus omphalodes	T	168 Pleurage curvicolla	B, T	232 Trichosporon beigelii	B, T
46 Coemansia interrupta	B, T	108 Lenzites spp[24]	T	169 Pleurotus corticatus	T[2]	233 T. minor	T
47 Colletotrichum circinans	O	109 Lepiota amiantina & procera	T	170 Polyporus spraguei	O	234 Tubaria furfuracea	T
48 C. lindemuthianum[12]	O	110 Lophodermium pinastri	B, I, T	171 Polystictus versicolor	T	235 Typhula variabilis	T
49 Collybia spp[13]	T	111 Madurella americana	O	172 Psalliota bispora	B or T	236 Ustilago spp[42]	T
50 C. dryophila	B, T	112 Malassezia furfur	O	173 P. campestris	T	237 Ustilago spp[43]	O
51 Coprinus spp[6]	T	113 Marasmius spp[25]	O	174 Pseudopeziza ribis	B	238 Ustulina vulgaris	O
52 Cordyceps militaris	O	114 M. perforans	B, T	175 Pyronema confluens	T	239 Valsa ceratophora	T
53 Coryne sarcoides	B, T	115 Melanconium betulinum	B, I, T	176 P. domesticum	O	240 V. pini	B, I, T
54 Cudonia circinans	O	116 Melanospora destruens	B, T	177 Pythiomorpha oryzae	O	241 Venturia inaequalis	O
55 Cunninghamella spp[14]	O	117 Memnoniella echinata	B	178 Pythium spp[32]	T	242 Xylaria arbuscula	O
56 Cyathus striatus	T	118 Merulius lachrymans	O	179 Pythium spp[33]	T	243 X. hypoxylon	T
57 Dacryomyces stillatus	T	119 Microsporum spp[26]	O	180 Rhizopogon roseolus	B[17], T	244 Zygorhynchus spp[44]	O
58 Daedalea spp[15]	T	120 M. audouini	N, Px[17]	181 Rhizopus spp[6]	O	245 Zygosaccharomyces spp[45]	B, T
59 Daldinia concentrica	O	121 Monascus purpurea	O	182 Rhodotorula spp[34]	T[2]	246 Z. lactis & marxianus	B, N
60 Dasyobolus immersus	T	122 Monilinia fructicola	O	183 R. aurantiaca	Pa	247 Z. nadsonii & pastori	B, Pn
61 Debaryomyces spp[16]	B	123 M. laxa	T[17]	184 R. aurea & glutinis	O	248 Z. japonicus	B, I, Pn, T
62 D. membranefaciens	B, T			185 Rosellinia arcuata	B	249 Z. pini	B
				186 R. necatrix & thelena	O	250 Z. priorianus	B, I, Pn
				187 Saccharomyces carls-bergensis	Px		

/1/ Spp: caerulea, glauca, orchidis, repens, spinosa. /2/ Required only pyrimidine portion of molecule. /3/ Plus an unknown "cofactor" which is neither nicotinic acid nor biotin. /4/ Can be replaced by pyrimidine + thiazole. /5/ Spp: denudatus, furfuraceus, leveillei. /6/ All species tested. /7/ Spp: elegans, granulatus, luteus, piperatus, variegatus, viscidus. /8/ Spp: fimbriata (2 isolates require thiamine only), ips, microspora, montium, penicillata, piceaperda, pini. /9/ Spp: multiannulata, pluriannulata; pilifera, pseudotsugae (partial requirement for thiamine). /10/ Spp: bostrychodes, cochlioides, elatum, globosum. /11/ Spp: alexandri, aurantiaca, clavipes, cyathiformis, geotropa, infundibuliformis, nebularis, odora, pithyophila. /12/ Certain isolates; certain other isolates have a partial requirement for inositol. /13/ Spp: ambusta, butyracea; tuberosa (cf Fn 2). /14/ Spp: bertholletiae, echinulata, elegans. /15/ Spp: confragosa, quercina, unicolor. /16/ Spp: fabrii, guillermondi, hudeloi, matruchoti, subglobosus. /17/ Partial requirement, some synthesis of the vitamin presumably takes place. /18/ Spp: annosus, igniarius, pinicola. /19/ Most species tested. /20/ One strain only. /21/ Spp: gramineum, victoriae. /22/ Spp: auriscalpium, corrugatum, erinaceus. /23/ Spp: corni-maris, hicoriae, pruni, viburni. /24/ Spp: abietina, trabea (cf Fn 17); betulina, saepiaria. /25/ Spp: alliaceus, chordalis, epiphyllus, foetidus, fulvo-bulbillosus, graminum, perforans, peronatus, putillus, ramealis, rotula, scorodonius. /26/ Spp: canis, ferrugineum, fulvum. /27/ Spp: circinelloides, genevensis, griseolilacinus, hiemalis, mucilagineus, stolonifer, tenuis. /28/ Spp: crassa, sitophila, tetrasperma. /29/ All other species tested. /30/ Spp: candida, fraxinea, junipericola, septentrionalis, violaceo-livida. /31/ Spp: compactum, jeanselmei, pedrosoi, verrucosa. /32/ Spp: debaryanum, deliense, graminicolum, hyphalosticton, intermedium, irregulare, mamillatum, scleroteichum, splendens. /33/ Spp: ascophallon, polymostum; arrhenomanes (cf Fn 37); butleri, oligandrum, polycladon (cf Fn 2). /34/ Spp: aurantiaca; flava, mucilaginos, rubra, sonnieri (cf Fn 2). /35/ Spp: azaleae, callistephi, chrysanthemella, nodorum. /36/ Spp: beurmanni, councilmanni, gougeroti. /37/ Requires only thiazole portion of molecule. /38/ Spp: cinnabarina, heteromorpha, serialis. /39/ Spp: albobrunneum, flavobrunneum, imbricatum, nudum, personatum, pessundatum. /40/ Spp: rubrum, sabouraudi, tonsurans. /41/ Spp: interdigitale, rosaceum, sulfureum, violaceum. /42/ Spp: pinguiculae, scabriosae, vinosa, violacea. /43/ Spp: avenae, bromivora, hordei, levis, nuda, striiformis, tritici, zeae. /44/ Spp: dangeardi, exponens, heterogamus, moelleri. /45/ Spp: bisporus, mandshuricus.

This table illustrates the ability (or inability) of certain yeasts to utilize nutrients in the following capacities: (1) fermentation, involving the production of gas, of six sugars; (2) assimilation of various carbon compounds; (3) nitrate assimilation; and (4) growth in a vitamin-free medium. + = production of gas (fermentation), or growth (assimilation); - = no production of gas (fermentation), or growth (assimilation); L = latent growth; V = variable reactions; 1/3 = fermentation of 1/3 of raffinose molecule; 3/3 = melibiose also fermented.

| | Fermentation[1] | | | | | | Assimilation of Carbon Sources | | | | | | | | | | | | | | | | | | | | | | | | | | | | | | | | | | | | | | | | | Nitrate assimilation[2] | Growth without added vitamins |
Yeast Species	Dextrose	Galactose	Maltose	Sucrose	Lactose	Raffinose	Dextrose	Galactose	L-Sorbose	Maltose	Sucrose	Cellobiose	Trehalose	Lactose	Melibiose	Raffinose	Melezitose	Inulin	Starch, soluble	Xylose	L-Arabinose	D-Arabinose	D-Ribose	Rhamnose	D-Glucosamine HCl	Ethanol	Glycerol	Erythritol	Adonitol	Dulcitol	Mannitol	Sorbitol	a-Methyl glucoside	Salicin	Potassium gluconate	Calcium 2-ketogluconate	Potassium 5-ketogluconate	Potassium sodium saccharate	Sodium pyruvate	Sodium lactate	Sodium succinate	Sodium citrate	Ethyl acetoacetate	Inositol		
1 Candida albicans	+	V	+	-	-	-	+	+	L	+	+	-	+	-	-	-	+	-	+	+	V	-	-	-	V	+	+	-	+	-	+	+	+	-	V	+	+	-	+	+	+	+	V	-	-	+
2 C. krusei	+	-	+	-	-	-	+	-	-	-	-	-	+	-	-	-	-	-	+	+	-	-	-	-	L	+	+	-	-	-	+	-	-	V	-	-	-	-	+	+	+	+	V	-	-	+
3 C. lipolytica	-	V	-	-	-	1/3-3/3	+	V	+	-	-	-	-	-	-	-	-	-	-	-	V	V	V	V	-	+	+	+	V	-	+	+	-	V	V	+	-	-	+	+	+	+	V	-	-	-
4 C. membranaefaciens[3]	+	V	-	-	-	-	+	+	+	+	+	+	+	+	-	-	+	+	+	+	+	+	+	+	+	+	V	+	+	-	+	+	+	V	V	+	-	-	+	+	+	+	-	+	-	+
5 C. parapsilosis[4]	+	V	-	-	-	1/3	+	+	+	+	+	+	+	-	-	-	+	+	+	+	+	+	+	-	+	+	+	+	+	-	+	+	+	V	V	+	-	-	+	+	+	+	-	-	-	+
6 C. pulcherrima	+	-	-	-	-	-	+	-	+	-	+	+	+	-	-	-	+	+	+	+	-	-	-	-	L	+	V	+	+	-	L	L	V	V	V	+	-	-	L	L	+	+	-	-	-	+
7 Debaryomyces globosus	+	V	+	+	-	1/3	+	+	+	+	+	+	+	+	+	+	+	-	-	+	+	+	+	+	+	+	V	+	+	-	+	+	+	+	+	+	-	-	+	+	+	+	-	-	-	+
8 Endomycopsis chodati[5]	+	V	+	+	-	1/3	+	+	+	+	+	+	+	+	-	-	+	-	+	+	+	-	V	-	+	+	V	+	V	-	V	+	V	+	V	+	-	-	+	+	+	V	-	+	-	+
9 E. guilliermondii[6]	+	V	V	+	-	1/3-3/3	+	+	+	+	+	+	+	-	+	+	+	+	+	+	+	+	+	+	+	+	V	+	+	-	+	+	+	+	V	V	V	-	+	+	+	+	-	-	-	+
10 E. ohmeri[7]	+	V	+	+	-	1/3	+	+	+	+	+	+	+	-	-	-	+	-	-	+	-	+	+	+	+	+	V	+	+	-	+	+	V	+	-	+	-	-	+	+	+	+	V	-	-	+
11 Hanseniaspora valbyensis	+	-	-	-	-	-	+	-	-	-	-	+	+	-	-	-	-	-	-	-	-	-	-	-	-	+	+	-	-	-	-	-	-	-	V	+	-	-	L	L	+	V	-	-	-	+
12 Hansenula anomala	+	V	V	+	-	1/3	+	+	+	+	+	+	+	-	-	+	+	V	+	+	+	+	+	+	+	+	V	+	V	-	+	+	V	+	V	+	V	-	+	+	+	+	V	-	+	+
13 H. capsulata	-	-	-	-	-	-	+	-	-	-	-	+	+	-	-	-	+	+	+	+	V	-	V	-	-	+	V	+	V	-	+	+	V	V	V	V	-	-	V	V	+	+	-	-	+	+
14 H. saturnus	+	V	V	+	-	1/3	+	+	V	+	+	+	+	-	-	+	V	V	+	V	+	+	V	+	-	+	+	+	+	-	+	+	+	V	V	+	-	-	+	+	+	V	-	-	+	+
15 Kloeckera apiculata	+	V	-	-	-	-	+	+	-	-	-	+	+	-	-	-	-	-	-	-	-	-	-	-	-	+	+	-	-	-	-	-	-	-	V	+	-	-	L	L	+	+	-	-	-	+
16 Pichia farinosa	V	V	-	-	-	-	+	-	+	+	+	+	+	-	-	-	+	-	+	+	-	-	-	+	V	+	V	V	V	-	+	+	V	V	V	+	-	-	V	V	+	+	-	+	-	+
17 P. membranaefaciens	-	-	-	-	-	-	+	-	+	-	-	-	-	-	-	-	-	-	-	-	-	-	-	-	+	+	+	+	+	-	+	+	-	-	+	+	-	-	V	V	+	V	-	-	-	+
18 Saccharomyces cerevisiae	+	+	+	+	-	1/3	+	+	-	+	+	+	+	-	+	+	V	V	-	-	-	-	-	-	-	+	+	-	-	-	V	V	+	V	V	V	-	-	+	+	+	V	-	-	-	+
19 S. fragilis	+	+	-	+	+	1/3	+	+	+	-	+	+	+	+	+	+	-	+	-	V	+	V	+	-	V	+	+	-	V	-	L	L	V	V	V	+	-	-	+	+	+	+	-	-	+	+
20 S. lactis[8]	+	+	-	-	+	1/3	+	+	V	-	-	+	+	+	+	-	-	+	-	-	-	-	V	+	+	+	+	-	V	-	V	L	V	+	V	+	-	-	+	+	+	+	-	-	+	+
21 S. pastori[9]	+	V	-	+	-	1/3	+	+	+	+	+	+	V	-	-	+	V	+	-	+	V	V	V	-	+	+	+	+	V	-	+	+	+	V	V	+	-	-	V	V	+	+	-	-	-	+
22 S. rosei[10]	+	+	V	-	-	1/3	+	+	+	+	+	+	+	-	+	+	V	+	-	V	V	V	V	-	+	L	L	+	V	-	L	L	+	L	V	+	-	-	L	L	+	V	-	-	-	+
23 S. veronae	+	V	+	+	-	1/3	+	+	+	+	+	+	+	-	+	+	+	+	-	+	V	-	V	-	+	+	+	-	V	-	V	V	+	L	L	+	-	-	L	L	+	V	-	-	-	+
24 Saccharomycodes ludwigii	+	-	-	-	-	-	+	+	-	-	+	-	-	-	+	+	-	-	-	-	-	-	-	-	-	+	+	-	-	-	-	-	-	-	V	+	-	-	+	+	+	V	-	-	-	+
25 Torulopsis colliculosa	+	V	+	+	-	1/3	+	+	+	+	+	+	+	-	-	+	V	-	-	-	-	-	-	-	V	+	+	-	-	-	V	+	+	L	+	+	-	-	+	+	+	+	-	-	-	+
26 T. lactis-condensi[11]	-	-	-	-	-	1/3	+	+	-	+	+	+	+	+	+	+	+	+	+	V	+	V	V	+	+	+	+	-	V	-	V	V	V	+	V	+	-	-	+	+	+	+	-	-	+	+
27 T. utilis[12]	+	+	+	+	-	1/3	+	+	+	+	+	+	+	-	-	+	+	-	-	+	+	+	+	+	+	+	+	-	-	-	+	V	V	L	+	+	-	-	+	+	+	+	V	-	+	+
28 Zygosaccharomyces dobzhanskii	+	V	+	-	-	1/3	+	+	-	+	+	-	+	-	-	V	-	-	-	V	V	-	-	-	-	+	L	-	V	-	V	V	+	+	+	-	-	-	V	V	+	V	+	-	-	-
29 Z. pini	V	V	-	-	-	-	+	+	V	+	+	+	+	-	+	+	+	+	+	+	V	-	-	+	-	+	+	-	V	-	+	+	+	+	+	-	-	-	+	+	+	+	-	-	-	+

/1/ Sugar commonly used for taxonomic differentiation of yeast species. /2/ All yeasts listed assimilate ammonium sulfate. /3/ Candida melibiosi var. membranaefaciens. /4/ Candida krusoides. /5/ Candida chodati. /6/ Candida guilliermondii. /7/ Candida guilliermondii var. membranaefaciens; C. chalmersi. /8/ Zygosaccharomyces lactis. /9/ Zygosaccharomyces pastori. /10/ Torulaspora rosei. /11/ Torulopsis caroliniana. /12/ Candida utilis.

If an organism cannot achieve typical growth, health, or reproduction in the absence of an element, the element is listed as R (or r). If addition of an element not required improves growth, health or reproduction, the element is listed as s. Accumulation in the tissues of an organism is not, alone, taken as sufficient evidence of requirement. Characterizations are subject to change with further study and increasing purity of materials.

R = Required by all forms studied; R̸ = Not required by any forms studied; r = Required by one or more species or strains; "u=" = Utilized as effectively, replaces wholly or is interchangeable with another element for one or more species or strains; u< = Can partially replace or spare another element for one or more species or strains; s = Stimulates growth or other processes for one or more species or strains; a = Accumulated in the tissue of one or more forms; c = Commonly present in the food of some forms and in the tissues at similar concentrations but requirement is uncertain.

	Nutrient	Higher Green Plants[1]	Fungi	Yeasts	Bacteria	Algae	Green Phyto-flagellates[2]	Protozoa[3]	Invertebrates Insects	Invertebrates Other	Vertebrates
1	Aluminum	r,s,a	R̸	R̸	R̸, u<[4]	R̸	R̸	R̸	R̸		R̸
2	Arsenic	R̸	R̸	R̸	R̸	R̸	R̸	R̸	R̸	a	R̸
3	Boron	R	R̸,s	R̸	r	r	r?	R̸	R̸	R̸	R̸
4	Bromine	R̸	R̸	R̸	R̸	R̸,a	R̸	R̸	R̸	r?[5],a?	R̸
5	Calcium	R	r,s,a	r,u=[6]	r,s	R	r	R	r,c	r	R
6	Carbon	R	R	R	R	R	R	R	R	R	R
7	Chlorine	r,s	R̸	R̸	R̸	a	R̸	R̸	r,c	r	R
8	Chromium	R̸	R̸	R̸	u=[7]	R̸	R̸	R̸	R̸		R̸
9	Cobalt	r	R̸	u=[6]	r	r	r	r	r?,s?		r
10	Copper	R	R	r	r,u<[4]	r		r	r,c	r	r
11	Fluorine	R̸,a	R̸	R̸	R̸	R̸	R̸	R̸	R̸	a	R̸,s
12	Gallium	r	r,s	R̸	R̸	R̸	R̸	R̸	R̸	R̸	R̸
13	Hydrogen	R	R	R	R	R	R	R	R	R	R
14	Iodine	R̸,s	R̸	R̸,s	R̸,s	R̸,a	R̸	R̸	R̸	r?,a	R
15	Iron	R	R	R	r,u<[4]	R	R	R	R	r	R
16	Magnesium	R	R	R	r	R	R	R	R	R	R
17	Manganese	R	r,s	r,u=[6]	r,u=	r	r	r	r,c,a	r[8]	R
18	Molybdenum	R,a	R̸[9],s	r	r[9]	r[9]	R̸				R[10]
19	Nitrogen	R	R	R	R	R	R	R	R	R	R
20	Oxygen	R	R	R	R	R	R	R	R	R	R
21	Phosphorus	R	R	R	R	R	R	R	R	R	R
22	Potassium	R	R	r	r	R,a	R	R	r,c,a	R	R
23	Rubidium	R̸	R̸	R̸	u=[11]	R̸	R̸	R̸	R̸		R̸
24	Selenium	R̸,a	R̸	R̸	R̸	R̸	R̸	R̸	R̸		R̸
25	Silicon	r								r	
26	Sodium	r?,s,a	R̸	R̸	r	R̸,a	R̸	r	r?,c		R
27	Strontium	R̸	R̸	R̸	u=[12]	R̸,u=	R̸	R̸	R̸		R̸
28	Sulfur	R	R	R	R	R	R	R	R	R	R
29	Tungsten	R̸	s	R̸	R̸	R̸	R̸	R̸	R̸		R̸
30	Vanadium	R̸	R̸,s	R̸	u<[13]	r	R̸	R̸,s?	R̸	r[14]	R̸
31	Zinc	R	R	r	r,u=	r	r	r	r	r?,a	R

/1/ Spermatophytes (the intact plant). /2/ = Green phytoflagellates, chrysomonads, dinoflagellates. /3/ Including the colorless phytoflagellates. /4/ u< = Mn or Cr for Aerobacter aerogenes. /5/ Occurs in scleroprotein of certain corals as di-bromotyrosine. /6/ "u=" = Ca in yeast cocarboxylase. /7/ "u" = Mn for Aerobacter aerogenes. /8/ In blood respiratory pigment of Pinna squamosa (mollusk). /9/ R for NO_3^- utilization by some fungi and some algae; R for N_2 fixation by some bacteria and algae. /10/ "Xanthine oxidase factor." /11/ "u=" = Ca by some. /12/ "u=" = Ca by Azotobacter. /13/ u< = Mo in N_2 fixation. /14/ In blood pigment of certain tunicates (Chordata).

R = Required by all forms studied; R̸ = Not required by any forms studied; r = Required by one or more species or strains; rm = Required by one or more mutants; U = Utilized by all forms studied; U̸ = Not utilized by any forms studied; u = Utilized by one or more species or strains; u̸ = Not utilized by one or more species or strains; s = Stimulates growth or other processes for one or more species or strains; * = Serves as adequate or partial N-source for one or more species or strains; ** = Simplest adequate N-source for one or more species or strains.

	Nutrient	Higher Green Plants	Fungi	Yeasts	Bacteria	Algae	Green Phyto-flagellates	Protozoa	Invertebrates Insects	Invertebrates Other	Vertebrates
					Inorganic Nitrogen Sources						
1	Nitrogen, molecular, N_2	u[1]	R̸,u?[2]	R̸	u**[3]	R̸,u**[4]	U̸	U̸	U̸		U̸
2	Ammonia, -ium, NH_3, $-NH_4^+$	R̸,U**	rm,u**[5]	R̸,u**	R̸,u*	R̸,u**[6]	R̸,U**	r,u**	R̸,u?		R̸,u[7]
3	Hyponitrite, $HN_2O_2^=$ or $-N_2O_2^=$	R̸,u[8]	R̸,u̸		R̸,u[9]	R̸	R̸	R̸	R̸		R̸
4	Nitrite, $-NO_2^-$	R̸,u*[10]	rm,u**[11]	R̸,u*	R̸,u*	R̸,u*[12]	R̸	R̸	R̸		R̸
5	Nitrate, $-NO_3^-$	R̸,U*	rm,u**[13]	R̸,u*[14]	R̸,u*[15]	R̸,U*	R̸,u*	R̸,u	R̸		R̸
6	Nitrohydroxamate, $-HN_2O_3^-$	R̸,u[16]	R̸,u*[17]	R̸	R̸	R̸	R̸	R̸	R̸		R̸
7	Cyanide, $-CN^-$	R̸	R̸,u[18]	R̸	R̸	R̸	R̸	U̸[19]	U̸[19]		U̸[19]
8	Thiocyanate, $-CNS^-$	U̸	R̸,u?	R̸,u	R̸,u*	R̸	R̸	U̸	U̸		U̸
9	Cyanamide, $-NHCN^-$	U̸	u*[20]		R̸,u*[20]	R̸	R̸	U̸	U̸		U̸
					Organic Nitrogen Sources						
10	Oximino compounds, $RONH_2$	R̸,U[21]	R̸,u*	R̸,u?	R̸,u*[22]	U̸[23]	R̸	R̸	R̸		R̸
11	Amines, RNH_2	R̸	R̸,u*	R̸,u*	R̸,u*	R̸,u*[24]	R̸	R̸	R̸		R̸
12	Acid imides, $(RCO)_2NH$	R̸	R̸,u*	R̸,u*	R̸,u*	R̸	R̸	R̸	R̸		R̸
13	Acid amides, $RCONH_2$	R̸,u*[25]	R̸,u*[26]	r,u*	R̸,u*	R̸,u*	R̸	R̸	R̸		R̸
14	Urea, $(NH_2)_2CO$	R̸,U*	R̸,u*	R̸,u*	R̸,u*	R̸,u*	R̸,u*	R̸,u*[27]	R̸		R̸,u[28]
15	Amino acids, $RCH(NH_2)COOH$	R̸,u*	r,rm,U*	r,U*	r,U*,s	R̸,u*[29]	r,u*	r,u*	R,U**	R,U**	R,U**[7]
16	Peptides, polypeptides	R̸,u*	R̸,u*	R̸,u*	r,u*,s	R̸,u*	R̸,u*	r,u*	R̸,U*		R̸,U*
17	Proteins	R̸	R̸,u*	R̸	R̸,u*	R̸	R̸	r,u*	R̸,U*	U*	R̸,U*,s
18	Imidazole compounds	R̸	R̸,u*	R̸,u*	R̸,u*	R̸	R̸	R̸	R̸		R̸
19	Pyridine compounds	R̸	R̸	r	r,u*	R̸	R̸	r	r		R
20	Pyrimidine compounds	R̸	R̸,u*,s	R̸,u*,	R̸,u*,s	r	r	r,u*	r		R
21	Purine compounds	R̸,u	rm,u*,s	R̸,u	R̸,u*,s	R̸	R̸	r,u*	R̸		R̸
22	Indole compounds	R̸,s	rm,u*		R̸,u*,s	R̸,s	R̸	r	r		R

/1/ U by virtue of symbiotic bacteria as in root nodules or legumes. /2/ Evidence for N_2 fixation conflicting. /3/ U by N_2 fixing bacteria. /4/ N_2 "fixation" by blue-green algae, Nostocaceae. U̸ if H_2 or CO present. /5/ U by Phycomyces blakesleeanus, Mucorales. Probably U by all fungi. /6/ U in preference to NO_3^- by Chlorella. /7/ Dietary NH_4^+ U by ruminants; possibly others; NH_4^+ originating as metabolic intermediate U in amino acid synthesis. /8/ U̸ by tobacco plant. /9/ U by Clostridium pasteurianum, but not for growth; U̸ for denitrification by Pseudomonas stutzeri. /10/ Toxic to many plants, poorly U by tobacco plant. /11/ U as sole N-source by many fungi. /12/ U poorly by Chlorella pyrenoidosa. /13/ Acts as sole H acceptor in anaerobic metabolism of Aspergillus niger. R by some when mannitol is carbon source. Some R NO_3^-, cannot substitute NH_4^+. /14/ U poorly by most yeasts. /15/ U̸ by purple photosynthetic bacteria. /16/ Good N-source for tobacco plant. /17/ Good N-source for Aspergillus niger. /18/ U by Aspergillus niger when N-starved. /19/ Toxic. /20/ Cyanamide and derivatives U by many. /21/ Hydroxylamine poor N-source. /22/ Hydroxylamine by Clostridium welchii, U in non-toxic concentration by Nitrosomonas. /23/ Hydroxylamine toxic. /24/ Glucosamine U. /25/ Acetamide U by some. /26/ Formamide and others U by Aspergillus. Both amino and amide N of asparagine U by Aspergillus. /27/ U by Astasia longa (colorless phytoflagellate). /28/ U by ruminants via rumen microflora. /29/ L-arginine, glutamine, cysteine, L-asparagine support more rapid growth of Chlorella than does NH_4^+.

181. NUTRIENTS: AMINO ACIDS, PEPTIDES, PROTEINS (SUMMARY)

R = Required by all forms studied; Ɍ = Not required by any form studied; r = Required by one or more species or strains; rm = Required by one or more mutants; U = Utilized as a source of nitrogen and/or carbon by all forms studied although not a specific requirement for all; u = Utilized by one or more species or strains as a source of nitrogen and/or carbon although not a specific requirement; "u=" = Replaces effectively one or more other amino-acids, one of the interchangeable series being required in the diet; ɥ = Not utilized by one or more species or strains; s = Stimulates growth or other processes for one or more species or strains; * = Serves as complete nitrogen source for one or more species or strains; ** = Serves as simplest complete nitrogen source for one or more species or strains.

	Nutrient	Higher Green Plants[1]	Fungi	Yeasts	Bacteria	Algae	Green Phytoflagellates[2]	Invertebrates Protozoa[3]	Invertebrates Insects	Vertebrates
1	Organic N (per se)	Ɍ,u*	r,rm,u*[4]	r,rm,u*[4]	r,u*[4]	r,u*	r,u*	r,U*	R,U*	R,U*
2	Proteins (per se)	Ɍ,u*	Ɍ,u*	Ɍ,u*	Ɍ,u*	Ɍ	u	r[5],u*	Ɍ[6],s,U*	Ɍ[6],s,U*
3	Polypeptides[7], peptones	Ɍ,u*[10]	Ɍ,u*	Ɍ,u*	r,u*[8]	Ɍ,u*	u=[9],u*	r,u*	Ɍ	Ɍ,U
4	Amino acids	Ɍ,u*[10]	r,rm,u*	rm,u*[11]	r[12],rm,u*	Ɍ,u*[13]	r,u=[9],u*[14]	r[15],u*	R,U**	R,U**
5	Alanine	Ɍ,u*	u*,u=[16]	u*	r,u*	Ɍ,u*	Ɍ,u*	u	r[17],u=	Ɍ,U
6	Arginine	Ɍ,u*	rm,u*	rm,u*	r,rm,u*	Ɍ,u*	Ɍ,u*	r[18],s,u	r[17]	r[19],U
7	Aspartic acid[20]	Ɍ,u*	u*,u=[16]	u*	r,u*	Ɍ,u*	r,u*	u,s	r[17],u=	Ɍ,U
8	Citrulline	Ɍ	rm,u*		r,u*	Ɍ		u	r,u=[21]	Ɍ,u=[21],U
9	Cysteine	Ɍ,u*	rm,u*	u*	r,u*	Ɍ,u*		u	r,u=	Ɍ,U
10	Cystine	Ɍ,u*	rm,u*	r,u*	r,rm,u*	Ɍ		u	r[17],u=	R,U
11	Glutamic acid[20]	Ɍ,u*	rm,u=[16],u*	u*	r,u*	Ɍ,u*	Ɍ,u*	u,s	r[17]	r[22],U
12	Glycine	Ɍ,u*	rm,u*	u*	r,u*	Ɍ,u*	Ɍ,u*	r[18],u	r	r[23],U
13	Histidine	Ɍ,u*	r,rm,u*	r,u*	r,rm,u*	Ɍ,u*	r,u*	r[18],s,u	r[17]	R[24]
14	Isoleucine	Ɍ,u*	rm,u*	rm,u*	r,rm,u*	Ɍ,u*		r[18],u	r[17]	R[24]
15	Leucine	Ɍ,u*	rm,u*	rm,u*	r,rm,u*	Ɍ,ɥ		r[18],u	r[17],u=	R[24]
16	Lysine	Ɍ,u*	rm,u*	u*	r,rm,u*	Ɍ,ɥ		r[18],u	r[17]	R[24]
17	Methionine	Ɍ,u	r,rm,u*	r,u*	r,rm,u*	Ɍ,ɥ	r	r[18],u	r[17]	R[24, 25]
18	Phenylalanine	Ɍ,u*	rm,u*	rm,u*	r,rm,u*	Ɍ,ɥ		r[18],u	r[17]	R[24, 25]
19	Proline	Ɍ,u*	rm,u*	u*	r,u*	Ɍ,u*	Ɍ,u*	r[18],u	r[17]	r,U
20	Serine	Ɍ,u*	rm,u*	u*	r,u*	Ɍ,ɥ	Ɍ,u*	r[18],s,u	r[17]	Ɍ,U
21	Threonine	Ɍ,u*	rm,u*	r,u*	r,u*	Ɍ,ɥ		r[18],u	r[17],u=	R[24]
22	Tryptophan[26]	Ɍ,u*	r,rm,u*	u*	r,rm,u*	Ɍ,ɥ	Ɍ,ɥ	r[18],u	r[17],s,u=	R[24]
23	Tyrosine	Ɍ,u*	rm,u*	u*	r,rm,u*	Ɍ,ɥ	Ɍ,ɥ	r[18],u	u=	Ɍ,U
24	Valine	Ɍ,u*	rm,u*	u*	r,rm,u*	Ɍ,ɥ	Ɍ,u*	r[18],s,u	r[17],u=	R[24]

/1/ Spermatophytes (the intact plant). /2/ Green phytoflagellates, chrysomonads, dinoflagellates. /3/ Including colorless phytoflagellates. /4/ Most grow better on organic than on inorganic N. /5/ Many require living prey. /6/ On assumption that suitable amino acid combinations can replace complete proteins. /7/ See strepogenin (table 185). /8/ Entire peptides, polypeptides, low molecular weight proteins directly assimilated by some. /9/ Either 3 or 4 required by photoautotrophs growing in dark. /10/ Several tested intact plants grow on single amino acids as sole N-source. Growth attained on some amino acids is superior to that achieved with NH_4^+, NO_3^-, as N-source, on other amino acids inferior. Some plants grow less well on amino acids than on inorganic N. Marked differences exist between species with respect to amino acid utilization. Some amino acids are toxic, under the experimental conditions used, for some plants. Among plants tested are: tomato, tobacco, clover, peas, orchid embryos, young orchid. /11/ Amino acid mixtures superior to NH_4^+ as N-source for some, e. g. Saccharomyces cerevisiae, S. carlsbergensis. /12/ Wide differences of requirement exist between species, species mutants, e. g. Leuconostoc mesenteroides R all the amino acids listed except 5 and 8, Lactobacillus bifidus R only 9. /13/ Based mainly on Chlorella pyrenoidosa. /14/ Marked differences between various species and varieties with respect to amino acid utilization; environmental conditions sharply modify. /15/ Best known requirement are those of Tetrahymena, Trichomonas foetus, Herpetomonas culicidarum, Glaucoma scintillans. /16/ Interchangeable for a Neurospora mutant. /17/ Basic common requirements of Tribolium confusum, Drosophila melanogaster, Aedes aegypti, Blattella germanica are covered by 6, 10, 13-18, 21, 22, 24. For A. aegypti 18 or 21 + 22 + 24 may be eliminated from diet. For B. germanica 5, 7, 11 u=, but one at least must be present; male also R 19, 20; 9, 10, 17 u=, and may be replaced by homocysteine, cysteic acid, isethionic acid, inorganic SO_4; 15, 24 u=; 18-23 u=, and may be replaced by 3, 4-dihydroxyphenylalanine, phenylacetic, 2, 4-dihydroxybenozic, shikimic, orsellinic acids. /18/ R by Tetrahymena geleii, Glaucoma scintillans, Trichomonas foetus, Herpetomonas culicidarum are 6, 13-18, 22, 24; in addition G. scintillans, T. foetus R 12, 19-21 and H. culicidarum R 23. T. geleii needs no other carbon source. /19/ R by rat, chicken. /20/ Asparagine (amide of 7) and glutamine (amide of 11) U by at least some in all the groups listed and R by some. /21/ 6, 8 interchangeable for some. /22/ R by chick. /23/ R by chick for rapid growth. /24/ R by man, mouse, rat, chicken. 13 not required to maintain nitrogen balance in adult human. /25/ Amount of methionine R by man depends on amount of cystine in diet. Amount of phenylalanine R by man depends on amount of tyrosine in diet. /26/ Precursor of niacin which it spares for some organisms.

182. NUTRIENTS: LIPIDS (SUMMARY)

Ɍ = Not required by any form studied; r = Required by one or more species or strains; rm = Required by one or more mutants; u = Utilized by one or more species or strains; "u=" = Utilized as effectively as a related substance by one or more species or strains; s = Stimulates growth or other processes for one or more species or strains; i = Inhibits growth or other processes for one or more species or strains.

	Nutrients	Higher Green Plants[1]	Fungi	Yeasts	Bacteria	Algae	Green Phytoflagellates[2]	Invertebrates Protozoa[3]	Invertebrates Insects	Vertebrates
				Steroids						
1	Cholesterol	Ɍ	r[4]	u	u	Ɍ	Ɍ	r[5]	r	Ɍ
2	7-Dehydrocholesterol	Ɍ	Ɍ	Ɍ	Ɍ	Ɍ	Ɍ	Ɍ,u=[6]	u=	u[7]
3	Ergostanol acetate	Ɍ	Ɍ	Ɍ	Ɍ	Ɍ	Ɍ	Ɍ,u=[6]		s[8]
4	Ergosterol	Ɍ	Ɍ	u,s	Ɍ	Ɍ	Ɍ	Ɍ,u=[6]	u=	u[9]
5	Stigmasterol	Ɍ	Ɍ	Ɍ	Ɍ	Ɍ	Ɍ	Ɍ	u=	Ɍ,s
			Long Chain Fatty Acids and Their Derivatives							
6	Arachidonic acid[10]	Ɍ		Ɍ		Ɍ	Ɍ		s	r,u=
7	Linoleic acid[10]	Ɍ	rm	Ɍ	s,i	Ɍ	Ɍ	u=[11]	r	r,u=
8	Linolenic acid[10]	Ɍ		Ɍ		Ɍ	Ɍ		u=	r,u=
9	Oleic acid	Ɍ	rm,s	Ɍ	s,i	Ɍ	Ɍ	s,i	r	Ɍ
10	"Tween 80, 85"[12]	Ɍ	Ɍ	Ɍ	Ɍ,s,i	Ɍ	Ɍ	Ɍ,s	Ɍ	Ɍ
11	"Myrj G 2144"[12]	Ɍ	Ɍ	Ɍ	Ɍ	Ɍ	Ɍ	Ɍ,s	Ɍ	Ɍ
				Phospholipids						
12	Lecithin	Ɍ	Ɍ	Ɍ	Ɍ	Ɍ	Ɍ	Ɍ	u=,s	Ɍ

/1/ Spermatophytes (the intact plant). /2/ Green phytoflagellates, chrysomonads, dinoflagellates. /3/ Including the colorless phytoflagellates. /4/ r by Labyrinthula vitellina (var. pacifica only). /5/ For several individual insect species various steroids u=. /6/ u= in place of 1 by Trichomonas. /7/ Precursor of vitamin D_3. /8/ Relieves "stiffness syndrome" of guinea pig. /9/ Precursor of vitamin D_4. /10/ The "essential fatty acids" of vertebrates. /11/ u = a required ether soluble factor of blood serum by Trichomonas. /12/ Synthetic detergents; "Tweens" = sorbitan esters of fatty acids, e. g. oleic; "Myrj G 2144" = polyoxalkalene derivative of oleic acid.

R = Required by all forms studied; Ɍ = Not required by any form studied; r = Required by one or more species or strains; rm = Required by one or more mutants; u = Utilized by one or more species or strains; "u=" = Utilized as effectively as the related compound(s) or vitamin by one or more species or strains; u> = Utilized more effectively than the related compound(s) or vitamin and considered to be required by one or more species or strains; u< = Utilized less effectively than the related vitamin by one or more species or strains; u<< = Utilized as well or less effectively than the related vitamin by one or more species or strains; ʉ = Not utilized in place of the related vitamin by one or more species or strains; s = Stimulates growth or other processes for one or more species or strains; i = Inhibits growth or other processes for one or more species or strains.

	Compound	Related Compound[2]	Higher Green Plants[3]	Fungi	Yeasts	Bacteria	Algae	Green Phyto-flagel-lates[4]	Invertebrates Protozoa[5]	Invertebrates Insects	Vertebrates
1	Vitamin A	(inc)A₁,A₂,A₃,(rel) 21A	Ɍ,s	Ɍ	Ɍ	Ɍ	Ɍ	Ɍ	r?	Ɍ	R
2	Ascorbic acid		Ɍ,s	Ɍ,s	Ɍ	Ɍ,s	r?,s	Ɍ	r,s	Ɍ	R
3	Biotin	(rel)20A,24A,30A,34A	Ɍ	r,rm,s	r,s	r	r	Ɍ	r,s	Ɍ	r
4	Choline group[6]		Ɍ,s	r,rm	Ɍ	r	r	Ɍ	r,s	r	r
5	Cobalamin[7]	(rel)39A,45A	Ɍ,s	Ɍ	Ɍ	r[8]	r	r	r	r?,s	r
6	Vitamin D[9]	(inc)D₂,D₃,D₄ etc.	Ɍ	Ɍ	Ɍ	Ɍ	Ɍ	Ɍ	r		R[9]
7	Vitamin E	(inc)α,β,γ,σ-Tocopherols	Ɍ	Ɍ	Ɍ	Ɍ	Ɍ	Ɍ	Ɍ	Ɍ,s	r
8	Inositol[10]	= meso-Inositol	Ɍ,s	r,rm,s	r,s	r?,s	Ɍ	Ɍ	r	r	r
9	Vitamin K	= K₁,K₂	Ɍ	Ɍ	Ɍ	Ɍ	Ɍ	Ɍ	Ɍ	r	r
10	Nicotinic acid	(rel)11A,25A,48A	Ɍ,s?	r,rm,s	r	r,s	r	Ɍ	r	r	r
11	Nicotinamide	(rel)10A	Ɍ,s?	r,rm,s	u=	r,u=,s	r	Ɍ	u=	u=	u=
12	Pantothenic acid	(rel)19A,22A,31A,35A	Ɍ,s	r,rm,s	r	r,s	r	Ɍ	u=	u=	R?
13	Pteroylglutamic acid[11]	(rel)27A,40A,44A,49A	Ɍ	Ɍ	Ɍ	r[12]	Ɍ	Ɍ	r	r	R
14	Pyridoxal[13]	(rel)15A,16A,41A,42A	Ɍ	u=	u=,s	r,u>	Ɍ	Ɍ	r	r	R
15	Pyridoxamine[13]	(rel)14A,16A,41A,42A	Ɍ	u=	u=,s	r,u>	Ɍ	Ɍ	u=	u=	u=
16	Pyridoxine[13]	(rel)14A,15A,41A,42A	Ɍ,s	r,rm,s	r,s	r,s	Ɍ,s	Ɍ	r	u=	R
17	Riboflavin		Ɍ	rm	Ɍ	Ɍ	Ɍ	Ɍ	r	r	R
18	Thiamine	(rel)26A,32A;(co)43A+47A	Ɍ,s	r,rm,s,i[14]	r,i[15]	r,s	r	r	r	r	R
19	β-Alanine	(po)12A	Ɍ	rm,u=	Ɍ,u=	Ɍ,u=	Ɍ	Ɍ	Ɍ,ʉ	Ɍ	Ɍ,s
20	Biocytin	(rel)3A	Ɍ	Ɍ	Ɍ	Ɍ	Ɍ	Ɍ	Ɍ	Ɍ	Ɍ
21	β-Carotene[16,17]	(pre)1A	Ɍ	Ɍ	Ɍ	Ɍ	Ɍ	Ɍ	Ɍ	Ɍ	Ɍ,u<
22	Coenzyme A	(co)12A+ADP+PO₄	Ɍ	Ɍ	Ɍ	r,u>	Ɍ	Ɍ	Ɍ	Ɍ	Ɍ,u<
23	5,6-Dimethylbenzimidazole	(po)5A	Ɍ	Ɍ	Ɍ	u	Ɍ	Ɍ	Ɍ	Ɍ	Ɍ,u<
24	Desthiobiotin	(rel)3A,30A,34A	Ɍ	Ɍ	Ɍ	Ɍ,u<	Ɍ	Ɍ	Ɍ	Ɍ	Ɍ,u<
25	DPN[18]	(co)10A+ribose PO₄	Ɍ	r,u>,s	Ɍ,u=	r,u=	Ɍ	Ɍ	Ɍ	Ɍ,u=<	Ɍ,u=<
26	Diphosphothiamine	(co)18A+PO₄	Ɍ	Ɍ,u<	Ɍ,u=	r,u>	Ɍ	Ɍ,u=	Ɍ,u	Ɍ,u=	Ɍ,u=
27	Folic acid conjugates[19]	(co)13A+glutamate	Ɍ·	Ɍ	Ɍ	Ɍ,u=	Ɍ	Ɍ	Ɍ,u=	Ɍ,u=	Ɍ,u=
28	Folinic acid[20]	(rel)13A	Ɍ	Ɍ	Ɍ	r	Ɍ	Ɍ	Ɍ,u=		Ɍ,u<
29	Hesperidin[21]	(po)"Vitamin P" series	Ɍ,s	Ɍ	Ɍ	Ɍ	Ɍ	Ɍ	Ɍ		Ɍ,s
30	O-Heterobiotin	(rel)3A,24A,34A	Ɍ	Ɍ	Ɍ	Ɍ,u<,ʉ	Ɍ	Ɍ	Ɍ	Ɍ	Ɍ
31	L. B. factor[22]	(rel)12A	Ɍ	Ɍ	Ɍ	r,u>	Ɍ	Ɍ	Ɍ	Ɍ	Ɍ
32	Lipothiamide	(co)18A+lipoic acid	Ɍ	Ɍ	Ɍ	Ɍ	Ɍ	Ɍ	Ɍ	Ɍ	Ɍ,u=
33	Lyxoflavin	(rel)17A	Ɍ	Ɍ	Ɍ	Ɍ,u<	Ɍ	Ɍ	Ɍ	Ɍ	Ɍ,s,u<
34	Oxybiotin	(rel)3A,24A,30A	Ɍ	Ɍ	Ɍ	Ɍ,u<	Ɍ	Ɍ	Ɍ	Ɍ	Ɍ
35	"Pantothenic acid conjugate"	(co)12A+adenine+glutamate	Ɍ	Ɍ	Ɍ	r?,u>	Ɍ	Ɍ	Ɍ	Ɍ	Ɍ
36	Pantoic acid	(po)12A	Ɍ	Ɍ	Ɍ,u	Ɍ,u	Ɍ	Ɍ	Ɍ	Ɍ	Ɍ,ʉ
37	Para-aminobenzoic acid	(po)40A	Ɍ	r,rm	r	r	Ɍ	Ɍ	r	Ɍ	Ɍ,s
38	Pimelic acid	(rel po)3A	Ɍ	Ɍ,s	Ɍ	Ɍ,u=<	Ɍ	Ɍ	Ɍ,u<	Ɍ	Ɍ,ʉ
39	Pseudovitamin B₁₂	(rel)5A	Ɍ	Ɍ	Ɍ	Ɍ,u=	Ɍ	Ɍ,u=	Ɍ	Ɍ	Ɍ,ʉ
40	Pteroic acid	(po)13A	Ɍ	Ɍ	Ɍ	Ɍ,u<	Ɍ	Ɍ	Ɍ,u=,ʉ	Ɍ	Ɍ,ʉ
41	Pyridoxal-PO₄	(rel)14A	Ɍ,u=	Ɍ,u=	Ɍ,u=	r,u>	Ɍ	Ɍ	Ɍ,u=	Ɍ,u=	Ɍ,u=
42	Pyridoxamine-PO₄	(rel)15A	Ɍ,u=	Ɍ,u	Ɍ,u	r,u>	Ɍ	Ɍ	Ɍ,u=	Ɍ,u=	Ɍ,u=
43	Pyrimidine[23,24]	(po)18A	Ɍ	r,rm,u[23,24]	r,s[23,24]	r,u[23,24]	r[23,24]	r,u[23,24]	r,u[23,24]	Ɍ,u=	Ɍ,ʉ
44	Rhizopterin	(rel po)13A	Ɍ	Ɍ	Ɍ	Ɍ,u=	Ɍ	Ɍ	Ɍ	Ɍ	Ɍ,ʉ
45	α-Ribazole	(po)5A	Ɍ	Ɍ	Ɍ	Ɍ,u=	Ɍ	Ɍ,u<	Ɍ	Ɍ	Ɍ,ʉ
46	Rutin[21]	(po) "Vitamin P" series	Ɍ	Ɍ	Ɍ	Ɍ	Ɍ	Ɍ	Ɍ	Ɍ	Ɍ,s
47	Thiazole[24,25]	(po)18A	Ɍ	r,rm,u[24,25]	r,s[24,25]	r,u[24,25]	r[24,25]	r,u[24,25]	r,u[24,25]	Ɍ	Ɍ,ʉ
48	TPN	(co)10A+ribose+PO₄	Ɍ	r,u>,s	Ɍ,u=	Ɍ,u=	Ɍ	Ɍ	Ɍ	Ɍ	Ɍ,u=
49	Xanthopterin	(rel po)13A	Ɍ	Ɍ	Ɍ	Ɍ,u<	Ɍ	Ɍ	Ɍ	Ɍ	r?[26],u>[26],s

/1/ Vitamin = an organic compound, other than an amino-acid, carbohydrate or essential fatty acid, required in the diet by at least one vertebrate animal. /2/ (co) = composed of; (po) = part of; (pre) = precursor of; (rel) = related to; (inc) = includes. /3/ Spermatophytes (the intact plant). /4/ Green Phytoflagellates, chrysomonads, dinoflagellates. /5/ Including the colorless phytoflagellates. /6/ Includes: choline, betaine and other methyl donors./7/ Generic term including cyanocobalamin, hydroxocobalamin, vitamins B₁₂, B₁₂ₐ, B₁₂ᵦ. /8/ For some, thymine desoxyriboside, hypoxanthine, adenine, guanine may substitute in certain media. /9/ D₂ active for mammals only; D₃ active for all and R by chicken. /10/ Of doubtful status as a vitamin. /11/ = Folic acid, folacin. /12/ For one or more, pteroic acid (q. v. 40A) or thymine + thymidine will substitute. /13/ Member of the pyridoxine group (Vitamin B₆). /14/ Inhibits growth of Rhizopus nigricans. /15/ Inhibits growth of strains of Saccharomyces cerevisiae. /16/ And other carotenoid precursors of Vitamin A. /17/ R? by certain crustacea whose eyes contain vitamin A. /18/ Diphospho-pyridine nucleotide. /19/ Di-, tri- and hepta-glutamates of pteroylglutamic acid. /20/ = The citrovorum factor, R by Leuconostoc citrovorum. /21/ 29, 46 and citrin = "vitamin P" series. /22/ Lactobacillus bulgaricus factor which = pantetheine, pantethine, (N-(pantothenyl) β-amîno-ethanol and corresponding di-sulfide?). /23/ Thiamine or pyrimidine moiety, (thiazole moiety is synthesized). /24/ Thiamine or pyrimidine + thiamine moieties, (pyrimidine and thiazole moieties combined to give thiamine). /25/ Thiamine or thiazole moiety, (pyrimidine moiety is synthesized). /26/ More active than pteroylglutamic (folic) acid in relieving anemia of Chinook salmon, (fish).

Ɍ = Not required by any form studied; r = Required by one or more species or strains; rm = Required by one or more mutants; u = Utilized by one or more species or strains; ɰ = Not utilized by one or more species or strains; "u=" = Utilized as effectively as (or interchangeably with) one or more related compounds, the presence of at least one of the series being required by one or more species or strains. u< = Partially replaces or spares one or more required or interchangeably required compounds for one or more species or strains; s = Stimulates growth or other processes for one or more species or strains; i = Inhibits growth or other processes for one or more species or strains.

	Nutrient	Higher Green Plants	Fungi	Yeasts	Bacteria	Algae	Green Phyto-flagellates	Invertebrates		Vertebrates
								Protozoa	Insects	
1	Pyrimidine compounds	Ɍ	r, rm, s	r, s	r, s, u	r	r	r, s	r	Ɍ, s
2	Purine compounds	Ɍ	rm, s, u	s, u	r, s, u	Ɍ	Ɍ	r, s	r	Ɍ, s
3	Cytidine	Ɍ	Ɍ, rm, s	Ɍ	u=[1]	Ɍ	Ɍ	u=, i	Ɍ	Ɍ
4	Cytidylic acid	Ɍ	Ɍ, rm, s[2]	Ɍ	u=[1]	Ɍ	Ɍ	u=, s	Ɍ	Ɍ
5	Cytosine	Ɍ	rm	Ɍ	u=[3]	Ɍ	Ɍ	r?, ɰ[4], i	Ɍ	Ɍ
6	Orotic acid	Ɍ	rm, s[2]	Ɍ	r[5], s	Ɍ	Ɍ	Ɍ, ɰ[4]	Ɍ	Ɍ, s
7	Pyrimidine	(See table H16)								
8	Thymine	Ɍ	Ɍ	Ɍ	u=[6], u<[7]	Ɍ	Ɍ, u<[8]	r?, u<[9]	r	Ɍ, s
9	Thymidine	Ɍ	Ɍ	Ɍ	u<[7]	Ɍ	Ɍ	u<[9]	Ɍ	Ɍ, s
10	Uracil	Ɍ	rm, s[2]	Ɍ	u=[1], s	Ɍ	r?	r, u=[10]	r[11]	Ɍ
11	Uridine	Ɍ	Ɍ, rm, s	Ɍ	u=[1], s	Ɍ	Ɍ	u=	Ɍ	Ɍ
12	Uridylic acid	Ɍ	Ɍ, rm, s[2]	Ɍ	u=[1], s	Ɍ	Ɍ	u=	Ɍ	Ɍ
13	Adenine	Ɍ	rm	r[12]	u=[13]	Ɍ	Ɍ, u<[8]	r?, u<[14]	r[11]	Ɍ, s
14	Adenosine	Ɍ	Ɍ	Ɍ	u=[13]	Ɍ	Ɍ	r, u<[14]	Ɍ	Ɍ
15	Adenosine triphosphate	Ɍ	Ɍ	Ɍ	u=[13]	Ɍ	Ɍ	Ɍ, s	Ɍ	Ɍ
16	Adenylic acid	Ɍ	Ɍ	Ɍ	u=[13]	Ɍ	Ɍ	r, u<[14]	r[11]	Ɍ, s
17	Guanine	Ɍ	r, rm, s	Ɍ	u=[13], s	Ɍ	s	r[15]	Ɍ	Ɍ
18	Guanosine	Ɍ	Ɍ	Ɍ	u=[13]	Ɍ	Ɍ	r?, u=, u<[16], i	Ɍ	Ɍ
19	Guanylic acid	Ɍ	Ɍ	Ɍ	u=[13]	Ɍ	Ɍ	u=, s	Ɍ	Ɍ
20	Hypoxanthine	Ɍ	r, rm	Ɍ	u=[13], s	Ɍ	s	u=, u<[14]	Ɍ	Ɍ
21	Xanthine	Ɍ	Ɍ	Ɍ	u=[12]	Ɍ	Ɍ	r?[17], ɰ[4]	Ɍ	Ɍ
22	Others							s[18]		

/1/ At least one required, but interchangeable, for several species, e.g. Clostidium tetani, Hemophilus parainfluenzae. /2/ Stimulates mutants of Neurospora. /3/ Lactobacillus arabinosus, Leuconostoc mesenteroides r 5 or 17 (interchangeable). /4/ ɰ by Tetrahymena. /5/ r by Lactobacillus bulgaricus 09. /6/ Clostridium tetani r either 13 or 20 (interchangeable). /7/ Spares folic acid for Streptococcus lactis; 8 + 9 replaces folic acid for S. lactis. /8/ Spares, and given with amino-acids, substitutes for para-aminobenzoic and folic acids for Euglena gracilis. /9/ Spares folic acid for Tetrahymena. /10/For Tetrahymena, 10 or 3, 4, 11 or 12 r. /11/ Drosophila melanogaster r 10 + sucrose, 10 + 13 + 17 or nucleic acid. /12/ r by Saccharomyces octosporus on certain media. /13/ Items 13-21 variously interchangeable for different bacteria, but at least one must be present, e.g. Streptococcus hemolyticus r at least one of 13, 14, 16, 17, 18, 19, 21 (the requirement is relieved by CO₂ in high concentration); 13, 17, 20 or 21 r Streptococcus lactis; 14 r by B. megaterium for spore germination. /14/ Spares but cannot replace 17, 18, 19, for Tetrahymena. /15/ r by Tetrahymena, replaceable by 18 or 19. /16/ Spares folic acid (as does adenosine) for Herpetomonas culicidarum. /17/ In vitro studies indicate a possible requirement of 21 and also 5, 7, 10, 13, 18 by Plasmodium. /18/ Methyl purines e.g. theobromine, theophylline, caffeine s some ciliates and Suctoria.

R = Required by all forms studied; Ɍ = Not required by any forms studied; r = Required by one or more species or strains; rm = Required by one or more mutants; "u=" = Replaces effectively or utilized interchangeably with one or more other substances, but one of the interchangeable substances must be present; s = Stimulates growth or other processes for one or more species or strains; i = Inhibits growth or other processes for one or more species or strains.

	Nutrient	Higher Green Plants	Fungi	Yeasts	Bacteria	Algae	Green Phyto-flagellates	Invertebrates		Vertebrates
								Protozoa	Insects	
1	Adenylthiomethylpentose	Ɍ	Ɍ	Ɍ	Ɍ	Ɍ	Ɍ	Ɍ	Ɍ	Ɍ, s
2	Anthranilic acid	Ɍ	r, rm[1]	Ɍ	u=[1]	Ɍ	Ɍ	Ɍ, s	Ɍ	Ɍ, s
3	Antibiotics	Ɍ, s	Ɍ, s	Ɍ	r[2]	Ɍ	Ɍ	Ɍ	Ɍ	Ɍ, s
4	Asparagine	Ɍ	Ɍ	Ɍ, s, i	r[3]	Ɍ	Ɍ	Ɍ	Ɍ	Ɍ
5	"Bifidus" factor[4]	Ɍ	Ɍ	Ɍ	r	Ɍ	R	Ɍ	Ɍ	Ɍ
6	Carbon dioxide	R	r[5], s, i	Ɍ	r[5], s	R	R[6], s	r[7]	r[8]	Ɍ
7	Carnitine	Ɍ	r	Ɍ	Ɍ	Ɍ	Ɍ	Ɍ	Ɍ	Ɍ
8	Coprogen	Ɍ	r	Ɍ	Ɍ	Ɍ	Ɍ	Ɍ	Ɍ	Ɍ
9	N-D-Glucosylglycine ester	Ɍ	Ɍ	Ɍ	r[3], s	Ɍ	Ɍ	Ɍ	Ɍ	Ɍ
10	Glutamine	Ɍ	Ɍ, s, i	s, i	r[9]	Ɍ	Ɍ	Ɍ	s[10]	Ɍ
11	Glutathione	Ɍ	Ɍ	Ɍ	r[9]	Ɍ	Ɍ	r?[11]	Ɍ	Ɍ
12	Guanidine	Ɍ	Ɍ	Ɍ	Ɍ	Ɍ	Ɍ	Ɍ	Ɍ	Ɍ
13	Indole-3-acetic acid[12]	r?, s	r?, s	Ɍ	Ɍ, s	Ɍ, s	Ɍ, s[13]	Ɍ[13], i	r	Ɍ, s?
14	Hematin	Ɍ	r	Ɍ	r	Ɍ	r[14], s	Ɍ, s[14]	Ɍ	Ɍ
15	Krebs cycle intermediates	Ɍ	r	Ɍ	r[15]	Ɍ	Ɍ	Ɍ	Ɍ	Ɍ, s
16	Mucin	Ɍ	Ɍ	Ɍ	r[16]	Ɍ	Ɍ	Ɍ	Ɍ	Ɍ
17	Mycobactin	Ɍ	Ɍ	Ɍ	rm	Ɍ	Ɍ	Ɍ	Ɍ	Ɍ
18	Parahydroxybenzoic acid	Ɍ	rm	Ɍ	rm	Ɍ	Ɍ	Ɍ	Ɍ	Ɍ
19	Putrescine	Ɍ	rm	Ɍ	r, u=[17]	Ɍ	Ɍ	Ɍ	u=[18]	Ɍ
20	Quinic acid	Ɍ	rm	Ɍ	rm	Ɍ	Ɍ	Ɍ	u=[18]	Ɍ
21	Shikimic acid	Ɍ	rm	Ɍ	rm	Ɍ	Ɍ	Ɍ	Ɍ	Ɍ
22	Spermidine	Ɍ	Ɍ	Ɍ	r, u=[17]	Ɍ	Ɍ	Ɍ	Ɍ	Ɍ, s?
23	Strepogenin	Ɍ	Ɍ, s?	Ɍ	r, rm, s	Ɍ	Ɍ	r[19]	Ɍ	Ɍ
24	Thioctic acid	Ɍ	Ɍ	Ɍ	r	Ɍ	Ɍ	r	r	Ɍ
25	Unidentified factors				r				r	r

/1/ Substitutes for tryptophan and/or indole. /2/ R by "dependent" mutants. /3/ R as growth factor and not replaceable by aspartic or glutamic acids. /4/ ɑ- and β-Methyl-N-acetyl-d-glucosaminide? /5/ R by some in higher than atmospheric concentrations. /6/ R although another carbon source is available, particularly in darkness. /7/ R by some colorless phytoflagellates. /8/ R by Tenebrio molitor; interchangeable with γ-amino-β-hydroxy-butryic acid. /9/ R by Neisseria gonorrhoeae. /10/ Favors larval growth of Drosophila and Aedes aegypti. /11/ Possibly R by Plasmodium in vitro; Ɍ by Tetrahymena. /12/ And related auxins. /13/ s Euglena gracilis (green phytoflagellate), ineffective for Astasia (colorless counterpart of Euglena). /14/ Several utilized for growth by the "acetate" flagellates; acetate utilized by most; wide variation among species with respect to utilization or availability of individual Krebs intermediates and related compounds such as pyruvate. /15/ Corynebacterium diphtheriae. /16/ Mycobacterium johnei. /17/ Interchangeable with spermidine for some. /18/ Spares or replaces phenylalanine, tyrosine for Blatella germanica. /19/ R by Tetrahymena geleii (8 strains), T. vorax (2 strains); spared but not replaced by acetate; R? by Peranema trichophorum.

A sulfur source is required by organisms in all categories listed below.

R = Required by all forms studied; R̸ = Not required by any forms studied; r = Required by one or more species or strains; rm = Required by one or more mutants; U = Utilized by all forms studied; U̸ = Not utilized by any forms studied; u = Utilized by one or more species or strains.

Nutrient	Higher Green Plants	Fungi	Yeasts	Bacteria	Algae	Green Phyto-flagellates	Invertebrates Protozoa[1]	Invertebrates Insects	Vertebrates
Inorganic Sulfur Sources									
1 Sulfur[2] (elemental), S	R̸,U̸	u[3]	u	r[4]	R̸,U̸	R̸	R̸	R̸	R̸,u[5]
2 Sulfhydryl, (SH)	R̸	u			R̸	R̸	R̸	R̸	R̸
3 Sulfide, (S)	R̸	u[6]		u[7]	R̸,u[8]	R̸	R̸	R̸	R̸,U̸
4 Bisulfite, (HSO3)	R̸	u[9]			R̸	R̸	R̸	R̸	R̸,U̸
5 Sulfite, (SO3)	R̸,u	u[9]		u[10]	R̸	R̸	R̸	R̸	R̸,U̸
6 Sulfate, (SO4)	U	u[9]	u	r	U	U	r	R̸	R̸,u[11]
7 Thiosulfate, (S2O3)	R̸,u	rm,u		u[12]	R̸	R̸	R̸	R̸	R̸,U̸
8 (S2O8)[13]	R̸	u?			R̸	R̸	R̸	R̸	R̸
9 Tetrathionate, (S4O6)	R̸			u	R̸	R̸	R̸	R̸	R̸
10 Sulfoxylate, (SOOH)	R̸	u[14]		u	R̸	R̸	R̸	R̸	R̸
11 (SO) as Sulfur hydrate, H2SO	R̸			u	R̸	R̸/	R̸	R̸	R̸
12 Thiocyanate, (SCN)	R̸	u		u[15]	R̸	R̸	R̸	R̸	R̸
13 Persulfate	R̸	u[9]			R̸	R̸	R̸	R̸	R̸
Sulfur Containing Amino Acids, Sulfoproteins[16]									
14 Cystathionine	R̸	u		u	R̸	R̸	R̸,u	u	u
15 Cysteine	R̸,u	u[6]	u	r	R̸,u[17]	R̸,u	u	u[18]	U
16 Cystine	R̸,u	u[6]	u	r	R̸	R̸,u	u	u	U
17 Homocysteine	R̸	U		u	R̸	R̸	R̸,u	u	u
18 Homocystine	R̸	U		u	R̸	R̸	R̸,u	u	u
19 Methionine	R̸,u	U	u	r	R̸,U̸	r	r	r[19]	R
20 Peptones	R̸,u	U	u	u	R̸,u	u	r	u	R̸,U
Sulfur Containing Vitamins and Growth Factors[16]									
21 Biotin[20]	R̸	u	u	u	R̸	r	r?	r	R?,U
22 Coenzyme A	R̸	R̸	R̸	R̸	R̸	R̸	R̸	R̸	R̸,U
23 Glutathione ("G-SH")[21]	R̸	u	u	r	R̸	u	R̸,u	r	R̸,U
24 Thiamine[22]	R̸	U̸	r	r	u	r	r	r	R
25 Thiazole[22]	R̸	u?[23]	r[24]	r[24]	r	r[24]	r[24],u	R̸	R̸
26 Thioctic acid[25]	R̸	R̸	R̸	r[26]	R̸	R̸	r[27]	R̸	R̸
Miscellaneous Sulfur Compounds									
27 Alkylsulfides, R-S-S-R	R̸	u[28]			R̸	R̸	R̸	R̸	R̸
28 Alkylsulfinates, R-SO2-R	R̸	u			R̸	R̸	R̸	R̸	R̸
29 Alkylsulfonates, R-SO3-R	R̸	u			R̸	R̸	R̸	R̸	R̸
30 Dithionate	R̸	u[29]			R̸	R̸	R̸	R̸	R̸
31 Ethereal sulfates	R̸	U			R̸	R̸	R̸	R̸	R̸
32 Sulfamate, (SO3-NH2)	R̸	u			R̸	R̸	R̸	R̸	R̸
33 Sulfonic acid amides	R̸	rm		U̸	R̸	R̸	R̸	R̸	R̸
34 Sulfoxides, R2SO	R̸	u		u	R̸	R̸	R̸	R̸	R̸
35 Taurine	R̸	u		U̸	R̸	R̸	R̸	R̸	R̸
36 Thioacetamide	R̸	u		u	R̸	R̸	R̸	R̸	R̸
37 Thioacetate	R̸	r,u[6]		u?[30]	R̸	R̸	R̸	R̸	R̸
38 Thiocarbonate	R̸	r,u[6]			R̸	R̸	R̸	R̸	R̸
39 Thioglycolate	R̸	r,u[6]		u?[31]	R̸	R̸	R̸	R̸	R̸
40 Thiols, R-SH	R̸	u			R̸	R̸	R̸	R̸	R̸
41 Thiooxalate	R̸	u			R̸	R̸	R̸	R̸	R̸
42 Thiourea	R̸	u[6]	u[32]	u?[33]	R̸	R̸	R̸	R̸	R̸

/1/ Including the colorless phytoflagellates. /2/ The substance not in combination with other elements. /3/ U by Fusarium lini. /4/ U by Thiobacillus thio-oxidans, Sporovibrio desulfuricans, S. aestuarii, Thiorhodacae. /5/ Bacteria, in ruminants, build the element into amino acids (methionine; cystine). /6/ Some aquatic fungi, e.g., members of the Blastocladiales and Saprolegniales, U̸ oxidized sulfur; these require a reduced sulfur source, e.g., H2S, cysteine, cystine, methionine, thioacetate, thiocarbonate, thioglycolate, thiourea. /7/ U, e.g., by Beggiatoa, Thiothrix, Thioploca, Thiobacilli. /8/ Synechococcus, grown in an atmosphere of N2, U Na2S (with reduction of CO2); Oscillaria and Pinnularia also reduce CO2 with H2S, depositing S in their cells. Scenedesmus also U sulfide. H2S toxic to Chlorella. /9/ U by Brevilegnea gracilis; U̸ by many other Saprolegniaceae. /10/ U by Sporovibrio desulfuricans, S. aestuarii. /11/ U for formation of chondroitin sulfate and heparin; U by laying hen by conversion to cystine. /12/ U by Thiobacillus novellus, Pseudomonas aeruginosa, P. fluorescens, Achromobacter stutzeri, others. /13/ Decomposes on contact with H2O. /14/ Inorganic sulfur, less oxidized than sulfinate, not efficiently U by Aspergillus niger. /15/ NH4SCN can be U by Bacillus thiocyan-oxidans as sole source of C, N, and S. /16/ R, r, U, u, may mean as a sulfur source, or the compound may be R for its molecular structure, not synthesized by the organism. /17/ U as N-source (and sulfur source?) by Chlorella pyrenoidosa. /18/ Also U cysteic acid, isethionic acid. /19/ Also U methionine sulfoxide, taurine. /20/ Biotin R by numerous fungi, yeasts, bacteria and by most of the vertebrates and invertebrates studied. The replacement of S in the biotin molecule does not affect the activity for some bacteria. /21/ Complex of cysteine, glycine, and glutamic acid. /22/ Thiamine, containing pyrimidine and thiazole (the latter an imidazole ring with one C replaced by sulfur), is R by numerous organisms; probably also a sulfur source? /23/ U̸ as sulfur source by Aspergillus niger (cannot rupture the thiazole ring?). /24/ Satisfies thiamine requirement for some (cf. Fn 22); probably a sulfur source? /25/ = Protogen, or α-lipoic acid. /26/ R by Streptococcus fecalis for oxidation of pyruvate. /27/ R by Tetrahymena geleii (8 strains), T. vorax (2 strains). /28/ U by Scopulariopsis (Penicillium brevicaulis, Schizophyllum commune). /29/ U̸ by Saprolegniaceae. /30/ U̸ as carbon source by many; improbable sulfur source. /31/ Surface active in culture media for many fastidious forms; powerful reducing agent; U̸ as carbon source; improbable as sulfur source. /32/ U by Torula monosa, T. dattila. /33/ U as nitrogen source by many bacteria; probable sulfur source?

187. DIETS, LOW AND MODERATE COST: MAN, U.S.A.

These food plans (low cost=L; moderate cost=M) represent quantities per week, as purchased, that will furnish nutritionally adequate diets as judged by the National Research Council's recommended allowances (1948). Both the low and moderate cost plans have the same adjustment for losses of vitamins in cooking. Values are in kilograms, except for milk (liters) and eggs (number).

Family Members		Leafy, Green and Yellow Vegetables kg		Citrus Fruit, Tomatoes kg		Potatoes, Sweet-potatoes kg		Other Vegetables and Fruit kg		Milk[1] L		Meat, Poultry, Fish kg		Eggs no.		Dry Beans and Peas, Nuts kg		Flour, Cereals[2] kg		Fats and Oils[3] kg		Sugar, Sirups, Preserves kg	
		L	M	L	M	L	M	L	M	L	M	L	M	L	M	L	M	L	M	L	M	L	M
	Children																						
1	9-12 mo	0.68	0.68	0.79	0.79	0.23	0.23	0.45	0.45	5.68	5.68	0.11	0.11	5	5	0.03	0.03	0.28	0.28	0.03	0.03	0.03	0.03
2	1-3 yr	0.79	0.91	0.79	0.91	0.45	0.23	0.45	0.79	5.20	5.68	0.23[4]	0.34[4]	5	6	0.03	0.03	0.57	0.57	0.06	0.06	0.06	0.06
3	4-6 yr	0.79	1.02	0.79	1.02	0.68	0.45	0.57	1.02	5.20	5.68	0.45	0.57	5	7	0.06	0.03	0.79	0.68	0.17	0.17	0.17	0.23
4	7-9 yr	0.91	1.13	0.91	1.13	1.13	0.79	0.68	1.13	5.20	6.15	0.68	0.79	5	7	0.11	0.06	1.02	0.91	0.23	0.23	0.28	0.34
5	10-12 yr	1.02	1.36	1.02	1.25	1.36	1.02	0.79	1.13	5.68	6.62	0.79	1.02	5	7	0.11	0.06	1.47	1.25	0.34	0.34	0.34	0.40
	Girls																						
6	13-15 yr	1.02	1.59	1.02	1.25	1.47	1.13	0.79	1.59	6.15	6.62	0.91[4]	1.25[4]	5	7	0.11	0.06	1.59	1.25	0.34	0.40	0.34	0.40
7	16-20 yr	1.02	1.59	1.02	1.25	1.36	1.13	0.79	1.59	4.73	5.68	0.91[4]	1.25[4]	5	7	0.11	0.06	1.47	1.13	0.34	0.34	0.28	0.40
	Boys																						
8	13-15 yr	1.13	1.59	1.13	1.36	1.81	1.59	1.02	1.59	6.15	6.62	0.91	1.36	5	7	0.23	0.11	2.04	1.81	0.45	0.51	0.40	0.51
9	16-20 yr	1.25	1.81	1.13	1.59	2.27	2.04	1.13	1.59	6.15	6.62	0.91	1.47	5	7	0.23	0.17	2.61	2.38	0.62	0.62	0.45	0.57
	Women																						
10	Sedentary	1.02	1.47	0.91	1.13	1.02	0.79	0.79	1.47	4.73	4.73	0.91	1.13	5	7	0.11	0.03	0.91	0.79	0.28	0.28	0.28	0.34
11	Mod. active	1.02	1.59	0.91	1.13	1.36	1.13	0.79	1.59	4.73	4.73	0.91	1.25	5	7	0.11	0.06	1.47	1.13	0.34	0.40	0.34	0.40
12	Very active	1.13	1.70	1.13	1.36	1.81	1.47	0.91	1.81	4.73	4.73	0.91	1.36	5	7	0.17	0.11	1.93	1.70	0.45	0.51	0.45	0.51
13	Pregnant	1.36	1.81	1.13	1.59	1.13	1.02	0.91	1.36	7.10	7.10	1.02[4]	1.36[4]	7	7	0.11	0.06	1.13	1.02	0.28	0.28	0.23	0.28
14	Nursing	1.59	1.81	1.70	2.04	1.81	1.36	1.02	1.59	9.94	9.94	1.13[4]	1.36[4]	7	7	0.11	0.06	1.36	1.13	0.28	0.34	0.23	0.34
15	60 yr or over	1.13	1.59	1.02	1.25	1.13	0.91	0.79	1.36	4.73	5.20	0.91	1.13	4	6	0.06	0.03	1.02	0.79	0.23	0.23	0.23	0.28
	Men																						
16	Sedentary	1.02	1.59	0.91	1.13	1.36	1.13	0.79	1.59	4.73	4.73	0.91	1.25	5	7	0.11	0.06	1.47	1.13	0.34	0.40	0.34	0.40
17	Phys. active	1.13	1.70	1.13	1.36	1.81	1.47	0.91	1.81	4.73	4.73	0.91	1.36	5	7	0.17	0.11	1.93	1.70	0.45	0.51	0.45	0.51
18	Heavy work	1.13	1.81	1.13	1.59	2.72	2.27	1.13	1.93	4.73	4.73	0.91	1.59	5	7	0.28	0.17	3.52	3.18	0.85	0.91	0.45	0.57
19	60 yr or over	1.13	1.59	1.02	1.25	1.47	1.25	0.79	1.36	4.73	5.20	0.91	1.25	4	6	0.06	0.06	1.47	1.13	0.28	0.34	0.28	0.34

/1/ Or its equivalent in cheese, evaporated milk, or dried milk. /2/ Count 0.68 kg bread as 0.45 kg flour. /3/ For small children, and pregnant and nursing women, cod-liver oil or some other source of vitamin D is also needed. For elderly persons and those who have no opportunity for exposure to clear sunshine, a small amount of vitamin D is also desirable. /4/ To meet iron allowance, 1 large or 2 small servings of liver or other organ meats should be served each week.

188. DIETS: LABORATORY AND DOMESTIC ANIMALS

These diets have been selected from a large number of possible diets. They are not necessarily optimal, nor do they suit all conditions and feeding purposes. Consult texts on feeding for more detailed information. Unless otherwise indicated, values are grams per 100 grams of ration, the daily food or feed intake is expressed as kg per animal, and the values are for adult animals.

	Animal	Intake[1], kg	Diet
1	Cattle, beef[2], 408 kg	I-9.4; II-9.0; III-17.9	Diet I: alfalfa hay, 20; oat hay, 80. Diet II: corn fodder, 50; barley straw, 25; alfalfa hay, 25. Diet III: corn silage, 69; oat straw, 27; cottonseed meal (41% protein), 4.
2	Chicken, Rhode Island Red[3], 2.5 kg	0.092	Corn, ground yellow, 49; standard wheat middlings, 15; wheat bran, 10; alfalfa meal, 5 (meal contains 75,000 or more I.U. of vitamin A per lb); soybean oil meal, 4; fish meal, 4; meat meal, 4; dried whey, 4; steamed bone meal, 1; ground limestone, 3.5; salt, 0.5; vitamin A and D feeding oil (300 International Chick Units vitamin D, 1500 I.U. vitamin A, per gram), 0.3; anhydrous $MnSO_4$, 0.0125 g, and riboflavine 0.1 mg per 100 g feed.
3	Dog[4]	Varies with breed	Meat, meat by-products including bone, or fish, 20; soybean meal, wheat germ, corn germ, or nut meal, 20; corn, wheat, or barley, 50; carrots, beet by-products, or tomato by-products, 2-5; iodized salt, 0.24-0.5; milk, liver meals, or fermentation solubles, q.s.; liver oils and irradiated yeast, q.s.
4	Fish[5], 0.002-0.05 kg	0.04-3 at 10°C	Diet I: pork or beef spleen, 35; beef liver, 15; salt, 2; fish meal, 12; wheat middlings, 12; dried skim milk or distillers' solubles, 12; cottonseed meal, 12. Diet II: beef liver, 33; beef spleen, 33; horse meat, 34. Diet III: cooked carp or other rough fish, 45; oatmeal, 5; beef liver, 15; beef or pork spleen, 35.
5	Horse[6], 544 kg	11.4	Timothy hay, 26; alfalfa hay, 20; oats, 32; corn, 22.
6	Monkey[7], 1.5-3 kg	0.06-0.12	Sucrose, 71; "de-vitaminized" casein, 18; corn oil, 4; salt mixture, 3 (composed of $CaCO_3$, 300 g; K_2HPO_4, 470 g; $CaHPO_4$, 680 g; $MgSO_4$, 100 g; NaCl, 670 g; KCl, 115 g; $FeC_6H_5O_7$, 55 g; KI, 1.6 g; $MnSO_4 \cdot H_2O$, 9 g; $ZnCl_2$, 4 g; $CuSO_4$, 2.4 g; $CoCl_2$, 0.2 g); whole liver substance, 2; liver concentrate powder, 2. To each 18 g of casein, add: thiamine hydrochloride, 350 µg; pyridoxine hydrochloride, 350 µg; nicotinamide, 2.5 mg; choline chloride, 100 mg; inositol, 100 mg; para-aminobenzoic acid, 30 mg; calcium pantothenate, 2 mg; riboflavin, 350 µg; folacin, 200 µg; biotin, 20 µg; ascorbic acid, 10 mg. To each 4 g of corn oil, add: 90% β-carotene, 90 µg; calciferol, 0.8 µg; α-tocopherol, 5 mg; menadione, 100 µg.
7	Rat[8], 0.18 kg	0.007	Casein, 35; corn starch 37; lard, 15; butter fat, 9; salt mixture, 4 (composed of $CaCO_3$, 134.8 g; Na_2CO_3, 34.2 g; $MgCO_3$, 24.2 g; K_2CO_3, 141.3 g; H_3PO_4, 103.2 g; HCl, 53 g; H_2SO_4, 9.2 g; citric acid·H_2O, 111 g; Fe citrate·xH_2O, 6.3 g; KI, 0.02 g; $MnSO_4$, 0.079 g; NaF, 0.248 g; $K_2Al_2(SO_4)_4$, 0.0245 g). To this ration, add 0.5 g yeast, 25 g lettuce.
8	Sheep[9], 32 kg	I-3.8; II-1.2; III-1.5	Diet I: barley (corn, oats, or sorghum), 10.1; beet pulp, wet, 70; alfalfa hay, 20. Diet II: corn (barley or sorghum), 42; alfalfa, 58. Diet III: corn, 32; soybean meal, 5.9; alfalfa hay, 32; corn silage, 30.
9	Swine[10], 45 kg	I, II, III, IV, or V-2.4	Diet I: corn (yellow), 63; oats, 15; soybean meal, 7.8; middlings, 5.0; meat scrap, 3.0; alfalfa meal (dehydrated), 5.0; limestone, 0.7; salt, 0.5. Diet II: barley, 50; oats, 40; linseed meal, 3.0; fish meal, 1.0; meat scrap, 3.0; minerals (iodized salt, 20%; steamed bonemeal, 37.7%; ground limestone, 40%; ferrous sulfate, 2%; manganese sulfate, 0.2%; copper sulfate, 0.1%), 3.0; A and D oil (to supply 45,000 I.U. vitamin A and 9,000 I.U. vitamin D per 45 kg of feed). Diet III: barley, 83; tankage, 3; soybean meal, 8; alfalfa meal (deh.), 4.5; bone meal, 0.5; limestone, 0.5; salt, 0.5. Diet IV: corn, 82; soybean meal, 6.5; meat and bone scrap, 2.5; fish meal, 2.5; cottonseed meal, 2.5; alfalfa meal (deh.), 2.5; limestone, 0.5; bone meal, 0.5; salt, 0.5. Diet V: corn, 79; soybean meal (solvent extracted), 13.5; alfalfa meal (sun cured), 5.0; mineral mix (same as Diet II), 2.0; vitamin mix (each lb contains riboflavin, 200 mg; pantothenic acid, 500 mg; B_{12}, 2 mg; and an antibiotic in an amount suited to its kind)

/1/ The numerals I, II, etc., refer to alternative dietary mixtures given in column C. /2/ Wintering pregnant cow. /3/ Mature, breeding. /4/ For more detailed diets, see Report of Committee on Animal Nutrition, National Research Council, 8, Dec. 1953. /5/ Brook, brown and rainbow trout, age 3-9 months. /6/ Lactating mare. /7/ Rhesus, juvenile. /8/ White, age 1-6 months. /9/ Fattening lambs. /10/ About 1/4 grown.

189. DIETS: ZOO ANIMALS
Part I: ZOO DIETS: MAMMALIA AND AVES

Diets illustrate the feeding practices successfully in use in the New York, Chicago, and San Diego zoological parks. Differences in diet reflect climatic conditions, food availability, and individual variation within species. Body weights and feed values are estimates and are for a single animal of the species listed.

No.	Species	Zoo[1]	Sex	Body Weight[2] (lb)	Total Feed[2] (lb/wk)	Horse Meat (lb/wk)	Liver, Kidney (lb/wk)	Miscellaneous[3] (lb/wk)
	Monotremata							
1	Platypus (Ornithorhynchus anatinus)	NY	M	3.3				Earthworms, 7; crayfish (105–140); mealworms (1400); frogs (14); eggs (14).
	Marsupialia							
2	Kangaroo, red (Macropus rufus)	SD	M	54	57			Alfalfa, 21; apples, 7; bread, 5; lettuce, 21; browse, 3.
3	Wombat (Vombatus hirsutus)	NY	M	130	49.1			Rolled oats, 5.3; apples, 3.5; bananas, 1.8; bread, 3.5; cabbage, 2.1; carrots, 3.5; crushed oats, 1.4; clover hay, 21; lettuce, 3.5; white potatoes, 3.5.
	Primates							
4	Gorilla, lowland (Gorilla gorilla)	NY	F	20	10.3			Rolled oats, 1; apples, 3.5; bananas, 0.7; bread, 2.1; carrots, 1; crushed oats, 1; white potatoes, 1.
5		NY	F	296	53.9+	2.3		Powdered whole milk, 1; cereal, 1; malted milk powder, 0.2; honey, 42 g; eggs, 1.4; sugar, 0.6; dicalcium phosphate, 14 g; carrots, 17; celery, 3.5; bananas, 7; oranges, 2.7; apples, 5.4; cabbage, 1.8; lettuce, 2.3; grapes, 2.3; sweet potatoes, 2.3; green beans, 2.3; spinach, 0.5; scallions, 0.3; vitamins, 12 drops.[4]
6	Mandrill (Mandrillus sphinx)	SD	M	25	25.6			Apples, 5.3; bread, 0.8; fruit, 5.3; sweet potatoes, 0.1; lettuce, 5.6; onions, 0.5; corn, 2; tomatoes, 3.5; avocados, 1.5; string beans, 1.
7	Orangutan (Pongo pygmaeus)	NY	M	105	31.5+	7.0		Apples, 3.5; bananas, 5.3; bread, 0.8; cabbage, 1.8; carrots, 8.8; eggs (14); grapes, 0.8; lettuce, 3.5; dog biscuit[5], (28); milk mixture[6], 7 gal.
8		SD	M	150	60.6	1.8		Bread, 2.1; fruit, 10.5; string beans, 2.3; tomatoes, 10.5; lettuce, 8.8; sweet corn, 1.5; bananas, 1.8; sweet potatoes, 3.9; grapes, 1.5; milk, 0.6; peanuts, 0.8; avocados, 3.0; rice & raisins, 1.
	Carnivora							
9	Badger, Canadian (Taxidea taxus)	SD		30	6			Dog food mix[7], 6.
10	Bear, Eurasian brown (Ursus arctos)	SD	M	450	72+	15		Mackerel, 21; eggs (24); lettuce, 1.5; apples, 1.5; fruit, 3; bran & honey[8], 3; celery, 9; bread, 12; tomatoes, 1.5; avocados[9], 4.5.
11	Bear, grizzly (Ursus horribilis)	SD	M	700	85.5±	24		Mackerel, 12; eggs (24); lettuce, 3; apples, 3; fruit, 4.5; bran & honey[8], 6; celery, 13.5; bread, 12; tomatoes, 1.5; avocados[9], 6.
12	Bear, kodiak (U. middendorfii)	NY	M	800	132–150	42		Butterfish, 30; mackerel, 30; apples, 18; bread[10], 12.
13	Bear, polar (Thalarctos maritimus)	SD	F	300	76.5±	24		Mackerel, 2.4; eggs (36); apples, 3.6; fruit, 9; bran & honey[8], 9; celery, 13.5; bread, 9; tomatoes, 1.5; avocados, 4.5.
14	Bear, sloth (Melursus ursinus)	SD	F	350	13.5–15	4.5		Eggs (24); lettuce, 1.5; fruit, 3; bran & honey[8], 3; avocados[11], 3.
15	Cheetah (Acinonyx jubatus)	SD	M	120	38	35		Jungle fowl, rabbit, or guinea pig, 2.
16	Dingo (Canis dingo)	SD	M	50	25+	2.5		Dog food mix[7], 12.5; jungle fowl, rabbit, or guinea pig, 2; milk, 7; eggs (12).
17	Fox, Arctic (Alopex lagopus ungava)	SD		15	6		1	Dog food mix[7], 6.
18	Hyena, spotted (Crocuta crocuta)	SD	M	100	18	15	1	Jungle fowl, rabbit, or guinea pig, 2.
19	Jaguar (Panthera onca)	SD	M	175	33	30	1	Jungle fowl, rabbit, or guinea pig, 2.
20		NY	M	175	39.5+	34	5	Bone meal, 0.5; cod-liver oil, 48 ml.
21		LP	M		18+	18		Vitamin and mineral supplement.
22	Leopard (Panthera pardus)	SD	M	120	33	30	1	Jungle fowl, rabbit, or guinea pig, 2.
23		NY	F	125	22.7+	21.5	1	Bone meal, 0.2; cod-liver oil, 30 ml.
24		LP	M		9+	9		Vitamin supplement.
25	Lion (Panthera leo)	SD	M	250	75	72	1	Jungle fowl, rabbit, or guinea pig, 2.
26		NY	M	350	57.5+	55	2	Bone meal, 0.5; cod-liver oil, 57 ml.
27		LP	F		45+	45		Vitamin and mineral supplement.
28	Lynx, Yukon (Felis canadensis mollipilosus)	SD		35	14.4+	12	2	Eggs (6); milk, 2.4.
29	Ocelot (Felis pardalis)	SD		16	12	10		
30	Panda, lesser (Ailurus fulgens)	SD		14	18+			Milk, 3.5; eggs (14); apples, 1.75; fruit, 1.75; dates, 1.75; raisins, 0.4; grapes, 1.75; bananas, 7; Pablum, 0.1; fresh bamboo, ad lib.
31	Raccoon (Procyon lotor)	LP			4.8	3.6		Whole wheat bread, 1.2.
32	Tiger, Bengal (Panthera tigris)	SD	M	350	87	84	1	Jungle fowl, rabbit, or guinea pig, 2.
33	Wolf, N. American (Canis lupus nubilis)	SD	M	80	33	5	1	Dog food mix[7], 25; jungle fowl, rabbit, or guinea pig, 2.
	Pinnipedia							
34	Sea lion (Zalophus californianus)	NY	M	600	96			Butterfish, 48; mackerel, 24; smelts, 24.
35	Seal, harbor (Phoca vitulina geronimensis)	NY	F	70	28			Mackerel, 28.
	Rodentia							
36	Chinchilla	LP		1.25	9 oz			Rabbit chow (Purina), 3.1 oz; timothy hay, 2.7 oz; carrots, 1.8 oz; rolled oats, 0.4 oz; yellow corn, 0.4 oz; wheat germ, 0.05 oz; flax seed, 0.1 oz; CaHPO$_4$, 0.1 oz; raisins, 0.03 oz; oyster shells, 0.1 oz; apple bark, 0.2 oz.

#	Order / Common name (Scientific name)	Zoo	Sex				Diet
	Proboscidea						
	Elephant, Indian (Elephas maximus)						
37		SD	F	4500	879		Grain mix[12], 28; avocados[13], 15; celery, 70; apples, 35; oat hay, 630; bread, 14; sweet corn[14], 105,
38		NY	F	5500	846–966		Alfalfa[15], 350; timothy[15], 490; GLF[16], 42; crushed oats, 38.5; bread, 15; cabbage, 15; potatoes, 15.
39		LP	F				Apples (168); rye or whole wheat bread, 42; carrots, 168 qt; beets, 1.6 bu; timothy, 560; alfalfa, 28; oats, 7 pk; bran, 7 pk; cornstalks.
	Artiodactyla						
40	Alpaca (Lama pacos)	SD	M	200	45		Alfalfa pellets[17], 14; grain mix[12], 6; lettuce, 3; carrots, 9; browse, 7.
41	Antelope, sable (Hippotragus niger rooseveltii)	SD	M	550	86		Alfalfa pellets[17], 49; grain mix[12], 6; avocados, 6; carrots, 6; celery, 9, browse, 10.
42	Buffalo, African (Syncerus caffer)	SD	M	3600	402±		Alfalfa pellets[17], 350; grain mix[12], 12; avocados[13], 15; browse, 25 (occasionally).
43		NY[18]	M	1400	252.8±		Clover, 140; GLF[16], 26.3; crushed oats, 24.5; cabbage, 51.5; lettuce, 10.5; green leaves 1 or 2 x/wk.
44	Camel, dromedary (Camelus dromedarius)	NY[18]	F	1310	140		Clover, 105; GLF[16], 35.
45	Deer, red (Cervus elaphus)	SD	M	350	93		Alfalfa pellets[17], 35; grain mix[12], 6; avocados, 6; carrots, 6; celery, 30; browse, 10.
46	Giraffe, uganda (Giraffa camelopardalis rothschildii)	SD	M	2500	622.9		Alfalfa pellets[17], 105; grain mix[12], 45; carrots, 60; apples, 90; potatoes, 42; onions, 35; tea, 0.9; acacia browse, 245.
47		NY[18]	F	1300	254.3		Clover, 140; GLF[16], 31.5; crushed oats, 31.5; apples, 2.3; bananas, 14; bread, 21; cabbage, 3.5; white potatoes, 5.6; carrots, 3.5; lettuce, 1.4.
48	Hippopotamus (Hippopotamus amphibius)	SD	M	4000	693		Alfalfa pellets[17], 420; grain mix, 18; avocados, 15; lettuce, 60; celery, 60; sweet corn, 120.
49	Llama (Lama glama)	SD	M	275	90		Alfalfa pellets[17], 35; grain mix, 6; avocados, 9; carrots, 30; browse, 10.
50		NY[18]	M	285	59.5		Clover, 38.5; GLF[16], 14; crushed oats, 7.
	Perissodactyla						
51	Moose (Alces americana)	SD	M	750	609		Grain mix[12], 91; avocados, 21; lettuce, 42; carrots, 60; apples, 150; browse, 245.
52	Rhinoceros, black (Rhinoceros bicornis)	NY	M	2800	615.5		Alfalfa[15], 140; timothy[15], 210; GLF[16], 10.5; bread, 210; cabbage, 15; carrots, 15; potatoes, 15.
53	Zebra, Chapman (Equus burchelli antiquorum)	SD	M	600	124		Alfalfa pellets[17], 7; grain mix[12], 6; carrots, 6; oat hay, 105.
54		NY	F	650	90.3		Timothy, 70; crushed oats, 16.8; carrots, 3.5.
	Struthioniformes						
55	Ostrich, N. African (Struthio camelus)	SD	M	250	28.8±	7	Bread, 5.3; lettuce, 6; alfalfa, 3.5; barley, 7; oyster shell.
	Casuariiformes						
56	Cassowary (Casuarius unappendiculatus occipitalis)	SD	F	100	45.6+	1.8	Apples, 14; bananas, 7; mice (28); fruit, 14; tomatoes, 8.8.
57		SD	M	100	29.8	1.8	Bread, 5.2; lettuce, 7; barley, 7; apples, 8.8.
58	Emu (Dromiceius novaehollandiae)	NY	M	60	22.1+	1.3	Apples, 3.5; bread, 7; lettuce, 5.2; rolled oats, 2.5; GLF[16], 2.6; whole corn, 7 pt in winter; scratch, 7 pt in summer.
	Sphenisciformes						
59	Penguin, king (Aptenodytes p. patagonica)	NY		45	24.5±19		Mackerel, 24.5.
	Pelecaniformes						
60	Pelican, European white (Pelecanus occidentalis	SD		15	17.5		Anchovies & sardines, 17.5.
61	onocrotalus)	NY		14	15.6+20		Butterfish[21], 15.6.
	Ciconiiformes						
62	Heron, cocoi (Ardea cocoi)	NY		5	3		Butterfish, 3.
63	Shoebill (Balaeniceps rex)	SD	F	12	16		Anchovies & sardines, 7; liver, 9.
64		NY		16	12.5		Butterfish, 12.5.
	Falconiformes						
65	Condor, Andean (Vultur gryphus)	SD		50	14		Anchovies & sardines, 14.
66		NY		22	10	10±	Rats (2) instead of horse meat 2 x/mo.
67	Eagle, bald (Haliaeetus leucocephalus)	SD		6	3.5		Anchovies & sardines, 3.5.
68		NY		12	5.8	3.8	Butterfish, 2.
	Strigiformes						
69	Owl, snowy (Nyctea scandinaca)	SD		3	2.5+		Anchovies & sardines, 2.5.
70		NY		3	2.5		Rat (1).
	Micropodiformes						
71	Hummingbird, ruby-throated (Archilochus colubris)	NY		2.5 g	122 ml		Mellin's formula[22], 112 ml; honey formula[23], 9.8 ml.

/1/ NY=New York Zoological Park, New York, N.Y.; SD=San Diego Zoological Gardens, San Diego, California; LP=Lincoln Park Zoo, Chicago, Illinois. /2/ Based on 7 da/wk feeding except for the order Carnivora in which the animals are fed 6 da and fasted the 7th. /3/ Lb/wk, unless otherwise indicated; figures in parentheses are no./wk. /4/ Vitamin formula: A, 5000 USP units; D_3, 1000 USP units; B_1, 1.0 mg; B_2, 1.0 mg; B_6, 0.5 mg; calcium pantothenate 3.0 mg; nicotinamide, 10.0 mg; ascorbic acid, 60.0 mg; B_{12}, 1.0 μg; folic acid, 0.25 mg. /5/ Dog biscuit formula: wheat flour, meat meal, bone meal, wheat bran, wheat germ meal, tomato pulp, irradiated dried yeast; dried corn fermentation solubles, calcite flour, manganese sulphate, potassium iodide, iron sulphate, copper carbonate, salt, Vitamin A feeding oil, dried skim milk, Brewer's yeast, turmeric, charcoal. Protein, 20%; fat, 1%; fiber, 2%. /6/ Milk mixture formula: salt, 2 t; sugar, 2 T; malted milk powder, 2 t; cereal, 1¼ lb; evaporated milk, 26 oz; water, 26 oz. /7/ Dog food mix (lbs): meat, 100; kibbled dog biscuit, 25; powdered milk, 5; bone meal, 5; NaCl, 1; water, 5 gal. /8/ Equal parts honey and bran. /9/ In winter only. /10/ 30 lb in summer. /11/ 1.5 lb in winter. /12/ Grain mix formula (lbs): beet pulp, 300; rolled barley, 300; bran, 100; rolled oats, 75; ground corn, 100; linseed meal, 40; bone meal, 5; salt, 5; live yeast culture, 3. /13/ 9 lbs in summer. /14/ During corn season. /15/ Hay consumption is decreased 25% in summer months. /16/ GLF formula (lbs): 34% linseed meal, 200; wheat bran, 200; hominy feed and corn meal, 400; crushed oats, 419. 5; cane molasses, 200; beet pulp, 200; chopped alfalfa, 240; wheat germ meal, 60; Brewer's yeast, 40; irradiated yeast, 0.5; salt, 20; dicalcium phosphate, 15; ground limestone, 5. /17/ Fresh-cut alfalfa, approximately twice the amount of alfalfa pellets, is fed 3 da per week for 10 months of the year in place of alfalfa pellets. /18 Salt block available. /19/ Eats almost twice as much for 10 da before and after annual moult; during moult, almost complete inappetence. /20/ Eats about 50% more daily for 2 autumn months. /21/ 23 lb in winter. /22/ Mellin's formula (given in a.m.): Mellin's food, 4 t; honey, 5 t; condensed milk, 1 t; vitamins, 4 drops; beef extract, 5 ml; warm water, 1 qt. /23/ Honey formula (given in p.m.): honey, 5 t; beef extract, 5 ml; vitamins, 4 drops; warm water, 1 qt.

189. DIETS: ZOO ANIMALS (Concluded)

Parts II and III list diets, as developed and used by the Philadelphia Zoological Garden, for captive wild animals. Although the diets are completely adequate for the majority of animals given below, certain rare species have not been tested.

Part II: BASIC DIETS

Values are g/100 g of ration, unless otherwise indicated.

Ingredient	Diet A[1]	Diet B	Diet C	Diet D	Diet E	Diet F
1 Basic Mixture			31[2]	50[2]		
2 Ground yellow corn	15	15				
3 Ground whole wheat	15	10				
4 Ground whole barley	10					
5 Ground rolled oats	10	10				
6 Peanut meal	10					
7 Soybean meal	10	10				
8 Brewers' yeast	10	5				
9 Dried skimmed milk	10					
10 Alfalfa leaf meal	5	26				
11 Oystershell flour	2	2.5			2	
12 Iodized salt	1	0.5				
13 A-D feeding oil	2	0.5		3	2	
Additional						
14 Linseed meal		10				
15 Brewers' grains		10				
16 Dry beet pulp[3]		45%[4]				
17 Whole milk					2x/day	
18 Ground cooked meat	1:9 Basic Mix.[5]			20		
19 Raw horse meat			55[6]		90	20-100[7]
20 Ground raw meat						
21 Raw liver						10-50[8]
22 Chopped raw cabbage		5%	10	20		
23 Ground raw carrots		5%		7		
24 Hard-cooked eggs, shells[6]						
25 Deterioration	2 wk[9]	2 wk[9]	48 hr[9]	48 hr[9]		

/1/ Press and refrigerate 24-28 hr before using. /2/ Basic mixture for Diet A. /3/ Mix with equal amounts water; let stand 1-2 hr before adding to other ingredients. /4/ Of total dry weight. /5/ Plus broth to make stiff mash. /6/ Ground. /7/ Or whale or beef, g/kg per body weight, daily. /8/ g/kg body weight, twice weekly. /9/ Refrigerated.

Part III: ANIMAL FEEDING

Diets are for adult animals, unless otherwise indicated.

Animal	Diet[1]		Animal	Diet[1]		Animal[7]	Diet[1]
Omnivorous[2]			Omnivorous[2] (concluded)			Carnivorous[7] (concluded)	
Mammalia			Aves (concluded)			Aves (concluded)	
1 Primates	A,S-1		18 Eurypygidae	1/2A,1/2C;S-1		34 Strigiformes	C
2 Rodentia	A,S-1		19 Cariamidae	1/2A,1/2C;S-1		35 Ardeidae	C
3 Hyracoidea	A,S-1		20 Psophiidae	A,S-1		36 Cochleariidae	C
4 Ursidae	1/2A,1/2 raw meat or fish; S-1		Herbivorous Mammalia[5]			37 Laridae	C
			21 Artiodactyla[6]	B,S-2,S-3		38 Corvidae	C
5 Suidae	A,S-1		22 Proboscidea	B,S-2,S-3		Reptilia	
6 Tayasuidae	A,S-1		23 Perissodactyla	B,S-2,S-3		39 Iguanidae	C
Aves			24 Hippopotamidae	B,S-2,S-3		40 Heloderma	C
7 Struthioniformes	1/2A,1/2B;S-1		25 Macropodidae	B,S-2,S-3		41 Testudinidae	C
8 Rheiformes	1/2A,1/2B;S-1		Carnivorous[7]			42 Eunueces	C
9 Psittaciformes[3]	A,S-1		Mammalia			43 Ophisaurus	C
10 Casuariiformes	A,S-1		26 Viverridae	C		Aves (Cage)[7,9]	
11 Phasianoidea	A,S-1		27 Canidae	C		44 Passeriformes	D,S-5
12 Columbidae	A,S-1		28 Felidae,immature	E		45 Trogoniformes	D,S-5
13 Anatidae	A,S-1		29 Felidae[8], adult	F		46 Musophagidae	D,S-5
14 Threskiornithidae	1/2A,1/2C;S-1		30 Mustelidae	C,S-4		47 Momotidae	D,S-5
15 Phoenicopteridae	A,S-1		31 Procyonidae	C,S-4		48 Coraciidae	D,S-5
16 Gruidae	A,S-1		32 Didelphidae	C		49 Bucerotidae	D,S-5,S-6
17 Rallidae	A,S-1		Aves			50 Capitonidae	D,S-5
			33 Falconiformes	C		51 Rhamphastidae	D,S-5

/1/ Diets may be supplemented: S-1=citrus fruits, green vegetables, carrots (for bulk, increase these items); S-2=hay, q.s., green leaves, or fresh-cut grass (5-10g/kg body weight); S-3=equal quantities apples, carrots, green lettuce, or cabbage (10-50 g/kg); S-4=apples and carrots; S-5=oranges, apples, grapes, cherries, and green lettuce; S-6=1-2 mice. /2/ Daily intake: 5-50 g/kg of body weight, depending on weight and activity. /3/ Small lories and parakeets need whole seed also. /4/ To start on diet, form a mash with water. /5/ Daily food intake: 10-40 g/kg of body weight. /6/ Except swine. /7/ Daily food intake: 25-75 g/kg of body weight. /8/ Daily food intake: 20-100 g/kg of body weight with twice-weekly supplement of liver (see Part II, Diet F). /9/ Diet D may be combined with Diet C in varying proportions.

190. SYNTHETIC DIET MEDIA: INSECTS

These are representative diets for a number of insects studied in nutritional research. Values for sterile diets are in brackets; insects maintained on sterile diets are from bacteria-free eggs. All values calculated (and rounded) as grams or milligrams per 100 grams or milliliters of diet.

Nutrient	Orthoptera — Cockroach, German (Blattella germanica)[1] per 100g	Coleoptera — Meal Worm, Yellow (Tenebrio molitor)[2,3] per 100 g	Flour Moth (Ephestia sp)[2] per 100g	Lepidoptera — Corn Borer (Pyrausta nubilialis)[2] per 100g[4]	Rice Stem Borer (Chilo simplex)[2] per 100ml[4]	Bollworm, Pink (Pectinophora gossypiella)[2] per 100ml[4]	Diptera — Fruit Fly (Drosophila melanogaster)[2] per 100ml[4]	Mosquito, "Yellow Fever" (Aedes aegypti)[2] per 100ml	Onion Maggot (Hylemya antiqua)[2] per 100ml[4]	Parasite of Spruce Budworm (Pseudosarcophaga affinis)[2] per 100ml[4]
1 Calcium chloride, mg							[1.3]	[1.2]		
2 Iron sulfate (ferrous), mg							[1.3]	[1.2]		
3 Magnesium sulfate-7H$_2$O, mg							[25.0]	[20.0]		
4 Manganese sulfate-7H$_2$O, mg							[1.3]	[1.2]		
5 McCollum's salt mixture, g		2.0	2.0							[0.172]
6 Potassium hydroxide, g						[+][5]				
7 Potassium orthophosphate (mono-H), mg							[6]	[60]		
8 Potassium orthophosphate (di-H), mg							[6]	[60]		
9 Sodium chloride, mg							[1.3]	[1.2]		
10 U.S.P. salt mixture No.1, g	[3.0]									
11 U.S.P. salt mixture No.2, g										
12 Wesson's salt mixture, g									[0.2]	[0.066]
13 Casein[6], g	4.0	17.0	17.0	[0.30]	[0.6]	[0.7]		[0.6]		
14 Cystine, mg	30[29]			[4.0]		[5.0]		[20.0]		
15 Glutathione, mg						[100]		[1.0]		
16 Glycine, mg	[0.5]									
17 Amino acid mixture, g					[3.5][7]	[150]	[3.1][8]		[2.4][7]	[2.0][7]
18 Inosine, mg									[3.0]	
19 Ribonucleic acid, g							[0.1]	[0.1]	[0.1]	[0.1]
20 Thymine, mg									[0.4]	
21 Dextrin, g	[63]									
22 Glucose, g	31	69.0	68	[4.0]	[5.0]	[8.0]			[1.5]	[0.5]
23 Sucrose, g			1.0		[2.0]			[0.2]		
24 Cholesterol[9], g	1.0[0.5]	0.9		[0.15]	[0.06]	[0.3]	[0.75]	[0.003]	[0.01]	[0.1]
25 Ergosterol, g	[0.5]						[0.04]			
26 Linoleic acid, g				[0.15]		[1.0]				
27 Oil, corn, g	3.0									
28 Oil, soybean, g	[1.0]		1.0							
29 Oil, wheat germ,[10] g										
30 Fatty acid mixture[10], g										
31 Biotin, mg	0.06[0.025]	0.02	0.02		[0.05]	[0.002]	[0.02]	[0.005]	[0.002]	[0.4]
32 Cobalamin (vitamin B$_{12}$), mg	400[100]	30.0				[0.002]	[0.003]		[0.004]	[0.0001]
33 Choline chloride, mg	200[97]		50	[0.06]	[10.0]	[100]	[7.5]	[2.0]	[2.0]	[9.8]
34 Inositol, mg	10.0[10.0]	1.6	50		[5.0]			[4.0]		[9.8]
35 Niacin, mg			5.0		[0.5]	[4.0]	[1.0]	[0.2]	[1.0]	[1.5]
36 Niacinamide, mg								[1.0]		
37 Pantothenic acid (Ca salt), mg	4.0[10.0]	0.8	5.0		[0.5]	[2.0]	[0.6]	[0.6]	[0.6]	[1.5]
38 Para-aminobenzoic acid, mg	[10.0]				[0.5]					[1.5]
39 Pyridoxine (HCl), mg	1.6 [10.0]	0.2	5.0		[0.25]	[0.5]	[0.3]	[0.4]	[3.0]	[1.5]
40 Pyridoxamine (HCl), mg								[0.002]		
41 Riboflavin, mg	1.8[10.0]	0.2-0.8	5.0		[0.25]	[1.0]	[0.24]	[0.2]	[0.24]	[1.5]
42 Thiamine (HCl), mg	1.2[10.0]	0.1	5.0	[1.5]	[0.5]	[0.5]	[0.15]	[0.2]	[0.15]	[0.5]
43 Brewer's yeast, g										
44 Carnitine, mg		0.15								
45 Co-enzyme A, mg										
46 Leaf factor, g									[0.15]	
47 Pteroylglutamic acid, mg	0.5[0.4]	0.0125-0.025	0.2	[1.2]	[0.05]	[0.5]	[0.6]	[0.06]	[0.6]	[0.5]
48 Thioctic acid, g					[1.0]	[3.0]			[0.05]	[0.75]
49 Agar-agar, g				[2.3]	[3.0]	[4.0]	[2.0]		[2.0]	
50 Cellulose, g	30			[1.8]		[0.5]				
51 Sodium alginate, g										
52 Water, ml	[2.0]	9.0		[100]	[100]	[100]	[100]	[100]	[100]	[100]

/1/ Nymphs and adults. /2/ Larvae. /3/ Also for confused flour beetle (Tribolium confusum), except that carnitine is not required, and for Palorus ratzburgi. /4/ Agar base. /5/ 2 M solution to adjust pH to 6.5. /6/ Vitamin free. /7/ Mixture of 18 pure amino acids. /8/ Mixture of 19 pure amino acids. /9/ Cholesterol essential for all insects critically studied. /10/ Mixture of palmitic, stearic, oleic, linoleic and linolenic acids.

	Component	Gautheret[1] mg/L	White[2] mg/L		Component	Gautheret[1] mg/L	White[2] mg/L
1	$Ca(NO_3)_2 \cdot 4H_2O$	285	288	13	$MnSO_4 \cdot 4H_2O$	0.4	4.5
2	$CaSO_4$	0.2		14	$NiCl_2$	0.01	
3	$Fe_2(SO_4)_3 \cdot 6H_2O$	20	2.5	15	KI		0.8
4	$MgSO_4 \cdot 7H_2O$	72	360	16	$Ti_2(SO_4)_3$	0.8	
5	KCl	72	65	17	$ZnSO_4 \cdot 7H_2O$	0.2	1.5
6	KNO_3	72	80	18	Glucose	20,000	
7	$KH_2PO_4 \cdot H_2O$	72		19	Sucrose		20,000
8	$NaH_2PO_4 \cdot H_2O$		16.5	20	Niacin		1.0
9	Na_2SO_4		200	21	Pyridoxine		0.1
10	H_3BO_3	0.02	1.5	22	Thiamine		0.1
11	$CoCl_2$	0.01		23	Naphtheleneacetic acid	0.1	
12	$CuSO_4$	0.01		24	Glycine		3
				25	Agar	12,000	6000

/1/ For callus tissues. /2/ For callus and tumor tissues.

192. SYNTHETIC CULTURE MEDIA: PLANTS
All values are mg of component per liter of culture media. Those for amino acids are for DL-isomers.

Higher Plants

	Component	Value
1	H_3BO_3	2.86
2	$Ca(NO_3)_2 \cdot 4H_2O$	1680
3	$CuSO_4 \cdot 5H_2O$	0.08
4	$FeSO_4 \cdot 7H_2O$	5[1]
5	$MgSO_4 \cdot 7H_2O$	493
6	$MnCl_2 \cdot 4H_2O$	1.8
7	$H_2MoO_4 \cdot H_2O$	0.02
8	KNO_3	505
9	KH_2PO_4	136
10	$ZnSO_4 \cdot 7H_2O$	0.22

Algae: Chlorella[2]

	Component	Value
11	NH_4VO_3	0.02
12	H_3BO_3	2.86
13	$CaCl_2$	55[3]
14	$Co(NO_3)_2 \cdot 6H_2O$	0.05[3]
15	$CuSO_4 \cdot 5H_2O$	0.08
16	$FeSO_4 \cdot 7H_2O$	20
17	$MgSO_4 \cdot 7H_2O$	250
18	$MnCl_2 \cdot 4H_2O$	1.8
19	KNO_3	2000
20	K_2HPO_4	1740
21	KH_2PO_4	1360
22	Na_2MoO_4	0.02
23	$ZnSO_4 \cdot 7H_2O$	0.02
24	Na citrate	200

Algae: Blue-green

	Component	Value
25	NH_4VO_3	0.02[3]
26	H_3BO_3	2.86
27	$CaCl_2$	55
28	$Co(NO_3)_2 \cdot 6H_2O$	0.05[3]
29	$CuSO_4 \cdot 5H_2O$	0.08
30	$FeSO_4 \cdot 7H_2O$	20
31	$MgSO_4 \cdot 7H_2O$	250
32	$MnCl_2 \cdot 4H_2O$	1.8
33	KNO_3	2000[4]
34	K_2HPO_4	2580
35	$NaCl$	40
36	Na_2CO_3	1500[5]
37	Na_2MoO_4	0.2
38	Na_2CO_3	1500
39	$ZnSO_4 \cdot 7H_2O$	0.02
40	Na citrate	200

Fungi: Aspergilli and Penicillia

	Component	Value
41	$FeSO_4 \cdot 7H_2O$	10
42	$MgSO_4 \cdot 7H_2O$	500
43	KCl	500
44	K_2HPO_4	1000
45	$NaNO_3$	3000
46	Sucrose	30,000

Fungi: Basidiomycetes[6]

	Component	Value
47	$(NH_4)_6Mo_7O_{24} \cdot 4H_2O$	0.02
48	H_3BO_3	0.57
49	$CuSO_4 \cdot 5H_2O$	0.04
50	$FeSO_4 \cdot 7H_2O$	0.15
51	$MgSO_4 \cdot 7H_2O$	500
52	$MnCl_2 \cdot 4H_2O$	0.04
53	KH_2PO_4	1500
54	$ZnSO_4 \cdot 7H_2O$	0.31
55	Glucose	10,000
56	Glutamic acid	1260
57	Thiamine·HCl	1

Fungi: Neurospora

	Component	Value
58	NH_4NO_3	1000
59	$(NH_4)_2C_4H_4O_6$	5000
60	H_3BO_3	0.06
61	$CaCl_2$	100
62	$CuSO_4 \cdot 5H_2O$	0.40
63	$FeSO_4 \cdot 7H_2O$	0.72
64	$MgSO_4 \cdot 7H_2O$	500
65	$MnCl_2 \cdot 4H_2O$	0.07
66	KH_2PO_4	1000
67	$NaCl$	100
68	Na_2MoO_4	0.04
69	$ZnSO_4 \cdot 7H_2O$	8.8
70	Sucrose	15,000
71	d-Biotin	0.005

Bacteria: Photosynthetic

	Component	Value
72	NH_4Cl	1000
73	H_3BO_3	2.8
74	$CaCl_2$	100
75	$Co(NO_3)_2 \cdot 6H_2O$	0.05
76	$CuSO_4 \cdot 5H_2O$	0.02
77	$FeSO_4 \cdot 7H_2O$	20
78	$MgSO_4 \cdot 7H_2O$	250
79	$MnCl_2 \cdot 4H_2O$	0.05
80	K_2HPO_4	500
81	$NaCl$	3000[7]
82	Na_2CO_3	2000[8]
83	Na_2S	1000[8]
84	Na_2CO_3	2000
85	$ZnSO_4 \cdot 7H_2O$	0.5
86	Glutamic acid	2000[9]
87	d-Biotin	0.004[9]
88	Thiamine·HCl	1.0[9]

Bacteria: Bacillus subtilis

	Component	Value
89	$(NH_4)_2HPO_4$	8000
90	$FeCl_3 \cdot 6H_2O$	33
91	$MgSO_4 \cdot 7H_2O$	614
92	$MnSO_4$	15
93	KCl	400
94	$NaCl$	300
95	Na_2SO_4	4000
96	$ZnCl_2$	10
97	Sucrose	100,000
98	Glutamic acid	2000
99	d-Biotin	0.02
100	Thiamine·HCl	4
101	Asparagine	2000
102	Choline·Cl	10
103	Folacin	0.02
104	l-Inositol	10
105	Niacin	2
106	DL-Ca pantothenate	4
107	Para-aminobenzoic acid	0.02
108	Pyridoxine·HCl	2
109	Pyridoxamine·HCl	2
110	Riboflavin	4
111	Adenine sulfate	40
112	Guanine·HCl	40
113	Uracil	40
114	Xanthine	40
115	Citric acid	2000

Bacteria: Hemophilus parainfluenzae

	Component	Value
116	$CaCl_2$	3
117	$FeSO_4 \cdot 7H_2O$	12.8
118	$MgSO_4 \cdot 7H_2O$	82
119	KH_2PO_4	3120
120	Glucose	1000
121	Glutamic acid	2000
122	d-Biotin	0.001
123	Thiamine·HCl	1
124	Alanine	1000
125	Arginine·HCl	400
126	Aspartic acid	1000
127	Cystine	200
128	Glycine	100
129	Histidine·HCl	200
130	Isoleucine	200
131	Leucine	200
132	Lysine·HCl	400
133	Methionine	200
134	Phenylalanine	200
135	Proline	200
136	Serine	200
137	Threonine	200
138	Tryptophan	200
139	Tyrosine	200
140	Valine	200
141	Choline·Cl	5
142	Folacin	0.01
143	l-Inositol	20
144	Niacin	0.5
145	DL-Ca-pantothenate	1
146	Para-aminobenzoic acid	0.001
147	Pyridoxine·HCl	2
148	Riboflavin	0.1
149	Adenine sulfate	10
150	Guanine·HCl	10
151	Uracil	10
152	Coenzyme I	0.1
153	Putrescine	500
154	Na acetate	6000

Bacteria: Lactobacillus leichmannii[10]

	Component	Value
155	NH_4Cl	280
156	$FeSO_4 \cdot 7H_2O$	10
157	$MgSO_4 \cdot 7H_2O$	1400
158	$MnSO_4$	203
159	K_2HPO_4	2000
160	KH_2PO_4	2000
161	Na citrate	5000
162	Glucose	20,000
163	Glutamic acid	400
164	d-Biotin	0.005
165	Thiamine·HCl	1
166	Alanine	200
167	Arginine·HCl	200
168	Asparagine	200
169	Aspartic acid	200
170	Cystine	400
171	Glycine	300
172	Histidine·HCl	200
173	Isoleucine	300
174	Leucine	100
175	Lycine·HCl	600
176	Methionine	100

Bacteria: L. leishmannii[10] (concluded)

	Component	Value
177	Phenylalanine	500
178	Proline	400
179	Serine	100
180	Threonine	100
181	Tryptophane	50
182	Tyrosine	400
183	Valine	200
184	Folacin	0.06
185	Niacin	1
186	DL-Ca-pantothenate	1
187	Para-aminobenzoic acid	0.04
188	Pyridoxine·HCl	2
189	Pyridoxamine·HCl	0.4
190	Riboflavin	1
191	Adenine sulfate	5
192	Guanine·HCl	5
193	Uracil	5
194	Xanthine	8
195	Na acetate	3600
196	Tween 80	1

Bacteria: Streptococcus faecalis

	Component	Value
197	NH_4Cl	2500
198	$FeSO_4 \cdot 7H_2O$	27
199	$MgSO_4 \cdot 7H_2O$	512
200	$MnSO_4$	30
201	K_2HPO_4	5000
202	$NaCl$	15
203	Na citrate	5000
204	Glucose	20,000
205	Glutamic acid	1000
206	d-Biotin	0.01
207	Thiamine·HCl	0.5
208	Alanine	500
209	Arginine·HCl	400
210	Asparagine	500
211	Aspartic acid	500
212	Cystine	200
213	Glycine	100
214	Histidine·HCl	200
215	Isoleucine	200
216	Leucine	200
217	Lysine·HCl	400
218	Methionine	200
219	Phenylalanine	200
220	Proline	400
221	Serine	500
222	Threonine	200
223	Tryptophane	200
224	Tyrosine	200
225	Valine	200
226	Folacin	0.02
227	Niacin	1
228	DL-Ca-pantothenate	0.5
229	Para-aminobenzoic acid	0.2
230	Pyridoxine·HCl	0.5
231	Pyridoxamine·HCl	0.5
232	Riboflavin	0.5
233	Adenine sulfate	10
234	Uridine	0.2
235	Glutathione	20
236	Na acetate	5000
237	Tween 80	10

/1/ To be added twice weekly or as indicated by iron deficiency. /2/ And other simple green algae. /3/ Not yet shown to be generally required. /4/ May be omitted for nitrogen-fixing forms. /5/ For those strains which grow only at an alkaline pH. /6/ Wood-rotting types. /7/ For marine forms. /8/ For purple and green sulfur bacteria. /9/ For non-sulfur purple bacteria; additional compounds not listed (mg/L): Na succinate, 4000; glycerol, 2000; malic acid, 3000; K acetate, 1000; niacin, 1.0. /10/ Additional components not listed (mg/L): cysteine, 800; glutamine, 100; hydroxyproline, 50; norleucine, 200; cobalamin, 0.01; pyridoxal·HCl, 2; pyridoxal phosphate, 1; cytidylic acid, 10; sodium ethyl oxalacetate, 100.

193. DILUENTS FOR CULTURE MEDIA: ANIMAL TISSUES

In general, these diluents are used only in combination with naturally occurring body substances (e.g., blood serum, tissue extracts) and/or more complex chemically defined feeding solutions, as presented in the next table. pH of the final medium must be regulated. Values are mg/liter.

#	Component	Tyrode I 1910	Earle	Hanks	#	Component	Tyrode I 1910	Earle	Hanks
1	NaCl	8000	6880	8000	6	$NaHCO_3$	1000	2200	340
2	KCl	200	400	400	7	Na_2HPO_4			60
3	$CaCl_2$	200	200	140	8	$NaH_2PO_4 \cdot H_2O$	58[2]	125	
4	$MgCl_2 \cdot 6H_2O$	214[1]		100	9	KH_2PO_4			60
5	$MgSO_4 \cdot 7H_2O$		200	100	10	Glucose	1000	1000	1000

/1/ Calculated from 100 mg/L $MgCl_2$ in original formula. /2/ Calculated from 50 mg/L NaH_2PO_4 in original formula.

194. CHEMICALLY DEFINED CULTURE MEDIUM: ANIMAL TISSUES
Data adapted from Healy, G. M., et al., Proc. Soc. Exp. Biol. & Med. 89:71, 1955.

#	Component	Value mg/L	#	Component	Value mg/L
1	L-Alanine	25	32	α-Tocopherol phosphate	0.01
2	L-Arginine	70	33	Cholesterol	0.2
3	L-Aspartic acid	30	34	Tween 80 (oleic acid)	5
4	L-Cysteine	260	35	Cocarboxylase (88% pure)	1
5	L-Cystine	20	36	Coenzyme A (75% pure)	2.5
6	L-Glutamic acid	75	37	Diphosphopyridine nucleotide (95% pure)	7
7	Glycine	50	38	Flavin adenine dinucleotide (60% pure)	1
8	L-Histidine	20	39	Glutathione	10
9	L-Hydroxyproline	10	40	Triphosphopyridine nucleotide (80% pure)	1
10	L-Isoleucine	20	41	Uridine triphosphate (90% pure)	1
11	L-Leucine	60	42	Adenine desoxyriboside	10
12	L-Lysine	70	43	Cystosine desoxyriboside	10
13	L-Methionine	15	44	Guanine desoxyriboside	10
14	L-Phenylalanine	25	45	5-Methyldesoxycytidine	0.1
15	L-Proline	40	46	Thymidine	10
16	L-Serine	25	47	Ethanol[1]	16
17	L-Threonine	30	48	D-Glucose	1000
18	L-Tryptophan	10	49	L-Glutamine	100
19	L-Tyrosine	40	50	Phenol red[2]	20
20	L-Valine	25	51	Sodium acetate	50
21	Vitamin A	0.1	52	Sodium glucuronate	4.2
22	Ascorbic acid	50	53	NaCl	6800
23	Biotin	0.01	54	KCl	400
24	Calciferol	0.1	55	$CaCl_2$	200
25	Choline	0.5	56	$MgSO_4 \cdot 7H_2O$	200
26	Folic acid	0.01	57	$NaH_2PO_4 \cdot H_2O$	140
27	Inositol	0.05	58	$NaHCO_3$	2200
28	Menadione	0.01	59	$Fe(NO_3)_3$	0.1
29	Para-aminobenzoic acid	0.05	60	n-Butyl parahydroxybenzoate	0.2
30	Pyridoxal	0.025	61	Dihydrostreptomycin sulfate	100
31	Pyridoxine	0.025	62	Sodium penicillin G	1

/1/ As an initial solvent for fat-soluble constituents. /2/ pH indicator.

195. CULTURE MEDIA: SELECTED PROTOZOA
Part I: PARASITIC AMEBAE
In presence of bacterial flora derived from intestinal tract of host.

#	Medium — Solid Phase	Medium — Liquid Phase	Species Showing Growth[1]
	Diphasic		
1	Slant of coagulated whole egg[2] with or without rice starch, rice flour or powder[3]	Ringer's or Locke's solution, or 0.85% NaCl with serum or liquid egg white overlay[4]	Dientamoeba fragilis, Entamoeba aulostomi, E. coli, E. gingivalis, E. histolytica, Endolimax nana
2	Same as 1 above	Same as 1 above, plus liver extract	Entamoeba coli, E. histolytica
3	Same as 1 above	No enrichment	D. fragilis, E. coli, E. histolytica, E. invadens, E. terrapini
4	Slant of coagulated serum	Same as 1 above	D. fragilis, E. coli, E. histolytica, Endolimax nana
5	Slant of liver infusion agar	Same as 1 above	Entamoeba coli, E. histolytica, E. invadens, E. terrapini
	Monophasic		
6	Same as liquid phase of 1 above, plus rice starch[5]		E. barreti, E. histolytica, E. invadens, E. ranarum, E. terrapini, E. thomsoni
7	Bacto-beef heart infusion, plus rice starch		E. histolytica, Iodamoeba buetschlii
8	Egg infusion with or without liver extract, blood clot extract, etc., with rice starch		D. fragilis, E. coli, E. histolytica, Endolimax nana
9	Alcoholic extract of egg yolk, and/or certain tissues, with rice starch		Entamoeba histolytica

/1/ Entamoeba aulostomi, E. coli, E. gingivalis, E. histolytica, Endolimax nana and Iodamoeba buetschlii cultivated at 37°C, transferred at 48 to 72 hr intervals; others cultivated at 25°C or lower and transferred less frequently. /2/ From 3 to 5 ml of egg emulsion, tubed, slanted, inspissated, and sterilized. /3/ Several mg per tube, sterilized by dry heat and added separately. /4/ Exact formulae unimportant; from 5 to 12.5% of enrichment is used. /5/ Only serum enrichment has been reported, from 5 to 12.5%; rice starch not always used.

Part II: ENTAMOEBA HISTOLYTICA

#	Medium — Solid Phase	Medium — Liquid Phase	Microbial Associate
	Diphasic		**Monoxenic[1] Culture**
1	Slant of coagulated whole egg[2] with rice starch or flour[3]	Locke's solution with or without serum[4]	Actinomyces muris, Aerobacter aerogenes, Aplanobacter stewartii, Bacillus mesentericus, B. subtilis, Bacterium coronofaciens, Clostridium perfringens[5], Escherichia coli, Klebsiella pneumoniae, Neisseria catarrhalis, organism t[6,7], Proteus rettgeri, Salmonella paratyphi, S. schottmuelleri, S. typhosa, Serratia marcescens, Shigella ambigua, S. dysenteriae, S. paradysenteriae, S. sonnei, Staphylococcus albus, S. aureus, Streptococus fecalis, S. hemolyticus, S. viridans, S. zymogenes
2	Slant of coagulated egg-white with rice flour[3]	Locke's solution with cholesterol, with or without B vitamins	Aerobacter aerogenes (n), Escherichia coli (n), organism t (w)[6]

/1/ Only one of the microbial associates or symbionts listed is required, in conjunction with the respective medium, to permit growth of the ameba. /2/ From 3 to 5 ml of egg emulsion, tubed, slanted, inspissated, and sterilized. /3/ Several mg per tube, sterilized by dry heat and added separately. /4/ Exact formulae unimportant; from 5 to 12.5% of enrichment is used. /5/ Dientamoeba fragilis also grows in this medium (Line 1) in the presence of C. perfringens. /6/ Probably a species of Clostridium. /7/ Entamoeba coli also grows in this medium (Line 1) in the presence of organism t.

Part II: ENTAMOEBA HISTOLYTICA (Concluded)

Medium		Microbial Associate
	Monoexenic[1] Culture	
	Diphasic (concluded)	
3 Slant of liver infusion agar with rice starch or flour	0.85% NaCl 9 parts, serum 1 part	Bacillus brevis, B. circulans, B. mesentericus, B. subtilis, Clostridium botulinum, C. pasteurianum, C. perfringens, C. tetani, Escherichia coli, Neisseria catarrhalis, Para-colobactrum coliforme, Staphylococcus albus, S. aureus, Vibrio comma
Monophasic		
4 Egg yolk infusion with rice flour		Aerobacter aerogenes, A. cloacae, Kurthia zenkeri, Proteus vulgaris, Streptococcus equinus, S. fecalis, S. liquefaciens
5 0.85% NaCl 9 parts, serum 1 part, with rice starch, and methylene blue as indicator		Escherichia coli
6 Thioglycollate medium (BBL)[8] with serum, trypticase medium (BBL) with serum		Streptobacillus[9] (generic and specific identification not determined), Trypanosoma cruzi[10]
7 Proteose peptone, with liver extract, L-cystine, methionine, cholesterol, and rice flour, in balanced salt solution		Organism t[6]
8 Twelve amino acids, B vitamins, nucleic acid, cholesterol, rice flour, in balanced salt solution		Organism t[6]
9 Same as 8 above, with 20 amino acids		Organism t[6]
	Axenic[11] Culture	
10 Whole egg medium with heat-killed bacteria and rice flour		Entamoeba histolytica[12] grows in this medium without microbial associate or symbiont
11 Mixed chick embryo cells, serum, in balanced salt solution		E. invadens and E. histolytica[13]
12 Proteose peptone with glucose		Mayorella pasteurensis
13 Proteose peptone without glucose		Acanthamoeba castellanii

/1/ Only one of the microbial associates or symbionts listed is required, in conjunction with the respective medium, to permit growth of the amebae. /6/ Probably a species of Clostridium. /8/ BBL: A Baltimore Biological Laboratories product. /9/ The streptobacillus is grown separately under a petroleum seal; amebae and dosage of penicillin are added. /10/ T. cruzi is grown separately and amebae added. /11/ No microbial associate or symbiont required, in conjunction with the respective medium, to permit growth of the amebae. /12/ Indefinite serial transfer not attained. /13/ E. histolytica requires anaerobiasis in H_2 or N_2 with 5% CO_2.

Part III: TRYPANOSOMATIDAE

Culture in absence of commensal organisms (axenic culture).

Medium[1,2]		Species[3] Showing Growth
	Diphasic	
Solid Phase	Liquid Phase[4]	
1 15.6 g agar, 7 g NaCl, 330 ml defibrinated rabbit blood	Water of condensation	Leishmania tropica, Trypanosoma cruzi, T. duttoni, T. lewisi, T. melophagium, T. theileri, T. rotatorium, avian trypanosomes: various spp[3]
2 50 g bacto beef, 25 g bacto peptone, 7 g NaCl, 10 g bacto agar, 50 ml 1% glucose solution, 50 ml defibrinated guinea pig blood	Equal parts of peptone broth and dextrose solution	T. cruzi
3 50 g bacto beef, 20 g neopeptone, 5 g NaCl, 20 g bacto agar, 100 or 300 ml defibrinated rabbit blood	Locke's solution	L. brasiliensis, L. donovani, L. tropica, T. conorhini, T. cruzi, T. lewisi, T. pipistrelli, T. rangeli
4 3 g bacto beef, 5 g bacto peptone, 8 g NaCl, 15 g bacto agar, 330 ml citrated human or rabbit blood	Locke's solution	T. gambiense, T. rhodesiense
	Solid	
5 10-15 g agar, 10 g glucose, 100 ml horse meat broth, 1 L horse meat broth, 1 L defibrinated horse blood		L. brasiliensis, L. donovani, L. tropica, T. cruzi, T. melophagium, T. theileri, avian trypanosomes[3], T. rotatorium, Leptomonas ctenocephali, L. fasciculata
6 50 g bacto beef, 20 g neopeptone, 5 g NaCl, 20 g nobel agar, 100 ml defibrinated human or rabbit blood		Leishmania tropica, T. cruzi
7 31 g nutrient agar, 165 ml human citrated, inactivated plasma, 165 ml human red cells		T. gambiense, T. rhodesiense
	Semi-solid[5]	
8 1 part 3% agar, 8 parts Locke's solution with 0.2% glucose, 1 part rabbit serum		L. donovani, L. tropica, T. cruzi, Herpetomonas culicidarum
9 3 g agar, 150 ml defibrinated rabbit blood, 100 ml normal saline		L. donovani, L. tropica
	Liquid	
10 0.5 ml human or monkey blood, 0.5 ml 2% sodium citrate in 0.85% NaCl solution, 1 ml Ringer's solution (with 0.6% NaCl)		T. congolense, T. gambiense
11 2-2.5 ml Ringer's solution (with 0.6% NaCl), or 2-2.5 ml Tyrode solution, 2 ml citrated (1%) human blood		T. congolense, T. gambiense
12 Overlay of 3 above for T. cruzi, or overlay of 4 above for T. gambiense and T. rhodesiense		T. cruzi, T. gambiense, T. rhodesiense
13 10 g peptone, 10 g "casamino acids," 5 g NaCl, 2 g glucose, 100 mg each of alanine and glycine, 20 mg each of folic acid, nicotinamide, thiamin and choline		T. cruzi
	Synthetic	
14 Mixture of salts, metals, amino acids, vitamins, sorbitol, and hemin		H. culicidarum
	Dialysate	
15 Cellophane loop filled with Locke's solution suspended in tubes of 3		T. cruzi
	Chick Embryo and Tissue Culture	
16 Chorio-allantoic membrane		L. donovani, L. tropica, T. cruzi, T. gambiense
17 Blood or organs		T. cruzi, T. equiperdum, T. evansi, T. gambiense, T. rhodesiense
18 Tissue culture		L. donovani, T. cruzi

/1/ Ingredients of solid phase media, Lines 1 to 4, and of media given on Lines 5-13 are in amounts to be added to 1 L distilled water unless otherwise specified; test tube cultures usually contain 5 ml base (Lines 1-4), flask or plate cultures (Lines 1-7) contain varying amounts of base depending on size of container. /2/ Lines 1-15: cultures grown on media are usually maintained at temperatures of approximately 22-25°C; Lines 16 and 17: at 25-35°C; Line 18: at 37-39°C. /3/ Mammalian trypanosomatidae: Leishmania brasiliensis, L. donovani, L. tropica, Trypanosoma conorhini, T. cruzi, T. duttoni, T. lewisi, T. melophagium, T. pipistrelli, T. theileri, T. rangeli, T. congolense, T. equiperdum, T. evansi, T. gambiense, T. rhodesiense; avian trypanosomatidae: various species, not named because of uncertain taxonomic status; frog trypanosomatidae: T. rotatorium; insect trypanosomatidae: Herpetomonas culicidarum, Leptomonas ctenocephali, L. fasciculata. /4/ Lines 2 and 3: receive 2 to 3 ml overlay, flask cultures approximately 15 ml. /5/ Lines 8-14: varying amounts are used depending upon size of container.

196. FACTORS AFFECTING NUTRIENT REQUIREMENTS: MAN

The daily requirement of a nutrient may be altered -- either increased or decreased -- by a change in the daily intake of some other nutrient or by changes in other existing conditions of health or disease. The actual minimum requirement of many of the nutrients is as yet undetermined for man. Factors affecting the requirement are not available for "essential" fatty acids, vitamin E, inositol, pantothenic acid, para-aminobenzoic acid, chlorine, cobalt, copper, magnesium, manganese, and silicon.

Part I: FACTORS INFLUENCING BIOLOGICAL AVAILABILITY OF NUTRIENTS

	Increase	Decrease		Increase	Decrease
	Energy: Total Calories			**Vitamin K (concluded)**	
1		Decreased absorption, increased loss from the body, or defective utilization of protein, carbohydrate and fats. (See Items 2 to 14.)	29		Defective absorption. (See Item 15 (b), (c), (f).)
	Protein		30		Inadequate intestinal flora in newborn infants.
2	Adequate energy production from carbohydrate and fat.	Inadequate energy production from carbohydrate and fat: (a) low intake; (b) diabetes mellitus.	31		Defective utilization in advanced liver disease.
3	Proper amino acid balance in ingested protein.	Amino acid deficiency or imbalance in ingested protein.		**Niacin**	
			32		Oral antibiotics.
4	Anabolic hormones; growth hormones.	Anti-anabolic hormones; adrenal cortical hormones.	33		Decreased absorption caused by desease of the gastrointestinal tract.
5		Excessive heat or chemical treatment of protein.	34		Decreased formation from tryptophan in vitamin B_6 deficiency.
6		Defective absorption caused by: (a) deficiency of digestive enzymes; (b) diarrhea; (c) intestinal parasites; (d) disease of the gastrointestinal tract.		**Pyridoxine Group (Vitamin B_6)**	
			35		Loss in urine caused by isonicotinic acid hydrazide therapy.
7		Loss of protein in: (a) urine; (b) exudates; (c) transudates; (d) hemorrhage.		**Riboflavin**	
			36		Decreased absorption caused by disease of the gastrointestinal tract.
8		Loss of nitrogen from tissues in: (a) caloric deficiency; (b) burns; (c) trauma; (d) surgery.	37		Increased excretion in association with protein breakdown.
	Carbohydrate			**Thiamine**	
9		Decreased absorption caused by: (a) gastrointestinal diseases; (b) sprue; (c) hypoadrenalism; (d) hypothyroidism (e) panhypopituitrism.	38		Decreased absorption caused by: (a) thiaminase in raw fish; (b) administration of live yeast and alkali; (c) low gastric acidity; (d) gastrointestinal diseases.
10		Increased loss: glycosuria.	39		Loss caused by diuresis.
11	Increased gluconeogenesis.	Impaired gluconeogenesis.		**Calcium**	
12		Diabetes mellitus.	40	High dietary acidity.	Decreased absorption caused by: (a) low gastric acidity; (b) low dietary acidity; (c) phytic, oxalic, or benzoic acids in diet; (d) phosphorus in diet; (e) fatty acids in diet; (f) impaired fat absorption (caused by deficiency of bile salts, pancreatic disease, sprue syndrome, celiac disease, and idiopathic steatorrhea).
	Fat				
13	Increased absorption caused by emulsifying agents.	Poor absorption caused by: (a) deficiency of fat-splitting enzymes; (b) deficiency of bile salts; (c) sprue, celiac disease and idiopathic steatorrhea.			
14		Loss from body caused by: (a) chyluria; (b) chylous transudates.	41		Increased loss of calcium caused by: (a) bed rest, immobilization; (b) anti-anabolic hormones; (c) primary and secondary hyperparathyroidism; (d) renal rickets.
	Vitamin A and Precursors				
15	Increased absorption caused by: (a) ready release of food carotene; (b) emulsifying agents.	Decreased absorption caused by: (a) food carotene not readily released; (b) deficiency of bile salts; (c) defective absorption of fat in sprue, celiac disease, idiopathic steatorrhea, and deficiency of fat-splitting enzymes; (d) ingestion of mineral oil; (e) destruction of vitamin A in gastrointestinal tract by oxidizing agents (rancid fat, ferric iron); (f) low dietary fat.	42	Protein in diet.	
			43	Lactose in diet.	Decreased ionized calcium caused by: (a) phosphorus retention; (b) alkalosis.
			44	Citrates in diet.	
			45	Vitamin D.	
			46	Anabolic hormones.	
				Iron	
16		Defective storage in liver disease (?).	47	Absorption increased by: (a) protein in diet; (b) ascorbic acid; (c) iron deficiency; (d) hemochromatosis.	Absorption decreased by: (a) low gastric acidity; (b) phytate in diet; (c) phosphate in diet.
17		Defective conversion of carotene to vitamin A: (a) diabetes; (b) hypothyroidism.			
	Ascorbic Acid				
18		Gastric achlorhydria.	48		Utilization decreased by infections.[1]
19		Administration of alkali.	49		Increased urinary excretion in nephrosis.
20		Destruction during preparation or storage of food: (a) high temperature; (b) alkali; (c) copper; (d) iron.		**Phosphorus**	
			50	Vitamin D.	Decreased absorption caused by: (a) phytate in diet; (b) excess calcium in diet; (c) administration of aluminum.
21		Increased loss in urine caused by certain drugs.	51		Increased excretion of phosphorus caused by: (a) alkalosis; (b) bone injury; (c) hyperparathyroidism; (d) immobilization.
	Biotin				
22		Raw egg white in diet.		**Potassium**	
23		Oral antibiotics.	52	Retention of potassium caused by: (a) anuria; (b) adrenal insufficiency.	Loss of potassium caused by: (a) metabolic alkalosis and acidosis; (b) administration of ACTH and adrenal cortical hormones; (c) negative nitrogen balance; (d) diarrhea; (e) recovery phase following acute renal failure.
	Choline				
24	Oral antibiotics.				
	Cobalamin (Vitamin B_{12})				
25		Poor absorption caused by lack of intrinsic factor in gastric juice (pernicious anemia).		**Sodium**	
	Vitamin D		53	Retention of sodium caused by: (a) administration of ACTH and adrenal cortical hormones; (b) hyperadrenalism; (c) hyperpituitrism.	Excessive loss in sweat caused by: (a) high environmental temperature; (b) fever.
26		Decreased absorption. (See Item 15 (b), (c), and (f).)			
	Folic Acid Group (Folacin)				
27		Decreased absorption caused by gastrointestinal disease.	54		Excessive loss in urine caused by: (a) adrenal insufficiency; (b) diuresis; (c) certain injuries and infections of the central nervous system.
	Vitamin K				
28	Synthesis by intestinal microorganisms.	Oral antibiotics.	55		Excessive loss from gastrointestinal tract in diarrhea and vomiting.

/1/ Poor utilization cannot be corrected by iron administration.

196. FACTORS AFFECTING NUTRIENT REQUIREMENTS: MAN (Concluded)

The daily requirement of a nutrient may be altered -- either increased or decreased -- by a change in the daily intake of some other nutrient or by changes in other existing conditions of health or disease. The actual minimum requirement of many of the nutrients is as yet undetermined for man. Factors affecting the requirement are not available for "essential" fatty acids, vitamin E, inositol, pantothenic acid, para-aminobenzoic acid, chlorine, cobalt, copper, magnesium, manganese, and silicon.

Part II: FACTORS INFLUENCING NUTRIENT REQUIREMENTS PER SE

#	Increase	Decrease
	Energy: Total Calories	
1	Growth.	Aging after maturity.
2	Pregnancy and lactation.	
3	Large body size.	Small body size.
4	Physical activity.	Physical inactivity.
5	Cold climate; exposure to cold.	Tropical climate.
6	Hypermetabolic states, such as: (a) fever; (b) hyperthyroidism; (c) leukemia; (d) acromegaly; (e) hyperadrenalism; (f) induced by certain drugs.	Hypometabolic states, such as: (a) hypothyroidism; (b) panhypopituitrism; (c) hypoadrenalism.
	Protein	
7	Growth.	
8	Pregnancy and lactation.	
9	Large body size.	Small body size.
10	Hypermetabolic states. (See Item 6.)	Hypometabolic states. (See Item 6.)
11	Protein deficiency syndromes: (a) Kwashiorkor; (b) starvation; (c) simple protein depletion, primary or secondary. (See Part I, Items 2 to 8.)	
	Carbohydrate	
12	Hyperinsulinism.	
	Vitamin A and Precursors	
13	Growth (e.g., bones, teeth).[1]	
14	Vitamin A deficiency syndromes: (a) night blindness; (b) xerophthalmia; (c) follicular hyperkeratosis.	
	Ascorbic Acid	
15	Pregnancy and lactation.	
16	Growth.	
17	Metabolic stress:[1] (a) infectious disease; (b) hypermetabolic states; (c) trauma, burns, surgery; (d) toxic reactions from certain drugs.	
18	Tissue repair.	
19	High intake of tyrosine and phenylalanine in premature infants.	
20	Vitamin C deficiency: scurvy.	
	Choline	
21	Methyl group deficiency (fatty liver).	Methionine or methyl precursors in diet.
	Cobalamin (Vitamin B$_{12}$)	
22	Cobalamin deficiency: (a) nutritional megaloblastic anemia; (b) pernicious anemia; (c) sprue (at times); (d) certain nutritional neuropathies.	
	Vitamin D	
23	Inadequate exposure to ultraviolet radiation.	Exposure to ultraviolet radiation.
24	Growth and dentition.	High dietary calcium and phosphorus.
25	Pregnancy and lactation.	
26	Vitamin D deficiency: (a) rickets; (b) osteomalacia.	
27	Hypoparathyroidism.	
	Folic Acid Group (Folacin)	
28	Pregnancy and lactation.	
29	Folic acid deficiency: (a) sprue; (b) nutritional megaloblastic anemia; (c) megaloblastic anemia of infancy; (d) megaloblastic anemia of pregnancy.	

#	Increase	Decrease
	Vitamin K	
30	Pregnancy.	
31	Vitamin K deficiency: (a) hemorrhagic disease of newborn; (b) obstructive jaundice; (c) hypoprothrombinemia caused by oral antibiotics.	
	Niacin	
32	Large body size.	Small body size.
33	Increased caloric requirement.	Decreased caloric requirement.
34	Hypermetabolic states. (See Item 6.)	Hypometabolic states. (See Item 6.)
35	Niacin deficiency: pellagra.	High tryptophan intake.
	Pyridoxine Group (Vitamin B$_6$)	
36	Pregnancy.	
37	Pyridoxine deficiency (primary and secondary).	
	Riboflavin	
38	Growth.	
39	Pregnancy and lactation.	
40	Increased caloric requirement.	Decreased caloric requirement.
41	Hypermetabolic states. (See Item 6.)	Hypometabolic states. (See Item 6.)
42	Riboflavin deficiency.	
	Thiamine	
43	Increased caloric requirement.	Decreased caloric requirement.
44	Hypermetabolic states. (See Item 6.)	Hypometabolic states. (See Item 6.)
45	Increased proportion of calories derived from carbohydrate sources.	Increased proportion of calories derived from non-carbohydrate sources.
46	Thiamine deficiency: (a) beriberi: heart disease, neuropathy; (b) polyneuritis of chronic alcoholism and pernicious vomiting of pregnancy; (c) Wernicke's encephalopathy; (d) Korsakoff's psychosis; (e) delirium tremens.	
	Calcium	
47	Growth and dentition.	
48	Pregnancy and lactation.	
49	Rickets and osteomalacia.	
50	Calcium deficiency with or without tetany.	
	Fluorine	
51	Dental caries.[2]	
	Iodine	
52	Iodine deficiency: endemic goiter.	
	Iron	
53	Growth.	Menopause.
54	Pregnancy and lactation.	
55	Blood loss: (a) physiological (menstruation); (b) pathological.	
	Phosphorus	
56	Growth.	
57	Pregnancy and lactation.	
58	Phosphorus deficiency caused by rickets.	
	Potassium	
59	Potassium deficiency.	
	Sodium	
60	Sodium deficiency.	

/1/ Available evidence suggests this but definite proof is lacking. /2/ Fluorine has not been demonstrated to be an essential nutrient, but in amounts of 1 ppm is useful in prevention of dental caries.

The functions listed in the table require the specific elements noted. In addition, carbon, hydrogen, nitrogen, oxygen, phosphorus, and sulfur are required for the functions of synthesis of structural proteins, carbohydrates, fats and other organic compounds, and for formation of end products of metabolism.

1	**BROMINE**
	Ingestion and Absorption: Traces in many foods. Probably completely absorbed from gastrointestinal tract. Distribution: Same as chloride in mammals. In Tyrian Purple (= brominated indigo) derived from viscera of marine gastropod (Purpura aperta); in dibromotyrosine in protein gorgonin, from coral (Primnoa lepadifera). Function: Not known.
2	**CALCIUM**
	Ingestion and Absorption: Almost entirely as salts of inorganic or organic acids. Partial absorption from gastrointestinal tract. Absorption aided by vitamin D and low pH. Distribution: Insoluble calcium phosphate complex in bones, teeth in vertebrates. In exoskeleton of numerous invertebrates as calcium carbonate. Minute concentrations as soluble salts in body fluids, all species. As calcium carbonate in shell of certain eggs. Function: Component of supporting structure in higher forms, many lower forms. Vital electrolyte of cell and extracellular fluid. Protective shell of eggs.
3	**CHLORINE**
	Ingestion and Absorption: Ingested principally as NaCl (see SODIUM, below). Distribution: Distribution similar to that of sodium but, in general, milliequivalent concentrations are lower. Chief anion of gastric juice. Also present in all other gastrointestinal secretions and extracellular fluids. Function: Although principal anion of extracellular fluid, function is unknown. Variation in Cl concentration appears to be better tolerated than in Na and most other electrolytes.
4	**COBALT**
	Ingestion and Absorption: Trace constituent of many foods. Absorbed from gastrointestinal tract. Distribution: Trace distribution in many tissues, particularly glands and visceral organs, e.g., liver. Function: Component of vitamin B_{12} (cobalamin), required by some species from lowest to highest forms. Cobalt deficiency occurs in ruminants as "Pine" disease, salt sickness, bush sickness, "coast" disease. Cobalt enhances activity of certain peptidases.
5	**COPPER**
	Ingestion and Absorption: Minute amounts in food as copper protein complexes. Poorly absorbed from intestine. Distribution: Higher concentrations in invertebrates than in vertebrates. Highest concentrations in hepatopancreas and gonads of Mollusca; lowest concentration in muscle. High concentration in gut of insects. Present in turacin (red pigment of feathers of turaco bird). Injected Cu accumulates in liver, kidney. Liver is principal site of storage. Function: Erythropoiesis. Myelinization of central nervous system. Maintenance of mammalian pigmentation. Trace quantities essential for hemoglobin and possibly iron-porphyrin-protein enzyme synthesis. Constituent of several enzymes present in animal tissues (polyphenol oxidase, tyrosinase, laccase, catechol oxidase, and ascorbic acid oxidase). Component of hemocyanin, respiratory pigment of numerous marine animals; component of hepatocuprein, hemocuprein-protein complexes found in liver, blood of certain mammals. Nutritional deficiency disease occurs in cattle, sheep, with inadequate intake or with increased intakes of molybdenum. Molybdenum and copper are mutually antagonistic in ruminant metabolism.
6	**FLUORINE**
	Ingestion and Absorption: Traces in various foods, significant quantities in water in certain areas. Distribution: Present in bones, teeth. High concentration of 0.6-1.6% F in bones of sea animals. Function: Decreases incidence and severity of dental caries.
7	**IODINE**
	Ingestion and Absorption: Trace amounts in various foods mostly as iodide or as component of organic compounds. Amount in food related to iodine content of soil. Absorbed from intestine and, in lower forms, through cell membranes. Distribution: Principally in thyroid of vertebrates. Component of thyroxine, diiodotyrosine and thyroglobulin. Trace amounts in other tissues. Relatively more iodide in marine fish and other marine animals. Function: Minute intake essential for growth and for prevention of goiter.
8	**IRON**
	Ingestion and Absorption: Mainly as ferrous compounds from gastrointestinal tract. More absorption with iron deficiency states. Distribution: In blood hemoglobin, muscle hemoglobin, cytochrome of all cells. Stored in liver and spleen as ferritin (iron phosphoprotein). Function: Respiratory pigments of higher and lower forms. (Platyhelminthes contain hemoglobin.) Cytochrome is present in practically all cells.
9	**MAGNESIUM**
	Ingestion and Absorption: Widely distributed in foods. Ingested as salt of inorganic or organic acid. Absorbed from intestine. Distribution: Minute amounts in plasma and extracellular water. Large amounts in intracellular fluid. Function: Essential electrolyte. Low concentrations increase cell irritability. Required for activity of several animal enzymes.
10	**MANGANESE**
	Ingestion and Absorption: Traces present in most plant and animal foods. Poorly absorbed from gastrointestinal tract. Distribution: Particularly in liver, pancreas and hair. Also in all other tissues. Blood pigment of shellfish (Pinna squamosa) contains Mn rather than Fe or Cu. Function: Component of enzyme arginase. Enhances effect of certain proteinases. Necessary for growth of young animals (rabbits, rats). Also required for reproductive processes in many adult forms. Required for fertility of hen's eggs. Needed to prevent perosis in chicks.
11	**PHOSPHORUS**
	Ingestion and Absorption: Occurs as phosphate in most foods. Absorbed from gastrointestinal tract in higher forms. Absorbed through cell membranes in lower forms. Distribution: Large quantities as phosphate complex of calcium in bone of vertebrates. Component of phospholipids (nerve and other tissues), phosphocreatine or phosphoarginine (muscle); as inorganic PO_4 in cell, extracellular fluid; as nucleprotein in all tissues; and as adenosine triphosphate (ATP) in variety of cells of higher and lower species. Intracellular inorganic phosphate phosphorus low compared to that of phosphate esters. Function: Important structural component of bone. Component of high energy P compounds (ATP, phosphocreatine, phosphoarginine, acetyl phosphate). Combines with intermediates in carbohydrate metabolism. Buffer in urine. Constituent of nucleoprotein. Component of phospholipids (intermediates in lipid metabolism).
12	**POTASSIUM**
	Ingestion and Absorption: Ingested as inorganic salt in variety of foods. Absorbed from intestine. Absorbed through gills and cell membranes in many lower marine forms. Distribution: Principal cation of intracellular water. Small amount in extracellular water. Function: Essential cation of intracellular fluid.
13	**SILICON**
	Ingestion and Absorption: Absorbed from intestine. Inhaled particles deposit in lungs and give rise to serious effects. Absorbed through cell membrane of lower forms. Distribution: In skeletal structures and in supporting structures of certain Protozoa, Porifera and higher forms. Function: Protective and structural component of various lower animals forms.
14	**SODIUM**
	Ingestion and Absorption: Widely distributed in foods as inorganic salt. More in foods of animal origin than in foods of plant origin. Taken as NaCl by many higher vertebrates including man. Absorbed from intestine in higher forms and through gills and cell membranes in lower forms. Distribution: Major part of body sodium is extracellular, much in bone. Some intracellular. Tissues vary in concentration of intracellular sodium, muscle containing only small amounts. Data on other than mammalian forms not avalable. Function: Chief cation of extracellular water. Essential for proper external environment of cells. Chief cation of intestinal secretions. Salts are important buffers of plasma, extracellular water and urine.
15	**SULFUR**
	Ingestion and Absorption: As inorganic sulfates, organic sulfates and sulfhydryl sulfur of cystine and methionine. Distribution: Small amount of sulfate in extracellular H_2O. Relatively large amount in proteins and small amount in certain lipids. Function: Essential component of many proteins. Sulfuric acid secreted as digestive fluid in Ascidia. Sulfate is important anion in intracellular fluid. Sulfate used in detoxification reactions.
16	**VANADIUM**
	Ingestion and Absorption: Extracted from marine muds by Ascidai. Distribution: In blood respiratory pigment of marine worm, Ascidia. Function: Component of respiratory pigment which provides oxygen transport in Ascidia.
17	**ZINC**
	Ingestion and Absorption: Traces present in most foods. Absorbed from gastrointestinal tracts; in lower forms through cell membrane. Distribution: Largest quantities in pancreas, hair, nails, bone. Very large concentrations in certain oysters and herring. Function: Prosthetic group of carbonic anhydrase. Indispensable for nutrition of growing rat. Also required by adult for reproduction. Needed for activation of certain proteinases.

Element[1]	Occurrence and/or Function	Symptoms of Deficiency[2]	Symptoms of Excess[2]
1 B	Inverse relationship between boron level and water permeability of membranes and moisture content of tissues. (May be a constituent of cytoplasmic membranes). Necessary for cell division, and translocation of sucrose and possibly other sugars.	Terminal leaves necrotic, shed prematurely; internodes of terminal shoots shortened, usually rosetting; apical meristems blacken and die, general breakdown of meristematic tissue; roots short, stubby. Plants dwarfed, stunted. Flower development and seed production usually impaired or lacking.	Marginal necrosis in lower leaves, remainder of leaves dark green; death of most plants if present in considerable concentration.
2 Ca	Precipitates organic acids. Calcium pectate may be a constituent of the middle lamella.[3]	Leaves chlorotic, rolled, curled; breakdown of meristematic tissues in stems and roots, in acute cases death; roots poorly developed, lack fiber, may appear gelatinous. Symptoms appear near growing points of stems and roots. Little or no fruiting.	Chlorosis similar to iron or manganese deficiency.[4] Zinc and boron deficiency may be induced when soil reaction, e. g., pH, is high.
3 Cu	Associated with tyrosinase, a polyphenoloxidase involved in reduction of molecular oxygen. In ascorbic acid oxidase, which may be concerned in respiratory oxidation.[5] In laccase.[6]	Wilting of terminal shoots, often followed by death; leaf color often faded; carotene formation and pigmentation reduced.	Chlorosis similar to iron deficiency, followed by necrosis; permanent wilting of upper leaves; leaves may become wrinkled and necrotic at margins; fibrous roots stubby, poorly developed, brownish at tips; reduced growth; extreme cases death.
4 Fe	Associated with peroxidase, which breaks down peroxides and transfers active oxygen to oxidizable substances. In cytochrome oxidase, which plays a role in reduction of molecular oxygen.[5] In catalase, which effects the release of molecular oxygen from hydrogen peroxide.	Interveinal white chlorosis, appearing first on young leaves; tendency for chlorosis of all aerial parts, often becoming necrotic; in some cases leaves may be completely bleached, margins and tips scorched. Usually has an overall effect.	Usually on interveinal necrosis.
5 Mg	In chlorophyll, which is essential for photosynthesis. Associated with co-carboxylase, which is the co-enzyme for the carboxylases; in enolase, which is necessary in glycolysis (from 2-phosphoglyceric acid to 2-phosphopyruvic acid); in hexokinase, which brings about transphosphorylation of glucose. Magnesium pectate may be a constituent of the middle lamella.[3]	Mottled chlorosis with veins green, leaf web tissue yellow or white, appearing first on old leaves; severely affected leaves may wilt and shed, or may abscise without the wilting stage; brittleness of leaves common, necrosis often occurs.	Usually on interveinal necrosis.
6 Mn	Associated with arginase (?), which converts arginine to urea. In an unidentified enzyme, which brings about catabolism of oxaloacetic acid to pyruvic acid and carbon dioxide in respiration.	Mottled chlorosis with veins green and leaf web tissue yellow or white, appearing first on young leaves, may spread to old leaves; stems yellowish green, often hard and woody. Carotene development reduced.	Leaves pale, necrotic, bronzing at margins; similar to iron deficiency. With potato, small black spots on stem.
7 Mo	Associated with an unidentified enzyme (?), which is apparently required in ascorbic acid synthesis. Appears to effect the reduction of nitrate to ammonia.[7]	Light yellow chlorosis of leaves; leaf blade may fail to expand.	Lower leaves yellow with brown necrotic areas; in severe cases, upper leaves may be stunted, chlorotic and abscise.
8 N	In proteins, the chief organic constituents of protoplasm. In chlorophyll, which is essential for photosynthesis. Important in the assimilation of sugars. In many organic compounds.	In young plants stunted growth and yellowish green leaves; older leaves light green, followed by yellowing and drying or shedding, often abundant anthocyanins in veins; shoots short, thin, growth upright and spindly; flowering reduced; with apple and peach, fruit highly colored develop slowly, small when mature. Appears first on older leaves, but usually has an overall effect.	Leaves dark green, excessive vegetative growth; high transpiration; reduced yield of seed and fruit crops; may secure satisfactory yield of leafy vegetables of reduced quality.
9 P	In phospholipids, e. g., lecithin, which are constituents of cytoplasmic membranes. In nucleoprotein, a constituent of the nucleus and chromosomes. In adenosine di- and triphosphates, which are required for phosphorylation reactions, glycolysis and synthesis of sucrose, starch and proteins. Di- and triphosphopyridine nucleotide, coenzymes which accept and/or donate hydrogen in oxidation-reduction reactions.	Young plants stunted, leaves dark blue-green, sometimes purplish (with potato and certain other vegetables, leaves pale green); stems slender; often anthocyanins in veins, may become necrotic; with potato, meristematic growth ceases; fruits ripen slowly; plants often dwarfed at maturity.	
10 K	May be involved in action of fructokinase and other enzyme systems. Facilitates carbohydrate synthesis and translocation of carbohydrates.	Leaves of potato usually dark blue-green and leaves of monocotyledons pale green or streaked with yellow, with marginal chlorosis and necrosis, appearing first on old leaves; usually wrinkled, corrugated or crinkled between veins.	Leaves yellowish green; reduced growth; tendency toward calcium and magnesium deficiency.
11 S	In cystine and cysteine, which are present in all plant proteins. In glutathione, which may function as a hydrogen carrier in respiration. In mustard oil glycosides, which may tie up reserve food substances which would otherwise be toxic to cells.	Leaves light green to yellow, appearing first along veins of young leaves; stems often slender.	Necrosis or firing of older leaves of certain species or varieties.
12 Zn	Associated with an unidentified enzyme, which is directly necessary for synthesis of tryptophan, the precursor of indoleacetic acid.	Leaves chlorotic and necrotic, appearing first on young growth; rosetting; premature shedding; whitish chlorotic streaks between veins in older leaves and whitening of upper leaves in monocotyledons; chlorosis of lower leaves in dicotyledons.	Leaves yellow from zinc-induced iron chlorosis.

/1/ Carbon, hydrogen and oxygen have been intentionally omitted from table. These elements are consitutents of carbohydrates, fats, proteins, vitamins, hormones, chlorophyll and other organic compounds occurring in plants. The bicarbonate ion is involved in ion absorption or exchange. Oxygen is the final receptor of hydrogen in aerobic respiration. Many of the metallic elements (as ions) that are indicated as being associated with enzymes serve as activators for the enzyme. /2/ Data applicable primarily to herbaceous crop plants. /3/ The middle lamella is an intercellular layer flanked on each side by the primary cell walls. /4/ Chlorosis due to the physiological unavailability of iron and manganese or reduced potassium. /5/ Terminal step in aerobic respiration. /6/ The enzyme is of limited distribution in plants and its function is a matter of speculation. /7/ Nature of relationship undetermined.

199. NUTRITIONAL CHARACTERISTICS OF CHEMICAL ELEMENTS: BACTERIA AND FUNGI

The specific elements listed are either required or exert an effect on the associated functions. Carbon, hydrogen, nitrogen, oxygen, phosphorus, and sulfur are required for the synthesis of structural proteins, carbohydrates, fats, and other organic compounds, and for formation of end-products of metabolism.

	Species	Chemical Element	Occurrence and/or Function
		Heterotrophic Bacteria[1]	
1	Aerobacter aerogenes	Fe	Growth.
2		Mg, Mn	Associated with pyruvate → acetylmethylcarbinol.
3		Cr or Mn (partially replaceable by Al, Cu, Fe, Zn)	Fermentation.
4	A. indologenes	Fe	Associated with hydrogenase, formic dehydrogenase, formic hydro-genlyase[2], and cytochrome.
5	Azotobacter spp	Fe	Growth.
6		Ca (replaceable by Sr); Mo (partially re-placeable by V)	Nitrogen fixation.
7		Co, Mg, Mn, Zn	Associated with oxalacetate decarboxylase.
8	Bacillus anthracis	Ca, Fe, K, Mg, Mn	Growth.
9	B. cereus	K	Spore formation.
10	B. subtilis	Fe, K, Mg, Mn, Zn	Growth and production of subtilin (antibiotic).
11	Brucella abortus	Mg or Mn	Normal growth of antigenic non-smooth variants.
12	B. suis	Fe, Mg, Mn	Growth.
13	Cellulomonas spp	Mg	Growth.
14	Clostridium acetobutylicum	Fe	Fermentation.
15		Mn, Zn	Associated with phosphatase.
16		Mo (partially replaceable by V)	Nitrogen fixation.
17	C. botulinum, C. histolyticus	Fe	Associated with polypeptidase.
18	C. butyricum	Mo (partially replaceable by V)	Nitrogen fixation.
19	C. perfringens	Mg	Cell division.
20		Fe	Fermentation.
21	Corynebacterium diphtheriae	Fe	Growth and formation of toxin and porphyrin.
22	Escherichia coli	Fe	Growth.
23		Mg, Mn	Associated with pyruvic dehydrogenase and enolase.
24	Hemophilus influenzae	Fe	In growth factor, hemin.
25	Klebsiella pneumoniae	Fe	Growth.
26	Lactobacillus arabinosus, L.casei	K, Mn	Growth.
27	L. lactis, L. leichmanii	Co	In growth factor, vitamin B_{12}.
28	Leuconostoc mesenteroides	K, Mn, P	Growth.
29	Propinonibacterium jensenii	Mg, Zn	Associated with phosphatase.
30	Pseudomonas spp	B, Ca, Co, Cu, Fe, Mn, Mo, Zn	Growth
31	P. aeruginosa	Fe, S	Production of pyocyanine (antibiotic).
32		Mg, P, S	Production of fluorescent pigment.
33		Fe	Associated with cytochrome, cytochrome oxidase, catalase, & peroxidase.
34		Mg	Growth.
35	Serratia marcescens	Fe, Mg	Pigment formation.
36	Sporocytophaga myxococcoides	Fe, Mg	Growth and decomposition of cellulose.
37	Streptococcus fecalis	K, Mn, P	Growth.
38	Streptomyces fradiae	Fe, Zn	Production of neomycins.
39	S. griseus	Co	Production of vitamin B_{12}.
40		Fe, Cr, Zn, Co, Cu, Mn, Ni, Se	Production of streptomycins.
41		Fe, Zn.	Production of grisein.
42	S. lavendulae	Fe, Zn	Production of streptothricin.
		Photosynthetic Bacteria[3]	
43	All species	Mg	In bacteriochlorophyll.
44	Non-sulfur purple bacteria	H_2[4]	Molecular hydrogen oxidized as source of energy.
45	Sulfur purple bacteria	S, as sulfide, sulfite, or thiosulfate	Indispensable reducing agent in photosynthesis.
46	Sulfur green bacteria	S, as sulfide or thiosulfate	Indispensable reducing agent in photosynthesis.
		Chemoautotrophic Bacteria[5]	
47	Iron bacteria	Fe, Mn	Substrates, oxidized as source of energy.
48	Nitrifying bacteria	Cu	Nitrification (oxidation of ammonia and nitrite).
49	Ammonia-oxidizing nitrifiers Nitrosomonas spp	N, as ammonia	Indispensable substrate, oxidized as source of energy.
50	Nitrite-oxidizing nitrifiers Nitrobacter spp	N, as nitrite	Indispensable substrate, oxidized as source of energy.
51	Sulfur-oxidizers, aerobic Thiobacillus spp	S, as sulfide or thiosulfate	Substrate, oxidized as source of energy.
52	Sulfur-oxidizer, anaerobic Thiobacillus denitrificans	S, as sulfide or thiosulfate	Substrate, oxidized as source of energy.
53		N, as nitrate	Indispensable oxidizing agent.
54	Sulfate-reducer Sporovibrio desulfuricans	S, as sulfate	Indispensable oxidizing agent.
55	Clostridium aceticum	H_2	Molecular hydrogen oxidized as source of energy.
56		CO_2	Employed as oxidizing agent.
57	Hydrogenomonas spp	H_2	Molecular hydrogen oxidized as source of energy.
58	Methanobacterium omelianski	H_2	Molecular hydrogen oxidized as source of energy.
59		CO_2	Employed as oxidizing agent.
		Fungi	
60	Aspergillus fumigatus	Fe, Zn	Production of gliotoxin and helvolic acid.
61	A. niger	Fe, Ni, Co, Al, Zn, Cr, Mn, Mo, Se, Pb, Cu, Ag, Te, U, Sb, W	Production of citric acid.
62		Fe	Production of gluconic acid.
63	Aspergillus sp	Fe, Zn	Production of citrinin.
64	Candida gulliermondia, C.flareri	Fe	Production of riboflavin.
65	Penicillium citrinum	Fe, Mn	Production of citrinin.
66	P. notatum (chrysogenum group)	Zn, Fe, Mn, Cr, Cu, Al, Sn	Production of penicillin.
67		Fe, Zn	Production of gluconic acid.
68	P. patulum	Mn, Fe, Cu	Production of patulin and gentisic acid.
69	Rhizopus delemar	Al	Production of amylase.
70	R. nigricans	Zn, Fe, Cu, Mn	Production of fumaric and lactic acids, and ethanol.

/1/ Utilize such organic materials as sugars, fatty acids, amino acids, and alcohols as sources of carbon and energy for growth. /2/ Not established as a separate and distinct enzyme. Considered by many investigators to be a mixture of formic acid dehydrogenase and other enzymes. /3/ Capable of growing with CO_2 as carbon source, by utilizing light energy. /4/ Also organic compounds, e.g., alcohols and acids. /5/ Capable of growing with CO_2 as carbon source and with energy derived from oxidation of inorganic materials. A few of these organisms grow only auto-trophically, but most of them can develop either as heterotrophs or as autotrophs.

200. EFFECT OF CERTAIN SOIL FACTORS ON CHEMICAL ELEMENT DEFICIENCY AND EXCESS

The effects of soil pH and general soil characteristics on chemical element availability, uptake, or toxicity, is manifested by the appearance of deficiency or excess symptoms in the indicator organisms growing in the soil medium specified. Parenthetical expressions associated with pH values describe the pH-symptom relationship as follows: High = symptoms rarely occur outside the stated pH. Medium = symptoms occur most commonly within the stated pH. Low = symptoms occur at all pH values. For symptoms of deficiency and excess, see Table

Part I: FACTORS AFFECTING DEFICIENCY

Element	Soil pH	General Soil Characteristics	Indicator Organism	Element	Soil pH	General Soil Characteristics	Indicator Organism
1 Al[1]	5.5-8.0 (High)	Any soil of pH indicated.	Hydrangea.	10 I	(Low)	Areas of calcareous rocks, river flats, alluvial soils. Inland areas.	Animals feeding on I-deficient plants.
2 B	<5.0;7.5-8.5 (Medium to low)	Calcareous soils with high Ca:B ratio; on leached acid sandy soils low in organic matter, particularly under intensive cropping.	Many, including apple, beet, cauliflower, kale, turnip, celery, legumes, tobacco.	11 Fe	>7.0 (Medium to high)	Particularly on calcareous soils; may be induced on acid soils by high concentration of heavy metals or P.	Apple, pear, sugar beet, citrus; peach, plum, etc.; grapes, pineapple, raspberry, strawberry.
3 Co	(Low)	Soils of high pH[2] and low Co content. Localized areas only.	Ruminants and other animals feeding on Co-deficient plants.	12 Mg	<5.0 (Low)	Coarse-textured acid sandy soils; may be induced by heavy application or high content of K and Ca.	Apple, sugar beet, cauliflower, cereals, citrus, corn, hops, kale, lettuce, oats, potato, tobacco, tomato, tung tree.
4 Cu	<5.0;7.6-8.5 (Medium to low)	Heath soils; peat; acid and calcareous sands and gravels.	Apple, pear, cereals, citrus, flax, legumes, lettuce, onion; peach, plum, etc.; tomato.		>9.0 (Medium)	Alkali soils with high exchangeable -Na- percentage (>40%).	Alfalfa.
5 Mn	6.5-8.0 (High)	Calcareous soils, muck and peat.	Bean, beet, tree and bush fruits (except citrus), grasses, oats and other cereals, peas, potato, tomato.	13 N	<5.5 (Low)	Particularly coarse-textured acid soils and soils with low organic matter content.	Non-legumes. Legumes at low pH (caused by molybdenum deficiency).
6 Mo	4.5-6.5 (Medium)	Coarse-textured, leached acid soils, low molybdenum content.	Particularly legumes, sugar beet, brussels sprouts, cauliflower, kale, swede, citrus, lettuce, tomato.	14 P	<6.5;7.5-8.2 (Medium to high)	Particularly acid soils; sands and certain calcareous and muck or peat soils.	Barley, beet, grasses, legumes, cotton, potato, swede, turnip.
7 Na	<5.5 (Medium)	Sandy, leached, inland soils.	Beet, carrot, celery, swede, turnip.[3]	15 K	<5.5; >7.5 (Medium to low)	Sandy soils, particularly when leached; coarse-textured calcareous soils.	Beet, corn, tree and bush fruits, legumes, potato, tobacco, tomato, tung tree.
8 Zn	<5.0;7.6-8.5 (Medium to low)	Leached sands and gravels; muck and peat; calcareous soils.	Sugar beet, cacao, cereals, citrus and other tree fruits, clover, flax, various grasses, potato, swede, tomato, tung tree.	16 S	<5.0 (Low)	Particularly on leached, eroded soils of areas remote from urban and industrial districts.	Cabbage, other brassicas, cotton, flax, legumes, tea.
9 Ca	<5.0 (High)	Coarse-textured sandy soils; highly acid soils.	Alfalfa, celery, clover, flax, peas, tomato.				
	>9 (Medium)	Alkali soils with high exchangeable - Na - percentage (>40%).	Alfalfa.				

/1/ Data refer to the role of aluminum in producing blue pigments in hydrangea flower. /2/ Availability of the element decreases with increasing soil pH. /3/ Sodium promotes vigor of certain higher plants, particularly celery, beet, and other root crops.

Part II: FACTORS AFFECTING EXCESS

Element	Soil pH	General Soil Characteristics	Indicator Organism	Element	Soil pH	General Soil Characteristics	Indicator Organism
1 Al	<5.5 (High)[1]	Any soil of pH indicated.	Barley, French bean, sugar beet, carrot, celery, flax, leek.	8 Zn	<5.0	See cobalt.	Sugar beet, cauliflower, tomato.
2 B	>8.5 (High)	Coarse-textured soil irrigated with B-rich water.	Avocado, beans, blackberry, cereals, citrus; peach, plum, etc.; peas, potato, sunflower.	9 As	8.5 (Medium)	Soils with minerals containing As, or soils receiving continued As-sprays. Sandy soils low in Fe_2O_3.	Alfalfa, apricot, barley, oats, peach, tomato.
3 Co	<6.0	Acid soils with high concentration of heavy metals, particularly from industrial effluent.	Sugar beet, cauliflower, tomato.	10 Cl	6.5-8.0 (Medium) >8.5 (High)	Saline soils containing chlorides, or soils irrigated with water high in chlorides.	Avocado, citrus, stone-fruits, grape.
4 Cu	<6.0	See cobalt.	Sugar beet, cauliflower, tomato.	11 F	<6.0 (High)	Soils in areas of industrial pollution.	Barley, buckwheat, collards, tomato.
5 Mn	<5.5 (High)	Often in rather impervious mineral soils.	Alfalfa, barley, French bean, kale, swede, lespedeza, potato, sweetclover, tomato, turnip, vetch.	12 Li	>8.2	Certain irrigated soils.	Citrus, corn, tomato, wheat.
6 Mo	>8.5 (High)	Soils derived from rocks high in molybdenum content, or receiving phosphate high in molybdenum.	Ruminants feeding on molybdenum-rich plants[2].	13 Ni	<6[2]	Soils in areas of industrial pollution.	Beet, cabbage, clover, kale, oats, potato, tomato, turnip.
7 Na	>8.5 (High)	Alkali soils with exchangeable - Na - percentage (>15%). Saline soils or soils irrigated with water high in Na.	Almond, avocado, bean, cotton, oats, peas, wheat.	14 Se		Soils derived from Upper Cretaceous rocks and Upper Carboniferous limestone. Non-ferruginous soils in arid and semi-arid regions.	Animals feeding on Se-rich plants.

/1/ May occur with P deficiency. /2/ Inconsistent results with field plants.

201. EFFECT OF pH ON MACRONUTRIENT ABSORPTION: PLANTS

Plants were grown at pH 5-6 for 5 weeks in a dilute nutrient solution. At the end of this period they were placed for 3 days in a second solution containing (mEq per liter of solution): KNO_3, 5; $MgSO_4$, 2; KH_2PO_4, 0.06, and micronutrients. Following transfer to a third solution, containing 5 mEq KNO_3, 1 mEq $Ca(NO_3)_2$, 1 mEq $MgSO_4$, 0.06 mEq KH_2PO_4, and 0.5 mg B (as H_3BO_3) per liter of solution, uptake of ions during a 96 hour period was measured. Positive values indicated net absorption; negative values, loss from plant to the solution.

Nutrient	Rate of Nutrient Uptake at pH[1]						
	3[2]	4	5	6	7	8	9
	mEq per plant per 96-hour period						
Bermuda grass (Cynodon dactylon)							
1 K	3.38	4.61	4.53	4.53	4.33	5.17	4.53
2 Ca	0	0.35	0.90	0.90	0.90	1.25	1.25
3 Mg	0.82	1.07	1.07	1.15	1.15	1.48	1.23
4 NO3	10.69	10.14	10.14	10.08	10.14	10.08	10.45
5 H2PO4	0.29	0.72	0.67	0.64	0.78	0.47	0.09
Lettuce (Lactuca sativa)							
6 K	-0.44	3.14	5.07	6.66	6.09	5.86	6.53
7 Ca	-0.30	0.45	0.65	0.90	0.90	0.90	1.55
8 Mg	-0.33	0.66	0.99	1.15	0.99	0.82	1.15
9 NO3	1.01	5.25	7.23	9.13	7.87	7.02	8.29
10 H2PO4	-0.11	0.26	0.45	0.65	0.58	0.42	0.16
Tomato (Lycopersicon esculentum)							
11 K	-0.51	5.40	9.80	9.11	10.32	9.80	10.98
12 Ca	0	1.30	4.29	4.29	4.59	4.29	3.64
13 Mg	0	2.14	3.95	6.25	6.00	6.82	5.75
14 NO3	4.69	26.48	25.12	25.84	24.94	20.61	20.29
15 H2PO4	0.03	1.51	1.85	1.89	2.86	1.52	0.14

/1/ pH adjusted by addition of either NaOH or H_2SO_4. /2/ Roots were visibly injured and plants failed to grow.

202. EFFECT OF pH ON ZINC ABSORPTION: EXCISED ROOTS

Data are applicable to excised, segmented roots of barley (Hordeum vulgare var. Sacramento), placed in solutions containing 0.0005 mEq zinc per liter. Values are mEq per 1000g roots, wet-weight, per 3 hr period.

	Acid-Base[1]	pH	Zn Uptake mEq/1000g roots		Acid-Base[1]	pH	Zn Uptake mEq/1000g roots
1	HCl-KOH	4.8	0.07	25	HCl-Ca(OH)2	4.5	0.02
2		5.3	0.18	26		5.0	0.04
3		6.4	0.33	27		6.1	0.12
4		7.0	0.32	28		7.0	0.15
5		8.0	0.30				
6		9.0	0.26	29		9.0	0.18
7	HNO3-KOH	4.6	0.05	30	HNO3-Ca(OH)2	4.6	0.02
8		5.2	0.09	31		4.8	0.03
9		6.4	0.25	32		6.1	0.08
10		7.0	0.29	33		7.0	0.12
11		8.0	0.31	34		8.0	0.14
12		9.0	0.24	35		9.0	0.19
13	H2SO4-KOH	4.4	0.04	36	H2SO4-Ca(OH)2	4.3	0.01
14		4.9	0.08	37		4.8	0.03
15		5.8	0.23	38		5.4	0.05
16		7.0	0.30	39		7.0	0.12
17		8.0	0.32	40		8.0	0.15
18		9.0	0.25	41		9.0	0.17
19	H3PO4-KOH	4.4	0.03	42	H3PO4-Ca(OH)2	4.0	0.01
20		5.2	0.10	43		4.3	0.01
21		6.6	0.27	44		6.2	0.11
22		7.0	0.31	45		7.0	0.16
23		8.0	0.31	46		8.0	0.17
24		9.0	0.14	47		9.0	0.14

/1/ Solutions made to pH 9 or above with base, then acidified with requisite amounts of acid. Initial concentration of KOH, 0.082 mEq per liter of H_2O; that for $Ca(OH)_2$, 0.090 mEq per liter.

203. EFFECT OF SOIL REACTION ON AVAILABILITY: CHEMICAL ELEMENTS

Diagram illustrates the general trend of relation of soil reaction (pH) and associated factors to the availability of plant nutrient elements. Each element is represented by a band as labeled. The width of the band at any particular pH value indicates the relative favorableness of this pH value and associated factors to the presence of the elements in question in readily available forms (the wider the band the more favorable the influence), but not to actual amount necessarily present. The latter is influenced by other factors, e.g., cropping and fertilization. The width of the heavily cross-hatched area between the curved lines at any pH is proportional to the hydrogen-ion concentration (intensity of acidity) to the left of pH 7, and to the OH-ion concentration (intensity of alkalinity) to the right of pH 7.

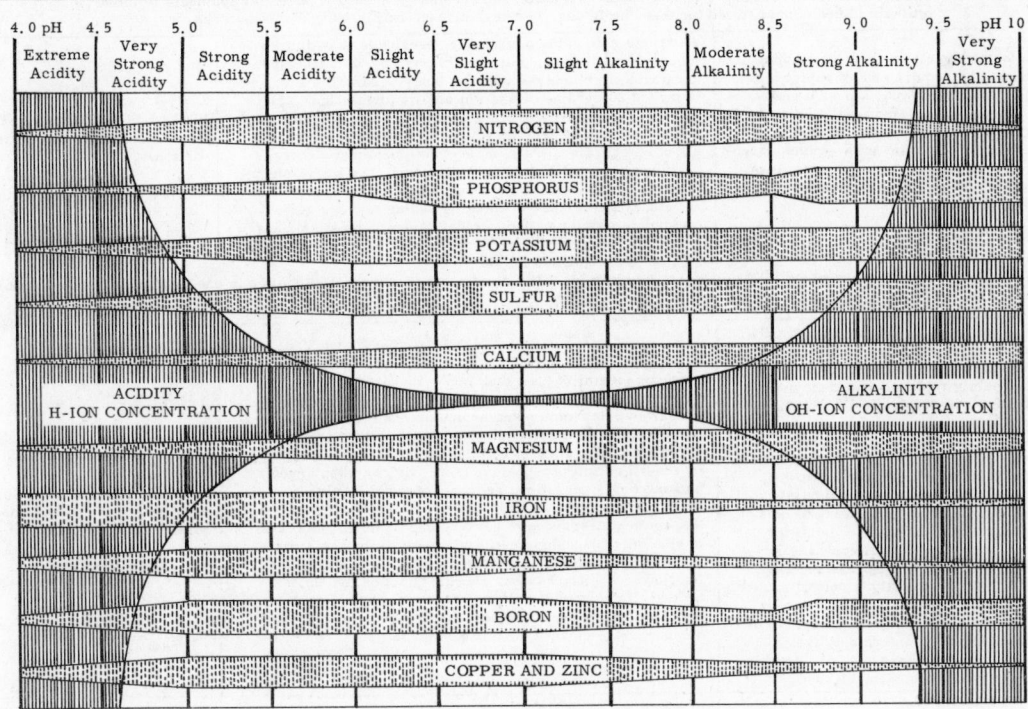

Functions	Deficiency Signs	Excess Signs

1

VITAMIN A
(Anti-xerophthalmia factor, axerophthol)

Required by all vertebrates studied (man, cattle, dog, guinea pig, hedgehog, horse, monkey, rabbit, rat, chicken, turkey). May be formed within the organism from one of the carotenoid provitamins, alpha-, beta-, gamma-carotene, or cryptoxanthin. Exists as vitamin A_1 in marine fishes and land vertebrates, as both A_1 and A_2 in amphibia and anadromous and catadromous fishes, and as A_2 (in place of or in addition to A_1) in fresh-water fishes.

Functions	Deficiency Signs	Excess Signs
Stimulates growth and development. Maintains epithelium. Vitamin A is a precursor for retinene which, with the visual proteins, forms the photosensitive visual pigments (rhodopsin, porphyropsin, iodopsin).	Retarded growth of young (man, rat, chick, turkey); inability to stand on hind legs (swine). Localized overgrowth of bone (cattle, rat). Night blindness; photophobia (man). Degenerative changes in epithelium of eye; xerophthalmia, keratomalacia in severe deficiency (man, rat). Skin (man, rat) and mucosae (man), metaplasia, hyperkeratinization, cornification, desquamation. Optic nerve degeneration, possible result of skull overgrowth and pressure (cattle, rat). Decreased egg production (chicken); irregular estrus-- sterility, male (rat). Odontoblast atrophy (man, rat). Deficiency accentuated by: factors impairing digestion or absorption of fat, excessive ingestion of mineral oil, hyperthyroidism (inhibits conversion of provitamins to vitamin A_1).	Hypoprothrombinemia (rat); increased serum lipids, phosphatase; decreased serum proteins (man). Fragility, hyperostosis, cortical thickening of long bones, periosteal swellings, pain (man). Dry, exfoliated epithelium. Mouth desquamation, hyperemia of skin and mucosae (man). Liver enlargement (man). Telangiectasis.

2

ASCORBIC ACID
(Vitamin C; anti-scorbutic factor)

Required by man, other primates; guinea pig.

Functions	Deficiency Signs	Excess Signs
Protects hydrogen carriers. Promotes oxidation of fatty acids, oxidation of aromatic amino acids, conversion of folic acid to folinic acid, formation of intercellular substances. Increases phagocytic activity. Prevents and cures scurvy. Alleviates some effects of vitamin A lack and moderate excess. Prevents development of deficiency signs of vitamin E deficient diets (chick, guinea pig). Treatment of shock, wounds, infections. Protects adrenal oxy-steroids from destruction by liver (rat).	Loss of appetite, decline in physical activity; defective wound healing. Follicular keratosis (man); loss of luster, roughening of hair. Disorientation of cells in growing region of bone and teeth; beading of ribs; failure of chondroblast and osteoblast and ameloblast differentiation and maturation. Loosening of teeth; swollen gums. Anemia with decreased red cells; increase in circulating leukocytes. Failure of differentiation and maturation of fibroblasts. Capillary hemorrhages, particularly in subcutaneous and intramuscular areas. Swelling, atrophy, soreness of muscles leading to "face ache posture." Increased cholesterol in adrenals in early deficiency, decrease in late deficiency. Reduction of cytoplasm and indistinctness of cell membrane, increased respiration rate early in deficiency, decrease in late stages; lowering of temperature in late stages.	Hypervitaminosis doubtful if calcium content of diet is sufficient. Massive doses by injection lead to sudden death.

3

BIOTIN
(Anti-egg-white factor; vitamin H)

The need for the vitamin may be met under normal circumstances by intestinal bacterial synthesis in most animals. Need demonstrated for man, calf, dog, monkey, mouse, rabbit, rat, chicken, turkey.

Functions	Deficiency Signs	Excess Signs
Growth factor for all vertebrates studied. Believed to be required by all rapidly growing tissues. Involved in such metabolic processes, as: carboxylation and decarboxylation of Krebs Cycle acids; deamination of aspartic acid, serine, threonine; synthesis of citrulline, synthesis of unsaturated fatty acids. Prevention of "slipped tendon" (chick).	Seborrheic skin pathology. Scaly, greasy dermatitis (dog, monkey, rat, rabbit, chicken) followed by extreme hyperkeratosis after long deficiency. Scaly dermatitis in volunteers fed 200 grams of egg white daily (man). Spectacle alopecia (rodents); alopecia (monkey) may be extreme. Atrophy of lingual papillae (man). Spasticity (rat); paralysis of hindquarters (rat). Precordial distress; electrocardiographic changes (man). Anorexia, lassitude, sleeplessness, muscle pain (man); perosis (chick). Spontaneous deficiency rare, seen in chick. Feeding raw egg white (avidin) necessary to produce deficiency in most animals.	1 g/kg body weight not toxic to mice. Relatively non-toxic to all animals.

4

CHOLINE
(No single analogue can carry out all functions of the vitamin; several compounds can replace choline in one or more of its functions).

Required by most or all vertebrates, especially the young, including dog, guinea pig, rat, chicken, turkey.

Functions	Deficiency Signs	Excess Signs
Source of transferable (labile) methyl (CH_3) groups; is enzymatically transformed to betaine which transfers the methyl group. May be readily replaced as a methyl donor by betaine, dimethyl thetine, or methionine. Donor of methyl groups for synthesis of methionine (in presence of homocysteine), purines, etc. Synthesis of phospholipids, i.e., lecithin. Participates in creatine formation (rat). Precursor of acetylcholine. Essential for normal nutrition and egg production (chicken). Essential for lactation (hamster, rat). Necessary for normal liver function (dog, mouse, rat, chicken). A direct catalytic role of choline in intermediate metabolism has not been demonstrated. Therapeutic uses: cure of fatty liver and certain forms of liver cirrhosis (dog, rat); prevention of perosis ("slipped tendon" (chicken, turkey)).	Increased mortality (chicken, turkey). Liver: fatty degeneration and cirrhosis of liver (dog, rabbit, rat); prolonged prothrombin and bromsulphalein times, changes being marked in animals on high protein diets (rat); liver carcinoma from chronic deficiency (mouse, rat, chick). Increased serum phosphatase (rat). Kidney is enlarged, hemorrhagic congestion, necrosis of renal tubule, epithelium and glomeruli (rat); granular atrophy; hypertension in consequence of early kidney lesions, decrease in alkaline phosphatase activity and fat deposition (rat). Paralysis (young rat). Muscle weakness (guinea pig). Decreased egg production, ovarian abortion (chicken, turkey). Intracranial bleeding in young, born of choline deficient females (rat). Small subcutaneous and adrenal hemorrhages; marked anemia (guinea pig).	Inhibition of erythrocyte formation (dog). Diarrhea (man). Edema of legs (man).

Functions	Deficiency Signs	Excess Signs

5

COBALAMIN
(Vitamin B_{12}; vitamin B_{12a}; vitamin B_{12b}; cyanocobalamin; hydroxycobalamin)

Required by most or all vertebrates studied. Probably the anti-pernicious anemia principle of liver.

Functions	Deficiency Signs	Excess Signs
Growth factor (man, mouse, rat, swine, chicken, turkey). Utilization of oral cobalamin potentiated by gastric juice; in man, "intrinsic" factor necessary for the utilization of cobalamin, the "extrinsic" factor. In methylation reactions (rat, chick). Combined action with folic acid group. Therapeutic uses: pernicious anemia -- the vitamin is anti-anemic, relieves lingual manifestations and reverses degenerative changes in the spinal cord unless damage is irreversible (man); sprue (man).	Megaloblastic bone marrow (man). Macrocytic, hyper-chromic anemia (man). Degenerative changes in the spinal cord. Glossitis (man).	Polycythemia of non-ruminant animals.

6

VITAMIN D
(Anti-rachitic factor; calciferol; vitamin D_2; 7-dehydrocholesterol, vitamin D_3)

Required by most vertebrates studied. Ultraviolet light converts the provitamins ergosterol and 7-dehydrocholesterol to D_2 and D_3 respectively.

Functions	Deficiency Signs	Excess Signs
Normal development of bone. Enhances absorption and retention of Ca and P; promotes P reabsorption by the renal tubules. Maintains alkaline phosphatase at the bone site.	Retardation of growth (man, others). Rickets. Skeletal abnormalities and deformities varying with degree and duration of deficiency (man, rat, others). Skeletal abnormalities are scars of functional and structural change and may persist long after the deficiency has been relieved. Degree of restoration may be extensive and continue over long periods. Rapidly growing regions of bones are most affected; persistent over-proliferation of cartilage; enlargement of ends of long bones; softness, weakness of bones, and deformation of stress and posture; osteomalacia: decalcification, fragility of non-growing bone. Faulty calcification of teeth, similar to deficiencies of vitamins A and C. Hypocalcemia, hypophosphatemia. Increase in plasma phosphatase. Myasthenia; atony, skeletal and gut muscle. Tetany, convulsions, spasmodic closure of glottis (man, rat). Deficiency accentuated by factors impairing digestion or absorption of fat, excessive ingestion of mineral oil; pregnancy; lactation. Degree of toxicity is an individual characteristic.	Early symptoms: anorexia, thirst, lassitude. Later symptoms: nausea, vomiting, diarrhea, abdominal discomfort, weight loss and debility. Hypercalcemia, hyperphosphatemia. Deposition of Ca salts in various organs. Dense calcification in long bone metaphyses at the expense of disphyseal calcification, in infants and growing young (man). Ca deposits, kidney damage and renal dysfunction; increased urinary excretion of Ca and P. Continued hypervitaminosis leads to death. Excessive doses may be cumulative. Hypercalcemia, high urinary Ca and renal damage have been noted eight months after treatment (125,000 - unit doses daily). The amount of dietary vitamin D which will produce signs of excess varies with individuals within the same species, and at different times within the same individual.

7

VITAMIN E
(Alpha-, beta-, gamma-, delta-tocopherols; anti-sterility factor)

Required by cattle, dog, guinea pig, hamster, mink, mouse, rabbit, rat, swine, chicken, duck, turkey. Significance, if any, in human nutrition, has not yet been established.

Functions	Deficiency Signs	Excess Signs
Biological anti-oxidant; protects unsaturated fatty acids, vitamin A against peroxidation. Participates in oxidation-reduction reactions. Therapeutic uses: treatment of skin collagenoses (man); protects against such toxic agents as carbon tetrachloride, chloroform, alloxan.	Irreparable degeneration of the testicular germinal epithelium (bull, mouse, rat, chicken); uterine necrosis, seminal vesicle necrosis (rat). Reproductive failure (swine, rat). Reduced egg hatchability, death of the embryo (chicken). Acute muscle degeneration (dog, guinea pig, hamster, rabbit, rat, chicken, duck, turkey). Acute encephalomalacia, degeneration of the cerebellum, nerve cell degeneration (chick). Ataxia, tremors, weakness, opisthotonos (chicken). Paralysis (suckling rat, born of vitamin E deficient mother). Creatinuria. Generalized exudative diathesis (chick). Liver necrosis, degeneration (mouse, rat, swine). Some causes of deficiency signs, other than dietary deficiency of the vitamin are: any factor impairing digestion or absorption of fat, as inflammation of intestinal mucosa, sprue, or chronic diarrhea; excessive ingestion of mineral oil; relatively greater requirement during pregnancy and lactation.	None listed.

8

FOLIC ACID GROUP
(Folacin; pteroylglutamic acid (PGA); folinic acid; citrovorum factor; vitamin M; vitamin B_c; vitamin B_{10}; factor U; L. casei factor; Norite eluate factor)

Required by most vertebrates studied, except ruminants and others whose need is satisfied by intestinal bacterial synthesis. Essential for man, dog, guinea pig, fox, mink, chicken, duck, goose, turkey, fish, sulfa-treated lamb and rat.

Functions	Deficiency Signs	Excess Signs
Growth and hematopoietic factor (monkey, fox, mink, chick, on purified rations). Production and utilization of formate. Methylation reactions. Introduction of the 2- and 8-carbon atoms into the purine ring and the amidine carbon into histidine. (Continued on next page)	Retardation of growth. Sprue (man, monkey), megaloblastic bone marrow (man, monkey, others), macrocytic, hyper-chromic anemia (man, monkey); macrocytic anemia, with ultimate anisocytosis (chick, turkey); cytopenia (monkey, (Continued on next page)	Relatively non-toxic. Males more resistant than females (mouse). (Continued on next page)

Functions	Deficiency Signs	Excess signs

8 — FOLIC ACID GROUP (concluded)

Functions	Deficiency Signs	Excess signs
Tyrosine oxidation. p-Aminobenzoic acid is a part of folic acid molecule. Vitamin-like action of PABA caused by above relations. Therapeutic uses: treatment of sprue (man); nutritional macrocytic anemia; certain megaloblastic, macrocytic anemias of infancy (man); macrocytic anemia of pregnancy (man); added to practical rations as a growth stimulant (mink).	chick); leukocyte abnormalities (monkey, rat, chick); infarction of the spleen (rat). Poor feather structure (chicken, turkey); abnormal feather pigmentation (chicken); graying of the pelage (rat). Perosis (chick, turkey). Impaired reproduction (rat, chicken); lowered hatchability of eggs (chicken). Impaired lactation (rat, mouse). Neck paralysis (goose, turkey). Diarrhea and the absorptive difficulties in sprue (disorders of calcium metabolism; impaired absorption of fat and of vitamins).	Death by obstruction of the renal tubules with precipitated folic acid follows intake of toxic amounts. Intravenous LD_{50} = 600 mg/kg body weight (mouse); 500 mg/kg (rat); 410 mg/kg (rabbit); 120 mg/kg guinea pig.

9 — INOSITOL (Myo-)
(Mouse anti-alopecia factor; Bios I)

Required by mouse and possible cotton rat and hamster.

Functions	Deficiency Signs	Excess signs
Has been reported to stimulate growth when added to rations deficient in thiamine (rat) and to rations containing sulfonamides (rat, swine). Lipotropic factor. Prevents encephalomalacia and exudative diathesis in vitamin E deficiency (chick). Suggested essential for reproduction (hamster). Of doubtful significance as a vitamin.	Characteristic alopecia (loss of hair) followed by severe dermatitis -- mouse (under certain dietary conditions).	Non-toxic, so far as known.

10 — VITAMIN K
(Anti-hemorrhagic factor; phylloquinone)

Required by man, dog, mouse, rabbit, rat, canary, chicken, duck, goose, pigeon, turkey, and others. In mammals, bacterial synthesis may satisfy the need in whole or in part.

Functions	Deficiency Signs	Excess signs
Essential for the production of prothrombin in liver. A number of synthetic products having a quinoid nucleus have vitamin K activity, e.g., menadione (2-methyl-1,4-naphthoquinone).	Decline or failure of prothrombin synthesis. Decrease in blood prothrombin content, resulting in increased bleeding tendency after even slight trauma, multiple hemorrhages throughout all tissues (man, chicken); increased clotting time (man, others).	Toxicity relatively low. Vomiting (man); vomiting after oral dose of 180 mg of menadione (synthetic vitamin) (dog). Porphyrinuria (man, dog), albuminuria (dog). Prolonged clotting time (rabbit); cytopenia, hemoglobinemia (mouse). Lethal dose is 350 to 500 mg/kg body weight (rats).

11 — NIACIN (-AMIDE)
(Nicotinic acid (-amide); pellagra preventive (P.P.) factor; anti-blacktongue factor).

Required by all vertebrates studied except calf, horse, sheep, whose need is supplied by intestinal flora. Most animals synthesize niacin from tryptophan. Animal tissues contain niacinamide; plant tissues contain mainly niacin.

Functions	Deficiency Signs	Excess signs
A component of di- and triphosphopyridine nucleotides (DPN, Coenzyme I; TPN, Coenzyme II) which function as hydrogen acceptors in more than 50 metabolic reactions. Stimulates gastric secretion.	Delayed growth and development of young; diarrhea, dermatitis, and dementia, the "triad" of pellagra. Bilateral, symmetrical dermatitis, aggravated by sunlight, heat, inflammation (man, only); rarefaction of corium, keratinization, atrophy of sebaceous glands, desquamation. Swollen gills (trout). Poor feathering (chick). Stomatitis (man, dog, fox, swine, chicken, turkey); smooth glossitis (man); blacktongue (dog, cat, chick); large intestine -- atrophy, ulceration, cyst formation (man, dog, swine); diarrhea (man, dog, calf, rabbit, chick, duck, turkey); achlorhydria (man, swine); salivary drooling (dog). Macrocytic anemia (man, dog, rabbit, swine); leukopenia (dog, rabbit). Retrobulbar neuritis (man); encephalopathy, headache, dizziness, depression, delusions, dementia; locomotor difficulties, tremors, jerky movements, rigidity; altered tendon reflexes, numbness, paralysis (man). Perosis ("slipped tendon" -- chick, turkey poult). The syndrome of deficiency symptoms is referred to as "pellagra" in man and "blacktongue" in dogs, cats, and other animals.	Death follows very large doses; dogs on 2 grams/day die within 20 days; 2% niacinamide in diet inhibits growth (chick); 1% causes fatty livers; large doses of niacin cause ketosis (rat). Burning and itching of skin; elevation of skin temperature (man). Peripheral vasodilation (man). Paralysis of the respiratory center (rat). Ratio therapeutic dose: toxic dose = 1:1000.

12 — PANTOTHENIC ACID

Required by most or all vertebrates studied, including calf, dog, fox, guinea pig, hamster, monkey, mouse, swine, rat, chicken, duck, pigeon, turkey, and possibly man.

Functions	Deficiency Signs	Excess signs
Growth factor for the animals mentioned above. As a component of Coenzyme A, functions in: enzymatic acetylation; fat, protein and carbohydrate metabolism; fat, phospholipid, and steroid synthesis.	Retarded growth in all animals. Specific dermatitis of mouth and feet (chicken); eczematous dermatitis (rat). Achromotrichia (monkey, dog, fox, rat, mouse), spectacle alopecia (rat). Myelin degeneration of peripheral nerves (chick); chromatolysis of dorsal root ganglion cells (chick, swine). Spastic abnormalities of hindquarters, abnormal gait, ataxia (dog, mouse, swine); convulsions (dog). Hemorrhagic necrosis of adrenals. Secretion of red pigment by the Harderian gland ("bloody pigment" -- rat). Diarrhea with bloody stools (dog); anorexia, diarrhea, colitis (monkey, swine); necrosis of intestinal epithelium, abscesses followed by ulceration (rat). Anemia (dog, rat, monkey, swine). Necrosis of kidney (rat). Increased deposition of liver fat (dog, chick). Failure and abnormalities in reproduction; ocular changes. Burning sensations of hands, feet (man); increased non-protein nitrogen in severe deficiency (dog); death in severe deficiency.	100 grams have been given to man without ill effects. LD_{50} mouse: orally, 10 g; subcutaneously, 2.7 g; intraperitoneally, 0.9 g. LD_{50} rat: subcutaneously, 3.4 g/kg body weight.

Functions	Deficiency Signs	Excess Signs

13

PYRIDOXINE (VITAMIN B$_6$) GROUP
(Pyridoxal, pyridoxamine, anti-acrodynia factor; factor Y)

Required by most or all vertebrates studied, including man, synthesized by intestinal organisms in rat. Requirement by animals is increased with increased dietary protein, linseed oil meal, sucrose, and apparently decreased with increased dietary essential fatty acids, aureomycin. Occurs largely as pyridoxal in animal products and as pyridoxamine in plant products. In animals the three forms (pyridoxine, -al, -amine) are equally active when given by injection, but pyridoxine is the most active when administered orally.

Functions	Deficiency Signs	Excess Signs
As coenzyme (pyridoxal phosphate) for transaminase and codecarboxylase systems, kynurinase, cystathionase, serine and threonine dehydrase, cysteine desulfhydrase, and racemizing enzymes; in deamination of amino acids and the formation of urea nitrogen; in conversion of tryptophan to niacin; in metabolism of fatty acids. Necessary for normal adrenal-cortical function. Therapeutic uses: treatment of muscular dystrophies associated with pellagra (man); hyperemesis gravidarum (nausea of pregnancy); seborrheic dermatitis sicca (man).	Retarded growth (man; infant; guinea pig, rabbit, monkey, rat, chick); appetite and weight loss, reduced egg production, death (chick). Hypochromic anemia (man: infant); polymorphonuclear leukocytosis, lymphopenia (man); hypocromic, microcytic anemia with anisocytosis and irregular reticulocytosis (dog, swine, monkey, duck, chick); poikilocytosis (cattle), dilation, hypertrophy of right auricle and ventricle; increased plasma urea and NPN tachycardia and cardiac embarrassment (rat); mucus accumulation in thorax (dog); impaired antibody production (rat); degeneration in myelin sheaths of peripheral nerves and spinal cord (dog, swine); convulsions, epileptiform fits (rat, swine, chicken); ataxia (swine); convulsions (man; infant); weakness, nervousness, irritability, insomnia (man); deficiency signs produced by ingestion of desoxypyridoxine; seborrhea-like lesions about eyes, nose, mouth; cheilosis, glossitis, stomatitis (man); denudation of hair from paws, snout, eartips, thickening of ears (rat); dermatitis, bald patches (monkey). Increased urea, ammonia, uric acid, creatinine (dog); tryptophan metabolites in urine (dog, hamster, mouse, rat); large amounts of xanthurenic acid (man). Anorexia, unthriftiness (cattle).	Convulsions 24 hr after LD$_{50}$ dose (rat). Daily feeding of 10 mg/kg body weight for 3 months had no effect (monkey, dog, rat). LD$_{50}$ rat: subcutaneously, 3 g/kg body weight; orally, 4 g/kg.

14

RIBOFLAVIN
(Vitamin B$_2$, or G; lactoflavin, ovoflavin, hepatoflavin)

Required by most or all vertebrates studied.

Functions	Deficiency Signs	Excess Signs
As riboflavin-5-phosphate in flavo-protein enzymes, e.g., "Warburg's yellow enzyme," cytochrome-c-reductase, riboflavin-adenine-nucleotide. As prosthetic group in enzymic hydrogen carriers, e. g., D-amino acid oxidase, xanthine oxidase, succinic dehydrogenase. Role in the visual mechanism of the retina.	Cessation or retardation of growth (rat, others). Epidermal atrophy, dermatitis, greasy scaling especially of nasolabial folds, cheeks, chin (man); cheilosis, angular stomatitis, lesions of lip and mouth corners (man). Myelin degeneration of nerves (dog, mouse, rat, swine, chicken); central neuritis (man); lack of coordination, faulty grasp reflex (monkey); curled toe paralysis (chicken); partial paralysis of legs (rat). Muscle weakness (dog, monkey). Mild photophobia, dimness of vision and decline of visual acuity; soreness of eyes and lids (man); cornea -- cloudiness, vascularization, cataract, opacity, ulceration (man, dog, rat). Congenital skeletal malformations in offspring of riboflavin-deficient females (rat). Requirement increased in pregnancy and lactation.	5,000 times the therapeutic dose is tolerated (rat, mouse). Toxic amounts intraperitoneally cause anuria, renal concretions (rat). Paresthesia, itching (man).

15

THIAMINE
(Vitamin B$_1$; aneurin)

Required by most or all vertebrates studied, except ruminants whose need is satisfied by intestinal synthesis.

Functions	Deficiency Signs	Excess Signs
Essential for normal growth, appetite, digestion, gastrointestinal tonus, nerve activity, carbohydrate metabolism (as cocarboxylase participates in decarboxylations, oxidations, dismutations, and condensations leading to CO$_2$ formation).	Retardation of growth; anorexia (man, others). No peripheral nerve degeneration (mammals). Convulsions, hyperesthesia, anesthesia, opisthotonos (pigeon, chicken, turkey). Dilation of the heart, myocardial lesions (dog, fox, rat, swine); bradycardia (monkey, cat, dog, rat, swine). Edema (dog, fox, rat, swine). Gastrointestinal disturbances (man). Accumulation of pyruvic acid in blood and tissues. Decrease in urinary citric acid (rat). Deficiency disease in man: beriberi (sometimes subdivided into cardiac, wet, and dry [neuritic, paraplegic] beriberi).	Vascular: hypotension (man, dog, rabbit).

16

ESSENTIAL UNSATURATED FATTY ACIDS
(Arachidonic acid, linoleic acid, linolenic acid)

Required by rat, mouse, guinea pig, swine, others. Ordinarily not regarded as a vitamin.

Functions	Deficiency Signs	Excess Signs
Essential to growth and reproduction (rat). Serve as building units of the phospholipids. Catalyze the oxidation of saturated fatty acids in vitro. Exercise a protective action in pyridoxine deficiency (rat).	Eczema (man). Retardation or cessation of growth; metabolic rate; scaliness on feet and tail; alopecia; disturbances in reproduction; kidney and urinary tract lesions; increased water intake (rat).	Changes from normal in composition of stored fat.

205. NUTRIENTS: CALORIE VALUE

Values are Calories per gram of ingested nutrient.

P = plant; A = animal; F = fiber; M = mixed; NFE = nitrogen-free extract.

	Nutrients for:		Total[1]	Lost, Rumen Gas[2]	Lost, Feces	Virtually Absorbed[3]	Lost Urine	Metabolized Net[4]	Av.[5]
	Man								
1	Protein	P	5.65		0.85	4.80	1.06	3.74	4.0
2		A	5.65		0.15	5.50	1.21	4.29	
3	Carbohydrate	P	4.15		0.15	4.00	0	4.00	4.0
4		A	3.90		0.10	3.80	0	3.80	
5	Fat	P	9.30		0.95	8.35	0	8.35	9.0
6		A	9.40		0.45	8.95	0	8.95	
	Monkey								
7	Protein	P	5.65		0.56	5.09	1.68	3.41	3.0
8		A	5.65		0.56	5.09	2.04	3.05	
9	Carbohydrate	P	4.1		0	?	0	?	
10	Fat	P	9.3		0	?	0	?	
	Cattle								
11	Protein	P	5.65		1.64	4.01	1.30	2.71	2.7
12	Carbohydrate	F	4.25	0.33	1.89	2.03	0	2.03	
13		NFE	4.23	0.47	0.95	2.81	0	2.81	2.6
14	Fat	P	8.72[6]		2.90	5.82	0	5.82	5.8
	Chicken								
15	Protein	M	5.70		1.37	4.33	0.8?	3.46	3.5
16	Carbohydrate	M	4.20		0.84	3.36	0	3.36	3.4
17	Fat	M	9.47[7]		1.89	7.58	0	7.58	7.6

/1/ By bomb calorimeter. /2/ From fermentation of fiber and NFE. A 550 kg cow may lose 4000 Calories/da (400 liters methane). /3/ Total calorie value minus that lost in feces (in rumen gas and feces for ruminants). /4/ Net physiological energy available for heat, activity, growth. /5/ Average values rounded off. /6/ Mean of 7.96 for fat from roughage and 9.47 for fat from grain. /7/ From grain.

206. FEED UTILIZATION, ACCUMULATIVE EFFICIENCY FOR GROWTH: VERTEBRATES

Unless otherwise indicated, values are grams gain in body weight per gram of feed[1] consumed (or pounds gain per pound of feed consumed). Values are calculated by dividing gain in weight from birth to per cent of mature weight by total weight of feed consumed since birth. MW = mature weight.

	Species		10% MW	25% MW	50% MW	90% MW
1	Cattle, dairy, large	♂	0.45	0.26	0.17	
2		♀	0.54	0.31	0.16	0.05
3	Cattle, dairy, small	♂	0.39	0.33	0.16	
4		♀	0.47	0.27	0.20	0.07
5	Cattle, beef	♂	0.62	0.30	0.15	
6		♀	0.61	0.25	0.14	
7	Rat, Sprague-Dawley	♂	0.41	0.31	0.15	
8		♀				
9	Rat, Wistar	♂	0.44	0.34	0.14	
10		♀				
11	Swine[2]	♂	0.373	0.273[3]	0.203[3]	
12		♀				
13	Chicken, white leghorn	♂	0.45	0.41	0.33	
14		♀	0.45	0.4	0.3	0.14
15	Chicken, heavy breeds	♂	0.53	0.45	0.35	
16		♀	0.54	0.43	0.33	
17	Turkey, Beltsville small[4]	♂	0.55	0.42	0.34	0.19
18		♀	0.50	0.37	0.31	

/1/ On a dry weight basis. /2/ Based on 56-day weaning weight, and feed consumption figures calculated for periods: 56-98 days, 98-140 days, and 140-180 days. /3/ Extrapolated. Calculated on basis of mature weight of 600 pounds. /4/ Values for broad-breasted bronze turkeys are the same, but a value of 0.23 is given at 90% mature weight.

207. NUTRIENTS, APPARENT DIGESTIBILITY AND ABSORBABILITY: VERTEBRATES

Values are grams of protein, fat or carbohydrate digested and virtually absorbed per 100 grams of the nutrient ingested as a component of the food or feed listed. The quantity digested and absorbed is taken as the quantity of the nutrient ingested minus the quantity subsequently found in the feces. Values for man are for food as commonly prepared for ingestion.

	Food- or Feedstuff	Man Protein	Man Carbohydrate	Man Fat	Cattle[1] Protein	Cattle Carbohydrate Fiber	Cattle Carbohydrate NFE[2]	Cattle Fat	Horse[1] Protein	Horse Carbohydrate Fiber	Horse Carbohydrate NFE[2]	Horse Fat	Chicken Protein	Chicken Carbohydrate	Chicken Fat
1	Animal products[3]	97	98	95											
2	Bone meal				69			0							
3	Buttermilk, dried				90		94	98					87	34	93
4	Eggs	97	98	95									69	71	95
5	Fats			95											
6	Fish meal				88			95					75	35	83
7	Meat and fish	97		95											
8	Meat scrap				82			97					61	60	90
9	Milk, milk products	97	98	95	95		98	98							
10	Milk, skim, dried				90		93	100					75	66	57
11	Plant products[3]	85	97	90	70?	40?	76?	77?					76?	69?	80?
12	Barley				70		88	63	88	39	87	25	73	80	75
13	Corn, whole ground	60	96	90	63		88	83	69		89	59	86	94	90
14	Cottonseed meal				81	57	80	92	85	29	49	90	70	36	97
15	Macaroni, spaghetti	86	98	90									78	97	85
16	Oatmeal, rolled oats	76	98	90	90	80	98	96							
17	Oats, whole grain				74		76	84	79	44	79	80	56	66	92
18	Rice, white	84	99	90											
19	Soybean oil meal[4]				90	57	91	38					74	34	79
20	Wheat, 85-93% extraction	83	94	90									100	95	100
21	Wheat bran				76	30	76	74	73	22	53	27	59	37	86
22	Fruit	85	90	90											
23	Potatoes	74	96	90	55		91	1	63	75	101	42			
24	Sugar		98				97		70	32	83	50			
	Green roughages														
25	Kentucky bluegrass				71	70	64	51							
26	Pasture grass, mixed				75	74	77	42	66	33	62				
27	Silage, corn				53	66	69	74							
28	Timothy				59	68	72	57							
	Dried roughages														
29	Alfalfa hay				71	44	70	34	74	39	68				
30	Alfalfa meal				73	45	67	21							
31	Clover hay				63	56	69	58	56	38	64	29	56	34	55
32	Timothy hay				46	58	57	46	43	43	53	13			

/1/ Digestibility of roughages is determined by feeding one roughage alone, while that of concentrates and grains is determined by difference, e.g., feeding the material in conjunction with a roughage the digestibility of which has been determined. /2/ Nitrogen-free extract. /3/ Variety not specified. /4/ Solvent extracted.

208. PATHWAYS OF CARBOHYDRATE DIGESTION AND ABSORPTION: MAN, LABORATORY MAMMALS

Carbohydrate digestion is the enzymatic hydrolysis of poly- and oligosaccharides into their monosaccharide components which are then absorbed into the blood stream. Monosaccharides are phosphorylated to hexose-6-PO_4(?) as they enter the intestinal mucosa and then dephosphorylated before they enter the blood stream. A = salivary amylase (ptyalin); B = pancreatic amylase (amylopsin); C = maltase; D = sucrase (invertase); E = lactase.

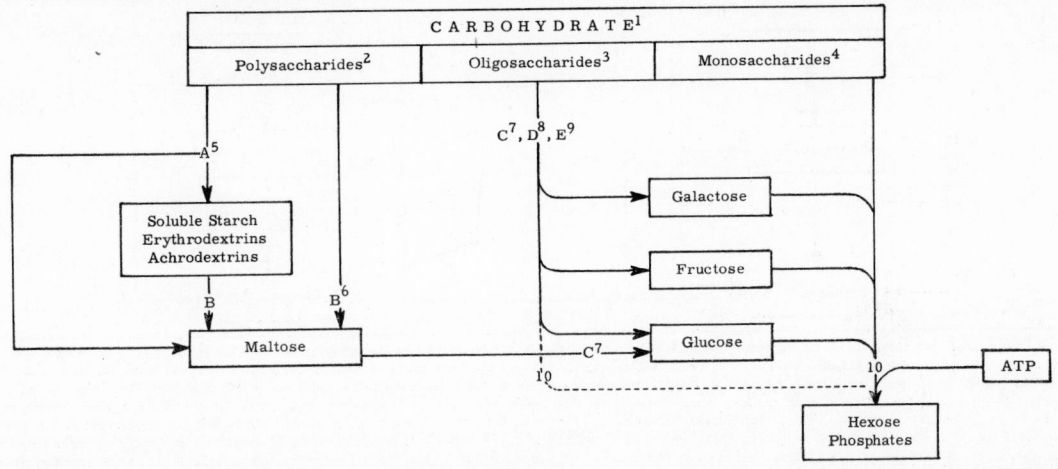

/1/ Ingested. /2/ Polysaccharides including glycogen, starch dextrins and cellulose are made up of many monosaccharide (simple sugar) molecules. Cellulose, although made up of glucose molecules is not digestible by mammals. /3/ Oligosaccharides are carbohydrates composed of only a few (down to two in the case of disaccharides) molecules of monosaccharide. Sucrose contains glucose and fructose; maltose is composed of two molecules of glucose; and lactose contains glucose and galactose as constituents. /4/ Ingested monosaccharides are absorbed into the blood stream without breakdown. /5/ Salivary amylase not only converts polysaccharides to soluble starch, etc., but also breaks off some maltose. /6/ Pancreatic amylase hydrolyzes starches, dextrins and glycogen to maltose; uncooked starch is hydrolyzed to some degree by pancreatic but not by salivary amylase. The concentration of pancreatic amylase is increased by high carbohydrate intake. /7/ Maltase, in intestinal secretion, hydrolyzes each molecule of maltose to two molecules of glucose. /8/ Sucrase, in intestinal secretion, hydrolyzes sucrose to glucose and fructose. /9/ Lactase, in intestinal secretion, hydrolyzes sucrose to glucose and fructose. /9/ Lactase, in intestinal secretion, hydrolyzes lactose to glucose and galactose. /10/ Possibly other hexoses.

209. PATHWAYS OF LIPID DIGESTION AND ABSORPTION: MAN, LABORATORY MAMMALS

Details of digestion and absorption of lipids are not as well established as those for protein and carbohydrate. The pathways as presented may be expected to undergo modification with further research in the field. A = pancreatic lipase (steapsin); B = lecithinase.

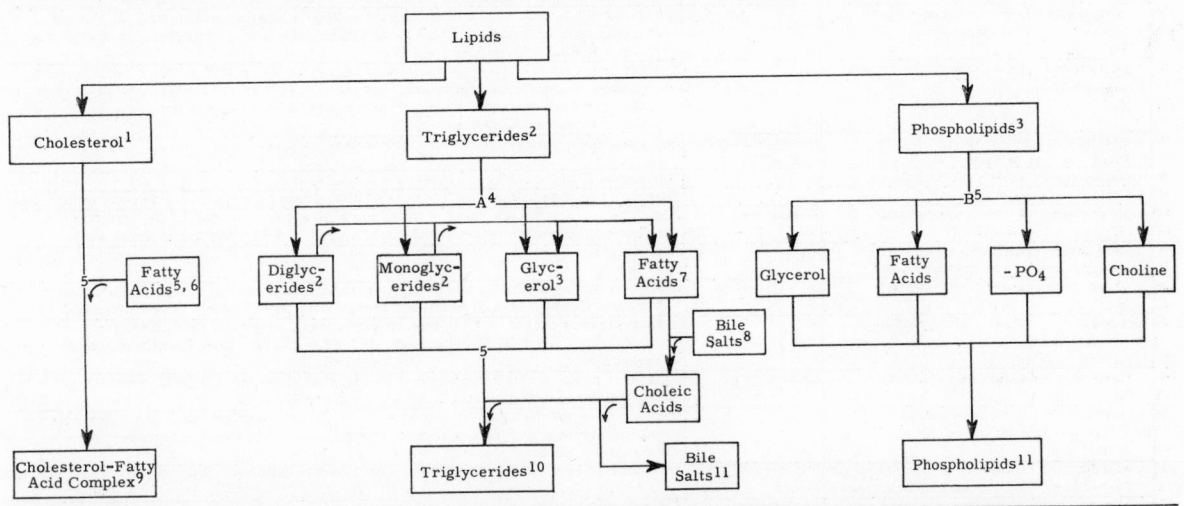

/1/ Absorbed in the presence of fat (except in rabbits); excess cholesterol may hinder fat absorption. Some conversion to coprosterol by intestinal bacteria and excreted as such. Plant sterols are not absorbed(?)./2/ Tri-, di-, and monoglycerides = compounds of glycerol and 3 or 2 or 1 molecule fatty acid. Some absorption(?)./3/ Absorbed. Include (a) lecithins (= glycerol + fatty acids + phosphoric acid + choline) although there is some question whether unchanged lecithin can be absorbed; (b) cephalin (= glycerol + fatty acids + phosphoric acid + cholamine or serine, or inositol); (c) sphingomyelins (= fatty acid + phosphoric acid + choline + sphingosine). /4/ Lipolytic enzyme activated in intestinal lumen by bile salts, soaps, and certain proteins and amino acids. /5/ In succus entericus from intestinal mucosa. /6/ From hydrolysis of glycerides or phospholipds. /7/ Short-chain (i.e., 10 carbon or less) fatty acids, being water soluble, are readily absorbed into the intestinal mucosa; long chain fatty acids absorbed with the aid of bile salts (q.v.). /8/ In addition to forming choleic acid complexes with fatty acids, bile salts serve as emulsifying agent to hasten absorption of lipid digestion end products. /9/ Absorbed into lymphatic system. /10/ Mono- and diglycerides and fatty acids (from triglyceride or phospholipid hydrolysis) combine in the intestinal mucosa with endogenous glycerol (from dihydroxyacetone) to form triglycerides of different composition from those ingested. Those containing short-chain fatty acids are absorbed chiefly into the portal blood stream; the more insoluble fats containing long-chain fatty acids are absorbed through the lacteals into the lymphatic system. /11/ Formed in intestinal mucosa and absorbed into lymph and portal blood.

210. PATHWAYS OF PROTEIN DIGESTION AND ABSORPTION: MAMMALS

Protein digestion, in the alimentary canal, comprises the enzymatic cleavage of the protein molecule into its component amino acids which are absorbed into the blood stream. Although the diagram is a summary of present knowledge of the field, controversy still exists with regard to some of the details. A = pepsin; B = rennin; C = trypsin; D = chymotrypsin; E = carboxypolypeptidase; F = aminopolypeptidase; G = dipeptidase.

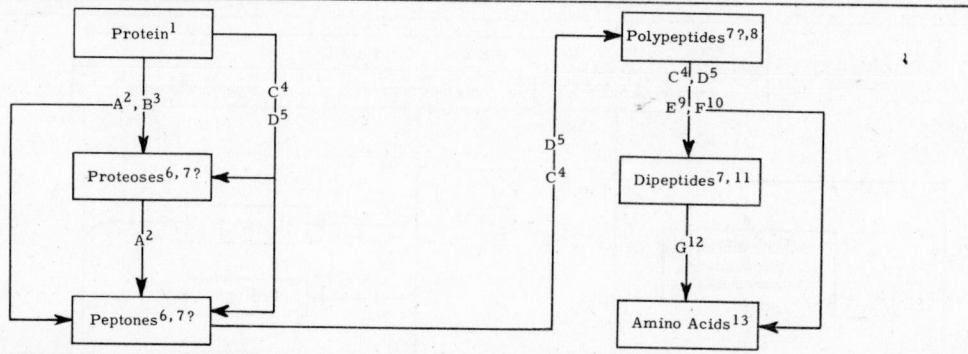

/1/ Native, denatured, or coagulated; some native protein may be absorbed. /2/ Secreted by the gastric mucosa as pepsinogen; activated by HCl. Pepsin is an autocatalytic endopeptidase, hydrolyzing peptide bonds in the interior of the protein molecule. /3/ In gastric juice of the young of some mammals, but probably not the adults; converts soluble calcium caseinate to insoluble calcium paracaseinate (clot). /4/ Secreted in pancreatic juice as trypsinogen in response to secretin from the small intestine; activated by enterokinase. Trypsin is an autocatalytic endopeptidase, hydrolyzing native proteins to proteoses, peptones, and polypeptides by splitting peptide bonds involving a basic nitrogen (as in lysine, arginine). /5/ Secreted in pancreatic juice as chymotrypsinogen in response to secretin; activated by trypsin. Chymotrypsin is an endopeptidase, hydrolyzing native proteins to proteoses, peptones, and polypeptides by splitting peptide bonds involving an aromatic group (as in tyrosine, phenylalanine). /6/ Secondary protein derivatives of molecular weight less than 1000, exclusive of polypeptides and simpler degradation products. /7/ Some absorption. /8/ A compound containing more than two amino acids joined by peptide linkages. /9/ An exopeptidase in pancreatice juice removing successively amino acids with free carboxyl groups from the end of the peptide chain, thus hydrolyzing polypeptides to simpler peptides and amino acids. /10/ Secreted by intestinal mucosa in succus entericus in response to enterocrinin, secretin, and presence of food; an exopeptidase, removing amino acids with free amino groups from the end of the peptide chain, thus hydrolyzing polypeptides to simpler peptides and amino acids. /11/ Dipeptides contain two amino acids. /12/ Secreted by intestinal mucosa in succus entericus; hydrolyzes dipeptides to amino acids by breaking the peptide linkage. /13/ Absorbed by intestinal mucosa; probably a stereochemical mechanism favoring absorption of L-amino acids.

211. PATHWAYS OF AMINO ACID METABOLISM

	Amino Acid	Product of Oxidative Deamination or Transamination	Product of Decarboxylation	Pathways and Products of Metabolism[1]
1	L-Alanine	Pyruvic acid		
2	L-Arginine	α-Keto-δ-guanidovaleric acid	Agmatine	Arginine → ornithine + urea; arginine → citrulline + NH_3.
3	L-Asparagine	α-Ketosuccinamic acid		Asparagine $\rightleftharpoons$ aspartic acid + NH_3; α-ketosuccinamic acid → NH_3 + oxalacetic acid.
4	L-Aspartic acid	Oxalacetic acid	α-Alanine, β-alanine	Aspartic acid + carbamyl phosphate → $PO_4^{\equiv}$ + carbamyl aspartic →pyrimidines; aspartic acid $\rightleftharpoons$ (a) fumaric acid + NH_3, (b) homoserine $\rightleftharpoons$ threonine.
5	L-Citrulline	α-Keto-δ-carbamido-valeric acid		Citrulline + aspartic acid + ATP → ADP + $PO_4^{\equiv}$ + arginosuccinic acid $\rightleftharpoons$ arginine + fumaric acid; citrulline + $PO_4^{\equiv}$ $\rightleftharpoons$ ornithine + carbamyl phosphate; carbamyl phosphate + ADP $\rightleftharpoons$ CO_2 + NH_3 + ATP.
6	L-Cysteine & L-cystine	β-Mercaptopyruvic acid		β-Mercaptopyruvic acid → pyruvic acid + S; cysteine → H_2S + NH_3 + pyruvic acid; cysteine → cysteine sulfenic acid → cysteine sulfinic acid → (a) cysteic acid → taurine, (b) hypotaurine, (c) via transamination → β-sulfinylpyruvate → pyruvate + $SO_3^{=}$; 2 cysteine $\rightleftharpoons$ cystine.
7	L-Glutamic acid	α-Ketoglutaric acid	γ-Aminobutyric acid	See ornithine, proline, histidine, glutamine.
8	L-Glutamine	α-Ketoglutaramic acid		Glutamine $\rightleftharpoons$ glutamic acid + NH_3; α-ketoglutaramic acid → NH_3 + α-ketoglutaric acid.
9	Glycine	Glyoxylic acid		Glycine + 1 carbon fragment (CH_2O or HCOOH) $\rightleftharpoons$ serine; glyoxylic acid →formate + CO_2.
10	L-Histidine	β-Imidazolepyruvic acid	Histamine	Histidine → (a) urocanic acid → glutamic acid + NH_3 + formate, (b) carnosine, (c) anserine; histamine → imidazole acetic acid → NH_3 + formyl aspartic acid.
11	L-Hydroxy-proline	α-Keto-γ-hydroxy-δ-aminovaleric acid		See proline.
12	L-Isoleucine	D-α-Keto-β-methyl-valeric acid		α-Keto-β-methylvaleric acid → CO_2 + α-methylbutyryl CoA $\rightleftharpoons$ tighlyl CoA $\rightleftharpoons$ α-methyl-β-hydroxybutyryl CoA $\rightleftharpoons$ α-methyl acetoacetyl CoA $\rightleftharpoons$ acetyl CoA + propionyl CoA.
13	L-Leucine	α-Ketoisocaproic acid		α-Ketoisocaproic acid → CO_2 + isovaleryl CoA $\rightleftharpoons$ senecioyl CoA $\rightleftharpoons$ β-hydroxyiso-valeryl CoA $^{=}$ + CO_2 $\rightleftharpoons$ β-hydroxy, β-methyl glutaryl CoA $\rightleftharpoons$ acetoacetic acid + acetyl CoA.
14	L-Lysine	α-Keto-ε-aminocaproic acid	Cadaverine	Lysine → α-aminoadipic acid → α-ketoadipic acid → glutaric acid; α-keto-ε-amino-caproic acid → dihydropicolinic acid → pipecolic acid.
15	L-Methionine	α-Keto-γ-methiolbutyric acid		Methionine → labile CH_3 + homocysteine → (a) homocysteic acid, (b) H_2S + NH_3 + α-ketobutyric acid, (c) + serine → cystathionine →cysteine + homoserine → α-ketobutyric acid.
16	L-Ornithine	Glutamic-γ-semialdehyde or α-keto-δ-aminovaleric acid	Putrescine	Ornithine $\rightleftharpoons$ (a) proline, (b) glutamic acid; see citrulline.
17	L-Phenyl-alanine	Phenylpyruvic acid	Phenylethyl-amine	Phenylalanine → (a) tyrosine, (b) phenylpyruvic acid → phenylacetic and phenyl-lactic acids.
18	L-Proline	Glutamic-γ-semialdehyde or α-keto-δ-aminovaleric acid		Proline $\rightleftharpoons$ (a) ornithine, (b) glutamic acid, (c) → hydroxyproline.
19	L-Serine	β-Hydroxypyruvic acid	Ethanolamine	Serine → NH_3 + H_2O + pyruvic acid; serine + indole $\rightleftharpoons$ tryptophan; see glycine.
20	L-Threonine	D-α-Keto-β-hydroxy-butyric acid		Threonine → (a) NH_3 + H_2O + α-ketobutyric acid, (b) glycine + acetaldehyde; see aspartic acid.
21	L-Tryptophan	β-Indolepyruvic acid	Tryptamine	Tryptophan → formylkynurenine → formate + kynurenine → (a) kynurenic acid, (b) anthranilic acid + alanine, (c) 3-hydroxykynurenine → 3-hydroxyanthranilic acid → nicotinic acid.
22	L-Tyrosine	p-Hydroxyphenylpyruvic acid	Tryptamine	p-Hydroxyphenylpyruvic acid → 2, 5-dihydroxyphenylpyruvic acid → CO_2 + homogen-tesic acid → fumarylacetoacetic acid → fumaric acid + acetoacetic acid.
23	L-Valine	α-Ketoisovaleric acid		α-Ketoisovaleric acid → CO_2 + isobutyryl CoA $\rightleftharpoons$ methacrylyl CoA $\rightleftharpoons$ β-hydroxy-butyryl CoA → CO_2 + propionyl CoA.

/1/ ADP = adenosine diphosphate; ATP = adenosine triphosphate; CoA = coenzyme A.

The pathway from stored or ingested carbohydrate to pyruvate is one of release of stored energy by anaerobic oxidation (glycolysis). Released energy is partly dissipated as heat and partly stored (temporarily) in the labile energy pool as "high energy phosphate" ($\sim PO_4$) by combination of $\sim PO_4$ with continuously available ADP (adenosine diphosphate) to form ATP (adenosine triphosphate). In the conversion of 1 mole of glucose (180 g), or of other monosaccharide to 2 moles of pyruvate (174 g), 2 moles of ATP are converted to ADP and 4 moles are formed from ADP, making a net gain of 2 moles of ATP, or approximately 20 kilocalories of readily available energy. If glucose-6-PO_4 has come from metabolic breakdown of glycogen, the cost is only 1 mole of ATP, making a net gain of 3 moles of ATP (approximately 30 kilocalories). The ATP is an immediate source of energy whose utilization (e.g., for muscular activity) is independent of oxygen supply. Aerobic oxidation (to carbon dioxide and water) begins where the present pathway ends and yields an additional 650 kilocalories per mole of hexose.

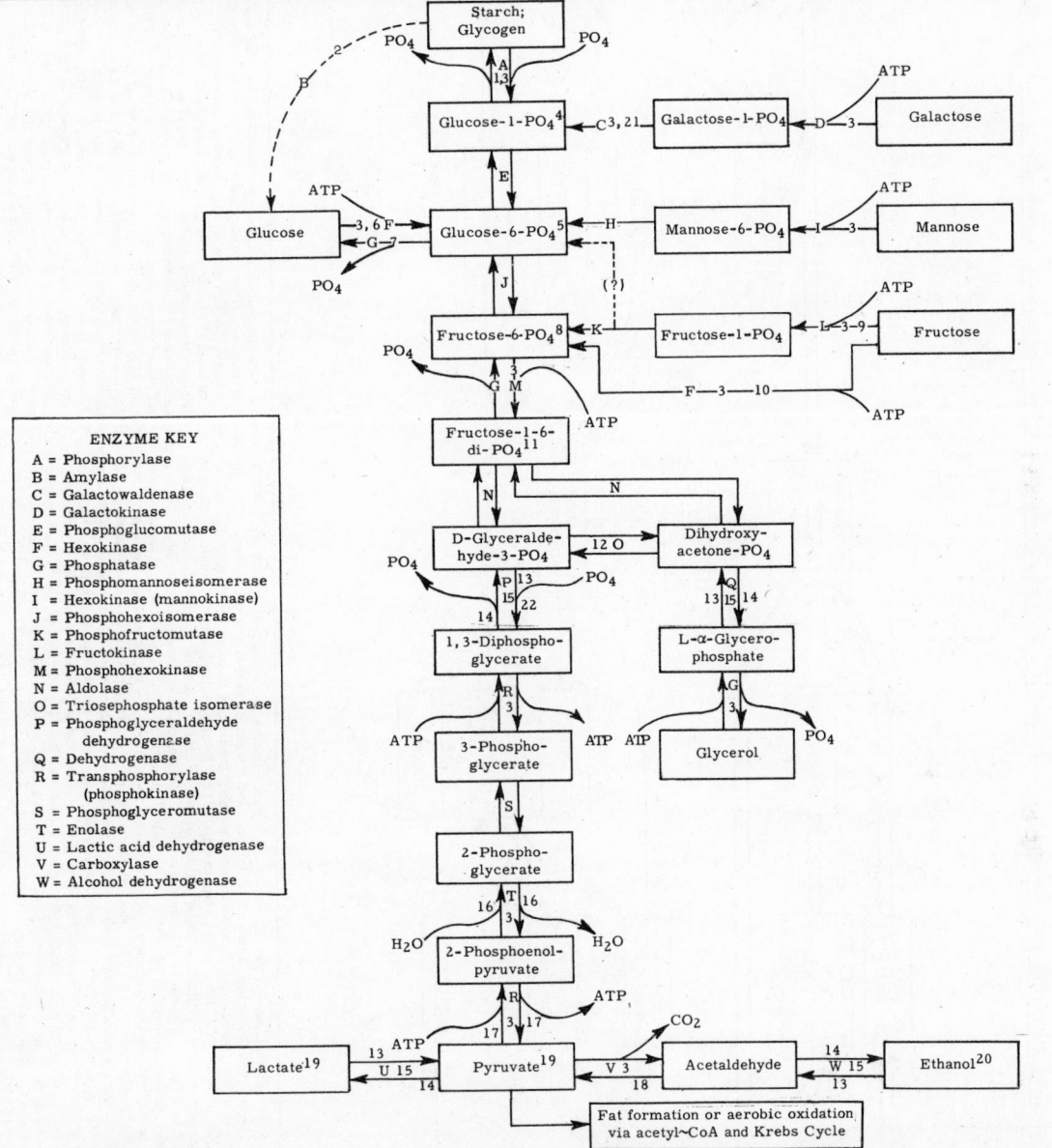

ENZYME KEY

A = Phosphorylase
B = Amylase
C = Galactowaldenase
D = Galactokinase
E = Phosphoglucomutase
F = Hexokinase
G = Phosphatase
H = Phosphomannoseisomerase
I = Hexokinase (mannokinase)
J = Phosphohexoisomerase
K = Phosphofructomutase
L = Fructokinase
M = Phosphohexokinase
N = Aldolase
O = Triosephosphate isomerase
P = Phosphoglyceraldehyde
        dehydrogenase
Q = Dehydrogenase
R = Transphosphorylase
        (phosphokinase)
S = Phosphoglyceromutase
T = Enolase
U = Lactic acid dehydrogenase
V = Carboxylase
W = Alcohol dehydrogenase

/1/ Adenylic acid and PO_4 required for activity in either direction. /2/ Digestion; glycogen and/or starch hydrolyzed to glucose in intestinal lumen. /3/ Mg^{++} required for this reaction. /4/ "Cori Ester." /5/ "Robison Ester." /6/ "Hexokinase reaction," assumed to be inhibited by growth hormone plus adrenal cortex hormone; and inhibition by these substances blocked by insulin, which thus favors conversion of glucose to glucose-6-phosphate. /7/ The reaction, glycogen to glucose-6-PO_4 to blood glucose, takes place in liver only; conversion of glucose to glucose-6-PO_4 to glycogen takes place in liver, muscle, and other tissues. /8/ "Neuberg Ester." /9/ In liver and muscle. /10/ In all tissue. /11/ "Harden-Young Ester." /12/ This reaction (to left) causes each step in the conversion to pyruvate to be doubled quantitatively; thus 1 mole of glucose gives rise to 2 moles of pyruvate. /13/ Hydrogen ions released. /14/ Hydrogen enters into the reaction. /15/ DPN acts as acceptor of released hydrogen ions, becoming DPNH in oxidative direction of the reaction; DPNH gives up hydrogen ions, becomes DPN, in reverse direction. Hydrogen ions accepted by DPN passed on in turn, to flavoprotein, cytochrome-c, cytochrome oxidase, molecular O_2. If molecular O_2 not sufficiently available, hydrogen ions may be passed from DPNH to pyruvate forming lactate. /16/ Inhibited by fluoride. /17/ K^+ also required. /18/ Thiamine pyrophosphate is required as coenzyme. /19/ Pyruvate, followed by conversion to lactate when oxygen supply is deficient (cf Fn 15), ends glycolysis in animal tissues. If oxygen is available pyruvate is oxidized via the Krebs Cycle, q.v. /20/ End of fermentation plant tissue. /21/ Uridine diphosphate glucose required as coenzyme. /22/ Inhibited by iodoacetate.

213. PATHWAYS OF LIPID METABOLISM: MAMMALS

These pathways are believed to occur in the lipid metabolism of animal forms in general. They are based on studies confined chiefly to mammals.

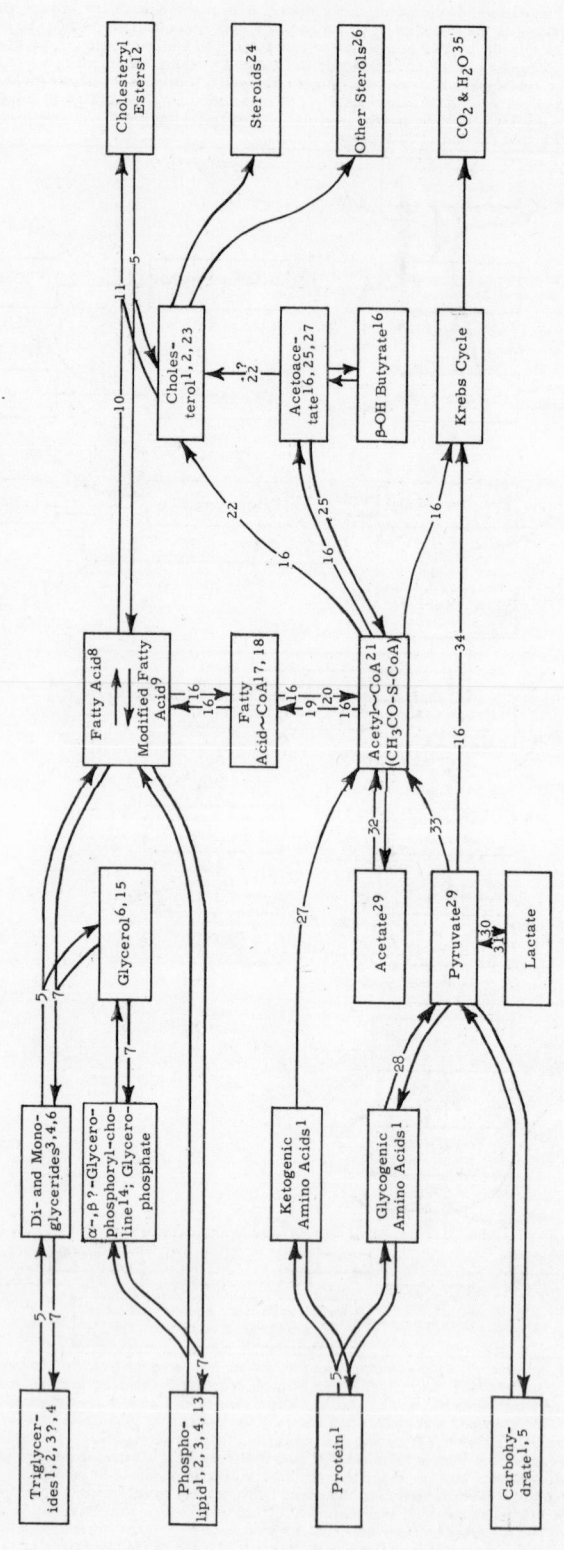

/1/ In intestinal lumen, blood, liver, other tissues. /2/ In chyle. /3/ Some absorption by intestinal mucosa. /4/ Formed in intestinal mucosa, or absorbed from lumen, pass into chyle, short chains possibly also into portal blood. /5/ Digestion in intestinal lumen. /6/ Probably transitory in tissues. /7/ In intestinal mucosa, liver, other tissues. /8/ Occur free (ionized) in intestinal lumen, blood, liver; free existence in chyle, questioned; free existence probably transitory in other tissues, if it occurs. /9/ In liver, carbon chains lengthened or shortened (cf Fn 20), and H added to not in brain, red cells. /10/ Chiefly (?) unsaturated. /11/ Synthesis probably in intestinal mucosa, liver, blood. /12/ In chyle, blood, and small amounts in liver, other tissues; liver (?), other tissues (?). /13/ Chiefly lecithin, cephalins (phosphatides of ethanolamine, serine, inositol, acetal, and polyglyceride phosphatides) some sphingomyelin. /14/ In intestinal mucosa, tabolized to pyruvate. /16/ In liver, other tissues. /17/ Fatty acid ester of coenzyme A, i.e., acyl∿CoA ester, formed by intestinal mucosa, where resynthesized into glycerides, including phospholipids. Me-other CoA ester. /18/ Coenzyme A probably = pantetheine (pantothenic acid + β-alanine + thioethanolamine) + ADP, with a third PO₄ at C3 of the ribose; forms fatty acid thiol esters via the SH in the thioethanolamine. /19/ Reverse of β-oxidation (cf Fn 20). bly the hexokinase reaction in carbohydrate metabolism. /20/ Fatty acid-CoA ester shortened 2 carbons at a time by β-oxidation, breaking off a molecule of acetyl∿CoA at each step, and re-esteri-fying the remainder with CoA. /21/ Acetic acid ester of coenzyme A known also as S-acetyl coenzyme A, active acetyl. /22/ Via squalene (?). /23/ Adrenal steroids (C₁₁oxy) promote synthesis (?). /24/ Hormones, bile acids. /25/ Acetyl∿CoA → Acetoacetyl∿ CoA → Acetoacetate. Transported from liver via blood to other tissues, where oxidized, via acetyl∿CoA and Krebs Cycle, to CO₂ and H₂O. Some conversion to acetone. /26/ Coprosterol, epicoprosterol excreted. /27/ Tyrosine, leucine, isoleucine also converted directly to acetoacetate. /28/ Aspartate enters Krebs Cycle not via pyruvate, but by conversion directly to oxalacetate. /29/ Occurs in blood, liver, muscle, other tissues. /30/ Occurs in muscle, especially in exercise, the lactate diffusing into the blood stream. /31/ Occurs in liver, muscle, brain, other tissues. /32/ ATP-dependent reaction with CoA. /33/ Diphosphothiamine (= cocarboxylase), lipoic acid, Mg⁺⁺ required. /34/ Pyruvate + CO₂ → oxalacetate, malate, components of Krebs Cycle. Oxalacetate condenses with acetyl∿CoA by oxalacetate (i.e., by pyruvate), occurring when acetyl∿CoA is being formed in active fat catabolism, may explain antiketogenic action of carbohydrate (and protein). /35/ And energy liberation.

214. PATHWAYS OF NUCLEOPROTEIN CATABOLISM

Nucleoproteins generally are composed of basic proteins, histones or protamins, associated with nucleic acids. The nucleic acids are complex molecules, each composed of many nucleotide units, joined by phosphate sugar linkages. Each nucleotide is made up of a purine or pyrimidine base, linked to a pentose or desoxypentose, and this in turn to a molecule of phosphoric acid. Upon hydrolysis of the nucleotide in the digestive tract or tissues, the phosphoric acid is removed. The remaining compound, a nucleoside, contains the purine or pyrimidine base and the sugar residue.

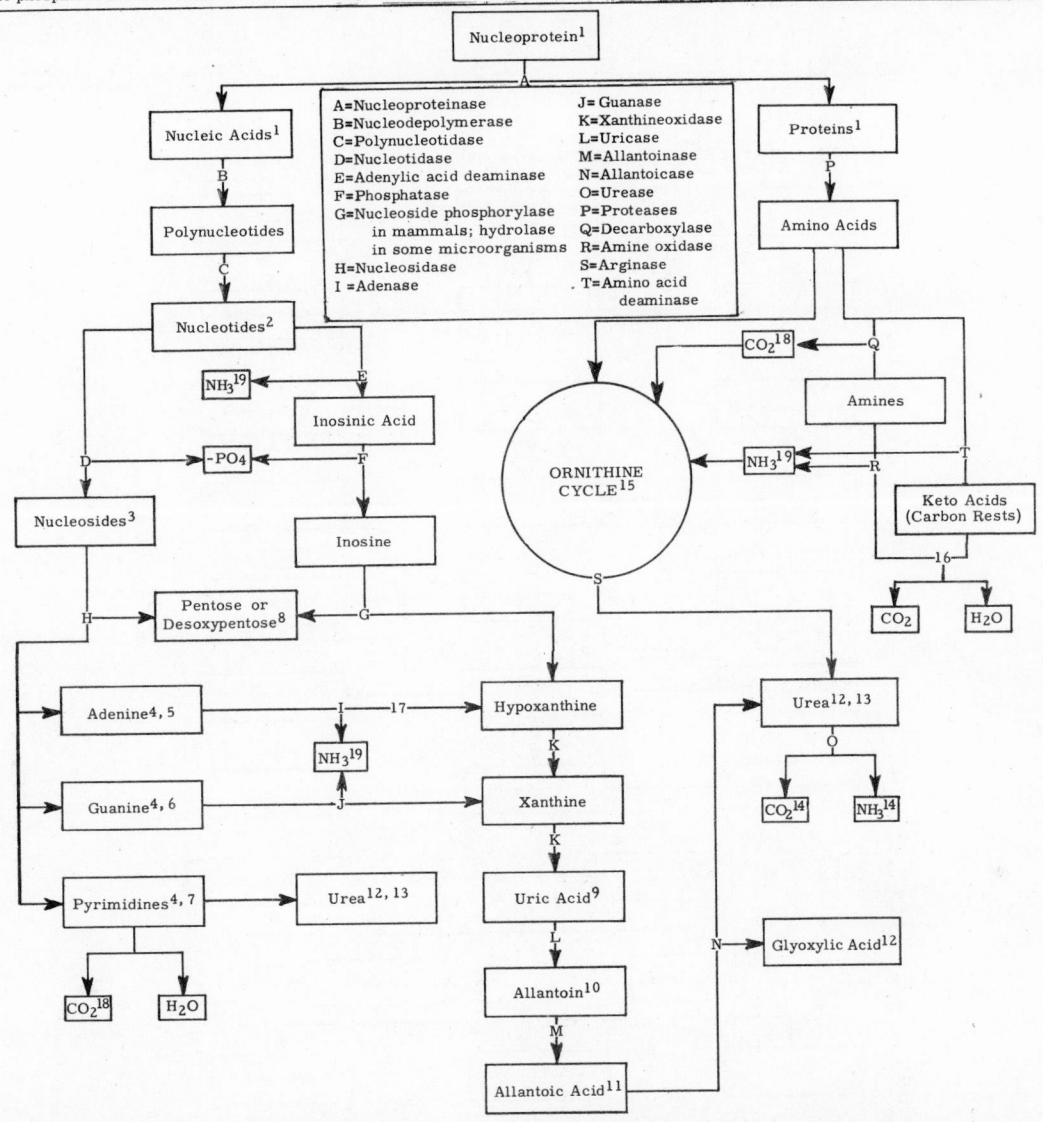

/1/ Catabolism of nucleoprotein, nucleic acid, and protein may take place in the alimentary canal or in the tissues. See Table 251 for detailed pathways of purine and pyrimidine nucleotide catabolism. /2/ Some intestinal absorption. Nucleotidase in liver splits both pyrimidine and purine nucleotides to nucleosides. /3/ Absorbed in the intestine. Purine nucleosides are split into purines and pentoses by purine nucleosidase present in tissues. /4/ Mammals do not require exogenous purines or pyrimidines, but can synthesize them from products of protein metabolism. /5/ Adenine and guanine are the only naturally occurring purines in nucleic acids. /6/ Excreted by pig and spider. /7/ Little is known about the stages in pyrimidine catabolism. It is thought that pyrimidine nitrogen is largely converted to urea, indicating disruption and metabolism of the pyrimidine ring. /8/ D-ribose and D-2-desoxyribose have been definitely established as present in nucleoproteins, and are degraded via the Warburg-Dickens-Lipmann pathway; other pentoses may be present. /9/ Excreted as end product of purine catabolism by primates, Dalmation dog, some reptiles, some insects; and as end product of catabolism of proteins as well as purines and pyrimidines by birds (no urea formation by birds). /10/ Excreted by most mammals, gastropods, and some insects. /11/ Excreted by some teleost fishes. /12/ Excreted by most fishes, amphibia, fresh-water lamellibranches. /13/ Urea is excreted as the end product of amino acid metabolism by mammals, and as an end product of purine (and pyrimidine?) metabolism by some other forms. /14/ Crustacea, gephyrean worms, marine lamellibranchs do not excrete urea but break it down to CO_2 and NH_3 which are excreted. /15/ Urea formation in the mammalian liver is via the "Ornithine Cycle" (Krebs-Henseleit Cycle). The pathway through the cycle is: ornithine $\longrightarrow$ citrulline $\longrightarrow$ arginine succinate $\longrightarrow$ arginine $\longrightarrow$ ornithine. CO_2 and NH_3 enter the cycle via carbamyl glutamic acid at ornithine; NH_3 enters the cycle via aspartic acid at citrulline. Arginine succinate is split to arginine and fumaric acid, after which arginine is converted to ornithine with the release of urea. /16/ Via Krebs Cycle. In the course of amino acid metabolism, previous to entry into the Krebs Cycle, sulfur-containing amino acids lose their sulfur -- usually in the form of SO_4. /17/ There is little likelihood that the route adenine $\longrightarrow$ hypoxanthine is of any importance in animals. Adenase is not found to any extent in mammals. /18/ May enter into metabolic processes, into the Ornithine Cycle and be incorporated into and excreted as urea, or be excreted as such. /19/ NH_3, as in the case of CO_2, is also used to synthesize many tissue constituents. Hence, it may enter into metabolic processes, be built into amino acids, incorporated into urea and excreted, or excreted as such across the kidney tubule (in appropriate animal species).

215. PATHWAYS OF PURINE AND PYRIMIDINE NUCLEOTIDE CATABOLISM

Nucleotides are composed of a purine or pyrmidine base linked to a pentose or desoxypentose sugar which, in turn, is linked to phosphate. Removal of the phosphate leaves a compound designated as a nucleoside. See Table 252 for pathways of nucleoprotein catabolism in general.

A = Phosphatase; B = Adenylic acid deaminase; C = Adenosine deaminase; D =Adenase(?);E = Nucleoside phosphorylase; F = Xanthine oxidase; G = Guanylic acid deaminase; H = Guanosine deaminase; I = Guanase; J = Phosphorylase or hydrolase; K = Cytidine deaminase; L = Cytosine deaminase; M = Uracil-thymine oxidase; N = Barbiturase; O = Urease.

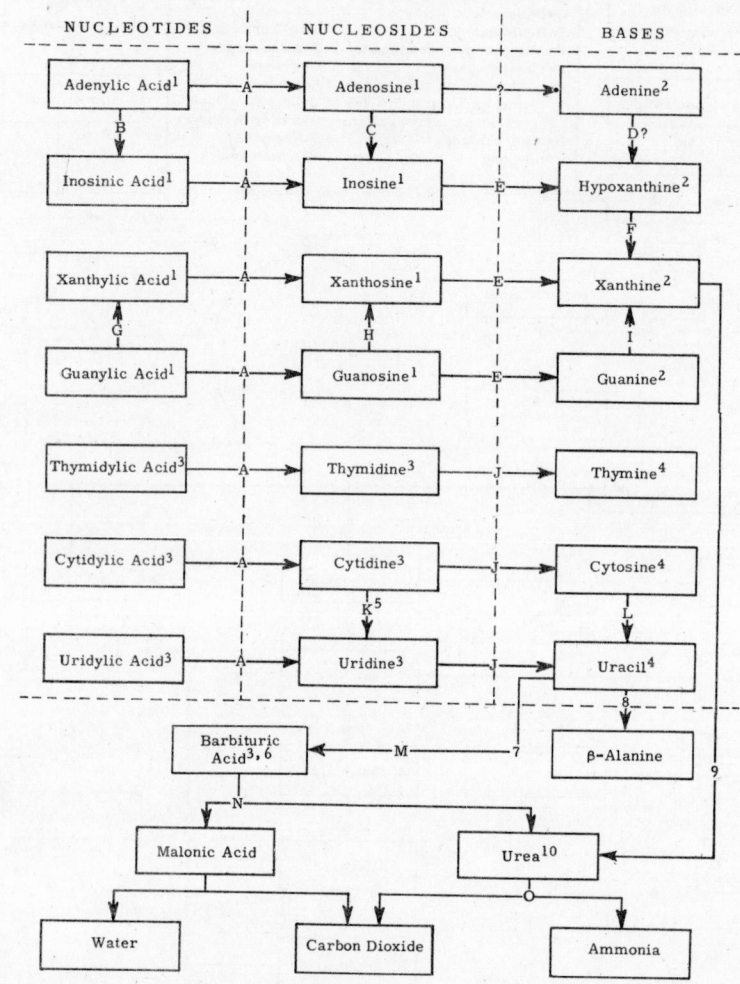

/1/ A purine derivative or contains purine ring.   /2/ A purine.   /3/ A pyrimidine derivative or contains pyrimidine ring.   /4/ A pyrimidine. /5/ Demonstrated in yeast and Escherichia coli.   /6/ Thymine yields 5-methyl barbituric acid.   /7/ Pathway demonstrated with Corynebacterium and Mycobacterium.   /8/ In animal tissues; methyl uracil (thymine) yields β-aminoisobutyric acid.   /9/ Via: uric acid, allantoic acid, and glyoxylic acid.   /10/ Urea is excreted as the end product of amino acid metabolism by mammals, and as an end product of purine and pyrimidine metabolism by most fishes, amphibia and fresh-water lamellibranches.

The Krebs Cycle (tricarboxylic acid cycle) is a major pathway for the final aerobic oxidation of carbohydrates, fats, and proteins. These three nutrients are channeled into the cycle via their two key metabolites, pyruvate and acetyl~CoA ("active acetate"). Each "revolution" of the cycle oxidizes acetate to CO_2 and H_2O. One mole (59 g) of acetate thus oxidized releases approximately 200 kilocalories of energy. A portion of the released energy (approximately 144 kilocalories) enters the phosphate pool as ATP. Twelve moles of ATP are formed from ADP and PO_4 (by energizing PO_4 to $\sim PO_4$). The remainder of the released energy appears as heat. Oxidation of 1 mole (87 g) of pyruvate, proceeding via acetyl~CoA, contributes a total of 14 moles of ATP to the energy pool.

A=Pyruvic decarboxylase; B=Malic enzyme; C=Transaminase; D=Condensing enzyme; E= Aconitase; F=Isocitric dehydrogenase; G=Oxalosuccinic carboxylase; H= α-Ketoglutaric dehydrogenase; I=Succinic dehydrogenase; J=Fumarase; K=Malic dehydrogenase; L=Oxalacetic decarboxylase.

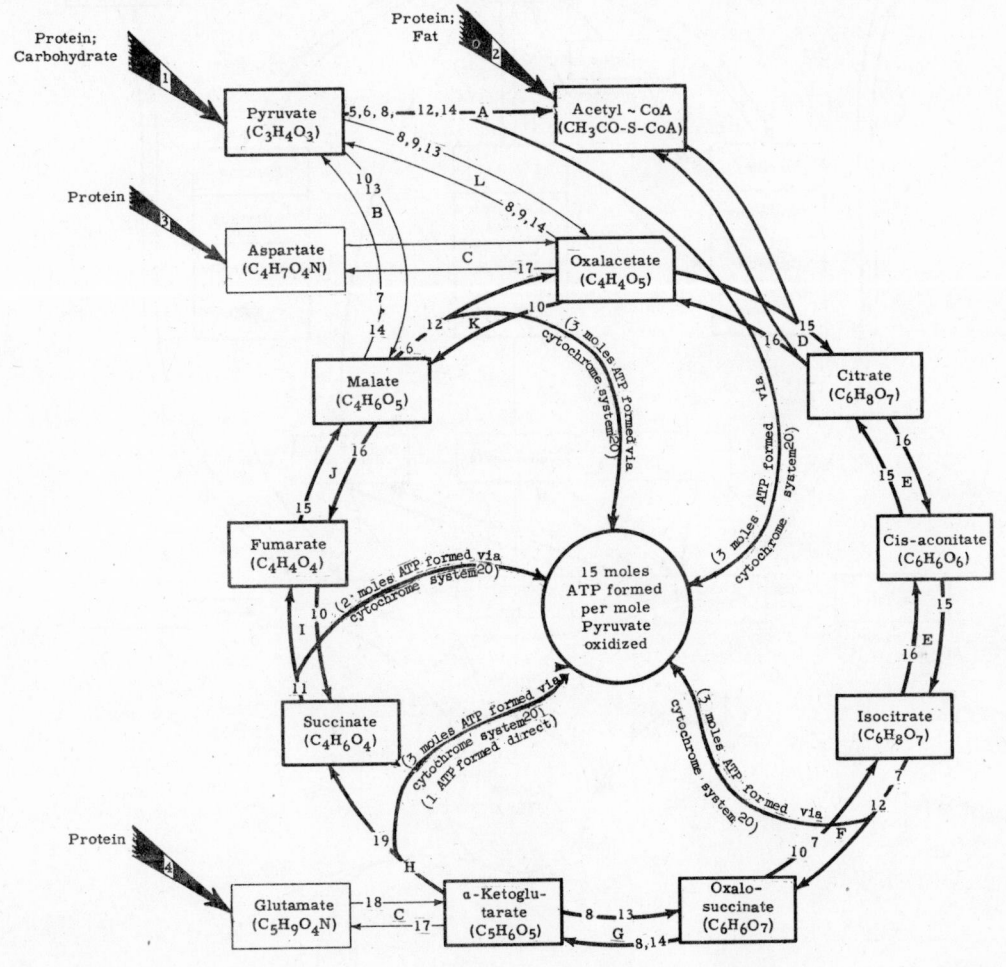

/1/ Glucogenic amino acid precursors for pyruvate are: alanine, glycine, serine, threonine, methionine, cysteine, valine. /2/ Ketogenic amino acid precursors for acetyl~CoA are: leucine, isoleucine, phenylalanine, tyrosine. /3/ Aspartic acid occurs as a component of protein. /4/ Glutamic acid occurs as a component of protein or may be formed from: arginine, proline, hydroxyproline, histidine, ornithine. /5/ Coenzyme-A (=ATP-pantoyl-β-alanyl-thioethanolamine) and α-lipoic acid required. /6/ In the oxidative direction, DPN (=diphosphopyridine nucleotide, a compound of nicotinamide, D-ribose, H_3PO_4 and adenine; also known as coenzyme I) acts as hydrogen acceptor; in the reverse direction $DPNH_2$ is hydrogen donor. /7/ In the oxidative direction, TPN (=triphosphopyridine nucleotide; coenzyme II) acts as hydrogen acceptor; in the reverse direction, $TPNH_2$ is hydrogen donor. /8/ DPT (=diphosphothiamine; thiamine pyrophosphate; cocarboxylase) required as coenzyme for the carboxylase (A); also Mg^{++} or Mn^{++}, is required as activator for the enzyme. /9/ Biotin required as coenzyme for decarboxylation. /10/ 2H enters into the reaction. /11/ 2H released and their electrons transferred to cytochrome. /12/ Hydrogen ions transferred to DPN (or, in the case of isocitrate → oxalsuccinate, to TPN) and pass in turn to flavoprotein, cytochrome-c, cytochrome oxidase, and finally to combination with molecular oxygen. For each H thus passed and finally oxidized, 1.5 moles of ATP are formed by the addition of energized phosphate ($\sim PO_4$) to ADP. /13/ CO_2 enters into the reaction. /14/ CO_2 released. /15/ H_2O enters into the reaction. /16/ H_2O released. /17/ NH_3 enters into the reaction by transamination. /18/ NH_3 transferred from glutamate by transamination, then enters into Krebs Cycle via α-ketoglutarate. /19/ Footnotes 5,6,8,12, 14 apply to this reaction. /20/ For details, see table on cytochrome system.

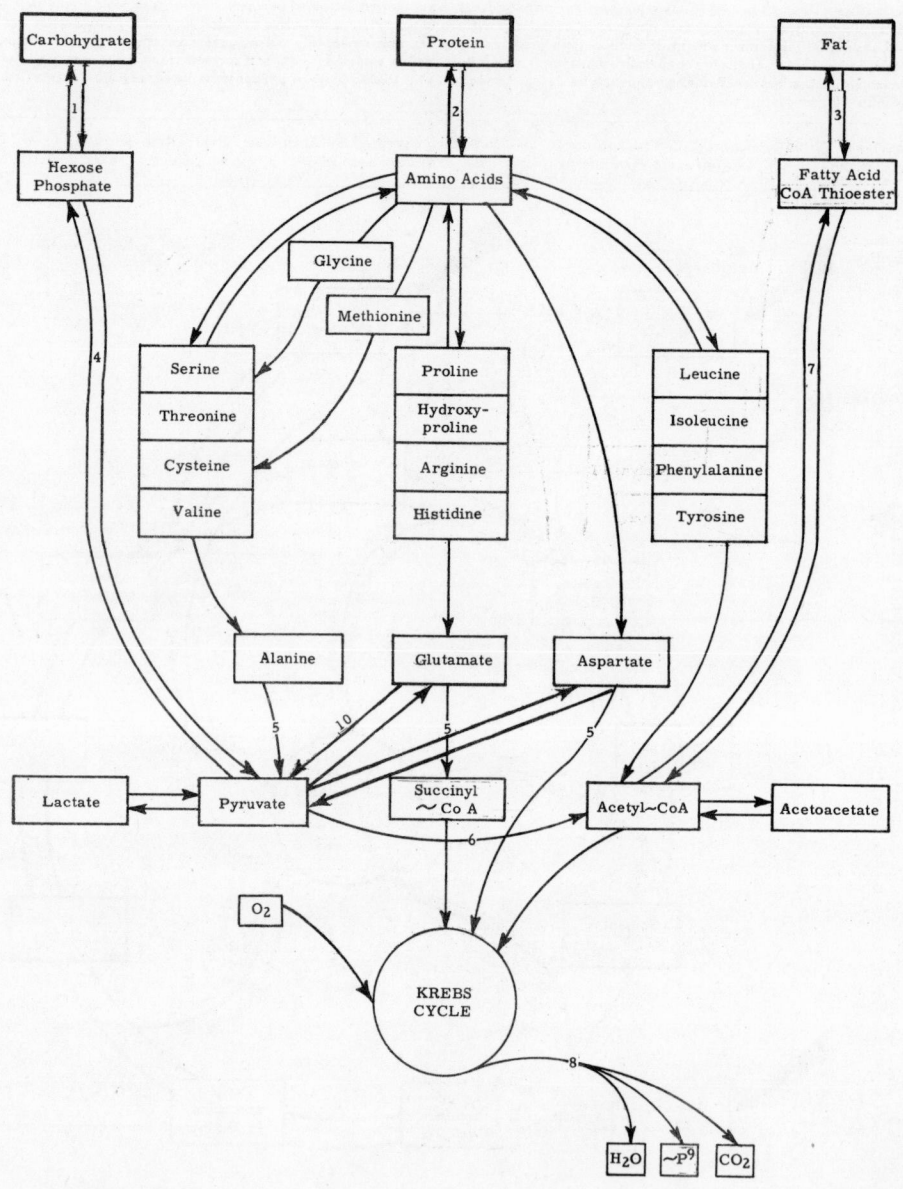

/1/ Phosphorylase and PO_4 phosphorylate hexose units in stored polysaccharides; hexokinase and ATP phosphorylate hexoses. /2/ Proteolysis by proteases in digestive tract or tissues. Synthesis by proteases of tissues. /3/ Lipase splits fat into fatty acids and glycerol; glycerol, via glycerol phosphate and dihydroxyacetone phosphate, enters the glycolytic cycle. Fatty acid then is acted upon by coenzyme A. /4/ Glycolysis. /5/ Oxidative deamination. /6/ Oxidative decarboxylation. /7/ β-oxidation. /8/ Chain of electron-transmitting enzymes. /9/ "High energy" phosphorus. /10/ Transamination.

The cytochromes (iron-containing compounds) in association with certain other compounds constitute the "Cytochrome System." The system operates as the final pathway by which an intermediate metabolite ("substrate"), under the influence of its specific dehydrogenase, releases hydrogen to the first member in a series of carriers for ultimate combination with oxygen to form water. Each step in the process involves both oxidation and reduction. The cytochrome system oxidizes the hydrogen of the substrate by removing electrons from it, thereby producing oxidized substrate and hydrogen ions, and the system itself is reduced in the process and is finally oxidized by molecular oxygen. For each gram of hydrogen thus passed and finally oxidized enough energy is produced to form 1.5 moles of ATP from ADP and PO$_4$.

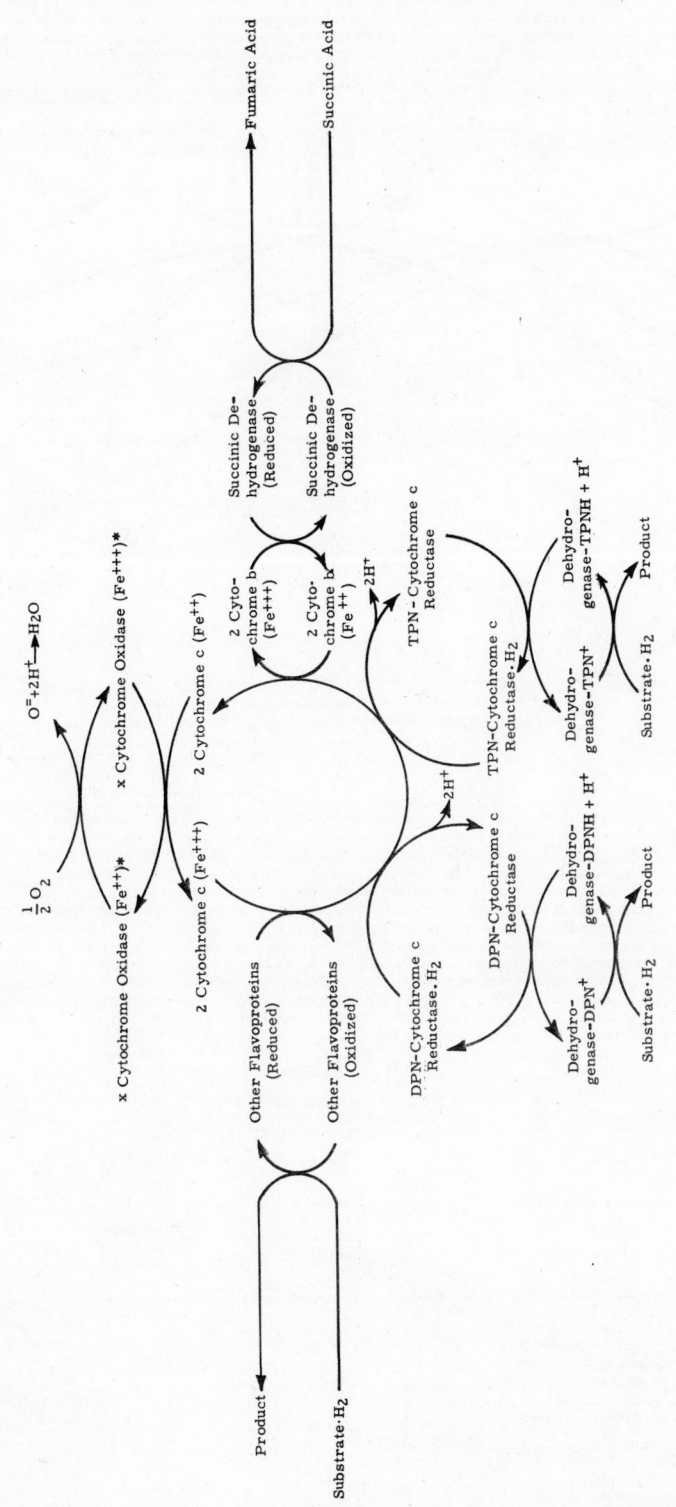

*Cytochrome a and cytochrome a$_3$ have not been proved to be separate enzymes. For the present, therefore, there is only one enzyme that acts between cytochrome c and molecular oxygen. This component is termed cytochrome oxidase.

219. PATHWAYS OF ENERGY METABOLISM: MUSCLE

Excitation of the muscle (cell) is accompanied by reversal of polarity of the cell membrane. The first identifiable metabolic event to follow is dephosphorylation of ATP. The breaking off of the terminal PO_4 of ATP is accompanied by release of energy previously stored in the molecule. The compound, minus one phosphate, is left as ADP. This compound can accept phosphate and again form ATP. If the presence of such acceptor is viewed as the stimulus to the subsequent steps in activity-metabolism, the presence of ADP causes progression of glucose-1-PO_4 to pyruvate (or to lactate if DPNH has accumulated as a result of O_2 inadequacy), and also brings about the progression of pyruvate to CO_2 and H_2O. In so doing, ADP is reconverted to ATP, (and other phosphate-acceptors that may be present are similarly rephosphorylated). The stimulus to extra release of energy from carbohydrate stores thus disappears, and the cell returns to its basal state of respiration and energy release.

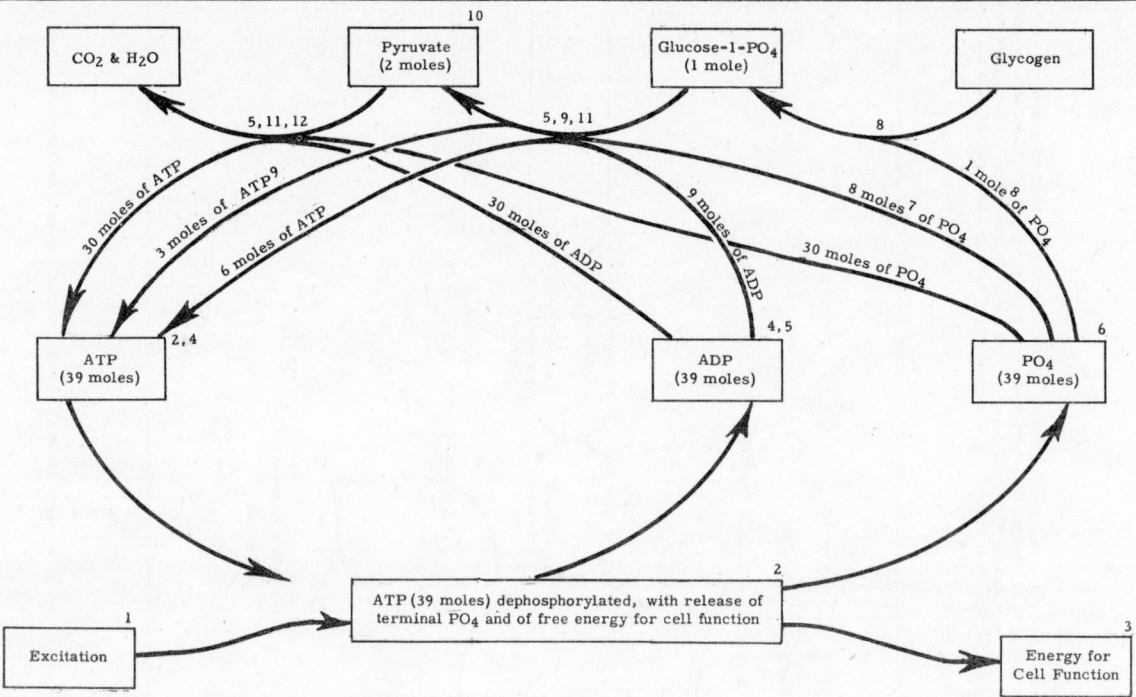

/1/ "When the stimulus is withdrawn, respiration continues at the elevated rate only until the organ is restored to its original state....With no compounds remaining in the unphosphorylated state, the respiration machinery stops with the various enzymes blocked in the acylated and/or phosphorylated states." /2/ The quantity of ATP assumed, 39 moles, is adjusted to the catabolism of 1 mole of glucose-1-PO_4 or 1 mole of 6-carbon unit, component of glycogen. /3/ Approximately 10 kilocalories (a compromise figure; values of 7-12 have been reported recently) of free energy per mole of ATP converted to ADP, or about 400 kilocalories for the quantities represented in the diagram. Energy used for muscle contraction, and for synthesis. /4/ Other high energy carriers than ATP (adenosine triphosphate) and other phosphate acceptors than ADP (adenosine diphosphate) may also function (e.g., creatine phosphate and creatine-- also phosphates of guanosine, cytidine and uridine). /5/ Rate of energy release from stored carbohydrate probably controlled by concentration of phosphate acceptors capable of forming high energy carriers (cf Fn 4). /6/ In inorganic phosphate pool. /7/ These 8 moles include 2 that combine with 2 moles of ᴅ-glyceraldehyde-3-phosphate (= "substrate phosphorylation") and are then transferred to ADP; and 6 that combine directly with ADP in association with the oxidation of hydrogen previously released by ᴅ-glyceraldehyde-3-phosphate to DPN (to form DPNH = "electron transport phosphorylation"). /8/ One PO_4 combines with one 6-carbon unit in glycogen to form glucose-1-PO_4, with no appreciable energy change. /9/ Not shown in diagram: One mole of ATP is required at an early step in the reaction glucose-1-$PO_4 \rightarrow$ pyruvate, and 4 moles of ATP are formed at later steps. The net gain is 3 moles of ATP. The 3 moles of PO_4 have come from the 1 mole combined into glucose-1-phosphate (cf Fn 8) and 2 of the 8 moles covered by Fn 7. /10/ Pyruvate is converted to lactate by reaction with DPNH, if the latter has accumulated, as in conditions of relative oxygen deficiency. /11/ Energy from carbohydrate metabolites is built into the ATP molecule. /12/ Via Krebs Cycle.

220. PATHWAYS OF IRON METABOLISM: MAMMALS
Adapted from Walker, Boyd and Asimov, "Biochemistry and Human Metabolism," Baltimore: Williams and Wilkins, 1952.

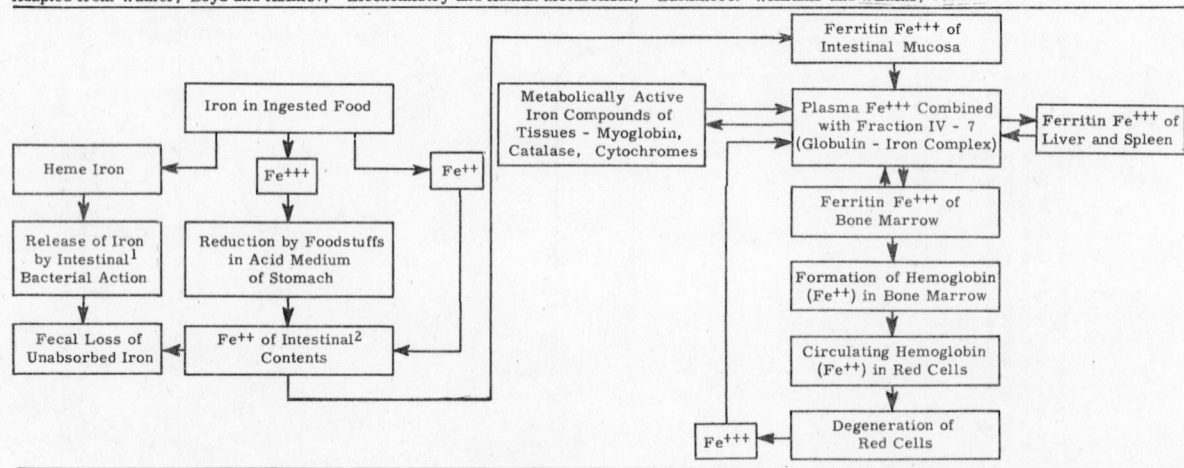

/1/ Large intestine. /2/ Small intestine.

221. PATHWAYS OF MINERAL METABOLISM: MAMMALS

The system of letters and numbers used in this table traces the course(s) of various ions through the diagram. The classifications as to extent of absorption are in general as follows: A, more than 70%; B, 5-70%; C, less than 5%. Underscoring indicates radioactive elements, or that data were obtained, at least in part, from studies using radioactive isotopes. Plus signs (+) indicate valence states to which the data apply. Observations were made on a wide variety of mammalian species. As far as possible, "Other Known Pathways" are listed in order of decreasing importance. Tissue predilections are also listed in this order. There are instances in which different isotopes of the same element show different predilections, but there is usually no difference in their absorption or route of excretion. In some cases an insufficient amount of the ion is absorbed from the alimentary tract to permit a study of its metabolism. In these cases the results of parenteral administration are shown, if available; in other instances less important alternatives to the primary oral pathways are shown. The term "Soft Tissues Generally" refers primarily to muscle, skin, and extracellular fluids.

Part I: PATHWAY DIAGRAM

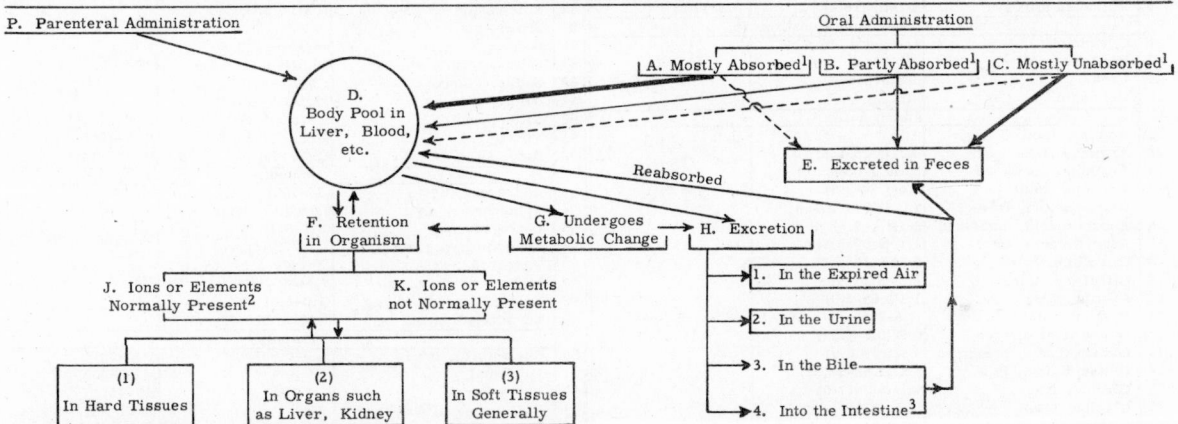

/1/ This classification is obviously rather arbitrary, since extent of absorption may depend on the amount offered; for example, the absorption of physiologically essential elements may be nearly complete when fed at or near the level of minimum requirement. It is assumed that the various ions are offered in the form of simple soluble compounds, or metallic oxides. /2/ This group includes some trace elements with no known function. /3/ Other than in the bile, or by route not definitely established.

Part II: INDIVIDUAL CATIONS

Information inadequate for classification, but probably poorly absorbed[1]: actinium, berkelium, californium, iridium, osmium, rare earth elements not mentioned below, rhodium, tantalum, and technetium.

	Element	Primary (Oral) Pathways[2]	Other Known Pathways		Element	Primary (Oral) Pathways[2]	Other Known Pathways
1	Aluminum	CE	PDH2, PDH3, PDFJ(2)	30	Niobium	CE	PDH2, PDFK(3)
2	Americium	CE	PDH4, PDFK(2,1), PDH2	31	Palladium	Probably CE[2]	PDH2, PDFK(2,1), PDH4
3	Antimony[+++]	BE, BDH2	PDFK(2,3), PDH4	32	Platinum	Probably CE[2]	PDH2, PDFK(2), PDH4
4	Arsenic[+++]	BE, BDH2	BDFK(2,3), BDH4	33	Plutonium	CE	PDFK(1,2), PDH4, PDH2
5	Barium	BE, BDH4	BDFK(1), BDH2	34	Polonium	CE	PDFK(2,1,3), PDH4, PDH2
6	Beryllium	CE	PDFK(3,2,1), PDH2, PDH4	35	Potassium	ADH2	ADFJ(3,2), ADH3, ADH4
7	Bismuth[+++]	CE	PDH2, PDFK(1,2,3), PDH4	36	Praesodymium	CE	PDFK(1,2), PDH3, PDH4
8	Cadmium	CE	PDFK(2), PDH4, PDH2	37	Promethium	CE	PDFK(1,2), PDH3, PDH4
9	Calcium	BE, BDFJ(1)	BDH3, BDH4, BDH2, BDFJ(3)	38	Protactinium	Probably CE[2]	PDFK(1)
10	Cerium	CE	PDH3, PDH4, PDFK(1,2)	39	Radium D	Probably BE, BDH2[2]	PDH2, PDH4, PDFK(1)
11	Cesium	ADH2	ADH3, ADH4, ADFJ(3)	40	Radium	BE, BDFK(1,2)	BDH4, BDH2
12	Cobalt[++]	BE, BDH2	BDH3, BDH4, BDFJ(2)	41	Rubidium	ADH2	ADFJ(3,2), ADH3
13	Copper[++]	BE, BDH2	BDH3, BDFJ(2)	42	Ruthenium	CE	PDFK(2)
14	Curium	Probably CE[2]	PDFK(1,2), PDH4, PDH2	43	Samarium	CE	PDFK(1,2), PDH3
15	Francium	Probably ADH2[2]	PDFK(2,3)	44	Scandium	Probably CE[2]	CDH2, CDFJ(1,3)
16	Gallium	CE	PDH2, PDFK(1,2), PDH4	45	Selenium[++++]	ADH2 ·	ADGH1, ADFK(2,3)
17	Germanium	ADH2	ADH4	46	Silver	CE	PDH3, PDFK(2,3), PDH2, CDGFK[4]
18	Gold[+++]	CE	PDFK(2), PDH2, PDH4				
19	Indium	ADH2		47	Sodium	ADH2	ADFJ(3,1,2), ADH3, ADH4
20	Iron[++]	CE	PDH4, PDFJ(2)	48	Strontium	BE, BDFK(1)	BDH2, BDH4
21	Lanthanum	CE	PDH2, PDH3, PDFK(2,1)	49	Tellurium[++++]	BE, BDGH2	BDGH3, BDGH1, BDGFK(2)
22	Lead[++]	BE, BDH3	PDFK(1,2), PDH2	50	Thallium[+]	ADH2	ADH4, ADFK(2,3)
23	Lithium	ADH2	ADH4, ADFJ(3,2)	51	Thulium	CE	PDFK(1,2), PDH2
24	Magnesium	BE, BDH2	BDH3, BDFJ(1,2,3)	52	Tin[++]	BE, BDH2	BDFJ(2,3), BDH4
25	Manganese[++]	CE	PDH3, PDH4, PDFJ(2,3)	53	Titanium	Probably CE[2]	CDFJ(2)
26	Mercury[++]	BE, BDH2	BDFK(2,3), BDH3, BDH4	54	Uranium[++++++]	BE, BDH2	BDFK(2,1)
27	Neodymium	Probably CE[2]	PDH4, PDFK(2,1)	55	Yttrium	CE	PDFK(1,2), PDH2, PDH4
28	Neptunium	CE	PDFK(1)	56	Zinc	CE	CDFJ(2,3), CDH3, CDH4, CDH2
29	Nickel[++]	BE, BDH2	BDH4, BDFJ(2)	57	Zirconium	CE	PDFK(1)

/1/ As would be judged from its position in the periodic table, or on solubility at neutral pH values. /2/ Cations absorbed orally may be assumed to follow the same pathways when given parenterally. /3/ Administered as a soluble complex. /4/ Skin.

Part III: INDIVIDUAL ANIONS

Information inadequate for classification: cyanate, ferricyanide, periodate.

	Element	Primary (Oral) Pathways[1]	Other Known Pathways		Element	Primary (Oral) Pathways[1]	Other Known Pathways
1	Bicarbonate	ADH1, ADH2, ADH3	ADH4, ADFJ(all tissues)	16	Nitrite	ADG(to nitrate)	
2	Borate	ADH2		17	Oxalate	ADH2	
3	Bromate	ADH2	ADG(to bromide)	18	Perchlorate	ADH2	
4	Bromide	ADH2	ADH3, ADH4, ADFK(3,1,2)	19	Permanganate	CE(reduced to MnO2)	
5	Chlorate	ADH2		20	Perrhenate	Probably CE[2]	PDH2, PDFK(2)
6	Chloride	ADH2	ADH3, ADH4, ADFJ(3,1,2)	21	Persulfate	ADG(to sulfate)	
7	Chromate	ADH2	ADH4, ADGH2, ADGH3, ADGFK(2)	22	Phosphate	BE, BDH2	BDFJ(1,2,3)BDH3, BDH4
8	Cyanide	ADH2	ADH1, ADG(to SCN⁻)	23	Silicate	BE, BDH2	BDFJ(2)
9	Ferrocyanide	ADH2		24	Sulfate	BE, BDH2	BDH3, BDH4
10	Fluoride	ADH2	ADFJ(1,3), ADH4	25	Sulfide	ADG(to sulfate)	ADH1
11	Hypophosphite	ADH2		26	Thiocyanate	ADH2	ADFK(3), ADH3, ADH4
12	Iodate	ADG(to iodide)		27	Thiosulfate	BE, BDG(to sulfate)	
13	Iodide	ADH2	ADFJ(3,2), ADH3	28	Tungstate	BE, BDH2	BDFK(1,2)
14	Molybdate	ADH2	ADH4, ADFJ(1,2)	29	Vanadate	ADH2	ADFJ(2), ADH4
15	Nitrate	ADH2	ADG, ADFK(3)				

/1/ Anions absorbed orally may be assumed to follow the same pathways when given parenterally. /2/ As would be judged from its position in the periodic table, or on solubility at neutral pH values.

Values, widely variable with changes in diet, are based on "normal" dietary intake, including approximately 10 grams of nitrogen per day. Values are per kilogram of body weight per day and are expressed as milligrams unless otherwise noted. Values in parentheses are ranges and conform with estimate "d" of the 95% range (cf Introduction).

#	Constituent	Excreted in Urine	Excreted in Feces
1	Water, total	17,000(7,800-27,500)	(910-1820)
2	Solids, total	860(780-1000)	394(140-560)
3	Nitrogen, total[1,2]	160(112-268)	24(11.4-36.0)
4	Protein nitrogen	(0.0046-0.018)	
5	Amino acid nitrogen	2.5(2.2-4.4)	
6	Ammonia nitrogen	9.2(4.0-18.2)	(0.36-1.2)
	Principal N-Containing Constituents		
7	Creatinine	15(12-25)	
8	Hippuric acid	8(1-12)	
9	Urea	300(215-500)	
10	Uric acid	9(5-12)	
	Amino Acids		
11	Alanine, total	0.55	
12	Arginine, free	0.31(0.15-0.5)	
13	Arginine, combined	0.1(0.0-0.2)	
14	Arginine, total	0.4(0.34-0.5)	3.8(2.9-5.0)
15	Aspartic acid, free	0.02(0.014-0.26)	
16	Aspartic acid, combined	2.3(1.2-3.7)	
17	Aspartic acid, total	2.32(0.37-3.7)	
18	Citrulline, free[3]	0.58(0.26-0.7)	
19	Citrulline, total	(0.345-0.79)	
20	Cystine, free	1.3(0.65-2.0)	
21	Cystine, total	(1.5-2.4)	
22	Glutamic acid, free	0.52(0.0-1.07)	
23	Glutamic acid, combined	4.5(1.0-10.0)	
24	Glutamic acid, total	5.27(1.58-11.55)	
25	Glycine, free	10.1(9.0-12.0)	
26	Glycine, total	(2.3-18.0)	
27	Histidine, free	2.7(0.94-4.8)	
28	Histidine, combined	0.6(0.07-1.8)	
29	Histidine, total	3.0(0.98-6.59)	1.7(1.4-2.1)
30	Hydroxyproline, total	0.02	
31	Isoleucine, free	0.085(0.03-0.3)	
32	Isoleucine, combined	0.2(0.06-0.4)	
33	Isoleucine, total	0.3(0.11-0.6)	4.3(3.3-5.5)
34	Leucine, free	0.14(0.05-0.25)	
35	Leucine, combined	0.2(0.05-0.4)	
36	Leucine, total	0.32(0.20-0.52)	5.6(4.3-6.9)
37	Lysine, free	0.5(0.25-1.13)	
38	Lysine, combined	0.6(0.2-1.1)	
39	Lysine, total	1.04(0.48-2.0)	5.7(4.5-6.9)
40	Methionine, free	0.11(0.05-0.18)	
41	Methionine, combined	0.03	
42	Methionine, total	0.14(0.12-0.17)	
43	Ornithine, free[3]	0.15	
44	Phenylalanine, free	0.23(0.1-0.43)	
45	Phenylalanine, combined	0.1(0.04-0.2)	
46	Phenylalanine, total	0.33(0.21-0.6)	
47	Proline, free	0.12(0.05-0.21)	
48	Proline, combined	0.5(0.3-0.8)	
49	Proline, total	0.61(0.33-0.9)	
50	Serine, free	0.4(0.21-0.52)	
51	Serine, combined	0.25(0.0-0.5)	
52	Serine, total	0.65(0.35-1.4)	
53	Threonine, free	0.37(0.17-0.62)	
54	Threonine, combined	0.4(0.3-0.8)	
55	Threonine, total	0.77(0.36-1.2)	4.0(3.3-5.2)
56	Tryptophan, free	0.37(0.12-0.7)	
57	Tryptophan, combined	0.3(0.009-0.4)	
58	Tryptophan, total	0.7(0.23-1.3)	
59	Tyrosine, free	0.3(0.17-0.55)	
60	Tyrosine, combined	0.5(0.08-0.9)	
61	Tyrosine, total	0.79(0.35-1.45)	
62	Valine, free	0.065(0.04-0.125)	
63	Valine, combined	0.2(0.09-0.4)	
64	Valine, total	0.3(0.21-0.45)	4.6(3.6-6.2)
	Electrolytes and Minor Minerals		
65	Aluminum, μg	(0.7-1.6)	0.6
66	Arsenic, μg	0.46(0.0-1.15)	33(1-116)
67	Bromine, μg	(12-110)	
68	Calcium, μg	2900(1100-4910)	7490(5,000-10,000)
69	Chloride	115(84-193)	(0.21-0.5)
70	Cobalt, μg	0.07(0.05-0.12)	0.007(0.002-0.02)
71	Copper, μg	2.38(0.0-7.52)	27(23-37)
72	Fluoride, μg	(6.7-100)[4]	
73	Iodide, μg	1.4(0.2-2.13)	
74	Iron, μg	0.7(0.7-1.4)	120(65-208)
75	Lead, μg	0.5(0.06-2.1)	4.2(2.2-19.8)
76	Magnesium, μg	1850(950-4500)	2500(1510-3185)
77	Manganese, μg	(0.095-1.4)	(18-120)
78	Mercury, μg	(0.007-0.01)	0.14
79	Nickel, μg	2.1(2.0-4.0)	(1.2-2.5)

#	Constituent	Excreted in Urine	Excreted in Feces
	Electrolytes and Minor Minerals (concluded)		
80	Nitrates, μg	7140	
81	Phosphorus	15(10-19)	9.86(7.1-20)
82	Potassium	34(14-46)	6.7
83	Selenium, μg	1.0(0.0-3.3)	
84	Silicon, μg	108(14-200)	
85	Silver, μg		0.8
86	Sodium	46(38-91)	1.7
87	Sulfur, total	16.5(4-40)	2.0
88	Sulfur, ethereal	1.0(0.6-4.3)	
89	Sulfur, inorganic	12.5(3.5-18.25)	
90	Sulfur, neutral	1.9(1.0-3.0)	
91	Tin, μg	(0.13-0.31)	(170-450)
92	Zinc, μg	18(11-33)	100(58-144)
	Hormones		
93	Androgens, μg	(30-100)	
94	Epinephrine, μg	0.16(0.07-0.31)	
95	Estrogens, μg	(0.1-0.5)	
96	Formaldehydogenic steroids, μg	(3-140)	
97	17-Ketosteroids, μg	♂ 160, ♀ 100	
98	Oxycorticosteroids, μg	(1.0-6.0)	
99	Noradrenaline, μg	0.41(0.18-0.9)	
	Lipids		
100	Cholesterol, total	(0.0-0.007)	8(10-20)[5]
101	Fat, total		56(30-100)
102	Fat, neutral		(10-45)
103	Fat, unsaponifiable		33(22-38)[6]
104	Fatty acids, total		30(4-64)
105	Fatty acids, free		16(4-38)
106	Soaps		53(40-66)[6]
	Organic Acids		
107	Citric acid	(3-17)	
108	Creatine[7]	2.9(1.1-3.86)	
109	Guanidoacetic acid	(0.23-0.51)	
110	Formic acid	(0.42-2.0)	
111	Indoleacetic acid	(0.03-0.06)	
112	Lactic acid	40	
113	Oxalic acid	0.285(0.23-0.5)	
114	Phenols	4.0(0.19-6.6)	(0.0-3.0)
	Pigments		
115	Bilirubin, μg	70	
116	Coproporphyrin I and III, μg	(0.24-1.4)	
117	Porphyrins, μg	(0.0-0.4)	
118	Urobilin, μg	(7-20)	
119	Urobilinogen, μg	(0.6-3.0)	2.0(0.57-4.0)
	Vitamins		
120	Vitamins A, D, K, μg	(0-trace)	
121	Ascorbic acid, μg	380(130-790)	70(60-70)
122	Biotin, μg	0.4(0.33-0.75)	1.9(0.63-6.64)
123	Carotenes, μg		(20-600)[8]
124	Choline, μg	90(80-130)	
125	Cobalamin, μg	0.0004(0.00023-0.00079)	
126	Vitamin E, μg		308(226-391)
127	Folic acid group, μg	0.2(0.03-0.3)	4.3(1.8-7.7)
128	Inositol, μg	170(170-220)	
129	Nicotinic acid, μg	(11-105)	52(12-124)
130	N-methyl nicotinamide, μg	130(73-400)	
131	Pantothenic acid, μg	44(20-100)	31.4(3.85-63.4)
132	Para-aminobenzoic acid, μg	2.11(2.0-3.0)	3.5(1.01-8.2)
133	Pyridoxal, μg	3.0(0.7-5.4)	
134	Pyridoxamine, μg	1.6(0.3-2.1)	
135	4-Pyridoxic acid, μg	51(9-160)	
136	Riboflavin, μg	14.3(0.2-22.5)	14.7(8.0-23.0)
137	Thiamine, μg	2.6(0.43-5.6)	7.8(0.67-18.0)
138	Trigonelline, μg	(30-300)	
	Miscellaneous Compounds		
139	Acetone bodies	0.285(0.03-0.7)	
140	Allantoin	0.27(0.18-0.36)	
141	Histamine	(0.2-1.0)	
142	Hydroxytyramine, μg	(1.4-2.8)	
143	Imidazole derivatives	(1.35-9.4)	(0.0-0.2)
144	Indican	0.14(0.06-0.45)	
145	Methionine sulfoxide	(0.0-0.31)	
146	Purine bases	0.41(0.18-0.92)	(2-3)
147	Reducing substances	(7-20)	
148	Sugars, as glucose	1.4	
149	Taurine	(0.105-0.2)	
150	Volatile acids, total, ml of 0.1 N		2.66(1.61-4.45)

/1/ Present in nitrogen compounds, not as free nitrogen. /2/ Calculated from nitrogen of principal N-containing constituents, plus ammonia- and amino acid nitrogen. /3/ Identity not proven. /4/ Including regions in Texas where dental fluorosis is endemic. /5/ Age 10 mo. /6/ Age 8-12 yr. /7/ Not normally present in urine of adult males. /8/ Carotene and xanthophyll; 8-100 μg/kg body wt/da for xanthophyll alone.

223. EXCRETED NITROGEN, PARTITION: ANIMALS

Values are grams of nitrogen per 100 grams of total nitrogen excreted. Values in parentheses are ranges and conform to estimate "d" of the 95% range (cf Introduction).

#	Species	Allantoin-N	Amino Acid-N	Ammonia-N	Creatine-N	Creatinine-N	Creatine+Creatinine (Combined)	Purine-N[1]	Urea-N	Uric Acid-N	Other Specified-N	Unidentified
	Vertebrata											
	Mammalia											
1	Man (Homo sapiens)			4.8(3.2-5)		3.6	(3.1-4.9)		87(85-90)	0.65(0.5-1.5)		4(2-6.4)
2	Alpaca (Auchenia vicunna)		0.96	4.5	2.7	4.6			60	0.3		28
3	Bat (Xantharpyia spp)			6		8.5	8.5		63	0.87		20.3
4	Camel (Camelus dromedarius)		(0.2-1.7)	15(12-19) (3.9-8.1)	3.8	14	(17.6-18.1)		44(33-56)	0.3		16.2(13-20)
5	Cat (Felis catus)			3.5(3.5-28)		(0.57-1.9)	(0.9-10)		91(46-92)	(0.2-0.22)		5(1.4-22)
6	Dog (Canis familiaris)	1.75	0.95	4.0		0.8	0.88		89	0.06		2.8
7	Hyena (Hyaena spp)	0.52	0.86	3.2		0.59	1.32	0.23	87	0.06		
8	Leopard (Panthera pardus)	21.4	1.4(1.3-1.4)	2.0(1.8-2.2)		0.88	(9.1-11.7)	0.25	64(61-68)	0.8		
9	Llama (Lama glama)			2.2		8.3	(9.1-31)		(61-90)			
10	Seal (Phoca vitulina)		0.95	(2-7.5)						(6-11)		3.4
11	Tiger (Panthera tigris)	1.3		3.3	0.43	1.29	1.72	0.18	89	0.06		2.6
12	Weasel (Mustela spp)	0.48	0.89		1.37	0.3	1.67	0.58	91	0.16		(2.7-3.1)
13	Whale (Balaenoptera physalus)			(1.9-3.6)		Trace	(0.3-3.8)		(85-93)	3(1.6-4.4)		
	Aves											
14	Duck (Anas spp)			3.2					4.2	72		20.7
15	Fowl (Gallus domesticus)		6	1.5(1.5-17)		8	(7.4-9.1)	8	0.9(0.9-10)	70(63-87)		28
16	Goose (Anser spp)			13.5						80		6.5
17	Swan (Cygnus spp)			13.8					2.6	69		13.9
	Reptilia											
18	Alligator (Alligator spp)	2.7		(37-81)					(1.3-17)	(7-19.8)		(0.2-23)
19	Lizard (Chalcides ocellatus)		2.3	8.7						93		
20	Python (Python spp)		1.1	5.7						89		
21	Snake (Eryx thebaicus)		(5.4-18.4)	(29-51)	2.6		(5.2-11.5)			63	0.95[2]	29.1
22	Tortoise (Chelonia mydas)	(4.4-25)				0.9	0.23	0.3	(0-12)	(1.4-6.3)	8-23[2]	(2.4-22)
	Amphibia											
23	Frog (Rana catesbiana)			(3-38)					(62-88)	(Trace-0.4)		7.5
	Pisces											
24	Carp (Cyprinus spp)		2.6	(75-77)					(12.5-14.5)	(1.7-2.4)		(5.5-12.5)
25	Catfish (Ictalurus furcatus)		20	20			7.9		24.6			16.9
26	Cod (Gadus callarias)						(53-56)		(6.5-11.2)			(15.2-19)
27	Flounder (Pseudopleuronectes americanus)		14.8(14.8-21.4)	2.2(1.8-2.6)		20.5	(15-26)		17.3(13-21)	1.2(1.2-1.3)	0.4-1[3]	50(48-51)
28	Goosefish (Lophius piscatorius)		8.9(8.2-9.7)	0.6(0.3-1.3)		2.6	(24-64)		0.9(0.1-2.7)	0.2(0.2-0.4)	37[3]	(28-63)
29	Lungfish (Protopterus aethiopicus)		8.4(5.3-15)	41		6.28			18.5	0.8		
30	Sheepshead (Archosargus probatocephalus)		(15-19.9)	(8.4-9.6)	0.54		(15.1-15.5)		(22.9-23)	(6.4-8.4)		(25-26)
	Invertebrata											
	Arthropoda											
31	Amphipod (Gammarus locusta)		(5-8)	(74-91)				(2-4)	(Trace-3)	Trace		(3-22)
32	Blowfly, larva (Calliphora spp)			Trace	Trace				Trace			11.5(4-11.5)
33	Crab (Cancer pagurus)		20	43				10	12.9	2.8		14.7
34	Crayfish (Astacus fluviatilis)		10(5-12)	60(53-65)				4.4(3.2-6.4)	11(10-12)	0.8(0.3-1.2)		
35	Grasshopper (Melanoplus spp)		17.7	3.3				(14-38)	8.7	70		(8-25)
36	Isopod (Oniscus asellus)		(0-12)	(44-50)						(4-5)		
37	Moth (Tinea pellionella)		10	10.2					17.6	47.3		
	Mollusca											
38	Clam (Mya arenaria)		18	21.5				5	4.5	Trace		51
39	Mussel (Mytilus edulis)		24(17-36)	7.4(Trace-11.4)				9.7(Trace-16)	Trace	Trace		58(37-79)
40	Octopus (Octopus vulgaris)		20	50					15	1		14
41	Oyster (Gryphoea angulata)		13.2	7.2				29	3.2	1.6		75
42	Periwinkle (Littorina littorea)		7	12.6				(15-167)	40	4.6		11
43	Sea hare (Aplysia limacina)		13	34(30-37)				16.6(3-20)	8.7(7.4-10)	4.6(Trace-9.2)		(24-45)
44	Slug (Arion empiricorum)		18(11.3-18)	9.8(7.1-9.8)				19	2.8	3.3(1.4-10.3)		(52-80)
45	Snail (Helix pomatia)		7	22.2				27.2	16.8	7		35
46	Snail, pond (Limnaea stagnalis)		20	9.0						4.0		31.6
	Annelida											
47	Earthworm (Lumbricus terrestris)		(12.2-15)	(20.4-47)				17.5	(10.0-38.1)			10
48	Leech (Hirudo medicinalis)		4.5	78				4.3	3.8	1.1		9.1
49	Sea-mouse (Aphrodite aculeata)		35	13.3					11.1			39
	Echinodermata											
50	Sea-cucumber (Holothuria tubulosa)		18(18-18.7)	39(39-41)				12(12-12.5)	6(6-6.25)			25(18-25)

/1/ Minus uric acid-N. /2/ Hippuric acid-N. /3/ Trimethylamine oxide-N.

Many of the "reactions" diagrammed probably consist in reality of two or more sequential enzymatic conversions, the resolution of which awaits future developments.

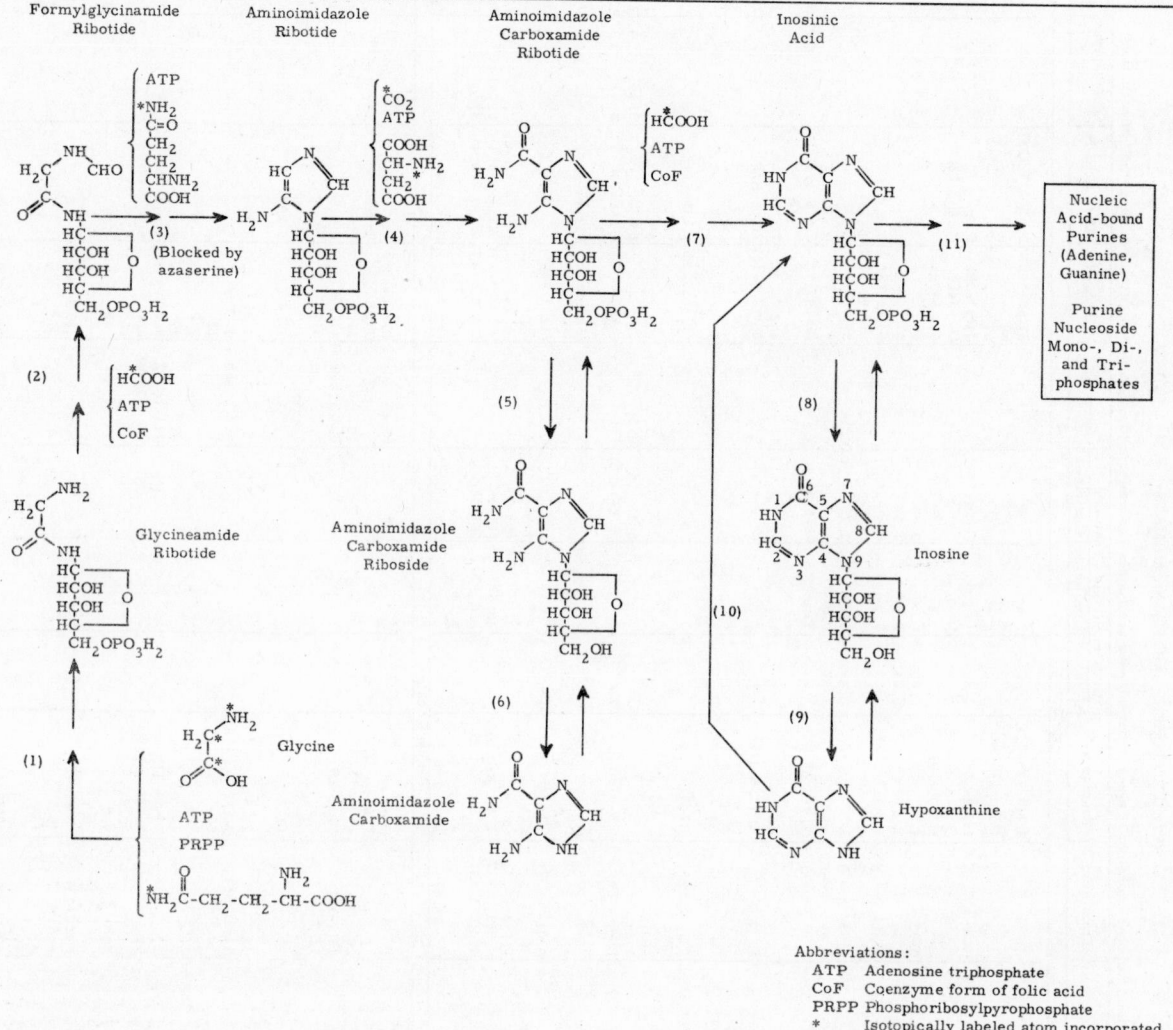

Abbreviations:
ATP   Adenosine triphosphate
CoF   Coenzyme form of folic acid
PRPP   Phosphoribosylpyrophosphate
*   Isotopically labeled atom incorporated
        into next product

/1/ Simple precursors utilizable in purine biosynthesis in several organisms include ammonium salts, glycine, which contributes purine carbons 4 and 5 and nitrogen 7, and glutamine, the amide nitrogen of which contributes purine nitrogen 9. ATP and PRPP (5'-phosphoribosylpyrophosphate) also are involved in the enzymatic synthesis of the intermediate glycinamide ribotide. /2/ Glycinamide ribotide is formylated in the presence of citrovorum factor or related derivatives to yield α-N-formylglycinamide ribotide. Labeled formate incorporated in this reaction ultimately contributes purine carbon 8. /3/ An aminoimidazoleriboside derivative accumulates in cultures of a purineless Escherichia coli mutant. In the presence of ATP and glutamine, the amide nitrogen of which contributes purine nitrogen 3, formylglycinamide ribotide is converted enzymatically to aminoimidazole ribotide; the conversion is blocked by azaserine, which therefore enhances accumulation of formylglycinamide ribotide and its precursor. Formylglycinamidine ribotide is reported to be an intermediate in aminoimidazole ribotide formation in pigeon liver preparations. /4, 5, 6/ In de novo purine biosynthesis from simple precursors, labeled CO_2 contributes carbon 6. Aspartic acid (the nitrogen of which contributes the nitrogen 1 of purines), ATP, and CO_2 are required in the conversion of aminoimidazole ribotide to aminoimidazole carboxamide ribotide. Accumulation of aminoimidazolecarboxamide and its riboside and ribotide occurs in sulfa-inhibited E. coli cultures; accumulation of the carboxamide has been studied also in purineless E. coli mutant cultures. Aminoimidazolecarboxamide can be utilized as a purine precursor by several organisms. Enzymatic interconversions of the free base, riboside, and ribotide forms have been reported, including direct conversion of the free base to the ribotide in the presence of PRPP. /7/ The initial purine compound produced in de novo biosynthesis is inosinic acid. Formate, shown in early work to contribute purine carbon 2, reacts with aminoimidazolecarboxamide ribotide to form inosinic acid, in a conversion involving the citrovorum factor or other activated derivatives of reduced folic acid which may be formed enzymatically in the presence of ATP. Copper is an additional cofactor in the exchange of formate with inosinic acid. /8, 9, 10/ Inosine and hypoxanthine arise secondarily via breakdown of inosinic acid; enzymatic interconversions of these metabolites occur, as well as direct conversion of hypoxanthine to inosinic acid in the presence of ribose-5-phosphate. /11/ The conversion of inosinic acid to other purine compounds (adenine, guanine) may involve as intermediates derivatives such as adenylosuccinic acid. Little is known of the mechanisms of polymerization of nucleotides into nucleic acids; however, a recent report indicates there may be involved the formation of long-chain polynucleotides by linking nucleoside diphosphates together by means of a phosphorylase type of reaction with the liberation of inorganic phosphate. Mono-, di-, and triphosphates of the purines as well as of the pyrimidines have been found to occur free in tissues, and considered as possible precursors in nucleic acid polymerization.

Many of the "reactions" diagrammed probably consist in reality of two or more sequential enzymatic conversions.

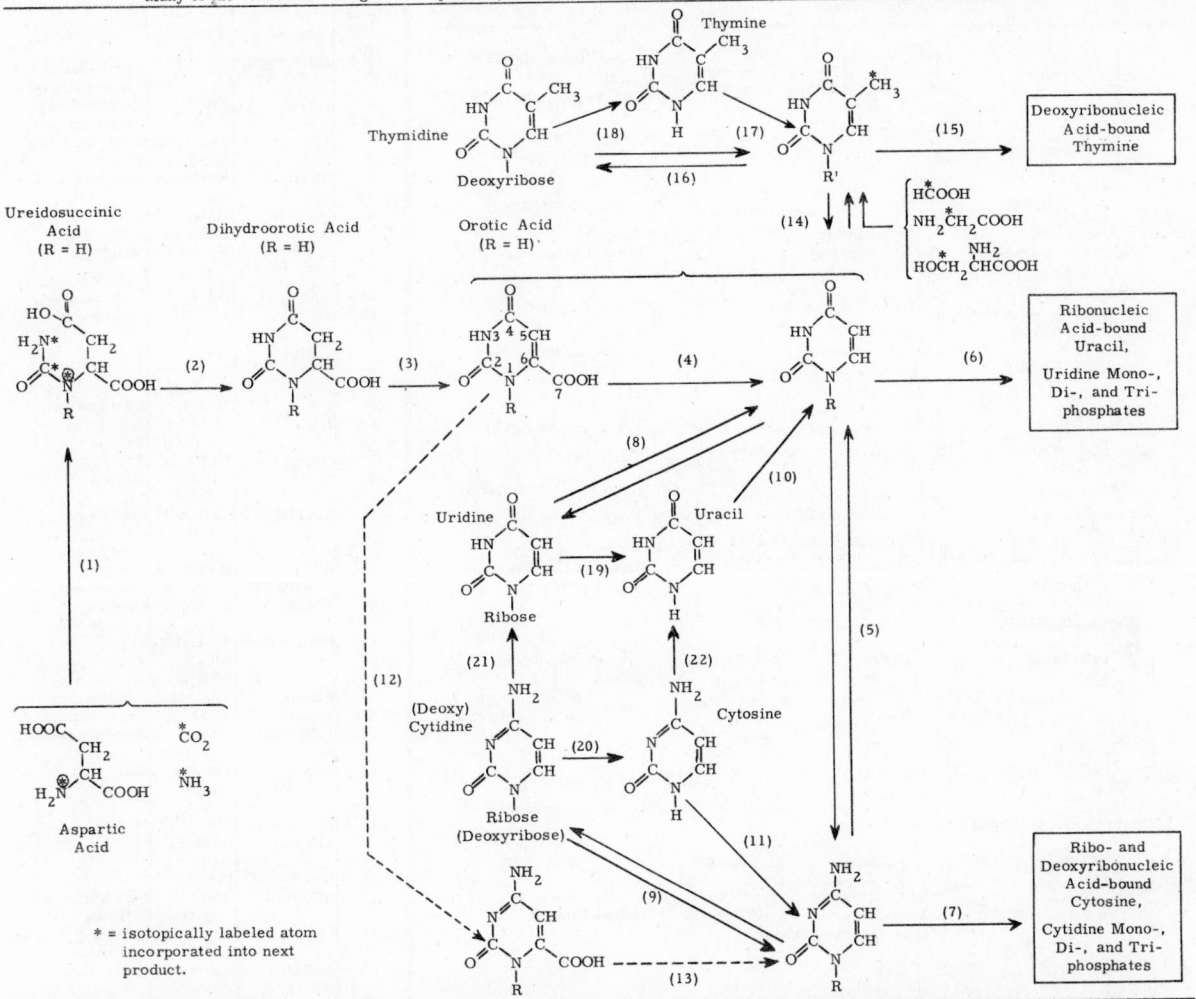

/1/ Aspartic acid contributes preferentially nitrogen 1, ⊕ and less effectively N-3, (ammonium-N contributes preferentially N-3) as well as carbons 4, 5, 6, and 7 to orotic acid in rat liver slices; it contributes the imido-N of ureidosuccinic acid in rat liver mitochondria, and has been shown to be involved in pyrimidine biosynthesis in lactobacilli. Labeled ammonium-N enters nucleic acid cytosine and thymine of pigeons, and enters combined pyrimidines in rats; it is an effective precursor of orotic acid N-1 and N-3 (equally) in rat liver, and of uracil N-1 in rat liver. Labeled ammonium-N contributes the carbamino-N of ureidosuccinic acid in rat liver mitochondria, in a reaction dependent upon ATP, aspartate, and carbamylglutamate. The carbamylation of aspartic acid may be closely analogous to that of ornithine. Labeled bicarbonate, or carboxyl of acetate, enters position 2 of uracil in rats, and of orotic acid in rat liver slices. Labeled CO_2 is fixed into nucleic acid pyrimidines of certain microorganisms. Labeled formate-C does not extensively enter nucleic acid uracil in rats, nor in yeast; the carbons of glycine are not extensively incorporated into the pyrimidine bases of rats. /2,3/ Ureidosuccinic acid replaces orotic acid for Lactobacillus bulgaricus 09, which utilizes no other simple pyrimidine derivatives except as more recently reported, uridine-5'-phosphate and dihydroorotic acid. Ureidosuccinic acid is utilized for orotic acid synthesis in rat liver; it is converted to orotic acid through dihydroorotic acid by certain bacteria. The suggestion has been made that conjugation, such as ribosidation, of an acyclic pyrimidine precursor precedes ring closure and decarboxylation; more recently the free compounds (R=H in diagram) have been suggested as the true intermediates in orotic acid biogenesis. /4/ Orotic acid is utilized by a pyrimidineless Neurospora mutant and by L. bulgaricus 09 (see above). Orotic acid labeled with N^{15} or C^{14} enters the uridine and cytidine components of liver polynucleotides in rats. Orotic acid-6C^{14} enters uracil of yeast. /5,6,7/ Presumably a conjugated form of uracil is aminated to form a cytosine derivative; such interconversion may take place in the polynucleotide stage. The stage at which pentose is replaced by deoxyribose is not definitely known; labeled C-2 of uracil deoxyriboside incubated with tissue suspensions was incorporated only into DNA thymidine, and no other DNA or RNA component. Little is known of the mechanisms of polymerization of nucleotides into nucleic acids. Mono-, di-, and triphosphates of the pyrimidine ribonucleosides have been found to occur free in tissues, and considered as possible precursors in nucleic acid polymerization; uridine-5'-phosphate is formed from orotic acid by pigeon liver in the presence of 5-phosphoribosylpyrophosphate. /8,9/ N^{15}-Labeled cytidine, and uridine (with much more isotope dilution), are incorporated by rats into nucleic acids; deoxycytidine is utilized for thymine and cytosine synthesis. /10,11/ Certain pyrimidineless Neurospora mutants utilize uridine or cytidine, or the corresponding free pyrimidines much less effectively. Cytidine and uridine may not be intermediates in uracil utilization in a Neurospora strain. Many organisms utilize uracil, cytosine, and their conjugated derivatives interchangeably as growth factors; however, for other microorganisms a specific pyrimidine requirement, e.g. for uracil or uridine, cannot be replaced by other pyrimidines. Although orotic acid (see above) is utilized by rats in nucleic acid formation, neither uracil nor cytosine is so utilized. /12,13/ It has been suggested that orotic acid after amination may be converted to cytidine and the latter deaminated to uridine. /14,15/ The stage of pyrimidine synthesis at which the methyl group is introduced to form thymine derivatives is not definitely known. 5-Nitrouracil competitively inhibits uracil utilization for the formation of a product replaceable by thymine. Uracil is converted to thymine by certain microorganisms. Labeled formate-C, alpha-C of glycine, or beta-C of serine provides the 5-methyl-C of deoxyribonucleic acid thymine in rats. /16,17/ Some organisms, e.g. Leuconostoc mesenteroides, utilize thymine and uracil interchangeably. Thymine is not utilized by rats in nucleic acid formation. Thymidine but not thymine in certain organisms prevents the toxicity of folic acid antagonists of sulfonamides; thymidine is utilized for synthesis of DNA-thymine in rats. In other organisms thymidine and thymine function interchangeably. Lactobacillus bifidus utilizes thymidine, thymidylic acid or certain other pyrimidine derivatives for growth. /18,19,20/ Nucleosidases for the pyrimidines have been reported. /21,22/ Enzyme preparations and other biological systems have been reported which deaminate cytosine. An Escherichia coli enzyme preparation specifically deaminates cytidine or cytosine deoxyriboside.

Tryptophan (TRYP)[3] — CH_2CHNH_2COOH (indole)
Indole(IND)
Intermediate(s)(I-7)
Intermediate(I-1)[3]
Anthranilic acid(AN) — $COOH$, NH_2
Formyl anthranilic acid (FAN) — $COOH$, $NHCHO$
Formyl kynurenine(FK)[4] — $COCH_2CHNH_2COOH$, NH_2
Kynurenic acid(KIC) — OH, N, $COOH$
2-Amino benzoyl pyruvic acid(ABPV) — $COCH_2COCOOH$, NH_2
Kynurenine(K)[6] — $COCH_2CHNH_2COOH$, NH_2
Xanthurenic acid (XIC) — OH, N, $COOH$, OH
2-Amino-3-hydroxybenzoyl pyruvic acid (AHBPV) — $COCH_2COCOOH$, NH_2, OH
Hydroxykynurenine(HK)[9] — $COCH_2CHNH_2COOH$, NH_2, OH
Hydroxyanthranilic acid phosphate (HANP) — $COOH$, NH_2, OPO_3H_2
Hydroxy-kynurenine phosphate (HKP) — $COCH_2CHNH_2COOH$, NH_2, OPO_3H_2
3-Hydroxyanthranilic acid (HAN)[11] — $COOH$, NH_2, OH
(I-3), (I-2), H_2(I-6), Nicotinic acid (NIC) — $COOH$, N
(I-4), (I-5), Quinolinic acid(Q)[21], Nicotinamide(N) — $CONH_2$, N
(Postulated intermediates reaction 6)
Nicotinuric acid(NICGL) — $CONHCH_2COOH$, N
N'Methyl-6-pyridone-3-carboxylamide — $O=N^+$-CH_3 (NMENPO), $CONH_2$
N'Methylnicotinamide (NMEN) — $CONH_2$, N^+-CH_3
DPN, TPN
Dinicotinyl ornithine(DNICOR) — $CONH(CH_2)_3CHNHCO$ $COOH$, N
Trigonelline(TRIG) — $COOH$, N^+-CH_3

Reaction No.	Reactants	Products	Enzyme
1	$TRYP+H_2O_2$	I-1+?	TRYP-peroxidase oxidase
2	$I-1+O_2$	FK	TRYP-peroxidase oxidase
3	$FK+H_2O$	K+HCOOH	K-formamidase
4	K+?	HK+?	?
5	$HK+H_2O$	HAN+ALA	Kynureninase
4a	K+?	HKP+?	?
5a	HKP+?	HANP+?	?
5b	AN+?	HANP+?	?
6	$HAN+\frac{3}{2}O_2$	$NIC+H_2O+CO_2$	Many?
6a	$HAN+\frac{1}{2}O_2$	$I-2+H_2O$	HAN-oxidase
6b	$I-2+H_2O$	$I-3+NH_3$	Spontaneous
6c	I-2+2(H)+2(O)	I-4	?
6d	I-4	I-5	?
6e	I-5	$I-6+CO_2$	?
6f	I-6	$Q+H_2O$	Spontaneous
6g	I-6	$NIC+H_2O$	?
6h	Q	$NIC+CO_2$	?
7	NIC+?	N+?	?
8	N	DPN^+, TPN^+	Many
9a	METH+ATP	$SADMETH+3P_i$	METH-activating enzyme
9b	N+SADMETH	NMEN+SA-HCYS	N-methylpherase
10	$NMEN+O_2$	$NMENPO+\frac{1}{2}H_2O_2$	Quinine oxidase
11	$NMEN+H_2O$	$TRIG+NH_3$	?
12		NICGL	?
13		DNICOR	?
14	$FK+H_2O$	FAN+ALA	Kynureninase
15	$K+H_2O$	AN+ALA	Kynureninase
16	$FAN+H_2O$	AN+HCOOH	K-formamidase
17	$AN+O_2$	Various products	Many
18	Precursors	AN	Many
19	AN+?	$I-7+CO_2+?$	?
20	I-7+?	IND+?	?
21	IND+SER	$TRYP+H_2O$	IND-SER ligase
22	$TRYP+H_2O$	$IND+PVA+NH_3$	Tryptophanase
23	K+AKG	ABPV+GLU	K-transaminase
24	ABPV	$KIC+H_2O$	Spontaneous
25	HK+AKG	AHBPV+GLU	K-transaminase
26	AHBPV	$XIC+H_2O$	Spontaneous

/1/ For definition of most abbreviations see flow diagram; ALA=alanine; METH=methionine; ATP=adenosine triphosphate; AKG=ketoglutaric acid; GLU= glutamic acid; SER=serine; PVA=pyruvic acid; DPN=diphosphopyridine nucleotide; TPN=triphosphopyridine nucleotide. /2/ Dietary TRYP substitutes for N and causes increased formation of NMEN, NIC, Q, and pyridine nucleotides. Tracer experiments have shown that: $TRYP-9-C^{14}\rightarrow K-8-C^{14}$ + $KIC-3-C^{14}$; $TRYP-3-C^{14}\rightarrow NMEN-7-C$; $TRYP-1-N^{15}\rightarrow K-N^{15}$ + $KIC-N^{15}$ + $XIC-N^{15}$ + $NMENPO-N^{15}$; $K-N^{15}\rightarrow XIC-N^{15}$; $TRYP-5,6,7,8-D_4-1-N^{15}\rightarrow$ $Q-D_2-1-N^{15}$; $IND-1-N^{15}\rightarrow NIC-1-N^{15}$; $AN-N^{15}$, $IND-N^{15}$, or $TRYP-1-N^{15}$ + $Q-1-N^{15}$. /3/ Reactions 1 and 2 have not been separated and intermediate not identified. The activity (amount?) of these enzymes is dependent upon the dietary intake of TRYP and is subject to hormonal control. /4/ Suggested compound identified as product of reaction 2. /5/ This enzyme catalyzes reactions 3 and 16 and also acts on other N-formyl compounds. /6/ As N-Acetyl-K, is accumulated by niacinless mutant of Neurospora. Dietary K can substitute for N and causes increased excretion of NMEN. /7/ This reaction postulated because of activity of K (Fn 6), HAN (Fn 10), and, subsequently, HK (Fn 9). It has not been shown in cell-free system. /8/ B_2 involved as catalyst in oxidation or oxidative phosphorylation of K. /9/ HK postulated as precursor of HAN. It is a naturally occurring substance and can serve as substitute for NIC in Neurospora. /10/ This enzyme catalyzes reactions 5, 14, and 15. It requires pyridoxal phosphate as coenzyme. It is inhibited by amines. /11/ A compound accumulated by niacinless mutant of Neurospora, identified as HAN, can substitute for NIC in diet. It is converted to NIC, causes increased excretion of NMEN, and is oxidized to Q by liver preparations. /12/ Reaction and reaction product postulated (see also Fn 13). /13/ Reactions 4a, 4b, and 5b postulated on basis of report that TRYP, K, and AN are oxidized by liver homogenate to product tentatively identified as HANP, whereas HK is split to HAN. However, most authors find that AN is not a source of NIC in mammals. /14/ Reaction well established (see Fn 10) but details still obscure (see reactions 6a-6h). /15/ Reaction 6a or 6c requires O_2 and Fe^{++}. It is inhibited by a, a-dipyridyl, p-chloromercuribenzoate, H_2O_2, and HCN. /16/ Intermediate tentatively identified on basis of absorption spectrum, chemical properties, and conversion to I-3. /17/ This reaction, catalyzed by H^+, gives a product, tentatively identified as I-3, that cannot be converted to Q. /18/ I-4 and I-5 tentatively identified by absorption spectra and chemical properties. /19/ Reaction postulated because of low activity of Q (see Fn 21). /20/ Reaction has not been shown in cell-free system. /21/ Acid-labile substance accumulated in urine identified as Q and is accumulated by niacinless mutant strain of Neurospora and mammals. To a limited extent, Q is utilized by Neurospora and mammals. May or may not be an intermediate. /22/ Although all mammals appear to utilize either NIC or N interchangeably, the reaction has not been demonstrated in cell-free system. NIC is not necessarily an intermediate. /23/ In some bacteria, AN is oxidized by way of catechol, and cis, cis-muconic acid to β-keto adipic acid. /24/ The ultimate origin of AN from carbohydrate is closely linked with the origin of other aromatic compounds. /25/ The carboxyl group of AN is lost during these reactions. /26/ Enzyme requires pyridoxal phosphate as coenzyme. /27/ Reaction requires pyridoxal phosphate as coenzyme. /28/ Enzyme requires pyridoxal phosphate as coenzyme. Either a-ketoglutaric or pyruvic acid can accept the amino group. With model compounds which cannot undergo ring closure the reaction is reversible. K can be oxidatively deaminated slowly by L-amino acid oxidase to form ABPV which spontaneously dehydrates to KIC. The relative rates of reactions 4, 5, 23, 25 depend upon the dietary intake of B_1, B_2, and B_6.

Part II: COMPOUNDS INCORPORATING NICOTINAMIDE[1]

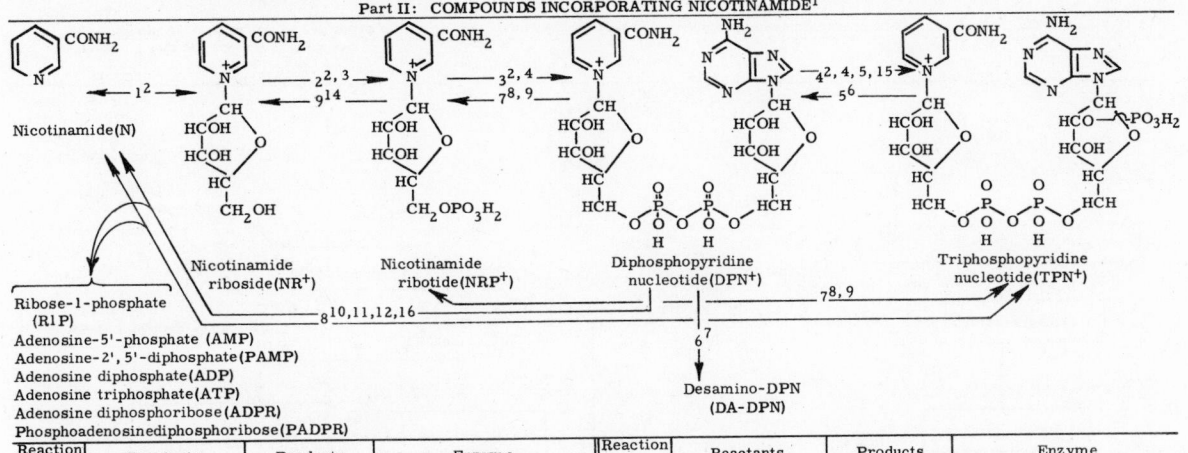

Nicotinamide(N)

Nicotinamide riboside(NR⁺)

Nicotinamide ribotide(NRP⁺)

Diphosphopyridine nucleotide(DPN⁺)

Triphosphopyridine nucleotide(TPN⁺)

Ribose-1-phosphate (R1P)
Adenosine-5'-phosphate (AMP)
Adenosine-2',5'-diphosphate (PAMP)
Adenosine diphosphate(ADP)
Adenosine triphosphate(ATP)
Adenosine diphosphoribose(ADPR)
Phosphoadenosinediphosphoribose(PADPR)

Desamino-DPN (DA-DPN)

Reaction No.	Reactants	Products	Enzyme	Reaction No.	Reactants	Products	Enzyme
1	N + R1P	NR⁺ + Pi + H⁺	Unnamed phosphorylase	7	DPN⁺ + H₂O	NRP⁺ + AMP	Nucleotide pyro-phosphatase
2	NR⁺ + ATP	NRP⁺ + ADP	Unnamed kinase		TPN⁺ + H₂O	NRP⁺ + PAMP	
3	NRP⁺ + ATP	DPN⁺ + PPi	DPN-pyrophosphorylase	8	DPN⁺ + H₂O	N + ADPR	DPN nucleosidase
4	DPN⁺ + ATP	TPN⁺ + ADP	DPN-kinase		TPN⁺ + H₂O	N + PADPR	(DPNase)
5	TPN⁺ + H₂O	DPN⁺ + Pi	Phosphatase	9	NRP⁺ + H₂O	NR + Pi	5-Nucleotidase
6	DPN⁺ + H₂O	DADPN⁺ + NH₃	Adenosine deaminase				

/1/ For definition of most abbreviations see flow diagram; Pi = inorganic phosphate; PPi = inorganic pyrophosphate. /2/ Mammalian liver. /3/ Mammalian erythrocytes (intact). /4/ Yeast. /5/ Pigeon liver. /6/ Mammalian prostate gland. /7/ Takadiastase. /8/ Mammalian kidney. /9/ Potato. /10/ Mammalian brain. /11/ Mammalian spleen. /12/ Neurospora. /13/ Mammalian semen. /14/ Also acts on purine ribosides. /15/ Yeast enzyme also acts on reduced coenzyme I (DPNH), whereas that from pigeon liver is inhibited by DPNR. /16/ Enzyme from spleen can catalyze reversible exchange of N or other pyridine compounds to form analogs of DRN, or can irreversibly transfer ADPR to primary amines.

Part III: THIAMINE AND DERIVATIVES[1]

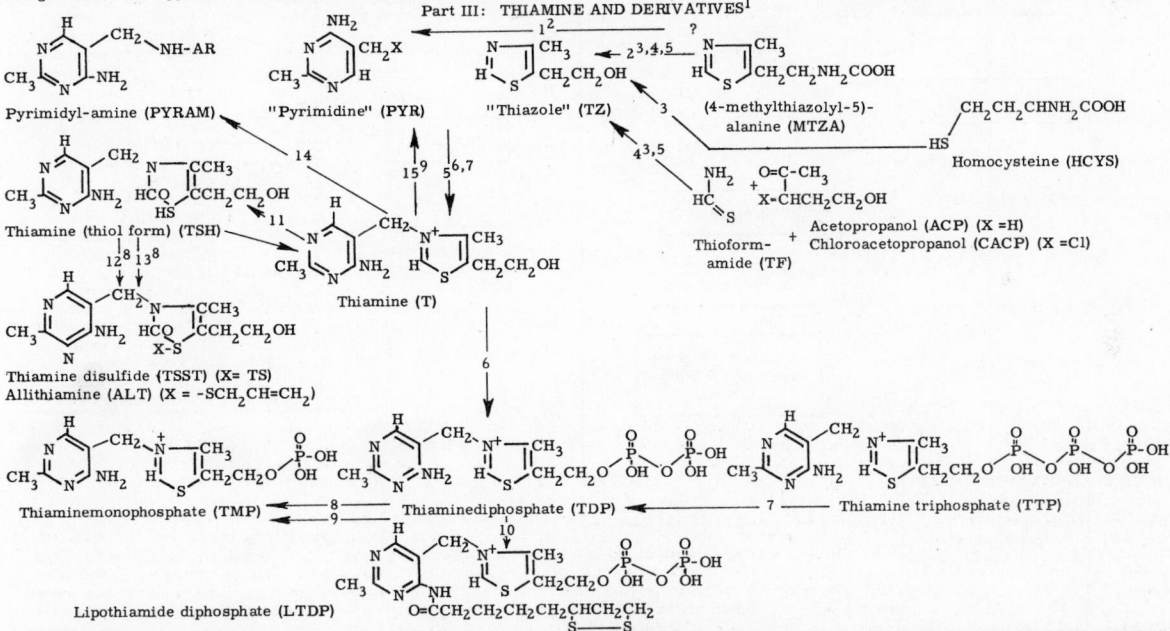

Pyrimidyl-amine (PYRAM)

"Pyrimidine" (PYR)

"Thiazole" (TZ)

(4-methylthiazolyl-5)-alanine (MTZA)

Homocysteine (HCYS)

Thiamine (thiol form) (TSH)

Thioformamide (TF)

Acetopropanol (ACP) (X =H)
Chloroacetopropanol (CACP) (X =Cl)

Thiamine (T)

Thiamine disulfide (TSST) (X= TS)
Allithiamine (ALT) (X = -SCH₂CH=CH₂)

Thiaminemonophosphate (TMP)

Thiaminediphosphate (TDP)

Thiamine triphosphate (TTP)

Lipothiamide diphosphate (LTDP)

Reaction No.	Substrates	Products	Enzyme	Reaction No.	Substrates	Products	Enzyme
1	? + ?	PYR + ?	?	9	TDP + H₂O	TMP + Pi	Nucleotide pyrophosphatase
2	MTZA + ?	TZ + NH₃ + CO₂	?	10	TDP + LA + ATP + CoA	LTDP + ?	Lipoic acid conjugase
3	HCYS + ?	TZ + ?	?				
4	TF + ACP	TZ + ?	?	11	T + OH	TSH + H₂O	Spontaneous?
	TF + CACP	TZ + ?	?	12	TSH + TSH	TSST + 2H	Thiamine disulfyrlase
5	PYR + TZ	T	Unnamed	13	AL + ?	ALC + ?	Allinase
6	T + ARP	TDP + AMP	Thiamine pyrophosphorylase		TSH + ALC	ALT + ?	Spontaneous
7	TTP + H₂O	TDP + Pi	Potato apyrase	14	T + AR-NH₂	PYRAM + TZ	Thiaminase I
8	TDP + H₂O	TMP + Pi	Potato apyrase	15	T + H₂O	PYR + TZ	Thiaminase II

/1/ For definition of abbreviations see flow diagram; ATP=adenosine triphosphate; AMP=adenosine monophosphate; Pi=inorganic phosphate; AL=alliin; CH₂=CHCH₂SOCH₂CHNH₂COOH; ALC=allicin, CH₂=CHCH₂SSOCH₂CH₂=CH₂; AR-NH=any of a variety of aromatic amines; LA=lipoic acid; CoA=coenzyme A. /2/ Constitution and origin of PYR not established; presumably, X=OH or NH₂. /3/ Growing pea roots. /4/ Intact yeast cells. /5/ Natural occurrence of MTZA, TF, ACP, CACP not established. /6/ There is evidence that this may not be sole or predominant pathway. /7/ The name "thiaminase" was first used for this enzyme, but is now reserved for the enzyme(s) which catalyze reactions 14 and 15. /8/ TSST and ALT are nutritionally equivalent to T. /9/ In the product (PYR), X=OH.

The diagram summarizes present knowledge and hypothesis of the pathway leading to the synthesis of chlorophyll in plants.

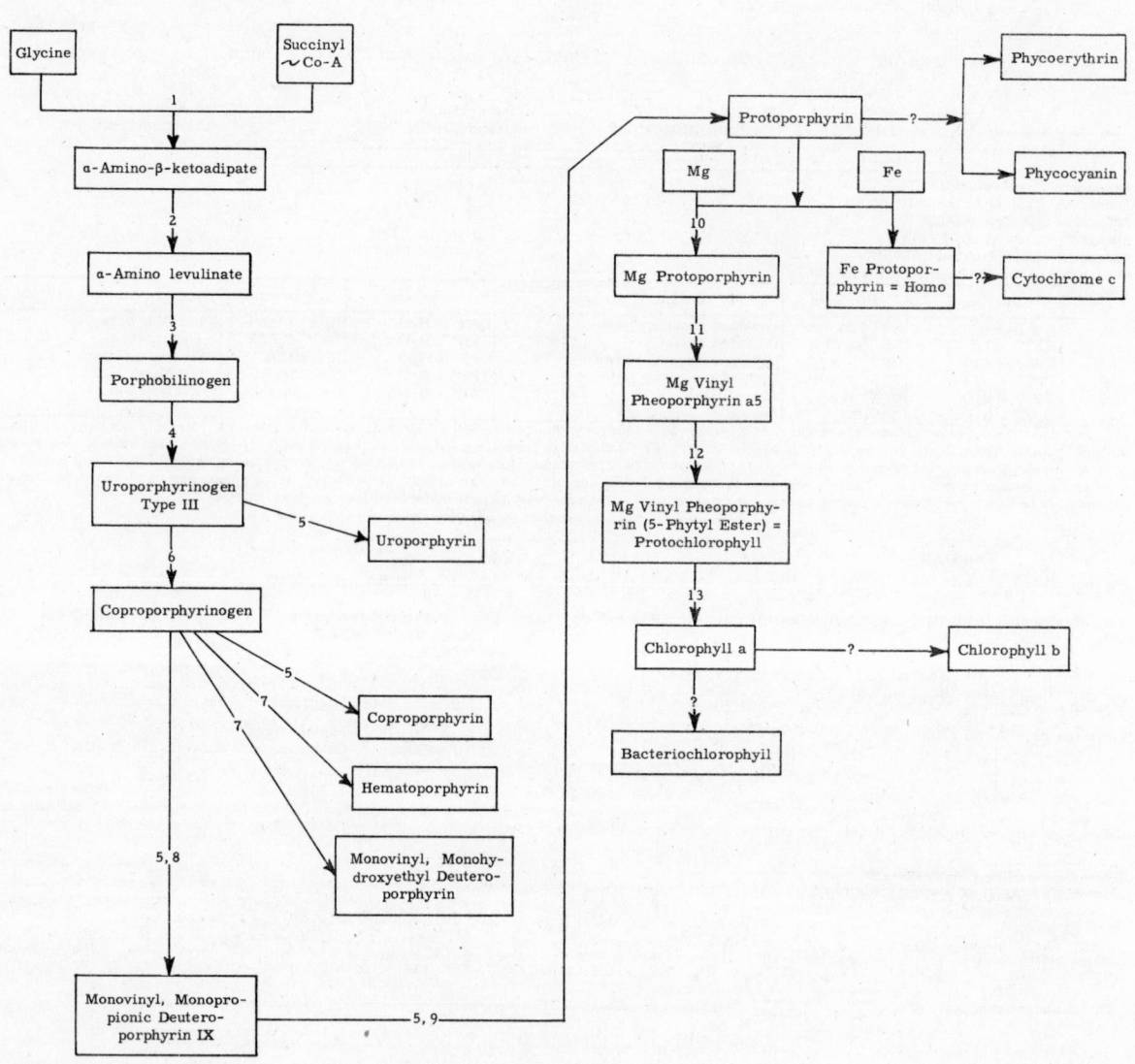

/1/ Condensation of glycine with "succinyl ∼ Co-A" produces α-amino-β-ketoadipate. /2/ Decarboxylates to α-amino levulinate. /3/ Two mole-cules of α-amino levulinate condensed by a dehydrase enzyme, forming the pyrrole amine, porphobilinogen. /4/ Four molecules of porphobilinogen condensed, forming a reduced porphyrin, uroporphyrinogen, isomer III. /5/ It is uncertain how far along the biosynthetic chain tetrapynole remains in the reduced form. /6/ Decarboxylation of uroporphyrinogen III to coproporphyrinogen III. /7/ It is uncertain whether these compounds are in-termediates or side products. Found in chlorella mutant. /8/ Oxidation of one propionic side chain to vinyl. /9/ Oxidation of one propionic side chain to vinyl, producing protoporphyrin. Found in a chlorella mutant devoid of chlorophyll and carotenoids. /10/ Mg protoporphyrin found in chlorel-la mutant. /11/ Four or five steps postulated, including reduction of vinyl side chain to ethyl, oxidation of propionic group and cyclization to a cyclopentanone ring, and esterification with methanol. Found in a chlorella mutant. /12/ Esterification of a propionic acid group with phytol, a C-20 alcohol. /13/ Open chain bile pigment chemically bound to protein.

Photosynthetic carbon dioxide-reduction follows the same general pathway in all plants. The first reaction results in formation of two molecules of phosphoglycerate from carbon dioxide and ribulose diphosphate. Phosphoglycerate is then reduce via the reverse of glycolysis reactions to give hexose-phosphates for synthesis of sucrose and polysaccharides. A portion of the intermediates undergoes the following sequence of reactions leading to regeneration of the carbon dioxide acceptor, ribulose diphosphate. Heavy arrows indicate directions of material transfer during steady state photosynthesis. A = Ribulose diphosphate carboxylase (carboxydismutase); B = Triosephosphate dehydrogenase; C = Triosephosphate isomerase; D = Aldolase, E = Phosphatase; F = Transketolase; G = Transaldolase; H = Phosphoketopentose epimerase; I = Phosphoriboisomerase; J = Phosphoribulokinase:

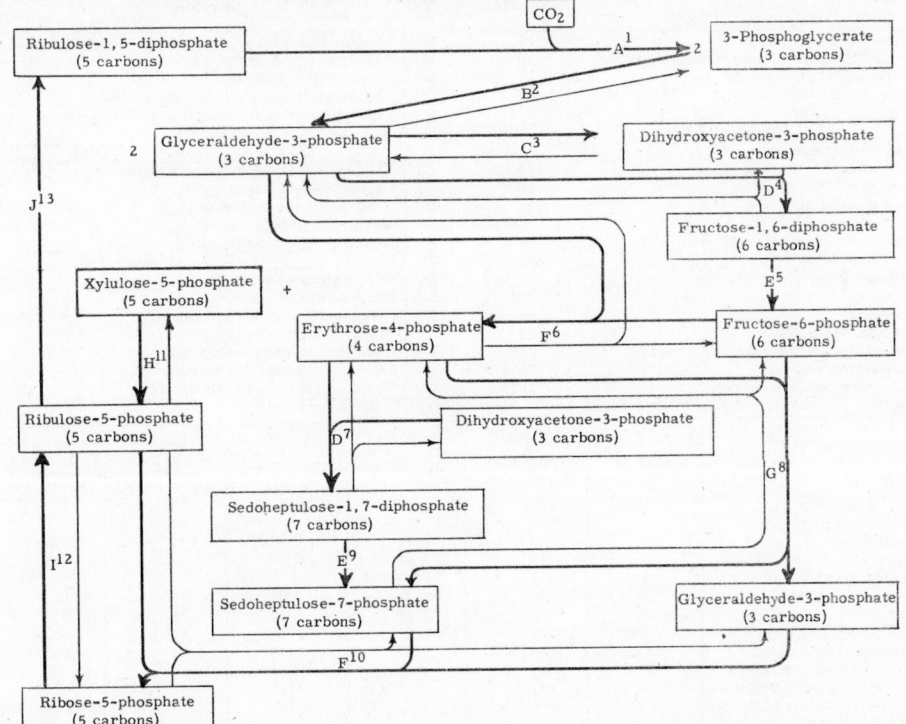

/1/ Ribulose diphosphate adds CO_2 at carbon-2 and splits hydrolytically to give two molecules of 3-phosphoglycerate. /2/ The carboxyl group is reduced to an aldehyde group with the aid of ATP and reduced TPN. /3/ Isomerization involves transfer of 2H from carbon-2 to carbon-1. /4/ Aldol condensation of carbon-1 of glyceraldehyde-3-P with carbon-1 of dihydroxyacetone-3-P. /5/ Removal of phosphate ester group from carbon-1 by hydrolysis. /6/ Glycolyl group (carbon-1,2) of fructose transferred to glyceraldehyde-P to form xylulose-5-P, leaving erythrose-P. /7/ Aldol condensation of carbon-1 of erythrose-4-P with carbon-1 of dihydroxyacetone-3-P obtained from step 3. /8/ Transfer of triose group (carbon-1,2,3) from fructose-6-P to carbon-1 of erythrose-4-P, leaving glyceraldehyde-3-P from carbon-4,5,6 of the fructose-6-P. /9/ Hydrolysis of phosphate ester group on carbon-1 to give inorganic phosphate. /10/ Transfer of glycolyl group (carbon-1,2) of sedoheptulose-7-P to carbon-1 of glyceraldehyde-3-P to give ribulose-5-P, leaving ribose-5-P. /11/ Epimerization of carbon-3 of ketopentose. Xylulose-5-P isomerizes to ribulose-5-P with phosphoketopentose epimirase. /12/ Isomerization of aldose to ketose by transfer of two H atoms. /13/ Phosphorylation of carbon-1 by reaction with ATP.

229. PATHWAYS OF SUCROSE SYNTHESIS: INTERMEDIATES

Sucrose synthesis, common to all green plants, is the first free sugar formed by a series of steps involving phosphorylated intermediates. Photosynthesis supplies reduced pyridine nucleotides and adenosine triphosphate (ATP). Phosphoglycerate, supplied by the photosynthetic carboxylation reaction, is reduced and condensed to form hexose molecules. Energy required to form sucrose from hexose phosphates comes largely from high energy uridine triphosphate (UTP) which becomes uridine diphosphate glucose (UDPG) for condensation with fructose phosphate. A = Triosephosphate dehydrogenase, two types; B = Triosephosphate isomerase; C = Aldolase; D = Phosphatase; E = Phosphoglucoisomerase; F = Phosphoglucomutase; G = Uridyl transferase; H = Sucrose phosphorylase; I = Sucrose phosphatase.

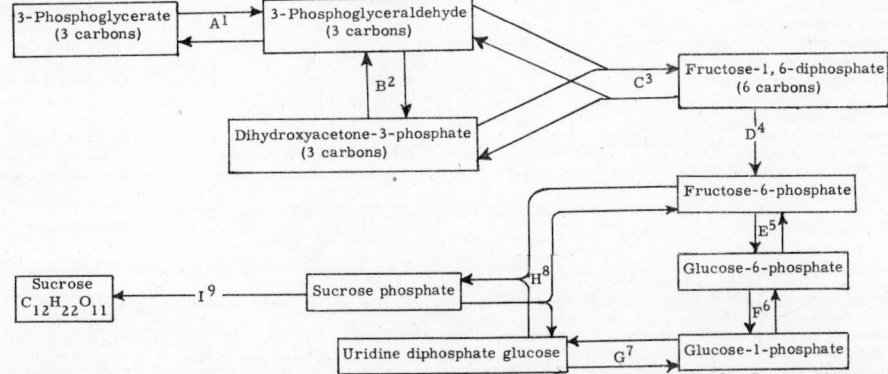

/1/ DPNH or TPNH are oxidized to supply hydrogen for reduction of carboxyl to aldehyde group. ATP and Mg^{++} are required for this reaction. /2/ Two hydrogen atoms shift from carbon-2 to carbon-1 to form isomeric phosphoketose from 3-phosphoaldotriose. /3/ Aldol condensation of carbon-1 of phosphoketotriose and carbon-1 of 3-phosphoaldotriose. /4/ Phosphate group on carbon-1 hydrolyzed. /5/ Hydrogen atom on carbon-1 shifts to carbon-2 forming the epimer, glucose-6-phosphate. Furanose ring structure changed to pyranose. /6/ Phosphate group on carbon-6 transferred to carbon-1 through the required coenzyme intermediate, glucose-1,6-diphosphage. Mg^{++} required. /7/ UTP reacts with glucose-1-phosphate to form pyrophosphate and UDPG. /8/ Fructose-6-phosphate and UDPG react to give UDP and an unstable sucrose phosphate. /9/ Hydrolysis to give free sucrose and orthophosphate.

230. PHOTOSYNTHESIS: RATES

Photosynthesis under natural conditions is complicated by such factors as light intensity, temperature, CO_2 concentration, and by certain internal conditions of the plant. For a comparison of the rates of photosynthesis, Part I presents maximum rates for natural conditions; Part II, maximum rates for controlled, near-optimum conditions. Part III gives rates as influenced by controlled conditions of temperature, light, and CO_2. Values are apparent rates, i.e., uncorrected for respiration.

Part I: APPARENT MAXIMUM RATES OF PHOTOSYNTHESIS: NATURAL CONDITIONS
Values are mg CO_2/100 sq cm per hr.

Species	CO_2 Fixation[1]	Species	CO_2 Fixation[1]
Arctic Zone		**Desert Zone**	
1 Dock (Rumex acetosella); 10°C	12	20 Atriplex (Atriplex vesicarium)	10
2 Chamaenerium (Chamaenerium latifolium); 0°C	10	21 Date (Phoenix dactylifera)	3.4
3 Cloudberry (Rubus chamaemorus)	8	22 Grape (Vitis vinifera)	16.1
4 Willow (Salix glauca); 10°C	4	23 Heliotrope (Heliotropium arguzioides)	27
5 Willow (S. glauca); 20°C	6	24 Limoniastrum (Limoniastrum feei)	1.3
Temperate Zone		25 Oleander (Nerium oleander)	10.3
6 Anemone (Anemone nemorosa)	(6-11)	**Tropical Zone**	
7 Apple (Pyrus malus)	20(20)	26 Calophyllum (Calophyllum inophyllum)	7.3
8 Corn (Zea mays)	10	27 Cassia (Cassia fistula)	10.9(8.6)
9 Dock (Rumex acetosella)	9	28 Coconut (Cocos nucifera)	0.9
10 Elder (Sambucus nigra)	4.6(1.7)	29 Mango (Mangifera indica)	14.8
11 Fern, polypody (Polypodium virginiana)	(5.6)	30 Sugarcane (Saccharum officinarum)	5
12 Horse-bean (Vicia faba)	17	**Mountain Zone**	
13 Mustard (Sinapis alba)	20-26	31 Barley (Hordeum sativum)	≥ 30
14 Oat (Avena sativa)	13	32 Eurotia (Eurotia ceratoides)	≥ 44
15 Pine (Pinus taeda)	14.3(2.5)	33 Gentiana (Gentiana algicola)	≥ 100
16 Potato (Solanum tuberosum)	20	34 Geum (Geum montanum)	48
17 Rhododendron (Rhododendron brachycarpum)	(2.8)	35 Homogyne (Homogyne alpina)	43(18)
18 Sunflower (Helianthus annuus)	5.5-24	36 Soldanella (Soldanella alpina)	39(19)
19 Tomato (Lycopersicon esculentum)	16.8	37 Veronica (Veronica bellidioides)	65

[1] Values from determinations made in shade are enclosed in parentheses; all others, in sunlight.

Part II: APPARENT MAXIMUM RATES OF PHOTOSYNTHESIS: NEAR-OPTIMUM CONDITIONS

Species	CO_2 in Air %	Temperature °C	CO_2 Fixation, g CO_2/hr per 100 g wet wt	per 100 g dry wt	per sq dm x 1000	per g chlorophyll ($\sqrt{A}$)[1]	Assimilation Time $(T_A)^2$, sec
1 Basswood (Tilia cordata)	5	25	1.88	5.8	28	6.6	24
Elder (Sambucus nigra)							
2 Green leaves	5	25	1.96	5.3	34	6.6	24
3 Yellow leaves	5	25	0.88	4.7	18	120	1.3
Maple (Acer pseudoplatanus)							
4 Young leaves	5	25	0.98	3.0	16	11.8	13
5 Old leaves	5	25	2.07	5.8	26	5.2	30
6 Poplar (Populus pyramidalis)	5	25	1.90	6.0	40	10.0	16
7 Sunflower (Helianthus annuus)	5	25	2.30	13.4	80	14.0	11
Chlorella (Chlorella pyrenoidosa)							
8 In shade, ← carbonate buffer 9				11.5		4.1	36
9 In light, ← carbonate buffer 9				13.4		2.8	56
10 Sea lettuce (Ulva lactuca)		25			11.8		
11 Sea weed (Gigartina harveyana)[3]		16			14		
12 Water net (Hormidium flaccidum)		20				6.8	23

[1] $\sqrt{A}$, the assimilation number, i.e., the maximum quantity of CO_2 that can be reduced in unit time by unit quantity of chlorophyll. [2] The shortest time in which one molecule of chlorophyll can reduce one molecule of CO_2. [3] In artificial sea water containing 0.016 M bicarbonate/carbonate buffer.

Part III: APPARENT RATES OF PHOTOSYNTHESIS: SPECIFIED CONDITIONS

Species	Temperature[1] °C	Light[1] ft-c	CO_2 in Air[1]	Photosynthesis Rate[2]	Unit of Expression per hr
1 Barley (Hordeum vulgare)	24	500	N	9-16	mg CO_2/sq dm
2 Bean (Phaseolus vulgaris)	25	1400	N	5.8-16.6	mg CO_2/sq dm
3 Dogwood (Cornus florida)	30	2000	N	2(3.1)	mg CO_2/sq dm
4 Laurel (Prunus laurocerasus)	29.5	Noon sun	N	23.2	mg CO_2/sq dm
5 Lemon (Citrus limonia)		1300	1.5%	3-5	ml O_2/sq dm
6 Oak (Quercus rubra)	30	2000	N	5(6)	mg CO_2/sq dm
7 Orange (Citrus sinensis)		1300	1.5%	4-6	ml O_2/sq dm
8 Pelargonium (Pelargonium zonale)	24	500	N	5.3	mg CO_2/sq dm
9 Pine (Pinus taeda)	30	2000	N	2(3.9)	mg CO_2/sq dm
10 Potato (Solanum tuberosum)	24	>5000	N	16-20	mg CO_2/sq dm
11 Spruce (Picea pungens)	24	2200	N	0.03	mg CO_2/100 leaves
12 Sugar cane (Saccharum officinarum)	36	N	N	3-6	mg CO_2/sq dm
13 Sunflower (Helianthus annuus)		4460	5%	(80)	mg CO_2/sq dm
14 Sphagnum (Sphagnum girgensohnii)		110-260		2.8	mg CO_2/g dry wt
15 Chlorella (Chlorella vulgaris viridis)	22.4	26,700 lux	Buffer 9[3]	195	cu mm O_2/100 mil cells
16 Chlorella (C. saccharophila)	22.4	26,700 lux	Buffer 9[3]	452	cu mm O_2/100 mil cells
17 Kelp (Macrocystis pyrifera)	N	Low	Sea water	17.5	ml O_2/sq dm

[1] N=under natural conditions. [2] Values in parentheses are maximum rates; all others, average rates. [3] Carbonate buffer 9.

231. PHOTOSYNTHESIS: EFFICIENCY AND CARBON PRODUCTION

Part I: ESTIMATED ANNUAL CARBON PRODUCTION

	Region	Area sq km	Carbon Fixed, ton/yr per sq km	total
1	Forest	44×10^6	250	11×10^9
2	Cultivated land	27×10^6	149	4.3×10^9
3	Grassland	31×10^6	43	1.1×10^9
4	Desert	47×10^6	7	0.2×10^9
5	Total land	149×10^6		16.6×10^9
6	Ocean	361×10^6	340	16.6×10^9

Part II: EFFICIENCY OF PHOTOSYNTHESIS

	Specification	Value
1	Energy utilized in photosynthesis by one acre of corn plants in synthesis of 8732 kg glucose[1].	3.3×10^7 Cal
2	Total solar energy available on the acre during growing season.	2.043×10^9 Cal
3	Photosynthetic efficiency of corn plants, i.e., per cent of available energy used in photosynthesis.	1.6%
4	Energy equivalent of earth's carbon production.	$(13.6\pm8.1) \times 10^{17}$ Cal
5	Mean solar radiation.	7.4×10^{20} Cal
6	Photosynthetic efficiency of the world.	0.18(±0.12%)

[1] Total sugar, as glucose, manufactured by one acre of corn plants.

232. PHOTOCHEMICAL ACTIVITIES: PLANTS

Data are concerned with the following: photosynthesis (light dependent reduction of CO_2 with evolution of equimolar O_2), hill reaction (light dependent reduction of a hydrogen acceptor other than CO_2 with evolution of equivalent O_2), photoreduction (light dependent reduction of CO_2 with oxidation of equivalent exogenous hydrogen donor), photofermentation (light dependent evolution of H_2 and CO_2 from endogenous reserves of exogenous substrate), and photochemical phosphorylation (light dependent esterification of inorganic phosphate). Except where otherwise indicated, light intensity is incident.

Part I: REDUCTION OF CO_2 WITH EVOLUTION OF O_2: INTACT CELLS

	Species	Sample Units	Total Sample	Temp °C	Radiant Energy Type	Intensity ergs/sq cm x sec	Rate of Reaction
1	Chlorella ellipsoidea	0.192 mg dry wt/ml	20 ml	25	Tungsten lamp	1.15×10^3	1.9×10^{-4} μM O_2/mg/sec
2						2.41×10^3	3.9×10^{-4} μM O_2/mg/sec
3						5.30×10^3	7.6×10^{-4} μM O_2/mg/sec
4						1.04×10^4	1.2×10^{-3} μM O_2/mg/sec
5						2.41×10^4	1.5×10^{-3} μM O_2/mg/sec
6						3.84×10^4	1.5×10^{-3} μM O_2/mg/sec
7						Saturation	1.6×10^{-3} μM O_2/mg/sec
8	C. pyrenoidosa	$1.5\text{-}2.0 \times 10^7$ cells/ml	1.0 ml	28	6500 Å	616 ergs/sec absorbed	8.2×10^{-4} μl O_2/sec
9		1.2 μl cells/ml	8.2 ml	26	Tungsten lamp	1.51×10^4	9.9 μl O_2/10 min
10	C. vulgaris	1.15×10^7 cells/ml	2.4×10^8 cells	23-25	Tungsten lamp	8.37×10^2	0.8 μl O_2/min
11						2.39×10^3	1.8 μl O_2/min
12						5.98×10^3	3.7-3.8 μl O_2/min
13						3.29×10^4	4.7-6.1 μl O_2/min
14	C. vulgaris viridis	10 μl cells/ml	2.0 ml	29.8	Na-vapor lamp	1.45×10^4	175 μl CO_2/hr
15	Chlorobium thiosulfatophilum	2.5 mg wet wt/ml	3.0 ml		Tungsten lamp	0.2	25 μl CO_2/hr
16						0.4	60 μl CO_2/hr
17						0.6	80 μl CO_2/hr
18	Alfalfa (Medicago sativa)	Whole plant	560 g	15.6	Sunlight	2.02×10^5	18 g CO_2/80 min
19			560 g	15.6		3.37×10^5	28 g CO_2/80 min
20			665 g	29.7		5.73×10^5	39 g CO_2/80 min
21	Corn (Zea mays)	Whole plant	Entire leaf	18-34	Sunlight	3.02×10^4	0.4-2.3 g CO_2/sq m/hr
22				18-34		1.21×10^5	1.7 g CO_2/sq m/hr
23				18-34		1.51×10^5	0.9-3.5 g CO_2/sq m/hr

Part II: REACTIONS OTHER THAN AN EXCHANGE OF CO_2 AND O_2: INTACT CELLS

	Species	Sample Units	Total Sample	Temp °C	Radiant Energy Type	Intensity erg/sq cm/sec	H_2 Acceptor or [Donor]	Rate of Reaction
				Photochemical Reduction, with H_2O as H_2 Donor				
1	Chlorella pyrenoidosa	16 μl cells/ml	3.0 ml	10	Fluorescent lamp	Saturation	p-Quinone	85 μl O_2/30 min
2		50 μl cells/ml	2.0 ml	20	Tungsten lamp	Saturation	p-Quinone	165 μl O_2/15 min
3		96 mg dry wt/ml	1.0 ml	28	Tungsten lamp	1.36×10^4	Benzaldehyde	50 μl O_2/20 min
4		96 mg dry wt/ml	1.0 ml	28	Tungsten lamp	1.36×10^4	Acetaldehyde	40 μl O_2/20 min
				Photochemical H_2 Evolution: Photofermentation				
5	Chlamydomonas moewusii	24 μl cells/ml	4.0 ml	25	Fluorescent lamp	6.0×10^2	[Endogenous material]	8.9 μl H_2/mg dry wt/hr
6	Chromatium sp	30 μl cells/ml	1.8 ml	30	Tungsten lamp	Optimal	[Endogenous material]	510 μl H_2/7.5 hr
7	Rhodopseudomonas gelatinosa	35 μl cells/ml	2.0 ml	30	Tungsten lamp	Optimal	[Endogenous material]	93 μl H_2/120 min
8							[Acetic acid]	560 μl H_2/120 min
9							[Malic acid]	470 μl H_2/120 min
10	Rhodospirillum rubrum	25 μl cells/ml	2.0 ml	30	Tungsten lamp	Optimal	[Malic acid]	170 μl H_2/100 min
11		30 μl cells/ml					[Malic acid]	1275 μl H_2/20 min
12		32 μl cells/ml					[Oxalacetic acid]	520 μl H_2/240 min
13	Scenedesmus obliques			25	Tungsten lamp	Optimal	[Endogenous material]	3.7 μl H_2/mg dry wt/hr
				Photochemical Oxidation of H_2: Photoreduction				
14	Chlorobium thiosulfatophilum	2.5 mg wet wt/ml	3.0 ml		Tungsten lamp	0.2	CO_2	45 μl H_2/hr
15						0.4		110 μl H_2/hr
16						0.6		185 μl H_2/hr
17	Scenedesmus, strain D3	18 μl cells/ml		21	Above 5500 Å	4.5×10^2	CO_2	43 μl H_2/10 min
				Photochemical Phosphorylation				
18	Chlorella pyrenoidosa		2.0 μl cells	20	Tungsten lamp	Saturation		3.5×10^{-5} μM P/μl cells/sec
19	Chromatium, strain D	5 μl cells/ml	50 μl cells	29	Tungsten lamp	$1.2\text{-}1.3 \times 10^4$		2.4 μg P/120 min

Part III: PHOTOCHEMICAL REDUCTION: CELL-FREE PREPARATIONS
Data are photochemical reductions, with water as hydrogen donor (Hill reaction).

	Species	Amount mg[1]	Rate of Reaction[2] μl O_2/mg x hr		Species	Amount mg[1]	Rate of Reaction[2] μl O_2/mg x hr
	Algae, Liverworts, Horsetails				Spermatophytes: Broadleaf (concluded)		
1	Chlorella pyrenoidosa	0.24	400	13	Beet (Beta vulgaris)	0.64	1490
2	C. vulgaris	0.38	210	14	Cabbage (Brassica oleracea)	0.70	590
3	Conocephalum conicum	0.19	200	15	Chickweed (Stellaria media)	0.72	540
4	Equisetum arvense	0.83	240	16	Duckweed (Lemna minor)	0.56	430
5	E. scirpoides	1.60	700	17	Duckweed (Wolffia punctata)	0.24	680
	Spermatophytes: Grasses			18	Lettuce (Lactuca sativa)	0.38	1010
6	Barley (Hordeum vulgare)	1.50	540	19	Melon (Cucumis melo)	0.61	620
7	Corn (Zea mays)	1.16	270	20	New Zealand spinach (Tetragonia expansa)	0.61	950
8	Millet (Panicum miliaceum)	0.71	2300	21	Parsley (Petroselinum hortense)	0.68	130
9	Oat (Avena sativa)	1.40	660	22	Spinach (Spinacea oleracea)	0.56	1940
10	Rye (Secale cereale)	1.60	890	23	Sweetpea (Lathyrus odoratus)	1.54	170
11	Wheat (Triticum aestivum)	1.14	760	24	Tobacco (Nicotiana alatea grandiflora)	1.01	100
	Spermatophytes: Broadleaf			25	Tobacco (N. tabacum)	0.80	190
12	Bean (Phaseolus vulgaris)	0.48	370	26	Tomato (Lycopersicon esculentum)	1.60	300

	Species	Sample Type	Unit	Total Sample	Radiant Energy Type	Intensity[3]	H_2 Acceptor	Rate of Reaction μl O_2/min
27	Spinach (Spinacea oleracea)	Granula	0.75-1.0 mg chlorophyll/ml	2 ml	Tungsten lamp	2.85×10^4	p-Quinone	6.0
28							1,2-Naphthoquinone-4-sulfonate	5.0
29							1,4-Naphthoquinone-2-sulfonate	4.0
30							9,10-Anthroquinone-4-sulfonate	1.5

/1/ mg chlorophyll. /2/ Data, expressed as μl O_2/mg chlorophyll/hr, are applicable to the following specifications: preparation, chloroplasts; hydrogen acceptor, $K_3Fe(CN)_6 + K_2C_2O_4$; radiant energy source, >5350 Å; intensity, 4.8×10^4 erg/sq cm/sec. /3/ erg/sq cm/sec.

233. NITROGEN FIXATION

Certain organisms fix atmospheric nitrogen in organic combination. Part I presents estimated amounts of nitrogen fixed per acre by symbiotic (rhizobia-legumes) and saprophytic bacteria. The amount of nitrogen fixed from the air by the symbiotic relation of rhizobia and legumes is influenced by effectiveness of the rhizobia, host species, soil and climatic conditions, and individual handling of the crop. Part II reveals strain and host specificity. Part III shows characteristics of various nitrogen-fixing organisms.

Part I: NITROGEN FIXING: BACTERIA, LEGUMES

	Organism	N Fixed Kg/acre
	Rhizobium spp - Legumes	
	Inoculated with Rhizobium meliloti	
1	Alfalfa (Medicago sativa)	88(25-170)
2	Burclover (M. denticulata)	35(23-49)
3	Fenugreek (Trigonella foenum-graecum)	37
4	Sourclover (Melilotus indica)	45
5	Sweetclover (M. alba)	54(30-75)
	Inoculated with R. trifolii	
6	Clover (Trifolium incarnatum)	42(32-53)
7	Clover (T. pratense)	52(19-78)
8	Clover (T. repens)	47(35-65)
9	Clover (T. repens giganteum)	81(72-91)
	Inoculated with R. leguminosarum	
10	Lentil (Lens culinaris & esculenta)	47
11	Pea (Pisum arvense)	23(20-28)
12	Pea (P. sativum)	33(13-60)
13	Vetch (Vicia spp)	36(20-63)
	Inoculated with R. phaseoli	
14	Bean (Phaseolus vulgaris)	18
	Inoculated with R. japonicum	
15	Soybean (Glycine soja)	26(7-48)
	Inoculated with R. lupini	
16	Lupine (Lupinus angustifolius)	68
	Inoculated with Rhizobium spp	
17	Cowpea (Vigna sinensis)	41(26-53)
18	Garbanzo (Cicer arietinum)	30
19	Kudzu (Pueraria thunbergiana)	49(40-57)
20	Lespedeza (Lespedeza striata & stipulaceae)	39(15-94)
21	Peanut (Arachis hypogaea)	19
22	Velvetbean (Stizolobium deeringianum)	30
23	Pastures with legumes	48(5-91)
	Saprophytic Bacteria	
24	Azotobacter	12-17
25	Clostridium	1-2

Part II: NITROGEN FIXING: STRAIN-HOST RELATION

	Organism	N Fixed with Rhizobia Strains[1]			
		RT 1	RT 16	RT 8	RT 13
		mg/8 plants			
1	Clover (Trifolium pratense)	54	34	3	2
2	Clover (T. repens)	60	46	10	7
3	Clover (T. subterranean)	8	7	138	154

/1/ Strains of Rhizobium trifolii. RT 1 isolated from Trifolium pratense; RT 16, from T. repens; RT 8 and 13, from T. subterranean.

Part III: NITROGEN-FIXING: ORGANISMS

	Organism	Essential Symbiotic Relationship	O_2 Relation	Type[1]
	Rhizobium[2]			
1	R. meliloti[3]	Medicago, Melilotus	Aerobic	Het.
2	R. trifolii	Trifolium	Aerobic	Het.
3	R. leguminosarum	Pisum	Aerobic	Het.
4	R. phaseoli	Phaseolus	Aerobic	Het.
5	R. japonicum	Glycine	Aerobic	Het.
6	R. lupini	Lupinus	Aerobic	Het.
7	Various spp	Vigna, Lespedeza	Aerobic	Het.
8	Azotobacter[3]	None	Aerobic	Het.
9	Clostridium[4]	None	Anaerobic	Het.
10	Desulfovibrio	None	Anaerobic	Het.
11	Rhodopseudomonas and Rhodospirillum	None	Anaerobic[5]	Het.
12	Chromatium	None	Anaerobic	Aut.
13	Chlorobacterium	None	Anaerobic	Het.
14	Rhodomicrobium	None	Anaerobic	Het.
15	Nostoc & Calothrix[3]	None	Aerobic	Aut.

/1/ Het. = heterotropic; Aut. = autotrophic. /2/ Nitrogen fixation inhibited by 2,4-D and by seed treatments containing Cu; slightly inhibited by DDT. /3/ Inhibited by NH_4 and NO_3; stimulated by Mo. /4/ Inhibited by NH_4, stimulated by Mo. /5/ Fixation is best under anaerobic conditions in light only; traces under aerobic in dark. Organism is facultative.

234. THE NITROGEN CYCLE IN NATURE

Adapted from Thimann, K. V., "The Life of Bacteria," Macmillan Co., 1955.

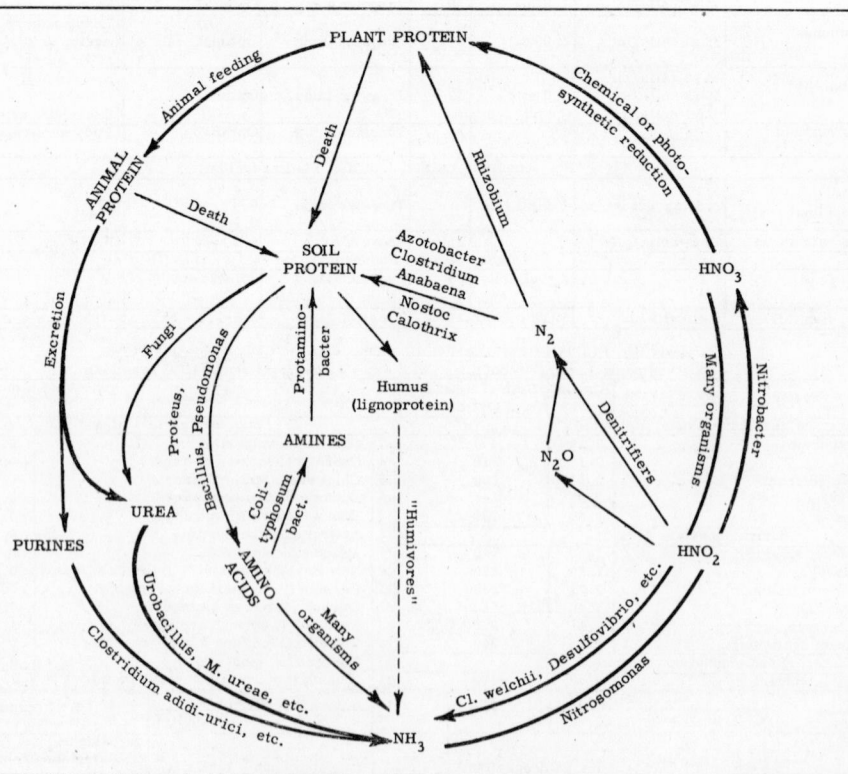

Products listed include only compounds (both diffusible and confined to the mycelium) produced on media containing glucose or sucrose, by the more common fungi (Mucor, Rhizopus, Aspergillus, Penicillium, Alternaria, Helminthosporium). The well-known antibiotics have been omitted. The organisms listed do not constitute the only species producing the compound but, for the most part, the more common ones or those used industrially. Most figures on yield are approximate, frequently based on weights of crude product or pure material after losses in purification. Yields may differ widely among strains of the same species.

	Metabolic Product	Produced By	Yield
		Organic Acids, Aldehydes, Alcohols and Related Compounds	
1	Acetaldehyde	Various Penicillia, Aspergilli, A. niger, Mucor species, and many other genera. By fixation with intercepting agents.	Up to 60% of theory when grown on sucrose with Aspergillus niger.
2	Acetic acid	Fomes annosus, Marasmius chordalis, Merulius confluens, M. lachrymans, M. niveus, M. tremellosus.	0.6% - 0.9% of glucose used for Merulius lachrymans and Marasmius chordalis.
3	Ascorbic acid	Aspergillus niger.	0.2% of the glucose consumed.
4	Clavacin[1] (claviformin or patulin)	Aspergillus clavatus, Penicillium expansum, P. claviforme, P. patulum.	2.2% of glucose added.
5	Citric acid	Citromyces, Penicillium luteum, P. citrinum, P. spinulosum, Aspergillus niger, A. clavatus, A. itaconicus, A. wentii, Mucor pyriformis, many other species. Commercial production on beet and cane molasses. Submerged production possible but not yet commercially successful.	As high as 90% of theory.
6	i-Erythritol	Penicillium brevi-compactum, P. cyclopium.	0.7% of the weight of the organism.
7	Ethyl acetate	Penicillium digitatum.	0.6% of the sugar consumed.
8	Ethyl alcohol	Fusarium species, Mucor species, Merulius species, various Penicillia and Aspergilli, Fomes annosus. Production much slower than by yeast.	Stoichiometric yield with Fusaria, Merulius species, Fomes annosus grown on hexoses and pentoses.
9	Formic acid	Aspergillus oryzae.	
10	Fumaric acid	Various species of Rhizopus; Aspergillus fumaricus, Penicillium griseofulvum, Caldariomyces fumago. Most species other than Mucorales give small amounts.	50% of theoretical yield after 30 days.
11	Fumigacin[1]	Aspergillus fumigatus, A. fumigatus mut. helvola.	0.02 - 0.15% of the glucose added.
12	Gentisyl alcohol	Penicillium patulum.	2.3% of the glucose added.
13	Gladiolic acid	Penicillium gladioli.	94 mg/liter of Raulin-Thom medium.
14	Gluconic acid	Penicillium chrysogenum, P. luteum, P. purpurogenum, Aspergillus species, Fusarium lini bolley.	Practically quantitative conversion in 24 hours.
15	Glucose	Aspergillus niger. From tartaric acid, lactic acid, mannitol and quinic acid.	
16	Glutaric acid	Aspergillus niger strains.	
17	Glycerol	Mucor racemosus, Aspergillus wentii, white Aspergilli, Clasterosporium and Helminthosporium.	Usually small amounts; some species, 3% of the glucose consumed.
18	Glycolic acid	Aspergillus niger (from acetate).	Traces.
19	Glycuronic acid	Ustulina vulgaris.	
20	Glyoxylic acid	Aspergillus niger (from acetate), Merulius lachrymans.	Traces.
21	Itaconic acid	Aspergillus terreus, A. itaconicus.	As high as 50% of theoretical yield.
22	Itatartaric acid	Aspergillus terreus mutant.	1.5% of glucose added.
23	Kojic acid	Aspergillus flavus - oryzae - tamarii group, A. wentii.	45-55% in 12 days. 63-66% reported.
24	ᴅ-Lactic acid	Practically confined to Mucorales. Various Rhizopus species, i.e., R. stolonifer, oryzae, japonicus, tritici, arrhizus. Fumaric acid produced by altering conditions.	Up to 62% with R. oryzae, 39-40% with R. japonicus.
25	Malic acid	White species of Aspergillus, A. flavus, Clasterosporium sp. Accompanied by succinic and fumaric acids.	Fair yields by submerged growths when growing at low temperatures.
26	Malonic acid	Penicillium funiculosum.	
27	Mannitol	White species of Aspergillus, many Aspergilli, Byssochlamys fulva, Penicillium griseofulvum. Not produced from fructose.	45-50% of theory.
28	Mellein[2] (ochracin)	Aspergillus melleus, A. ochraceus.	300 mg/l of medium on sucrose.
29	Methyl glyoxal	Aspergillus niger. On hexosediphosphate.	16% of the substrate consumed.
30	Methyl salicylic acid	Penicillium griseofulvum, P. flexuosum.	2.4% of the glucose consumed.
31	Oxalic acid	Citromyces, Aspergillus, Penicillium and many other genera. Can be produced more economically by other methods.	50% of the sugar consumed.
32	Penicillic acid[1]	Penicillium cyclopium, P. puberulum, Aspergilli.	4.2% of the glucose consumed.
33	Propionic acid	Botrytis cinerea. On lactate.	
34	Pyruvic acid	Aspergillus niger (in presence of sodium sulfite as interceptor), Fusaria.	8.2% of the glucose consumed.
35	Saccharic acid	Aspergillus niger.	
36	Spiculosporic acid[3]	Penicillium spiculisporum, P. crateriforme, P. minio-luteum.	Approx. 2% of the sugar utilized.
37	Succinic acid	Mucor stolonifer, Aspergillus terreus, Ustulina vulgaris, Penicillium aurantio-virens, P. spiculosporum, Fusarium oxysporum, F. heterosporum, F. lini bolley, Fomes annosus, Merulius confluens, M. niveus, M. tremellosus.	Yields very small, except for Fusarium species.
38	Ustic acid	Aspergillus ustus.	0.6% of glucose added.
		Pigments	
39	Alboleersin (colorless)[4]	Helminthosporium leersii.	0.4% of mycelial weight.
40	Aurofusarin	Fusarium culmorum, F. graminearum.	Up to 4.4% of mycelial weight.
41	Auroglaucin	Aspergillus glaucus sp.	More than 13% of the dry growth.
42	β-Carotene	Neurospora, Mucor hiemalis, Phycomyces blakesleanus.	Traces.
43	γ-Carotene	Allomyces species.	Traces.
44	Carviolacin	Penicillium roseopurpureum (P. carminoviolaceum).	3.0% of mycelium (crude pigment).
45	Carviolin	Penicillium roseopurpureum (P. carminoviolaceum).	3.0% of mycelium (crude pigment).
46	Catenarin[5] (1-hydroxyemodin)	Helminthosporium catenarium, H. gramineum, H. velutinum, H. tritici-vulgaris.	As much as 10% - 40% of the mycelial weight in Helminthosporium gramineum, 20% in H. catenarium.
47	Chrysogenin	Penicillium chrysogenum.	
48	Chrysophanic acid (chrysophanol)	Penicillium islandicum.	0.1% of dried mycelium.
49	Citrinin[1]	Penicillium citrinum, Aspergillus terreus.	3.4% of the sugar consumed.
50	Citromycetin	Citromyces glabrum (Penicillium frequentans group).	As much as 20% sugar metabolized.
51	Cynodontin[5]	Helminthosporium cynodontis, H. euchlaenae, H. avenae.	Up to 4.2% of mycelium.
52	Emodic acid	Penicillium cyclopium.	0.1% (as acetyl derivative) of glucose supplied.

/1/ Possesses antibiotic properties but is not in clinical use. /2/ Converted to methyl salicylic acid on KOH fusion. /3/ Related to minioluteic acid. /4/ Related to luteoleersin. /5/ Compare Items 46, 51, 59, and 78. Different species of Helminthosporium have different proportions of these pigments.

	Metabolic Product	Produced By	Yield
		Pigments (concluded)	
53	Ergoflavin	Sclerotium clavus.	
54	Erythroglaucin	Aspergillus glaucus group, 15 species.	0.25% of the mycelium (pure).
55	Flavoglaucin	Aspergillus glaucus.	More than 25% of the dry growth weight.
56	Fulvic acid	Penicillium griseofulvum, P. flexuosum, P. brefeldianum.	15-20% of the mycelium, 2.7% of the glucose consumed.
57	Fumigatin	Aspergillus fumigatus.	0.35% of the glucose consumed (crude material).
58	Fusarubin	Fusarium solani	On sucrose 25 mg/liter of medium.
59	Helminthosporin[5]	Helminthosporium gramineum, H. catenarium, H. tritici-vulgaris, H. cynodontis.	As much as 22% - 40% of the mycelial weight in H. gramineum.
60	ω-Hydroxyemodin	Penicillium cyclopium, P. citreo-roseum, P. cyaneo-fulvum.	0.1/ of glucose (tetraacetyl derivative) supplied.
61	Islandicin	Penicillium islandicum.	3% of the mycelium.
62	Javanicin	Fusarium javanicum.	0.05% of the glucose added (pure).
63	Luteoleersin[6]	Helminthosporium leersii.	1.8% of the mycelium.
64	Lycopersin	Fusarium lycopersici.	
65	Monascoflavin	Monascus purpureus.	
66	Monascorubrin	Monascus purpureus.	
67	Nalgiovensin	Penicillium nalgiovensis.	1% of dry mycelium.
68	Oosporein	Oospora colorans.	9.5% of the substrate added.
69	Oxy-javanicin	Fusarium javanicum.	0.02% of the glucose added (pure).
70	Penetrinic acid	Penicillium notatum.	
71	Penicilliopsin	Penicilliopsis clavariaeformis.	7.5% of the mycelium.
72	Phoenicin	Penicillium phoeniceum, P. rubrum (also Bacillus pyocyaneus).	1.2% (pure) of mycelium.
73	Physcion (Emodin monomethyl ether)	Aspergillus glaucus species.	0.65% of the mycelium (pure).
74	Ravenelin	Helminthosporium ravenelii, H. turcicum.	10% of the mycelium.
75	Rugulosin	Penicillium rugulosum.	
76	Solanione	Fusarium solani D_2 purple.	
77	Spinulosin (6-hydroxyfumigatin)	Penicillium spinulosum, P. cinerascens, Aspergillus fumigatus.	0.11% of the glucose consumed (A. fumigatus).
78	Tritisporin[5]	Helminthosporium tritici-vulgaris, Helminthosporium species.	1.4% of the mycelium.
		Chlorine-containing Compounds	
79	Caldariomycin	Caldariomyces fumago.	0.4% of the glucose consumed.
80	Erdin[7]	Aspergillus terreus.	0.6% of the sugar consumed.
81	Geodin[7]	Aspergillus terreus.	0.5% of the sugar consumed.
82	Griseofulvin[1]	Penicillium griseofulvum, P. janczewskii.	2% of the mycelium.
83	Nalgiolaxin[8]	Penicillium nalgiovensis.	0.18% of dry mycelium.
84	Sclerotiorine	Penicillium sclerotiorum.	2% of the mycelium.
		Polysaccharides	
85	Capreolinose[9]	Penicillium capreolinum.	
86	Glycogen[10] (red-brown I_2 color)	White species of Aspergillus, Penicillium digitatum.	
87	Gums	Oidium sp., Penicillium lactis, P. guttulosum, Monilia candida, Mucor racemosus.	38% on 10% mannose.
88	Levan[11]	Aspergillus sydowii.	(From sucrose only).
89	Luteic acid (Luteose)[12]	Penicillium luteum.	10-12%.
90	Mold starch[10] (blue I_2 color)	Penicillium species.	
91	Mycodextran[10] (no I_2 color)	Penicillium expansum, Aspergillus niger.	2% of the growth.
92	Mycogalactan[13]	Aspergillus niger (produced along with Mycodextran).	
93	Polygalactose[13] (galactocarolose)	Penicillium charlesii.	Approx. 4% of the sugar consumed (crude).
94	Polymannose[14]	Penicillium charlesii.	Approx. 4% sugar consumed (crude).
95	Rugulose[13]	Penicillium rugulosum.	
96	Sclerotiose[10]	Penicillium sclerotiorum.	10% of the mycelial weight.
97	Varianose[15]	Penicillium varians.	Approx. 1% of the glucose consumed (crude material).
		Sterols and Lipids	
98	Ergosterol	Aspergillus niger, A. oryzae, Fusarium lycopersici, F. lini bolley, Helminthosporium avenae, H. ravenelii, H. velutinum, Lentinus lepideus, Penicillium expansum, P. puberulum.	0.13% - 1.7% of mycelium.
99	Ergosteryl palmitate	Penicillium brevi-compactum, P. italicum.	0.5% of the growth, 0.6% of the glucose consumed.
100	Fat	All organisms.	Various.
101	Lecithin	Aspergillus oryzae (spores).	
102	Lecithin and cephalin	Aspergillus sydowii.	0.43-0.73%.
103	Phosphatides	Aspergillus oryzae, A. sydowii, A. citromyces.	
104	Sterols	Aspergillus fischeri, Penicillium puberulum, Paecilomyces varioti, Fusaria.	0.13%-1.0% of the dry mycelium.
		Nitrogen-containing Compounds	
105	Adenine	Aspergillus niger.	0.05%.
106	Aspergillic acid	Aspergillus flavus.	1% of the carbohydrate added.
107	Betaine	Aspergillus oryzae (spores).	
108	Choline sulfate	Aspergillus sydowii (from hydrolysis of mycelium).	
109	Hypoxanthine	Aspergillus oryzae, Rhizopus japonicus.	
110	Lycomarasmin (asparagyl-glycylhydroxyalanine)	Fusarium lycopersici.	110 mg/l of medium on glucose.
111	Stachydrine (n-methyl-proline-methyl betaine)	Aspergillus oryzae, Rhizopus japonicus.	
112	Thiamine	Fusarium lini bolley.	20 gammas/gram of mycelium.
113	Urea	Penicillium johannioli, Aspergillus niger, Rhizopus nigricans.	
114	Uric acid	Aspergillus oryzae (spores).	

/1/ Possesses antibiotic properties but is not in clinical use. /5/ Compare Items 46, 51, 59, and 78. Different species of Helminthosporium have different proportions of these pigments. /6/ Related to alboleersin. /7/ Geodin and erdin are closely related compounds. /8/ Mono-chloronalgiovensin. /9/ Hydrolysis yields mannose, glucose, galactose and mannonic acid. /10/ Hydrolysis yields glucose. /11/ Hydrolysis yields fructose. /12/ Hydrolysis yields β-glucose-malonic acid (2:1), demalonylated luteic acid. /13/ Hydrolysis yields galactose. /14/ Hydrolysis yields mannose. /15/ Hydrolysis yields D-glucose, D-galactose and D-idose or L-altrose.

236. METABOLIC RATES: SOIL ORGANISMS

In columns B D F I K the following symbols are used: μμ = a millionth of a millionth (10^{-12}); μ = a millionth (10^{-6}); m = a thousandth (10^{-3}); M = million (10^{6}). Values in columns I J K are included only to indicate the order of magnitude of the metabolic activity of representative groups of organisms.

Organism (A)	Weight mg (B)	Temperature[1] °C (C)	Metabolic Rate — Calories[2] Cal/ind/hr[4] (D)	Cal/kg/hr (E)	Metabolic Rate — Oxygen Consumption ml/ind/hr[5] (F)	L/kg/hr (G)	Respiratory Quotient[3] (H)	Typical Estimates, Natural Soils — Number Per sq m (I)	Mass g/sq m (J)	Metabolism Cal/hr/sq m (K)
Bacteria								200-1200 MM	200-1200	330 m
Acetobacter	1mμ					250[6]				
Azotobacter						750[6]				
Escherichia coli						25-75[6]				
Sarcina lutea		20.5	33 mμμ	33	7 μμ	7	0.71			
Fungi								100-500 M	40-400	21-32 m
Mycoderma sp	100 mμ	20.0	0.024 mμ	238	4.9 mμ	49	(0.82)			
Saccharomyces sp	180 mμ	20.0	8.7 μμ	48.1	1.8 mμ	10	(0.82)			
Protozoa								0.2-20 M	38	4-107 m
Chaos chaos (ameba)	0.05	22.5	42-62 mμ	0.8-1.2	8.6-12.9 μ	0.17-0.25	(0.82)		0.7-17.8	
Nematoda										
Monhystera	0.2-0.3	16.0	1.4-2.2 μ	6.1-8.3	300-450 μ	1.3-1.7	0.83			
Plectus	0.5-1.0	16.0	2.9-5.8 μ	4.8-6.8	600-1200 μ	1-1.4	0.83			
Dorylaimus	0.5-56	16.0	1.9-216 μ	2.4-4.5	400-45,000 μ	0.5-1.1	0.83			
Annelida										
Lumbricus terrestris (earthworm)	500	17-20	0.14 m	0.29	0.03	0.06	(0.82)	50-2000	1.6	0.5 m
	5000	20-23	1.4 m	0.29	0.3	0.06	(0.82)			
	1200	13.0	0.42 m	0.35	0.09	0.07	(0.82)			
Mollusca								0-8500	0-50	0-15 m
Helix aspersa (garden snail)	10,000	10.0	2.1 m	0.21	0.43	0.04	(0.82)			
	10,000	20.0	4.2 m	0.42	0.88	0.09	(0.82)			
Arthropoda										
Crustacea								0-200	0-1.2	0-2.4 m
Talorchestia megalopthalma	120	12-13	0.1 m	0.87	0.02	0.18				
	390	12-13	0.16 m	0.40	0.03	0.08				
	110	22-23	0.18 m	1.6	0.04	0.34				
	270	22-23	0.28 m	1.0	0.06	0.22	(0.82)			
Acari (mites)								2000-120,000	4.5	6.7 m
Oribatei	0.25	14.5	150-190 mμ	0.6-0.8	30-40 μ	0.12-0.16	(0.82)		0.07-0.8	0.1-1.2 m
Euzetes aterrimus	0.03	11.3	48 mμ	1.6	10 μ	0.33	(0.82)			
Notaspis coleoptratus										
Parasitiformes								200-7400	0.09-0.2	0.1-0.3 m
Macrocheles sp	0.25	12.0	480 mμ	1.9	100 μ	0.4	(0.82)	175-640	0.64	0.4-1.4 m
Araneae (spiders)								1.6-38	0.005-0.15	0.02-0.5 m
Lycosa sp	15.1	13.0	33 μ	2.2	6900 μ	0.45	(0.82)			
Opiliones										
Nemastoma sp	3.8	13.0	9.2 μ	2.4	1900 μ	0.5	(0.82)			
Insecta								40-40,000	6.8	27-46 m
Collembola										
Pogonognathus plumbens	1.3-2.5	13.0	6.5-9.3 μ	3.7-5.0	1400-1900 μ	0.77-1.0	(0.82)			
Orchesella flavescens	1.8-3.5	13.0	5.3-11.7 μ	2.9-3.3	1100-2400 μ	0.61-0.69	(0.82)			
Diptera									1.0	1.3 m
Tipula sp (larva)	275	13.0	285 mμ	1.0	0.06	0.21	(0.81)			
	605	13.0	500 μ	0.82	0.1	0.17	(0.82)			
Coleoptera									3.8	6.1 m
Carabus nemoralis (ground beetle)	645	13.0	765 μ	1.2	0.16	0.25	(0.82)			
Epaphius secalis (ground beetle)	1.2-2.2	13.0	7-9.8 μ	5.9	1.5-2.0 m	1.2	(0.82)			
Notiophilus biguttatus (ground beetle)	7.5	13.0	36 μ	4.8	7.6 m	0.88	(0.82)			
Staphylinus olens (rove beetle)	245	13.0	285 μ	1.1	0.06	0.24	(0.82)			

/1/ Temperature used in determining values in columns D-G. Values in column K are reduced to the common standard at 16°C according to Krogh's curve. /2/ Kilocalories. /3/ CO_2 liberated ÷ O_2 consumed. Values in parentheses are assumed. /4/ Kilocalories per individual per hour. /5/ Milliliters per individual per hour. /6/ Assuming a water content of 75% of the fresh weight.

237. BIOCHEMICAL ACTIVITIES, PROCESSES, PRODUCTS, AND USES: MICROORGANISMS USEFUL TO MAN

This table lists only a few of the vast number of microbial reactions that are known, and is merely representative of types of processes used commercially. Most processes are patented; and recent information on yields and process modifications is not generally available. Industry is continually seeking better yielding strains of microorganisms through selection and mutation.

Part I: GENERAL ORGANIC COMPOUNDS

	Product	Microorganism	Substrate[1]	Type of Culture[1]	pH	Temp °C	Time da	Yield	Industrial Uses
1	Acetone-butanol	Clostridium saccharoaceto-butylicum, and others	Molasses diluted to 5-7% sugar, with addition of NH₃ compounds and CaHPO₄ as required.	Anaer.	5.0-7.0	29-34	1.7-2	28-33% mixed solvents (sugar basis); 74% butanol, 23% acetone, 4% ethanol.	Solvents; chemical manufacturing.
2	2,3-Butanediol	Bacillus polymyxa; Aerobacter aerogenes	Grain mash, or starch plus nutrients, or sugars plus nutrients.	Preferably aer.	6.2	33	1.3-3	26-30% weight of carbohydrates.	Solvent; humectant; chemical intermediate.
3	Dihydroxyacetone	Acetobacter suboxydans	5% glycerol, 0.5% yeast extract, 0.25% KH₂PO₄.	Aer., sub. or surf.	5.5-7.0	28-30	3-10	90% of theory.	Fine chemical.
4	Ethanol	Saccharomyces cerevisiae	Molasses diluted to 12% sugar. Amm. sulfate or phosphate added as nutrients.	Aer. in early stages only	4.0-4.5	21-35	2.1	90% of theory based on fermentable sugar.	Solvent; fuel; chemical intermediate.
5	Glycerol	S. ellipsoideus var. Cal. wine yeast; S. cerevisiae	Molasses diluted to 17.5-20% sugar. Soda ash to 5% of mash added during fermentation.	Aer. in early stages only	7-8	30-32	5	20-25% of theory based on fermentable sugar.	Solvent; explosives, drugs and cosmetics; humectant.
6	Citric acid	Aspergillus niger, or A. wentii	10-20% sucrose, or purified molasses mashes plus nutrients.	Sub., aer. or surf.	3.0-4.1	25-30	3-10	60-90% based on sugar.	Food products, medicinal citrates; in blood for transfusion.
7	Fumaric acid	Rhizopus nigricans	5-10% invert sugar, plus nutrient salts and CaCO₃.	Sub., aer.	5-6	33	4	58-64% based on sugar utilized.	Manufacture of alkyd resins, wetting agents.
8	Gluconic acid	Aspergillus niger, strain 67	Corn sugar, MgSO₄, KH₂PO₄, (NH₄)₂HPO₄, CaCO₃. Glucose conc. 15.2 g/100 ml.	Sub., aer.	5.0	30	1	93-97% based on glucose utilized.	Pharmaceutical products.
9	2-Keto-gluconic acid	Pseudomonas spp	Glucose, gluconic acid.	Aer.	4.5-7	30-35	1.4-1.5	90%.	Intermediate for D-araboascorbic acid.
10	5-Keto-gluconic acid	Acetobacter suboxydans	Glucose.	Aer.	4.5-7	30-35	1.5-2.5	90-95%.	Intermediate for tartaric acid.
11	Itaconic acid	Aspergillus terreus	6.6-27.5% glucose or sucrose (molasses) plus (NH₄)₂SO₄, MgSO₄, corn steep liquor. Sugars plus mineral nutrients.	Sub. or surf., aer.	1.8-2.2	35	2-3	38-60% based on sugar.	Manufacture of alkyd resins, wetting agents.
12	Kojic acid	A. flavus		Aer.	2.0-3.5	29-35	12	45-60% based on sugar.	No uses developed.
13	Lactic acid	Lactobacillus delbrueckii	Acid hydrolyzed corn starch or whey, plus nutrients and CaCO₃.	Anaer.	5.5-6.5	45	5-10	93-94% based on sugar.	Food products, textile and laundry, chem. mfg., deliming hides.
14	Bacitracin(s)	Bacillus licheniformis	Dextrose, sucrose or starch, plus soybean or peanut meal or other protein.	Sub., aer.	6.2-7.7	37	2-3	1.5 grams per liter.	Active against Gram-pos. bacteria topically.
15	Carbomycin (Magnamycin)	Streptomyces halstedii	Media of organic composition.	Sub., aer.	6-8		3-5	100 mg per liter.	Active against some Gram-pos. bact., rickettsia, large viruses.
16	Chloramphenicol (Chloromycetin)	S. venezuelae	1% maltose, 0.5% casamino acids, 0.5% distillers' solubles, 0.5% NaCl.	Sub., aer.	6.7	23-27	3-6	170 mg per liter.	Same as aureomycin.
17	Chlortetracycline (Aureomycin)	S. aureofaciens	0.5-5.0% starch or monosaccharoses; amino acids, casein, fish meal, soybean meal, urea, nitrates, NH₃ compounds or corn steep liquor; inorg. salts of K, Ca, Mg, Fe, S, Cu, Mn, and Zn.	Sub., aer.	6.0-7.0	26-28	1-3	500-1300 mg per liter.	Effective orally against Gram-pos. and some Gram-neg. bacteria, some rickettsia and some viruses.
18	Cycloheximide (Actidione)	S. griseus	Glucose, salts, soybean meal, and butyl fermentation residue.	Aer.	6-8	24	3-5	80-250 mg per liter.	Antibiotic: yeasts, fungi, esp. plant disease fungi.
19	Erythromycin (Ilotycin)	S. erythreus	Glucose, soybean meal, corn steep liquor.	Sub., aer.	6.4-7.2	26-30	3-5	350 mg per liter.	Same as aureomycin.
20	Fumagillin (Phagopedin Sigma)	Aspergillus fumigatus	Dextrin and corn steep liquor.	Sub., aer.	6.5-7.5	24-30	1.5-4	300 mg per liter.	Amebicide.
21	Neomycin (complex)	Streptomyces fradiae	Glucose, soya peptone, meat extract, NaCl, ZnSO₄.	Sub., aer.	6.5-6.8	24-30	3.8-6	2-3 grams per liter.	Active against Gram-pos. and Gram-neg. bacteria.
22	Oxytetracycline (Terramycin)	S. rimosus	Soybean meal, starch, casein digest, salts.	Sub., aer.	7.0-8.0	24-30	2	>1 gram per liter.	Broad spectrum antibiotic.
23	Penicillin	Penicillium chrysogenum Q176 or derived mutants	Corn steep liquor, lactose, dextrose, animal or vegetable oil, salts, phenylacetic acid.	Sub., aer.	5.5-7.5	23-25	2-6	1000-3000 International Units per ml.	Active against many Gram-pos. organisms.
24	Polymyxins	Bacillus polymyxa	Glucose, yeast extract, salts.	Sub., aer.	6.3-7.9	25	5	163-358 units polymyxin D per ml.	Active against Gram-neg. bacteria.
25	Streptomycin	Streptomyces griseus[2]	Glucose, soybean meal, corn steep liquor, NaCl, and animal or vegetable oil.	Sub., aer.	6.0-7.5	24-30	3-6	150-900 mg per liter.	Active against many bacteria, particularly Myco. tuberculosis.
26	Viomycin (Vinactin)	S. floridae or S. puniceus	Glucose, hydrolyzed casein, yeast hydrolyzate, salts.	Sub., aer.	6.0-8.0	24-26	3-6	600 mg per liter.	Active against Myco. tuberculosis.
27	Bacterial amylase	Bacillus subtilis	Vegetable protein plus sugar for surf.; starch, cereal grain and protein for sub.	Surf., aer. or sub., aer.	6.5-7.0	30-40	1-3	400-500 grams amylase concentrate from 100 liters culture.	Modified starches; sizing paper; desizing textiles.

No.	Product	Microorganism	Method of Preparation / Medium	Conditions	pH	Temp	Time	Yield	Function / Use
28	Bacterial protease	B. subtilis	1% protein, 6% carbohydrate, salts.	Surf., aer.	6.5-7.0	37	3-5		Bating hides; desizing fibers; spot remover; tenderizing meat.
29	Pectinases	Aspergillus wentii or A. aureus (Nakazawa)	1000 kg bran plus 800 liters H_2O. Inoculate with 100 liters spore suspension.	Aer.		33-37	2-3	10-95%.	Clarifying agents in fruit juice industries.
30	11-γ-Hydroxyprogesterone	Rhizopus arrhizus, R. nigricans, others	Progesterone, plus lactalbumin digest, corn steep liquor, glucose.	Aer.	4.4-6	24-28	2-3	10-40% of sucrose used.	Intermediate for 17-γ-hydroxycorticosterone.
31	Dextran	Leuconostoc mesenteroides	Sucrose plus nutrients.	Anaer.		20-30	1-5		Stabilizer in food products; blood plasma substitute.
32	Sorbose	Acetobacter suboxydans	25% sorbitol plus yeast extract or corn steep liquor.	Aer., sub., or surf.	5.1-6.8	28-30	3-10	90-95% of theory.	Manufacture of ascorbic acid.
33	Cobalamin	Streptomyces olivaceus; Propionbacterium freudenreichii	Distillers' solubles, dextrose, $CaCO_3$, $CoCl_2$.	Sub., aer. agitation.	6.5-8.0	27-29	3-5	1.2 mg per liter, average.	Pernicious anemia; food and feed supplementation.
34	Ergosterol	Saccharomyces carlsbergensis	Saccharine materials with nutrients.	Aer.	7.0-7.5	25	1-2	2-2.7% of weight of yeast.	Manufacture vitamin D.
35	Riboflavin[3]	Eremothecium ashbyii, Ashbya gossypii, and others	For E. ashbyii, carbohydrates and protein; for A. gossypii, glucose, corn steep and animal steep liquor.	Sub., aer.	4.5-7.5	27-30	5-10	0.5-2.5 grams per liter.	Food and feed supplementation.

/1/ Sub.=submerged culture; surf.=surface culture; aer.=aerobic; anaer.=anaerobic. /2/ Improved strains obtained by exposing organism to UV light or nitrogen mustard. /3/ See U.S. Patent 2,605,210.

Part II: FOODS AND BEVERAGES

Product	Microorganism	Method of Preparation	Factors Influencing Reaction	Function of Microorganism
1 Acidophilus milk	Lactobacillus acidophilus	Fresh, whole milk sterilized at 120°C for 15 min is cooled and inoculated with the organism.	Microaerophilic, pH 6.6, 35-37°C, 20-48 hr.	Produces lactic acid from milk sugar[1].
2 Cheese Camembert and Brie types	Penicillium camemberti Thom and others	Curd cut into cakes 3-4 cm thick, containing 55-60% H_2O and salted on surface.	4 wk at 10-16°C, in a ripening room at 88% relative humidity. Partially aerobic.	Mold grows on cheese surface, gradually softening whole mass of curd.
3 Roquefort and Gorgonzola types	P. roqueforti	Raw curd pressed to leave irregular cracks and channels; inoculated with mold grown on bread.	Aerated during ripening at 9°C by piercing with wires.	Produces caproic, caprylic, other acids imparting characteristic flavor.
4 Pickles	Mixed natural lactic acid organisms, including Lactobacillus plantarum	Cucumbers in tanks allowed to undergo spontaneous lactic fermentation in salt brine. For dill pickles, dill spices added before fermentation. For others, salt is leached, and pickles packed with vinegar, sugar, spices, etc.	Salt concentration and availability of O_2 affect rate and kind of fermentation. Optimum temp is 21-27°C.	Converts fermentable substances, forming particularly lactic acid. Final titratable acidity, as lactic acid, 0.5-1.0%, pH = 3.5-3.8.
5 Sauerkraut	Same as for pickles	Shredded cabbage placed in vats with salt. Undergoes spontaneous lactic fermentation.	Anaerobic fermentation. Optimum temp 16-24°C.	Converts fermentable substances into lactic acid, mainly, plus acetic acid and ethanol. Final acidity, as lactic, 1.5-2.0%.
6 Vinegar	Acetobacter aceti, A. pasteurianum and other Acetobacter spp	Alcoholic solutions (e.g., wine, cider) derived from fermentation of grapes, apples, or grain are "acetified" by acetic acid bacteria.	Aerobic requiring 8-10 da at 28-40°C, or less depending on process conditions.	Alcohol oxidized to acetic acid, 5% acid being formed from approximately 5% alcohol.
7 Yeast, bakers'	Saccharomyces cerevisiae (selected baker's strains)	Molasses solutions with ammonium salts, phosphates, and Mg salts seeded with pure yeasts strains. Increments of medium added frequently as nutrients are exhausted.	Very vigorous aeration throughout process. pH 3.4-4.5. Temp 24-30°C. Growth complete in 11 hr.	Converts 100 parts molasses to equivalent of 100 parts pressed yeast (27% dry matter).
8 Beer	S. cerevisiae or S. carlsbergensis	Barley malt and starch adjuncts mixed with warm water. After enzymic starch conversion, wort is filtered, then boiled with hops, and finally fermented with yeast.	Aerobic in early stages, but quickly becomes anaerobic. Temp 8-12°C. pH at start 5.0-5.4; at end 4.0-4.8. Primary fermentation lasts 5-9 da.	Converts sugar into alcohol and CO_2; produces changes in proteins and other minor constituents which modify flavor.
9 Rum	S. cerevisiae or other yeasts	Blackstrap molasses containing 12-14% fermentable sugar. Ammonium sulfate and occasionally phosphates may be added as nutrients. Distilled after fermentation.	Optimum pH 4.0-4.7. Initial temp 21°C rising to final temp of 35.5. Fermentation lasts 3-7 da.	Sugar converted to alcohol which is then removed by distillation.
10 Whisky, Scotch	S. cerevisiae (generally a top yeast)	Grain mash cooked, saccharified with peated malt and fermented. Batch distilled and distillate aged in oak casks at least 3 yr; then blended with grain whiskey.	Optimum pH 4.0-5.0. Initial temp 26°C. Fermentation completed in 72 hrs.	Produces alcohol and congeneric substances (acids, esters, various alcohols) which with the peated malt give characteristic Scotch flavor.
11 Whiskey, bourbon	S. cerevisiae	Grain mash consistency of corn (at least 51%); generally with rye, cooked and saccharified with malt and fermented. Distillate, between 110-130° proof, matured in charred oak barrels.	Same as for Scotch whisky.	Same as for Scotch whisky, but the flavor is characteristic of bourbon whiskey.
12 Wine	S. ellipsoideus, various strains	Grape must with sugar concentration up to 22° Balling is sulfited to reduce rate of fermentation. Allowed to ferment with special strain of yeast, or with yeast naturally present on the grape. Primary fermentation succeeded by a period of storage for maturation.	Aerobic in early stages, but mainly anaerobic later. Temp below 29.4°C, but varies according to local conditions, yeast strain, and type of wine. Fermentation lasts 7-11 da[2].	Converts sugar into alcohol, and also produces changes in minor constituents which modify flavor and bouquet. Amount of alcohol varies according to type of wine.

/1/ Lactic acid plus large quantities of organism produced are used for various disorders of the gastrointestinal tract. /2/ 14-20°C with S. cerevisiae.

238. BASAL AND RESTING ENERGY METABOLISM: VERTEBRATES

Animal	Stage	Approximate Age		Body Weight kg		Body Surface Area sq m		Resting Metabolism[2] Cal/kg/da		Cal/sq m/da		Oxygen Consumption liters/kg/da		Basal Metabolism Cal/kg/da		Cal/sq m/da		Oxygen Consumption liters/kg/da	
		♂	♀	♂	♀	♂	♀	♂	♀	♂	♀	♂	♀	♂	♀	♂	♀	♂	♀
Man	Adult			65	56	1.83	1.65							25.5	23.2	910	790		
Baboon	Adult			6.2		0.40								48		760			
Beef cattle	Young	1.8 mo		70		1.4	1.3	43.8	51.1	2190	2385	9.1	10.6						
	Half-grown	11 mo		300	250	3.2	2.9	25.6	26.3	2420	2295	5.3	5.5						
	Adult	1.7 yr		500	400	4.2	3.7	21.2	21.1	2515	2270	4.4	4.4			1595	1635	3.8	3.2
Cat	Adult			3.0		0.2								50		750			
Chimpanzee	Adult			38		1.1								29.2		980			
Dairy cattle	Young	6 mo		150		2.4			34.4		2100		7.1						
	Half-grown	1.2 yr		300		3.6			26.0		2170		5.4						
	Adult	2 yr		500		5.0			21.1		2180		4.4				770		
Dog	Adult			15.5	11.7	0.65	0.58							33.5	38.5	800	770		
Elephant	Adult			3670		23.8								13.3		2060			
Elephant, small	Adult			1360		13.7								11.8		1170			
Goat	Young			2				130	125										
	Half-grown			20				63	54										
	Adult			70				42	34										
Guinea pig	Young	82 da	30 da	0.2		0.029		115	120	780	805	23	24	110	110	735	765	23	24
	Half-grown	290 da	87 da	0.4		0.046		90	95	800	825	29		85	90	755	790	18	19
	Adult		270 da	0.8		0.071		63	68	710	765	13	13	60	63	675	710	13	13
Horse	Young	2.8 mo	2.9 mo	200		2.8		32.2	32.7	2280	2320	6.7	6.8						
	Half-grown	9.5 mo	8.5 mo	350		4.0		24.6	25.3	2150	2210	5.0	5.2						
	Adult	4.2 yr	2.8 yr	650		5.9		25.2	24.7	2770	2710	5.2	5.1						
Macaque	Adult			4.2		0.31								49.3		675			
Marmot	Adult			2.6		0.18								28.3		420			
Monkey, rhesus	Adult			3.2		0.26								48.4		610			
Mouse, albino	Adult			0.02		0.005								170		525			
Mouse, dwarf	Adult			0.008		0.004								125		280			
Mouse, obese	Adult			0.06		0.01								130		550			
Mule	Young	4 mo		200		2.9		39.2		2700		8.1							
	Half-grown	13 mo		400		4.5		30.6		2705		6.3							
	Adult	38 mo		600		5.8		26.4		2710		5.5							
Pony, shetland	Adult			280		4.4								16.7		1060			
Rabbit	Adult			3.5		0.2								47		810			
Rat	Young	29 da		0.05		0.013		280		1085		60		240		1060		51	
	Half-grown	50 da	60 da	0.15	0.1	0.026		195	165	1120	970	39	34	160	155	930	930	34	33
	Adult	60 da	120 da	0.2	0.2	0.031		155	135	1000	870	32	28	140	120	905	760	30	25
Sheep	Adult			49.5	42.7	1.10	0.95							26.3	25.7	1180	1160		
Swine	Young	9.4 mo	8.3 mo	75		1.5		37.3	40.5	1880	2040	7.7	8.4	30.9	30.2	1550	1520	6.4	6.3
	Half-grown	1.3 yr	1.1 yr	150		2.3		28.9	25.1	1880	1625	6.0	5.2	21.9	18.7	1420	1210	4.5	3.9
	Adult	2.1 yr		250		3.2		23.7	17.8	1860	1390	4.9	3.7	17.4	14.1	1360	1100	3.6	2.9
Birds, wild	Adult			3.0		0.2								57		830			
Canary				0.016		0.006								310		760			
Chicken	Young	4 wk		0.25	0.2	0.04	0.03	195	210	1220	1230	40	43	90	90	870	830	19	19
	Half-grown	13 wk		1.1	0.9	0.11	0.1	105	100	1020	900	21	20	85	70	1075	800	18	15
	Adult	25 wk		2.6	2.0	0.21	0.17	95	75	1160	880	19	16						
Dove, ring	Adult			0.15		0.03								130		700			
Duck	Adult			0.93		0.1								90		855			
Goose	Adult			5.0	3.3	0.29	0.23							54	61	940	880		
Parakeet	Adult			0.03		0.009								225		690			
Pigeon	Adult			0.28		0.04								100		670			
Lizard				1.2		0.11								2.5		29			
Turtle				0.14		0.02								11.4		64			
Frog				to 0.05												130			
Toad				to 0.05												130			
Fish				to 0.25												33			
Fish, sturgeon				1400		11.8								0.3		31			

/1/ Surface area in sq m calculated from k x W^0.67, or, in sq cm, from the following equations (W=body weight in grams): man, 3.81 W^0.425 x H^0.725 (where H=height in cm); baboon, 11.7 W^0.667; chimpanzee, 10 W^0.667; dog, 11.2 W^0.667; guinea pig, 9.85 W^0.64; monkey, rhesus, 11.7 W^0.667; mouse, 15.18 W^0.667; rabbit, 56.33 W^0.436; sheep, 8.5 W^0.667; chicken, 8.19 W^0.705; reptiles, amphibians, fish, 9 W^0.67. Surface area in sq m (W=body weight in kg): beef cattle, 0.13 W^0.56; dairy cattle, 0.15 W^0.56; horse, 0.1 W^0.63; mule, 0.1 W^0.636, rat, 0.0011 W^0.63 (W in grams); swine, 0.097 W^0.633.

/2/ Resting metabolism refers to heat production when animal is at rest, although neither in a strictly thermo-neutral environment, nor in a post-absorptive state. Cattle, goats, swine, and chickens were measured in a recumbent position. Resting metabolism, as thus defined, is considerably greater than basal metabolism, exact values depending on nature of diet, time after feeding, and environmental temperature.

239. BASAL METABOLISM: MAN

Values are smoothed means of basal Calories per sq m per hr from the three largest and most authoritative sets of original data, representing a total of 4016 measurements. The three sets of data used are: (1) The Mayo Foundation Standards of Boothby, Berkson and Dunn, based upon 639 males and 828 females; (2) the British measurements of Robertson and Reid, based upon 987 males and 1323 females; (3) The Carnegie Nutrition Laboratory data of Harris and Benedict, based upon 136 males and 103 females. The height-weight formula of DuBois and DuBois was used in computing the sq m of body surface area: $SA = 0.007184 \times W^{0.425} \times S^{0.725}$, where SA is the surface area in square meters, W is the body weight in kilograms and S is the height in centimeters. Ranges, given in parentheses, are calculated from an average coefficient of variation[1] of 6.9% and represent estimate "b" of the 95% range. Somewhat higher values are to be expected on first tests (i.e., on persons not accustomed to the procedures). For comparison of these standards with previous American and other important standards, see table below.

	Age yr	Males Cal/sq m/hr	Females Cal/sq m/hr		Age yr	Males Cal/sq m/hr	Females Cal/sq m/hr
1	Three	60.1(51.8-68.3)	54.5(47.0-62.0)	24	Twenty-six	38.2(32.9-43.5)	35.0(30.2-39.8)
2	Four	57.9(49.9-65.9)	53.9(46.5-61.3)	25	Twenty-seven	38.0(32.8-43.2)	35.0(30.2-39.8)
3	Five	56.3(48.5-64.1)	53.0(45.7-60.3)	26	Twenty-eight	37.8(32.6-43.0)	35.0(30.2-39.8)
4	Six	54.0(46.5-61.5)	51.2(44.1-58.3)	27	Twenty-nine	37.7(32.5-42.9)	35.0(30.2-39.8)
5	Seven	52.3(45.1-59.5)	49.7(42.8-56.6)	28	Thirty	37.6(32.4-42.8)	35.0(30.2-39.8)
6	Eight	50.8(43.8-57.8)	48.0(41.4-54.6)	29	Thirty-one	37.4(32.2-42.6)	35.0(30.2-39.8)
7	Nine	49.5(42.7-56.3)	46.2(39.8-52.6)	30	Thirty-two	37.2(32.1-42.3)	34.9(30.1-39.7)
8	Ten	47.7(41.1-54.3)	44.9(38.7-51.1)	31	Thirty-three	37.1(32.0-42.2)	34.9(30.1-39.7)
9	Eleven	46.5(40.1-52.9)	44.1(38.0-50.2)	32	Thirty-four	37.0(31.9-42.1)	34.9(30.1-39.7)
10	Twelve	45.3(39.0-51.6)	42.0(36.2-47.8)	33	Thirty-five	36.9(31.8-42.0)	34.8(30.0-39.6)
11	Thirteen	44.5(38.4-50.6)	40.5(34.9-46.1)	34	Thirty-six	36.8(31.7-41.9)	34.7(29.9-39.5)
12	Fourteen	43.8(37.8-49.8)	39.2(33.8-44.6)	35	Thirty-seven	36.7(31.6-41.8)	34.6(29.8-39.4)
13	Fifteen	43.7(37.7-49.7)	38.3(33.0-43.6)	36	Thirty-eight	36.7(31.6-41.8)	34.5(29.7-39.3)
14	Sixteen	42.9(37.0-48.8)	37.7(32.5-42.9)	37	Thirty-nine	36.6(31.5-41.7)	34.4(29.7-39.1)
15	Seventeen	41.9(36.1-47.7)	36.2(31.2-41.2)	38	Forty	36.5(31.5-41.5)	34.3(29.6-39.0)
16	Eighteen	40.5(34.9-46.1)	35.7(30.8-40.6)	39	Forty-five	36.3(31.3-41.3)	33.9(29.2-38.6)
17	Nineteen	40.1(34.6-45.6)	35.4(30.5-40.3)	40	Fifty	36.0(31.0-40.0)	33.4(28.8-38.0)
18	Twenty	39.8(34.3-45.3)	35.3(30.4-40.2)	41	Fifty-five	35.4(30.5-40.3)	32.9(28.4-37.4)
19	Twenty-one	39.4(34.0-44.8)	35.2(30.3-40.1)	42	Sixty	34.8(30.0-39.6)	32.4(27.9-36.9)
20	Twenty-two	39.2(33.8-44.6)	35.2(30.3-40.1)	43	Sixty-five	34.0(29.3-38.7)	31.8(27.4-36.2)
21	Twenty-three	39.0(33.6-44.4)	35.2(30.3-40.1)	44	Seventy	33.1(28.5-37.7)	31.3(27.0-35.6)
22	Twenty-four	38.7(33.4-44.0)	35.1(30.3-39.9)	45	Seventy-five and above	31.8(27.4-36.2)	31.1(26.8-35.4)[2]
23	Twenty-five	38.4(33.1-43.7)	35.1(30.3-39.9)				

/1/ Coefficient of variation = 6.9 = average of values from five sources. /2/ Value and range extrapolated from smoothed curve.

240. COMPARATIVE STANDARDS OF BASAL METABOLISM: MAN

Column F is the standard commonly employed heretofore in America. The underlying measurements include many first tests (on persons unaccustomed to the procedure). Values are accordingly high -- the highest of the standards. Values in column D, the British standard, are based on the lowest of repeated measurements on trained persons under rigorously basal conditions. Values in column E are based on measurements on well trained children and are generally the lowest of those given for children. Adult values in columns B and C are so similar that either standard can be used safely in clinical medicine. For children, choice between columns E or C and columns B or D will depend on the experience of the testing laboratory. Some laboratories tend to find higher basal values and some laboratories, lower. Each laboratory may accordingly develop its own standard. A variation of as much as 14% above or below the standard may occur in healthy persons (estimate "b" or "d" of the ordinary range).

	Age yr (A)	Boothby[1] 1952 Cal/sq m/hr Male (B)	Boothby[1] 1952 Cal/sq m/hr Female	Fleisch[2] 1951 Cal/sq m/hr Male (C)	Fleisch[2] 1951 Cal/sq m/hr Female	Robertson and Reid[3] 1952 Cal/sq m/hr Male (D)	Robertson and Reid[3] 1952 Cal/sq m/hr Female	Lewis, Duval and Iliff[4] 1943 Cal/sq m/hr Male (E)	Lewis, Duval and Iliff[4] 1943 Cal/sq m/hr Female	Boothby, Berkson and Dunn[5] 1936 Cal/sq m/hr Male (F)	Boothby, Berkson and Dunn[5] 1936 Cal/sq m/hr Female
1	Two			52.4	52.4			56.9	52.9		
2	Four	57.9	53.9	50.3	49.8	57.9	53.9	52.6	49.9	53.0	50.5
3	Six	54.0	51.2	48.3	47.0	54.2	51.8	49.6	46.9	51.5	46.7
4	Eight	50.8	48.0	46.3	43.8	50.1	48.4	46.6	44.0	48.0	45.7
5	Ten	47.7	44.9	44.0	42.5	46.6	44.3	43.6	41.4	46.8	43.9
6	Twelve	45.3	42.0	42.5	41.3	43.8	40.6	41.5	39.7	46.4	41.1
7	Fourteen	43.8	39.2	42.1	39.2	41.8	37.8	41.1	36.8	45.5	38.6
8	Sixteen	42.0	37.2	41.4	36.9	40.3	36.0			42.9	37.0
9	Eighteen	40.8	35.8	40.0	35.9	39.2	34.9			41.6	36.3
10	Twenty	39.9	35.3	38.6	35.3	38.4	34.3			40.3	36.0
11	Twenty-five	38.4	35.1	37.5	35.2	37.1	34.0			39.6	35.8
12	Thirty	37.6	35.0	36.8	35.1	36.4	34.1			38.9	35.7
13	Thirty-five	36.9	34.8	36.5	35.0	35.9	33.5			38.3	35.5
14	Forty	36.5	34.3	36.3	34.9	35.5	32.6			37.6	35.3
15	Forty-five	36.3	33.9	36.2	34.5	34.3[6]	32.4[6]			37.0	34.4
16	Fifty	36.0	33.4	35.8	33.9	33.9[6]	32.1[6]			36.3	33.4
17	Fifty-five	35.4	32.9	35.4	33.3	33.6[6]	31.8[6]			35.7	32.8
18	Sixty	34.8	32.4	34.9	32.7	33.2[6]	31.4[6]			35.1[7]	32.4
19	Sixty-five	34.0	31.8	34.4	32.2	32.8[6]	31.2[6]			34.5[7]	32.2
20	Seventy	33.1	31.3	33.8	31.7	32.6[6]	30.8[6]			33.4[7]	32.0[7]
21	Seventy-five[8]	31.8	31.1[9]	33.2	31.3	32.0	30.5[9]				

/1/ These are the values used in the top table; they are based on values in cols. D, F and values from Harris and Benedict, 1919. /2/ Based on values from 24 reports in the literature, including those in cols. E, F, of this table and values from Harris and Benedict, 1919. /3/ The British standard. These values constitute part of the basis for those in col. B. /4/ These values constitute part of the basis for those in col. C. /5/ These values are part of the basis for those in cols. B and C. /6/ Interpolated. Original data given for pentades 40-44, 45-49, etc. /7/ Extrapolated by authors. /8/ Values are for age 75 or over. /9/ Extrapolated.

241. TISSUE OXYGEN CONSUMPTION: ANIMALS

Oxygen consumed by tissue in a buffered medium is measured in a closed chamber at approximately 1 atm. pressure and at 37°C. Further definition of the medium is given in the key below; where only the substrate is named the medium contains that substrate in Ringer solution. The oxidation quotient ($-QO_2$) is expressed in cu mm O_2 per mg dry-weight tissue in one hour. A = serum; B = Ringer glucose; C = saline; D = Ringer phosphate; E = Ringer solution; F = horse serum; G = horse serum glucose; H = glutamate; I = lactate; J = succinate; K = pyruvate; L = glucose; M = no substrate added; N = alanine; O = butyrate.

No.	Tissue	Medium	$-QO_2$
Man			
1	Cerebral cortex	B	6.0-10.3
2	Decidua	A	2.5
3	Lung, embryo	B	3.7
4	Lymph nodes	B	3.8-5.9
5	Mucosa, gastric	B	9.6
6	Muscle, smooth, gastric	H	1.3
7	Uterine	B	0.6
8	Salivary gland	B	6.3
9	Skin, adult	B	2.1
10	Fetus	D	1.8
11	Sperm	D	0.54
12	Tonsil	B	5.1
Rat			
13	Adrenal	A	10.0
14	Brain cortex	D[1]	26.3
15	Cerebral cortex	M	2.9
16	Cerebral cortex	L	10.8
17	Cerebral cortex	H	8.0
18	Cerebral cortex	E	13.6
19	Cerebral cortex	J	9.5
20	5 da	B	6.2
21	50 da	B	14.7
22	Adult	B	8.5-17.1
23	Chorion	B	13.5
24	Diaphragm	M	6.3[2]
25	Diaphragm	L	5.4[3]
26	Diaphragm	J	9.4[4]
27	Diaphragm	K	6.3[4]
28	Embryo, 1-3 mg	A	10.5-14.6
29	13-14 da	E	7.2-11.0
30	Ganglion, dorsal root	E	8.0
31	Hypothalamus	M	10.4
32	Kidney	M	15.8[5]
33	Kidney	N	38.0
34	Kidney	O	23.2
35	Kidney	L	23.1[6]
36	Kidney	I	34.0
37	Kidney cortex	K	26.0
38	Kidney cortex	M	38.2
39	Liver	M	7.2[7]
40	Liver	O	8.1
41	Liver	L	9.0
42	Liver	J	10.7
43	Liver	I	26.0
44	Liver	D[1]	17.2
45	Liver, fetus	AB	7.1
46	3-21 da	B	13.2
47	Adult	E	9.8-10.2
48	Adult	B	6.5-11.6
49	Lung	D[1]	8.6
50	Adult	C	7.9
51	Adult	B	4.4-7.8
52	Embryo	A	10.0
53	Lymph nodes	B	4.4
54	Mammary, term. of preg.	B	1.3
Rat (concluded)			
55	Mammary, 15-22 da lactation	B	10.0
56	2 da after weaning	B	5.5
57	Medulla, 5 da	B	3.4
58	50 da	B	9.0
59	Adult	B	2.5-4.9
60	Mucosa, colon	B	3.4-14.6
61	Duodenal	B	8.8
62	Gastric	B	7.2
63	Ileum	B	3.7
64	Jejunal	B	12.4
65	Muscle, diaphragm	C,E	4.1-5.9
66	Diaphragm	A	5.9
67	Heart	B	3.8-10.4
68	Skeletal	B	2.3-3.1
69	Smooth, gastric	B	3.5
70	Smooth, intest.	C	7.1
71	Smooth, intest.	E	5.7
72	Ovary	C	3.7
73	Pancreas	B	5.2
74	Pancreas	B	5.9
75	Pituitary, anterior	B	6.6
76	Posterior	A	12.0
77	Young	F	3.9
78	Placenta	B	7.3
79	20 da	B	7.6
80	Prostate	B	22.0-32
81	Retina	B	11.6-16.6
82	Salivary gland	B	3.5
83	Skin, newborn	B	4.9-3.6[8]
84	10-36 da	B	1.8-1.2[8]
85	79 da, adult	M	7.7
86	Sperm	D[1]	12.7
87	Spleen	B	7.2-12.9
88	Spleen	B	13.0
89	Spleen	A	11.0
90	Testis	B	7.2-14.3
91	Testis	B	11.0
92	Thymus	B	12.5-5.13
93	Thyroid	A	7.6
94	Uterus	E	5.2
95	Castrate	E	7.9
Mouse			
96	Castrate		
97	Castrate, plus estrogen		
98	Adrenal	A	6.0
99	Brain cortex	D[1]	32.9
100	Cerebral cortex	E	11.0
101	Cerebral cortex	B	10.4
102	Kidney cortex	D[1]	46.1
103	Liver	C	8.8-13.8
104	Liver	E	18.7
105	Liver	B	23.1
106	Lung	B	7.3-8.0
107	Lung	B	12.0
Mouse (concluded)			
108	Ovary	A	9.0
109	Placenta, 0.4mg	A	7.5
110	10.9-3.7 mg	A	6.4
111	Pituitary	A	8.0
112	Skin, newborn	B	
113	Spleen	D[1]	16.9
Guinea Pig			
114	Adrenal	A	6.0
115	Brain cortex	D[1]	27.3
116	Cerebral cortex	C	6.9
117	Cerebral cortex	C,L[9]	11.7
118	Epithelium[10]	B	6.1
119	Of castrate	B	22.7
120	Kidney cortex	D[1]	31.8
121	Liver	C	13.0
122	Liver	E	5.0
123	Liver	E	7.4
124	Fatty	B	6.1
125	Lung	C	7.4
126	Lung	D[1]	8.5
127	Lung	B	1.7
128	Muscle, smooth[9]	B	1.4
129	Of castrate	C	2.7
130	Pancreas	C	5.0
131	Salivary gland	B	3.0
132	Skin	D	8.0
133	Sperm	A	18.4
134	Sperm	D[1]	11.6
135	Spleen	C	8.13
136	Spleen		
Rabbit			
137	Brain cortex	D[1]	28.2
138	Cerebral cortex	B	7.3-10.4
139	Embryo	B	8.5
140	Ganglion, celiac	A	4.0
141	Kidney cortex	D[1]	34.5
142	Liver	B	11.6
143	Liver	D[1]	4.2-7.7
144	Lung	B	8.0
145	Lung	B	6.7
146	Marrow, erythroid cells	A	9.0
147	Myeloid cells	A	6.0
148	Mucosa, colon	B,A	11.1
149	Uterine	A	6.1
150	Muscle, diaphragm	B	2.4
151	Smooth, intest.	B	2.6
152	Pancreas	D[1]	4.6
153	Placenta, fetal side	A	5.3
154	Uterine side	A	3.4
155	Sperm, ejaculated	D[1]	14.2
156	Spleen	B	7.7
157	Testis	B,A	11.7
158	Thyroid		
Cat			
159	Brain cortex	D[1]	26.9
Cat (concluded)			
160	Cerebral cortex	B	8.5-12.2
161	Kidney cortex	D[1]	22.7
162	Liver	D[1]	13.2
163	Lung	B	3.9
164	Lung	B	3.5
165	Medulla	B	2.5
166	Muscle, heart	B	1.4
167	Smooth, intest.		
168	Pancreas	B	5.8
169	Salivary, acetyl-choline stimulation	B	13.6
170	Esterine + AcCH	B	22.7
171	Resting	B	1.3
172	Spinal cord		
173	Spleen	D[1]	8.4
Dog			
174	Brain cortex	D[1]	21.2
175	Caudate nucleus	C,L[9]	1.36
176	Cerebellum	C,L[9]	1.07
177	Cerebral cortex	C,L[9]	1.16
178	Cerebral cortex	B	6.7
179	Heart	M	2.6
180	Heart	L	2.7
181	Heart	I	4.6
182	Heart	K	6.3
183	Kidney cortex	B	27.0
184	Liver	B	6.0
185	Liver	D[1]	11.7
186	Lung	D[1]	0.69
187	Medulla	C,L[9]	1.2
188	Muscle, skeletal	L	1.3
189	Muscle, skeletal	I	1.7
190	Muscle, skeletal	B	1.9
191	Diaphragm, young	B	4.2
192	Diaphragm, juvenile	B	2.6
193	Heart	B	3.2
194	Pancreas	B	20.8
195	Retina	B	10.6
196	Salivary	B	0.5
197	Spinal cord	C,L[9]	6.6
198	Spleen	A	1.01
199	Thalamus	B	9.1
200	Thyroid	B	2.0
201	Thyroid		
202	Midbrain	C,L[9]	0.92
Horse			
203	Brain cortex	D[1]	15.7
204	Kidney cortex	D[1]	21.5
205	Liver	D[1]	5.4
206	Liver	D[1]	2.1
207	Liver	D[1]	4.4
208	Spleen	D[1]	4.2
Cattle			
209	Brain cortex	D[1]	17.2
210	Kidney cortex	D[1]	23.5
Cattle (concluded)			
211	Liver	D[1]	8.2
212	Cow	B	2.6
213	Lung	D[1]	4.3
214	Retina, ox	B	10.7
215	Sperm	D	6.6
216	Sperm	F	11.2
217	Sperm	G	12.8
218	Sperm, epididymal	D	2.6
219	Spleen	D[1]	4.4
220	Thyroid, calf	B	2.6
Swine			
221	Cerebral cortex, 29-60 da fetus	E	5.5
222	99 da fetus	E	6.5
223	Birth to adult	E	8.5
224	Retina	B	17.7
225	Thyroid, hog	B	2.1
Sheep			
226	Brain cortex	D[1]	19.7
227	Kidney cortex	D[1]	27.5
228	Liver	B	2.5
229	Liver	B	8.5
230	Lung	D	5.4
231	Sperm, ejaculated	D	9.0
232	Spleen	D	6.9
233	Trigeminal, nerve	D[1]	0.5
234	Ganglion	E	0.3
Chick			
235	Allantois	B	22.3
236	Embryo, 0.1-1.2g	A	15.9-21.4
237	4.7 g	E	8.1
238	5-6 da	E	10-12
239	12 da	E	9.9
240	19 da	E	7.7
241	Brain	A	25.0
242	Heart, 4 da	A	30
243	Heart, 6-7 da	A	14.9
244	Liver, 6 da	B	7.5
245	Liver, 12 da	B	4.5
246	Liver, 20 da	B	1.5
Fowl			
247	Liver, hen	A	14.5
248	Sperm, ejaculated	D	2.8
Pigeon			
249	Cerebral cortex	C,L[9]	14.6
250	Lung	C	2.1
251	Muscle, skeletal	C	8.7
252	Pancreas	C	
Frog			
253	Hippocampus	E	2.4
254	Muscle, skel., rest.	E	.18-.24
255	Elect. stim.	E	.79-4.24
256	Nerve, sciatic	E	.28
257	Retina	E	0.3
258	Retina	B	3.5
259	Spinal cord		

1/ Medium essentially Ca-free Ringer phosphate, but containing pyruvate (or lactate), fumarate, glutamate and glucose. 2/ Value of 5.4 also reported. 3/ Value of 8.1 also reported. 4/ Value of 9.8 also reported. 5/ Value of 17.8 also reported. 6/ Value of 19.4 also reported. 7/ Value of 8.1 also reported. 8/ Range shows a decrease with age. 9/ Phosphate saline medium containing glucose. 10/ From seminal vesicles.

</...>

Data unless otherwise specified are for adults in resting or basal state. Rate values for protozoa are cubic millimeters oxygen per million cells per hour, and for metazoa, cubic millimeters oxygen per gram fresh weight per hour (= cubic centimeters per kilogram per hour). Rates for poikilo-thermic vertebrates and invertebrates were measured at the indicated ambient temperatures.

Organism	Rate	Organism	Rate	Organism	Rate
Mammalia		**Amphibia**		**Annelida (concluded)**	
1 Man, maximum work	4000	80 Molge vulgaris, 20°C	123	153 Nereis virens, 15°C	26
2 Man, resting	200	81 Rana esculenta, winter, 20°C	85	154 Sipunculus nudus, 16°C	50
3 Anteater, spiny	1100	82 R. esculenta, summer, 20°C	437	155 Tubifex sp, 15°C	200
4 Armadillo	201	83 R. fusca, winter, 20°C	100	**Mollusca**	
5 Bat, brown, big	800	84 R. fusca, summer, 20°C	210	156 Aplysia limacina, 16°C	30
6 Bat, brown, little	1500	85 R. temporaria, winter, 19°C	85	157 Eledone moschata, 16°C	181
7 Bear, polar, cub	700	86 R. temporaria, summer, 19°C	554	158 Helix pomatia, 20°C	94
8 Cat, Australian, native	560	**Pisces**		159 Limax agrestis, 20°C	350
9 Cow	390	87 Anguilla vulgaris, 25°C	128	160 Mytilus edulis, 14°C	13
10 Dog	580	88 Arapaima gigas, 25°C	9	161 M. galloprovincialis, 25°C	18
11 Dormouse, awake	852	89 Cobitis fossilis, 20°C	51	162 Octopus vulgaris, 16°C	47-87
12 Dormouse, hibernating	15	90 Crenichthys baileyi, 37°C	546	163 Pleurobranchea meckeli, 25°C	36
13 Elephant, Indian, 37 yr, ♀	155	91 Cyprinus tinca, 20°C	104	164 Pterotrachea coronata, 16°C	7.8
14 Fox, arctic, white	505	92 Esox lucius, 18°C	102	165 Sepia officinalis, 15°C	320
15 Guinea pig	1250	93 Heliasis chromis, 20°C	162	166 Tethys leporina, 16°C	12
16 Hamster	1050	94 Lepidosiren paradoxa, 20°C	42	**Echinodermata**	
17 Hamster, golden, awake	2900	95 Salmo trutta, 12°C	226	167 Asterias rubens, 15°C	30
18 Hamster, golden, hibernating	70	96 Scomber scombrus, 20°C	726	168 Holothuria impatiens, 25°C	17
19 Horse	130	97 Serranus scriba, 20°C	151	169 Ophioderma longicauda, 25°C	8-32
20 Lemming	1700	98 Sphoeroides maculatus, 20°C	62	170 Strongylocentrotus lividus, 25°C	15
21 Manatee, Florida sea cow	120	99 Stenotomus chrysops, 20°C	174	**Nemathelminthes**	
22 Marmoset	1040	100 Tautoga onitis, 20°C	62	171 Ascaridia galli, 37°C	525
23 Monkey, night	510	101 Tautogolabus adspersus, 21°C	120	172 Ascaris lumbricoides, large, 37°C	72
24 Mouse, house, basal	1530	**Cephalochordata and Tunicata**		173 A. lumbricoides, small, 37°C	156
25 Mouse, house, resting	3500	102 Amphioxus lanceolatus, 16°C	35	174 A. lumbricoides, ♂, 37°C	112
26 Opossum, Australian	700	103 A. lanceolatus, 20°C	45	175 A. lumbricoides, ♀, 37°C	61
27 Platypus, duckbilled	460	104 Ascidia mentula, 25°C	4.8	176 Heterakis spumosa, 38°C	880
28 Porpoise	360	105 Salpa pinnata, 16°C	8	177 Litomosoides carinii, 37.5°C	800
29 Rabbit	460-850	106 S. pinnata, 20°C	12	178 Nematodirus sp, 37°C	1070
30 Raccoon	395	107 S. tilesii, 16°C	2.0	179 Neoaplectana glaseri, 30°C	2600
31 Rat	2000	108 S. tilesii, 20°C	2.8	180 Nippostrongylus muris, 37°C	1430
32 Rat, kangaroo	950	**Arthropoda**		181 Ostertagia circumcincta, 38°C	1480
33 Seal	540	109 Apis mellifera, resting, 20°C	17,466	182 Setaria equinum, 38°C	250
34 Sheep	340	110 A. mellifera, true flight, 20°C	87,000	183 Strongylus equinus, 38°C	511
35 Shrew, Monterey	7200	111 Asellus aquaticus, 17°C	348	184 Syphacia obvelata, 38°C	1010
36 Shrew, long-tailed	13,700	112 Astacus leptodactylus, 20°C	70	**Platyhelminthes**	
37 Shrew, short-tailed	5200	113 Callianax subterranea, 15°C	930	185 Dendrocoelum lacteum, 2.5°C	4.4
38 Shrew, Sonoma, ♂	6100	114 Carcinus maenus, 15°C	625	186 D. lacteum, 25°C	26.3
39 Shrew, Sonoma, ♀	5500	115 Cryptocercus punctulatus, 5°C	28.5	187 Diphyllobothrium latum[2], 37°C	243
40 Sloth, two-toed	216	116 Culex sp, 20°C	575	188 Fasciola hepatica, 37.5°C	330
41 Sloth, three-toed	168	117 Dronia vulgaris, 15°C	3000	189 Paramphistomum cervi, 38°C	3
42 Squirrel, arctic, ground	600	118 Drosophila americana, resting, 20°C	1560	190 Planaria torva, 2.5°C	18.9
43 Squirrel, flying	2000	119 D. america, true flight, 20°C	21,800	191 P. torva, 25°C	75.8
44 Swine	220	120 Emerita talpodia, 20°C	112	192 Ttiaenophorus nodulosus[3], 22°C	418
45 Weasel	5000	121 Eriphia spinifrons, 15°C	1828	**Ctenophora**	
46 Woodchuck, awake	262	122 Formica sp, 20°C	532	193 Beroe ovata, 16°C	5
47 Woodchuck, hibernating	14	123 Geotrupes sp, 21°C	447	194 Cestus veneris, 16°C	2.6
Aves		124 Homarus americanus, 15°C	507	195 C. veneris, 25°C	25
48 Bunting, snow	3350	125 Ilia nucleus, 15°C	253	**Coelenterata**	
49 Canary	2900	126 Limnophilus vittatus, 10°C	500	196 Anemonia sulcata, 18°C	13.4
50 Dove	950	127 Lucilia sericata[1], 20°C	95,600	197 Aurelia aurita, 13°C	3.4
51 Duck	800	128 Maja verrucosa, 15°C	1460	198 Carmarina hastata, 16°C	6
52 Fowl, hen	630	129 Melanotus communis, 27°C	2400	199 Rhizostoma pulmo, 16°C	7.2
53 Goose	547-592	130 Melolontha sp, 20°C	724-960	**Porifera**	
54 Gull, arctic	1640	131 Musca sp, 20°C	3200-5112	200 Suberites massa, 22.4°C	0.0241
55 Hawk, night	1750	132 Ocypode albicans, 26°C	139	**Protozoa**	
56 Hummingbird, day	13	133 Paguristis maculata, 15°C	1600	201 Amoeba chaos chaos, 20°C	7050
57 Manakin	4620	134 Palaemon squilla, 19°C	128	202 A. chaos chaos, 25°C	9010
58 Pigeon	710	135 Palinurus vulgaris, 15°C	12,874	203 A. chaos chaos, 30°C	13,244
59 Sparrow	2100	136 Pandalina brevirostrus, 15°C	20	204 Astasia klebsii, young, 25.2°C	3.8
Reptilia		137 Passalus cornutus, 17°C	30	205 Chilomonas paramecium, 25°C	16.4
60 Alligator lucius, 25°C	64	138 Periplaneta orientalis, 20°C	277	206 Leishmania braziliensis, 32°C	0.32
61 A. mississippiensis, 22°C	8.9	139 Pilumnus hirtellus, 15°C	160	207 Leptomonas ctenocephali, 28°C	0.27
62 Coluber natrix, 20°C	92-150	140 Pugettia producta, 15°C	100	208 Paramecium aurelia[4], 20°C	354
63 Constrictor constrictor, 16°C	4.9	141 Sicyonia sculpa, 15°C	443	209 P. aurelia[4], 25°C	616
64 C. constrictor, 22°C	10	142 Spirontocaris cranchi, 15°C	6	210 P. aurelia[4], 35°C	1512
65 C. constrictor, 30°C	24	143 Talorchestis megalopthalma, 17°C	180	211 P. caudatum[4], 20°C	2110
66 Crotalus atrox, 16°C	6.8	144 Venessa sp, resting, 20°C	600	212 P. caudatum[4], 25°C	3860
67 C. atrox, 22°C	16.4	145 Venessa sp, true flight, 20°C	100,000	213 P. multimicronucleatum[5], 25°C	1021
68 C. atrox, 30°C	35.5	146 Zootermopsis angusticollis, 20°C	400	214 Plasmodium cathemerium, 38°C	0.25
69 Drymarchon corais couperi, 16°C	10.1	**Annelida**		215 P. knowlesi, 38°C	0.34
70 D. corais couperi, 22°C	20	147 Arenicola sp, 12°C	30	216 Strigomonas fasciculata, 28°C	0.37
71 D. corais couperi, 30°C	47	148 Chaetopterus pergamentaceus 15°C	8	217 Tetrahymena geleii[6], 26.8°C	632.5
72 Iguana tuberculata, 22°C	22.2	149 Glycera siphonostoma, 25°C	15	218 Trichomonas foetus, 28°C	2.15
73 I. tuberculata, 30°C	52	150 Lumbricus communis, 21.5°C	206	219 Trypanosoma congolense, 37°C	1.53
74 Lacerta agilis, 20°C	1980	151 L. herculeus, 10°C	45	220 T. cruzi, 37°C	1.24
75 Malaclemys centrata, 24°C	35	152 L. terrestris, 20.5°C	138	221 T. gambiense, 37°C	1.70
76 Python reticulatum, 22°C	12.2			222 T. lewisi, old, 37°C	0.51
77 Storeria dekayi, ♂, 20°C	266			223 T. rhodesiense, 37°C	1.94
78 S. dekayi, ♀, 20°C	183				
79 Testudo vicina, 22°C	22				

/1/ True flight. /2/ Proglottids. /3/ Strobilia. /4/ No substrate. /5/ Bacteria present. /6/ Substrate present.

243. RESPIRATION RATES: PLANTS
Part I: FUNGI

Values for rates of gaseous exchange are μl/mg dry weight/hour, except as otherwise specified. Data for aerobic CO_2 production are enclosed in parentheses; those for anaerobic CO_2 production in brackets. Values not enclosed are O_2 consumption.

	Species	Material	Temp °C	Substrate	Specifications	$[Q_{CO_2}]$ or Q_{O_2}	RQ
					Myxomycetes		
1	Physarum polycephalum	Plasmodium	22		Endogenous	(1.0) 2.4[1]	0.75-0.85
					Phycomycetes		
2	Allomyces arbuscula	Mycelial mat	20	Carbohydrate	Starved	0.8	
3	A. moniliformis	Mycelial mat	20	Carbohydrate	Starved	1.0	
4	Cystopus candidus	Mycelial mat		Natural	Host, host + fungus		0.93, 0.95
5	Leptomitus lacteus	Pellets	20		Endogenous; at 0, 4, 8 days	20, 15, 10	0.98
6	Mucor guillermondi	Mycelial mat	25		Endogenous; mycelial phase	5.7-10 [7.1]	
7		Mycelial mat	25	Carbohydrate	+ Glucose; mycelial phase	5.6-21.4 [18.82]	
8		Mycelial mat	25		Endogenous; yeast phase	7.1-8.6	
9		Mycelial mat	25	Carbohydrate	+ Glucose; yeast phase	7.8-39 [31-142]	
10	M. stolonifer	Mycelial mat	20, 30	Carbohydrate			1.53, 1.72
11	Phycomyces blakesleeanus	Mycelial mat	20	Carbohydrate	At 1.5, 3.5, 7 days	(27, 13, 3)	
12	Rhizopus sp	Mycelial mat	28	Carbohydrate		(4.7)	
					Ascomycetes		
13	Ashbya gossypii	Mycelium[2]	30		Endogenous; at 1, 2, 3 days	19, 11, 8	
14		Mycelium[2]	30	Carbohydrate	+ Glucose; at 1, 2, 3 days	32, 20, 12	
15		Mycelium[2]	30	Carbohydrate	+ Sucrose; at 1, 2, 3 days	30, 17, 13	
16		Mycelium[2]	30	Carbohydrate	+ Lactose; at 1, 2, 3 days	0, 0, 0	
17		Mycelium[2]	30	Complex	+ Pyruvate; at 1, 2, 3 days	8, 3, 0	
18		Mycelium[2]	30	Complex	+ Ethanol; at 1, 2, 3 days	12, 8, 3	
19	Erysiphe graminis tritici	Growing culture	22	Natural	Host, host + fungus	1.7, 6.0[3]	
20	Melanospora destruens	Mycelial mat	30	Carbohydrate	+ Glucose	6	
21	Neurospora crassa	Mycelial mat	30	Organic comp'd	Endogenous	11-38 [0-5]	
22	N. tetrasperma	Sexual spores	25		Endogenous; dormant	0.2-0.6 [0.03]	
23		Sexual spores	25		Endogenous; germinating	9-22 [1-2]	
24	Saccharomyces cerevisiae R	Cell suspension		Carbohydrate	No stored reserves	83-109 [278-299]	
25		Cell suspension			Fat as reserves	76 [322]	
26		Cell suspension			Glycogen as reserves	0 [116]	
27	S. cerevisiae U	Cell suspension		Carbohydrate	No stored reserves	10-137 [276-284]	
28		Cell suspension			Fat as reserves	125 [261]	
29		Cell suspension			Glycogen as reserves	47 [83]	
30	Sclerotinia sp	Pellets	23-25	Carbohydrate			1.15
31	Zygosaccharomyces acidifaciens	Mycelium[2]	28		Endogenous; at 24, 48, 72 hr	16, 7, 7	
32		Mycelium[2]	28	Carbohydrate	+ Glucose; at 24, 48, 72 hr	60, 35, 35	
					Basidiomycetes		
33	Boletus luridus	Sporophore	17		Endogenous	(1.5)	
34	Bovista tunicata	Sporophore			Endogenous	(1.8-1.1) [8.7-5.6]	
35	Coprinus comatus	Sporophore	17		Endogenous	(2.7)	
36	Exidia glandulosa						0.7
37	Lactarius serifluus	Sporophore	17		Endogenous	(2.7)	
38	Polyporus squamosus	Sporophore	17		Endogenous	(1 0)	
39	Polystictus versicolor	Mycelial mat	17.5	Complex	At 2, 21, 100% O_2	3. 8.5, 10.4[3]	
40		Mycelial mat	29.5	Complex	At 2, 21, 100% O_2	7.4, 4.2, 17.2[3]	
41	Psalliota campestris	Growing culture	25			1.9-2.9	
42	Puccinia pruni	Growing culture		Natural	Host, host + fungus		1.06, 0.82
43	Ustilago sphaerogena	Conidia			Endogenous	75	
44		Conidia		Carbohydrate	+ Sugars	150-375	
					Fungi Imperfecti		
45	Aspergillus clavatus	Mycelial mat	15-25	Carbohydrate		12.4	
46		Mycelial mat		Complex		44	
47	A. flavus	Mycelial mat	30	Carbohydrate	At 4-6 days	6-7	
48	A. niger	Mycelial mat	19, 35	Carbohydrate	+ Glucose		0.98, 1.30
49		Mycelial mat	18, 35	Carbohydrate	+ Sucrose		0.91, 1.22
50		Mycelial mat	36	Carbohydrate	+ Glycerol		0.82-0.86
51		Mycelial mat	35	Carbohydrate	+ Mannitol		1.20
52	Blastomyces dermatitidis	Cell suspension	37		Endogenous; at pH 2, 6, 8	0.5, 12, 11[4]	
53		Cell suspension	37	Carbohydrate	+ Glucose; at pH 2, 6, 8	1, 12, 12[4]	
54	Candida albicans	Cell suspension	30		Endogenous	5	
55		Cell suspension	30	Carbohydrate	+ Glucose	40	
56	Fusarium avenaceum	Pellets	23-25	Natural			5.46
57	F. dianthi	Pellets	23-25	Natural			1.85
58	F. trichothecioides	Mycelium[2]	30		Endogenous; at 1-4 hrs[5]	31-11	
59		Mycelium[2]	30	Carbohydrate	+ Glucose; at 1-4 hr[5]	64-56	
60	Helminthosporium gramineum	Pellets	23-25		Endogenous		1.31
61	H. inaequalis	Pellets	23-25		Endogenous		1.16
62	Memnoniella echinata	Conidia	30		Endogenous; at pH 4, 6, 8	1.0, 1.5, 1.3	
63		Conidia		Carbohydrate	+ Glucose; at pH 4, 6, 8	2.6, 3.1, 2.7	
64		Conidia		Carbohydrate	+ Lactose; at pH 4, 6, 8	0.7, 1.3, 1.2	
65	Myrothecium verrucaria	Conidia	30	Carbohydrate	+ Glucose; at pH 4, 6, 8	19, 25, 30	
66		Conidia		Carbohydrate	Endogenous; at pH 4, 6, 8	2.9, 2.6, 5.6	
67		Pellets			Starved, sucrose grown	42	
68	Penicillium chrysogenum	Pellets	23-25	Carbohydrate	3 strains		1.10-1.27
69	P. digitatum	Pellets	23-25		4 strains		1.39-1.63
70	P. notatum	Mycelial mat	23-25	Carbohydrate	At 4-8-11 days	46-198-152[4]	
71	Torulopsis utilis	Cell suspension	30		Glycine	3.7[1]	0.86
72		Cell suspension	30		Urea	3.5[1]	1.15
73		Cell suspension	30		α-Alanine	5.2[1]	0.89
74		Cell suspension	30		β-Alanine	4.2[1]	1.16

/1/ μl/mg wet wt/hr. /2/ Homogenized. /3/ μl/sq cm area/hr. /4/ μl/10 μl tissue volume/hr. /5/ 1-day old.

243. RESPIRATION RATES: PLANTS (Continued)

Part II: BACTERIA

Data are applicable to bacterial suspensions in the presence of glucose. Values are ml/mg dry weight/hr.

	Species	Temp °C	Culture Age hr	Q_{O_2}
1	Azotobacter chroococcum	22	36	2,000-10,000
2	Aerobacter aerogenes	36, 30	17, 48	47, 50
3	Bacillus cereus (short)	30?	18	42-86
4	B. cereus (filamentous)	30?	18	3-49
5	B. subtilis	37	6-8	170
6	Escherichia coli	40, 32	20	200, 272
7	Lactobacillus bulgaricus	37, 45	8	34, 55
8	Leuconostoc citrovorum	38	16	8
9	Micrococcus luteus	35	30-34	15
10	M. flavus	35	30-34	8
11	M. auranticus	35	30-34	14
12	M. cinnebareus	35	30-34	32
13	M. freundenreichii	35	30-34	20
14	Mycobacterium phlei	38	84	28
15	M. smegmatis	38	84	23
16	M. stercoris	38	84	15
17	M. sp Karlinski	38	84	22
18	M. ranae	38	84	32
19	M. leprous kedrowsky	38	84	8
20	M. butyricum	38	84	13
21	M. tuberculosis hominis	38	252	4
22	M. tuberculosis avian	37	84	1
23	Pneumococcus, Type I	37	18	27
24	Pseudomonas fluorescens	26	20	58
25	Streptococcus faecalis, B33A	38	18	106
26	S. faecalis, 10Cl	37	15	57-80
27	S faecalis, Lancefield D	37	12-15	7
28	S. thermophilus, C3	37, 50	8	4, 5
29	S. thermophilus, MC	37, 50	8	9, 10

Part IV: LICHENS

Values are µl/100 mg dry weight/hr.

	Species	Q_{O_2} 30°C	Q_{O_2} 10°C	Q_{O_2} 0°C
1	Alectoria nigricans	33	14	8
2	Cetraria chrysantha	19	9	3.9
3	C. glauca	61	31	10
4	C. islandica	48	19	8
5	Cladonia scholanderi	13	7.5	3.1
6	C. sylvatica	24	6.8	2.9
7	Cornicularia divergens	40	11	5
8	Lobaria linita	72	22	10
9	L. scrobiculata	50	29	12
10	Parmelia nigrociliata	25	13	4
11	Peltigera aphthosa	90	33	17
12	Ramalina alludens	13	3.3	2.2
13	Solorina crocea	43	24	10
14	Sticta laciniata	28	11	7
15	S. weigelii	40	14	6.7
16	Thamnolia vermicularis	28	14	4.2
17	Umbilicaria cinereorufescens	30	9.8	4.1
18	U. proboscidea	18	6.5	3.5

	Species	Temp °C	Q_{O_2}	RQ
19	Cladonia rangiferina	50	10	0.80
20	Evernia prunastri	50	40	0.78
21		60	30	0.88
22	Orthotrichum affine	55	17	0.70
23	Pertusaria communis			0.84
24	Physica aipolia			0.73
25	P. ciliaris	45	18	0.80
26	Ramalina farinacea	50	25	0.77

Part III: ALGAE

Values for rates of gaseous exchange are µl/100 mg dry weight/hr, except as otherwise specified. Data for O2 consumption are enclosed in brackets; those for CO2 production are not enclosed.

	Species	Temp °C	Q_{CO_2} or $[Q_{O_2}]$	RQ
	Cyanophyta (Blue Green)			
1	Anabaena sp	25	414	0.90
2	Nostoc commune	19	0.16	0.40
	Chlorophyta (Green)			
3	Chara vulgaris	18	1.5[1]	
4	Chlorella ellipsoidea	25	[147]	
5	C. pyrenoidea	20	89	0.89
6	C. vulgaris	20	[475-192][2]	
7	Cladophora rupestris	20	[33]	
8	Coelastrum proboscideum	20	[170]	
9	Enteromorpha compressa	20	27	3.6
10	E. linza	19	66	0.62
11	Haematococcus pluvialis	20	[180]	
12	Nitella flexilis	18	1.6	
13	Scenedesmus obliquus	25	[50]	
14	Spirogyra majuscula	10.4	[0.5][1]	
15	S. varians	10.4	[0.6][1]	
16	Ulva lactuca	20	13-16	2.4-6.1
17	Valonia utricularis	20	8.4	1.5-5.7
	Phaeophyta (Brown)			
18	Ascophyllum nodosum	20	1.6[1]	0.80
19	Chorda tomentosa	9	[74]	
20	Cutleria multifida	20	7.2-17	0.5-2.1
21	Cystoseira abrotanifolia	20	4.5-10	1.2-3.7
22	C. amentacea	20	17	3.9
23	C. barbata	20	13-17	2.1-4.0
24	Desmarestia aculeata	14	[24]	
25	D. viridis	14	[14][1]	
26	Dictyota dichotoma	20	9.4-9.2	0.98-1.04
27	Ectocarpus siliculosus	12	[41][1]	
28	Fucus serratus	18	18[1]	0.54
29	F. vesiculosus	17	11	0.60
30	Laminaria digitata	17	[2][1]	
31	Taonia atomaria	20	6.7-20	0.9-3.1
	Rhodophyta (Red)			
32	Ceramium rubrum	17	45	0.89
33	Chondrus crispus	14	[18]	
34	C. crispus	20	[28]	
35	Cladostephus spongiosus	20	[39]	
36	Cryptonemia lomation	20	7.5-9.9	2.4-3.8
37	Delesseria alata	20	[41]	
38	Furcellaria fastigiata	14	[7]	
39	Gelidium corneum	20	13	3.26
40	Gracilaria compressa	20	9	1.4
41	Laurencia papillosa	20	18	4.88
42	Phyllophora nervosa	20	4.6	1.56
43	Plocamium coccineum	14	[21]	
44	Polyides lumbricoides	14	[5]	
45	Polysiphonia urceolata	12	[10][1]	
46	P. violacea	11	107	1.02
47	Porphyra laciniata	17	[39]	

/1/ µl/100 mg fresh wt/hr. /2/ µl/10[9] cells/hr.

Part V: LIVERWORTS, MOSSES

Values are µl/100 mg dry weight/hr, except as otherwise specified. Data for O2 consumption are enclosed in brackets; those for aerobic CO2 are not enclosed.

	Species	Temp °C	Q_{CO_2} or $[Q_{O_2}]$
	Liverworts (Hepaticae)		
1	Chiloscyphus fragilis	25	[60-100]
2	Marchantia polymorpha	20	0.6[1]
3	Riccia fluitans	25	[250-300]
	Mosses (Musci)		
4	Fontinalis antipyretica	25	[70-140]
5	Hylocomium parietinum	30	92
6		20	46
7		0	15
8	H. proliferum	30	92
9		20	46
10		0	15
11	H. squarrosum	30	100
12		20	61
13		0	15
14	Hypnum cupressiforme	18.5	[2-30]
15	H. fluitans	18	0.83[2]
16	Polytrichum juniperium, shoot[3]	18	1.2-0.7[2]
17	Sphagnum girgensohnii	30	130
18		20	71
19		5	20

/1/ µl/sq cm/hr. /2/ µl/100 mg fresh wt/hr. /3/ Data show changes during growth, development, maturation.

Part VI: HORSETAILS, FERNS

Values for gaseous exchange are µl/100 mg wet weight/hr. Data for O2 consumption are enclosed in brackets; those for aerobic CO2 production are not enclosed.

	Species	Material	Temp °C	Q_{CO_2} or $[Q_{O_2}]$	RQ
	Horsetail (Equisetineae)				
1	Equisetum maximum	Shoot	20	6	0.78
2		Fruiting shoot	20	100	0.83
3		Stem	RT	9.6	0.80
4		Branchlet	RT	19	0.69
	Ferns (Filicineae)				
5	Asplenium adiantum nigrum	Leaf	20	13	0.86
6		Leaf with sori	20	17	1.01
7		Leaf blade	RT	13.4	0.80
8		Petiole	RT	8.3	0.80
9	Dryopteris austriaca	Leaf	48	122	
10		Leaf	30	36	
11		Leaf	10	25	
12	Eupteris aquilina	Leaf	48	168	
13		Leaf	30	46	
14		Leaf	10	15	
15	Polypodium virginiana	Leaf	20	10	0.92
16		Leaf with sori	20	19	1.06
17	Pteris aquilina	Leaf	22	19	0.84
18		Leaf with sori	22	35	1.01
19	Scolopendrium scolopendrium	Leaf	30	[31]	
20		Leaf	22	[17.5]	
21		Leaf	13	[9.9]	
22		Leaf	3	[2.2]	

Values for rates of gaseous exchange are μl/100 mg wet weight/hour, except as otherwise specified. Data for anaerobic CO_2 production are enclosed in parentheses; those for O_2 consumption in brackets. Values not enclosed are aerobic CO_2 production.

Part VII: SEEDS AND PARTS

	Species	Material[1]	Temp °C	Q_{CO_2}	RQ
1	Apple (Pyrus malus	Resting	19	2.8[2]	0.86
2	Alfalfa (Medicago sativa)	Resting	18	41	1.08
3		Germinating	18	91	0.86
4	Barley (Hordeum vulgare)	Resting		8.7	
5		Embryo		63	
6		Endosperm		3.6	
7	Bean (Phaseolus coccineus)	Resting	28		1.75
8	Broadbean (Vicia faba)	Resting	28		0.99
9	Broom (Cytisus laburnum)	Resting	28		1.16
10	Buckwheat (Fagopyrum esculentum)	Germinating	25	41-306	0.8-1.0
11	Castor bean (Ricinus communis)	Resting	28		1.03
12		Endosperm	30	54	0.38
13	Cherry (Prunus cerasus)	Moist	25	5.6	0.87
14	Coconut (Cocos nucifera)	Moist	30	100-200	
15		Endosperm	30	0	
16		Hypocotyl	30	50	
17	Corn (Zea mays)	Resting		1.7	
18		Embryo		22.6	
19		Endosperm		0.36	
	Cotton (Gossypium herbaceum)				
20	Coker	Resting	26	0.1-1.5	0.92-1.05
21	Delfos	Resting	26	0.03-6.0	0.96-1.12
22	Flax (Linum usitatissimum)	Resting	17	21.8	0.91
23		Germinating	18	117	0.55
24	Hemp (Cannabis sativa)	Resting	18	9.0	0.82
25	Lamb's-quarters (Chenopodium album)	Moist	25	8.9	0.93
26	Peach (Prunus persica)	Moist	25	3.9	0.68
27	Plum (P. domestica)	Resting	28		0.80
28	Plum, blue gage (P. domestica)	Moist	25	5.6	0.70
29	Plum, Burbank (P. domestica)	Moist	25	4.3	0.91
30	Pumpkin (Cucurbita pepo)	Germinating	25	10-117	0.94-0.62
31	Radish (Raphanus sativus)	Resting	20	6.0	0.86
32		Germinating	20	60	0.58
33	Red cedar (Juniperus virginiana)	Resting	25	0.05	0.76
34		Germinating	25	6.6-25	0.84-0.97
35	Rice (Oryza sativa)	Resting		0.03[2]	1.15
36		Moist		5.5[2]	1.96
37		Germinating		9.7[2]	1.98
38		Seedling		1.1[2]	1.00
39	Rye (Secale cereale)	Resting	38	0.002-0.12[2]	
40	Smartweed (Polygonum scandens)	Moist	6		0.90
41		Moist	30		0.92
42	Sorghum (Sorghum vulgare)	Resting	37.8	0.01-0.3[2]	
43	Sorrel (Rumex crispus)	Moist	25	7.8	1.16
44	Sunflower (Helianthus annuus)	Resting	28		1.05
45	Walnut (Juglans regia)	Resting	28		0.52
46	Watermelon (Citrullus vulgaris)	Resting	28		0.90
47	Wheat (Triticum aestivum)	Resting	65		0.3[2]
48		Resting	55		0.7[2]
49		Resting	35		0.03[2]
50		Resting	4		0.005[2]

/1/ Condition of seeds: resting=dormant, air-dry; moist=with imbibed water. /2/ μl/100 mg dry wt/hr.

Part VIII: STEMS

	Species	Temp °C	Q_{CO_2} or [Q_{O_2}]	RQ
1	Apple, Jonathan (Pyrus malus)[2]	6	2.3-4.6	
2	Apple, McIntosh (P. malus)[2]	6	1.7-3.8	
3	Asparagus (Asparagus officinalis)[3]	24	35-13.2	1.04-0.95
4		10	9.7-3.6	1.03-0.86
5		0.5	3.0-2.0	0.98-0.95
6	Borage (Borago officinalis)	RT	6.1	0.81
7	Broadbean (Vicia faba)	RT	6.2 (5.6)	
8	Broom (Spartium junceum)	RT	16	0.80
9	Charlock (Raphanus raphanistrum)	RT	10.5	0.87
10	Cinquefoil (Potentilla reptans)	RT	11.0	0.83
11	Clematis (Clematis cirrhosa)	RT	12.4 (7.5)	
12	Cotton (Gossypium herbaceum)[4]	38	168-42[5]	
13	Elder (Sambucus nigra)	RT	9.8 (7.7)	
14	Nettle (Urtica membranacea)	RT	8.8	0.88
15	Oak (Quercus coccifera)	21	31-11	0.89-0.83
16	Oxalis (Oxalis corniculata)[4]	RT	15.4	0.97
17	Pea (Pisum sativum)	RT	14.9	0.86
18	Smartweed (Polygonum persicaria)	RT	6.9	0.82
19	Sorrel (Rumex lunaria)	RT	10 (8.1)	
20	Sorrel (R. pulcher)	RT	11.8	0.85
21	Sugar cane (Saccharum officinarum)[4]	28	27-4[5]	
22	Vetch (Vicia sativa)	RT	14.9	0.86

/1/ RT=room temperature. /2/ Tissue precooled. /3/ Material observed under conditions of storage or starvation. /4/ Data applicable to conditions of growth, development, maturation. /5/ μl/100 mg dry wt/hr.

Part IX: FLOWERS AND PARTS

	Species	Material	Temp °C	Q_{CO_2} or [Q_{O_2}]	RQ
1	Agave (Agave attenuata)[1]	Stamen	15	24-21	0.78-0.74
2		Pistil	14	34-13-11	0.92-0.69
3	Aloe (Aloe arborescens)[1]	Stamen	17	36-21-11	
4		Pistil	17	26-23-25	0.93-0.94
5	Arum (Arum italicum)	Spadix	18	[2800]	
6	Begonia (Begonia rex)	Sepal	20	39	
7		Petal	20	37	
8		Stamen	20	43	
9		Pistil	20	31	
10	Cacalia (Cacalia verbascifolia)	Flower	18	34(15)	
11	Canna (Canna indica)	Petal	22	27	0.79
12		Stamen	22	65	0.72
13		Pistil	22	45	0.78
14	Columbine (Aquilegia vulgaris)	Ovule	20	[190][2]	
15	Cucumber (Cucumis sativus)[1]	Pistil	22	48-43-29	
16	Cyclamen (Cyclamen persicum)	Flower	28		1.03
17	Dahlia (Dahlia variabilis)	Petal	28		0.94
18	Delphinium (Delphinium sinense)	Flower	28		0.94
19	Eel-grass (Vallisneria spiralis)	Flower	20	[30][2]	
20	Elder (Sambuscus nigra)	Flower	28		0.95
21	Fleabane (Erigeron annua)	Flower	18	[40] (23)	
22	Gladiolus (Gladiolus gandavensis)	Petal	24	15	0.72
23		Stamen	24	27	0.77
24		Pistil	24	71	0.90
25	Lilac (Syringa vulgaris)	Flower	20	40	
26	Jasmine (Jasminum nudiflorum)	Flower	28		0.01
27	Lily (Lilium elegans)	Pollen	25	[610] (240)[2]	
28	Lily (L. hansoni)	Pollen	25	[340] (260)[2]	
29	Lily (L. philippinensis)	Pollen	25	[1140] (980)[2]	1.04
30	Marsh marigold (Caltha palustris)	Ovule	20	[360][2]	
31	Mullein (Verbascum thapsus)	Stamen	23	76	0.83
32		Pistil	23	82	0.92
33	Peony (Paeonia albiflora)	Pollen	25	[700] (170)[2]	
34	Pine (Pinus densiflora)	Pollen	25	[160] (150)[2]	
35	Poppy (Papaver orientale)	Pollen	25	[520] (0)[2]	
36	Poppy (P. rhoeas)	Sepal	21	39	
37		Petal	21	37	
38		Stamen	21	104	
39		Pistil	21	69	
40	Primrose (Primula obconica)	Flower	28		0.96
41	Sweetpea (Lathyrus odoratus)	Ovule	20	[420][2]	
42		Ovary	20	[300][2]	
43		Filament	20	[160][2]	
44	Tulip (Tulipa genneriana)	Flower	28		0.95

/1/ Data show changes during growth, development, maturation. /2/ μl/ per 100 mg dry wt/hr.

Part X: STORAGE ORGANS

	Species	Material	Temp °C	Q_{CO_2} or [Q_{O_2}]	RQ
1	Arrow-head (Sagittaria latifolia)	Rhizome	25	4.1 (3.2)	
2	Artichoke (Cynara scolymus)[1]	Tuber	25	1.4-0.8 (0.5)	
3	Beet (Beta vulgaris)	Root	15.5	0.8	
4	Bur-reed (Sparganium eurycarpum)	Rhizome	25	[2.3] (1.6)	
5	Carrot (Daucus carota)[1]	Root	24	3.3-1.5	1.10-1.18
6			10	1.5-0.5	1.08-1.01
7			0.5	0.4-0.2	0.92-1.16
8	Cattail (Typha latifolia)	Rhizome	25	2.4(2.1)	
9	Dahlia (Dahlia variabilis)	Root	25		0.99
10	Gladiolus (Gladiolus sp)	Corm	23	8.5[2]	
11	Milkweed (Asclepias incarnata)	Rhizome	25	3.7(4.3)	
12	Onion (Allium cepa)	Bulb	21	0.7-1	
13			10	0.4-0.5	
14			0	0.1-0.2	
15	Oxalis (Oxalis cernua)	Rhizome	RT	5	1.18
16	Potato (Solanum tuberosus)[1]	Tuber	24	0.6-0.3	1.02-0.75
17			10	0.2-0.15	0.86-0.99
18			0.5	0.07-0.15	0.45-0.66
19	Sedge (Scirpus validus)	Rhizome	25	2.8(3.4)	
20	Sweetflag (Acorus calamus)	Rhizome	25	3.7(3.7)	
	Sweetpotato (Ipomoea batatus)				
21	Puerto Rico	Root	35	6.2	
22			25	4.0	
23			15	1.9	
24	Triumph	Root	35	5.6	
25			25	3.2	
26			15	1.4	
27	Turnip (Brassica rapa)	Root	15.5	1.6	
28			4.5	0.1	
29			0	0.02	
30	Waterlily (Nuphar advenum)	Rhizome	25	3.0(2.6)	

/1/ Material observed under conditions of storage or starvation. /2/ μl/100 mg dry wt/hr.

Values for rates of gaseous exchange are μl/100 mg wet weight/hour, except as otherwise specified. Data for anaerobic CO_2 production are enclosed in parentheses; those for O_2 consumption in brackets. Values not enclosed are aerobic CO_2 production.

Part XI: LEAVES

	Species	Temp[1] °C	Q_{CO_2} or $[Q_{O_2}]$	RQ
1	Almond (Prunus amygdalus)	14	29	1.00
2	Bamboo (Bambusa nana)[2]	22.5	22-8.5	
3	Barley (Hordeum vulgare)	23	26.6(11.6)	0.85
4	Barley (H. vulgare), etiolated	23	21.6(11.2)	0.83
5	Bean (Phaseolus vulgaris)	26	26-57	
6	Beech (Fagus sylvatica)	21	34	
7	Beet (Beta vulgaris)	27	23	
8	Begonia (Begonia rex)	20	30	
9	Broadbean (Vicia faba), blade	RT	11.1(5.1)	
10	Broadbean (V. faba), petiole	RT	4.1(4.3)	
11	Broom (Spartium junceum), blade	RT	17	0.71
12	Buttercup (Ranunculus glacialis)	20	28	
13		10	19	
14		0	5.1	
15	Catalpa (Catalpa bignonioides aurea)	14	18	
16	Catalpa (C. bignonioides koehnei)	14	25	
17	Cattail (Typha latifolia)[2]	22.5	26-15-19	
18	Charlock (Raphanus raphanistrum), blade	RT	13.3	0.73
19	Charlock (R. raphanistrum), petiole	RT	6.2	0.86
20	Cinquefoil (Potentilla reptans), blade	RT	31.9(12.5)	0.67
21	Cinquefoil (P. reptans), petiole	RT	10.7(5.6)	0.83
22	Coffee (Coffea arabica)	20	1.5[3]	
23	Corn (Zea mays)	26	68(17.1)	0.99
24	Corn (Z. mays), etiolated	26	54(18.1)	0.97
25	Dandelion (Taraxacum officinale)	19	46	0.95
26	Duckweed (Lemna minor)	25	300[4]	
27	Elm (Ulmus montana)	16	24	
28	Elm (U. montana aurea)	16	22	
29	Elm (U. montana atropurpurea)	16	23	
30	Eucalyptus (Eucalyptus globulus)	19	8.5	0.80
31	Gladiolus (Gladiolus gandavensis)	24	18	0.64
32	Horsechestnut (Aesculus hippocastanum)	12	49	
33	Horsechestnut, white (A. hippocastanum)	12	26	
34	Ivy (Hedera helix)	32	40	1.00
35		18	18	1.00
36	Lettuce (Lactuca sativa)[2]	24	3.3-2.6	1.12-1.02
37		10	1.3-0.7	1.09-1.00
38		0.5	0.95-0.4	0.88-0.98
39	Lime (Citrus aurantium)	20	3.0[3]	
40	Mallow (Malva parviflora), blade	RT	32	0.84
41	Mallow (M. sylvestris), blade	RT	12.3	0.71
42	Maple (Acer pseudoplatanus)	10	33	
43	Maple (A. pseudo. atropurpureum)	16	23	
44	Maple (A. pseudo. cupreum)	16	24	
45	Maple (A. pseudo. luteo-virescens)	10	28	
46	Mullein (Verbascum thapsus)	26	38	0.84
47	Nettle (Urtica membranaceae), blade	RT	10.8	0.69
48	Nightshade (Solanum nigrum), blade[2]	16	34-10	0.78-0.67
49	Olive (Olea europaea)[2]	22	24-13	0.78-0.75
50	Optunia (Optunia versicolor)	65	6	
51		55	21	
52		45	33	
53		35	15	0.70
54	Pine (Pinus canariensis)	29	42	0.90
55	Pine (P. maritama)	36	5	0.87
56		20	12	0.84
57		0	2	0.83
58	Potato (Solanum tuberosum)	48	137	
59		30	41	
60	Purslane (Atriplex hortensis)	18	44	
61	Reed (Phragmites communis)[2]	22.5	31-12	
62	Rye (Secale cereale)	25	44	
63		15	26	
64	Sorrel (Rumex acetosa), blade	RT	21.6	0.76
65	Sorrel (R. pulcher), blade	RT	14.7	0.76
66	Spinach (Spinacia oleracea)[2]	24	16.2-12.8	0.94-0.83
67		10	4.2-2.0	0.90-0.86
68		0.5	1.5-5.8	0.85-0.73
69	Squill (Scilla peruviana)	20	4	0.78
70	Sunflower (Helianthus annuus)	42	24.3[3]	
71		31	16.6[3]	
72		20	5.8[3]	
73	Tea (Thea sinensis), sections	36	16.4(8.6)	
	Tomato (Lycopersicon esculentum)			
74	Gem	28	260[4]	
75	Rutgers	28	210[4]	
76	Vetch (Vicia sativa), blade	RT	30.1	0.75
77	Vetch (V. sativa), petiole	RT	16.7	0.88
78	Vetch (V. sativa), tendril	RT	27.7	0.90
79	Wheat (Triticum aestivum)	25	40(10.6)	0.97
80	Wheat (T. aestivum), etiolated	25	38(11.7)	0.98
81	Yew (Taxus baccata)	46	55	0.89
82		16	6	0.86
83	Yucca (Yucca gloriosa)[2]	22.5	13.6-5.1	

/1/ RT = room temperature. /2/ Material observed under conditions of storage or starvation. /3/ μl/sq cm/hr. /4/ μl/100 mg dry wt/hr.

Part XII: FRUITS

	Species	Temp °C	Q_{CO_2} or $[Q_{O_2}]$	RQ
	Apple (Pyrus malus)			
1	Delicious[1]	20	1.7-0.4-0.4	
2	Jonathan[1]	27	7.2-4.5	0.45-0.92
3	Maiden blush[2]	25	4.2-20	
4		0	1.4-2.4	
5	Winesap[2]	25	1.9-0.9	
6		0	1.8-0.6	
7	Apricot (Prunus armeniaca)[2]	18	2.8-4.1	
8		4	1.1-1.0	
9	Avocado (Persea gratissima)[2]	5	1	
10		25	7-15	
11	Banana (Musa paradisca sapientum)	31	3.1	
12		20	1.8	
13		12.5	0.9	
14		0	0.4	
15	Barberry (Berberis vulgaris)	25		1.20
16	Bean (Phaseolus vulgaris)[2]	24	16.4-6.6	1.1-1.0
17		0.5	0.95-0.6	0.94-0.96
18	Bryony (Bryonia dioica)[1]	25	64-8.5	
19	Cherry (Prunus avium)[1]	20	68-2	
20	Corn (Zea mays)[1]	30	21-18(12-9)	
21	Cranberry (Vaccinium)[1]	24	32-14	
22	Cucumber (Cucumis sativus)[2]	24	2.3-0.8	1.01-0.91
23		10	1.0-0.4	1.01-1.10
24		0.5	0.2-0.7	0.97-0.88
25	Elder (Sambucus nigra)	18	12(11)	
26	Grape (Vitis vinifera)	28		1.6
27	Grapefruit (Citrus grandis)	38	2.5	2.1
28		21	1.0	1.1
29		10	0.4	1.4
30		0	0.1	1.2
31	Guava (Psidium guajava)[2]	30	20-3.6	
32	Hawthorn (Crataegus punctata)	28		1.26
33	Ivy (Hedera helix)[1]	20	13-50-19	
34	Lemon (Citrus limonia)	38	4.1	1.4
35		10	0.5	1.1
36		0	0.15	1.2
37	Lilac (Syringa vulgaris)[1]	25	42-8.5	
38	Oak (Quercus alba)	30	14.9[3]	0.71
39		10	4.8[3]	0.30
40		2.5	2.7[3]	0.16
41	Oak (Q. rubra)	30	6.4[3]	0.46
42		10	3[3]	0.13
43		2.5	1.6[3]	0.08
44	Okra (Hibiscus esculentus)[2]	30	306-104	
45	Orange (Citrus nobilis)	28		1.07
	Orange (C. sinensis)			
46	Washington navel	21	2.0	1.1
47		10	0.8	1.1
48		0	0.2	1.2
49	Valencia	38		1.7
50		21	1.8	1.0
51		21	0.2	1.1
52	Papaya (Carica papaya)	15.6	0.83	
53		10	0.46	
54		4.4	0.24	
55	Pea (Pisum sativum)[2]	24	20-12	1.32-1.06
56		10	7.9-3.1	1.13-1.00
57		0.5	2.2-1.4	1.00-0.96
58	Peach (Prunus persica)	18	1.4-2.0[2]	
59		4	0.4-0.3[2]	
60		25	7-5[1]	
61		25	8-2[2]	
62	Pear (Pyrus communis)	18	6.3-1-1.2[1]	
63		18	1-0.9-2.2[2]	
64	Pepper (Capsicum frutescens)[2]	24	4.0-1.4	1.12-0.88
65		10	1.2-0.6	1.27-0.88
66		0.5	0.4-0.3	0.96-0.96
67	Persimmon, Hachiya (Diospyros kaki)	20-27	1.8	1.2
68	Persimmon, Fuyu (D. kaki)	20-27	1.4	1.1
69	Pigeon pea (Kajanus indicus)[1]	21	30-0	
70	Pimento (Pimenta officinalis)	30	40[3]	
71	Plum (Prunus domestica)	18	8.7(5.6)	
72	Poppy (Papaver somniferum)	20	38	1.5
73	Rye (Secale cereale)[1]	28	[240-12][3]	
74	Smartweed (Polygonum scandens)	30		0.87
75	Snowberry (Symphoricarpos ramosus)	17	33	
76	Strawberry, missionary (Fragaria sp)	20	3.3-5.1	0.84-0.91
77	Strawberry (F. vesca)	28		1.27
78	Tobacco (Nicotiana tabacum)	28		0.94
79	Tomato (Lycopersicon esculentum)	24	2.5-1.6[2]	1.11-1.13
80		10	0.8-0.6[2]	1.39-1.06
81		0.5	0.4-0.2[2]	1.11-1.02
82		28	2.6-2.5[1]	1.8-1.4
83	Wheat (Triticum aestivum)[1]	28	[340-8][3]	

/1/ Data show changes during growth, development, maturation. /2/ Material observed under conditions of storage or starvation. /3/ μl/100 mg dry wt/hr.

244. RESPIRATORY MEDIA: CHARACTERISTICS

Water and nitrogen are the two major ecological variations of respiratory media available to organisms. These media are the solvents, mechanically inspired by the actively ventilated respiratory organ, through which occurs the exchange of oxygen and carbon dioxide. Values identified with an asterisk (*) are averages of many determinations but vary widely with conditions of measurement.

	Variable	Water		Atmosphere (N_2)	
		Ocean	Fresh	Sea Level	Altitude[1]
1	Temperature, °C	-2.0 to 30.0	2.0-32.0	0.7-15.7	-28.1 to -15.1
2	Pressure, total, mm Hg	760-760,000	760-20,000	760	347.5-360.2
3	Density, g/L	1027* (20°C)	1000* (4°C)	1.223-1.290	0.649-0.659
		Concentration			
4	H_2O, vol %	100.00	100.00	1.00[2]	1.00[2]
5	N_2, vol %	1.03* (15°C)	1.33* (15°C)	78.03 (STP)	78.03 (STP)
6	CO_2, vol %	0.02* (15°C)	0.03* (15°C)	0.03 (STP)	0.03 (STP)
7	O_2, vol %	0.58* (15°C)	0.72* (15°C)	20.99 (STP)	20.99 (STP)
8	Salts, vol %	3.46*	0.18*		
9	pH	7.5-8.4	3.2-10.6		
10	Inert gases, vol %	Trace	Trace	0.95 (STP)	0.95 (STP)
		Partial Pressure (Tension)			
11	H_2O (mm Hg)	12.79 (15°C)	6.10 (4°C)	6.40[3] (15°C)	0.72[3] (-15°C)
12	N_2 (mm Hg)	593.02 (STP)	593.02 (STP)	593.02 (STP)	281.06[4] (STP)
13	CO_2 (mm Hg)	0.23* (STP)	0.23* (STP)	0.23 (STP)	0.11[4] (STP)
14	O_2 (mm Hg)	159.52* (STP)	159.52* (STP)	159.52 (STP)	75.61[4] (STP)
15	Inert gases	7.46 (STP)	7.46 (STP)	7.46 (STP)	3.42[4] (STP)
16	Total pressure	760.00	760.00	760.00	360.20
		Diffusion Coefficient ml/min/sq cm x cm (760 mm Hg, 20°C)			
17	H_2O				
18	N_2	0.000018[5] (0.53)[6]			
19	CO_2	0.000078[5] (23.1)[6]			
20	O_2	0.000034[5] (1.0)[6]	11.0		

/1/ 6000 meters. /2/ Varies, but never absent and always of biological significance. /3/ Calculated for 50% relative humidity. /4/ Calculated from Lines 5,6,7,10 and 16. /5/ Calculated from measured value for O_2 (Line 20) and relative coefficients (Lines 18,19). Values in parentheses are relative coefficients with O_2 as unity.

245. RESPIRATORY MOLECULES: CHARACTERISTICS

Values, unless otherwise indicated, are for standard conditions (STP) of temperature (0°C) and pressure (760 mm Hg).

	Type	Weight (0=16)	Diameter[1] cm x 10^{-8}	Density g/L	Mean Free Path cm x 10^{-6} (750 mm Hg)	Collision Frequency (20°C)	Average Velocity cm x 100/sec	Water Solubility STP	Water Solubility 20°C	Vol % (40°C)
1	N_2	28.02	3.15-3.53	1.251	8.50	5070	454	2.35	1.54	1.18
2	H_2O	18.02	3.0-5.0	0.005-0.030[2]			566			
3	CO_2	44.01	3.34-3.40	1.977	5.56	6120	362	171.3	87.8	53.0
4	O_2	32.00	2.92-2.98	1.429	9.05	4430	425	4.89	3.10	2.31

/1/ Range indicates variability with method of measurement (e.g. viscosity, heat conductivity). /2/ Water vapor in saturated air, i.e., in equilibrium with water, at 0°C and 30°C.

246. RESPIRATORY EXCHANGE CHARACTERISTICS: MAN

Part I: VENTILATION

Gas	Inspired Air Composition vol %[1]	Inspired Air Partial Pressure mm Hg[2]	Alveolar Air Composition vol %[1,3]	Alveolar Air Partial Pressure mm Hg[3,4]	Expired Air Composition vol %[1]	Expired Air Partial Pressure mm Hg[4]
A	B	C	D	E	F	G
1 H_2O	0.00	5.7	00.0	47	00.0	47
2 N_2	79.02	596.0	80.4	573	79.2	565
3 O_2	20.95	158.0	14.0	100	16.3	116
4 CO_2	0.03	0.3	5.6	40	4.5	32

/1/ Dry air, partial pressure in mm Hg, = B/100 x 760 mm Hg (Dalton's Law). /2/ Ambient air (slight variations exist), in vol %, = 100 C/760 (Dalton's Law). /3/ "Alveolar" air, actually last part of expired samples. /4/ Physiological air, normal temperature (37°C) and standard pressure (760 mm Hg).

Part II: TRANSPORT

Values in parentheses are ranges.

Gas	Arterial vol %	Arterial mm Hg	Capillary vol %	Capillary mm Hg	Tissue Fluid vol %	Tissue Fluid mm Hg	Venous vol %	Venous mm Hg
1 H_2O	83(81-86)	47	83(81-86)	47	83(81-86)	47	83(81-86	47
2 N_2	0.975	573	0.975	573	0.975	573	0.975	573
3 O_2	19.6(17.3-22.3)	94	1-22.3[1]	1-94[1]	0.185[1]	30[1]	12.9(11.0-16.1)[2]	40
4 CO_2	48.2(44.6-50.4)	40	44.6-57.7[1]	40-50	3.046[1]	50[1]	54.8(51.0-57.7)[2]	46

/1/ Variable, depending on blood flow, tissue activity and relation of sample to capillary length or field. /2/ Internal jugular.

247. RESPIRATORY EXCHANGE CHARACTERISTICS: VERTEBRATES

Volume per cent values are for dry air.

	Animal	Inspired Air vol % O_2	Inspired Air vol % CO_2	Alveolar Air vol % O_2	Alveolar Air vol % CO_2	Expired Air vol % O_2	Expired Air vol % CO_2	RQ CO_2/O_2
1	Man (Homo sapiens)	20.95	0.03	14.00	5.60	16.30	4.50	0.850
2	Dog (Canis familiaris)			13.66	5.68	16.30	3.46	0.780
3	Albino rat (Rattus norvegicus)							0.894 (0.754-1.072)
4	Horse (Equus caballus)							0.960
5	Guillemot (Cepphus grylle)					15.05	4.83	
6	Chicken (Gallus domesticus)					13.50	6.50	0.764[1] (0.71-0.96)[2]
7	Turtle (28°C) (Malaclemys centrata)			16.46	4.69			0.71[3]
8	Frog (20°C), cutaneous (Rana esculenta)							1.92
9	Frog (20°C), pulmonary (R. esculenta)							0.32
10	Puffer fish (20°C)	0.31		0.31		0.149		

/1/ Average for 5 days including day of last feeding. /2/ Range for 1-5 hr and 4 days after feeding. /3/ Data for painted turtle (Chrysemys marginata) included in calculation.

248. LUNG VENTILATION: VERTEBRATES

Values, unless otherwise noted, are averages of means for the resting state. Ranges in parentheses are estimate "d" of the 95% range (cf Introduction).

	Species	Respiration Frequency breath/min	Tidal Volume[1] ml	Minute Volume[2] L
	Man (Homo sapiens)			
1	Premature	33	12.4(8.4-17.3)	0.41(0.28-0.58)
2	Newborn, asleep	43(24-116)	16.7(10.0-27)	0.72(0.43-1.41)
3	Adult ♂	11.7(10.1-13.1)[3]	750(757-895)[4]	7.4(5.8-10.3)[5]
4	♀	11.7(10.4-13.0)[6]	339(285-393)[7]	4.5(4.0-7.0)[8]
5	Cat (Felis catus)	26	12.4	0.32
6	Cow (Bos taurus)	31(27-40)	2850(2200-3800)	86(59-104)
7	Dog	18(11-38)	320(251-432)	5.2(3.3-7.4)
8	Goat	19.0	310	5.7
9	Guinea pig (Cavia cobaya)	90(69-104)	1.8(1.0-3.9)	0.16(0.09-0.38)
10	Hamster (Mesocricetus auratus)	74(33-127)	0.83(0.42-1.2)	0.054(0.025-0.083)
11	Horse (Equus caballus)[9]	11.9(10.6-13.6)	9000(8520-9680)	107
12	Manatee, Florida (Trichechus latirostris)	7.0(6.0-8.0)	(5000-9000)	45(35-60)
13	Marmot (Marmota marmota)	8.0[10]	22.0[11]	0.17[12]
14	Monkey (Macaca mulatta)	40(31-52)	21(9.8-21)	0.86(0.31-1.41)
15	Mouse (Mus musculus)	163(84-230)	0.15(0.09-0.23)	0.023(0.011-0.036)
16	Porpoise (Tursiops truncatus)	1.1(0.9-1.3)	9,000(8,000-10,000)	9.7(9.0-10.4)
17	Rabbit (Lepus cuniculus)	51(38-60)	21(19.3-24.6)	1.07(0.80-1.14)
18	Rat (Rattus norvegicus)		1.5(1.4-1.6)	0.100(0.075-0.130)
19	Rat, cotton (Sigmodon hispidus)	94(75-115)	0.35(0.24-0.70)	0.04(0.023-0.071)
20	Sloth (Choleopus hoffmanii)	13.0		0.84(0.80-1.0)
21	Sloth (Bradypus griseus)	(4.5-8.0)		0.49(0.33-0.73)
22	Turtle (Maleclemys centrata)	3.7	14.0	0.05

/1/ Air inspired per breath. /2/ Respiration frequency x tidal volume. /3/ Resting. Light work, 17.1(15.7-18.2); heavy work, 21.2(18.6-23.3). /4/ Resting. Light work, 1670(1510-1770); heavy work, 2030(1900-2110). /5/ Resting. Light work, 29(27-31); heavy work, 60(50-90). /6/ Resting. Light work, 19; heavy work, 30(25-33). /7/ Resting. Light work, 860(836-885); heavy work, 880(490-1270). /8/ Resting. Light work, 16.3(15.9-16.8); heavy work, 24.5(17.3-32.0). /9/ Percheron, gelding. /10/ Hibernating, 0.68. /11/ Hibernating, 13(11.3-15.0). /12/ Hibernating, 0.009.

249. PULMONARY VALUES, EQUATIONS, DEFINITIONS: MAN

Part I: LUNG AIR VOLUME, RECUMBENT

Values are from smoothed curves plotted from mean values, and are for the following conditions: $37^{\circ}C$, ambient pressure, saturated with water vapor. Ranges in parentheses are from smoothed curves of ranges, and are estimate "d" of the 95% range (cf Introduction).

	Age yr	Total Lung Capacity[1] L	Vital Capacity[2] L
1	Six ♂	1.6(1.3-2.1)	1.2(0.9-1.7)
2	♀	1.6(1.3-2.1)[3]	1.2(0.9-1.7)[3]
3	Ten ♂	2.5(2.2-3.1)	1.9(1.6-2.4)
4	♀	2.5(2.2-3.1)[3]	1.9(1.6-2.4)[3]
5	Fourteen ♂	4.6(3.5-6.1)	3.7(3.0-4.7)
6	♀	3.6(2.8-4.3)[3]	2.7(2.2-3.5)[3]
7	Eighteen ♂	5.9(4.3-8.0)	4.6(4.0-5.8)
8	♀	4.1(3.1-5.3)[3]	3.0(2.4-4.2)[3]
9	Twenty ♂	6.3(4.3-8.5)	4.9(4.0-6.0)
10	♀	4.2(3.1-5.3)[3]	3.0(2.4-4.4)[3]
11	Twenty-five ♂	6.4(4.3-9.0)	4.9(3.3-6.0)
12	♀	4.2(3.1-5.4)	3.0(2.2-4.2)[3]
13	Thirty-five ♂	6.1(4.3-8.5)	4.5(2.3-6.0)
14	♀	4.3(3.0-5.6)	3.0(2.0-3.8)
15	Forty-five ♂	5.9(4.3-8.0)	4.3(2.8-5.1)
16	♀	4.3(2.9-5.7)	2.9(1.8-3.7)
17	Fifty-five ♂	5.8(4.3-8.0)	4.1(2.6-5.5)
18	♀	4.2(2.8-5.7)	2.7(1.6-3.5)
19	Sixty-five ♂	5.6(4.3-7.0)	3.7(2.5-5.0)
20	♀	3.9(2.8-5.5)[3]	2.3(1.4-3.4)[3]
21	Seventy-five ♂	5.2(4.3-7.0)	3.3(2.5-4.5)
22	♀	3.9(2.8-5.0)[3]	2.2(1.4-3.3)[3]

/1/ Total volume of air contained in lungs after deepest possible inspiration. Total lung capacity minus vital capacity equals residual capacity or residual air. /2/ Volume of air expired in deepest possible expiration following deepest possible inspiration. /3/ Values are estimates; a sex difference may exist.

Part II: INTRAPULMONIC (INTRA-ORAL) PRESSURE

Values are for males only. Mean lung volumes are given as per cent of vital capacity. Ranges in parentheses are estimate "b" of the 95% range (cf Introduction).

	Volume %	mm Hg
		Maximum Expiratory Pressure
1	9.7	42(14.7-68)
2	25.0	52(10.9-94)
3	44	70(30-109)
4	60	90(47-133)
5	75	93(58-128)
6	83	107(74-144)
7	100	120(86-145)
		Maximum Inspiratory Pressure
8	3.9	86(47-125)[1]
9	21.7	75(46-103)[1]
10	35	63(26-101)[1]
11	56	57(26-88)[1]
12	76	45(16.8-73)[1]
13	91	24(2.2-49)[1]
		Relaxation Pressure
14	0	-19.2(-32 to -6.6)
15	13.9	-8.5(-15.5 to -1.5)
16	31	-1.3(-9.9 to 7.3)
17	51	4.1(-1.9 to 10.1)
18	72	10.5(1.9 to 19.1)
19	87	14.9(0.3 to 29.5)
20	100	20.6(10.2 to 31)

/1/ Negative pressure.

Part III: INTRAPLEURAL PRESSURE

Values are cm H_2O relative to atmospheric pressure.

	Condition	Inspiration	Expiration
1	Adults, at rest	-5 to -10	-3 to -5
2	Deep breathing	-30	
3	Müller's[1]	-50 to -60	
4	Valsalva's[2]		60
5	Normal[3]	-0.7(-0.5 to -1.0)	0.4(0-1.0)
6	Labored[3]	-1.1(-0.5 to -1.5)	2.4(1.0 to 3.0)
7	Normal[4]	-1.3(-1.0 to -1.5)	2.6(1.0 to 3.5)
8	Infants, end of inspiration	-5	
9	End of expiration		0

/1/ Inspiration with glottis closed. /2/ Expiration with glottis closed. /3/ Air pressure at posterior pharynx. /4/ Air pressure at tracheal bifurcation.

Part IV: PREDICTION EQUATIONS

Equations are applicable for the following conditions: $37^{\circ}C$, ambient pressure, saturated with water vapor. MBC=maximum breathing capacity, L/min; SA=body surface area, sq m; V=pulmonary ventilation, L/min; W=weight, kg; VC=vital capacity, L; H=height, cm; A=age, yr.

	Subject	Equation
1	Infants, <1 week, resting	V = 0.139 + 0.00367 W[1]
2	Males, 10-17 yr	VC = 0.0562 H + 0.0097 AW - 6.27
3	140-160 cm	VC = 0.0492 H - 4.82
4	160-190 cm	VC = 0.0799 H - 9.75
5	Males, standing	VC = 0.025 H^2
6	Females, standing	VC = 0.020 H^2
7	Males	MBC = [86.5 - (0.522 x A)] x SA[3]
8	Females	MBC = [71.3 - (0.474 x A)] x SA[3]
9	Both sexes	MBC = H x (1.24 - 0.0095 A)[3]

/1/ Weight in ounces. /2/ Age correction for vital capacity: 46-55 yr = -4%; 56-65 yr = -8%; 66-75 yr = -16%; over 75 yr = -30%. /3/ Values vary widely with equipment and laboratory methods.

Part V: SUMMARY OF VALUES USED IN EVALUATION OF PULMONARY FUNCTION

	Variable	Average "Normal"[1] Values for Men
1	Maximal breathing capacity (MBC)	100-150 liters/min.
2	Vital capacity (VC)	3500-5000 cc.
3	Residual air	1000-1500 cc.
	Ventilation volume per min/sq m BSA	
4	Rest	2.6-3.8 liters
5	Exercise	8.0-10.5 liters
	Oxygen uptake from air breathed	
6	Rest	4.0-5.0% (40-50 cc/liter).
7	Exercise	5.0-6.0% (50-60 cc/liter).
	Carbon dioxide addition to air breathed	
8	Rest	3.2-4.0% (32-40 cc/liter).
9	Exercise	3.4-4.2% (34-42 cc/liter).
	Arterial blood	
	Carbon dioxide content[2]	
10	Rest	48.5 vol %.
11	Exercise	42.5 vol %.
	Oxygen content[2]	
12	Rest	19.0 vol %.
13	Exercise	19.2 vol %.
	Hemoglobin saturation	
14	Rest	96+ %.
15	Exercise	96+ %.
	Mean resting tensions[3]	
16	Oxygen (pO_2)	95 mm Hg.
17	Carbon dioxide (pCO_2)	40 mm Hg.
18	Dyspnea following mild exercise[4]	60 seconds.

/1/ Pathological findings: pulmonary fibrosis, as in silicosis, tuberculosis, bronchiectasis, sarcoidosis, post-radiation fibrosis, pleuritis, hydrothorax, spondylitis and kyphoscoliosis, causes pulmonary insufficiency; the findings are reduction in lung volumes and maximum breathing capacity, normal spirogram, hyperventilation, low blood carbon dioxide and high areterial pH. In emphysema residual air is increased. Maximum breathing capacity and vital capacity are reduced; arterial oxygen content is low, while carbon dioxide content is elevated. In pulmonary edema arterial anoxia results from disturbance of diffusion of gases across the alveolocapillary membrane. Pulmonary hypertension occurs in emphysema, cardiac failure, mitral stenosis, Ayerza syndrome and polycythemia. /2/ Van Slyke method. /3/ Riley method. /4/ 30 step-ups in one min on stool 20 cm high.

Part VI: STANDARDIZED NOMENCLATURE IN RESPIRATORY PHYSIOLOGY

	Standardized Measurement	Previous Measurement
1	Inspiratory reserve volume	Complemental air. Complementary air. Complemental air minus tidal air. Inspiratory capacity minus tidal volume.
2	Expiratory reserve volume	Supplemental air. Reserve air.
3	Tidal volume	Tidal air.
4	Residual volume	Residual air. Residual capacity.
5	Vital capacity	Vital capacity.

Part VII: STANDARD SYMBOLS IN RESPIRATORY PHYSIOLOGY

	Symbol	Variable[1]
		General
1	V	Gas volume in general. (Pressure, temperature and % saturation with H_2O vapor to be stated.)
2	$\dot{V}$	Gas volume per unit time.
3	P	Gas pressure in general.
4	F	Fractional concentration in dry gas phase.
5	$\dot{Q}$	Quantity flow of blood.
6	C	Concentration in blood phase.
7	F	Respiratory frequency-breaths per unit time.
8	R	Respiratory exchange ratio in general (vol CO_2/vol O_2).
9	D	Diffusing capacity in general (volume per unit time per unit pressure difference).
		Gas Phase
10	I	Inspired gas.
11	E	Expired gas.
12	A	Alveolar gas.
13	T	Tidal gas.
14	D	Dead space gas.
15	B	Barometric.
		Blood Phase
16	b	Blood in general.
17	a	Arterial (exact location to be specified).
18	v	Venous (exact location to be specified).
19	c	Capillary (exact location to be specified).
		Special
20	$\bar{X}$	Dash above any symbol indicates a mean value.
21	$\dot{X}$	Dot above any symbol indicates a time derivative.
22	S	Subscript to denote the steady state.
23	STPD	Standard temperature, pressure, dry. (0°C, 760 mm Hg).
24	BTPS	Body temperature, pressure, saturated with water.
25	ATPD	Ambient temperature, pressure, dry.
26	ATPS	Ambient temperature, pressure, saturated with water.

/1/ Definitions, dimensions and conditions must be specified.

Part VIII: GLOSSARY

TIDAL VOLUME: Volume of air inhaled and exhaled during a single quiet cycle. Wide variability in clinically normal individuals reduces the significance of this determination and complicates its interpretation. INSPIRATORY RESERVE VOLUME: Some investigators consider total volume of air from the beginning of quiet respiration and others from the conclusion of quiet respiration. EXPIRATORY RESERVE VOLUME: Volume of air that can be forcibly expired following a quiet expiration. VITAL CAPACITY: Sum of tidal and inspiratory and expiratory reserve volumes. The volume obtained may be any volume but to be of value should be compared to the "normal" standard tables based on surface area, weight, or standing height. RESIDUAL VOLUME: Air in lungs following a full forced expiration. Included with this volume is the minimal air volume which, although present in the alveoli, cannot be readily measured. TOTAL LUNG CAPACITY: Total volume of air in lungs after full inspiration. FUNCTIONAL RESIDUAL CAPACITY: Air present within lungs at midpoint during a quiet respiration; also classified as midcapacity and subtotal volume. RESTING MINUTE VENTILATION: Total volume of air ventilated in one minute under conditions of rest. It varies widely with individuals but rarely in any one individual. MAXIMUM MINUTE VENTILATION: Maximum volume of air ventilated in one minute in conditions of forced breathing (also known as maximum minute volume). VENTILATORY FACTOR: Quotient of maximum minute ventilation divided by resting minute ventilation, but value is widely variable. Inasmuch as the minute resting ventilation is fixed for an individual, its division into the maximum minute ventilation gives a fairly accurate value for the ventilatory factor. The ventilatory factor may be greatly reduced before appearance of dyspneic symptoms upon exertion.

250. ARTIFICIAL RESPIRATION: MANUAL

Values are mean tidal volumes in cu cm/cycle obtained with manual methods of artificial respiration. They are the results of comparative studies on various types of non-breathing human subjects.

	Method	Warm Corpses[1,2]	Passive Suspension of Respiration[1,3]	Apnea — Induced by Curare-pentothal-cyclopropane Mixture[1,4]	Apnea — Induced by Anesthesia and Curare Drugs[5,6]	Apnea — Intra-cranial Pathology[5,7]	Apnea — Intra-cranial Pathology[8]	Conscious, Passive[9] — Male	Conscious, Passive[9] — Female
1	Prone pressure (Schafer)	185	810	485		155	365	466	296
2	Hip Lift (Emerson)	270	883	635			352	871	753
3	Silvester (Arm-lift chest-pressure)	520	1529	1069		285		1087	795
4	Back-pressure arm-lift (Holger Nielsen)	580	1367	1056	474	245	577	1060	748
5	Hip-roll back-pressure	537	1417	967		350		1140	858
6	Hip-lift back-pressure	530	1650	1140	864	405	680		

/1/ University of Illinois investigation. /2/ 26 subjects immediately after death and before onset of rigor mortis. /3/ 10 normal adult male subjects. /4/ 26 normal adult males. /5/ University of Pennsylvania investigation. /6/ 8 pre-operative patients. /7/ 4 patients. /8/ Harvard University investigation; 6 patients. /9/ Springfield College investigation; 15 normal males, 11 normal females.

Part I: TEMPERATURE CHANGES
VS. CO_2 AND O_2 TENSIONS

This nomogram illustrates the effect of changes in temperature on CO_2 and O_2 tensions in human or dog blood sealed in an anaerobic environment. The values are applicable to either in vitro or in vivo conditions as, for example, blood sampled into an oil-filled syringe, or blood cooling as it flows through an artery. Nomogram error increases progressively as pH and temperature deviate from standard values of 7.4 and 37°C respectively.

ΔT = temperature change in $^\circ$C.

Part II: CALCULATION OF SERUM pK

This nomogram allows for calculation of serum pK' for carbonic acid in man and dog when pH and temperature are known. Mean pK' at 37.5°C and pH 7.40 = 6.090.

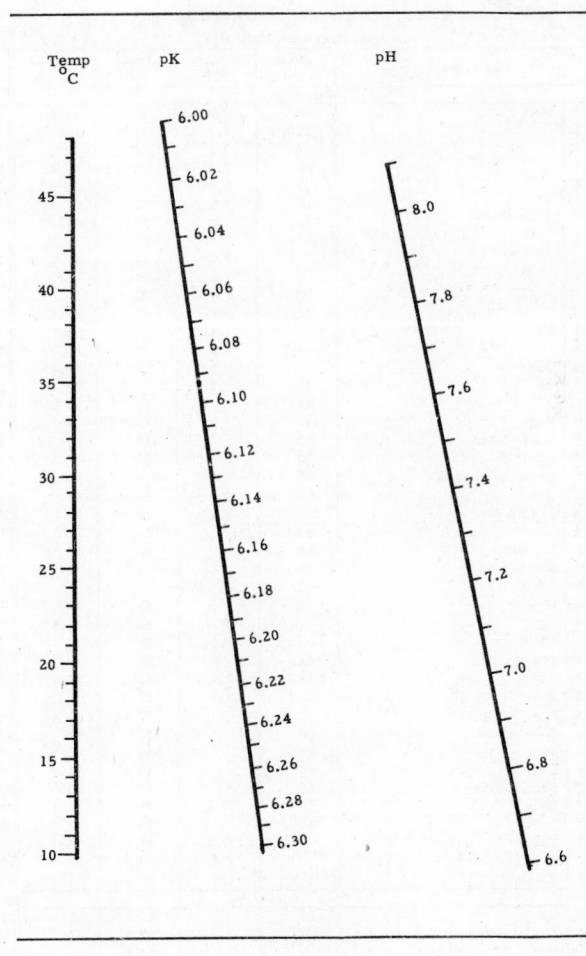

Part III: EFFECT OF BODY TEMPERATURE ON ARTERIAL pH and CO_2 TENSION: DOG

These values illustrate the effect of body temperature on arterial pH and CO_2 tension when tidal volume and rate are constant during cooling in curarized dogs.

	Measurement	At 37°C	At 25°C		Measurement	At 37°C	At 25°C		Measurement	At 37°C	At 25°C
1	Oxygen consumption, ml/min	56	18	3	Plasma CO_2 content, mM/L	19.7	16.5	5	Alveolar pCO_2, mm Hg (end expiratory)	35	19
2	pH	7.28	7.37	4	Arterial blood pCO_2, mm Hg	40	23[1]				

/1/ The pCO_2 in normal blood (37°, pH 7.4, pCO_2 40) when cooled anaerobically to 25° is, by coincidence, also 23 mm Hg.

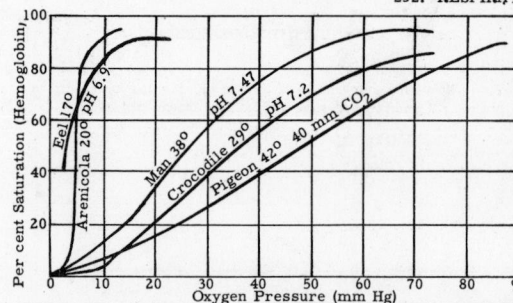

The oxygen tension, in mm Hg, at which the respiratory blood pigment (hemoglobin, unless otherwise indicated) is 95 or more per cent saturated, is referred to as the tension of saturation; that at which the pigment is 50% saturated (i.e., when unoxygenated pigment equals oxygenated pigment) is called the tension of half-saturation and indicated as "t.½ sat." The tension of half-saturation for a specific pigment establishes the upper limit of tissue oxygen tension and the lower limit of environmental oxygen for the function of that pigment. When per cent saturation is plotted as ordinate against oxygen pressure as abcissa, the "position" (O₂ pressure required to produce 50% saturation) of the resultant dissociation curve differs from species to species, and varies greatly within the same species with changes in pH and temperature. The figure to the left illustrates dissociation curves for two animals whose blood has a low affinity for oxygen, i.e., a high t.½ sat (pigeon, crocodile), and for two others (arenicola, eel) showing a high affinity and low t.½ sat. In the table below, values in parentheses are extrapolations.

Species		pCO₂ mm Hg	pH	Temp °C	t.½ sat mm Hg
Mammalia					
1	Man	142	7.0	37	(39)
2		110	7.1	37	(35.5)
3		84	7.2	37	32.2
4		60	7.3	37	29.2
5		31	7.5	37	23.5
6		22	7.6	37	21.0
7		15	7.7	37	(18.5)
8			7.4	0	(1.7)
9			7.4	10	(3.8)
10			7.4	20	8.1
11		(48)	7.4	30	16.2
12		(42)	7.4	40	31.5
13	Cat		7.4	37	38
14		44	7.4	37	35
15	Dog		7.1	37	29.4
16		38	7.4	37.5	28
17		40		38	31.5
18	Fox	40		37.5	37
19	Goat, adult	50		38	28-33
20	Goat, fetal	50		38	25
21	Goat, maternal	50		38	40
22	Horse	50	7.4	37.5	27
23	Llama		7.4	39	20
24		43		38	22
25	Marmot	40		38	23.8
26	Marten	40			38
27	Mink	40			37
28	Mouse	40		38	72
29	Ox		(7.4)	37	29.8
30	Peccary		7.4	37	29
31	Porpoise	46		38	30
32	Rabbit	32	7.4	38.6	31.6
33	Rat		7.4	37	40
34	Rat, kangaroo	40		37	51
35	Rat, white	40		37	56
36	Sea lion	44		38	40
37	Seal	40		38	31
38	Seal, harbor	40		37	28
39	Sheep		(7.4)	37	39
40		40		39	37
41	Swine		(7.4)	37	33.7
42	Vicuna		7.4	39	18
43	Viscacha		7.4	38.6	26
Aves					
44	Crow	40		42	53
45	Duck, domestic	40		37.5	42
46	Duck, domestic		7.1	37.5	45
47	Fowl	37	7.4	40	51
48		31		38	58
49	Goose		7.1	37.5	45
50		50		42	37.5
51	Huallata		7.35	40	33
52	Ostrich		7.35	40	26
53	Pheasant		7.1	37.5	50
54	Pigeon	40		37.5	35
55		40		42	51
Reptilia					
56	Alligator	42	7.6	20	28
57	Chuckwalla	37	7.6	20	24
58		(55)		37	62
59	Crocodile	(50)	(7.4)	29	26
60		(45)	(7.4)	37	53
61	Gila monster	36	7.4	20	32
62		(32)	7.4	37	59
63	Turtle	40		25	20
64		27		25	28
65			7.4	25.5	20.3[1,2]
Amphibia					
66	Amphiuma		7.38	25.4	15

Species		pCO₂ mm Hg	pH	Temp °C	t.½ sat mm Hg
Amphibia (concluded)					
67	Bufo		7.38	25.4	30
68	Cryptobranchus		7.38	25.4	18
69	Desmognathus		7.38	25.4	5
70	"Eel," congo	43		26	30
71	Frog, adult		7.3	25.4	27
72	Frog, tadpole		7.38	25.4	7
73	Triturus		7.38	25.4	7.5
Pisces					
74	Baiara	0		28	8
75	Bom-bom	0		28	11
76	Bowfin	0-1		15	4
77	Carp	1-2		15	5
78		30		18	13
79	Catfish	0-1		15	1.4
80	Cod	<0.3		14	15
81	Eel, salt-water	0.3		17	4
82	Eel, electric	0		28	12
83	Haimara	0		28	8
84	Hassa	0		28	20
85	Mackerel	1		20	16
86		1	8.0	20	17
87	Plaice	0.3		16.5	12
88	Paku	0		28	12
89	Ray		7.38	25	26[2]
90	Ray	1		25	45
91	Ray, sting		7.4	25.5	13-15[2]
92	Scup		7.38	25	6.4[2]
93	Sea robin		7.38	25	21[2]
94		1	7.7	20	17
95	Shark	1		25	7
96	Shark, sand		7.4	25.5	7.6[2]
97	Shark, bonnet nose		7.4	25.5	7[2]
98	Salmon, fresh water	1-2		15	21
99	Salmon, brackish	1-2		15	23
100	Skate	1		0.2	11
101		1	7.8	10.4	20
102		1		25	45
103		1		37.5	98
104	Sucker	1-2		15	12
105	Tautog		7.38	25	6[2]
106	Toadfish		7.38	25	3-4.4[2]
107		1	7.7	20	13
108	Trout, brook	1-2		15	17
109	Trout, common	0-3		15	18
110	Trout, rainbow	1-2		15	15
Invertebrata					
111	Arenicola	0	7.3	17	1.8
112	Busycon[3]	13.5		23	6
113	Cancer[3]	0		23	12
114	Ceriodaphnia	0		17	0.8
115	Chironomus	0		17	0.2-0.6
116	Daphnia	0		17	3.1
117	Gastrophilus	0		39	4.9
118		0		39	0.2[2]
119	Helix, summer[3]	0		20	12
120	Helix, winter[3]		8.2	20	11
121	Homarus[3]		7.2		90
122	Limulus[3]		7.7		13
123	Loligo[3]	0		23	36
124	Octopus[3]	0.6		25	3
125	Phascolosoma[4]			19	8
126	Planorbis	0		20	7
127		0		17	1.9
128	Sepia[3]	2.3		25	14
129	Sipunculus[4]	0.07-80		19	8
130	Spirographis[5]		7.7	20	27
131	Tubifex	0		17	0.6
132	Urechis[4]	8.6		19	12.3

/1/ Inter-species range 12-28.5. /2/ Dilute hemoglobin solution. /3/ Hemocyanin. /4/ Hemerythrin. /5/ Chlorocruorin.

253. ACID-BASE BALANCE: VERTEBRATES
Part I: GENERAL
Values in parentheses are ranges and represent estimate "b" or "c" of the 95% range (cf Introduction).

				Whole Blood						Plasma			
Animal	Body Temp °C	Sample[1]	pH[2]	Hemoglobin mM/L[3]	Cell Volume %	CO_2 Comb. Power[4] mM/L	CO_2 Total mM/L	CO Pressure[5] mm Hg	Na^+ mEq/L	Cl^- mEq/L	H_2O g/L	Protein g/L
Man												
1 Birth-10 da	37	C	7.42(7.31-7.53)[b]	10.0			22.7(18-27)[b]	34(27-42)[b]				
2	37	V	7.38(7.30-7.46)[b]	10.3			23.6(20-28)[b]	38				60
3 1 mo-2 yr	37	V	7.38	7.0			24.2(19-29)[b]	38				
4 6-15 yr, ♂♀	37	A	7.40(7.33-7.47)[b]	8.2			25(22-28)[b]	38(29-47)[b]				
5	37	V	7.38(7.32-7.44)[b]	8.2			27(23-30)[b]	43(35-50)[b]				
6 16-50 yr, ♂	37	A	7.39(7.33-7.45)[b]	9.0			27(25-29)[b]	42(36-47)[b]				
7	37	C	7.39(7.33-7.45)[b]	9.4			27	43(35-50)[b]				
8	37	V	7.35(7.27-7.43)[b]	9.0			29(24-34)[b]	49	139(133-143)[c]			73
9 16-50 yr, ♀	37	C	7.41(7.35-7.47)[b]	7.9			26	39(34-44)[b]				
10	37	V	7.37(7.31-7.43)[b]	7.9			27(24-31)[b]					
11 Over 50 yr, ♂	37	A	7.42(7.32-7.52)[b]	7.7			25	37(29-45)[b]				
12	37	C	7.39(7.32-7.46)[b]	8.8			27	42(33-50)[b]				
13 Over 50 yr, ♀	37	A	7.42(7.34-7.50)[b]	7.8			25	36(28-54)[b]				
14 Adult, ♂	37	A	7.39(7.33-7.45)[b]	9.0	45	25.7	27(25-29)[b]	42(36-47)[b]	138(132-144)[b]	102(97-108)[b]	940	68
15 Cat	38.6	M	7.35(7.24-7.40)[c]			18.0	20.4(17-24)[b]	36	153(150-156)[b]	120(117-123)[b]	941	
16 Anesthetized	38.6		7.28(7.18-7.35)[c]	6.8	40	17.0	21.8(19-25)[c]	45(34-52)[c]		108(105-111)[c]	942	74
17 Cow	38.5	A	(7.35-7.50)[6]	7.0	40	21.5					930	83
18 Dog	38.9	A	7.36(7.31-7.42)[c]	9.0	46	18.6	21.4(17-24)[c]	38	147(140-154)[b]	114(108-119)[b]	941	67
19 Guinea pig	38.6	H(A)	7.35(7.17-7.55)[c]	8.7	42	18.5	22(16-26)[c]	40(19-59)[c]	141(138-144)[c]	104(100-108)[c]	954	47
Hamster												
20 Anesthetized	38	H(V)	7.39(7.37-7.44)[c]	8.4	46	26.0	37.3(35-39)[c]	59(54-61)[c]	144(140-151)[e]	106(103-108)[c]	945	
21 Hibernating	5	H(V)	7.44(7.34-7.56)[c]				42.4(35-50)[c]	32(26-42)[c]				
22 Horse	37.8	V	(7.20-7.55)[c]	6.8	33	23.0	28.1(24-32)[c]	47	135	96	931	68
23 Rabbit	39.4	A	7.35(7.21-7.57)[c]	7.2		19.5	22.8(13-33)[c]	40(22-51)[c]	140(139-142)[c]	102(99-105)[c]	944	
24 Rat	38.2	A	7.35(7.26-7.44)[c]	9.0	46	19.5	24(20-28)[b]	42	144(135-155)[b]	104(99-112)[b]	946	60
25 Sheep	39.1	V	7.44(7.32-7.54)[c]	7.6	32	20.5	26.2(21-28)[c]	38	153(146-161)[c]	103(98-109)[c]	947	57
26 Chicken	41.7	V	7.54(7.45-7.63)[c]	6.8	32		23(21-26)[c]	26	154(148-161)[c]	117(109-120)[c]	960	36
27 Alligator	5	H(M)	7.74	4.2	25	34.5	36.1	15		110	958	41
28	26	H(M)	7.30(6.87-7.66)[c]	4.3	22		18.8(15-27)[c]	38	144(130-148)[c]	107(83-128)[c]	952	50
29 Chameleon	26	H(M)	7.26(6.93-7.63)[c]	4.2	28		15.4(10-22)[c]	27	157(139-186)[c]	127(113-133)[c]	958	41
30 Iguana, black	26	H(M)	7.22(7.05-7.42)[c]	3.6	35		14.5(10-22)[c]	28	159(158-163)[c]	133(128-137)[c]	940	68
31 Snake, garter	26	H(M)	7.25(7.12-7.50)[c]		28		6.6(3-16)	27	156(151-169)[c]	130(122-143)[c]		42
32 Carp	20	H(V)	7.39(7.33-7.45)[c]	6.4	31		17.7(14-22)[c]	22	130(126-137)[c]	107(96-121)[c]	957	42
33 Skate	10.4	A	7.82	2.7	20	8.4	3.5	1.3	254(219-289)[c]	255(230-285)[c]	967	27

/1/ A=arterial blood; C=cutaneous; H=heart; M=mixed arterial and venous; V=venous. /2/ "Blood" pH is actually plasma pH. /3/ Assumed concentration of 20 mM hemoglobin per liter red cells. One mM (single Fe-atom structure, molecular weight 16,500) combines with 22.4 ml of O_2, S.T.P., when saturated. /4/ Total CO_2 concentration of oxygenated whole blood at pCO_2 of 40 mm (normal alveolar pCO_2 for many animals) and at body temperature, unless otherwise indicated. /5/ Calculated from pH and total CO_2 of plasma at body temperature by the Henderson-Hasselbalch equation. /6/ Venous blood.

Part II: CHLORIDE-BICARBONATE SHIFT
Exchange of Cl^- and HCO_3^- between red blood cells and plasma in tissues and lungs. Heavy arrows indicate the direction of the changes.

Tissues	Plasma	RBC	Plasma	Lungs
CO_2	CO_2	CO_2	CO_2	CO_2
60 mm Hg	+	+	+	40 mm Hg

H_2O
H_2CO_3
$H^+ + HCO_3^-$
$NaHCO_3 \rightleftharpoons$ Na
$KHbO_2 \rightleftharpoons$ K $\rightleftharpoons KHCO_3$
$NaCl \rightleftharpoons Cl$
$+ Hb + O_2$
HCO_3^-
Cl
$Na \rightleftharpoons NaHCO_3$
$HCO_3^- + H^+$
$Cl \rightleftharpoons NaCl$
Cl
KCl

Part III: ACIDOSIS AND ALKALOSIS
Biochemical characteristics of uncompensated and compensated acidosis and alkalosis. + = increase; - = decrease; N = normal.

Plasma	Normal Values	Acidosis				Alkalosis			
		HCO_3^- Deficit		H_2CO_3 Excess		HCO_3^- Excess		H_2CO_3 Excess	
		Uncomp.	Comp.	Uncomp.	Comp.	Uncomp.	Comp.	Uncomp.	Comp.
1 HCO_3^-	26(23-28) mM/liter; 58(51-62) vol %	--	-	+	+	++	+	-	-
2 CO_2 combining power	30(24-35) mM/liter; 65(53-78) vol %	--	-	+	+	++	+	-	-
3 H_2CO_3	1.3(1.1-1.5) mM/liter; 2.9(2.4-3.3) vol %	-	-	++	+	+	+	--	-
4 pCO_2	40(35-45) mm Hg	-	-	++	+	+	+	--	-
5 CO_2, total	28(24-33) mM/liter; 62(53-75) vol %	-	-	++	+	++	+	--	-
6 $\dfrac{HCO_3^-}{H_2CO_3}$	20	-	N	-	N	+	N	+	N
7 pH	7.4(7.35-7.45)	-	N	-	N	+	N	+	N
8 Urinary acidity and ammonia	<27 ml/kg 0.1 M acid (+NH_3)/24 hr	+	+	+	+	-	-	-	-

254. BLOOD GASES: MAN

The values from which this table has been synthesized are in many instances derived by calculation from basic assumptions, factors, and constants, and do not have the same validity as measured values. Those for women are in general less well-founded than those for men. A = arterial blood; V = venous blood.

	Variable		ml Gas in 100 ml Whole Blood	ml Gas in ♂45.0 ml ♀40.0 ml RBC	ml Gas in ♂55.0 ml ♀60.0 ml Plasma	ml Gas in 100 ml RBC (In Contact)	ml Gas in 100 ml Plasma	Blood Gas Pressure (Tension) mm Hg
1	Oxygen capacity	♂	20.4			45.3		
		♀	18.0			45.3		
2	Total oxygen	A[1] ♂	20.3	20.1	0.142	44.7	0.258	94
3		♀	17.9	17.7	0.155	44.7	0.258	94
4	oxygen	V[1] ♂	15.3	15.2	0.060	33.9	0.110	40
5		♀	13.7	13.6	0.068	34.4	0.113	41
6	"Free"	A ♂	0.285	0.144	0.142	0.319	0.258	94
7		♀	0.282	0.126	0.156	0.319	0.258	94
8	oxygen	V ♂	0.122	0.061	0.061	0.136	0.110	40
9		♀	0.124	0.055	0.068	0.139	0.113	41
10	Combined	A ♂	20.0	20.0	0	44.4	0	94
11	oxygen	♀	17.6	17.6	0	44.4	0	94
12	(HbO2)	V ♂	15.2	15.2	0	33.6	0	40
13		♀	13.6	13.6	0	34.3	0	41
14	Total	A[1] ♂	49.0	16.2	32.8	36.0	59.6	41
15	carbon	♀	48.0	13.6	34.4	34.3	57.0	39
16	dioxide	V[1] ♂	53.1	18.0	35.1	40.1	63.8	46
17		♀	51.4	14.9	36.5	37.7	60.4	43
18	"Free"	A ♂	2.62	1.06	1.56	2.36	2.84	41
19	carbon	♀	2.53	0.89	1.64	2.25	2.72	39
20	dioxide	V ♂	3.00	1.21	1.79	2.69	3.25	46.5
21		♀	2.78	0.96	1.82	2.44	3.01	43
22	Total	A ♂	46.4	15.1	31.2	33.6	56.8	41
23	combined	♀	45.5	12.7	32.8	32.1	54.3	39
24	carbon	V ♂	50.1	16.8	33.3	37.4	60.5	46.5
25	dioxide	♀	48.6	14.0	34.7	35.3	57.4	43
26	Carbamino	A ♂	2.2	1.7	0.4	3.9	0.8	41
27	carbon	♀	1.9	1.5	0.5	3.7	0.8	39
28	dioxide	V ♂	3.1	2.6	0.5	5.8	0.8	46.5
29		♀	2.7	2.2	0.5	5.5	0.8	43
30	Bicarbonate	A ♂	44.2	13.4	30.8	29.8	56.0	41
31	carbon	♀	43.6	11.2	32.3	28.3	53.5	39
32	dioxide	V ♂	47.0	14.2	32.8	31.6	59.7	46.5
33		♀	46.0	11.8	34.2	29.8	56.6	43
35	Nitrogen	A & V ♂	0.979	0.494	0.484	1.099	0.881	572
36		♀	0.970	0.437	0.534	1.103	0.884	574

/1/ Difference between arterial and venous values for O2 and CO2 can vary, depending on vein from which blood was drawn, the presence of local vascular constriction or dilatation, degree of cold or warmth, or metabolic activity.

255. IONIC BALANCE AND BUFFER BASE, ARTERIAL BLOOD, CELLS, AND PLASMA: MAN

Values shown in these diagrams are for adult male, and are mEq per liter of plasma, red cells, and whole blood, respectively. X^- = undetermined anion residue. HbO_2 includes other red cell buffer ions, such as organic phosphate. pH of whole blood = plasma pH. $pCO_2 = CO_2$ tension. B^+ = mEq total base (Na^+, K^+, etc.) on basis of hematocrit values of 45% red cells. Buffer Base = that quantity of total base equivalent in amount (in terms of mEq) to the labile portion of the total anions, i.e., protein, bicarbonate, oxyhemoglobinate, organic phosphate (and other red cell buffer ions).

PLASMA (mEq/L; Total 150)
- Cation: Na^+ 139, K^+ 4.2, Ca^{++} 5.2, Mg^{++} 1.7
- Anion: Protein⁻ 16, HCO_3^- 26, Cl⁻ 103, X⁻ 5
- Buffer Base 42
- PLASMA Vol 55%, pH 7.39, pCO_2 41mm

RED CELLS (Total 119)
- Cation: K^+ 95, Na^+ 18.6, Mg^{++} 5.1
- Anion: HbO_2^- 42, HCO_3^- 15, Cl⁻ 52, X⁻ 10
- Buffer Base 57
- RED CELLS Vol 45%, pH 7.19, pCO_2 41mm

BLOOD (mEq/L; Total 136)
- Cation: B^+ 136
- Anion: Protein⁻ 28, HCO_3^- 21, Cl⁻ 80, X⁻ 7
- Buffer Base 49
- BLOOD Vol 100%, pH 7.39, pCO_2 41mm

256. RESPIRATORY CHARACTERISTICS, ARTERIAL AND VENOUS BLOOD: MAN, ADULT AND NEWBORN

Adult values are averages of means. Ranges in parentheses are estimates "c" and "d", as indicated, of the 95% range (cf Introduction). A = arterial; V = venous. In the newborn (before first breath), where the oxygenated blood goes from the placenta to the fetus via the umbilical vein, A refers to the vena umbilicalis and V to the arteria umbilicalis.

	Measurement		Adult[1]	Newborn
1	O2 Tension, mm Hg	A	95.2(80.0-104.0)c	24.4(13.5-34.0)d
2		V	39.4(29.5-48.5)d	10.4(1.2-19.0)d
3	O2 Content, vol %	A	19.4(17.3-22.3)c	10.6(5.6-17.9)d
4		V	15.0(12.6-16.4)c	2.9(0.4-8.4)d
5	O2 Capacity, vol %	A	20.2(16.8-23.1)c	22.2(17.2-26.2)d
6		V	4.6(3.2-6.0)c,2	7.2(2.1-12.5)d,3
7	O2 Saturation, %	A	96.4(90.5-101.0)c	47.7(25.7-73.8)d
8		V	73.3(63.0-81.9)c	13.9(2.4-37.6)d
9	CO2 Tension, mm Hg	A	41.0(35.0-47.0)c	44.9(35.0-60.0)d
10		V	43.3(33.0-54.3)c	59.2(43.5-68.0)d
11	CO2 Content, vol %	A	48.9(42.8-57.1)c	40.9(31.2-51.8)d
12		V	51.2(45.2-61.5)c	48.0(37.4-55.2)d
13	pH	A	7.426(7.37-7.49)c	7.32(7.23-7.41)d
14		V	7.40(7.36-7.47)c	7.25(7.14-7.37)d

/1/ Arterial blood from femoral or brachial artery, mixed venous blood from pulmonary artery. /2/ Arterio-venous O2 difference. /3/ Venous-arterial O2 difference.

257. H2CO3 DISSOCIATION CONSTANTS IN BLOOD, SERUM, AND RBC: MAN, OX, DOG[1]

	Medium	Temp °C	Dissociation Constant (pK)		
1	Serum[2]	38	6.11(6.097-6.122)[3]		
2	Plasma	42	6.0674	6.0735	6.0636
3		37	6.094	6.0985	6.0886
4		31	6.114	6.1165	6.1076
5		25	6.124	6.125	6.1206
6	RBC				
6	Reduced	37	5.98		
7	Oxidized	37	6.04		

/1/ Same values found for all three forms. /2/ Normal men. /3/ Range. /4/ At pH 7.4. /5/ At pH 7.1. /6/ At pH 7.6.

	Altitude	Temperature			Pressure					O₂ Part. Press.	Weight	Density		Pressure
	ft	°C	°F	°K	atm	psi	mm Hg	in. Hg	millibars	mm Hg	lb/cu ft	g/ml	Ratio	Ratio
1	0	15.0	59	288.0	1.000	14.67	760.0	29.92	1013.2	159.2	0.07651	1.25x10⁻³	1.00	1.00
2	5,000	5.1	41.2	278.1	0.835	12.23	632.3	24.89	842.9	132.5		1.08x10⁻³	8.62x10⁻¹	8.32x10⁻¹
3	10,000	-4.8	23.3	268.2	0.690	10.11	522.9	20.58	697.1	109.5	0.05649	9.22x10⁻⁴	7.38x10⁻¹	6.88x10⁻¹
4	15,000	-14.7	5.5	258.3	0.566	8.29	428.6	16.87	571.4	89.8		7.86x10⁻⁴	6.29x10⁻¹	5.64x10⁻¹
5	20,000	-24.6	-12.3	248.4	0.460	6.76	348.8	13.75	465.0	73.1	0.04075	6.66x10⁻⁴	5.33x10⁻¹	4.59x10⁻¹
6	25,000	-34.5	-30.2	238.5	0.372	5.46	282.0	11.10	375.9	59.1		5.60x10⁻⁴	4.48x10⁻¹	3.71x10⁻¹
7	30,000	-44.4	-48.0	228.6	0.296	4.36	225.7	8.88	300.9	47.3	0.02861	4.67x10⁻⁴	3.74x10⁻¹	2.97x10⁻¹
8	35,000	-54.3	-65.8	218.7	0.236	3.46	178.6	7.03	238.1	37.4		3.87x10⁻⁴	3.10x10⁻¹	2.35x10⁻¹
9	40,000	-55.0	-67.0	218.0	0.191	2.72	140.6	5.54	187.4	29.4	0.01872	3.06x10⁻⁴	2.45x10⁻¹	1.85x10⁻¹
10	50,000	-55.0	-67.0	218.0	0.115	1.69	87.4	3.44	116.5	18.3	0.01161	1.90x10⁻⁴	1.52x10⁻¹	1.15x10⁻¹
11	60,000	-55.0	-67.0	218.0	0.071	1.05	54.1	2.13	72.1	11.3	0.00720	1.18x10⁻⁴	9.41x10⁻²	7.12x10⁻²
12	70,000	-55.0	-67.0	218.0	0.044	0.649	33.6	1.32	44.8	7.0	0.00447	7.30x10⁻⁵	5.84x10⁻²	4.42x10⁻²
13	80,000	-55.0	-67.0	218.0	0.027	0.403	20.8	0.82	27.8	4.3	0.00277	4.52x10⁻⁵	3.62x10⁻²	2.74x10⁻²
14	90,000	-55.0	-67.0	218.0	0.017	0.250	12.9	0.51	17.2	2.7	0.00172	2.80x10⁻⁵	2.24x10⁻²	1.70x10⁻²
15	100,000	-55.0	-67.0	218.0	0.011	0.155	8.0	0.31	10.6	1.7	0.00107	1.74x10⁻⁵	1.39x10⁻²	1.05x10⁻²
16	200,000	33.8	93.0	306.8	3.2x10⁻⁴	4.6x10⁻³	0.24	9.5x10⁻³	0.32	0.05		3.28x10⁻⁷	2.63x10⁻⁴	3.14x10⁻⁴
17	300,000	-2.2	28.0	270.8	7.3x10⁻⁶	1.1x10⁻⁴	0.0055	2.2x10⁻⁴	0.0073	0.00011		8.57x10⁻⁹	6.86x10⁻⁶	7.23x10⁻⁶

259. ARTERIAL BLOOD GASES AT ALTITUDE: MAN

Values in parentheses are estimate "b" of the 95% range (cf Introduction).

	Altitude[1]			Oxygen				Carbon Dioxide	
				Tension	Content[2]	Capacity[2,3]	Saturation	Tension	Content
	ft	m	mm Hg	mm Hg	ml/100ml	ml/100ml	%	mm Hg	ml/100ml
				Simulated Ascent in Low-Pressure Chamber[4]					
1	0	0	760	94	21.1	21.5	98	41	49
2	5,000	1,524	632	66	19.6	21.5	91(87-95)	36.5	
3	8,000	2,458	564	60	19.1	21.5	89(84.5-93.5)	37.4	
4	10,000	3,048	523	53	18.4	21.5	85.4(79-92)	35.8	
5	12,000	3,658	483	52	18.3	21.5	84.9(77-92.5)	34.8	
6	14,000	4,267	446	44	17.0	21.5	79.2(71-87.5)	35.4	
7	16,000	4,877	412	41	16.4	21.5	76.2(65-87.5)	33.8	
8	18,000	5,486	379	36	15.3	21.5	71.2(57-85.5)	31.8	
9	20,000	6,096	349	35	15.2	21.5	70.8(57.5-84)	29.4	
				Ascent to Altitudes Necessitating Use of Pure Oxygen[4]					
10	35,000	10,668	179		19.8	21.5	92(84-100)		
11	37,500	11,430	159	74	20.2	21.5	94	40.6	46.3
12	39,300	11,979	146	57	19.1	21.5	88.7	39.4	50.0
13	40,000	12,192	141	55	18.9	21.5	88.1(81-95)	35(26-44)	42.7(35-50)
14	41,000	12,497	134	54	18.6	21.5	86.4(85-88)	38.1	44.8
15	42,000	12,802	128	49	17.8	21.5	83(71-95)	40(36-44)	47.1(45-50)
16	43,000	13,106	122	42	16.9	21.5	78.5(65-92)		41.5(31-52)
17	44,000	13,411	116	36	15.5	21.5	72.2(58-86)	33.2	44.9
18	45,000	13,716	111		14.6	21.5	68(53-83)		
				Permanent Residents in Mountainous Regions					
19	492	150	746	90	20.7	21.7	95.4	41	46
20	7,840	2,390	568	68	21.2(18.5-24)	23.1(19-27.5)	91.7(86.5-97)	37.8(34-42)	41.1(37-45)
21	10,300	3,140	517	66	21.8(19-25)	24.0(22-26)	91.0(87-95)	36.4(31-42)	39.3(34.5-44)
22	12,238	3,730	479	57	21.9(18.5-25)	25.0(21.5-28.5)	87.6(84.5-91.5)		36.0(33-39)
23	14,896	4,540	431	47	23.0(19.5-26.5)	28.3(24-32.5)	81.4(75.5-87)	34.7(29-40)	33.5(32-35)
24	15,950	4,860	413	46	23.4(20.5-26.5)	29.0(25-33)	80.7(76-85)	33.0(28-38)	34.0(31-37)
25	17,521	5,340	387	43	23.0	30.2	76.2	29.3	31.8
				Newcomers to Mountainous Regions[5]					
26	11,319	3,450	496	55	20.5	24.1	85	31	41
27	15,421	4,700	429	44	18.7	24.1	78	29.3	38.3
28	17,521	5,340	387	43	18.6	24.5	76.2	27.7	35.0
29	20,145	6,140	347	35	18.6	24.9	65.6	24	30.2

/1/ U.S. Standard Atmosphere. /2/ Combined oxygen only; does not include physically dissolved oxygen. /3/ Values in lines 1-18 assume a uniform hemoglobin content of 15.8 g/100 ml. /4/ For a period not longer than one hour. /5/ Up to 16 days.

260. HEMOGLOBIN, SEA LEVEL AND ALTITUDE: MAN
Values are for residents unless otherwise indicated.

	Country	Place	Altitude		Hb Conc.[1]	Corp. Hb[2]		Country	Place	Altitude		Hb Conc.[1]	Corp. Hb[2]
			Ft	m	g/100ml	μμg				Ft	m	g/100ml	μμg
1	U.S.A.	Portland, Ore.	<1300	<400	15.8	29.3	10	Switzerland	Zurich	1,640	500	15.0	30.0
2	U.S.A.	New Orleans, La.	<1300	<400	15.9	27.2	11	U.S.A.	Denver	4,920	1,500	16.5	30.4
3	U.S.A.	Omaha, Nebr.	<1300	<400	15.0	32.0	12	So. Africa	Johannesburg	5,900	1,800	14.7	24.5
4	Argentina	Buenos Aires	<1300	<400	14.8	27.9	13	Mexico	Mexico City	7,550	2,300	17.7	32.9
5	Germany	Jena	<1300	<400	16.0	31.6	14	Chile	Ollague[3]	12,140	3,700	17.0	30.7
6	Hawaii	Honolulu	<1300	<400	15.1	29.7	15	Peru	Morococha	14,760	4,500	20.8	33.8
7	India	Calcutta	<1300	<400	14.8	27.6	16	Chile	Quilcha	17,390	5,300	22.6	30.7
8	Norway	Oslo	<1300	<400	16.2	29.3	17	Chile	Punta[3]	20,000	6,100	18.3	31.7
9	Peru	Lima	<1300	<400	16.0	31.1	18	India	Nanga Parbat[3]	22,970	7,000	24.7	30.5

/1/ = g hemoglobin per 100 ml blood. /2/ = μμg hemoglobin per RBC. /3/ Sojourners.

Part I: ERYTHROCYTE AND HEMOGLOBIN VALUES AT ALTITUDE: MAN
Values in parentheses are ranges, estimate "d" of the 95% range (cf Introduction).

#	Altitude ft	Exposure Time	RBC millions/cu mm	#	Altitude ft	Exposure Time	Hemoglobin g/100 ml	#	Altitude ft	Exposure Time	Hematocrit %
1	Gr. level	Resident	4.93(4.0-5.65)	39	Gr. level	Resident	15.1(13.1-17.4)	75	Gr. level	Resident	48.4(42.0-56.0)
2	1840	Resident	4.75	40	1800	Resident	14.3	76	5000	Resident	♂48.4(43.8-53.6)
3	2200	Resident	5.04	41	5000	Resident	♂16.5(15.0-18.3)	77		Resident	♀43.2(37.1-46.1)
4		Resident	4.65	42		Resident	♀14.5(12.7-15.7)	78	10,000	1 da	50.0(41.0-56.0)
5	5000	Resident	♂5.42(4.83-6.07)	43	5750	Resident	14.7	79		2 da	49.2(44.0-55.0)
6		Resident	♀4.63(4.41-5.0)	44		3 wk	15.6	80		4 da	51.0(45.0-59.0)
7	5200	Resident	6.55	45	6000	Resident	15.0	81		5 da	50.6(47.0-58.0)
8	5750	Resident	5.99(5.12-6.82)	46	7450	Resident	♂17.7(14.4-20.1)	82		6 da	49.1(44.0-54.0)
9		3 wk	5.19	47		Resident	♀15.2(12.8-17.7)	83		7 da	50.3(47.0-55.0)
10	7400	Resident	♂5.39(4.53-6.17)	48	7800	Resident	16.4	84		8 da	49.3(46.0-56.0)
11		Resident	♂5.01(4.27-6.01)	49	9500	Resident	16.9	85		9 da	50.4(42.0-56.0)
12	8650	Resident	5.44	50	10,000	1 da	16.7(12.7-19.6)	86		11 da	49.4(43.0-57.0)
13	9200	1-55 da	5.24(4.72-5.67)	51		2 da	16.0(14.0-18.3)	87		13 da	50.4(45.0-55.0)
14	10,000	1 da	5.34(4.32-6.40)	52		4 da	16.0(13.7-19.5)	88	12,240	Resident	54.1(47.8-65.4)
15		2 da	5.58(5.04-6.11)	53		5 da	16.5(14.6-20.0)	89	12,900	Resident	64.3(50.5-86.0)
16		3 da	5.48(4.34-6.90)	54		6 da	16.5(15.2-18.2)	90	14,900	2 da	50.6
17		4 da	5.60(4.14-6.95)	55		7 da	16.2(14.0-18.1)	91		4 da	50.5
18		5 da	5.70(4.37-6.75)	56		8 da	16.3(15.4-18.3)	92		6 da	52.1
19		6 da	5.60(4.91-6.29)	57		9 da	16.6(15.1-18.7)	93		7-21 da	55.6(50.5-63.0)
20		7 da	5.66(4.97-6.56)	58		11 da	15.6(13.3-17.3)				
21		9 da	5.87(5.22-6.72)	59		12 da	15.7(13.3-17.2)				
22		11 da	5.48(4.07-6.51)	60		13 da	16.0(14.2-18.8)				
23		13 da	5.47(4.44-6.54)	61	10,100	Resident	17.2				
24	10,740	Resident	5.82	62	10,300	Resident	16.7				
25	11,400	3 da	♂6.20	63	11,300	Resident	17.5				
26		3 da	♀520	64	12,240	Resident	18.8(16.4-22.1)				
27	12,000	Resident	7.50	65	14,100	Resident	18.1				
28		1-7 da	5.54(4.74-5.92)	66	14,200	Resident	18.9				
29	12,200	Resident	5.67(4.70-6.28)	67	14,800	Resident	19.4(15.7-25.0)				
30	12,300	Resident	6.31	68	14,900	Resident	20.8(18.1-25.4)				
31	14,200	Resident	7.05	69		Arr.[1]	16.9				
32	14,800	Resident	6.46	70		2 da	18.4				
33		7-21 da	6.43	71		4 da	17.7				
34	14,900	Resident	6.66(4.80-10.4)	72		6 da	18.3				
35	15,500	2 hr-11 da	5.84(4.66-6.63)	73		1-3 wk	18.6				
36	17,500	Resident	7.37	74	17,500	Resident	22.9				
37		1-16 da	5.93(4.96-6.89)								
38	20,800	3 hr - 6 da	5.77(5.41-6.52)								

/1/ On arrival at altitude.

Part II: LUNG ALVEOLAR O_2, CO_2 AT ALTITUDE: ACCLIMATIZED MAN

#	Altitude[1] m	Altitude[1] ft	Bar. Press.[1] mm Hg	pCO2 mm Hg	pO2 mm Hg
1	Sea level	Sea level	760	38.0	106.0
2	305	1000	733	37.7	100.3
3	800	2600	690	37.0	96.0
4	1900	6200	610	33.6	79.5
5	2370	7780	573	30.7	
6	2800	9200	543	34.0	64.0
7	3050	10,000	522	30.5	61.9
8	3457	11,300	496	31.2	55.5
9	3820	12,500	489	30.0	58.0
10	4700	15,400	429	28.0	46.9
11	5340	17,500	401	25.6	42.3
12	6140	20,100	356	21.4	37.7
13	6460	21,200	331	17.7	42.5
14	6950	22,800	310	15.6	37.0

/1/ U. S. Standard Atmosphere.

Part III: CERTAIN RESPIRATION AND CIRCULATION CHARACTERISTICS AT SIMULATED ALTITUDES: MAN
Data compiled from tests in a low-pressure chamber in which the inspired oxygen was always 20.9%. Values in parenthese are percentages of ground level values. Ground level altitude = 540 ft above sea level.

Simulated Altitude	Respiration Frequency, breaths/min Ground Level	10	20	30	40	50	60	Ventilation Volume, L/min Ground Level	10	20	30	40	50	60
1 12,000 ft [483 mm Hg]	13 (100)	14 (107.7)	13 (100)	14 (107.7)	14 (107.7)	14 (107.7)	14 (107.7)	8.85 (100)	9.45 (106.8)	9.48 (107.1)	9.50 (107.4)	9.66 (109.2)	9.61 (108.6)	9.77 (110.4)
2 16,000 ft [412 mm Hg]	13 (100)	12 (92.2)	11 (84.6)	13 (100)	12 (92.2)	12 (92.2)	11 (84.6)	8.25 (100)	9.32 (113.0)	9.14 (110.8)	9.74 (118.0)	8.79 (106.5)	9.39 (113.8)	10.50 (127.3)
3 18,000 ft [379 mm Hg]	12 (100)	11 (91.7)	12 (100)	11 (91.7)	11 (91.7)	12 (100)	11 (91.7)	8.42 (100)	10.9 (129.5)	11.24 (133.5)	11.06 (131.4)	11.73 (139.4)	10.66 (126.6)	10.83 (128.5)
4 20,000 ft [349 mm Hg]	11 (100)	11 (100)	11 (100)	12 (109.1)	13 (118.2)			8.40 (100)	12.36 (147.1)	11.76 (139.9)	12.46 (148.3)	13.44 (159.9)		
5 22,000 ft [321 mm Hg]	11 (100)	12 (109.1)	14 (127.3)	15 (136.4)				8.64 (100)	14.61 (169.0)	15.21 (176.0)	15.31 (177.1)			

Simulated Altitude	Alveolar O_2, [CO_2], mm Hg Ground Level	10	20	30	40	50	60	Pulse Rate, beats/min 10	20	30	40	50	60
1 12,000 ft [483 mm Hg]	101.0 [37.6]	52.1 [35.4]	51.0 [35.1]	50.4 [34.9]	51.4 [34.5]	50.9 [34.3]	50.7 [34.0]	(113)	(115)	(113)	(106)	(104)	(99)
2 16,000 ft [412 mm Hg]	106.1 [34.9]	45.6 [30.8]	44.8 [30.0]	45.4 [28.6]	43.2 [29.4]	44.4 [28.2]	44.2 [28.0]	(111)	(110)	(103)	(103)	(101)	(105)
3 18,000 ft [379 mm Hg]	107.1 [35.0]	43.1 [28.4]	41.3 [27.3]	40.1 [27.0]	40.8 [26.2]	39.8 [26.2]	41.1 [25.1]	(107)	(109)	(108)	(111)	(108)	(104)
4 20,000 ft [349 mm Hg]	104.8 [35.5]	37.6 [26.6]	36.7 [24.4]	36.4 [24.4]	37.9 [23.4]			(124)	(112)	(117)	(107)		
5 22,000 ft [321 mm Hg]	103.3 [35.3]	34.0 [25.1]	32.7 [24.6]	32.0 [23.5]				(131)	(126)	(124)			

Part IV: CERTAIN RESPIRATION AND CIRCULATION CHARACTERISTICS AT ALTITUDES: MAN
Values in parentheses are ranges, estimate "d" of the 95% range (cf Introduction).

#	Altitude ft	Exposure Time min	Respiration Frequency breaths/min	Expiratory Minute Volume[1] L/min	Stroke Volume[2] ml	Work, Left Ventricle g/cm x 10^{-4}
1	610[3]		16.8(9.4-24.2)	6.50(4.14-8.86)	72.6(43.0-102.2)	67.4(31.4-103.4)
2	10,000	5	16.5(9.2-23.8)	6.17(4.55-7.79)	74.3(31.6-117.0)	81.2(32.7-129.7)
3		10	16.3(8.0-24.6)	7.10(5.06-9.14)	76.9(34.3-119.5)	76.4(16.8-136.0)
4	18,000	5	17.9(7.8-28.0)	8.55(4.33-12.77)	82.0(37.6-126.4)	98.1(17.4-178.8)
5		10	18.5(10.0-27.0)	8.06(5.42-10.70)	88.4(45.4-131.4)	105.3(37.6-173.0)
6		15	18.1(10.4-25.8)	8.10(4.92-11.28)	93.9(49.6-138.2)	94.5(32.6-156.3)
7		20	15.6(12.5-18.7)	7.09(3.85-10.33)	99.3(50.9-147.7)	106.9(31.4-182.4)

Part V: PULSE RATE AND SYSTOLIC BLOOD PRESSURE IN CHRONIC HYPOXIA (8660 FEET): MAN

#	Age yr	Pulse Rate beats/min	Systolic Pressure mm Hg
1	7-10	♂81; ♀102	♂160; ♀150
2	10-20	♂83; ♀91	♂170; ♀180
3	20-30	♂75; ♀83	♂190; ♀200
4	30-40	♂72; ♀80	♂180; ♀140
5	50-60	♂81; ♀89	♂200; ♀220
6	60-70	♀84	♂180; ♀230

/1/ Total volume of air expired per minute. /2/ Amount of blood discharged from left ventricle with each contraction. /3/ Ground level.

262. ERYTHROCYTE AND PLATELET VALUES: VERTEBRATES

Values in parentheses are ranges and where accompanied by superscript, conform to "b" or "c" estimate of the 95% range (cf Introduction).

Animal	RBC millions/cu mm	Hematocrit ml/100 ml	Reticulocytes % of total RBC	RBC Diameter[1] (dry film) μ	RBC Volume[2] cu μ	Blood Hb Concentration g/100 ml blood	RBC Hb Concentration[3] g/100 ml RBC	RBC Hb Content[4] μμg	Platelets thousands/cu mm
1 Man, birth[5]	5.7(4.8-7.1)[c]	56.6	4.35(2.5-6.5)[c]		106.0	21.5(18.0-27.0)[c]	38.0	38.0	227(140-290)[c]
2 1 wk	5.3(4.5-6.4)[c]	52.7	1.12(0.1-4.5)[c]		101.0	19.6(16.2-25.5)[c]	37.2	37.0	235(150-320)[c]
3 2 wk	5.1(4.3-6.0)[c]	49.6	0.67(0.2-1.5)[c]		96.0	18.0(14.5-24.2)[c]	36.3	35.0	247(163-340)[c]
4 3 wk	4.9(4.1-6.0)[c]	46.6	0.63(0.2-1.3)[c]		93.0	16.6(13.2-23.0)[c]	35.6	34.0	267(177-367)[c]
5 4 wk	4.7(3.9-5.9)[c]	44.6	0.73(0.1-1.0)[c]		91.0	15.6(12.0-21.8)[c]	35.0	33.0	280(185-390)[c]
6 3 mo	4.5(3.8-5.8)[c]	38.9	1.2(0.5-3.1)[c]		85.0	13.3(10.8-18.0)[c]	34.2	30.0	315(200-428)[c]
7 5 mo	4.5(3.8-5.5)[c]	36.5	1.66(0.9-2.94)[c]		79.0	12.4(10.2-15.0)[c]	34.0	27.0	338(205-465)[c]
8 7 mo	4.6(3.9-5.3)[c]	36.2	1.38(0.72-2.3)[c]		78.0	12.3(10.0-15.0)[c]	34.0	27.0	340(205-470)[c]
9 9 mo	4.6(4.0-5.4)[c]	35.8	1.12(0.65-1.9)[c]		77.0	12.1(9.8-15.0)[c]	33.8	26.0	345(210-473)[c]
10 11 mo	4.6(4.0-5.5)[c]	35.5	0.97(0.62-1.8)[c]		77.0	11.7(9.2-15.5)[c]	33.5	25.0	345(212-470)[c]
11 3 yr	4.7(3.8-5.4)[c]	35.5			78.0	12.1(9.8-15.0)[c]	34.0	27.0	
12 5 yr	4.7(3.8-5.4)[c]	37.1			80.0	12.6(9.6-15.5)[c]	33.5	27.0	
13 7 yr	4.7(3.8-5.4)[c]	37.9			80.0	12.7(10.0-15.5)[c]	33.2	27.0	
14 9 yr	4.7(3.8-5.4)[c]	38.9			80.0	12.9(10.3-15.5)[c]	33.3	27.0	
15 11 yr	4.8(3.8-5.4)[c]	39.0			80.0	13.0(10.7-15.5)[c]	33.3	27.0	
16 >14 yr, male	5.4(4.6-6.2)[b]	47(40-54)[b]	1.5(0.1-3.8)	7.5(7.2-7.8)[b][6]	87(70-104)[7]	15.8(14.0-18.0)[b]	33.5(27-40)[b]	29(25-34)[b]	409(273-545)
17 female	4.8(4.2-5.4)[b]	42(37-47)[b]	1.5(0.1-3.8)		87(74-98)[b]	13.9(11.5-16.0)[b]	33.5(30-40)[b]	29(24-33)[b]	409(273-545)
18 Pregnancy, 6 mo	4.0(3.5-4.8)[b]	37(32-42)[b]			92.0	11.4(10.2-14.0)	31.0	28.5	
19 9 mo	4.2(3.7-5.0)[b]	37.5(33-43)[b]			89.0	12.0(10.8-14.4)[b]	32.0	28.5	
20 labor	4.4(4.0-5.0)[b]	39(34-44)[b]			89.0	12.6(11.2-15.0)[b]	32.0	28.6	
21 Post-partum, 10 da	4.5(4.0-5.0)[b]	40(35-45)[b]			89.0	12.8(11.4-15.4)[b]	32.0	28.4	
22 Buffalo, domestic	6.8	44.3(38-52)		5.5	72.0	13(11.0-15.2)	19.0	29.0	345(164-500)
23 Carp	0.84(0.65-1.13)	31.3(21-40)[b]	0.2	6(5.0-7.0)	311(278-340)	10.5(9.4-12.4)[b]	33.5	72(63-78)	
24 Cat	8.0(6.5-9.5)	40(28-52)			57(51-63)	11.2(7.0-15.5)	28(23-31)	14(12-16)	
25 Chicken	2.8(2.0-3.2)	35.6(24-43.3)		11.2x6.8	127(120-137)	10.3(7.3-12.9)	29(27-30)	36.6(33-41)	
26 Chimpanzee	5.1(3.4-6.0)	41.6(24-51)		7.4	81.4(70-91)	12.3(6.5-15.1)	30.6(29-34)	24.5(20-27)	684(542-975)
27 Cow	8.1(6.1-10.7)[c]	40(33-47)[b]		5.9	50(47-54)	11.5(8.7-14.5)[b]	29.0		461(188-960)[c]
28 Dog	6.3(4.5-8.0)	45.5(38-53)	0.7(0-2.7)	7(6.2-8.0)	66(59-68)	14.8(11.0-18.0)	33(30-35)		
29 Dogfish	0.073(0.06-0.09)	6.8(5.5-7.6)		23.7x17.0	946(650-1180)	1.4(1.0-1.8)	23(21-25)	201(126-282)	
30 Duck[8]	2.5(1.8-3.3)		0.2(0.1-0.5)	12.8x6.6	149.0	14.8(9-21)[b]	38.1		
31 Eel	2.4			13.3x8.1		9.3	26.0		
32 Frog, bull	0.44	29.3(26.6-32.0)		24.8x15.3	670(625-716)	(10-12)	34(33-36)		
33 Goat	16.0(13.3-17.9)	33(27.0-34.6)	0.9(0.4-1.8)	4.0	19.4	10.5(8.8-11.4)	34(33-35)	6.4	783(525-900)
34 Guinea pig	5.6(4.5-7)	42(37-47)		7.4(7.0-7.5)	77(71-83)	14.4(11-16.5)	21.0	26(24.5-27.5)	
35 Hagfish	0.14(0.12-0.19)	22.2(19.3-27.6)			1530(1470-1560)	4.6(4.0-5.7)	32.0	318(303-330)	
36 Hamster	6.96(3.96-9.96)[c]	49(39-59)[c]	1.8(1.0-3.4)	5.6(5.4-5.8)	70.0	16(2-30)[c]	33.0	23.0	338(160-516)[c]
37 Horse	9.3(8.21-10.35)	33.4(28-42)[b]		5.5		11.1(8-14)[b]	26.0		335(249-461)
38 Lamprey	0.333			14.3	710.0	5.8	30.0	177.0	
39 Mackerel	3.9(3.6-4.2)	57.5(56-59)		12.4x8.3	146(140-152)	14.8(14.5-15.2)	36(33-39)	37.5(36-39)	
40 Monkey, rhesus		42(32-52)[b]			49(48-51)	12.6(10-16)	29(27-31)		267(155-424)
41 Mouse	9.3(7.7-12.5)	41.5	4.0	6.0	61(60-68)	14.8(10-19)	32(30-35)	16(15.5-16.5)	278(246-339)
42 Pike	1.1(0.4-1.37)	(16-33.0)			61(57-65)	(10-12)	34.5		
43 Rabbit	5.7(4.5-7.0)	41.5(33-50)	2.2(2-3)	7.5(6.5-7.5)	126.4	11.9(8.0-15.0)	31.0	21(19-23)	533(170-1120)[c]
44 Rat	8.9(7.2-9.6)[b]	46(39-53)	2.9(0.6-4.9)	7.5(6.0-7.5)	130.0	14.8(12-17.5)	35.0	17(15-19)	754(702-796)
45 Sea gull	2.6			13.7x8.1		10.2			
46 Sea robin	1.93			10.4x7.3		6.2			
47 Sheep	10.3(9.4-11.1)	31.7(29.9-33.6)		4.8	31(30-32)	10.9(10-11.8)	31.2	11.0	441(284-659)
48 Skate, barn door	0.265			21.9x15.6	727.0	3.6			
49 Snake, garter	1.05(0.71-1.39)	28(19-37)		18.1x10.3	267.0	8.5(5.8-11.3)		82.0	
50 Stingray	0.30			20.6x14.3	612.0	3.0			
51 Swine	6.4	41.5(30-53)[b]			63.0	13.3(10-16.5)[b]		22.0	403(296-616)
52 Trout	2.3	27.2(22-36)		♂15.5x7.5		8.5(6.2-11.5)	23.5		
53 Turkey	1.01(0.74-1.5)	38.0			314(284-348)	11.2		75(61-82)	
54 Turtle, box	0.647	25(21-27)[b]	2.0	9.0x19.0	442.0	7.2(6.1-9.1)[b]	20.6	91.0	

/1/ Ranges in parentheses are for diameter only. Values otherwise represent length x width. /2/ Mean corpuscular volume. /3/ Mean corpuscular hemoglobin concentration x hematocrit. /4/ Blood hemoglobin concentration x hematocrit. /5/ Erythrocyte and hemoglobin values are higher during first week of life if cord is clamped after placental separation. /6/ In plasma = 8.4(7.4-9.4). /7/ Ordinary range of mean corpuscular volume among individuals, 81-95. /8/ As ducks mature, all hematologic values progressively increase, with the exception of reticulocytes which progressively decrease. /9/ In plasma.

263. LEUKOCYTE VALUES: VERTEBRATES

Values are in thousands/cu mm; in most cases they are also given as per cent of total leukocytes. Ranges are in parentheses. Those on lines 1-18, 20, 22, 24 and 28-31 conform to estimate "d" of the 95% range (cf Introduction). Other values and ranges are approximate averages of highly variable unweighted means and ranges from the literature.

	Animal	Leukocytes Total	Neutrophils Total	Neutrophils Band[1]	Neutrophils Segmented	Eosinophils	Basophils	Lymphocytes	Monocytes
1	Man[2], birth	18.1(9.0-30.0)	11.0(6.0-26.0)	1.65	9.4	0.4(0.02-0.85)	0.1(0.0-0.64)	5.5(2.0-11.0)	1.05(0.4-3.1)
	%	100	61(40-80)	9.1	52	2.2	0.6	31	5.8
2	12 hr	22.8(13.0-38.0)	15.5(6.0-28.0)	2.33	13.2	0.45(0.02-0.95)	0.1(0.0-0.50)	5.5(2.0-11.0)	1.20(0.4-3.6)
	%	100	68(40-80)	10.2	58	2.0	0.4	24	5.3
3	24 hr	18.9(9.4-34.0)	11.5(5.0-21.0)	1.75	9.8	0.45(0.05-1.00)	0.10(0.0-0.30)	5.8(2.0-11.5)	1.10(0.20-3.1)
	%	100	61(40-75)	9.2	52	2.4	0.5	31	5.8
4	1 wk	12.0(5.0-21.0)	5.5(1.5-10.0)	0.83	4.7	0.50(0.07-1.10)	0.05(0.0-0.25)	5.0(2.0-17.0)	1.10(0.30-2.7)
	%	100	45(25-65)	6.8	39	4.1	0.4	41	9.1
5	2 wk	11.4(5.0-20.0)	4.5(1.0-9.5)	0.63	3.9	0.35(0.07-1.00)	0.05(0.0-0.23)	5.5(2.0-17.0)	1.00(0.20-2.4)
	%	100	40	5.5	34	3.1	0.4	48	8.8
6	4 wk	10.8(5.0-19.5)	3.8(1.0-9.0)	0.49	3.3	0.30(0.07-0.90)	0.05(0.0-0.20)	6.0(2.5-16.5)	0.70(0.15-2.0)
	%	100	35	4.5	30	2.8	0.5	56	6.5
7	2 mo	11.0(5.5-18.0)	3.8(1.0-9.0)	0.49	3.3	0.30(0.07-0.85)	0.05(0.0-0.20)	6.3(3.0-16.0)	0.65(0.13-1.8)
	%	100	34	4.4	30	2.7	0.5	57	5.9
8	4 mo	11.5(6.0-17.5)	3.8(1.0-9.0)	0.45	3.3	0.30(0.07-0.80)	0.05(0.0-0.20)	6.8(3.5-14.5)	0.60(0.10-1.5)
	%	100	33	3.9	29	2.6	0.4	59	5.2
9	6 mo	11.9(6.0-17.5)	3.8(1.0-8.5)	0.45	3.3	0.30(0.07-0.75)	0.05(0.0-0.20)	7.3(4.0-13.5)	0.58(0.10-1.3)
	%	100	32	3.8	28	2.5	0.4	61	4.8
10	8 mo	12.2(6.0-17.5)	3.7(1.0-8.5)	0.41	3.3	0.30(0.07-0.70)	0.05(0.0-0.20)	7.6(4.5-12.5)	0.58(0.08-1.2)
	%	100	30	3.3	27	2.5	0.4	62	4.7
11	10 mo	12.0(6.0-17.5)	3.6(1.0-8.5)	0.40	3.2	0.30(0.06-0.70)	0.05(0.0-0.20)	7.5(4.5-11.5)	0.55(0.05-1.2)
	%	100	30	3.3	27	2.5	0.4	63	4.6
12	12 mo	11.4(6.0-17.5)	3.5(1.5-8.5)	0.35	3.2	0.30(0.05-0.70)	0.05(0.0-0.20)	7.0(4.0-10.5)	0.55(0.05-1.1)
	%	100	31	3.1	28	2.6	0.4	61	4.8
13	2 yr	10.6(5.0-17.0)	3.5(1.5-8.5)	0.32	3.2	0.28(0.04-0.65)	0.05(0.0-0.20)	6.3(3.0-9.5)	0.53(0.05-1.0)
	%	100	33	3.0	30	2.6	0.5	59	5.0
14	6 yr	8.5(5.0-14.5)	4.3(1.5-8.0)	0.25(0.0-1.0)	4.0(1.5-7.0)	0.23(0.0-0.65)	0.05(0.0-0.20)	3.5(1.5-7.0)	0.40(0.0-0.8)
	%	100	51	3(0.0-10)	48(16-60)	2.7	0.6	42	4.7
15	10 yr	8.1(4.5-13.5)	4.4(1.8-8.0)	0.24(0.0-1.0)	4.2(1.8-7.0)	0.20(0.0-0.60)	0.04(0.0-0.20)	3.1(1.5-6.5)	0.35(0.0-0.8)
	%	100	54	3(0.0-10)	51(16-60)	2.4	0.5	38	4.3
16	14 yr	7.9(4.5-13.0)	4.4(1.8-8.0)	0.24(0.0-1.0)	4.2(1.8-7.0)	0.20(0.0-0.50)	0.04(0.0-0.20)	2.9(1.2-5.8)	0.38(0.0-0.8)
	%	100	56	3(0.0-10)	53(16-60)	2.5	0.5	37	4.7
17	18 yr	7.7(4.5-12.5)	4.4(1.8-7.7)	0.23	4.2	0.20(0.0-0.45)	0.04(0.0-0.20)	2.7(1.0-5.0)	0.40(0.0-0.8)
	%	100	57	3.0	54(25-70)	2.6	0.5	35	5.2
18	21 yr	7.4(4.5-11.0)	4.4(1.8-7.7)	0.22(0.0-0.7)	4.2(1.8-7.0)	0.20(0.0-0.45)	0.04(0.0-0.20)	2.5(1.0-4.8)	0.30(0.0-0.8)
	%	100	59	3(0.0-6)	56(37-75)	2.7	0.5	34	4.0
19	Cat	16.0(9.0-24.0)	9.5(5.5-16.5)			0.85(0.2-2.5)	0.02(0.0-0.1)	5.0(2.0-9.0)	0.65(0.05-1.4)
	%	100	59.5(44-82)			5.4(2-11)	0.1(0.0-0.5)	31(15-44)	4(0.5-7.0)
20	Cow	(5-12)	(1.2-4.8)			(0.18-1.8)	(0.0-0.1)	(2.7-6.9)	(0.15-1.8)
21	Dog	12.0(8.0-18.0)	8.2(6.0-12.5)			0.6(0.2-2.0)	0.09(0.0-0.30)	2.5(0.9-4.5)	0.65(0.3-1.5)
	%	100	68(62-80)			5.1(2-14)	0.7(0.0-2.0)	21(10-28)	5.2(3.0-9.0)
22	Goat	(5-14)	(2.1-3.4)			(0.0-1.1)	(0.0-0.6)	(2.1-11.3)	(0.05-0.60)
23	Guinea pig	10.0(7.0-19.0)	4.2(2.0-7.0)[3]			0.40(0.2-1.3)	0.07(0.0-0.30)	4.9(3.0-9.0)	0.43(0.0-2.0)
	%	100	42(22-50)			4.0(2-12)	0.7(0.0-2.0)	49(37-64)	4.3(3-13)
24	Horse	(5-11)	(3.0-6.9)			(0.05-0.60)	(0.0-0.1)	(1.2-4.8)	(0.1-1.5)
25	Mouse	8.0(4.0-12.0)	2.0(0.7-4.0)			0.15(0.0-0.5)	0.05(0.0-0.10)	5.5(3.0-8.5)	0.30(0.0-1.3)
	%	100	25.5(12-44)			2.0(0.0-5.0)	0.5(0.0-1.0)	68(54-85)	4.0(0.0-1.5)
26	Rabbit	9.0(6.0-13.0)	4.1(2.5-6.0)[3]			2.0(0.0-5.0)	0.18(0.0-0.4)	3.5(2.0-5.6)	0.70(0.3-1.3)
	%	100	46(36-52)			2.0(0.5-3.5)	2.0(0.0-6.0)	39(30-52)	8.0(4-12)
27	Rat	14.0(5.0-25.0)	3.1(1.1-6.0)			0.3(0.0-0.7)	0.1(0.0-0.20)	10.2(7.0-16.0)	2.3(0.0-0.65)
	%	100	29(9-34)			2.2(0.0-6.0)	0.5(0.0-1.5)	73(65-84)	2.3(0.0-5.0)
28	Sheep	(4-10)	(1.0-4.5)			(0.05-0.70)	(0.0-0.20)	(2.5-7.0)	(0.05-0.80)
29	Swine	(7-20)	(2.4-10.0)			(0.05-2.0)	(0.0-0.80)	(3.2-12.0)	(0.05-2.0)
30	Chicken	(16-40)	(4.0-16.0)			(0.4-4.0)	(0.2-1.6)	(8.0-24.0)	(1.0-6.0)
31	Duck					1.0(0.0-4.5)		45.8(13.0-73.5)	4.4(0.5-11.5)

/1/ Includes a small percentage of myelocytes during the first several days after birth. /2/ Values and ranges from birth through 12 months are from fragmentary data. A few prolymphocytes may be found in the blood of healthy infants up to 4 years of age. /3/ Cells classed as "neutrophils" include "pseudoeosinophils," "amphophils" or "heterophils."

264. HEART RATES

Heart rates are widely variable and influenced by such conditions as breed, sex, age, environment, size, temperature and many others. Although temperature is particularly important in determining invertebrate heart rates, it is not specified in many of the literature sources. Ranges are given in parentheses and correspond with estimate "d" of the 95% range (cf Introduction).

Animal	Beats/min		Animal	Beats/min		Animal	Beats/min
VERTEBRATES			**VERTEBRATES** (continued)			**VERTEBRATES** (concluded)	
Mammalia			**Mammalia** (concluded)			**Pisces** (concluded)	
Man (Homo sapiens)		81	Swine (Sus scrofa), newborn	227	153	Eel (Anguilla spp)	(39-68)
1 Embryo, 5 mo	156(150-160)	82	Tapir (Tapirus indicus)	44	154	Eel, marine (Conger conger)	(33-50)
2 6 mo	154(141-155)	83	Tiger (Panthera tigris)	64	155	Goldfish (Carassius auratus)	(36-40)
3 7 mo	149(118-156)	84	Wallaby (Macropus spp)	125	156	Gurnard (Trigla hirundo)	(62-86)
4 8 mo	142(129-152)	85	Weasel (Mustela frenata)	182(172-192)	157	Haddock (Melanogrammus sp)	(30-40)
5 9 mo	146(131-173)	86	Weasel, shorttail (M. erminea)	357(300-420)	158	Perch (Perca fluviatilis)	(52-66)
6 Newborn, premature	(110-185)	87	Whale (Beluga spp)	16(12-23)	159	Pike (Esox lucius)	(30-54)
7 Newborn	134(101-160)		**Aves**		160	Plaice (Pleuronectes platessa)	(54-76)
8 2 yr	108(84-134)				161	Pogge (Agonus cataphractus)	(81-90)
9 4 yr	103(80-133)	88	Blackbird (Turdus merula)	(390-590)	162	Ray (Tetranarce spp)	(16-50)
10 6 yr	93(72-128)	89	Bramblefinch (Fringilla sp)	(900-920)	163	Rockling (Montella mustela)	(64-82)
11 8 yr	89(72-114)	90	Buzzard (Buteo spp)	300(206-351)	164	Scorpion fish (Scorpaena scrofa)	(11-24)
12 10 yr	87(56-106)	91	Canary (Serinus canarius)	(514-1000)	165	Sculpin (Cottus scorpius)	(55-74)
13 15 yr	83(66-112)	92	Cassowary (Casuarius galeatus)	70	166	Shad, gizzard (Dorosoma sp)	20(5-50)
14 20 yr	71(59-99)	93	Catbird (Dumetella sp)	330(318-354)	167	Shark (Carcharodon carcharias)	(18-30)
15 20-24 yr	74(41-100)	94	Cardinal (Richmondena sp)	(375-800)	168	Shark (Squalus acanthias)	(16-50)
16 25-30 yr	72(52-102)	95	Chaffinch (Fringilla coelebs)	700	169	Skate (Raja spp)	(16-50)
17 30-35 yr	70(58-104)	96	Chickadee (Parus atricapillus)	(480-1000)	170	Stickleback (Gasterosteus sp)	(60-100)
18 35-40 yr	72(56-100)	97	Cowbird (Molothrus sp)	(315-779)	171	Tench (Tinca tinca)	(31-42)
19 40-45 yr	72(50-104)	98	Crane (Arthropoides paradisea)	120	172	Trout (Salmo trutta)	(30-46)
20 45-50 yr	72(49-100)	99	Crow (Corvus cornix)	378(312-492)	173	Wrasse (Labrus mixtus)	(40-81)
21 50-55 yr	72(52-94)	100	Dove (Columba spp)	282(185-300)		**Tunicates**[2]	
22 55-60 yr	75(48-108)	101	Duck (Anas spp)	268(212-317)	174	Sea squirt (Molgula sp)	(43-80)
23 60-65 yr	73(54-100)	102	Falcon (Falco senchris)	367	175	(Appendicularia sp)	250
24 65-70 yr	75(52-96)	103	Finch (Carduelis elegans)	920(914-925)	176	(Ascidia depressa)	(31-33)
25 70-75 yr	75(54-104)	104	Fowl (Gallus spp)	312(178-458)	177	(A. mentula)	(16-20)
26 75-80 yr	72(50-94)	105	Goose (Anser a. domesticus)	(80-144)	178	(Ciona intestinalis)	(17-32)
27 80 and over	78(63-98)	106	Goshawk (Accipiter gentilis)	347	179	(Clavellina lepardiformis)	(23-50)
28 Recumbent	66(40-100)	107	Greenfinch (Chloris hortensis)	740(703-848)	180	(Cyclosalpa pinnata)	(26-30)
29 Sitting	73(31-110)	108	Gull (Larus canus)	401(360-483)	181	(Perophora annectens)	43
30 Standing	82(54-124)	109	Hawk (Astur palumbarius)	347	182	(Phallusia mammillata)	(9-12)
31 Sleeping	♂ 59; ♀ 65	110	Hummingbird (Archilochus colubris)	615[1]	183	(Pyrosoma giganteum)	(38-58)
32 Waking, male	78(61-119)	111	Jackdaw (Corvus monedula)	342(326-358)	184	(Salpa bicaudata)	(13-40)
33 Waking, female	84(67-121)	112	Kestrel (Tinnunculus alaudarius)	367	185	(S. fusiformis)	(41-69)
34 Ass (Equus asinus)	50(40-56)	113	Kingfisher (Alcedo ispida)	440		**INVERTEBRATES**	
35 Badger (Taxidea taxus)	138(128-144)	114	Kite (Milvus spp)	258		**Arthropoda**	
36 Bat (Plecotus auritus)	750(100-970)	115	Ostrich (Struthio camelus)	(60-70)	186	Aphid (Aphis sp)	74(66-80)
37 Beaver (Castor canadensis)	140	116	Parrot (Psittacus erithacus)	320	187	Beetle (Chrysopa sp)	(53-63)
38 Camel (Camelus bactrianus)	30(25-32)	117	Penguin (Aptenodytes spp)	240	188	Botfly (Gastrophilus equi), larva	(40-44)
39 Cat (Felis catus)	120(110-140)	118	Pigeon (Columba spp)	170(141-244)	189	Cockroach (Periplaneta sp)	(60-90)
40 Newborn	(168-300)	119	Redstart (Ruticilla phoenicurus)	890	190	Crab (Limulus polyphemus)	20(8-28)
41 Cattle (Bos taurus)	70(40-100)	120	Robin (Turdus migratorius)	570(520-620)	191	Crab (Maia sp)	(25-46)
42 Chipmunk (Eutamias minimas)	684(660-702)	121	Rook (Corvus frugilegus)	380(352-440)	192	Crab, cocoa-nut (Porcellana sp), larva	170
43 Dog (Canis familiaris)	(100-130)	122	Sparrow (Passer domesticus)	804(745-850)	193	Crayfish (Astacus marinus)	50(30-87)
44 Newborn	(160-180)	123	Sparrow, song (Melospiza sp)	(450-1020)	194	Crayfish (Cambarus clarkii)	116(75-136)
45 Dolphin (Delphinus spp)	150	124	Starling (Sturnus vulgaris)	388(375-400)	195	Daphnia (Daphnia pulex)	(140-166)
46 Dormouse (Muscardinus sp)	646(580-780)	125	Stork (Ciconia sp)	161	196	Lobster (Homarus grammarus)	60(50-100)
47 Elephant (Elephas maximus)	35(22-53)	126	Swan (Sthenelides olor)	257	197	Lobster, rock (Palinurus sp)	35(30-50)
48 Ferret (Mustela vison)	231(216-242)	127	Thrasher, brown (Toxostoma sp)	278(270-294)	198	Moth (Cossus cossus)	15
49 Giraffe (Giraffa camelopardalis)	66	128	Titmouse (Parus major)	870	199	Moth (Sphinx ligustri), larva	61(39-82)
50 Goat (Capra hircus)	90(70-135)	129	Towhee (Pipilo erythrophthalmus)	(445-810)	200	Shrimp (Mysis sp)	260(140-320)
51 Newborn	(145-240)	130	Turkey (Meleagris gallopavo)	211(93-330)	201	Shrimp (Lysmata seticaudata)	175(50-200)
52 Guinea pig (Cavia porcellus)	280(260-400)	131	Vulture (Gyps fulvus)	199	202	Silkworm (Bombyx mori), larva	(30-40)
53 Hamster (Cricetus cricetus)	450(300-600)	132	Wren (Troglodytes aedon)	(450-950)	203	Spider (Eperia diadema)	132(130-134)
54 Hedgehog (Erinaceus europaeus)	300(189-320)		**Reptilia**			**Mollusca**	
55 Hibernating	(3-15)	133	Adder (Bitis sp)	40	204	Chiton (Cryptochiton sp)	(5-7)
56 Horse (Equus caballus)	44(23-70)	134	Adder (Tropidonotus natrix)	(23-68)	205	Chiton (Ischnochiton sp)	(12-25)
57 Newborn	(100-120)	135	Blindworm (Anguis fragilis)	64	206	Clam (Dreissensia polymorpha)	(30-60)
58 Hyena (Hyaena hyaena)	(55-58)	136	Crocodile (Crocodilus acutus)	(10-70)	207	Clam (Pisidium sp)	(60-75)
59 Lemming (Dicrostonyx rubricatus)	416(348-465)	137	Lizard (Lacerta viridis)	64(60-66)	208	Clam (Mya arenaria)	(5-14)
60 Lion (Panthera leo)	40	138	Ringsnake (Coluber natrix)	(23-41)	209	Cuttlefish (Sepia officinalis)	(18-40)
61 Manatee (Trichechus spp)	(50-60)	139	Tortoise (Testudo spp)	(11-60)	210	Cuttlefish (Loligo spp)	(60-80)
62 Marmot (Marmota marmota)	180(120-206)	140	Turtle (Emys orbicularis)	(6-9)	211	Mussel (Anodonta cygnea)	(2-29)
63 Monkey (Macaca mulatta)	192(165-240)	141	Turtle (Terrapene sp)	(6-70)	212	Mussel (Mytilus edulis)	(15-25)
64 Mouse (Mus musculus)	600(328-780)		**Amphibia**		213	Octopus (Octopus vulgaris)	(12-59)
65 Mouse, deer (Peromyscus sp)	534(324-858)	142	Frog (Rana pipiens)	(4-50)	214	Oyster (Ostrea edulis)	(25-30)
66 Opossum (Didelphis virginiana)	(120-240)	143	Salamander (Salamandra spp)	(30-40)	215	Sea hare (Aplysia sp)	(8-35)
67 Panther (Felis concolor)	60	144	Toad (Bufo spp)	(40-50)	216	Sea hare (Pterotrachea sp)	67(50-80)
68 Porcupine (Erethizon dorsatus)	(280-320)		**Pisces**		217	Scallop (Pecten jacobeus)	(22-50)
69 Porpoise (Tursiops truncatus)	150	145	Barbel (Barbus fluviatilis)	(35-90)	218	Slug (Ariolimax agrestris)	(20-40)
70 Rabbit (Oryctolagus cuniculus)	205(123-304)	146	Bass (Micropterus salmoides)	20(5-50)	219	Snail (Helix pomatia)	(10-60)
71 Rat (Rattus spp)	328(261-600)	147	Blenny (Zoarces viviparus)	(71-86)	220	Snail (Haliotis tuberculata)	(40-45)
72 Newborn	161(81-241)	148	Bullhead (Ameiurus sp)	22(5-50)	221	Snail (Valvata piscinalis)	100
73 Seal (Phoca vitulina)	100(10-140)	149	Carp (Cyprinus spp)	(40-78)	222	Snail (Natica sp)	(5-7)
74 Sheep (Ovis aries)	75(60-120)	150	Chub (Leuciscus dobula)	18	223	Snail (Bulla sp)	(10-18)
75 Shrew (Blarina brevicauda)	699(618-780)	151	Cod (Gadus morrhua)	(26-40)	224	Snail (Limnaea auricularis)	(42-100)
76 Shrew (Sorex cinereus)	782(588-1320)	152	Dragonet (Callionymus lyra)	(60-84)	225	Snail, land (Helix hortensis)	40
77 Skunk (Mephitis mephitis)	166(144-192)				226	Whelk (Sycotypus sp)	(5-8)
78 Squirrel (Sciurus vulgaris)	354(320-372)					**Miscellaneous**	
79 Squirrel (Citellus spp)	249(96-378)				227	Clamworm (Nereis virens)	8
80 Swine (Sus scrofa)	(55-86)				228	Earthworm (Lumbricus terrestris)	17(15-20)
					229	Leech (Hirundo medicinalis)	6
					230	Lugworm (Arenicola sp)	7(6-8)

/1/ Basal rate.   /2/ Chordates, but neither vertebrates nor invertebrates.

P wave = 1st wave of the electrocardiogram (EKG) = auricular activation; Q wave = 1st downward wave of ventricular QRS complex = ventricular activation; R wave = 1st upward wave of QRS complex; S wave = 2nd downward wave of QRS complex; T wave = slow final wave of ventricular complex = restitution of the resting state in ventricles.

Part I: AMPLITUDE: MAN
Values are millimeters (1 mm = 0.1 mV). Values in parentheses conform to estimate "d" of the 95% range (cf Introduction).

	Lead[1]	Age yr	P Wave mm	Q Wave mm	R Wave mm	S Wave mm	T Wave mm
1	I	0-10	0.8(0.04-1.2)	0.3(0-1.4)	4.8(1.5-12.3)	2.2(0-6.0)	2.7(0.20-5.0)
2		12-16	0.94(0-2.0)	0.99(0-3.0)	6.35(1.0-16.0)	2.07(0-11.0)	2.65(1.0-6.0)
3		Adults	0.55(0-1.1)	0.33(0-1.5)	6.81(1.5-19.4)	1.67(0-5.0)	2.21(1.0-5.5)
4	II	0-10	1.0(0.4-2.0)	0.6(0-2.8)	10.1(4.3-18.2)	1.0(0-4.1)	3.4(0.3-6.3)
5		12-16	1.62(1.0-3.0)	1.18(0-2.5)	14.0(5.0-25.5)	2.25(0-7.0)	3.48([±]-8.5)
6		Adults	1.25(0.3-2.5)	0.43(0-2.0)	11.99(4.0-22.0)	1.53(0-8.0)	2.97(1.0-6.0)
7	III	0-10	0.5(-0.9 to 2.0)	1.0(0.0-5.7)	7.4(0.2-19.0)	2.0(0-11.0)	0.7(-2.0 to 3.4)
8		12-16	0.73(-0.5 to 2.0)	1.56(1.0-5.0)	9.03(1.0-26.5)	1.92(0-9.0)	0.89(-1.5 to 3.5)
9		Adults	0.80(-1.0 to 2.0)	0.54(0-2.0)	8.50(1.2-18.0)	1.27(0-13.0)	1.49(-1.3 to 3.0)
10	aVR	0-10	-0.8(-1.0 to -2.0)	2.5(0-11.4)	2.3(0-5.7)	1.2(0-11.0)	-2.8(-6.1 to -0.2)
11		12-16	-1.14(-2.0 to -0.5)	7.90(0-14.0)	1.4(0-3.5)	10.0(0-15.0)	-2.85(-5.0 to 0)
12		Adults	-0.08(-1.5 to -0.1)	2.81(0-7.6)	0.76(0-3.0)	2.56(0-10.5)	-1.66(-3.3 to -0.8)
13	aVL	0-10	0.4(-0.7 to 1.0)	0.02(0-1.0)	2.4(0.2-8.7)	3.5(0-12.8)	1.3(-1.2 to 7.2)
14		12-16	0.28(-1.0 to 1.0)	1.34(0-6.0)	2.59(0-12.0)	3.98(0-20.1)	1.10(-1.0 to 5.0)
15		Adults	0.2(-1.0 to 1.2)	0.21(0-1.5)	1.13(0-7.0)	2.00(0-7.0)	0.05(-1.0 to 1.0)
16	aVF	0-10	0.8(0.5-1.5)	0.8(0-3.1)	8.3(1.8-18.0)	1.6(0-8.0)	2.0(-1.6 to 4.8)
17		12-16	1.18(0-2.0)	1.28(0-3.0)	10.9(3.0-23.0)	1.73(0-4.0)	2.28([±]-8.0)
18		Adults	0.7(-1.8 to 1.6)	0.29(0-1.2)	6.68(0-13.0)	0.80(0-6.5)	1.46(0.2-2.8)
19	V$_1$	0-10	1.0(0-1.9)	0.0(0.0-0.0)	8.5(1.8-15.7)	12.3(2.4-25.6)	-2.5(-6.8 to 1.7)
20		12-16	0.44([±]-1.5)	0.0(0.0-0.0)	5.62(0.5-16.0)	14.5(5.0-46.0)	-1.2(-4.0 to 7.5)
21		Adults	0.6(-0.8 to 1.6)	0.0(0.0-0.0)	2.3(0.0-7.0)	10.5(2.0-24.0)	1.23(-4.0 to 5.6)
22	V$_2$	0-10	1.0(0-1.8)	0.0(0.0-0.0)	10.8(3.3-23.4)	16.3(4.4-37.8)	-1.5(-8.2 to 5.6)
23		12-16	1.08([±]-2.0)	0.0(0.0-0.0)	9.13(2.0-20.0)	23.7(8.0-52.0)	6.0([++]-13.5)
24		Adults	0.8(0.2-1.6)	0.0(0.0-0.0)	4.7(0.0-12.0)	13.4(5.0-38.0)	6.22(0.3-11.0)
25	V$_3$	0-10	0.9(0-1.7)	0.05(0.0-0.1)	12.0(1.6-34.1)	14.3(1.5-26.9)	-0.2(-6.2 to 10.1)
26		12-16	1.02(0.5-1.5)	0.0(0.0-0.0)	11.66(2.5-26.0)	12.6(3.0-35.0)	5.6([++]-13.5)
27		Adults	0.6(-1.8)	0.0(0.0-0.0)	8.6(2.0-27.0)	8.8(3.0-21.0)	6.26(0.4-12.0)
28	V$_4$	0-10	0.8(0-1.6)	0.2(0.0-2.0)	15.4(4.5-37.8)	11.9(0.0-28.0)	0.7(-2.0 to 1.4)
29		12-16	0.96(0.25-1.5)	0.0(0.0-0.5)	23.8(6.5-51.0)	6.0(0.5-17.0)	7.5([++]-17.0)
30		Adults	0.6(0.1-2.3)	0.76(0.0-2.0)	13.0(2.0-25.0)	5.4(0.5-14.0)	5.66(0.3-11.0)
31	V$_5$	0-10	0.7(0-1.3)	0.7(0.0-3.4)	15.9(6.7-37.5)	6.0(0.0-1.0)	0.6(0.0-1.0)
32		12-16	0.94(0.25-1.0)	1.31(0.0-4.1)	18.1(6.0-34.0)	3.0(0.0-7.0)	5.93(2.0-13.0)
33		Adults	0.06(0-2.4)	0.24(0.0-1.0)	10.7(3.0-21.0)	1.7(0.0-10.0)	4.59(0.2-9.6)
34	V$_6$	0-10	0.7(0.2-1.3)	0.8(0.0-3.7)	13.4(1.0-21.5)	4.2(0.0-23.1)	0.6(0.0-1.0)
35		12-16	0.73(0.25-1.0)	1.30(0.0-2.5)	13.8(5.0-20.0)	1.4(0.0-5.0)	3.98(1.0-7.0)
36		Adults	0.06(0-1.4)	0.49(0.0-2.0)	9.2(3.0-19.0)	0.42(0.0-3.0)	2.55(0.2-5.2)

/1/ Leads: I = between right arm (R) and left arm (L); II = between right arm and left leg (F); III = between left arm and left leg; aVR = between point connected to (L) and (F) through large equal resistances and (R); aVL = between point connected to (R) and (F) through large equal resistances and (L); aVF = between point connected to (R) and (L) through large equal resistances and (F); V$_1$ = between central terminal (point connected to (R), (L), and (F)) through large equal resistances and 4th intercostal space (ICS) at right sternal border; V$_2$ = central terminal to 4th ICS at left sternal border; V$_3$ = central terminal to point midway between V$_2$ and V$_4$; V$_4$ = central terminal to 5th ICS at midclavicular line; V$_5$ = central terminal to anterior axillary line at ht of V$_4$; V$_6$ = central terminal to midaxillary line at ht of V$_4$.

Part II: DURATION: VERTEBRATES
Values are milliseconds and, except where noted, apply to adult animals.

	Species	P Wave[1] msec	P-R Interval[2] msec	QRS Interval[3] msec	Q-T$_c$[4,5] msec
	Man				
1	0-1 da	52(40-68)	104(80-120)	65(40-100)	421
2	1 da-1 wk	49(36-68)	100(80-120)	56(40-80)	402(322-476)
3	1 wk-1 mo	48(40-60)	97(80-160)	55(40-70)	385(345-434)
4	1-3 mo	47(40-64)	100(80-120)	62(50-80)	397(304-500)
5	3-6 mo	52(48-64)	103(80-130)	68(50-80)	392(348-458)
6	6 mo-1 yr	55(40-70)	108(80-140)	65(40-80)	408(350-455)
7	1-3 yr	59(65-88)	115(80-150)	64(40-80)	394(338-435)
8	3-5 yr	67(40-96)	123(100-160)	69(40-96)	402(349-465)
9	5-8 yr	68(40-96)	130(100-180)	70(40-90)	414(350-514)
10	8-12 yr	73(40-100)	137(100-200)	74(50-96)	419(350-536)
11	12-16 yr	78(50-104)	146(100-200)	76(40-100)	408(302-455)
12	Adult ♂	90(70-120)	160(110-210)	83(50-100)	397(337-433)
13	♀	90(70-120)	160(110-210)	72(50-100)	415(380-456)
14	Bull	80	180(160-200)	50	310(300-320)
15	Cat	40	80(60-110)	30	(330-400)
16	Cow	110(100-120)	225(220-230)	80	350(260-410)
17	Dog	70(60-80)	120(70-150)	45(30-80)	220(200-240)
18	Donkey	80	200	60	(270-360)
19	Elephant	160(120-200)	350(280-410)	150(120-180)	600(590-790)
20	Goat	80	130(120-140)	50	290(260-320)
21	Guinea pig	40	65(60-100)	30(10-50)	(200-430)
22	Hamster		43(40-46)	21(19-23)	
23	Horse	195(170-220)	370(320-420)	100(80-120)	520(440-600)
24	Monkey		71(54-88)	31(20-44)	(330-400)
25	Mouse, white	20	43(39-47)	22(20-24)	320
26	Mule	101(83-143)[b]	259(227-293)[b]	87(80-97)[b]	440(404-469)[b]
27	Rabbit	40(30-50)	60(50-100)	30(15-40)	(280-360)
28	Rat, white	20	42(35-53)	10(8-13)	(170-190)
29	Sheep	38(20-40)	(80-140)	(50-70)	(240-360)
30	Spermophile		48(38-58)	28(26-30)	
31	Swine	(40-70)	130(120-140)	60(40-80)	250(220-280)
32	Whale		300	(90-120)	240
33	Frog	60	(200-400)	80	600
34	Elasmobranch		190(120-260)	50(40-60)	
35	Teleost		250(200-440)	50(40-160)	750(400-1000)

/1/ Duration of P, measured from the beginning to the end of the P wave. /2/ P-R interval measured from the beginning of the P wave to the beginning of the QRS complex and corresponding to the atrio-ventricular conduction. /3/ QRS interval, measured from the beginning to the end of the QRS complex, and corresponding to duration of intraventricular conduction. /4/ Q-T interval, measured from the beginning of the QRS complex to the end of the T wave. /5/ = $\dfrac{Q-T}{\sqrt{\text{cycle length}}}$.

266. CARDIAC OUTPUT UNDER VARYING CONDITIONS: VERTEBRATES

Values in parentheses are ranges and, where accompanied by superscript, conform to estimate "b" of the 95% range (cf Introduction).

#	Species	Body Weight kg	Surface Area sq m	Physiological State	Heart Rate beats/min	Stroke Volume ml/beat	Oxygen Consumption L/min	Cardiac Output L/min	Cardiac Index L/sq m/min	Method
1	Man	18.0	0.82	Basal, age 5	96	23.8		2.28	2.78	Wezler - Böger
2		31.2	1.19	Basal, age 10 1/2	90	36.3		3.27	2.75	Wezler - Böger
3		66.0	1.79	Basal, age 16 1/3	60	86.2		5.18	2.90	Wezler - Böger
4		68.5	1.85	Basal, age 25	65	78.4		5.10	2.76	Wezler - Böger
5		70.0	1.83	Basal, age 33 1/3	68	62.8		4.27	2.33	Wezler - Böger
6		72.4	1.85	Basal, age 47	72	55.8		4.02	2.17	Wezler - Böger
7		69.8	1.79	Basal, age 60	80	57.0		4.55	2.54	Wezler - Böger
8		65	1.78[1]	Sitting				6.6(4.7-8.0)	3.7	Ind. Fick - CO_2
9		65		Standing[2]		29.2(21.9-35.2)	0.285(0.256-0.309)	2.21(1.61-2.85)	2.7(2.0-3.9)	Wezler - Böger
10			1.84	Tilting to 70°			0.248(0.220-0.272)	4.86(3.94-6.20)		Direct Fick
11				Acute hypoxia, 760 mm Hg	59.8	72.7		4.35		Broemser - Ranke
12				600 mm Hg	66.8	76.0		5.08		Broemser - Ranke
13				376 mm Hg	75.9	81.3		6.17		Broemser - Ranke
14				260 mm Hg	85.7	105.9		9.08	2.20(1.38-2.99)	Broemser - Ranke
15				Hemorrhagic shock	113	31	0.154(0.119-0.223)	3.5		Direct Fick
16				"Vagotonia"	40	42	0.204	1.7		Wezler - Böger
17				"Sympatheticotonia"	106	110	0.327	9.1		Wezler - Böger
18				Bicycle ergometer, 102 W m/min			0.630(0.621-0.638)	8.8	4.91	Ind. Fick - CO_2
19		65	1.78[1]	Basal, age 23 1/2[5]	63.3(49-80)	54.9(29-72)		3.43(2.0-5.3)	1.90	Broemser - Ranke
20		68.1[3]	1.81[4]	150 kg m/min[6]	77.5(51-99)	78.4(51-101)		6.08(3.3-8.6)	3.36	Broemser - Ranke
21				300 kg m/min[6]	86.3(59-113)	88.4(68-119)		7.62(4.6-10.2)	4.21	Broemser - Ranke
22				450 kg m/min[6]	97.8(69-127)	108.1(77-170)		10.62(5.9-17.9)	5.87	Broemser - Ranke
23		65	1.78[1]	525 kg m/min			1.369(1.348-1.390)	14.1(13.8-14.4)	8.0	Ind. Fick - CO_2
24		64	1.75	840 kg m/min			2.08(2.05-2.10)	19.2(19.0-19.4)	11.0	Acetylene
25		75	1.98	1200 kg m/min			2.92(2.83-2.98)	23.9(23.0-25.1)	12.1	Acetylene
26		75	1.98	1680 kg m/min			3.84(3.79-3.94)	33.8(28.9-37.3)	17.1	Acetylene
27				Treadmill, 6 MPH, 0°			2.41(2.120-2.900)	21.6(18.3-27.5)		Ind. Fick - CO_2
28				7 MPH, 0°			2.657(2.530-3.530)	27.0(22.0-33.0)		Ind. Fick - CO_2
29	Bass	2.5		Anesthetized	20	2.0-2.4	(0.05-0.09)[7]	0.271(0.168-0.352)b	1.55(0.36-2.74)b	Fick
30	Cat	4.1		Basal[7]	178.8	3.15	0.56			Wetterer
31					19	0.12-0.28		(0.3-1.0)b		Physical
32	Catfish									Physical
33	Chick embryo									
34	Cow				60	244		14.6		Physical
35	Dog	6.4	0.39[9]	Basal[10]	60		0.057(0.042-0.068)	1.12(0.65-1.57)	2.9	Direct Fick
36		14.4	0.66[9]	Anesthetized				1.82(1.14-2.50)b	2.8(1.97-4.18)	Stew. NaCl
37		23.9	0.93[9]	Anesthetized				2.66(2.00-3.32)b	2.9	Stew. NaCl
38		11.8[1]		Basal[12]	170.5(123.3-226.0)	6.91(4.42-9.74)		1.18(0.80-1.59)	3.1	Wetterer
39		16.1	0.71[9]	Basal			0.106(0.063-0.184)	2.21(1.20-3.84)	6.6	Direct Fick
40		15	0.68[9]	Shivering			0.234(0.232-0.236)	4.49(3.66-5.31)	6.1	Direct Fick
41		21.6	0.879	Treadmill, 3 MPH, 0°			0.459(0.393-0.616)	5.30(4.2-7.8)	4.5	Direct Fick
42		21.5	0.879	Standing			0.210(0.193-0.238)	3.9(3.6-4.1)	6.7	Direct Fick
43		21.5	0.879	Treadmill, 3 MPH, 5°			0.609(0.598-0.620)	5.8(5.7-5.9)	14.0	Direct Fick
44		21.5	0.879	Treadmill, 5 MPH, 10°			1.402(1.380-1.420)	12.15(12.1-12.2)		Direct Fick
45	Dogfish				36	(0.4-1.5)	(0.014-0.054)	0.139(0.082-0.20)		Physical
46	Ferret				227			(0.13-0.20)[13]		Cardiometer
47	Goat, kid	23.7	0.91[1]	Basal			0.176(0.078-0.329)	3.1(1.37-5.60)	3.4	Direct Fick
48	mature			Basal						Direct Fick
49	Horse	283	4.30[14]	Standing			1.364	18.8	4.4	Direct Fick
50		283	4.30[14]	Treadmill, 47.6 m/min, 0°			2.965	31.4	7.3	Direct Fick
51		342	4.90[14]	Treadmill, 56.9 m/min, 6.5°			4.414(4.315-4.513)	53.1(46.6-59.5)	10.8	Direct Fick
52		342	4.90[14]	Standing			2.480	24.0	4.9	Direct Fick
53	Monkey, rhesus	3.2	0.21	Standing	120	8.8		1.06		Direct Fick
54	Rabbit, white	4.13[15]		Anesthetized			0.021(0.014-0.028)	0.35(0.26-0.48)	1.7	Direct Fick
55				Basal[16]		2.48(1.27-3.79)		0.53(0.25-0.75)		Wett. & Broem. -Ran.
56	Rat	0.18	0.03	Anesthetized	214.5(169.5-288.5)	1.3-2.0[17]		0.047(0.015-0.079)b	1.6	Direct Fick

/1/ = 0.11 x $W^{2/3}$. /2/ Average of 5 persons standing about 15 minutes. /3/ Range: 57.3-86.5. /4/ Range: 1.65-2.03. /5/ Range: 18-30. /6/ Duration 2 minutes. /7/ Chloral-urethane narcosis. /8/ Gram/200-400 gram weight of fish. /9/ = 0.112 x $W^{2/3}$. /10/ Morphine. /11/ Range: 8-17. /12/ "Pernocton" narcosis. /13/ Expressed as L/kg. /14/ = 0.10 x $W^{2/3}$. /15/ Range: 3.0-5.2. /16/ Urethane narcosis. /17/ Based upon 0.5 ml/kg, animals weighing between 2.5 and 4.0 kg.

267. EFFECT OF INORGANIC IONS AND pH ON THE HEART

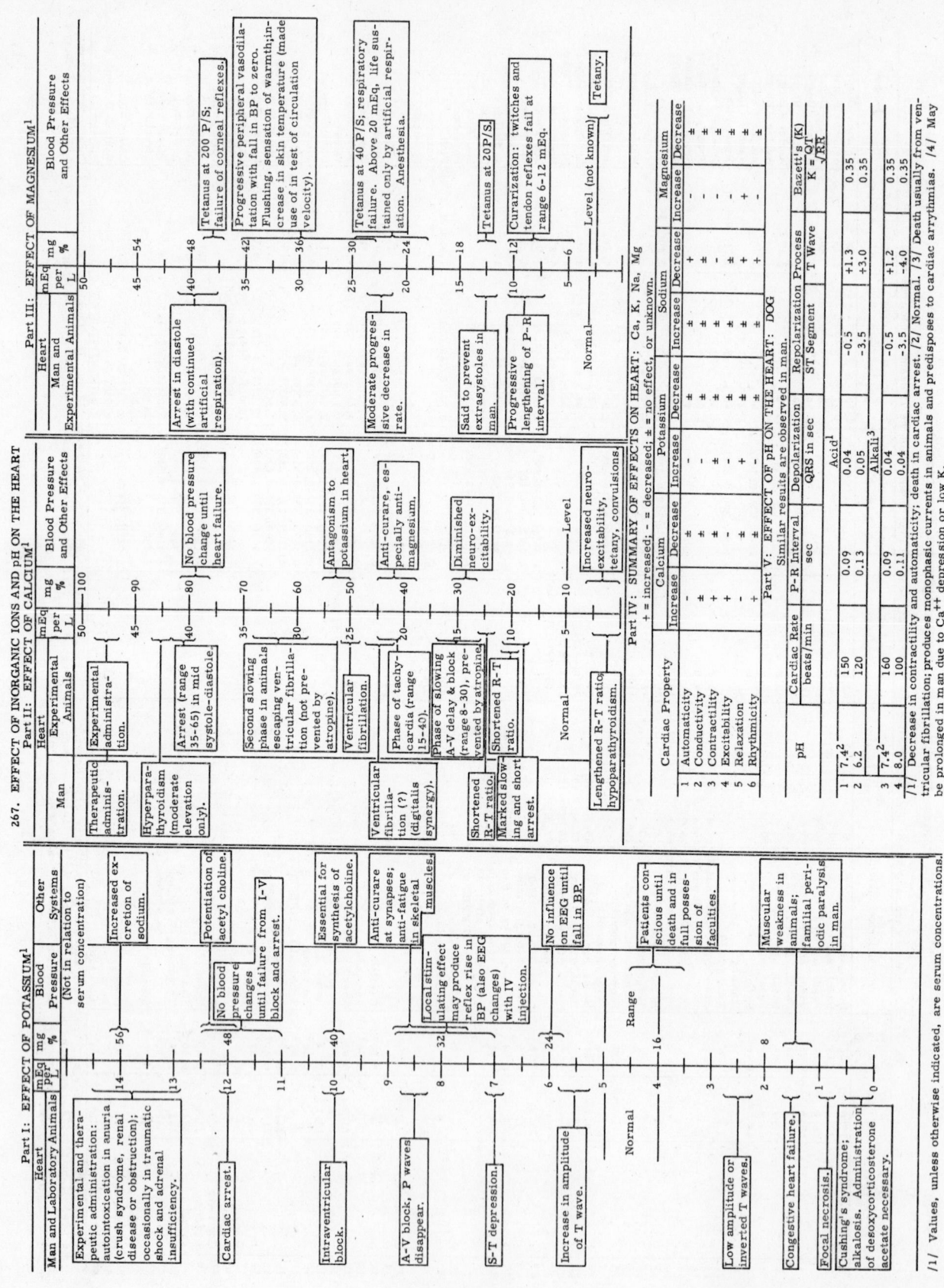

Part I: EFFECT OF POTASSIUM[1]
(Heart — Man and Laboratory Animals; Blood Pressure; Other Systems; Not in relation to serum concentration)

Part II: EFFECT OF CALCIUM[1]
(Heart — Man, Experimental Animals; Blood Pressure and Other Effects)

Part III: EFFECT OF MAGNESIUM[1]
(Heart — Man and Experimental Animals; Blood Pressure and Other Effects)

Part IV: SUMMARY OF EFFECTS ON HEART: Ca, K, Na, Mg
+ = increased; − = decreased; ± = no effect, or unknown.

Cardiac Property	Calcium Increase	Calcium Decrease	Potassium Increase	Potassium Decrease	Sodium Increase	Sodium Decrease	Magnesium Increase	Magnesium Decrease
1 Automaticity	−	±	−	±	±	±	−	+
2 Conductivity	±	±	−	±	±	±	−	+
3 Contractility	+	±	±	±	±	±	−	±
4 Excitability	+	±	±	+	±	±	−	±
5 Relaxation	−	±	+	±	±	±	+	±
6 Rhythmicity	±	±	+	±	±	±	±	±

Part V: EFFECT OF pH ON THE HEART: DOG
Similar results are observed in man.

	pH	Cardiac Rate beats/min	Depolarization P-R Interval sec	Depolarization QRS in sec	Repolarization Process ST Segment	Repolarization Process T Wave	Bazett's (K) $K = \dfrac{QT}{\sqrt{RR}}$
				Acid[1]			
1	7.4[2]	150	0.09	0.04	−0.5	+1.3	0.35
2	6.2	120	0.13	0.05	−3.5	+3.0	0.35
				Alkali[3]			
3	7.4[2]	160	0.09	0.04	−0.5	+1.2	0.35
4	8.0	100	0.11	0.04	−3.5	−4.0	0.35

/1/ Decrease in contractility and automaticity; death in cardiac arrest. /2/ Normal. /3/ Death usually from ventricular fibrillation; produces monophasic currents in animals and predisposes to cardiac arrythmias. /4/ May be prolonged in man due to Ca++ depression or low K.

/1/ Values, unless otherwise indicated, are serum concentrations.

Part I: VASCULAR PRESSURES: MAN

	Chamber or Vessel	Systolic mm Hg	Diastolic mm Hg	Mean mm Hg
1	Small veins[1]			18
2	Medium veins[2]			4-7
3	Venae cavae[3]			-5 to 5
4	Right atrium[3]	1-5	0-2	1-3
5	Right ventricle[3]	20-30	0-4	
6	Pulmonary artery[3]	20-30	8-12	15-18
7	Pulmonary capillary[3]			8-10
8	Left atrium[4]	8-12	5-9	8-10
9	Left ventricle[5]	90-130	2-8	
10	Aorta	90-130	60-90	70-115

/1/ From animal and human data. /2/ Direct measurement. /3/ Right heart catheterization. /4/ Transthoracic needle puncture. /5/ Direct measurement, open chest.

Part III: RELATIONSHIP OF CENTRAL AND PERIPHERAL ARTERY PRESSURES: MAN

Values are expressed as percentage of pressure of aorta or subclavian near the aorta. Values are means.

	Condition and Measurement	Artery Brachial	Radial	Femoral
	Supine, at rest			
1	Systolic	109	112	110
2	Diastolic	96	93	94
3	Mean	98	94	96
	Supine, during exercise			
4	Systolic	111	113	101
5	Diastolic	97	93	95
6	Mean	97	93	97
	70° Head-up tilt			
7	Systolic	111	115	123
8	Diastolic	98	95	98
9	Mean	99	98	100

Part II: CAPILLARY BLOOD PRESSURE: VERTEBRATES

Values in parentheses are estimate "d" of the 95% range (cf Introduction). A = arterial; V = venous.

	Animal	Region		Pressure cm H_2O
1	Man	Nail bed of finger.	A	43.5(28.6-65.0)[1]
2			V	16.5(8.0-24.5)[1]
3		Skin, hyperemia.	A	66.0(71.0-93.0)
4			V	(54.5-66.5)
5		Skin, hypertensive.	A	48.5(10.1-95.1)
6			V	30.8(12.8-58.0)
7	Guinea pig[2]	Mesentery, veronal ether anesthesia.	A	38.5(31.0-49.0)
8			V	17.0(13.0-19.5)
9	Rat[2]	Mesentery.	A	30.0(22.0-34.0)
10			V	17.0(15.0-20.0)
11	Frog	Mesentery.	A	14.4(5.0-22.0)[3]
12			V	10.1(6.7-18.0)[3]
13		Muscle, normal, urethane.	A	14.9(11.0-18.0)
14			V	9.5(7.0-12.7)
15		Muscle, hyperemia.	A	20.1(17.0-26.0)
16			V	16.0(12.0-17.5)
17		Web, normal, urethane.	A	13.9(10.0-19.0)
18			V	9.6(8.5-13.0)
19		Web, normal, curare.	A	14.5(0.0-20.5)
20			V	10.0(8.5-15.5)
21		Web, hyperemia.	A	19.5(14.0-26.5)
22			V	16.5(15.0-17.5)

/1/ Varies directly with venous pressure as affected by hydrostatic pressure or venous obstruction. Varies directly with arteriolar vasodilatation as produced by emotion, heat, or trauma. Varies inversely with arteriolar vasoconstriction as produced by emotion or cold. Varies minimally in a single capillary with time and also from capillary to capillary. /2/ Decerebrate. /3/ Pithed.

269. PULSE CHARACTERISTICS AND CONFIGURATIONS

Part I: PULSE WAVE VELOCITY FROM CENTRAL TO PERIPHERAL RECORDING SITE: MAN

	Recording Site	Velocity M/sec		Recording Site	Velocity M/sec
1	Aorta to radial artery	8.8(6.6-13.8)	3	Aorta to femoral artery	6.3(4.7-10.4)
2	Aorta to brachial artery	7.2(5.4-8.5)	4	Brachial artery to radial artery	12.5(9.3-22.5)

Part II: MEAN BLOOD PRESSURE AND VASCULAR INTERRELATIONS: DOG (SCHEMATIC)

Reference plane is 5 cm anterior to the dorsal surface with the animal supine; ranges are averages of those in the anesthetized dog during expiratory rest. The horizontal line at the level of 10 mm Hg is the pressure at each point during circulation arrest (mean static pressure).

Part III: CARDIAC CYCLE INTERRELATIONS

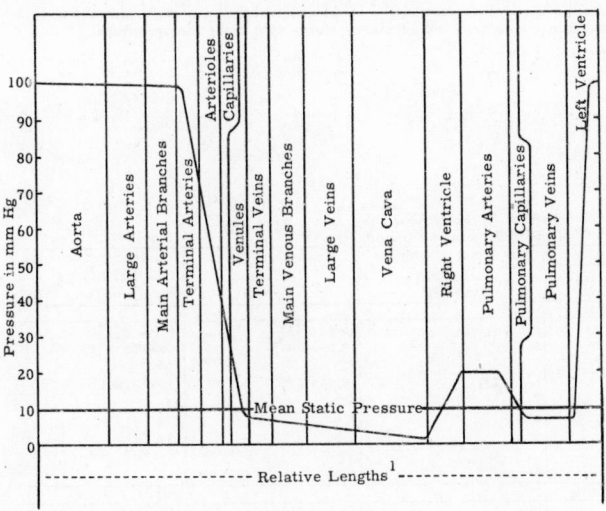

/1/ Arterioles, capillaries and venules should be shorter than indicated.

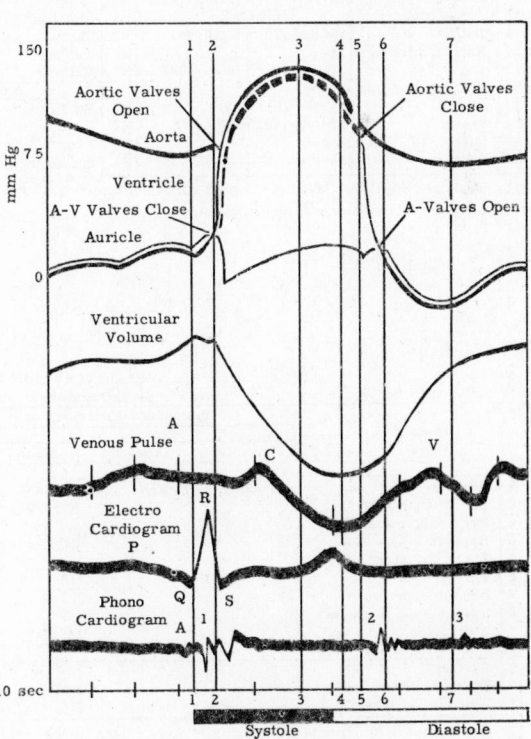

270. ARTERIAL BLOOD PRESSURE: MAN

Values are mm Hg. Ranges in parentheses are estimates of the 95% range, those on Lines 1-13 estimate "b," and those on Lines 14-26 estimate "a" (cf Introduction).

	Age yr	Male Systolic	Male Diastolic	Female Systolic	Female Diastolic
1	Birth	74	38		
2	4	89(78-100)	60(46-74)	89(76-102)	60(47-73)
3	5	92(80-104)	62(47-77)	92(79-105)	62(49-75)
4	6	94(81-107)	64(49-79)	94(80-108)	64(50-78)
5	7	97(84-110)	65(50-80)	97(83-111)	66(51-81)
6	8	100(87-113)	67(53-81)	100(86-114)	64(50-78)
7	9	101(88-114)	68(55-81)	101(87-115)	69(55-83)
8	10	103(90-116)	69(57-81)	103(89-117)	70(57-83)
9	11	104(91-117)	70(59-81)	104(90-118)	71(58-84)
10	12	106(93-119)	71(61-81)	106(92-120)	72(58-86)
11	13	108(95-121)	72(62-82)	108(95-121)	73(58-88)
12	14	110(97-123)	73(63-83)	110(97-123)	74(57-74)
13	15	112(98-126)	75(64-86)	112(98-126)	76(59-95)
14	16	118(95-142)	73(53-93)	116(92-140)	72(54-91)
15	17	121(96-146)	74(56-93)	116(93-139)	72(54-90)
16	18	120(96-143)	74(55-94)	116(94-139)	72(55-89)
17	19	122(92-151)	75(54-95)	115(92-138)	71(54-89)
18	20-24	123(96-150)	76(57-96)	116(93-139)	72(53-91)
19	25-29	125(100-150)	78(60-95)	117(94-139)	74(56-92)
20	30-34	126(99-153)	79(60-98)	120(92-147)	75(54-96)
21	35-39	127(99-155)	80(60-101)	124(97-151)	78(58-98)
22	40-44	129(100-159)	81(63-100)	127(94-161)	80(59-100)
23	45-49	130(97-163)	82(61-103)	131(92-169)	82(59-104)
24	50-54	135(97-172)	83(61-106)	137(96-179)	84(59-108)
25	55-59	138(101-175)	84(62-106)	139(97-180)	84(61-106)
26	60-64	142(100-183)	85(60-109)	144(100-188)	85(60-110)

271. ARTERIAL BLOOD PRESSURE: ANIMALS OTHER THAN MAN

Values are mm Hg. Ranges in parentheses are estimate "d" of the 95% range (cf Introduction).

VERTEBRATES — Mammals

	Species	Systolic	Diastolic
1	Bat[1]	50[2]	
2	Cat[2]	155	100
3	Cat, birth	(25-30)	
4	Cattle[3]	134(124-166)	88(80-102)
5	Cattle, young	130(110-140)[2]	
6	Dog[3]	148(108-189)	100(75-122)
7	Dog, birth	50	
8	Goat[3]	120(112-126)	84(76-90)
9	Guinea pig	(81-90)[2]	
10	Hamster[1]	(90-100)[2]	
11	Horse[1]	169(115-188)	
12	Horse, young	80	50
13	Horse, gelding[3]	98(90-104)	(57-71)
14	Horse, stallion	(70-98)	(40-58)
15	Horse, mare	(86-98)	(53-65)
16	Jackass	(90-104)	(54-60)
17	Mouse[3]	147(133-160)	106(102-110)
18	Opossum	(120-135)[2]	
19	Rabbit[3]	110(95-130)	80(60-90)
20	Rabbit, birth	35	
21	Rat	116(88-130)	90(60-100)
22	Rat, 20 da embryo	12[2]	
23	Seal	(130-140)[2]	
24	Sheep	114(90-140)	68(64-76)
25	Sheep, 106 da embryo[3]	37[2]	
26	Swine	169(144-185)	108(98-120)

VERTEBRATES (continued) — Birds

	Species	Systolic	Diastolic
27	Buzzard	171[2]	
28	Canary[1]	220(200-250)	154(150-160)
29	Crow	(147-151)[2]	
30	Duck	162[2]	
31	Falcon	103[2]	
32	Fowl[3]	150	120
33	Goose	162(129-176)[2]	
34	Gull	179[2]	
35	Hawk	178[2]	
36	Jackdaw	119[2]	
37	Kite	194[2]	
38	Pigeon[3]	135(120-140)	105(100-115)
39	Red-hawk	103[2]	
40	Robin	118(110-125)	80
41	Rook	115[2]	
42	Sparrow[1]	180	140
43	Sparrow, fledgling[1]	(115-130)	
44	Starling[1]	180(150-210)	130(100-160)
45	Stork	161[2]	
46	Turkey	193[2]	
47	Vulture	171[2]	

Amphibians and Reptiles[4]

	Species	Systolic	Diastolic
48	Bull-frog	(26-34)	(12-18)
49	Crocodile	(30-50)[2]	
50	Frog	43(36-56)	31(24-44)
51	Snake, ring	89[2]	

VERTEBRATES (concluded) — Amphibians and Reptiles (concluded)

	Species	Systolic	Diastolic
52	Toad	48[2]	
53	Turtle[3]	44(38-55)	37(28-47)

Fish

	Species	Systolic	Diastolic
54	Barbel	42[2]	
55	Bass, large mouth	50	40
56	Bullhead	22	13
57	Carp[1]	43(40-45)	
58	Catfish	37	23
59	Dogfish	32(30-37)	28
60	Eel	(65-70)[2]	
61	Pike	(35-84)[2]	
62	Ray	16	7
63	Salmon	75(47-120)	
64	Sand-shark	32	
65	Shad, gizzard	48	38
66	Shark	(30-37)[2]	
67	Skate	20	
68	Torpedo	17(16-18)	10

INVERTEBRATES

	Species	Systolic	Diastolic
69	Crab	4	
70	Earthworm	9.3[2]	
71	Lobster	10	
72	Mussel	3	
73	Octopus	60	
74	Sea-hare	(20-40)	
75	Squid	(25-80)	

/1/ Anesthetized. /2/ Mean pressure. /3/ Unanesthetized. /4/ Values change with body temperature, rising with raised temperature.

272. PULMONARY CIRCULATION DYNAMICS: MAN AND DOG

Ranges in parentheses are estimate "d" of the 95% range (cf Introduction).

	Condition	Arterial Systolic	Arterial Diastolic	Arterial Mean	Venous[2]	Pulmonary Vascular Gradient mm Hg	Pulmonary Blood Flow L/min	Pulmonary Vascular Resistance (dyne sec)/(cm x 10⁵)
		Pulmonary Pressure, mm Hg[1]						
	Man							
1	Resting	(23-25)[3]	(9-14)[3]	(14-18)[3]	(7-9)	(6-9)	(5.4-7.4)[3]	(67-238)[3,4]
2	Exercise, supine			(15[3]-21)	10	11	(9.6-10.4[3])	(90-115[3,4])
3	Exercise, standing[3]	26	9	16		12		76[4]
4	Hypoxia	26[3]	12[3]	(18[3]-20)	(7-8[3])	(10[3]-13)	(5.5-8.0[3])	(119[3]-189)
5	Saline infusion[3]			23	16	7	6.7	84
6	Epinephrine[3]			19	7	12	7.9	121
7	Norepinephrine	28	11	21	15	6	4.5	118
8	Tetraethylammonium chloride			15	10	5	4.7	85
	Dog							
9	Resting[5]			(17-18)	(4-10)	(8-13)	(2.3-3.2)	(285-325)
10	Hypoxia, moderate[5]			(22-26)	(4-8)[6]	(14-22)	(2.4-3.8)	(463-467)
11	Hypoxia, severe[5]			26	9[6]	17	8.1	167

/1/ Zero point = 10 cm anterior to back in man; = back in dog. /2/ Pulmonary "capillary" mean pressure used except where indicated. /3/ Pressure approximately corrected to 10 cm zero point. /4/ Total pulmonary resistance, utilizing pulmonary arterial mean minus pulmonary "capillary" mean as pressure gradient. /5/ Anesthetized. /6/ Pulmonary venous or left atrial mean pressure.

273. BLOOD FLOW, TISSUES AND ORGANS: MAMMALS

Values in parentheses are ranges and, where accompanied by superscript, conform to the "b" or "c" estimate of the 95% range (cf Introduction).

	Species	Body Wt kg	Tissue or Organ	Physiological State	Tissue Weight kg	Tissue Weight % body wt	Blood Flow ml/100g tissue per min[1,2]	Blood Flow ml/total tissue per min[2,3]	Blood Flow ml/sq m/min[2,4]	% of Cardiac Output[5]
1	Man	70	Total body, arterial (systemic circulation or cardiac output)	Basal	68.8	98.3	7.5(5.7-8.3)	5200	3000	100
2				Exercise			20.1	13,840	8000	100
3				Oligemic shock			4.5	3114	1800	100
4			Lungs (pulmonary circ.)	Basal	1.2	1.7	433(333-485)	5200	3000	100
5				Exercise			1153	13,840	8000	100
6				Oligemic shock			259	3114	1800	100
7			Adrenals	Basal	0.011	0.02	590	65	38	1.2
8			Brain	Basal	1.35	1.93	54(40-71)	729(540-959)		14.0
9				Inhalation 5-7% CO_2			93(65-141)			
10				85-100% O_2			45(34-55)			
11				10% O_2			73(39-107)			
12				Anesthesia, thiopental			61(33-117)			
13				Oligemic shock			32(24-38)	432(324-513)		
14				Sleep			65(48-85)			
15				Supine			64.7(50-103)			
				Position change						
16				Supine			67.0(52-97)			
17				65° (head up)			53.1(40-81)			
				Position change						
18				Supine (40°-65°)			65.1(52-97)			
19				Erect			51.6(40-81)			
20				L-Norepinephrine			61(42-83)			
21				L-Epinephrine			66(40-98)			
22				USP Epinephrine			71(42-97)			
23				Age, <45 yr			52(40-63)			
24				>45 yr			46(30-64)			
25			Heart (coronary circ.)	Basal	0.3	0.43	70(50-75)	210(150-225)	121	4.0
26				Exercise			576	1730	1000	12.5
27				Oligemic shock			86.5	259	150	8.0
28			Kidney	Basal	0.16	0.23	750(400-900)	1200(1000-1500)	695	23.0
29				Exercise[6]			415	1245	650	8.0
30				Oligemic shock[6]			28.8	86.5	50	3.0
31			Muscle	Basal	28.0	40.0	3.0(2.3-6.5)	850(500-1820)	491	16.3
32				Exercise			19.7	6920	4000	50.0
33				Oligemic shock			1.97	692	400	22.0
34			Liver, hepatic[7] portal[7]	Basal	1.5	2.14	20.0	300	173	5.8
35							80.0	1200	695	23.1
36			Splanchnic flow[8]	Basal	1.843	2.63		1470	850	28.2
37				Exercise				1038	600	7.5
38				Oligemic shock				605	350	19.4
39			Extremities Hand[9]	Basal, 21°C[10]			3.5(1.2-5.3)c			
40				24°C[11]			5.9(2.7-9.6)c			
41				25°C[10]			9.3(5.1-13.5)b			
42				21-24°C[12]			2.1(0.5-6.4)c			
43				25-29°C[12]			9.3(5.8-16.5)c			
44			Forearm	Basal, 15-20°C[10]			2.3(1.2-3.0)c			
45				15-20°C[13]			2.7(1.9-3.8)c			
46				15-20°C[11]			4.2(1.5-7.0)			
47				18.5°C[12]			3.1(2.6-3.6)b			
48				25-27°C[14]			4.5(2.8-6.3)c			
49				27-29°C[12]			4.9(1.7-7.3)c			
50			Calf	Basal, 25°C[10]			1.4(0.4-2.4)b			
51			Foot	Basal, 21°C[10]			2.0(0.5-4.4)c			
52				24-26.5°C[10]			3.9(1.4-7.8)c			
53			Finger	Comfortable[12]			(15-40)			
54			Skin & subcutaneous	Basal	18.0[15]	25.71	1.4(1.2-1.8)	260(220-330)	150	5.0
55				Exercise			4.61	692	400	5.0
56				Oligemic shock			0.57	86.5	50	3.0
57			Thyroid	Basal	0.03	0.04	550	165	96	3.2
58	Monkey	3-6	Brain	Anesthesia, barbiturate			47(33-74)			
59				Hemorrhagic shock			24(13-30)			
60				Anesthesia, thiopental			24(14-26)			
61	Cat		Liver	Anesthesia			(33-48)			
62	Rat		Liver	Basal[16]			79(75-92)			
63	Dog	9-19	Heart	Basal	0.054[17]		133(79-220)	70.1(52-103)		
64		12-19	Liver	Basal	0.53		82(46-112)	387(216-612)		
65		10-16	Hind leg	Basal				55(35-75)		

/1/ = $\frac{\text{(ml/sq m/min x 1.73)}}{\text{organ wt}} \times \frac{1}{10}$. /2/ Body surface 70 kg man = 1.73 sq m. /3/ = (ml/sq m/min) x 1.73. /4/ = $\frac{\text{(ml/100g tissue/min) x (0.1 organ wt)}}{1.73}$

/5/ = $\frac{\text{(ml/sq m/min) x 1.73}}{\text{Cardiac output}}$. /6/ Values based on organ weight of 0.3 kg. /7/ Calculated from relative hepatic artery flow and portal vein flow as measured in dog. /8/ = portal drained viscera, including intestines, pancreas, spleen, stomach. /9/ Values for extremity flows are ml/min/100 ml segment. Water plethysmography, unless otherwise noted. /10/ Bath temp. 32°C. /11/ Bath temp. 35°C. /12/ Air plethysmography. /13/ Bath temp. 33°C. /14/ Stewart dye principle. /15/ Skin, 4 kg; subcutaneous, 14 kg. /16/ Thermo-electric. /17/ Left ventricle alone.

274. CAPILLARY VASCULARITY, SKELETAL AND CARDIAC MUSCLE: VERTEBRATES

"Capillary" counts from injected cross-section may not exclude other minute vessels (e.g., arterioles, venules). By statistical estimation, numbers of arterioles per capillary per venules = 1/39/2.7 in membranous hamster cheek pouch in vivo; endothelial surface areas = 10/60/30; capacities = 21/18/61. By camera lucida drawings, endothelial surface areas = 21/25/54; capacities = 22/4/74.

Part I: SKELETAL MUSCLE
A = asphyxiated; R = resting; T = trained; U = untrained; V = vasodilated; W = working.

	Animal	Muscle		Capillaries per sq mm Cross-section[1,2]	Capillaries per Fiber	Capillary Diameter[3] μ	Capillary Capacity[2,4,5] cu mm/cu mm	Capillary Surface Area[2,5,6] sq mm/cu mm
1	Cat	Gastrocnemius	V	2341		6.0	0.066	44.1
2		Rectus femoris	V	2474		6.0	0.070	46.6
3		Tibialis anterior	V	2214		6.0	0.063	41.7
4	Dog, adult	Semimembranosus	R	3240	0.6	7.1	0.128	72.3
5			V	5900	1.6	7.1	0.234	131.6
6			V	2630		7.2	0.107	59.5
7		Gracilis	R	1050	0.6	7.1	0.042	23.4
8			W[7]	2010	1.2	7.1	0.080	44.8
9			V	2580		7.1	0.102	57.5
10	Dog, puppy	Gracilis	R	1690	0.7	7.1	0.067	37.7
11	Guinea pig	Abdominal wall	R	85		3.0	0.001	0.8
12			R	270		3.8	0.003	3.2
13			V	1400		4.6	0.023	20.2
14		Diaphragm	W[8]	2570		5.0	0.050	40.4
15			W[8]V	3000		8.0	0.151	75.4
16		Gastrocnemius	R	1136		7.5	0.050	26.8
17			U	1378		7.5	0.061	32.5
18			T	1924		7.5	0.085	45.3
19			W[7]	2000		7.5	0.088	47.1
20			A	2600		7.5	0.115	61.3
21			V	2614		7.5	0.115	61.6
22	Mouse	Gastrocnemius	R	3060		6.6	0.105	63.4
23			W[7]	3600		6.6	0.123	74.6
24			A	4650		6.6	0.159	96.4
25		Masseter	W[7]	4393		6.6	0.150	91.1
26			W[7]V	5100		6.6	0.174	105.7
27			A	6800		6.6	0.233	141.0
28	Rabbit	Adductor magnus (white)	V	1550	0.7	2.5	0.008	12.3
29		Gastrocnemius	V	1344	1.6	1.8[9]	0.004	7.5
30		Gluteal	U		0.5	7.5		
31			T		1.2	7.5		
32		Semitendinosus (red)	V	790	1.2	5.2	0.017	13.0
33			V	1198	3.1	2.3[9]	0.005	8.8
34		Rectus femoris	V	1475	1.2	1.6[9]	0.003	7.4
35	Rat	Rectus femoris	V	3573		7.5	0.158	84.2
36		Tibialis anterior	V	3402		7.5	0.150	80.2
37	Frog (Rana	Gastrocnemius	V	382	2.6	9.8	0.029	11.8
38	temporaria)	Gracilis	V	406	1.9	9.7	0.030	12.4
39		Obliquus oculi inferior	V	393	0.2	15.0	0.069	18.5
40		Sartorius	R	90		4.4	0.001	1.2
41			W[7]	325		6.8	0.012	7.0
42			V	400		15.0	0.071	19.0
43			V	426	1.8	8.6	0.025	11.5
44		Submaxillarus	V	652	0.7	11.1	0.063	22.7
45	Trout	Eyeball muscle	W[8]	276		10.6	0.024	9.2
46		Parietal	R	123		9.8	0.009	3.8
47		Rectus lateralis	W[8]	400		8.3	0.022	10.4

/1/ Differences in counts during rest, work and vasodilation are now attributed to precapillary sphincter action. /2/ Counts are averages. Assumed capillary length = 1 mm. Actual capillary length <0.5 mm. /3/ Based on RBC diameter, excluding Items 11-15, 37-38, 40-41, 43-47. /4/ Capillary capacities determined by pressure injection are maximal, and differ from capacities (all vessels) by isotope and spectrophotometric methods, which may be minimal and indicate effective in vivo capacities. E.g., vascular capacities (cu mm/cu mm), assuming that muscle density = 1.0: skeletal muscle of cat, 0.027; dog, 0.018; rat, 0.004; cardiac muscle of cat, 0.084; dog, 0.066; rat, 0.042. From micrometry in hamster cheek pouch, in vivo compared with injected, effective capillary capacity/maximum capacity = 1/6. /5/ Calculated, excluding Items 28-34, 40-42, 45-47. /6/ By both hydrodynamic and injection methods, mammalian capillary surface area = 7.0 cu mm/cu mm, assuming that muscle density = 1.0. /7/ Muscle or animal stimulated before injection. /8/ Classified as working (W) on basis of habitual use. /9/ Low values for RBC diameter may be caused by shrinkage upon fixation.

Part II: CARDIAC MUSCLE
A = atrophied; H = hypertrophied; T = trained; U = untrained.

	Animal	Heart Area		Capillaries per sq mm Cross-section[1]	Capillaries per Fiber	Capillary Diameter[2] μ	Capillary Capacity[1,3,4] cu mm/cu mm	Capillary Surface Area[1,4] sq mm/cu mm
1	Man, 5.9 yr			3744	0.3	8.4	0.207	98.8
2	49.8 yr			3343	0.8	8.4	0.185	88.2
3	51.0 yr		H	2483	0.8	8.4	0.138	65.5
4	63.3 yr		A	4613	0.6	8.4	0.256	121.7
5	Guinea pig			1970		7.5	0.087	46.4
6			U	1948		7.5	0.086	45.9
7			T	2819		7.5	0.125	66.4
8				3407		7.5	0.151	80.3
9			H	2950		7.5	0.130	69.5
10	Rabbit	Left ventricle		3420	1.1	7.5	0.151	80.6
11			H	2670	1.2	7.5	0.118	62.9
12		Right ventricle		3310	1.0	7.5	0.146	78.0
13			H	2740	1.2	7.5	0.121	64.6
14		Papillary		3230		5.0	0.063	50.7
15	Snake (Tropido-	Inner		500		14.5[5]	0.083	22.8
16	notus natrix)	Periphery		1000	14.5[5]	14.5[5]	0.165	45.6

/1/ See Fn 2, Part I. /2/ Based on RBC diameter, excluding Item 14. /3/ See Fn 4, Part I. /4/ Calculated, excluding Item 14. /5/ Based on RBC dimensions of Natrix sp, 18.3 x 14.4 μ.

275. CIRCULATION TIME: VERTEBRATES

Circulation time is the time required for an indicator substance introduced into the blood stream to traverse the normal vascular path from a specified point, usually the point of introduction (as the antecubital vein in the arm), and to arrive at another point or area in sufficient concentration to register its arrival in some characteristic and recognizable manner. Values in parentheses are ranges, estimate "d" of the 95% range (cf Introduction).

No.	Species	Circuit	Registration Time sec	Indicator
1	Man	Arm to heart, left ventricle	8(6-9)	Diodrast
2	Adult	Arm to heart, right atrium	3.6(1.6-10)	Acetylcholine
3		Arm to lung	6(3-9)	Ether
4			6.3(3.5-8)	Paraldehyde
5		Arm to carotid sinus	11(3-24)	Lobeline
6			9.5(8-11)	α-Lobeline
7			15.6(9-21)	Sodium cyanide[1]
8		Arm to lips	17.5(15-20)	Fluorescein[2]
9		Arm to mouth	12(9-15)	Calcium chloride
10		Arm to face	21.5(13-30)	Histamine
11		Arm to tongue	12(9-15)	Calcium chloride
12			13(10-16)	Calcium gluconate
13			14.4(8-20)	Decholin
14			15(5-24)	Macasol[3]
15			12.4(7-17.8)	Magnesium sulfate
16		Arm to tongue and nose	11.6(9-16)	Saccharin
17		Arm to throat	8.5(5-13)	Thiamine
18			18(12-25)	Calcium gluconate
19			14(7-22)	Macasol[3]
20			14(11-17)	Magnesium sulfate
21		Arm to conjunctiva	10.6(7-16)	Fluorescein
22		Arm to ear	12.5(9-16)	Methylene blue[4]
23			14(10-21)	Dye(T-1824)[5]
24		Arm to respiratory center	15(12-19)	Aminophylline
25			21(15-27)	Papaverine
26		Arm to arm	23(18-30)	Fluorescein
27			17.5(12-23)	Radium-C
28			19(14.5-26.2)	Riboflavine
29			15(10-20)	Thorium-X
30		Arm to opposite hand	25.5(23-28)	Fluorescein
31			27(26-28)	Macasol[3]
32		Arm to foot, open wound	23	Fluorescein
33		Arm to foot, intact skin	35(34-36)	Fluorescein
34			32.5(28-37)	Macasol[3]
35		Arm to perineum	26	Macasol[3]
36		Arm to rectum	18	Fluorescein
37		Right to left heart (lesser)	6.5	Radium-C
38		Through heart	1	Radium-C
39		Lung to face	19.5(14-25)	Amyl nitrite
40		Lung to medulla	7(5-10)	Carbon dioxide
41		Lung to ear	5.2(4-7)	Acetylene
42		Lung to opposite lung	(10-15)	Nitrogen, 100%[6]
43		Foot to tongue	41(22-75)	Histamine
44		Foot to groin	18(6-49)	Radioactive sodium
45		Foot to carotid sinus	33(27-39)	Sodium cyanide
46		Portal circ., rectum to lung	(11-25)	Ether
47		Total circulation	8(7-9)	Radioactive phosphorus[7]
48	Children	Arm to carotid sinus	10.6[8](9-14.5)	Sodium cyanide
49		Arm to tongue or nose	6(4-8)	Thiamine
50		Arm to opposite arm	11(5-17)	Radioactive sodium
51	Newborn	Arm to conjunctiva	(5-14)	Riboflavine
52			(3.1-7)	Fluorescein
53		Umbilical vein to lip	(3.3-6)	Fluorescein
54		Ductus venosus to lip	(30-60)	Fluorescein
55		Umbilical vein to umbilical vein		Congo red
56	Cat	Left common carotid art. to right auricle	6(3-9.5)	Radium-C
57		Femoral vein to carotid artery	3.2(3-3.5)	Conductivity
58			4(3-5)	Radioactive phosphorus[7]
59		Femoral artery to carotid artery	10(9-11)	Radioactive phosphorus[7]
60		Femoral artery to femoral vein	6(4-8)	Radioactive phosphorus[7]
61	Chicken	Sciatic vein to systemic arterioles	3	Acetylcholine
62	Cow	Mammary vein to opposite mammary vein	52	Fluorescein
63	Dog	Root of aorta to sino-atrial node	1.3(1.1-1.7)	Acetylcholine
64		Apex left ventricle to s-a node	1.8(1.7-2.1)	Acetylcholine
65		2-3 cm above root of aorta to s-a node	3.4(2.6-4.3)	Acetylcholine
66		Main pulmonary artery to s-a node	5.2(3.9-7.6)	Acetylcholine
67		Right ventricle to s-a node	6(4.4-6.8)	Acetylcholine
68		Leg vein to s-a node	6.7(4.0-9.5)	Acetylcholine
69		Superior vena cava to s-a node	6.7(6.4-9.9)	Acetylcholine
70		Femoral vein to right atrium	17(16-18)	Bismuth oil
71		Systemic (greater circulation)	5.3(5.3-7.1)	Conductivity
72		Pulmonary (lesser circulation)	5.8(4.0-7.6)	Conductivity
73		Right to left ext. jugular vein	9.25	Conductivity
74		Complete circulation	10.8(8.9-12.8)	Conductivity
75		Femoral vein to conjunctiva	12.6	Fluorescein
76		Right to left jugular vein	7.9(4.9-10.2)	Hexamethylene tetramine
77		Right to left ext. jugular vein	7.8	Lithium acetate
78		Right to left jugular vein	7.8(4.9-10.2)	Lithium benzoate
79		Femoral vein to carotid artery	7(6-8)	Radioactive phosphorus
80		Jugular vein to right heart	1.7(1-2.5)	Shadacol[9]
81		Right to left heart	5.5	Shadacol[9]
82		Left to right heart	6.0	Sodium cyanide
83		Femoral vein to carotid sinus	8.0	Sodium cyanide
84		Ext. jugular vein to carotid sinus	(9-13)	Sodium sulfocyanide
85		Left ventricle or aorta to femoral artery	4.0	Sodium sulfocyanide
86		Complete circulation	10.5(10-11)	Sodium sulfocyanide
87	Goat	Pulmonary circulation, fetal	4.7	Iodine
88		Pulmonary circulation, birth	2.7	Iodine
89	Horse	Jugular vein to opposite jugular vein	22.5(20-25)	Potassium ferrocyanide
90	Sheep	Pulmonary circulation, fetal	2.7	Iodine
91	(lamb)	Pulmonary circulation, birth	1.4	Iodine
92		Complete circulation	(5-8)	Iodine
93	Rabbit	Pulmonary circulation	2.85	Conductivity
94		Crural artery to crural vein	3.8	Conductivity
95		Hepatic portal circulation	5.4(3.85-6.95)	Conductivity
96		Renal circulation	8	Conductivity
97		Jugular vein to crural vein	8.4	Conductivity
98		Complete circulation	10.5	Conductivity
99		Ear vein to eye	5.5(5-6)	Fluorescein
100		Right to left ear vein	4.8(3.4-7.2)	Hexamethylene tetramine
101			4.7	Lithium acetate
102			4.5(3.5-5.8)	Lithium chloride
103		Ear vein to medulla	6.0	Methylene blue[4]
104		Ear vein to carotid sinus	4(3.3-5.2)	Sodium cyanide
105			3.9	Sodium cyanide
106		Right jugular vein to right carotid art.	(2.4-3.4)	Sodium chloride
107		Left jugular vein to right femoral art.	(3.85-4.0)	Sodium chloride
108		Left right jugular vein	(4.1-6.1)	Sodium chloride
109		Left jugular vein to right renal artery	(3.8-5.4)	Sodium chloride
110		Left jugular vein to right renal vein	(10.8-12.7)	Sodium chloride

1/ Warm subject, 18.5; cold subject, 32.3. 2/ During exercise, 6. 3/ Magnesium sulfate compound. 4/ Photoelectric method. 5/ Photocell. 6/ With oximeter. 7/ Labelled cells. 8/ For ages 14 days to 5.9 yr; 10.4 for ages 6-12.9 yr. 9/ Iodophthalein sodium.

276. BLOOD VESSELS: MAN

ant.=anterior; ext.=external; inf.=inferior; int.=internal; lt.=left; mid.=middle; post.=posterior; rt.=right; sup.=superior; trans.=transverse.

Listed arteries represent important blood pathways. A complete atlas is not intended and branches of main arteries, in many cases, are not shown.

Part I: ARTERIES

No.	Artery	Origin	Distribution
1	Alveolar, inferior	Internal maxillary	Lower teeth, gums, mandible, lower lip, chin.
2	Superior, anterior	Infraorbital	Incisors, canines of upper jaw.
3	Superior, posterior	Internal maxillary	Molars, bicuspids of upper jaw; maxillary sinus.
4	Aorta, abdominal	Thoracic aorta	Abdominal viscera, wall; pelvis; lower limbs.
5	Ascending, arch	Left ventricle	Heart muscle, head, neck, upper limbs.
6	Thoracic	Aortic arch	Thoracic wall, mediastinal structures.
7	Appendicular	Ileocolic	Mesentery of vermiform appendix.
8	Arcuate (renal)	Interlobar	Kidney parenchyma.
9	Auditory, internal	Anterior inf. cerebellar	Internal ear.
10	Auricular, anterior	Superficial temporal	Lat. surface auricle, external meatus.
11	Auricular, posterior	External carotid, 5th branch	Middle ear, mastoid cells, auricle, parotid gland, digastric and other muscles.
12	Axillary	Subclavian	Upper extremity, axilla, chest, shoulder.
13	Basilar	Right and left vertebral	Brain stem, internal ear, cerebellum, posterior cerebrum.
14	Brachial	Axillary	Shoulder, arm, forearm, hand.
15	Superficial	Brachial or axillary	Radial, or radial and ulnar arteries.
16	Bronchial	Aorta or intercostal	Bronchi, lungs.
17	Carotid, common	Innominate, right; aortic arch, left	Origin of external and internal carotids.
18	External	Common carotid	Neck, face, skull.
19	Internal	Common carotid	Mid-ear, brain, pituitary, orbit, choroid plexus of lateral ventricle.
20	Celiac	Abdominal aorta	Esophagus, stomach, duodenum, spleen, pancreas, liver, gallbladder.
21	Central of retina	Ophthalmic	Retina.
22	Cerebellar, ant. inf.	Basilar	Lower anterior cerebellar cortex.
23	Posterior inferior	Vertebral	Lower cerebellum, medulla, choroid plexus 4th ventricle.
24	Superior	Basilar	Upper cerebellum, mid-brain, pineal body, choroid plexus 3rd ventricle.
25	Cerebral, anterior	Internal carotid	Frontal lobe, medial surface cerebrum, corpus callosum.
26	Middle	Internal carotid	Lateral surface cerebrum and basal ganglia.
27	Posterior	Basilar	Occipital, temporal lobes, basal ganglia, choroid plexus of lateral ventricle.
28	Cervical, ascending	Inferior thyroid	Neck muscles, vertebrae, spinal canal.
29	Deep	Costocervical	Deep muscles of back of neck; first intercostal space.
30	Transverse	Thyrocervical trunk	Posterior muscles of neck, interscapular region.
31	Choroid	Internal carotid	Choroid plexus of lateral ventricle, hippocampus fimbria.
32	Ciliary, ant., post.	Ophthalmic and lacrimal	Iris, conjunctiva, choroid.
33	Circumflex, femoral, lateral	Profunda femoris	Hip joint, thigh muscles.
34	Medial	Profunda femoris	Hip joint, thigh muscles.
35	Iliac, deep	External iliac	Abdominal muscles.
36	Superficial	Femoral	Inguinal glands, skin of thigh and abdomen.
37	Colic, left	Inferior mesenteric	Descending colon.
38	Middle	Superior mesenteric	Transverse colon.
39	Right	Superior mesenteric	Ascending colon.
40	Collateral, ulnar	Brachial	Lower arm and elbow.
41	Communicating, ant.	Anterior cerebral	Anterior perforated substance.
42	Posterior	Internal carotid	Uncinate gyrus, thalamus.
43	Coronary, left	Left aortic sinus	Heart.
44	Right	Right aortic sinus	Heart.
45	Cystic	Hepatic	Gallbladder, under surface of liver.
46	Digital (of fingers)	Metacarpals	Fingers.
47	Digital (of toes)	Metatarsals	Toes.
48	Diploic	Pericranial, meningeal	Diploe of skull.
79	Innominate	Arch of aorta	Right side of head, neck, upper limb.
80	Intercostal	Int. mammary, thoracic aorta	Thoracic walls, muscles, vertebrae.
81	Interlobar (renal)	Renal	Kidney lobes.
82	Interosseous, anterior	Ulnar	Deep structures of forearm.
83	Lacrimal	Ophthalmic	Lacrimal gland, eye muscles, cheek, eyelids.
84	Laryngeal, inferior	Inferior thyroid	Larynx, upper trachea, esophagus.
85	Superior	Superior thyroid	Larynx, pharynx.
86	Lenticular	Middle cerebral	Lenticular nucleus.
87	Lingual	External carotid	Tongue, tonsil, sublingual gland, epiglottis.
88	Lumbar (4 pairs)	Abdominal aorta	Abdominal walls, vertebrae, lumbar muscles, renal capsule.
89	Mammary, internal	Subclavian	Anterior thoracic wall, mediastinal structures.
90	Maxillary, external	External carotid	Face, tonsil, palate, submaxillary gland.
91	Internal	External carotid	Both jaws, teeth, chewing muscles, ear, meninges, nose, nasal sinus, palate.
92	Median	Volar interosseous	Median nerve, muscles of front forearm.
93	Medullary (arteriolae rectae)	Arcuate of kidney	Renal pyramids.
94	Meningeal, anterior	Ophthalmic, interior carotid	Bones, dura mater of anterior cranial fossa.
95	Middle or great	Internal maxillary	Bones, dura mater of middle cranial fossa.
96	Posterior	Ascending pharyngeal	Bones, dura mater of posterior cranial fossa.
97	Mesenteric, inferior	Abdominal aorta	Lower half of colon, rectum.
98	Superior	Abdominal aorta	Small intestine, proximal half of colon.
99	Metacarpal, dorsal	Radial, ulnar, interosseous.	Hand and fingers, dorsal.
100	Metatarsal, dorsal	Dorsalis pedis	Foot and toes, dorsal.
101	Musculophrenic	Internal mammary	Diaphragm; abdominal, thoracic walls.
102	Obturator	Hypogastric	Pelvic muscles, hip joint, ant. thigh.
103	Occipital	External carotid	Scalp, neck muscles, post.
104	Ophthalmic	Internal carotid	Eye, orbit, adjacent facial structures.
105	Ovarian	Abdominal aorta	Ovary, ureter, uterus, uterine tube.
106	Palatine, ascending	External maxillary	Soft palate, tonsil, auditory tube.
107	Descending	Internal maxillary	Soft, hard palates; tonsil.
108	Pancreatic	Splenic	Pancreas.
109	Pancreaticoduodenal		
110	Inferior	Superior mesenteric	Pancreas, duodenum.
111	Superior	Gastroduodenal	Pancreas, duodenum.
112	Penis, deep, dorsal.	Internal pudendal	Penis.
113	Perforating	Profunda femoris	Muscles of thigh.
114	Pericardiacophrenic	Internal mammary	Pericardium, diaphragm, pleura.
115	Perineal	Internal pudendal	Perineum, skin of external genitalia.
116	Peroneal	Posterior tibial	Outside and back ankle, deep calf muscles.
117	Phrenic, inferior	Aorta, abdominal	Diaphragm, suprarenal glands.
118	Plantar arch	Lateral plantar	Sole of foot, toes.
119	Pontine	Basilar	Pons, brachia pontis, trigeminal roots.
120	Popliteal	Femoral	Knee, post. leg.
121	Princeps pollicis	Radial	Thumb ventrally.
122	Profunda brachii	Brachial	Humerus, posterior arm structures.
123	Profunda femoris	Femoral	Thigh muscles, hip joint.
124	Pudendal, external	Femoral	External genitalia, medial thigh muscles.
125	Internal	Hypogastric	Perineum, anal canal, external genitalia.
126	Pulmonary	Right ventricle	Lungs.
127	Radial	Brachial	Forearm, wrist, hand.
128	Renal	Abdominal aorta	Kidney.
129	Sacral, lateral	Hypogastric	Structures about coccyx and sacrum.
130	Scapular, trans.	Thyreocervical	Clavicle, scapula, shoulder muscles, joint.
131	Scrotal, anterior	External pudendal	Anterior part of scrotum.
132	Posterior	Perineal	Posterior part of scrotum.

No.	Artery	Origin	Distribution
49	Dorsalis pedis	Anterior tibial	Dorsum of foot, toes.
50	Epigastric, inferior	External iliac	Abdominal muscles, cremaster, peritoneum.
51	Superficial	Femoral	Skin of abdomen, superficial fascia.
52	Superior	Internal mammary	Abdominal muscles, diaphragm.
53	Esophageal	Gastric, inferior thyroid, thoracic left phrenic, !aorta.	Esophagus.
54	Ethmoidal anterior	Ophthalmic	Dura mater, nose, frontal sinus, ant. and mid. ethmoidal cells.
55	Posterior	Ophthalmic	Posterior ethmoidal cells, nose, dura mater.
56	Femoral	External iliac	Lower abdominal wall, ext. genitalia, lower limb.
57	Deep	Femoral	Thigh muscles, hip joint.
58	Frontal	Ophthalmic	Anterior scalp.
59	Gastric, left	Celiac	Esophagus, lesser curvature of stomach.
60	Right	Hepatic	Lesser curvature of stomach.
61	Short	Splenic	Left portion greater curvature of stomach.
62	Gastroduodenal	Hepatic	Stomach, duodenum, pancreas.
63	Gastroepiploic, left	Splenic	Stomach, greater omentum.
64	Right	Gastroduodenal	Stomach, greater omentum.
65	Gluteal	Hypogastric	Hip joint, gluteal region.
66	Hemorrhoidal, sup.	Inferior mesenteric	Upper part of rectum.
67	Middle	Hypogastric	Middle portion of rectum.
68	Inferior	Internal pudendal	Anal canal.
69	Hepatic	Celiac	Stomach, pancreas, duodenum, liver.
70	Left	Hepatic	Left lobe of liver.
71	Right	Hepatic	Right lobe of liver.
72	Hypophyseal	Internal carotid	Hypophysis.
73	Intestinal	Superior mesenteric	Ileum, jejunum.
74	Ileo-colic	Superior mesenteric	Cecum, appendix, ascending colon.
75	Iliac, common	Abdominal aorta	Pelvis, abdominal wall, lower limb.
76	Int. and ext.	Common iliac	Abdominal wall, external genitals, lower limb.
77	Iliolumbar	Posterior hypogastric	Pelvic muscles, bones; 5th lumbar segment.
78	Infra-orbital	Internal maxillary	Maxilla, maxillary sinus, upper teeth, lower lid, cheek, side of nose.
133	Septal (nasal)	Sphenopalatine	Mucous membrane of nasal septum, palate.
134	Sigmoid	Inferior mesenteric	Sigmoid flexure of colon.
135	Spermatic, internal	Abdominal aorta	Testis.
136	Sphenopalatine	Internal maxillary	Interior of nose and nasal sinus.
137	Spinal, ant., post.	Intercostal, lumbar	Spinal cord.
138	Splenic	Celiac	Spleen, pancreas, stomach, greater omentum.
139	Stapedial	Stylomastoid	Stapedius muscle.
140	Stylomastoid	Posterior auricular	Tympanic cavity walls, mastoid cells, semicircular canals.
141	Subclavian	Innominate (right side), aortic arch (left side)	Neck, thoracic wall, spinal cord, brain, meninges, upper limbs.
142	Subcostal	Thoracic aorta	Region below 12th rib in abdominal wall.
143	Submental	External maxillary	Tissues under chin.
144	Subscapular	Axillary	Back of axilla, shoulder and scapular muscles.
145	Supra-orbital	Ophthalmic	Forehead, upper muscles of orbit.
146	Suprarenal, inferior	Renal	Suprarenal gland.
147	Middle	Aorta	Suprarenal gland.
148	Superior	Inferior phrenic	Suprarenal gland.
149	Temporal, superficial	Exterior carotid	Parotid, auricle, scalp.
150	Thymic	Internal mammary	Mediastinum, thymus.
151	Thyroid, inferior	Thyreocervical trunk	Larynx, esophagus, trachea, neck muscles, thyroid.
152	Superior	External carotid	Hyoid muscles, larynx, thyroid, pharynx.
153	Thyreoidea ima	Aortic arch, innominate	Thyroid gland.
154	Tibial, anterior	Popliteal	Leg, ankle, foot, dorsal.
155	Posterior	Popliteal	Leg, sole of foot, heel.
156	Tonsillar	Ascending palatine	Tonsil, neighboring tissues.
157	Tympanic	Int.maxillary, ext.carotid	Tympanic cavity.
158	Ulnar	Brachial	Forearm, wrist, hand.
159	Uterine	Hypogastric	Uterus, vagina, fallopian tube, round ligament.
160	Vaginal	Hypogastric, uterine	Vagina, base of bladder, rectum.
161	Vertebral	Subclavian	Neck muscles, vertebrae, spinal cord, brain, cerebellum, interior of cerebrum.

Part II: VEINS

Veins, venous sinuses and plexuses having no accompanying artery of the same name, or differing considerably from the accompanying artery, are listed. Veins having tributaries with the same distribution and name as the accompanying arteries are not shown.

No.	Vein	Location	Drains Into:
1	Accessory hemiazygos	Lt. side of vertebral column.[1]	Either azygos or hemiazygos.
2	Anterior facial	Anterior face.	With post., forms common facial.
3	Anterior jugular	Near midline of neck.	Ext. jugular or subclavian.
4	Azygos	Rt. side of vertebral column.[1]	Superior vena cava.
5	Basilic	Medial side of arm.	Joins brachial to form axillary.
6	Cavernous sinus	Middle cranial fossa.	Int. jugular via sup. petrosal sinus.
7	Cephalic	Lateral side of arm.	Axillary.
8	Common facial	Below angle of mandible.	Internal jugular.
9	Coronary sinus of heart	Post. part coronary sulcus.	Right atrium.
10	Coronary of stomach	Lesser curvature of stomach.	Portal.
11	Emissary	Various apertures of skull.	Intracranial venous sinuses, connecting with veins external to skull.
12	External jugular	Side of neck, superficial.	Subclavian.
13	Great cardiac	Ant.longitudinal sulcus of heart.	Coronary sinus.
14	Great cerebral	Below and behind splenium of corpus callosum.	Straight sinus.
15	Hemiazygos	Lt. side of vertebral column.[1]	Azygos.
16	Hemorrhoidal plexus	Rectum.	Sup., mid., inf. hemorrhoidal veins.
17	Hepatic	Posterior surface liver.	Inferior vena cava.
18	Inf. petrosal sinus	Inferior petrosal sulcus of skull.	Internal jugular.
19	Inf. sagittal sinus	Lower edge of falx cerebri.	Straight sinus.
20	Inf. vena cava	Front of lumbar vertebral column, right of aorta.	Right atrium.
21	Innominate	Root of neck.	Superior vena cava.
22	Internal jugular	Side of neck.	Innominate.
23	Oblique of left atrium	Back of left atrium.	Coronary sinus.
24	Parumbilical	Round ligament of liver.	Portal.
25	Portal	Lesser omentum.	Sinusoids of liver.
26	Prostatic plexus	Fascial sheath of prostate.	Pudendal and vesical plexuses.
27	Pterygoid plexus	Between pterygoid muscles.	Internal maxillary.
28	Pudendal plexus	Behind symphysis pubis, in front of bladder.	Vesical and hypogastric veins.
29	Pyloric	Lesser curvature of stomach.	Portal.
30	Sigmoid sinus	Groove on internal surface of temporal bone on petrous and mastoid parts.	Internal jugular.
31	Small saphenous	Back of leg.	Popliteal.
32	Straight sinus	Junction of falx cerebri with tentorium cerebelli.	Transverse sinus.
33	Sup. sagittal sinus	Attached margin falx cerebri.	Confluence of sinuses or transverse sinus.
34	Sup. vena cava	Behind first and second intercostal spaces and right margin of sternum.	Right atrium.
35	Trans. sinus	Attached margin tentorium cerebelli.	Internal jugular via sigmoid sinus.
36	Vertebral plexus	Within vertebral canal (internal) and around vertebrae (external).	Intracranial venous sinus, segmental tributaries of various parietal and visceral veins.
37	Vesical plexus	Lower bladder, base prostate gland.	Hypogastric.
38	Vorticose	Eyeball.	Ciliary, ophthalmic veins.

/1/ In thorax.

277. BLOOD COAGULATION: THEORIES

At the present time the concept of blood coagulation is more uncertain than it was before discovery of the newer clotting factors. It must be recognized that these charts are merely guides and will require modification as new data become available.

Part I: THEORY OF M. STEFANINI

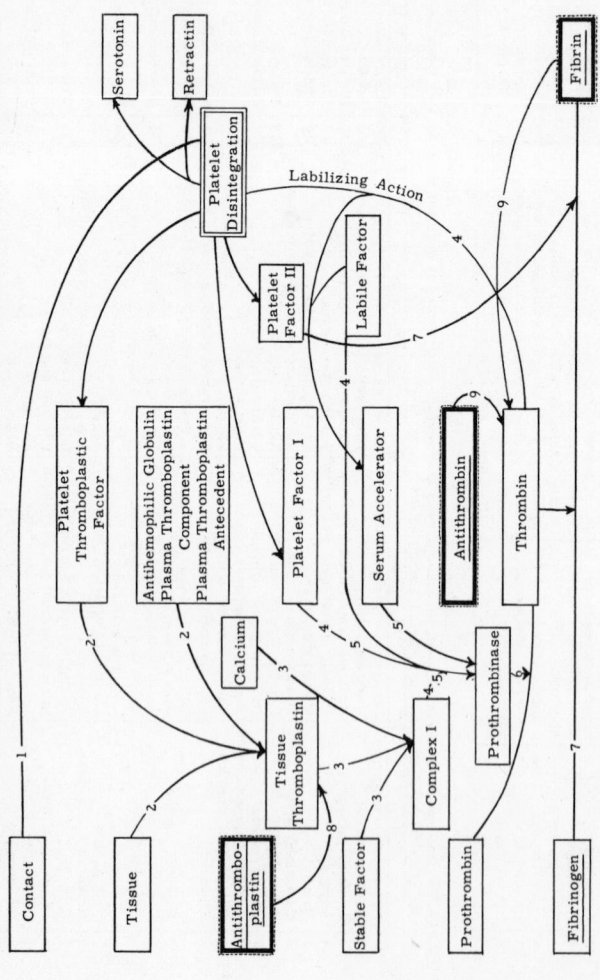

Part II: THEORY OF A. J. QUICK

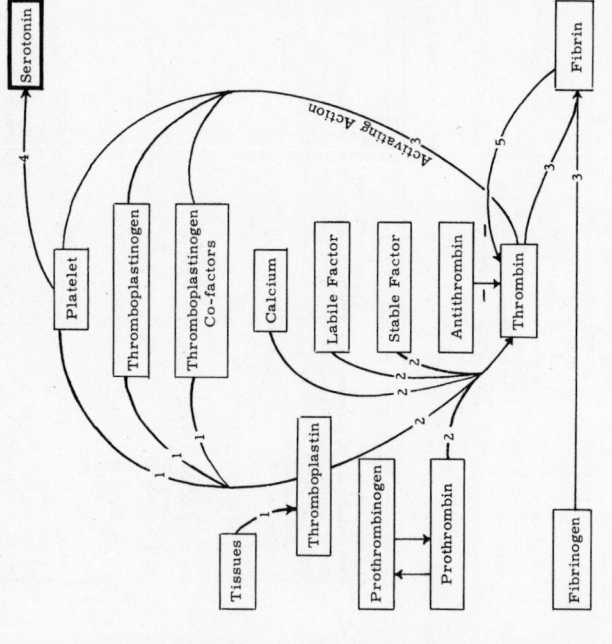

/1/ Contact with foreign surface (wounded vessel wall) causes disintegration of platelets. This is followed by the liberation of a number of agents present in or carried by platelets: serotonin (factor of vascular contractility), retractin (clot retraction agent), thromboplastic factor, platelet factors I and II. There is increasing evidence that platelet factor I is only a labile factor absorbed on platelets. Evidence for platelet factor II is somewhat meager and this factor might be disregarded in future theories. /2/ Platelet thromboplastin factor interacts with a number of plasma factors (antihemophilic globulin, plasma thromboplastin component, plasma thromboplastic antecedent, possibly others) to form the equivalent of tissue thromboplastin. This, of course, may be supplied directly from tissue. /3/ Tissue thromboplastin, calcium and stable factor (proconvertin, factor VII, etc.) interact to form an intermediary complex (convertin). /4/ The intermediary complex (complex I) reacts with the labile factor (proaccelerin, factor V) to form a new agent (prothrombinase). Some prothrombin is then converted to thrombin and this initiates the "autocatalytic phase" of blood coagulation. Thrombin then determines further disintegration of platelets and also conversion of the labile factor to a more active accelerator of the conversion of prothrombin, the serum accelerator (accelerin). /5/ As result of the autocatalytic reaction, the formation of prothrombinase proceeds at an even more acclerated speed. A factor liberated from platelets (factor I) takes part in this reaction. /6/ Prothrombinase, formed in large quantities, converts almost completely prothrombin to thrombin. /7/ Thrombin converts fibrinogen to fibrin. A platelet factor (factor II) and a hypothetical plasma factor (not shown in the diagram) accelerate the formation of fibrin. /8/ Inhibitors exist for each phase and each blood coagulation factor. Antithromboplastin is a well documented one and antagonizes the activity of tissue thromboplastin. /9/ The conversion of fibrinogen to fibrin is also antagonized by two factors: a plasma antithrombin and the fibrin clot itself, through its property of adsorbing thrombin.

/1/ Thromboplastin is (a) released by injured tissue and is (b) formed in the blood by the interaction of a platelet factor, thromboplastinogen (antihemophilic factor), and one or more co-factors (PTC, PTA, etc.) through the activating action of thrombin. /2/ Thromboplastin, prothrombin, calcium and labile factor interact stoichiometrically and, in addition, stable factor is needed to form thrombin. In adult human blood a large fraction of the prothrombin is in an inactive state: prothrombinogen (probably as a prothrombin inhibitor complex). During storage or clotting all prothrombinogen becomes activated. /3/ The thrombin formed not only converts fibrinogen to fibrin but participates in the activation of plasma factors (probably thromboplastinogen or one of its co-factors), thereby bringing about lysis of platelets and initiating a chain reaction. /4/ The platelets release a vasoconstrictor, serotonin, through the action of thrombin, which probably functions in local hemostasis. /5/ The prompt removal of thrombin by fibrin holds in check the autocatalytic reaction mediated through the action of thrombin on platelets, thromboplastinogen and its co-factors.

Part III: THEORY OF L. M. TOCANTINS

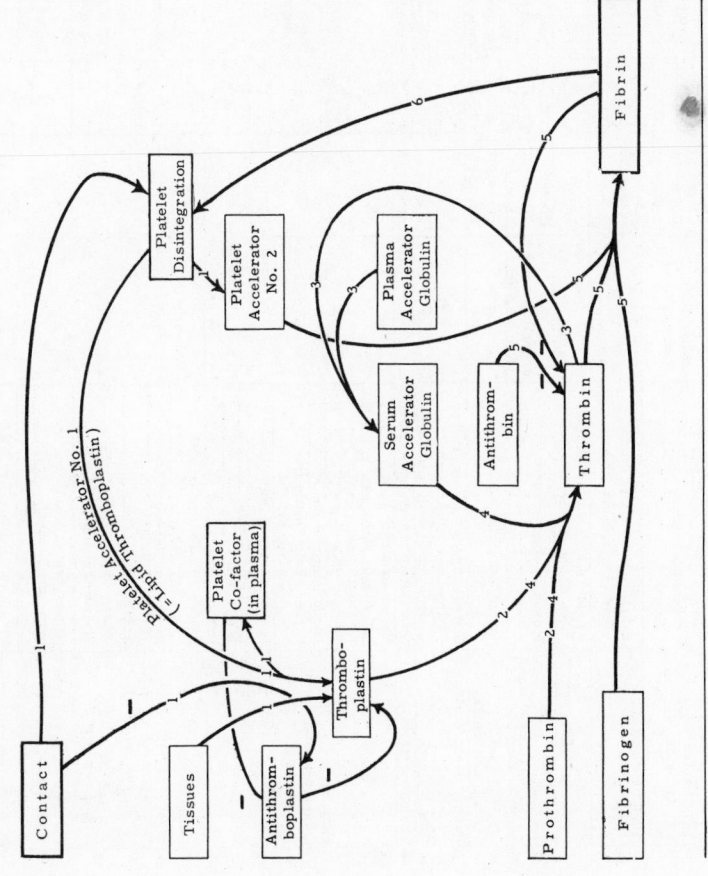

/1/ Contact of the blood with certain surfaces (damaged blood vessel endothelium, glass) initiates the first changes which lead to the inception of clotting; blood platelets agglutinate, adhere to the surface and/or disintegrate, releasing (a) cephalin like accelerator and (b) fibrinoplastic factor (platelet accelerator No. 2). There is dissociation of the platelet co-factor/lipid inhibitor complex, with freeing of the platelet co-factor. The latter conjugates with the platelet lipid accelerator and forms plasma thromboplastin. Some of the thromboplastin of the blood is offset or neutralized by the antithromboplastin; some of the antithromboplastin is itself adsorbed or neutralized at the contacting surface. /2/ Thromboplastin (from tissues and/or platelets) brings about a minimal conversion of prothrombin to thrombin. /3/ This initially formed thrombin activates the accelerator system, that is, the conversion of inactive plasma accelerator globulin to active serum accelerator globulin. /4/ Thromboplastin together with serum accelerator globulin causes acceleration of the conversion of prothrombin to thrombin. /5/ Some of the thrombin may be inactivated by antithrombin. The thrombin that escapes such inactivation acts, with the aid of platelet accelerator No. 2, to cause the conversion of fibrinogen to fibrin. Some of the excess thrombin is removed from the plasma by adsorption on fibrin. /6/ Fibrin probably causes further disintegration of platelets.

Part IV: THEORY OF P. A. OWREN

Section 1: THE INTRINSIC BLOOD COAGULATION SYSTEM

Section 2. THE EXTRINSIC (TISSUE-BLOOD) COAGULATION SYSTEM

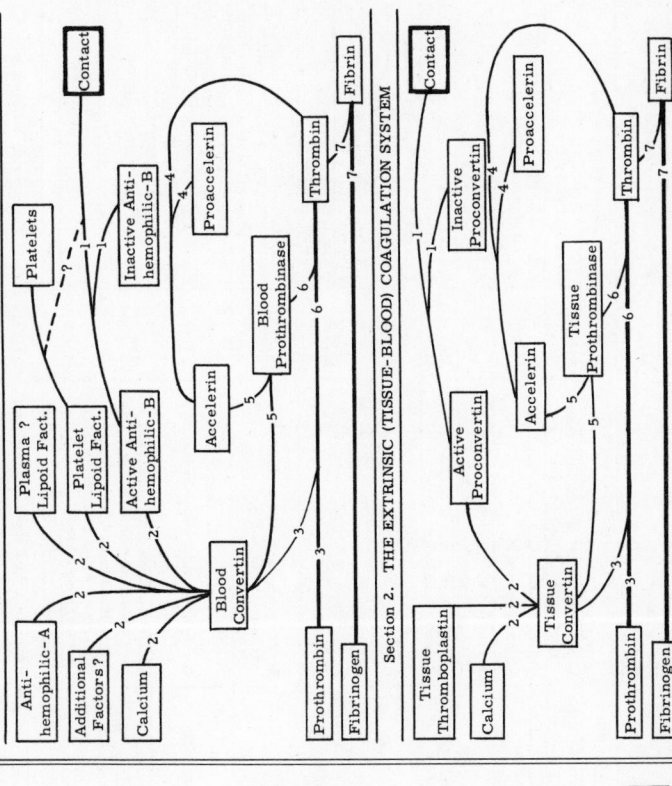

(1) The intrinsic blood coagulation system: /1/ Contact activates the inactive antihemophilic B factor. (Plasma thromboplastin component, Christmas factor.) /2/ Reactions take place between plasma thromboplastin factors (antihemophilic A-factor (A.H.G.) and active antihemophilic B factor), lipid factors with cephalin-like activity (from platelets and possibly also in plasma) and calcium to form an intermediate complex termed blood convertin. This reaction possibly requires one or more additional factors such as: plasma thromboplastin antecedent, the IV thromboplastic factor, factor X, Prower factor. The problems of platelet disintegration and the significance of contact influence on platelets are still unsolved. /3/ Blood convertin brings about a minimal conversion of prothrombin to thrombin. /4/ This initially formed thrombin starts the accelerator system, i.e., the conversion of proaccelerin to accelerin. /5/ Blood convertin and accelerin interact in the presence of calcium to form blood prothrombinase. /6/ Blood prothrombinase produces rapid conversion of prothrombin to thrombin. /7/ Thrombin is now formed in sufficient quantity to convert fibrinogen to fibrin. NB: Proconvertin does not take part in the intrinsic blood coagulation system.

(2) The extrinsic (tissue-blood) coagulation system: /1/ Contact activates inactive proconvertin to active proconvertin. /2/ Tissue thromboplastin (liberated by tissue injury), active proconvertin and calcium interact to form tissue convertin. /3/ Tissue convertin brings about a minimal conversion of prothrombin to thrombin. /4/ This initially formed thrombin starts the accelerator system, i.e., the conversion of proaccelerin to accelerin. /5/ Tissue convertin and accelerin interact in the presence of calcium to form tissue prothrombinase. /6/ Tissue prothrombinase produces rapid conversion of prothrombin to thrombin. /7/ Thrombin is now formed in sufficient quantity to convert fibrinogen to fibrin. NB: Platelets and antihemophilic factors do not take part in the extrinsic blood coagulation system.

278. CARDIOVASCULAR REFLEXES: MAMMALS

CIC = cardio-inhibitor center; CAC = cardio-accelerator center; VCC = vasoconstrictor center; N = nerve; NN = nerves.

#	Reflex	Effective Stimulus	Receptor	Afferent	Center	Efferent	Response	Species[1]	Conditions in which Reflex is Increased
1	Veno-cardiac (Bainbridge)	Blood pressure↑ in great veins, R auricle.	Walls of great veins entering R auricle; wall of R auricle(?).	Vagus N (afferent fibers).	CIC↓ CAC↑	Vagus N; sympathetic(?).	Heart rate↑.	Man, dog(?)[2]	Exercise; inspiration; R ventricular failure.
2	Veno-arterial (McDowall)	Blood pressure↑ in great veins.			VCC↑	Sympathetic NN.	General arterial vasoconstriction retards↓ in arterial blood pressure.	Man	Hemorrhage; erect posture.
3		Blood pressure↑ in great veins, R auricle.			VCC↑		General arterial vasoconstriction; arterial blood pressure↑.	Dog, cat	Exercise.
4	Pulmonary vaso-cardiac[3]	Pulmonary blood pressure↑; distension lung vessels.	Pulmonary arteries(?);VV(?); capillaries(?).	Vagus N (afferent fibers).	CIC↑ CAC↓	Vagus N.	Heart rate↓.	Man	Exercise; L ventricular, L auricular failure.
5	Pulmonary alveolo-cardiac[3]	"Collapse of lung alveoli."	Pulmonary alveoli.	Vagus N (afferent fibers).	CIC↓ CAC↑	Vagus N; sympathetic(?).	Heart rate↑.	Man	Lung consolidation, collapse; extreme expiration.
6	Aorto-cardiac (D,e,p,f)	Aortic pressure↑↓.	Wall of aortic arch.	Vagus N (afferent fibers).	CAC↓ CIC↑	Vagus N;	Heart rate↓.	Man, rabbit	Exercise; recumbent posture or lowered head; hypertension.
7	Aorto-arterial				VCC↓	sympathetic NN(?).	Vasodilatation; arterial and venous blood pressure↓; syncope.		
8	Carotid sinus: Cardiac (s,o)	Carotid blood pressure↑↓; direct pressure on sinus.	Adventitia of carotid sinus.	Glosso-pharyngeal N; vagus N[5].	CIC↑ CAC↓	Vagus N; sympathetic(?).	Heart rate↓.	Man	Exercise; recumbent posture or lowered head; pressure on neck.
9	Arterial (s,r)				VCC↓	Sympathetic.	Vasodilatation; arterial and venous blood pressure↓; syncope[6].		
10	Aortic & carotid body: Cardiac	Arterial blood O2↓; blood free CO2↑; blood pH↓.	Carotid-aortic body chemo-receptors.		CAC↑ CIC↓		Heart rate↑.	Man	Acetylcholine; acidosis; anemia; asphyxia; deep anesthesia.
11	Arterial				VCC↑		Blood pressure↑; vasoconstriction.		
12	Antigravity vascular reflexes[7]	Pressure & voluntary changes associated with erect posture.	Brain(?); pacinian corpuscles(?).	Multiple(?).	VCC↑	Sympathetic NN.	Heart rate↑; splanchnic vasoconstriction; venous tone↑.	Man	Assumption of erect posture.
13	Myo-arterial (Loven)	Muscular contraction.	Receptors among fibers of skeletal muscle.	Afferent fibers in "motor" nerve trunks.	VCC↑ (local↓)	Vasodilatation NN; sensory NN.	Local vasodilatation; remote vasoconstriction; blood pressure↑.	Man(?), dog	Muscular activity.
14	Myo-cardiac	Anoxic muscular activity.			CIC↓ CAC↑	Vagus N.	Heart rate↑.	Man	Arterial compression; arterial obstruction (thrombosis, endarteritis).
15	Myo-arterial (Alam and Smirk)				VCC↑ (local↓)	Sympathetic; vasodilatation NN.	Blood pressure↑.		
16	Pain N fibers: cardiac	Strong stimulated pain fibers; stimulated splanchnics.			CIC↓ VCC↑		Heart rate↑; splanchnic vasodilatation; blood pressure↑.	Man	Blow to jaw, epigastrium; painful injury or disease, e.g. colic.
17	arterial				VCC↑				
18	Cold N fibers	Stimulation of skin cold receptors.		Cutaneous, sensory.	VCC↑	Cutaneous, sensory.	Cutaneous vasoconstriction.	Man	Exposure to cold.
19	Thermo-arterial	Stimulation of skin heat receptors.		sensory NN	VCC↓	Sympathetic.	Cutaneous vasodilatation[8].	Man	Exposure to heat.
20	Medullary cardio-inhibitor center (CIC) (vagus)	Reflex inhibition, cf 1,4,5,10,12,14.			CIC↑ CAC↓	Vagus N; sympathetic NN.	Heart rate↑.	Man	Exercise; L or R heart failure; shock; erect posture.
21		Arterial blood free CO2↑, O2↓, pH↓.							Exercise; anemia; acetylcholine; asphyxia; acidosis.
22		Blood temperature↑.							Pyrexia.
23		Higher center inhibition (hypothalamus).	CIC						Emotion[9]: fear, anxiety, (usual response).
24		Higher center stimulation (hypothalamus).							Emotion[9]: disgust; anxiety, fear (less frequent response).
25		Blood flow↓.							Cerebral compression; tumor.
26		Reflex stimulation, cf 6,8,16.			CIC↑ CAC↓	Vagus N; sympathetic NN.	Heart rate↑; syncope or faintness ("vasovagal attack").	Man	Hypertension; blow to epigastrium.
27		Reflex stimulation, cf 2,3,11, 12,13,15,18.							Exercise; R heart failure; erect posture; shock; hemorrhage.
28		Arterial blood free CO2↑,pH↓.			VCC↑	Sympathetic NN.	Vasoconstriction; blood pressure↑.	Man	Exercise; CO2 inhalation; apnea.
29		Blood flow↓.							Shock: hemorrhage; heart failure with↓ output; tumor.
30	Medullary vasoconstrictor center (VCC)	Higher center stimulation (hypothalamus, cortex).	VCC			Vagus N; sympathetic NN.	Splanchnic vasoconstriction; cutaneous vasodilatation or constriction; systolic blood pressure↑.	Man	Emotion[9]: excitement, anger, rage.
31		Higher center inhibition (hypothalamus).			VCC↓	Vagus NN; sympathetic NN.	Splanchnic vasodilatation; blood pressure↓; fainting.		Emotion[9]: fear, anger, rage.
32		Blood temperature↑.							Fever.
33		Reflex inhibition, cf 7,9,17.					Cutaneous vasodilatation (flushing).		Rise of blood pressure.

/1/ These reflexes have been demonstrated only in the forms listed, but may have wide mammalian distribution. /2/ Best seen in animals with marked tonic vagal inhibition of heart rate; not seen in frog, rabbit; slight in cat. /3/ May be the same as Hering-Breuer reflex by irradiation from respiratory center to CIC. /4/ ↑ blood pressure has opposite effects. /5/ For aortic sinus and body. /6/ When sinus is hyperactive. /7/ A depressor reflex (↓blood pressure) from mesenteric vessels has been described for man, cat. /8/ Stimulation of heat receptors may actually cause vasoconstriction, the reflex vasodilatation resulting from removal of cold stimulus. /9/ Emotion is also associated with secretion of adrenalin.

279. ELECTRICAL PROPERTIES MEASURED WITH ALTERNATING CURRENTS: BODY TISSUES

Temperature coefficient of specific resistance: (a) -2%/°C whenever frequency dependence is small; (b) complicated function of frequency, but always above -2%/°C when frequency dependence is pronounced.

Temperature coefficient of dielectric constant: (a) Smaller than 0.5% when frequency dependence is small; (b) positive, but complicated function of frequency when frequency dependence is pronounced.

cps=cycles per second; kc=kilocycles per second; Mc=megacycles per second.

Specific Resistance (ohm cm)

Frequency	Muscle	Heart Muscle	Liver	Lung*	Spleen	Kidney	Brain	Fatty Tissue	Bone	Bone Marrow	Whole Blood	Plasma	0.9% NaCl
10 cps			1220[1]								166[2]		
100 cps		750[1]	1060[1]								166[2]	60[2]	
	800[1]		800[1]	1000[1]							147[4]		
1 kc		830-900[5]	970[1]	400-850[3]									
	980[6]		1000-1600[5]	1400-1900[5]			500-800[5]	1500-5000[1]			120-135[5]		
	880[6]		700-1300[7]		260-430[7]		450-550[7]	1700-2500[3]			130-180[8]		
10 kc			850[1]								147[4]		
			460[1]										
100 kc	170-250[9]	190-240[9]	220-550[9]	165-200[9]	250-500[9]	150-270[9]	460-850[9]				140[4]		
			550-800[7]										
	520[6]		420[10]										
1 Mc	160-210[9]	180-230[9]	210-420[9]	150-280[9]	230-380[9]	140-250[9]	430-700[9]						
			400-550[7]										
	250[6]		400[10]								90[4]		
10 Mc	150-170[9]	140-180[9]	180-260[9]	110-150[9]	150-170[9]	120-170[9]	300-450[9]						
	100-130[11]		250[10]	95-130[11]	85-105[11]	100-120[11]	160-230[11]	1170-1250[11]			82[12]	70[12] / 61[11]	
	120-160[9]	130-170[9]	150-200[9]	100-140[9]	110-150[9]	100-150[9]	200-300[9]	1500[9]					
100 Mc	140-200[13]		180-210[13]		150[13]	130-160[13]	220-260[13]	2200-4300[13]		4100-5300[13]	120-150[13]	80[13]	
	120-150[13]		150-180[13]		120[13]	90-140[13]	180-200[13]	1700-2500[13]		3000-5000[13]	80-100[13]	60[13]	
								700-1400[14]	2000[14]	1000-2300[14]	64-72[14]	54[14]	49[14]
1000 Mc	75-79[14]		98-106[14]					1100-3500[15]			80[15]		56[15]
	81-84[15]		92-100[15]	137[15]		81-82[15]					11[14]		
	77[16]		100[16]					250[16]	150[14]	60-200[14]			
10,000 Mc	12[14]		15-17[14]					240-370[14]	130[17]	100[17]	9.5[17]	9[14]	9[14]
	13[17]							210[17]			9.3[18]		

Dielectric Constant (Relative to Vacuum)

Frequency	Muscle	Heart Muscle	Liver	Lung*	Spleen	Kidney	Brain	Fatty Tissue	Bone	Bone Marrow	Whole Blood	Plasma	0.9% NaCl
10 cps	2500x10³[13]		900x10³[1]	450x10³[1]				150x10³[1]					
100 cps	800x10³[1]	800x10³[1]											
	1000x10³[19]												
1 kc	130x10³[1]	300x10³[1]	150x10³[1]	90x10³[1]				50x10³[1]			2900[4]		
	170x10³[19]												
	100x10³[6]												
10 kc	50x10³[1]	100x10³[1]	50x10³[1]	30x10³[1]				20x10³[1]			2810[4]		
	90x10³[19]												
	50x10³[6]		7,000-12,000[7]										
100 kc	30x10³[19]										2740[4]		
	20x10³[6]		1200-2000[7]								2040[4]		
1 Mc	2x10³[6]												
10 Mc											2000[4]		
100 Mc	69-73[13]		65-75[11]		88-90[13]	83-84[13]	70-75[13]	8-13[11]		7-8[13]	72-74[13]	82[13]	
	71-76[13]		72-74[13]		100-101[13]	87-92[13]	81-83[13]	11-13[13]			73-76[13]	76[13]	
	49-52[14]		76-79[13]					4.3-7.5[14] / 3.2-6[15]	8[14]	4.3-7.8[14]	58-62[14]	69[14]	72[14]
1000 Mc	53-55[15]	53-57[15]	46-47[14]	35[15]	53-56[15]	53-56[15]		9.5[16]			63[15]		78[15]
	61[16]		44-52[15]										
			50[16]								50-52[14]		
10,000 Mc	40-42[14]		34-38[14]					3.5-3.9[14]	8[14]	4.4-6.6[14]	45[17]	61[14]	
	29[17]							3.6[17]	6.6[17]	5.8[17]	48[18]		66[14]

* Partially or totally deflated, except material described in Footnote 1.

/1/ Dog, material in situ at body temperature. /2/ Sheep, material at 18°C, except plasma at 37°C (Line 3). /3/ Dog, in situ at body temperature. /4/ Rabbit, at room temperature. /5/ Rabbit, excised material at 37°C. /6/ Rabbit, excised piece at room temperature. /7/ Man and various animals, excised pieces and minced material at 23°C. /8/ Sheep, 18°C. /9/ Man, minced material at 23°C. /10/ Rabbit, minced material at 23°C. /11/ Man, minced material at 37°C. /12/ Sheep, at 20°C. /13/ Beef and pork, excised material at 20°C (Lines 20, 42). /14/ Dog and horse, blood and excised tissues measured at 38°C, except bone and bone marrow at 25°C. /15/ Man, excised piece at 25°C. /16/ Beef, minced material at 22°C. /17/ Man, excised piece at 37°C. /18/ Man, excised material at 35°C. /19/ Frog, excised piece at 25°C.

Resting and action potential data are restricted to intracellular recording, unless otherwise noted. Values obtained with intracellular electrodes filled with 3M KCl are considered as corrected for junction potential. Values in parentheses are ranges. Space constant of fiber (λ) in paraffin oil = $\sqrt{[r_m \div (r_o + r_i)]}$, in cm, where r_o = resistance of outside fluid per unit length, in ohm·cm^{-1}; r_i = internal resistance of fiber per unit length, in ohm·cm^{-1}; and r_m = transverse resistance times unit length of fiber, in ohm·cm. Time constant of the membrane ($\mathcal{T}$) = $R_m \cdot C_m$, in msec, where R_m = D.C. resistance of fiber membrane, in ohm·cm^2, and C_m = membrane capacity = $\mathcal{T} \div R_m$, in μF·cm^{-2}. R_m also = $r_m \cdot 2\pi a$ (where a= fiber radius). Specific resistance of internal protoplasm (R_i), in ohm·cm, = $r_i \cdot 2\pi a$. Specific resistance of outside fluid (R_o), in ohm·cm, has following values: Woods Hole sea water, 20.9 ohm·cm (25°C); Tyrode's solution, 51 ohm·cm (37°C); frog Ringer's, 94 ohm·cm (18°C), 92 ohm·cm (19°C), 90 ohm·cm (20°C), 83 ohm·cm (22°C); myelin sheath, sciatic nerve, 800 megohm·cm.

#	Tissue and Property	Value
	Squid (Loligo forbesi)	
	Unmyelinated nerves[1]	
1	Fiber diameter, μ	500
2	Resting potential, observed, mV	50
3	Action potential, amplitude, mV	90
	Unmyelinated nerves[1]	
4	Fiber diameter, μ	500
5	Resting potential, observed, mV	45
6	After correction for junction potential, mV	60
7	Action potential, amplitude, mV	90
	Unmyelinated nerves[1]	
8	Fiber diameter, μ	500-700
9	Temperature, °C	20
10	Resting potential, observed, mV	48(40-53)
11	After correction for junction potential, mV	62
12	Action potential, amplitude, mV	88(82-89)
13	Maximum rate of rise, V·sec^{-1}	630
14	Maximum rate of fall, V·sec^{-1}	380
	Unmyelinated nerves[2]	
15	Fiber diameter, μ	500-700
16	Temperature, °C	20
17	Resting potential after correc. junct. pot., mV	47
18	Action potential, amplitude, mV	80
19	Maximum rate of rise, V·sec^{-1}	500
20	Maximum rate of fall, V·sec^{-1}	301
	Squid (Loligo pealei)	
	Unmyelinated nerves[3]	
21	Fiber diameter, μ	500
22	Resting potential, observed, mV	51(46-59)
23	After correction for junction potential, mV	61
24	Action potential, amplitude, mV	108(77-168)
	Unmyelinated nerves[2]	
25	Fiber diameter, μ	400
26	Temperature, °C	21-28
27	Resting potential after correc. junct. pot., mV	48.6(27.5-68)
28	Action potential, amplitude, mV	85.3(46-127)
29	Duration, msec	0.35-0.5[4]; 4.5[5]
30	Conduction speed, m·sec^{-1}	19.2
	Unmyelinated nerves	
31	Fiber diameter, μ	500
32	Temperature, °C	10
33	Membrane capacity[6], μF·cm^{-2}	1.1
	Unmyelinated nerves	
34	Fiber diameter, μ	500
	Resistance[6]	
35	Specific; internal protoplasm, ohm·cm	71
36	Membrane capacity[6], μF·cm^{-2}	1.8
	Unmyelinated nerves	
37	Fiber diameter, μ	500
38	Temperature, °C	22-25
39	Space constant, mm	2.3(1.8-3.8)
40	In sea water, mm	6.0(5.0-9.3)
	Resistance[7]	
41	Specific; internal protoplasm, ohm·cm	29
42	D.C.; fiber membrane, ohm·sq cm	700[8](400-1100)
	Unmyelinated nerves	
43	Fiber diameter, μ	500
	Resistance[6]	
44	D.C.; fiber membrane, ohm·sq cm	<200
	Unmyelinated nerves	
45	Fiber diameter, μ	500
	Resistance[9]	
46	D.C.; fiber membrane, ohm·sq cm	23(14.4-40.5)
	Unmyelinated nerves	
47	Fiber diameter, μ	500
	Resistance[10]	
48	D.C.; fiber membrane, ohm·sq cm	350[11]
	Unmyelinated nerves	
49	Fiber diameter[12], μ	527; 463; 426
50	Temperature, °C	21-25
51	Conduction speed[12], m·sec^{-1}	34.8; 31.1; 29.2

#	Tissue and Property	Value
	Cuttlefish (Sepia officinalis)	
	Unmyelinated nerves[2]	
52	Fiber diameter, μ	200
53	Temperature, °C	12-17
54	Resting potential after correc. junct. pot., mV	62(53-67)
55	Action potential[13], amplitude, mV	120
56	Duration, msec	1[4]; 7[5]
57	Maximum rate of rise, V·sec^{-1}	840(650-1150)
58	Conduction speed, m·sec^{-1}	6.7
	Unmyelinated nerves[2]	
59	Fiber diameter, μ	204(126-306)
60	Temperature, °C	12-17
61	Space constant[14], mm	5.7(2.0-10.3)
	Resistance[14]	
62	Specific; internal protoplasm, ohm·cm	63(34-105)
63	D.C.; fiber membrane, ohm·sq cm	9,200(1,400-31,700)
64	Membrane capacity[14], μF·cm^{-2}	1.17(0.46-3.76)
	Lobster (Homarus vulgaris)	
	Unmyelinated nerves	
65	Fiber diameter, μ	75
66	Resting potential, observed, mV	62
67	Action potential[13], amplitude, mV	106
	Unmyelinated nerves	
68	Fiber diameter, μ	75
69	Action potential[13], amplitude, mV	110
	Unmyelinated nerves	
70	Fiber diameter, μ	75
71	Temperature, °C	15-20
72	Space constant[14], mm	1.61(0.81-2.95)
	Resistance[14]	
73	Specific; internal protoplasm, ohm·cm	60.5(43.2-83.6)
74	D.C.; fiber membrane, ohm·sq cm	2290(564-7330)
75	Membrane capacity[14], μF·cm^{-2}	1.3(0.46-3.24)
	Crab (Carcinus maenas)	
	Unmyelinated nerves	
76	Fiber diameter, μ	25-35
77	Space constant[14], mm	1.98(0.89-2.82)
	Resistance[14]	
78	Specific; internal protoplasm, ohm·cm	90.0(67.1-115.8)
79	D.C.; fiber membrane, ohm·sq cm	7,653(2,050-15,600)
80	Membrane capacity[14], μF·cm^{-2}	1.11(0.62-2.02)
81	Action potential[13], amplitude, mV	116
	Unmyelinated nerves	
82	Fiber diameter, μ	30
83	Resting potential, observed, mV	71-94
84	Action potential[13], amplitude, mV	116-153
	Unmyelinated nerves	
85	Fiber diameter, μ	30
86	Temperature, °C	21
87	Conduction speed, m·sec^{-1}	3-4
	Crab (Carcinus maenas and Portunus depurator)	
	Extensor muscle, carpopodite[2]	
88	Fiber diameter, μ	100-600[15]
89		70-500[16]
90	Temperature, °C	20
91	Space constant[17], mm	(0.4-2.65)
	Resistance[17]	
92	Specific; internal protoplasm, ohm·cm	69
93	D.C.; fiber membrane, ohm·sq cm	100(20-2000)
94	Membrane capacity[17], μF·cm^{-2}	40
95	Resting potential after correc. junct. pot., mV	70±0.5[18](56-93)
96	Action potential, amplitude, mV	61±1.2[18](0-84)[19]
97	Duration, msec	3.5(2-17)
98	Maximum rate of rise, V·sec^{-1}	20.5±1
99	Conduction speed, m·sec^{-1}	0.3
	Locust (Locusta migratoria migratoriodes R. and F.) and Cockroach (Periplaneta americana L.)	
	Extensor tibialis muscle, metathoracic leg[2]	
100	Resting potential after correct. junct. pot., mV	60
101	Action potential amplitude, mV	60-75

/1/ Solution in internal electrode used to depolarize: sea-water. /2/ Solution in internal electrode used to depolarize: 3M KCl. /3/ Solution in internal electrode used to depolarize: isotonic KCl. /4/ Spike. /5/ Positive after-phase. /6/ Determined by alternating current and transverse electrodes. /7/ Resistance length measurements made with direct current. /8/ 1000 ohm·cm^2 adopted as best value. (Value for axons in better physiological condition.) /9/ Determined by direct current pulses and internal electrodes. /10/ Determined by alternating current and longitudinal electrodes. /11/ Assuming membrane capacity=1.1. /12/ Passing from the proximal to the distal end of the giant axon. /13/ Determined by external electrodes. /14/ Determined by direct current pulses and longitudinal electrodes. /15/ Carcinas maenas. /16/ Portunus depurator. /17/ Determined by square wave pulses and internal electrodes. /18/ Standard error of mean. /19/ Value of zero omitted in averaging.

	Tissues and Property	Values		Tissues and Property	Values
	Locust (Locusta migratoria migratoriodes R. and F.) and Cockroach (Periplaneta americana L.) (concluded)			**Frog, bull (Rana catesbeiana)**	
				Sciatic nerve	
102	Maximum rate of rise, $V \cdot sec^{-1}$	17[20]	156	Conduction speed, $m \cdot sec^{-1}$	32-46
103		36[21]		**Frog (Rana pipiens)**	
104	End-plate potential, rate of rise, $V \cdot sec^{-1}$	14[20]		Myelinated fiber[2]; sciatic nerve[2]	
105		38[21]	157	Fiber diameter[28], μ	7-22
	Eel, electric (Electrophorus electricus L.)		158	Resting potential, observed, mV	60-80
	Electroplates[2]		159	Action potential, amplitude, mV	100-130
106	Fiber diameter[22], μ	100	160	Conduction speed, $m \cdot sec^{-1}$	14-43
107	Temperature, ^{o}C	24-25		Sartorius muscle[2, 3]	
	Resistance[9]		161	Temperature, ^{o}C	20-22
108	Specific; internal protoplasm, ohm·cm	50	162	Resting potential, observed, mV	78.4±5.3
109	D.C.; fiber membrane, ohm·sq cm	10[23]	163	After correction for junction potential, mV	97.6±5.7
110		0.23[24]		End-plate[30], sartorius muscle[2]	
111	Resting potential after correc. junct. pot.[25], mV	84	164	Temperature, ^{o}C	22-23
112	Action potential, amplitude[26], mV	151	165	Resting potential after correc. junct. pot.[31], mV	94.6±0.8
113	Duration, msec	2.3	166	Action potential, amplitude[31], mV	120.9±1.5
114	Conduction speed, $m \cdot sec^{-1}$	1.7	167	Maximum rate of rise[31], $V \cdot sec^{-1}$	670±22
	Electroplates[2]			End-plate[30], sartorius muscle[2]	
115	Temperature, ^{o}C	22-24	168	Temperature, ^{o}C	22-23
116	Resting potential after correc. junct. pot., mV	73.1±4.76	169	Resting potential after correc. junct. pot.[32], mV	94.9±0.9
117	Action potential, amplitude, mV	126±15.55	170	Action potential, amplitude[32], mV	117.4±1.4
118	Duration, msec	2.16±0.55	171	Maximum rate of rise[32], $V \cdot sec^{-1}$	750±31
119	Conduction speed, $m \cdot sec^{-1}$	1.05(0.71-1.59)		End-plate[32], sartorius muscle[2]	
	Spinal nerves		172	Temperature, ^{o}C	
120	Temperature, ^{o}C	24	173	Resting potential after correc. junct. pot.[33], mV	92.8±0.5
121	Conduction speed, $m \cdot sec^{-1}$	13-17	174	Action potential, amplitude[33], mV	130.8±0.5
	Lateral nerves		175	Maximum rate of rise[33], $V \cdot sec^{-1}$	650±25
122	Temperature, ^{o}C	24		Ventricle[2]	
123	Conduction speed, $m \cdot sec^{-1}$	25	176	Temperature, ^{o}C	12-16
	Spinal cord		177	Resting potential after correc. junct. pot., mV	62(50-90)
124	Temperature, ^{o}C	24	178	Action potential, amplitude, mV	80.8(65-115)
125	Conduction speed, $m \cdot sec^{-1}$	44-50	179	Duration[34], msec	(400-1000)
	Chick Embryo			Ventricle[2]	
	Auricle		180	Temperature, ^{o}C	19
126	Resting potential after correc. junct. pot., mV	29.2±1.3(10-41)	181	Resting potential after correc. junct. pot., mV	64.5±17.5
127	Action potential, amplitude, mV	39.2±2.0(11-81)	182	Action potential, amplitude, mV	77.2±22.3
	Ventricle		183	Duration, msec	8-257[35]
128	Resting potential after correc. junct. pot., mV	39.3±0.7(10-70)	184	Maximum rate of rise, $V \cdot sec^{-1}$	10
129	Action potential, amplitude, mV	53.5±1.4(13-100)	185	Maximum rate of fall[34], $V \cdot sec^{-1}$	0.8
	Toad (Bufo bufo)			Ventricle[2]	
	Tactile fibers		186	Temperature, ^{o}C	22-29
130	Fiber diameter, μ	8-15	187	Resting potential after correc. junct. pot., mV	54±8(40-80)
131	Temperature, ^{o}C	22-26	188	Action potential, amplitude, mV	74.9±9(50-110)
132	Conduction speed, $m \cdot sec^{-1}$	20-35	189	Duration[34], msec	420-1000
	Pressure fibers			**Frog (Rana temporaria)**	
133	Fiber diameter, μ	4-5		Sartorius muscle[2]	
134	Temperature, ^{o}C	22-26	190	Fiber diameter, μ	80
135	Conduction speed, $m \cdot sec^{-1}$	5-8	191	Temperature, ^{o}C	18
	Nociceptive nerve, large		192	Resting potential, observed, mV	88
136	Fiber diameter, μ	6-9	193	After correction for junct. potential, mV	88
137	Temperature, ^{o}C	22-26	194	Action potential, amplitude, mV	119
138	Conduction speed, $m \cdot sec^{-1}$	10-15	195	Duration, msec	1.5[4]; 4[36]
	Nociceptive nerve, small		196	Maximum rate of rise, $V \cdot sec^{-1}$	470
139	Fiber diameter, μ	3-5	197	Maximum rate of fall, $V \cdot sec^{-1}$	86
140	Temperature, ^{o}C	22-26		Sartorius muscle[37, 2]	
141	Conduction speed, $m \cdot sec^{-1}$	3-9	198	Fiber diameter[38]	137
	Unmyelinated nerves		199	Temperature, ^{o}C	19-20
142	Fiber diameter, μ	<2	200	Space constant[39], mm	2.4(2.2-2.6)
143	Temperature, ^{o}C	22-26		Resistance[39]	
144	Conduction speed, $m \cdot sec^{-1}$	1.0-0.1	201	Specific; internal protoplasm, ohm·cm	250[40]
	Frog		202	D.C.; fiber membrane, ohm·sq cm	4100
	Motor fibers, isolated[27]		203	Membrane capacity[39], $\mu F \cdot cm^{-2}$	8
145	Resting potential after correc. junct. pot., mV	71	204	Resting potential after correc. junct. pot., mV	88±0.6
	Ventral root fibers, small diameter[28]		205	Action potential, amplitude, mV	123±1
146	Conduction speed, $m \cdot sec^{-1}$	2-8	206	Conduction speed, $m \cdot sec^{-1}$	1.4
	Ventral root fibers, large diameter[29]			Sartorius muscle[2]	
147	Conduction speed, $m \cdot sec^{-1}$	8-40	207	Fiber diameter[38], μ	137
	Sciatic nerve (stripped of epineurium)		208	Temperature, ^{o}C	19-20
148	Space constant, mm	2.8	209	Space constant[41], mm	2.4; 2.15
	Sartorius muscle[3]			Resistance[41]	
149	Resting potential after correc. junct. pot., mV	72(max 90)	210	Specific; internal protoplasm, ohm·cm	250[40]
	Iliofibularis muscle[2]		211	D.C.; fiber membrane, ohm·sq cm	3300; 4100
150	Resting potential after correc. junct. pot., mV	90	212	Membrane capacity[41], $\mu F \cdot cm^{-2}$	6.5
151	Action potential, amplitude, mV	120		Sartorius muscle[2]	
	Ventricle[2]		213	Resting potential after correc. junct. pot., mV	88.1-0.6
152	Resting potential after correc. junct. pot., mV	64.34±12		Sartorius muscle	
153	Action potential, amplitude, mV	84.44±10.9	214	Fiber diameter[38], μ	129
	Ventricle[2]		215	Temperature, ^{o}C	20
154	Resting potential after correc. junct. pot., mV	64.5±2.7(27-112)	216	Space constant[17], mm	1.6
155	Action potential, amplitude, mV	72.2±2.9(30-132)			

/2/ Solution in internal electrode used to depolarize: 3M KCl. /3/ Solution in internal electrode used to depolarize: isotonic KCl. /4/ Spike. /9/ Determined by direct current pulses and internal electrodes. /17/ Determined by square wave pulses and internal electrodes. /20/ Locust. /21/ Cockroach. /22/ Ant.-post. direction, or non-nervous to nervous face. /23/ Nervous face. /24/ Non-nervous face. /25/ Across each face of electroplate. /26/ Electrode penetrating nervous face. /27/ Potentiometric method. /28/ Innervate slow muscle fiber system. /29/ Innervate twitch muscle fiber system. /30/ Max. rate of rise of end-plate potential, 220 $V \cdot sec^{-1}$. /31/ End-plate center. /32/ 35μ from end-plate center. /33/ Distant from end-plate. /34/ Depends on cycle length. /35/ Temp. range, 30-0.2°C. /36/ Calculated on basis of conduction speed in $m \cdot sec^{-1}$ being twice fiber diameter in micra. /37/ End-plate response during normal impulse transmission reaches 40 mV in first 0.5 sec. /38/ Calculated from fiber diamaeter = $\sqrt{(4\pi x R_i / r_i)}$. /39/ Determined by square wave pulses and longitudinal electrodes. /40/ Assumed. /41/ Determined by end-plate potential and internal electrodes.

	Tissue and Property	Value		Tissue and Property	Value
	Frog (Rana temporaria) (concluded)			**Dog (Canis familiaris)**	
	Sartorius muscle			Purkinje fibers, ventricle[2]	
	Resistance[17]		269	Fiber diameter, μ	30
217	D.C.; fiber membrane, ohm·sq cm	2064	270	Temperature, °C	37-38
218	Membrane capacity[17], μF·cm^{-2}	10.6	271	Resting potential after correc.	
	End-plate, sartorius muscle[2]			junct. pot., mV	90±6
219	Temperature, °C	20	272	Action potential, amplitude, mV	121
220	Resting potential after correc.		273	Duration[4], msec	240-400
	junct. pot., mV	90(75-107)	274	Maximum rate of rise, V·sec^{-1}	500-1000
	Bundles, adductor magnus		275	Conduction speed, m·sec^{-1}	2±0.5
221	Fiber diameter, μ	75(30-130)		Purkinje fibers, ventricle[2]	
222	Temperature, °C	22.5	276	Temperature, °C	38-40
223	Space constant[14], mm	0.65(0.47-1.15)	277	Resting potential after correc.	
	Resistance[14]			junct. pot., mV	89±3.2
224	Specific; internal protoplasm, ohm·cm	176(131-280)	278	Action potential, amplitude, mV	121±4
225	D.C.; fiber membrane, ohm·sq cm	1500(650-4500)	279	Duration[44], msec	500
226	Membrane capacity[14], μF·cm^{-2}	6(4.5-10)	280	Conduction speed, m·sec^{-1}	2.5
	Extensor muscle, dig. IV			Ventricle[2]	
227	Fiber diameter, μ	43	281	Resting potential after correc.	
228	Temperature, °C	22.5		junct. pot., mV	90
229	Space constant[14], mm	1.1(0.75-1.53)	282	Action potential, amplitude, mV	120-130
	Resistance[14]			Ventricle[2]	
230	Specific; internal protoplasm, ohm·cm	255(206-355)	283	Resting potential after correc.	
231	D.C.; fiber membrane, ohm·sq cm	4300(1500-9500)		junct. pot., mV	80.7±7(65-95)
232	Membrane capacity[14], μF·cm^{-2}	4.4(2.9-5.9)	284	Action potential, amplitude, mV	100±8(80-120)
	Cells, spinal ganglion			Auricle[2]	
233	Fiber diameter, μ	80-90	285	Resting potential after correc.	
234	Resting potential, observed, mV	50-90		junct. pot., mV	85±9
235	Action potential, amplitude, mV	50-90	286	Action potential, amplitude, mV	100±1
	Frog (Rana temporaria) and Cat (Felis catus)			Auricle[2]	
	Myelinated root fibers[2]		287	Temperature, °C	37-38
236	Resting potential, observed, mV	85-95	288	Resting potential after correc.	
	Cat (Felis catus)			junct. pot., mV	85
	Motor neurones, spinal cord[2]		289	Action potential, amplitude, mV	105
237	Fiber diameter, μ	100	290	Duration[45], msec	150-250
238	Temperature, °C	37.	291	Conduction speed, m·sec^{-1}	1
239	Resting potential after correc.			Papillary muscle[2]	
	junct. pot., mV	70	292	Temperature, °C	37-38
240	Action potential, amplitude, mV	(90-100)	293	Resting potential after correc.	
241	Duration, msec	(300-500)		junct. pot., mV	85
242	Maximum rate of rise, V·sec^{-1}	(200-250)	294	Action potential, amplitude, mV	105
	Auricle[2]		295	Duration[45], msec	150-250
243	Fiber diameter, μ	30	296	Conduction speed, m·sec^{-1}	1
244	Temperature, °C	36-38		**Calf and Sheep**	
245	Resting potential after correc.			Purkinje fibers, ventricle[2]	
	junct. pot., mV	60.4±4.68	297	Temperature, °C	38
246		(36-91)		Resistance[17]	
247	Action potential, amplitude, mV	65.2±7.67	298	Specific; internal protoplasm, ohm·cm	154
248	Maximum rate of rise, V·sec^{-1}	10	299	D.C.; fiber membrane, ohm·sq cm	1220
249	Maximum rate of fall[34], V·sec^{-1}	0.8-2	300	Membrane capacity[17], μF·cm^{-2}	11.3
	Cat		301	Resting potential after correc.	
	Sartorius muscle[2]; vastus m.[2]			junct. pot., mV	94
250	Fiber diameter, μ	20	302	Action potential, amplitude, mV	129
251	Resting potential after correc.			**Goat (Capra hircus)**	
	junct. pot., mV	79.5±5.7		Purkinje fibers, ventricle	
252	Action potential, amplitude, mV	116	303	Fiber diameter[46], μ	75
253	Duration, msec	1[42]	304	Temperature, °C	37
254	Maximum rate of rise, V·sec^{-1}	730	305	Space constant, mm	1.9
255	Maximum rate of fall, V·sec^{-1}	160		Resistance[17]	
	Guinea Pig		306	Specific; internal protoplasm, ohm·cm	105
	Sartorius muscle[2]; pectoralis major[2]; biceps m.[2]		307	D.C.; fiber membrane, ohm·sq cm	1940(760-3380)
256	Fiber diameter, μ	20	308	Membrane capacity[17], μF·cm^{-2}	12.4
257	Resting potential after correc.		309	Conduction speed, m·sec^{-1}	2.2±0.5
	junct. pot., mV	84.5±5.7		Purkinje fibers, ventricle[2]	
258	Action potential, amplitude, mV	121	310	Fiber diameter, μ	40-100
259	Duration, msec	1[42]; 1-6[36]	311	Temperature, °C	37
260	Maximum rate of rise, V·sec^{-1}	730	312	Resting potential after correc.	
261	Maximum rate of fall, V·sec^{-1}	160		junct. pot., mV	94±8
	Taenia coli[2]; longitudinal smooth muscle[2]		313	Action potential, amplitude, mV	135
262	Fiber diameter, μ	<10		**Man (Homo sapiens)**	
263	Resting potential after correc.			Ulnar nerve (most rapidly conducting fibers to	
	junct. pot.[43], mV	60±9.18		muscles of hypthenar eminence)	
	Rabbit		314	Conduction speed, m·sec^{-1}	57[47]
	Smooth muscle, sphincter pupillae[2]			**Mammalia**	
264	Fiber diameter, μ	<10		Myelinated nerve fibers	
265	Temperature, °C	35	315	Fiber diameter, μ	1-20
266	Resting potential after correc.		316	Conduction speed, m·sec^{-1}	5-120
	junct. pot.[44], mV	60		Myelinated nerve fibers (preganglionic, autonomic)	
	Mouse, white		317	Fiber diameter, μ	<3
	Anterior tibialis muscle[2]		318	Conduction speed, m·sec^{-1}	3-15
267	Temperature, °C	24-30		Unmyelinated nerve fibers (somatic, autonomic)	
268	Resting potential after correc.		319	Conduction speed, m·sec^{-1}	0.6-2
	junct. pot., mV	99.8±6.5			

/2/ Solution in internal electrode used to depolarize: 3M KCl. /14/ Determined by direct current pulses and longitudinal electrodes. /17/ Determined by square wave pulses and internal electrodes. /34/ Depends on cycle length. /36/ Calculated on basis of conduction speed in m·sec^{-1} being twice fiber diameter in micra. /38/ Calculated from fiber diameter = $\sqrt{(4\pi \times R_1/r_1)}$. /42/ With negative after potential of 1-6 msec; value of negative after-potential varies from 5-28 mV. /43/ At in situ length; membrane potential varies inversely with length. /44/ No spontaneous movements; cf Fn 43. /45/ At heart rates of 130-150 beats per min. /46/ May vary 1.8 times over same fiber. /47/ Varies with age.

281. MUSCLE: PHYSICAL PROPERTIES

When a muscle is stimulated, after a brief latent period, the contractile substance shortens against a force P with a velocity v. When shortening is prevented, it exerts a maximum force P_o; when shortening is unrestrained, no force is exerted and it shortens at a maximum velocity v_o. P_o is often expressed as the force per unit area of muscle cross section (P_o/S) and v_o in muscle lengths per sec. Experimentally it is found in all muscles studied that P and v can be related by an equation of the form $(P + a)(v + b) = b(P_o + a)$, where "b" is a constant and has the dimensions of velocity, and "a" the shortening heat constant with the dimensions of force (cf Part II, Item 15). a/P_o is approximately 1/4 and largely independent of temperature. The contractile material of muscle is in series with an elastic component which must be stretched before external tension is manifest. This takes time and, in a single muscle twitch, relaxation usually sets in before P_o can be reached. The ratio of the peak twitch tension to P_o is called the twitch/tetanus ratio, and the time after the stimulus at which the peak tension is reached is known as the contraction time. The velocity of the action potential provides an index to the way in which the process of contraction spreads from the active to the inactive parts of the muscle. Resting muscle gives out a small amount of heat as a result of its metabolism. During activity the rate of heat production is much greater. The initial heat has two components: maintenance or activation heat produced when the contractile machinery is activated; and shortening heat, produced in addition in proportion to the shortening of the muscle. For a long time after activity the rate of heat production is slightly greater than the resting rate. The total amount of heat is the recovery heat.

Part I: MECHANICAL CHARACTERISTICS

	Species	Muscle	Temp °C	Latency msec I[1]	Latency msec II[2]	P_o/S kg/sq cm	a/P_o	Ratio: Twitch Tetanus	Contract. Time msec	Velocity Action Potential cm/sec	Velocity Max. of shorten. lengths/sec[3]
1	Man	Flexors of elbow	37			2.4	0.36		70-80	400	6
2	Cat	Soleus	34-37		10			0.3	100		
3		Gastrocnemius	34-37		6.5			0.3	40		
4		Internal rectus	34-37					0.09	7.5-10		
5		Nictitating membrane			144[4]				800-1900	50-80	
6	Rabbit	Glycerol extracted fiber[5]	20			1-4	0.1				0.2
7	Rat	Diaphragm	37	1.0	1.5	1.6	0.25	0.14	16	500	11
8	Fowl	Gastrocnemius	36					0.13	50		
9	Tortoise	Retractor penis[6]	0		70	2.5	0.28		4000		0.1
10	Frog	Sartorius	20-22	1.5	2.9	2.1	0.18	0.22	25	160	10
11		Sartorius	0	7.1	15	1.7	0.25	0.72	400	55	2
12		Semimembranosus, single fibers	18-26			3.3			70		9.2
13		Semimembranosus, single fibers	0			2.8	0.16		400		3.0
14	Toad	Sartorius and semimembranosus	0	9.5	20	1.2	0.3		800	80	0.8
15	Dogfish and ray	Coracohyoid, coracomandibula	0			0.6	0.35		200	65	2.0
16	Snail	Pharyngeal retractor	15			5	0.28		300		0.15
17	Mytilus	Anterior byssal retractor	14		50	3.5	0.16	0.13		17.6	0.06
18		Pedal retractor	14		20	2.5	0.1	0.33			0.06
19	Sea anemone	Wall muscle				10,000	40		40,000		

/1/ From stimulus to beginning of early tension relaxation. /2/ From stimulus to beginning of development of positive tension or shortening. /3/ Maximum velocity of shortening. Muscle lengths/sec. /4/ Includes conduction time and neuromuscular delay. /5/ Activated by ATP. /6/ And ileofibularis.

Part II: MISCELLANEOUS PROPERTIES OF FROG MUSCLE

	Property	Value		Property	Value
1	Density, g/cu cm	1.062	9	Active state, time to fall to 50%, 0°C, ($Q_{10} \cong 2$), msec	250
2	Diffusion constant of oxygen, at 20°C, ml/min for 1 sq cm area, 1 μ thickness; 760 mm/Hg pressure difference	0.14	10	Series elastic component, stretch produced by maximum tetanic tension, % of muscle length	4
3	Thermal conductivity, cal/min for 1 sq cm area, 1 cm thickness; 1°C temperature difference	1.18×10^{-3}	11	Membrane potential, 17.4°C, mV	90
4	Volume coefficient of thermal expansion, (unloaded, resting), ml/ml x °C	0.16×10^{-3}	12	Action potential, 17.4°C, mV	124
5	Linear coefficient of thermal expansion, (unloaded, resting), cm/cm x °C	$(-0.1 \text{ to } 0.6) \times 10^{-3}$	13	Resting heat[1], cal/g x minutes	3.75×10^{-3}
6	Temperature coefficient of resting tension, (small tensions), dyne/dyne x °C	$(2.4 - 6) \times 10^{-3}$	14	Initial heat[1]: Maintenance, cal/g x seconds	2.3×10^{-3}
7	Latency relaxation, maximum drop in tension, % of tetanic tension	0.1	15	Initial heat[1]: Shortening, cal/cm shortening x sq cm (equals "a" of Part I, if expressed in force units)	8.2×10^{-3}
8	Active state, duration of plateau, °C, ($Q_{10} = 2.20$), msec	35	16	Recovery heat[1], total energy developed by contraction / initial energy developed	2
			17	Maximum efficiency[1], work done x 100 / energy consumed	20

/1/ Sartorius, 0°C.

Part III: MICROSCOPIC STRUCTURE AND BIREFRINGENCE CHARACTERISTICS OF MUSCLE

	Species	Muscle	Conditions	Myofibril Diameter μ	Protofibril Diameter Å	At Rest[4] A μ	At Rest[4] J μ	At Rest[4] A+J μ	At Rest[4] (A/A+J) x 100	Contraction[5] A μ	Contraction[5] J μ	Contraction[5] A+J μ	Contraction[5] (A/A+J) x 100	Birefringence At Rest x 10^-3	Birefringence Contraction[6] Decrease % of Rest
1	Dog	Sartorius	Living fibers											2.60	
2	Guinea pig	Gluteus maximus[7]	Single fiber, static			1.41	0.84	2.25	62.7	1.20	1.06	2.26	53.1	1.98	
3	Mouse	Rectus abdominis	Living, whole muscle											2.61	
4	Rabbit	Psoas		0.8-1.8	200										
5		Leg muscle		0.5-1.0	50-250										
6	Lizard	Thoracalis abdominus		1.0	160	1.34	0.90	2.24	59.9						
7	Toad	Leg muscle		0.5-1.0	50-250										
8	Frog	Semitendinosus[8]	Living fiber		40	1.37	0.81	2.18	62.9	1.13	1.05	2.18	51.9	2.0[9]	20-30
9		Gastrocnemius	Static											2.07	12-14
10		Sartorius[10]	Whole muscle static												
11	Crayfish	Leg flexor				3.5	2.8	6.3	55.5						
12	Crab	Leg flexor				3.4	2.6	6.0	56.6	3.2	2.9	6.1	52.5		

/1/ Composed of filaments denoted as protofibrils. /2/ Anisotropic. /3/ Isotropic. /4/ Equilibrium length (at which tension = 0.5% of maximum tension in isometric tetanic contraction. /5/ Isometric tetanic contraction, equilibrium length. /6/ Isometric. /7/ 37°C. /8/ 17-20°C. /9/ Corrected for deviation from circular X-section by adding 18.5%. Birefringence increases with decreasing temperature by 0.5%/°C. /10/ 0°C.

282. MUSCLES: MAN

Table represents an abridged listing of muscles. In no case is a complete atlas intended.

Ant. = anterior; ext. = external; inf. = inferior; int. = internal; lat. = lateral; med. = medial; post. = posterior; trans. = transverse; vert. = vertebra(e); cart. = cartilage.

	Muscle	Origin	Insertion	Action
1	Abductor digiti quinti (hand)	Pisiform; flexor carpi ulnaris tendon.	Med. surface base proximal phalanx little finger.	Abducts little finger.
2	Abductor digiti quinti (foot)	Med. and lat. tubercles calcaneus; plantar fascia.	Lat. surface base proximal phalanx little toe.	Abducts little toe.
3	Abductor hallucis	Med. tubercle calcaneus; plantar fascia.	Med. surface base proximal phalanx great toe.	Abducts, flexes great toe.
4	Abductor pollicis brevis	Navicular; ridge greater multangular; trans. carpal ligament.	Lat. surface base proximal phalanx thumb.	Abducts thumb.
5	Abductor pollicis longus	Posterior surfaces radius and ulna.	Radial side base 1st metacarpal bone.	Abducts, extends thumb.
6	Adductor brevis	Outer surface inferior ramus of pubis.	Upper part of linea aspera of femur.	Adducts, rotates, flexes thigh.
7	Adductor hallucis	Plantar fascia; base 2nd, 3rd, 4th metatarsals.	Lat. side base proximal phalanx great toe.	Adducts great toe.
8	Adductor longus	Crest, symphysis of pubis.	Linea aspera of femur.	Adducts, rotates, flexes thigh.
9	Adductor magnus	Inf. ramus pubis; ramus ischium.	Linea aspera of femur.	Adducts thigh.
10	Adductor minimus	Sup. portion adductor magnus.	Adductor tubercle of femur.	Extends thigh.
11	Adductor pollicis	Multangular; capitate; bases 2nd, 3rd, 4th metacarpals.	Ischium; body, ramus of pubis.	Adducts thigh.
12	Anconeus	Back lat. epicondyle of humerus.	Med. aspect base proximal phalanx of thumb.	Adducts, opposes thumb.
13	Arrectores pilorum	Papillary skin layer.	Olecranon; dorsal surface of ulna.	Extends forearm.
14	Articularis genu	Distal 4th anterior surface of femur.	Hair follicles.	Elevates skin hairs.
15	Aryepiglotticus	Apex arytenoid cartilage.	Synovial membrane of knee joint.	Lifts capsule of knee joint.
16	Arytenoideus, obliquus	Base muscular process arytenoid cartilage.	Lateral margin epiglottis.	Closes larynx inlet.
17	transversus	Base muscular process arytenoid cartilage.	Apex opposite arytenoid cartilage.	Closes larynx inlet.
18	Auricularis, anterior	Superficial temporal fascia.	Continuous with thyroarytenoid, base opposite cart.	Approximates arytenoid cartilages.
19	posterior	Mastoid process.	Cartilage of ear.	Draws ear pinna forward.
20	superior	Galea aponeurotica.	Cartilage of ear.	Draws pinna backward.
21	Biceps brachii	Tip coracoid process scapula; supraglenoid tuberosity.	Cartilage of ear.	Raises ear pinna.
22	Biceps femoris	Linea aspera of femur; ischial tuberosity.	Radius tubercle; forearm deep fascia.	Flexes forearm, supinates hand.
23	Brachialis	Anterior aspect humerus.	Head fibula; lat. condyle tibia; deep fascia lat. knee.	Flexes knee joint, extends hip.
24	Brachioradialis	External supracondyloid ridge of humerus.	Coronoid process of ulna.	Flexes forearm.
25	Buccinator	Alveolar processes maxilla, mandible, pterygomandible raphé.	Lower end of radius.	Flexes forearm.
26	Bulbocavernosus	Central point perineum; median raphé of bulb.	Orbicularis oris at angle of mouth.	Compresses cheek, retracts mouth.
27	Caninus	Canine fossa of maxilla.	Fascia of penis (clitoris).	Constricts bulbus urethrae.
28	Chondroglossus	Inner side, base lesser cornu of hyoid bone.	Orbicularis oris; skin at angle of mouth.	Raises angle of mouth.
29	Ciliaris	Scleral spur; sphincter of ciliary body.	Substance of tongue.	Depresses, retracts tongue.
30	Coccygeus	Ischial spine; sacrospinous ligament.	Ciliary process.	Visual accommodation.
31	Constrictor pharyngis, inf.	Under surfaces cricoid and thyroid cartilages.	Lat. border lower sacrum; upper coccyx.	Supports, raises coccyx.
32	medius	Cornua of hyoid; stylohyoid ligament.	Med. raphé posterior wall of pharynx.	Constricts pharynx.
33	superior	Med. pterygoid lamina; pterygomandibular raphé.	Middle of posterior wall of pharynx.	Constricts pharynx.
34	Coracobrachialis	Coracoid process of scapula.	Posterior median raphé.	Constricts pharynx.
35	Corrugator cutis ani	Submucous tissue within anus.	Medial aspect shaft of humerus.	Flexes, adducts arm.
36	Corrugator supercilii	Superciliary arch of frontal bone.	Skin surrounding anus.	Corrugates skin around anus.
37	Cremaster	Inferior margin internal oblique muscle of abdomen.	Skin of forehead.	Moves eyebrows; wrinkles forehead.
38	Crico-arytenoideus, lateralis	Lateral surface cricoid cartilage.	Pubic tubercle.	Elevates testis.
39	posterior	Back of cricoid cartilage.	Muscular process arytenoid cartilage.	Approximates vocal folds.
40	Cricothyroideus	Front, side of cricoid cartilage.	Muscular process arytenoid cartilage.	Separates vocal folds.
41	Deltoideus	Clavicle, acromion, spine of scapula.	Lamina of thyroid cartilage.	Tenses vocal cords.
42	Depressor alae nasi	Incisor fossa of maxilla.	Deltoid tuberosity of humerus.	Abducts, flexes, extends arm.
43	Diaphragma	Xiphoid process; costal cartilages; lumbar vertebrae.	Ala and septum of nose.	Contracts nostril; depresses ala.
44	Digastricus, anterior belly	Inner surface mandible near symphysis.	Central tendon.	Respiration and expulsive acts.
45	posterior belly	Mastoid notch.	Hyoid bone; intermediate tendon.	Elevates hyoid bone, lowers jaw.
46	Epicranius (frontalis et occipitalis)	Forehead skin, occipital bone.	Hyoid bone; intermediate tendon.	Elevates hyoid bone, lowers jaw.
47	Extensor carpi radialis brevis	External epicondyle of humerus.	Galea aponeurotica.	Raises eyebrows; draws scalp backward.
48	longus	External supracondyloid ridge of humerus.	Base 3rd metacarpal bone.	Extends, abducts wrist joint.
49	Extensor carpi ulnaris	External epicondyle of humerus.	Base 2nd metacarpal.	Extends, abducts wrist joint.
50	Extensor digiti quinti proprius	External epicondyle of humerus.	Base 5th metacarpal bone.	Extends, adducts wrist joint.
51	Extensor digitorum brevis	Dorsal surface of calcaneus.	Dorsum proximal phalanx of little finger.	Extends little finger.
52	communis	Lateral epicondyle of humerus.	Extensor tendons 1st, 2nd, 3rd, 4th toes.	Extends toes.
53	longus	Ant. fibula; lat. condyle tibia; interosseous membrane.	Common extensor tendon of each finger.	Extends wrist joint and phalanges.
54	Extensor hallucis longus	Front of tibia; interosseous membrane.	Common extensor tendons 4 lateral toes.	Extends toes.
55	Extensor indicis proprius	Dorsal surface of ulna.	Base of terminal phalanx of great toe.	Dorsiflexes ankle joint; extends toe.
56	Extensor pollicis brevis	Dorsal surface radius and interosseous membrane.	Common extensor tendon of index finger.	Extends index finger.
57	Extensor pollicis longus	Dorsal surface ulna and interosseous membrane.	Dorsal surface proximal phalanx of thumb.	Extends thumb.
58	Flexor carpi radialis	Medial epicondyle of humerus.	Dorsal surface distal phalanx of thumb.	Extends, abducts thumb.
59	Flexor carpi ulnaris	Medial epicondyle humerus; medial border ulna.	Base 2nd metacarpal. / Pisiform; hamulus of hamate; proximal end 5th metacarpal.	Flexes, abducts wrist joint. / Flexes, adducts wrist joint.

#	Muscle	Origin	Insertion	Action
60	Flexor digiti quinti brevis (foot)	Base 5th metatarsal; plantar fascia.	Lateral aspect base proximal phalanx little toe.	Flexes little toe.
61	Flexor digiti quinti brevis (hand)	Hamulus of hamate; transverse carpal ligament.	Medial side base proximal phalanx little finger.	Flexes little finger.
62	Flexor digitorum brevis	Medial tuberosity calcaneus; plantar aponeurosis.	Four tendons to middle phalanx of 4 lateral toes.	Flexes toes.
63	Flexor digitorum longus	Shaft of tibia; posterior surface.	Distal phalanges lesser toes.	Flexes toes; extends foot.
64	Flexor digitorum profundus	Shaft of ulna; coronoid process.	Distal phalanges of fingers.	Flexes distal phalanges.
65	Flexor digitorum sublimis	Med. epicondyle humerus; coronoid process ulna; ant. margin of radius.	Four tendons to base of middle phalanx of each finger.	Flexes middle phalanges.
66	Flexor hallucis brevis	Under surface cuboid; 3rd cuneiform.	Base proximal phalanx of great toe.	Flexes great toe.
67	Flexor hallucis longus	Posterior aspect of fibula.	Base of distal phalanx great toe.	Flexes great toe.
68	Flexor pollicis brevis	Transverse carpal ligament; ridge great multangular.	Base proximal phalanx of thumb.	Flexes thumb.
69	Flexor pollicis longus	Volar surface radius; coronoid process of ulna.	Base distal phalanx of thumb.	Flexes thumb.
70	Frontalis	Anterior portion of Epicranius; skin of forehead.	Galea aponeurotica.	Draws scalp forward, raises eyebrows.
71	Gastrocnemius	Lateral and medial condyles of humerus.	Posterior surface of calcaneus via tendo calcaneus (tendon of Achilles).	Plantar flexes ankle joint. Flexes knee joint.
72	Gemellus inferior	Tuberosity of ischium.	Greater trochanter of femur.	Rotates thigh laterally.
73	Gemellus superior	Spine of ischium.	Greater trochanter of femur.	Rotates thigh laterally.
74	Genioglossus	Mental spine of mandible.	Hyoid bone; under surface of tongue.	Protrudes and depresses tongue.
75	Geniohyoideus	Mental spine of mandible.	Body of hyoid.	Elevates, draws hyoid forward.
76	Glossopalatinus	Under surface soft palate.	Side of tongue.	Elevates tongue; constricts fauces.
77	Gluteus maximus	Lat. surface ilium; post. surface sacrum, coccyx; sacrotuberous ligament.	Gluteal tuberosity of femur; iliotibial tract.	Extends, abducts, rotates thigh outward.
78	Gluteus medius	Lateral surface of ilium.	Greater trochanter.	Abducts femur.
79	Gluteus minimus	Lateral surface of ilium.	Greater trochanter.	Abducts, medially rotates femur.
80	Gracilis	Inferior ramus of pubis.	Medial surface of tibia.	Adducts femur; flexes knee joint.
81	Hyoglossus	Body, greater cornu of hyoid bone.	Side of tongue.	Depresses tongue.
82	Iliacus	Iliac fossa and sacrum.	Lesser trochanter.	Flexes thigh, trunk on extremity.
83	Iliocostalis cervicis	Angles 3rd, 4th, 5th, 6th ribs.	Trans. processes 4th, 5th, 6th cervical vertebrae.	Extends cervical spine.
84	Iliocostalis dorsi	Upper borders angles of six lower ribs.	Angles upper 6 ribs; trans. process 7th cervical vert.	Extends thoracic spine.
85	Iliocostalis lumborum	Along with sacrospinalis.	Angles lower 6 or 7 ribs.	Extends lumbar spine.
86	Infraspinatus	Infraspinous fossa of scapula.	Greater tubercle of humerus.	Rotates humerus laterally.
87	Intercostales, ext. (11 pairs)	Lower border of rib above.	Superior border of rib below.	Draws ribs together; respiration; expulsion.
88	Intercostales, int. (11 pairs)	Lower border costal cartilage and rib above.	Lower border costal cartilage and rib below.	Draws ribs together; respiration; expulsion.
89	Interossei dorsales (foot)	Surfaces adjacent metatarsal bones.	Extensor tendons 4 lateral toes.	Abducts, flexes toes.
90	Interossei dorsales (hand)	Two heads from adjacent sides metacarpal bones.	Extensor tendons 2nd, 3rd, 4th fingers.	Abducts, flexes proximal phalanx.
91	Interossei plantares	Medial side 3rd, 4th, 5th metatarsals.	Extensor tendons 3rd, 4th, 5th toes.	Adducts, flexes toes.
92	Interossei volares	Sides of 2nd, 4th, 5th metacarpals.	Extensor tendons 2nd, 4th, 5th fingers.	Adducts, flexes proximal phalanx.
93	Interspinales	Under surface of spines of vertebrae near apex.	Posterior part of upper surface of spine below.	Supports spinal column.
94	Intertransversarii	Transverse process of vertebra.	Transverse process of vertebra.	Lateral flexion vertebral column.
95	Ischiocavernosus	Ramus of ischium.	Crus of penis.	Assists in erection of penis.
96	Latissimus dorsi	Spines of thoracic, lumbar vertebrae; lumbodorsal fascia; ilium crest; lower ribs; inf. angle of scapula.	Groove of intertubercular sulcus of humerus.	Adducts, extends humerus.
97	Levator ani	Pelvic surface ischial spine; int. obturator fascia.	Point of perineum; anococcygeal raphé; coccyx.	Draws anus upward, forward; supports viscera.
98	Levator palpebrae superioris	Upper border optic foramen.	Upper tarsal plate.	Raises upper lid.
99	Levator scapulae	Trans. processes 4 upper cervical vertebrae.	Medial angle of scapula.	Raises scapula.
100	Levator veli palatini	Apex petrous part temporal bone; eustachian tube.	Aponeurosis of soft palate.	Raises soft palate.
101	Levatores costarum (12 pairs)	Trans. processes 7th cervical, upper 11 thoracic vertebrae.	Medial to angle of corresponding rib below.	Aid in raising ribs in inspiration.
102	Lingualis inferior	Under surface of tongue at base.	Tip of tongue.	Shortens tongue.
103	Lingualis superior	Submucosa and septum of tongue.	Tip of tongue.	Shortens tongue; raises edges, tip.
104	Longissimus capitis	Trans. process upper thoracic, lower 4 cervical vertebrae.	Mastoid process of temporal bone.	Draws head backward; rotates head.
105	Longissimus cervicis	Trans. process upper thoracic vertebrae.	Trans. processes 2nd to 6th cervical vertebrae.	Extends cervical vertebrae.
106	Longissimus dorsi	Trans., articular processes lumbar vertebrae; fascia.	Lower ribs; trans. processes thoracic vertebrae.	Extends thoracic vertebrae.
107	Longus capitis	Trans. processes 3rd to 6th cervical vertebrae.	Basal portion occipital bone.	Flexes head.
108	Longus colli	Bodies of 1st to 3rd thoracic vertebrae.	Trans. processes 5th to 6th cervical vertebrae.	Flexes cervical vertebrae.
109	Lumbricales (foot)	Tendons of flexor digitorum longus pedis.	Extensor tendon of 4 lateral toes.	Flexes proximal phalanges, extends distal phalanges.
110	Lumbricales (hand)	Tendons of flexor digitorum profundus.	Extensor tendon of each finger.	Flexes proximal phalanges, extends distal phalanges.
111	Masseter	Arch of zygoma.	Ramus and angle of mandible.	Raises mandible, closes jaws.
112	Mentalis	Incisive fossa of mandible.	Skin of chin.	Puckers chin.
113	Multifidus	Sacrum, sacroiliac ligament; mammillary processes of lumbar vertebrae; thoracic, cervical vertebrae.	Spines of vertebrae.	Extends, rotates vertebral column.
114	Mylohyoideus	Mylohyoid line of mandible.	Hyoid.	Elevates hyoid; supports mouth floor.
115	Nasalis	Maxilla.	Skin over bridge of nose.	Muscle of facial expression.
116	Obliquus abdominis externus	Lower 8 ribs at costal cartilages.	Crest of ilium; linea alba through rectus sheath.	Flex and rotate vertebral column; compress abdominal viscera.
117	Obliquus abdominis internus	Inguinal ligament; iliac crest; lumbar aponeurosis.	Lower 3 or 4 costal cartilages; linea alba; conjoined tendon to pubis.	Flex and rotate vertebral column; compress abdominal viscera.

282. MUSCLES: MAN (Concluded)

Ant. = anterior; ext. = external; inf. = inferior; int. = internal; lat. = lateral; med. = medial; post. = posterior; trans. = transverse; vert. = vertebra(e); cart. = cartilage.

Table represents an abridged listing of muscles. In no case is a complete atlas intended.

	Muscle	Origin	Insertion	Action
118	Obliquus capitis inferior	Spine of axis.	Transverse process of atlas.	Rotates atlas and head.
119	Obliquus capitis superior	Transverse process of atlas.	Occipital bone.	Extension and lateral head movements.
120	Obliquus oculi inferior	Orbital plate of maxilla.	Sclera.	Rotates eyeball upward and outward.
121	Obliquus oculi superior	Lesser wing sphenoid above optic foramen.	Sclera.	Rotates eyeball outward and downward.
122	Obturator externus	Pubis, ischium, superficial surface obturator memb.	Trochanteric fossa of femur.	Rotates thigh laterally.
123	Obturator internus	Pubis, ilium, ischium, deep surface obturator memb.	Greater trochanter of femur.	Rotates thigh laterally.
124	Occipitalis	Posterior portion of Epicranius; occipital bone.	Galea aponeurotica.	Draws scalp backward.
125	Omohyoideus	Superior border of scapula.	Lateral border of hyoid bone via central tendon.	Depresses hyoid.
126	Opponens digiti quinti	Hamulus of hamate; transverse carpal ligament.	Medial aspect of 5th metacarpal.	Rotates, adducts 5th metacarpal.
127	Opponens pollicis	Ridge greater multangular; trans. carpal ligament.	First metacarpal volar.	Opposes thumb.
128	Orbicularis oculi	Medial aspect of orbit.	Skin about eyelids.	Closes lids.
129	Palmaris brevis	Palmar aponeurosis.	Skin of medial border of hand.	Tenses palm of hand.
130	Palmaris longus	Medial epicondyle of humerus.	Transverse carpal ligament; palmar aponeurosis.	Flexes wrist joint.
131	Pectineus	Iliopectineal line; pubis.	Femur distal to lesser trochanter.	Flexes; adducts thigh.
132	Pectoralis major	Clavicle, sternum, first 6 ribs, aponeurosis of obliquus abdominis externus.	Crest of intertubercular sulcus of humerus.	Adducts, flexes, medially rotates arm; depresses shoulder.
133	Pectoralis minor	Third to 5th ribs.	Coracoid process of scapula.	Draws shoulder forward and downward.
134	Peroneus brevis	Lateral surface of fibula.	Base of 5th metatarsal.	Abducts, plantar flexes foot.
135	Peroneus longus	Lateral condyle tibia; lateral surface fibula.	First cuneiform, 1st metatarsal.	Abducts, everts, plantar flexes foot.
136	Peroneus tertius	Medial surface of fibula.	Fifth metatarsal.	Everts, dorsiflexes foot.
137	Pharyngopalatinus	Soft palate.	Aponeurosis of pharynx.	Aids swallowing.
138	Piriformis	Ilium, 2nd to 4th sacral vertebrae.	Upper border of great trochanter.	Rotates thigh outward.
139	Plantaris	Lateral condyle of femur.	Posterior part of calcaneus.	Plantar flexes foot.
140	Platysma	Fascia of cervical region.	Mandible and skin around mouth.	Wrinkles neck skin; depresses jaw.
141	Popliteus	Lateral condyle of femur.	Back of tibia.	Flexes leg; rotates leg inward.
142	Procerus	Skin over nose.	Skin of forehead.	Draws down eyebrows.
143	Pronator quadratus	Volar surface of ulna.	Volar surface of radius.	Pronates hand.
144	Pronator teres	Medial epicondyle of humerus; coronoid of ulna.	Lateral surface of radius.	Pronates hand.
145	Psoas major	Lumbar vertebrae and fascia.	Lesser trochanter of femur.	Flexes trunk; flexes, medially rotates thigh.
146	Psoas minor	Last thoracic, first lumbar vertebrae.	Iliopectineal eminence of pubis.	Flexes trunk on pelvis.
147	Pterygoideus externus	Sphenoid; lateral pterygoid plate.	Mandible neck; temporomandibular joint capsule.	Protrudes mandible; opens jaws.
148	Pterygoideus internus	Lateral pterygoid plate; maxilla tuberosity.	Medial surface of mandible angle.	Closes jaws.
149	Pyramidalis	Front of pubis; anterior pubic ligament.	Linea alba.	Tenses abdominal wall.
150	Quadratus femoris	Ischial tuberosity.	Quadrate tubercle of femur.	Adducts, laterally rotates femur.
151	Quadratus labii inferioris	Mandible.	Skin about mouth.	Depresses lower lip.
152	Quadratus labii superioris	Maxilla.	Skin about mouth.	Raises upper lip.
153	Quadratus lumborum	Iliac crest; lumbodorsal fascia; lumbar vertebrae.	Last rib.	Laterally flexes lumbar vertebrae.
154	Quadratus plantae	Calcaneus and plantar fascia.	Tendons of flexor digitorum longus.	Aids in flexion of toes.
155	Quadriceps femoris	Rectus femoris and 3 vastus muscles.		Extends leg.
156	Rectus abdominis	Pubic crest.	Xiphoid; 5th to 7th costal cartilage.	Flexes lumbar vertebrae; supports abdomen.
157	Rectus capitis anterior	Lateral portion of atlas.	Occipital bone.	Flexes, supports head.
158	Rectus capitis lateralis	Upper surface transverse process of atlas.	Jugular process occipital bone.	Flexes, supports head.
159	Rectus capitis post. major	Spine of epistopheus.	Occipital bone.	Extends head.
160	Rectus capitis post. minor	Posterior tubercle of atlas.	Occipital bone.	Extends head.
161	Rectus femoris	Ant. inf. spine of ilium; dorsum ilii.	Patella; tubercle of tibia.	Extends leg; flexes thigh.
162	Rectus oculi inferior	Circumference of optic foramen.	Under side of sclera.	Adducts, rotates eye downward and inward.
163	Rectus oculi lateralis	Margin optic foramen, sphenoidal fissure.	Outer side of sclera.	Abducts eyeball.
164	Rectus oculi medialis	Circumference of optic foramen.	Inner side of sclera.	Adducts eyeball.
165	Rectus oculi superior	Upper border optic foramen.	Upper aspect of sclera.	Adducts, rotates eye upward and inward.
166	Rhomboideus major	Spines of 2nd to 5th thoracic vertebrae.	Vertebral margin of scapula.	Retracts, elevates scapula.
167	Rhomboideus minor	Spines 7th cervical to 1st thoracic vertebrae.	Vertebral margin of scapula.	Retracts, elevates scapula.
168	Risorius	Fascia over masseter.	Skin at angle of mouth.	Draws angle of mouth laterally.
169	Rotatores spinae (11 pairs)	Transverse process of thoracic vertebrae below.	Lamina of thoracic vertebrae above.	Extend, rotate vertebral column.
170	Sartorius	Anterior superior spine of ilium.	Tibia, upper medial.	Flexes thigh and leg.
171	Scalenus anterior	Transverse processes 3rd to 6th cervical vertebrae.	Tubercle of first rib.	Raises 1st rib.
172	Scalenus medius	Transverse processes 2nd to 6th cervical vertebrae.	First rib.	Raises 1st rib.
173	Semimembranosus	Tubercles 4th to 6th cervical vertebrae.	Second rib.	Raises 1st and 2nd ribs.
174	Semispinalis capitis	Ischial tuberosity.	Medial condyle of tibia.	Flexes leg; extends thigh.
		Trans. processes upper 6 thoracic, lower 4 cervical vertebrae.	Occipital bone.	Extends head.

No.	Muscle	Origin	Insertion	Action
175	Semispinalis cervicis	Trans. processes upper 6 thoracic, lower 4 cervical vertebrae.	Spines 2nd to 5th cervical vertebrae.	Extends, rotates vertebral column.
176	Semispinalis dorsi	Trans. processes 6th to 10th thoracic vertebrae.	Spines last 2 cervical, first 4 thoracic vertebrae.	Extends, rotates vertebral column.
177	Semitendinosus	Ischial tuberosity.	Medial aspect proximal portion of tibia.	Flexes leg; extends thigh.
178	Serratus anterior	Upper 8 or 9 ribs.	Vertebral border of scapula.	Draws scapula forward; rotates scapula to raise shoulder in abduction of arm.
179	Serratus posterior inferior	Spines 2 lower thoracic, upper 2-3 lumbar vertebrae.	Inferior border of 4 lower ribs.	Lowers ribs in expiration.
180	Serratus posterior superior	Ligamentum nuchae; spines upper thoracic vertebrae.	Second to 5th ribs.	Raises ribs in inspiration.
181	Soleus	Fibula; popliteal fascia; tibia.	Calcaneus by tendo calcaneus (Achilles).	Planter flexes ankle joint.
182	Sphincter ani externus	Tip of coccyx; surrounding fascia.	Tendinous center of perineum.	Closes anus.
183	Sphincter pupillae	Circular fibers of iris.		Contracts pupil.
184	Sphincter urethrae membranaceae	Ramus of pubis.	Median raphé of urethra.	Compresses urethra.
185	Spinalis capitis	Spines upper thoracic, lower cervical vertebrae.	Occipital bone.	Extends head.
186	Spinalis cervicis	Spines lower cervical, upper thoracic vertebrae.	Spines 2nd to 4th cervical vertebrae.	Extends vertebral column.
187	Spinalis dorsi	Spines of lower 2 thoracic, upper 2 lumbar vertebrae.	Spines upper thoracic vertebrae.	Extends vertebral column.
188	Splenius capitis	Ligamentum nuchae; last cervical, upper thoracic vertebrae.	Occipital bone.	Extends, rotates head.
189	Splenius cervicis	Spinous processes 3rd to 6th thoracic vertebrae.	Transverse processes 2-3 upper cervical vertebrae.	Extends, rotates head and neck.
190	Stapedius	Interior of pyramid of tympanum.	Posterior surface of neck of stapes.	Retracts stapes.
191	Sternocleidomastoideus	Two heads, sternum and clavicle.	Mastoid process.	Flexes, rotates head.
192	Sternohyoideus	Manubrium of sternum.	Lower border of body of hyoid.	Depresses hyoid and larynx.
193	Sternothyroideus	Manubrium of sternum.	Thyroid cartilage.	Depresses thyroid cartilage.
194	Styloglossus	Styloid process.	Side of tongue.	Raises and retracts tongue.
195	Stylohyoideus	Styloid process.	Hyoid.	Draws hyoid and tongue upward.
196	Stylopharyngeus	Styloid process.	Lateral wall of pharynx.	Raises and dilates pharynx.
197	Subanconeus	Posterior distal surface of humerus.	Posterior aspect of elbow joint.	Pulls capsule back in elbow joint extension.
198	Subclavius	1st costal cartilage and rib.	Clavicle.	Depresses lateral end of clavicle.
199	Subcostales	Inner surface of ribs.	Inner surface 1st, 2nd, 3rd rib below.	Raises ribs in inspiration.
200	Subscapularis	Subscapular fossa of scapula.	Lesser tubercle of humerus.	Rotates humerus medially.
201	Supinator	Lat. epicondyle of humerus; ulna, elbow joint fascia.	Radius.	Supinates hand.
202	Supraspinatus	Supraspinous fossa of scapula.	Greater tubercle of humerus.	Abducts humerus.
203	Temporalis	Temporal fossa and fascia.	Coronoid process of mandible.	Closes jaws.
204	Tensor fasciae latae	Iliac crest.	Iliotibial band of fascia lata.	Flexes, abducts thigh.
205	Tensor tympani	Cartilaginous portion of auditory tube.	Manubrium of malleus.	Tenses membrana tympani.
206	Tensor veli palatini	Scaphoid fossa of sphenoid; wall of auditory tube.	Aponeurosis of soft palate.	Tenses soft palate; opens auditory tube.
207	Teres major	Axillary margin of scapula.	Crest of intertubercular sulcus of humerus.	Adducts, extends, medially rotates arm.
208	Teres minor	Axillary margin of scapula.	Greater tubercle of humerus.	Laterally rotates arm.
209	Thyro-arytenoideus	Lamina of thyroid cartilage.	Muscular process of arytenoid cartilage.	Relaxes, shortens vocal cords.
210	Thyro-epiglotticus	Lamina of thyroid cartilage.	Epiglottis.	Closes inlet of larynx.
211	Thyrohyoideus	Thyroid cartilage.	Lower border greater cornu of hyoid.	Raises and changes form of larynx.
212	Tibialis anterior	Tibia and interosseous membrane.	First cuneiform and metatarsal, dorsal.	Dorsiflexes and inverts foot.
213	Tibialis posterior	Fibula; tibia; interosseous membrane.	Bases metatarsals and tarsals, except talus.	Plantar flexes and inverts foot.
214	Transversus abdominis	Costal cartilages lower 6 ribs; lumbodorsal fascia; iliac crest; inguinal ligament.	Lines alba through rectus sheath; conjoined tendon to pubis.	Compresses abdominal viscera.
215	Transversus linguae	Median raphé of tongue.	Dorsum and sides of tongue.	Alters shape of tongue.
216	Transversus perinei profundus	Inferior ramus of ischium.	Median raphé of perineum.	Draws back central point of perineum.
217	Transversus perinei superficialis	Tuberosity of ischium.	Central tendon of perineum.	Tensor of central point of perineum.
218	Transversus thoracis	Mediastinal surface of xiphoid and body of sternum.	Second to 6th costal cartilage.	Narrows the chest.
219	Trapezius	Occipital bone; ligamentum nuchae; spines of 7th cervical and all thoracic vertebrae.	Clavicle; acromion; spine of scapula.	Rotates scapula to raise shoulder in abduction of arm; draws scapula backward.
220	Triangularis	Lower border of mandible.	Angle of mouth.	Pulls mouth corners downward.
221	Triceps brachii	Infraglenoid tuberosity; shaft of humerus; (three heads).	Olecranon of ulna.	Extends forearm; adducts, extends arm.
222	Uvulae	Posterior nasal spine.	Uvula.	Raises uvula.
223	Vastus intermedius	Anterior, lateral aspects of femur.	Patella; common tendon of quadriceps femoris.	Extends leg.
224	Vastus lateralis	Capsule of hip joint; lateral aspect of femur.	Patella; common tendon of quadriceps femoris.	Extends leg.
225	Vastus medialis	Medial aspect of femur.	Patella; common tendon of quadriceps femoris.	Extends leg.
226	Verticalis linguae	Dorsal aspect of tongue.	Sides and base of tongue.	Alters shape of tongue.
227	Vocalis	Thyroid cartilage.	Vocal process of arytenoid cartilage.	Shortens vocal cords.
228	Zygomaticus	Zygomatic bone in front of temporal process.	Angle of mouth.	Draws mouth backward, upward.

Part I: MORPHOLOGY
Numbers represent areas of Brodmann.

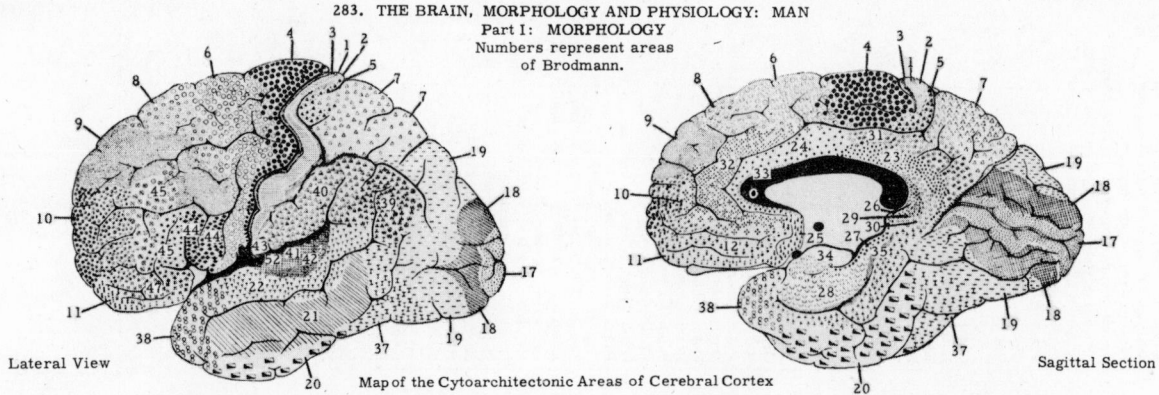

Lateral View   Map of the Cytoarchitectonic Areas of Cerebral Cortex   Sagittal Section

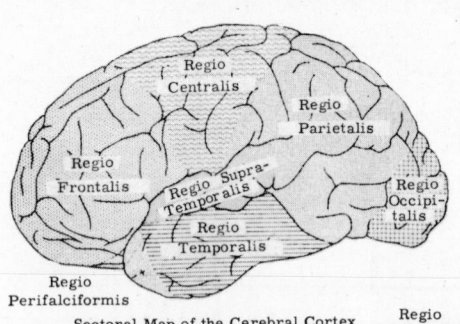

Sectoral Map of the Cerebral Cortex

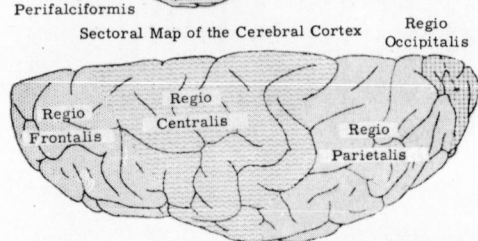

Median Sagittal Section Through Brain Stem

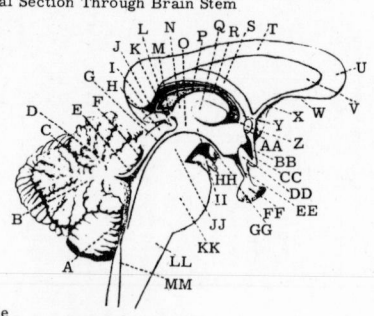

A=Epithelial roof and chorioid plexus of 4th ventricle
B=Inferior vermis of cerebellum
C=Fissura prima
D=Sup. verm. of cerebellum
E=4th ventricle
F=Anterior medullary velum
G=Cerebral aqueduct
H=Lamina quadrigemina
I=Splenium of corpus callosum
J=Pineal body
K=Posterior commissure
L=Suprapineal recess
M=Habenular commissure
N=Habenula
O=Hypothalamic sulcus
P=Chorioid plexus of 3rd ventricle
Q=Massa intermedia
R=Epithelial roof of 3rd ventricle
S=Body of fornix
T=Corpus callosum
U=Genu of corpus callosum
V=Septum pellucidum
W=Ros. of cor. callosum
X=Lamina rostralis
Y=Columna fornicis
Z=Interventricular foramen
AA=Anterior commissure
BB=Lamina terminalis

CC=Optic recess
DD=Optic chiasma
EE=Infandibulum
FF=Hypophysis
GG=Mammillary body
HH=Oculomotor nerve
II=Subthalamus
JJ=Tegmentum of mesencephalon
KK=Pons
LL=Medula
MM=Central canal

Part II: VARIOUS BRAIN REGIONS AND THEIR FUNCTIONS

	Region	General Functions	Sub-regions	Known Functions
			Telencephalon	
1	Cerebral cortex	Highest level of integration; symbolism, memory, forecasting.	Prefrontal, frontal, parietal, occipital, temporal.	Association: autonomic; general motor, sensory; visual; auditory.
2	Rhinencephalon	Olfaction, "visceral brain," emotion.	Olfactory bulb, cortex; amygdala; hippocampus; fornix; mammillary bodies.	Association: autonomic-visceral integration; olfaction.
3	Corpus striatum	Smoothing of motor behavior; inhibition of posture, movement patterns; extrapyramidal relay.	Caudate nucleus, putamen, globus pallidus.	Forebrain association centers; motor relay (globus pallidus) for putamen.
			Diencephalon	
4	Epithalamus		Habenular nucleus.	
5	Thalamus	Sensory relay to cortex; thalamocortical circuits.	Anterior, midline, medial, lateral, posterior, pulvinar, ventral.	Cortical relay nuclei: anterior, emotion(?); medial and ventral, sensory; pulvinar, gnostic and practic. Unspecific intralaminar nuclei. Basal ganglia relay ventromedian.
6	Metathalamus		Medial, lateral geniculate.	Medial: acoustic to supratemporal plane; lateral: visual to striate area.
7	Subthalamus		Subthalamic nucleus.	Hemiballismus.
8	Hypothalamus	Principal forebrain center for integration of visceral functions involving autonomic nervous system. /1/	Anterior, middle, lateral, posterior.	Generally anterior part trophotropic (parasympathetic); posterior part ergotrophic (orthosympathetic).
9	MESENCEPHALON	Postural reflexes; nuclei for cranial nerves.	Superior colliculus, inferior colliculus, substantia nigra, red nucleus, tegmentum, reticular formation (part of), basis peduncles, nucleus N III, IV, V (part of).	Relay for visual reflexes (protective), auditory reflexes, extrapyramidal junction of striatal and cortical influences; contributes to righting reflexes, tracts; facilitatory and inhibitory influences on motor performance.
			Metencephalon	
10	Cerebellum	Maintenance of posture; equilibrium; coordination, smoothing of complex movements.	Corpus cerebelli, anterior posterior lobe; flocculonodular lobe.	"Vestibulocerebellum" (equilibration, maintenance of posture); postural reflexes, stabilizing, smoothing more complex movements initiated in cortex, facilitation of posture change.
11	Pons		Pontine nucleus, reticular formation, cerebellar peduncles, tracts, nucleus V (part of).	Relay between cerebro-cerebellar, motor inhibitory areas.
			Myelencephalon	
12	Medulla oblongata	Reflex center for cardiac vasomotor, vomiting, deglutition, respiratory, gustatory, facial reflexes.	Nucleus V (part of), IX, XI, XII; inferior olivary, tracts; reticular nuclei of medullary tegmentum.	Posture.

Left margin region labels: PROSENCEPHALON (rows 1–8), RHOMBENCEPHALON (rows 10–12)

/1/ Energy and water exchange; sexual function; sleep; vasomotor.

Part III: META- AND DORSAL THALAMUS

A = associational; D = diffuse associational; I = internal relay; E = external relay; U = unclassified or doubtful.

	Nucleus	Function	Afferents	Efferents
1	Medialis dorsalis	A	Principal: some from medio ventral region (hypothalamus).	Frontal granular cortex.
2	Lateralis posterior	A	Principal: parietal cortex. Diffuse: sensorimotor, limbic, auditory, visual, frontal cortices. Nuclei, Lines 5-9 (q.v.).	Parietal field.
3	Lateralis anterior	A	Principal: parietal cortex. Diffuse: sensorimotor, auditory, visual cortices. Nuclei, Lines 5-9 (q.v.).	
4	Pulvinar	A	Principal: parietal association. Diffuse: frontal, sensorimotor, limbic, auditory, visual cortices. Subcortical: ventral posterior nucleus of thalamus. Nuclei, Lines 5-9 (q.v.).	Posterior parietal and temporal cortex, superior parietal lobule, posterior Sylvian region, supramarginal gyrus, temporo-occipital region, area 18, superior colliculus and pretectum, posterior parietal, temporal and occipital (parasensory) fields.
5	Centrum medianum	D	Subcortical: reticular formation, other intralaminar[1] thalamic nuclei.	Subcortical: caudate nucleus, corpus striatum.
6	Centralis medialis			
7	Centralis lateralis	D	Reticular formation. Intralaminar thalamic nuclei.	Cortical associational areas: frontal, cinguate, orbital. Caudate nucleus.
8	Ventralis anterior			
9	Reticularis anterior	D	Reticular formation; other intralaminar thalamic nuclei.	
10	Anterodorsalis	I	Corresponding opposite nucleus.	Retrosplenial region(?).
11	Anteromedialis	I	Mammillothalamic tract; limbic cortex. Nuclei, Lines 5-9, (q.v.).	Anterior gyrus cinguli.
12	Anteroventralis	I	Subcortical: nuclei, Lines 5-9, (q.v.); mammillothalamic tract. Cortical: gyrus cinguli.	Posterior gyrus cinguli.
13	Ventral anterior	I	Principal: globus pallidus. Diffuse from orbital, parietal, frontal, sensorimotor, limbic cortices. Nuclei, Lines 5-9 (q.v.).	Globus pallidus; prefrontal cortex.
14	Ventralis lateralis	I	Principal: superior cerebellar peduncle.	Precentral motor cortex; areas 4 and 6. Brachium conjunctivum.
15	Ventral medial	I		Globus pallidus; lateral frontal cortex.
16	Medial geniculate body	E	Inferior colliculi and parabigeminal body; auditory cortex.	Auditory cortex; parvicellular and magnocellular to temporal cortex in lower wall of Sylvian fissure.
17	Lateral geniculate body	E	Ganglion cell layer of retina.	
18	Ventral posterolateral	E	Medial lemniscus; spinothalamic tracts; sensorimotor cortex.	Sensorimotor cortex.
19	Ventral posteromedial	E	Trigeminal lemniscus; trigeminal thalamic tract.	Sensorimotor cortex.
20	Reticularis lateralis (posterior)	U	Unclassified or doubtful.	Cortex.
21	Midline[2]	D/U	Spinothalamic tract; medial lemniscus.	Hypothalamus; basal ganglia; lateral thalamus nuclei.

/1/ Denotes nuclei not only adjacent to internal medullary lamina of thalamus but also others (such as midline nuclei, reticularis anterior and ventralis anterior), which when stimulated can evoke cortical and intrathalamic recruiting responses. /2/ Midline nuclei: rhomboideus, reuniens, paracentralis, parafascicularis, paraventricularis (anterior and posterior), parataenialis.

Part IV: VARIOUS CORTICAL CEREBRAL REGIONS AND THEIR FUNCTIONS

	Function	Gross Region	Diagram	Area[1]	Principal Connected Pathways and Areas		Function	Gross Region	Diagram	Area[1]	Principal Connected Pathways and Areas
1	Vision	Occipital (striate cortex)		17(OC)	Optic radiation; lateral geniculate body of the thalamus; optic tract; chiasm; optic nerve; retina.	5	Equilibration	Temporal (first convolution)		22(TA) (?)	Probably similar to auditory mechanism.
						6	Olfaction	Temporal (Piriform area)		28(HB) 34(HA)	Lateral root; olfactory tract; olfactory bulb; fila olfactoria.
2	Visual elaboration	Occipital (parastriate) and Parietal (preoccipital)		18(OB) 19(OA)	Reticular formation of brain stem; areas PH, FC, LC$_2$ and TE of Economo; areas 37, 8, 23, 21 of Brodman.	7	Somatic sensation	Parietal (post central convolution)		3(PA) 1(PB) 2(PC)	Connected through posteroventral nuclei with mesial and trigeminal fillets and spinothalamic tract; dorsal root; sensory root ganglion; peripheral sensory nerves.
3	Hearing (auditosensory)	Temporal (Heschl's gyrus)		41(TC)	Auditory radiation; medial geniculage body inferior colliculus; nucleus of lateral lemniscus; superior olive: dorsal and ventral cochlear nucleus in brain stem; cochlear nerve; spiral ganglion; hair cells in Organ of Corti.	8	Sensory elaboration (leg skills)	Parietal (superior parietal lobule)		5(PE$_m$) 7a(PE$_p$)	Association fibers with areas PC, FD$_p$, FEB$_m$, OA, FC, FD$_\Delta$ of Economo; areas 1, 44, 19, 8, 46 of Brodmann.
4	Hearing (auditopsychic)	Temporal		42(TB) 22(TA)							

/1/ Areas of Brodmann are given numerically, followed in parentheses by associated areas of Economo. The latter have literal designations.

Part IV: VARIOUS CORTICAL CEREBRAL REGIONS AND THEIR FUNCTIONS (Concluded)

	Function	Gross Region	Diagram	Area[1]	Principal Connected Pathways and Areas		Function	Gross Region	Diagram	Area[1]	Principal Connected Pathways and Areas
9	Sensory elaboration (arm skills)	Parietal (inferior parietal lobule)		40(PF) 39(PG)	Association fibers with areas PC, TB and OA of Economo; areas 1, 42, 19 of Brodmann.	13	Elaboration of concious thought	Frontal		9, 10, 11, 12, 13, 14(FD and variants) 24(LA)	Orbitofrontal cortex (areas 9, 10, 11, 12 of Brodmann) and posterior and medial orbital gyri (areas 13 and 14 of Walker) are connected to dorsomedial nuclei of thalamus which has hypothalamic connections. The anterior cingulate gyrus (area 24) is projection area of anterior nuclei of thalamus.
10	Speech (motor)	Frontal (3rd convolution, dominant hemisphere) Broca's area		44(FCB$_m$)	Receives afferents from PB of Economo, area 3 of Brodmann, sends impulses to areas FA and PE of Economo, areas 4 and 5 of Brodmann.						
11	Speech (sensory) (Gnosia)	Parietal (lower parietal lobule, dominant hemisphere)		40(PF) 39(PG)	Association fibers with areas PC, TB, OA of Economo; areas 1, 42, 19 of Brodmann.	14	Motion	Frontal (precentral area, motor and premotor)		4(FA) 6(FB)	Internal capsule, pyramidal decussation, corticospinal tracts, anterior horn cells, motor roots. Connected by way of lateroventral nucleus and the superior cerebellar peduncle with the spinocerebellar afferents.
12	Memory	Temporal		Areas not definite							

/1/ Areas of Brodmann are given numerically, followed in parentheses by associated areas of Economo. The latter have literal designations.

Part V: BRAIN TRACTS
C = cervical; S = sacral; T = thoracic.

	Tract	Origin	Termination	Pathway	Function
1	Acoustico-optic	Inferior colliculus.	Homolateral superior colliculus.	Diffuse.	Unknown.
2	Allen's fasciculus[1]	Solitary nucleus.	Ventral column: C3-T6.	Lateral funiculus along dorsolateral edge of ventral column.	Associated with respiratory control.
3	Part of central tegmental fasciculus	Central gray of cerebral aqueduct.	About sac of inferior olive.	Flattened bundle running through tegmentum, oblique to horizontal plane, lateral to medial longitudinal fasciculus	
4	Arcuate fasciculus	Cerebral cortex of basal frontal lobes.	Cortex of temporal, lower parietal and occipital regions	Through base of angular gyrus into interior and middle frontal gyrus; in parietal and frontal opercula over upper border of insula.	Association bundle.
5	Bigeminopontine	Nucleus of parabigeminal body.	Pontine nuclei (lateral cells).	Lateral to medial lemniscus to middle strata of pons.	
6	Central acoustic	Contralateral and homolateral cochlear nucleus and olivary complex; nuclei of central acoustic tract.	Medial geniculate body.	With lateral lemniscus to ventrolateral surface of inferior colliculus; runs in brachium of inferior colliculus.	Auditory.
7	Cortico-habenular fibers	Hippocampus (and cinguate gyrus).	Medial habenular nucleus.	Via fornix and medullary stria of diencephalon.	
8	Corticospinal, lateral	Cerebral cortex.	Contralateral ventral column.	Internal capsule; cerebral peduncle; decussation of pyramids, lateral corticospinal tract.	Motor.
9	Corticospinal, ventral	Cerebral cortex.	Ipsilateral ventral column.	Internal capsule; peduncle, ventral corticospinal tract about anterior median fissure of cord.	Motor.
10	Cortico-tegmental fasciculus	Anterior central gyrus.	Diffuse tegmental nucleus.	Intermingled with corticospinal fibers, mostly in lateral 2/5 of cerebral peduncle.	
11	Cuneate fasciculus	Dorsal root ganglia C 1-T6.	Cuneate nucleus.	Lateral portion of dorsal funiculus above T6.	Proprioception. Discriminative touch (upper extremities).
12	Dorsolateral fasciculus (Lissauer)	Dorsal root ganglia.	Substantia gelatinosa (Rolando), and nucleus proprius within 2-4 segments.	Dorsolateral to substantia gelatinosa of dorsal horn of gray matter.	Pain, temperature and light touch.
13	Fastigiobulbar fasciculus	Fastigial nuclei.	Tegmental motor nuclei	Mingled with uncinate fasciculus of Russel in juxtarestiform body.	Cerebellar inhibitory path from anterior lobe to inhibitory region of bulbar reticular substance.
14	Fastigiospinal fasciculus	Fastigial nuclei.	Upper cervical segments of cord.	By way of spinal root of vestibular nerve.	Vestibular reflex connections to cervical musculature.
15	Fastigiovestibular fasciculus	Fastigial nucleus.	Contralateral superior, lateral, medial and spinal vestibular nuclei.	Through brachium conjunctivum in front of dentate nucleus, forming three limbs to distribute to vestibular nuclei.	
16	Frontal fasciculus, superior (Burdach's)	Basal frontal regions of cortex.	Temporal, lower parietal and occipital cortex.	Dorsal to insula.	Association fibers.
17	Frontopontine fasciculus	Posterior portions of superior and middle frontal gyri bordering on precentral gyrus.	Pontine nuclei.	Extreme medial and lateral portions of cerebral peduncle.	Cortical relay fibers to middle lobe of cerebellum.
18	Fasciculus gracilis (Goll)	Dorsal root ganglia T6-S5.	Nucleus gracilis.	Medial portion of dorsal funiculus.	Proprioception. Discriminative touch (lower extremities).
19	Habenulo-peduncular fasciculus[2]	Habenular nuclei.	Interpeduncular nucleus.	Runs ventrolaterally; arches beneath centrum medianum through medial border or red nucleus and down along midventral line.	

/1/ Solitario spinal. /2/ Retroflex bundle of Meynert.

	Tract	Origin	Termination	Pathway	Function
20	Habenulo-tegmental	Habenular nuclei.	Dorsal tegmental nucleus.		
21	Descending hypothalamic[3]	Dorsomedial nuclei, posterior and lateral hypothalamic areas and perifornical areas.	Autonomic cells in medulla oblongata and intermediolateral cell column of cord.	Decends between mammillary body and red nucleus to ipsilateral reticular formation; dorsal to substantia nigra, then to region of vestibular fiber complex.	
22	Interfascicular fasciculus (Schultze)	Descending fibers of posterior funiculus.	Nucleus proprius of gray matter.	Between and mingled with fasciculus gracilis and cuneatus.	Reflex collaterals.
23	Interstitiospinal (of Cajal)	Mesencephalon, region of posterior commissure.	Intermediolateral cell column of cord (C8-T1).	Descends along ventromedian sulcus of cervical cord.	
24	Laterocerebellar	Lateral nucleus of medulla.	Cerebellum.	Runs with external arcuate fibers.	
25	Longitudinal fasciculus, dorsal (Schutz)	Hypothalamus and dorsal tegmental nucleus.	Somato-motor and autonomic motor nuclei of brain stem.	Continued into ventral fasciculus proprius of cord.	
26	Longitudinal fasciculus, inferior	Occipital cortex.	Temporal cortex.		Association fibers.
27	Longitudinal fasciculus, medial	Mesencephalon, at level of posterior commisural nuclei.	Through medulla, continued in cord as sulcomarginal fasiculus of Marie.	Bilateral, about midventral line between central gray matter and tectospinal fasiculus (in medulla).	Contains vestibular reflex fibers, fibers from reticular nuclei, abducens nucleus.
28	Mammillary fasciculus	Medial mammillary nuclei.	Anterior thalamic nuclei and tegmentum.	Runs dorsally from mammillary bodies, then bifurcates; one limb continues dorsally, the other caudally.	
29	Mammillotegmental fasciculus	Medial and lateral mammillary nuclei.	Tegmentum.	Initially a component of the principal mammillary fasciculus which it leaves to run caudally.	
30	Mammillothalamic fasciculus (Vicq d'Azyr)	Medial and lateral mammillary nuclei.	Anterior nuclear mass of thalamus.	Dorsorostrally through medial thalamic wall.	
31	Olfactohabenular	Basal olfactory region, olfactory striatum, and medial part of amygdaloid complex.	Lateral habenular nucleus.	Lateral portion of medullary stria of diencephalon.	
32	Olfactopeduncular	Region about olfactory tubercle and putamen.	Region of substantia nigra.	Caudally beneath pallidum; ventral to internal capsule; medial border of peduncle.	
33	Olfactory	Olfactory bulb.	In three stria; medial, intermediate, and lateral olfactory stria.	Lies between gyrus rectus and medial orbital gyrus, covering olfactory sulcus.	Olfaction.
34	Olivo-cochlear bundle	Nuclei of olivary complex.	Organ of Corti.	Via auditory nerve.	Inhibition of neural response from Organ of Corti.
35	Olivospinal (Helweg)	Inferior olive.	Spinal gray, ventral column.	At junction of lateral and ventral funiculi.	
36	Optic	Ganglion cells of retina.	Lateral geniculate and/or supperior colliculus.	Tract encircles thalamus ventrally.	Vision.
37	Perpendicular fasciculus	Inferior parietal lobule.	Fusiform gyrus.	Obliquely dorsomedially and ventrolaterally.	Association.
38	Probst's	Sensory cells associated with nucleus V in area of cerebral aqueduct or lateral reticular nucleus of the mesencephalon.	Intercalated nucleus and dorsal vagal nucleus.	Ventrolateral to solitary fasciculus and dorsomedial to the nucleus of the spinal tract of V.	Appears to link various parts of the trigeminal system; relates masticatory movements with salivation.
39	Reticulospinal fasciculus, lateral, direct	Reticular substance.	Gray matter of cord.	Lies in region of overlap of lateral corticospinal and rubrospinal tracts.	Extrapyramidal aspects of motor function.
40	Reticulospinal fasciculus, ventral, crossed	Reticular substance.	Gray matter of cord.	Ventrolateral to ventral corticospinal fibers.	Inhibitory pyramidal motor function.
41	Rubrospinal	Red nucleus.	Gray matter of cord.	Ventromedial to, and overlapping, lateral corticospinal tract.	Extrapyramidal function in man obscure.
42	Septomarginal fasciculus	Collaterals of dorsal funiculus fibers (fasciculus cuneatus).	Gray matter of cord.	Along posterior median sulcus in middle of posterior funiculus.	Proprioceptive reflex connections.
43	Solitary fasciculus	Fibers from cranial nerves VII, IX, and X.	Solitary nucleus.	Dorsomedial to spinal root of V; extends from level of medullary stria to caudal end of medulla.	Visceral afferent; oral end concerned with taste.
44	Spinal of trigeminal nerve	Cells of origin in semilunar ganglion.	Nucleus of spinal trigeminal tract.	Medial to restiform body; in position of Lissauer's zone and gelatinous substance of spinal cord.	Pain and temperature from face region.
45	Spinocerebellar fasciculus, ventral	Border cells about medial border of centralateral ventral column and cells about dorsal nucleus of Clark.	Vermis of anterior lobe of cerebellum.	On periphery of cord ventral to dorsal spinocerebellar, and lateral to lateral spinothalamic tract.	Exteroceptive.
46	Spinocerebellar fasciculus, dorsal (Flechsig)	Dorsal horn and dorsal nucleus of Clark.	Cortex of anterior cerebellar lobe, uvula and pyramis of vermis.	On periphery of lateral funiculus of cord.	Proprioceptive and exteroceptive.
47	Spinoölivary (Helweg)	Dorsal horn of spinal cord.	Inferior olive.	Ventral and superficial part of lateral funiculus between lateral and ventral spinothalamic tracts.	

/3/ Not yet demonstrated anatomically.

283. THE BRAIN, MORPHOLOGY AND PHSIOLOGY: MAN (Concluded)
Part V: BRAIN TRACTS (Concluded)
C = cervical; S = sacral; T = thoracic.

	Tract	Origin	Termination	Pathway	Function
48	Spinothalamic, lateral	Dorsal horn of gray matter.	Tectum of midbrain.	Ventral and superficial part of lateral funiculus.	
		Proper nucleus of contra-lateral dorsal horn.	Posterolateral ventral nucleus of thalamus.	Lateral funiculus just medial to ventral spinocerebellar tract.	Pain and temperature from limbs and trunk.
49	Spinothalamic, ventral	Proper nucleus of contra-lateral dorsal horn.	Posterolateral ventral nucleus of thalamus.	Lateral portion of ventral funiculus.	Light touch.
50	Subcallosal fasciculus	Frontal cortex (Brodmann area 9).	Striate body.	Dorsal to caudate nucleus below radiation of corpus callosum.	
51	Tectospinal (Lowenthal)	Superior colliculus.	Spinal gray matter.	Ventromedial portion of ventral funiculus.	
52	Tegmental fasciculus central	Variable composition.		In reticular formation of medulla lateral to crossed vestibulospinal tract.	
53	Thalamic fasciculus	Fibers of brachium conjunctivum going to thalamus through tegmental field of Forel. Also fibers from globus pallidus.	Pallium. Thalamus.	Ventrally through Forel's field H1, between mammillothalamic tract and lenticular fasciculus.	
54	Vestibulofastigial	Vestibular nuclei and spinal nucleus of V.	Fastigial nucleus and vermian cortex.	Between restiform body and periventricular gray matter; in juxtarestiform body.	
55	Vestibulo-flocculo-nodular	Cells of origin in vestibular ganglion (Scarpa).	Cortex of flocculus and nodulus of cerebellum.		Vestibular.
56	Vestibuloglobose	Vestibular nuclei and spinal nucleus of V.	Globose nucleus and vermian cortex.	Between restiform body and periventricular gray matter in juxtarestiform body.	
57	Vestibulospinal, crossed, ventral	Medial, inferior and spinal vestibular nuclei.	Gray matter of cord.	Medial portion of ventral funiculus in sulcomarginal fasiculus of Marie.	Vestibular reflex.
58	Vestibulospinal, direct, lateral	Lateral vestibular nucleus.	Gray matter of cord.	Ventrolateral part of ventral funiculus and ventromedial portion of lateral funiculus.	Vestibular reflex.

284. ENCEPHALIC INDICES, EVOLUTIONARY SIGNIFICANCE: VERTEBRATES
Adapted from F. Tilney's "The Brain From Ape to Man," New York: Paul B. Hober, 1928.

	Animal	Volume Index			Weight Index		
		Forebrain %	Midbrain %	Hindbrain %	Forebrain %	Midbrain %	Hindbrain %
	Index: 82 and Above	Hands, Fingers, Fingernails					
1	Man (Homo sapiens)	88	1	11	87	1	12
2	Gorilla (Gorilla gorilla)	84	2	14	84	2	14
3	Orangutan (Simia satyrus)	83	5	12	83	5	12
4	Monkey, Indian (Macaca rhesus)	83	2	15	84	2	14
5	Marmoset (Callithrix jacchus)	83	2	15	83	2	15
6	Gibbon (Hylobates hoolock)	82	2	16	82	2	16
	Index: 70 to 80	Paws, Hoofs, Claws					
7	Dog (Canis familiaris)	80	7	13	80	5	15
8	Cattle (Bos taurus)	80	2	18	80	2	18
9	Horse (Equus caballus)	80	2	18	80	2	18
10	Camel (Camelus bactrianus)	79	2	19	79	2	19
11	Cat (Felis catus)	77	6	17	75	4	21
12	Anteater, giant (Myrmecophaga sp)	75	6	19	73	5	22
13	Elephant (Elephas indicus)	72	2	26	71	2	27
14	Sloth, three-toed (Bradypus tridactylus)	70	10	20	70	10	20
	Index: 20 to 60	Wings, Fins, Paddles					
15	Ostrich (Rhea americana)	58	16	26	60	13	27
16	Turtle, soft-shelled (Aspidonectes ferox)	57	15	28	53	20	27
17	Frog (Rana sylvatica)				21	37	42
18	Codfish (Gadus morrhua)	20	40	40	20	40	40
19	Dogfish (Squalus acanthias)				23	27	50

285. THE BRAIN, PLANIMETRIC COEFFICIENTS: PRIMATES
Planimetric coefficient = ratio of planimetric measurement of the structure adapted to that of the total axis hemisection at a fixed magnification.
Adapted from F. Tilney's "The Brain From Ape to Man," New York: Paul B. Hober, 1928.

	Structure	Man	Gorilla	Chimpanzee	Orang	Gibbon	Baboon	Macaque	Mycetes	Marmoset	Lemur	Tarsier
1	Pyramid	.183	.161	.172	.160	.138	.143	.147	.137	.064	.110	.032
2	Pontine nuclei	.550	.480	.400	.300	.200	.164	.150	.103	.095	.055	.057
3	Cerebral peduncle	.321	.187	.223	.110	.110	.190	.169	.144	.079	.086	.017
4	Inferior olive	.226	.186	.174	.172	.155	.125	.128	.120	.038	.060	.042
5	Nucleus dentatus	.176	.152	.136	.160	.134	.165	.155	.130	.077	.110	.059
6	Nucleus globosus	.023	.0095	.018	.015	.020	.023	.014	.032	.050	.032	.037
7	Red nucleus	.128	.096	.086	.087	.051	.060	.057	.081	.044	.012	.034
8	Superior cerebellar peduncle	.088	.047	.047	.064	.063	.044	.046	.036	.048	.033	.032
9	Inferior colliculus	.070	.111	.132	.131	.130	.155	.175	.182	.210	.223	.337
10	Superior colliculus	.104	.140	.125	.124	.132	.173	.158	.161	.154	.140	.230
11	Nucleus of Goll	.064	.086	.050	.048	.034	.086	.076	.131	.068	.041	.026
12	Nucleus of Burdach	.100	.081	.073	.093	.068	.065	.086	.113	.043	.049	.029
13	Nucleus of Dieters	.065	.072	.077	.054	.085	.060	.075	.114	.077	.082	.180
14	Nucleus of Schwalbe	.075	.070	.080	.055	.092	.095	.087	.090	.060	.045	.062

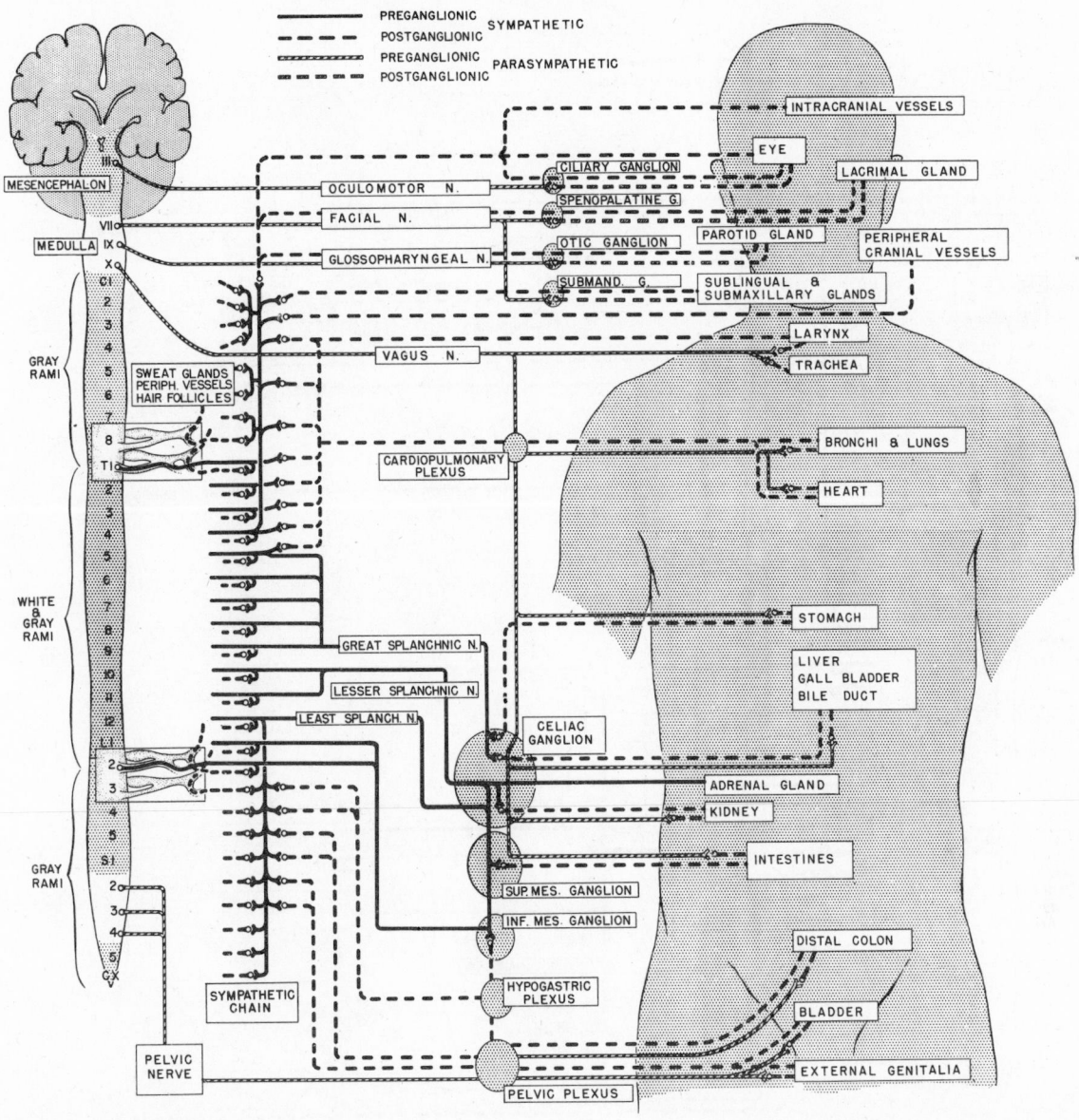

Division		Preganglionic Neurons	Outflow	Ganglia	Distribution	Effects of Increased Activity
1	S	Intermediolateral column, in spinal cord, C 8 to L 3.	Thoracic, lumbar nerves.	Sympathetic trunk.	Thoracic viscera, cardiovascular system, peripheral smooth muscle, sweat glands.	Inhibition of bronchial and gastrointestinal musculature; cardiac acceleration; increased vascular tonus, activation of peripheral smooth muscle and sweat glands.
				Abdominal and pelvic plexuses.	Abdominal, pelvic viscera and blood vessels.	Inhibition of visceral musculature; increased splanchnic vascular tonus.
2	P	Edinger-Westphal nucleus.	Cranial nerve III.	Ciliary.	Intraocular muscles.	Activation of ciliary muscle and circular muscle of iris.
3		Salivatory nuclei.	Cranial nerves VII, IX.	Sphenopalatine, otic, submandibular lingual.	Smooth muscle and glands.	Activation of salivary glands and glands in mucous membranes.
4		Vagus nucleus.	Cranial nerves X, XI.	Cardiac, pulmonary, enteric	Heart, some blood vessels, visceral musculature, glands.	Cardiac inhibition; activation of bronchial and gastrointestinal musculature and glands.
5		Visceral nuclei in sacral segments of spinal cord.	S2, S3, S4.	Pelvic.	Pelvic viscera.	Activation of pelvic visceral musculature; control of bladder sphincter.
6	E[1]	Vagus nuclei.	Vagus nerves.	Enteric.	E musculature, glands.	Activation of E musculature and glands.
7		Visceral nuclei in sacral segments of spinal cord.	S2, S3, S4.	Enteric.	Musculature and glands of colon and rectum.	Activation of musculature and glands of colon and rectum.

/1/ Actually a subdivision of P.

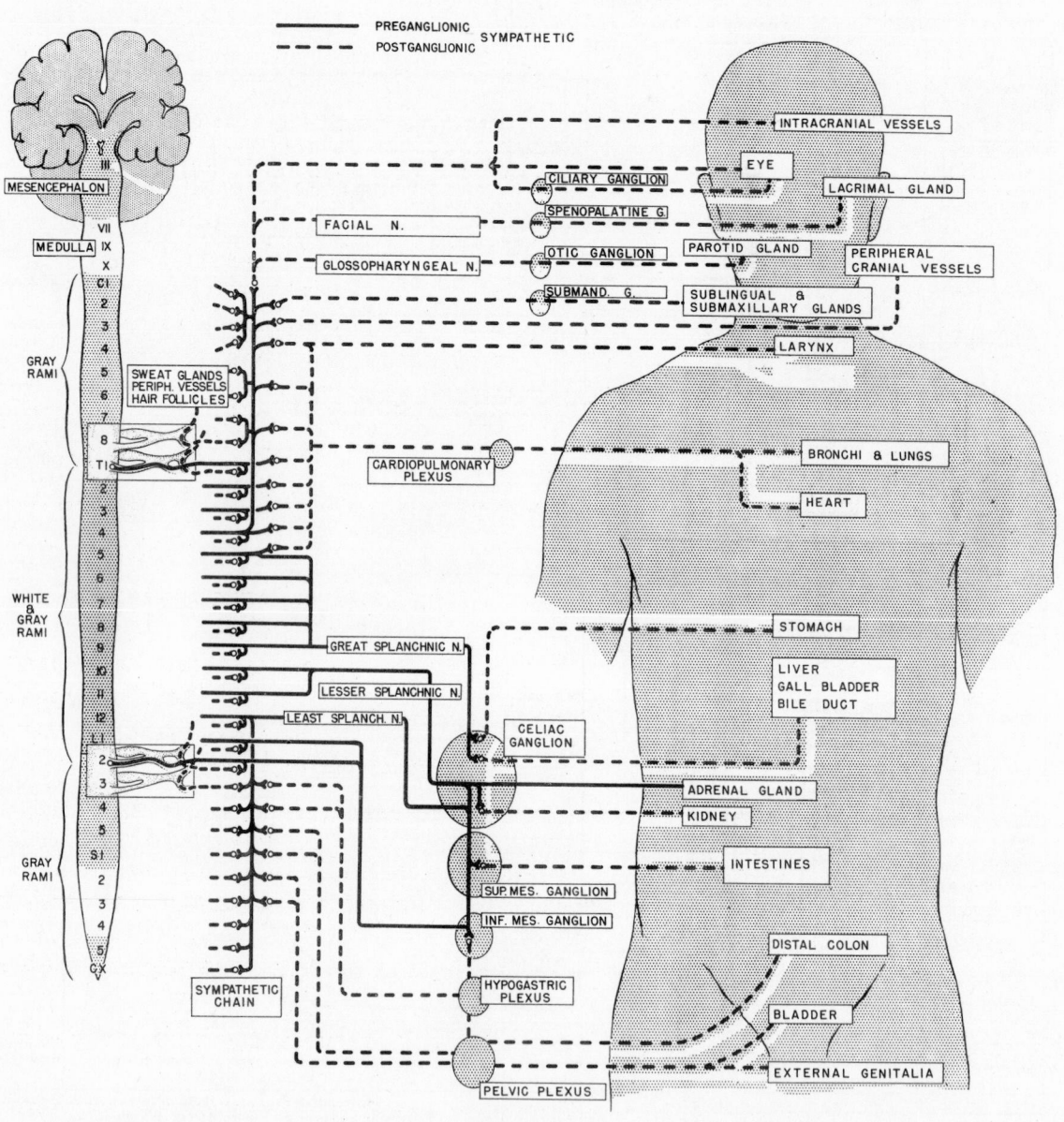

SC = sympathetic chain; WRC = white ramus communicans.

	Organ	Species	Effector	Preganglionic Neurone		Postganglionic Neurone		Action
				Cell Body	Pathway	Cell Body	Pathway	
1	Eye	Man	Dilator pupillae.	T1,2,3(Oc.C8&T4).	WRC, SC.	Superior cervical ganglion.	Carotid plexus -- short and long ciliary nerve.	Dilatation.
2				C8, T1, 2.				
3		Cat					Superior carotid nerve; ophthalmic nerve; ciliary nerve.	
4		Man	Muscle orbitalis.	T1, 2, 3.			Carotid plexus; ophthalmic nerve.	(?).
5		Cat	Bulbar, conjunctival vessels.	T2, 3, 4, 5.			Superior carotid nerve; ophthalmic nerve; ciliary nerve.	Vaso-constriction.
6			Nictitating membrane.	T1, 2, 3, 4.				Retraction.
7	Lacrimal gland	Man	Blood vessels.	T1, 2, 3.	WRC, SC.	Superior cervical ganglion.	Internal carotid plexus and branches.	Vaso-constriction.

Part II: SYMPATHETIC CONNECTIONS (Continued)

SC = sympathetic chain; WRC = white ramus communicans.

	Organ	Species	Effector	Preganglionic Neurone		Postganglionic Neurone		Action
				Cell Body	Pathway	Cell Body	Pathway	
8	Heart	Man	Mostly ventricular muscle, some auricular.	T1, 2, 3, 4, 5.	WRC, SC.	Superior cervical ganglion; middle cervical ganglion; inferior cervical ganglion; stellate ganglion; upper 2 or 3 thoracic ganglia.	Superior cervical cardiac nerve; middle cervical cardiac nerve; inferior cervical cardiac nerve; cardiac plexus.	Augmentation and acceleration.
9		Dog	Mostly ventricular muscle, some auricular.	T1-4.	WRC, SC.	Middle cervical ganglion.	Middle cardio-sympathetic nerve (accelerator nerve).	Augmentation and acceleration.
10		Cat		T1, 2-4, 5.		Stellate ganglion.	Cardio-accelerator nerve; coronary arteries; ventricles.	
11	Coronary artery	Man	Smooth muscle.	T1, 3, 4, 5.	WRC, SC.	Superior cervical ganglion; middle cervical ganglion; inferior cervical ganglion; stellate ganglion; and upper 2 or 3 thoracic ganglia.	Superior cervical cardiac nerve; middle cervical cardiac nerve; inferior cervical cardiac nerve; cardiac plexus.	Dilatation.
12	Blood vessels	Man	Meningeal arteries.	T1, 2.	WRC, SC.	Superior cervical ganglion.	External carotid plexus; middle meningeal artery.	Vasoconstriction.
13			Cerebral arteries.				Internal carotid plexus and branches.	
14			Vertebral system of brain.			Stellate ganglion.	Vertebral plexus.	
15	Blood vessels, sweat glands, and pilo-erection muscles	Man	Head, neck.	T1, 2, 3 (Oc. C8 & T4).	WRC, SC.	Superior cervical ganglion.	Gray rami to cervical plexus.	Vasoconstriction, sweating, pilo-erection.
16			Upper limb.	T1, 2-9, 10.		Superior cervical ganglion; middle cervical ganglion, inferior cervical ganglion; stellate ganglion.	Gray rami; brachial plexus and subclavian artery.	
17			Thoracic and upper abdominal wall.	T2-10.		Middle cervical ganglion; inferior cervical ganglion; stellate ganglion; upper thoracic ganglia.	Gray rami; intercostal nerves.	Sweating, pilo-erection.
18			Lower limb, trunk.	T6-L2.		Lumbar 1-4; sacral 1-3.	Gray rami; lumbar and sacral nerves.	
19	Adrenal medulla	Man	Cells of medulla.	T5-9, 10-L1, 2.	WRC, SC. (splanchnic).	Cells of adrenal medulla.	No postganglionic pathway.	Secretion.
20	Spleen	Dog	Smooth muscle of capsule, trabeculae and artery.	T5, 6-8, 9-12.	WRC, SC (splanchnic).	Thoracic ganglia 6-11, and celiac plexus.	Splenic nerve; celiac plexus; plexus on splenic artery.	Spleno-, vasoconstriction.
21			Splenic veins.	T5.		Stellate ganglion.	Gray rami; phrenic nerve; plexus on splenic artery.	Vasoconstriction(?).
22	Lung	Man	Trachea, bronchi	T2-4.	WRC, SC.	Inferior cervical, stellate, and upper 4 thoracic ganglia.	Cardiac accelerator -- deep cardiac and pulmonary plexus.	Tracheal, bronchial, dilatation.
23			Blood vessels.					Vasoconstriction.
24		Cat	Trachea, bronchi, blood vessels.	T3-7.				Tracheal, bronchial dilatations.
25	Submaxillary, sublingual glands	Man	Gland, vessels.	T1, 2, 3.	WRC, SC.	Superior cervical ganglion.	External carotid plexus and branches.	Vasoconstriction; weak secretion.
26	Parotid gland	Man	Gland, vessels.	T1, 2, 3.	WRC, SC.	Superior cervical ganglion.	External carotid plexus and branches.	Vasoconstriction; weak secretion(?).
27	Lower esophagus	Man	Smooth muscle.	T1-3, 4-6.	WRC, SC (great splanchnic).	Inferior or stellate, upper thoracic, celiac ganglia.	Esophageal rami, aortic plexus; left gastric, phrenic nerves.	Inhibits peristalsis.
28	Cardiac sphincter	Man	Smooth muscle.	T1-3, 4-6.	WRC, SC (great splanchnic).	Inferior or stellate, upper thoracic, celiac ganglia.	Esophageal rami, aortic plexus; left gastric, phrenic nerves.	Contraction.
29	Stomach	Man	Smooth muscle, gland.	T5, 6-10, 11.	WRC, SC (splanchnic).	Celiac ganglion.	Accompanies gastric artery.	Inhibits peristalsis.
30			Pyloric sphincter.					Contraction.
31			Blood vessels.					Vasoconstriction.
32	Pancreas	Man	Gland.	T5, 6-10, 11.	WRC, SC (splanchnic).	Celiac ganglion.	Accompanies pancreatic artery.	Secretion(?).
33			Blood vessels.					Vasoconstriction.
34	Liver	Man	Blood vessels.	T5, 6, 7-10.	WRC, SC (splanchnic).	Celiac ganglion.	Periarterial plexus of hypogastric artery.	Vasoconstriction.

Part II: SYMPATHETIC CONNECTIONS (Concluded)

SC = sympathetic chain; WRC = white ramus communicans.

No.	Organ	Species	Effector	Preganglionic Neurone Cell Body	Pathway	Postganglionic Neurone Cell Body	Pathway	Action
35	Gallbladder	Man	Smooth muscle	T5,6,7-10.	WRC,SC (splanchnic).	Celiac ganglion.	Periarterial plexus of hepatic artery.	Relaxation.
36			Sphincter of common bile duct.				Periarterial plexuses.	Contraction.
37	Small intestine, upper colon	Man	Smooth muscle, glands.	T5,6-10,11.	WRC,SC (splanchnic).	Celiac and superior mesenteric ganglia.	Celiac and superior mesenteric rami.	Inhibitory.
38	Iliocecal sphincter	Man	Blood vessels, sphincter muscle.	T5,6-10,11.	WRC,SC (splanchnic).	Celiac and superior mesenteric ganglia.	Celiac and superior mesenteric rami.	Vasoconstriction and contraction.
39	Lower colon, rectum	Man	Smooth muscle.	T12,L1,2,3.	WRC,SC (lumbar splanchnic).	Inferior mesenteric ganglion.	Plexus of inferior mesenteric artery.	Contraction, inhibition.
40			Blood vessels.					Vasoconstriction.
41	Internal sphincter ani	Man	Blood vessels, sphincter muscle.	L1,2,3.	WRC,SC (lumbar splanchnic).	Aortic ganglion.	Aortic and hypogastric plexus.	Vasoconstriction and contraction.
42	Kidney	Man	Blood vessels, smooth muscle.	T5-L2.	WRC,SC (splanchnic).	Aortic or renal ganglion.	Renal plexus.	Vasomotor changes.
43	Ureter	Man	Blood vessels, smooth muscle.	T5-12.	WRC,SC (splanchnic).	Aortic or renal ganglion.	Renal plexus and hypogastric nerve.	Rhythmic contraction.
44	Bladder	Man	Detrussor vesicae.	L1-3.	WRC,SC (hypogastric nerve, pelvic plexus).	Vesical plexus, intramural ganglia.		Relaxation.
45			Sphincter vesicae.			Vesical plexus.	Intramural plexus.	Constriction for ejaculation.
46	Urethra	Man	Compressor urethrae.	L1-3.	WRC,SC (hypogastric nerve, pelvic plexus).	Vesical plexus; intramural ganglia.	Prostatic plexus.	Contraction.
47	Prostate	Man	Smooth muscle.	T12-L2	WRC,SC (hypogastric nerve, pelvic plexus).	Vesical plexus, prostatic plexus.	Prostatic plexus.	Contraction; ejaculation.
48	Seminal vesicles, vas deferens	Man	Smooth muscle.	T12-L2	WRC,SC (hypogastric nerve; pelvic plexus).	Vesical plexus.	Plexuses of seminal vesicles and vas deferens.	Contraction; ejaculation.
49	Testes	Man	Blood vessels.	T6-12.	WRC,SC.	Probably lower thoracic ganglia of sympathetic chain.	Splanchnic nerve, aortic and renal plexuses, spermatic plexus.	Vasoconstriction.
50	Corpora cavernosa	Man	Blood vessels.	T12-L2.	WRC,SC.	Lumbar, sacral ganglia of sympathetic chain.	Hypogastric plexus, prostatic plexus, cavernous plexus.	Vasoconstriction.
51	Clitoris, labia minora	Man	Blood vessels.	T12-L2.	WRC,SC.	Lumbar, sacral ganglia of sympathetic chain.	Hypogastric plexus, vaginal plexus, cavernous plexus.	Vasoconstriction.
52	Vagina	Man	Smooth muscle.	T12-L2.	WRC,SC (hypogastric nerve).	Pelvic plexus, uterovaginal plexus.	Vaginal plexus.	Contraction.
53	Uterus (non-pregnant)	Dog	Smooth muscle.	T12,L1,2,3-5.	WRC,SC (hypogastric nerve).	Pelvic plexus, uterovaginal plexus.	Uterine plexus.	Relaxes.
54	Uterus (pregnant)	Dog	Smooth muscle.	T12,L1,2,3-5.	WRC,SC (hypogastric nerve).	Pelvic plexus, uterovaginal plexus.	Uterine plexus.	Contracts.
55	Uterus (non-pregnant)	Cat	Smooth muscle.	T12,L1,2,3-5.	WRC,SC (hypogastric nerve).	Pelvic plexus, uterovaginal plexus.	Uterine plexus.	Contracts.
56	Uterine tube (lower)	Dog	Smooth muscle	T12,L1,2,3-5.	WRC,SC (hypogastric nerve).	Pelvic plexus, uterovaginal plexus.	Uterine plexus.	Contracts.
57	Ovary, upper uterine tube	Man	Vascular bed, stroma.	T6-12.	WRC,SC	Probably lower thoracic ganglia of sympathetic chain.	Splanchnic nerve; aortic, renal plexuses; ovarian plexus.	Vasoconstriction, contraction.

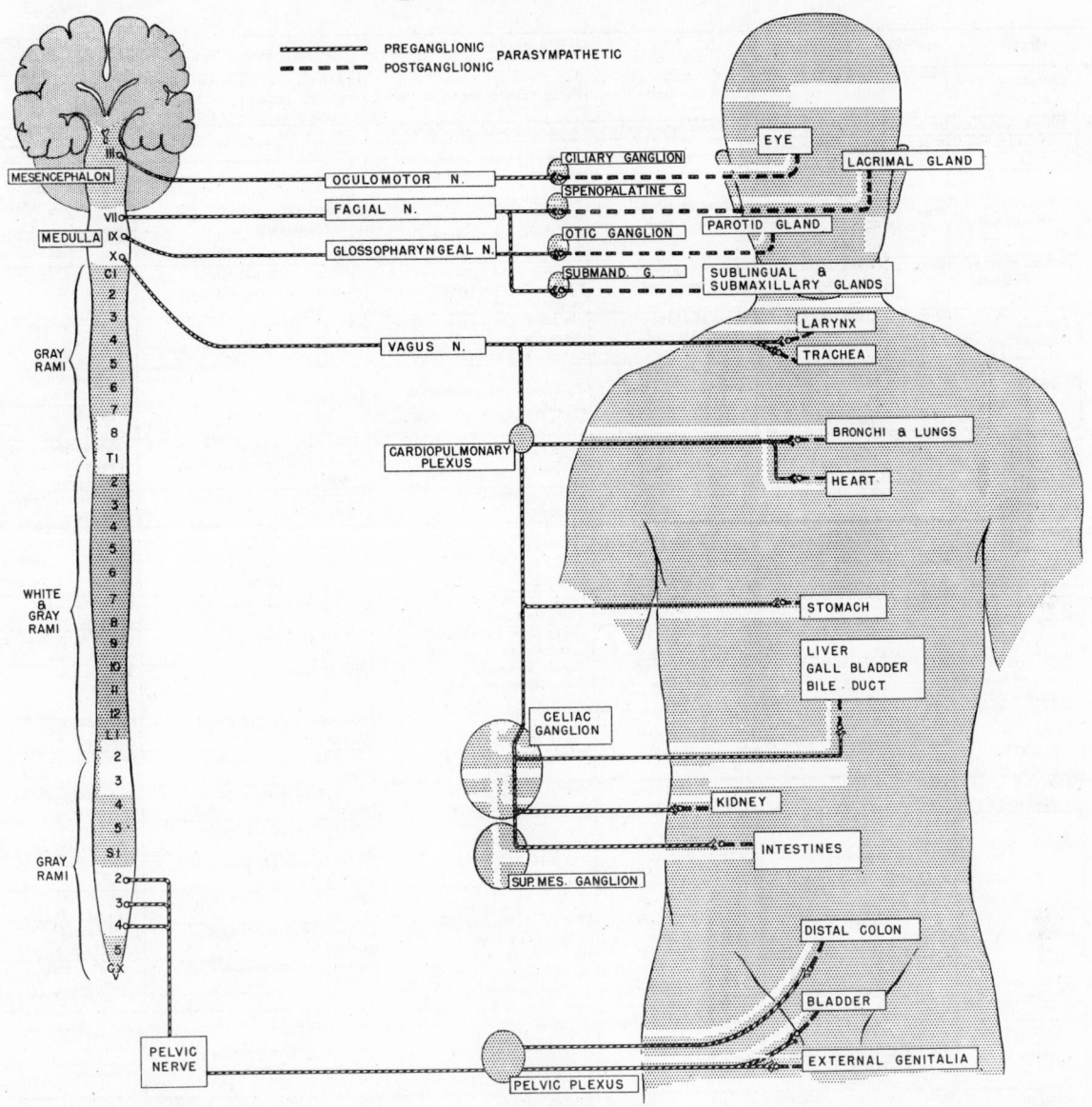

Organ	Species	Effector	Preganglionic Neurone		Postganglionic Neurone	Action
			Cell Body	Pathway		
1	Man	Sphincter pupillae.	Visceral oculo-motor nucleus of Edinger-Westphal.	Oculomotor nerve; motor root; ciliary ganglion.	Ciliary ganglion -- short ciliary nerve.	Constriction of pupil.
2 Eye		Ciliary muscle.				Accommodation.
3	Bird	Sphincter pupillae, ciliary muscle (striated).	Visceral oculo-motor nucleus of Edinger-Westphal (very large).		Ciliary ganglion -- short ciliary nerve (all fibers very large).	Constriction of pupil, accommodation (rapid).
4 Lacrimal gland	Man	Gland cells.	Nucleus saliva-torius superior.	Nervus intermedius; great superficial petrosal nerve; vidian nerve.	Sphenal-palatine ganglion; zygomatic nerve; lacrimal nerve.	Secretion.
5	Man	Sino-atrial node; atrio-ventricular node, conduction system; auricular muscle.	Dorsal motor nucleus of vagus.	Superior, inferior, thoracic cardiac rami of vagus.	Intrinsic cardiac ganglia in wall of atrium and auricle.	Inhibitory; decreases heart rate.
6 Heart	Dog			Right cardiovagal nerve; accelerater nerve; deep cardiac plexus. Left cardiovagal nerve; deep cardiac plexus.	Intrinsic ganglia on or above coronary sulcus in atrium.	

Part III: PARASYMPATHETIC CONNECTIONS (Concluded)

	Organ	Species	Effector	Preganglionic Neurone		Postganglionic Neurone	Action
				Cell Body	Pathway		
7	Coronary artery	Man	Smooth muscle.	Dorsal motor nucleus of vagus.	Superior, inferior, thoracic cardiac rami of vagus.	Intrinsic cardiac ganglia, adventitia, small branches of coronary artery.	Constriction.
8	Blood vessels	Man	Smooth muscle.	Demonstrated only for brain, meninges, face, and most glands.			Vaso-constriction.
9	Adrenal medulla	Man	None demonstrated.				
10	Spleen	Man	None demonstrated.				
11	Lung and trachea	Man	Smooth muscle of of trachea, bronchial tree.	Dorsal motor nucleus of vagus.	Vagal branches; anterior, posterior pulmonary; deep cardiac plexuses.	Intramural tracheal, bronchial ganglia.	Tracheal, bronchial constriction
12			Tracheal, bronchial glands.				Secretion.
13	Submaxillary, sublingual glands	Man	Gland cells, blood vessels.	Nucleus salivatorius superior.	Nervus intermedius; 7th nerve; chorda-tympani; lingual nerve.	Submaxillary ganglion; submaxillary, sublingual branches.	Secretion, vasodilatation.
14	Parotid gland	Man	Gland cells, blood vessels.	Nucleus salivatorius inferior.	9th nerve; tympanic nerve; lesser superficial petrosal nerve; lingual nerve.	Otic ganglion; auriculotemperal nerve.	Secretion, vasodilatation.
15	Lower esophagus	Man	Smooth muscle.	Dorsal motor nucleus of vagus.	Vagus nerve; esophageal plexus.	Myenteric ganglianated plexus.	Increases tonus, peristalsis.
16			Cardiac sphincter.				Relaxation.
17	Stomach	Man	Smooth muscle.	Dorsal motor nucleus of vagus.	Vagus nerve; gastric branches.	Myenteric ganglionated plexus.	Contraction; increases tonus, peristalsis secretion.
18			Gastric glands.			Submucosal ganglionated plexus.	
19	Pyloric sphincter	Man	Smooth muscle.	Dorsal motor nucleus of vagus.	Vagus nerve; gastric branches.	Myenteric ganglionated plexus.	Diminishes tonus, inhibitory.
20	Pancreas	Man	Gland cells, blood vessels.	Dorsal motor nucleus of vagus.	Vagus nerve; pancreatic branches.	Pancreatic ganglia.	Secretion, vasodilatation.
21	Liver	Man	Hepatic cells.	Dorsal motor nucleus of vagus.	Vagus nerve; hepatic branches.	Intramural ganglia.	Secretion (?).
22	Gallbladder	Man	Smooth muscle.	Dorsal motor nucleus of vagus.	Vagus nerve; hepatic, gastroduodenal plexus.	Intramural ganglia.	Emptying of gallbladder.
23	Biliary tree	Man	Smooth muscle.	Dorsal motor nucleus of vagus.	Vagus nerve; hepatic, gastroduodenal plexus.	Intramural ganglia.	Elevates pressure of bile ducts.
24	Sphincter of common bile duct	Man	Smooth muscle.	Dorsal motor nucleus of vagus.	Vagus nerve; hepatic, gastroduodenal plexus.	Intramural ganglia.	Relaxation.
25	Small intestine	Man	Smooth muscle.	Dorsal motor nucleus of vagus.	Vagus nerve; celiac mesenteric branches.	Myenteric ganglionated plexus.	Contraction, peristalsis.
26			Gland.			Submucosal ganglionated plexus.	Secretion.
27	Iliocecal sphincter	Man	Smooth muscle.	Dorsal motor nucleus of vagus.	Vagus nerve; celiac mesenteric branches.	Myenteric ganglionated plexus.	Inhibitory, diminishes tonus.
28	Upper colon	Man	Smooth muscle.	Dorsal motor nucleus of vagus.	Vagus nerve; celiac mesenteric branches.	Myenteric ganglionated plexus.	Contraction, peristalsis.
29			Glands.			Submucosal ganglionated plexus.	Secretion.
30	Lower colon	Man	Smooth muscle	S2, 3, 4.	Pelvic nerve; hypogastric nerve -- inferior mesenteric plexus.	Myenteric ganglionated plexus.	Contraction, vasodilatation, peristalsis, secretion.
31			Glands.			Submucosal ganglionated plexus.	
32			Internal sphincter ani.			Myenteric ganglionated plexus.	Inhibition; vasodilatation.
33	Kidney	Man	None demonstrated.				
34	Ureter	Man	None demonstrated.				
35	Bladder	Man	Detrussor vesicae.	S2, 3, 4.	Pelvic nerve (nerve eregentes).	Pelvic plexus; vesical, intramural ganglia.	Contraction.
36			Sphincter vesicae.				Relaxation.
37	Urethra	Man	Smooth muscle.	S2, 3, 4.	Pelvic nerve.	Pelvic plexus; vesical plexus; prostatic plexus.	Control of sphincter.
38	Prostate	Man	Smooth muscle.	S2, 3, 4.	Pelvic nerve.	Pelvic plexus; vesical plexus; prostatic plexus.	(?).
39	Seminal vesicles and vas deferens	Man	Smooth muscle.	S2, 3, 4.	Pelvic nerve.	Pelvic plexus; vesical plexus.	(?).
40	Testes	Man	None demonstrated.				
41	Corpora cavernosa	Man	Erectile tissue.	S2, 3, 4.	Pelvic nerve.	Pelvic plexus; cavernous plexus.	Vasodilatation; erection.
42	Clitoris and labia minora	Man	Erectile tissue.	S2, 3, 4.	Pelvic nerve.	Pelvic plexus; utero-vaginal plexus.	Vasodilatation; erection.
43	Vagina	Man	None demonstrated.				
44		Cat	None demonstrated.				
45	Uterus	Monkey	Smooth muscle.	S2, 3, 4.	Pelvic nerve.	Probably uterocervical ganglion.	Motility (?).
46	Cervix of uterus	Man	Smooth muscle.				
47	Uterine tube	Man	None demonstrated.				
48	Ovary	Man	None demonstrated.				
49	Thyroid gland	Man	No true secretory fibers present.				
50	Face	Man	Blood vessels.	Nucleus salivatorius superior(?)	Nervus intermedius, 7th nerve.	(?).	Vasodilation; blushing.

310

Part IV: GANGLIA

	Ganglia	Class.	Location	Preganglionic Connections	Postganglionic Distribution
1	Accessory	S	In relation to ventral nerve roots, communicating rami and S roots.	Ventral nerve roots.	Primary ventral rami of spinal nerves, visceral nerves.
2	Aortico-renal	S	Root of renal artery.	Splanchnic nerves.	Renal and aortic plexuses.
3	Bronchial	P	Bronchial plexuses.	Vagus nerves.	Bronchial musculature and glands.
4	Cardiac	P	Cardiac plexus.	Vagus nerves.	Heart, coronary vessels, pulmonary plexuses.
5	Celiac	S	Celiac plexus.	Splanchnic nerves.	Abdominal viscera and blood vessels.
6	Cervical sympathe- tic, inferior	S	Sympathetic trunk, level of vertebra T 1.	Thoracic nerves.	Brachial plexus, inferior cardiac nerve, common carotid plexus, vertebral nerve.
7	Intermediate	S	Sympathetic trunk, level of vertebra C 8.	Thoracic nerves.	Ansa subclavia, inferior cardiac nerve, sympathetic roots of nerves C 6, 7, 8.
8	Middle	S	Symp. trunk, level of vertebra C 6.	Thoracic nerves.	Middle cardiac nerve, S roots of nerves C 5, 6.
9	Superior	S	Sympathetic trunk, 2nd, 3rd, 4th cervical vertebrae.	Thoracic nerves.	Internal, external carotid nerves, sympathetic roots of nerves C 1-3, superior cervical cardiac nerves.
10	Cervical of uterus	P, S	Pelvic plexus adjacent to cervix of uterus.	Pelvic nerves, hypo- gastric plexus.	Uterus and vagina.
11	Ciliary	P	Orbit, between optic nerve and lateral rectus muscle.	Oculomotor.	Short ciliary nerves.
12	Enteric	E	Wall of enteric canal.	Vagus and sacral nerves.	Enteric muscles and glands.
13	Impar (or coccygeal)	S	Ventral surface of coccyx.	Lumbar spinal nerves.	Caudal spinal nerves.
14	Lingual	P	Posterior portion of tongue.	Facial and chorda tympani.	Lingual glands.
15	Mediastinal	S	Posterior mediastinum in relation to splanchnic nerves.	Splanchnic nerves.	Celiac plexus.
16	Mesenteric, inferior	S	Adjacent to inferior mesenteric artery.	Splanchnic nerves.	Inferior mesenteric and hypogastric plexuses.
17	, superior	S	Adjacent to root of superior mesenteric artery.	Splanchnic nerves.	Superior mesenteric, aortic, and renal plexus.
18	Myenteric	E	Between longitudinal and circular enteric muscle layers.	Vagus and pelvic nerves.	Enteric muscles.
19	Otic	P	Medial to mandibular nerve, just below foramen ovale.	Glossopharyngeal nerve.	Supplies auriculo-temporal nerve with fibers to parotid gland.
20	Pelvic	P, S	Adjacent to pelvic viscera.	Pelvic nerves, hypo- gastric plexus.	Pelvic viscera and blood vessels.
21	Pulmonary	P	Pulmonary plexuses.	Vagus nerves.	Bronchial plexuses.
22	Semilunar	S	Celiac plexus.	Splanchnic nerves.	Abdominal viscera and blood vessels.
23	Sphenopalatine [1]	P	Pterygopalatine fossa.	Facial nerve.	Pharyngeal, palatine, nasal, and orbital nerves.
24	Submaxillary	P	Between lingual nerve and duct of submaxillary gland.	Chorda tympani (through facial).	Submaxillary, sublingual, and lingual glands.
25	Submucous	E	Submucosa of enteric canal.	Vagus and pelvic nerves.	Enteric muscles and glands.
26	Sympathetic trunk	S	Ventrolateral to vertebral column.	Spinal nerves T 1-L 3.	Sympathetic roots of spinal nerves, cephalic sympathetic, cardiac and splanchnic nerves.
27	Terminale	P	Adjacent to olfactory tract.	Nervus terminalis.	Anterior cerebral artery, vomero nasal organ, nasal mucosa.
28	Tracheal	P	Tracheal wall.	Vagus nerves.	Tracheal and bronchial plexus.

/1/ Supplied by greater superficial petrosal through facial nerve.

Part V: PLEXUSES

	Plexus	Class.	Origin	Distribution
1	Adrenal	S	Celiac plexus.	Adrenal artery and gland.
2	Aortic	S	Sympathetic trunks.	Aorta and proximal portions of its branches.
3	Cardiac, superficial	P, S	Cervical and thoracic sympathetic cardiac nerves, branches of vagus nerves.	Heart, coronary vessels, anterior pulmonary plexuses.
4	Cardiac, deep	P, S	Right superior, middle and inferior cervical and thoracic sympathetic cardiac nerves, all cardiac branches of right vagus, left middle and inferior cervical and thoracic cardiac nerves, superior cervical and cardiac branches of left vagus.	Heart, coronary vessels, anterior pulmonary plexuses.
5	Carotid, common	S	Sympathetic trunk.	Common carotid artery.
6	Carotid, external	S	Superior cervical ganglion, common carotid plexus.	External carotid artery and its branches.
7	Carotid, internal	S	Superior cervical ganglion, common carotid plexus.	Internal carotid artery and its branches, caroticotympanic and deep petrosal nerves, cavernous plexus.
8	Cavernous	S	Internal carotid plexus.	Cavernous sinus, oculomotor, trochlear and ophthalmic nerves, ciliary ganglion, hypophysis.
9	Celiac	S	Intrinsic ganglia, splanchnic nerves.	Celiac artery and its branches.
10	Colic	S	Inferior mesenteric plexus.	Colon.
11	Duodenal	S	Superior mesenteric and pancreatic plexuses.	Duodenum and pancreas.
12	Enteric	E	Vagus, sacral nerves, intrinsic ganglia, esopha- geal, celiac, mesenteric and pelvic plexuses.	Enteric canal.
13	External maxillary	S	External carotid plexus.	External maxillary artery, submaxillary and otic ganglia.
14	Hepatic	P, S	Vagus nerves and celiac plexus.	Biliary system, hepatic blood vessels.
15	Hypogastric	S	Celiac, aortic, inferior mesenteric plexuses.	Pelvic plexuses.
16	Spermatic	S	Aortic and renal plexuses.	Spermatic artery, spermatic cord, testis.
17	Mesenteric, inferior	S	Celiac plexus, lumbar splanchnic nerves.	Inferior mesenteric artery and its branches.
18	Mesenteric, superior	S	Celiac plexus.	Superior mesenteric artery and its branches.
19	Meningeal, middle	S	External carotid plexus.	Middle meningeal artery.
20	Ovarian	S	Aortic and renal plexuses.	Ovarian artery, ovary.
21	Pancreatic	P, S	Vagus nerves, intrinsic ganglia, sympathetic trunks.	Pancreas, pancreatic ducts and vessels.
22	Pelvic	P, S	Hypogastric plexus, pelvic nerves, intrinsic ganglia.	Pelvic viscera and blood vessels.
23	Pulmonary	P, S	Vagus nerves, intrinsic ganglia, sympathetic trunks.	Bronchial plexuses, pulmonary vessels.
24	Phrenic	S	Celiac plexus, lesser and least splanchnic nerves.	Renal blood vessels; supplies adrenal gland, diaphragm, esoph- agus, inferior cava.
25	Prostatic	P, S	Pelvic plexus.	Prostate gland.
26	Renal	S	Celiac plexus, splanchnic nerves.	Renal blood vessels.
27	Sigmoid	S	Inferior mesenteric plexus.	Sigmoid colon.
28	Splenic	S	Celiac plexus.	Spleen, pancreas, stomach.
29	Tympanic	P, S	Internal carotid nerve, ramus from petrosal ganglion.	Tympanum, mastoid cells, auditory tube.
30	Uterine	P, S	Pelvic plexus.	Uterus.
31	Vaginal	P, S	Pelvic plexus.	Vagina.
32	Vesical	P, S	Pelvic plexus.	Urinary bladder.

287. NERVES: MAN

Cranial nerves are indicated by Roman numerals; spinal nerves by Arabic numerals and literal designation as follows: C = cervical; Th = thoracic; L = lumbar; S = sacral; Coc = coccygeal. Nerves listed are those considered most important; a complete atlas is not intended.

No.	Nerve(s)	Distribution
	Cranial Nerves	
1	Olfactory (I)	Nasal mucous membrane.
2	Optic (II)	Retina.
3	Oculomotor (III)	Levator palpebrae, recti (medial, superior and inferior) and inferior oblique muscles of eye. Sphincter pupillae and ciliary muscles via ciliary ganglion and short ciliary nerves.
4	Trochlear (IV)	Superior oblique muscle of eye.
	Trigeminal (V)	
	Ophthalmic division	
	Frontal	
5	Tentorial	Tentorium and dura of anterior cranial fossa.
6	Supraorbital	Skin of upper eyelid, forehead, anterior scalp, mucosa of frontal sinus.
7	Supratrochlear	Medial forehead, root of nose, medial commissure of eye.
8	Lacrimal	Lacrimal gland, conjunctiva, lateral commissure of eye.
	Nasociliary	
9	Long ciliary	Intraocular structures (sensory).
10	Posterior ethmoidal	Mucosa of posterior ethmoid cells and of sphenoid sinus.
11	Anterior ethmoidal	Mucosa of upper and anterior nasal septum, lateral wall of nasal cavity, skin of lower bridge and tip of nose.
12	Infratrochlear	Root and upper bridge of nose, conjunctiva, skin of eyelids, lacrimal sac.
	Maxillary division	
13	Middle meningeal	Dura of anterior cranial fossa.
14	Zygomatic	
15	Zygomaticofacial	Skin over zygomatic bone.
16	Zygomaticotemporal	Skin of anterior temple.
17	Posterior superior alveolar	Upper molar teeth and gum, mucosa of maxillary sinus.
18	Superior dental	Upper molar teeth.
	Infraorbital	Skin of anterior cheek, side of nostril, skin and conjunctiva of lower eyelid.
19	Middle and ant.sup.alveolar	Upper teeth (except molars), mucosa of maxillary sinus.
	Sphenopalatine nerves via ganglion	
20	Post. sup. lat. nasal	Mucosa of superior and middle nasal conchae.
21	Post. sup. medial nasal	Mucosa of posterior part of nasal septum; post. ethmoid sinus.
22	Post. inferior nasal	Mucosa of middle and inferior nasal conchae.
23	Palatines	Soft palate and tonsil via greater petrosal nerve and Vidian nerve.
	Mandibular division	
24	Spinous	Dura mater of middle cranial fossa.
	Masticator	
25	Masseter	Masseter muscle.
26	Deep temporal	Temporal muscle.
27	Pterygoid ext. and int.	Pterygoid muscles.
28	Buccinator	Skin of mid-cheek, mucosa of mouth.
29	Auriculotemporal	Skin of temple, superior part of ear, external acoustic meatus, tympanic membrane.
30	Lingual	Mucosa of anterior 2/3 of tongue, lateral wall and floor of mouth.
	Inferior alveolar	
31	Mylohyoid	Mylohyoid muscle, anterior belly of digastric muscle.
32	Dental, inferior	Lower teeth.
33	Mental and inf. labial	Skin of chin, mucosa of lower lip.
34	Abducens (VI)	Lateral rectus muscle of eye.
35	Facial (VII)	Posterior auricular muscle, occipital belly of epicranius muscle, posterior belly of digastric muscle, stylohyoid, platysma and buccinator muscles, lip, chin and nose muscles, orbicularis oculi muscle, stapedius muscle.
	Nervus intermedius[2]	
36	Greater superficial petrosal	Lacrimal gland via vidian nerve, sphenopalatine ganglion, anastomotic zygomaticotemporal nerve and lacrimal nerve', from soft palate and tonsil via posterior palatine nerve and sphenopalatine ganglion.

No.	Nerve(s)	Distribution
	Nerves of Shoulder Girdle and Upper Extremity (concluded)	
78	Median (C6-Th1)	Intrinsic muscles of hand (abductor brevis, opponens and flexor brevis of thumb, medial two lumbricals), pronators quadratus and teres, long forearm flexors (of hand and fingers, except flexor profundus IV and V), skin of radial half of palm and fingers I-IV.
79	Ulnar (C8 and Th1)	Intrinsic muscles of hand (adductor pollicis, short muscles of little finger, all interossei, lateral two lumbricals), long forearm flexors (flexor carpi ulnaris, flexor profundus of fingers IV and V), skin of ulnar half of hand and of fingers IV and V.
80	Radial (C5-Th1)	Extensor muscles of forearm, brachioradialis and extensor carpi, radialis longus.
81	Posterior interosseous	Supinator, extensor carpi radialis brevis, extensor muscles to hand and fingers, intrinsic extensor muscles of thumb.
82	Post. cutaneous of arm	Skin of back of arm.
83	Lower lat. cutaneous of arm	Skin of lateral side of arm.
84	Post. cutaneous of forearm	Skin of back of forearm.
85	Dorsal digital	Skin of dorsal aspect of hand at base of thumb, index and middle fingers, and contiguous proximal surface of thumb, index and middle fingers.
86	Medial cutaneous of arm (C8, Th1)	Skin of medial side of arm.
87	Medial cutaneous of forearm (C8 and Th1)	Skin of medial side of forearm.
	Nerves of Trunk, Thorax and Abdomen	
88	Intercostobrachial (Th1-Th3)	Skin of axilla and medial side of arm.
89	Thoracic (Th2-Th12) (intercostal and post. rami)	Intercostal: skin of thorax and abdomen, intercostal muscles; post rami: skin of trunk, longitudinal back muscles.
90	Thoracic (Th7-Th12)	Oblique, transverse and rectus abdominal muscles.
91	Lumbar, sacral and coccygeal (posterior rami)	Skin of lower back from spinous process L1 through coccyx, deep muscles of lower back.
	Nerves of Abdomen. Pelvic Region, Perineum, Bladder and Genitals	
92	Iliohypogastric (L1)	Skin above pubis and lateral gluteal region.
93	Ilioinguinal (L1)	Skin of pubis, inguinal region and upper 1/3 of penis.
94	Genitofemoral (L1 and L2)	Cremaster muscle, skin of upper scrotum and groin.
95	Superior gluteal (L4-S1)	Gluteus medius and minimus muscles.
96	Inferior gluteal (L5-S2)	Gluteus maximus muscle.
97	Pudendal plexus (S2-S4)	
98	Pelvic (erigentes)	Lower colon via hypogastric plexus. Detrusor muscle and internal sphincter muscle of bladder via vesical plexus, rectum via pelvic plexus.
99	Muscular (S4)	Levator ani and coccygeus muscles.
100	Pudendal (S2-S4)	
101	Inferior hemorrhoidal	External sphincter of anus, skin around anus.
	Perineal	External sphincter of anus, transverse perineal and bulbocavernosus muscles, skin of lower scrotum (labia majorum), mucosa of urethra, bulb and corpus spongiosus of penis.
102	Dorsal, of penis (of clitoris)	Skin of lower 2/3 of penis (clitoris), crus and corpus cavernosus of penis (clitoris).
103	Coccygeal plexus (S5-Coc 1)	Skin over coccyx (anococcygeal nerves).
	Nerves of Lower Extremity	
104	Lat. cutaneous of thigh (L2 and L3)	Skin of lateral side of thigh.
105	Post. cutaneous of thigh (S1-S3)	Skin of back of thigh and lower buttock.
106	Femoral (L2-L4)	Muscles of front of thigh.
107	Ant. cutaneous of thigh	Skin of front of thigh and medial side of knee.
108	Saphenous	Skin of medial side of knee and ankle.
109	Obturator (L2-L4)	Adductor muscles of thigh, obturator externus skin of medial side of knee.
110	Sciatic (L4-S3)	
	Nerve to hamstring muscles (L4-S3)	Muscles of back of thigh.

No.	Nerve	Distribution
37	Chorda tympani[3]	Submaxillary and sublingual glands via lingual nerve and submaxillary ganglion, anterior 2/3 of tongue.
	Acoustic (VIII)	
38	Auditory (Cochlear)	Organ of Corti in cochlea.
39	Vestibular	Macula of utricle in vestibule, cristae of ampullae in semicircular canals.
	Glossopharyngeal (IX)	
40	Tympanic	Tympanic cavity, tympanic membrane, mastoid air cells.
41	Pharyngeal	Mucosa of pharynx (from level of eustachian tube to the epiglottis).
42	Stylopharyngeal	Stylopharyngeus muscle.
43	Tonsillar	Fauces, including tonsil.
44	Lingual	Posterior 1/3 of tongue, posterior rim of soft palate, uvula.
45	Parotid	Parotid gland via nerve to digastric muscle, facial nerve, anastomotic nerve, otic ganglion and auriculotemporal nerve.
	Vagus (X)	
46	Meningeal	Dura mater of floor of posterior cranial fossa.
47	Auricular	External acoustic meatus, tympanic membrane, skin between ear and mastoid.
48	Pharyngeal	Pharyngeal and palatine muscles, mucosa of pharynx.
49	Superior laryngeal	Inferior pharyngeal constrictor and cricothyroid muscles, mucosa of larynx, epiglottis.
50	Sup. and inf. cardiac[1]	Heart via cardiac plexuses.
51	Recurrent laryngeal	Intrinsic muscles of larynx (inferior laryngeal nerve) except cricothyroid, heart via cardiac plexus, trachea and esophagus via periaortic plexus.
52	Bronchial[1]	Bronchi via pulmonary plexuses.
53	Esophageal[1]	Esophageal muscle and mucosa via esophageal plexus.
54	Abdominal[1] Anterior branch (right)	Anterior surface and lesser curvature of stomach and pylorus and duodenum via gastric plexuses, liver via celiac and hepatic plexuses.
55	Posterior branch (left)	Posterior surface of stomach (posterior gastric nerve), small intestine and ascending colon via superior mesenteric plexus, spleen and kidney via celiac, splenic and renal plexuses.
56	Spinal accessory (XI)	Sternocleidomastoid and trapezius muscles.
57	Hypoglossal (XII)	Intrinsic and extrinsic tongue muscles.
	Cervical Nerves	
	Sensory	
58	Greater occipital (C2)	Scalp of medial half of back of head.
59	Lesser occipital (C2 and C3)	Scalp of lateral half of back of head.
60	Great auricular (C2 and C3)	Most of ear, skin at angle of jaw.
61	Anterior cutaneous of neck (C2 and C3)	Skin of front of neck.
62	Supraclaviculars (C3 and C4)	Skin over shoulder girdle and upper 3 ribs.
	Motor	
63	Roots C1-C3	Infrahyoid muscles (via ansa hypoglossi), occipito-vertebral muscles.
64	Roots C2 and C3	Sternocleidomastoid muscle.
65	Roots C3 and C4	Levator scapulae and trapezius muscles.
66	Roots C3-C7	Longus colli and scalenus muscles.
67	Phrenic (C3-C5)	Diaphragm.
	Nerves of Shoulder Girdle and Upper Extremity	
68	Long thoracic (C5-C7)	Serratus anterior muscle.
69	Anterior thoracis (C5-Th1)	Pectoralis major and minor muscles.
70	Dorsal scapular (C5)	Levator scapulae and rhomboid major and minor muscles.
71	Subclavian (C5 and C6)	Subclavius muscle.
72	Suprascapular (C5 and C6)	Supraspinatus and infraspinatus muscles.
73	Thoracodorsal (C6-C8)	Latissimus dorsi muscle.
74	Subscapulars (C5 and C6)	Subscapular and teres major muscles.
75	Axillary (C5 and C6)	Deltoid and teres minor muscles, skin over shoulder.
76	Musculocutaneous (C5-C7)	Biceps coracobrachialis, brachialis muscles.
77	Lateral cutaneous of forearm.	Skin of radial side of forearm.

No.	Nerve	Distribution
111	Tibial (L4-S3) Posterior tibial	Muscles of back of calf, skin of heel.
112	Med. and lat. plantar	Skin of bottom of foot and toes, intrinsic muscles of foot.
113	Sural	Skin of back of calf and lateral side of foot.
114	Common peroneal (L4-S2)	Skin of lateral side of knee and upper calf.
115	Lat. cutaneous of calf	Skin of back of calf and lateral side of foot.
116	Sural communicating Superficial peroneal	Peroneus longus and brevis muscles of calf, skin of lower lateral side of calf and dorsum of foot.
117	Deep peroneal	Anterior muscles of calf, extensor digitorum brevis, skin of dorsum of foot in region of toes I and II.
	Sympathetic Nervous System	
	Nerve or ganglion	
118	Superior cervical Nerve to internal carotid artery	Vasoconstrictor fibers to circle of Willis and cerebral arteries, dilatator pupillae and ciliary muscle[4], lacrimal gland.
119	Nerve to external carotid artery	Blood vessels and sweat glands of face, submaxillary and sublingual glands[5], parotid gland[7].
120	Carotico-tympanic nerves	Tympanic plexus.
121	Laryngo-pharyngeal nerves	Pharyngeal and laryngeal plexus via superior laryngeal nerve.
122	Rami communicantes (C2-C4)	Cervical plexus, blood vessels and sweat glands of posterior scalp and neck.
123	Superior cardiac	Heart via cardiac plexuses.
124	Middle cardiac	Heart via cardiac plexuses.
125	Rami communicantes	Upper brachial plexus.
126	Inferior cardiac	Heart via cardiac plexuses.
127	Pulmonary nerves	Bronchi and pulmonary vessels via pulmonary plexuses.
128	Rami communicantes	Brachial plexus.
129	Vertebral ramus	Vasoconstrictor fibers to vertebral artery.
130	Thoracic, abdominal and pelvic Rami communicantes (Ganglia 1-12)	Intercostal nerves.
131	Thoracic cardiac nerves (Ganglia 1-4)	Heart via cardiac plexuses.
132	Pulmonary nerves (Ganglia 1-4)	Bronchi and pulmonary vessels via pulmonary plexuses.
133	Esophageal nerves (Th5-Th6)	Upper esophagus via esophageal plexus, lower esophagus and upper gastric orifice via periaortic plexus.
134	Greater splanchnic (Ganglia 5-9), lesser splanchnic (Ganglia 10 and 11) and least splanchnic (Ganglion 12)	Celiac and aortico-renal ganglia. Via celiac plexus to following plexuses: (a) left gastric (esophagus and stomach), (b) hepatic (liver, gallbladder, stomach, duodenum and pancreas), and (c) splenic (spleen, pancreas, and stomach). Also via following plexuses with branches from periaortic plexus: adrenal (adrenal gland), renal (kidney) and superior mesenteric (small intestine, cecum, appendix, ascending and transverse colon).
135	Splanchnics plus fibers from lumbar ganglia	Aortic plexus to spermatic (or ovarian) plexus (gonads) and inferior mesenteric plexus (descending colon and rectum).
136	Rami communicantes	Lumbosacral plexus, blood vessels and sweat glands of lower extremities.
137	Hypogastric nerves (continuation of aortic plexus)	Inferior hypogastric, hemorrhoidal (rectum), vesical (bladder), prostatic and uterovaginal plexuses.

/1/ Parasympathetic. /2/ Part of VIIth cranial nerve. /3/ Branch of facial nerve but carries fibers to and from nervus intermedius. /4/ Via ciliary ganglion and short ciliary nerves. /5/ Via deep petrosal nerve, vidian nerve and sphenopalatine ganglion. /6/ Via submaxillary ganglion. /7/ Via external carotid artery.

288. REPRESENTATIVE NERVES, CONDUCTION VELOCITY AND FIBER SIZE

Values in parentheses are ranges and represent estimate "c" of the 95% range (cf Introduction).

Vertebrata

No.	Species	Nerve, Fiber Type	Conduction Velocity m/sec[1]	Fiber Diameter μ	Temperature °C
	Mammalia				
1	Man	Large motor fibers	(30-65)	(1-30)	In vivo
2		Ulnar and median (to hand)	(49-69)		In vivo
3		Ulnar and median (to forearm)	(66-69)		In vivo
4		Tibia & peroneus (to foot)	120		In vivo
5		Sciatic	(47-58)		
6			65		18.7
7					
8	Cat	Large motor fibers	110	20	20
9			80	15	
10			50	10	
11		N. to gastrocnemius		(11-16)	
12		N. to soleus		(9-12)	
13		N. to tibia ant.		(9-15)	
14		Saphenous, α fibers[2]	60		
15		Small motor fibers	40	8	
16			30	6	
17			20	4	
18			10	2	
19		N. to gastrocnemius		(3-8)	
20		N. to soleus		(3-6)	
21		N. to tibia ant.		(3-6)	
22		Splanchnic, β fibers[2]	(70-81)	(13-15)	35
23		Afferent fibers — Flexor hamstrings	(47-111)	(13-22)	37.5
24		Pre-tibial	(27-99)	(13-22)	37.5
25		Gastrocnemius	(30-104)	(13-22)	37.5
26		Spinal cord — Pyramidal tract	(1.8-164)	(1-12.5)	37
27		Dorsal columns	(22-66)		
28		Dorsal spinocerebellar	85-160	(16-18)	
29		A fibers (fastest)[2]	100		
30		B fibers[2]	4.5	3	
31		C fibers[2]	0.6	1-5	
32	Dog	Sciatic	(59-102)		
33		Chorda tympani	36.4	8.2	38
34		Splanchnic	55.0		38
35		Saphenous	(72-83)	(14.4-17)	38
36	Rabbit (Oryctolagus cuniculus)	Depressor	5	(2-4)	38
37		Peroneal	69	20.4	37.5
38	Rat (Rattus rattus)	Tibial	37.8	(2.6-12.5)	20
	Reptilia				
39	Blow snake (Pituophis catenifer)	Spinal motor pathways	(11.0-36.9)		14-24
40	Bull snake (Pituophis sp)	Hypoglossal	(7.5-11.2)		22-27
41	Garter snake (Thamnophis sp)	Spinal motor pathways	(3.42-35.1)		10.5-22
42	King snake (Lampropeltis sp)	Hypoglossal	10		
	Amphibia				
43	Frog (Rana sp)	Sciatic, A fibers[2]	2 x d[1], 40 max	(3-20)	24[1]
44		Muscle nerve	(10-40)	15	22
45			(4-8)	5	22
46	Frog (R. catesbeiana)	Large motor fibers		(7-11)	
47		Small motor fibers		(4-6)	
48		C fibers[2]	(0.2-0.6)	<1	
49		Large motor fibers	30	15	
50			25	12	
51			20	10	

Vertebrata (concluded)

No.	Species	Nerve, Fiber Type	Conduction Velocity m/sec[1]	Fiber Diameter μ	Temperature °C
	Amphibia (concluded)				
52	Frog (Rana catesbeiana) (concluded)	Small motor fibers	15	8	
53			10	5	
54			7	4	
	Pisces				
55	Bullhead (Ameiurus sp)	Spinal pathway[3]	50-60	22-43	10-15
56	Catfish	Optic n. (proximal)	3-8		
57		(peripheral)	15-25		
58	Pike (Esox)	Olfactory n.	16-24	2-17	20
59	Ray (Raja squalus)	Dorsal roots	8-36		18-19
60	Torpedo (Torpedo sp)	Electric organ (aff.)	20-30		

Invertebrata

No.	Species	Nerve, Fiber Type	Conduction Velocity m/sec[1]	Fiber Diameter μ	Temperature °C
	Arthropoda				
	Crustacea				
61	Crab (Carcinus maenas)	Leg	4.4(3.9-5.5)	30	21
62	Crayfish (Cambarus sp)	Lateral giant fibers	(10-15)	(75-150)	20
63		Median giant fibers	(15-20)	(100-250)	20
64	Lobster (Homarus spp)	Leg nerve fibers	4(2-10)	(35-70)	23
65	Mud shrimp (Callianassa sp)	Giant fibers	(6.0-7.5)	(35-40)	20-22
66	Prawn (Leander sp)	Giant fibers	(18-23)	35	17
	Insecta				
67	Cockroach (Periplaneta sp)	Giant fibers	(9-12)	(10-40)	
	Xiphosura				
68	King crab (Limulus sp)	Ambulacral n.	(1.3-4.6)		
69		Heart plexus	1.5		
	Mollusca				
70	Cuttlefish (Sepia sp)	Giant fibers	(6-13)	200	
71		Stellar n.	(2.2-8.1)	(30-180)	
72	Octopus (Octopus sp)	Stellar n.	2		
73	Slug (Ariolimax columbianus)	Mantle	0.83	1-35	21.8
74		Pedal n.	0.50	1-35	7.6
75	Snail (Helix pomatia)	Intestinal n.	(0.05-0.48)	10-15	
76	Squid (Loligo forbesi)	Stellar n.	(4.7-22.3)	(40-718)	
77	Squid (L. pealii)	Giant fibers	18	260	20.8-24.3
78		Giant fibers	23.5(21.5-25)	350	20.8-24.3
79		Giant fibers	30(27.5-32)	450	20.8-24.3
80		Giant fibers	35	520	20.8-24.3
	Annelida				
81	Clamworm (Neanthes virens)	Lateral giant fibers	5(4-6)	(30-37)	24
82		Median giant fibers	4.5	(15-18)	24
83		Median giant fibers	2.5	(7-9)	24
84	Earthworm (Lumbricus terrestris)	Lateral giant fibers	11.3(7.5-15)	(40-60)	21-24
85		Median giant fibers	30(15-45)	(50-90)	21-24
86	Leech (Hirudo sp)	Ganglionic cords	(0.02-0.03)		
87	Lugworm (Arenicola sp)	Giant fiber	2	25	24
88	Sabellid (Myxicola sp)	Giant fiber	(6-20)	(100-1000)	
89	Sandworm (Lumbrineris hebes)	Median dorsal fiber	10	130	24
90		Median ventral fiber	4.5	27	24
91	Sea mouse (Aphrodita sp)	Nerve cord	0.5		
	Coelenterata				
92	Aurelia (Aurelia sp)	Nerve net	0.229		
93	Portug. man-of-war (Physalia sp)	Filaments[4]	0.121		
94	Sea anemone (Calliactis parasitica)	Column n. net, longit.	0.1		26
95		circular	0.15		
96		radial	0.04		
97		Mesentery n. net, longit.	1.2		

[1]/ Velocity (v) in m/sec (myelinated fibers) in vertebrates is directly proportional to outside diameter in μ; v = kd, k≈6 in mammals; k≈2 in frogs. Temperature coefficient of velocity is 1.8 for 10°. [2]/ A fibers = myelinated fibers of somatic system, subdivided into α, β, γ and δ; B fibers = myelinated (usually preganglionic) fibers of autonomic nervous system; C = non-myelinated fibers. /3/ Presumed to be Mauthner's fibers. /4/ Presumably nerve net.

289. DELAYS AT SYNAPSES AND PERIPHERAL JUNCTIONS

Synaptic delay is the time between first electrical sign of impulse in presynaptic terminals and first electrical sign of response in the postsynaptic unit. The latter is often a synaptic potential and not a spike. Values are not strictly comparable because of varying interpretations with regard to the exact moment an impulse enters presynaptic terminals or with respect to bases for correction for conduction. Because spike may be initiated any time up to or slightly beyond crest of junction potential, values for crest time (foot to summit) of such potentials are listed separately.

	Species	Preparation, Junction, Condition	Corrected Delay msec	Temp °C
		Synapses		
1	Cat (Felis catus)	Neuromuscular junction, soleus and other muscles.	0.55-0.65[1]	37-39
2		Monosynaptic reflex, ventral horn motoneurons, wire electrodes.	0.3-0.45[2]	37
3		Cochlear nucleus in medulla.	0.8[3]	
		Sympathetic ganglion.		
4		Superior cervical, synapse facilitated.	2.0[4]	35
5		Stellate ganglion, in situ.	3.0-4.0[2]	37-39
6	Cockroach (Periplaneta americana)	Last abdominal ganglion, cercal afferents to ascending giant fibers.	0.6-1.5	
	Crayfish (Cambarus sp)	First synapse in proprioceptive pathway		
7		Exposed ventral ganglia.	3.5-4.5[5]	
8	Crayfish (C. clarkii)	Lateral giant fibers, segmental, septal synapse.	<0.1	
9		Lateral giant fibers, commissural synapse.	0.5	
10		Ipsilateral medial giant to 3rd root motor fiber, slightly fatigued.	0.6	
11	Earthworm (Lumbricus terrestris)	Oblique septum between segmental giant fiber units.	0.1[5]	24
12	Frog (Rana sp)	Neuromuscular junction, semitendinosus.	0.8	22.5
13	Plume worm (Protula intestinum)	Natural synapse between giants, in brain, fresh to fatigued.	0.8-6.5	16
14		"Quasi-artificial" jumping between giant fibers, fresh to fatigued.	0.6-7+	16
15	Rabbit (Oryctolagus cuniculus)	Trochlear motoneurons.	0.5-0.9[6]	37
16	Sea anemone (Metridium senile)	Mesentery nerve net, through-conduction pathway	<2.5[5]	
17	Shrimp, ghost (Callianassa californiensis)	Last abdominal ganglion, giant central fiber to motor fibers in telson	0.25	20-22
18	Slug (Ariolimax columbianus)	Isolated pedal ganglion.	33.0	7.6
19		Isolated pedal ganglion	19.0	21.8
20	Squid (Loligo opalescens)	Synapse in stellate ganglion, 2nd and 3rd order giant fibers.	0.5	24
	Turtle (Pseudemys sp)	Superior cervical ganglion		
21		B-fibers, pre- and post-ganglion.	8.0[7]	
22		C-fibers, pre- and post-ganglion.	25.0[7]	
		Artificial Synapses		
23	Cat (Felis catus)	Cut end of nerve, A-fibers, motor to sensory.	0.1-0.3[8]	
24		Cut end of dorsal columns of spinal cord, dorsal root to dorsal root.	0.1-0.3[9]	
25	Crab (var. spp)	Two isolated nerves or fibers in contact.	7+	
	Cuttlefish (Sepia officianalis)	Two isolated nerves or fibers in contact.		
26		Giant fibers, normal or citrated.	2.5[10]-5.0	
27		Citrated, rhythmic subthreshold activity.	>40.0[10]	
28	Earthworm (lumbricus terrestris)	Single giant fiber, after discharge arising near anodally depressed locus.	5+	
		Mechanoreceptors		
29	Cat (Felis catus)	Pacinian corpuscle, single mesenteric.	0.5-1.5[8]	
30		Baroreceptors in carotid body, single fibers.	<10[5,10,11]	
31		Auditory nerve spikes, click stimulus.	0.6-0.8	
32	Crayfish (Cambarus sp)	Tactile hairs on telson.	0.5-1.5	
33	Frog (Rana temporaria)	Touch receptors, dorsal skin.	0.7-14.6[5]	20.6-29.6
34	Guinea pig (Cavia porcellus)	Cochlear microphonic to action potential.	0.15	
		Radiation Receptors		
35	Cat (Felis catus)	Electroretinogram (ERG), a-wave.	4.0	
36		ERG, b-wave.	25-80[4,10]	
37	Clam (Mya arenaria)	Photoreceptors in siphon, electrogram.	720-16,000	20
38	Crab, horseshoe (Limulus polyphemus)	Spikes in optic nerve, near-maximal and near-threshold stimuli.	77-750	
39		ERG, intracellular electrode in ommatidial receptor.	70	
40		ERG, near-maximal light flash.	10[12]-55	25-28
41	Fly (Calliphora erythrocephala)	ERG, near-maximal stimuli, compound eye.	6.0[10,12]	
42	Frog (Rana sp)	ERG, a-wave, isolated eye, maximal stimuli.	28-120	
43	Grasshopper (Melanoplus differentialis)	ERG, near-maximal stimuli.	9.3[12]-59.6	
44	Pigeon (Columba sp)	ERG, a-wave.	8.0	
45	Rattlesnake (Crotalus viridis)	Infrared receptor in facial pit organ.	15-50+[13]	23
46	Slater, rock (Ligia occidentalis)	ERG, compound eye, near-maximal stimuli.	6[12]-20	22
		Crest Times		
47	Cat (Felis catus)	Neuromuscular junction, circulated soleus strip.	0.8[13]	37-39
48		Spinal cord, ventral horn motoneuron, internal electrode.	0.6-1.0[14]	36-38
49	Crab (var. spp)	Various leg muscles, end-plate potential.	3.0	17
	Frog (Rana temporaria)	Neuromuscular junction.		
50		Isolated skeletal muscle, internal electrode.	1.2[13]	20
51	Frog (Hyla aurea)	Isolated fiber; external microelectrode on single end-plate.	0.5	
52	Plume worm (Protula intestinum)	Giant synapse in brain, in situ.	1.0	16
53	Rabbit (Oryctolagus cuniculus)	Sympathetic ganglion, stellate, in situ.	10-20	37-39
54		Sympathetic ganglion, isolated superior cervical.	25-35[13]	35

/1/ Decerebrate or nembutal. /2/ Nembutal. /3/ Avertin. /4/ Decerebrate. /5/ Uncorrected for conduction time. /6/ Decorticate. /7/ Measured from 1st reversal of sign of prespike; conduction-time correction not stated. /8/ Decerebrate or chloralose. /9/ Dial. /10/ Measured from illustrations. /11/ Chloralose-urethane. /12/ Probably minimum, i.e. light intensity probably nearly maximal. /13/ Curarized. /14/ Pentobarbitone.

290. THE VISUAL MECHANISM: MORPHOLOGY AND PHYSIOLOGY
(For definition of terms, see Glossary, Part XVI.)

Part I: ANATOMY OF THE EYE: MAN

Diagram labels: Visual Axis; Optic Axis; Angle α = 5-7°; Diam. Cornea 12-13 mm; Diam. Pupil 5-6 mm; Cornea; Diam. Cryst. Lens about 8 mm; Vitreous; Optic Disk[1]; Macula; Fovea; Retina; Choroid; Sclera; Right Eye; Temporal Side; Nasal Side; 1.2 mm

Anterior Surface of Cornea; Post. Surf. of Cornea; Ant. Surf. of Lens; Post. Surf. of Lens

15.6 mm; 7.6 mm; 3.5 mm; 24.7 mm

Anterior Focal Length f_1 = 17.1 mm; Posterior Focal Length f_2 = 22.9 mm

1st Prin. Point; 2nd Prin. Point; 1st Nodal Point; 2nd Nodal Point — 1.5 mm; 1.9 mm; 7.3 mm; 7.6 mm

/1/ Blind spot.

Part II: OPTICAL CONSTANTS OF EYES: MAMMALS
Values in brackets refer to state at maximal accommodation.

	Constant	Eye Area or Measurement	Man	Cat	Dog	Horse	Ox	Sheep	Swine
1	Refractive index	Cornea	1.37	1.37	1.37	1.37	1.37	1.37	1.38
2		Aqueous humor	1.33	1.33	1.33	1.33	1.33	1.33	1.33
3		Lens capsule	1.38[1]	1.33	1.37	1.38	1.38	1.36	1.36
4		Outer cortex, lens		1.38		1.39	1.38	1.37	1.38
5		Ant. cortex, lens	1.41	1.46	1.38	1.39	1.38	1.38	
6		Post. cortex, lens	1.41	1.52	1.38	1.39	1.38	1.38	
7		Center, lens			1.44	1.45	1.46	1.45	1.44
8		Calc. total index	1.41			1.50	1.55	1.53	1.48
9		Vitreous body	1.33	1.33	1.33	1.33	1.33	1.33	1.33
10	Radius of curvature, mm	Cornea	7.7	9.5	8.7	18.7	16.8	12.7	11.0
11		Ant. surface, lens	9.2-12.2	6.7	6.5	14.0	11.3	8.9	7.2
12		Post. surface, lens	5.4-7.1	6.4	5.5	10.1	9.7	7.9	6.3
13	Distance from cornea, mm	Post. surface, cornea	1.2	0.8-1	0.5	1-1.5	1.5-2	0.8-1.2	1-1.2
14		Ant. surface, lens	3.5	4.5	4.8	5.5	4.4	3.0	2.8
15		Post. surface, lens	7.6	12	12	18	16	13	11
16		Retina	24.8	21	21	42	36	28	25
17	Focal distance, mm	Ant. focal length	17.1						
18			[14.2]						
19		Post. focal length	22.8						
20			[18.9]						
21	Position of cardinal points measured from corneal surface, mm	1. Focus	-15.7						
22			[-12.4]						
23		2. Focus	24.4						
24			[21.0]						
25		1. Principal point	1.5						
26			[1.8]						
27		2. Principal point	1.9						
28			[2.1]						
29		1. Nodal point	7.3						
30			[6.5]						
31		2. Nodal point	7.6						
32			[6.8]						
33	Diameter, mm	Optic disk	2-5						
34		Macula	1-3						
35		Fovea	1.5						
36	Depth, mm	Anterior chamber	2.7-4.2						

/1/ Cortex of lens and its capsule.

Part III: VOLUME OF EYEBALL AND ITS PARTS: MAMMALS
Values are milliliters; those in parentheses are ranges.

	Animal	Eyeball	Lens	Anterior Chamber	Posterior Chamber	Vitreous
1	Man	5.4	0.2	0.2	0.3	3.9
2	Cat	3.9	0.6	0.3	0.3	2.8
3	Dog	4.4(1-5)	0.5	0.4	0.2	3.2
4	Horse	45(40-47)	2.8	2.4	1.6	28.8
5	Ox	32(28-44)	2.2	1.7	1.5	20.9
6	Rabbit	3.0	0.2	0.3	0.1	2.0
7	Sheep	12.2(8-14)	0.9	0.8	0.5	7.0
8	Swine	7.22(3-9)	0.8	0.3	0.3	5.7

Part IV: DIMENSIONS OF EYEBALL: VERTEBRATES
Values are millimeters.

	Animal	Horizontal	Vertical	Sagittal
1	Man	24.0	23.5	24.0
2	Elephant, Indian	41.0	40.0	35.1
3	Fox	16.0	16.0	15.4
4	Gorilla	22.5	22.5	22.5
5	Horse	50.5	50.5	45.5
6	Lion	35.0		37.5
7	Mole	1	1	
8	Swine	26.9	26.0	24.8
9	Whale, great blue	145	129	107
10	Goose	12	12	10
11	Alligator	20.0	20.0	
12	Iguana	16.6	13.7	14.6
13	Frog	5.8	5.6	5.3
14	Bowfin	12.5	12	10
15	Herring	11.5	11.5	7.5
16	Lamprey	4.9	4.5	4.0

Part V: RETINA: MAN

Section 1: General Characteristics

	Designation	Cones	Rods
1	20 min angle = 100 μ		
2	Thickness, extrafovea, 300 μ		
3	Thickness, fovea, 125-135 μ		
4	Approx. diam. of fovea, 300 μ		
5	No. nerve fibers in optic nerve, 800,000-1,000,000		
6	No. receptors for each eye	7 million	125 million
7	Total receptors in fovea	12,000	0
8	Diam. of receptor, μ	1.0-5.0	1.0-2.5
9	Photochemical substance	(Iodopsin)[1]	Rhodopsin
10	Wave length for max. sensitivity, μ	0.56	0.51
11	Approx. range of response, μ	0.4-0.75	0.40-0.65
12	Sensation	Chromatic	Mono-chromatic
13	Absolute threshold, millilamberts	0.01	0.000001
14	Approx. time for dark adaptation, min	2	30

/1/ Found only in retina of chicken.

Section 2: Rod and Cone Population and Cone Acuity[1]
Values in parentheses are ranges.

	Angular Eccentricity[2] (degrees)	Rods/sq mm (thousands)	Cones/sq mm (thousands)	Visual Angle Subtended at Eye (minutes)
1	0	0	136	0.7(0.5-1.0)
2	1/4	0	84.4	0.8(0.6-1.1)
3	1/2	7.22	57.5	1.0(0.7-1.3)
4	3/4	12.4	49.1	1.1(0.8-1.5)
5	1	34.2	41.3	1.2(0.8-1.5)
6	1 1/2	53.0	29.3	1.4(0.8-2.0)
7	6	56.9	25.3	1.7(1.0-2.3)
8	8	105	12.1	4.5(1.5-6.7)
9	12	125	7.64	6.1(2.5-10)
10	20	158	7.08	10(5.0-17)
11	40	132	5.95	27.5(14-48)
12	50	108	5.79	42.5(21-72)
13	70	80.4	5.47	$100(47 - X^3)$
14	90	57.7	6.84	$X^3(126 - X^3)$

/1/ At or near horizontal meridian. /2/ From fovea. /3/ Unmeasurably poor acuity.

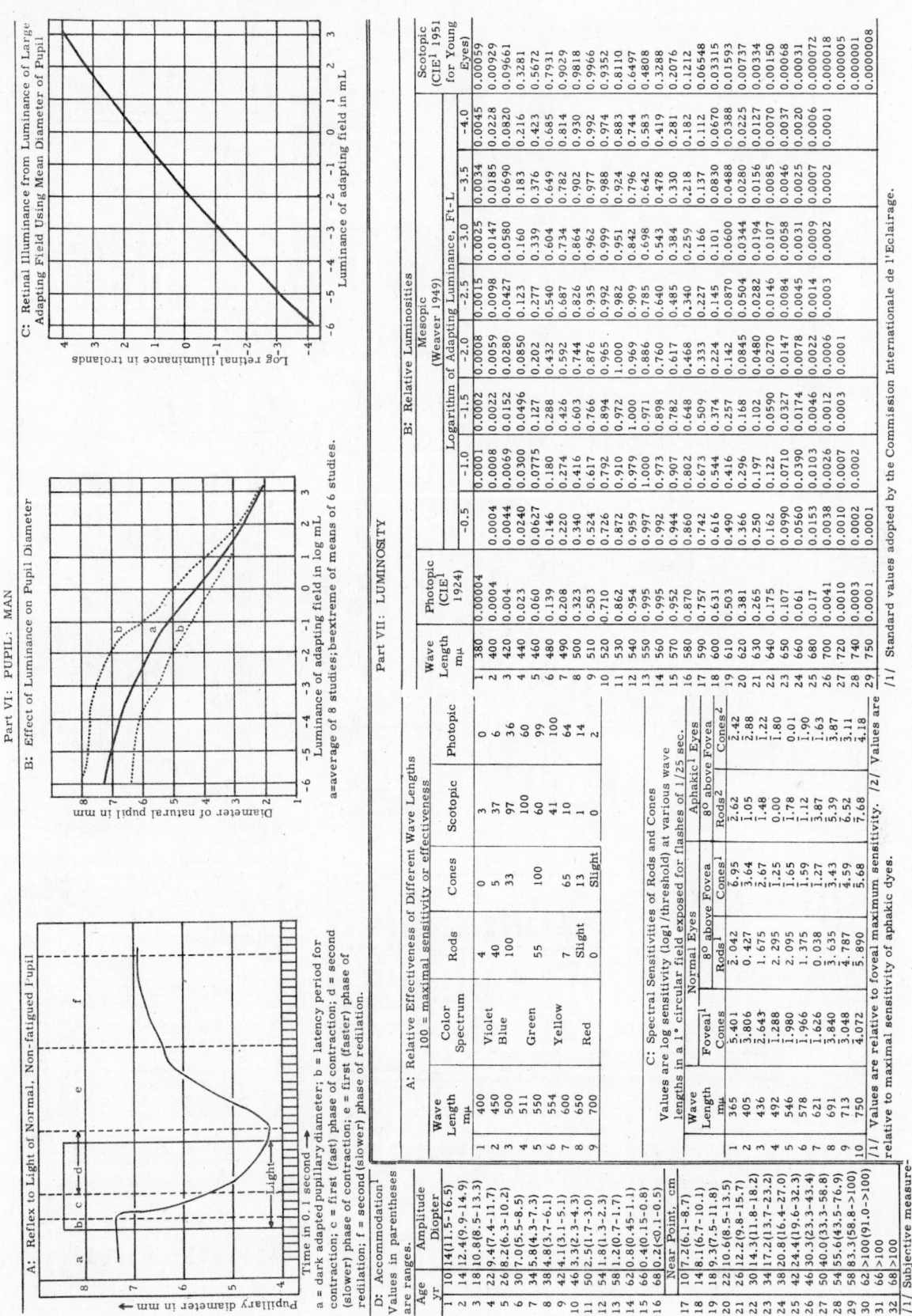

Part VI: PUPIL: MAN

A: Reflex to Light of Normal, Non-fatigued Pupil

(Pupillary diameter in mm vs. Time in 0.1 second; curves marked a, b, c, d, e, f; "Light" interval shown)

a = dark adapted pupillary diameter; b = latency period for contraction; c = first (fast) phase of contraction; d = second (slower) phase of contraction; e = first (faster) phase of redilation; f = second (slower) phase of redilation.

B: Effect of Luminance on Pupil Diameter

(Diameter of natural pupil in mm vs. Luminance of adapting field in log mL; curves a and b)

a = average of 8 studies; b = extreme of means of 6 studies.

C: Retinal Illuminance from Luminance of Large Adapting Field Using Mean Diameter of Pupil

(Log retinal illuminance in trolands vs. Luminance of adapting field in mL)

D: Accommodation[1]
Values in parentheses are ranges.

#	Age yr	Amplitude Diopter
1	10	14(11.5-16.5)
2	14	12.4(9.9-14.9)
3	18	10.8(8.5-13.3)
4	22	9.4(7.4-11.7)
5	26	8.2(6.3-10.2)
6	30	7.0(5.8-8.5)
7	34	5.8(4.3-7.3)
8	38	4.8(3.7-6.1)
9	42	4.1(3.1-5.1)
10	46	3.3(2.3-4.3)
11	50	2.5(1.7-3.0)
12	54	1.8(1.3-2.3)
13	58	1.2(0.7-1.7)
14	62	0.8(0.45-1.1)
15	66	0.4(0.15-0.8)
16		0.2(<0.1-0.5)

Near Point, cm

#	Age yr	Near Point, cm
17	10	7.2(6.1-8.7)
18	14	8.1(6.7-10.1)
19	18	9.3(7.5-11.8)
20	22	10.6(8.5-13.5)
21	26	12.2(9.8-15.7)
22	30	14.3(11.8-18.2)
23	34	17.2(13.7-23.2)
24	38	20.8(16.4-27.0)
25	42	24.4(19.6-32.3)
26	46	30.3(23.3-43.4)
27	50	40.0(33.3-58.8)
28	54	55.6(43.5-76.9)
29	58	83.3(58.8->100)
30	62	>100(91.0->100)
31	66	>100
32	68	>100

/1/ Subjective measurements.

Part VII: LUMINOSITY

A: Relative Effectiveness of Different Wave Lengths
100 = maximal sensitivity or effectiveness.

#	Wave Length mμ	Color Spectrum	Rods	Cones	Scotopic	Photopic
1	400	Violet	4	0	3	0
2	450	Blue	40	5	37	6
3	500		100	33	97	36
4	511	Green		60	100	60
5	550		55	100	60	99
6	554				41	100
7	600	Yellow	7	65	10	64
8	650		Slight	13	1	14
9	700	Red	0	Slight	0	2

B: Relative Luminosities

#	Wave Length mμ	Photopic (CIE[1] 1924)	Mesopic (Weaver 1949) -0.5	-1.0	-1.5	-2.0	-2.5	-3.0	-3.5	-4.0	Scotopic (CIE[1] 1951 for Young Eyes)
1	380	0.00004									0.00059
2	400	0.0004	0.0004	0.0001	0.0002	0.0008	0.0015	0.0025	0.0034	0.0045	0.00929
3	420	0.004	0.0044	0.0008	0.0022	0.0059	0.0098	0.0147	0.0185	0.0228	0.09661
4	440	0.023	0.0240	0.0069	0.0152	0.0280	0.0427	0.0580	0.0690	0.0820	0.3281
5	460	0.060	0.0627	0.0300	0.0496	0.0850	0.123	0.160	0.183	0.216	0.5672
6	480	0.139	0.146	0.0775	0.127	0.202	0.277	0.339	0.376	0.423	0.7931
7	490	0.208	0.220	0.180	0.288	0.432	0.540	0.604	0.649	0.685	0.9029
8	500	0.323	0.340	0.274	0.426	0.592	0.687	0.734	0.782	0.814	0.9818
9	510	0.503	0.524	0.416	0.603	0.744	0.826	0.864	0.902	0.930	0.9966
10	520	0.710	0.726	0.617	0.766	0.876	0.935	0.962	0.977	0.992	0.9352
11	530	0.862	0.872	0.792	0.894	0.965	0.982	0.999	0.988	0.974	0.8110
12	540	0.954	0.959	0.910	0.972	1.000	1.000	0.951	0.924	0.883	0.6497
13	550	0.995	0.997	0.979	1.000	0.969	0.909	0.842	0.796	0.744	0.4808
14	560	0.995	0.992	1.000	0.971	0.886	0.785	0.698	0.642	0.583	0.3288
15	570	0.952	0.944	0.973	0.898	0.760	0.640	0.543	0.478	0.419	0.2076
16	580	0.870	0.860	0.907	0.782	0.617	0.485	0.384	0.330	0.281	0.1212
17	590	0.757	0.742	0.802	0.648	0.468	0.340	0.259	0.218	0.182	0.06548
18	600	0.631	0.616	0.673	0.509	0.333	0.227	0.166	0.137	0.112	0.03315
19	610	0.503	0.490	0.544	0.374	0.224	0.145	0.101	0.0830	0.0670	0.01593
20	620	0.381	0.366	0.416	0.257	0.142	0.0870	0.0600	0.0488	0.0388	0.00737
21	630	0.265	0.250	0.296	0.168	0.0845	0.0504	0.0344	0.0280	0.0225	0.00334
22	640	0.175	0.162	0.197	0.102	0.0480	0.0282	0.0194	0.0156	0.0127	0.00150
23	650	0.107	0.0990	0.122	0.0590	0.0270	0.0146	0.0107	0.0085	0.0070	0.00068
24	660	0.061	0.0560	0.0710	0.0327	0.0147	0.0084	0.0058	0.0046	0.0037	0.00031
25	680	0.017	0.0153	0.0390	0.0174	0.0078	0.0045	0.0031	0.0025	0.0020	0.000072
26	700	0.0041	0.0038	0.0103	0.0046	0.0022	0.0014	0.0009	0.0007	0.0006	0.000018
27	720	0.0010	0.0010	0.0026	0.0012	0.0006	0.0003	0.0002	0.0002	0.0001	0.000005
28	740	0.0003	0.0002	0.0007	0.0003	0.0001					0.000001
29	750	0.0001	0.0001	0.0002							0.0000008

Logarithm of Adapting Luminance, Ft-L

C: Spectral Sensitivities of Rods and Cones (log1/threshold) at various wave lengths in a 1° circular field exposed for flashes of 1/25 sec.

#	Wave Length mμ	Normal Eyes Foveal[1] Cones[1]	Normal Eyes 8° above Fovea Rods[1]	Normal Eyes 8° above Fovea Cones[1]	Aphakic[1] Eyes 8° above Fovea Rods[2]	Aphakic[1] Eyes 8° above Fovea Cones[2]
1	365	5.401	2.042	6.95	2.62	2.42
2	405	3.806	0.427	3.64	1.05	2.88
3	436	2.643	1.675	2.67	1.48	1.22
4	492	1.288	2.295	1.25	0.00	1.80
5	546	1.980	1.375	1.65	1.78	0.01
6	578	1.966	0.038	1.27	1.12	1.90
7	621	1.626		1.59	3.87	1.63
8	691	3.840	3.635	3.43	5.39	3.87
9	713	3.048	4.787	4.59	6.52	3.11
10	750	4.072	5.890	5.68	7.68	4.18

/1/ Values are relative to foveal maximum sensitivity. /2/ Values are relative to maximal sensitivity of aphakic dyes.

/1/ Standard values adopted by the Commission Internationale de l'Eclairage.

A: Tristimulus Values of the Spectrum

Values represent the magnitudes of each of the 3 standard primaries necessary to match the given spectral light. These primaries are imaginary; for convenience, $\bar{y}$ corresponds to the overall luminosity function of the standard observer, but, as an approximation, $\bar{x}$ may be regarded as red, $\bar{y}$ as green, and $\bar{z}$ as blue.

Wave Length mμ	$\bar{x}$	$\bar{y}$	$\bar{z}$	Wave Length mμ	$\bar{x}$	$\bar{y}$	$\bar{z}$
380	0.0014	0.0000	0.0065	585	0.9786	0.8163	0.0014
400	0.0143	0.0004	0.0679	590	1.0143	0.7570	0.0011
410	0.0435	0.0012	0.2074	595	1.0567	0.6949	0.0010
420	0.1344	0.0040	0.6456	600	1.0622	0.6310	0.0008
430	0.2839	0.0116	1.3856	605	1.0456	0.5668	0.0006
440	0.3483	0.0230	1.7471	610	1.0026	0.5030	0.0003
450	0.3362	0.0380	1.7721	615	0.9384	0.4412	0.0002
460	0.2908	0.0600	1.6692	620	0.8544	0.3810	0.0002
470	0.1954	0.0910	1.2876	625	0.7514	0.3210	0.0001
480	0.0956	0.1390	0.8130	630	0.6424	0.2650	0.0001
485	0.0580	0.1693	0.6162	635	0.5419	0.2170	
490	0.0320	0.2080	0.4652	640	0.4479	0.1750	
495	0.0147	0.2586	0.3533	645	0.3608	0.1382	
500	0.0049	0.3230	0.2720	650	0.2835	0.1070	
505	0.0024	0.4073	0.2123	655	0.2187	0.0816	
510	0.0093	0.5030	0.1582	660	0.1649	0.0610	
515	0.0291	0.6082	0.1117	665	0.1212	0.0446	
520	0.0633	0.7100	0.0782	670	0.0874	0.0320	
525	0.1096	0.7932	0.0573	675	0.0636	0.0232	
530	0.1655	0.8620	0.0422	680	0.0468	0.0170	0.0000
535	0.2257	0.9149	0.0298	690	0.0227	0.0082	
540	0.2904	0.9540	0.0203	700	0.0114	0.0041	
545	0.3597	0.9803	0.0134	710	0.0058	0.0021	
550	0.4334	0.9950	0.0087	720	0.0029	0.0010	
555	0.5121	1.0002	0.0057	730	0.0014	0.0005	
560	0.5945	0.9950	0.0039	740	0.0007	0.0003	
565	0.6784	0.9786	0.0027	750	0.0003	0.0001	
570	0.7621	0.9520	0.0021	760	0.0002	0.0001	
575	0.8425	0.9154	0.0018	770	0.0001	0.0000	
580	0.9163	0.8700	0.0017	775	0.0000	0.0000	

B: Classification and Characteristics of Abnormal Color Vision Systems

Type[1]	Designation	Common Name	Discrimination Possible	No. of Lights to Match Spectrum	Neutral Points	Appearance of Spectrum (Achromatic)	λ2 of Max. Luminosity, mμ (Red monochromats (cone monochromats) 560)	Saturation Characteristics
Monochromatic	Achromatopsia	Total color blindness	Light-dark	1 (can match all stimuli by adjusting to equal brightness)	All	Achromatic	Red monochromats 510[3]	0 (Throughout spectrum)
Dichromatic	Protanopia	Red-green blind	Light-dark; yellow-blue	2 (yellow and blue)	493	Blue (short λ); Yellow (long λ)	540	0 at neutral point; ↑ toward long and short ends of spectrum
	Deuteranopia	Red-green blind	Light-dark; yellow-blue	2 (yellow and blue)	497	Yellow (long λ)	560[4]	
	Tritanopia	Yellow-blue blind	Light-dark; red-green	2 (red and green)	572	Green (short λ); Red (long λ)	560	
Anomalous trichromatic	Protanomaly	Red-green weak	Light-dark; yellow-blue; red-green weak	3 (in different proportions from those required by normals)	None	Intermediate between normal and respective dichromatic types	540[5]	Intermediate between normal and respective dichromatic types
	Deuteranomaly	Red-green weak	Light-dark; yellow-blue; red-green weak	3	None		560[4]	
	Tritanomaly	Yellow-blue weak	Light-dark; red-green; yellow-blue weak	3	None		560[4]	

/1/ According to number of components (lights required to match spectrum). /2/ Wave length. /3/ As in dark-adapted normals. /4/ Similar to normals. /5/ Deficient at long wave lengths.

C: Incidence of Color Defectiveness: European-American Males

Values are percentages of populations.

	Degree of Color Defectiveness		
Total	Anomalous Trichromats	Dichromats	Monochromats
8.2	5.8	2.4	0.004[1]
	Protanomalous 2.2 → 1.0	Protanopes 1.2	
	Deuteranomalous 4.8	Deuteranopes 1.2	
	Tritanomalous 0.00015	Tritanopes 0.00005	

Type of Color Defectiveness

Total	Protans	Deutans	Tritans
8.2	2.2	6.0	0.00020

/1/ (Estimated) rod 0.004; cone 0.00001.

D: Incidence of Defective Color Vision: Various Populations

Values are per cent failing Ishihara[1] test.

Population	Male	Female
U.S.A.	6.8-9.7	0.2-1.3
European, Caucasian (Brit., Scot., Norway, Ger.)	7.5-8.0	0.4-0.6
Chinese	4.0-6.9	0.4-1.7
Japanese	2.4-6.9	0.35
American Negro	3.9	0.2
American Indian	1.1-2.0	0-0.7
Mexican	2.3	0.5

/1/ Criterion of failure: 2 or more plates miscalled on 5th edition Ishihara, or equivalent.

E: Wave Length Discrimination[1]

Values are given in mμ for λ (wave length) and Δλ (just noticeable difference in wave length, averaged from Δλ's at graduated stimulus intensities).

#	λ	Δλ	#	λ	Δλ	#	λ	Δλ
1	430	6.5	15	515	2.4	29	585	1.4
2	435	5.0	16	520	2.7	30	590	1.3
3	440	3.8	17	525	2.9	31	595	1.3
4	445	3.3	18	530	3.1	32	600	1.4
5	450	3.5	19	535	3.2	33	605	1.5
6	460	3.3	20	540	3.1	34	610	1.6
7	470	2.5	21	545	2.9	35	615	1.7
8	475	2.2	22	550	2.7	36	620	1.9
9	480	1.8	23	555	2.4	37	625	2.1
10	490	1.6	24	560	2.2	38	630	2.2
11	495	1.6	25	565	1.9	39	635	3.0
12	500	1.7	26	570	1.7	40	640	3.6
13	505	1.8	27	575	1.6	41	645	4.5
14	510	2.0	28	580	1.5	42	650	5.9

/1/ Monocular observations by 5 subjects (with normal color vision) of matching bipartite field at 2°. Illumination averaged 70 photons with a dark surround; an artificial pupil had 1.016mm diameter.

F: Color Vision: Animals

#	Animal	Predominant Retinal Elements	Wave Length Discrimination	Spectral Range	Probable No. Primary Colors
1	Man, chimpanzee, rhesus monkey	Rods, cones	1-2 mμ at optimal	400-700 mμ, approximately	3
2	Cebus monkey	Rods, cones	Good except at yellow (589 mμ) and longer	↓ toward long λ's	2
3	Cat, cow, dog, mouse, rabbit	Rods	Weak or absent	↑ toward long λ's	Unknown
4	Chicken, pigeon	Cones	Equivalent to man	Slight shift toward long λ's	3
5	Turtle (Clemmys caspica)	Cones	Very good	Equivalent to man	3
6	Fish (Phoxinus laevis)	Rods, cones	Very good	Possible shift toward short λ's	3
7	Calliphora	Compound eye	Fair	Shift toward long λ's	Unknown
8	Dronefly (Eristalis tenax)	Compound eye	Present	Unknown	Unknown
9	Honey bee, bumble bee, hawkmoth, Vanessid butterfly	Compound eye	Fair	Shift toward short λ's	Unknown
10	Popilionid and Pieridid butterflies	Compound eye	Fair	Range equivalent to man	Unknown

Part IX: PHOTOCHEMISTRY OF VISION

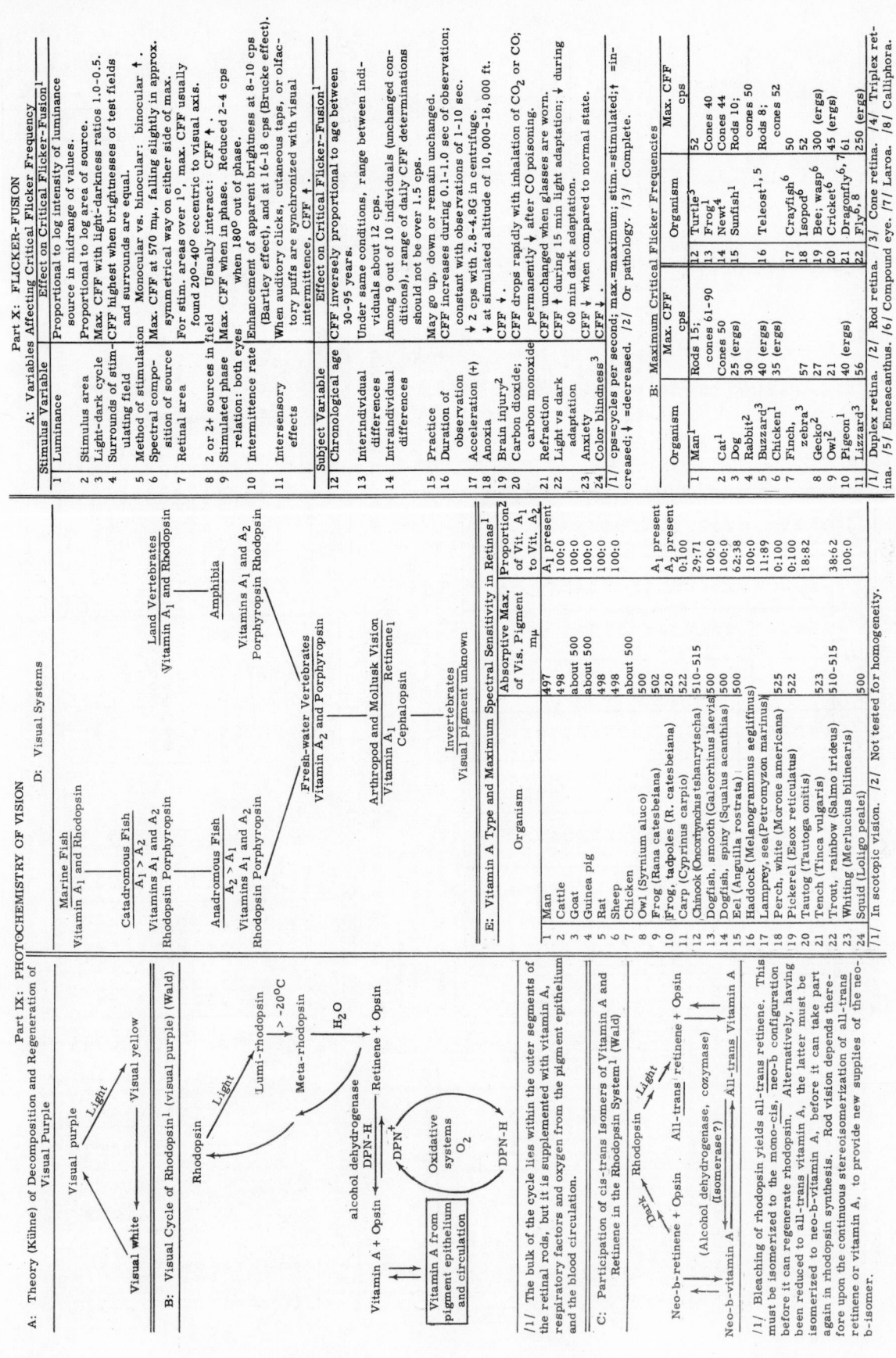

A: Theory (Kühne) of Decomposition and Regeneration of Visual Purple

Visual purple → (Light) → Visual yellow

Visual white ← Visual purple

B: Visual Cycle of Rhodopsin[1] (visual purple) (Wald)

Rhodopsin → (Light) → Lumi-rhodopsin → (> -20°C) → Meta-rhodopsin → (H_2O) → Retinene + Opsin

alcohol dehydrogenase DPN-H / DPN+ Oxidative systems O_2 DPN-H

Vitamin A + Opsin ⇄ Retinene + Opsin

Vitamin A from pigment epithelium and circulation

C: Participation of cis-trans Isomers of Vitamin A and Retinene in the Rhodopsin System[1] (Wald)

Neo-b-retinene + Opsin → (Dark) → Rhodopsin → (Light) → All-trans retinene + Opsin

(Alcohol dehydrogenase, cozymase) (isomerase?)

Neo-b-vitamin A ⇄ Neo-b-retinene + ... ⇄ All-trans Vitamin A

D: Visual Systems

- Marine Fish — Vitamin A1 and Rhodopsin
- Catadromous Fish A1 > A2 — Vitamins A1 and A2, Rhodopsin Porphyropsin
- Land Vertebrates — Vitamin A1 and Rhodopsin
- Amphibia — Vitamins A1 and A2, Porphyropsin Rhodopsin
- Anadromous Fish A2 > A1 — Vitamins A1 and A2, Rhodopsin Porphyropsin
- Fresh-water Vertebrates — Vitamin A2 and Porphyropsin
- Arthropod and Mollusk Vision — Vitamin A1 Retinene1, Cephalopsin
- Invertebrates — Visual pigment unknown

E: Vitamin A Type and Maximum Spectral Sensitivity in Retinas[1]

	Organism	Absorptive Max. of Vis. Pigment mμ	Proportion[2] of Vit. A1 to Vit. A2
1	Man	497	A1 present
2	Cattle	498	100:0
3	Goat	about 500	100:0
4	Guinea pig	about 500	100:0
5	Rat	498	100:0
6	Sheep	about 500	
7	Chicken	500	
8	Owl (Syrnium aluco)	500	A1 present
9	Frog (Rana catesbeiana)	502	A2 present
10	Frog, tadpoles (R. catesbeiana)	520	0:100
11	Carp (Cyprinus carpio)	522	29:71
12	Chinook (Oncorhynchus tshanrytscha)	510-515	100:0
13	Dogfish, smooth (Galeorhinus laevis)	500	100:0
14	Dogfish, spiny (Squalus acanthias)	500	62:38
15	Eel (Anguilla rostrata)	500	11:89
16	Haddock (Melanogrammus aeglifimus)		0:100
17	Lamprey, sea (Petromyzon marinus)	525	18:82
18	Perch, white (Morone americana)	522	
19	Pickerel (Esox reticulatus)	523	38:62
20	Tautog (Tautoga onitis)	510-515	100:0
21	Trout, rainbow (Salmo irideus)		
22	Tench (Tinca vulgaris)		
23	Whiting (Merlucius bilinearis)	500	
24	Squid (Loligo pealei)		

/1/ In scotopic vision. /2/ Not tested for homogeneity.

/1/ The bulk of the cycle lies within the outer segments of the retinal rods, but it is supplemented with vitamin A, respiratory factors and oxygen from the pigment epithelium and the blood circulation.

/1/ Bleaching of rhodopsin yields all-trans retinene. This must be isomerized to the mono-cis, neo-b configuration before it can regenerate rhodopsin. Alternatively, having been reduced to all-trans vitamin A, the latter must be isomerized to neo-b-vitamin A, before it can take part again in rhodopsin synthesis. Rod vision depends therefore upon the continuous stereoisomerization of all-trans retinene or vitamin A, to provide new supplies of the neo-b-isomer.

Part X: FLICKER-FUSION

A: Variables Affecting Critical Flicker Frequency

	Stimulus Variable	Effect on Critical Flicker-Fusion[1]
1	Luminance	Proportional to log intensity of luminance source in midrange of values.
2	Stimulus area	Proportional to log area of source.
3	Light-dark cycle	Max. CFF with light-darkness ratios 1.0-0.5.
4	Surrounds of stimulating field	CFF highest when brightnesses of test fields and surrounds are equal.
5	Method of stimulation	Monocular vs. binocular: binocular ↑.
6	Spectral composition of source	Max. CFF at 570 mμ, falling slightly in approx. symmetrical way on either side of max.
7	Retinal area	For stim. areas over 1°, max. CFF usually found 20°-40° eccentric to visual axis.
8	2 or 2+ sources in field	Usually interact: CFF ↑.
9	Stimulated phase relation: both eyes	Max. CFF when in phase. Reduced 2-4 cps when 180° out of phase.
10	Intermittence rate	Enhancement of apparent brightness at 8-10 cps (Bartley effect), and at 16-18 cps (Brucke effect).
11	Intersensory effects	When auditory clicks, cutaneous taps, or olfactory puffs are synchronized with visual intermittence, CFF ↑.

	Subject Variable	Effect on Critical Flicker-Fusion[1]
12	Chronological age	CFF inversely proportional to age between 30-95 years.
13	Interindividual differences	Under same conditions, range between individuals about 12 cps.
14	Intraindividual differences	Among 9 out of 10 individuals (unchanged conditions), range of daily CFF determinations should not be over 1.5 cps.
15	Practice	May go up, down or remain unchanged.
16	Duration of observation	CFF increases during 0.1-1.0 sec of observation; constant with observations of 1-10 sec.
17	Acceleration (+)	↓ 2 cps with 2.8-4.8G in centrifuge.
18	Anoxia	↓ at simulated altitude of 10,000-18,000 ft.
19	Brain injury[2]	CFF ↓.
20	Carbon dioxide; carbon monoxide	CFF drops rapidly with inhalation of CO_2 or CO; permanently ↓ after CO poisoning.
21	Refraction	CFF unchanged when glasses are worn.
22	Light vs dark adaptation	CFF ↑ during 15 min light adaptation; ↓ during 60 min dark adaptation.
23	Anxiety	CFF ↓ when compared to normal state.
24	Color blindness[3]	

/1/ cps=cycles per second; max.=maximum; stim.=stimulated;↑ =increased;↓ =decreased. /2/ Or pathology. /3/ Complete.

B: Maximum Critical Flicker Frequencies

	Organism	Max. CFF cps		Organism	Max. CFF cps
1	Man	Rods 15; cones 61-90	12	Turtle[3]	52
2	Cat[1]	Cones 50	13	Frog[1]	Cones 40
3	Dog	25 (ergs)	14	Newt[4]	Cones 44
4	Rabbit[2]	30	15	Sunfish[1]	Rods 10; cones 50
5	Buzzard[3]	40 (ergs)	16	Teleost[1,5]	Rods 8; cones 52
6	Chicken[1]	35 (ergs)	17	Crayfish[6]	50
7	Finch, zebra[3]	57	18	Isopod[6]	52
8	Gecko[2]	27	19	Bee; wasp[6]	300 (ergs)
9	Owl[2]	21	20	Cricket[6]	45 (ergs)
10	Pigeon[1]	40 (ergs)	21	Dragonfly[6,7]	61
11	Lizzard[3]	56	22	Fly[5,8]	250 (ergs)

/1/ Duplex retina. /2/ Rod retina. /3/ Cone retina. /4/ Triplex retina. /5/ Enneacanthus. /6/ Compound eye. /7/ Larva. /8/ Calliphora.

290. THE VISUAL MECHANISM: MORPHOLOGY AND PHYSIOLOGY (Concluded)

Part XI: WAVE LENGTH OF MAXIMAL SENSITIVITY[1]: ANIMALS AND PLANTS

	Organism	Wave Length mμ
1	Man	560
2	Cat	560
3	Guinea pig	500
4	Rat	500
5	Chicken	560-580
6	Pigeon	580
7	Snake	560
8	Tortoise	620
9	Frog	560
10	Fish, fresh-water	540-610
11	Salt-water	500
12	Crab	480-500
13	Squid	480-500
14	Bee	360[2]
15	Drosophila	360
16	Blowfly larvae	503
17	Tenebrio larvae	535
18	Mya	500
19	Balanus larvae	560-578
20	Arenicola	483
21	Volvox	494
22	Hydra	430-490
23	Eudendrium	460-480
24	Pandorina	524
25	Phacus	483
26	Ameba	430-490
27	Euglena	483
28	Green plants	465
29	Seedlings	blue
30	Avena	440
31	Phycomyces	449

/1/ Photopic conditions. /2/ Also green.

Part XII: DARK ADAPTATION: MAN

A: Following Light Adaptation to Various Brightnesses[1]
Values in boxes indicate color was apparent at threshold.

	400,000 Photons Time min	Log B μ pho²	38,900 Photons Time min	Log B μ pho²	19,500 Photons Time min	Log B μ pho²	3800 Photons Time min	Log B μ pho²	263 Photons Time min	Log B μ pho²
1	0.19	8.26	0.10	7.16	0.17	6.96	0.18	6.22	0.14	4.78
2	0.52	7.58	0.57	6.53	0.42	6.41	0.67	5.60	0.36	4.38
3	1.1	7.07	1.0	6.11	0.97	6.11	0.67	5.25	0.50	4.12
4	1.5	6.80	2.5	5.90	1.7	5.94	1.3	4.92	0.90	3.88
5	2.2	6.37	3.3	5.81	2.7	5.75	2.1	4.72	1.4	3.71
6	2.7	6.19	4.1	5.76	4.1	5.59	2.9	4.54	2.9	3.57
7	3.4	6.00	5.3	5.75	5.1	5.42	3.8	4.41	4.1	3.45
8	4.4	5.92	7.1	5.67	6.3	5.17	4.9	4.15	5.3	3.33
9	6.4	5.80	8.1	5.61	7.6	4.81	5.9	3.96	6.2	3.24
10	7.7	5.73	8.9	5.45	9.2	4.38	7.7	3.60	7.2	3.07
11	9.5	5.68	9.9	4.99	10.7	3.98	9.4	3.40	8.9	3.02
12	10.7	5.66	10.8	4.77	11.9	3.70	10.6	3.16	10.5	2.91
13	12.6	5.34	12.5	4.28	13.5	3.50	13.5	2.89	11.5	2.82
14	14.3	4.78	14.4	3.81	14.4	3.28	15.0	2.80	13.1	2.80
15	16.0	4.28	15.3	3.52	15.3	3.07	16.4	2.77	15.1	2.72
16	16.7	4.11	16.8	3.29	17.8	2.92	18.2	2.62	17.3	2.61
17	18.0	3.79	18.6	3.13	18.8	2.83	21.9	2.56	19.7	2.58
18	19.6	3.55	20.5	2.99	20.0	2.78	23.7	2.49	23.5	2.51
19	21.5	3.27	22.5	2.92	21.1	2.64	25.4	2.46	25.8	2.55
20	23.0	3.20	23.9	2.88	24.5	2.57	28.8	2.47	27.5	2.51
21	24.3	3.13	26.0	2.79	26.1	2.57			29.6	2.53
22	25.9	3.08	29.3	2.69	27.7					
23	28.5	2.97	32.0	2.55	29.8					
24	30.8	2.88								
25	33.4	2.84								
26	36.0	2.78								
27	38.6	2.72								

/1/ Values, from one observer, are least amounts necessary to produce response. Adapting field: 30° in diameter; white light, fixated 30° nasally on the retina, exposed for 2 minutes. Test field: 5° diameter containing a centered opaque cross 30' wide, violet light, fixated 30° nasally on the retina, exposed for 0.2 second. /2/ Microphotons.

B: Time-Luminance Relation

	Time in Dark min	Log Brightness millilamberts	Adapting Element
1	½	-1.5	
2	1	-2.0	
3	2	-2.3	
4	3	-2.5	Cones
5	4	-2.6	
6	5	-2.7	
7	6	-2.73	
8	7	-2.75	
9	8	-3.3	→ 2
10	9	-3.8	
11	10	-4.2	
12	15	-5.1	Rods
13	20	-5.3	
14	25	-5.5	
15	30	-5.6	

/1/ Values are least amount necessary to produce positive responses. /2/ Adaptation curve breaks caused by change from cone to rod vision.

C: Relative Sensitivity of Dark-adapted Eye

	Wave Length mμ	Relative Sensitivity[1] Periphery[2]	Fovea
1	400	-20	+10
2	450	-10	+24
3	500	-3	+26
4	525	0	0
5	550	0	+23
6	600	-4	+6
7	650	-10	-10
8	700	-27	-27
9	750	-40	-40

/1/ In decibels. /2/ 8° above fixation.

Part XIII: VISUAL ACUITY

A: Visual Phenomena as Functions of Luminance: Man

	Log B[1] mL	Pupil Diameter mm	Visual Acuity[2]	Intensity Discrimination, ΔB/B
1	-6.0	7.17		
2	-5.0	7.02		
3	-4.0	6.78		0.521
4	-3.5		0.08	0.350
5	-3.0	6.37	0.11	0.225
6	-2.5		0.13	0.137
7	-2.0		0.19	0.080
8	-1.5	5.80	0.29	0.048
9	-1.0		0.52	0.035
10	-0.5	5.10	0.80	0.027
11	0	4.74	1.14	0.021
12	0.5	4.39	1.48	0.017
13	1.0	4.05	1.74	0.015
14	1.5	3.64	2.0	0.012
15	2.0	3.19	2.15	0.015
16	2.5	2.77	2.22	0.017
17	3.0	2.43	2.25	0.024
18	3.5	2.09	2.26	0.037

/1/ White light. /2/ An acuity of 1.00 represents a visual angle of a 1' arc.

B: Visual Acuity and Illumination: Man
Test object: Landolt's ring.

	Red (λ=670 mμ) Log I photons	Log V.A.[1]	Blue (λ=490 mμ) Log I photons	Log V.A.[1]	White Log I photons	Log V.A.[1]
1	-2.88	-1.43	-4.87	-1.47	-3.44	-1.47
2	-2.55	-1.19	-4.09	-1.07	-2.87	-1.16
3	-2.25	-0.95	-3.79	-0.95	-2.42	-0.98
4	-1.85	-0.66	-2.97	-0.78	-2.13	-0.90
5	-1.53	-0.44	-2.32	[-0.65]	-1.85	[-0.84]
6	-1.23	-0.27	-2.02	[-0.56]	-1.85	-1.00
7	-0.81	-0.10	-1.72	[-0.48]	-1.45	-0.73
8	-0.49	0.02	-1.28	-0.38	-1.16	[-0.65]
9	-0.19	0.12	-0.97	-0.28	-1.16	-0.52
10	0.14	0.21	-0.67	-0.14	-0.88	[-0.45]
11	0.46	0.26	-0.25	0.02	-0.88	-0.33
12	1.08	0.30	0.36	0.21	-0.19	-0.04
13	1.71	0.33	1.19	0.30	0.09	0.06
14	2.43	0.36	1.83	0.35	0.77	0.21
15	3.15	0.37	2.44	0.39	1.50	0.29
16	3.77	0.38	3.18	0.39	2.47	0.37
17					3.44	0.40

/1/ Underlined values are rod determinations in a subjectively colorless field; those in brackets, with parafoveal rod and cone vision in a colored field; balance of values, with foveal cone vision in a colored field.

C: Resolving Power of Eyes

	Organism	Test Object	Background Illumination	Minimum Resolvable Angle
1	Man	Dark square	Bright sky	14.2 sec
2		Dark line	0.006 μL	10-11 min
3		Fine wire	Bright sky	0.43 sec
4		Grating	0.006 μL	20-30 min
5		Grating	30.2 mL	0.5-1 min
6	Cat	Grating	37.8 ft. cand.	0.45-1 min
7	Monkey	Grating	3.85 mL	0.95 min
8	Rat, albino	Grating		56 min
9	pigmented	Grating		26 min
10	Chick	Grating	3.85 mL	4.07 min
11	Pigeon	Grating	14.4 ft. cand.	0.38-0.5 min
12	Lizard	Grating	Lowest I[1]	0.5-1°
13		Grating	Highest I[1]	1.3-11.5 min
14	Frog	Pendulum		29.4 min
15	Crab, fiddler	Dark line	263 ft. cand.	3.87°
16	Bee	Grating	100 mL	0.9-1.0°
17		2 cm square[2]	Daylight	2.8°
18	Fly, fruit	Dark line	14.6 mL	9.28°

/1/ Intensity. /2/ At 40 cm.

D: The Stiles-Crawford Effect[1]

Rays entering the eye near the edge of the pupil are less effective than rays entering near the center. Their relative effectiveness is denoted by γ:

$$\gamma = 1 - 0.0850\, x^2 + 0.0020\, x^4,$$

where x is the distance (mm) from the center of the pupil.

	Distance mm	γ for Single Ray	Pupil Diameter mm	γ for Light Filling Entire Pupil
1		1.000	1	1.000
2	0.5	0.980	1.5	0.958
3	1.0	0.917	2.0	0.935
4	1.5	0.819	2.5	0.908
5	2.0	0.692	3.0	0.876
6	2.5	0.548	3.5	0.841
7	3.0	0.397	4.0	0.802
8	3.5	0.260	4.5	0.761
9	4.0	0.152	5.0	0.717
10			5.5	0.672
11			6.0	0.627
12			6.5	0.580
13			7.0	0.536
14			7.5	0.492
15			8.0	

/1/ Occurs only in cone vision.

Part XIV: CONVERSION FACTORS FOR BRIGHTNESS (LUMINANCE AND LUMINOUS EMITTANCE) UNITS

Value in unit in left hand column times the conversion factor equals the value in unit shown at the top of the column.

#	Units	C/sq mm	C/sq cm	C/sq m	Stilb (H)	C/sq in.	C/sq ft	L	mL	μL	Apostilb (H)	Ft-L	Photons[1]
1	Candles per square millimeter	1	1×10^{2}	1×10^{6}	1.111×10^{2}	6.452×10^{2}	9.290×10^{4}	3.142×10^{2}	3.142×10^{5}	3.142×10^{8}	3.491×10^{6}	2.919×10^{5}	7.854×10^{5}
2	Candles per square centimeter (C.I.E. Stilb)	1×10^{-2}	1	1×10^{4}	1.111	6.452	9.290×10^{2}	3.142	3.142×10^{3}	3.142×10^{6}	3.491×10^{4}	2.919×10^{3}	7.854×10^{3}
3	Candles per square meter	1×10^{-6}	1×10^{-4}	1	1.111×10^{-4}	6.452×10^{-4}	9.290×10^{-2}	3.142×10^{-4}	3.142×10^{-1}	3.142×10^{2}	3.491	2.919×10^{-1}	7.854×10^{-1}
4	Hefner candles per square centimeter (Stilb (H))	9.0×10^{-3}	9.0×10^{-1}	9.0×10^{3}	1	5.806	8.361×10^{2}	2.828	2.828×10^{3}	2.828×10^{6}	3.142×10^{4}	2.627×10^{3}	7.069×10^{3}
5	Candles per square inch	1.550×10^{-3}	1.550×10^{-1}	1.550×10^{3}	1.722×10^{-1}	1	1.440×10^{2}	4.869×10^{-1}	4.869×10^{2}	4.869×10^{5}	5.411×10^{3}	4.524×10^{2}	1.217×10^{3}
6	Candles per square foot	1.076×10^{-5}	1.076×10^{-3}	1.076×10	1.196×10^{-3}	6.944×10^{-3}	1	3.382×10^{-3}	3.382	3.382×10^{3}	3.758×10	3.142	8.454
7	Lamberts (equivalent centimeter candles, apparent lumens per square centimeter)	3.183×10^{-3}	3.183×10^{-1}	3.183×10^{3}	3.537×10^{-1}	2.054	2.957×10^{2}	1	1×10^{3}	1×10^{6}	1.111×10^{4}	9.290×10^{2}	2.500×10^{3}
8	Millilamberts	3.183×10^{-6}	3.183×10^{-4}	3.183	3.537×10^{-4}	2.054×10^{-3}	2.957×10^{-1}	1×10^{-3}	1	1×10^{3}	1.111×10	9.290×10^{-1}	2.500
9	Microlamberts	3.183×10^{-9}	3.183×10^{-7}	3.183×10^{-3}	3.537×10^{-7}	2.054×10^{-6}	2.957×10^{-4}	1×10^{-6}	1×10^{-3}	1	1.111×10^{-2}	9.290×10^{-4}	2.500×10^{-3}
10	Milli-microlamberts (micro-millilamberts)	3.183×10^{-12}	3.183×10^{-10}	3.183×10^{-6}	3.537×10^{-10}	2.054×10^{-9}	2.957×10^{-7}	1×10^{-9}	1×10^{-6}	1×10^{-3}	1.111×10^{-5}	9.290×10^{-7}	2.500×10^{-6}
11	Apostilb (Hefner lumens per square foot)	2.864×10^{-7}	2.864×10^{-5}	2.864×10^{-1}	3.183×10^{-5}	1.848×10^{-4}	2.661×10^{-2}	9.0×10^{-5}	9.0×10^{-2}	9.0×10	1	8.360×10^{-2}	2.249×10^{-1}
12	Foot-lamberts (equivalent foot candles; apparent lumens per square foot)	3.426×10^{-6}	3.426×10^{-4}	3.426	3.807×10^{-4}	2.210×10^{-3}	3.183×10^{-1}	1.076×10^{-3}	1.076	1.076×10^{3}	1.196×10	1	2.691
13	Photons[2]	1.273×10^{-6}	1.273×10^{-4}	1.273	1.414×10^{-4}	8.213×10^{-4}	1.183×10^{-1}	4.000×10^{-4}	4.000×10^{-1}	4.000×10^{2}	4.444	3.716×10^{-1}	1

/1/ In converting measures of brightness into photons, it is necessary to multiply the conversion factor by the square of the pupil diameter in millimeters. /2/ In converting photons to measures of brightness, it is necessary to divide the conversion factor by the square of the pupil diameter in millimeters.

Part XV: MISCELLANEOUS

A: Characteristic Luminances

Values in parentheses are ranges.

#	Specification	Luminance ft-L[1]
1	Noon sun on snow	10,000
2	Hazy sky	1,000
3	Foliage in landscape	(100-400)
4	Living room walls	(7-10)
5	Television screens in homes	(3.5-10)
6	Motion pictures (theater)	1.6(0.4-5)
7	Drive-in	0.7(0.1-2.2)
8	Photopic vision	>0.01
9	Mesopic vision	(0.001-0.01)
10	Scotopic vision	<0.001
11	Cones take over	0.006±
12	Rods take over	0.008±
13	Lower limit of useful color vision	0.019±
14	Night automobile driving	(0.003-4)
15	Asphalt roads	(0.045-1.1)
16	Cement roads	(0.08-3.2)
17	Pedestrian on road	(0.012-0.35)
18	Moonlight	0.01
19	Clear starlight, no moon	0.0001
20	Hazy starlight, no moon	0.00001
21	Threshold	0.00001

/1/ Foot-lamberts.

B: Color Temperatures

#	Source	Degrees Kelvin
1	Candle	1900
2	Carbon filament lamp	2100
3	Gas-filled lamp, 40 watt	2700
4	60 watt	2800
5	100 watt	2870
6	1000 watt	3020
7	Ribbon filament lamp, 108 w	2950
8	CIE[1] source A	2854
9	Fluorescent "Warm White"	3000
10	Photoflood	3400
11	Carbon (solid) arc	3750
12	Fluorescent "Cool White"	4500
13	Average noon sunlight	5000
14	CIE[1] source B	4870
15	Carbon (sunshine) arc	6260
16	Fluorescent "Daylight"	6500
17	Overcast sky	6500
18	CIE[1] source C	6740
19	Light overcast sky	7500
20	Hazy blue sky	9000
21	Clear blue sky	25000

/1/ Commission Internationale de l'Eclairage. Source A is characteristic of tungsten light, source B of sunlight and source C of daylight. For details see Hardy, A. C., "Handbook of Colorimetry," Cambridge, Mass.: Technology Press, 1939.

Part XVI: GLOSSARY

APHAKIC. Destitute of the lens of the eye.

APOSTILB. 9×10^{-2} mL (see also LAMBERT).

CANDLE (C). Unit of luminous intensity defined by reference platinum standard.

CANDLEPOWER. Luminous intensity (I) expressed in candles. $I = dF/d\omega$, where F is luminous flux and ω is solid angle in steradians (see LUMEN).

DECIBEL. A logarithmic measure of the ratio between two quantities. The number of decibels denoting the ratio is 10 times the logarithm to the base 10 of the ratio.

DIOPTER. Refractive power of a lens (reciprocal of focal length, expressed in meters).

ERG. Energy of 1 dyne through 1 cm.

FLUX. Time rate of flow of light.

FOOT-CANDLE (see FOOT-LAMBERT). Unit of illumination (lumen/sq ft).

FOOT-LAMBERT (ft-L). 1 ft-L = $1/\pi$ candles/sq ft, and is the same as the apparent foot-candle, and numerically equal to the equivalent foot-candle.

ILLUMINATION (E). The density of luminous flux on a surface. $E = dF/dA$, where A is area.

INTENSITY (I). Light-giving power of a source of light (see CANDLEPOWER).

LAMBERT (L). Unit of luminance equal to $1/\pi$ candles/sq cm. It is equal to the uniform luminance of a perfectly diffusing surface emitting or reflecting 1 lumen/sq cm. 1 Apostilb (Blondel) = 9×10^{-2} mL.

LUMEN (lm). Unit of luminous flux; it is equal to the flux through a unit solid angle (steradian) from a uniform point source of one candle.

LUMINANCE (B). Photometric brightness. It is the luminous intensity (I) of any surface in a given direction per unit of projected area of the surface as viewed from that direction. $B = dI (dA \cos \theta)$, where A = surface area, and θ = angle between direction of observation and 90° line to the surface.

MESOPIC. Pertaining to vision intermediate between photopic and scotopic (q.v.).

PHOTON (TROLAND). Retinal illumination for 1 sq mm of pupil area from a luminance of 1 c/sq m.

PHOTOPIC. Pertaining to vision in bright light.

SCOTOPIC. Pertaining to vision in dim light.

STILB. Unit of luminance equal to 1 C/sq cm.

TROLAND (see PHOTON).

VISUAL ACUITY (V.A.). Reciprocal of angle (1' arc) between 2 black bars just visibly separate.

λ = Wave length.

Part I: MORPHOLOGY OF THE EAR: MAN

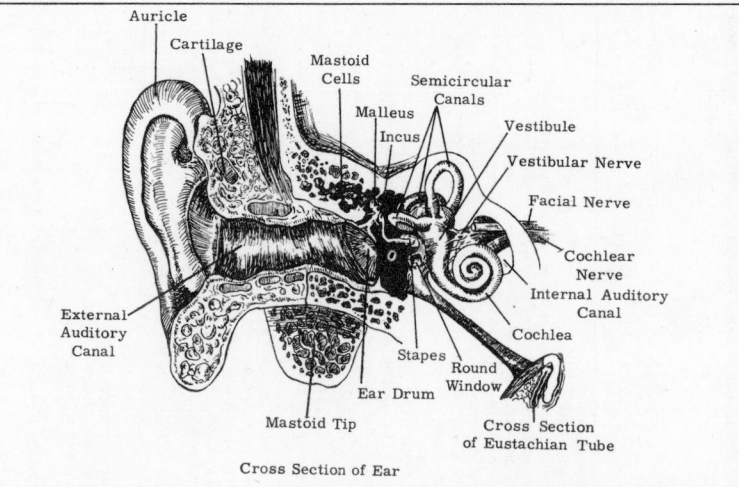

Cross Section of Ear

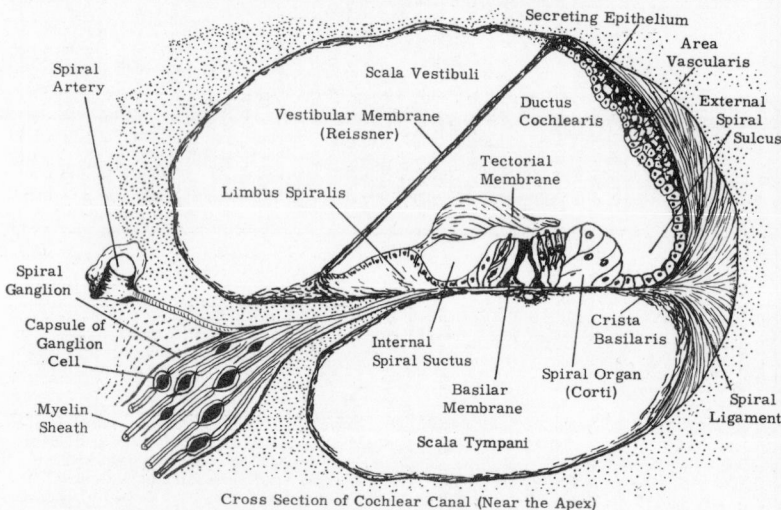

Cross Section of Cochlear Canal (Near the Apex)

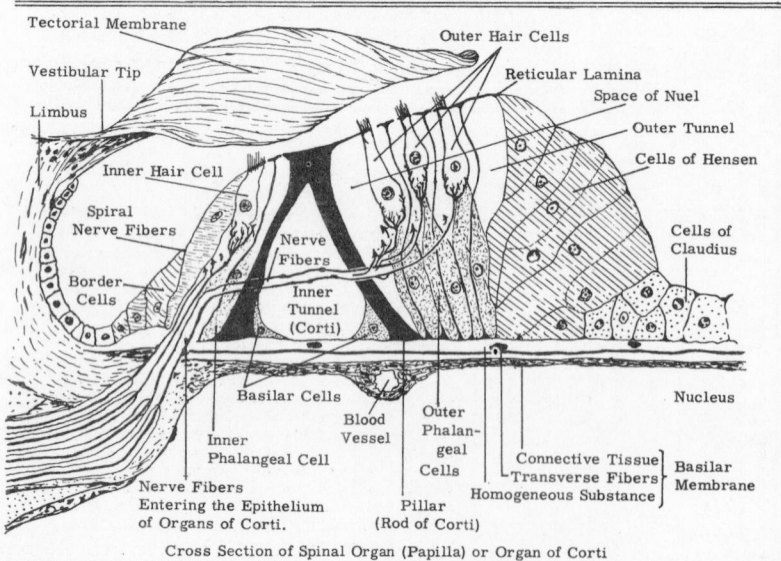

Cross Section of Spinal Organ (Papilla) or Organ of Corti

The external auditory canal extends inward (medially) to the tympanic- or drum-membrane. Medial to this, embedded in the bone, lies the irregular air chamber, the middle ear, and medial to the latter is the fluid-filled inner ear or labyrinth. The tympanic membrane is set in the lateral (external) wall of the middle ear, opposite the oval and round windows in the medial wall. Positioned across the chamber from the tympanic membrane to the oval window are the three ossicles (malleus, incus, and stapes), to which are attached the tensor tympanic and stapedial muscles. The handle of the malleus is attached to the drum. The incus is joined at its outer end to the head of the malleus by a flexible joint, and the stapes in turn articulates with the incus. The footplate of the stapes fits into the oval window and is joined to the bony window around its edge by an elastic ligament. The round window is an opening in the bony labyrinth closed by a membrane. The ear receives sound waves on the drum; the vibrations are conducted by the ossicles and are transmitted through the oval window to the fluid and sensory elements in the inner ear (ultimately to the round window). The inner ear consists of the osseous labyrinth, a complicated group of communicating cavities in the bone (the vestibule adjoining the middle ear, the cochlea, and the semicircular canals) and the membranous labyrinth contained in and coextensive with the osseous labyrinth. The membranous labyrinth consists of the semicircular canal, utricle, saccule, and membranous cochlea (ductus cochlearis, scala media). A clear fluid, the perilymph, surrounds the membranous labyrinth; within the membranous labyrinth is the endolymph. (The semicircular canals, utricle, and saccule are involved in equilibrium and are not considered here.) The bony cochlea, a short cone resembling a snail shell, has in it the sense organ for sound perception (organ of Corti, papilla basilaris). Its bony spiral tube is divided by the spiral (bony) lamina, an incomplete partition which is completed by the ductus cochlearis, thus making three tubes, the scala vestibuli, the scala media (ductus cochlearis) and the scala tympani. The scala media has the following structures: Reissner's membrane separating it from the scala vestibule, the stria vascularis (secretory organ), the tectorial membrane resting on the organ of Corti (papilla basilaris), the organ of Corti consisting of supporting cells, pillar cells (tunnel of Corti) and external and internal hair cells (neuro-sensory elements). These structures rest on the basilar membrane which separates it from the scala tympani. The cochlear division of the 8th nerve enters the modiolus of the cochlea to form the spiral ganglion. The dendrites of the ganglion cells are distributed to the spiral organ of Corti, supported by the basilar membrane. The axons of the ganglion cells go to the medulla.

Part II: COMPARATIVE MORPHOLOGY OF AUDITORY MECHANISMS

Species	Outer Ear — External Canal			Tympanic Membrane			Middle Ear — Cavity	Malleus		Incus	Stapes			
	Opening Area sq cm	Length cm	Volume ml	Diameter mm	Area sq mm	Thickness mm	Volume ml	Weight mg	Length Total mm	Weight mg	Weight mg	Footplate Length mm	Width mm	Area sq mm
1 Man	0.3-0.5	2.3-3.0	1.04	8-10	56-85	0.1	2	23-27	7.6-9.1	25-32	2.0-4.3	2.6-3.4	1.1-1.7	2.6-3.7
2 Cat				5.5-8.6	32-48	0.03		10-11.4		3-4.5	0.2-0.9	1.6	1	1.1-1.3
3 Dog														
4 Guinea pig				23-28										0.8-0.9

Species	Middle Ear (concluded) — Muscles				Inner Ear		Cochlea							
	Tensor Tympani Cross Section sq mm	Length mm	Stapedius Cross Section sq mm	Length mm	Oval Window Area sq mm	Round Window Area sq mm	Turns no.	Volume cu mm	Scala Vestibuli Volume cu mm	Max. Diam. mm	Scala Tympani Volume cu mm	Area Helicotrema[1] sq mm	Scala Media Volume cu mm	Length mm
1 Man	4.8-6.9	23-26	4.9	6.3	2.0-3.7	2	2.2-2.9	98	54	3.5	37	0.08-0.2	6.7	35
2 Cat					1.1-1.3	2.8-3.3	3+			2.7				25
3 Dog							3.2			3.0				16-17
4 Guinea pig					1.4	1.0	4							18.8

Inner Ear (concluded)

Species	Cochlea (concluded) — Basilar Membrane			Organ of Corti							
	Length mm	Thickness mm	Fibers no.	Cross Sectional Area sq mm	Inner Hair Cells no.	Height mm	Outer Hair Cells no.	Height mm	Inner Pillar Cells no.	Outer Pillar Cells no.	Total Ganglion Cells no.
1 Man	25-35	<0.003	24000	0.005-0.022[2]	3500	0.034	20000	0.028-0.066[3]	5600	3850	30500
2 Cat	19-25		15700	0.005-0.020[3]	2600	0.03	9900		4700	3300	
3 Dog	14-16		10500[4]		1600	0.03	6100	0.03-0.036[3]	2800	1940	
4 Guinea pig	18.8	0.007-0.0013[2]		0.012-0.017[5]							

/1/ Communicating part between scala tympani and scala vestibuli. /2/ From base to apex. /3/ Measurement made at midpoint of the length of the basilar membrane. /4/ The tympanic layer. /5/ The maximum is for a point near the apex of the cochlea; at the extreme apex the area diminishes to 0.015 sq mm.

Part III: COMPARATIVE AUDITORY SYSTEMS

Species	Organ Type	Location	Accessory Structures
		Vertebrates	
1 Man	Organ of Corti. Pillars, tunnel, outer and inner hair cells, Hensen's cells, Claudius' cells, tentorium, Reissner's membrane.	Cochlea, 2½ to 3 turns.	Mastoid tip well developed. Mastoid area more or less pneumatic in adult. Apex pneumatic, semipneumatic, or containing either fatty or hemapoietic marrow. Stapes with posterior crus bowed. Arachnoid tissue fills aqueduct.
2 Bat	Organ of Corti, with tall pillars and stiff rod spiralling in basilar membrane in floor of tunnel.	Cochlea, 2 turns. Fibers of VIIIth cochlear branch pass straight up modiolus to apical ganglion cells. Some species spiral.	Middle ear muscles large, especially tensor tympani, with heavy nerve supply. Stapediovestibular ligament composed of discrete fiber cells. Cartilaginous trap door for closing external ear. Drum membrane very thin. Stapedius muscle unseparated by bone from jaw muscles, i.e., no bony enclosure posteriorly for middle ear. No bulla, mastoid or pneumatization. Large supply of fat in bones and among head muscles. Stapedial artery present in some species.
3 Cat and dog	Organ of Corti; no unique characteristics described.	Cochlea, 3 turns.	Bulla divided into 2 compartments separating oval and round windows. Middle ear muscles relatively large. Superior sinus of Eustachian tube widely patent. Wide cochlear aqueduct.
4 Guinea pig	Well-developed organ of Corti. High or tall Hensen's cells.	Cochlea, 4½ turns. Spiral ganglion follows through modiolus to apex.	Persistent stapedial artery and bony bar. Middle ear competely enclosed by bulla. Coils of cochlea exposed in molded form on medial wall of middle ear. Wide cochlear aqueduct.
5 Monkey	Spiral organ of Corti.	Cochlea, 2½ turns.	Middle ear, mastoid, and petrous apex completely enclosed in bone. No mastoid tip developed. Pneumatization extreme in both mastoid and apex. Bony Eustachian tube difficult to identify because of pneumatization of apex. Internal carotid artery courses through apex. No stapedial artery. Long bony external auditory canal. Cochlear aqueduct narrow.
6 Opossum	Spiral organ of Corti rests on basilar membrane.	Cochlea, 2 turns. Ganglion follows through modiolus to top coil, but is untwisted.	Incipient bulla. Membrana tympani on half-shell of bone. No bony external auditory canal. Ossicles small and fragile. Styloid process participates in articulation near head of stapes. Stapedius muscle large (derived from depressor mandibulae), occupying whole posterior wall of middle ear. Tensor tympany small (derived from pterygoid). Malleus fan-shaped anterior process. VIIth nerve passes uncovered by bone through middle ear and emerges at level of round window. Cochlear aqueduct is Y-shaped, one limb entering scala tympani and one directed toward middle ear. Large IXth ganglion in floor of middle ear.

Part III: COMPARATIVE AUDITORY SYSTEMS (Concluded)

	Species	Organ Type	Location	Accessory Structures
			Vertebrates (continued)	
7	Platypus[1]	Organ of Corti. Lagena sense organ.	Lagena. Incipient cochlea.	Recessus scala tympani narrows into funnel-shaped tube to form cochlear aqueduct.
8	Birds		Papilla lagena, basilaris and, neglecta. Papilla lagena elongated. Developed tegmentum vasculosum. Saccule reduced. No crus commune. Superior semicircular canal large and encircling others. Posterior canal smallest and communicating perilymph with horizontal.	Membrana tympani, columella, Eustachian tube, oval and round windows. Round window separates perilymph and intracranial arachnoid spaces from middle ear. Single columella. First appearance of external ear.[2]
9	Turtle	Sensory cells bathed in fluid. Papilla basilaris.	Papilla lagena, basilaris, and neglecta. Shows mound of Corti.	Membrana tympani, columella of two articulating pieces, Eustachian tube, oval and round windows. Latter separates perilymph and arachnoid spaces from middle ear.
10	Frog			Membrana tympani, columella, Eustachian tube, oval and round windows. Latter separates perilymph and intracranial arachnoid spaces from middle ear.
11	Toad[3]	Also, probably some sensation through skin of foot pads.	End-organs as in fish.	Vestibulo-scapular conduction through forefeet. Vestibulo-squamosal conduction direct from ground.
12	Fish	Sensory hair cells bathed in fluid. Lagena saccule.	Lateral line organs for slow vibrations. Labyrinth in head, bilateral, developed from lateral line organs. Cristae of 3 semicircular canals in 3 planes of space. Macula of utricle. Lagena and macula of very large saccule. Large otoliths. Papilla neglecta present in most fishes.	Forerunner of middle ear in carp, goldfish, catfish, etc. Weberian ossicles. Oval window.
			Invertebrates	
13	Cricket	Membrani tympani. Sensory cells of graded sizes.	Front leg below knee. May be second one in 2nd abdominal section.	
14	Grasshopper[4]	Membrani tympani connected with leg tracheal vesicles. Sensory cells of graded sizes.	Front segment of abdomen.	
15	Grasshopper[5]	Membrani tympani with external ear and ear slit. Sensory cells of graded sizes.	Tibia of foreleg.	

/1/ Duckbill. /2/ External ear of rooster can be closed when crowing. /3/ Tree toad; also salamander. /4/ Short antennae. /5/ Long antennae, Katydid.

Part IV: FUNCTIONS OF AUDITORY COMPONENTS: VERTEBRATES

	Species	Segment	Component	Function
1	Man[1], all mammals	External ear	Auricle.	Collects sound waves. Protects ear mechanism.
			External ear canal.	Passageway for sound waves.
		Middle ear	Ear drum (tympanic membrane).	Picks up sound waves and starts rocking of ossicles.
			Ossicles: malleus, incus, stapes.	Rocking motion transmits sound waves to perilymph and membranous cochlea through oval window.
			Eustachian tube.	Carries air from nasopharynx to middle ear.
			Antrum, mastoid cells.	Lightens skull; helps maintain air on medial side of drum.
		Internal ear	Osseous labyrinth: vestibule; horizontal semicircular canal; anterior and posterior vertical semicircular canals. Bony cochlea.	Protects membranous labyrinth.
			Membranous labyrinth: utricle, semicircular canals attached; saccule, cochlea attached;	Static equilibrium. Orientation in space.
			3 semicircular canals.	Equilibrium, in motion (canals).
			Cochlea: basilar membrane, organ of Corti.	Organ of hearing.
2	Birds and reptiles[2]	External ear	Auditory meatus.	
		Middle ear	Tympanic membrane, columella[3].	Transmits sound.
		Internal ear	Utricle, lagena saccule, papilla basilaris.	Dual function of equilibrium and hearing.
3	Amphibians	No external ear		
		Middle ear	Tympanic membrane, columella[4].	Transmits sound.
		Internal ear	3 semicircular canals. Vestibule: utricle, lagena saccule, papilla basilaris.	Dual function of equilibrium and primitive auditory organ.
4	Fishes	No external ear		
		No middle ear		
		Internal ear	3 semicircular canals[5]. Vestibule: utricle, lagena saccule.	Dual function of equilibrium and primitive auditory organ.

/1/ Cochlea highly developed. In all except aquatic mammals, middle ear has three ossicles. External ear present. /2/ Bird organs are similar in structure to those of reptiles, including basilar membrane. Tympanic organs also have hairs beneath the tympanum. /3/ Two bones, inner one acts as stapes. No middle ear in snakes. /4/ Bony rod, action similar to stapes. /5/ Higher fishes have three canals, hagfish one, and lamprey two.

Part V: HEARING THRESHOLDS FOR PURE TONES: MAMMALS

The least "strength" of a given stimulus that can just elicit a response from an organism or its parts is the threshold for the type of stimulation employed. For the sense of hearing, the "strength" (intensity) of a sound stimulus is expressed in terms of the rate of flow of sound energy at the hearing point. For binaural hearing, this is the midpoint of the position of the listener's head when the head is placed in the sound field. The unit of power (rate of energy flow) is commonly watts/sq cm. Measurements of hearing are often made, however, in terms of sound-wave pressure (dynes/sq cm) in the air at the hearing point. As the rate of energy flow is proportional to the square of the sound pressure, both are convertible to the decibel (db) scale. The least sound pressure (dynes/sq cm) at which a tone having a frequency of 1000 cycles/sec (cps) can be heard by a human observer is approximately 0.0002 dynes/sq cm. This value is used as a basis for comparison of sound intensity levels, serving as the zero reference level for a logarithmic intensity scale. The unit of this scale is the db. The intensity level of sound, in db, is 10 x the $\log_{10}$ of the ratio of the intensity of this sound to the reference intensity. As the intensity is also proportional to the square of the sound pressure, the level of a sound in db can be calculated from sound pressure in dynes/sq cm by the formula $db = 20 \log p_1/p_2$, where p_1 is the pressure of a sound of a given frequency, and p_2 is 0.0002 dynes/sq cm (the threshold pressure of a 1000 cps tone). Negative values for decibels indicate that less energy is required to make the sound audible than is required for a tone of 1000 cps.

	Sound Wave Frequency[1] cps	Man[2] db	Cat db	Chim-panzee db	Dog db	Guinea Pig db	Monkey db	Rat db
1	64	46				60	45	
2	100	37	38		34			
3	128	30		20		41	20	
4	200	23	24		21			
5	256	16		8		26	10	
6	400	10	9		9			
7	500	6	6		8		7	
8	512	5		-3		11		65
9	1,000	0	-1		1		-3	
10	1,024	0		-10		2		41
11	2,000	-4	-2		-3		-5	
12	2,048	-5		-14		18		40
13	2,896	-7						31
14	3,000	-8	-7		-7			
15	4,000	-8	-6		-6		3	
16	4,096	-7		-6		14		30
17	5,000	-4	-8		-10			
18	5,792	1						30
19	8,000	7	-7		-3		-14	
20	8,192	8		-9		34		-14
21	10,000	9	-7		-6			
22	11,584	10						0
23	14,000	13	-9		-5			
24	16,000	20	-4		2			

/1/ Each frequency corresponds to a different pure tone. /2/ The sound is generated at intensity just sufficient to be heard binaurally, the experimental subject is then removed, and the intensity at the hearing point is measured.

Part VI: RANGE OF HEARING: ANIMALS

Unless otherwise indicated, values are based upon changed behavior of the intact animal in response to tonal stimuli. The data, however, are inhomogenous, and the values are not strictly comparable with one another because of different criteria used in determining the lower and upper limits. The limits are not actually single numbers as they depend both on the intensity of the stimulus and the endpoint chosen to define "hearing."

	Species	Frequency Limit Lower cps	Frequency Limit Upper cps
1	Man	15[1]	20,000[1]
2	Bat	30[2]	98,000[2]
3	Cat	30[2]	45,000[3]
4	Chimpanzee		33,300
5	Dog		40,000
6	Dolphin, Tursiops	100	130,000[4]
7	Guinea pig		40,000
8	Monkey		33,600
9	Mouse, deer	500	95,000
10	Mouse, harvest		17,500
11	Opossum	100	19,000[3]
12	Rat		40,000
13	Pigeon	100	12,000
14	Alligator		340
15	Turtle		1,200
16	Axolotl		240
17	Frog	50	10,000
18	Catfish		13,000
19	Characinidae		10,000
20	Goldfish		2,700[4]
21	Minnow		7,000
22	Cricket (Acridium aegyptium)		20,000
23	Cricket (Gryllus assimilis)	300	8,000
24	Grasshopper (Arphia sulfurea)	300	20,000
25	Katydid (Pterophylla camellifolia)	430	45,000[2]

/1/ At the lower end the sense of hearing merges into the sense of feeling and vibration. On the musical scale (equal tempered chromatic), the note low C (C_0) has a frequency of 16, middle C (C_4, four octaves higher) 256, middle A (American Standard Pitch) 440, and high C (C_8) 4186. /2/ By recording electrical potentials from the region of the sensory organ; does not necessarily represent the capacities of the entire auditory system. /3/ Electrical responses of the cochlea up to 30,000 cps have been reported. /4/ At least as high as this figure.

Part VIII: PURE TONES OF EQUAL LOUDNESS: MAN

The greater the intensity of a pure tone, the greater is its loudness up to the level of discomfort or pain. However, the loudness of a sound is a subjective estimate, whereas its intensity is measured objectively. In general, two tones of equal intensity but different frequency are not necessarily equally loud to the hearer. Each successive column, 10-120, contains values that are equal in loudness in the same column, but louder than values in the preceding column. The intensity levels for 1000 cps (Line 9) have been used as a scale of reference and appear at the head of each column.

	Pure Tone cps	10 db	20 db	30 db	40 db	50 db	60 db	70 db	80 db	90 db	100 db	110 db	120 db	Threshold of Feeling db	Threshold of Feeling cps
1	Thirty	5	9	12	15	17	20	22	25	29	36	46	64	82	35
2	Fifty	5	11	15	18	22	25	29	32	38	46	57	72	92	
3	Seventy	6	12	16	21	25	28	33	37	44	53	65	80	94	75
4	One hundred	7	14	19	24	28	33	38	44	51	62	72	85	101	
5	Two hundred	8	16	23	29	37	44	51	58	67	77	87	100	109	
6	Three hundred	8	17	25	32	40	48	57	66	75	85	95	107	116	400
7	Five hundred	10	19	28	36	45	54	65	74	84	95	105	115		
8	Seven hundred	11	20	30	39	48	59	69	79	89	99	110	120	130	800
9	One thousand	10	20	30	40	50	60	70	80	90	100	110	120		
10	Two thousand	10	21	32	43	53	64	74	83	92	100	110	118	132	1500
11	Three thousand	10	21	32	43	54	65	74	83	91	100	109	118	133	3100
12	Five thousand	11	23	34	44	55	65	74	82	90	99	106	115		
13	Seven thousand	10	21	32	44	56	65	74	83	90	98	105	112	125	6500
14	Ten thousand	10	21.	32	43	55	64	74	82	90	96	104	111		

	Animal	End Organ or Region of Body	Substance	Medium[1]	Method[2]	Mean or Median Threshold
1	Tongue worm	General integument	HCl	SW	W	0.002N
2	(Balanglossus sp)		NaOH or KOH	SW	W	0.0025N
3			KCl	SW	W	0.005N
4			Quinine	SW	W	0.001M
5	Tunicate	Oral siphon	HCl	SW	W	0.0016N
6	(Ascidia atra)		Formic acid	SW	W	0.0018N
7			NaOH or acetic acid	SW	W	0.010N
8			NH_4OH	SW	W	0.015N
9			KSCN	SW	W	0.10N
10			K acetate	SW	W	0.15N
11			KCl	SW	W	0.20N
12			NH_4Cl	SW	W	0.30N
13			NaCl	SW	W	0.40N
14			Strychnine	SW	W	0.00005M
15			Morphine[3]	SW	W	0.001M
16			Quinine	SW	W	0.004M
17			Ethyl ether[4]	SW	W	0.02M
18			Ethyl alcohol	SW	W	0.75M
19	Lancelet	Mouth	HCl	SW	W	0.002N
20	(Amphioxus)	Mid-trunk	HCl	SW	W	0.10N
21		Tail	HCl	SW	W	0.01N
22	Lamprey	Mouth	HCl	SW	W	0.008N
23	(Petromyzon sp)		NaOH	SW	W	0.001N
24	ammocoetes larvae		NaCl	SW	W	0.025N
25			Quinine	SW	W	0.0016M
26		Mid-trunk	NaOH	SW	W	0.01N
27			HCl or NaCl	SW	W	0.05N
28			Quinine	SW	W	0.10M
29		Tail	NaOH	SW	W	0.002N
30			HCl	SW	W	0.025N
31			NaCl	SW	W	1.0N
32			Quinine	SW	W	0.05M
33	Dogfish, smooth	Mouth	NaOH	SW	W	0.01N
34	(Mustelus sp)		HCl	SW	W	0.013N
35		Mid-trunk	HCl	SW	W	0.02N
36			$NaOH^5$	SW	W	0.05N
37		Tail	HCl	SW	W	0.025N
38	Catfish	Mouth	NaOH	SW	W	0.01N
39	(Aniurus sp)		NaCl	SW	W	0.02N
40			HCl	SW	W	0.05N
41			Quinine	SW	W	0.007M
42		Mid-trunk	HCl	SW	W	0.02N
43			$NaOH^5$	SW	W	0.05N
44		Tail	HCl	SW	W	0.025N
45	Rat	Tongue (taste buds)	NaCl	FW	E	0.0081% (0.0075-0.0095%)
46	(Rattus rattus		NaCl	FW	A	0.06%
47	norvegicus, and		$HgCl_2$	FW	R	0.004% (0.001-0.007%)
48	var. albinus		As_2O_3	FW	R	0.0065% (0.002-0.02%)
49			Glucose	FW	A	0.20% (0.1-0.4%)
50			Galactose	FW	A	1.6% (0.5-2.8%)
51			Lactose	FW	R	4.8% (2.8-6.5%)
52			Maltose	FW	A	0.06% (0.04-0.08%)
53			Sucrose	FW	A	0.57% (0.1-0.8%)
54			Quinine HCl	FW	A	0.00005% (0.000012-0.0002%)
55			Quinine HCl	FW	R	0.0003% (0.0001-0.0012%)
56			Quinine SO_4	FW	R	0.00072% (0.00038-0.0016%)
57			Phenylthiocarbamide	FW	R	0.0003% (0.00005-0.02%)
58			α-Naphthylthiourea	FW	R	0.001% (0.0005-0.002%)
59			Phenylthiourea	FW	R	0.002% (0.0001-0.008%)
60			Thiosemicarbazide	FW	R	0.0023% (0.0005-0.005%)
61			Strychnine SO_4	FW	R	0.008% (0.005-0.02%)
62	Adrenalectomized		NaCl	FW	E	0.0104% (0.0048-0.017%)
63	Rabbit, European	Tongue (taste buds)	HNO_3	FW	R	0.085N
64	(Oryctolagus cuniculus)		HCl	FW	R	0.12N
65			H_2SO_4	FW	R	0.14N
66			Acetic acid	FW	R	0.17N
67			NaI	FW	R	0.79N
68			$NaNO_3$	FW	R	0.81N
69			NH_4Cl	FW	R	1.0N
70			KCl	FW	R	1.1N
71			Na acetate or $NaSO_4$	FW	R	1.3N
72			NaCl or $CaCl_2$	FW	R	1.4N
73			LiCl	FW	R	1.8N
74			Sucrose	FW	A	0.031M
75	Cat, domestic	Tongue (taste buds)	HCl	FW	E	0.02N(0.007-0.07N)
76	(Felis catus)		NaCl	FW	E	0.1-0.3N
77			Quinine	FW	E	0.001-0.005M
78	Monkey	Tongue (taste buds)	Quinine HCl	FW	A	0.0031%(0.0003-0.006%)
79	(Macaca mulatta)		Quinine HCl	FW	R	0.025% (0.0015-0.05%)
80	Chimpanzee	Tongue (taste buds)	Quinine HCl	FW	A	0.0003%
81	(Pan troglodytes)		Quinine HCl	FW	R	0.0062%

/1/ Dispersion medium for the stimulating substance. SW=sea water; FW=fresh water. /2/ Experimental procedure used to indicate reception. W=generalized avoidance reaction or withdrawal of part of body; E=electro-physiological methods; A=acceptance thresholds for materials offered in food or water; R=rejection thresholds. /3/ Same value for amyl alcohol. /4/ Same value for chloral hydrate. /5/ Same value for tail, NaOH.

293. TASTE AND OLFACTION THRESHOLDS: MAN

Values derived from early literature were excluded from this table. It is considered that publication of the older values might perpetuate certain ambiguities, if not errors, that have arisen in translation and recalculation. Data presented below have been selected from the more recent research publications.

Part I: TASTE THRESHOLDS

Values are lowest molar concentrations that can be distinguished as different from water alone.

	Substance	Threshold Mole/L		Substance	Threshold Mole/L
1	Formic acid	0.0018	13	n-Pentanol	0.016
2	Acetic acid	0.0028	14	n-Hexanol	0.002
3	Butyric acid	0.0035	15	n-Heptanol	0.0013
4	Valeric acid	0.0037	16	n-Octanol	0.0006
5	Tartaric acid	0.0011	17	1,2-Butanediol	0.052
6	Glutaric acid	0.00225	18	1,3-Butanediol	0.016
7	Succinic acid	0.0016	19	1,4-Butanediol	0.031
8	Lactic acid	0.0028	20	1,5-Pentanediol	0.017
9	Oxalic acid	0.0010	21	1,6-Hexanediol	0.013
10	Ethanol	0.32	22	1,8-Octanediol	0.016
11	n-Propanol	0.11	23	Ethylene glycol	0.063
12	n-Butanol	0.028	24	Trimethylene	0.037

Part II: THRESHOLDS OF TASTERS vs NON-TASTERS

Tasters are individuals relatively sensitive to phenylthiourea; non-tasters are relatively insensitive. Values are lowest molar concentrations that can be distinguished as different from water alone.

	Substance	Tasters Mole/L	Non-Tasters Mole/L
1	Urea	0.132	0.132
2	Phenylurea	0.00551	0.00551
3	Thiourea	0.00295	0.0553
4	Phenylthiourea	0.000020	0.00306
5	Diphenylthiourea	0.000013	0.000070
6	Acetylthiourea	0.000093	0.00719
7	Diacetylthiourea	0.000106	0.002068
8	Thioglyoxaline	0.000155	0.00845
9	Thio-methylhydantoin	0.000508	0.00217
10	Uracil	0.011	0.008928
11	Methyl-thiouracil	0.000296	0.001204

Part III: OLFACTION THRESHOLDS

P_{olf} = partial pressure of substance for olfactory recognition; P^O = vapor pressure of pure substance; $A_{olf} = P_{olf} \div P^O$ = the fraction of saturated vapor of substance that allows threshhold recognition.

	Substance	Concentration mg/L	P_{olf} atm x 10^{-7}	P^O atm (37°C)	A_{olf} x 10^{-3}
1	Amyl acetate	0.039	90	0.013	1
2	Ethyl acetate	0.69	1760	0.23	1
3	Butyric acid	0.009	18	0.003	1
4	Ethyl ether	5.83	13,000	1.1	1
5	Chloroform	3.30	6700	0.4	2
6	Artificial musk	0.00004	0.029	0.0000013	2
7	Carbon tetrachloride	4.53	6700	0.24	3
8	Valeric acid	0.029	50	0.001	5
9	Amyl alcohol	0.225	500	0.007	7
10	Nitrobenzene	0.146	300	0.0007	40
11	Methyl salicylate	0.10	150	0.00026	60

	Substance	Threshold A_{olf} x 10^{-4}
1	Methyl alcohol	500
2	Ethyl alcohol	300
3	n-Butyl alcohol	7
4	n-Hexyl alcohol	7
5	n-Octyl alcohol	30
6	n-Decyl alcohol	200
7	n-Dodecyl alcohol	1000
8	Ethane	170
9	n-Butane	8
10	n-Pentane	10
11	n-Heptane	50
12	n-Nonane	200
13	n-Undecane	450
14	n-Butyl chloride	5
15	n-Heptyl chloride	30
16	n-Decyl chloride	100

294. PAIN SENSITIVITY: MAN

Specific thresholds of pain are necessarily arbitrary, since the variations between individuals, and within an individual under differing conditions and accommodations, are great. Widely accepted standards for measurement have not yet been achieved. Body locus of stimuli materially affects mechanical and electrical thresholds, and chemical pain stimulation is generally in proportion to the pH extreme. An accepted thermal pain threshold of 0.21 gram-calories/sec/sq cm reported (Woodson, W. E., Human Engineering Guide, 1954). The data in this table, from the research of J. D. Hardy, H. G. Wolff, and H. Goodell, are based on only limited samplings of subjects and should under no circumstances be considered standards.

Part I: PRICKING PAIN THRESHOLDS

Values are for a final skin temperature of 34°C, corrected from observed threshold values by the formula: $Q_{34} = Q + 20(T_s - 34)$, where Q_{34} = pain threshold for 34°C; Q = observed pain threshold in millicalories per second x square centimeter; and T_s = final skin temperature. Values in parentheses are estimate "b" of the 95% range (cf Introduction).

	Skin Area[1]	Final Skin Temp. °C	Pain Threshold millical.[2]/sec/sq cm		Skin Area[1]	Final Skin Temp. °C	Pain Threshold millical.[2]/sec/sq cm
1	Forehead	45.7	235(181-289)	19	Arch	44.3	200(144-256)
2	Cheek (zygoma)	44.6	210(156-264)	20	Heel	53.7	390(202-478)
3	Nose	44.8	215(151-279)	21	Heel, corneal layer shaved off		250
4	Lips	44.1	200(124-276)				
5	Chin	45.0	220(166-274)	22	Shoulder	44.8	215(143-287)
6	Chest	44.8	215(127-303)	23	Neck (nape)	43.8	195(147-286)
7	Nipple	43.8	200(136-264)	24	Back (upper)	43.5	185(121-249)
8	Abdomen	43.9	200(164-236)	25	Back (middle)	43.8	195(147-242)
9	Groin	43.3	185(137-233)	26	Back (lower)	42.2	160(104-216)
10	Thigh (posterior)	42.8	175(119-231)	27	Buttock	42.4	165(89-241)
11	Thigh (anterior)	42.6	170(114-226)	28	Arm (upper)	43.4	185(117-253)
12	Kneecap	42.7	175(139-211)	29	Forearm (volar)	44.4	210(146-274)
13	Popliteal space	43.5	190(150-230)	30	Forearm (outer)	44.0	200(152-248)
14	Calf	43.0	185(129-241)	31	Hand (back)	43.8	195(131-259)
15	Shin	43.9	190(146-234)	32	Finger pad	47.1	260(180-340)
16	Ankle	44.0	190(146-234)	33	Fingernail		215(185-245)
17	Foot, dorsum	43.2	180(124-236)	34	Palm, center	45.1	220(152-288)
18	Toes, dorsum	43.4	185(117-253)	35	Palm, over callus	45.6	230(158-312)

/1/ Ink-blackened skin areas exposed to radiant heat stimulus for three seconds. /2/ Millicalories = small calories/1000.

Part II: SCALE OF PRICKING PAIN INTENSITY

It is not usually possible to discriminate between stimuli less than two steps apart; therefore, for purposes of this table, the unit of pain sensation is equivalent to two steps and is designated as a dol. Ceiling pain intensity has a value of $10\frac{1}{2}$ dols, as there are 21 steps between pain threshold and ceiling pain, under conditions specified.

Stimulus Intensity[1] millicalories[2]/second/sq cm	Increments of Intensity Discrimination		Step	No. of dols	Stimulus Intensity[1] millicalories[2]/second/sq cm	Increments of Intensity Discrimination		Step	No. of dols
1	220	◄——Pain threshold——			12	300	10		11th
2	227	7		1st	13	310	10	90	12th	6
3	234	7	14	2nd	1	14	320	10	13th
4	241	7		3rd	15	335	15		14th	7
5	248	7	28	4th	2	16	350	15	115	15th
6	255	7		5th	17	365	15		16th	8
7	262	7	42	6th	3	18	380	15	145	17th
8	269	7		7th	19	395	15		18th	9
9	276	7	56	8th	4	20	425	30	175	19th
10	283	7		9th	21	480	55		20th	10
11	290	7	70	10th	5	22	680	——Pain ceiling——	260

/1/ Stimulus is intense radiant heat applied for three seconds to ink-blackened skin of forehead or forearm. /2/ Millicalories = small calories/1000.

Part III: PRESSURE PAIN THRESHOLDS

	Surface	Threshold[1] g/sq mm
1	Cornea	0.2
2	Conjunctiva	2
3	Abdomen	15
4	Forearm, front	20
5	Forearm, back	30
6	Calf	30
7	Back of hand	100
8	Sole of foot	200
9	Finger tip	300

/1/ Pressure applied with sharp needle.

295. BIOLUMINESCENCE
Table adapted from data presented in E. Newton Harvey's "Bioluminescence," Academic Press, 1952.

	Groups and Typical Luminous Genera	Habitat[1]	Type of Light[2]	Knowledge of Histology[3]	Necessity for Oxygen[4]	Luciferin-Luciferase Reaction[5]	Adenosine Triphosphate Reaction[6]	Inhibition by Light[7]	Color of Fluorescence[8]	Color of Bioluminescence[9]
1	Bacteria (Photobacterium, Achromobacter, Vibrio)	M, F[10]	I	±	+	+	-	±	-	Bluish to greenish (470, 490, 495)
2	Fungi basidiomycetes (Panus, Omphalia, Pleurotus, Polyporus, etc.)	T	I	±	+	-	-	-	-	White (528, 520)
3	Radiolaria (Thalassicola, Sphaerozoum, Collozum, Myxosphaera, Collosphaera)	M	I	±	-	-		-	-	Faint bluish
4	Dinoflagellata (Noctiluca, Ceratium, Gonyaulax, Gymnodinium, Pyrocystis, etc.)	M	I	±	+			±DN		White or bluish
5	Porifera (Grantia)	M	I?	-		-		-		Yellowish
	Hydroidea									
6	Hydroids (Campanularia, Obelia, Aglaophenia, etc.)	M	I?					-		Yellowish
7	Hydromedusae (Aequorea, Halistaura, Phialidum, etc.)	M	I?	-	-	-	-	-		Bluish green
8	Siphonophora (Diphyes, Hippopodius, Agalma, etc.)	M	I?							Faint bluish
9	Scyphomedusae (Pelagia, etc.)	M	E?	±	-	-	-	-[11]	-	Greenish blue
10	Pennatulacea (Cavernularia, Pennatula, Renilla, Pteroeides, etc.)	M	I	±	+		+-[12]	±[13]	-	Yellowish
11	Gorgonacea (Ceratoisis, Primnoisis, etc.)	M	?	-						Pale lilac
12	Ctenophora (Mnemiopsis, Beroë, Pleurobrachia, Bolinopsis, Eucharis, etc.)	M	I	±				+	Greenish	Blue-green
13	Nemertinae (Emplectonema)	M	I	+						Bluish white
	Polychaeta									
14	Polynoinae (Acholoë, Polynaë, Harmothoë, etc.)	M	I	+	+	-		-	Yellowish	Yellowish
15	Alciopidae (Calizonella, Corynocephalus, etc.)	M	-							Bluish
16	Tomopteridae (Tomopteris)	M	I?	±		-			-	Yellowish
17	Syllidae (Odontosyllis, etc.)	M	E	±		+				Bluish
18	Eunicidae (Onuphis)	M	I	-						Bluish green
19	Chaetopteridae (Chaetopterus, Mesochaetopterus, etc.)	M	E	+	+	-	-	-	Bluish	Bluish
20	Cirratulidae (Cirratulus, Heterocirrus, etc.)	M	E	+						Yellow-green
21	Terebellidae (Thelepus, Polycirrus)	M	E	+	+	-				Bluish
22	Oligochaeta (Microscolex, Eisenia, Pontodrilus, Octochaetus, etc.)	T[14]	E	+	+	-[15]			Yellow-green	Yellow-green (550)
23	Nudibranchia (Plocamopherus, Phyllirhoë, Kaloplocamus, etc.)	M	E[16]	+						Bluish white
	Pulmonata									
24	Ariophantidae (Dyakia)	T	I	-						Bluish
25	Latiidae (Latia)	F	E	+		+				Bluish green
26	Prosobranchia (Planaxis)	M	I	-		-	-			Bluish
27	Bivalvia (Pholas, Rocellaria)	M	E	+	+	+	-			Greenish blue
28	Vampyromorpha (Vampyroteuthis)	M	I	+						
	Decapod squid[17]									
29	Oegopsida (Watasenia, Lycoteuthis, Histioteuthis, Calliteuthis, Chiroteuthis, Cranchia, etc.)	M	I	+	+					Bluish[18] or yellowish
30	Myopsida (Inioteuthis, Rondeletia, Sepiola, Spirula, etc.)	M	Bs or Bp	+	+				-	Bluish[19]
31	(Heteroteuthis, Stoloteuthis)[20]	M	E	+	+	-	-	-		Yellowish blue
32	Ostracoda (Cypridina, Pyrocypris, Conchoecia, etc.)	M	E	+	+	+	-	+	Yellow	Blue (480-470)
33	Copepoda (Pleuromma, Leuckartia, Heterochaeta, Oncaea, etc.)	M	E	±	+	-		±DN	Greenish[21]	Greenish
34	Isopoda (Megaligia, Porcellio)	MT	Bp		+					Bluish
	Amphipoda									
35	Gammaridea (Talitrus, Orchestia, etc.)	M	Bp		+					Bluish
36	Hyperiidea (Scyphlolanceola, Streetsia, Parapronoë)	M	I?	±						Greenish yellow[22]

/1/ F = fresh water; M = marine; T=terrestrial. /2/ Bp=light emission owing to parasitic luminous bacteria; Bs=light emission owing to symbiotic luminous bacteria; E = self-luminosity with extracellular light emission from secreted material; I = self luminosity with intracellular material. /3/ + = cytology of the photogenic cell or histology of the light organ is well known; - = cytology or histology unknown; ± = further study of cytology or histology is desirable. /4/ + = dissolved molecular oxygen is necessary for light production; - = light will appear in complete absence of oxygen (Pt and H$_2$, or, in excess, hydrosulfite). /5/ + = positive reaction if light appears when a hot water extract of the luminous cells allowed to cool (luciferin) is mixed with a cold water extract of the luminous cells allowed to stand until the light disappears (luciferase); - = a negative reaction. /6/ + = positive reaction if a non-luminous water extract of the luminous tissue containing magnesium emits light when the sodium salt of adenosine triphosphate is added; - = a negative reaction. /7/ + = marked inhibition of luminescence of single-celled organisms or of luminescent extracts by sunlight; - = no marked inhibition; ± = some species show light inhibition, others do not; DN = day-night rhythm of luminescence such that the intact living organism does not luminesce in the daytime even if kept in the dark. /8/ - = no marked fluorescence in near ultraviolet light or after functional activity. /9/ Figures in parentheses are wave lengths of maximum emission where spectrophotometric curves are known. /10/ Some luminous bacteria live on the flesh of terrestial animals. /11/ Inhibition has been observed. /12/ Adenosine triphosphate reaction positive in Renilla Kollikeri and negative in R. reniformis. /13/ In Renilla, inhibition and no inhibition have been observed. /14/ Pontrodilus matsushimensis lives in sand, wet by the sea. /15/ Thermolabile and thermostable components demonstrated. /16/ Kaloplocamus reported to have intracellular luminescence. /17/ The location of luminous organs has been tabulated by G. Grimpe and H. Hoffman (Tab. Biol. 6:462-4, 1930). /18/ Red, white, and blue in Lycoteuthis diadema. /19/ Greenish yellow in Spirula. /20/ No luminous bacteria demonstrated in Stoloteuthis. /21/ Bluish in Oncaea. /22/ Regarding Parapronoë.

Table adapted from data presented in E. Newton Harvey's "Bioluminescence," Academic Press, 1952.

	Groups and Typical Luminous Genera	Habitat[1]	Type of Light[2]	Knowledge of Histology[3]	Necessity for Oxygen[4]	Luciferin-Luciferase Reaction[5]	Adenosine Triphosphate Reaction[6]	Inhibition by Light[7]	Color of Fluorescence[8]	Color of Bioluminescence[9]
37	Mysidacea (Gnathophausia, Mysis, Siriella, Gastrosaccus)	M	E	±						Greenish
38	Schizopoda (Nyctiphanes, Euphausia, Nematoscelis, etc.)	M	I	+		-			Greenish?	Bluish
	Decapod shrimp									
39	(Sergestes, Hoplophorus, etc.)	M	I	+		-	-			Greenish yellow
40	(Systellaspis, Plesiopenaeus, Heterocarpus, etc.)	M	E	+		+				Bluish
41	(Xyphocaridina)	F	Bp		+					Bluish
42	Diplopoda (Luminodesmus, Spirobolellus)	T	I, Bs?	-	+				Blue-green	Greenish white
43	(Trigoniulus)	T	Bp							Blue-green
44	Chilopoda (Stigmatogaster, Orya, Geophilus, Scolioplanes, etc.)	T	E	+	+				Bluish?	Blue-green
45	Collembola (Neanura, Onychiurus, etc.)	T	I[23]	-						Blue-green or greenish yellow
46	Orthoptera (Gryllotalpa)	T	Bp?	-						Greenish white
47	Ephemerida (Caenis, Telognodes)	T	Bp?	-						Pale blue
48	Hemiptera (Fulgora)	T	?	-						White
49	Diptera (Ceroplatus, Platyura, Arachnocampa, etc.)	T	I	±		-	-			Bluish
50	(Chironomus)	T	Bp							Greenish
51	Lepidoptera (Mamestra, Agrotis larvae, Asteroscopus adult)	T	Bp							Bluish
52	Hymenoptera (Camponotus, Iridomyrmex)	T	Bp?							Greenish-yellow
	Coleoptera									
53	Lampyridae (Photinus, Photuris, Luciola, Lampyris, etc.)	TF	I	+	+	+	+-	-[24]	Greenish yellow[25]	Orange (565), yellow (570), or green (550)
54	Phengodidae (Phengodes, etc.)	T	I	+	+		-	-	+, yellowish?	Yellow-green
55	Rhagophthalmidae (Dioptoma)	T	I	-						Green
56	Drilidae (Diplocladon)	T	I	-						Greenish blue
57	(Phrixothrix)	T	I	+	+	-	-	-	-	Red and yellow-green
58	Elateridae (Pyrophorus, etc.)	T	I	+	+	+	+	-[24]	Yellow	Greenish and orange (518 and 530)
59	Ophiuroidea[26] (Amphiura, Ophioscolex, Opiopsila, etc.)	M	I	+	+				Yellow-green	Green
60	Enteropneusta (Ptychodera, Balanoglossus)	M	E	+	+	-		-DN[27]	-	Bluish or greenish
61	Tunicata (Pyrosoma, Appendicularia, Salpa, etc.)	M	I or Bs?	+		-	-			Various colors
62	Elasmobranchii (Etmopterus, Laemargus, Centrosyllium, etc.)	M	I	+						Greenish or white
	Teleostomi									
63	Macrouridae (Malacocephalus, Coelorhynchus, etc.)	M	Bs	+	+	+				Greenish blue (510)
64	Gadidae (Physiculus, Lotella)	M	Bs	+						Greenish blue
65	Monocentridae (Monocentris)	M	Bs	+			-			Weak bluish
66	Anomalopidae (Photoblepharon, Anomalops, Kryptophaneron)	M	Bs	+						Greenish blue
67	Acropomatidae (Acropoma)	M	Bs	+						Bluish white
68	Leiognathidae (Leiognathus, Gazza, Secutor)	M	Bs	+						Bluish white
69	Serranidae (Apogon)	M	I?	+						Bluish green
70	Cerratioidea (Dolopichthys, Ceratias, Linophryne, etc.)	M	Bs?	+						Bluish green or purplish
71	Saccopharyngidae (Saccopharanx)	M	Bs?	-						White
72	Batrachoididae (Porichthys, etc)	M	I	+						White
73	Stomiatoidea (Echiostoma, Gonostoma, Maurolicus, Polyipnus, Argyropelecus, Chauliodus, Stomius, etc.)	M	I[28]	+		-	-	-	Greenish[29]	Yellowish to greenish or bluish
74	Myctophoidea (Myctophum, Diaphus, Lampadena, Neoscopelus)	M	I	+		-	-		Greenish	Bluish or greenish

/1/ F = fresh water; M = marine; T=terrestrial. /2/ Bp=light emission owing to parasitic luminous bacteria; Bs=light emission owing to symbiotic luminous bacteria; E = self-luminosity with extracellular light emission from secreted material; I = self luminosity with intracellular material. /3/ + = cytology of the photogenic cell or histology of the light organ is well known; - = cytology or histology unknown; ± = further study of cytology or histology is desirable. /4/ + = dissolved molecular oxygen is necessary for light production; - = light will appear in complete absence of oxygen (Pt and H_2, or, in excess, hydrosulfite). /5/ + = positive reaction if light appears when a hot water extract of the luminous cells allowed to cool (luciferin) is mixed with a cold water extract of the luminous cells allowed to stand until the light disappears (luciferase); - = a negative reaction. /6/ + = positive reaction if a non-luminous water extract of the luminous tissue containing magnesium emits light when the sodium salt of adenosine triphosphate is added; - = a negative reaction. /7/ + = marked inhibition of luminescence of single-celled organisms or of luminescent extracts by sunlight; - = no marked inhibition; ± = some species show light inhibition, others do not; DN = day-night rhythm of luminescence such that the intact living organism does not luminesce in the daytime even if kept in the dark. /8/ - = no marked fluorescence in near ultraviolet light or after functional activity. /9/ Figures in parentheses are wave lengths of maximum emission where spectrophotometric curves are known. /23/ It has been claimed that the light comes from a fungus in some species. /24/ Intense illumination of the luminous organ inhibits luminescence by affecting nerve stimulation. /25/ The purified luciferin is blue fluorescent in acid, yellow-green in alkali. /26/ The location of luminous organs has been tabulated by G. Grimpe (Tab. Biol. 6:449-501, 1930). /27/ In Ptychodera at Bermuda. /28/ No luminous bacteria demonstrated in Yarella or Polyipnus. /29/ Argyropelecus photophores show no marked fluorescence.

	Species	Geographic Distribution	Specialized Structures	Remarks
			Sarraceniaceae (Pitcher-plants)	
1	Darlingtonia californica	California, Oregon.	Erect, hooded, pitcher-like leaves from 1.5 to 100 cm long, lined with "nectar" glands and hairs. "Digestive" glands absent.	Cf Heliamphora.
2	Heliamphora spp[1]	Northern South America.	Pitcher-like leaves, 30-50 cm long when mature, lined with "nectar" glands and unicellular hairs. "Digestive" glands absent.	Any digestion of animal "prey" must be attributed to adventitious bacterial action because of the reported absence of digestive glands or secretions. Ability of plant to absorb products of digestion not determined.
3	Sarracenia spp[2]	Eastern North America.	Pitcher-like leaves, 10-40 cm long when mature, lined with "nectar" glands, unicellular hairs, "digestive" glands; non-cuticular "absorptive" areas present.	Absorption of liquid from pitchers has been demonstrated. pH of pitcher contents in the field varies from 2 to 8. Mature pitchers contain considerable amounts of decayed insect residues. Presence of various enzymes, i.e., maltase, lipase and proteinases, reported in pitcher liquid. Role of bacteria in digestion of animal "prey" not determined.[3]
			Nepenthaceae (Nepenthes)	
4	Nepenthes (±65 spp)[4]	Southwest Pacific to Ceylon and Madagascar.	Leaves tendril-like, up to one meter long, terminating in pitcher-like erect hooded cups 5-30 cm long. Pitchers are lined with "nectar" glands, various types of hairs, and "digestive" glands.	Cf Sarracenia.
			Droseraceae (Sundews)	
5	Aldrovanda vesiculosa	Europe, Asia, Africa, Australia.	Leaves in whorls of 8, bearing at their tips bilobed "traps" (somewhat similar to Dionaea); inner aspects of lobes bear "secreting" glands and 3 kinds of hairs.	Traps close on appropriate stimulation, as in Dionaea. Insects thus trapped disintegrate. Action of bacteria and enzymes not determined.[5]
6	Dionaea muscipula (Venus fly-trap)	Peat bogs of North and South Carolina.	Leaves bilobed, with marginal spines and six "trigger" hairs in center of upper surface. Upper leaf-surface bears "nectar" glands and "digestive" glands, both types sessile.	When an insect comes in contact with a trigger hair, the leaf-lobes close rapidly (±0.25 sec), forming with the marginal spines a box-like structure within which the "prey" may be entrapped. Closure is followed by the secretion of an acid substance in which various proteolytic enzymes have been reported. Role of bacteria in digestion uncertain. Absorption of products of digestion reported; significance on nutrition not determined.
7	Drosera (±90 spp)	World-wide.	Leaves orbiculate, spatulate or linear, 2-35 cm long, with tentacles yielding a viscid secretion.	Tentacles inflect to cover insects entrapped in tentacular secretion. Secretion contains sugars and enzymes capable of proteolysis at pH 2. Digestion independent of bacterial action; absorption not clearly demonstrated.[6]
8	Drosophyllum lusitanicum	Portugal, Spain, Morocco.	Similar to Byblis (cf below) but larger, shrubbier; leaves with stalked "mucilage" glands and sessile "digestive" glands.	Insects captured in mucilaginous secretion. Digestion by secreted enzymes reported, possibly affected by bacteria. Beneficial absorption of proteolytic products reported.
			Cephalotaceae (Cephalotus)	
9	Cephalotus follicularis	Australia.	Leaves of 2 kinds: foliage (to 15 cm) and pitcher-like (pitchers to 5 cm long, at right angle to petiole). Pitcher lined with glands and modified stomata which are secretory in function.	Insects entrapped in pitchers disintegrate; whether this is caused by bacterial action, by enzymes produced by the plant, or by both, not determined. No evidence of absorption of products of proteolysis.
			Byblidaceae	
10	Byblis gigantea, B. linifolia	Australia.	Semi-shrubs with linear leaves, 10-20 cm long, bearing stalked "muscilage" glands and sessile "digestive" glands.	Small, wingless insects live on leaves and feed on other insects entrapped by mucilage. Digestion of egg-white in contact with secretion of digestive glands reported. Role of bacteria in digestion and absorption of products of digestion not determined.
11	Roridula (2 spp)	South Africa	Leaves equipped with tentacular glands furnishing a "resinous" secretion.	Digestion by bacteria or secreted enzymes not reported. Certain insects habitually feed on entrapped "victims." Cf Byblis.
			Lentibulariaceae (Bladderworts)	
12	Genlisea (±10 spp)	Tropical Africa, South America.	Small submersed plants with "foliage" and "trapping" leaves, which are forked at tip, spirally twisted and connected with a basal bulb or receptacle. Grooves formed by twisted portion are transversely ridged and supplied with glandular hairs secreting mucilage.	Disintegrated insect remains are commonly found in grooves of leaves and in basal receptacles. Digestion or absorption of digestive products not determined.
13	Pinguicula (±30 spp)	Northern Temperate and Sub-arctic Zones.	Rosette plants with entire leaves bearing "muscilage" and "digestive" glands.	Small insects become entangled in muscilage secretions, and leaf margins slowly enroll. Disintegration of insects ensues. Bacterial or enzymatic action uncertain. Absorption of products of digestion not determined.[7]
14	Utricularia (±275 spp)	World-wide.	Aquatic plants bearing on submersed portions small vesicles or "bladders" lined with glandular hairs. Absorption of water within bladders leads to formation of a partial vacuum; a door closes the bladder. On the outer surface of the door are 4-6 "tripping" hairs or bristles.	When an aquatic insect encounters the tripping hair, the door opens and the inrushing water carries the insect into the bladder. After an interval the partial vacuum is reestablished, again setting the trap. Entrapped insects disintegrate and are apparently absorbed. Bacterial action not determined.
15	Biovularia (2 spp)	Antilles, South America.	Cf Utricularia.	Cf Utricularia.
16	Polypompholyx (3 spp)	Australia.	Cf Utricularia.	Cf Utricularia.

/1/ Species: H. macdonaldae, H. minor, H. nutans, H. tatei, H. tyleri. /2/ Species: S. adunca, S. drummondii, S. flava, S. jonesii, S. minor, S. oreophila, S. psittacina, S. purpurea, S. rubra, S. sledgii, S. variolaris. /3/ Insect larvae, especially of mosquitoes, have frequently been found growing in the pitcher liquid. This raises questions as to the proteolytic property of the plant secretions. /4/ Five distinct types of nepenthes are: N. villosa, N. lowii, N. rajah, N. hookeriana, N. rafflesiana. /5/ There is evidence that the plant can grow indefinitely on inorganic nutrients, and no evidence that organic nutrition through the capture of animals is essential for growth. /6/ Plants have survived 15 years, in aseptic culture, on inorganic nutrients + sucrose. /7/ Laplanders reported to use leaf secretion to curdle milk.

297. FACTORS AFFECTING CILIARY ACTIVITY
Part I: CHEMICAL
Cilia cease beating when underlying muscle contracts, resume beating when muscle relaxes.

	Ciliated Material	Chemical Factors	Results
		Protozoa	
1	Paramecium	Novocaine, 0.5%	Ciliary coordination may be interrupted; partial disappearance of metachronal activity [1], or merely slowing of rate.
2		Ions (Na, K, Li, etc.)	Reversal of ciliary beat.
		Invertebrates	
3	Actinian larvae, longitudinal band	Ca, Mg ions	Neuromuscular movement inhibited, ciliary movement stimulated.
4	Ctenophora, meridional combs	H, K, and NH_4 ions	Neuromuscular movement stimulated, then depressed; ciliary
5	Veliger (Mollusca) larvae, lobes		movement depressed, then recovers.
6	Trochophore larvae, peristomal;	Li and Na ions	Neuromuscular movement stimulated, ciliary movement inhibited.
7	Annelida larvae		
8	Nemerteans, surface	Atropine, 2% ⎫	Strong initial stimulus; actively moving after 4 hours.
9	epithelium	Curare, 2% ⎟	Strong initial stimulus; actively moving after 4 hours.
10		Ether, 2% ⎟	Cilia continued beating, undiminished for a long time.
11		Lithium chloride, 2% ⎟ in sea	Cilia at rest after 15 minutes.
12		Magnesium chloride, 2% ⎬ water	Muscular contraction inhibited, but not cilia.
13		Nicotine, 2% ⎟	Cilia brought to rest after a few minutes.
14		Pilocarpine, 2% ⎟	Very active ciliary movement, undiminished after 2 hours.
15		Strychnine, 2% ⎭	Ciliary movement stimulated initially, then becomes inactive.
16	Pecten yessoensus (Mollusca),	pH 3.7 ± 0.1: HCl at 13°C ⎫	
17	terminal cilia on end of gill	3.8 ± 0.4: H_3PO_4 at 20°C ⎟	
18		5.45 ± 0.15: CH_3COOH at 20°C ⎬	Stop cilia in 1 minute; order of efficiency: $H_2CO_3 > CH_3COOH >$
19		5.5 ± 0.5: H_2CO_3 at 20°C ⎟	$H_3PO_4 > HCl$.
20		6.15 ± 0.05: H_2CO_3 at 13°C ⎭	
21	Anodonta (Mollusca), gill	Caffeine, 2%	Ciliary movement accelerated for 3 minutes, ceased in 6 minutes.
22		Chloral hydrate, 0.5%	Cilia quiet in 4 to 5 minutes.
23		Novocaine, 1%	Cilia quiet in 9 minutes.
24		Pilocarpine HCl, 1.5%	Metachronal activity[1] continues until cilia become quiet (2 minutes).
25		Strychnine sulfate, 1%	Cilia quiet in 10 minutes.
26		Veratrine sulfate, 1-1.5%	Metachronal activity[1] continues until cilia quickly cease movement.
		Vertebrates	
27	Frog, buccal membrane (excised)	Acetic acid vapor ⎫ gas	Ciliary movement stimulated initially, then stopped.
28		Ammonia vapor, 1.5% ⎬ chamber	Initial strong movement of cilia, then cessation.
29		Alcohol, amyl	Cessation of ciliary movement in 18 minutes.
30		butyl 1:10 dilution	Cessation of ciliary movement in 3 hours.
31		ethyl ⎬ in normal	Cessation of ciliary movement after 30 hours.
32		methyl saline	Cessation of ciliary movement after 30 hours.
33		propyl	Cessation of ciliary movement after 25 hours.
34		Acids	Cilia brought to rest.
35		Alkalies (KOH, NaOH)	Ciliary activity slowly stimulated, then became vigorous.
36		Ions (Na, K, Li, etc.)	Reversal of ciliary beat.
37		Sodium bicarbonate, conc. vapor	Quick cessation of ciliary movement.
38		Sodium chloride, 0.3-0.5%	Cilia beat all day, no cessation.
39		Sodium chloride, 0.5%, or blood serum in gas chamber, + CO_2	Initial cessation of ciliary movement, followed by vigorous activity; cilia beat longer in dilute solutions of CO_2
40	Frog, esophageal mucosa (in situ)	Benzedrine, 0.1%	46 to 52% depression of ciliary movement.
41		Ephedrine HCl, 0.1%	25 to 32% depression of ciliary movement.
42		m-Synephrine HCl, 0.1%	17 to 25% depression of ciliary movement.
43	Frog, esophagus (in vitro)	Alcohol	Slight depression of ciliary activity.
44		Chloroform	Depressed ciliary activity.
45		Ethylene	Initial stimulation of ciliary activity.
46		Nitrous oxide	No effect on ciliary activity.
47		Sodium amytal	Depressed ciliary activity.
48		Sodium veronal	Depressed ciliary activity.
49	Frog, pharynx	Acetylcholine, 0.001%	No stimulation to moderate stimulation of ciliary activity.
50		Arecoline, 0.01%	Strong stimulation of ciliary movement.
51		Atropine, 0.001%	No effect on ciliary activity.
52		Caffeine, 2%	Ciliary movement accelerated for 3 minutes, ceased in 6 minutes.
53		Chloral hydrate, 0.5%	Cessation of ciliary movement in 5 minutes.
54		Chloretone, 0.1%	Cessation of ciliary movement in 5 minutes.
55		Choline, 1%	Slight stimulation of ciliary activity.
56		Epinephrine, 0.001%	Slight stimulation of ciliary activity.
57		Ether, 7.3%	Cessation of ciliary movement in 5 minutes
58		Physostigmine, 0.01%	No effect to strong stimulation of ciliary activity.
59		Pilocarpine, 0.01%[2]	Strong stimulation of ciliary activity.
60		Strychnine sulfate, 1%	Ciliary movement ceased in 10 minutes.
61		Veratrine sulfate, 1-1.5%	Metachronal activity[1] continues until cilia become quiet.
62	Frog, pharynx tissue culture	Cresols, o-, m-, and p-	m-Cresol accelerated, o- and p- retarded, ciliary activity.
63		Phenol, cresol, thymol	Toxic effect on ciliary activity decreases in order listed.
64		α- and β- Naphthol	Toxic effect on ciliary activity decreases in order listed.
65		Zootoxin, (Lytta spp): cantharidin crystal	Slight irritation; finally a decrease in ciliary activity, with separation of individual cells, cilia still beating.
66		Zootoxin, fish (Synancea verrucosa), diluted	Acceleration of ciliary movement followed by gradual reduction.
67		Zootoxin, toad dermal glands, 1:10,000 dilution	Intense acceleration of ciliary activity, followed by depression.
68	Cat, upper bronchi and trachea	Morphine, 0.125 mg/kg, and codeine, 0.75 mg/kg	Apparently little or no effect on ciliary movement.
69	Ox, tracheal tissue (excised)	Acetylcholine chloride, veratrine SO_4, caffeine, pilocarpine HCl, strophanthin ⎬	Accelerating effect decreases in order listed.
70		Barium chloride, chloral, cocaine ⎬ HCl, quinine HCl, saponin	Retard ciliary movement.

/1/ Metachronal activity: characteristic ciliary beating of any ciliated cell or tissue in one direction in a regular sequence. /2/ Pilocarpine, 1.5%, caused ciliary movement to cease in 6 minutes.

297. FACTORS AFFECTING CILIARY ACTIVITY (Concluded)
Part I: CHEMICAL (Concluded)
Cilia cease beating when underlying muscle contracts, resume beating when muscle relaxes.

	Ciliated Material	Chemical Factors	Results
		Vertebrates (concluded)	
71	Man, dog, guinea pig: mucous membrane strips, upper	Cocaine, 10-20%	Ciliary activity slowed; good recovery (5% cocaine does not decrease, may even increase, ciliary activity).
72	respiratory tract (man and dog	Ephedrine HCl, 3%	Not harmful, may increase activity.
73	tissue strips in chamber,	Epinephrine HCl, 0.1%	Definitely detrimental, slowing to stoppage.
74	guinea pig tissues in situ)	Eucalyptol, 1%	Depresses or stops ciliary activity, with fair or no recovery (0.5% no harmful effect).
75		Menthol, 0.5%	Mildly depresses ciliary activity (1% more depressing than 0.5%).
76		Mercurochrome, 2%	Definitely detrimental, slowing to stoppage of ciliary activity.
77		Silver nitrate, 0.5%	Immediately detrimental to ciliary activity; no recovery.
78		Silver proteinate, 5, 10, and 20%	Initial acceleration of ciliary activity, then retardation.
79		Thymol, 0.5-1%	Detrimental to ciliary activity, or cessation, with fair or no recovery.
80		Zinc sulfate, 2%	Definitely detrimental, slowing to stoppage.
81	Man, nose (extirpated mucous	Chlorbutanol	Slows, stops cilia; recovery from weak solutions.
82	membrane)	Penicillin (5000 units/ml normal saline) applied directly	Non-irritating to cilia.
83		Tuamine sulfate, 1%	No slowing of cilia during 41 minutes of observation.
84		Turamine sulfate, 1%	Average slowing time 97 minutes; recovery from weaker solutions.
85		Sulfadiazine, 2%, in triethanolamine and butoben	Ciliary movement stops, recovers when washed; effect caused by solvent (?).
86		Sulfadiazine, sulfanilamide, sulfathiazole, as powders	No effect on ciliary movement.
87		Sulfanilamide, in saline	No permanent deleterious effect.
88		Sulfathiazole, sodium, 5% (isotonic solution)	In 50% of tests cilia did not recover after immersion; caused by pH (10.17) (?).

Part II: PHYSICAL

	Ciliated Material	Physical Factors		Results
1	Paramecium	Electricity:	Direct current, 0.1-0.15 mA in water.	Animal stopped with anterior end toward the positive pole.
2	Beroe spp (Ctenophora), swimming plate		2 mA/ml passed longitudinally, at <20°C.	Inhibition effect, from cathode.
3	Turtle trachea		A C electrodes on trachea.	No change in ciliary frequency.
4	Paramecium	Hydrostatic pressure:	1-300 atmospheres.	No effect on ciliary rate.
5			400-600 atmospheres.	Ciliary action ceased.
6	Mytilus (Mollusca), lateral cilia of gill		Gill in pressure bomb; pressures up to 1000 or 3000 lb/sq in.; (stroboscopic measurement).	Ciliary rates increase immediately, 7-20%; gradual return to normal.
7			Incr. in successive equal steps of pressure.	Increase in ciliary movement constant.
8			Pressure 5000 lb/sq in.	Basic ciliary frequency falls rapidly.
9			Pressure 6000 lb/sq in.	Irreversible damage.
10			Sudden decrease from 5000 or 1000 to 0 lb/sq in.	Immed. decrease of 3-25% in ciliary movement, with gradual return to normal.
11	Frog, pharynx tissue culture		From -7 to +7 atmospheres.	Little or no effect on ciliary rate.
12			-8 atmospheres.	Slight decrease in rate.
13	Frog, pharynx tissue culture	Light:	300-400 mμ (UV), short exposure.	Intense acceleration of ciliary movement.
14			500-620 mμ.	No effect.
15			650-722 mμ.	Temporary acceleration of ciliary movement.
16	pharynx in toto on slide		Darkness.	Cilia come to rest in about 45 minutes.
17			Light: after cilia come to rest in darkness.	Activity resumed in about 2 minutes.
18	Frog, pharynx in toto on slide	Mechanical influences:	Floating cells.	Stimulation.
19	pharynx in situ		Base line: no substances.	Cilia inactive.
20			Ringer's solution.	Cilia active until fluid is removed.
21			Carbon particles.	Cilia active until particles are removed.
22			Camphor crystal.	Cilia active in front of crystal, inactive after its passage.
23	Paramecium bursaria	Radiation:	X-rays above 200,000 roentgens.	Decreased ciliary activity.
24			X-rays, 1,000,000 roentgens.	Ciliary activity decreased to very low level.
25	Frog, pharynx tissue culture		Radium bromide, 100 mg, 3 hr.	Temporary inhibition.
26	Toad (Bufo viridis), pharynx epithelium tissue culture		X-rays, 1-4 million roentgens.	Ciliary movement completely inhibited.
27	Oyster, Japanese (Ostrea circumpicta)	Osmotic effects:	Sea water, dil. to 50% normal salinity.	Ciliary activity stimulated.
28			Sea water, dil. from 50 to 20% normal salinity.	Ciliary activity declines to nearly zero.
29	Frog, buccal membrane, excised		Distilled water.	Initial strong stimulation of cilia; cells develop vesicles in 1 minute; ciliary movement ceases in 5 to 10 minutes.
30	Oyster (intact), feeding organs	Temperature:	4-6°C	Decreased ciliary activity; normal feeding above this range, almost none below.
31			25-30°C	Optimum for ciliary activity; coordination of cilia decrease at temp below 15°C and above 25°C.
32	Modiolus (Mollusca) gill, lateral cilia		10-35°C	Ciliary vibration rate increases with temperature, from 3.5-15.8/second.
33	Frog, pharynx in toto on slide		20-27°C	Ciliary rate increases.
34			28°C	Ciliary rate increases notably.
35			35-38°C	Maximum increase in ciliary rate.
36			42°C	Cilia stop moving.
37	Rabbit, sinus in situ		7-12°C	Cilia stop moving.
38			18-33°C	Ciliary activity greatest (7 to 10 vibrations/second).
39			40°C	Movement of cilia greatly retarded.
40			43-44°C	Cilia stop moving; no recovery.

298. AMEBOID MOVEMENT: RATE

In this table ameboid movement means actual locomotion of the ameba by means of ectoplasmic contraction, protoplasmic streaming, or both.

f = fresh water; s = sea water.

	Species[1]	Dimensions		Number of Nuclei[2]	Habitat	Average Rate of Movement[3]		Optimum (Highest Rate) Temp. °C
		Length μ	Width μ			μ/sec	°C	
1	Trichamoeba, Pantin's "A"	120	50		s	1.9	22	20-24
2	Trichamoeba, Pantin's "B"	150	135		s	3.3	20	20-24
3	Trichamoeba, caerulea	150	42	10-20	f	1.9	22	
4	T. clava	100	25		f	3.2	25	34-36
5	T. fusa	175	40		f	11.4	22	
6	T. gumia	100	41		s	2.0	22	
7	T. limax[4]				f	1.0		
8	T. osseosaccus	125	32		f	2.5	22	
9	T. pallida	60	12		s	2.0	27	
10	T. schaefferi	175	33		s	5.9	22	20-24
11	T. sphaerarum	25	6		s	1.1	27	
12	Pelomyxa clara	175	100	10-20	f	3.3	22	28.5-31
13	P. minima	78	35		f	0.55	23	34-36
14	P. palustris	580	200	300+	f	5.6	23	
15	P. scheidti	75	33	2[5]	f	1.6	22	
16	Striolatus tardus	60	16	2[5]	s	0.5	27	
17	Polychaos dubia	400	300		f	3.3	22	
18	Metachaos discoides[6]	450	45		f	2.5	26	34-36
19	M. fulvum[6]	70	24		s	2.5	27	
20	M. granulosa[6]	225	70		f	4.2	26	
21	M. gratum[6]	200	60		f	2.5	22	
22	M. oxyuris[6]	130	27		f	1.5	22	
23	M. rarum[6]	125	53		f	1.6	22	
24	Chaos chaos	1800	130	to 300	f	12.0	23	
25	Chaos nobilis	725	95	10-20	f	1.0	23	
26	Amoeba proteus pallas[7]	600	85		f	10.0	21	
27	A. proteus pallas[6,7,8]				f	10.4	22	34-36
28	A. proteus pallas[6,7]				f	4.6[7]	23	
29	A. proteus[6,9]	460	65		f	6.8	23	
30	Flabellula citata	20	37		s	2.0	25	
31	F. citata				s	1.2	27	34-36
32	F. crassa	50	58		s	0.4	27	
33	F. mira	25	20		s	1.2	27	
34	F. mira				s	0.5[10]	23	
35	F. pellucida	30	80	10-20	s	0.9	27	
36	Mayorella augusta	250	74		f	1.7	22	
37	M. bigemma	200	110		f	2.6	25	
38	M. bulla	100	51		f	1.7	22	
39	M. conipes	45	23		s	0.8	25	34-36
40	M. conipes				s	2.0	27	
41	M. crystallus	30	22		s	0.5	27	
42	M. gemmifera	50	28		s	0.7	27	
43	Vexillifera aurea	80	31		s	0.8	27	
44	Astramoeba stella	40	18		f	0.4	22	
45	A. torrei	120	55		f	1.2	27	
46	Gibbodiscus gemma	35	30		s	0.6	27	
47	Flamella magnifica	50	50		s	0.8	27	
48	Dactyllosphaerium acuum	60	60		s	0.3	27	
49	Pelomyxa lentissima	100	50	2[5]	f	0.03	27	
50	Rugipes bilzi	70	34		f	1.7	23	
51	R. vivaz	12	8		s	0.4	27	
52	Thecamoeba hilla	80	45		s	2.5	27	
53	T. rugosa	70	35		s	0.5	27	
54	T. verrucosa[11]	150	90		f	0.5	25	34-36
55	Hyalodiscus aureus	80	70		s	0.4	21	
56	H. elegans	40	40		s	1.3	21	
57	Cochliopodium clarum	40	39		s	0.3	21	
58	C. gulosum	80	55		s	0.4	21	

/1/ Grouped according to characteristic body shape during locomotion. General body shape: Lines 1-16, clavate; Lines 17-29, antler-shaped with large indeterminate pseudopods; Lines 30-49, 55-58, fan-shaped to triangular with small determinate pseudopods; Lines 50-54, oval without pseudopods. /2/ Unless otherwise indicated, the amebas listed have one nucleus, occasionally 2-4, except Flamella magnifica (Line 47) which has no formed nucleus. /3/ Rates at culturing temperatures during well-coordinated movement in clear culture fluid on glass surfaces, except Amoeba proteus pallas (Line 28), which was in 0.001 N NaCl after washing in distilled water. /4/ Original report in literature: Trichamoeba limax = Amoeba limax. /5/ Occasionally has only one nucleus. /6/ Rates determined while in clavate shape. /7/ Amoeba proteus pallas is North American name for Chaos diffluens. /8/ Mixture of Amoeba proteus pallas and Metachaos discoides. /9/ Chaos nitida is European name for Amoeba proteus. /10/ Mean rate. /11/ Original report in literature: Thecamoeba verrucosa = Amoeba verrucosa.

299. PROTOPLASMIC STREAMING

Protoplasmic streaming as considered in this table includes the shuttle-type flow of protoplasm in slime molds, cyclosis in higher plants, and streaming of protoplasm within rigid cell walls of algae. Streaming rates have been studied by use of many techniques, and results vary according to methods and conditions of measurement. Values were interpolated, where necessary, for comparison from graphic and tabular data in the literature. Parts I, II, and III show the effect of temperature on rate of streaming. Part I shows typical rates; Part II gives the temperature coefficient of Avena (oat) coleoptile. Part III reveals the effect of sudden changes of temperature, with estimates of temperature sensitivity. Because energy available for streaming has been associated with respiration, the effect of oxygen concentration is shown in Part IV. In Part V is presented the effect of various agents generally known specifically to affect respiration. Part VI demonstrates the effect of light on non-chlorophyll containing cells of Avena coleoptile observed in the orange-red phototropically inactive spectral region after exposure to various doses of blue light (4360 Å), at 23°C. Data show the fitness of the product rule (intensity x time), as well as the effect of total energy (dosage). Part IX shows the spectral sensitivity of this effect. The term "chemodinesis" (Part VII) is used to describe the action of certain alpha amino acids and other compounds which in very high dilution initiate protoplasmic streaming in leaf cells of Vallisneria. The lower concentration thresholds are presented in Part VIII. The action of various other agents on streaming is indicated in part VIII.

Part I: EFFECT OF TEMPERATURE

Material (Investigator)	Rate of Streaming, μ/sec							
	5°C	10°C	15°C	20°C	25°C	30°C	35°C	40°C
1 Chara foetida (Velton, 1876)	20.4	26	38	42	52	76	93	72
2 Elodea canadensis (Velton, 1876)	4.8	7.7	8.8	10.5	11.5	13.3	16.7	0
3 Vallisneria spiralis (Velton, 1876)	4.7	8.7	15.1	20	26	31	38	
4 Nitella sp (Ganong, 1908)	10.5	15.3	20	27	34	43	47	37
5 Chara foetida (Lambers, 1926)	11.2	24.5	41	56	74	90		
6 Nitella mucronata (Lambers, 1926)	12.7	28	41	60	75	96	109	
Avena coleoptile (Bottelier, 1934)								
7 90 hr old	3.4	4.8	7.0	8.2	8.3	8.5		
8 200 hr old	3.6	5.7	7.9	10.4	12.8	15.8		

Part II: TEMPERATURE COEFFICIENT

	Temp, °C	Avena Coleoptile	
		Age: 90 hr Q_{10}	Age: 140-200 hr Q_{10}
1	5-10	1.8-2.1	1.9-2.2
2	10-15	1.8	1.8
3	15-20	1.1	1.8
4	20-25	1.1	1.7
5	25-30	0.9	1.5
6	30-35	0.7	1.1
7	35-40	0.9	

Part III: EFFECT OF SUDDEN CHANGES OF TEMPERATURE

T_O = initial temperature; T = final temperature prevailing during the test; R_O = average streaming rate (μ/sec) at T_O

	Temp, °C T	T_O	R_O	Rate of Streaming, μ/sec, at Specified Interval (min)												Sensitivity[1]
				10	20	30	40	50	60	70	80	90	100	110	120	
								Nitella flexilis								
1	24.5	13.8	28.5		55	55	55	55	55	55	55	55	55	55	55	
2	31.5	13.8	28.5		80	80	80	80	80	80	80	80	80	80	80	
3	37.5	13.8	28.5		99	99	99	99	99	99	99	99	99	99	99	
4	12.8	19	55		36	36	36	36	36	36	36	36	36	36	36	
5	12.8	22	62.5		36	36	36	36	36	36	36	36	36	36	36	
6	12.8	24.3	70		36	36	36	36	36	36	36	36	36	36	36	$\frac{100}{12}$ = 8.3
7	12.8	26	74		24	28	32	34	36	36	36	36	36	36	36	
8	20	25	86		71	71	71	71	71	71	71	71	71	71		
9	20	27.5	93		64	68	69	70	71	71	71	71	71	71		
10	20	30	100		62	65	66	68	69	70	71	71	71	71		$\frac{100}{6}$ = 16.6
11	20	35	114		45	50	52	54	56	58	60	62	63	64	65	
12	25	30	100		83	83	83	83	83	83	83	83	83	83		
13	25	32.5	104		83	83	83	83	83	83	83	83	83	83		
14	25	33	106		83	83	83	83	83	83	83	83	83	83		
15	25	35	113		77	80	82	82	83	83	83	83	83	83		$\frac{100}{9}$ = 11.1
16	25	38.5	125		71	74	76	77	78	80	81	81	82	83	83	
17	25	40	131		25	40	48	54	58	62	65	68	70	71	72	
								Avena coleoptile								
18	13	21	12	6.0	6.2	6.4	6.6	6.6	6.6	6.6	6.6	6.6	6.6	6.6		
19	13	24	12.8	0.9	0.1	2.1	3.2	4.4	5.1	5.9	6.3	6.9	7.5	7.6	7.6	$\frac{100}{7.5}$ = 13
20	13	28	12.6	12.6	0	0.4	1.2	2.6	4.5	5.8	6.6	7.3	7.7	7.7		
21	21	25	11	4.2	9.1	9.9	10.2	10.3	10.3	10.3	10.3	10.3	10.3	10.3		
22	21	27	10	0	4.5	9.9	11.9	12.1	12.1	12.1	12.1	12.1	12.1	12.1		$\frac{100}{3.5}$ = 30
23	21	36	3.4	0	0.1	0.1	0.2	0.1	0.2	0.1	0.1	0.2	0.4	1.4	3.6	

/1/ Sensitivity = 100 ÷ maximum temp difference giving no rate lag.

Part IV: EFFECT OF OXYGEN

	Material	O_2 Conc. % Sat. (ml/L)	Streaming Rate	Per Cent of Normal Rate of: Streaming	Respiration		Material	O_2 Conc. % Sat. (ml/L)	Streaming Rate	Per Cent of Normal Rate of: Streaming	Respiration
1		21(6.27)	Normal	100	100	12	260 hr old, 26°C	21(5.85)	13.4 μ/sec	100	
2	Physarum	2.4(0.72)	Normal		60	13	260 hr old, 21°C	4(1.23)	9.0 μ/sec	88	
3	polycephalum,	1.0(0.30)	Reduced		30	14	260 hr old, 26°C	4(1.02)	9.1 μ/sec	68	
4	at 22°C	0.3(0.08)	Reduced		9			O_2 Conc. % Sat. (ml/L)			
5		0.1(0.03)	Reduced		3		Avena coleoptile				
6		0(0)	Reduced	0	0	15	80 hr old, 25°C	10.8-14.6[1](3.1-4.1)		100	100[2]
	Avena coleoptile					16	80 hr old, 25°C	14.6[1]-21(4.1-5.7)			50[2]
7	96 hr old, 21°C	100(30.4)	9.9 μ/sec	99		17	95 hr old, 25°C	10.8-18.2[1](3.1-5.3)		100	100[2]
8	96 hr old, 26°C	100(27.8)	10.1 μ/sec	132		18	95 hr old, 25°C	18.8[1]-21(5.3-5.7)			50[2]
9	96 hr old, 21°C	21(6.32)	10.0 μ/sec	100		19	130 hr old, 25°C	11.6-12.4[1](3.2-3.5)		100	100[2]
10	96 hr old, 26°C	21(5.85)	10.1 μ/sec	100		20	130 hr old, 25°C	12[1]-21(3.5-5.7)			50[2]
11	260 hr old, 21°C	21(6.32)	10.2 μ/sec	100							

/1/ Critical O_2 tension. /2/ Rates uniform within indicated O_2 ranges, there being a sharp change in rate at the critical oxygen tension.

Part V: EFFECT OF CHEMICAL RESPIRATORY AGENTS

	Agent	Residual Respiration % Control	Effect on Streaming
		Physarum polycephalum[1]	
1	KCN, 1×10^{-4} M	77	
2	KCN, 5×10^{-4} M	47	
3	Air, control[2]	100	++++ (indefinitely).
4	Air + KCN, 1×10^{-3} M[2]	15.1	+++ (after 7 hr).
5	2.4% O_2, control[2]	59	++++ (indefinitely).
6	2.4% O_2 + KCN, 1×10^{-3} M[2]	5.2	
7	After 2 hr in 2.4% O_2 and 3 hr in KCN[2]		+++
8	After 5 hr in KCN (2 hr of which in air)[2]		++
9	1.0% O_2, control[2]	30.5	
10	1.0% O_2 + KCN, 1×10^{-3} M[2]	1.4	
11	After 2 hr in 1.0% O_2 and 3 hr in KCN[2]		+++
12	After 7 hr in KCN (2 hr of which in air)[2]		+
13	DNP, 2×10^{-4} M	122-137	Stopped within 5 min (reversible).
14	DNP, 1.25×10^{-4} M	138-143	Stopped within 10 min (reversible).
15	Na iodacetate, 5×10^{-3} M	35	Not stopped until disintegration occurs.
16	NaN_3, 1×10^{-4} M	30	Stopped quickly (reversible).
17	Na pyrophosphate, $2(10^{-2}$ to 10^{-4} M)	No effect	No effect.
		Avena coleoptile	
18	KCN, 3×10^{-4} M		53%[3] (reversible).
19	KCN, 1×10^{-2} M	54-67	53-61%[3] (reversible).
20	KCN, 1×10^{-1} M		Stopped within 22 min (irreversible).
21	DNP, 5×10^{-6} M		100%[3].
22	DNP, 1×10^{-5} M	100[4]	
23	DNP, 2.5×10^{-4} M	37[4]	52%[3].
24	DNP, 5×10^{-4} M	3[4]	Stopped within 22 min (irreversible).
		Nicotiana tabacum[5]	
25	KCN, 8×10^{-4} to 2×10^{-3} M	40-50	40%[3].

/1/ Streaming measurements not absolute because of irregular change of rate and direction of movement. Relative rates presented as number of plus signs. /2/ Data applicable to same plasmodium. /3/ Per cent of control. /4/ Rates sustained 30 minutes after rinsing. /5/ Data applicable to marginal cells of leaf.

Part VI: EFFECT OF VARIOUS DOSES OF LIGHT (4360 Å): AVENA COLEOPTILE

	Dosage[1] ergs/sq cm	Illumination Intensity ergs/sq cm/sec	Time sec	Reaction[2]		Dosage[1] ergs/sq cm	Illumination Intensity ergs/sq cm/sec	Time sec	Reaction[2]		Dosage[1] ergs/sq cm	Illumination Intensity ergs/sq cm/sec	Time sec	Reaction[2]
1	10	2	5	-29	14	110	11	10	-118	26	440	11	40	-84
2	12	23.6	0.5	-54	15	118	23.6	5	-92	27	472	23.6	20	-54
3	20	2	10	-49	16	120	2	60	-112	28	480	2	240	-107
4	20	5	4	-67	17	142	23.6	6	-97	29	600	5	120	-69
5	22	11	2	-74	18	160	5	32	-103	30	660	11	60	-22
6	24	23.6	1	-75	19	180	2	90	-160	31	746	23.6	32	-15
7	40	2	20	-72	20	189	23.6	8	-136	32	944	23.6	40	+32
8	47	23.6	2	-87	21	220	11	20	-169	33	1320	11	120	+132
9	55	11	5	-70	22	236	23.6	10	-105	34	1420	23.6	60	+42
10	66	11	6	-74	23	240	2	120	-118	35	2100	23.6	90	+28
11	80	2	40	-91	24	360	2	180	-104	36	2800	23.6	120	+26
12	88	11	8	-78	25	378	23.6	16	-81	37	4200	23.6	180	+4
13	94	23.6	4	-77										

/1/ Energy (intensity x time). /2/ Algebraic sum (average of 1-20 separate experiments for each energy value) of per cent departures from normal rate. Negative values indicate a decrease in streaming; positive values, an increase.

Part VII: CHEMODINESIS: VALLISNERIA

	Compound	Molarity	Threshold %		Compound	Molarity	Threshold %		Compound	Molarity	Threshold %
1	L-Histidine	5×10^{-8}	7.7×10^{-7}	5	Benzoic acid	1×10^{-5}	1×10^{-4}	8	Histamine	8×10^{-5}	4×10^{-4}
2	L-Asparagine	1.5×10^{-6}	2×10^{-6}	6	Cinnamic acid	1×10^{-5}	1×10^{-4}	9	Na-β-indole acetate	1×10^{-4}	1.9×10^{-3}
3	L-Alanine	1×10^{-6}	8.9×10^{-6}	7	Salicylic acid	1×10^{-5}	1×10^{-4}	10	Leaf extract (Vallisneria)		2.5×10^{-5}
4	D-Galacturonic acid	5×10^{-6}	1×10^{-4}								

Part VIII: EFFECT OF CERTAIN PHYSICAL AND CHEMICAL AGENTS

	Agent	Material	Effect on Streaming		Agent	Material	Effect on Streaming
1	Ethyl chloride, 25%	Physarum	Stops in 10-15 sec.	15	3-Indoleacetic acid, 0.005-0.5 mg/L	Avena	Increases up to 13%[1].
2	Ethyl chloride, 18%	Physarum	Stops in 20 sec.	16	Heavy metals, 5×10^{-6} to 5×10^{-2} M	Physarum	Decreases: Ag>Hg>Cd>Tl>Cu>Pb>Zn>Y>Sr>La>Rb.
3	Ethyl chloride, 5%	Physarum	No effect.	17	pH 3-8	Chara	Max. at pH 5.5 & 7.
4	$LiCl_3$, 0.1 M	Chara	Stops in 5 hr.	18	pH 5-7	Hordium[2]	Max. at pH 5.8 & 6.4.
5	$CaCl_2$, $BaCl_2$, 0.1 M	Chara	Stops in 6 hr.	19	Hydrostatic pressure, 400 atmos.	Nitella	Stops(reversible).
6	Ethyl ether, low conc.	Physarum	Accelerates.	20	Hydrostatic pressure, 600 atmos.	Elodea	-50%(reversible).
7	Ethyl ether, high conc.	Physarum	Inhibits.	21	X-radiation, 25-70,000 r.	Tradescantia	Inhibits.
8	Ethyl ether, 10-32 mg/L	Avena	Inhibits.	22	Electric current, 3.1×10^{-8} amps.	Chara, Nitella	Stops temporarily.
9	Sodium chlorate	Elodea	Inhibits.	23	Electric current, 1 to 5×10^{-6} amps.	Avena	Inhibits, stops temporarily.
10	Menotoxin extract	Elodea, Nitella	Stops.				
11	Quinine hydrochloride, 1:150	Physarum	Accelerates, then stops.				
12	Morphine, 1:20	Physarum	Stops in 2-3 min.				
13	Colchicine, 1:1000	Elodea	Accelerates.				
14	Ethylene chlorhydrin, 0.025-0.075 M	Elodea, Nitella	Accelerates.				

/1/ No effect has been reported at concentration of 0.01-10 mg/L. /2/ Observation from cells of root hairs.

Part IX: EFFECT OF VARIOUS WAVE LENGTHS: AVENA COLEOPTILE

	Wave Length Å	Dosage[1]	Reaction[2]	Equivalent Energy[3]	Sensitivity		Wave Length Å	Dosage[1]	Reaction[2]	Equivalent Energy[3]	Sensitivity
1	3660	270	-46	16	6	6	4360	Cf Part VI			100
2		760	-85	90	12	7		230	-16	7	3
3		21	-15	7	33	8	5460	240	-15	7	3
4	4550	67	-33	13	20	9		1790	-60	30	1.7
5		190	-90	95	50	10	5780	9000	+1		<1
						11	6200	Cf Fn 4	+1		<1

/1/ Intensity x time. /2/ Algebraic average of per cent departures from normal rate. Negative values indicate a decrease in streaming; positive values, an increase. /3/ Equivalent energy required at 4360 Å for comparable effect. /4/ Approximately 70 ergs/sq cm/sec.

300. TRANSPIRATION RATES

Factors influencing transpiration include solar radiation, humidity, temperature, and wind. Part I (Section 1) presents the rate of water loss as influenced by these conditions. Certain soil factors indicated in Part I (Section 2) are involved in water absorption, giving a corresponding effect on transpiration. Part II gives hourly and day and night variations of corn (Zea mays). Values are averages for 30 days during July and August, Nebr. Agr. Exp. Sta. Part III reveals diurnal transpiration of mullein (Verbascum thapsus). Part IV gives the total water loss during the growing season. Part V denotes the water required to produce one gram of dry matter, the transpiration ratio.

Part I: TRANSPIRATION RATES: VARIOUS CONDITIONS
Section 1.

	Species	Temp °C	Light	RH[1] %	Water Loss g/sq dm/hr
	Herbaceous Plants				
1	Corn (Zea mays)		12-2 PM		2.5
2	Sorghum, kafir (Sorghum vulgare)		12-2 PM		2.2
3	Sorghum, milo (S. vulgare)		12-2 PM		4.3
4	Sunflower (Helianthus annuus)	27		22[3]	0.7;0.9
5		38		22[3]	1.2;2.8
6		49		22[3]	2.1;4.9
7	Tobacco (Nicotiana tabacum)	23-26		68	1.5
8		37-38		68	3.6
	Woody Plants				
9	Box elder (Acer negundo)	38	Shade	32	0.6
10	Buckeye (Aesculus glabra)	38	Shade	32	0.7
	Germander (Teucrium scorodonia)				
11	Sun leaves	26-30	Sun	38-46	0.7
12	Shade leaves	26-30	Sun	38-46	0.4
13	Sun leaves	18-19	Shade	75-76	0.3
14	Shade leaves	18-19	Shade	75-76	0.1
15	Maple (Acer saccharinum)	13-17		58-78	1.0
16	Oak (Quercus rubra)	38	Shade	32	0.8
17	Orange (Citrus sinensis)	21-38		40-98	0.2
18	Peach (Prunus persica)	21-38		40-98	0.7
19	Pecan (Carya illionensis)	24	Day	45-60	1.07
20		20-23	Night	61-65	0.09
21	Pine (Pinus ponderosa)	13-17		58-78	0.2
22	Pineapple (Ananas comosus)	31		59	2.0
23		24		85	0.03
24	Spruce (Picea engelmannii)	13-17		58-78	0.2
25	Sycamore (Platanus occidentalis)	38	Shade	32	0.8
26	Walnut (Juglans nigra)	75	Day	45-60	0.09
27		68-73	Night	61-65	0.08

/1/ Relative humidity. /2/ g per sq dm leaf surface per hr. /3/ Wind, 6 mi/hr.

Section 2.

	Species	Specified Condition	Water Loss mg/sq cm/hr[1]
1	Apple (Pyrus malus)	Straw mulch	17.2
2		Without mulch	14.3
3	Cotton (Gossypium herbaceum)	Soil of low salt conc.	15
4		With 0.8% Ca (NO3)2	1.6
5	Euphorbia (Euphorbia capitellata)	10 AM - 2 PM	4.5
6		Evaporation 0.01 g/sq cm[2]	
7		10 PM - 7 AM	0.1
8		Evaporation 0.01 g/sq cm[2]	
9	Grapefruit (Citrus grandis)	Soil temp 27°C	4.6
10		Soil temp 35°C	3.1
11	Houseleek (Sempervium howorthii)	Wind velocity 1100 cm/sec	0.6
12		Wind velocity 570 cm/sec	0.2
13	Pepper (Capsicum annuum)	Soil moisture 50%[3]	3.5
14		Soil moisture 25%[3]	1.1
15	Wheat (Triticum aestivum)	Good loam soil	2.1
16		Poor soil	1.1

/1/ Mg per sq cm leaf surface per hr. /2/ Evaporation from free water surface. /2/ Per cent water holding capacity of soil.

Part II: TRANSPIRATION RATES; CORN: DIURNAL VARIATION

	Period	Temp °C	RH[1] %	Wind mi/hr	Water Loss Per Plant[2] g	Water Loss Evaporation[3] g
1	8 AM	23.1	80	6	84	4.8
2	9	25.5	73	7	111	7.7
3	10	27.6	67	8	167	11.6
4	11	29.3	63	8	215	15.0
5	12	30.8	58	9	279	19.2
6	1 PM	31.9	55	9	329	23.7
7	2	32.7	53	9	356	24.5
8	3	32.9	52	9	354	23.8
9	4	32.8	50	9	343	22.2
10	5	32.2	51	8	294	18.5
11	6	31.2	53	8	217	14.1
12	7	28.4	58	7	132	10.2
13	8	27.6	64	7	64	6.4
14	Av. for day	29.8	59.8	8	226	15.5
15	Av. for night	22.7	81.5	6	16	2.3

/1/ Mean relative humidity. /2/ Water transpired from one plant. /3/ Water evaporated from 36 sq in. free-water surface, under identical conditions.

Part III: TRANSPIRATION RATES, MULLEIN: DIURNAL VARIATION

	Period	Temp °C	Diffusion Pressure Deficit mm Hg	Sunlight %	Water Loss g/sq dm/hr[1]
1	1:00 AM	18.3	6.40		0.09
2	2:00	17.8	6.21		0.09
3	3:00	17.2	5.98		0.09
4	4:00	16.7	5.79		0.09
5	5:00	16.1	5.57		0.09
6	6:00	15.7	5.30	0	0.16
7	7:00	15.7	5.30	70	0.33
8	8:00	16.7	5.54	100	0.53
9	9:00	21.1	8.37	100	1.33
10	10:00	26.7	15.61	100	2.48
11	11:00	29.4	22.83	100	2.68
12	12:00	32.2	27.51	100	3.06
13	1:00 PM	33.9	31.48	100	2.80
14	2:00	35.0	34.26	100	2.42
15	3:00	33.9	31.48	100	1.65
16	4:00	32.2	28.22	10	1.60
17	5:00	29.4	22.83	0	0.68
18	6:00	25.6	14.63		0.13
19	7:00	23.3	9.56		0.13
20	8:00	22.2	7.55		0.13
21	9:00	22.2	7.35		0.13
22	10:00	21.7	7.13		0.13
23	11:00	21.1	6.88		0.13
24	12:00	21.1	6.88		0.13

/1/ g per sq dm leaf surface per hr.

Part IV: TRANSPIRATION RATES: GROWING SEASON

	Species	Length of Season; Location	Water Loss L
1	Apple (Pyrus malus)	188 da; New York	8,200
2	Coconut (Cocus nucifera)	365 da; Philippines	19,000
3	Corn (Zea mays)	May 5-Sept 8; Kansas	245
4	Cowpea (Vigna sinensis)	May 19-Sept 2;Kansas	60
5	Date (Phoenix dactylifera)	365 da; Sahara Desert oasis	160,000
6	Potato (Solanum tuberosum)	Apr 18-July 30;Kansas	115
7	Ragweed (Ambrosia sp)	June 1-Aug 30	640
8	Sunflower (Helianthus annuus)	May 26-Aug 23;Kansas	560
9	Tomato (Lycopersicon esculentum)	May 19-Sept 2;Kansas	155
10	Wheat, winter (Triticum aestivum)	Oct 15-June 28;Kansas	115

Part V: TRANSPIRATION RATIO: SEASONAL VARIATION

	Species	Seasonal Water Requirement 1912	1913	1914	1915	1916	1917	Av
	Colorado							
1	Alfalfa (Medicago sativa)	657	834	890	695	1047	822	824
2	Amaranth (Amaranthus retroflexus)		320	306	229	340	307	300
3	Barley (Hordeum vulgare)	443		501	404	664	522	507
4	Corn (Zea mays)	280	399	368	253	495	346	357
5	Cotton (Gossypium hirsutum)	488	657	574	443	612	522	549
6	Cowpea (Vigna sinensis)		571	659	413	767	481	578
7	Grama-grass (Bouteloua gracilis)			389	312	336	290	332
8	Oat (Avena sativa)	449	617	615	445	809	636	595
9	Rye (Secale cereale)			622	469	800	625	629
10	Setaria (Setaria italica)	187	286	295	202	367	284	273
11	Sorghum (Sorghum vulgare sudan.)			394	260	426	378	365
12	Wheat, durum (Triticum aestivum)	394	496	518	405	636	471	487
	South Dakota							
13	Alfalfa (Medicago sativa)	735	735	1038	696	673	866	790
14	Setaria (Setaria italica)	239	293	311	171	233	278	254
15	Sorghum (Sorghum vulgare sudan.)			272	314	344	310	
16	Wheat, durum (Triticum aestivum)	463	436	528	333	352	487	433

336

301. ION ABSORPTION AND ACCUMULATION: PLANTS

Parts I and II indicate the differential absorption among cations present in the culture solution. The accumulation ratio (internal: external), shown in Parts I and III, is the ratio of concentration in cell sap to that in the external medium. Ratios greater than 1 indicate the movement of ions against a concentration gradient, i.e., from a region of lesser concentration to a region of greater concentration for each ion that accumulates. Part III reveals the influence of temperature on absorption by excised barley roots (Hordeum vulgare). Values were determined at end of 10 hours. Part IV shows the factors of time and distance from apex of excised barley roots on Rb absorption. Roots were placed in 0.005 M RbBr during the specific periods. Part V presents the course of ion absorption from 0.001 M $MnCl_2$ by root discs of beet (Beta vulgaris) as influenced by pretreatments. The root discs were washed at 25°C for 24 hr in distilled water (through which moist N_2, O_2, or air was passed) prior to transferring in the $MnCl_2$ solution. Because data have been greatly condensed, values should be considered with caution.

Part I: ION ABSORPTION AND ACCUMULATION: ALGAE

		Chara ceratophylla			Nitella clavata			Valonia macrophysa		
		Ion Concentration		Accumulation Ratio	Ion Concentration		Accumulation Ratio	Ion Concentration		Accumulation Ratio
Ion		Cell Sap	Brackish Water		Cell Sap	Pond Water		Cell Sap	Sea Water	
		mole x 10^{-3}			mole x 10^{-3}			mole x 10^{-3}		
1	Ca	5.3	1.8	2.9	10.2	0.8	12.8	1.7	12	0.1
2	Mg	15.5	6.5	2.4	17.7	1.7	10.4	Trace	57	
3	Na	140	60	2.3	10.0	0.2	50	90	500	0.2
4	K	88	1.4	63	54	0.05	1080	500	12	42
5	Cl	225	73	3.1	91	0.9	100	600	520	0.9
6	SO_4	3.9	2.8	1.4	8.3	0.3	28	Trace	36	

Part II: ION ABSORPTION AND ACCUMULATION: HIGHER PLANTS

	Species	Cations Absorbed							Species	Cation Absorbed					
		Na	K	Mg	Ca	Sr	Total			Na	K	Mg	Ca	Sr	Total
		Equivalent Percentages[1]					mEq/kg dry wt			Equivalent Percentages[1]					mEq/kg dry wt
1	Buckwheat (Fagopyrum esculentum)	0.9	39	27	33	0.011	3230	8	Saltbush (Atriplex litorale)	10.7	56	23	10	0.006	4340
2	Corn (Zea mays)	2.9	70	16	11	0.005	2420	9	Spinach (Spinacia oleracea)	4.5	52	31	13	0.006	6520
3	Oat (Avena sativa)	3.7	73	14	8	0.004	2040	10	Sunflower (Helianthus annuus)	2.3	54	17	27	0.008	3020
4	Pea (Pisum sativum)	6.0	62	12	20	0.008	2140	11	Tobacco (Nicotiana tabacum)	4.0	51	24	21	0.006	4440
5	Plantain (Plantago lanceolata)[2]	12.2	45	18	24	0.010	3690	12	Tomato (Lycopersicon esculentum)	4.1	44	25	27	0.010	4290
6	Plantain (P. maritima)[2]	28	39	11	21		4370	13	Vetch (Vicia sativa)	10.6	44	19	26	0.011	2470
7	Saltbush (Atriplex hortensis)	19.7	39	31	10	0.004	4790	14	Culture solution	25	25	25	25	0.006	

/1/ The sum of equivalents of all fixed cations in 1 kg dry wt of plant tissue (cf Total) was determined and the amount of each cation expressed as percentage of this total. Analyses of entire plants (shoot and root), except as otherwise specified. /2/ Analyses of shoots.

Part III: EFFECT OF TEMPERATURE: BARLEY ROOTS

	Temp °C	Ion Concentration						Accumulation Ratio		
		Culture Solution			Expressed Sap					
		K mEq/L	NO_3 mEq/L	Br mEq/L	K mEq/L	NO_3 mEq/L	Br mEq/L	K	NO_3	Br
1	6	9.62	8.35	4.84	34.7	4.8	5.9	3.6	0.6	1.2
2	12	9.32	8.27	4.76	47.7	11.1	8.8	5.1	1.3	1.9
3	18	8.45	7.75	4.64	73.2	23.7	14.6	8.7	3.1	3.1
4	24	7.98	7.29	4.30	97.8	38.1	30.9	12.3	5.2	7.2
5	30	7.42	6.70	3.96	112	47.8	39.9	15.1	7.1	10.1

Part IV: EFFECT OF TIME AND DISTANCE: EXCISED BARLEY ROOTS

Values are mEq/kg fresh weight.

	Distance from Apex cm	Root Weight[1] mg	Rubidium Absorbed		Per Cent Gain 25-50 hr
			End of 25 hr mEq/kg	End of 50 hr mEq/kg	
1	to 1	33	32	44	38
2	1-2	38	26	34	29
3	2-3	39	25	27	8
4	3-4	38	24	26	8
5	4-5	40	24	25	6

/1/ Weight of 30 roots.

Part V: EFFECT OF PRETREATMENT: BEET ROOT DISCS

Values for manganese are followed, in parentheses, by those for chloride. Negative values indicate loss from the tissue to the bathing solution.

	Observation Period hr	Percentage Absorption of Mn and Cl					Observation Period hr	Percentage Absorption of Mn and Cl			
		Untreated	Pretreatment					Untreated	Pretreatment		
			Nitrogen	Oxygen	Air				Nitrogen	Oxygen	Air
1	5	18.3(-2.0)	18.7(-0.2)	21.9(5.3)	19.1(2.3)		3	120	58.5(51.8)	76.2(60.1)	78.4(72.6)	79.6(74.6)
2	48	21.3(1.5)	27.9(16.2)	40.7(35.4)	32.9(27.3)		4	192	77.4(73.2)	84.3(79.1)	100(83.8)	100

302. TRANSLOCATION RATES: PLANTS

Values are linear rates of movement in phloem.

	Substance	Species	Translocation Rate cm/hr	Method of Determination		Substance	Species	Translocation Rate cm/hr	Method of Determination
	Virus				11	Sugars	Oak (Quercus robor)	130-400	Conc. change
1	Curly top	Sugar beet (Beta vulgaris)	150		12	Assimilates[2]	Pumpkin, squash (Cucurbita spp)	55-160	Dry wt gain
2	Curly top, Argentine	Sugar beet (B. vulgaris)	7.5		13	Sucrose	Bean (Phaseolus vulgaris)	84	C^{14} tracer
3	Curly top	Dodder (Cuscuta sp), acropetal	10	Infectivity of tissue	14	Sucrose	Soybean (Glycine soja)	84	C^{14} tracer
4	Curly top	Dodder (Cuscuta sp), basipetal	0		15	Indoleacetic acid	Cucumber (Cucumis sativus)	18.5	
5	Curly top	Tobacco (Nicotiana tabacum)	1.2		16		Oat (Avena sativa)	1.0-1.2	Auxin assay
6	Mosaic	Tobacco (N. tabacum)	17.8		17		Squash (Cucurbita sp)	20	
7	Streak	Corn (Zea mays)	20[1]		18	2,4-D	Alligator weed (Alternanthera sp)	4.2	Bending of stem
8		Various species	2-50		19		Bean (Phaseolus vulgaris)	10-100	
9	Fluorescein	Bryonia sp	50(15-65)	Observation of movement	20	Iron		>43	Fe^{55} tracer
10		Geranium (Pelargonium zonale)	20-35		21	Phosphate	Bean (P. vulgaris)	60(45-90)	P^{32} tracer
					22	Sulfate		>41	S^{35} tracer

/1/ Minimum rate. /2/ Unspecified carbohydrates.

Osmotic pressure (O.P.), a direct function of cell sap concentration, effects movement of water into roots and throughout the plant. Diffusion pressure gradients influencing translocation of solutes appear to arise primarily from osmotic differences between adjacent supplying and receiving cells. Diffusion pressure deficit (D.P.D.) = O.P.-T.P. (turgor pressure). Part I presents variation in leaves. Part II shows effect of specified factors. Part III gives seasonal values of shoots, plants grouped by depth of rooting. Part IV reveals changes with age of seedling, wheat (Triticum aestivum). Part V indicates values for tissues and organs. Parts VI and VII present diurnal and seasonal variations. Part VIII shows effect of soil water and soil nutrient contents on corn (Zea mays). Part IX specifies habitats, and Part X presents plant-group values. Values are atmospheres.

Part I: LEAVES VS O.P.

	Species	O.P.		Species	O.P.
	Herbaceous Plants			Trees	
1	Bedstraw (Galium aparine)	9.6	18	Ash (Fraxinus americana)	16.4
2	Beet (Beta vulgaris)	14	19	Birch (Betula lutea)	12.6-16.0
3	Bluegrass (Poa pratensis)	12.6-18.6	20	Cottonwood (Populus deltoides)	21.3
4	Burdock (Arctium minus)	9.8-13.7	21	Dogwood (Cornus florida)	11.1-16.7
5	Cattail (Typha latifolia)	9.7-11.8	22	Lemon (Citrus limonia)	15.1-21.4
6	Cinnamon fern (Osmunda cinnamomea)	9.8	23	Locust (Robinia pseudoacacia)	9.8-14.3
7	Cocklebur (Xanthium sp)	8.4-10.7	24	Maple (Acer rubrum)	11.2-16.7
8	Cotton (Gossypium sp)	22	25	Oak (Quercus alba)	15.8-18.4
9	Dandelion (Taraxacum officinale)	8.5-10.8	26	Oak (Q. coccinea)	19.1
10	Goldenrod (Solidago sp)	10.3	27	Pine (Pinus spp)	16.0-18.4
11	Iris (Iris germanica)	13.1	28	Poplar (Populus alba)	19.7-20.1
12	Lamb's-quarters (Chenopodium album)	13.2	29	Spruce (Picea engelmannii)	11.5-23.5
13	Mullein (Verbascum thapsus)	8.0-10.1	30	Sweetgum (Liquidambar styraciflua)	13.3-15.5
14	Pea (Pisum sativum)	9.2	31	Sycamore (Platanus occidentalis)	13.5
15	Pokeweed (Phytolacca decandra)	8.5-9.5	32	Walnut (Juglans nigra)	12.6-18.3
16	Sunflower (Helianthus annuus)	13.8-18.0	33	Willow (Salix alba)	12.3-14.2
17	Touch-me-not (Impatiens biflora)	4.6-8.4	34	Yellow-poplar (Liriodendron tulipifera)	11.3-16.4

Part II: FACTORS VS D.P.D., O.P.

	Factors	D.P.D.	O.P.
	Temperature		
1	0°C	0.7	14.3
2	13°C	2.0	13.5
3	23°C	3.3	12.7
4	30°C	4.0	11.1
	Height on tree		
5	16 m		18.3
6	13 m	10.5	18.3
7	12 m	9.9	17.2
8	10 m	9.3	18.2
9	6 m		17.8
10	2 m	7.5	16.8
	Distance from growing point (root)		
11	1.5 mm	7.4	11.3
12	3.0 mm	7.7	11.7
13	5.0 mm	10.0	12.7
14	8.0 mm	0.4	9.8

Part III: SHOOTS VS O.P.

	Species	Apr 19	Apr 24	May 8	May 28	Jun 8	Jun 20	Jul 2	Jul 9	Jul 31
					Osmotic Pressure					
	Shallow-rooted Plants									
1	June grass (Koeleria cristata)	16.4	17.4	24.1	35					
2	Lomatium (Lomatium foeniculacum)	11.5	14.6	16.1	20.2					
3	Milk vetch (Astragalus crassicarpus)	10.9	13.2	15.4	18.7					
	Relatively Deep-rooted Plants									
4	Bluestem (Andropogon scoparius)	8.1	9.6	9.9	25.3	18.1	17.4	31.3		
5	Goldenrod (Solidago glaberrima)		12.0		12.8	14.3	16.8			
6	Sunflower (Helianthus rigidus)			12.6	19.9	15.2	22.9	36.9		
	Deep-rooted Plants									
7	False-indigo (Baptisia leucophaea)	8.6	10.8	12.0	14.8	16.0	16.7	17.3		
8	Lead plant (Amorpha canescens)		11.6	13.1	20.8	16.2	15.1	17.2	20	22.1
9	Scurf pea (Psoralea tenuiflora)		12.2	14.2	17.8	16.0	16.8	15.2	17.2	15.8

Part IV: WHEAT SEEDLING: AGE VS O.P.

	Age	Entire Plant	Shoot	Root
1	2 da	10.7		
2	3 da	9.8		
3	4 da	8.0		
4	5 da	7.8		
5	6 da	7.1		
6	7 da	6.6		
7	8 da	6.0		
8	9 da	5.4		
9	10 da	5.1	6.06	3.06
10	13 da	4.9		
11	18 da	5.4	7.04	3.03
12	25 da	6.0		

Part V: TISSUE-ORGAN VS O.P., D.P.D.

	Tissue-Organ	Beech[1]	Hellebore[2]	Nettle[3]
	Leaf			
1	Epidermis	15	19.2	18.8
2	Spongy parenchyma	22.4	22.5	24.7
3	Palisade parenchyma	37.7	32.9	37.7
	Stem			
4	Cambium	24.6	21.9	21.5
5	Xylem parenchyma	36.6	22.2	23
6	Pith		20.6	18.7
7	Wood rays	35.2		
8	Cortex	26.1	20.8	19.2
9	Phloem parenchyma	22.5		20.4

	Tissue-Organ	D.P.D.
	Root, absorption zone	
10	Epidermis	0.7
	Cortex	
11	1st row	1.4
12	3rd row	1.5
13	4th row	2.1
14	5th row	2.8
15	6th row	3.0
16	Endodermis	1.7
17	Wood parenchyma	0.9

	Tissue-Organ	D.P.D.
18	Petiole	8.4
19	Stem, 225 cm high	5.0
20	Stem, 35 cm high	2.9
21	Root, older portion	2.4
22	Root, absorption zone	1.6
		O.P.
23	Sieve-tubes	15.6-17.1
24	Stem wood	7.5-11.8
25	Root wood	6.3
26	Stem cambium	11.1-12.9
27	Root cambium	9.7-11.0

/1/ Fagus sp. /2/ Helleborus sp. /3/ Urtica sp.

Part VI: TIME OF DAY VS O.P.

	Species	6 AM	10 AM	2 PM	5 PM	8 PM
				O.P.; (D.P.D.)		
	King-weed (Ambrosia trifida)					
1	Top leaf	12.5;(7.5)	15.3;(15)	17.4;(17.5)	16.5;(15)	16.3;(15)
2	1st leaf from top	12.5	15.6	17.2	15.7	14.9
3	2nd leaf from top	12.9;(8)	15;(14.5)	17.1;(17)	15.7	14.9;(15)
4	Lowest leaf	10.1;(6.5)	13;(13.5)	15.9;(15.5)	14.3	14;(14)

		8 AM	1 PM	3 PM	7 PM
	Dock (Rumex patientia)				
5	Guard cell	16.6	21	20.2	13.2
6	Subsidiary cell	16.6	16.6	17.8	15.5
7	Epidermal cell	14.4	14.4	14.4	13.2

		12 N	2 PM	4 PM	6 PM	8 PM	10 PM	4 AM	8 AM
	Bluestem (Andropogon scoparius)								
8	Shoots (extreme drought)	23	25	27	26	21.5	20.5	21	25

Part VII: SEASON VS O.P.

	Species	Oct	Dec	Jan	Feb	Mar	Apr	May	June
				Osmotic Pressure					
1	Aspen (Populus tremuloides)	15	16.8	16.2	13.7	17		10.6	
2	Spruce (Picea glauca)	17.1	20.3	20		24.9	20.1	21	19.7
3	Twin-flower (Linnaea borealis)	19.6	25		25.6		14.3		
4	Wintergreen (Pyrola rotundifolia)		24.6		23.9		17.2		12.6

Part VIII: SOIL MOISTURE-SOLUTES VS O.P.

	Soil Water, g/100g	Corn Plant	
		Shoots O.P.	Roots O.P.
1	31	22.1	5.9
2	16	24.4	7.8
3	14	25.0	9.2
4	11	26.5	12.0

	Soil Solution, O.P.	Shoots	Roots
5	1.2	6.2	4.6
6	2.0	7.1	5.5
7	3.4	7.0	6.6
8	5.0	7.2	7.5
9	7.2	7.3	8.2

Part IX: HABITAT VS O.P.

	Habitat	Woody Plants O.P.	Herbaceous Plants O.P.
	Jamaica		
1	Ruinate	13	10
2	Ridge forest	12	9
3	Leeward ravines	11	8
4	Windward	10	8
	Arizona		
5	Rocky slopes	22	16
6	Canyons	21	13
7	Arroyos	17	13
8	Bajada slopes	30	20
9	Salt spots	45	24

Part X: PLANT GROUPS VS O.P.

	Plant Group	O.P.
1	Summer ephemerals	8-42
2	Succulents and winter ephemerals	4-24
3	Xerophytes	14-57
4	Hydrophytes	8-13
5	Air leaves	18-21
6	Water leaves	8-9
7	Epiphytes	3-6
8	Halophytes	30-115
9	Parasites[1]	14-17
10	Hosts	11-14

/1/ As for example, mistletoe (Phoradendron flavens), 15.8; host, 11.6.

304. OSMOTIC REGULATION: ANIMALS

	Organism	Osmotic Characteristics	Regulatory Mechanisms
1	Marine invertebrate eggs; Phascolosoma	Osmotic adjustment	No volume regulation known.
2	Marine mollusks; maja; Nereis pelagica; N. cultrifera		Volume regulation.
3	N. diversicolor	Limited osmoregulation	Low permeability; salt reabsorption in nephridia.
4	Gunda		Water storage.
5	Carcinus	Fair osmoregulation in hypotonic media	Selective absorption of salts from medium; kidney reabsorption or secretion; low permeability.
6	Uca	Regulation in hypertonic and hypotonic media except at extremes	Unknown.
7	Crayfish; fresh-water teleosts; amphibia	Unlimited (?) regulation in hypotonic media	Hypotonic copious urine; salt reabosprtion or water secretion; low surface permeability.
8	Fresh-water embryos		Water impermeability in some.
9	Elasmobranchs	Maintenance of hypertonicity in both media	Urea retention.
10	Some marine teleosts	Regulation in hypertonic media	Extrarenal salt excretion; low water intake.
11	Artemia		Unknown.
12	Earthworm; amphibians	Regulation in moist air	Low skin permeability; salt absorption from medium; salt re-absorption in kidney.
13	Insects	Regulation in dry air	Impermeable cuticle; hypertonic urine.
14	Birds, reptiles, mammals		Hypertonic urine; water reabsorption in kidney.

305. WATER BALANCE: ANIMALS

Part I: TERRESTRIAL ANIMALS
Values are for the resting state. Body weight values are g; others are g/100g body weight per day.

	Animal	Body Weight g	Water Turnover	Water Intake[1]	Metabolic Water[2]	Output Urine	Output Other[3]
1	Man	65,000	4.0	3.5	0.5	1.9	2.1
2	Cat	2,900	8.4	7.2	1.2	4.1	4.3
	Cattle						
3	Brahman, dry	409,000	6.1	5.5	0.6		
4	Holstein, dry	745,000	6.7	6.0	0.7		
5	Holstein, milking	529,000	15.9	14.8	1.1		
6	Jersey, milking	403,000	12.8	11.8	1.0		
7	Steer	584,000	4.8	4.0	0.8	0.9	3.9
8	Dog	18,600	6.0	4.6	1.4	1.9	4.1
9	Elephant	3,670,000	4.6	4.2	0.4	1.3	3.3
10	Guinea pig	450	17.0	14.5	2.5		
11	Hamster, golden	70	21.6	18.4	3.2		
12	Horse	420,000	6.2	5.5	0.7	1.2	4.3
13	Monkey, rhesus	4,900	8.2	7.0	1.2	5.3	2.9
14	Mouse, albino	21	20.4	10.1	10.3	4.3	16.1
15	Mouse, deer	20	15.4	9.0	6.4		
16	Rabbit	3,670	13.0	11.3	1.7	7.4	5.6
17	Rat, albino	225	16.3	13.9	2.4	5.8[4]	10.5
18	Rat, cotton	130		17.7			
19	Rat, kangaroo	106	8.2	5.5	2.7		
20	Vole	29	27.3	21.1	6.2		
21	Chicken	1,550	16.1	13.0	3.1		

/1/ In drink and food. /2/ Water of oxidation of foods or body protoplasm. /3/ Water lost in sweat, respiratory tract, feces, and incorporation into new protoplasm. /4/ A value of 3.8 has been reported.

Part II: AQUATIC ANIMALS

Values are for the resting state. Body volume values are ml and those for water turnover are per cent body volume per day at the indicated temperature.

	Animal	Body Volume ml	Water Turnover % body/day	Temp °C		Animal	Body Volume ml	Water Turnover % body/day	Temp °C
	In Fresh Water					Protozoa (concluded)			
	Amphibia				15	Euplotes	3×10^{-7}	10^4	25
1	Bufo vulgaris	22	117		16	Lembus	2×10^{-9}	6×10^4	26
2	Rana esculenta	65	22		17	Leucophrys	4.7×10^{-7}	3,300	21
3	Rana pipiens	32	40	20	18	Paramecium	1.9×10^{-7}	6,200	22
4	Rana temporaria	9	100		19	Rhabdostyla	8×10^{-9}	1.1×10^4	15
5	Salamandra	20	53		20	Spirostomum	2.2×10^{-6}	550	
6	Triton marmoratus	5	43		21	Zoöthamnium	1.4×10^{-8}	5,500	15
	Insecta					**In Sea Water**			
7	Chironomus larva	0.1	22			Pisces			
8	Corethra larva	6.2	19	20	22	Anguilla	250	6.5	
	Crustacea				23	Myoxocephalus	180	11.5	
9	Cambarus	13	5.3			Crustacea			
10	Eriocheir	60	3.6	13	24	Cancer	300	6.5	
11	Potamobius	46	4.1		25	Carcinus	40	10.0	
	Annelida				26	Maia	2,200	2.7	
12	Lumbricus	4	60	19		Protozoa			
	Protozoa				27	Amoeba mira	6×10^{-9}	4,300	
13	Amoeba proteus	3×10^{-6}	360	23	28	Cothurnia	1.2×10^{-8}	700	15
14	Cyclidium	2×10^{-9}	2.2×10^4		29	Zoöthamnium marinum	1.2×10^{-7}	750	15

Values in parentheses are ranges and unless followed by superscript, are estimate "b" of the 95% range (cf Introduction). * = range is only an estimate from comparable data in other animals.

Animal	Total Body Water			Extracellular Body Water			Plasma Volume[1]	
	Specifications	ml/kg	Method[2]	Specifications	ml/kg	Method[2]	Specifications	ml/kg
1	Fetus, <100g	914(871-957)	Des	Infant, premature	435(300-570)	Na[24]		
2	100-499g	882(837-927)	Des					
3	500-999g	852(792-912)	Des	Infant, full term	391(275-510)	Na[24]		
4	1000-1499g	832(798-866)	Des		346(275-419)[d]	Inulin[3]	<1 yr	47.7(34.0-61.4)
5	1500-2499g	783(710-856)	Des		353(297-414)[d]	Ferrocy[3]		
6	Newborn	757(703-811)	D$_2$O	<1 mo	412(354-470)	Thio		
7	1-12 mo	626(509-745)	D$_2$O	1-12 mo	364(268-460)	Thio		
8	1-10 yr	589(548-630)	D$_2$O	1-6 yr	309(236-382)	Thio	1-9 yr	46.9(34.8-59.0)
9	10-16 yr ♂	590(516-664)	D$_2$O	10-18 yr ♂	286(228-344)	Thio	10-18 yr ♂	49.0(37.0-61.0)
10	♀	561(489-633)	D$_2$O				♀	42.6(30.0-55.2)
11	Adult ♂	635	Des	Adult ♂	248(188-308)	Thio	Adult ♂	46.2(33.7-58.7)
12	♂	592(472-712)	D$_2$O	♂♀	158(131-185)	Inulin[3]		
13	♂	542(426-658)	AP	♂♀	178(143-213)	Sucrose[3]		
14	♂	532(462-602)	T$_2$O	♂♀	159(141-189)[d]	Mannitol[3]		
15	♂<70kg	626(517-735)	D$_2$O	♂<60kg	248(154-342)	Thio		
16	♂>70kg	560(470-650)	D$_2$O	♂60-69kg	249(196-302)	Thio	♂18-29 yr	46.0(34.7-57.3)
17	♂17-39 yr	602(502-702)	D$_2$O	♂70-79kg	241(176-306)	Thio	♂30-49 yr	43.8(31.8-55.8)
18	♂40-59 yr	572(471-673)	D$_2$O	♂>80kg	221(182-260)	Thio	♂50-69 yr	46.0(30.6-61.4)
19	♂>60 yr	541(478-628)[d]	D$_2$O	♂♀20-60+ yr	260(220-290)[c]	Cl[38]	♂>70 yr	48.7(35.3-62.1)
20	♀	560	Des	♀	208(144-272)	Thio	♀	43.5(32.5-54.5)
21	♀	496(404-588)	D$_2$O	♀40-70+ kg	245(185-305)	Bromide		
22	♀	448(336-556)	AP					
23	♀<60kg	505(415-595)	D$_2$O	♀<50kg	220(160-280)	Thio		
24	♀>60kg	486(395-577)	D$_2$O	♀50-69kg	198(138-258)	Thio		
25	♀<40 yr	511(430-592)	D$_2$O	♀>70kg	183	Thio		
26	♀>40 yr	468(389-547)	D$_2$O	Pregnant, 1st 1/3	281(196-366)	Thio		
27	♀20-39 yr	444	AP	2nd 1/3	284(221-347)	Thio		
28	♀40-59 yr	446	AP	3rd 1/3	303(233-373)	Thio		
29	♀60-79 yr	422	AP	60-69kg	310(250-370)	Thio		
30	♀>80 yr	488	AP	80-89kg	278(227-329)	Thio		
31	Pregnant, 2nd 1/3	547(485-600)	D$_2$O	>100kg	241(191-291)	Thio	Pregnant[4]	50.7(36.0-76.8)
32	3rd 1/3	544(485-590)	D$_2$O					
33	Post-partum	520(435-580)	D$_2$O					
34	Newborn	807	Des					
35	Cat 2 wk	738	Des					
36	12 wk	666	Des					
37	Adult	580		Adult	288	Thio	Adult	46.4(32.2-56.4)
38	Cattle Fattened	539(431-647)	AP				Adult	38.8(36.0-41.6)
39	Newborn	779(737-803)[d]	Des	Adult	299(240-360)[d]	Na[24]		
40	Dog Young	700(670-730)	Des		312(290-340)[c]	Cl[36]		
41	Adult, lean	700(619-756)[d]	Des		320(239-408)	Thio	Adult	52.7(35.0-70.4)
42	obese	596(503-690)	Des		198(145-251)	Inulin[3]		
43	unspecified	628(550-662)[d]	Des		216(166-214)	Mannitol[3]		
44	Goat 18.6kg	717	AP					48.0(42-54)[5]
45	44.2kg	706	AP					52.8(45-59)
46	Fetus <12g	894(863-966)[d]	Des					
47	71-112g	716(684-754)[d]	Des					
48	Guinea pig Newborn	710	Des					
49	Adult	635(524-746)	Des				Adult	43.0
50	Monkey	691(650-720)[d]	Des	Adult	208(121-195)	Thio	Adult	44.9(27.1-62.7)
51	Fetus, 1/2 time	871	Des					
52	Mouse Newborn	833	Des					
53	15 da	757	Des					
54	30 da	766	Des				Adult	57.4
55	Fetus, <1g	915(914-915)[d]	Des					
56	>50g	816(815-818)[d]	Des					
57	Rabbit Newborn	830(772-888)*	Des					
58	Young	720(651-767)[d]	Des					
59	Adult 2.7-4.0kg	667(550-785)	AP	Adult 2.7-4.0kg	246(200-295)	Thio	Adult 2.7-4.0kg	38.0(27-48)
60	Fetus, <0.20g	922(918-926)	Des					
61	0.5-1.0g	900(892-908)	Des					
62	2.5-5.0g	874(867-881)	Des					
63	Newborn	868(851-885)*	Des					
64	6 da	814(773-855)	Des					
65	10-15 da	757(719-795)	Des				Very young	54.7(49.6-59.8)
66	Rat 1-2 mo	697(662-732)*	Des					
67	2-3 mo	684(643-725)*	Des				Pubescent	65.0(59.2-70.8)
68	Adult, lean ♂	690(676-704)*	Des	Adult	300(260-340)	Thio	Adult	41.5(29.5-53.5)
69	♀	684(670-698)*	Des					
70	average ♂	660(620-700)*	Des					
71	♀	650(610-690)*	Des					
72	obese ♂	558(508-608)*	Des					
73	♀	586(516-656)*	Des					
74	♂ 250-390g	674(505-840)	AP	♂ 290-350g	269(190-350)	Thio	♂ 290-350g	45.1(31-59)
75	Swine Newborn	834	Des					
76	17 da	799(796-802)[d]	Des					

/1/ Measured by the dye method using T-1824 (Evans blue). /2/ AP = antipyrine; Cl[36], Cl[38] = radioactive isotopes of chlorine; Des = desiccation; D$_2$O = deuterium oxide; Ferrocy = ferrocyanide; Na[24] = radioactive isotope of sodium; Thio = thiocyanate; T$_2$O = tritium oxide. /3/ Constant infusion technique. /4/ Third trimester. /5/ Measured by radio-iodinated albumin.

307. KIDNEY FUNCTION: MAMMALS

Values in parentheses are ranges and, unless accompanied by superscript, are estimate "b" of the 95% range (cf Introduction).

Species	Age Group	ERBF[1] ml/min	ERBF[1] ml/min per sq m S.A.[8]	ERPF[2] ml/min	ERPF[2] ml/min per sq m S.A.[8]	Glom. Filtration Rate[3] ml/min	Glom. Filtration Rate[3] ml/min per sq m S.A.[8]	Filtration Fraction[4]	Tm p-Aminohippurate mg/min per sq m S.A.	Tm Diodrast mg/min per sq m S.A.[8]	Tm Glucose mg/min per sq m S.A.[8]	Urea[6] ml/min per sq m S.A.[8]	Creatinine[7] ml/min per sq m S.A.[8]
Man	Infant Premature, 4-28 da				149		45(26-64)	34	12.9			32(20-43)	
	Full term, 2-8 da				73		38(17-60)	49	16(6-26)		77	23.2	53.4(36-71)
	10-22 da				229		50(32-69)	24	21.4			36	
	1-5 mo				326		77(39-114)	24	51			55(23-88)	
	6-11 mo				480		103(49-157)	22(8-36)	50			68	
	12-19 mo				519(419-619)		127(62-191)	25(15-35)	61(19-104)			71	
	Children, 2-12 yr				654(533-775)		127(89-164)	19(11-27)	74(36-112)			75(38-112)	139(115-192)
	Adult♀		1166		655(544-761)c		127(117-140)c	20(12-28)	80(46-113)	51.8(34-69)	543(285-828)	75(59-95)	148(117-181)
	Adult♀		940		600(518-669)c		118(109-127)c	19(11-27)	77(56-99)	42.6(24-62)	375(295-455)	75(59-95)	186(102-317)
	Pregnancy, 2-8 mo		1359(964-1799)		727(590-865)		170(147-193)	22		45.6	303(248-358)	104(86-122)	153(120-231)
	near term		919(632-1773)		561(461-570)		126(69-183)	19.5				79(50-108)	
Dog	Adult[9]	300[10]	480	166	265(135-400)	53	84(45-120)	32(26-38)	19	20(13-48)c	300(170-390)c	56(28-83)	
Rabbit	Adult[9]	78	430	54	300(180-410)	9.2	50(30-70)	17		33(30-37)	79(55-105)	25.5	
Rat	Adult[9]	8	221	4.4	145	1.7	40(23-96)	28	20	9.3		10.9(5-17)	

[1] Effective Renal Blood Flow calculated from Effective Renal Plasma Flow ÷ 1 minus hematocrit. [2] Effective Renal Plasma Flow measured by PAH(p-aminohippurate) or diodrast clearance. Values require upward correction of about 10% for incomplete extraction by kidney to yield values for total renal plasma flow. [3] Glomerular filtration rate (GFR) measured for man by inulin or mannitol; for dog, rabbit, and rat, by inulin, mannitol or creatinine. [4] GFR/ERPF (% of plasma filtered). [5] Minimum volume of blood required to furnish the amount of substance excreted in urine in one minute. [6] Maximum whole blood clearance, or when urine flow rate is 2 ml or more per minute. Urea concentration in blood. [7] Exogenous. [8] In clinical medicine, values are usually based on body surface area of 1.73 sq m (adult, 70 kg ♂, 60 kg ♀), whereas for other animals values are per sq m; in this table, values are based on dog 13 kg, 0.623 sq m; rabbit 3 kg, 0.18 sq m; rat 0.2 kg, 0.03 sq m. [9] Unanesthetized. [10] Hematocrit = 0.45.

308. KIDNEY CONCENTRATING POWER AND ELECTROLYTE EXCRETION: MAMMALS

Values in parentheses are ranges, estimate "c" of the 95% range (cf Introduction).

Species	Urine Output ml/kg/da	Max. Conc. Urea mOs/L[2]	Max. Conc. Osmolar mOs/L[2]	Maximum Specific Gravity[3]	Max. U/P Osmotic Gradient[4]	Chloride Excretion mEq/da	Chloride Conc. mEq/L	Bicarbonate[1] Excretion mEq/da	Bicarbonate[1] Conc. mEq/L	Ammonia Excretion mEq/da	Ammonia Conc. mEq/L
1 Man	(9-29)	1000	(1200-1400)	1.040	4.2	118(58-250)	110(49-210)	1.5(0-36)	1.1(0-26)	38(30-70)	27(20-50)
2 Cat	26(22-30)										
3 Cow	14					282(127-610)	76(0-400)				
4 Dog	31(25-41)	1600	(1700-3000)	1.060	5.5-10	40(0-222)	41(3.4-94)	18(0.01-71)	39(0-150)	25(2.9-82)	69(4-190)
5 Rabbit	90(20-300)	2400	2400	1.056	8.2	3.6(0.8-9.8)	96(31-144)				
6 Rat	43(24-77)					1.30(0.4-1.9)				0.7	118(37-188)

Species	Sodium Excretion mEq/da	Sodium Conc. mEq/L	Potassium Excretion mEq/da	Potassium Conc. mEq/L
1 Man	120(40-186)	114(35-167)	64(53-91)	50(27-150)
2 Cat				
3 Cow	360(89-475)	74(2-530)	2370(1650-2980)	84(18-540)
4 Dog	32(1-209)	60	31(3-128)	
5 Rabbit				
6 Rat	1.4(0.2-1.9)	90(35-164)	0.9(0.4-1.9)	118(37-188)

Species	Sulfate Excretion mEq/da	Sulfate Conc. mEq/L	Phosphate Excretion mEq/da	Phosphate Conc. mEq/L	Calcium Excretion mEq/da	Calcium Conc. mEq/L	Magnesium Excretion mEq/da	Magnesium Conc. mEq/L	Water Excretion ml/da
7 Man	37(11-56)	26(13-56)	36(22-54)[5]	28(0-120)	8(2-18)	7.5(1.4-13)	9(6-16)	8.2(5.8-11.6)	1400(500-3000)
8 Cat					0.11	3.0	0.4	11.9	36
9 Cow	26(1-48)	48(6-800)	22		18.0(4.5-74.3)		339(154-578)		420(122-2000)
10 Dog			7(0-38)	(0-120)	1.3(0.1-7.0)	2.1(0.2-76)	3.9(0.7-20.7)	8.3(2.8-26.9)	258(34-935)
11 Rabbit	0.17(0.13-0.21)	5.5	1.4(0.6-2.1)	4.6(1.5-6.9)	1.7(0.5-3.4)	5.2(1.6-11.4)	2.7	8.5	12(4.3-24)
12 Rat			0.5(0.27-0.55)		0.09(0.02-0.16)		0.17(0.04-0.3)		

[1] Bicarbonate excretion is a function of urine pH. For man little is excreted at pH 5.2; 1.5 mEq at 6.0; 6 mEq at 6.6; 14 mEq at 7.0; 36 mEq at 7.4. [2] Milliosmols per liter. [3] Specific gravity during imposed thirst (water deprivation for 12 or 24 hours) is a measure of kidney concentrating power used in clinical medicine. [4] Ratio of osmolar concentrations of solutes in urine and plasma. [5] Base equivalence assumed as 1.0. Proportion of BH_2PO_4 to B_2HPO_4 varies with pH of urine. At pH 5.4, proportion 0.96 to 0.04, and the base equivalence is 1.04. At pH of plasma, the proportion is 0.2 to 0.8, and the equivalence is 1.8.

309. GASTRIC SECRETION, TESTS: MAN

Values in parentheses are ranges, and, unless followed by superscript, are estimate "d" of the 95% range (cf Introduction).

	Condition	Age Group	Volume ml/hr	Free HCl mEq/liter[1]	Total HCl mEq/liter[1]	pH	Pepsin units/ml[2]	Mucin mg/100 ml
1		Adult, 20-39 yr, ♂	77(0-164)	32(0-95)				
2		♀	70(0-160)	24(0-74)				
3	Fasting	40-59 yr, ♂	84(0-176)	30(0-87)	66(13-118)[3]	♂♀(2.2-2.7)[3,4]	♂♀65(0-162)[3]	♂♀181(11-351)[3]
4		♀	66(0-155)	17(0-74)	43(5-70)[3]			
5		60-79 yr, ♂	65(0-149)	16(0-60)				
6		♀	48(0-103)	10(0-32)				
7	Basal, one hour	Adult, 20-59 yr, ♂	79(0-176)	26(0-95)				
8		♀	65(0-160)	20(0-74)				
9	Nocturnal	Adult[3] ♂	54(14-99)	30(1-90)		♂♀(1.1-2.6)	♂♀205[5]	
10		♀	38(12-75)	27(3-72)				
11		Adult, 20-39 yr, ♂	114(13-217)	47(13-80)	62(29-96)			
12		♀	99(20-178)	50(21-80)				
13	After test meal	40-59 yr, ♂	99(13-192)	44(6-79)	58(19-96)	(1.6-1.8)[3]	♂♀7(3-15)[3,6]	
14		♀	93(16-172)	33(4-62)	50(20-80)			
15		60-79 yr, ♂	91(0-192)	36(0-76)	52(17-91)			
16		♀	82(13-156)	33(1-65)	50(16-85)			
17		Children, 6-11 mo, ♂♀	18(6-54)C	(0-50)C	(8-110)C	(1.3-1.5)		
18		1-15 yr, ♂♀	50(6-180)C	(15-115)C	(26-145)C	(1.2-2)		
19		Adult, 20-39 yr, ♂	131(6-256)	76(11-142)				
20	After histamine	♀	99(2-203)	62(0-126)				
21		40-59 yr, ♂	137(0-283)	69(0-156)			32[3]	♂♀136(0-330)[3]
22		♀	101(0-229)	53(0-125)			43[3]	
23		60-79 yr, ♂	108(0-257)	44(0-130)				
24		♀	84(0-195)	45(0-113)				
25	After insulin	Adult[3] ♂	140(85-204)	123(103-140)	128(111-144)	♂♀(1.2-1.8)	58	♂♀225(83-367)
26		♀	109(70-176)	123(105-133)	128(112-138)			

/1/ One mEq/liter is the same as one "clinical unit" or one "degree of acidity" = ml of 0.1 N NaOH required to neutralize 100 ml of gastric secretion. /2/ Unless otherwise indicated, "units" refer to proteolytic units in the Anson and Mirsky method. /3/ Age not specified. /4/ Range of means. The range for one normal person may be 1.5-5.0. /5/ Micrograms per ml (refers to equivalent activity of a standard pepsin). /6/ mg/ml (refers to equivalence to a standard pepsin).

310. LIVER FUNCTION, TESTS: MAN

Values in parentheses are ranges, estimate "d" of the 95% range (cf Introduction).

	Test or Constituent	Method	Normal Values	Abnormal Levels
		Tests Related to Bilirubin Metabolism		
1	Serum bilirubin, total	Van den Bergh	<0.2 mg/100 ml	Increased
2	Serum bilirubin, total	Photoelectric	0.25-1.5 mg/100 ml	Increased
3	Serum bilirubin, direct	Photoelectric	0-1.5 mg/100 ml	Increased
4	Icterus index	Acetone	1-5 units	Increased
5	Bilirubin clearance	I.V. injection	<5% retention at 4 hr	>5% retention
6	Urobilinogen, urine	Quantitative	<4 mg in 24 hr	Increased[1]
7	Urobilinogen, urine	Simplified quantitative	<1.9 "Ehrlich units" in 2 hr	Increased[1]
8	Urobilinogen, fecal	Quantitative	40-280 mg in 24 hr	Increased; decreased[2]
		Dye Excretion Tests		
9	Bromsulfalein	Photoelectric; dose 5 mg/kg	<6% at 45 min	>6%
10	Rose Bengal	Spectroscopic	<55% at 8 min	>55%
		Tests Related to Carbohydrate Metabolism		
11	Galactose tolerance	Urine, after oral administration	<3 g in 5 hr	>3 g[3]
12	Galactose tolerance	Blood, after I.V. administration	0 at 75 min	Positive[3]
13	Levulose tolerance	Blood, after I.V. administration	<20 mg at 1 hr	>20 mg
14	Lactic acid tolerance	Blood, after I.V. administration	<5 mg at 30 min	>5 mg
		Tests Related to Protein Metabolism		
15	Serum albumin	Sodium sulfate	4.89(3.6-5.6) g/100 ml	Decreased
16	Serum globulin	Sodium sulfate	2.12(2.0-3.7) g/100 ml	Increased
17	Albumin/globulin	Sodium sulfate	2.31(1.5-2.5) g/100 ml	Decreased
18	Zinc turbidity	Zinc sulfate	6-12.5 units	>12.5 units
19	Prothrombin	Quick	70-100% of normal control	Decreased
20	Prothrombin response	Response to vitamin K	>10% rise in prothrombin	<10% rise
21	Cephalin flocculation[4]	Hanger	<2+, 24 hr; up to 2+, 48 hr	3-4+, 48 hr
22	Thymol turbidity	MacLagan	<5 units at 30 min	>5 units
23	Thymol flocculation	Neefe	0-1 plus at 18 hr	2+ or more
24	Colloidal Red	Ducci	0-1 plus at 24 hr	>2+
25	Takata-ara		No flocculation	Flocculation
		Tests Related to Lipid Metabolism		
26	Cholesterol, total	Chemical	194-235 mg/100 ml	Increased[2]
27	Cholesterol, esterified	Chemical	70-75% of total cholesterol	<50% total cholesterol
28	Phospholipid	Chemical	145-280 mg/100 ml	Increased; decreased[3]
29	Lipids, total	Chemical	591-720 mg/100 ml	Increased; decreased[3]
		Miscellaneous Tests		
30	Serum alkaline phosphatase	Bodansky	1-4 units	>4 units[2]
31	Serum cholinesterase	Potentiometric (Michel)	0.66-1.06	Decreased
32	Hippuric acid	Sodium benzoate; 3 g, oral	2.5-3.5 g in urine after 4 hr	Decreased

/1/ In liver disease and hemalytic states. /2/ In complete obstruction of biliary passages. /3/ Parenchymal liver damage. /4/ Cephalin cholesterol.

Part I: MAMMALS

Temperatures are daytime rectal or cloacal averages.

	Species	Temperature, °C		Species	Temperature, °C
1	Man (Homo sapiens)	36.9(36.2-37.6)	84	Jackal (Canis aureus indicus)	38.3
2	Agouti (Dasyprocta acouchy)	38.9(38.7-39.0)	85	Kangaroo, red (Macropus rufus)	35.8(35.0-36.8)
3	Agouti (D. aguti)	38.5(37.9-39.0)	86	Kangaroo, great gray (M. major)	36.0(34.7-36.0)
4	Agouti (D. azare)	39.0(38.9-39.1)	87	Kinkajou (Potos caudiovolvus)	36.8(36.4-37.2)
5	Agouti (D. prymnolopha)	38.9(37.9-39.0)	88	Koala (Phascolarctos cinereus)	36.4(34.9-38.4)
6	Anteater, three-toed (Tamandua tetradactyla)	33.8(32.0-35.2)	89	Lemming, collared (Dicrostonyx rubricatus)	38.3(35.4-41.2)
7	Anteater, two-toed (Cyclopes sp)	30.7(30.2-31.1)	90	Lemur (Lemur variegatus)	38.2(37.5-38.9)
8	Ape (Cynopithecus niger)	37.9(37.1-38.8)	91	Loris (Perodicticus potto)	36.9(34.9-38.9)
9	Armadillo (Dasypus citellus)	31.3(30.0-32.5)	92	Macaque (Macaca macacus)	38.4(36.4-40.0)
10	Armadillo (D. novemcinctus)	32.5(30.0-32.5)	93	Manatee (Trichechus manatus)	39.5[2]
11	Armadillo (D. sexcinctus)	33.2(32.2-35.0)	94	Marmot (Actomys marmota)	34.2(31.2-37.2)
12	Armadillo (D. villosus)	33.4(31.8-35.0)	95	Marmot (Marmota marmota)	36.2(31.2-39.0)
13	Ass (Equus asinus taeniopus)	37.4(37.0-37.8)	96	Marmot, hoary (M. caligata)	36.4(33.5-39.3)
14	Baboon (Papio hamadryas)	38.1(37.3-38.7)	97	Mole, common (Scalopus aquaticus)	35.8(34.6-37.0)
15	Bat (Eptesicus fuscus)	38.1(36.2-40.0)	98	Monkey (Macaca mulatta)	38.8(37.2-40.2)
16	Bat (Pipistrellus noctula)	31.5(30.0-33.0)	99	Monkey (M. syanomolgus)	37.8(36.7-38.5)
17	Bat (Plecotus auritus)	36.6(35.0-38.2)	100	Monkey (Papio hamadryas)	38.1(37.3-38.7)
18	Bat, big brown (Eptesicus tenuipinnis)	35.7(32.2-39.2)	101	Monkey, night (Aotes trivirgatus)	38.2(37.4-40.0)
19	Bat, big brown (E. serotinus)	38.1(36.2-40.0)	102	Monkey, velvet (Cercopithecus pattus)	38.0(37.4-38.5)
20	Bat, horseshoe (Hipposideros caffra)	34.9(31.4-38.4)	103	Monkey, velvet (C. pygerythrus)	38.7(36.9-40.5)
21	Bat, horseshoe (H. cyclops)	34.8(31.4-38.2)	104	Moose (Alces americana)	39.4
22	Bat, horseshoe (Rhinolophus ferrum-equinum)	35.8(29.1-42.5)	105	Mouse, deer (Peromyscus leucopus)	37.4(33.6-41.2)
23	Bat, horseshoe (R. hipposideros)	35.9(34.4-37.4)	106	Mouse, deer (P. maniculatus)	37.9(35.7-40.1)
24	Bat, horseshoe (R. landeri)	32.8(28.0-37.6)	107	Mouse, house (Mus musculus)	36.5(35.2-37.9)
25	Bat, little brown (Myotis myotis)	37.6(35.6-39.6)	108	Mouse, jumping (Zapus hudsonicus)	37.3(35.3-39.3)
26	Bat, little brown (M. mystacinus)	37.2(36.2-38.2)	109	Mouse, meadow (Microtus pennsylvanicus)	39.3(34.7-43.1)
27	Bat, short-tailed (Carollia perspicillatum)	37.4(36.4-37.8)	110	Mouse, pocket (Perognathus hispidus)	36.5(34.9-38.1)
28	Bear, black (Ursus americanus)	38.3(31.3-39.0)	111	Mouse, red-backed (Clethrionomus gapperi)	37.3(35.3-39.3)
29	Bear, brown (U. arctos)	38.0(37.0-38.0)	112	Mouse, red-backed (C. rutilus)	38.3(36.6-40.0)
30	Bear, polar (U.-Thalarctos-maritimus)	37.5(37.1-37.8)	113	Muntjac (Muntiacus muntjac)	38.6
31	Bison (Bison bison)	39.0	114	Musk ox (Ovibos moschatus)	40.0
32	Buffalo, water (Bubalus spp)	38.2(37.4-38.7)	115	Muskrat (Ondatra zibethica)	38.0(37.0-39.1)
33	Camel (Camelus bactrianus)	37.5(36.9-38.0)	116	Nutria (Myocastor coypus)	38.0(37.2-38.8)
34	Caribou (Rangifer tarandus stonei)	39.0(38.5-40.0)	117	Opossum (Didelphis marsupialis)	34.6(31.9-36.4)
35	Cat (Felis catus)	38.6(37.2-39.9)	118	Opossum (D. virginiana)	34.2(32.6-36.6)
36	Cat, ring-tail (Bassariscus astutus)	37.6(37.2-37.9)	119	Opossum, brown (Metachiuris nudicaudatus)	34.4(32.4-36.4)
37	Cat, tiger (Dasryurus maculatus)	35.6(32.2-37.2)	120	Opossum, brush-tail (Trichosurus vulpecula)	36.1(35.4-36.8)
38	Chimpanzee (Pan troglodytes)	37.2(36.3-37.8)	121	Opossum, Murine (Marmosa mexicana)	32.7(28.9-36.5)
39	Chipmunk (Tamias striatus)	38.6(36.5-40.1)	122	Opossum, ring-tail (Pseudocheirus vulpina)	35.1(33.1-36.6)
40	Chipmunk, least (Eutamias minimas)	38.7(35.8-41.6)	123	Orangutan (Pongo pygmaeus)	37.0(36.2-37.8)
41	Coati (Nasua rufa)	38.2(37.1-39.2)	124	Otter, sea (Enhydra lutris)	38.5
42	Cow, beef (Bos taurus)	38.3(36.7-39.1)	125	Panther (Felis concolor)	38.1(37.2-39.1)
43	Cow, dairy (B. taurus)	38.6(38.0-39.3)	126	Peccary (Tayassu angulatus)	38.7
44	Cow, Holstein	39.6(38.2-41.0)	127	Pig (Sus scrofa)	39.3(38.7-40.3)
45	Cow, Jersey	39.3(37.9-40.7)	128	Pika, collared (Ochotona collaris)	39.0
46	Deer (Odocoileus virginianus)	38.2(37.9-38.5)	129	Platypus (Ornithorhynchus paradoxus)	30.5(24.8-35.3)
47	Dog (Canis familiaris)	38.9(36.7-40.6)	130	Porcupine (Coendou villosus)	36.8(35.3-38.3)
48	Dog, Eskimo (C. familiaris)	38.5(37.2-40.0)	131	Porcupine (Erethrizon dorsatum)	37.4(36.5-38.3)
49	Dormouse (Glis glis)	35.5(35.1-35.9)	132	Rabbit (Oryctolagus cuniculus)	38.8(37.5-40.1)
50	Dormouse (Muscardinus avellanaris)	34.5(31.0-37.9)	133	Rabbit, cottontail (Sylvilagus floridanus)	39.4(38.7-40.1)
51	Echidna (Tachyglossus sp)	29.9(24.9-34.5)	134	Raccoon (Neyctoreutes procyonoides)	37.4(37.0-37.8)
52	Echidna (T. aculeatus)	29.4(27.4-31.4)	135	Raccoon (Procyon lotor)	38.3(37.3-39.7)
53	Echidna (T. hystrix)	28.7(25.7-31.7)	136	Rat (Rattus rattus)	35.1(32.1-38.1)
54	Echidna (Zaglossus sp)	29.0(26.2-31.8)	137	Rat, spiny (Proechimys semispinosus)	37.9(36.5-39.3)
55	Eland (Taurotragus oryx)	38.8	138	Rat, white (Rattus norvegicus)	37.3(34.5-40.0)
56	Elephant (Elephas maximus)	36.2(35.7-37.8)	139	Reedbuck (Redunca arundinum)	38.4
57	Ferret (Mustela putoris)	39.3(37.9-40.4)	140	Reindeer (Rangifer tarandus)	38.8(37.5-39.8)
58	Fox (Vulpes melanotus)	37.9(36.5-39.3)	141	Rhinoceros (Rhinoceros unicornis)	37.6(37.4-37.8)
59	Fox, Alaska red (V. vulpes alascensis)	40.1	142	Seal (Callorhinus ursinus)	38.3(37.4-39.5)
60	Fox, Arctic (Alopex sp)	38.6(35.4-41.8)	143	Seal, bearded (Erignathus barbatus)	37.2(36.8-37.3)
61	Fox, Arctic (Vulpes lagopus)	38.7(38.1-39.3)	144	Sealion, Steller's (Eumetopias jubata)	38.5
62	Fox, Arctic white (Alopex lagopus)	38.6(36.6-41.5)	145	Sheep (Ovis aries)	38.8(37.2-40.5)
63	Fox, flying (Pteropus gaddei)	35.4(32.2-38.6)	146	Shrew, short-tail (Blarina brevicauda)	35.7(34.5-37.7)
64	Fox, flying (Rousettus angolensis)	36.5(34.4-38.6)	147	Skunk (Mephitis mesomelas)	36.4(36.3-36.5)
65	Fox, red (Vulpes fulva)	38.8(37.5-40.1)	148	Sloth, three-toed (Bradypus cuculliger)	31.0(24.4-37.6)
66	Fox, red (V. vulpes)	37.8(37.6-38.0)	149	Sloth, three-toed (B. griseus)	33.2(29.9-37.7)
67	Goat (Capra hircus)	39.5(38.3-40.8)	150	Sloth, two-toed (Choloepus hoffmanni)	34.5(33.4-35.8)
68	Goat, domestic (C. sp)	39.2(37.8-40.5)	151	Squirrel, Arctic ground (Citellus undulatus)	38.5(32.5-41.0)
69	Goat, Indian (C. sp)	38.6(35.2-40.5)	152	Squirrel, flying (Glaucomys volans)	37.0(35.0-39.0)
70	Goat, mountain (Oreamnos americanus)	38.6(37.8-39.0)	153	Squirrel, Franklin (Citellus franklini)	36.6(33.9-39.3)
71	Gopher, pocket (Geomys bursarius)	34.8(33.8-35.8)	154	Squirrel, red (Tamiasciurus hudsonicus)	39.6(37.6-41.6)
72	Guinea pig (Cavia sp)	39.1(38.4-39.8)	155	Squirrel, thirteen-lined (Citellus tridecemlineatus)	36.9(33.0-40.8)
73	Guinea pig (C. porcellus)	37.9(36.0-40.5)	156	Squirrel, Yukon ground (Citellus parryii)	38.1(35.5-40.7)
74	Hamster (Citellus auratus)	36.9(36.4-37.4)	157	Wallaby (Petrogale xanthopus)	36.0(35.4-36.6)
75	Hamster (Mesocricetus auratus)	36.0(35.0-37.0)	158	Walrus (Odobenus divergens)	36.1
76	Hare, Arctic (Lepus timidus)	38.3	159	Weasel, least (Mustela rixosa)	40.4(38.4-42.4)
77	Hare, showshoe (L. americanus)	38.5(38.0-39.0)	160	Whale, blue (Balaenoptera musculus)	35.7(35.6-35.8)
78	Hare, varying (L. americanus)	39.6(38.9-40.3)	161	Whale, fin (B. physalus)	36.3(34.4-38.2)
79	Hare, white (L. timidus)	38.7(38.1-39.3)	162	Whale, gray (Rachianectes glaucus)	36.5(35.0-38.0)
80	Hedgehog (Erinaceus europaeus)	35.1(32.0-36.5)	163	Whale, humpback (Megaptera nodosa)	36.3(35.2-37.8)
81	Hippopotamus (Hippopotamus amphibius)	25.0[1]	164	Whale, sperm (Physeter catodon)	35.8(34.6-37.0)
82	Horse (Equus caballus)	37.7(37.2-38.1)	165	Wolf (Canis lupus)	40.5
83	Hutia (Capromys pilorides)	38.3(36.2-40.3)			

/1/ Skin temperature. /2/ Old report; may be for a seal.

Part II: BIRDS
Temperatures are cloacal averages taken usually at room temperatures.

	Species	Temperature, °C		Species	Temperature, °C
1	Albatross, wandering (Diomedea exulans)	40.7(39.5-41.9)	81	Hawk, marsh (Circus hudsonius)	41.9(41.4-42.4)
2	Albatross, yellow-nosed (Thalassogeron chlororhynchus)	41.0(40.7-41.3)	82	Hawk, red-tailed (Buteo borealis)	41.2(40.9-41.4)
3	Amazon, blue-fronted (Amazona aestiva)	41.0[1]	83	Heron, black-crowned night (Nycticorax nycticorax hoactli)	42.3(41.9-42.4)
4	Auk, razor-billed (Alca torda)	39.1[1](39.9-41.1)	84	Ibis, white (Guara alba)	42.3(42.2-42.4)
5	Bittern, American (Botaurus lentiginosus)	40.2[1]	85	Jackdaw (Coloeus monedula)	41.2(41.0-42.6)
6	Bittern, sun (Eurypyga helias)	39.1[1]	86	Jaeger, parasitic (Stercorarius parasiticus)	41.2
7	Blackbird, rusty (Euphagus carolinus)	42.3[1]	87	Jay, blue (Cyanocitta cristata)	43.6(42.0-44.4)
8	Bluebird, eastern (Sialia sialis)	42.6(42.2-43.0)	88	Jay, brown (Psilorhinus morio)	43.3[1]
9	Bobolink (Dolichonyx oryzivorus)	42.6(40.9-43.4)	89	Junco, slate-colored (Junco hyemalis)	43.0(41.2-44.0)
10	Brant (Branta bernicla)	42.7[1]	90	Kittiwake (Rissa tridactyla)	41.4(39.9-42.2)
11	Bullfinch (Pyrrhula pyrrhula)	42.2	91	Kiwi, large gray (Apteryx haasti)	38.1[1]
12	Bunting, snow (Plectrophenax nivalis)	43.1(42.9-43.4)	92	Kiwi, north island (A. mantelli)	37.8(37.4-38.2)
13	Bunting, yellow (Emberiza citrinella)	43.2	93	Knysna Lourie (Tauracus corythaix)	40.1[1]
14	Cardinal, red-crested (Paroaria cucullata)	44.2[1]	94	Lark, northern horned (Otocoris alpestris)	43.9[1]
15	Cassowary, Beccari's (Casuarius beccarii)	39.2	95	Motmot, Brazilian (Momotus paraensis)	40.0[1]
16	Cassowary, two-wattled (C. bicarunculatus intensus)	38.8	96	Murre (Uria troille)	40.3(39.4-41.0)
17	Catbird (Dumetella carolinensis)	41.2(40.0-42.3)	97	Murre, Atlantic (U. aalge)	40.9(40.4-41.4)
18	Chickadee, black-capped (Penthestes atricapillus)	43.8(43.2-44.3)	98	Murre, thick-billed (U. lomvia)	40.5(39.7-41.5)
19	Chough, Alpine (Pyrrhocorax alpinus)	42.0	99	Ostrich (Struthio camelus)	39.2(37.8-40.0)
20	Coot, European (Fulica atra)	40.5[1]	100	Owl, great-horned (Bubo virginianus)	40.5(40.3-40.8)
21	Cormorant, common (Phalacrocorax carbo)	39.6(38.9-40.3)	101	Owl, northern barred (Strix varia)	40.0(39.6-40.5)
22	Cormorant, double-crested (P. auritus)	41.3(41.0-41.5)	102	Owl, snowy (Nyctea nyctea)	41.0(40.4-41.7)
23	Cowbird (Molothrus ater)	43.2(42.5-43.5)	103	Peacock (Pavo cristatus)	40.0(39.5-40.3)
24	Crane, demoiselle (Anthropoides virgo)	41.1[1]	104	Pelican, white (Pelecanus erythrorhynchos)	40.5[1]
25	Crane, sandhill (Grus canadensis)	41.3(41.0-41.4)	105	Penguin, little (Eudyptula minor)	39.0(37.8-40.1)
26	Crossbill, red (Loxia curvirostra pusilla)	43.3(43.1-43.6)	106	Petrel, pintado (Daption capensis)	39.8(39.3-40.2)
27	Crossbill, white-winged (L. leucoptera)	43.0(42.5-44.0)	107	Petrel, snow (Pagophila eburnea)	40.4(39.9-41.2)
28	Crow, eastern (Corvus brachyrhynchos)	43.0[1]	108	Petrel, storm (Hydrobates pelagica)	39.7[1]
29	Curassow, black (Crax bigra)	42.0	109	Pewee, eastern wood (Myiochanes virens)	41.6(39.6-43.0)
30	Curassow, Central American (C. rubra)	41.3	110	Pheasant, Amherst (Chrysolophus amherstiae)	42.2(41.9-42.4)
31	Dove, eastern turtle (Streptopelia decaocto)	43.3(43.0-43.9)	111	Pheasant, golden (C. pictus)	42.5(42.2-42.5)
32	Dove, mourning (Zenaidura macroura)	43.4(42.9-43.6)	112	Pheasant, ring-necked (Phasianus colchicus mongolicus)	42.1(41.7-42.4)
33	Dove, quail (Oreopelia montana)	43.3[1]	113	Pheasant, ring-necked (P. torquatus)	41.5
34	Duck, black (Anas rubripes)	41.0(40.7-41.5)	114	Pheasant, silver (Gennaeus nycthemerus)	42.3(42.2-42.4)
35	Duck, domestic (A. platyrhynchos domesticus)	41.5(40.9-42.0)	115	Pigeon, Cape Rock (Columba phaeonota)	43.3[1]
36	Duck, mallard (A. platyrhynchos)	43.1(42.8-43.4)	116	Pigeon, domestic (C. livia)	41.1(39.9-41.9)
37	Duck, muscovy (Cairina moschata)	42.0(40.8-42.3)	117	Pintail (Dafila acuta tzitzihoa)	43.0(42.8-43.2)
38	Duck, sheld (Tadorna tadorna)	42.7(42.4-42.9)	118	Puffin, Atlantic (Fratercula arctica)	40.8(40.7-40.8)
39	Duck, wood (Aix sponsa)	42.0	119	Quail, Calif. (Lophortyx californica vallicola)	42.9[1]
40	Eider, American (Somateria mollissima dresseri)	42.5(40.1-43.2)	120	Rail, clapper (Rallus crepitans)	40.1
41	Emu (Dromiceius novaehollandiae)	39.0	121	Redwing (Agelaius phoeniceus)	42.7(42.1-43.0)
42	Falcon, prairie (Falco mexicanus)	41.4[1]	122	Road runner (Geococcyx californianus)	41.9
43	Field fare (Turdus pilaris)	43.6	123	Robin, eastern (Turdus migratorius)	43.6(43.2-44.2)
44	Finch, eastern purple (Carpodacus purpurens)	43.2(42.5-43.8)	124	Scaup, greater (Marila marila)	42.6(42.2-43.2)
45	Finch, green (Ligurinus chloris)	41.5(41.2-42.2)	125	Scoter, black (Oidemia nigra)	41.3(40.9-41.7)
46	Flamingo (Phoenicopterus chilensis)	40.5(40.4-40.6)	126	Screech-owl, eastern (Otus asio naevius)	40.1[1]
47	Fowl, domestic (Gallus gallus)	41.4(40.9-41.9)	127	Shag (Phalacrocorax graculus)	40.4(39.4-40.9)
48	Francolin, gray-winged (Francolinus natalensis)	42.2	128	Shearwater, slender-billed (Puffinus tenuirostris)	38.6(37.8-39.6)
49	Fulmar (Fulmarus glacialis)	38.8(38.1-39.6)	129	Sheathbill (Chionis minor)	40.0
50	Gadwall (Anas strepera)	42.9[1]	130	Skua (Megalestris skua)	40.1(39.5-40.8)
51	Gannet (Moris bassana)	40.9(40.2-41.5)	131	Snow-goose, greater (Chen hyperborea atlantica)	40.8(40.6-41.2)
52	Goldeneye (Clangula clangula)	40.4[1]	132	Sparrow, Cassin's (Aimophila cassinii)	42.2[1]
53	Goose, barnacle (Branta leucopsis)	40.2(39.9-41.5)	133	Sparrow, eastern chipping (Spizella passerina)	41.7(39.8-42.9)
54	Goose, bean (Anser fabalis)	40.9	134	Sparrow, eastern fox (Passerella iliaca)	43.8(42.7-44.3)
55	Goose, blue (Chen caerulescens)	40.4(40.2-40.8)	135	Sparrow, eastern song (Melospiza melodia)	41.1(40.2-43.0)
56	Goose, cackling (Branta canadensis minima)	41.1(40.7-41.5)	136	Sparrow, eastern tree (Spizella arborea)	43.0(42.3-44.0)
57	Goose, Canada (B. canadensis)	40.5(39.8-41.3)	137	Sparrow, house (Passer domesticus)	41.5(37.3-43.5)
58	Goose, Chinese (Cygnopsis cygnoldes)	42.8(42.4-43.1)	138	Sparrow, Lincoln's (Melospiza lincolnii)	43.6
59	Goose, domestic (Anser anser domesticus)	41.3(40.2-42.0)	139	Sparrow, sharp-tailed (Passerherbulus caudacutus)	42.9
60	Goose, Hutchins (Branta canadensis hutchinsi)	40.5(40.0-41.0)	140	Sparrow, white-crowned (Zonotrichia leucophrys)	43.4(41.4-44.7)
61	Goose, white-fronted (Anser albifrons)	40.5(40.6-42.7)	141	Sparrow, white throated (Z. albicollis)	43.2(41.5-44.2)
62	Goshawk, crested (Accipiter trivirgatus)	41.8(40.2-42.2)	142	Sparrow hawk (Falco sparvarius)	42.3(42.0-43.2)
63	Grackle, bronzed (Quiscalus quiscula aeneus)	43.5(42.5-44.0)	143	Starling (Sturnus vulgaris)	43.5(38.8-43.7)
64	Grosbeak, Canadian pine (Pinicola enucleator leucura)	42.6(42.0-43.2)	144	Swan, black (Chenopsis atrata)	40.6(40.0-41.0)
65	Grosbeak, eastern evening (Hesperiphona vespertina)	43.3(42.8-43.9)	145	Swan, mute (Cygnus olor)	41.0(40.9-41.2)
66	Grosbeak, rose-breasted (Hedymeles ludivicianus)	43.6(43.2-43.9)	146	Swift, European (Micropus apus)	44.0
67	Grouse, ruffed (Bonasa umbellus togata)	42.5[1]	147	Thrasher, brown (Toxostoma rufum)	43.1[1]
68	Guillemot, black (Cepphus grylle)	40.7(40.0-41.0)	148	Thrush, red-winged (Turdus musicus)	41.0(38.4-42.7)
69	Guinea fowl (Numida meleagris)	42.2(42.0-43.3)	149	Thrush, wood (Hylocichla mustelina)	40.9(39.2-42.1)
70	Gull, American herring (Larus argentatus smithsonianus)	41.4(40.8-41.9)	150	Tinamou, rufescent (Rhynchotus rufescens)	40.8
71	Gull, black-headed (L. ridibundus)	41.4[1]	151	Tinamou, spotted (Nothura maculosa)	40.5(39.2-42.4)
72	Gull, common (L. canus)	41.8(41.0-42.0)	152	Titmouse, great (Parus major)	44.0
73	Gull, glaucous (L. hyperboreus)	40.8(39.8-41.7)	153	Tree-duck, black-bellied (Dendrocygna autumnalis)	42.3[1]
74	Gull, great black-backed (L. marinus)	41.9(41.2-42.4)	154	Turkey (Meleagris gallopavo)	42.8
75	Gull, herring (L. argentatus)	42.3(41.6-43.0)	155	Vulture, bearded (Gypaetus barbatus)	41.0
76	Gull, laughing (L. atricilla)	42.3(41.7-42.8)	156	Warbler, Connecticut (Oporornis agilis)	42.5[1]
77	Gull, lesser black-backed (L. fuscus)	41.7(41.2-42.1)	157	Waxwing, Bohemian (Bombycilla garrula)	42.5(41.2-42.1)
78	Hawk, Amer. rough-legged (Buteo lagopus johannis)	42.0(41.9-42.0)	158	Waxwing, cedar (B. cedrorum)	42.9(42.0-44.4)
79	Hawk, broad-winged (B. platypterus)	41.0[1]	159	Wigeon, European (Mareca penelope)	42.5(41.4-43.0)
80	Hawk, rough-legged (Archibuteo lagopus)	41.0[1]	160	Wren, eastern house (Troglodytes aedon)	41.1(39.2-42.1)

/1/ Only one measurement recorded.

Hibernation in mammals is defined as a state characterized by a lowering of body temperature to near that of the environment with a concurrent decrease in metabolism, but with the ability to regain the elevated body temperature without heat from external sources. Among reptiles and amphibians hibernation is arbitrarily defined as the state where body temperature approaches or equals ambient temperature, and metabolic, respiratory and heart rates are greatly reduced.

	Species	Geographical Distribution	Temperature Air °C	Temperature Rectal °C	Heart Rate per min	Respiration Rate per min	O_2 Consumption ml/g/hr[1]	CO_2 Produced ml/g/hr	RQ[2]
			Mammalia						
	Insectivora								
1	Hedgehog (Erinaceus europaeus)	Great Britain to Spain, Italy, Greece	2-3	6.2-7.7	18-24		0.014-0.033		
2			3.5	5			0.88	0.83	0.68
3			6				0.40	0.29[3]	0.73
4			9.7	12.0			0.126	0.056	
	Chiroptera								
5	Bat, big brown (Eptesicus fuscus)	U.S.A., southern Canada	8	9		3-10[4]			
6			22-26				0.8		
7	Bat, little brown (Myotis lucifugus)	Northern U.S.A., southern Canada, and southern Alaska	23	23.2		72-80	0.45		
8			0.5				0.113		
9				2		7-10	0.022-0.039		
10	Bat, greater horseshoe (Rhinolophus ferrum-equinum)	England to Korea, Japan to Morocco	13	13			0.150	0.089	
11			19	19			0.426	0.366	0.77
12	Bat, lesser horseshoe (R. hipposideros)	Europe to Asia Minor, north-western India to Sudan	15	15			2.23	1.80	0.80
13	Bat, Keen (Myotis keenii)	Eastern U.S.A., British Columbia	21.5	22.7		140-168	0.85		
14	Bat, long-eared (Plecotus auritus)	Europe to Japan, eastern Siberia to Sudan	0				0.037		
15			5	6.5			0.069	0.049[3]	0.71
16			10	10.7			0.094	0.079[3]	0.84
17	Bat, large mouse-eared (Myotis myotis)	Europe to China to Afghanistan	1.7				0.020	0.009	
18			2.5				0.051	0.033	0.65
19	Bat, noctule (Nyctalus noctula)	Europe to Siberia, Japan to Palestine	4.3				0.51	0.38[3]	0.75
20			12.5				3.49[5]	2.58[3]	0.74
21			20				0.403[3]	0.314	0.78
22			30				0.682[3]	0.484	0.71
23	Bat, parti-colored (Vespertilio murinus)	Europe to Japan, north-western India	0				0.037		
24			7.05	7.05	50-55				
25			8				0.020		
26	Pipistrelle (Pipistrellus pipistrellus)	Europe to North Asia, Japan		5			0.247	0.175[3]	0.71
27			5				0.053	0.038[3]	0.72
	Rodentia								
28	Dormouse, common (Muscardinus avellanarius)	Southern Italy to England and Sweden	6			9-10			
29			10.1				0.80	0.57[3]	0.71
30			11.6			10-12			
31	Dormouse, fat (Myoxus glis)	Central and southern Europe	6				0.029	0.021[3]	0.72
32			11.8				0.024		
33	Hamster, golden (Mesocricetus auratus)	Rumania, eastern Asia Minor, Syria, Palestine, north-western Iran	5	5-6			0.183	0.132[3]	0.72
34			5.5	5.5[6]			0.032		
35			5.8	6.4[6]			0.06		
36			5	5	4-15		0.060-0.080		
37	Marmot, European (Marmota marmota)	Alps	10	10.5		0.35[4]	0.018	0.012	0.68
38	Squirrel, arctic ground (Citellus undulatus)	Northeastern Siberia, Alaska, northern Canada		5.2	68[7]	10			
39			5.9	5.9		6			
40	Squirrel, thirteen-lined ground (C. tridecimlineatus)	Central U.S.A., Canada		3-10[6]	5-20		0.081-0.191		
41			4.0	5.7		1	0.081		
42			8.6	10.2		1.6	0.125		
43			12.5	13.6		1.8	0.197		
44	Suslik (Citellus citellus)	Central Asia, southern Russia to Austria		6			0.320	0.230[3]	0.72
45			7	7.2			0.015		
46			11	11.7		5			
47			13	15.5			0.034		
48	Woodchuck (Marmota monax)	Eastern U.S.A., Canada, Alaska		4-7	4-5		0.008-0.034		
49			8	8		6			
	Carnivora								
50	Bear, black (Ursus americanus)[8]	North America, north of Mexico	-3.5	31.2					
51			4.4	35.5		2-3			
			Aves						
52	Hummingbird, Allen's (Selasphorus sasin)	U.S.A. (California)	16	21.5					
53			22				1.24		
54	Hummingbird, Anna (Calypte anna)	U.S.A. (California)	24				0.84		
55	Swift, European (Micropus apus)		19	23[9]		8-10[4]	0.7	0.31	
56	Poorwill (Phalaenoptilus nuttalli)	Western U.S.A., Mexico	17.5	19.8					
			Reptilia						
57	Lizard, horned (Phrynosoma cornutum)	U.S.A. (Kansas to Texas), northern Mexico to Colorado	4-6[10]				0.051	0.022	
58			0-20[11]				0.043	0.033	0.73
			Amphibia						
59	Frog (Rana esculenta)		0	1			0.043	0.059	
60			6.1	6.4			0.342	0.449	

/1/ Milliliters per gram of body weight per hour. /2/ Respiratory quotient. Probably does not reflect actual exchange of gases or the true nature of combustion of foods during hibernation. /3/ Calculated. /4/ Respiration rates are very irregular in deep hibernation and there may be several minutes with no respiration followed by several respirations. Cheyne-Stokes respiration is not uncommon; range is average of several minutes. /5/ During awakening from hibernation. /6/ Oral temperature. /7/ Feeble heart beat in deep hibernation, becoming more evident as awakening progresses. /8/ Not a true hibernator, as indicated by the discrepancy between rectal and ambient temperature. /9/ Proventriculus temperature, taken orally. /10/ Body temperature in reptiles and amphibians presumably at or near ambient temperature. /11/ Range is result of long duration of experiments.

Diapause may be defined generally as a stoppage or radical decline of growth or physiological processes, usually for purposes of enduring extremes of such environmental factors as temperature and humidity. The degree to which purely physiological factors induce diapause cannot be stated with accuracy, if at all. There is no complete agreement on the nature or scope of the phenomenon, nor even whether it be a single phenomenon described inter- or intra-specifically.

Species	Dormant Stage[1]	Type of Diapause[2]	Observed Characteristics[3]		Species	Dormant State	Type of Diapause[2]	Observed Characteristics[3]
Acarina					**Lepidoptera (concluded)**			
1 Metatetranychus ulmi	E-1	F	abcd		Bombyx mori			
2 Tetranychus telarius	A	F	acd	28	bivoltine races	E-1	F	acdhi
Coleoptera				29	univoltine races	E-1	O	acdhi
3 Anatolica eremita	A	?	di	30	Chorizabrotis auxiliaris	A	O	dk
4 Dytiscus marginalia	A	O	g	31	Cydia pomonella	L-2	F	acd
5 Epilachna corrupta	A	F		32	Dendrolimus pini	L-1 to L-2	F	c
6 Leptinotarsa decemlineata	A	F	cdgi	33	Diataraxia oleracea	P	F	acd
Diptera				34	Euproctis chrysorrhoea	L-1	F	c
7 Epistrophe balteata	A	F		35	Grapholitha molesta	L-2	F	acd
8 E. bifasciata	L-2	O	di	36	Harrisina brillians	P	F	c
9 Lucilia sericata	L-2	F	d	37	Loxostege sticticalis	L-2	F	
10 Sitodiplosis mosellana	L-2	O		38	Lymantria dispar	E-2	O	d
Hemiptera				39	Malacosoma disstria	E-2	O	
11 Eurydema ornatum	A	F	ad	40	Mamestra brassicae	P	F	acd
12 Eurygaster integriceps	A	O		41	Operophtera brumata	P	O	d
13 Psylla pyri	A	F	acd	42	Philosamia cynthia	P	F	dei
14 Reduvius personatus	L-1 to L-2	F	ad	43	Pieris brassicae	P	F	acd
Hymenoptera				44	Platysamia cecropia	P	O	deij
15 Apanteles glomeratus	PP	F	c	45	Polychrosis botrana	P	F	c
16 Cephus cinctus	PP	O	de		Pyrausta nubilalis			
17 Exeristes roborator	L-2	F	d	46	bivoltine race	L-2	F	ad
18 Gilpinia polytoma	PP	O	d	47	univoltine race	L-2	O	ad
19 Sceliphron caementarium	L-2	?	i	48	Telea polyphemus	P	?	adei
20 Spalangia drosophilae	L-2	F	a		**Odonata**			
21 Trichogramma cacaeciae	L-2	?		49	Anax imperator	L-2	F	c
Neuroptera					**Orthoptera**			
22 Sialis lutaria	L-2	?	f	50	Austroicetes cruciata	E-1	O	d
Lepidoptera				51	Dociostaurus maroccanus	E-1	O	d
23 Acronicta rumicis	P	F	ac	52	Gryllulus commodus	E-1	O	d
24 Alsophila pometaria	E	O	d	53	Gryllus campestris	L-2	?	e
25 Antheraea pernyi	P	F	cde	54	Locusta migratoria gallica	E-1	O	d
26 Aporia crataegi	L-1	O	d	55	Locustana pardalina	E-1	?	d
27 Araschnia levana	P	F	c	56	Melanoplus bivittatus	E-2	O	d
				57	M. differentialis[4]	E-2	O	di

/1/ A = adult; E = egg; E-1 = embryo small or half-grown; E-2 = embryo fully grown and nearly ready to hatch; L-1 = larva at close of early or intermediate instar; L-2 = larva at close of final or penultimate instar; P= pupa; PP = prepupa. /2/ F = facultative; O = obligate. /3/ a = dormant condition evoked by certain temperatures; b = dormant condition evoked by nutritional factors; c = dormant condition evoked by day lengths; d = diapause terminated by adequate exposure to a specific (often rather low) temperature range ; e = failure of brain responsible for growth arrest in larvae and pupae; f = failure of prothoracic gland hormones responsible for growth arrest in larvae and pupae; g = corpus allatum involved in reproductive diapause of adult; h = egg diapause elicited when maternal blood contains secretion from subesophageal ganglion; i = diapause usually accompanied by striking fall in metabolic rate; j = metabolic rate decrease mediated by enzymatic processes, particularly in disappearance of cytochrome-c from tissues; k = diapause termination affected by rising humidity. /4/ Example of species in which diapause does not necessarily occur in all individuals. By selection over several generations, 100% non-diapausing or 100% long-diapausing embryos may be obtained.

314. PHYSIOLOGICAL CHANGES IN SLEEP: MAN

Data are intended to reflect changes caused by sleep alone as opposed to changes caused by rest, relaxation, or recumbency. Entries designated by "no change" are not to be construed to contraindicate profound changes sometimes found from the daytime active state to the relaxed horizontal state. ↑ = Increase; ↓ = Decrease.

Function or Property	Change in Sleep or Night/Day Ratio(N/D)		Function or Property	Change in Sleep or Night/Day Ratio(N/D)
1 Calcium, total, serum	No change; ↓ with rest	31	Effective renal plasma flow	No change
2 Chloride, serum	No change	32	H_2O, tubular reabsorption	N/D: 1.4
3 CO_2, combining power	No change or ↓	33	17-Ketosteroid excretion	N/D: 0.7
4 Creatinine, plasma	No change	34	Nitrogen, amino acid excretion	↓
5 Eosinophil count	↑	35	Nitrogen, total excretion	No change, or ↓
6 Glucose	No change	36	Phosphate excretion	↑
7 Hematocrit	No change; ↓ with rest	37	Phosphate excretion, fasting state	↑
8 Hemoglobin	No change; ↓ with rest	38	Potassium excretion	N/D: 0.25-0.5
9 pH	No change	39	Purine body excretion	↑
10 O_2, arterio-venous difference	No change	40	Sodium excretion	N/D:0.14-0.72
11 Phosphorus, inorganic	↑	41	Specific gravity, urine	↑
12 Potassium, serum	No change	42	Titratable acidity	↑
13 Protein, plasma	No change; ↓ with rest	43	Urea excretion	No change
14 Sodium, serum	No change	44	Uric acid excretion	↑
15 Volume, plasma	No change; ↑ with rest	45	Urine flow	N/D: 0.5-0.83
16 Blood pressure, systolic	↓ 15-30 mm Hg	46	Uropepsin, urine	N/D: 0.7
17 Blood pressure, diastolic	↓ 5-10 mm Hg	47	Metabolic rate[2]	No change or ↓10%
18 Cardiac output	↓	48	Babinski sign	Positive
19 Heart rate	↓	49	Knee jerk	↓ or abolished[3]
20 Pulse pressure	↓ 10 mm Hg	50	Pupillary light reflex	↓
21 Vessels of extremities	Dilate	51	Time spent in movements	↓; 20-43 sec/hr
22 Gastric acidity, total	↑; 74 ml N/10 NaOH equiv.	52	Number of major movements	↓; 11-28/night
23 Gastric acidity, free HCl	↑; 59 ml N/10 NaOH equiv.[1]	53	Cerebral blood flow	N/D: 1.08[4]
24 Gastric motility	↑	54	Electroencephalogram	Delta waves appear[5]
25 Saliva, pH	↓ to 6.3	55	Intracranial pressure	↓
26 Ammonium excretion, rate	↓	56	Temp., cortical and hypothalmic	↓
27 Bicarbonate excretion, rate	↓	57	Respiration rate	No change, ↓ or ↑
28 Calcium excretion, rate	No change or ↓	58	Respiratory rhythm, light sleep	Irregular
29 Chloride excretion, rate	N/D: 0.1-0.16	59	Respiratory rhythm, deep sleep	Regular
30 Creatinine excretion, rate	No change	60	Ventilation	↓ to 4.5 L/min

/1/ Almost none present, also reported. /2/ Slight decrease in body temperature also occurs. /3/ Similar response during relaxation. /4/ Calculated. /5/ Also, alpha waves eventually disappear.

Wherever necessary in calculating these values, the following assumptions were made: surface area of the average man = 1.8 sq m (height, 173 cm; weight, 68 kg); surface area of the average woman = 1.65 sq m (height, 165 cm; weight, 60 kg).

	Activity	Subjects no.	Tests no.	Age yr	Weight kg	Cal/min	Increase over Supine %
	Men						
1	Supine, basal	82				1.17	
2	Supine, basal	5	15	19-25		1.19	
3	Lying, at ease	5	15	19-25		1.5	28
4	Sitting at ease	5	5	19-25		1.8	54
5	Sitting, calculating	5	7	19-25		1.78	52
6	Sitting, writing	4	4	19-25		1.91	63
7	Sitting, reading	2	2	19-25		1.98	69
8	Standing, at ease	5	8	19-25		1.98	69
9	Standing, relaxed	2	47			1.25	7
10	Dressing	9		18-20	69	4.0	242
11	Brushing clothes	1	3	28		2.57	120
12	Washing hands, face, neck; brushing hair	1	3	28		2.74	134
13	Cleaning shoes	2	2	19-25		3.49	198
14	Dressing, washing, shaving	5	8	19-25		3.56	204
15	Walking (indoors), 2.4 mi/hr	4	4	19-25		4.3	268
16	Walking (indoors), 3.0 mi/hr	4	6	19-25		5.1	336
17	Walking (outdoors), 4.0 mi/hr	1	1	19-25		8.2	601
18	Walking (outdoors), 4.2 mi/hr	4	5	19-25		9.1	678
19	Walking (outdoors), 4.4 mi/hr	4	8	19-25		9.5	712
20	Walking (outdoors), 4.6 mi/hr	3	4	19-25		9.9	746
21	Walking (outdoors), 4.8 mi/hr	5	6	19-25		10.7	815
22	Walking up and down stairs, 97/min	5	10	19-25		8.4	618
23	Walking up and down stairs, 116/min	5	5	19-25		9.3	695
24	Climbing 15 cm stairs, 14.8 m/min				75	9.8	736
25	Climbing 15 cm stairs, 17.6 m/min				75	10.3	780
26	Climbing ladder, 17 cm step, 50° angle, 9.1 m/min					7.7	558
27	With 50 lb					14.3	1122
28	Climbing ladder, 17 cm step, 90° angle, 11.9 m/min					11.5	883
29	With 50 lb					25.4	2071
30	Walking, hard snow, 6 km/hr	1			83	11.9	917
31	Walking, loose snow, 20 kg load, 4 km/hr	1			83	20.2	1627
32	Walking, snow shoes, soft snow, 4 km/hr	1			83	13.8	1080
33	Skiing, level hard snow, 6 km/hr	1			83	9.9	746
34	Driving car	3	19		64	2.8	139
35	Driving motor cycle	3	19		64	3.4	191
36	Bicycling, 5.5 mi/hr	1			71	4.5	285
37	Bicycling, 9.4 mi/hr	1			71	7.0	498
38	Bicycling, 13.1 mi/hr	1			71	11.1	849
39	Rowing, 33 strokes per minute	5	7			19.0	1524
40	Rowing, 22 strokes per minute	2	2			12.3	951
41	Peeling potatoes	1	1	19-25		2.7	131
42	Laboratory work	5	5	19-25		3.2	174
43	Washing dishes	3	3	19-25		3.3	182
44	Making beds	1	1	19-25		7.0	498
45	Cleaning windows	10		27	61	3.7	216
46	Copper tooling (sitting)	2	2	41		1.8	54
47	Hand loom weaving (sitting)	1	1	40		1.9	62
48	Chip carving (reclining)	1	2	40		2.0	71
49	Miscellaneous office work, sitting	10	36	55-72		1.6	37
50	Miscellaneous office work, standing	10	45	55-72		1.8	55
51	Shoemaking, shoe repair	6	17			2.7	131
52	Shoemaking, shoe manufacturing	4	16			3.0	156
53	Locksmith, working	1	5	19	53	2.5	114
54	Tailor, cutting	2		21	63	2.6	122
55	Tailor, pressing	2				3.9	233
56	Armature winding	2	8			2.2	88
57	Radio mechanics	4	8			2.7	131
58	Printing, hand compositor	1	1			2.2	88
59	Printing, printer	1	1			2.2	88
60	Watch and clock repairer trainee		8			1.6	37
61	Light assembly line		3			1.8	54
62	Draftsman		5			1.8	54
63	Light machine work (engineering)		8			2.4	105
64	Typewriter mechanic trainee		6			2.1	80
65	Medium assembly work		14			2.7	131
66	Sheet metal worker		8			3.0	156
67	Machinists (engineering)		12			3.1	165
68	Plastic moulding		9			3.3	182
69	Joiners		18			3.6	208
70	Turners		4			3.7	216
71	Tool room workers		4			3.9	233
72	Machine fitting		12			4.2	259
73	Casting lead balls in mould		2			4.8	310
74	Loading chemicals into mixer		2			6.0	413
75	Unloading battery boxes from oven		4			6.8	481
76	Shoveling, 8 kg load, 1 m lift, 12/min					7.5	541
77	Hewing with pick					7.0	498
78	Pushing wheelbarrow, 57 kg load, 4.5 km/hr					5.0	327
79	Bricklaying					4.0	242
80	Mixing cement					4.7	302
81	Stonemasonary, shaping stones					3.8	225
82	Plaster lathing					3.1	165
83	Plastering walls					4.1	250
84	Carpentry, measuring wood	1	35		62	2.4	105

315. ENERGY COST, WORK: MAN (Continued)

Wherever necessary in calculating these values, the following assumptions were made: surface area of the average man = 1.8 sq m (height, 173 cm; weight, 68 kg); surface area of the average woman = 1.65 sq m (height, 165 cm; weight, 60 kg).

	Activity	Subjects no.	Tests no.	Age yr	Weight kg	Cal/min	Increase over Supine %
	Men (concluded)						
85	Carpentry, machine sawing	1	35		62	2.4	105
86	Carpentry, joining floorboards	1	35		62	4.4	276
87	Carpentry, chiselling	1	31		65	5.7	387
88	Carpentry, sawing soft wood	1	31		65	6.3	439
89	Carpentry, drilling hard wood	1	35		62	7.0	498
90	Carpentry, sawing hard wood	1	31		65	7.5	541
91	Carpentry, planing soft wood	1	31		65	8.1	592
92	Carpentry, planing hard wood	1	31		65	9.1	678
93	Farming, mowing with horse drawn reaper	15		15-55		4.3	268
94	Farming, threshing, throwing sheaves to thresher	7		15-41		5.6	379
95	Farming, hoeing, deep ridging	5	13	24-36	57	9.5	712
96	Farming, hoeing		12			4.4	276
97	Farming, hand milking	1		28	64	4.7	302
98	Farming, machine milking	1		28	64	3.7	216
99	Farming, horse ploughing	7	16	18-39	57-86	5.9	404
100	Farming, tractor ploughing	7	22	18-39	57-86	4.2	259
101	Lumbering, tree felling	11				10.7	815
102	Lumbering, tree trimming	11				10.2	772
103	Lumbering, tree barking	11				10.1	763
104	Lumbering, crosscutting with bucksaw	11				9.0	669
105	Lumbering, stacking firewood	2				6.3	439
106	Lumbering, chopping, vertical, 1.25 kg ax, 19/min	1		23	82	6.9	490
107	Lumbering, chopping, horizontal, 1.25 kg ax, 34/min	1		23	82	13.2	1028
108	Coal mining, hewing	18				7.0	498
109	Coal mining, loading	20				7.1	507
110	Coal mining, timbering	13				5.7	387
111	Coal mining, drilling	30				5.8	396
112	Coal mining, pushing tubs	12				8.0	584
	Women						
113	Supine, basal	49	265	22	55	.98	
114	Sitting	57	338	22	55	1.09	11
115	Standing	16	47	22	55	1.11	13
116	Dressing and undressing	12		8-12	34	2.3	135
117	Washing, dressing, undressing	3		43-55	70	3.3	237
118	Walking, 2.8 mi/hr	1	3	29		2.00	104
	Walking, 2.8 mi/hr, carrying a 20 lb load						
119	Load carried with shoulder yoke	1	3	29		1.94	98
120	Load carried on one shoulder	1	3	29		2.07	111
121	Load carried in two bundles in either hand	1	3	29		2.19	124
122	Load carried on tray in front of body	1	3	29		2.25	130
123	Load carried on tray in front of body with strap around shoulder	1	3	29		2.28	133
124	Load carried on head	1	3	29		2.49	154
125	Load carried on hip	1	3	29		2.72	1.78
126	Horizontal walking, 1.1 mi/hr	9	60	24		1.99	103
127	Horizontal walking, 2.2 mi/hr	9	64	24		2.84	190
128	Horizontal walking, 3.4 mi/hr	9	51	24		2.90	196
129	Skiing, level hard snow, moderate speed	1			57	10.8	1002
130	Skiing, uphill hard snow, maximum speed	1			68	18.6	1798
131	Washing dishes, top of pan 42 in.from floor (ht of subject 66 in.)	1	3			1.37	40
132	Washing dishes, top of pan 32 in.from floor (ht of subject 66 in.)	1	3			1.53	56
133	Paring potatoes (sitting)	7	24	27		1.23	26
134	Paring potatoes (standing)	7	26	27		1.29	32
135	Beating batter (standing)	7		22		1.43	46
136	Kneading dough (standing)	7		22		2.04	108
137	Step up 7 inches	9	36	26		2.77	183
138	Arm reach and trunk bend to 3 in. above floor (average ht of sub. 62 in.)	9	36	26		2.88	194
139	Arm reach and knee bend to 3 in. above floor (average ht of sub. 62 in.)	7	28	26		4.12	320
140	Arm reach and body pivot 36 in. above floor (average ht. of sub. 62 in.)	9	36	26		1.75	77
141	Arm reach 72 in. above floor (average ht of subjects 62 in.)	9	36	26		1.82	86
142	Hand sewing sheets, 18 stitches/min	1	5			1.18	20
143	Hand sewing sheets, 30 stitches/min	1	6			1.25	28
144	Darning	1	2	22		1.26	29
145	Crocheting, 32 stitches/min	1	5	22		1.27	30
146	Knitting, 23 stitches/min	1	4	22		1.29	31
147	Machine sewing (foot-operated)	1	8			1.43	46
148	Washing clothes, by hand	7	25	22		2.69	175
149	Rinsing clothes	7	21	22		2.42	147
150	Drying clothes (in extractor)	7	21	22		2.08	112
151	Wringing clothes, by hand	7	23	22		2.21	125
152	Putting up and removing clothes line	2	7	23		2.14	118
153	Hanging up clothes from basket on the floor	7	21	22		2.63	168
154	Ironing, standing (high board)	7	7	22		1.64	67
155	Ironing, standing (normal board)	7	7	22		1.69	72
156	Washing floor (on knees)	1	3	22		1.63	66
157	Sweeping floor	1	4	22		1.85	89
158	Vacuum-cleaning rug (moving 1 ft per sec)	1	10			1.63	66
159	Vacuum cleaning rug (moving 3 ft per sec)	1	12			2.58	163
160	Bedmaking, stripping	1		55	80	5.4	451
161	Typing, electric, 40 words per min	6			45-52	1.31	34
162	Typing, mechanical, 40 words per min	6			45-52	1.48	51
163	Typing, 59 words per min	1	4	18		1.34	37
164	Typing, 115 words per min	1	3	31		1.72	76
165	Leather tooling (reclining)	3	3	36		1.13	15
166	Leather tooling (sitting)	16	41	20		1.28	31
167	Leather stamping (sitting)	14	38	20		1.33	36

Wherever necessary in calculating these values, the following assumptions were made: surface area of the average man = 1.8 sq m (height, 173 cm; weight, 68 kg); surface area of the average woman = 1.65 sq m (height, 165 cm; weight, 60 kg).

	Activity	Subjects no.	Tests no.	Age yr	Weight kg	Cal/min	Increase over Supine %
	Women (concluded)						
168	Leather carving (sitting)	11	44	23		1.65	68
169	Leather lacing (sitting)	12	27	22		1.39	42
170	Copper tooling (sitting)	3	3	29		1.39	42
171	Chip carving (sitting)	17	53	22		1.61	64
172	Hand loom weaving	3	3	29		1.58	61
173	Table loom weaving	17	47	22		1.69	72
174	Floor loom weaving	3	4	42		2.12	116
175	Chisel carving, hardwood (sitting)	5	5	32		2.14	118
176	Chisel carving, softwood (sitting)	5	5	33		2.16	120
177	Printing (floor press, standing)	5	26	22		2.31	136
178	Hand sawing (standing)	16	47	22		3.27	234
179	Turning and finishing	8	36	19-33	47-65	3.0	206
180	Forging	4	20	22-32	55-69	3.1	216
181	Stamping	2	12	35-44	44-55	3.2	227
182	Hoisting shelf with pulley	1	5	54	56	3.3	237
183	Tool setting	5	25	21-26	45-59	3.4	247
184	Gauging	4	19	18-44	52-55	4.0	308
185	Laboring (general industrial)	5	14	35-51	44-86	5.1	420

316. ENERGY COST, PROGRESSION: MAN

Values for speed are kilometers per hour, unless otherwise indicated. Those for Calories are calculated on assumption that one liter of excess oxygen = 5.05 Calories, and that the resting level (included in the values) = 0.3 liters/min (1.46 Calories)[1].

	Progression	Subject	Speed km/hr	Cal/min	LO_2/min		Progression	Subject	Speed km/hr	Cal/min	LO_2/min
1	Walking, horizontal,	Normal,	4	3.5-4.5	0.7-0.9		Carrying 20 kg load				
2	treadmill	75 kg	6	5.0-5.5	1.0-1.1	39	Walking, horizontal	70 kg	1.6	3.5	0.7
3			8	9.0-10.1	1.8-1.9	40			3.2	4.5	0.9
4			10	14.6-17.6	2.9-3.5	41			4.8	6.0	1.2
5		Athlete,	8	8.0	1.6	42			6.4	9.0	1.8
6		63 kg	10	11.6	2.3	43	Running, horizontal		8.0	14.1	2.8
7			12	16.1	3.2	44	Walking, grade 36%		0.8	6.0	1.2
8	Walking, grade, 0%	Normal,	4.2	4.0-4.5	0.8-0.9	45			2.4	15.6	3.1
9	treadmill, +5%	70-79 kg		5.5-6.0	1.1-1.2	46	Bicycling, level	70 kg + cycle	8.9	3.0	0.6
10	uphill +10%			7.5-8.0	1.5-1.6	47		and gas-	15.1	6.0	1.2
11	+15%			10.0-10.5	2.0-2.1	48		meter = 21 kg	21.3	10.0	2.0
12	+20%			12.6-13.1	2.5-2.6		Bicycling, grade[3]				
13	+25%			15.1-16.1	3.0-3.2	49	Free-wheeling, DH	79 kg + cycle	8.6	2.5	0.5
14	downhill -5%	Normal,	4.2	3.5-4.0	0.7-0.8	50	Cycling, DH, -2%	and gas-		2.5	0.5
15	-10%	70-79 kg		3.5	0.7	51	DH, -10%	meter = 16kg		4.0	0.8
16	-15%			3.5	0.7	52	UH, +2%			6.0	1.2
17	-20%			4.0-4.5	0.8-0.9	53	UH, +10%			17.6	3.5
18	-25%			5.0	1.0		Swimming				
19	Walking, horizontal, hard surface road	68-69 kg plus	5.5	5.5	1.1	54	Breast stroke,	Excellent	16 m/min	7.0	1.4
20	grass covered road	9 kg clothing	5.6	6.5	1.3	55	steady state	swimmer	32	10.0	2.0
21	furrow in field	and apparatus	5.4	7.0	1.4	56			44	14.6	2.9
22	harvested field		5.2	7.0	1.4	57			56	20.2	4.0
23	plowed field		5.3	8.0	1.6	58	short sprint,	Good	60	39[3]	7.8[3]
24	harrowed field		5.1	10.5	2.1	59	20-40 m	swimmer	72	72[3]	14.3[3]
25	hard snow	83 kg	6.0	11.9	2.3	60	Crawl, steady	Excellent	36	10	1.9
26			9.1	16.1	3.2	61	state	swimmer	58	17	3.3
27	soft snow	83 + 20 kg[2]	3.9	20.7	4.1	62	short sprint,	Good	60	23[3]	4.5[3]
28	Running, horizontal,	74 kg	12	15.1-16.1	3.0-3.2	63	20-40 m	swimmer	80	45[3]	9.0[3]
29	treadmill; values		14	17.6-18.7	3.5-3.7	64			104	124[3]	24.5[3]
30	for Cal. and O_2 are		16	20.2-21.7	4.0-4.3	65	Skiing, horizontal,	83 kg	4.16	8.5	1.7
31	for work and		18	24.2-25.8	4.8-5.1	66	loose snow,		10.67	15.6	3.1
32	recovery		20	30.3-34.3	6.0-6.8	67	steady state		14.73	26.2	5.2
33	Running, horizontal,	75 kg	19.2	28-31	5.5-6.1	68		Carrying 20 kg	4	13.1	2.6
34	on track; values for	74 kg	26.3	66-91	13-18	69	Snow-shoeing, horiz.		4	14.1	2.8
35	Cal. and O_2 are for	70 kg	28.1	76-167	15-33	70		Carrying 20 kg	4	15.6	3.1
36	work and recovery	72 kg	28.8	106-232	21-46	71	Rowing; assistant	70 kg	3.2	5.0	1.0
37	Running, grade 8.6%	70 kg	9.3	13.1	2.6	72	also in boat		5.6	10.0	2.0
38			11.3	16.2	3.2	73	Skating, smooth ice	70 kg	14.5	8.0	1.6
						74			20.9	13.5	2.7

/1/ At the resting level or for light work a satisfactory conversion factor is one liter of oxygen = 4.9 Calories, but work requiring 1.5-2 liters of oxygen per minute will use glycogen, and a factor of one liter O_2 = 5.05 Calories is considered more valid. /2/ Extra load carried. /3/ Work plus recovery.

317. MOTOR PERFORMANCES: ANIMALS
Part I: MAMMALS

Running

#	Species	Velocity mi/hr	Remarks
1	Antelope, prong-horned (Antilocapra americana)	70	Maximum in short burst.
2	Ass, Asiatic wild (Equus hemionus)	20-36	Normal gait.
3	Bison, American (Bison bison)	30	Average, 16 miles.
4		30-32	Maximum, pressed.
5	Camel, dromedary (Camelus dromedarius)	9-10	Racing, 115 miles in 12 hr.
6			Normal walking, loaded.
7	Caribou, barren ground (Rangifer arcticus)	25+	Average maximum.
8	Cheetah (Acinonyx jubatus)	65-70	Maximum, 440 yards.
9	Chipmunk, least (Eutamias sp)	10	Pressed, 50 yards.
10	Coyote (Canis latrans)	28-43	Maximum, short dash.
11		24	Average, 1 mile.
12	Deer, white-tailed (Odocoileus virginianus)	49	Maximum, pressed.
13		15-18	
14	Dog, domestic (Canis familiaris)	43	Maximum for saluki.
15		30-36	Average, 1 mile, foxhound.
16		22	Racing greyhound, average.
17	Elephant, African (Loxodonta africana)	25	Charging, 120 yards.
18	Elk, American (Cervus canadensis)	18	Unhurried, 1 mile.
19	Fox, gray (Urocyon cinereoargenteus)	40	Pressed, 3/4 mile.
20	Fox, red (Vulpes fulva)	26	Average maximum, 1 mile.
21	Gazelle, Grant's (Gazella granti)	50+	1/2 mile.
22	Giraffe (Giraffa camelopardalis)	28-32	Pressed.
23	Goat, mountain (Oreamnos americanus)	20+	Maximum.
24	Hare, arctic (Lepus groenlandicus)	30-40	Pressed, 3 miles.
25	Horse, domestic (Equus caballus)	42.3	Running, 440 yards.
26		39.1	Running, 1 mile.
27		31.1	Trotting, 1 mile.
28		11.2	Trotting, 100 miles.
29	Kangaroo, great (Macropus sp)	25	Chased.
30	Mink, common (Mustela vison)	7-8	Average maximum.
31	Mole, common (Scalopus aquaticus)	1.5	On surface.
32	Monkey, langur (Presbytis senex)	23+	On ground, 70 yards.
33	Moose (Alces americana)	35	Pressed to maximum, 1/4 mile.
34	Rabbit, white-tailed jack (Lepus townsendii)	34	50 yards.
35	Rat, Calif. kangaroo (Dipodomys heermanni)	5.4-12	Pressed, 16-52 feet.
36	Reindeer (Rangifer tarandus)	13.3	Pulling sled, 1.6 miles.
37	Rhinoceros, black (Diceros bicornis)	20+	Sustained maximum.
38	Sheep, bighorn (Ovis canadensis)	30	Pressed, 1/4 mile.
39	Sloth	0.5	
40	Squirrel, gray (Sciurus carolinensis)	15	40 or 50 feet.
41	Squirrel, southern flying (Glaucomys volans)	4-5	Maximum.
42	Swine, domestic (Sus scrofa)	11	
43	Warthog (Phacochoerus aethiopicus)	30	
44	Wildebeest (Connochaetes sp)	50+	Maximum, 1/4 mile.
45	Wolf (Canis lupus)	28-40	Maximum up to 200 yards.
46	Woodchuck (Marmota monax)	10	Maximum, 1 minute.

Leaping, Horizontal

#	Species	Distance ft	Remarks
47	Antelope, pronghorned (Antilocapra americana)	12-20	Bound at high speed.
48	Chipmunk (Tamias striatus)	6	Maximum.
49	Deer, mule (Odocoileus hemionus)	18-25	Effortless bounding.
50	Dog, domestic (Canis familiaris)	15	Stride, racing whippet.
51	Fisher (Martes pennanti)	40	Descending diagonally.
52	Hare, varying (Lepus americanus)	4-10	Normal bounds.
53	Impala (Aepyceros melampus)	30-40	Estimated maximum.
54	Jerboa (Dipus sagitta)	12-15	Estimated maximum.
55	Kangaroo, great (Macropus sp)	35	Chased, maximum leap.
56	Lynx, Canadian (Lynx canadensis)	12-15	Normal maximum leap.
57	Marten, American (Martes americana)	3	Normal maximum bound.
58	Mink (Mustela vison)	0.8-1.2	Normal bound.
59	Mouse, woodland jumping (Napaeozapus insignis)	10-12	Frightened, maximum leap.
60	Puma (Felis concolor)	1-3	Normal leap.
61		40-47?	Maximum leap.
62	Rabbit, white-tailed jack (Lepus townsendii)	18-21	Maximum bound.
63		6-9	Slow speed hop.
64	Rat, kangaroo (Dipodomys sp)	9-12	Frightened, maximum leap.
65	Squirrel, southern flying (Glaucomys volans)	152	Max. diagonal descending glide.
66	Squirrel, red (Tamiasciurus hudsonicus)	15-20	Max. diagonal descending leap.
67	Squirrel, gray (Sciurus carolinensis)	2	Normal bound.
68	Weasel, long-tailed (Mustela frenata)	2.5-3.5	Average maximum bound.

Leaping, Vertical

#	Species	Distance ft	Remarks
69	Antelope, pronghorned (Antilocapra americana)	5	"Spy-hop."
70	Coyote (Canis latrans)	4	Pressed.
71	Deer, white-tailed (Odocoileus virginianus)	8	Pressed.
72	Elk, American (Cervus canadensis)	8	
73	Impala (Aepyceros melampus)	8	Estimated maximum.
74	Jerboa (Dipus sagitta)	3+	
75	Kangaroo, great (Macropus sp)	9	
76	Kangaroo, rat (Bettongia penicillata)	8	
77	Mouse, meadow jumping (Zapus hudsonius)	3+	
78	Mouse, kangaroo (Microdipodops megacephalus)	1.5	
79	Muskrat (Ondatra zibethicus)	2.5	
80	Peccary (Tayassu sp)	4	
81	Puma (Felis concolor)	10-18?	
82	Rabbit, antelope jack (Lepus alleni)	2.5-5.5	Easy bound.
83	Rat, large kangaroo (Dipodomys spectabilis)	1.5-2	
84	Squirrel, red (Tamiasciurus hudsonicus)	3	"Spy-hop."

Swimming

#	Species	Velocity mi/hr	Remarks
85	Beaver, American (Castor canadensis)	2	Maximum.
86	Caribou, woodland (Rangifer caribou)	4	Estimated maximum.
87	Deer, white-tailed (Odocoileus virginianus)	4±	Estimated maximum.
88	Dolphin	35-37+	Playing before ship.
89	Dolphin, bottle-nosed (Tursiops truncatus)	21	Maximum.
90	Mink (Mustela vison)	1-1.5	Normal.
91	Mole, common (Scalopus aquaticus)	0.7	
92	Muskrat (Ondatra zibethicus)	3	Maximum.
93	Porcupine (Erethizon dorsatum)	2±	Cruising.
94	Whale, blue (Sibbaldus musculus)	16	Chased.

Flying

#	Species	Velocity mi/hr	Remarks
95	Bat	20	

Part II. BIRDS, REPTILES, FISH

Birds: Flying

Species	Velocity mi/hr	Remarks[1]
1 Blackbird, tricolored (Agelaius tricolor)	46-48	To and from nest.
2 Bluebird, mountain (Sialia currucoides)	18	Side wind.
3 Bobwhite (Colinus virginianus)	28-49	Normal to frightened.
4 Bunting, yellow (Emberiza citrinella)	26-35	Easy flight.
5 Canvasback (Aythya valisineria)	72‡	Air speed, pressed.
6 Catbird (Dumetella carolinensis)	12-16	
7 Crane, sandhill (Grus canadensis)	31-35	Headwind to calm.
8 Crow, American (Corvus brachyrhynchos)	17-35	
9 Cuckoo, European (Cuculus canorus)	27	Pressing some.
10 Curlew, long-billed (Numenius americanus)	35-55	Normal to maximum, pressed.
11 Dove, ring (Columba palumbus)	27-51	Easy flight to pressing hard.
12 Eagle, golden (Aquila chrysaëtos)	28-120	Migrating to diving.
13 Egret, American (Casmerodius albus e.)	17-32	Normal to pressed.
14 Falcon, peregrine (Falco peregrinus)	26-180	Cruising to diving.
15 Flicker, red-shafted (Colaptes cafer)	25-44	Normal to alarmed.
16 Gannet (Moris bassana)	25-48	
17 Goldfinch, European (Carduelis carduelis)	26	Normal.
18 Goose, Canada (Branta canadensis)	20-60	Cruising to pressed (air speed).
19 Grackle, bronzed (Quiscalus versicolor)	20-30	
20 Grouse, ruffed (Bonasa umbellus)	30-51	Flying in brush and to cover..
21 Gull, herring (Larus argentatus)	12-36	Easy flight.
22 Harrier, American marsh (Circus cyaneus)	21-38	Migrating, 2/3 mile.
23 Hawk, Cooper's (Accipiter cooperii)	21-55	Migrating, 2/3 mile.
24 Heron, great blue (Ardea herodias)	18-36	Cruising to pressed.
25 Hummingbird, ruby-throated (Archilochus colubris)	45-55	Easy flight.
26 Ibis, white-faced glossy (Plegadis guarauna)	30-33	Cruising.
27 Jay, blue (Cyanocitta cristata)	20	
28 Kestrel (Falco tinnunculus)	35-44	Easy flight.
29 Killdeer (Charadrius vociferus)	25-55	
30 Kingfisher, belted (Megaceryle alcyon)	36	Easy flight.
31 Lark, horned (Eremophila alpestris)	17-54	Short to long flight.
32 Linnet (Carduelis cannabina)	53	5 miles.
33 Loon, common (Gavia immer)	26-36	Normal to pressed.
34 Magpie (Pica pica)	19-35	Normal to pressed (air speed).
35 Mallard (Anas platyrhynchos)	26-60	
36 Martin, house (Chelidon urbica)	24-27	Cruising.
37 Meadowlark, western (Sturnella neglecta)	26-40	
38 Merganser, American (Mergus merganser a.)	30	1.4 mile, not pressed.
39 Oriole, Bullock's (Icterus bullockii)	28-32	
40 Osprey (Pandion haliaetus)	20-56	Migrating, 2/3 mile.
41 Owl, tawny (Strix aluco)	40-45	Deliberate flight to pressed.
42 Partridge, European (Perdix perdix)	25-35	Normal flight.
43 Pelican, brown (Pelecanus occidentalis)	14-26	Maintain 26 mph for 8 miles.
44 Pheasant, ring-necked (Phasianus colchicus)	27-38	
45 Pigeon, green (Dendrophasa sp)	44-48	2 miles.
46 Pintail (Anas acuta)	49-65+	Pressed (air speed).
47 Plover, European golden (Pluvialis apricaria)	60-70	Air speed, chased.
48 Quail, California (Lophortyx californica)	38-58	
49 Raven (Corvus corax)	24-40	Normal, to 1300 yards.
50 Redhead (Aythya americana)	31-55	Cruising to pressed.
51 Robin (Turdus migratorius)	17-36	
52 Rook (Corvus frugilegus)	24-45	
53 Sandpiper, western (Ereunetes mauri)	44-55	Level flight to maximum air speed.
54 Shoveller (Spatula clypeata)	25-53+	
55 Shrike (Lanius ludovicianus)	22-45	
56 Sparrow, house (Passer domesticus)	24-35	Calm to pressed.
57 Starling, European (Sturnus vulgaris)	18-51	
58 Stork, white (Ciconia ciconia)	48	Migrating, air speed.
59 Swallow, barn (Hirundo rustica)	20-46	
60 Swan, whistling (Cygnus columbianus)	18-55	Cruising to pressed (air speed).
61 Swift	68+	Passed plane at this air speed.
62 Teal, European (Anas crecca)	44-68	Cruising to pressed (air speed).
63 Tern, common (Sterno hirundo)	13-29	Cruising.
64 Thrasher, sage (Oreoscoptes montanus)	22-29	Cruising.
65 Thrush, song (Turdus philomelus)	31	Pressed.
66 Titmouse, blue (Parus caeruleus)	21	Tree to tree, 40 yards.
67 Turkey, wild (Meleagris gallopavo)	55	Pressed, 1 mile.
68 Vulture, turkey (Cathartes aura)	15-34	Normal to migrating, 2/3 mile.
69 Warbler, willow (Phylloscopus trochilis)	24-27	Pressed.
70 Woodcock (Philohela minor)	5-13	

Birds: Running

Species	Velocity mi/hr	Remarks[1]
71 Avocet (Recurvirostra americana)	8	Pressed, 50 feet.
72 Chicken, domestic (Gallus gallus)	9	
73 Curlew, long-billed (Numenius americanus)	8-10	75 yards, pressed.
74 Emu (Dromiceius novaehollandiae)	35-40	Not maximum.
75 Grouse, sage (Centrocercus urophasianus)	2	Before car, 30 feet.
76 Killdeer (Charadrius vociferus)	5	30 feet.
77 Ostrich (Struthio camelus)	50+	1/2 mile.
78 Partridge, chuker (Alectoris graeca)	12-18	12 mph for 20 yards.
79 Pheasant, ring-necked (Phasianus colchicus)	8-21	30-200 yards.
80 Quail, California (Lophortyx californica)	12-15	Chased.
81 Road runner (Geococcyx californianus)	10-22	Pressed, 50-300 yards.
82 Sparrow, vesper (Pooecetes gramineus)	9	Upgrade, 100 feet.

Reptiles: Running

Species	Velocity mi/hr	Remarks[1]
83 Lizard, six-lined	18	Not pressed, 1 minute.
84 Red racer	3.6	Maximum.
85 Sidewinder	2.0	Maximum.
86 Snake, coral king	0.7	Maximum.

Fish: Swimming

Species	Velocity mi/hr	Remarks[1]
87 Carp	0.9	
88 Flying fish, biplane	22-40	Maximum in pre-flight taxi.
89 Mackerel-like fish	30	Cruising.
90 Perch	1.3	
91 Pike	1.0	
92 Salmon	7	

Fish: Leaping, Horizontal

Species	Distance ft Horizontal	Remarks
93 Flying fish, biplane (Cypselurus sp)	650-1300	Horizontal glide.
94 Flying fish, biplane (Parexocoetus sp)	7-25	Horizontal glide.
95 Flying fish, monoplane (Exocoetus sp)	33-67	Horizontal glide.
96 Flying fish, primitive (Oxyporhamphus sp)	17-27	Horizontal glide.

Fish: Leaping, Vertical

Species	Vertical	Remarks
97 Atherine, fresh-water	$10-20^2$	
98 Flying fish, monoplane (Exocoetus sp)	7-13	High point of glide.
99 Mullet, striped	$10-20^2$	
100 Tuna	Several	

/1/ First part of remark covers first figure of range in velocity column, second part of remark covers second figure. /2/ Times length of fish.

	Test	Subjects	Before	After	Gain %		Test	Subjects	Before	After	Gain %
			Training						Training		
1	Pushups, max. no.	Men	18.1	21.3	17.6	37	Basal O_2 consumption, ml/m	Men	228	208	9
2	of times	Women	10.7	15.6	46	38	O_2 cost in running	Men	13.57	14.13	4
3	Pullups, max. no.	Men	10.0	10.8	8	39	Respiratory efficiency	Men	55.3	46.1	17
4	of times	Women	5.5	8.7	59	40	Resp. quotient	Men	0.82	0.93	
5	Situps, max. no.	Men	38.4	51.1	34	41	Resp. rate, exercising	Runners[1]	44	48	
6	of times	Women	19.9	32.2	63	42	Resp. min. volume	Men	6.23	5.69	9
7	Shoulder strength, push, lb	Women	48.7	53.2	9.2	43	Vital capacity	Runners[1]	4.74	5.36	
8	pull, lb	Women	44.6	46.8	5.1	44	Alveolar pCO_2, mmHg	Men	41.5	41.3	
9	Muscular strength	Weight lifters	102.7	107.7	4.6	45	Alveolar pO_2, mmHg	Men	100.3	98.1	
10		Non-lifters	101.5	104.3	2.7	46	Blood gas capacity, vol. % O_2	Men	19.83	20.18	
11	Knee extension, kg	Trained limb	24.1	30.9	28.2	47	Hemoglobin, g/100ml	Men	14.8	15.2	
12		Untrained limb	24.5	33.6	37.0	48	Red blood cells, millions	Men	4.62	4.73	
13	Hand curl, kg	Trained limb	9.8	12.6	28.2	49	Hematocrit	Men	44.1	46.0	
14		Untrained limb	9.6	11.8	22.6	50	Alkaline reserve, CO_2	Men	47.8	46.6	
15	Finger ergograph,	Trained limb	13.2	26.1	97.4	51	combining power, vol. %	Runners[1]	48.0	48.1	
16	total work, kg	Untrained limb	10.9	16.6	52.7	52	Alk. res. after running, mM/L	Men	11.8	10	
17	Finger ergograph, no. times	Men	276	858	212	53	Exercise pulse rate	Men	151	146	
18	Left arm performance	Right arm trained	53.5	79.8	49.2	54		Runners[1]	134	111	
19		Right arm untrained	53.2	58.2	9.4	55	Pulse after 30 sec recovery	Runners[1]	115	77	
20	Shot put, 8 lb	Weight lifters	33.3	36.3	9.0	56	Resting pulse	Men	66.8	61.8	
21		Non-lifters	31.2	31.6	1.3	57	Resting blood pressure	Men	114/65	113/67	
22	Shot put, 12 lb	Weight lifters	27.2	29.5	8.5	58	Stroke volume, ml	Men	82	80	-2.5
23		Non-lifters	25.1	25.7	2.4	59	Cardiac output, liters/hr	Men	4.62	4.71	-2
24	Broad jump, standing, ft	Weight lifters	7.5	7.8	4.0	60	Systolic heart volume, ml	Men	565	469	-17
25		Non-lifters	7.1	7.1	0	61	Heart diameter, cm	Men	11.9	10.9	-8
26	Running, 60 yd, sec	Weight lifters	7.9	7.6	3.8	62	Heart volume, ml	Men	785	930	
27		Non-lifters	8.1	8.1	0	63		Women	560	790	
28	Running, 300 yd, sec	Men, 18-22 yr	44.3	42.7	3.6	64	Blood volume, ml	Men	5250	6580	
29	Running, 5 min, yd	Men	1490	1510	1.3	65		Women	4070	5670	
30	Obstacle course, sec	Men	24.7	22.0	10.9	66	Leukocytes, thousands	Men	5.96	6.1	
31	Muscle endurance	Weight lifters	220.4	267.8	21.0	67	Plasma chloride, mEq	Men	103.6	105.8	
32		Non-lifters	189.5	235.9	24.5	68	Plasma nitrogen, g/L	Men	10.3	10.8	
33	Endurance	Women	25.2	30.5	21	69	Blood sugar, max., mg/100ml	Men	127	134	
34	Walking efficiency	Men	15.3	16.9	10.4	70	Blood lactate, max., mg/100ml	Men	114	134	
35	Max. work, treadmill, kgM	Men	3786	6046	59.6	71	Blood lactate, exercise[2], 100ml	Men	146	192	
36	Work per liter O_2 debt	Men	484	737	52.2	72		Runners[1,3]	19.1	13.4	

/1/ Champion male runners; values before training are not necessarily for those men for whom values are given after training. /2/ After strenuous exercise. /3/ During mild exercise.

319. PHYSIOLOGICAL CHANGES DURING EXERCISE, EFFECT OF AGE: MAN

Values are results obtained with various age-groups of healthy, well-trained subjects during maximum physiological activity (treadmill or bicycle). Values in parentheses are estimate "c" of the 95% range (cf. Introduction).

	Specifications	4-6 yr	7-9 yr	10-11 yr	12-13 yr	14-15 yr	16-18 yr	20-33 yr
1	Body height, cm ♂	113.5(107-128)	135.0(125-143)	145.4(132-157)	154.4(139-169)	171.8(150-188)	176.9(165-187)	176.7(165-188)
2	♀	111.6(108-114)	132.0(121-142)	140.6(129-148)	158.5(150-175)	164.9(156-173)	165.8(155-175)	
3	Body weight, kg ♂	20.8(16.0-27.8)	30.7(25.1-36.5)	36.5(31.1-44.7)	43.6(31.8-60.6)	59.5(40.6-76.2)	64.1(45.2-73.4)	70.4(61.7-86.6)
4	♀	18.4(17.4-21.9)	27.2(20.6-33.0)	32.5(27.0-37.4)	46.7(39.6-60.5)	56.0(46.2-67.1)	57.3(50.5-63.7)	60.3(50.0-72.8)
5	Vital capacity[1], L ♂		2.21(1.84-2.51)	2.65(2.24-3.25)	3.22(2.52-4.33)	4.55(2.78-6.57)	5.17(3.20-6.48)	5.68(4.17-7.26)
6	♀		1.95(1.69-2.24)	2.30(1.88-2.63)	3.25(2.52-4.01)	3.74(2.94-4.32)	4.14(3.24-5.04)	4.28(3.15-5.76)
7	Max. heart rate ♂	203(188-214)	208(191-220)	211(200-227)	205(175-237)	203(178-222)	202(194-220)	194(171-212)
8	♀	204(176-214)	209(192-220)	207(188-222)	202(192-217)	206(188-214)	198(184-225)	
9	Max. O_2 intake[2], ♂	1.01(0.77-1.30)	1.75(1.40-2.01)	2.04(1.78-2.32)	2.46(1.79-3.40)	3.53(2.59-4.47)	3.68(2.84-4.35)	4.11(3.30-5.09)
10	L/min ♀	0.88(0.74-0.94)	1.50(1.21-1.79)	1.70(1.48-1.94)	2.31(2.01-2.72)	2.58(2.02-3.31)	2.71(2.25-3.08)	2.90(2.41-3.40)
11	Max. O_2 intake[2], ♂	49.1(43.2-57.6)	55.1(49.3-58.8)	56.5(51.1-61.5)	56.5(54.8-63.7)	59.5(54.8-63.7)	57.6(51.0-62.4)	58.6(51.1-67.4)
12	ml/min/kg ♀	47.9(42.4-52.2)	55.1(49.3-58.8)	52.4(46.4-56.1)	49.8(45.0-53.5)	46.0(42.5-52.5)	47.2(42.8-51.2)	48.4(43.2-59.6)
13	Max. pulmonary ven-♂	39.8(30.9-43.5)	61.8(44.1-75.2)	70.5(50.0-77.5)	75.2(58.1-105.0)	112.9(84.5-140.3)	110.3(79.6-139.3)	122.0(91.5-160.3)
14	tilation[1], L/min ♀	33.9(31.0-38.9)	57.3(48.2-67.6)	61.1(46.2-80.9)	79.9(65.5-102.6)	87.9(68.4-100.7)	93.8(73.6-119.1)	92.2(74.4-114.8)
15	Max. respiratory ♂	70.4(63-90)	67.0(55-83)	57.5(32-77)	54.1(31-68)	52.9(39-68)	44.7(28-60)	39.9(27-59)
16	rate ♀	66.4(56-81)	67.1(54-94)	61.3(51-82)	54.4(41-88)	51.6(40-58)	51.2(44-60)	46.0(28-63)
17	Max. respiratory ♂	0.60(0.43-0.87)	1.05(0.72-1.25)	1.33(1.12-1.62)	1.59(1.02-2.54)	2.52(1.62-3.26)	2.77(1.68-3.40)	3.05(2.26-4.72)
18	depth, L ♀	0.52(0.40-0.58)	0.91(0.64-1.22)	1.05(0.85-1.36)	1.64(1.28-2.54)	1.87(1.34-2.41)	1.95(1.43-2.28)	2.10(1.64-3.29)
19	Max. blood lactic ♂	56.3(33-76)	82.0(50-110)	84.0(50-125)	79.1(45-143)	90.4(74-113)	104.9(83-138)	112.0(71-158)
20	acid, mg/100ml ♀	60(51-69)	76.5(64-85)	82.2(56-116)	97.6(76-119)	100.5(73-145)	110.2(77-144)	103.6(69-134)

/1/ Body temperature, pressure; saturated. /2/ Standard temperature, pressure, density.

320. PHYSIOLOGICAL EFFECTS, SUBMAXIMAL WORK: MAN

Values are for young adults (20-30 yr) doing submaximal work on the bicycle ergometer. Values in parentheses are estimate "b" of the 95% range (cf. Introduction).

	Sex	Work Intensity kg m/min	O_2 Intake[1] L/min	Net Efficiency %	O_2 Intake [% of Max Intake] %	Heart Rate	Ventilation[2] L/min	Ventilation[2] per L O_2 Intake	Ventilation [% of Max Vent.] %
1	♀	600	1.48(1.32-1.64)	22.5(19.2-25.8)	52(41-63)	138(115-161)	34.7(24.9-44.5)	23.4(18.5-28.3)	39(27-51)
2	♀	900	2.06(1.88-2.24)	23.1(20.9-25.3)	73(60-86)	168(143-193)	50.6(37.3-63.9)	24.5(19.2-29.8)	56(38-74)
3	♂	900	2.09(1.90-2.28)	23.4(21.1-25.7)	50(42-58)	128(105-151)	41.9(32.1-51.7)	20.1(15.7-24.5)	34(23-45)
4	♂	1200	2.67(2.44-2.90)	23.7(21.4-26.0)	64(51-77)	148(125-171)	55.2(41.1-69.3)	20.6(15.8-25.4)	45(30-60)
5	♂	1500	3.33(3.00-3.66)	23.3(21.0-25.6)	79(67-91)	167(144-190)	70.9(55.3-86.5)	21.1(16.9-25.3)	58(39-77)

/1/ Standard temperature, pressure, density. /2/ Body temperature, pressure, saturated.

Values are to be considered as "estimates" because the newborn period is not a time when measurements are likely to be "normal." Ranges of values obtained from normal infants vary widely with the day of life and even with the hour within the first day. Variation will also depend on whether the cord is clamped early or late and whether the infant is full term or premature. The relatively high immunity to the usual infectious diseases of infants during the first 6-12 months of age is generally attributed to immune bodies obtained in utero by placental passage.

Part I: CHEMICAL AND PHYSICAL PROPERTIES

Blood

	Variable	Birth	Age One Week
1	Calcium serum, mg/100 ml	11.3(7.3-17)	10.5(7.5-13.9), IV-VII
2	Cholesterol, ester, plasma, mg/100 ml	82(50-130), I	140(100-190), V-XI
3	Cholesterol, free, plasma, mg/100 ml	32(22-44), I	50(40-70), V-XI
4	Citric acid, serum, mg/100 ml	(3-6)	
5	Fat, neutral, plasma, mg/100 ml	80(10-150), I	175(90-270), V-XI
6	Hemoglobin, capillary, g/100 ml	19.9(14-27)	19.6(16.2-25.5)
7	Hemoglobin, venous or cord, g/100 ml	17(13-24)	19(15-25)
8	Iron, serum, μg %	(30-120)	(30-120)
9	Lipids, total, plasma, mg/100 ml	221(120-320), I	470(300-650), V-XI
10	Nitrogen, blood urea, mg/100 ml	17(13-19), III	114(70-200), VI
11	Nitrogen, non-protein, mg/100 ml	54(44.5-61), III	40(26.5-48)
12	Phosphatase, serum, Bodansky units	7(4.5-10), I-III	9(6.5-11), IV-XIV
13	Phosphatides, plasma, mg/100 ml	27(0-94), I	100(20-200), I
14	Phosphorus, serum, mg/100	5.5(4.2-8)	5.9(3.5-7.6), IV-VII
15	Protein, total, serum, g/100 ml[2]	6(5.0-7.5)	

Bone Marrow

	Variable	Birth	One Week
16	Leukocytes, total, thousands/cu mm	186(54-358)	134(53-327), VIII
	Differential cell count, % of total		
17	Basophil	0	0, VIII
18	Eosinophil	2	1.7, VII
19	Erythroblast	1(0-5.2)	0.5(0-2.6), VIII
20	Erythrocyte, nucleated, total	31.9(16.4-49)	11.6(5-23), VIII
21	Lymphocyte	3.8	6.2, VIII
22	Megakaryocyte	0.1	0.1, VIII
23	Megaloblast	0.1	0.1, VIII
24	Myeloblast	0.8	1.5, VIII
25	Myelocyte, eosinophilic	0.6	0.6, VIII
26	Myelocyte, neutrophilic	16.3(7-29.6)	19.7(8-34), VIII
27	Neutrophil, non-segmented	33.9(16.4-46)	43.5(15.4-61), VIII
28	Neutrophil, segmented	7(0-17)	10.4(10-29.4), VIII
29	Normoblast	30.8(16.2-44.6)	11(4.4-22.4), VIII
30	Reticulum cell	0	0.1, VIII

Miscellaneous

	Variable	Birth	Age One Week
31	Blood pressure, systolic/diastolic, mm Hg	80/40	92/50
32	Bleeding time, min (Duke's method)	(1.5-2.5)	(1.5-2.5)
33	Cardiac output, ml/min	528(313-696)	580(438-855)
34	Circulation time, umbilical vein to lip, sec[3]	4.8(3.1-7)	4
35	Circulation time, sinus venosum to lip, sec[3]	4.4(3.3-5.8)	7
36	Clotting time, normal plasma, min	4	
37	Clotting time, platelet free plasma, min	5	
38	Erythrocytes, capillary, millions/cu mm	5.6(4-7.5)	5.3(3.6-7.6)
39	Erythrocytes, venous or cord, millions/cu mm	4.8(3.8-6)	
40	Erythrocytes, corpuscular volume, cu μ	113(90-124)	107(90-124)
41	Erythrocytes, nucleated, % nucleated cells	7(0-15)	>1%, III
42	Hematocrit, venous	53(45-60)	55(42-66)
43	Platelets, capillary, thousands/cu mm	227(140-290)	233(160-320)
44	Prothrombin time, venous, % of normal	76(37-100)	86(69-100), V
45	Pulse, beats/min	112(96-130), I	119(103-133), I
46	Respiration rate, breaths/min	25(14-34)	28(18-40)
47	Reticulocytes, % total erythrocytes	4.4(2.5-6.5)	1.1(0.1-4.5)
48	Tidal air, ml	(15-25)	(15-25)
49	Urine, pH	5.7(5.2-6.3), I	6.4(5.2-7.2)
50	Urine, specific gravity[4]	1.012(1.008-1.018), I	1.009(1.005-1.011)
51	Volume, blood[5], % body wt	9.4(7.2-12.8)	9.6(8-13.8), III
52	Volume, blood[6], % body wt	12.2(8-14.9)	12.1(8.2-16.2), III

White Blood Cells

	Variable	Birth	Age One Week
53	Leukocytes, total, thousands/cu mm blood	18(9-30)	12(5-21)
	Differential leukocyte count, % of total		
54	Basophil	0.1(0-0.6)	0.05(0-0.25)
55	Eosinophil	0.4(0.02-0.9)	0.5(0.07-1.1)
56	Lymphocyte	5.5(2-11)	5(2-17)
57	Monocyte	1.1(0.4-3.1)	1.1(0.3-2.7)
58	Neutrophil, banded	1.6	0.8
59	Neutrophil, segmented	9.4	4.7
60	Neutrophil, total	11(6-26)	5.5(1.5-10)

Part II: ORGAN AND BODY WEIGHTS AT GESTATION INTERVALS

Organ	Interval (days) between First Day of Last Menstrual Period and Delivery								
	167	195	217	248	258	272	279	287	291
	Body Weight, g								
	250-750	750-1250	1250-1750	1750-2250	2250-2750	2750-3250	3250-3750	3750-4250	Over 4250
	Organ Weights, g								
1 Adrenals	2.5	3.3	4.3	5.3	6.9	7.6	9.3	10.5	12.5
2 Brain	82.8	160.6	226.3	289.2	332.6	390.9	429.6	402.9	456.0
3 Heart	4.6	7.6	10.8	14.5	17.9	20.1	21.7	25.4	29.3
4 Kidneys	5.3	9.7	13.6	18.3	21.1	23.5	26.6	29.3	32.2
5 Liver	31.5	49.2	66.3	87.9	105.8	140.4	151.5	185.1	229.0
6 Lungs	15.0	25.2	33.7	44.2	49.5	54.7	59.4	64.0	77.9
7 Pancreas	0.6	1.2	1.6	2.1	2.8	3.4	3.6	3.9	4.6
8 Spleen	1.0	2.1	4.0	5.8	7.6	9.7	11.1	12.2	13.0
9 Thymus	1.4	3.1	5.1	8.5	9.3	9.9	10.8	15.3	12.8
10 Thyroid	0.5	4.1	1.1	1.4	1.8	1.8	2.4	2.4	2.9

/1/ Roman numerals indicate age in days when age varies from column headings. /2/ Cord blood. /3/ Fluorescein. /4/ RENAL FUNCTION TESTS. I. Glomerular filtration of H_2O: (a) Inulin Clearance (C_{IN}) for infants 6-30 da of age = 30-50% of adult value; C_{IN} = 48 ml/min/1.73 sq m Body Surface Area (BSA). (b) Creatinine Clearance/Inulin Clearance (C_{CR}/C_{IN}) = 1.00(0.86-1.30). II. Effective Renal Plasma Flow: p-Aminohippurate (PAH) or Diodrast at low (0.5-3 mg/100 ml) plasma concentration = 20-40% of adult value or 135-270 ml/min/1.73 sq m BSA. III Maximal Rate of Tubular Excretion: PAH or Diodrast at high (50-100 mg/100 ml) plasma concentration = 15-40% of adult value or 11.5-30.8 mg/min/1.73 sq m BSA. IV. Maximal Rate of Tubular Reabsorption: Glucose Clearance at high (up to 300 mg %) plasma concentration = 10-30% of adult value or 30-100 mg/min/1.73 sq m BSA. V. Urea clearance = 1.00 ml/min or 7.7 ml/min/1.73 sq m BSA when blood urea nitrogen (BUN) = 19(12-26) mg/100 ml, normal value. Maximal clearance, when BUN = 34(23.4-34.6) mg/100 ml, = 2 ml/min or 14.4 ml/min/1.73 sq m BSA. /5/ Early clamped cord. /6/ Late clamped cord.

Values are for males only unless otherwise indicated. Ranges in parentheses on Lines 1-39 conform to estimates "b," and those on Lines 43-46 to "d" of the 95% range (cf Introduction). Differences between values presented here and those in other tables giving more detailed data on one or more of the variables may be attributed to the differences in the sample of "normal" subjects studied by different investigators. The purpose of this table is to indicate the change (if any) of a variable with age, rather than to present a set of "standard values" for each age group.

322. PHYSIOLOGICAL VARIABLES: MAN

	Variable	Age Group, yr					
		20-29	30-39	40-49	50-59	60-69	70-79
1	Plasma volume, ml/kg body weight	42.3(31.1-53.5)	45.5(34.7-56.3)	42.3(36.3-48.3)	50.8(35.6-66.0)	46.6(32.2-61.0)	47.2(34.4-60.0)
2	Total blood volume, ml/kg body weight	77.3(61.1-93.5)	81.9(65.9-97.9)	73.5(61.3-85.9)	86.1(67.3-104.9)	78.3(58.1-98.5)	80.7(58.7-102.7)
3	Plasma vitamin A, μg/100 ml			47.6(28.6-66.6)	55.0(16.0-77.0)	49.9(22.7-77.1)	47.1(17.9-76.3)
4	Plasma β-carotene, μg/100 ml			126.7(42.7-210.7)	128.3(43.3-213.3)	111.0(22.0-200.0)	106.0(28.2-183.8)
5	Blood pH, capillary serum, 38°C	7.40(7.34-7.46)	7.38(7.33-7.45)	7.38(7.32-7.44)	7.38(7.34-7.42)	7.38(7.34-7.42)	7.37(7.33-7.41)
6	Total blood CO_2 content, capillary, mM/L	22.8(20.1-25.5)	22.8(19.9-25.7)	22.6(19.6-25.6)	22.3(18.8-25.8)	22.3(18.2-26.4)	22.3(19.4-25.2)
7	CO_2 tension, arterial blood, mm Hg	44.8(38.3-51.3)	45.2(38.3-52.1)	46.1(38.1-54.1)	45.0(36.2-53.8)	45.3(36.5-54.1)	45.8(38.9-52.7)
8	Serum bicarbonate content, arterial, mM/L	26.5(23.2-29.8)	26.5(23.2-29.8)	26.8(22.4-31.2)	26.0(21.9-30.1)	26.2(21.5-30.9)	25.8(22.3-29.3)
9	Cell volume, % red cells	47(43-51)	47(41-53)	48(36-60)	44(36-52)	45(39-51)	43(35-51)
10	Blood non-protein nitrogen, mg/100 ml			27.2(18.4-36.0)	27.2(19.2-35.2)	27.7(20.7-34.7)	28.5(18.5-28.5)
11	Blood urea nitrogen, mg/100 ml	9.7(4.7-14.7)	10.7(3.5-17.9)	10.6(4.4-16.8)	12.3(6.5-18.1)	13.5(6.3-20.7)	12.9(6.5-19.3)
12	Blood glucose, venous, mg/100 ml	82.1(68.9-95.3)			78.9(54.9-102.9)	79.0(62.0-96.0)	79.6(67.2-92.0)
13	Thiocyanate space (extracellular H_2O), L/sq m body surface area			17.0(10.6-23.4)	16.8(11.4-22.2)	16.3(12.3-20.3)	16.1(10.5-21.7)
14	Antipyrine space (total body H_2O), L/sq m body surface area			34.6(22.0-47.2)	33.1(20.9-45.5)	31(23.1-40.7)	30.2(20.4-40.0)
15	Heart rate, per min	77(52-102)	72(48-96)	70(50-90)	70(52-88)	63(43-83)	66(44-88)
16	Eye, minimum light threshold, 30 min dark adaptation, log μμLamberts	2.62(2.08-3.16)	2.67(1.79-3.55)		2.84(2.06-3.62)	3.16(2.22-4.10)	3.85(1.63-6.07)
17	Eye, pupil diameter (in light), mm	5.11(3.70-6.52)	4.64(3.27-6.01)	4.09(2.48-5.70)	3.77(2.20-5.34)	3.48(1.89-5.07)	3.52(2.15-4.89)
18	Eye, pupil diameter (in dark), mm	7.42(6.15-8.69)	6.72(4.96-8.48)	5.91(3.85-7.97)	5.89(3.75-8.03)	4.78(2.70-6.86)	5.10(3.53-5.67)
	Kidney function						
19	Tm glucose, mg/min/1.73 sq m body surface area	358.7	333.6(221.2-446.0)	315.1(224.7-405.5)	308.2(178.2-438.2)	260.2(131.0-389.4)	239.3(146.5-332.0)
20	Inulin clearance, ml/min/1.73 sq m B.S.A.	122.8(90.0-155.8)	115.0(93.4-136.6)	121.2(74.6-167.8)	99.3(70.1-128.5)	96.0(45.0-147.0)	89.0(49.2-128.8)
21	Diodrast clearance, ml/min/1.73 sq m B.S.A.	613.5(464.3-762.7)	649.3(414.7-883.9)	573.8(350.6-797.0)	500.4(326.4-674.4)	442.1(281.5-602.7)	354.0(187.2-520.5)
22	PAH clearance, ml/min/1.73 sq m B.S.A.		615.2(409.2-821.2)	511.8(289.0-734.6)	460.4(196.6-724.2)	429.7(244.7-614.7)	292.8(189.0-396.6)
23	Urea clearance, ml/min/1.73 sq m B.S.A.	63.1(30.7-95.5)	60.6(36.4-84.8)	64.6(42.4-86.8)	57.7(33.5-81.9)	46.9(26.5-67.3)	48.3(22.7-73.9)
24	Tm diodrast, mg/min/1.73 sq m B.S.A.	54.6(35.6-73.6)	51.0(33.8-68.2)	49.9(30.3-69.5)	45.3(32.8-58.0)	44.5(26.3-62.7)	39.1(24.5-53.7)
25	Tm PAH, mg/min/1.73 sq m B.S.A.		90.6(55.4-125.8)	83.4(50.8-116.0)	74.0(39.2-108.8)	67.2(40.9-93.5)	59.0(35.6-82.4)
26	Conduction velocity of ulnar nerve, m/sec	57.7(37.1-78.3)	58.8(45.1-72.5)	55.6(36.0-75.2)	53.6(36.9-70.3)	52.0(33.5-66.9)	52.6(32.0-73.2)
27	Basal metabolism, cal/sq m/hr			35.7(28.1-43.3)	34.5(25.7-43.3)	33.0(25.9-40.1)	32.6(25.3-39.9)
28	Oxygen uptake, ml/sq m/min			123.5(94.9-152.1)	121.9(86.2-157.6)	112.9(87.4-138.4)	113.1(87.6-138.6)
29	CO_2 elimination, ml/sq m/min			99.7(81.1-118.3)	98.9(75.0-122.8)	93.4(72.0-114.8)	90.5(68.4-112.6)
30	Ventilation volume, L/sq m/min	3.72(2.04-5.40)	3.54(1.64-5.44)	3.97(2.62-5.32)	4.03(2.70-5.36)	3.93(2.26-5.60)	4.13(2.78-5.48)
31	Cardiac output (cardiac index), L/sq m/min			2.96(1.46-4.46)	2.78(1.74-3.82)	2.58(1.52-3.64)	2.54(1.46-3.62)
32	Stroke index, ml/beat/sq m	48.9(30.7-67.1)	49.4(25.8-73.0)	43.3(24.9-61.7)	40.3(23.3-57.3)	41.5(24.3-58.7)	39.3(20.1-58.5)
33	Circulation time, arm to arm, sec	12.0(7.8-16.2)	13.5(7.9-19.1)	13.7(9.3-18.1)	13.9(7.5-20.2)	15.0(10.0-20.0)	14.9(8.5-21.3)
	Pulmonary function						
34	Resting tidal volume, ml/sq m	301(183-419)	297(155-438)	315(123-507)	338(184-492)	302(176-428)	305(175-432)
35	Vital capacity, supine, L/sq m B.S.A.	2.37(1.40-3.33)	2.19(1.36-3.03)	1.94(1.00-2.89)	1.89(1.26-2.53)	1.63(0.76-2.49)	1.40(0.74-2.07)
36	Vital capacity, standing, L/sq m B.S.A.	2.55(1.52-3.55)	2.35(1.52-3.18)	2.14(1.09-3.18)	2.04(1.09-3.18)	1.77(0.93-2.61)	1.51(0.79-2.23)
37	Total lung volume, L/sq m B.S.A.	3.06(1.95-4.17)	2.96(1.90-4.01)	2.88(1.87-3.90)	3.24(2.41-4.07)	2.78(1.82-3.74)	2.83(1.78-3.89)
38	Residual lung volume, L/sq m B.S.A.	0.70(0.29-1.10)	0.79(0.34-1.25)	0.95(0.32-1.59)	1.35(0.42-2.27)	1.15(0.33-1.97)	1.44(0.71-2.17)
39	Maximum breathing capacity (15 sec), L/sq m B.S.A.	69.5(29.5-109.5)	62.3(29.3-95.3)	58.3(19.7-96.9)	43.7(15.7-71.7)	40.4(8.6-72.2)	32.6(9.4-55.8)
	Gastric secretion[1]						
40	Total volume, ml	113.5 ♀99.0	109.5 ♀97.7	103.0 ♀95.0	96.3 ♀93.7	92.7 ♀85.5	91.0 ♀79.0
41	Free acidity, ml N/10 NaOH/100 ml	47.0 ♀33.0	47.0 ♀33.0	46.0 ♀33.0	42.6 ♀33.3	38.3 ♀33.5	33.5 ♀33.5
42	Total acidity, ml N/10 NaOH/100 ml	62.5 ♀50.5	61.7 ♀50.5	58.9 ♀50.5	57.6 ♀50.5	54.6 ♀50.5	50.5 ♀50.5
	Hearing loss >45 db, % individuals[2]						
43	At 440-880 cycles/sec	(0.0-0.1) ♀(0.1-0.4)	(0.3-1.1) ♀(0.8-1.2)	(1.4-1.7) ♀(0.6-2.1)	(2.2-2.6) ♀(0.7-4.0)	4.7 ♀1.2	
44	At 1760 cycles/sec	(0.0-0.3) ♀0.3	(0.6-2.3) ♀(0.8-1.4)	(2.6-3.6) ♀(1.5-2.0)	(6.0-8.4) ♀(2.2-3.0)	18.0 ♀9.0	
45	At 3520 cycles/sec	(2.7-5.0) ♀(0.3-0.7)	(6.0-7.0) ♀(0.6-1.6)	(13-16) ♀(2.4-3.0)	(27-30) ♀(2.7-7.0)	45.0 ♀12.0	
46	At 7040 cycles/sec	6.7 ♀0.0	7.1 ♀1.4	13.9 ♀3.4	35.1 ♀6.1	49.6 ♀23.6	

/1/ Test meal: 400 ml H_2O and 8 tapioca biscuits.   /2/ Samples taken at San Diego County Fair (1948) and World's Fair (Chicago, 1933).

Adapted from Adolph, E. F., Science 109:579-585 (1949).

	Variable	Symbol	Value		Variable	Symbol	Value
1	Water intake, ml/hr	I	$=.010\ B^{.88}$	17	Sulfur output, g/hr	S	$=.000\ 001\ 71\ B^{.74}$
2	Urine output, ml/hr	U	$=.0064\ B^{.82}$	18	O$_2$ consum., liver slices, ml STP/hr	O_L	$=3.3\ B^{.77}$
3	Urea clearance, ml/hr	C_{ur}	$=1.59\ B^{.72}$	19	Hemoglobin weight, g	H_b	$=.013\ B^{.99}$
4	Inulin clearance, ml/hr	C_{in}	$=1.74\ B^{.77}$	20	Myoglobin weight, g	M_y	$=.000\ 039\ B^{1.31}$
5	Creatinine clearance, ml/hr	C_{cr}	$=4.2\ B^{.69}$	21	Cytochrome weight, g	P_c	$=.000\ 10\ B^{.84}$
6	Diodrast clearance, ml/hr	C_{di}	$=2.14\ B^{.89}$	22	Nephra number	N	$=2600\ B^{.62}$
7	Hippurate clearance, ml/hr	C_{PAH}	$=5.4\ B^{.80}$	23	Diameter, renal corp., cm	D	$=.0081\ B^{.08}$
8	O$_2$ consum., basal, ml STP/hr	O	$=3.8\ B^{.734}$	24	Kidneys, weight, g	K	$=.0212\ B^{.85}$
9	Heartbeat duration, hr	H	$=.000\ 0119\ B^{.27}$	25	Brain weight, g	E	$=.081\ B^{.70}$
10	Breath duration, hr	Q	$=.000\ 047\ B^{.28}$	26	Heart weight, g	J	$=.0066\ B^{.98}$
11	Ventilation rate, ml/hr	V	$=120\ B^{.74}$	27	Lungs, weight, g	F	$=.0124\ B^{.99}$
12	Tidal volume, ml	T	$=.0062\ B^{1.01}$	28	Liver weight, g	L	$=.082\ B^{.87}$
13	Gut beat duration, hr	G	$=.000\ 093\ B^{.31}$	29	Thyroid, weight, g	M	$=.000\ 22\ B^{.92}$
	Nitrogen			30	Adrenals, weight, g	A	$=.0011\ B^{.80}$
14	Total output, g/hr	N_T	$=.000\ 074\ B^{.735}$	31	Pituitary weight, g	P	$=.000\ 13\ B^{.76}$
15	Endogenous output, g/hr	N_E	$=.000\ 042\ B^{.72}$	32	Stomach + intestines, weight, g	W	$=.112\ B^{.94}$
16	Creatinine-N output, g/hr	N_{cr}	$=.000\ 001\ 09\ B^{.90}$	33	Blood weight, g	R	$=.055\ B^{.99}$

Equations (Derived) Interrelating Quantitative Properties

34	$U = .46\ I^{.93} = .0108\ C_{ur}^{1.14} = .000\ 000\ 19\ N^{1.32}$
35	$C_{ur} = .35\ C_{PAH}^{.90} = 17,700\ N_T^{.98} = 42\ K^{.85}$
36	$O = 1300,000,000,000\ H^{2.72} = 11,900\ P^{.87}$
37	$V = 370,000,000,000,000\ H^{2.74} = 4900\ T^{.73}$
38	$N_T = .0068\ U^{.90} = 5.4\ N_{cr}^{.82} = .000\ 0162\ C_{cr}^{1.06}$
39	$O_L = 30\ L^{.89} = .81\ O^{1.05} = 1290\ M_y^{.59}$

324. ALIGNMENT CHART RELATING QUANTITATIVE VALUES: MAMMALS

The characteristics of one animal are read off along a horizontal straight-edge placed at a known value in any one of the variables. Several species chosen at random are indicated on the left at their appropriate scale positions. Ordinates are numbered as exponents of 10; but the subdivisions between ordinates read arithmetically. Thus, the number 1 means 10^1 and the subdivisions above it mean 20, 30, 40, etc. All values are in ml, g, cm, and hr, as shown in Table 323. The lines and scales represent, and are derived from, the equations of Table 323. Adapted from Adolph, E. F., Science 109:579-585 (1949).

325. ANTIMETABOLITES

Table adapted from D. W. Woolley's "A Study of Antimetabolites," John Wiley and Sons, 1952.

Part I: SOME METABOLITES AND THEIR ANTAGONISTIC STRUCTURAL ANALOGS

	Metabolite	Analog	Structural Alteration	Biological System Affected
1	Acetic acid	Fluoroacetic acid	F for H	Aconitase
2	Adenine	Benzimidazole and derivatives	2 C for 2 N; side-chain alterations	Microorganisms, animals
		Triazolopyrimidines	N for C	Microorganisms
		Diaminopurine	NH_2 for H	Bacteria
3	α-Alanine	Glycine	H for CH_3	Bacteria
4	β-Alanine	β-Aminobutyric acid	CH_3 for H	Yeast
		Propionic acid	H for NH_2	Bacteria
		Asparagine	COOH for H; $CONH_2$ for COOH	Yeast
5	Arginine	Canavanine	O for CH_2	Bacteria
6	Aspartic acid	Hydroxyaspartic acid	OH for H	Bacteria
		Aspartophenone	C_6H_5 for OH	Bacteria
7	Ascorbic acid	Glucoascorbic acid	Addition of CHOH and optical inversion	Animals, liver enzymes
8	p-Aminobenzoic acid	Sulfanilamide and derivatives	SO_2NH_2 or derivative for COOH	Microorganisms
		p-Aminobenzamide	$CONH_2$ for COOH	Microorganisms
		Carbarsone and related arsenicals	As for C in a COOH group; derivatives of this	Microorganisms, animals
		Phosphanilic acid	PO_3H_2 for COOH	Microorganisms
		Heterocyclic acids[1]	N or S for C	Bacteria
		Ring-substituted PAB	Halogen or alkyl for H	Bacteria
		p-Aminoacetophenone and derivatives	COR for COOH	Bacteria
		p-Nitrobenzoic acid	NO_2 for NH_2	Bacteria
9	Biotin	Desthiobiotin and derivatives	2 H for S	Microorganisms
		Biotin sulfone	SO_2 for S	Microorganisms
		Ureylenecyclohexyl aliphatic acids	2 C for S; and derivatives with shorter side chains	Microorganisms
		Desthioisobiotin	Loss of S, geometric isomerism	Insects
		Ureylenetetrahydrofuryl aliphatic sulfonic acids	O for S, SO_3H for COOH	Microorganisms
		Homobiotin	Addition of $- CH_2 -$	Microorganisms
10	Choline	Triethyl choline	3 ethyls for 3 methyls	Frog muscle and mice
11	Cocarboxylase	Thiamine-thiazole pyrophosphate	Loss of pyrimidine portion	Carboxylase
12	Cis- or trans- crocetin dimethyl ester	Trans- or cis-crocetin dimethyl ester	Geometric isomerism	Algae
13	Cytidine	Adenosine	OH for H, loss of imidazole ring	Neurospora mutant
14	Desthiobiotin	2-Oxyimidazole aliphatic acids	H for CH_3	Microorganisms
15	Glutamic acid	Methionine sulfoxide	$SOCH_3$ for COOH	Bacteria
		Hydroxyglutamic acid	OH for H	Bacteria
		N-Alkylglutamines	N-Alkyl for OH	Bacteria
16	Guanine	Triazolopyrimidines	N for C	Bacteria
		Benzimidazole	2 C for 2 N	Microorganisms
17	Histamine	Imidazole and derivatives	Elimination or substitution, part of molecule	Smooth muscle, histamine shock in animals
		Diphenhydramine	Opening of ring, O for N, alkylation of N, C	
		Tripelennamine	Opening of ring, alkylation of N	
18	Hypoxanthine	Hydroxytriazolopyrimidine	N for C	Bacteria
19	Indoleacetic acid	Phenyl butyric acid	Elimination of N and shift of one C	Plants
		Skatyl sulfonic acid	SO_3H for COOH	Plants
20	Inositol	Hexachlorocyclohexane	6 Cl for 6 OH	Fungi, plants, pancreatic amylase
21	Isoleucine	Leucine	Position isomerism of one CH_3	Bacteria
22	Leucine	D-Leucine	Optical inversion	Bacteria
23	Lysine	Arginine	Guanidino for amino, elimination of CH_2	Neurospora mutant
24	Methionine	Methoxinine	O for S	Bacteria
		Ethionine	CH_3 for H	Bacteria and animals
		Norleucine	CH_2 for S	Bacteria
25	Nicotinic acid, (or amide)	Pyridine-3-sulfonic acid or amide	SO_3H for COOH	Microorganisms; animals[2]
		3-Acetylpyridine	$COCH_3$ for COOH	Animals, not in microorganisms
		5-Thiazole carboxamide	S for CH=CH	Certain bacteria
26	Pantothenic acid[3]	Thiopanic acid (pantoyltaurine) and derivatives	SO_3H and derivatives for COOH	Microorganisms, pantothenate-utilizing enzymes, not animals
		Pantothenyl alcohol	CH_2OH for COOH	Microorganisms, not animals
		α- or β-Methyl pantothenic acid	CH_3 for H	Microorganisms
		Other substituted panto-amides	Alkyl or OH- and NH_2-alkyl for CH_2CH_2COOH	Microorganisms
		Phenyl pantothenone	COC_6H_5 for COOH	Microorganisms
		Salicylyl β-alanine	o-Hydroxy-benzoyl for pantoyl	Microorganisms
		γ'-Methyl pantothenic acid	CH_3 for H	Bacteria
27	Phenylalanine	β-Hydroxyphenylalanine	OH for H	Bacteria
		Thienylalanine	S for CH=CH	Microorganisms, animals
		Furylalanine	O for CH=CH	Microorganisms
		Halogenated phenylalanines	Halogen for H	Microorganisms
28	Pimelic acid	2,4-Dichlorosulfanilidocaproic acid	Dichlorosulfanilide for COOH	Biotin indepdt. microorganisms
29	Porphyrins[4]	Porphyrins lacking vinyl groups		Bacteria
30	Pteroylglutamic acid	Pteroyl-triglutamic acid	Addition of two glutamic acids	Transplanted tumors
		Xanthopterin	Loss of p-amino-benzoyl glutamic acid	Transplanted tumors
31	Pyridoxine	Desoxypyridoxine	H for OH	Microorganisms, animals
		2-Ethyl-3-amino-4-ethoxymethyl-5-amino-methyl pyridine	CH_3 for H, NH_2 for OH, Et for H	Microorganisms
32	Riboflavin	6,7-Dichlororiboflavin	2 Cl for 2 CH_3	Microorganisms
		Isoriboflavin	Shift in position of CH_3	Animals, not bacteria
		Corresponding phenazine	2 C for 2 N, 2 NH_2 for 2 OH	Microorganisms, animals
		Galactoflavin	Dulcityl for ribityl	Animals
		Lumiflavin	CH_3 for ribityl	Bacteria
		Araboflavin	Inversion of position of OH	Animals

/1/ e.g., 6-Aminonicotinic acid. /2/ Alcohol and lactic dehydrogenases, not animals in vivo. /3/ See also table on next page. /4/ e.g., hematin and protoporphyrin.

325. ANTIMETABOLITES (Concluded)

Table adapted from D. W. Woolley's "A Study of Antimetabolites," John Wiley and Sons, 1952.

Part I: SOME METABOLITES AND THEIR ANTAGONISTIC STRUCTURAL ANALOGS (Concluded)

	Metabolite	Analog	Structural Alteration	Biological System Affected
33	Succinic acid	Malonic acid	Loss of CH_2	Succinic oxidase
		Sulfonated succinic acid	SO_3H for H	Succinic oxidase
34	Testosterone	Estradiol	Benzene ring for cyclohexane ring, loss of CH_3	Animals
35	Thiamine	Pyrithiamine	CH=CH for S	Microorganisms, animals
		Oxythiamine	OH for NH_2	Animals, fish thiaminase
		Butylthiamine	Butyl for CH_3	Animals
		Aminobenzylmethylthiazolium chloride	2 C for 2 N, loss of side chains	Fish thiaminase
36	Thymine	5-Substituted dioxypyrimidines	NO_2 or Br or NH_2 or OH for CH_3	Bacteria
		2, 4-Diamino-or dithiothymine	NH_2 or SH for OH	Bacteria
37	α-Tocopherol	α-Tocopherol quinone	Opening of ring by addition of O	Animals
38	Thyroxine	Ethers of diiodotyrosine	p-Nitrobenzyl or p-nitrophenylethyl or benzyl for p-hydroxydiiodophenyl	Tadpoles
39	Tryptophan	Indole acrylic acid	Loss of NH_3	Bacteria
		Naphthylacrylic acid	Loss of NH_3, C=C for N	Bacteria
		Styrylacetic acid	Loss of NH_2, substitution of aliphatic unsaturated side chain for pyrrol ring	Bacteria
		Methyltryptophans	CH_3 for H	Bacteria
		Benzothienylalanine	S for N	Bacteria
		Indole	Loss of side chain	Bacteriophage plus bacteria
40	Tyrosine	3-Fluorotyrosine	F for H	Rats
41	Uracil	Barbituric acid	OH for H	Bacteria
		Thiouracil	S for O	Bacteria, plant seed germination
42	Vitamin K	Dicumarol and derivatives	O for C, side-chain alterations	Animals
		Iodinin	2 N for 2 C, side-chain alterations	Bacteria
		α-Tocopherol quinone	2 CH_3 for benzene ring	Animals
		2, 3-Dichloronaphthoquinone	2 Cl for alkyl side chains	Microorganisms
		2-Substituted-3-hydroxynaphthoquinones	OH for H, change in alkyl substituent	Animals, not bacteria
		Methoxynaphthoquinone	OCH_3 for CH_3	Microorganisms

Part II: SOME ANTIMETABOLITES TO PTEROYLGLUTAMIC ACID

	Structural Alteration	Organisms Affected	Reversing Effect of Folic Acid
1	x-CH_3 for H (x = 7 or 9)	Bacteria, chickens, rats, mice, swine, insects	Competitive
2	10-CH_3 for H	Bacteria	Competitive
3	10-CH_3 for H, loss of glutamic	Bacteria	Competitive
4	4-NH_2 for OH	Bacteria, rats, mice, chickens, guinea pigs, insects, humans	Present in some bacteria, poor or absent in animals
5	4-NH_2 for OH, 10-CH_3 for H	Bacteria, chickens, rats	Poor or absent in animals
6	4-NH_2 for OH, 6-phenyl for aminobenzoylglutamic, 7-phenyl for H	Bacteria, not animals	Present
7	6-Phenyl for aminobenzoylglutamic, 7-phenyl for H	Chickens, not bacteria	
8	7-OH for H, 9-O for H	Bacteria, rats	Competitive
9	Aspartic for glutamic	Bacteria, rats, mice, chickens	Competitive
10	Quinoxaline for pteridine	Bacteria, not rats	Competitive

Part III: SOME ANTIMETABOLITES TO PANTOTHENIC ACID

	Antimetabolite	Structural Alteration	Inhibition Index[1] L. arabinosus	Yeast	L. casei
		Alterations of β-Alanine Part			
1	Pantoyltaurine (thiopanic acid)	SO_3H for COOH	1,000		24,000
2	Pantoyltaurine amide	SO_2NH_2 for COOH			6,400
3	Pantoyltaurine anilides	$SO_2NHC_6H_5$ for COOH			
4	Phenylpantothenone	COC_6H_5 for COOH	4,500	Inhibition not reversible	700
5	Tolyl pantothenone	$COC_6H_4CH_3$ for COOH			100
6	Chlorophenyl pantothenone	COC_6H_4Cl for COOH			230
7	α-Methylpantothenic	CH_3 for H			1,000
8	β-Methylpantothenic	CH_3 for H	750		250
9	Pantothenol	CH_2OH for COOH	10,000		20,000
10	Methylpantothenol	$CH(CH_3)OH$ for COOH	50,000		100,000
11	α-Hydroxypantothenic[2]	OH for H	2,500		2,500
12	Pantoic hydrazide	NH_2 for CH_2CH_2COOH			240
13	Monopantoylalkyldiamines	Alkyl diamine for β-alanine			Approx. 100,000
14	Tolyl sulfone of pantothenic	$SO_2C_6H_4CH_3$ for COOH			6,400
15	Anisyl sulfone of pantothenic	$SO_2C_6H_4OCH_3$ for COOH			1,600
16	Pantoylpropylamine	CH_3 for COOH	7,500		10,000
17	Pantoylbutylamine	C_2H_5 for COOH	7,500/		15,000
18	Pantoylheptylamine	$(CH_2)_4CH_3$ for COOH	4,500		4,250
19	Pantoylphenylethylamine	C_6H_5 for COOH	40,000		10,000
		Alterations of Pantoyl Part			
20	γ,γ-Dimethyl-δ-hydroxyvaleryl-β-alanine	CH_2CH_2 for CHOH	Inhibitory to streptococci but not reversed by pantothenic		
21	γ-Hydroxybutyryl-β-alanine	Loss of methyls and of α-hydroxy			
22	γ'-Methylpantothenic[3]	CH_3 for H	5,000		300
23	Salicylyl-β-alanine	Hydroxybenzoic for pantoic		1,600	12,500
		Alterations of Both Portions			
24	β-δ-Dihydroxy-γ,γ-dimethylvaleryltaurine	Insertion of CH_2, SO_3H for COOH	Inhibitory to hemolytic streptococci		

/1/ The inhibition index represents the amount of antimetabolite required to overcome the effect of a unit weight of metabolite. The values in this table were calculated from the quantities required to produce maximal inhibition of growth. /2/ Complete inhibition of growth could not be achieved with this compound. /3/ Nomenclature used for pantothenic acid derivatives is sometimes confusing because some investigators name the α-carbon atom of the entire molecule, whereas others take the α-carbon atom of the pantoyl residue as the α-carbon atom. γ'-Methylpantothenic acid might more correctly be named ω-methylpantothenic acid.

357

326. BIOLOGICAL ANTIOXIDANTS

Biological antioxidants, as distinct from antioxidants that protect the unsaturated bonds of such materials as gasoline, rubber, and plastics, are compounds that decrease the rate of fatty peroxidase formation and oxygen uptake at carbon-to-carbon unsaturated bonds of food, feed, or tissue lipids. Compounds listed are only a few of the many occurring in living organisms and having antioxygenic activity in vivo or in vitro[1]. Some of the antioxidants are known to be toxic to animals, hence inclusion in the table is not to be construed as endorsement for use in foods or diets for animals. Naturally occurring synergistic type antioxidants (e.g., ascorbic acid, citric acid, cephalin, phosphoric acid, certain amino acids) are not included in this table. Synergistic type antioxidants do not impart any appreciable antioxygenic activity when used alone with a lipid substrate known to be free of inhibitols or other antioxidants, but when used in combination with one or more primary antioxidants they enhance antioxygenic activity.

	Antioxidant and Occurrence	Chemical Name and Composition
1	Arbutin. Leaves of the bearberry (Arctostaphylos uvae-ursi), a small evergreen shrub, and frequently occurs in plants particularly of the Ericaceae family.	Hydroquinone-β-D-glucoside. $C_{12}H_{15}O_6(OH)$.

------------------------------------ Physical and chemical properties ------------------------------------

Long, fine, silky, bitter tasting, colorless needles, MP (water free product) 194-195°C. Almost insol. in ether; slightly sol. in cold water and in alcohol; easily soluble in hot water. Arbutin hydrate (1 mol H_2O) shows $[\alpha]_D = -60.34°$. Loses water of crystallization at 110-115°C, decomposes on heating to glycosan and hydroquinone. Gives colors with $FeCl_3$, $BiCl_3$, and with HNO_3. Crystallizes from methyl alcohol as hygroscopic anhydrous crystals which acquire 2 mols H_2O at ordinary conditions. Fehling's solution not reduced, but ammonical $AgNO_3$ is, on heating.

2	Gossypol. In the "gland dots," "secretion cavities" or "resin glands" present in all parts of the cotton plant except the woody tissue.	2,2-bi-1,6,7-Trihydroxy-3-methyl-5-isopropyl-8-aldehydonaphthyl. $C_{30}H_{24}O_2(OH)_6$.

------------------------------------ Physical and chemical properties ------------------------------------

Brilliant yellow needles, MP 184°C; other crystal forms with MP of 199°C and 214°C; also a red isomeric crystalline form, MP 184-185°C. Very sol. in cold dioxane, diethylene glycol, methyl-, ethyl-, isopropyl-, and butyl alcohols, ether, ethyl acetate, acetone, chloroform, carbon tetrachloride, and pyridine; slightly sol. in glycerol, cyclohexane, and petroleum ether (BP 60-110°C); and insol. in pet. ether (BP 30-60°C); and in water; sol. in fat, alkali salts; very sol. in water and alcohol. Log molal extinction coefficient: (250 mμ) = 5; (300 mμ) ≥ 4; (360 mμ) ≤ 4. Alkaline solutions oxidize readily on exposure to air and are extremely sensitive to oxidizing agents. A number of color reactions occur with metallic and other reagents. O-R potential = + 408 mvolts.

3	Gum Guaiac. From heart wood resin of tropical American trees, Guaiacum officinale Linné and Guaiacum sanctum Linné.	Constituents: α- and β-guaiaconic acids (70.5%), guaiaretic (11%), guaiacinic, guaiacresinic, and guaiacic acids, guaiacsaponin, vanillin, an aromatic oil, a guttapercha-like substance called guaiaputtin, guaiac yellow. Analysis: 87-96% alc. sol.; 55-75% ether sol.; ash not greater than 3.5%; acid value 46-53; ester value 121-139; sap. value 167-192.

------------------------------------ Physical and chemical properties ------------------------------------

Occurs in irregular masses enclosing fragments of plant tissues, or in large, nearly homogeneous masses, occasionally in round or ovoid tears. Externally brownish black to dusky brown, acquiring a greenish color on long exposure; the fractured surface having a glassy luster, the thin pieces being translucent and varying in color from brown to yellowish orange. The powder is moderate yellowish brown, becoming olive brown on exposure to air. Balsamic odor and slightly acrid taste. Melting range 85-90°C. Incompletely but readily soluble in alcohol, ether, chloroform, creosote, solutions of alkalis, and in chloral hydrate T.S. Slightly sol. in carbon disulfide and benzene, not readily sol. in fat. An alcoholic solution on addition of $FeCl_3$ tincture or oxidizing agents or enzymes becomes blue changing rapidly to green.

4	Nordihydroguaiaretic acid. From a desert plant, the creosote bush (Larrea divaricata).	2,3-bis-(3,4-Dihydroxybenzyl)-butane. $C_{18}H_{18}(OH)_4$.

------------------------------------ Physical and chemical properties ------------------------------------

White crystalline solid, MP 184-185°C. Slightly sol. in water and dilute acids; moderately sol. in hot benzene and xylene; very sol. in diethyl ether, alcohol, and glacial acetic acid; sol. in fats to the extent of 0.5%.

5	Sesamol. Believed to occur as the glucoside sesamolin in sesame oil.	4-Hydroxy-1,2-methylenedioxy-benzene. $C_7H_5O_2(OH)$.

------------------------------------ Physical and chemical properties ------------------------------------

Colorless crystals with a phenolic odor, MP 65.8°C. Easily sol. in alcohol and ether; difficultly sol. in water and petroleum ether; sol. in alkali; sol. in conc. H_2SO_4 with a dark green color. Color reactions with aromatic aldehydes in the presence of HCl; gives a carmoisin red color with furfural in presence of HCl; gives color with ferric iron; azo derivatives colored.

6	Tannins. Widely distributed in vegetable kingdom. May occur in every part of the seed plant.	All contain polyhydroxy phenols or derivatives, often in complex, condensed ring structures. Hydrolyzable with acids to yield phenolic derivatives and in some instances sugars, usually D-glucose. Alkali fusion and dry distillation give decomposition products principally phenolic in character: catechol, pyrogallol, phloroglucinol, resorcinol, and hydroquinone, or their corresponding acids including pyrocatechuic, pyrogallic, and resorcylic.

------------------------------------ Physical and chemical properties ------------------------------------

Generally amorphous, rarely crystalline materials, having an astringent taste. Readily soluble in hot water to form colloidal sols. Precipitated from solution by potassium dichromate, lead acetate, albumin, gelatin, other proteins, and by alkaloids. Give colors (inks) with ferric salts; sols. develop a red color on the addition of potassium ferri-cyanide. When heated with dilute acids, insoluble, amorphous anhydrides or phlobaphenes produced in addition to hydrolysis products. Phlobaphenes are red brown substances practically insoluble in water, chemically relatively inert.

7	α-Tocopherol (natural or d-form). Non-saponifiable fraction of plant fats and oils; to some extent in land- and marine-animal fats and oils.	5,7,8-Trimethyltocol, a chroman derivative. $C_{29}H_{49}O(OH)$.

------------------------------------ Physical and chemical properties ------------------------------------

Transparent needles, MP 2.5-3.5°C; sol. in fats and fat solv., insol. in water. $E_{1\,cm}^{1\%}$ (292 mμ) = 71. Infrared maxima at 3.02 μ for hydroxy and 7.85 μ for phenolic C-O linkage; optically active, dextrorotatory in ethyl alc.; compound has 3 centers of asymmetry: carbon 2 of the chroman ring, and 4', 8' of the side chain; 8 isomers possible. Stable to heat, 200°C, when heated alone in absence of oxygen or to heat, 100°C, in presence of HCl or H_2SO_4. Stable in visible light, unstable in UV light. Acted on by alkali only slowly. Sensitive to oxidation. O-R potential = + 273 mvolts.

8	β-Tocopherol (natural form). Same occurrence as α-tocopherol.	5,8-Dimethyltocol. $C_{28}H_{47}O(OH)$.

------------------------------------ Physical and chemical properties ------------------------------------
Light yellow or colorless oil. $E_{1\,cm}^{1\%}$ (297 mμ) = 87.6. O-R potential = + 343 mvolts. Same general properties as those listed for α-tocopherol.

9	γ-Tocopherol (natural form). Same occurrence as α-tocopherol.	7,8-Dimethyltocol. $C_{28}H_{47}O(OH)$.

------------------------------------ Physical and chemical properties ------------------------------------
Transparent needles, MP -3 to -2°C. $E_{1\,cm}^{1\%}$ (298 mμ) = 93.2. Infrared maxima at 3.02 μ for hydroxy and 8.17 μ for phenolic C-O linkage. O-R potential = + 348 mvolts. Same general properties as those listed for α-tocopherol.

10	δ-Tocopherol (natural form). Same occurrence as α-tocopherol.	8-Methyltocol. $C_{27}H_{45}O(OH)$.

------------------------------------ Physical and chemical properties ------------------------------------
Yellow oil. $E_{1\,cm}^{1\%}$ (298 mμ) = 91.2. Infrared maxima at 3.01 μ for hydroxy and 8.28 μ for phenolic C-O linkage. O-R potential = + 405 mvolts. Same general properties as those listed for α-tocopherol.

[1] Some antioxidants not included are butylhydroxyanisole (synthetic), caffeic acid (wide distribution in plants), coffee bean, conidendrin (spruce resin, wood liquor wastes), dihydroquercetin (bark of Douglas fir, Jeffrey pine), diphenyl, p-phenylene-diamine ("DPPD," synthetic), eugenol (clove and nutmeg oils), gallic acid (many tannins), methylene blue (synthetic), pomiferin (fruit of osage orange tree), propyl gallate (synthetic), quercetin (rinds of many fruits, as glycosides of bark and leaves of some plants), vanillin (widely in plants, fruit of Vanilla plantifolia).

327. DETOXICATION MECHANISMS

Ar = aryl group; Et = ethyl or ethyl group; G = glucuronic acid group; Ph = phenyl group; R = alkyl group; X = any substituted group.

Part I: OXIDATION

The liver is the principal site of action for most of these oxidations.

	Substance	Reaction	Products[1]	Remarks
1	Alcohols, primary aliphatic	$RCH_2OH \rightarrow RCHO \rightarrow RCOOH \rightarrow CO_2 + H_2O$	Fatty acids and aldehydes.	Liver principal site of action.
2	Ethyl alcohol	$CH_3CH_2OH \rightarrow CH_3CHO \rightarrow CH_3COOH \rightarrow CO_2 + H_2O$	Acetic acid, acetaldehyde.	Liver principal site of action.
3	2-Ethylhexanol	$C_4H_9CHEtCH_2OH \rightarrow C_4H_9CHEtCOOH \rightarrow C_4H_9CHEtCOOC_6H_9O_6$	2-Ethylhexanoic acid.	Acid forms ester glucuronide.
4	Alcohols, secondary aliphatic	$RR'CHOH \rightarrow RR'CO + RR'CHOC_6H_9O_6$	Ketones.	Partly oxidized, partly conjugated.
5	Isopropyl alcohol	$(CH_3)_2CHOH \rightarrow (CH_3)_2CO$	Acetone	Mostly oxidized.
6	Higher secondary alcohols	Cf Item 4, above.	Ketones.	Conjugated and/or oxidized.
7	Alcohols, tertiary aliphatic	$RR'R''COH \rightarrow RR'R''COC_6H_9O_6$ (principal reaction)	Difficultly oxidized.	Mostly conjugated.
8	Alcohols, primary aromatic	$ArCH_2OH \rightarrow ArCOOH$	Aromatic acids.	
9	Benzyl alcohol	$C_6H_5CH_2OH \rightarrow C_6H_5COOH$	Benzoic acid.	Hippuric acid excreted.
10	Saligenin	$HO\text{-}C_6H_4CH_2OH \rightarrow HOC_6H_4COOH$	Salicylic acid.	Saligenin also directly conjugated.
11	Alcohols, secondary aromatic	$ArCHOHCH_3 \rightarrow ArCOOH + ArCHOGCH_3$	Aromatic acid.	Extensive conjugation as well as oxidation.
12	Methyl phenyl carbinol	$C_6H_5CHOHCH_3 \rightarrow C_6H_5COOH + C_6H_5CHOGCH_3$	Benzoic acid.	Forms glucuronide.
13	Aldehydes, aliphatic	$RCHO \rightarrow RCOOH \rightarrow CO_2 + H_2O$	Fatty acids.	Acid oxidized to CO_2.
14	Formaldehyde	$HCHO \rightarrow HCOOH \rightarrow CO_2 + H_2O$	Formic acid.	Acid oxidized to CO_2.
15	Aldehydes, aromatic	$ArCHO \rightarrow ArCOOH$	Aromatic acids.	
16	Benzaldehyde	$C_6H_5CHO \rightarrow C_6H_5COOH$	Benzoic acid.	Hippuric acid excreted.
17	Hydroxyaldehydes	$HOArCHO \rightarrow HOArCOOH + GOArCHO$	Hydroxyaromatic acid.	Some conjugated aldehyde also formed.
18	Ethers, aromatic	$ArOR \rightarrow HOAr'OR$ or $ArOH$	Phenols.	Formed either by oxidation or oxidative demethylation.
19	Methyl phenyl ether (anisole)	$C_6H_5OCH_3 \rightarrow p\text{-}HOC_6H_4OCH_3$	p-Methoxyphenol.	Oxidation of aromatic ring.
20	p-Nitroanisole	$p\text{-}NO_2C_6H_4OCH_3 \rightarrow p\text{-}NO_2C_6H_4OH + HCHO$	p-Nitrophenol.	Oxidative demethylation.
21	Glycols		Corresponding di- and monocarboxylic acids.	Oxidation not thoroughly studied.
22	Ethylene glycol	$(CH_2OH)_2 \rightarrow (COOH)_2$	Oxalic acid.	Glycol not conjugated with glucuronic acid.
23	2,2-Diethylpropane-1,3 diol	$Et_2C(CH_2OH)_2 \rightarrow Et_2C(CH_2OH)COOH$	α,α-Diethylhydracrylic acid.	Diol partly conjugated with glucuronic acid.
24	Ketones, aromatic	$ArCOR \rightarrow ArCOOH + ArCHOHR$	Benzoic or phenylacetic acid.	Reduction to carbinols (principal reaction).
25	Acetophenone	$C_6H_5COCH_3 \rightarrow C_6H_5COOH + C_6H_5CHOHCH_3$	Benzoic acid	All acylphenones yield benzoic acid.
26	Benzene	$C_6H_6 \rightarrow C_6H_5OH$ [also o- and p-$C_6H_4(OH)_2$, 1,2,4-$C_6H_4(OH)_3$, muconic acid]	Phenol, polyphenols.	Nearly half eliminated unchanged in expired air.
27	Toluene	$C_6H_5CH_3 \rightarrow C_6H_5COOH$	Benzoic acid.	Excreted as hippuric acid.
28	Xylenes	$C_6H_4(CH_3)_2 \rightarrow C_6H_4(CH_3)COOH$	Toluic acids.	Small amts. of xylenols formed.
29	Mono-substituted benzenes (except alkylbenzenes)	$C_6H_5X \rightarrow p\text{-}HOC_6H_4X$ (plus o- or p-isomer)	p-Substituted phenols (from all types of substituted benzenes).	Also m-phenols or o-phenols according to type.
30	Aniline	$C_6H_5NH_2 \rightarrow p\text{-}HOC_6H_4NH_2 + o\text{-}HOC_6H_4NH_2$	p-Aminophenol.	Some o-aminophenol.
31	Nitrobenzene	$C_6H_5NO_2 \rightarrow p\text{-}HOC_6H_4NO_2 + m\text{-}HOC_6H_4NO_2$	p-Nitrophenol.	Also m-nitrophenol.
32	Polysubstituted benzenes		Phenols.	
33	1,3,5-Trichlorobenzene	$1,3,5\text{-}C_6H_3Cl_3 \rightarrow 1,2,4,6\text{-}C_6H_2(OH)Cl_3$	2,4,6-Trichlorophenol.	
34	Alkylbenzenes		Secondary carbinols + benzoic or phenylacetic acids.	
35	Ethyl benzene	$PhCH_2CH_3 \rightarrow PhCOOH + PhCHOHCH_3 + PhCH_2COOH$	Benzoic and phenylacetic acids, methyl phenyl carbinol.	Carbinols excreted as glucuronides; acids as glycine conjugates.
36	Propylbenzene	$PhCH_2CH_2CH_3 \rightarrow PhCOOH + PhCH_2CHOHCH_3 + PhCHOHCH_2CH_3$	Benzoic acid; benzyl methyl and ethyl phenyl carbinols.	
37	Isopropylbenzene (cumene)	$PhCH(CH_3)_2 \rightarrow PhCOOH + PhCH(CH_3)CH_2OH + PhCH(CH_3)COOH$	Hydratropic acid, hydratropoyl alcohol, benzoic acid.	
38	tert.-Butylbenzene	$Ph(CH_3)_3 \rightarrow PhC(CH_3)_2CH_2OH$	2,2-Dimethyl-2-phenylethanol only.	

/1/ Other than CO_2 and H_2O.

Ar = aryl group; Et = ethyl or ethyl group; G = glucuronic acid group; Ph = phenyl group; R = alkyl group; X = any substituted group.

Part I: OXIDATION (Continued)

The liver is the principal site of action for most of these oxidations.

	Substance	Reaction	Product[1]	Remarks
	Alkylbenzenes (concluded)			
39	Styrene	$PhCH=CH_2 \rightarrow PhCOOH$	Benzoic acid (partly).	Excreted as hippuric acid.
40	Phenylacetylene	$PhC\equiv CH \rightarrow PhCH_2COOH$ (+ PhCOOH)	Phenylacetic and some benzoic acid.	Much eliminated unchanged in breath.
41	Polycyclic hydrocarbons		Phenols and trans-1,2-dihydro-1,2-diols.	Free and conjugated.
42	Naphthalene		trans-1,2-Dihydronaphthalene-1,2-diol.	Also 1- and 2-naphthols.
43	Anthracene		1,2-Dihydroanthracene-1,2-diol.	Free and conjugated.
44	Heterocyclic rings		Phenols or hydroxy compounds.	Usually conjugated.
45	Pyridine	(minor reaction)	3-Pyridinol (trace metabolite).	Major metabolites unknown; N-methyl-pyridium hydroxide formed in some animals.
46	3-Alkyl pyridines (e.g., nicotinamide)		3-Alkyl-6-ketopyridines.	
47	Quinoline	$\rightarrow$ 3-HO-5,6-di-OH + 2,6-di-OH substitutions	3-Quinolinol, 5,6- and 2,6-quinoline-diols.	Conjugated 2-hydroxy-quinoline formed in vitro.
48	Coumarin		3- and 7-Hydroxy-coumarins.	Conjugated, 3- is principal phenol.
49	3-Substituted coumarins		7-Hydroxy-coumarins.	
50	Phenothiazine		3-Hydroxy-3,7-dihydroxyphenothiazine, and 5-oxide.	Free and conjugated.
51	Chlorpromazine (10-dimethyl-amino-propyl-2-chloro-phenothiazine)		5-Oxide.	
52	Indole		3-Hydroxyindole (indoxyl).	
53	3-Substituted indoles		5-Hydroxy derivatives.	
54	Phenols		o- and p-Dihydric phenols (minor reaction).	Major reaction is conjugation.
55	Phenol	$C_6H_5OH \rightarrow$ O- and p-$C_6H_4(OH)_2$; (p- > o-).	Quinol.	Catechol also formed.
56	N-Methylamino compounds, aromatic.	$ArNHCH_3 \rightarrow ArNH_2 + HCHO.$	Aromatic amine + formaldehyde.	Oxidative demethylation.

/1/ Other than CO_2 and H_2O.

Ar = aryl group; Et = ethyl or ethyl group; G = glucuronic acid group; Ph = phenyl group; R = alkyl group; X = any substituted group.

Part II: REDUCTION

	Substance	Reaction	Products		Substance	Reaction	Products
1	Ketones, aliphatic and aromatic	$RR'CO \rightarrow RR'CHOH$	Secondary alcohols; also excreted conjugated.	10	Trinitrotoluene (2, 4, 6-)		2, 6-Dinitro-4-aminotoluene.
2	2-Heptanone	$C_5H_{11}COCH_3 \rightarrow C_5H_{11}CHOHCH_3$	2-Heptanol.				
3	Acetophenone	$PhCOCH_3 \rightarrow PhCHOHCH_3$	Methyl phenyl carbinol.	11	Azo compounds	$RN{=}NR' \rightarrow RNH_2 + R'NH_2$	Aromatic amines.
4	Aldehydes, trisubstitutes	$RR'R''CCHO \rightarrow RR'R''CCH_2OH$	Primary alcohols.	12	Prontosil rubrum		Sulfanilamide, 1, 2, 4-Triamino-benzene.
5	Chloral hydrate	$CCl_3CH(OH)_2 \rightarrow CCl_3CH_2OH$	Trichloroethyl alcohol.				
6	p-Quinones (benzo-quinone)		Quinols (quinol).				
7	2-Methyl-1, 4-naphtho-quinone		2-Methyl-1, 4-dihydroxy-naphthalene.	13	Disulfides	$RS{\cdot}SR' \rightarrow RSH + HSR'$	Sulfhydryl compounds.
8	Nitro compounds, aromatic	$ArNO_2 \rightarrow ArNH_2$	Aromatic amines (partly).	14	Antabuse	$Et_2NCS{\cdot}S{\cdot}S{\cdot}SCNEt_2 \rightarrow Et_2NCSSH$	Diethyldithio-carbamate.
9	Nitrobenzene	$C_6H_5NO_2 \rightarrow p\text{-}HOC_6H_4NH_2$	p-Aminophenol.	15	Pentavalent organic arsonic acids	$R{-}AsO(OH)_2 \rightarrow R{-}AsO$	Trivalent arsen-oxides + minor metabolites(?).
				16	Phenyl-arsonic acids	$C_6H_5AsO(OH)_2 \rightarrow C_6H_5AsO$	Phenylarsenoxide. Reduction a minor reaction.

Part III: SYNTHESIS OR CONJUGATION

	Substance	Reaction	End Products	Remarks
		Acylation		
1	Aliphatic primary amines	$RNH_2 + AcCoA \rightarrow RNHCOCH_3 + CoA$	Acetylamines.	Uncommon reaction; de-amination main reaction.
2	Glucosamine		N-Acetylglucosamine.	
3	Histamine		Acetylhistamine.	Extent of acetylation varies with species.
4	α-Amino acids	$RCH(NH_2)COOH \rightarrow RCH(NHCOCH_3)COOH$	N-Acetylamino acid.	Occurs in most species with foreign amino-acids and D-isomers. Natural amino acids are reversibly acetylated in intermediary metabolism.
5	γ-Phenyl-α-amino-butyric acid	$Ph\text{-}CH_2CH_2CH(NH_2)COOH \rightarrow Ph\text{-}CH_2CH_2CH(NHCOCH_3)COOH$	γ-Phenyl-α-acet-amidobutyric acid.	
6	S-Phenylcysteine	$Ph\text{-}SCH_2CH(NH_2)COOH \rightarrow PhSCH_2CH(NHCOCH_3)COOH$	Phenylmercapturic acid.	
7	Aromatic primary amines	$ArNH_2 \rightarrow ArNHCOCH_3$	Acetylated aromatic amine.	Extent varies with amine; does not occur in dog.
8	Isonicotinic hydrazide	$C_5H_4NCONHNH_2 \rightarrow C_5H_4NCONHNHCOCH_3$	1-Acetyl-2-iso-nicotinyl hydrazide.	In man, rhesus monkey; not in dog.
9	Sulfanilamide	$p\text{-}NH_2C_6H_4SO_2NH_2 \rightarrow p\text{-}CH_3CONHC_6H_4SO_2NH_2$	N-Acetyl-sulfanilamide.	In most animals except dog.
		Glycine Conjugation		
10	Aromatic acids	$ArCOOH \rightarrow ArCONHCH_2COOH$	Aroylglycines.	
11	Benzoic acid		Hippuric acid.	
12	α- and β-Naphtholic acids		α- and β-Naphthuric acids.	Type: ArCOOH. Also substituted benzoic acids. Reaction occurs in mammals, insects, some reptiles, but not in birds.
13	Nicotinic acid		Nicotinuric acid.	
14	Furoic acid		Furoylglycine (pyromucuric acid).	
15	Thiophene-2-carboxylic acid		Thiphenuric acid.	
16	Substituted acetic acids			Types: $ArCH_2COOH$, ArCHRCOOH, ArCRR'COOH, and possibly RR'R''CCOOH (some bile acids also form glycine conjugates).
17	Phenylacetic acid	$Ph\text{-}CH_2COOH \rightarrow Ph\text{-}CH_2CONHCH_2COOH$	Phenaceturic acid.	In mammals except man.
18	Indolylacetic acid		Indolylaceturic acid.	
19	Hydratropic acid	$Ph\text{-}CH(CH_3)COOH \rightarrow Ph\text{-}CH(CH_3)CONHCH_2COOH$	Hydratropoylglycine.	
20	Phellandric acid		Phelланduric acid.	

Ar = aryl group; Et = ethyl or ethyl group; G = glucuronic acid group; Ph = phenyl group; R = alkyl group; X = any substituted group.

Part III: SYNTHESIS OR CONJUGATION (Continued)

	Substance	Reaction	End Products	Remarks
		Glycine Conjugation (concluded)		
21	β-Substituted acrylic acids.			Type: ArCH=CHCOOH; ArCR=CHCOOH
22	Cinnamic acid	$Ph-CH=CHCOOH \rightarrow Ph-CH=CHCONHCH_2COOH$	Cinnamoylglycine.	
23	2-Furylacrylic acid	CH=CHCOOH → CH=CHCONHCH₂COOH	Furfuracrylic acid.	
24	β-Methylcinnamic acid	$Ph-C(CH_3)=CHCOOH \rightarrow Ph-C(CH_3)=CHCONHCH_2COOH$	β-Methylcinnamoylglycine.	
		Glutamine Conjugation		
25	Phenylacetic acid	$Ph-CH_2COOH \rightarrow Ph-CH_2CONHCH(COOH)CH_2CH_2CONH_2$	Phenylacetyl-glutamine.	Occurs in only man and chimpanzee.
		Ornithine Conjugation		
26	Aromatic acids		N, N'-Diaroyl-ornithines (or ornithuric acids).	Occurs only in birds and some reptiles.
27	Benzoic acid (also substituted benzoic acids)	$Ph-COOH \rightarrow Ph-CONHCH_2CH_2CH_2CH(COOH)NHCOC_6H_5$	Ornithuric acid.	
28	Furoic acid		Difuroylornithine.	
29	Nicotinic acid		Dinicotinyl-ornithine.	} Hens.
30	Phenylacetic acid		Diphenacetyl-ornithine.	
		Cysteine Conjugation		
31	Aromatic hydrocarbons	$ArH \rightarrow ArSCH_2CH(NHCOCH_3)COOH$	N-Acetyl-S-aryl-cysteines or mercapturic acids.	Not all polycyclic hydrocarbons form mercapturic acids.
32	Benzene	$C_6H_6 \rightarrow Ph-SCH_2CH(NHCOCH_3)COOH$	Phenylmercapturic acid.	
33	Naphthalene	→ SCH₂CH(NHCOCH₃)COOH	1-Naphthyl-mercapturic acid.	
34	Anthracene	→ S-CH₂CH(NHCOCH₃)COOH	1-Anthrylmercapturic acid.	
35	Halogenated aromatic hydrocarbons		Mercapturic acids.	Tetra- and penta-chlorobenzenes form little if any mercapturic acid.
36	Bromobenzene	$Ph-Br \rightarrow p-BrC_6H_4SCH_2CH(NHCOCH_3)COOH$	p-Bromophenyl-mercapturic acid.	In large amounts.
37	o- and m-Dichlorobenzene	e.g., Cl → ClSCH₂CH(NHCOOH₃)COOH	Dichlorophenyl-mercapturic acid.	p-Dichlorobenzene is not conjugated.
38	Benzyl chloride	$Ph-CH_2Cl \rightarrow Ph-CH_2SCH_2CH(NHCOCH_3)COOH$	Benzylmercapturic acid.	
39	Some chloronitrobenzenes		Mercapturic acids.	Conjugation occurs by replacement of chloro- or nitro-groups.
40	Pentachloronitrobenzene	$C_6Cl_5NO_2 \rightarrow C_6Cl_5SCH_2CH(NHCOCH_3)COOH$	Pentachlorophenyl-mercapturic acid.	Acetylcysteinyl denitration.
41	2, 4-Dichloronitrobenzene	→ SCH₂CH(NHCOCH₃)COOH	5-Chloro-2-nitrophenyl-mercapturic acid.	Acetylcysteinyl dechlorination.
		Glycoside Conjugation		
42	Primary alcohols	$RCH_2OH \rightarrow RCH_2OG$	Alkylglucuronides, RCH_2OG.	Minor metabolites; oxidation principal reaction.
43	Ethanol	$CH_3CH_2OH \rightarrow CH_3CH_2OC_6H_9O_6$	Ethyl glucuronide.	Minor metabolite.
44	2, 2-Dimethyl-2-phenyl ethanol	$Ph-C(CH_3)_2CH_2OH \rightarrow Ph-C(CH_3)_2CH_2OG$	2, 2-Dimethyl-2-phenylethyl-glucuronide.	Major metabolite.
45	Secondary alcohols	$RR'CHOH \rightarrow RR'CHOG$	Alkylglucuronides, RR'CHOG.	
46	Pentan-2-ol	$C_3H_7CHOHCH_3 \rightarrow C_3H_7CHOGCH_3$	2-Pentylglucuronide.	
47	Tertiary alcohols	$RR'R''COH \rightarrow RR'R''COG$	Alkylglucuronides, RR'R''COG.	
48	tert.-Butanol	$(CH_3)_3COH \rightarrow (CH_3)_3COG$	tert.-Butyl-glucuronide.	} Principally conjugation.
49	Phenols (all types)	$ArOH \rightarrow ArOG$	Arylglucuronides, ArOG.	
50	Phenol		Phenyl-glucuronide.	
51	Aliphatic acids		Acylglucuronides, RCOOG.	Occurs with α-substituted fatty acids.
52	Diethylacetic acid	$(C_2H_5)_2CHCOOH \rightarrow (C_2H_5)_2CHCOOG$	Diethylacetyl-glucuronide.	
53	Aromatic amines	$ArNH_2 \rightarrow ArNHG$	N-Glucuronides.	Probable.
54	Phenol	$Ph-OH \rightarrow Ph-OC_6H_{11}O_5(\beta-)$	β-Phenylglucoside.	Occurs in insects, not in mammals.
55	Imidazoleacetic acid	HC=C-CH₂COOH HC=C-CH₂COOH N—C—NH N—C—N-CHCHOHCHOHCHCH₂OH H H O	1-(3)-Ribosyl-imidazole-4-(5)-acetic acid.	Occurs in rats and mice.

Ar = aryl group; Et = ethyl group; G = glucuronic acid group; Ph = phenyl group; R = alkyl group; X = any substituted group.

Part III: SYNTHESIS OR CONJUGATION (Concluded)

	Substance	Reaction	End Products	Remarks
		Ethereal Sulfate Formation		
56	Phenols	$Ph\text{-}OH \rightarrow PhOSO_3H$	Arylsulfuric acids.	Occurs with phenols of pK_a 6-11.
57	Aromatic amines	$ArNH_2 \rightarrow ArNHSO_3H$	Sulfamates.	Probable.
		Thiocyanate Formation		
58	Cyanide ions	$CN^- \rightarrow CNS^-$	Thiocyanate.	Specific for CN^-.
		Methylation		
59	Monomethylaminoazobenzene	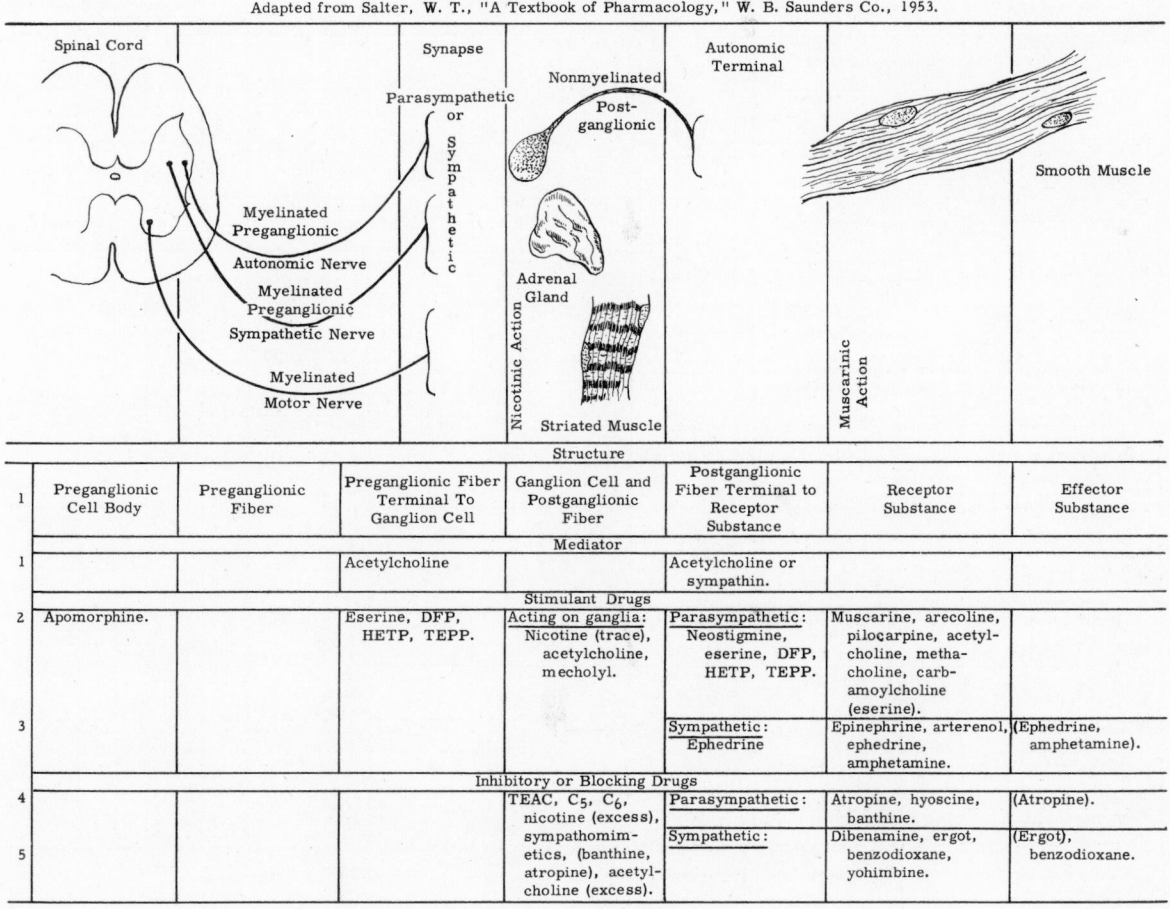	Dimethylamino-azobenzene.	Extremely rare.
60	Heterocyclic tertiary nitrogen			Occurs in many species, but only to a slight extent in rabbits.
61	Pyridine		N-Methylpyridium hydroxide.	Occurs in dog, swine, goat, hen, frog, to slight extent in rabbit, not in rat.
62	Quinoline		N-Methylquinolinium hydroxide.	
63	3, 5-Diiodo-4-hydroxy-benzoic acid		3, 5-Diiodo-4-methoxybenzoic acid.	In man only.
64	3, 4-Dihydroxyphenyl acetic acid		4-Hydroxy-3-methoxyphenyl-acetic acid.	In man and rabbit.

328. DRUGS AFFECTING THE AUTONOMIC NERVOUS SYSTEM
Part I: SITE OF ACTION
Adapted from Salter, W. T., "A Textbook of Pharmacology," W. B. Saunders Co., 1953.

			Structure			
1	Preganglionic Cell Body	Preganglionic Fiber	Preganglionic Fiber Terminal To Ganglion Cell	Ganglion Cell and Postganglionic Fiber	Postganglionic Fiber Terminal to Receptor Substance	Receptor Substance	Effector Substance
				Mediator			
1			Acetylcholine		Acetylcholine or sympathin.		
				Stimulant Drugs			
2	Apomorphine.		Eserine, DFP, HETP, TEPP.	Acting on ganglia: Nicotine (trace), acetylcholine, mecholyl.	Parasympathetic: Neostigmine, eserine, DFP, HETP, TEPP.	Muscarine, arecoline, pilocarpine, acetylcholine, metha-choline, carb-amoylcholine (eserine).	
3					Sympathetic: Ephedrine	Epinephrine, arterenol, ephedrine, amphetamine.	(Ephedrine, amphetamine).
				Inhibitory or Blocking Drugs			
4				TEAC, C_5, C_6, nicotine (excess), sympathomim-etics, (banthine, atropine), acetyl-choline (excess).	Parasympathetic:	Atropine, hyoscine, banthine.	(Atropine).
5					Sympathetic:	Dibenamine, ergot, benzodioxane, yohimbine.	(Ergot), benzodioxane.

The use of trade names in this table is for informative purposes only and in no way implies endorsement by The National Academy of Sciences -- The National Research Council.

Part II: CHEMISTRY AND TOXICOLOGY

TD = toxic dose; PO = oral; SC = subcutaneous; IP = intraperitoneal; IM = intramuscular; IV = intravenous.

	Common or Trade Name, Synonyms	Chemical Name	Structure	Pressor Activity (Epinephrine Equivalent)	Toxicity mg/kg Animal (Dose)	PO	SC	IP	IM	IV
			Sympathomimetic Drugs							
1	Amphetamine, (Benzedrine)	dl-α-Methylphenethylamine		1:100-1:300	Mouse (LD$_{50}$)		42	75		10
					Rabbit (LD$_{50}$)		11		10	
					Rat (LD$_{50}$)		39-165	30		
2	Phenylpropylmethyl-amine, (Vonedrine)	dl-N, β-Dimethylphen-ethylamine		1:600	Mouse (LD$_{50}$)		540			
					Rabbit (LD$_{50}$)		205		220	72
					Rat (LD$_{50}$)		850	165		
3	d-Desoxyephedrine HCl, (Pervitin)	d-N, α-Dimethylphen-ethylamine hydrochloride		1:100-1:300	Mouse (LD$_{50}$)			75		
					Rat (MLD)			17		
4	Mephentermine	N, α, α-Trimethylphen-ethylamine sulfate								
5	Mydriatine, (dl-Nor-ephedrine HCl)	α-(1-Aminoethyl) benzyl alcohol hydrochloride		1:60-1:300	Mouse (LD$_{50}$)		600	300		
					Rabbit (LD$_{50}$)		255		320	50
					Rat (LD$_{50}$)		380-860	160		
6	l-Ephedrine	l-Phenyl-2-methylamino-propanol		1:100-1:300	Mouse (LD$_{50}$)		600	325		
					Rabbit (LD$_{50}$)		165		175	60
					Rat (LD$_{50}$)		320-550	165		
7	l-N-Ethylephedrine HCl, (Nethamine HCl)	2-Methylethylamino-1-phenyl-1-propanol hydrochloride		Hypotensor						
8	Hydroxyamphetamine, (Paredrine)	dl-p-Hydroxy-α-methyl-phenethylamine		1:50-1:100	Guinea pig (LD$_{50}$)		180			
					Mouse (LD$_{50}$)			430		
9	p-(2-Methylamino-propyl)-phenol, (Veritol)	p-Hydroxy-N, α-dimethyl-phenethylamine		1:30-1:250	Rat (LD$_{50}$)			100		
10	Synephrin tartrate, (Sympatol)	p-Hydroxyphenolmethyl-aminoethanol tartrate		1:116	Mouse (MLD)		700-800			65
					Rabbit (MLD)					50
11	Phenylephrine HCl, (Neo-Synephrine HCl)	l-m-Hydroxy-α-(methyl-aminomethyl) benzyl alcohol		1:56	Mouse (LD$_{50}$)		22	330		
					Rabbit (LD$_{50}$)		22		7.2	0.5
					Rat (LD$_{50}$)		27-33	17		
12	Methoxyphenamine HCl, (Orthoxine HCl)	β-(o-Methoxyphenyl) iso-propylmethylamine hydrochloride		1:1000	Rat (LD$_{50}$)					60
13	Epinine HCl	3,4-Dihydroxyphenyl-ethylmethylamine hydro-chloride		1:10-1:12						
14	l-Arterenol, (l-Nor-epineprhrine; l-Noradrenaline)	l-α-(Aminomethyl)-3,4-		1:2-1:5	Mouse (LD$_{50}$)					5; 0.10[1]
					Rat (LD$_{50}$)					0.10; 1.40[1]
15	3,4-Dihydroxynoreph-edrine HCl, (Cobe-frine HCl)	3,4-Dihydroxyphenylpro-panolamine hydrochlo-ride		1:4-1:12	Rabbit (MLD)					11
					Rat (LD$_{50}$)					8
16	Butanefrine HCl	α-(1-Aminopropyl) proto-catechuyl alcohol hydrochloride		Hypotensor	Mouse (LD$_{50}$)					117
17	Epinephrine, (Adre-naline)	3,4-Dihydroxy-α-(methyl-aminomethyl) benzyl alcohol		1:1	Mouse (LD$_{50}$)			13[2]		2.7[2];50[3]
					Rat (LD$_{50}$)					0.04[2]; 0.80[3]
18	N-Methylepinephrine, (N-Methyladrenaline; Methadren)	α-(Dimethylaminomethyl) protocatechuyl alcohol		1:10-1:25	Mouse		250			
					Rabbit					40
19	Isopropylarterenol, (Isuprel)	α-(Isopropylaminomethyl) protocatechuyl alcohol		Hypotensor	Mouse (LD$_{50}$)			450		83
20	Methoxamine HCl, (Vasoxyl HCl)	2-Amino-1-(2,5-dimeth-oxyphenyl)-1-propanol hydrochloride			Mouse (LD$_{50}$)	92				
21	Naphazoline HCl, (Privine HCl)	2-(1-Naphthylmethyl) imidazoline hydrochlo-ride			Mouse (LD$_{50}$)		170			
					Rabbit (LD$_{50}$)		0.95		0.95	0.8
					Rat (LD$_{50}$)		325-385	50		
22	N-1-Dimethylhexyl-amine, (Oenethyl)	2-Methylaminoheptane	CH$_3$-CH$_2$-CH$_2$-CH$_2$-CH$_2$-CH-NH-CH$_3$ (CH$_3$)							
23	Tuaminoheptane, (Tuamine)	1-Methylhexylamine	CH$_3$-CH$_2$-CH$_2$-CH$_2$-CH$_2$-CH-NH$_2$ (CH$_3$)	1:320	Mouse (LD$_{50}$)		115	75		
					Rabbit (LD$_{50}$)		130		85	22
					Rat (LD$_{50}$)		135-169	34		
24	Octin	6-Methylamino-2-methylheptene	CH$_3$-C=CH-CH$_2$-CH$_2$-CH-NH-CH$_3$ (CH$_3$) (CH$_3$)		Dog (LD)	148	76.3			25.8
					Mouse (LD$_{50}$)		171			17.5
					Rabbit (LD$_{50}$)		101			17.6
25	N, α-Dimethylcyclo-hexaneethylamine, (Benzedrex)	N-Methyl-β-cyclohexyl-isopropylamine		1:333-1:500	Guinea pig (LD$_{50}$)			85		
					Rabbit (LD$_{50}$)		80-90			
					Rat (LD$_{50}$)		65-75			
26	Cyclopentamine HCl, (Clopane HCl)	N, α-Dimethylcyclo-pentaneethylamine hydrochloride								

/1/ Second value for d-arterenol. /2/ l-epinephrine. /3/ d-epinephrine.

The use of trade names in this table is for informative purposes only and in no way implies endorsement by The National Academy of Sciences -- The National Research Council.

Part II: CHEMISTRY AND TOXICOLOGY (Continued)

TD = toxic dose; PO = oral; SC = subcutaneous; IP = intraperitoneal; IM = intramuscular; IV = intravenous.

Sympatholytic Drugs

	Common Name	Structure				Adrenolytic Action			Toxicity	
						Rabbit Uterus	Guinea Pig Seminal Vesicle	Epinephrine Hypertensive Reversal, Dog mg/kg, IV	Species (Route)	LD_{50}[4] mg/kg
						Isolated (Ergotamine=1)				
	For lines 27-31: lysergic acid, [R], d-proline, and [R'] are joined in amide linkages.									
		R'	R_2	R	R_1					
27	Ergocornine	1-Valine	-CH(CH_3)(CH_3)	Dimethylpyruvic acid	-CH(CH_3)(CH_3)	0.5	2		Rabbit(IV)	1.17
28	Ergocristine	1-Phenylalanine	-CH_2-⬡	Dimethylpyruvic acid	-CH(CH_3)(CH_3)	1.0	4		Rabbit (IV)	2.17
29	Ergocryptine	1-Leucine	-CH_2-CH(CH_3)(CH_3)	Dimethylpyruvic acid	-CH(CH_3)(CH_3)	1.5	4		Rabbit(IV)	1.05
30	Ergotoxine	1-Phenylalanine	-CH_2-⬡	Dimethylpyruvic acid	-CH(CH_3)(CH_3)					
31	Ergotamine	1-Phenylalanine	-CH_2-⬡	Pyruvic acid	-NH_3					
32	Ergonovine	Lysergic acid-NH-CHCH_2OH CH_3				1	1	0.2-0.5	Mouse (IV) Rabbit(IV) Rat (IV)	62 3.55 80
33	Dihydroergotamine[5]	5,10-dihydro derivative of ergotamine				2.25	7	0.2-0.5	Mouse (IV) Rabbit(IV) Rat (IV)	118 25 110
34	Dihydroergocornine	5,10-dihydro derivative of ergocornine	— methane sulfonate "Hydergine"			2.5	25		Rabbit(IV)	35
35	Dihydroergocristine	5,10-dihydro derivative of ergocristine				3.5	35		Rabbit(IV)	27
36	Dihydroergocryptine	5,10-dihydro derivative of ergocryptine				5.0	35		Rabbit(IV)	19
		Chemical Name		Structure						
37	Yohimbine (Quebrachine; Corynine; Aphrodine)	(Chief alkaloid of Crynanthe johimbe; 10 isomers known)				1:200		1	Guinea pig (IP) Mouse (PO) Mouse (IV)	42(TD) (86.7-1000) (TD) 16 (TD)
38	N-(2-Chloroethyl)-dibenzylamine HCl (Dibenamine HCl)	β-Chloroethyldibenzylamine hydrochloride						10-20	Cat (IV) Mouse (SC) Mouse (IP) Mouse (IV)	35 400-500 75-100 50
39	Benzazoline HCl, (Priscoline HCl)	z-Benzyl-4,5-imidazoline hydrochloride						10		
40	Piperoxan HCl, (933F)	2-(1-Piperidylmethyl)-1,4-benzodioxan hydrochloride				1:100			Mouse (IP)	180 (TD)
41	Prosympal, (883F)	2-(Diethylaminoethyl)-benzodioxan				1:200		1	Frog (SC) Guinea pig (SC) Mouse (SC) Rabbit (SC) Rabbit (IV)	250 (TD) 400 (TD) 500 (TD) 300 (TD) 30 (TD)
42	Regitine, (C7337)	2-(N'-p-tolyl-N'-m-hydroxyphenylaminoethyl) imidazoline							Mouse (PO) Rabbit (PO) Rat (PO)	750 2000 1250

/4/ Unless otherwise indicated in parentheses. /5/ D. H. E. 45.

The use of trade names in this table is for informative purposes only and in no way implies endorsement by The National Academy of Sciences -- The National Research Council.

Part II; CHEMISTRY AND TOXICOLOGY (Continued)

TD = toxic dose; PO = oral; SC = subcutaneous; IP = intraperitoneal; IM = intramuscular; IV = intravenous.

Parasympathomimetic Drugs

#	Common or Trade Name, Synonyms	Chemical Name	Structure	Pressor Activity	Species (Dose)	PO	SC	IP	IM	IV
43	Acetylcholine, (Pragmoline; Acecoline)	(2-Hydroethyl)-trimethyl-ammonium Bromide or Chloride		1	Mouse (TD)	3000	170			20
					Rabbit (TD)					0.15
					Rat (TD)	2500	250			
44	Methacholine, (Mecholyl)	Acetyl-β-methylcholine bromide or chloride		1	Mouse (TD)	1100				
45	Carbachol, (Choline chloride carbamate; **carbamoylcholine chloride**	(2-Hydroxyethyl) tri-methylammonium chloride carbamate		5-10 (Dog); 1 (Rabbit)	Dog (TD)		0.1			
					Guinea pig (TD)		0.075			
					Mouse (TD)	25	0.5			0.5
46	Vasodilatateur 2249F, (Dilvasene)	(1, 3-Dioxolan-4-ylmethyl) trimethylammonium iodide		0.5-0.2	Guinea pig (TD)		5			
					Mouse (TD)	300	35			2.5
					Rat (TD)		25			
47	Furtrethonium Iodide, (Furmethide Iodide)	Furfuryltrimethylammo-nium iodide			Rat (LD50)		90			
48	Muscarine	Alkaloid of Amanita muscarina			Cat (TD)		2-4			
49	Pilocarpine	Alkaloid of Pilocarpus jaborandi								
50	Arecoline	Methyl-1,2,5,6-tetra-hydro-1-methylnicotinate			Mouse (TD)		65			
51	Physostigmine[6], (Eserine)	Main alkaloid of Calabar bean (Physostigma venenosum)			Cat (LD50)					0.68
					Mouse (LD50)	3	0.75			0.45
					Rabbit (LD50)		3			0.5-0.8
52	Neostigmine Bromide[6], (Prostigmine Bromide)	(m-Hydroxyphenyl) tri-methylammonium bromide or methylsulfate dimethylcarbamate			Mouse (LD50)	12-16	1			0.30
					Rabbit (LD50)		0.5-0.75			0.25
53	Benzpyrinium Bromide[6], (Stigmonene Bromide)	1-Benzyl-3-(dimethyl-carbamyloxy) pyridinium bromide								
54	DFP[6]	Diisopropyl fluorophos-phate			Cat (LD50)					1.63
					Dog (LD50)					3.43
					Mouse (LD50)	36.8	3.71			
					Rabbit (LD50)	9.78				0.34
					Rat (LD50)			1.82		

Parasympatholytic Drugs

#	Common or Trade Name, Synonyms	Chemical Name	Structure	Species (Dose)	PO	SC	IP	IM	IV
55	Atropine, (dl-Hyoscyamine)	dl-Tropyltropate		Cat (TD)		125-150			
				Dog (TD)		175-200			50-100
				Guinea pig (TD)					70
				Mouse (TD)		300-400			
				Mouse (LD50)	794		215		68-90.8
				Rabbit (TD)	1400-1500	200-500			
				Rat (TD)		700-750			
				Rat (LD50)			280		41
56	Scopolamine, (Hyoscine)								
57	Genatropine	Atropine-N-oxide		Dog (TD)					200

/6/ Inhibitor of cholinesterase.

328. DRUGS AFFECTING THE AUTONOMIC NERVOUS SYSTEM (Continued)

Part II: CHEMISTRY AND TOXICOLOGY (Concluded)

TD = toxic dose; PO = oral; SC = subcutaneous; IP = intraperitoneal; IM = intramuscular; IV = intravenous.

#	Common or Trade Name, Synonyms	Chemical Name	Structure	Species (Dose)	PO	SC	IP	IM	IV
58	Homatropine, (Mydriasine)	Mandeltropeine (methyl-bromide)	(structure) HBr or CH_3Br	Guinea pig (LD_{50}) / Mouse (LD_{50}) / Rat (LD_{50})	1000 / 1400 / 1200	650 / 800	120 / 60 / 82		
59	Amprotropine Phosphate, (Syntropan)	3-Diethylamino-2,2-dimethylpropyltropate phosphate	(structure) $\cdot H_3PO_4$	Mouse (LD)		1600			70
60	Eucatropine HCl	4-Hydroxy-1,2,2,6-tetramethylpiperidine mandelate hydrochloride	(structure) $\cdot HCl$						
61	Trasentine	2-Diethylaminoethyl α-phenyl cyclohexane-acetate HCl	(structure) $\cdot HCl$	Mouse (LD_{50}) / Rat (LD_{50})	780		220 / 250		27 / 32
62	Trocinate	β-Diethylaminoethyl-diphenylthioacetate hydrochloride	(structure) $\cdot HCl$						
63	Propivane, (117RP)	2-Diethylaminoethyl-propylphenylacetate hydrochloride	(structure) $\cdot HCl$						
64	Artane Trihexylphenidyl	α-Cyclohexyl-α-phenyl-1-piperidinepropanol hydrochloride	(structure) $\cdot HCl$	Mouse (LD_{50}) / Rat (LD_{50})			162 / 195		39 / 30
65	Pavatrine HCl	2-Diethylaminoethyl 9-fluorenecarboxylate hydrochloride	(structure) $\cdot HCl$	Mouse (LD)			320		
66	Cyverine HCl	Methyl-bis (β-cyclohexylethyl) amine hydrochloride	(structure) $\cdot HCl$						
67	Dibutoline Sulfate, (Dibuline Sulfate)	Bis [(dibutylcarbamate) of ethyl (2-hydroxyethyl) dimethylammonium] sulsulfate	$(C_4H_9)_2N-COO-CH_2-CH_2-N^+$ ... $\cdot SO_4$	Rat (LD_{50})			22		
68	Dicyclomine HCl, (Bentyl)	1-Cyclohexylhexahydrobenzoic acid, β-diethylaminoethyl ester hydrochloride	(structure) $\cdot HCl$						
			Curariform Drugs						
69	Diethazine Base, or HCl, (Diparcol Base or HCl; 2987RP)	10-(2-Diethylaminoethyl) phenothiazine	(structure)	Mouse (LD_{50}) / Rabbit (LD_{50})		450 / 200			45 / 25
70	Caramiphen HCl, (Parpanit)	1-Phenylcyclopentane-carboxylic acid 2-diethylaminoethyl ester hydrochloride	(structure) $\cdot HCl$	Cat (LD_{50}) / Mouse (LD_{50}) / Rabbit (LD_{50}) / Rat (LD_{50})	390		222.3 / 209		45.1 / 24.5
71	Gallamine Triethiodide, (Flaxedil; 3697RP; 2559F)	[v-Phenenyltris (oxyethylene)]-tris [triethylammonium iodide]	(structure)	Dog (LD_{50}) / Mouse (LD_{50}) / Rabbit (LD_{50}) / Rat (LD_{50})	425 / 100	15 / 25		2.3	0.8 / 4.5 / 24.5 / 5.5
72	Myanesin	3-o-Toloxy-1,2-propanediol	(structure)	Mouse (LD_{50})			560		
			Ganglion-Blocking Drugs						
73	T.E.A. Chloride, (Etamon); TEAB	Tetraethylammonium bromide or chloride	(structure) (X = Cl or Br)	Dog (LD_{50}) / Mouse (LD_{50}) / Rat (LD_{50})	900 / 2630	65		58 / 110	36.4 / 56.3
74	Hexamethonium Bromide (Hexameton)	Hexamethylenebis [trimethylammonium bromide]	(structure) (X = Cl or Br)						

The use of trade names in this table is for informative purposes only and in no way implies endorsement by the National Academy of Sciences--The National Research Council.

Part III: CLINICAL APPLICATIONS
Numbers in brackets refer to drugs listed in Part II.

Drug Number		Principal Uses	Possible Side Effects or Severe Reactions	Contraindications	Route of Administration[1]
			Sympathomimetic Drugs		
1	[1]	CNS stimulant in narcolepsy, certain depressive conditions, post-encephalitic parkinsonism.	May produce overstimulation, restlessness, insomnia, G.I. upset, chills; collapse and syncope may follow overdosage. Preliminary small test dosages obviate hypertensive reactions or cardiovascular disease.	Anxiety, hyperexcitability or restlessness	PO.
2	[2]	Nasal decongestant.			TOP.
3	[3]	CNS stimulant.	Euphoria, tachycardia, hypertension. Hypersensitivity may cause headache, irritability, vertigo, insomnia and collapse.	Hypertension, heart diseases, or thyrotoxicosis.	PO.
4	[4]	In severe hypotensive states; cardiac and general surgery, spinal anesthesia.		Peripheral vascular collapse.	IV, IM.
5	[5]	Bronchial dilation; nasal vasoconstriction.	Hypertension, tachycardia, and nervous excitation.	Severe hypertension or cardiac disease, thyrotoxicosis.	PO, TOP.
6	[6]	In asthma and allergic disorders; to increase blood pressure; locally, to shrink mucosa of nose; treatment of syncope due to complete heart block.	Nervous insomnia, tachycardia and cardiac consciousness, sweating, headache, hypertension, anxiety.	Thyrotoxicosis, heart disease, hypertension.	PO, IM, SC, TOP.
7	[7]	In bronchial asthma, allergic manifestations; vasomotor rhinitis.	Insomnia; nausea.	Diabetes, severe cardiovascular diseases, marked hyperthyroidism.	PO.
8	[8]	Vasoconstrictor; in postural hypotension, carotid sinus syndrome, nasal decongestion.	Nervous system stimulation, hypertension.	Severe hypertension, cardiac disease, or glaucoma.	PO, TOP.
9	[9]	In hypotension; for pupil dilatation.	Nervous system stimulation, hypertension.	Severe hypertension, cardiac disease.	
10	[10]	Hypertensive in mild collapse caused by failing peripheral blood flow.		Cardiac disease, diabetes, or thyroid disorders.	PO.
11	[11]	In paroxysmal tachycardia, shock, and shock-like states.	Tingling or coloring of skin; "fullness" of the head; transient precordial pain; hyperthyroidism; certain cardiac conditions; hypertension in the aged.		PO, TOP.
12	[12]	In bronchial asthma, acute urticaria, G.I. allergy.	Mild nervous excitation; nausea; hypotension; slight drop in systolic blood pressure, more pronounced in those with hypertension.	Advanced cardiac disease or hypotension.	PO.
13	[13]	Nasal vasoconstrictor.	Tachycardia, hypertension, nervous excitation.	Thyrotoxicosis.	TOP.
14	[14]	In acute hypotensive states, trauma, central vasomotor depression, hemorrhage.	Hypertensive and arteriosclerotic disease.	Use of cyclopropane anesthesia or myocardial ischemia.	IV.
15	[15]	Vasoconstrictor, particularly with local anesthetic.	Comparable to epinephrine (see [17]).		
16	[16]	In bronchial asthmatic paroxysms.		Hypersensitivity to "sympathomimetic amines."	IV, SC.
17	[17]	In asthma, hay fever, acute allergic states, shock; vasoconstrictor applied topically or with local anesthetic.	Anxiety, palpitation, vertigo, headache; acute elevation of blood pressure and vasomotor collapse may occur.	Thyrotoxicosis, cardiac disease, or cerebral arteriosclerosis; cyclopropane or ether anesthesia.	IM, SC, TOP.
18	[18]	Hyperglycemic with local anesthetic.	Hypertension, nervous excitation.	Severe hypertension, cardiac disease.	
19	[19]	Vasoconstrictor; in asthma, allergic states.	Acute hypertension, nervous excitation, palpitations, tachycardia.	Thyrotoxicosis, severe cardiac disease.	SL, IH.
20	[20]	In hypotension, post-operative collapse.			IM.
21	[21]	Nasal vasoconstrictor. As effective as epinephrine but more prolonged action.	Overdose may cause drowsiness, tachycardia, hypertension.	Thyrotoxicosis, severe hypertension, cardiac disease.	TOP.
22	[22]	In hypotension produced by spinal anesthesia.	Hypertension, nervous excitation, headache, dizziness, tachycardia, palpitations.	Thyrotoxicosis, cardiac disease.	IV, IM.
23	[23]	In rhinitis and allergic conditions.			TOP, IH.
24	[24]	Antispasmodic, in vesical and ureteral spasms.	Dizziness, headache.	G.I. obstruction.	PO, IV, SC.
25	[25]	Shrink nasal mucosa. Lacks centrally stimulating properties of amphetamine.			IH.
26	[26]	Nasal decongestant.	Overdose may cause rise in blood pressure, nervousness, occasional nausea, dizziness.		TOP, IH.
			Sympatholytic Drugs		
27	[27, 28, 29]	Peripheral vascular disorders; hypotensive agent.			
28	[30]	Oxytocic.	Hypertension, collapse, colic, nausea, vomiting.	Pregnancy, serious cardiac disease.	
29	[31]	Oxytocic; in migraine.	Hypertension, tachycardia, vomiting. Chronic reactions: gangrene of digits; mental confusion.	Pregnancy, early stages of labor; peripheral vascular disease; diseases of liver, kidneys.	SC, SL.
30	[32]	Oxytocic; in migraine.	G.I. disturbances, hypertension, tachycardia, tremor, excitement, convulsions, exophthalmus (?).	Pregnancy, serious cardiac disease.	

/1/ PO = orally; IV = intravenous; IM = intramuscular; SC = subcutaneous; TOP = topically; SL = sublingually; IH = inhalation; ION = iontophoresis; MI = miotic; REC = rectally.

The use of trade names in this table is for informative purposes only and in no way implies endorsement by The National Academy of Sciences--The National Research Council.

Part III: CLINICAL APPLICATIONS (Continued)
Numbers in brackets refer to drugs listed in Part II.

Drug Number		Principal Uses	Possible Side Effects or Severe Reactions	Contraindications	Route of Administration[1]
31	[33]	In migraine.	Nausea, vomiting, weakness, cardiac irregularity.	Pregnancy; peripheral vascular disease; diseases of the liver, kidneys.	IV, IM, SC.
32	[34, 35, 36]	Clinically used for adrenergic blocking and peripheral vasodilatation in peripheral vascular diseases.		Hypotension.	IM.
33	[37]	Formerly: aphrodesiac, local anesthetic, mydriatic.	Hypotension, kidney injury.	Renal disease.	
34	[38]	In Raynaud's disease, erythromelalgia, causalgia, hypertension, pheochromocytoma.	Usually: postural hypotension; occasionally: nausea, diarrhea, mental confusion.	Arteriosclerosis.	
35	[39]	Vasodilator; in peripheral disease.	Possible peptic ulcer or gastritis; may cause transient syncope.		IV, IM, SC.
36	[40]	Diagnostic agent: detection of epinephrine-producing tumors.	Tachycardia, palpitation, flushing; cold, clammy extremities; hypernoia, nervousness, mild headache, fright, dizziness.		IV.
37	[41]	Sympatholytic vasodilator; analgesic; angors.	Cardiac, digestive disturbances; sedation; bronchitis.		PO.
38	[42]	Diagnostic agent; pheochromocytoma. In vascular disease, hypertensive emergencies.			PO, IV, IM.
Parasympathomimetic Drugs					
39	[43]	In peripheral vascular diseases, attacks of paroxysmal tachycardia, hypertension, intestinal or bladder atony (post-operative), spasmic occlusion of retinal artery.	Flushing, sweating, vertigo, marked salivation, nausea, vomiting.		IV, IM, SC.
40	[44]	In auricular paroxysmal tachycardia, chronic ulcers, Raynaud's disease, low peripheral blood circulation.	Hypotension; cardiac slowing or arrest.	Allergy, asthma, hyperthyroidism; recent coronary occlusion or severe illness. Never administered IV or IM.	PO, SC, ION.
41	[45]	In urinary retention, post-operative abdominal distension, peripheral vascular diseases (vasospasm), threatened gangrene. Veterinary uses.	Flushing, abdominal pain, vomiturition, headache, asthmatic attacks. Counter-action by atropine.	Asthma or allergic patients suspected of latent asthma. Never administered IV or IM.	PO, SC, TOP, (MI).
42	[46]	Vasodilator; in hypotension, peripheral vascular (Raynaud's) disease.	Flushing, sweating, salivation. Counter-action by atropine.	Never administered IV.	PO, TOP (MI).
43	[47]	In bladder atony, glaucoma.	Cystitis.	Mechanical obstruction of bladder. Never administered IV.	PO, SC.
44	[48]	Experimental pharmacology.	Salivation; lacrimation; vomiting; profuse diarrhea; cardiac slowing; collapse; may progress to convulsions, coma and death in few hours.		
45	[49]	Miotic; in glaucoma, atropine poisoning. Formerly: to increase sweating.	Sweating, salivation, cardiac irregularities, pulmonary edema, increased G.I. motility.	Asthma; pulmonary, cardiac disease.	TOP(MI), SC.
46	[50]	Miotic; in glaucoma.	Cardiac slowing, salivation and miosis.		TOP(MI).
47	[51]	Miotic; in glaucoma; in stimulation of G.I. or bladder activity; myasthenia gravis distension or atony of intestines.	Salivation, lacrimation, tremor and depression of cardiorespiratory system.	Asthma.	IM, SC, TOP.
48	[52]	In glaucoma, atony of G.I. tract and bladder, myasthenia gravis, muscular spasms in poliomyelitis.	Salivation, lacrimation, nervous excitation and depression of cardiorespiratory system.	Asthma or mechanical obstruction of intestines.	PO, IM, SC.
49	[53]	In atony of G.I. tract and bladder, myasthenia gravis, migraine, tachycardia, muscular spasms in poliomyelitis.	Asthma.	Asthma or mechanical obstruction of intestines.	PO, IM.
50	[54]	In glaucoma.	Blurred vision, pain in eyes and brow, ciliary spasm and pericorneal injection. Orally: nausea, vomiting and diarrhea. Systemic administration: prolonged salivation, lacrimation, intestinal cramps, shock, collapse.	Never administered systemically.	TOP.
Parasympatholytic Drugs					
51	[55[2]]	Symptomatic treatment of post-encephalitic parkinsonism and paralysis agitans; cardio- and pyloro-spasm; mydriasis and cycloplegia; suppression of excessive salivation; syncope resulting from carotid sinus hypersensitivity or cardiac block.	Dryness of mouth, blurred vision, persistent cycloplegia, tachycardia, excitement and dermatitis.	Glaucoma, corneal ulcer.	PO, IM, SC. TOP.
52	[56]	Hypnotic and sedative. Locally: as substitute for atropine in ophthalmology.	Thirst, dryness of mouth, dilatation of pupil, tachycardia, delirium, ataxia and muscular weakness.	Glaucoma.	PO, SC, TOP.
53	[57]	G.I. disturbances.	Similar to but less toxic than atropine sulfate. Cf 51 [55].		
54	[58[3]]	Mydriatic, cycloplegic.	Similar to but less toxic than atropine sulfate. Cf 51 [55].	Glaucoma	TOP.

/1/ PO - orally; IV = intravenous; IM = intramuscular; SC = subcutaneous; TOP = topically; SL = sublingually; IH = inhalation; ION = iontophoresis; MI = miotic; REC = rectally. /2/ As atropine sulfate. /3/ As homatropine hydrobromide.

The use of trade names in this table is for informative purposes only and in no way implies endorsement by The National Academy of Sciences The National Research Council.

Part III: CLINICAL APPLICATIONS (Concluded)
Numbers in brackets refer to drugs listed in Part II.

Drug Number		Principal Uses	Possible Side Effects or Severe Reactions	Contraindications	Route of Administration[1]
55	[59]	Antispasmodic, for smooth muscle; in encephalitic parkinsonism.	Overdosage: may cause convulsions.		PO, IM, SC.
56	[60]	Mydriatic.		Glaucoma	TOP.
57	[61]	Antispasmodic.	Tachycardia, restlessness and nervous excitation.	Glaucoma.	PO, IM, REC.
58	[62]	Antispasmodic, for smooth muscle.	All the advantages of atropine sulfate, none of the disadvantages. Cf 51 [55].		PO.
59	[63]	Antispasmodic, for G. I. and urogenital disorders.	Ten times less toxic than atropine sulfate. Cf 51 [55].		PO, SC, REC.
60	[64]	Parkinsonism.	Blurring of vision, nausea, dryness of mouth, dizziness, "fullness" in head, agitation, confusion.	Glaucoma.	PO.
61	[65]	Antispasmodic.	Tachycardia, nervous excitability.	Glaucoma.	PO.
62	[66]	In pylorospasm, colitis.	Tachycardia, restlessness and nervous excitability.	Glaucoma.	
63	[67]	In G.I., urogenital, biliary spasm; mydriatic; cycloplegic.	Dryness of mouth, mydriasis, moderate hypotension.	Glaucoma.	TOP.
64	[68]	Antispasmodic, for smooth muscle.	Therapeutic dosages: virtually without pupillary, secretory, and cardiac effects of atropine sulfate. Cf 51 [55].		PO.
		Curariform Drugs			
65	[70]	In parkinsonism, muscular spasm, tremor.			
66	[71]	For muscular relaxation.	Neostigmine bromide (Cf 52 [56]) should be available.		
67	[72]	Depression of reflex excitability in such conditions as hemiplagia, paraplegia.	Paralysis.	Myasthenia gravis.	
		Ganglion-blocking Drugs			
68	[73]	Bromide: diagnostic and therapeutic in peripheral vascular affections; diagnostic in hypertension. Chloride: peripheral vascular disorders and arteriosclerosis; diagnostic in hypertension.	Bromide: hypotension. Chloride: reduction of blood pressure, disturbance of accommodation.	Bromide: severe cerebral or cardiac vascular occlusive disorders. Chloride: severe coronary heart disease or cerebral vascular arterial disease.	IV, IM.
69	[74]	ANS blocking agent.			

/1/ PO = orally; IV = intravenous; IM = intramuscular; SC = subcutaneous; TOP = topically; SL = sublingually; IH = inhalation; ION = iontophoresis; MI = miotic; REC = rectally.

329. EQUIVALENT ANESTHETIC EFFECTS OF GASES: INTACT ANIMALS AND ISOLATED EXCITABLE TISSUES

	Gas	ED_{50}[1]	Blockade[2] atm	Concentration of Gas in Non-aqueous Phase[3] (x 10^{-4} mole fraction)		Gas	ED_{50}[1]	Blockade[2] atm	Concentration of Gas in Non-aqueous Phase[3] (x 10^{-4} mole fraction)
1	Helium	163		125	6	Krypton	1.8		47
2	Nitrogen	18		80	7	Xenon	0.51	12	49
3	Argon	12.6	340	111	8	Nitrous oxide	0.58	13	66
4	Methane	2.9	110	60	9	Ethylene	0.47	12	58
5	Sulfur hexafluoride	1.87	None	41	10	Cyclopropane	0.045	1.9	

/1/ The partial pressure required to abolish the M.E.C. response to electroshock, in 50% of a large group of mice. /2/ The partial pressure required to abolish reversibly the impulse transmission in isolated rat sciatic nerve. /3/ ED_{50} times mole fraction in benzene at 1 atmosphere.

330. ANESTHESIA, STAGES AND PLANES: MAN

	Designation	Characteristics	General Signs	Drug
1	Stage I (Analgesia)	Senses benumbed; consciousness retained.	Appearance and feeling of well-being. Sense of pain diminished.	All drugs that will produce surgical anesthesia, stage III.
2	Stage II (Delirium)	Consciousness lost; respiration irregular; movement of skeletal muscles probable.	Eyeballs move from side to side, or strabismus may be present.	All drugs that will produce surgical anesthesia, stage III.
3	Stage III (Surgical anesthesia) Plane 1	Swallowing reflex abolished; muscle relaxation is minimal; respiration regular and even.	Eyeballs moving, or strabismus is present. Pupils are of pre-anesthetic size. Eyelid reflex is abolished.	Ethylene, nitrous oxide.
4	Plane 2	Muscle relaxation increased. Intercostal musculature still active in respiration (inspiration). Movements of diaphragm are of normal range. Respirations are regular and even.	Eyeballs are fixed in mid-line.	Chloroform, cyclopropane, di-vinyl ether, ether, ethyl chloride, morphine, pentothal, trichlorethylene.
5	Plane 3	Muscle relaxation further increased and suitable for intra-abdominal surgery. Inspirations are quickened and shortened. Expirations and the inter-respiratory pause are more prolonged.	Eyeballs are fixed in mid-line. Pupils are slightly larger than pre-anesthetic. The light reflex is present but sluggish.	All drugs as in plane 2.
6	Plane 4	Skeletal muscle relaxation is complete. Bronchial (cough) reflexes are dulled. Respiration becomes gasping, and is maintained entirely by the diaphragm. The expiratory phase is further prolonged. Cyanosis may be present. Blood and pulse pressure fall, while pulse rate increases.	Pupils are widely dilated and do not react to light. Conjunctivae are glassy.	Same as plane 2.
7	Stage IV (Overdose or respiratory paralysis)	Cessation of respiration. Extreme relaxation of skeletal musculature. Death in few minutes if respiration not restored.	Eyes fixed in mid-line. Pupils dilated and not reactive to light.	

331. DRUGS AFFECTING THE NEUROMUSCULAR JUNCTION

The use of trade names is for informative purposes only and should not be interpreted as endorsement by the National Academy of Sciences - National Research Council. Values for blocking potency are approximations. For further details on other effects of these drugs, consult appropriate tables.

#	Drug	Animal[1]	Neuromuscular Blocking Potency mg(cation)/kg	LD$_{50}$ mg(cation)/kg	Antagonist or Antidote	Other Effects
1	Decamethylene-1, 10-bis-trimethyl-ammonium dihalide (Decamethonium halide; C.10; Eulissin; Syncurine) $N(CH_3)_3$ | $[CH_2]_{10}$ -2X | $N(CH_3)_3$	Man	0.02-0.025		Hexa- or pentamethonium.	Cardiovascular.
2		Cat	0.015-0.018		Hexa- or pentamethonium, stilbazolinium salts.	
3		Monkey	0.125		Hexa- or pentamethonium.	
4		Mouse	0.35	0.4-0.5		
5		Rabbit	0.04-0.09		Hexa- or pentamethonium.	Anticholinesterase; muscarinic.
6		Rat	1.25	1.5		
7		Chick	0.025			Contracture.
8		Frog[2]	5.5-6.2	>123	Hexa- or pentamethonium.	
9	Dihydro-β-erythroidine ($C_{16}H_{21}NO_3$)	Man	0.7-1.4			Hypotensive; bradycardia.
10		Cat[3]		1.8-2.7		
11		Dog				Bradycardia.
12		Mouse[3]		8.4	Neostigmine.	
13		Rabbit[3]		9-18		
14		Rat[3]		207		
15		Frog[2]	0.45			
16	Triethiodide of 1,2,3-tri(diethyl-aminoethoxy)benzene (Flaxedil; Gallamine triethiodide) $C_6H_3[O-CH_2-CH_2-N(C_2H_5)_3]_3$ ·3I	Man	0.45-0.6		Neostigmine, tensilon.	Histamine release; parasympathetic.
17		Cat	0.3-1.1			
18		Dog	0.25	0.5	Tensilon.	
19		Mouse	1.2	1.9-2.7		
20		Rabbit	0.2-0.3	0.4	Neostigmine.	
21		Rat		3.3		Histamine release.
22		Frog[2]	6 and 36			
23	Decamethylene bis-[1-(3',4'-dimeth-oxybenzyl)-6,7-dimethoxy-2-methyl-1,2,3,4-tetrahydroisoquin-olinium]dimethosulfate (Laudolissin) $C_{54}H_{80}N_2O_{16}S_2$	Man	0.1		Neostigmine.	Histamine release.
24		Cat	0.1			Ganglion blocking.
25		Mouse	0.2	0.35		
26		Rabbit	0.02	0.04	Neostigmine.	
27		Rat	1.05	1.8		
28		Chick	0.25			
29	2,5-bis-(3-Diethylaminopropylamino)-benzoquinone-bis-benzyl chloride (Mytolon chloride; Win 2747; Benzo-quinonium chloride) $C_{34}H_{50}N_4O_2Cl_2$	Man	0.06-0.24			Bradycardia, salivation bronchorrhea.
30		Cat[4]	9.5	11.7		
31		Dog	0.1		Neostigmine.	
32		Mouse[3]	0.5	1.4(0.5 i.v.)		
33		Rabbit	0.025	0.04	Neostigmine.	
34		Rat		1.1		
35	bis-(Trimethylammonium-ethyl)succinate dihalide; Dimethohalide of bis-2-Dimethylaminoethyl succinate (Suxamethonium halide; Succinyl-choline; Succinoylcholine; Scoline; Brevedil M; Celocurine; Anectine; Lysthenon; Curacit) $CH_2-CO-O-CH_2-CH_2-N(CH_3)_3$ | ·2 halide $CH_2-CO-O-CH_2-CH_2-N(CH_3)_3$	Man	0.1-0.3		Plasmacholinesterase.	Anticholinesterase; nicotinic; initial stimulation of muscular contraction.
36		Cat	0.05-0.1			Nicotinic; initial stimulation of muscular contraction.
37		Dog	0.1	0.15	Plasmacholinesterase.	Anticholinesterase.
38		Mouse	0.05-0.1	0.25		
39		Rabbit	0.1	0.5		
40		Sparrow	5.0	10.0		Contracture.
41		Frog[2]	2.5			Nicotinic; contracture.
42	bis-(Dimethylethylammonium ethyl)succinate dihalide, or Diethohalide of bis-2-dimethylaminoethyl succinate (Suxethonium halide; Brevedil E; Tachycurine; 362.I.S.; M115; M and B 2210) $CH_2-CO-O-CH_2-CH_2-N(CH_3)_2C_2H_5$ | ·2 halide $CH_2-CO-O-CH_2-CH_2-N(CH_3)_2C_2H_5$	Man	0.5-13			
43		Dog	0.08-0.25	0.17	Plasmacholinesterase.	Anticholinesterase.
44		Rabbit	0.45	0.84		
45		Frog[2]	14.0			
46	Toxiferine I chloride (C-Toxiferine I chloride) $C_{20}H_{23}N_2OCl$ ·3H_2O	Man				Histamine release.
47		Cat	0.003-0.018	0.018	Neostigmine.	Ganglion blocking; salivation.
48		Dog	0.005			
49		Mouse	0.005-0.009	0.01		
50		Rabbit	0.004-0.01	0.007		
51		Frog[2]	0.005-0.013			
52	d-Tubocurarine chloride (Tubarine) $C_{38}H_{44}N_2O_6Cl_2 \cdot 5H_2O$	Man	0.08-0.19		Neostigmine, tensilon.	Cardiovascular; histamine release.
53		Cat	0.12-0.23			Histamine release; ganglion blocking.
54		Dog	0.08-0.15	0.38	Tensilon.	Ganglion blocking.
55		Monkey	0.06			
56		Mouse	0.06-0.09	0.11-0.15		
57		Rabbit	0.09-0.15	0.165	Neostigmine.	Ganglion blocking.
58		Rat	0.04-0.06	0.08		Histamine release.
59		Chick	0.13			
60		Frog[2]	1.4, 4.1 and 7.5	>20.0	Acetylcholine.	
61	d-O,O-Dimethyltubocurarine iodide (Dimethyl ether of d-tubocurarine iodide; Dimethine; Metubine) $C_{40}H_{48}N_2O_6I_2 \cdot 3H_2O$	Man	0.027		Tensilon, neostigmine.	
62		Cat	0.02			Ganglion blocking; histamine release.
63		Mouse	0.08-0.1	0.16		
64		Rabbit	0.01-0.015	0.02	Neostigmine.	
65		Rat	0.009	0.025-0.03	Neostigmine.	Histamine release.
66		Frog[2]	0.94	14.4		

/1/ Unless otherwise indicated, drug administered by intravenous injection. /2/ Ventral lymph sac injection. /3/ Subcutaneous injection.
/4/ Oral administration.

Data presented in this table are substantiated by experimental and clinical evidence. Except in a few instances, and so indicated, unauthenticated

	Characteristic	Gaseous Agents		
		Nitrous Oxide	Ethylene	Cyclopropane
	Physical and Chemical Characteristics			
1	Chemical formula	N_2O	$H_2C=CH_2$	$H_2C \overset{CH_2}{\diagdown} CH_2$
2	Molecular weight	44.02	28.05	42.08
3	Color, odor, taste	Colorless, odorless, tasteless or sweet.	Colorless, slightly sweet.	Colorless, odor like petroleum benzene, pungent.
4	Specific gravity[4]	1.53	0.97	1.45
5	Boiling point, $^{\circ}C$	-89	-103.9	-37
6	Range of flammability in[5]: Air	Not flammable, but supports combustion.	3.05-28.6%.	2.45-10.45%.
7	Oxygen		3.10-79.9%.	2.48-60.00%.
8	Stability to alkali[6]	Stable.	Stable.	Stable.
9	$\frac{Oil}{Blood}$ Ratio[7]	$\frac{0.437}{0.412}=1.06$	$\frac{1.599}{0.123}=13$	$\frac{6.99}{0.457}=15.3$
10	Potency[8], %	25	30	100
11	Methods of administration[9]	Semi-closed, closed.	Semi-closed, closed.	Closed.
12	Induction time[10], average	Less than 5 min without hypoxia.	2-3 min without hypoxia.	2-5 min.
13	Recovery time[11], average	Rapid, 2-3 min.	Rapid, 2 min.	Immediate to 15 min.
14	Concentration in inspired air for[12]: Analgesia, %	20-40	25-35	4-6
15	Surgery, %	85-90	80-85	13-25
16	Respiratory arrest, %	Not without anoxia.	Not without anoxia.	40
17	Blood concentration for[12]: Surgery	23.3 vol %.	11.2-12.6 vol %.	4.5-9.1 vol %; 16-20 mg %.
18	Respiratory arrest	Not without anoxia.	Not without anoxia.	39 vol %; 30 mg %.
19	Routes of elimination[13]	Lungs, small quantity through skin.	Lungs, small quantity through skin.	Lungs, small quantity through skin.
	Physiological Effects[14]			
20	Respiratory center	Not affected.[15]	Not affected.	Decreased response to carbon dioxide; decreased minute volume.
21	Carotid body	Not affected.[15]	Not affected.[15]	Not affected.[15]
22	Larynx	Reflex not abolished; no spasm without hypoxia.	Reflex not abolished; no spasm without hypoxia.	Frequent laryngospasm.
23	Cilia	None without hypoxia.	Initial stimulation.	
24	Bronchi	Minimal bronchoconstriction or not affected.	Not affected.	Tends to produce bronchoconstriction.
25	Carotid sinus	Increased sensitivity or not affected.	Little effect.	Little effect.
26	Heart	None without hypoxia.	None without hypoxia.	Bradycardia, A-V nodal rhythm, ventricular extrasystoles, ventricular tachycardia, ventricular fibrillation, reduction in cardiac reserve.

/1/ Marketed as Vinethene which has added to it 3.5% alcohol to decrease its rate of vaporization, and 0.01% phenyl-α-naphthylamine as a preservbe an improvement over diethyl ether. /3/ Stabilized with 0.01% thymol and tinted (for anesthetic use) to distinguish it from chloroform which has /5/ Range of inflammability for all inflammable agents lies within the anesthetic range. Non-inflammable agents either support combustion or prodroxide and calcium hydroxide, is used to absorb CO_2 in all closed systems. /7/ A loose term, sometimes refers to water or blood, or to vegetion is a partial function of the oil:blood ratio. /8/ A relative term indicating the ability of an anesthetic agent to take a patient from consciousness ularly the central nervous system. There is a progressive brain depression from cortex to lower centers, followed by an ascending paralysis of the administration of a volatile anesthetic by dropping the agent on a gauze-covered wire-mesh face mask. "Semi-open" is the same technique, with the rebreathes the same mixture of gas with suitable means for the absorption of carbon dioxide and the introduction of a continuous supply of oxygen and tion" is the blowing of the anesthetic vapor and oxygen into the pharynx or trachea in sufficient quantity and rate to maintain anesthesia. /10/ Averdividual metabolism, rate and depth of ventilation, cardiovascular system, effect of previously administered drugs, addiction to barbiturates or ation and average depth of anesthesia--particularly the depth at termination of surgery--effective ventilation, status of the cardiovascular system, oxide. /12/ Concentrations to produce a given plane of anesthesia vary considerably from individual to individual. Each patient must be carefully end products, probably related to the metabolism of chloroform and trichlorethylene, have been discovered in the urine. /14/ Those listed presupautonomic blocking agents, sympathicomimetic agents, endocrines, and muscle relaxants, significantly modify these effects. /15/ No data availamong anesthesiologists.

impressions and opinions have not been included. Blank spaces indicate unavailability of data.

Diethyl Ether	Divinyl Oxide[1]	n-Propyl Methyl Ether[2]	Chloroform	Trichlorethylene[3]	Ethyl Chloride	
Volatile Agents						
Physical and Chemical Characteristics						
$C_2H_5-O-C_2H_5$	$CH_2=CH-O-CH=CH_2$	$C_3H_7-O-CH_3$	$CHCl_3$	$HClC=CCl_2$	CH_3CH_2Cl	1
74.12	70.09	74.08	119.39	131.40	64.52	2
Colorless, pungent, irritating, sweetish, burning.	Colorless, odor like garlic.	Colorless, ethereal, unpleasant, non-irritating.	Colorless, ethereal, burning, sweet.	Colorless, similar to chloroform.	Colorless, ethereal, burning.	3
0.713-0.716 / 2.56	0.767-0.771 / 2.2	0.726	1.474-1.478 / 4.12	1.456-1.462 / 4.53	0.921 / 2.23	4
35	28-31	39	61	86-88	12-13	5
1.85-25.9%	1.70-27.0%	Same as diethyl ether.	Not flammable, but produces phosgene near naked flames.	Not flammable in air, but products of decomposition explosive.	4.0-14.8%	6
2.1-82.0%	1.8-85.0%			10.3-64.5%	4.05-67.2%	7
Stable.	Stable.		Little decomposition under anesthetic conditions; some carbon monoxide produced.	Decomposes, producing dichloracetylene and phosgene.	Hydrolysed slowly by alkali.	8
4.1	41.3	10±1	$\frac{147.5-275.0}{1.42-2.77}=99.1-103.5$	34.4	15.3	9
100	100	100	100	25-30	100	10
Open; semi-open; closed; semi-closed; insufflation, rectally.	Open; semi-open; closed; semi-closed.	Open; semi-open; closed; semi-closed; insufflation.	Open; semi-open; closed(?); semi-closed; insufflation.	Semi-closed; rectally.	Open; semi-open; closed.	11
10-15 min.	15 sec-5 min; average one min.	5 min.	5 min.	Difficult induction 5-10 min.	15 sec-5 min; average one min.	12
½-2 hr.	Rapid, almost immediate on discontinuing agent.	Prolonged up to 3 hr.	½-1 hr.	2-5 min.	Rapid, almost immediate.	13
	Almost impossible to produce.			0.5	2-3	14
6.1-13.7 vol %.	3.9		0.67	5.0-7.5	3.6-4.5	15
	10-12				6	16
120 mg %.	11-18 mg %.	40-70 mg %.	9.2 mg %.		20-30 mg %.	17
154 mg %.	68 mg %.		>16.5 mg %.		40 mg %.	18
87% by lungs; remainder in urine, perspiration and by exposed serous surfaces.	Lungs, small amount in urine.	Probably same as diethyl ether.	98% by lungs; some in urine possibly as trichlormethyl-glucoronate.	Lungs, urine.	Exclusively through lungs.	19
Physiological Effects[14]						
Decreased response to carbon dioxide; increased minute volume.	Stimulated in minimal dosage.	Irregular, fairly quiet respirations.	Depressed.	Tachypnea and shallow irregular breathing in deep planes; sudden respiratory arrest.	Depressed.	20
Markedly depressed.			Remains active[15].			21
Laryngospasm caused by direct irritant effect.	Laryngospasm infrequently.		Laryngospasm caused by high concentrations.	Minimal tendency to laryngospasm.	Infrequent laryngospasm.	22
Possibly initial stimulation, later decrease in activity.			Decreased activity.			23
Bronchodilatation.	Bronchodilatation.		Bronchodilatation.			24
Markedly depressed in deep planes.	Stimulated in light planes; depressed in deep planes.		Stimulated to 1%; but depressed by higher concentrations.			25
Auricular extrasystoles, A-V nodal tachycardia; in deep planes dilatation and decreased force of contraction.	A-V nodal tachycardia or no notable cardiac effect.	No change in electrocardiogram.	Ventricular extrasystoles, nodal and ventricular rhythms, ventricular tachycardia; incidence increased by adrenalin, overdosage, and anoxemia.	Nodal rhythm, ventricular extrasystoles, pulsus bigeminus.	Increase in cardiac irritability during induction; myocardial depression; slight decrease in cardiac output.	26

ative. /2/ Included here as an example of a recent product developed in the search for an ideal anesthetic agent, although it has not proved itself to
a similar odor. /4/ Water and air are the reference points and in each case equal unity. Upper figures of the volatile agents are the liquid phase.
duce toxic products in the presence of a flame. /6/ A mixture of sodium hydroxide and calcium hydroxide, or of barium hy-
table oils or brain lipids. The significance herein is that the rapidity of induction is a partial function of the air:blood ratio, and the rate of desatura-
to death without hypoxia, according to the accepted stages and planes (see Table 330). Anesthetic agents produce a depression of all tissues, partic-
spinal cord.   The respiratory and cardiovascular centers function until death is produced by an agent of 100% potency. /9/ "Open" means
addition of an occlusive material wrapped about the face mask to increase the concentration of the vapor. "Closed" is the method in which the patient
anesthetic agent. "Semi-closed" is the same technique except that expiration partly escapes into the atmosphere via an exhalation valve. "Insuffla-
age induction time depends on several factors including the following: chemical or physiological properties and concentration of the anesthetic, in-
narcotics, and experience of the anesthetist. /11/ Average recovery time is related to many factors including, fat solubility of the anesthetic, dur-
accidents during the anesthesia (such as the aspiration of pus, blood, or vomitus), bouts of severe hypoxia, and persistent accumulation of carbon di-
equilibrated with the anesthetic. /13/ It is assumed that many anesthetic agents are excreted, principally by way of the lungs, unchanged. However,
pose administration of a single agent with adequate oxygen and without accumulation of carbon dioxide. Other drugs, such as metabolic depressants,
able in the literature or available data sketchy and based on clinical impression or animal experiments. Statements are from consensus of opinion

Data presented in this table are substantiated by experimental and clinical evidence. Except in a few instances, and so indicated, unauthenticated

Characteristic		Gaseous Agents		
		Nitrous Oxide	Ethylene	Cyclopropane
Physiological Effects[14] (concluded)				
27	Eyeball activity	Present, becomes fixed in prolonged anesthesia.	Present at all times.	Fixed in 2nd to 3rd plane.
28	Pupillary size[16]	Dilated, becomes constricted in prolonged anesthesia.	No effect.	Constricted, becomes dilated in 3rd plane
29	Salivary glands	None without hypoxia.	None without hypoxia.	90% increase in secretion during induction.
30	Liver	Retention of bromsulfthalein for few post-operative days.	None without hypoxia.	Bromsulfthalein may be retained from 15-30% post-operatively, bile secretion increased.
31	Kidney	None without hypoxia.	None without hypoxia.	31% decrease glomerular filtration, 52% decrease renal plasma flow, 35% increase filtration fraction; slight decrease urine flow; increased tubular reabsorption.
32	Spleen	Not affected.[15]	Not affected.[15]	Dilated.[15]
33	Adrenals	No secretion without hypoxia.	No secretion without hypoxia.[15]	Some secretion of adrenalin (cats).
34	Stomach and intestines	Slight increase in peristalsis followed by decreased tone in recovery period.	Decreased gastric secretion and gastric emptying time; little effect, in deeper planes inhibition of peristalsis.	Little effect; in deeper planes inhibition of peristalsis; some increase in tone; some spasm of colonic muscles.
35	Uterus	Contractions essentially unaltered.	Slight decrease in strength of contractions.	Decreased strength of contractions.
36	Skeletal muscles	Inadequate relaxation.	Moderate relaxation.	Adequate muscle relaxation obtainable.
37	Blood volume[17]	Increased because of increase in red cell mass.	No significant change.[15]	Increased because of increase in red cell mass.
38	Body temperature	Not affected.[15]	Slight fall caused by muscular relaxation.	Skin temperature tends to rise.
39	Peripheral blood vessels	Vasodilatation.	Vasodilatation.	Vasodilatation; in capillaries rapid restricted flow and increased vasomotion.
40	Autonomic effect	None.	Not sympatheticomimetic, not parasympatheticomimetic.	Parasympatheticomimetic, late adrenolytic effect(?).
41	Metabolic rate	Decreased.	Decreased.	Decreased.
42	Acid base balance	None without anoxia.	None without anoxia.	Respiratory acidosis occurs; clinically unimportant tendency for fixed acids to rise.
43	Special features	Should not be used in conjunction with hypoxia.	Absence of sweating.	Post-anesthetic hypotension and delirium; concurrent use of epinephrine may lead to ventricular tachycardia and fibrillation.

/1/ Marketed as Vinethene which has added to it 3.5% alcohol to decrease its rate of vaporization, and 0.01% phenyl-α-naphthylamine as a preservbe an improvement over diethyl ether. /3/ Stabilized with 0.01% thymol and tinted (for anesthetic use) to distinguish it from chloroform which has drugs, such as metabolic depressants, autonomic blocking agents, sympathicomimetic agents, endocrines, and muscle relaxants, significantly modify are from consensus of opinion among anesthesiologists. /16/ May be modified by a narcotic, a barbiturate, or a belladonna derivative used in preand blood during surgery. Maintenance of body temperatures during surgery is also a factor in fluid shifts from one body compartment to another.

impressions and opinions have not been included. Blank spaces indicate unavailability of data.

		Volatile Agents				
Diethyl Ether	Divinyl Oxide[1]	n-Propyl Methyl Ether[2]	Chloroform	Trichlorethylene[3]	Ethyl Chloride	
		Physiological Effects[14] (concluded)				
Present plane 1; fixed plane 2.	Rhythmic activity in light stage III.	Eyeballs may remain eccentric in plane 4.	Strabismus in light planes.	Nystagmus during induction and recovery.	Rotate into plane 3.	27
Dilated stage II, constricted plane 1; dilated plane 3.	Pupillary reflex to light remains active.	Pupils may remain constricted in plane 4.	Dilated in stage II.	Usually constricted in surgical plane.	Dilated in light planes.	28
550% increase in secretion during induction, depressed in surgical plane.	Profuse salivation.	Increased secretion in some patients.	500% increase in secretion during induction.	Not stimulated.	Little secretion.	29
Bromsulfthalein may be retained from 15-30% post-operatively; bile secretion decreased.	No impairment in obstetrics after one hr of anesthesia; no impairment bile secretion; possible liver damage in humans; liver necrosis in dogs.	No histologic damage in dog, rat, and monkey.	Greater retention of bromsulfthalein and higher cephalin flocculation postoperatively than with other agents. Can be markedly damaging, and acute yellow atrophy may occur especially with hypoxia.	Clinically non-toxic; no histologic changes noted.	Jaundice and fatty degeneration noted after repeated administration.	30
21% decrease glomerular filtration, 39% decrease renal plasma flow, 25% increase filtration fraction, 51% decrease urine flow, increased tubular reabsorption.	Oliguria or anuria, with decreased urea clearances in dogs.	No histologic damage in dog, rat, and monkey.	Decrease in urea clearance and changes in other tests similar to those obtained with other agents.	No histologic changes noted.		31
Constricted			Constricted			32
Adrenalin secretion stimulated.	No stimulation of adrenalin secretion.		Effect undecided.			33
Decreased peristalsis, decreased tone, decreased colonic contractions.	Increased tone and decreased peristalsis of stomach; decreased tone and peristalsis of intestines, decreased colonic contractions.		Decreased peristalsis, decreased colonic contractions.		Spasm of colonic muscles.	34
Decreased contractions.	Contractions not decreased.		Marked decrease in strength of contractions.	Little effect.		35
Adequate relaxation; sensitizes myoneural junction to curare.	Adequate relaxation in proper plane.	Excellent relaxation in 2nd plane.	Excellent relaxation.	Usually inadequate relaxation.	Usually inadequate relaxation.	36
Increased with some decrease of plasma volume and increase of red cell mass.			Decreased.[15]			37
Usually decreased but patient poikilothermic.			Decreased.	Decreased.		38
Vasodilatation; in capillaries rapid unrestricted flow and decreased vasomotion.			Vasodilatation.	Constriction of vessels, relatively less capillary bleeding.	Vasodilatation.	39
Sympathicomimetic.	Sympathicomimetic[15] in some respects.		Sympathicomimetic.	May increase vagal tone.		40
Decreased.			Decreased.			41
Tendency for metabolic acidosis to occur.	Minimal disturbance of acid-base balance.		May result in metabolic acidosis.			42
Convulsions occasionally occur during narcosis probably associated with hypoxia or hypercardia.	Convulsions during induction, maintenance, or recovery in unpremedicated patients. Running movements in dogs.	Overdose produces marked depression of blood pressure.	Sudden death from ventricular fibrillation or arrest may occur during induction.	Convulsions may occur in children under 2 yr, specific anesthesia of 5th cranial nerve.	Ventricular fibrillation may occur during induction.	43

ative. /2/ Included here as an example of a recent product developed in the search for an ideal anesthetic agent, although it has not proved itself to a similar odor. /14/ Those listed presuppose administration of a single agent with adequate oxygen and without accumulation of carbon dioxide. Other these effects. /15/ No data available in the literature, or available data sketchy and based on clinical impression or animal experiments. Statements medication. /17/ These studies were done primarily on animals before literature appeared concerning adequate replacement of fluid, electrolytes,

The use of certain trade names is for informative purposes only and in no way is intended to imply

Part I: SPECIFIC HEMODYNAMIC

Values are per cent increase or decrease from level before administration of drug and are ranges or averages of effects on groups of subjects includ-
- = decreases; 0 = unchanged; ? = questionable. In some instances drugs are listed with no accompanying data. Other information, however, is pre-
in the column headings: MABP = mean systemic arterial pressure; Car. O = cardiac output; TSVR = total systemic vascular resistance; Cer. BF =
limb vessels; RBF = renal blood flow; RVR = renal vascular resistance; Hep. BF = hepatic blood flow; Hep. VR = hepatic vascular resistance; PABP =
vessels; Cor. BF = coronary blood flow; Cor. VR = coronary vascular resistance; Car. O_2 = cardiac oxygen uptake; Car. R = cardiac rate; Car. Ex. =

	Drug	MABP	Car. O.	TSVR	Cer. BF	Cer. VR	Cer. O_2	LBF	LELV	RBF
1	Acetazoleamide									
2	Acetylcholine									
3	Aconitine									
4	Alkavervir				-12	-28	+17			
5	Alseroxylon									
6	Ambonestyl									
7	Aminophylline	+7 to +8	+6 to +33	-4 to -19	-25 to -33	+8 to +24	0 to -18			+12 to +30
8	Ammonium chloride			+26 to +44	-21	+23	+5			
9	Amobarbital sodium	-8 to -13	-26							
10	Amphetamine sulfate				-2	+4	+4			
11	Amyl nitrite									
12	Atropine sulfate							+	Dilates	
13	Azamethonium bromide	-8	+23		-8 to 12	-20 to -35	+7 to +10	+	0	0 to -8
14	Azepetine phosphate							+		-7
15	Barium chloride									
16	Benzathine penicillin G									
17	Bishydroxycoumarin									
18	Caffeine and sodium benzoate				-13	+22 to +28	+8 to +9			
19	Calcium chloride									
20	Carbachol	-7	+12	-17						
21	Chloralose									
22	Chlorisondamine dimethochloride							+		
23	Chloroform									
24	Chloroquine diphosphate									
25	Chlorpromazine				-9	-24	+4			
26	Cocaine									
27	Corticotropin				0	0	-14			
28	Cortisone acetate	+	0							
29	Cyanocobalamin				-56	+177	+22			
30	Cyclopentamine									
31	Cyclopropane	0	0	0						
32	Deslanoside									
33	Desoxycorticosterone acetate				-5	+6	-10			
34	Dextran									
35	Dextroamphetamine sulfate									
36	Dibenamine hydrochloride	-6 to -9	-6 to +28	-4						
37	Digifolin									
38	Digilanid									
39	Digitalis	-5 to +	-2 to +46	-32 to +3	-4	-9	+13			
40	Digitoxin									
41	Digoxin	0 to +8	-15 to +29	-28 to 7						+12 to +19
42	Dihydroergocornine methanesulfonate				0 to -8	-12 to -31	-8 to +3	+	Constr.	
43	Dihydroergotamine methanesulfonate	+3	0	+45						
44	β-Dihydrosolasodine									
45	Diphenhydramine hydrochloride									
46	Diphenylhydantoin sodium									
47	1,1-Dimethyl-4-phenyl-piperazinium I									
48	Dioxyline phosphate									
49	Ephedrine sulfate	+10	+27	-13						
50	Epinephrine bitartrate	+ or -	+33 to +52	-35	-4 to +22	0	-3 to +28	+	Dil/constr.	-10 to -55
51	Erythrityl tetranitrate									
52	Ether	-5	+71 to +100	-44						
53	Ethyl alcohol	0	-5		-18 to +18	-35 to +12	-10 to +16	+	Dilates	
54	Ethyl chloride									
55	α-Fagarine									
56	Gelatin, 6% solution									
57	Gitalin									
58	Glyceryl trinitrate	0	+		-8	-4	-3			
59	Heparin				-3	0	+4			
60	Hexamethonium bromide or chloride	-20 to -35	-46 to +38	-12 to -60	-4 to -42	-11 to -45	-12 to +4	0 or +	0	-59 to +17
61	Histamine diphosphate				0	-30	+6		Dilates	+28
62	Hydergine	-4	0	-5				+	Constr.	-11 to +5
63	Hydralazine	-10 to -41	+27 to +110	-31 to -61				0 or +	Dilates	-30 to +38
64	Hydroxyamphetamine hydrobromide	+30	0	+						
65	Inositol hexanitrate									
66	Insulin			+11 to +16	-6 to -13	-21 to -42				
67	Isoproterenol hydrochloride	+ to -	+26					+	dilates	
68	Khellin	+5	0/-6							
69	Lanatoside c	+								
70	Levarterenol bitartrate	+15 to +30	-6 to +32	+12 to +31	-8 to -21	-8 to +53	-5 to -15	0	Constr.	-47 to +181
71	Lobeline									
72	Magnesium sulfate									-10
73	Mannitol hexanitrate									
74	Mecamylamine hydrochloride									-21
75	Meperidine									
76	Mephentermine sulfate	+	0	+						

/1/ Caffeine citrate.

endorsement by the National Academy of Sciences-National Research Council for use of the drug.

AND CARDIAC EFFECTS

ing hyper-, hypo-, and normotensive persons. Where quantitative data are not available, direction of action is indicated as follows: + = increases; sented in Parts II, III, and IV of this table where the drugs are identified by their number in Part I. The following abbreviations have been employed cerebral blood pressure; Cer. VR = cerebral vascular resistance; Cer. O_2 = cerebral oxygen uptake; LBF = limb blood flow; LELV = local effect on pulmonary arterial blood pressure; Pul. BF = pulmonary blood flow; Pul. VR = pulmonary vascular resistance; LEPV = local effects on pulmonary cardiac excitability; Car. RP = cardiac refractory period; Car. CT = cardiac conduction time; Car. Con. = cardiac contractility.

RVR	Hep. BF	Hep. VR	PABP	Pul. BF	Pul. VR	LEPV	Cor. BF.	Cor. VR	Car. O_2	Car. R	Car. Ex.	Car. RP	Car. CT	Car. Con.	#
															1
			+ or 0			Constr.	+128	-59		+ or -	+	-	+ or -		2
											+				3
															4
															5
											-	+			6
			+ to -25	+6 to +33	-37 to +4	Dilates	+1 to +76	-		+				+	7
															8
															9
										+				+	10
			0			+ to -	+20	-							11
										+	-	+	+ or -		12
-12 to -23															13
															14
											+			+	15
															16
															17
										+[1]			+[1]		18
											+			+	19
												+			20
															21
0	-														22
		+									+			-	23
											-	+			24
											-				25
															26
															27
															28
															29
															30
											+			-	31
															32
															33
			+50	+36											34
															35
			-21 to -27	-6 to +7	-17 to -34	?				-					36
															37
															38
			-40	+46	-					-	+ or -	+ or -	+	+	39
															40
			-12 to +7	0 to +29		0									41
															42
															43
			+28 to +38	0	+41 to +45	0				-	-				44
											-	+			45
											-				46
															47
															48
										+				+ or -	49
+270	+107		+20	+30	+ or -	Constr.	+35	-		+ or -	+ or -	-	+ or -	+	50
														-	51
											-				52
	+45														53
							+60 to +117	-46 to -57	+1						54
											-	+	+		55
															56
															57
							+10 to +80	-			-			+	58
															59
															60
-55 to +14	-28 to -33	+5	-14 to -35	0 to -16	-35 to +21	0	-14 to -15	- to +3	+2						61
-			+			Constr.	+128	-59							62
-8			0	0	0	0									63
	+34 to +58	-41 to -56	-9 to +45	+25 to +110	-60 to +27		+34	-35	-5						64
			+												65
															66
						Dilates				+	0				67
			0 to -4	0 to -6	0	0	+	-							68
			+ or -	+	-	0									69
										+ or -	+				70
-7 to +270	0 to -32	0 to +	+33	-6	0	Constr.									71
															72
															73
															74
0											-				75
			+	0	+									+	76

The use of certain trade names is for informative purposes only and in no way is intended to imply

Part I: SPECIFIC HEMODYNAMIC

Values are per cent increase or decrease from level before administration of drug and are ranges or averages of effects on groups of subjects includ-
- = decreases; 0 = unchanged; ? = questionable. In some instances drugs are listed with no accompanying data. Other information, however, is pre-
in the column headings: MABP = mean systemic arterial pressure; Car. O = cardiac output; TSVR = total systemic vascular resistance; Cer. BF =
limb vessels; RBF = renal blood flow; RVR = renal vascular resistance; Hep. BF = hepatic blood flow; Hep. VR = hepatic vascular resistance; PABP =
vessels; Cor. BF = coronary blood flow; Cor. VR = coronary vascular resistance; Car. O_2 = cardiac oxygen uptake; Car. R = cardiac rate; Car. Ex. =

	Drug	MABP	Car. O	TSVR	Cer. BF	Cer. VR	Cer. O_2	LBF	LELV	RBF
77	Merraluride sodium									
78	Mercurophylline sodium									
79	Mersalyl sodium		+19							
80	Metaraminol bitartrate	+50	0	+55	-9	+50	-6			-4
81	Methacholine chloride	-7	+29							
82	Methamphetamine hydrochloride							0	Dilates	
83	Methantheline bromide									
84	Methoxamine hydrochloride	+	-30	+						
85	Methoxyphenamine hydrochloride									
86	Methylhexeneamine									
87	Morphine									
88	Naphazoline hydrochloride									
89	Nicotine									
90	Nicotinic acid	1(?)	-4		+6	+9	-3	-	Dilates	
91	Nikethamide									
92	Nitrous oxide									
93	Nordefrine									
94	Oenanthyl hydrochloride									
95	Ouabain									
96	Papaverine hydrochloride				+8 to +12	-17 to -22	0 to +4			
97	Parephyllin				-4	+3	+23			-13 to -18
98	Pentaerythritol tetranitrate									
99	Pentamethonium chloride	-11	+29					+	0	
100	Pentobarbital sodium							+	Dilates	
101	Pentolinium tartrate									
102	Phenobarbital sodium									
103	Phenoxybenzamine hydrochloride				-12	-31	-14	+		+15 to +57
104	Phentolamine HCl or methanesulfonate				0	-21	0	+	Dilates	
105	Phenylephrine hydrochloride	+35	-28	+						
106	Phenylpropanolamine hydrochloride									
107	Phenylpropylmethylamine									
108	Piperoxan hydrochloride									
109	Pituitary extract (posterior)	-2	-2 to -54	-1						
110	Potassium chloride									
111	Potassium thiocyanate									
112	Procaine hydrochloride	- to +2	-2 to +23		-2 to -12	-16 to +8	-3 to -6	+ or -	Dilates	
113	Procaine amide hydrochloride	-17	-11	+5						
114	Procaine penicillin G				+18	-11	+10			
115	Propylhexedrine									
116	Protoveratrines A and B maleate							0	0	-7 to -25
117	Pyrilamine maleate									
118	Quinacrine hydrochloride									
119	Quinidine gluconate									
120	Quinidine hydrochloride									
121	Quinidine sulfate	0 to -25	0 to -4	- to +4						
122	Rauwolfia									
123	Rescinnamine									
124	Reserpine	0 or -	+ or -		-2	-17	-3			0
125	Roniacol tartrate							0		
126	Scillaren A									
127	Scillaren B									
128	Scopolamine hydrobromide									
129	Serotonin	+	+30	-3						
130	Sodium bicarbonate				+30 to +69	-25 to -39	-6 to +8			
131	Sodium chloride				0 to +12	-6 to -7	0 to -8			
132	Sodium cyanide									+4
133	Sodium lactate									
134	Sodium nitrite	-3 to -5	+10 to +21	-13 to -15						
135	Sodium salicylate	+3	+14							
136	Sodium sulfide									
137	Sodium thiocyanate	0	-18	+						
138	Strophanthin									
139	Succinylcholine chloride									
140	Synephrine									
141	Tetraethylammonium chloride or Br	-5 to -21	-32 to +35	-27 to -28				+	+ or -	
142	Thiamine hydrochloride									
143	Thiopental sodium	-4 to -19	-20 to -25	0 to +4	-25 to +11	-19	0 to -39			
144	Thiouracil				-13	+31	-14			
145	Tolazoline hydrochloride	+8	+28		-12 to +22	-25 to +6	-3	+	Dilates	
146	Trichlorethylene									
147	Triethanolamine trinitrate $BiPO_4$									
148	Trimetaphen camphorsulfonate	-5 to -38	-18 to -19	-8 to -22						0 to -18
149	Trimethadione									
150	Tripelennamine hydrochloride									
151	Tuaminoheptane sulfate									
152	Tubocurarine chloride								Dilates	
153	Urethane									

endorsement by the National Academy of Sciences-National Research Council for use of the drug.
AND CARDIAC EFFECTS (Continued)
ing hyper-, hypo-, and normotensive persons. Where quantitative data are not available, direction of action is indicated as follows: + = increases;
sented in Parts II, III, and IV of this table where the drugs are identified by their number in Part I. The following abbreviations have been employed
cerebral blood pressure; Cer. VR = cerebral vascular resistance; Cer. O_2 = cerebral oxygen uptake; LBF = limb blood flow; LELV = local effect on
pulmonary arterial blood pressure; Pul. BF = pulmonary blood flow; Pul. VR = pulmonary vascular resistance; LEPV = local effects on pulmonary
cardiac excitability; Car. RP = cardiac refractory period; Car. CT = cardiac conduction time; Car. Con. = cardiac contractility.

RVR	Hep. BF	Hep. VR	PABP	Pul. BF	Pul. VR	LEPV	Cor. BF.	Cor. VR	Car. O_2	Car. R	Car. Ex.	Car. RP	Car. CT	Car. Con.	
															77
															78
															79
+56			+95	0	+										80
										+ or -	+	-	+ or -		81
											-			+	82
															83
			-	-	-	0	-10 to +	+			0			-	84
															85
															86
	-6	-17													87
															88
															89
															90
							+3 to +45	-	+13						91
														-	92
															93
															94
							-11	+34	+4						95
			+			+1 or -	+20 to +60	-			-	+	+		96
															97
															98
															99
															100
															101
											-		-		102
-31 to -50															103
															104
			+70	-	+						0			0	105
															106
													+		107
													+		108
			+	-54	+	+ or -									109
											+ or 0		+		110
															111
	-24 to -33	+1 to +7	-17 to -34	-16 to -31			-52	+7	-53	+	-				112
			-	-11		0				+	-	+ or 0	+		113
															114
															115
+ or -															116
															117
															118
															119
															120
										+	-	+	+ or -	-	121
															122
															123
											-		-		124
															125
															126
															127
															128
			+	+/-	+50	constr.									129
															130
			+66	+19											131
															132
															133
			-10 to -18	+10 to +11	-19 to -20	+ or 0									134
															135
															136
															137
							-1 to +9	-3 to -5	-5 to +24						138
															139
															140
															141
			-3 to -29	-32 to +12	+ to -35	0				+	+				142
											0			-	143
															144
											-				145
											+				146
															147
-36 to +33															148
															149
															150
											+		+		151
															152
													-		153

The use of certain trade names is for informative purposes only and in no way is intended to imply

Part I: SPECIFIC HEMODYNAMIC

Values are per cent increase or decrease from level before administration of drug and are ranges or averages of effects on groups of subjects includ-
- = decreases; 0 = unchanged; ? = questionable. In some instances drugs are listed with no accompanying data. Other information, however, is pre-
in the column headings: MABP = mean systemic arterial pressure; Car. O = cardiac output; TSVR = total systemic vascular resistance; Cer. BF =
limb vessels; RBF = renal blood flow; RVR = renal vascular resistance; Hep. BF = hepatic blood flow; Hep. VR = hepatic vascular resistance; PABP =
vessels; Cor. BF = coronary blood flow; Cor. VR = coronary vascular resistance; Car. O_2 = cardiac oxygen uptake; Car. R = cardiac rate; Car. Ex. =

	Drug	MABP	Car. O	TSVR	Cer. BF	Cer. VR	Cer. O_2	LBF	LELV	RBF
154	Urginin									
155	Veratramine									
156	Veratridine									
157	Veratrone	-11 to -14	0	-6 to -21				-	0	-
158	Vergitryl									
159	Vertavis									
160	Vinyl ether									

Part II: SITES OF ACTION

Numbers in brackets refer to drugs listed in Part I.

	Site of Action	Stimulant Drugs	Depressant Drugs
	NERVOUS MECHANISMS CONTROLLING CIRCULATION		
	Central Nervous System (Direct Action)		
1	Vasoconstrictor center	Analeptics [18, 91][1].	General anesthetics [23, 31, 52, 54, 92, 143, 146, 160][1].
2	Cardioaccelerator center		
3	Cardioinhibitory center[2]	General anesthetics [23, 31, 52, 54, 92, 143, 146, 160][1].	Analeptics [18, 91][1].
4	Other areas, unidentified	None recognized.	Rauwolfia alkaloids [5, 122, 123, 124]; hydralazine [63]; morphine [87].
	Sensory Receptors in Heart, Lungs, and Blood Vessels		
5	Stretch receptors in carotid sinuses and aortic arch[3]	Activated indirectly, and by local application of sympathomimetics [10, 30, 35, 49, 50, 64, 70, 76, 80, 82, 84, 86, 88, 93, 94, 102, 105, 106, 115, 140, 151]; veratrum alkaloids [4, 116, 157, 158, 159].	Local anesthetics [112]; receptors inactivated indirectly by hypotensive drugs [2, 7, 11, 20, 48, 51, 53, 58, 65, 68, 73, 81, 96, 97, 98, 134, 147].
6	Chemoreceptors in carotid and aortic bodies[4]	Ganglion stimulants [89]; oxidation inhibitors (e.g., cyanide, sulfide) [132]; papaverine [96]; nikethamide [91]; aminophylline [7].	Local application of ganglionic blocking agents [13, 22, 60, 74, 99, 101, 141, 148] depresses action of ganglion stimulants; oxygen inhalation depresses action of cyanide.
7	Stretch receptors in heart, lung parenchyma, blood vessels[5]	Veratrum alkaloids [4, 116, 157, 158, 159].	Local anesthetics [112].
8	Various receptors in respiratory passages and joints[6]	Veratrum alkaloids [4, 116, 157, 158, 159]; low concentration of volatile anesthetics [23, 52, 160].	High concentration of volatile anesthetics [23, 52, 160].

	Site of Action	Stimulant Drugs	Depressant Drugs
	NERVOUS MECHANISMS CONTROLLING CIRCULATION (Concluded)		
	Autonomic Nervous System		
9	Sympathetic[7] and parasympathetic[8] ganglia	Ganglion stimulants [89].	Ganglion-blocking agents [13, 22, 60, 74, 99, 101, 141, 148]; high concentration of nicotine [89].
10	Post-ganglionic nerve terminations: sympathetic[7]	Sympathomimetics [10, 30, 35, 49, 50, 64, 70, 76, 80, 82, 84, 86, 88, 93, 94, 102, 105, 106, 115, 140, 151].	Adrenergic blocking drugs [13, 22, 60, 74, 99, 101, 141, 148].
11	Post-ganglionic nerve terminations: parasympathetic[8]	Parasympathomimetics [2, 20, 81].	Parasympathetic blocking agents [12, 83, 128].
	MUSCULAR COMPONENTS OF CIRCULATORY SYSTEM		
	Smooth Muscle of Blood Vessels		
12	With	Methacholine [81].	Atropine [12].
13	specific antagonist	Histamine [61].	Antihistamines [45, 117, 152].
14	Without specific antagonist	Musculotropic vasoconstrictors [109, 129].	Musculotropic vasodilators [7, 11, 48, 51, 53, 58, 65, 68, 73, 96, 97, 98, 134, 147].
	Heart		
15	Contractility of heart muscle	Digitalis glycosides [32, 37, 38, 39, 40, 41, 57, 69, 95, 126, 127, 138, 154].	Quinidine [121]; general anesthetics [23, 31, 52, 54, 92, 143, 146, 160].
16	Excitability of the heart	Profibrillatory drugs: chloroform [23]; cyclopropane [31].	Antifibrillatory drugs [6, 113, 119, 120, 121]; quinidine [121].

/1/ None selective. /2/ Reciprocal innervation with cardioaccelerator center. /3/ Type 1 receptors producing perfect inhibition of vasoconstrictor, cardioaccelerator, and respiratory centers. /4/ Type 3 receptors producing pure stimulation of vasoconstrictor, cardioaccelerator and respiratory centers. /5/ Type 2 receptors producing imperfect inhibition of vasoconstrictor, cardioaccelerator and respiratory centers. /6/ Type 4 receptors producing impure stimulation of vasoconstrictor, cardioaccelerator and respiratory centers. /7/ Sympathetic stimulation causes cardiac acceleration and constriction of most blood vessels (peripheral). /8/ Parasympathetic stimulation causes cardiac slowing and dilatation of most blood vessels.

CARDIOVASCULAR SYSTEM (Continued)

endorsement by the National Academy of Sciences-National Research Council for use of the drug.

AND CARDIAC EFFECTS (Concluded)

ing hyper-, hypo-, and normotensive persons. Where quantitative data are not available, direction of action is indicated as follows: + = increases; sented in Parts II, III, and IV of this table where the drugs are identified by their number in Part I. The following abbreviations have been employed cerebral blood pressure; Cer. VR = cerebral vascular resistance; Cer. O_2 = cerebral oxygen uptake; LBF = limb blood flow; LELV = local effect on pulmonary arterial blood pressure; Pul. BF = pulmonary blood flow; Pul. VR = pulmonary vascular resistance; LEPV = local effects on pulmonary cardiac excitability; Car. RP = cardiac refractory period; Car. CT = cardiac conduction time; Car. Con. = cardiac contractility.

RVR	Hep. BF	Hep. VR	PABP	Pul. BF	Pul. VR	LEPV	Cor. BF.	Cor. VR	Car. O_2	Car. R	Car. Ex.	Car. RP	Car. CT	Car. Con.	
															154
										-					155
															156
-	-	-	-10 to -29			0									157
															158
															159
														-	160

Part III: "CARDIOVASCULAR DRUGS": USES AND EFFECTS

"Cardiovascular Drugs," for the purposes of this table, refers to those drugs used primarily in treatment of circulatory system disorders. Numbers in brackets refer to drugs listed in Part I.

Drug Number, Synonyms, Trade Names	Route of Administration[1]	Effects: Desirable (D); Undesirable (U)		Drug Number, Synonyms, Trade Names	Route of Administration[1]	Effects: Desirable (D); Undesirable (U)
ANTIHYPERTENSIVE DRUGS[2]				**VASODILATORS[11] (concluded)**		
Veratrum Alkaloids				*Musculotropic Vasodilators*		
1 [4][3], Veriloid	PO, IM, IV	D: hypotension.	31	[1]	IH	D: subjective relief of
2 [116][4], Provell	PO	U: severe bradycardia,	32	[58] , Nitroglycerine	SL	angina.
3 [157[5], 158[5], 159[6]]	PO	nausea, vomiting,	33	[134]	PO	U: syncope, methemo-
		salivation, sweating.	34	[73]	PO	globinemia, develop-
Rauwolfia Alkaloids			35	[98] , Peritrate	PO	ment of tolerance.
4 [124][7], Serpasil, Serpiloid, Reserpoid, Raused, Serpate		D: hypotension. U: mental depression, nasal congestion, nausea, brady-	36	[51]	PO	
			37	[65]	PO	
			38	[147] , Metamine	PO	
			39	[7] , Theophylline ethylenediamine	PO, IM, IV	U: variable effects on coronary and limb blood
5 [123][8]	PO	cardia, weakness, fatigue.	40	[97] , Soluphylline	IM	flow; inconstant
6 [122][9], Raudixin, Rauwal			41	[96]	IV, IM	clinical results.
7 [5][10], Rauwiloid, Rautension, Rau-Tab, Rauwistan			42	[48] , Paveril	PO	
			43	[68] , Eskel	PO	
Miscellaneous			44	[53] , grain alcohol	PO	
8 [63] , Apresoline	PO	U: nausea, constipation.		**HYPERTENSIVE DRUGS[13]**		
9 [111] (or sodium salt)		U: drowsiness, vomiting.		*Sympathomimetic Amines: Systemic Pressure Action*		
VASODILATORS[11]			45	[50] , Adrenaline, Suprarenin	SC, IV	D: rise in systemic arterial pressure.
Ganglionic Blocking Drugs			46	[70] , Levophed, Nor-adrenaline	IV	U: some amines induce
10 [141] , Etamon	IV, IM	D: Increased blood flow to limbs; lowering of arterial pressure if hypertensive.	47	[49]	PO, SC, IM	cardiac arrhythmias and cerebral excitation.
11 [60] , Bistrium, Methium, Estomid, Hexameton, Hiohax	PO, IV, SC		48	[64] , Paredrine	IM, TOP	
			49	[76] , Wyamine	IM, IV, TOP	
12 [99]	IV	U: severe hypotension (unless intentional for hypertensive surgery; generalized ganglion blockade manifested by blurring of vision, dryness of mouth, tachycardia, constipation.	50	[82] , Methedrine, Desoxyephedrine, Desoxin, Dexoval, Droxyfed, Efroxine, Norodin	PO, SC, IM, IV, TOP	
13 [13] , Pendiomide	IV					
14 [22] , Ecolid	PO					
15 [74] , Inversine	PO		51	[84] , Vasoxyl	IM	
16 [101] , Ansolysen, Pentapyrrolidinium	PO		52	[105] , Neosynephrine Isophrin	SC, IM, IV TOP	
17 [148] , Arfonad	IV		53	[30] , Clopane	IV, IM, TOP	
Adrenergic Blocking Drugs			54	[94]	IV, IM	
18 [104] , Regitine	PO, IV, IM	D: increased blood flow to limbs; hypotensive action useful in diagnosis of pheochromocytoma.	55	[140] , Sympatol, Synthenate	SC, IM	
19 [108] , Benodaine	IV			*Sympathomimetic Amines: Local Application*		
20 [43]	IV, IM		56	[10] , Benzedrine, Actedrow	IH	D: local nasal decongestion. (With the exception
21 [42]	IV, IM		57	[35] , Dexedrine	TOP	of drugs [10] and [35] ,
22 [62][12]	SL, IV, IM	U: drowsiness, nausea, vomiting, tachycardia, nasal congestion.	58	[88] , Privine	TOP	which fall in the same
23 [14] , Ilidar	PO, IV		59	[115] , Benzedrex	IH	general category as [82],
24 [36]	IV		60	[151] , Tuamine	IH, TOP	these amines are too
25 [103] , Dibenzyline	IV, PO		61	[106] , Propadrine	TOP	toxic for parenteral use.)
26 [125]	PO		62	[107] , Vonedrine	IH, TOP	
27 [145] , Priscoline	PO, IV		63	[80] , Aramine	TOP	
Cholinergic Vasodilators			64	[86] , Forthane	IH	
28 [2]	IM, SC	U: peripheral vasodilatation accompanied by generalized parasympathomimetic actions.	65	[93] , Cobefrine	TOP	
29 [81] , Mecholyl	SC					
30 [20] , Doryl	SC					

/1/ PO = oral; IM = intermuscular; IV = intravenous; SC = subcutaneous; SL = sublingual; IH = inhalation; TOP = topical. /2/ For acute and chronic relief of essential and other forms of systemic hypertension. /3/ Mixture of alkaloids extracted from Veratum viride. /4/ From Viscum album. /5/ Partially purified extract of Veratum viride. /6/ Whole powdered preparation of V. viride. /7/ From Rauwolfia serpentina. /8/ Purified alkaloid. /9/ Powdered root of R. serpentina. /10/ Alkaloidal mixture from alseroxylon fraction of Rauwolfia extract. /11/ For improving blood flow in diseased limb and coronary vascular beds; for relief of systemic hypertension. /12/ Equal parts of dihydroergocornine-, dihydro-ergocristine-, and dehydroergokryptine methanesulfonates. /13/ Exert pressor action for correction of hypotensive states; local vasoconstrictor action for nasal decongestion.

333. DRUGS AFFECTING THE CARDIOVASCULAR SYSTEM (Concluded)

The use of certain trade names is for informative purposes only and in no way is intended to imply endorsement by the National Academy of Sciences-National Research Council for use of the drug.

Part III: "CARDIOVASCULAR DRUGS": USES AND EFFECTS (Concluded)

"Cardiovascular Drugs", for the purposes of this table, refers to those drugs used primarily in treatment of circulatory system disorders. Numbers in brackets refer to drugs listed in Part I.

	Drug Number, Synonyms, Trade Names	Route of Administration[1]	Effects: Desirable (D); Undesirable (U)		Drug Number, Synonyms, Trade Names	Route of Administration[1]	Effects: Desirable (D); Undesirable (U)
	CARDIOTONIC DRUGS[14]				CARDIOTONIC DRUGS[14] (concluded)		
	Digitalis Purpurea Glycosides		D: improve ventricular function of heart in failure with and without auricular fibrillation; A-V block. U: anorexia, vomiting, headache, ventricular axrhythmia; excessive A-V block.		Urginea maritina (Squill) Glycosides		Same as for Items 66-72.
66	[37, 39, 40, 57]	PO		73	[126, 154]	PO	
67	[41]	PO, IV		74	[127]	IV	
	Digitalis Lanata Glycosides				ANTIARRHYTHMIC DRUGS[15]		
68	[69], Cedilanid	PO			Cinchona Alkaloids		
69	[38]	PO, IV		75	[121]	PO	D: antifibrillatory action. U: cinchonism; vascular collapse following IV.
70	[32], Cedilanid D	IV		76	[119]	IM	
	Strophanthus Gratus, S. Kombe Glycosides			77	[120]	IM, IV	
					Synthetics		
71	[95], Strophanthin G	IV		78	[113], Pronestyl	PO, IV	U: Depression of cardiac muscle contracility; hypotension.
72	[138]	IV		79	[6]	IV	

/1/ PO = oral; IM = intermuscular; IV = intravenous; SC = subcutaneous; SL = sublingual; IH = inhalation; TOP = topical. /14/ For management of congestive heart failure. /15/ For prophylactic and curative control of cardiac arrhythmia.

Part IV: "NON-CARDIOVASCULAR DRUGS": USES AND EFFECTS

"Non-cardiovascular Drugs," for the purposes of this table, refers to those drugs used primarily in treatment of disorders other than those of the cardiovascular system. Numbers in brackets refer to drugs listed in Part I.

	Drug Number	Use in Clinical Disorder of Circulatory System	Nature of Cardiovascular Action		Drug Number	Use in Clinical Disorder of Circulatory System	Nature of Cardiovascular Action
		Analeptics				Hypnotics and Sedatives	
1	[91]	Stimulant to vasomotor and respiratory centers.	Direct effects (?) on heart and coronaries.	16	[9, 100, 102]	Sedative in hypertension and heart disease.	In large doses, depressant to cardiac contraction.
2	[18]		Direct stimulation of heart muscle and vasodilatation.			Ions	
		Analgesics		17	[8, 15, 19, 72, 110, 130, 133]	Limited clinical trial as antiarrhythmus or as stimulants to arrested ventricles.	Alterations in excitability and automaticity of heart.
3	[125]	Antipyretic for rheumatic carditis.	Claimed to have direct effect on cardiac lesion.				
4	[75, 87]	Sedative for acute myocardial infarction or acute congestive failure	In large doses, vasomotor depression and bradycardia.			Neuromuscular Blocking Agents	
		Anesthetics, General		18	[139, 152]	None.	Curare preparations cause hypotension through histamine liberation, ganglionic blockade, and decreased muscle tone.
5	[23, 31, 52, 54, 92, 143, 146, 160]	None directly. Cardiac patients may be subjected to general anesthetics if necessary.	Depressant to cardiac contraction. In general, all are vasodilators. [23, 31] can cause dangerous cardiac arrhythmias.				
						Parasympathetic Blocking Drugs	
		Anesthetics, Local and Spinal		19	[12, 83, 128]	Diagnosis and treatment of cardiac arrhythmia by virtue of increased vagal tone; antidote for anticholinesterase poisoning.	Cardioaccelerator.
6	[26, 112]	Applied locally to exposed heart to prevent arrhythmia during cardiac surgery.	Spinal anesthesia may reduce arterial blood pressure by sympathetic blockade and decreased thoracic movement.				
						Plasma Extenders	
		Antibiotics		20	[34, 56, 131]	Plasma expander in shock.	Increased cardiac output.
7	[16, 114]	Control of subacute bacterial endocarditis.	Secondary to arrest of infectious process.			Sympathomimetic Bronchodilators	
		Anticoagulants		21	[67, 85]	Relief of bronchial asthma.	Hypotension. Action unlike that of sympathomimetic amines [30, 49, 50, 64, 70, 76, 82, 84, 94, 105, 140].
8	[17, 59]	Prophylaxis against thromboembolic diseases.	Prevention of thromboses and emboli.				
		Anticonvulsants				Tranquilizers	
9	[46, 149]	None	Antiarrhythmic activity.	22	[25]	Prevention of nausea in uremia, eclampsia, and veratrum therapy and relief of mental aberrations.	Essentially secondary to actions on nervous system.
		Antihistaminics					
10	[45, 117, 150]	None.	Antifibrillatory action demonstrated in animals.			Vitamins	
		Antimalarials		23	[29]	None.	None.
11	[24, 118]	Antifibrillatory agent.	Decreased excitability of cardiac muscle.	24	[90]	Treatment of peripheral vascular disease.	Vasodilator(?).
		Anti-thyroids		25	[142]	Treatment of cardiac beri-beri.	None, unless deficiency symptoms exist.
12	[144]	Treatment of hyperthyroid heart disease.	None directly.			Miscellaneous[1]	
		Diuretics		26	[3]	None because of toxicity.	Proarrhythmic.
13	[1, 77, 78, 79]	Mobilization of sodium ion and water in congestive heart failure.	Decreased blood volume aids in treating congestive heart failure. In large doses is depressant to cardiac muscle.	27	[61]		Vasodilator.
				28	[129]		Vasoconstrictor.
				29	[47, 71, 89]		Ganglion stimulant.
				30	[55]		Antiarrhythmic.
		Endocrine Preparations		31	[44, 155]		Antiaccelerator.
14	[27, 28, 33, 66]	None.	None.	32	[132, 136]		Chemoreceptor stimulant.
				33	[156]		Visceral receptor stimulant.
15	[109]		Vasoconstrictor.	34	[21, 153]		General anesthetic.

/1/ For animal experimental use.

Part I: PHYSICAL AND CHEMICAL CHARACTERISTICS

† = decreased; ‡ = increased.

	Name, Synonyms, Chemical Formula (Systematic Name)	Properties[1]	Sources[1]	Assay Methods	Metabolites
			Adrenal Cortex		
1	Aldosterone; electrocortin; $C_{21}H_{28}O_5$ (Δ^4-pregnen-18-al-11β, 21-diol-3, 20-dione-11, 18-hemiacetal)	MW=360; MP=164; $[\alpha]_D$=160°(chl.); s. org. solv.; sl. s.w.	Adrenals (beef, hog, dog, monkey); human urine, placenta (?).	Urinary Na:K ratio in adre-x rats; recovery muscle fatigue (Everse and de Fremery test) in adre-x rats; muscular work performance (Ingle's test) in adre-x rats; deposition of liver glycogen (rats, mice);weight maintenance in adre-x dogs;survival and growth (Kuizenga test) in young adre-x rats; prevention of convulsions (anti-insulin test) in mice;protection against cold in adre-x rats; decrease in circulating eosinophils, circulating lymphocytes, thymus weight; chemical methods (formaldehydogenic, reducing properties, reaction with phenylhydrazine).	Unknown.
2	Desoxycorticosterone=DOC;acetate = DOCA or DCA; $C_{21}H_{30}O_3$ (Δ^4-pregnen-21-ol-3, 20-dione)	MW=330; MP=141-142; $[\alpha]_D$=+178°(al.); s. acet., bz.,chl., vol. solv., veg. oils; i.w.	Adrenal cortex;synth. commercially from cholesterol,diosgenin.		Pregnanediol; 17-ketosteroids; 17-OH-steroids(?).
3	Corticosterone; $C_{21}H_{30}O_3$ (Δ^4-pregnene-11β, 21-diol-3, 20-dione)	MW=346; MP=180-182; $[\alpha]_D$=+262°(al.); s. org. solv.; sl.s. veg. oils; v.s.sl.w.	Adrenal cortex;urine synth. from desoxycholic acid.		17-Ketosteroids (11-OH-androsterone and 11-keto-etiocholan-3-(α)-ol-17-one.
4	Dehydrocorticosterone; cortexone; $C_{21}H_{28}O_4$(Δ^4-pregnen-21-ol-3, 11, 20-trione)	MW=344; MP=178-180; $[\alpha]_D$=+258°(al.); s. org. solv.; i.w.			Similar to those of corticosterone; 11-keto-pregnenediol main metabolite.
5	Hydrocortisone; 17-hydroxycortisone; cortisol; $C_{21}H_{30}O_5$(Δ^4-pregnene-11β-17α-21-triol-3, 20-dione)	MW=362; MP=217-220; $[\alpha]_D$=+167°(al.); s. chl., eth., veg. oils; sl. s.w.	Adrenal cortex; synth. from desoxycholic acid.		Similar to those of corticosterone (17-ketosteroids); cortisone (?).
6	Cortisone; 17-OH-11-dehydrocorticosterone; $C_{21}H_{28}O_5$ (Δ^4-pregnene-17α-21-diol-3, 11, 20-trione)	MW=360; MP=220-224; $[\alpha]_D$=+209°(al.); s. acet., chl., bz., eth., veg. oils; sl. s.w.			17-Ketosteroids, in small quantities.
7	Fluorocortisone; $C_{21}H_{29}O_5F$ (9-α-Fluoro-17β-[1-keto-2-hydroxyethyl] -Δ^4-androstene-3, 11-dione-17α-ol)	MW=380; MP=233-234(acetate); $[\alpha]_D^{23}$= +123° (acetate).	Synthetic.		
			Ovaries		
8	Equilenin; $C_{18}H_{18}O_2$ ($\Delta^{1, 3, 5:10, 6, 8}$-estrapentaen-3-ol-17-one)	MW=266; MP=258-259; $[\alpha]_D$=+89°(diox.); s. vol. solv.; sl. s. al., veg. oils; i.w.	Synth.; 4 stereoisomers; natural estrogen from pregnant mare urine.		One inactive stereoisomer is produced by catalytic dehydrogenatior of estrone.
9	Equilin; $C_{18}H_{20}O_2$ ($\Delta^{1, 3, 5:10, 7}$-estratetraen-3-ol-17-one)	MW=268; MP=238-240; $[\alpha]_D$=+308°(diox.); s. vol. solv.; sl. s. veg. oils; i.w.	Pregnant mare urine.	Colorimetric: phenolsulfonic acid (Kober); $ZnCl_2$/benzoyl Cl, sulfanilic acid/$NaNO_2$ (Pincus); spectrophotometric; estrus changes in vagina (immature rats, mice, Allen-Doisy).	Easily dehydrogenated to equilenin.
10	β-Estradiol; dihydro[-theelin, -folliculin, -estrone] ; di-OH-estrin; $C_{18}H_{24}O_2$(3, 17β-di-OH-1, 3, 5:10-estratriene)	MW=272; MP=178; $[\alpha]_D$=+82°(diox.); s. alk., vol. solv.; sl. s. veg. oils; i.w.	Urine (pregnant mare, rabbit, man); ovary(swine); testes (stallion); human placenta; synth. from cholesterol.		β-estradiol ⇅ estrone ⇌ α-estradiol ↓ estriol
11	Estriol; theelol; tri-OH-estrin; $C_{18}H_{24}O_3$ ($\Delta^{1, 3, 5:10}$-estratriene-3, 16α, 17β-triol)	MW=288; MP=282; $[\alpha]_D$=+53-63°(diox.); s. vol. solv., alk.; sl. s. veg. oils; i.w.	Urine (pregnant ♀); placenta; synth. from estrone, β-estradiol.		estriol (principal metabolite in urine; excreted as water-soluble inactive glucuronide).
12	Estrone; theelin; folliculin; keto-OH-estrin; $C_{18}H_{24}O_2$($\Delta^{1, 3, 5:10}$-estratrien-3-ol-17-one)	MW=270; MP=255; $[\alpha]_D$=+170°(diox.); s. vol. solv., alk.; v. sl. s.w.; sl. s. veg. oils.	Adrenal cortex; urine (man, bull, steer); synth. from cholesterol, diosgenin.		
13	Progesterone; progestin; luteosterone; $C_{21}H_{30}O_2$(Δ^4-pregnene-3, 20-dione)	MW=314; MP(α) = 128, (β) = 121; $[\alpha]_D$=+172-182°(diox.); s. vol. solv.; sl. s. veg. oils; i.w.	Corpus luteum, placenta; adrenal cortex; synth. from cholesterol or stigmasterol.		Pregnanediol.
14	Relaxin	Polypeptide(?); IEP=5.5; s. w. and 95% al.	Serum (pregnant ♀); placenta; corpus luteum.	Degree of relaxation of pelvic ligaments (guinea pig).	Unknown.
			Placenta		
15	Chorionic gonadotropin[2] (HCG; prolan)	MW(HCG)=60,000-80,000; MW(PMS)=30,000(?);IEP(HCG)=3.2; IEP(PMS)=2.6; s.w., 50% acet., 60% al.; inactivated pH 2.0.	HCG-placenta, urine (pregnant woman; PMS-placenta; blood (pregnant mare).	Corpus luteum formation (mice); ovarian wt. (rat); ovulation (rabbit);repair ovarian cells (immature hypophysectomized rats).	HCG excretion; basis of Aschheim-Zondek pregnancy test.
			Testes (and Androgens from Urine)		
16	Testosterone; $C_{19}H_{28}O_2$(Δ^4-androsten-17β-ol-3-one)	MW=288; MP=155-156; $[\alpha]_D$ = 109° (al.); absorption maximum = 238 mμ; s. al., eth., vol. solv.; sl. s. veg. oils; i.w.	Testes (bull); synth. from cholesterol and dehydroandrosterone.	17-Ketosteroids (urine)[3]; alk. m-dinitrobenzene; $SbCl_3$-acetic anhydride (colorimetric);chromatography; capon comb growth; blackening of bill (sparrow);‡wt. seminal vesicle, prostate (castrated rats).	Androsterone; etiocholanolone.
17	Dehydroepiandrosterone; dehydroisoandrosterone; $C_{19}H_{28}O_2$(Δ^5-androsten-3β-ol-17-one)	MW=288; MP(leaflets) 152-153; $[\alpha]_D$=+10.9°(al.); s. al., eth., bz. precipitated by digitonin; i.w.	Urine (man, bull, pregnant cow);synth. from cholesterol.		Found only in urine in conjugated form.
18	Androsterone; $C_{19}H_{30}O_2$(androstan-3-(α)-ol-17-one)	MW=290; MP=185.5; $[\alpha]_D$=+87.8°(diox.); s. vol. solv.; sl. s. veg. oils; not precipitated by digitonin; i. w.	Urine (man, bull, pregnant cow);synth. from cholesterol or sitosterol.		Found only in urine (probably a metabolite of testosterone).
19	Pregnenolone; $C_{21}H_{32}O_2$(Δ^5-pregnen-3-(β)-ol-20-one)	MW=316; MP=193; $[\alpha]_D$=+28°(al.); s. chl., al., diox.; v. sl. s.w.	Testes (hog); synth. from stigmasterol, diosgenin and cholesterol.	None available.	Pregnanediol.

/1/ ac. = acid; acet. = acetone; al. = alcohol (ethanol, 95%); alk. = alkali; aq. = aqueous; bz. = benzene; chl. = chloroform; diox. = dioxane; eth. = ether; HCG = human chorionic gonadotropic; i. = insoluble; IEP = isoelectric point; me. = methyl alcohol; MP = melting point; MW = molecular weight; org. = organic; PMS = pregnant mare serum; pptd. = precipitated; s. = soluble; sl. = slightly; sol. = solution; solv. = solvents; synth. = synthesized; v. = very; vol. = volatile; w. = water; wt. = weight; -x = -ectomized (e.g., hypo-x = hypophysectomized). /2/ Placenta also produces estrogens and progesterone. /3/ Not applicable to testosterone.

$\dagger$ = decreased; $\ast$ = increased.

	Name, Synonyms, Chemical Formula (Systematic Name)	Properties[1]	Source[1]	Assay Methods	Metabolites
		Anterior Pituitary			
20	Adrenocorticotropin; adrenotropin; adrenocorticotropic hormone; corticotropin; ACTH	MW=4500; IEP=4.7-4.8; Sed_{20}= 2.08; s. w.; 60-70% al.; basic polypeptide(s).	Anterior pituitary (especially sheep, ox, swine).	Adrenal repair, wt. maintenance (hypo-x rats); $\ast$adrenal ascorbic acid (hypo-x rats); urinary excretion of corticoids (guinea pig).	
21	Follicle-stimulating hormone; thylakentrin; FSH	IEP=4.8; stable pH 7-8, 30 min at 75°; s. w., 50% acet., 70% al., 50% diox., $\frac{1}{2}$ saturated $(NH_4)_2SO_4$.	Anterior pituitary (especially sheep, swine); urine (castrates); PMS.	Follicular growth (hypo-x rats); $\ast$ weight, ovary and uterus (hypo-x immature ♀ rats); $\ast$ uterine weight (immature mice).	FSH-like protein.
22	Growth hormone; somatotropin; GH	IEP=6.85; $Diff_{20}$=7.15x10^{-7}; visc. coeff.=7.64; s.salt sol.; sl.s.w.; HNO_2 and acetylation destroy.	Anterior pituitary (various species).	$\ast$ tail length, tibial epiphyseal cartilage (hypo-x rats); body growth (hypo-x rats).	
23	Interstitial-cell-stimulating hormore; luteinizing hormone;ICSH; LH	Sheep: Sed_{20}=3.6x10^{-13}; IEP=4.6 Swine: Sed_{20}=6.8x10^{-13}; IEP=7.45 s.w.; 40% al., dilute salt solution.	Anterior pituitary (especially sheep, swine).	Repair interstitial cells; (hypo-x rats or mice); $\ast$ wt. ventral prostate (hypo-x rats); $\ast$testes wt. (pigeon).	
24	Lactogenic hormone; luteotropin; galactin; prolactin; LTH	$Diff_{20}$=9x10^{-7}; IEP=5.5-5.73; visc. coeff.=6.65 $[\alpha]_D 25°$= -40.5°; s. acid, al., me. al.; sl. s. w., dil. salt sol.	Anterior pituitary (especially ox, sheep); urine, in small amounts.	$\ast$ wt. crop sac, proliferation crop gland (pigeon); $\ast$ milk secretion (rabbit).	
25	Thyrotropic hormone[4]; thyrotropin; thyrotropic hormone; TSH	Inactivated by boiling, cysteine, ketene, trypsin, pepsin, chymotrypsin; non-diffusible.	Probably anterior pituitary (basophilic cells).	$\ast$ I_2 thyroid (chicks); $\ast$ thyroid cell height (chicks); $\ast$ wt. thyroid gland (guinea pig).	
		Pituitary Intermediate Lobe			
26	Intermedin; "B"-hormone; middle lobe hormone; melanophore-expanding hormone	IEP=4.1; dialyzable; moderately heat stable; destroyed by trypsin; stable acid, alk.; s.w.; i.eth., acet.	Intermediate lobe (animals changing skin color); anterior lobe (birds, porpoise).	Melanophore expansion (S. African clawed frog).	
		Posterior Pituitary			
27	Oxytocic hormone; oxytocin; pitocin; postlobin-O; posterior-lobe principle	IEP=7.7; not adsorbed on charcoal; destroyed by acid, trypsin, tyrosinase; s. w., concentrated acetic acid, me. al.	Posterior pituitary.	Contraction, isolated uterus (guinea pig); $\ast$ BP (chicken).	
28	Vasopressin; vasopressor principle; postlobin-V; vasopressor-antidiuretic principle; ADH; pitressin	IEP=10.8; adsorbed charcoal; inactivated by trypsin, not pepsin; solubility $\approx$to oxytocin.		$\ast$ BP (rat, dog); antidiuretic activity (rats).	ADH-like material.
		Parathyroid			
29	Parathormone; PTH	IEP=5.6; inactivated by proteases. alk.; stable dilute acid; s.w., saline, aq.al., 94% acetic acid, conc. phenol; 50% glycerol; i. vol. org. solv.	Parathyroids.	Rate and degree of rise in serum $Ca^{++}$and decrease in serum phosphate (dogs).	
		Thyroid			
30	Thyroid hormone[5]; thyroxine; $C_{15}H_{11}O_4NI_4$; β-[(3,5-diiodo-4-OH-phenoxy)-3,5-diiodophenyl]-alanine	MW=777; needles; MP=232-233; $[\alpha]_D$ = 3.2° (NaOH); s. alk. w., alk. or acid al.; i.w., al., vol. solv.	Thyroid gland; synth. from p-methoxyphenol and 3, 4, 5-triiodinitrobenzene.	$\ast$ BMR, thyroid-deficient subject; limb bud growth, amphibian larvae; $\ast O_2$ consumption.	Inactive iodinated compounds in bile; iodides.
		Pancreas			
31	Insulin	MW=36,000[6]; MP=223; IEP=5.3; s.w., al.; pptd. by protein precipitants; stable acid; destroyed by alk.	Islets of Langerhans (various species).	Convulsions, (mice); hypoglycemia (starved rabbit); $\ast$ blood glucose (adrenodemedullated, hypo-x, diabatic rats).	
		Adrenal Medulla			
32	Epinephrine; adrenalin, suprarenine, adrenine	MW=183; MP(L)=207-211; $[\alpha]_D$ = -50° to -53.5°; s. alk. ac.; sl. s. w.; v.sl.s.al.; i.eth., chl.	Adrenal medulla; synth. (commerc.) catechol; in vivo, tyrosine; methylation of nor-epinephrine.	Stimulation isolated heart (frog); relaxation uterus (cat); dilatation pupil (cat); $\ast$ peristalsis (rabbit); $\ast$BP(cat).	Cathechol derivatives.
33	Nor-epinephrine; arterenol, nor-adrenalin	MW=169; MP=(L-bitart.)=163-164, L-HCl=146-147; solubility $\approx$to epinephrine.	Adrenal medulla; various nerves, especially splenic; spleen, heart, blood vessels.	$\approx$epinephrine in all tests except pressor and contraction of gravid uterus.	Methylated to epinephrine by adrenals in presence of ATP.
		Gastrointestinal Tract			
34	Cholecystokinin; CCK	MW=5,000-10,000(?); IEP=5.0-5.5; dialyzable, s. w.	Upper intestinal mucosa.	Contraction of gallbladder (dog).	Metabolized as protein(?).
35	Enterocrinin	s.ac., w., al.; i. eth., acet.; salted out by NaCl.	Intestinal mucosa (hog, cat, dog, cow, man).	$\ast$ flow of intestinal juice in jejunum (dog).	
36	Enterogastrone	s.w.; i. org. solv.; dialyzable; destroyed by pepsin.	Duodenal mucosa.	$\ast$ stim. effect of exogenous histamine on HCl secretion.	Urogastrone (?).
37	Gastrin	IEP=8; heat stable; destroyed by UV, alk., pepsin; dialyzable.	Gastric mucosa, especially pylorus.	No standard assay method.	
38	Pancreozymin	Salted out by NaCl; s. absolute al., w.	Upper intestinal mucosa.	Increase in enzymes in pancreatic juice.	Unknown.
39	Secretin	MP=234; salted out by NaCl, CCl_3COOH; s. dilute acidic w.		Volume of pancreatic juice (dog).	
40	Urogastrone	Similar to enterogastrone; not destroyed by pepsin.[7]	Urine.	$\approx$enterogastrone.	
		Neuro			
41	Acetylcholine; ACh; [Br] Pragmoline; [Cl] Acecoline	MW=163; MP (Br)=143; quart. salt unstable; s. w., al., eth., oils; salts v. s. w.; i. eth.	Ganglia of parasymp. nervous system;brain; synth. commercially.	None.	

/1/ ac. = acid; acet. = acetone; al. = alcohol (ethanol, 95%); alk. 6 alkali; aq. = aqueous; bz. = benzene; chl. = chloroform; diox. = dioxane; eth. = ether; HCG = human chorionic gonadotropic; i. = insoluble; IEP = isoelectric point; me. al. = methyl alcohol; MP = Melting Point; MW = molecular weight; org. = organic; PMS = pregnant mare serum; pptd. = precipitated; s. = soluble; sl. = slightlyly; sol. = solution; solv. = solvents; synth. = synthesized; v. = very; vol. = volatile; w.= water; wt. = weight; -x = -ectomized (e.g., hypo-x= hypophysectomized). /4/ Evidence for 2 fractions of TSH: (1) stimulation hypertrophy of acinar cells and colloid secretion from gland; (2) acceleration I⁻ uptake from blood, hormone synthesis. /5/ Circulating hormone probably thyroxin protein. Thyroglobulin (MW 650,000 and IEP 5) isolated from gland; circulating hormone may be 1/4 of this. Triiodothyronine is probably the tissue active compound; it is 5-7 times as potent as thyroxine. /6/ A polymer of 6 units of MW about 6000. /7/ Only the motor-inhibitory effect.

Part II: BIOLOGICAL PROPERTIES
Numbers in brackets refer to hormones listed in Part I.
↓ = decreased; ↑ = increased; (S) = stimulated; PMS = pregnant mare serum.

Hormone Number	Targets	Principal Effects	Effect of Deficiency (−) Excess (+)	Secretion Inhibited by (I) Stimulated by (S)
		Adrenal Cortex		
1 [1]	See [3,4]; chiefly kidneys, interstitial fluid; (mineralo-corticoid).	Promotes renal excretion of K, and retention of Na and Cl; 25–100 times more potent than [2]. Some properties of gluco-corticoids (q.v.).	− Hemoconcentration; ↑Na, H_2O (blood, muscle); ↓ K retention. + Reverse of above; hypertension; congestive heart failure.	(S) low blood Na (?).
2 [2]	Same as [1]. (mineralo-corticoid).	Similar to [1].	Similar to [1], but effects much less pronounced.	
3 [3]	Muscles, liver, capillaries, kidneys, pancreas(?), integument, lymphoid organs and bone marrow, circulating blood cells; (gluco-corticoid).	Effects of gluco-corticoids [3,4,5,6] are qualitatively comparable but differ quantitatively as follows: for glycogen deposition in liver, muscle work performance, hypersensitivity reactions, and thymus involution, the relative potencies are [5]=1.5, [6]=1.0, [3]=0.5, [4]=0.5; gluconeogenesis, [5]>[4]=[3]; maintenance of renal function, [1]>[2]>[4]=[3]> [5]=[6]; K/Na ratio and H_2O balance, [1]>[2]>[4]=[3]; recovery muscular fatigue,[2]>[3]>[5]>[6]; cold protection, [6]>[4]>[3]>[2]; CHO metabolism,[5]> [3]>[2]; collagen maintenance,[6]; anti-inflammatory,[5,6,9]; normal capillary permeability,[5,6,4];protection against stress,[4,5,6]; protection against shock,[2].	− Asthenia; hemoconcentration; skin pigmentation; ↓ weight; blood glucose, liver glycogen, stress resistance, blood pressure; ↑ K/Na ratio in serum. + Reverse of above; Cushing's syndrome; hirsutism.	(S) ACTH.
4 [4]				
5 [5]	See [3,4]; particularly muscle, liver, connective tissue; (gluco-corticoid).			
6 [6]				
7 [7]	Synthetic. More potent than [5,6] in rheumatoid arthritis.			
		Ovaries		
8 [8]			Unknown.	
9 [9]		Estrogenic. Endometrial proliferation; development and maintenance of vaginal mucosa, cornification of superficial layer; antagonizes androgen effects; ↓development mammary gland ducts, uterine motility, growth axillary and pubic hair (♀ human), growth of down (♀ bird), growth all ♀ secondary sex organs, estrus. Potency [10]>[12]>[11].	− ↓ development accessory sex organs, mammary glands, secondary sex characteristics, and ♀ behavior pattern. + Precocious maturity; hypertrophy accessory sex organs and mammary glands; precocious epiphyseal maturation and closure; estrus changes; cystic hyperplasia of endometrium.	(S) LH; FSH + LH (?).
10 [10]	All female sex organs; mammary glands; mucous membranes; anterior pituitary.			
11 [11]				
12 [12]				
13 [13]	Uterus; mammary glands.	Luteinizing. Preparation of endometrium for implantation of zygote; ↓ uterine contractions; ↓ development mammary glands, metabolism and excretion of estrogens.	− ↑uterine motility and bleeding; abortion. + Prolongation of cycle;dysmenorrhea (?); ↓ Na, H_2O retention.	(S) LTH (?).
14 [14]	Pelvic ligaments.	Relaxation pelvic ligaments.	(?)	(S) estrogens (?).
		Placenta		
15 [15]	Ovaries (pregnancy, man and horse).	Mainenance corpus luteum in pregnancy: HCG → luteinizing corpus luteum;PMS → luteinization, follicle development.	− Abortion. + Toxemias of pregnancy (?).	(I) sex steroids.
		Testes (and Androgens from Urine)		
16 [16]		Androgenic. ↑ development ♂ secondary sex organs and sex characteristics, BMR, protein anabolism, retention Na and K, folliculoid and luteoid activity (♀ immature); ↑ creatinuria.	− ↓ development ♂ sex organs and sex characteristics, excretion 17-ketosteroids in urine. + Precocious sex development; rapid body growth; ↓ scalp hair (?);↑ hirsutism; ↑ excretion 17-ketosteroids.	(I) sex steroids.
17 [17]	All male sex organs; anterior pituitary; muscle.			
18 [18]				
19 [19]	Seminiferous tubules.	↑ spermatogenesis even in hypophysectomized or folliculoid-overdosed animals.	(?).	
		Anterior Pituitary		
20 [20]	Adrenal cortex.	↑ lipid and ascorbic acid content of adrenal cortex; ↑ secretion adrenal cortical hormones.	− Atrophy and hypofunction of adrenal cortex; ↓ response to stress. + Hyperfunction adrenal cortex.	(I) circulating adrenal cortex hormones. (S) stress; epinephrine(?).
21 [21]	Ovarian follicles; seminiferous tubules.	↑ spermatogenesis and growth seminiferous tubules, development follicles (not ova production or estrogen secretion unless ICSH present).	− Obesity; ↑H_2O metabolism, ovarian dysfunction. + No syndrome associated with FSH alone.	(I) circulating androgens and/or estrogens. (S) castration; low blood level of androgens and/or estrogens.
22 [22]	Bones, especially epiphyseal cartilage; most tissues.	↑ skeletal and soft-tissue growth, protein anabolism; ↑ pancreatic insulin (↓ in rat), maintenance muscle growth.	− Dwarfism and/or infantilism; delayed closure apiphyses. + Gigantism and/or acromegaly; hypertrophy of viscera[1]	(I) estrogens or androgens (large doses).
23 [23]	Maturing Graafian follicles and interstitial cells (ovaries); interstitial cells of Leydig (testes).	↑ follicle maturation (production but not maintenance corpus luteum), secretion estrogens, and androgens from testes.	− ↓ ovulation;atrophy of Leydig cells. + Secretion estrogens and androgens; precocious development or ovulation.	(S) high blood level of ovarian and testicular hormones.
24 [24]	Mammary glands; crop-sac (pigeon); ovarian corpus luteum.	↑ milk secretion, progesterone secretion by developed corpus luteum, uterine nidation and decidua, growth and secretion of crop gland (pigeon).	− ↓milk secretion, progesterone. + ↑milk secretion.	(I) or (S) by effects of androgens, FSH; ICSH, and progesterone on target organs.
25 [25]	Thyroid gland	↑ synthesis and secretion of thyroid hormone, cell height of thyroid epithelium, thyroid size, serum protein bound iodine; ↑ iodine and colloid content of thyroid.	− Myxedema; cretinism (some forms); ↓BMR. + Goiter; hyperthyroidism; ↑BMR; exophthalmos[2].	(I) ↑ circulating TH; (I) or (S) by nervous system. (S) ↓ circulating TH.

/1/ More characteristic of acromegaly, since long bones do not lenghten. /2/ May be caused by "exophthalmos factor" that can be separated from TSH.

Part II: BIOLOGICAL PROPERTIES (Concluded)

Numbers in brackets refer to hormones listed in Part I.

↓ = decreased; ↑ = increased; (S) = stimulated.

Hormone Number	Targets	Principal Effects	Effect of Deficiency (-) Excess (+)		Secretion Inhibited by (I) Stimulated by (S)
		Pituitary Intermediate Lobe			
26 [26]	Chromatophore cells in skin of lower vertebrates	Expands chromatophores → pigment granules to disperse and color skin.	-	Contraction chromatophores; ↓ skin pigment.	(S) central nervous system; ACTH (chromatophore expansion).
			+	↑ skin pigmentation, melanin synthesis; hyperglycenia.	
		Posterior Pituitary			
27 [27]	Uterine and other smooth muscles; mammary glands	Stimulates contraction uterine muscle, (and other smooth muscles too lesser degree), milk secretion.	-	Delayed uterine contraction (pre- or postpartum); ↓ milk flow.	(S) suckling (?).
			+	↑ milk flow; abortion (?).	
28 [28]	Capillaries; arterioles; coronary vessels; kidney vascular bed and tubules	↓ kidney excretion of H_2O[3]; ↑ excretion of Nacl and urea, ↑ blood pressure (constriction of capillaries).	-	Diabetes insipidus[3]; ↑ excretion NaCl and urea.	(S) ↑ plasma osmotic conc. (I) ↓ plasma osmotic conc.
			+	↑ H_2O retention.	
		Parathyroid			
29 [29]	Bones; kidneys	Controls Ca and PO_4 level in blood via mineral exchange between blood and bones, and PO_4 excreted by kidneys.	-	Tetany; convulsions; coma; death; ↑Ca, ↑ PO_4 (serum); muscle spasm; cataract, scaly skin, hair loss (?).	(S) low Ca, high PO_4 diet; ↑ serum PO_4, ↓ serum Ca (?).
			+	↑ PO_4, ↑ Ca (serum); ↑ alkaline phosphatase, excretion PO_4; decalcification bones; renal calcification.	
		Thyroid			
30 [30]	All body cells	↑ oxidations; regulation of rate of CHO, fat, protein, H_2O, mineral metabolism; stimulates growth, maturation, neuromuscular function, skin development, hematopoiesis, spermato- and oogenesis, lactation; regulation of TSH secretion.	-	Myxedema; cretinism (some types in fetus, child); retardation of ossification and epiphyseal maturation.	(I) anti-thyroid drugs. (S) TSH.
			+	Hyperthyroidism; Grave's disease; exophthalmos.[2]	
		Pancreas			
31 [31]	Skeletal muscle; probably adipose tissue	Regulation CHO metabolism; ↑oxidation tissue glucose (hexokinase) (?); ↓ gluco-genesis, ↓ ketogenesis (indirect) (?).	-	Diabetes mellitus (hyperglycemia, glycosuria, keto-nuria; ↓ weight and blood volume; - nitrogen balance); delayed wound healing; gangrene.	(I) Pituitary extracts; GH; in tissues by epinephrine, glucocorticoids. (S) ↑ blood glucose; vagus stimulation.
			+	Hyperinsulinism (hypoglycemia, convulsions, nausea, muscular weakness, anxiety and confusion).	
		Adrenal Medulla			
32 [32]	Sympathetic nervous system; heart muscle; smooth and skeletal muscles; liver	↑ contraction heart muscle (↑ output and rate), spleen, gravid uterus, iris muscle (radial), capillaries; relaxation non-gravid uterus, peripheral arterioles, bronchial muscles; ↓ peristalsis; ↑ glucogenolysis, BMR, blood coagulation; stimulates secretion ACTH (?), salivary, sweat glands.	-	No clinical syndrome.	(S) sympathetic nervous system, via splanchnic nerve; "stress."
			+	Over-secretion rare; may cause paroxistic hypertension, and, in some instances, sustained hypertension.	
33 [33]	See [32]	Similar to [32], but causes arteriole constriction, hyperglycemia; no effect on cardiac output; pressor effect is not reversed by ergotoxine (as is that of [32]).			
		Gastrointestinal Tract			
34 [34]	Gallbladder	Stimulates contraction and emptying of gallbladder.			(S) fat, protein, acid in duodenum.
35 [35]	Secretory cells of ileum, jejunum	↑ secretion succus entericus, volume rate and enzyme concentration.		(?)	(S) food in intestine.
36 [36]	Stomach	↑ motor activity and acid secretion of stomach.			(S) sugar, fat in intestine.
37 [37]	Parietal (HCl-producing) cells, stomach	↑ HCl secretion (but not pepsin) by gastric mucosa.			(S) mechanical distention; protein degradation products.
38 [38]	Enzyme-secreting cells of pancreas	↑ enzyme secretion by pancreas; no effect on volume rate.			(S) Peptones, amino acids, soaps, fats in duodenum.
39 [39]	Pancreas (acinar or exocrine), liver	↑ volume rate of pancreatic enzymes; no effect on concentration; stimulates bile secretion.	-	Hyposecretion pancreatic enzymes and bile.	(S) HCl, protein degradation products, digested fat or bile in small intestine.
			+	Excess doubtful.	
40 [40]	Gastric mucosa and muscularis	↑ HCl secretion, muscular contractions stomach.		(?)	
		Neuro			
41 [41]	Muscles, especially involuntary (ACh released at neuromuscular junctions, synapses)	Conduction electrical impulses along nerve fibers; ↑ heart rate; dilatation arterioles; effects (cholinergic) generally opposite to those of epinephrine (adrenergic).		(?)	

/2/ May be caused by "exophthalmos factor" that can be separated from TSH. /3/ Antidiuretic hormone (ADH) fraction.

Generic Name [Trade Name]	Structural Formula	Molecular Formula [Molecular Weight]	Solubility[1]	Mouse LD$_{50}$ mg/kg	Benadryl Ratio[2]	Anesthesia min[3]	Atropine Ratio[4]	Epinephrine Potentiation[5]	Side Effects[6]
1 Diphenhydramine HCl [Benadryl]	CH-O-CH$_2$CH$_2$N(CH$_3$)$_2$·HCl	C$_{17}$H$_{21}$NO·HCl [291.81]	s.w., al., chl.; sl.s. bz., eth.	31(IV) 83(IP) 206(PO) 129(SC)	1.0(a, b, c, d, e)	22	0.02	Yes	Sedation, dizziness, dry mouth, lassitude, excitement, nausea.
2 Antazoline HCl [Antistine]	N-CH$_2$-C (N-CH$_2$ / NH-CH$_2$)·HCl	C$_{17}$H$_{19}$N$_3$·HCl [301.82]	s.al.; sl.s w.; i.bz., eth.	39(IV-rats) 150(IP)	0.1(a) 0.5(b)	20	<0.001	No	Dry mouth, headache, tachycardia, nervousness, nausea.
3 Bromodiphenhydramine HCl [Ambodryl]	Br CH-O-CH$_2$CH$_2$N(CH$_3$)$_2$ ·HCl	C$_{17}$H$_{20}$BrNO·HCl [370.73]	s.w.	108(IP)	1.4(a) 2.2(b)		0.005	Yes	Dizziness, anorexia, dry mouth, diarrhea.
4 Carbinoxamine maleate [Clistin]	Cl CH-O-CH$_2$CH$_2$N(CH$_3$)$_2$ CHCO$_2$H ‖ CHCO$_2$H	C$_{16}$H$_{19}$ClN$_2$O ·C$_4$H$_4$O$_4$ [406.86]	s.w., al., chl.; sl.s. eth.	411(PO)	24.0(e)	0	Weak	No	Somnolence, dizziness, dry mouth, gastric pain.
5 Chlorcyclizine HCl [Perazil]	Cl CH-N (CH$_2$-CH$_2$ / CH$_2$-CH$_2$) N-CH$_3$ ·2HCl	C$_{18}$H$_{21}$ClN$_2$ ·2HCl [373.57]	s.w., chl., al.; i.bz., eth.	137(IP)	1.0(a) 7.0(b) 4.0(d)	22	Moderate	Yes	Dry mouth, headache, blurred vision, insomnia, palpitation, gastric disturbances.
6 Chlorothen citrate [Chlorothen; tagathen]	Cl S CH$_2$-N-CH$_2$CH$_2$N(CH$_3$)$_2$ N ·H$_3$C$_6$H$_5$O$_7$	C$_{14}$H$_{18}$ClN$_3$S ·C$_6$H$_8$O$_7$ [487.95]	s.w.; sl.s al., eth.	26(IV) 105(IP)	10.0(a)		0.01		Sedation, dizziness, headache, gastric disturbances.
7 Chlorpheniramine maleate [Chlor-trimeton]	Cl CH-CH$_2$CH$_2$N(CH$_3$)$_2$ N CHCO$_2$H ‖ CHCO$_2$H	C$_{16}$H$_{19}$ClN$_2$ ·C$_4$H$_4$O$_4$ [390.86]	s.w., al., chl.; sl.s. bz., eth.	40(IV) 77(IP) 176(PO) 104(SC)	3.0(a) 29.0(b) 35.0(e)	15	0.001	Yes	Jitteriness, dry mouth, gastric disturbances.
8 Doxylamine succinate [Decapryn]	C-O-CH$_2$CH$_2$N(CH$_3$)$_2$ N CH$_3$ ·C$_4$H$_6$O$_4$	C$_{17}$H$_{22}$N$_2$O ·C$_4$H$_6$O$_4$ [388.45]	s.w., al., chl.; sl.s. bz.	62(IV) 470(PO) 460(SC)	1.0(a) 2.5(e)	16	<0.001		Sedation, dizziness, headache, dermatitis, gastric disturbances.
9 Metaphenilene HCl [Diatrin]	S CH$_2$-N-CH$_2$CH$_2$N(CH$_3$)$_2$·HCl	C$_{15}$H$_{20}$N$_2$S ·HCl [296.86]	s.w.; sl.s al., chl.; i.eth.	117(IP)	1.7(a) 1.3(b)		0.007		Irritability, burning of the skin, gastric disturbances.
10 11 Methapyrilene (Thenylpyramine) HCl [Thenylene; Histadyl]	S CH$_2$-N-CH$_2$CH$_2$N(CH$_3$)$_2$·HCl N	C$_{14}$H$_{19}$N$_3$S ·HCl [297.85]	s.w., al.; i.bz., eth.	20(IV) 77(IP) 182(PO)	5.0(a) 4.0(b)	17	0.002	Yes	Dizziness, dry mouth, headache, nervousness, nausea.

/1/ Abbreviations: al. = alcohol (ethanol 95%); bz. = benzene; chl. = chloroform; eth. = ether; glyc. = glycerol; i. = insoluble; s. = soluble; sl. = slightly; w. = water. /2/ Benadryl Ratio as based on: (a) isolated guinea pig ileum; (b) bronchoconstrictor effect of histamine aerosol in guinea pigs; (c) vasodepressor response to histamine in dogs; (d) guinea pig tracheal chain; (e) bronchoconstrictor effect of intravenous histamine in guinea pigs. /3/ Corneal local anesthesia duration in rabbits or guinea pigs, using 1% solution. /4/ Anticholinergic effect on isolated rabbit intestine. /5/ Potentiation of epinepherine pressor effect. /6/ In addition to drowsiness, which is a side effect common to all drugs listed.

	Generic Name [Trade Name]	Structural Formula	Molecular Formula [Molecular Weight]	Solubility[1]	Mouse LD$_{50}$ mg/kg	Benadryl Ratio[2]	Anesthesia min[3]	Atropine Ratio[4]	Epinephrine Potentiation[5]	Side Effects[6]
12	Phenindamine tartrate [Thephorin]		C$_{19}$H$_{19}$N ·C$_4$H$_6$O$_6$ [297.82]	s.w.;sl.s. propylene glycol; i. al., glyc., eth.	23(IV) 88(IP) 280(PO) 300(SC)	2.0(b) 9.3(d)		0.003	No	Dizziness, headache, anorexia, palpitations, restlessness, depression, nausea.
13	Pheniramine maleate [Trimeton]		C$_{16}$H$_{20}$N$_2$ ·C$_4$H$_4$O$_4$ [356.41]	s.w., al.; sl.s.bz., eth.	60(IV) 65(IP) 225(PO) 132(SC)	2.0(b) 1.3(d) 2.0(e)	0	<0.001	Yes	Dry mouth, weakness, gastric disturbances.
14	Phenyltoloxamine HCl [Bristamin]		C$_{17}$H$_{21}$NO ·HCl [291.82]	s.w.	33(IV) 163(IP) 424(PO)	1.1(b)	Same as procaine q. v.	0.01	No	Dry mouth.
15	Promethazine HCl [Phenergan]		C$_{17}$H$_{20}$N$_2$S ·HCl [320.88]	s.w., al., chl.	55(IV) 200(PO) 190(IP)	2.5(a) 4-10(b)	69	Moderate	Yes	Dizziness, weakness, dry mouth, nausea, vomiting.
16	Pyrathiazine HCl [Pyrrolazote]		C$_{18}$H$_{20}$N$_2$S ·HCl [332.89]	s.w., al.	37(IV) 445(PO) 1340(SC)	4.0(a) 4.0(b)	53	0.004	No	Headache, nausea.
17	Pyrilamine maleate [Neoantergan]		C$_{17}$H$_{23}$N$_3$O ·C$_4$H$_4$O$_4$ [401.45]	s.w., al.; sl.s.bz., eth.	30(IV) 102(IP) 150(SC)	10.4(a) 28.0(b) 1.0(c) 17.1(d)	21	0.002	Yes	Vertigo, dry mouth, nervousness, headache, nausea.
18	Pyrrobutamine phosphate [Pyronil]		C$_{20}$H$_{22}$ClN ·2H$_3$PO$_4$ [507.86]	s.h.w.	54(IV) 1116(PO) 1270(SC)	14.0(a) 20.0(b)	92	Weak		Dizziness, dry mouth, headache, palpitation, nervousness, nausea, diarrhea.
19	Thenyldiamine HCl [Thenfadil]		C$_{14}$H$_{19}$N$_3$S ·HCl [297.85]	s.w.;sl. s.al.	14(IV) 55(IP) 277(PO) 36(SC)	1.0(c)		0.0025		
20	Thonzylamine HCl [Neohetramine]		C$_{16}$H$_{22}$N$_4$O ·HCl [322.83]	s.w., al., chl.; i. eth.	119(IP) 245(PO)	1.0(b) 4.0(d)	Same as procaine q. v.	Weak	No	Dry mouth, headache, nervousness, nausea.
21	Tripelennamine HCl [Pyribenzamine]		C$_{16}$H$_{21}$N$_3$ ·HCl [291.82]	s.w., al., chl.; i. bz., eth.	16(IV) 74(IP) 210(PO) 71(SC)	5.0(a) 6.5(b) 5.0(c) 5.1(d) 1.0(e)	17	0.0025	Yes	Dizziness, dry mouth, headache, excitement, gastric disturbances.

/1/ Abbreviations: al. = alcohol (ethanol 95%); bz. = benzene; chl. = chloroform; eth. = ether; glyc. = glycerol; i. = insoluble; s. = soluble; sl. = slightly; w. = water. /2/ Benadryl Ratio as based on: (a) isolated guinea pig ileum; (b) bronchoconstrictor effect of histamine aerosol in guinea pigs; (c) vasodepressor response to histamine in dogs; (d) guinea pig tracheal chain; (e) bronchoconstrictor effect of intravenous histamine in guinea pits. /3/ Corneal local anesthesia duration in rabbits or guinea pigs, using 1% solution. /4/ Anticholinergic effect on isolated rabbit intestine. /5/ Potentiation of epinepherine pressor effect. /6/ In addition to drowsiness, which is a side effect common to all drugs listed.

Blood levels and dosages indicated in this table are not to be interpreted as recommendations of the National Academy of Sciences - National Research Council, nor does the appearance of a trade name imply such endorsement for the product or its manufacturer. These are presented for informative purposes only.

	Therapeutic Agent	Common or Trade Name	Use	Dosage	Route of Administration[1]	Minutes After Administration[2]	Blood Concentration[3] mg/100 ml[2]
			Antibiotics				
1	Chloramphenicol	Chloromycetin	Infections caused by G+ and G- bacteria, viruses.	0.5 g	O	30	0.4(P)
2	Chlorotetracycline HCl	Aureomycin HCl	Broad spectrum antibiotic	250 mg	O	120-240	0.1-0.3 mg(P)
3	Erythromycin		Infections caused by G+ bacteria.	300 mg	O	60-120	0.015 mg
4	Oxytetracycline	Terramycin	Broad spectrum antibiotic.	250 mg	O	120-240	0.1-0.3 mg(P)
5	Penicillin G procaine		Infections caused by G+ bacteria.	300,000 units	IM	60-180	0.06 mg(S)
6	Tetracycline	Achromycin	Broad spectrum antibiotic.	250 mg	O	120-240	0.1-0.3 mg(P)
			Antihistaminics				
7	Diphenhydramine HCl	Benadryl HCl	Histamine antagonist.	50 mg	O	15-30	
8	Tripelennamine HCl	Pyribenzamine HCl	Histamine antagonist.	50 mg	O	15-30	<300 µg(P)
			Antimalarial Drugs				
9	Chloroquine di-PO_4	Aralen-SN 7618	Suppressive, therapeutic.	1 g (start); 500 mg (6 hr); 500 mg (2nd, 3rd da)[4]	O	Slow	0.015-0.020 mg (P)
10	Pyrimethamine	Daraprim	Suppressive antimalarial.	100 mg[5]	O	60-120	0.08-0.16
11	Quinacrine HCl	Atabrine	Suppressive, therapeutic.	200 mg (every 6 hr for 5 doses); then 100 mg (3 times daily for 6 da)[4]	O	Slow	0.002-0.003 mg (S)
			Antituberculosis Drugs				
12	Isoniazid		Tuberculosis therapy.	100 mg	O	120-180	0.13-0.34(P)
13	Para-amino-salicylic acid	PAS	Tuberculosis therapy.	4 g	O	30-60	10
14	Streptomycin SO_4		Tuberculosis therapy; infections caused by G- bacteria.	500 mg	IM	30-180	0.7-1.5(P)
			Autonomic Nervous System Drugs				
15	Atropine SO_4		Parasympatholytic.	0.5 mg	O	15	
16	Bethanechol Cl	Urecholine	Parasympathomimetic.	20 mg	O	30	
17	Ephedrine SO_4		Sympathomimetic.	25 mg	O, SC	20	
18	Epinephrine HCl	Adrenalin	Sympathomimetic.	0.5 mg / 2 mg	SC / IM	5 / 5	
19	Neostigmine Br	Prostigmine Br	Parasympathomimetic.	15 mg	O	15	9×10^{-3} (P)
20	Priscoline		Sympatholytic.	25 mg	O	15	<1
			Cardiovascular Drugs				
21	Aminophylline		Angina pectoris, coronary thrombosis, asthma.	200 mg	O	30-60	0.3-0.4 as theophylline
22	Digitoxin		Cardiac decompensation.	0.1 mg	O	30-120	<1 µg
23	Glyceryl trinitrate	Trinitroglycerine	Angina pectoris.	0.4 mg	SL	2-5	
24	Quinidine SO_4		Auricular fibrillation.	200 mg	O	60-120	0.2-0.4 mg
			Central Nervous System Depressants				
	Analgesics, hypnotics, and sedatives						
25	Acetophenetidine	Phenacetin	Analgesia.	300 mg	O	15-30	>0.1 (P)
26	Acetylsalicylic acid	Aspirin	Analgesia.	600 mg	O	15-30	2-3 (P)
27	Amobarbital sodium	Amytal sodium	Hypnosis.	100 mg	O	30	0.6-0.8
28	Codeine phosphate		Analgesia.	30 mg	O	30	
29	Meperidine HCl	Demerol	Analgesia.	100 mg	IM	15-30	0.125 (P)
30	Methadone	Amidone; Dolophine	Analgesia.	7.5 mg	O or SC	15-30	
31	Morphine SO_4		Analgesia.	15 mg	O or SC	15-30	250 µg
32	Paraldehyde		Analgesia[6].	4 (1-30) g[7]	R or O	30	11.8-24.4(S)
33	Pentobarbital sodium	Nembutal sodium	Hypnosis.	100 mg	O	15	0.2-0.3
34	Phenobarbital sodium	Luminal sodium	Sedation.	30 mg	O	30	5
35	Secobarbital sodium	Seconal sodium	Hypnosis.	100 mg	O	15	0.2-0.3
36	Sodium bromide		Sedation.	1 g	O	60	16-50
	Anesthetics						
37	Chloroform		Surgical anesthesia.	1.5 vol %	I	5	15-20
38	Cyclopropane		Surgical anesthesia.	20-30 vol %	I	2-3	15
39	Ether, ethyl		Surgical anesthesia.	6-10 vol %	I	15-20	50-130
40	Ether, ethyl vinyl	Vinamar	Surgical anesthesia.	6 vol %	I	2-4	50
41	Ether, methyl-n-propyl	Neothyl	Surgical anesthesia.	2.5-3 vol %	I	10-15	30-60
42	Ether, vinyl	Vinethene	Surgical anesthesia.	4 vol %	I	1-2	28
43	Ethyl alcohol		Euphoria.	30 ml	O	15-30	30
44			Hypnotic.	100 ml	O	15-30	100
45			Anesthesia (stupor).	300-400 ml	O	15-30	300-400
46	Ethyl chloride		Surgical anesthesia.	3-4.5 vol %	I	2	20-30
47	Ethylene		Anesthesia (Plane 1).	80-85 vol %	I	20	120-180
48	Nitrous oxide		Anesthesia (Plane 1).	85-92 vol %	I	2	23 vol %
49	Thiamylal sodium	Surital sodium	Short surgical procedures.	3-6 ml of 2.5% solution[8]	IV	1-10	1.5-2
50	Thiopental sodium	Pentothal sodium	Short surgical procedures.	2-3 ml of 2.5% solution[9]	IV	1-10	1.5-2
51	Tribromethanol (soln)	Avertin	Basal anesthesia.	80-100 mg/kg	R	30	6-9
	Anticonvulsants						
52	Diphenylhydantoin sodium	Dilantin	Anti-epileptic.	100 mg[10]	O	2-3 da	3-6
53	Trimethadione	Tridione	Anti-epileptic.	300 mg[11]	O	2-3 da	4-6(P)
			Central Nervous System Stimulants				
54	Caffeine		Central stimulant.	200 mg	O	15-30	0.1-0.2(P)
55	Dextroamphetamine SO_4	Dexedrine	Central stimulant.	5 mg	O	30	Not available
56	Pentylenetetrazol	Metrazol	Respiratory stimulant.	100 mg	IV, SC	5-15	Not available

/1/ I=inhalation; IM=intramuscular; IV=intravenous; N=nasal; O=oral; PA = parenteral; R=rectal; SC=subcutaneous; SL=sublingual. /2/ Unless otherwise indicated. /3/ (P)=plasma; (S)=serum. /4/ Therapeutic dose. /5/ Usual dose, 25 mg. /6/ Also as anti-convulsant and in alcoholic psychoses. /7/ Range, depending upon use. /8/ At rate of 1 ml per 5 sec. /9/ In 15 sec; repeat in 30 sec as required. /10/ 2-4 times per day. /11/ 3-6 times per day.

Blood levels and dosages indicated in this table are not to be interpreted as recommendations of the National Academy of Sciences - National Research Council, nor does the appearance of a trade name imply such endorsement for the product or its manufacturer. These are presented for informative purposes only.

	Therapeutic Agent	Common or Trade Name	Use	Dosage	Route of Administration[1]	Minutes After Administration[2]	Blood Concentration[3] mg/100 ml[2]
			Diuretics				
57	Acetazoleamide	Diamox	Diuretic.	250 mg	O	60-120	
58	Meralluride	Mercuhydrin	Diuretic.	1 ml[12]	PA	180	Not available
59	Mercaptomerin sodium	Thiomerin	Diuretic.	130 mg (in 1 ml)	PA	180	Not available
			Hematopoietic Drugs				
60	Ferrous sulfate		Secondary anemia.	300 mg	O	Variable	105 µg as Fe (P)
61	Vitamin B_{12}		Pernicious anemia.	15 µg	IM	60	
			Hormones				
62	Corticotropin		Adrenocorticotropic hormone.	10 U.S.P. Units[13]	IV	Slow	
63	Cortisone acetate		Collagen diseases.	25 mg[14]	O	Slow	
64	Diethylstilbestrol		As estrogen.	0.5 mg	O	Slow	
65	Hydrocortisone acetate		Collagen diseases.	10 mg[10]	O	Slow	
66	Insulin(s)		Diabetes.	No official dose	SC	60-360[15]	
67	Methyltestosterone		As androgen.	10 mg	O or SL	Slow	
68	Thyroxine		Mild hypothyroidism.				
			Sulfonamides				
69	Sulfadiazine		Antibacterial.	4 g[16]	O	180-240	8, free form
70	Sulfamerazine		Antibacterial.	4 g[16]	O	180-240	9.8, free form
71	Sulfamethazine		Antibacterial.	4 g[16]	O	180-240	7.8, free form
72	Sulfasoxazole		Antibacterial.	4 g[16]	O	180-240	6-8, free form
			Vitamins				
73	Ascorbic acid	Vitamin C	Vitamin deficiency.	75 mg[17]; 150 mg[18]	O	Readily	1-2(P)
74	Nicotinic acid		Vitamin deficiency.	100 mg	O	Slow	
75	Riboflavin	Lactoflavin, Vitamins B_2 and G	Vitamin deficiency.	3 mg[17]; 5 mg[18]	O	Readily	
76	Thiamine HCl	Vitamin B_1	Vitamin deficiency.	25 mg	O	Readily	
77	Vitamin A		Vitamin deficiency.	25,000 Units[18] (adult)	O	Slow	0.03 mg; vitamin A alcohol 5×10^{-4}
78	Vitamin D, oleo- (synthetic)		Vitamin deficiency.	50,000 U.S.P. Units	O	Slow	
			Miscellaneous				
79	Carbarsone		Amebic dysentery.	250 mg	O		

/1/ I=inhalation; IM=intramuscular; IV=intravenous; N=nasal; O=oral; PA = parenteral; R=rectal; SC=subcutaneous; SL=subingual. /2/ Unless otherwise indicated. /3/ (P)=plasma; (S)=serum. /10/ 2-4 times per day. /12/ Equivalent to 39 mg Hg and 45 mg theophylline. /13/ In 8 hr infusion. /14/ Four times daily. /15/ Dependent on type. /16/ Initial dose. /17/ Requirement. /18/ Therapeutic dose.

337. BARBITURATES: PLASMA LEVELS AT AWAKENING

With each dosage administered, objective was to produce sleep. Plasma concentrations were determined at time of awakening. For many investigations this is the critical dose level, inasmuch as any significantly greater concentration would be a hypnotic or anesthetic level. Ranges, in parentheses, conform to estimate "b" of the 95% range (cf Introduction).

	Barbiturate	Animal	Dosage mg/kg[1]	Route of Administration[2]	Plasma[1] Concentration mg/100 ml
1	Barbital	Man	200	O	1.5[3]
2		Man	600[4]	O	0.8[3]
3	Hexobarbital	Rat	100	IP	4.1
4	5-Isopropyl-5-(2-methylpentyl)-2-thio-barbiturate, sodium	Dog	21	IV	0.64(0.38-0.90)
5	Pentobarbital	Man	800[4]	O	0.8[3]
6		Man	2000[4]	O	1.0[3]
7		Man	750-1000[4]	IV	0.8[3]
8		Dog	20	IV	1.5(1.1-1.9)
9		Dog	25	IV	1.7(1.3-2.1)
10		Mouse	50	IP(?)	2.6
11		Rabbit	15	IV	1.0(0.8-1.2)
12		Rabbit	25	IV	1.0(0.6-1.4)
13		Rabbit	30	IV	1.2(0.8-1.6)
14		Rabbit	35	IP	1.2(0.4-2.0)
15		Rat	30	IP	2.9
16		Rat	60	IP	2.0
17	Phenobarbital	Man	(?)	O	1.2
18	Secobarbital	Man	600	O	0.8
19		Dog	20	IV	1.1(0.9-1.3)
20		Dog	25	IV	1.2(1.0-1.4)
21		Rabbit	15	IV	1.0(0.8-1.2)
22		Rabbit	25	IV	0.8(0.4-1.2)
23	Thiamylal	Dog	21	IV	0.95(0.83-1.07)
24	Thioethamyl	Dog	20	IV	2.3(0.7-3.9)
25	Thiopental	Man	22	IV	1.3
26		Man	33	IV	1.7
27		Man	36	IV	2.3
28		Man	40	IV	1.9
29		Man	43	IV	2.0
30		Man	50	IV	2.6
31		Man	54	IV	2.5
32		Man	59	IV	3.3
33		Man	65	IV	2.7
34		Man	67	IV	2.8
35		Dog	10	IV	0.9[5]
36		Dog	20	IV	1.2(1.1-1.3)
37		Dog	25	IV	1.7[6]
38		Dog	30	IV	1.5[5]
39		Dog	35	IV	1.8[5]
40		Dog	40	IV	2.4[6]
41		Mouse	30	IV	3.2[6]
42		Mouse	45	IV	4.9[6]
43		Mouse	70	IP	2.7(2.3-3.1)
44		Mouse	70	IV	2.2[5]
45		Rabbit	25	IV	2.3(1.7-2.9)
46		Rabbit	27	IV	1.9(1.1-2.7)

/1/ Unless otherwise indicated. /2/ O = oral; IP = intraperitoneal; IV = intravenous. /3/ Approximate. /4/ Mg per individual. /5/ Estimated from graph. /6/ Serum.

338. SOME ORGANIC COMPOUNDS AFFECTING CELL DIVISION

Data in this table are only a representative sample of the voluminous literature on the subject.

Part I: EFFECTS ON MITOSIS AND MEIOSIS

#	Compound	Organism, Part Affected	Effect	#	Compound	Organism, Part Affected	Effect
	Interphase				**Anaphase**		
1	Auxin	Cambium		42	Caffeine	Onion root	Incomplete chromosome separation.
2	Glucose	Mouse epidermis	Division stimulated.	43	Ryanodine	Sea urchin egg	
3	Hypoxanthine	Chick osteoblasts		44	Trypaflavine	Rabbit fibroblast	
4	Indoleacetic acid	Onion root			**Telophase**		
5	Acridines	Chick fibroblasts		45	Aureomycin	Chick fibroblasts	
6	Azaguanine	Mouse tumors	Initiation of prophase inhibited.	46	Caffeine	Onion root	
7	Dyes	Frog sperm		47	Carbamates	Sea urchin egg	
8	Nitrogen mustard	Animals		48	Nicotine	Tobacco anthers	Cytoplasmic division suppressed.
9	Phenylacetic acid	Onion root		49	Quinone	Worm egg	
10	Cortisone	Onion root	Chromosome doubling within nucleus.	50	Rotenone	Sea urchin egg	
11	Naphthaleneacetic acid	Bean internodes		51	Sulfanilamide	Onion root	
12	Folic acid antagonists	Mouse intestine		52	Theobromine	Onion root	
13	Hydroquinone	Mouse intestine	Pycnosis from pre-prophase damage.	53	Nicotine	Pea seedling	Spindle remnant persists.
14	Neotetrazolium	Onion root					
15	Urethane	Mouse intestine		54	Sulfhydryl compounds	Yeasts	Cytoplasmic division enhanced.
16	Trypaflavine	Onion root	Destruction of interphase nucleus.	55	Chloracetophenone	Chick osteoblasts	Nuclear reconstruction retarded.
	Prophase			56	Thiourea	Chick fibroblasts	
17	Dichlorophenoxyacetic acid	Onion root			**Chromosome Effects Not Confined to One Phase**		
18	Nitrophenols	Sea urchin egg	Prophase blocked.	57	Acenaphthine	Onion root	
19	Protoanemonin	Corn root		58	Acridines	Onion root	
20	Glutathione	Amoeba proteus	Prophase accelerated.	59	Coumarin	Onion root	Breaks.
21	Urethane	Rabbit fibroblasts		60	Phenols	Onion root	
22	Tropolones	Tradescantia stamen hairs.	Precocious chromosome split.	61	Uracil	Onion root	
23	Trypan blue	Rabbit fibroblasts	Spindle formation slowed.	62	Urethane	Bean root	
24	Aureomycin	Onion root	Membrane dissolution delayed.	63	Epoxides	Bean root	
				64	Ethoxy caffeine	Onion root	Rearrangement within chromosome.
25	Acridines	Onion root	Reversion to interphase.	65	Mustards	Onion root	
26	Purines	Arbacia egg		66	Urethane	Peony buds	
	Metaphase[1]			67	n-Butyl gallate	Onion root	Adhesion.
27	Methylnaphthoquinone	Onion root	Abnormal chromosome orientation.	68	Dyes	Onion root	
28	Testosterone, estrone	Rabbit fibroblasts.		69	Acridines	Onion root	Pseudochiasmata.
29	Diphenyl	Wheat root	Rotate spindle.	70	Coumarin	Onion root	
30	Indoleacetic acid	Wheat root		71	Aminoacridine	Onion root	
31	Colchicine	Onion root		72	Aminobenzoate	Onion root	Chromatin diminished.
32	Mustard gas	Chick osteoblasts	Induce monopolar mitotic figure.	73	Phenols	Onion root	
33	Narcotics	Onion root		74	Ammonia	Tradescantia hairs	
34	Phenyl urethane	Sea urchin egg		75	Ammonium thiocyanate	Impatiens pollen mother cells	Dispersion and despiralization.
35	Carbamates	Sea urchin egg		76	Urea	Drosophila salivary glands	
36	Diethyl bromacetyl carbamide	Onion root	Induce multipolar spindle.	77	Glutathione	Worm regenerating tissues	Chromosome widened.
37	Ethyl mercuric phosphate	Corn seedling		78	Antibiotics	Onion root	
38	Methylnaphthohydroquinone diacetate	Onion root		79	Cysteine	Protozoa	Induced reduction.
				80	Nucleic acid	Onion root	
39	Streptomycin	Onion root	Revert to interphase.	81	Acenaphthene	Onion root	Centromere misdivision.
40	Alcohol	Onion root	Nucleolus neoformation.	82	Mustard	Tradescantia pollen mother cells	
41	DDT	Onion root					

/1/ See Part 2 (below) for metaphase block.

Part II: MITOTIC POISONS: METAPHASE BLOCKING AGENTS

#	Substance	Concentration	Animal	Tissue	#	Substance	Concentration	Plant	Tissue
1	Acenaphthine	Vapor	Drosophila melanogaster		20	Acenaphthine	Saturated	Colchicum	Root
2	Aureomycin	100 ppm	Chick embryo	Fibroblast	21	Aureomycin	50 ppm	Allium cepa	Root
3	Benzene		Mammal	Marrow	22	Benzene	Saturated	Allium sativum	Root
4	Colchicine	10^{-5} M	Chortophaga viridifasciata	Neuroblast	23	Colchicine	20%	Colchicum autumnale	Root
5	Coumarin	0.1%	Arbacia punctulata	Egg	24	Coumarin	Saturated	Allium cepa	Root
6	DDT	Saturated	Arbacia punctulata	Egg	25	DDT	Saturated	Allium cepa	Root
7	Dibenzanthracene	0.1%	Chick embryo	Fibroblast	26	Dibenzanthracene	1.5 ppm	Secale cereale	Root
8	p-Dichlorobenzene	Saturated	Paracentrotus lividus	Egg	27	p-Dichlorobenzene	Vapor	Triticum vulgare	Root
9	Epinephrine	0.01%	Chick embryo heart	Fibroblast	28	Epinephrine	1/100	Tradescantia occidentalis	Pollen tube
10	Ethyl-p-aminobenzoate	Saturated	Paracentrotus lividus	Egg					
11	Hexachlorocyclohexane	0.02%	Sphaerechinus granularis	Egg	29	Ethyl-p-aminobenzoate	M/400	Allium cepa	Root
12	Methyl anthranilate	Saturated	Paracentrotus lividus	Egg	30	Hexachlorocyclohexane	10^{-4} M	Cucurbita pepo	Root
13	Morphine	10^{-4} M	Chick embryo	Iris epithelium	31	Methyl anthranilate	Vapor	Linum usitatissimum	
					32	Morphine	0.1%	Vicia lutea	Root
14	Naphthoquinone	10^{-2} M	Tubifex	Egg	33	Naphthoquinone	10^{-3} M	Allium cepa	Root
15	Nicotine	1/8000	Rabbit fibroblast		34	Nicotine	Vapor	Nicotiana tabacum	Bud
16	Phenyl urethane	2×10^{-3} M	Strongylocentrotus lividus	Egg	35	Phenyl urethane	0.02%	Allium cepa	Root
17	Physostigmine	0.1%	Arbacia punctulata	Egg	36	Physostigmine	0.05%	Allium cepa	Root
18	Podophyllotoxin	10^{-4} mM	Echinarachnius parma	Egg	37	Podophyllotoxin	Saturated	Allium cepa	Root
19	Sulfanilamide		Paracentrotus lividus	Egg	38	Sulfanilamide	1/2000	Allium cepa	Root

339. HERBICIDES: PHYSICAL, CHEMICAL, AND BIOLOGICAL CHARACTERISTICS

Common and [Chemical Name]	Structure	Properties[1]	Solubility[2]	Oral Toxicity, Single Dose[3] LD50 mg/kg	Hazard to Humans[4]	Type of Activity
1 2,4-D [2,4-dichlorophenoxy-acetic acid]	Cl-ring-Cl; O-CH2-C(=O)-OH	MW=221.0;MP=139.2-140.5; BP=24149.4;sp gr=1.56530.	sl.s. w. (0.05%); i. oils.acet.	375 rat;368 mouse; 541 chick;100 dog; 800 rabbit.	Injurious to eyes; dust, strong sol. irritating to skin, mucous membranes; not a sensitizer.	Systemic weed killer.
2 Methyl ester of 2,4-D [methyl 2,4-dichloro-phenoxyacetate]	O-CH2-C-O-CH3	MW=235.0;MP=33-38;BP= 1197; sp gr=1.37037.8/4.	i. w.;v.s. aromatic oils.	650 g. pig.	Very slight; concentrate causes transient injury to eyes, irritation to skin.	Systemic weed killer.
3 Isopropyl ester of 2,4-D [isopropyl 2,4-di-chlorophenoxyacetate]	O-CH2-C-O-CH(CH3)CH3	MW=263.1;MP=22.8(fr. p.); BP=17010;sp gr=1.25120 (com'l).	i. w.;s. kerosene; v.s. xylene.	700 rat; 541 mouse; 550 g. pig;1420 chick.	Concentrate slightly irritating to skin upon prolonged contact.	Systemic weed killer.
4 n-Butyl ester of 2,4-D [n-butyl 2,4-dichloro-phenoxyacetate]	O-CH2-C-O-(CH2)3-CH3	MW=277.1;MP9(fr. p.); BP=160-170 15-2;sp gr= 1.23525/4.	i. w.;s. kerosene; v. s. xylene.	620 rat;848 g. pig;424 rabbit.	Concentrate slightly irritating to skin upon prolonged contact.	Systemic weed killer.
5 Propylene glycol butyl ether esters of 2,4-D [poly-propylene glycol butyl ether 2,4-di-chlorophenoxyacetate]	O-CH2-C-O(C3H6O)x-(CH2)3-CH3	MW=356(av.); liquid; sp gr=1.188 20/0.	i. w.;s. kerosene; v.s. xylene.	570 rat.	Concentrate causes transient injury to eyes; slightly irritating to skin upon prolonged exposure.	Systemic weed killer.
6 2-Butoxyethyl ester of 2,4-D [2-butoxyethyl 2,4-dichlorophenoxy-acetate]	O-CH2-C-O-CH2-CH2-O-(CH2)3-CH3	MW=321.2; liquid.	i. w.;s. kerosene; v. s. xylene.		Concentrate causes transient injury to eyes; slightly irritating to skin upon prolonged exposure.	Systemic weed killer.
7 Triethanolamine salt of 2,4-D [2,4-dichlorophen-oxyacetic acid tri-ethanolamine salt]	O-CH2-C-OH : N-(CH2CH2OH)3	MW=361-365;MP=142-144; sp gr=1.23720.	v.s. w.;i. oil.	2000 g. pig; 500+ chick.	Injurious to eyes; irritating to skin upon prolonged contact.	Systemic weed killer.
8 2,4,5-T [2,4,5-trichloro-phenoxyacetic acid]	O-CH2-C-OH	MW=255.5;MP=153.5-155; sp gr=1.800/0.	sl. s. w. (0.02%); sl. s. oil.	500 rat; 389 mouse; 381 g. pig;100 dog.	Injurious to eyes; dust and concentrate irritating to skin, throat, lungs.	Systemic weed killer.
9 Methyl ester of 2,4,5-T [methyl 2,4,5-trichloro-phenoxyacetate]	O-CH2-C-O-CH3	MW=269.5;MP=89-90.	i. w;sl. s. kerosene; s. xylene.			Systemic weed and woody plant killer.
10 Isopropyl ester of 2,4,5-T [isopropyl 2,4,5-trichloro-phenoxyacetate]	O-CH2-C-O-CH(CH3)CH3	MW=297.6;MP=42-43;BP= 157±0.5;sp gr=1.243-1.2620.	i. w.;sl. s. kerosene;s. xylene.	495 rat;551 mouse;449 g. pig;850 chick.	Transient injury to eyes from concentrate; slightly irritating to skin upon prolonged contact.	Systemic weed killer.
11 Propylene glycol butyl ether esters of 2,4,5-T [poly-propylene glycol butyl ether 2,4,5-tri-chlorophenoxyacetate]	O-CH2-C-O-(C3H6O)x-(CH2)3-CH3	MW=390.5(av.);liquid;BP= 193-200 2.5;sp gr=1.24-1.2550.	i. w.;s. kerosene; v.s. xylene.	890 rat;820 mouse;1000 g. pig; 360 rabbit; 2400 chick.	Transient injury to eyes from concentrate; slightly irritating to skin upon prolonged contact.	Systemic weed and woody plant killer.
12 MCPA [2-methyl-4-chlorophenoxyacetic acid]	O-CH2-C-OH	MW=200.6;MP=119-120; sp gr=1.3515.	sl. s. w. (0.1%); i. oil.	700 rat.	Injurious to eyes; concentrate slightly irritating to skin upon long contact.	Systemic weed killer.
13 Triethanolamine salt of MCPA [4-chloro-O-toloxyacetic acid tri-ethanolamine salt]	O-CH2-C-OH:N-(CH2CH2OH)3	MW=340.6-345.6;sp gr= 1.20620.	v.s. w.;i. oil.	1200 rat.	Injurious to eyes; concentrate slightly irritating to skin upon long contact.	Systemic weed killer.
14 Maleic hydrazide (MH) [1,2-dihydropyridazine-3,6-dione]	pyridazine-3,6-dione structure	MW=112;MP=290-295; sp gr=1.6025 (tech. grade).	sl. s. w. (0.6%); i. acet.	5800 rat.	No effect on eyes or skin.	Translocated.

No.	Name	Structure	Properties	Solubility	Toxicity	Hazard to eyes/skin	Action
15	2,4-DES [sodium-2,4-dichlorophenoxy-ethyl sulfate]	Cl₂-C₆H₃-O-CH₂-CH₂-O-SO₃·Na	MW=309;MP=170;density approx. 27 lb/cu ft; purity=90%+.	s. w. (25%); i. oil.	730-1400 rat; 250 rabbit.	Injurious to eyes and skin.	Translocated through roots; pre-emergence weed killer.
16	Sodium TCA [sodium trichloroacetate]	Cl₃-C-C-O·Na (O)	MW=185.4;MP=d.; purity=90% minimum.	v. s. w. ; i. oil.	5000 rat;3640 mouse;4280 chick.	Concentrate injurious to eyes; irritating to skin.	Translocated through roots; pre-emergence.
17	CIPC [isopropyl N-(3-chlorophenyl)-carbamate]	Cl-C₆H₄-N(H)-C(O)-O-CH(CH₃)₂	MW=213.6;MP=41.4;BP=247 d.; sp gr=1.18 30/20; purity=98-99%.	sl. s. w. (108 ppm); v. s. aromatic solvents.	5000-7000 rat; 5000 rabbit.	No hazard to skin. No problem from absorption or sensitization.	Residual pre-emergence; translocated through roots.
18	Monuron [3-(p-chlorophenyl)-1,1-dimethyl-urea]	Cl-C₆H₄-N(H)-C(O)-N(CH₃)₂	MW=198.6;MP=170;sp gr=1.25;purity=80%.	sl. s. w. (230 ppm); sl. oil (229 ppm).	3500 rat;670 g. pig;1500 rabbit.	None. No problem from absorption or sensitization.	Translocated; sterilant; residual pre-emergence.
19	[Ammonium sulfamate]	NH₄O₃ / H₂N-SO₂	MW=114.3;MP=131-132 (tech.)purity=80%.	s. w. (232 g/100 g).	3900 rat.	No hazard to skin from irritation; not a sensitizer.	Translocated; contact sterilant.
20	[Potassium cyanate]	KOCN	MW=81.1;MP=315;sp gr=2.056;purity=92%.	s. w. (72%);i. oil; sl. s. bz., al.	780‡ rat;1050 mouse;230‡ rabbit.†	—	Contact.
21	[Phenylmercuri-triethanolammonium lactate]	Hg-N[CH₂CH₂OH]₃ · OCOCHOHCH₃	MW=515;MP=126;purity=99%.	v. s. w;sl. s. oil; s. al., gly.	>0.67 g. pig; >0.10 monkey.	Seriously injurious to eyes; concentrate seriously injurious to skin; readily absorbed through skin.	Contact; translocated through roots.
22	PCP [pentachlorophenol]	Cl₅-C₆-OH	MW=266.3;MP=191;BP=310 d.;sp gr=1.949 25; purity=83%.	sl. s. w. (15 ppm); s. xylene, acet.	50-500 rat, g. pig, rabbit; chick.	Injurious to eyes; concentrate injurious to skin; toxic amounts readily absorbed through skin. Poisonous to humans and other warm-blooded animals.	Contact and/or pre-emergence weed killer; translocated through roots.
23	DNBP [4,6-dinitro-2-sec.-butylphenol]	OH; CH(CH₃)CH₂CH₃; 2×NO₂	MW=239.1;MP=39.3±0.3; BP=d.;purity=95%.	i. w.;s. oil, kerosene;v. s. xylene.	40 rat;25 g. pig;26 chick.	Painful, not injurious to eyes; not irritating to skin, but readily absorbed in toxic amounts. Poisonous to humans and other warm-blooded animals.	Contact and/or pre-emergence weed killer.
24	Triethanolamine salt of 4,6-dinitro-2-sec.-butyl phenol [triethanolammonium 4,6-dinitro-2-sec.-butylphenate]	OH·N[CH₂CH₂OH]₃; CH(CH₃)CH₂CH₃; 2×NO₂	MW=378.1;sp gr=1.104 20; purity=3 lb/gal DNBP	v. s. w.;i. oil.	45 rat;35 g. pig;28 chick.	Same as DNBP (above).	Contact and/or pre-emergence weed killer.
25	NPA [N-(1-naphthyl)-phthalamic acid]	C₆H₄(COOH)(CO-NH-C₁₀H₇)	MW=291.4;MP=175-180; sp gr=1.35-1.45;purity=95% minimum.	sl. s. w. (0.02%); sl. s. organic solvents.	>8200 (test animal not specified).	No hazard to skin; not absorbed.	Selective systemic pre-emergence weed killer.
26	Dalapon, sodium salt [sodium 2,2-dichloro-propionate]	H₃C-C(Cl₂)-COONa	MW=164.9;MP=193-197; purity=88% in formulations.	s. w. (50%); sl. s. oil(0.25%).	6590-8120 rat; >4000 mouse; 3360 g. pig; 5660 chick.	Irritating and injurious to skin; concentrate irritating to skin; no problem from absorption.	Systemic post- and pre-emergence weed killer.
27	2-(2,4,5-TP) [2-(2,4,5-trichlorophenoxy)propionic acid]	Cl₃-C₆H₂-O-C(CH₃)(H)-C(O)-OH	MW=268.4;MP=179-181; purity=95%*.	i. w., oil.	650 rat;600-1400 (esters) rat, g. pig, mouse, chick.	Concentrate injurious to eyes; irritating to skin upon prolonged contact.	Systemic weed and woody plants killer.
28	[Ethyl xanthogen disulfide]	(C₂H₅OCS₂)₂	MW=242.4(calc.);MP=27-29;BP=112 d.;sp gr=1.26 25/15.5;purity=80%.	i. w.;100% s. bz., acet.	603 rat;504 g. pig;781 rabbit.	Concentrate irritating and readily absorbed in toxic amounts. It is a sensitizer.	Contact, some pre-emergence.
29	Cyanamid [calcium cyanamide]	Not established. May be CaN-CN or Ca=N-C≡N	MW=80.1;MP=1300(subl.); sp gr=2.3*;purity 44-57%.	sl. s. w.;i. al.	1400 rabbit.	Injurious to eyes; concentrate irritating and injurious to skin on long contact.	Contact; pre-planting sterilant.
30	[Methyl bromide]	CH₃Br	MW=95.0;MP=-93(fr. p); BP=3.5 760;sp gr=1.732 0/0.78 4/6/16.	sl. s. w. (0.09%); s. bz.	75 g. pig; 50 rabbit.	Injurious to eyes; concentrate injurious to skin on prolonged contact. Poisonous.	Sterilant (seeds).
31	[Stoddard solvent]		MP=not more than 50% distilled at 177°C;sp gr=0.78 16/16.	i. w.	2000 rat.	Irritant upon prolonged or repeated exposure.	Contact selective.

/1/ av. = average; BP = boiling point, °C, with superscript, where present, indicating pressure; calc. = calculated; com'l = commercial; d. = decomposes; fr. p. = freezing point; MP = melting point; MW = molecular weight; sp gr = specific gravity (or density), with superscript indicating temperature of measurement (for liquids, sp gr of the solution is referred to that of water at the same temperature, unless otherwise indicated; subl. = sublimes, tech. = technical. /2/ acet. = acetone; al. = ethyl alcohol(95%); arom. = aromatic; bz. = benzene; gly. = glycerol; i. = insoluble; ppm = parts per million; s. = soluble; sl. = slightly; sol. = solution; solv. = solvent(s); v. = very; w. = water. /3/ g. pig = guinea pig. /4/ sol. = solution. /5/ Refers to 4 lb acid equivalent aqueous formulation.

Data are based upon separate lists compiled and issued during 1949-1955 by weed control conferences of United States and Canada. Classifications and terminologies used by the various conferences differ and have undergone modification. For purposes of this table the following general descriptive terms apply: S = species can be killed by relatively low concentrations of at least one formulation of 2,4-D in one or more foliage applications and at some stage of growth other than the seedling stage (during which many resistant and intermediate species are susceptible); I = species is severely injured or controlled by above treatments or can be killed by one or more foliage applications of higher concentrations (woody plants and herbaceous perennials frequently show response in top kill only); R = species is only slightly or not at all damaged by foliage applications,and control by 2,4-D is not feasible. Species resistant to 2,4-D are listed in Fn 1 appearing on page 396. Low concentrations range up to 1 lb acid equivalent per acre or 1 lb acid equivalent in 100 gal carrier (for woody plants). Higher concentrations range from 1-4 lb/acre (or 1-4 lb/100 gal) in many parts of the country. Still higher concentrations for control of woody plants may range from 3-16 lb/100 gal carrier, depending on species and method of application. Variations in response (e.g.,more than one classification symbol) may be attributed to differences in climatic conditions, soil properties, varieties, or to ecotypes within the species.

Species[1]	Response	Species[1]	Response
Annual and Winter Annual Weeds		**Annual and Winter Annual Weeds** (concluded)	
1 Bassia, five-hooked (Bassia hyssopifolia)	I	66 Mustard, blue (Chorispora tenella)	S
2 Bedstraw (Galium spp)	I	67 Mustard, hares-ear (Conringia orientalis)	S
3 Beeplant, Rocky Mountain (Cleome serrulata)	S	68 Mustard, tansy (Descurainia pinnata)	S
4 Beet, wild (Beta maritima)	I	69 Mustard, tumbling (Sisymbrium altissimum)	S
5 Beggar-tick (Bidens frondosa)	I	70 Mustard, field [charlock] (Brassica arvensis)	S
6 Bitterweed (Helenium tenuifolium)	S	71 Mustard, wild (B. kaber)	S
7 Buckwheat, wild (Polygonum convolvulus)	I, R	72 Mustard, wormseed (Erysimum cheiranthoides)	S
8 Bur, blue [stickseed] (Lappula echinata)	S	73 Nightshade, black (Solanum nigrum)	S, R
9 Bush, burning [annual kochia] (Kochia scoparia)	S	74 Nightshade, cut-leaved (S. triflorum)	I
10 Buttercup, field (Ranunculus arvensis)	S	75 Nightshade, hairy (S. vilosum)	I
11 Butterfly weed (Gaura parviflora)	S	76 Orache [saltbush] (Atriplex hastata)	S
12 Buttons, Australian brass (Cotula australis)	S	77 Ox-tongue, bristly (Picris echiodes)	I
13 Careless weed (Amaranthus palmerii)	S	78 Peppergrass (Lepidium spp)	S
14 Carpetweed (Mollugo verticillata)	I, R	79 Pigweed, prostrate (Amaranthus blitoides)	I
15 Cheeseweed (Malva parviflora)	S	80 Pigweed, rough (A. retroflexus)	S, I
16 Chickweed, common (Stellaria media)	S, I	81 Pigweed, tumbling (A. graecizans)	S, I
17 Cinquefoil, rough (Potentilla monspeliensis)	S	82 Pimpernel (Anagallis arvensis)	I
18 Clover, bur (Medicago hispida)	S	83 Pineapple weed [wild marigold] (Matricaria	
19 Clover, sour (Melilotus indica)	I	matricarioides)	S
20 Cocklebur (Xanthium spp)	S	84 Poppy, Roemeria (Roemeria refracta)	S
21 Cockle, purple [corncockle] (Agrostemma githago)	I, R	85 Poppy, white prickly (Argemone intermedia)	I
22 Coreopsis (Coreopsis tinctoria)	I	86 Primrose, cut-leaved (Oenothera laciniata)	S
23 Corn flower (Centaurea cyanus)	I	87 Puncture vine [goat-head, bull-head, galtrop]	
24 Cucumber, wild (Sicyos angulatus)	S	(Tribulus terrestris)	S
25 Dodders (Cuscuta spp)	I	88 Purslane (Portulaca oleracea)	I, R
26 Elder, marsh (Iva xanthifolia)	S	89 Radish, wild (Raphanus rhaphanistrum)	S
27 Fanweed [Frenchweed, stinkweed, pennycress]		90 Ragweed, common (Ambrosia artemisiifolia)	S, I, R
(Thlaspi arvense)	S	91 Ragweed, giant (A. trifida)	S
28 Fiddleneck (Amsinkia spp)	I	92 Rape, annual (Brassica napus)	S
29 Filaree, red stem [storksbill] (Erodium cicutarium)	I	93 Rape, bird's [common yellow mustard] (Brassica	
30 Filaree, white stem [storksbill] (E. moschatum)	I	campestris)	S
31 Flax, false (Camelina spp)	S	94 Redweed (Melochia corchorifolia)	S
32 Fleabane, Canada (Erigeron canadensis)	I	95 Rocket, London (Sisymbrium irio)	S
33 Fleabane, daisy and others (E. annuus,		96 Rocket, yellow (Barbarea vulgaris)	S
Erigeron spp)	I	97 Saltbush (Atriplex spp)	S
34 Flower-of-an-hour [bladder Ketmia] (Hibiscus		98 Shepherd's purse (Capsella bursa-pastoris)	S, I
trionum)	S	99 Smartweed [lady's thumb and others]	
35 Foxtail, yellow (Setaria glauca)	I, R	(Polygonum persicaria)	I, R
36 Galinsoga (Galinsoga parviflora)	S	100 Speedwells (Veronica spp)	I
37 Goatsbeard (Tragopogon spp)	S	101 Spikeweed, common (Centromadia pungens)	I
38 Goosefoot, narrow-leaved (Chenopodium leptophyllum)	S	102 Spurge, mat (Euphorbia glyptosperma)	I
39 Goosefoot, nettleleaf (C. murale)	S	103 Spurge, spotted (E. maculata)	I, R
40 Goosefoot, oak-leaved (C. glaucum)	I	104 Sunflower, wild (Helianthus annuus)	S
41 Gromwell, corn (Lithospermum arvense)	I	105 Telegraph plant (Heterotheca grandiflora)	I
42 Groundcherry (Physalis spp)	S	106 Thistle, blessed (Cnicus benedictus)	I
43 Halogeton (Halogeton glomeratus)	S	107 Thistle, distaff (Carthamus lanatus)	I
44 Hemp (Cannabis sativa)	I	108 Thistle, milk (Silybum marianum)	S
45 Henbit [dead-nettle] (Lamium amplexicaule)	I	109 Thistle, Russian (Salsola kali)	S, I
46 Indigo [coffee-weed] (Sesbania macrocarpa)	S	110 Thistle, sow[common, annual] (Sonchus oleraceus)	S
47 Indigo, curly (Aeschynomene virginia)	I	111 Thistle, sow [spiny or prickly] (S. asper)	S, I
48 Jewelweed (Impatiens pallida)	S	112 Thistle, yellow star (Centaurea solstitialis)	S
49 Jimson weed (Datura stramonium)	S	113 Tocalote (C. melitensis)	I
50 Knotweed, common [doorweed] (Polygonum aviculare,		114 Vervain (Verbena bracteosa)	S
P. erectum)	I, R	115 Vetches, wild (Vicia spp)	S
51 Knotweed, silver-sheathed (P. argyrocoleon)	I, R	116 Wintercress, bitter (Barbarea vulgaris)	S
52 Lamb's quarter (Chenopodium album)	S, I	117 Wormwood (Artemisia spp)	S
53 Lettuce, prickly (Lactuca scariola)	S, I	**Herbaceous Biennial and Perennial Weeds**	
54 Lettuce, wild (Lactuca spp)	I	118 Agroseris (Agroseris spp)	S
55 Mallow (Malva neglecta)	I	119 Alfalfa (Medicago spp)	S
56 Mallow, bull (M. borealis)	S	120 Alligator weed (Alternanthera piloxeroides)	I
57 Mallow, Indian [velvetleaf, butterprint]		121 Arrowhead [arrow weed] (Sagittaria spp)	I
(Abutilon theophrasti)	S	122 Artichoke, Jerusalem (Helianthus tuberosus)	S
58 Mallow, roundleaved or common (Malva		123 Aster (Aster spp)	I
rotundifolia)	S, I	124 Aster, woody (Xylorrhiza parryi)	I
59 Mare's-tail [Canada fleabane] (Erigeron canadensis)	I	125 Avens, three-flowered (Geum triflorum)	I
60 Mayweed [dog fennel] (Anthemis cotula)	I	126 Bedstraws, northern (Galium boreale)	I, R
61 Medic, black [yellow trefoil] (Medicago lupulina)	S	127 Bindweed, field [small flowered morning-glory]	
62 Mexican weed (Caperonia castaneaefolia)	S	(Convolvulus arvensis)	S, I
63 Morning-glory, annual (Ipomoea spp)	S	128 Bindweed, hedge [large flowered morning-glory]	
64 Mellein, turkey (Eremocarpus setigerus)	S	(C. sepium)	S
65 Mustard, ball (Neslia paniculata)	S	129 Biscuit root (Lomatium leptocarpum)	S

Data are based upon separate lists compiled and issued during 1949-1955 by weed control conferences of United States and Canada. Classifications and terminologies used by the various conferences differ and have undergone modification. For purposes of this table the following general descriptive terms apply: S = species can be killed by relatively low concentrations of at least one formulation of 2,4-D in one or more foliage applications and at some stage of growth other than the seedling stage (during which many resistant and intermediate species are susceptible); I = species is severely injured or controlled by above treatments or can be killed by one or more foliage applications of higher concentrations   (woody plants and herbaceous perennials frequently show response in top kill only); R = species is only slightly or not at all damaged by foliage applications, and control by 2,4-D is not feasible. Species resistant to 2,4-D are listed in Fn 1 appearing on page 396. Low concentrations range up to 1 lb acid equivalent per acre or 1 lb acid equivalent in 100 gal carrier (for woody plants). Higher concentrations range from 1-4 lb/acre (or 1-4 lb/100 gal) in many parts of the country. Still higher concentrations for control of woody plants may range from 3-16 lb/100 gal carrier, depending on species and method of application. Variations in response (e.g., more than one classification symbol) may be attributed to differences in climatic conditions, soil properties, varieties, or to ecotypes within the species.

Species[1]	Response	Species[1]	Response
Herbaceous Biennial and Perennial Weeds (continued)		Herbaceous Biennial and Perennial Weeds (concluded)	
130 Blueweed (Echium vulgare)	I	196 Milkweed, whorled (Asclepias verticillata)	S, R
131 Blueweed (Helianthus ciliaris)	I	197 Moonseed (Menispermum canadense)	S
132 Bouncing Bet (Saponaria officinalis)	I	198 Mule's ear (Wyethia amplexicaule)	S
133 Buckwheat, false (Polygonum scandens)	I	199 Mullein, common [Mullen] (Verbascum thapsus)	S, R
134 Burdock (Arctium minus)	S	200 Nettle, hedge (Stachys palustris)	S
135 Burnet (Sanguisorba minor)	S	201 Nettle, stinging (Urtica dioica)	S
136 Buttercup, tall and others (Ranunculus acris, R. spp)	I	202 Nettle, stinging (U. gracilis)	I
137 Camas, death (Zygadenus gramineus)	S	203 Nettle, white horse (Solanum elaeagnifolium)	S, R
138 Carrot, false (Pseudocymopteris montanus)	S	204 Nutgrass, northern (Cyperus esculentus)	I
139 Carrot, wild (Daucus carota)	S	205 Nutgrass, southern (C. rotundus)	I
140 Catnip (Nepeta cataria)	S	206 Onion, wild (Allium canadense)	I
141 Cattail (Typha spp, esp. T. latifolia)	I	207 Onion, wild (A. acuminatum)	S
142 Chickweed, field (Cerastium arvense)	S, I	208 Parsnip, wild (Pastinaca sativa)	S
143 Chickweed, mouse-ear (C. vulgatum)	S, I, R	209 Pentstemon, Rydberg (Pentstemon rydbergii)	S
144 Chicory (Cichorium intybus)	S	210 Pennywort, lawn (Hydrocotyle rotundifolia)	S
145 Cinquefoil [fivefingers] (Potentilla fillipes, P. glaucaphylla)	S	211 Pignut, Indian (Hoffmannseggia densiflora)	S
146 Cinquefoil, silvery (P. argetea)	I	212 Plantains, common (Plantago major)	S
147 Comfrey (Symphytum officinale)	I	213 Plantains (English) [buckhorn] (P. lanceolata)	S
148 Coneflowers (Ratibida spp)	S	214 Pokeweed (Phytolacca americana)	I
149 Cress, Austrian field (Roripa austriaca)	S	215 Potato, wild sweet [man-of-the-earth] (Ipomoea pandurata)	S, I
150 Cress, hoary [whitetop, whiteweed] (Lepidium draba, Cardaria draba)	S, I, R	216 Poverty weed (Iva axillaris)	S, I, R
151 Cress, western yellow (Radicula sylvestris)	I	217 Poverty weed, silver-leaved [white franseria] (Franseria discolor)	S
152 Daisy, ox-eye (Chrysanthemum leucanthemum)	I, R	218 Primrose, evening (Oenothera spp)	S
153 Dandelions (Taraxacum spp, esp. T. officinale)	S	219 Puccoon, hoary (Lithospermum canescens)	I
154 Dandelion, fall (Leontodon autumnalis)	S	220 Ragweed, bur [Woolly-leaved poverty weed] (Franseria tomentosa)	I
155 Dock, curled and others (Rumex crispus, R. spp)	I	221 Ragweed, false (Iva ciliata)	S
156 Dogbane (Apocynum cannabinum)	S, I	222 Ragweed, western [perennial] (Ambrosia psilostachya)	S
157 Dragonhead (Dracocephalum parviflorum)	S	223 Ragwort, tansy (Senecio jacobaea)	I, R
158 Fleabane (Erigeron spp)	S	224 Rocket, yellow (Barbarea vulgaris)	I
159 Fiddleneck (Amsinkia spp)	S	225 Rosin weed (Silphium spp)	S
160 Figwort (Scrophularia lanceolata)	S	226 Rush, slender (Juncus tenuis)	S
161 Four-o'clock (Mirabilis jalapa)	S	227 Sage, pasture (Artemisia frigida)	S, I, R
162 Garlic, wild (Allium vineale, Allium spp)	S, I	228 Sage, sand (A. gnaphaloides)	S
163 Gaura (Gaura spp)	S	229 St. John's-wort [klamath weed, goatweed] (Hypericum perforatum)	S, R
164 Geranium [cranesbill] (Geranium carolinianum)	I	230 Skeleton weed (Lygodesmia juncea)	I
165 Goatsbeard (Tragopogon spp)	S, I	231 Smartweed, swamp [tanweed] (Polygonum coccineum, P. muhlenbergia)	I, R
166 Goatsrue (Galega officinalis)	S	232 Sneezeweed, orange (Helenium hoopesii)	S, I
167 Goldaster, hairy (Chrysopsis villosa)	S	233 Sorrel, sheep (Rumex acetosella)	I, R
168 Goldenrods (Solidago spp)	S, I	234 Spurges, leafy (Euphorbia esula)	I, R
169 Gourd, wild (Cucurbita foetidissima)	I, R	235 Stonecrop (Sedum acre)	S
170 Groundcherry, perennial (Physalis spp)	I, R	236 Sunflower, false (Heliopsis scabra)	S
171 Gumweed (Grindelia squarrosa, G. perennis)	S	237 Sunflower, perennial (Helianthus spp, H. maximiliani, H. grosseserratus)	S
172 Hawkweed, orange (Hieracium aurantiacum)	S, I	238 Sweetclover (Melilotus spp)	S
173 Heal-all (Prunella vulgaris)	S	239 Teasel (Dipsacus sylvestris)	I
174 Hemlock, poison (Conium maculatum)	S	240 Thistle, artichoke [cardoon] (Cynara cardunculus)	S
175 Hemlock, water (Cicuta spp)	S	241 Thistle, biennial (Cirsium spp)	S
176 Horsetail (Equisetum spp)	S, I	242 Thistle, bull (Cirsium lanceolatum)	S, I
177 Hound's-tongue (Cynoglossum officinale)	I	243 Thistle, bull (C. vulgare)	I
178 Hyacinth, water (Eichhornia crassipes)	S	244 Thistle, Canada (C. arvense)	I
179 Iron weed (Veronia baldwinii)	I	245 Thistle, perennial sow (Sonchus arvensis)	S, I
180 Ivy, ground [creeping Charlie] (Glecoma hederacea, Nepeta hederacea)	S, I	246 Tule (Scirpus acutus)	I
181 King devil [yellow-flowered hawkweed] (Hieracium spp)	I	247 Vervains (Verbena spp)	S, I, R
182 Knapweeds [esp. Russian knapweed] (Centaurea spp, C. picris)	S, I, R	248 Vetch, two-grooved (Astragalus bisulcatus)	S
183 Larkspur, low (Delphinium geyeri)	S, I, R	249 Vetch, narrow-leaved (A. bipinnata)	S
184 Larkspur, Menzesis (D. menzesi)	S	250 Vetch, crown (Coronilla varia)	S
185 Larkspur, tall (D. barbeyi)	S	251 Vetch, wild (Vicia spp)	S
186 Lettuce, blue (Lactuca pulchella)	S, I	252 Wormwood, biennial (Artemisia biennis)	S, I
187 Licorice, wild (Glycorrhiza lepidota)	S	253 Yarrow, common (Achillea millifolium)	I, R
188 Locoweed (Oxytropis lambertii)	S	254 Yarrow, western (A. lanulosa)	S
189 Loosestrife, purple (Lythrum salicaria)	I	Woody Plants	
190 Lupine, mountain (Lupinus alpestris)	S	255 Alder (Alnus spp)	S
191 Lupine, silvery (L. argentus)	S	256 Apple, American crab (Pyrus coronaria)	S
192 Mallow, poppy (Callirhoe involucrata)	S	257 Aspen (Populus spp, esp. P. tremuloides)	S
193 Mallow, round-leaved or common (Malva neglecta)	S, I	258 Barberry, common and others (Berberis vulgaris, Berberis spp)	I, R
194 Milkweed, purple-flowered (Asclepias purpurea)	I		
195 Milkweed, woolly-pod (A. eriocarpa)	S		

Data are based upon separate lists compiled and issued during 1949-1955 by weed control conferences of United States and Canada. Classifications and terminologies used by the various conferences differ and have undergone modification. For purposes of this table the following general descriptive terms apply: S = species can be killed by relatively low concentrations of at least one formulation of 2,4-D in one or more foliage applications and at some stage of growth other than the seedling stage (during which many resistant and intermediate species are susceptible); I = species is severely injured or controlled by above treatments or can be killed by one or more foliage applications of higher concentrations, (woody plants and herbaceous perennials frequently show response in top kill only); R = species is only slightly or not at all damaged by foliage applications, and control by 2,4-D is not feasible. Species resistant to 2,4-D are listed in Fn 1 appearing on page 396. Low concentrations range up to 1 lb acid equivalent per acre or 1 lb acid equivalent in 100 gal carrier (for woody plants). Higher concentrations range from 1-4 lb/acre (or 1-4 lb/100 gal) in many parts of the country. Still higher concentrations for control of woody plants may range from 3-16 lb/100 gal carrier, depending on species and method of application. Variations in response (e.g., more than one classification symbol) may be attributed to differences in climatic conditions, soil properties, varieties, or ecotypes within the species.

	Species[1]	Response		Species[1]	Response
	Woody Plants (continued)			Woody Plants (concluded)	
259	Barberry, native [Colorado] (Berberis fendleri)	S	302	Hazel (Corylus spp)	S
260	Basswood (Tilia americana)	I, R	303	Hickory (Carya spp)	S, I, R
261	Birch (Betula spp)	S	304	Honeysuckle (Lonicera japonica)	S
262	Blackberry, common (Rubus spp)	I, R	305	Honeysuckle, bush (Diervilla lonicera)	S
263	Blueberry (Vaccinium spp)	S	306	Hornbeam (Ostrya virginiana)	S
264	Brier, common, green (Smilax rotundifolia)	I	307	Ivy, poison (Rhus radicans , R. toxicodendron)	S, I
265	Broom, Scotch (Cytisus spp)	I	308	Juneberry (Amelanchier alnifolia)	S
266	Buckbrush [coralberry, Indian currant] (Symphoricarpos orbiculatus)	I	309	Lambkill [laurel, sheep] (Kalmia angustifolia)	S, R
267	Buckbrush, western [western snowberry, wolfberry] (S. occidentalis)	S	310	Lead plant (Amorpha canescens)	S
			311	Lilac (Syringa vulgaris)	R
268	Burroweed (Haplopappus tenuisectus)	I	312	Locust, black (Robinia pseudoacacia)	S
269	Cactus, cholla (Opuntia imbricata)	I	313	Lotebush (Condalia obtusifolia)	S, I
270	Ceanothus, wedgeleaf (Ceanothus cuneatus)	I	314	Maple (Acer spp)	I, R
271	Cedar, salt (Tamarix gallica)	S	315	Maple, Manitoba (A. negundo)	S
272	Cherry, wild [black and red] (Prunus spp)	S	316	Mesquite, honey (Prosopis juliflora var. glandulosa)	S,I
273	Chestnut (Castanea dentata)	I	317	Mulberry (Morus spp)	I
274	Chokecherry (Prunus virginiana)	S	318	Myrtle, wax (Myrica cerifera)	S
275	Cottonwood (Populus spp)	S	319	Oak, black jack (Quercus marilandica)	S, I
276	Creeper, Virginia (Parthenocissus quinquifolia)	S	320	Oak, post (Q. stellata)	I
277	Currant, Alpine (Ribes montigenum)	I, R	321	Oak, laurel (Q. imbricaria)	I
278	Currant, American black (R. americanum)	S	322	Oak, white (Q. alba)	I
279	Currant, Hudson Bay (R. hudsonianum)	S	323	Oak, scrub (Q. illicifolia)	I
280	Currant, prickly (R. lacustre)	I, R	324	Plum, wild (Prunus spp)	S, I
281	Currant, red-flowered (R. sanguineum)	S	325	Poplar, balsam (Populus balsamifera)	I
282	Currant, red swamp (R. triste)	S	326	Prickly-ash, northern (Xanthoxylum americanum)	I
283	Currant, Sierra Nevada (R. nevadense)	S	327	Rose, Cherokee (Rosa laevigata)	S
284	Currant, squaw (R. cereum)	S	328	Sage, black (Salvia mellifera)	I
285	Currant, stink (R. brateosum)	S	329	Sage, purple (S. leucophylla)	I
286	Currant, western black (R. petiolare)	S	330	Sage, white (S. apiana)	I
287	Dewberry (R. vilosus)	I	331	Sagebrush, big (Artemisia tridentata)	S, I
288	Dogwood (Cornus spp)	S	332	Sagebrush, black (A. nova)	S
289	Elderberry (Sambucus canadensis, Sambucus spp)	S	333	Sagebrush, California or coastal (A. californica)	S
290	Elder, box (Acer negundo)	S	334	Saltbush (Atriplex spp)	S
291	Elm (Ulmus spp)	S, I	335	Sassafras (Sassafras albidum)	S
292	Fern, sweet (Myrica asplenifolia, Comptonia perigrina)	S, R	336	Silverberry (Elaeagnus commutata)	S, I
			337	Spicebush (Benzoin aestivale)	S
293	Gooseberries, gummy (Ribes lobii)	S	338	Sumac, poison, staghorn and others (Rhus spp)	S
294	Gooseberries, Sierra (R. roezlii)	S			
295	Gooseberries, Siskiyou (R. binominatum)	S	339	Sycamore (Plantanus occidentalis)	S
296	Gooseberries, white-stemmed (R. inerme)	S, I	340	Tamarisk (Tamarix spp)	I
297	Grape, wild and cultivated (Vitis spp)	S	341	Tobacco, tree (Nicotiana glauca)	S
298	Gum, sweet (Liquidambar styraciflua)	S, I	342	Tree-of-heaven (Ailanthus glandulosa)	S, I
299	Gum, tupelo or black (Nyssa sylvatica)	S	343	Viburnum (Viburnum spp)	I
300	Hardhack (Spiraea spp)	I	344	Walnut, black (Juglans nigra)	I
301	Hawthorn [thornapple] (Crataegus spp)	S, R	345	Walnut, white (J. cinerea)	S
			346	Willow, species highly variable (Salix spp)	S, I

/1/ Resistant species. Annual and winter annual weeds: Buckwheat, tartary (Fagopyrum tataricum); bur, buffalo (Solanum rostratum); catchfly, night-flowering and others (Silene noctiflora, Silene spp); chess (Bromus secalinus); crabgrass (Digitaria sanguinalis); foxtail, green (Setaria viridis); grasses, all weedy annual species; hemp-nettle (Galeopsis tetrahit); oats, wild (Avena fatua); sorrel, wood (Oxalis spp); spurrey, corn (Spergula arvensis). Herbaceous biennial and perennial weeds: beardtongue (Penstemon laevigatus); bittersweet [climbing nightshade] (Solanum dulcamara); bracken (Pteris aquilina, Pteridium aquilinum); cactus, prickly pear (Opuntia spp); campion, bladder (Silene latifolia, S. cucubalus); catchfly, night-blooming (S. noctiflora); cinquefoil, shrubby (Potentilla fruticosa); cockle, white (Lychnis alba); danthonia, timber (Danthonia intermedia); dogbane, spreading (Apocynum androsaemifolium); ferns, many kinds; goutweed (Aegopodium podograria); grasses, all species; harebell [bellflower] (Campanula spp); knotweed [smartweed] (Polygonum spp); larkspur, tall (Delphinium occidentale); mallow, alkali [white malva] (Sida hederacea); milkweed, climbing (Gonolobus laevis, G. gonocarpus); milkweed (Asclepias spp, A. siniaca); milkweed, showy (A. speciosa); nettle, horse (Solanum carolinense); quackgrass [twitch grass] (Agropyron repens); sedges (Carex spp); sorrel, wood or red ox (Oxalis spp); spurges, cypress (Euphorbia cyparissias); spurges, snow-on-the-mountain (E. marginata); strawberry, wild (Fragaria spp); tansy (Tanacetum vulgare); tick-trefoil (Desmodium spp); toadflax (Linaria vulgaris); whitetop, globe-podded (Cardaria pubescens). Woody plants: apple, common (Pyrus malus); aborvitae [white cedar] (Thuja occidentalis); ash, green (Fraxinus pennsylvanica); ash, white (F. americana); beech (Fagus spp); buckthorn, common or European (Rhamnus cathartica); cedar, dryland (Juniperus pinchota); cedar, red (J. virginiana); chokeberry (Aronia melanocarpa); elm, red (Ulmus fulva); hackberry (Celtis occidentalis); hemlock (Tsuga spp); locust, honey (Gleditsia triacanthos); mahonia (Mahonia repens); meadowsweet (Spiraea latifolia); mesquite, velvet (Prosopis juliflora var. velutina); orange, osage ["hedge," hedgeapple] (Maclura pomifera); pines (Pinus spp); rabbitbrush, small (Chrysothamnus stenophyllus); raspberry, wild [black and red] (Rubus spp); rhododendron (Rhododendron canadense); rose, wild [species variable, mostly resistant] (Rosa spp); spruces (Picea spp).

341. GROWTH REGULATORS PROMOTING CELL ELONGATION, RELATIVE ACTIVITY: PLANTS

The elongation effect is determined by floating 15 apical sections (3mm in length) of decapitated Avena coleoptiles, 90-92 hours old, on the surface of 25 ml of solution in a covered Petri dish at 24°C for 24 hours. Where concentrations greater than $10^{-5}M$ are required for an elongation of 0.15 mm, the pH of the solutions is adjusted to 5.6 with NaOH.

$$\text{Activity Index} = \frac{\text{molar concentration of indole-3-acetic acid inducing an elongation of 0.15mm x 100}}{\text{molar concentration of growth regulator inducing an elongation of 0.15 mm}}$$

	Compound	Activity Index		Compound	Activity Index		Compound	Activity Index
1	Indole-3-acetic acid (5 x 10⁻⁸M)	100	28	m-Trifluomethylphenoxyacetic acid	7	59	Benzoic acid	Inactive
2	Indole-3-acetonitrile	250	29	o-Iodophenoxyacetic acid	0.1	60	o-Aminobenzoic acid	Inactive
3	4-Chloroindole-3-acetic acid	140	30	p-Iodophenoxyacetic acid	Inactive	61	o-Bromobenzoic acid	0.1
4	2-Methylindole-3-acetic acid	1.5	31	2,4-Diiodophenoxyacetic acid	Inactive	62	m-Bromobenzoic acid	Inactive
5	4,7-Dichloro-2-methylindole-3-acetic acid	0.1	32	o-Methoxyphenoxyacetic acid	Inactive	63	p-Bromobenzoic acid	Inactive
6	5,7-Dichloro-2-methylindole-3-acetic acid	1.5	33	m-Methoxyphenoxyacetic acid	0.1	64	o-Chlorobenzoic acid	0.05
7	Indole-3-butyric acid	15	34	p-Methoxyphenoxyacetic acid	0.03	65	m-Chlorobenzoic acid	Inactive
8	Indole-3-propionic acid	1.5	35	o-Methylphenoxyacetic acid	0.2	66	p-Chlorobenzoic acid	Inactive
9	Phenoxyacetic acid	0.03	36	m-Methylphenoxyacetic acid	0.07	67	2,4-Dichlorobenzoic acid	Inactive
10	o-Bromophenoxyacetic acid	0.1	37	p-Methylphenoxyacetic acid	0.05	68	2,5-Dichlorobenzoic acid	1
11	m-Bromophenoxyacetic acid	2.5	38	2,4-Dimethylphenoxyacetic acid	0.5	69	o-Fluobenzoic acid	Inactive
12	p-Bromophenoxyacetic acid	1.5	39	2,5-Dimethylphenoxyacetic acid	0.2	70	Pentachlorobenzoic acid	Inactive
13	2,4-Dibromophenoxyacetic acid	12.5	40	3,5-Dimethylphenoxyacetic acid	Inactive	71	o-Iodobenzoic acid	Inactive
14	2,6-Dibromophenoxyacetic acid	Inactive	41	2,4,6-Trimethylphenoxyacetic acid	Inactive	72	2-Amino-3,5-diiodobenzoic acid	Inactive
15	2,4,6-Tribromophenoxyacetic acid	Inactive	42	o-Nitrophenoxyacetic acid	Inactive	73	2,3,5-Triiodobenzoic acid	50
16	o-Chlorophenoxyacetic acid	0.06	43	m-Nitrophenoxyacetic acid	0.2	74	3,4,5-Triiodobenzoic acid	Inactive
17	m-Chlorophenoxyacetic acid	2	44	p-Nitrophenoxyacetic acid	0.1	75	2,6-Dimethylbenzoic acid	0.05
18	p-Chlorophenoxyacetic acid	5	45	2,4-Dinitrophenoxyacetic acid	Inactive	76	2,6-Dimethyl-3-bromobenzoic acid	3
19	2,4-Dichlorophenoxyacetic acid	25	46	Phenylacetic acid	1	77	2,6-Dimethyl-3-chlorobenzoic acid	2
20	2,6-Dichlorophenoxyacetic acid	Inactive	47	α-Aminophenylacetic acid	Inactive	78	2,6-Dimethyl-3-iodobenzoic acid	2.5
21	3,5-Dichlorophenoxyacetic acid	Inactive	48	p-Aminophenylacetic acid	0.05	79	2,6-Dimethyl-3-nitrobenzoic acid	0.1
22	2,4,5-Trichlorophenoxyacetic acid	25	49	m-Fluophenylacetic acid	1.5	80	o-Nitrobenzoic acid	0.1
23	2,4,6-Trichlorophenoxyacetic acid	Inactive	50	p-Fluophenylacetic acid	1.5	81	Benzothiazyl-2-oxyacetic acid	0.5
24	2,4-Dichloro-6-methylphenoxy-acetic acid	Inactive	51	2,5-Dihydroxyphenylacetic acid	0.02	82	α-Naphthaleneacetic acid	50
25	2,4-Dichloro-5-nitrophenoxy-acetic acid	0.2	52	p-Iodophenylacetic acid	Inactive	83	β-Naphthoxyacetic acid	0.7
26	2-Ethyl-4-chlorophenoxyacetic acid	Inactive	53	2,4-Dimethylphenylacetic acid	0.5	84	2-Phenanthreneacetic acid	Inactive
			54	3,5-Dimethylphenylacetic acid	0.5	85	α-Phenoxypropionic acid	0.5
27	p-Fluophenoxyacetic acid	6	55	2,4,6-Trimethylphenylacetic acid	Inactive	86	Phenylacetonitrile	2
			56	p-Nitrophenylacetic acid	Inactive	87	α-Naphthaleneacetonitrile	100
			57	p-Phenylphenylacetic acid	Inactive	88	γ-Phenylbutyric acid	1.5
			58	Diphenylacetic acid	Inactive	89	p-Chlorophenylglycine	1
						90	β-Phenylpropionic acid	Inactive

342. GROWTH REGULATORS, RELATIVE ACTIVITIES: PLANTS

Data indicate relative activity as tested by various methods. For each compound listed, as the concentration increases, the response occurs from 0 to +1, and then to a -1 when the substance becomes inhibitory. Values are applicable to the maximum positive response.

	Compound	Avena Curvature Test	Pea Curvature Test	Rooting of Cuttings[1]	Tomato Petiole Bending	Bud Inhibition[1]	Inhibition of Root Elongation[2]
		Activity Relative to Indoleacetic Acid, %					
1	Indoleacetic acid	100	100	100	100	100	100
2	Indolebutyric acid	8	190	150	6	>100	10
3	Indene-3-acetic acid	1	20	45		14	20
4	α-Naphthaleneacetic acid	2.5	300	150	50	>100	4
5	β-Naphthoxyacetic acid	0	200	25	15	100	
6	Phenylacetic acid	0.02	10	0	0.6	0	0.3
7	Phenoxyacetic acid	0	0	0	Trace		
8	2,4-Dichlorophenoxyacetic acid	0	800-1200		100		30

/1/ Variability encountered with species. Generally, indolebutyric acid is most effective; napththaleneacetic and indoleacetic acids are 2nd and 3rd, respectively. /2/ In oat (Avena sativa).

343. GROWTH REGULATORS: APPLICATIONS AND USES

	Principal Use	Chemical	Concentration Range; Treatment
1		Indoleacetic acid; indolebutyric acid.	1-80 mg/L H₂O; soak cuttings 5-24 hr.
2			1-15 mg/ml of 50-95% alcohol; dip cuttings.
3			1-12 mg/g; talcum powder preparation.
4	Propagation of plants (rooting of cuttings)	α-Naphthalene-acetic acid.	1-50 mg/L H₂O; soak cuttings 5-24 hr.
5			1-5 mg/g; talcum powder preparation.
6		Indolebutyric acid and α-naph-thaleneacetic acid mixture.	1-8 mg/g (equal parts); talcum powder preparation.
7			1-40 mg (equal parts)/L H₂O; soak cuttings 5-24 hr.
8		Indolebutyric acid.	0.3 g/L; foliage spray.
9	Preharvest drop of fruit	α-Naphthalene-acetic acid.	10-20 ppm; water solution for apple spray.
10		2,4-Dichloro-phenoxyacetic acid (2,4-D)	8-24 ppm; water solution for some varieties of apples and oranges.
11		α-(2-Chloro-phenoxy)-pro-pionic acid.	25-40 ppm; water solution sprayed on flowers and large buds.
12	Fruit set of tomatoes	4-Chlorophen-oxyacetic acid[1].	30-40 ppm; water solution sprayed on flowers and large buds.
13		Naphthaleneacetic acid and derivatives[1,2].	40-60 ppm; water solution sprayed on open flowers and large buds.
14	Inhibition of buds	Methyl ester of α-naphthalene-acetic acid.	Vapor, foliage spray.
15		Acids, salts, and esters of 2,4-D.	0.1-1% sprays or 1/8 lb to 3 lb per acre, or water solutions, emulsions, or various formulations depending upon purpose.
16	Selective weed killing	Acids, salts, and esters of 2,4,5-trichlorophen-oxyacetic acid (2,4,5-T); 2,4,5-trichloro-phenoxypro-pionic acid.	0.1-1% sprays or 1/8 lb to 3 lb per acre, (especially used for woody plants), or water solutions, emulsions, or various formulations depending upon purpose.

/1/ Chemical modifies leaves. /2/ Esters used where vapor is necessary.

	Name and Synonym	Source	Nature	Molecular Formula	Structure	Crystal Form and Color[1]	Melting Point[1] °C
1	Actinomycin(s)[3] A	Streptomyces antibioticus, S. chryso-mallus	Weakly basic chromopep-tides, quino-noid	$C_{41}H_{58}N_8O_{11}$	Unknown	Red-vermilion platelets	250, 252 d.
	C			$C_{62}H_{89}N_{11}O_{17}$ or $C_{60}H_{83}N_{11}O_{16}$ (?)		Hexagonal bipyr-amids, prisms or needles	C_1:241-243 d. C_2:237-239 d. C_3:232-235 d.
2	Amicetin	Streptomyces vinaceus-drappus; S. fasciculatis	Amphoteric	$C_{29}H_{44}N_6O_9$	Partial	Hydr.: fine needles; anhy.: tan to colorless powder	Hydr.: 165-169; anhy.: 244-245; HCl:190-192
3	Amimycin (P.A.105)	Streptomyces antibioticus	Basic	$C_{37}H_{67}NO_{13} \cdot HCl$	Unknown	White crystals	Dihydr.:134-135; HCl:125-128
4	Amphotericin B (Fungizone)	Streptomyces spp	Amphoteric conjugated polyene	Unknown	Unknown	Clusters of long, deep yellow needles	170 d.
5	Anisomycin (Flagecidin)	Streptomyces griseolus	Basic	$C_{14}H_{19}NO_4$	Unknown	Long white needles	140-141
6	Aureothricin	Streptomyces celluloflavus n. spp		$C_9H_{10}N_2O_2S_2$		Golden-yellow needles	256-257 d.
7	Azaserine (O-diazoacetyl-L-serine)	Streptomyces fragilis	Amphoteric	$C_5H_7N_3O_4$		Light yellow-green needles	146-162 d. before melting
8	Bacitracin(s)[4] (Ayfivin)	Bacillus subtilis	Polypeptides	$C_{65}H_{103}N_{17}O_{16}S$ (proposed)	Uncertain	White amorp. powder	
9	Carbomycin[5] (Magnamycin)	Streptomyces halstedii	Monobasic	$C_{41-42}H_{67-69}NO_{16}$	Unknown	White needles or rect. plates	210-218 d.
10	Celesticetin	Streptomyces caelestis	Amphoteric	$C_{24}H_{38}N_2O_9S$	Unknown	Base: white glass	Salicylate: 139
11	Cephalosporin N (Synnematin B, Salmotin)	Cephalo-sporium sp	A hydrophilic penicillin	$C_{14}H_{21}N_3O_6S$		Ba salt: white powder	
12	Chloramphenicol (Chloromyce-tin)	Streptomyces venezuelae, S. omiyoensis	Neutral	$C_{11}H_{12}N_2O_5Cl_2$		Colorless plates or fine needles	149.7-150.7 corr.
13	Chlortetracycline (Aureomycin)	Streptomyces aureofaciens	Amphoteric	$C_{22}H_{23}N_2O_8Cl$		Base: acicular to bladed; HCL: rhomboid, lemon-yellow	Base: 168-169 HCl: d. above 210
14	Cycloheximide (Actidione)	Streptomyces griseus	Weakly acidic	$C_{15}H_{23}NO_4$		Colorless plates	119-121

/1/ a. =acid; abs. =absolute; ac. =acetic; acet. =acetone; al. =alcohol; aliph. =aliphatic; alk. =alkali(ine); amorp. =amorphous; anhy. =anhydrous; aq. = dilute; eth. =ether; filt. =filtrate; glac. =glacial; h. =hot; hex. =hexagonal; hydr. =hydrated; i. =insoluble; inact. =inactivated; lab. =labile; me.al. = prop. =propylene; pwd. =powder; pyr. =pyridine; rect. =rectangular; rm. =room; s. =soluble; sev. =several; sl. =slight; sol. =solution; solv. =solvent; were made. /3/ Other forms are: actinomycin B, C_1, C_2, C_3, D, Io, I_1, X_1, X_2. /4/ Various forms are: A, A^1, B, C, D, E, F_1, F_2, F_3, G. /5/ Carbo-

Optical Activity[1,2] $[\alpha]_D^+$	Solubility[1]	Absorption Maxima,[1] UV, mμ	Stability[1]	Some Other Reactions [1]	
$-320^{25} \pm 5$ in al.	s. chl., bz., al., acet., 10% HCl; sl. s. w., eth., i. pet. eth., dil. min.a., dil. alk.	230-250, 450	Thermostable except in alk. and strong acid.	Transient purple color with conc. NaOH; neg. color with al. $FeCl_3$; reduced by $Na_2S_2O_4$, H, over PtO to pale yellow, reversed by exposure to air. Neg. ninhydrin; gray-brown ppt. with Nessler's; yellow-green fluorescence in me. al. or glac. ac.a.	1
C_1: -349^{20} ± 10	s. bz., chl., acet.; less s. al., glac. ac. a.				
$+116.5^{24}$ in 0.1 N HCl	s. n-butanol saturated with w., dil. a., alk.; almost i.w., most org. solv.	305 in w. at pH 6.75; 316 in 0.1 N HCl; 322 in 0.1 N NaOH	Stable as dry solid and pH 3-5; unstable at pH >8.	Neg. Bratton-Marshall and ninhydrin until after hydrolysis; forms sl.s. helianthate and picrate salts.	2
-54 in me. al.	Phosphate s.w.; s. methyl ethyl ketone.	286-289 (broad, low intensity maxima)	0.1% aq. sol. st. at least 24 hr pH 2.2-9.	(?)	3
$+410^{24}$ at pH 5 in dimethylformamide	s. glac. ac.a.; i.w., al., acet.	225, 263, 273, 283, 345, 362, 382, 405	st. in solid form room temp.; unstable in sol.	Green color with conc. H_2SO_4; neg. $FeCl_3$, ninhydrin, biuret, Tollen's, Fehling's; absorbs Br_2 in glac. ac. a.	4
-30^{23} in me. al.	s. dil. a., al., me.al., acet.; less s.w., i.eth., CCl_4.	224, 277, 283, 3.34 mg in 25 ml me. al.	st. rm.temp.; thermolab. acid pH.	Infrared: 3545, 3450, 3320, 2890; 2800, 1725, 1610, 1582, 1515, 1470 ...... to 962 (recip. cm).	5
Inactive	sl. s. org. solv.; more s. chl.; i.w.	248, 312(?), 388	Very thermo- and acid stable.	Similar to thiolutin; acid hydrolysis yields an amine, $C_6H_6N_2OS_2$, identical with one so obtained from thiolutin.	6
$+9.7^{28}$ in 2N HCl	s.w., h. aq. me. al., al., acet.; sl. s. abs.me.al., al., acet.	250.5 at pH 7	Acidification at pH 2 results in vigorous evolution of N_2 and loss of biological activity.	Pronounced infrared peak at 4.66μ. Neutral solutions are stable.	7
$+52^3 \pm 2.5$ in 0.02N HCl	s.al., me.al., w.; sl.s.acet., pyr., i.eth., chl., pet.eth.	A, B, D, E: 253; C, G: 250, 268; F_1, F_2, F_3: 253, 288	Fairly thermost., esp. at pH 4-5.	Pptd. by heavy metal salts, tannic a., conc. NaCl; pos. ninhydrin; neg. $FeCl_3$, biuret; inact. by Cu.	8
-58.6^{25} in chl.	Salts: s. w., most org. solv.; base: i.w., hexane.	238, 327 in abs. al.	st. at room temp. at pH 5-7.	Neg. ninhydrin, $FeCl_3$; pos. Fehling's, Tollen's; decolorizes Br; violet color with 40% H_2SO_4.	9
$+124^{24}$ in 1 N HCl (salicylate)	s.a., alk.; i.pH 7-10; salts s.w.	130.3 in 0.01 N al. KOH; 183.7 in 0.01 N H_2SO_4	st. pH 5-7 at 24°C; unst. above pH 9.	Pos. $FeCl_3$, Molisch, Ekkert; neg. Benedict's, ninhydrin, iodoform.	10
Ba salt: $+ 187^{20}$ in w.	i. most org. solv.; Ba salt: s.w.; sl.s. me. al.; i.al.		Unst. rm. temp. below pH 4 and above pH 9; inact. heavy metal ions pH 7.	Inact. by penicillinase; acid hydrolysis eventually forms a penicillamine; penicillin W is very similar in nature.	11
-25.5^{25} in ethyl acetate; $+19^{25}$ in al.	s.al., me.al., prop.glycol; sl.s.w., chl., alk.; i.a., bz., pet.eth., veg.oils.	278	Thermostable; alk. labile.	Chlorine non-ionic; neg. $FeCl_3$, Molisch, biuret; not hydrolyzed by papain, trypsin; chymotrypsin, pepsin.	12
Base: -274.9^{23} in me.al.; HCl: -295.9^{23} in me.al.	Base: s, dil.a., alk., pyr.; less s.al., me.al., acet.; bz.; i.eth., pet.eth.; HCl: s.w., me.al.; sl.s.al.	HCl: 226, 264, 365 in 0.1M H_3PO_4	Thermolab. in strong a.; st. at pH 2.5; unst. at pH 7 at 25°C.	Ppts. with picric a., Reinecke's a., ammonium molybdate; UV shifts in acids, alkali; fluoresces in basic sol.	13
-2.8^{25} in me. al.	s.w., all org. solv. except saturated hydrocarbons.	287	Thermostable.	Inactivated at room temp. by acetic anhydride, sodium acetate, dil. alkali.	14

aqueous; bz. =benzene; chl. =chloroform; colorl. =colorless; corr. =corrected; cryst. =crystal(line); cult. =culture; d. =decomposes; def. =definite; dil.= methyl alcohol; min. =mineral; MP = melting; MW = molecular weight; neg. =negative; org. =organic; pet. =petroleum; pos. =positive; ppt. =precipitate; st.=stable; unst.=unstable; veg.=vegetable; v.=very; w.=water; wh.=white. /2/ Superscripts in this column are temperatures at which determinations mycin B may be isomeric with carbomycin, and has the same antimicrobial spectrum.

	Name and Synonym	Source	Nature	Molecular Formula	Structure	Crystal Form and Color[1]	Melting Point[1] °C
15	Cycloserine (Isoxazolidone, D-4-amino-3-; Oxamycin; Seromycin)	Streptomyces garyphalus, n. spp; S. or-chidaceus n. sp	Amphoteric	$C_3H_6N_2O_2$	[structure]	Colorless cryst.; fine white needles	154-156
16	Erythromycin (Erythrocin, Ilotycin)	Streptomyces erythreus	Basic	$C_{37}H_{67-69}NO_{13}$ or $C_{38-39}H_{69-71}NO_{13}$	Not completely determined	White needles	Base:136-140; HCl: 170-173
17	Erythromycin C	Streptomyces erythreus	Basic	$C_{36}H_{65}NO_{13}$	Similar to Erythromycin	Colorless needles	121-125
18	Framycetin (Actiline, Soframycine)	Streptomyces sp, similar to S. lavendulae	Basic	MW 1400-1500	Unknown	Chlorhydrate: white amorp. powder	Picrate: 189 d., corr.
19	Fumagillin (Fugillin, Amibex, Fumidil?)	Aspergillus fumigatus	Weak monobasic acid	$C_{26-27}H_{34-36}O_7$	$[C_{16-17}H_{25-27}O_3]-O-C=O$ $(CH=CH)_4COOH$	Colorless or light yellow crystals	189-194 d.
20	Gliotoxin (Aspergillin)	Aspergillus fumigatus, and several unrelated spp of fungi including Trichoderma viride		$C_{13}H_{14}N_2O_4S_2$	[structure]	Colorless plates or needles	195 d.
21	Gramicidin[6] (A component of tyrothricin)	Bacillus brevis	Neutral polypeptide	Possibly C_{148} $\cdot H_{210}N_{30}O_{26}$	Unknown	Colorless platelets	228-231
22	Gramicidin S	Bacillus sp, similar to B. brevis	Cyclic decapeptide	MW 1060-1340	Uncertain	Thin colorless needles	268-270
23	Griseofulvin	Penicillium griseofulvum; other P. spp	Neutral	$C_{17}H_{17}O_6Cl$	[structure]	Colorless rhombic or octahedral crystals	218-221
24	Neomycin A[7], B, C (Flavomycin)	Streptomyces fradiae; other S. spp	Basic	A: $C_{12}H_{26}N_4O_6$; B,C: $C_{23}H_{48}N_6O_{13}$ (proposed)	Unknown	A, base: white; HCl: white amorp. pwd.	A: 256 d.
25	Novobiocin (Cathomycin)	Streptomyces spheroides n.sp	Acid	MW 600-618	Incomplete	Nearly colorless	Polymorphic 153; 175
26	Nystatin (Fungicidin, Mycostatin)	Streptomyces noursei; S. fungicidicus	Amphoteric	$C_{46}H_{77}NO_{19}$ (proposed)	A tetraene	Yellow needles	160+ d. without melting at 250
27	Oxytetracycline (Terramycin)	Streptomyces rimosus; S. platensis; S. armillatus	Amphoteric	$C_{22}H_{24}N_2O_9$	[structure]	Pale yellow needles, thick hex. plates	Dihydrate: 181-182 d.; HCl: 190-194 d.
28	PA 114 A[8]	Streptomyces olivaceous	Neutral	$C_{25}H_{31}N_3O_6$ or $C_{35}H_{42}N_4O_9$	Unknown	Colorless needles	200 d.
29	Patulin (Clavacin, Clavatin, Claviformin, Expansine, Penicidin)	Penicillium spp; Aspergillus spp	Neutral	$C_7H_6O_4$	[structure]	Colorless; rhomboid plates, prisms	111-112
30	Penicillic acid	Penicillium spp; Aspergillus spp; synthesis	Monobasic acid	$C_8H_{10}O_4$	[structure]	Colorless rhombic or hex. plates	Hydrate: 64-65; anhy. 86-87.

/1/ a.=acid; abs.=absolute; ac.=acetic; acet.=acetone; al.=alcohol; aliph.=aliphatic; alk.=alkali(ine); amorp.=amorphous; anhy.=anhydrous; aq.=aqueous; ether; filt.=filtrate; glac.=glacial; h=hot; hex.=hexagonal; hydra.=hydrated; i=insoluble; inact.=inactivated; lab.=labile; me. al.=methyl alcohol; min.=min-powder; pyr. =pyridine; rect. =rectangular; rm. =room; s. =soluble; sev. =several; sl. =slight; sol. =solution; solv. =solvent; st. =solvent; st. =stable; /6/ Gramicidin (20%±) and tyrocidin (80%±) are components of tyrothricin. /7/ Can be derived from B or C, and is identical with Neamine. /8/ PA

Optical Activity[1,2] $[\alpha]_D^+$	Solubility[1]	Absorption Maxima,[1] UV, mμ	Stability[1]	Some Other Reactions[1]	
+116²⁵ in w.;+112²⁵ in NaOH	Dimerizes in solution.	226	Stable to alkali.	Pos. ninhydrin; ½ of the N exists as a primary amino group; D(-)serine and hydroxylamine isolated from hydrolyzates.	15
Base:-78²⁵ in al.;complex:-47²⁵ in al.	s.al.,chl.,acet.;less s.eth., w.;HCl:v.s.w., lower alcohols.	Base: 278 Complex: 274	st. at -25 to +4°C; st. 4 da at 37°C; unst. at 60-100°C.	One titratable group with pKa 8.6; activity not reduced by serum.	16
	Same as Erythromycin.	285 in me. al.	Similar to Erythromycin		17
Picrate: -32 in me. al.	Chlorhydrate: s.w.,me.al.; i.acet., eth., most org.solv.		Thermostable.	No guanidinic grouping; all N as primary amine; forms picrate, reineckate; resembles streptomycin and neomycin, but differs from both.	18
-26.6²⁵ in me. al.	s. most org. solv., dil. alk.; i.w., dil. a.	239, 304, 322, 336, 351	Thermolabile; light sensitive.	Neg. FeCl₃, Millon, Fehling's, Molisch;properties change on exposure to air for one week.	19
-239 to -256 in chl.; -290±10²⁵ in al.	s.ac.a.,acet.,CCl₄, chl., dioxane, HCl, me.al.; sl.s.w., bz., al.	270, 450	st. to acids; unst. to alkali and light.	Readily oxidized with Br₂-water, forming sulfates; yields H₂S when reduced; black ppt. with lead acetate in boiling alkali; in alk. sol. decolorizes KMnO₄, giving a green color.	20
+3²⁰in al.	s. lower alcohols, ac.a., pyr.; sl.s.abs.acet.; i.w., ether, hydrocarbons.	271, 281.5, 290.5	Thermostable.	Neg. Millon; pos. to most protein tests; hydrolyzed by acid; not digested by enzymes; forms a gel with picric acid.	21
-292¹⁸ in al.	s.al.,chl.,acet.; less s. abs.al.; i.w., a., alk.		Thermo- and acid stable.	Positive ninhydrin, biuret; neg. Millon, xanthoproteic, Pauly, Voisenet, Sakaguchi.	22
+370¹⁷ in chl.; +337²¹in acet.	s.ac.a.,dioxane,bz., eth.,al., dimethyl formamide (12-14%); sl.s.chl., toluene; i.w., pet.eth.	236, 252, 291, 324	Thermostable.	Neg. FeCl₃, HBr, alk. Na nitroprusside, pyridine; yellow color with H₂SO₄ or HNO₃; reacted with phenylhydrazine, but not with diazomethane or semicarbazide. Solutions in dimethylformamide up to 1% can be diluted with H₂O without precipitating.	23
A, base: +112.8²⁵in w.;HCl:+83²⁵in w.	s.w.;sl.s.me.al.;i.other org. solv.	End absorption only.	Thermo-, acid and alkali stable.	Pos. ninhydrin, Molisch, carbazole; neg. glucosamine, Tollen's; yields furfural on acid hydrolysis; all N present as primary amino groups.	24
-63²⁴ in al.	s.al., me.al., acet.; i. w., chl.; Na salt s.w.	307 in 0.1N NaOH; 324 in 0.1N HCl in 90% me.al.	Thermostable.	Reacts as dibasic acid (pKa at about 4 and 9).	25
-10²⁵ in glac.ac.a.; +21²⁵in pyr.	sl.s.al.me.al.,dioxane;i w.,pyr.,glac.ac.a., dimethylformamide;s.pyr.	280, 291, 304, 318	st. in cold; unst. at pH 2 or 9.	Neg. FeCl₃, Millon; pos. Molisch; decolorizes KMnO₄, Br-CCl₄; in conc. H₂SO₄ color change from violet to blue to black.	26
Dihydrate: -196.6²⁵ in 0.1N HCl;-2.1²⁵ in 0.1N NaOH	s.a., alk.; sl.s.acet., al., chl., w.; i.eth.; HCl: s.w.; i.eth., pet.eth., bz.	270, 370 in me.al. Dihydrate: 249, 276, 353 in 0.1 M KH₂PO₄, pH 4.5.	st. at acid pH; decreasingly st. at pH 7 and above at 37°C.	Pos. FeCl₃, Pauly, Friedel-Crafts, Fehling's Molisch; HCl pKa 3.49, 7.55, 9.24 in aq. sol., forms complexes with inorg. salts; Ba-Ca and Ba-Mg very i. in w.and ppts. readily at pH 8.5-9.5.	27
-207 in me.al.	s.al.,acet.,bz.;sl.s. w.;i.pet.eth.	220-230, 275	Thermostable.	Green with FeCl₃; pos. copper acetate, Br₂ in CCl₄.	28
Inactive	s.w., al., acet., chl.eth., dil.alk.;i.pet.eth.; bz.	276	Thermostable; rather labile to alkali.	Neg. FeCl₃, Schiff's; red color with alk.; yellow color with dil. ammonia, asparagine, amino acids; inhibited by serum, cysteine.	29
Inactive	s.h.w., al., eth., bz., chl.; i.pet.eth.	227	Stable.	No color with FeCl₃ in cold, orange-brown when heated; reddish-purple with strong ammonia on standing; no color with conc. H₂SO₄ or NaNO₂.	30

bz.=benzene; chl.=chloroform; colorl.=colorless; corr.=corrected; cryst.=crystal(line); cult.=culture; d.=decomposes; def.=definite; dil.=dilute; eth.= eral, MP =melting point; MW = molecular weight; neg.=negative; org. =organic; pet. =petroleum; pos. positive; ppt. =precipitate; prop. =propylene; pwd. = unst. =unstable; veg. =vegetable; v. =very; w. =water; wh. =white. /2/ Superscripts in this column are temperatures at which determinations were made. 114 B, with different chemical properties, is also formed during the fermentation.

	Name and Synonym	Source	Nature	Molecular Formula	Structure	Crystal Form and Color[1]	Melting Point[1] °C
31	Penicillin(s)[9]	Penicillium notatum, Westling; Penicillium spp; Aspergillus spp	Strong monobasic carboxylic acids	F: $C_{14}H_{20}N_2O_4S$ G: $C_{16}H_{18}N_2O_4S$ K: $C_{16}H_{26}N_2O_4S$ X: $C_{16}H_{18}N_2O_5S$		Colorless prisms	Na salts: F: 204-205 d. G: 215 d. X: 228-235 d.
32	Penicillin V	Penicillium chrysogenum	Acidic	$C_{16}H_{18}N_2O_5S$	$R=$ phenyl$-O-CH_2-$ (See Penicillin)	White crystals	120-128 d. (indefinite)
33	Polymyxin A,B,C,D,E (Aerosporin)	Bacillus polymyxa, various strains	Basic polypeptides	D:4HCl:$C_{50}H_{97}$·$N_{15}O_{15}Cl_4$;B_1·5HCl:$C_{56}H_{104}N_{16}O_{14}Cl_5$	Unknown	Birefringent, no definite structure	228-235 d.
34	Prodigiosin	Serratia marcescens	Red pigment; monoacidic base	$C_{20}H_{25}N_3O$		Lustrous square pyramids; dark red with a green reflex	151-152
35	Puromycin (Stylomycin)	Streptomyces alboniger; synthesis	Diacidic base	$C_{22}H_{29}N_7O_5$		White crystals	Base: 175.5-177 (uncorr.)
36	Spiramycin (Rovamycin)	Streptomyces ambofaciens	Mixture of organic bases	$C_{22-24}H_{33-34}NO_{7-8}$	Unknown	Amorphous powder	
37	Streptolydigin	Streptomyces lydicus	Strong enol acid	$C_{32}H_{45}N_2O_9Br_3$	Unknown	Orthorhombic; yellow	144-150
38	Streptomycin	Streptomyces griseus; S. bikiniensis	Strong base	$C_{21}H_{39}N_7O_{12}$		Reineckate: thin plates; HCl: white amorp. pwd.; tri-HCl: monoclinic prisms	Reineckate: 164-165 d. Helianthate: 220-226 d.
39	Streptothricin (See Neomycin)	Streptomyces lavendulae	Basic	$C_{13}H_{25}N_5O_7$, or $C_{20}H_{34}N_8O_9$?	Unknown	HCl and SO_4: wh. pwd.	Reineckate; 192-194 d.
40	Subtilin	Bacillus subtilis	Basic polypeptide	MW 3420 (found)	Unknown	Amorp. white pwd.	
41	Tetracycline (Achromycin, Panmycin, Polycycline, Steclin, Tetracyn)	Streptomyces spp, and reductive dehalogenation of chlortetracycline	Amphoteric	$C_{22}H_{24}N_2O_8$		Base: orthorhombic	anhyd.: 170-173 d.; HCl: 214
42	Thiolutin	Streptomyces albus	Neutral	$C_8H_8N_2O_2S_2$		Yellow needles	270 d.
43	Tyrocidne[3]	Bacillus brevis	Basic polypeptides	A: $C_{66}H_{87}N_{13}O_{13}$	Uncertain	HCl: colorless needles	A: 240-242 d.
44	Viomycin (Vinactin A)	Streptomyces floridae	Basic polypeptide	$C_{17-18}H_{31-35}N_9O_8$	Unknown	White crystals	SO_4: 280 d. anhyd.: 252 d.

/1/ a.=acid; abs.=absolute; ac.=acetic; acet.=acetone; al.=alcohol; aliph.=aliphatic; alk.=alkali(ine); amorp.=amorphous; anhy.=anhydrous; aq.=aqueous; bz.=filt.=filtrate; glac.=glacial; h.=hot; hex.=hexagonal; hydr.=hydrated; i.=insoluble; inact.=inactivated; lab.=labile; me.al.=methyl alcohol; min.=powder; pyr.=pyridine; rect.=rectangular; rm.=room; s.=soluble; sev.=several; sl.=slight; sol.=solution; solv.=solvent; st.=stable; unst.=un-
/3/ Gramicidin (20%±) and tyrocidne (80%±) are components of tyrothricin. /9/ For penicillin F, R=$CH_3-CH_2=CH-CH_2-CH_2-$;for G, R= phenyl$-CH_2-$;

Optical Activity[1,2] $[\alpha]_D^+$	Solubility[1]	Absorption Maxima,[1] UV, mμ	Stability[1]	Some Other Reactions[1]	
F: +276-316[20-25] in w.; G:301-325[25] in w.; K: +258[25]; X: +267 in w.	Acids: s.al., eth., esters;sl. s.w.;i.aliph.hydrocarb.;Na salts: s.w., al., me.al.;sl.s. ketones, ethylacetate.	G: 252, 257.5, 264 X: 278 F, K: no characteristic bands.	aq. sol. st. when pure; labile to acids, alk., heat, penicillinase.	Free acids hygroscopic, rapidly inactivated unless completely dry; inactivated by heavy metals; pptd. from sol. by aliphatic hydro-carbons; Na salts inact. in glac. ac. a., primary alcohols.	31
	s. eth., chl., al., me.al., acet.	268, 274 in water.	Free acid has much greater acid stability than other penicillins.		32
A,HCl:-42[20] in w.; B, HCl:-40[23] in w.	s.w., me.al.;less s.higher alcohols; i.eth., esters; base: sl. s.w.	No characteristic bands.	Thermo- and acid stable; alkali labile.	Pos. biuret, ninhydrin; neg. Molisch, Sakaguchi, Pauly; ppts. with picric, helianthic, flavianic, Reinecke acids.	33
	s.al., chl., eth., bromoform, bz.; i.w.	pH 7.4 in al., 225, 288, 337, 471, 539. pH 11 in al., 257, 281, 335, 468. pH 2.9 in al., 216, 296, 371, 541.	Thermostable.	Forms picrate, MP 176°C; salicylate, MP 178°C; benzoate, MP 170°C; perchlorate, MP 228°C (uncorr.).	34
-11[25] in al.	HCl: s. lower alcohols, w.; sl.s.ethyl acetate; i.pet. eth., chl.;Base: s.aq. alcohols; i.w., eth., pet.eth.	275 in 0.1 N NaOH; 267.5 in 0.1 N HCl	Thermo- and pH stable.	Readily forms a dihydrochloride or monosulfate; neg. Brady's; infrared: 3309, 3200, 3125, 1645, 1600, 1560, 1512, 1428, 1403, 1345, 1303, 1248, 1230, 1184, 1158, 1107, 1070, 1040, 998, 968, 930, 871, 820, 791, 758 (recip. cm).	35
	sl.s.w.; s. most org. solv.	231-232		Silicotungstic acid → white ppt.; picric acid → yellow ppt.	36
-65.7[25] in al. KOH	s. most org. solv.; i.w.; Na and K salts s.w.	262, 291, 335 in al. KOH; 357, 370 in al. H_2SO_4	Stable alk.; labile acid.	Pos. FeCl$_3$, iodoform; neg. Fehling's, Molisch, biuret, ninhydrin.	37
HCl: -84 in w.; SO$_4$: -79[25] in w.; tri-HCl: -86.1[26.6] in w.	s.w.;less s.lower alcohols; i. other org. solv.	End absorption only.	Stable pH 3-7; less stable to heat, acid, alkali.	Maltol produced by alk. hydrolysis; inactivated by cysteine, reactivated by iodine; acid hydrolysis yields streptidine, streptobiosamine; pos. Sakagu-chi; reacts rapidly with carbonyl group reagents.	38
-51.3[25] in w.	HCl: s.w., dil. mineral a.; i. eth., pet. eth., chl.	End absorption only.	st. pH 1-8.5; ther-molab. in cult. filt.	Pos. biuret, ninhydrin, Pauly; neg. FeCl$_3$, Molisch, Sakaguchi, Schiff's, Millon.	39
-29 to 35[23] in ac. a.	s.w., me.al., ac.a.; i. anhyd.al., acet., eth., chl.		Stable, esp. at pH 2.5.	Inact. by light, trypsin, me. al.; blue with FeCl$_3$; dialyzable.	40
-239[25] in me. al.; -257.9[25] in 0.1 N HCl	Trihydrate: sl. s.w.; HCl: s.w.	220, 268, 355 in 0.1 N HCl; 268, 363 in 0.01 M me. HCl; 246, 372 in 0.01 M me. NaOH.	st. in sol. at pH 7.0; 50% loss in 12 hr at pH 8.85; no loss in 0.1 N H_2SO_4 48 hr.	pKa 8.3, 10.2 in 50% aq. dimethylformamide; orange-yellow color with Ehrlich's in dil. HCl; chlortetracycline dehalogenated in presence of palladium yields tetracycline.	41
Inactive	s. most org. solv.; sl. s.w.	250, 311, 388 in me. al.	Acid stable; alkali labile.	Raney nickel treatment yields "desthiolutin" (MP 130-131°C); acid hydrolysis yields an amine, $C_6H_6N_2OS_2$ (see aureothricin).	42
A: -101[25] in al.	s. al., me. al., ac.a.; sl. s.w., acet., i. eth., chl.	A: 290	Thermostable.	Pos. ninhydrin, Millon; red color with diazoben-zenesulfonic acid; not digested by enzymes.	43
SO$_4$: -32 in w.	SO$_4$ and HCl: s.w.; i. most org. solv	268 in 0.1 N HCl; 282.5 in 0.1 N NaOH 268.5 at pH 7	Very st. in acid; less st. in alk.	Pos. Sakaguchi, biuret, Fehling's, ninhydrin; neg. maltol, Molisch, Benedict's.	44

benzene; chl.=chloroform; colorl.=colorless; corr.=corrected; cryst.=crystal(line); cult.=culture; d.=decomposes; def.=definite; dil.=dilute; eth.=ether; mineral; MP=melting point; MW=molecular weight; neg.=negative; org.=organic; pet.=petroleum; pos.=positive; ppt.=precipitate; prop.=propylene; pwd.= stable; veg.=vegetable; v.=very; w.=water; wh.=white. /2/ Superscripts in this column are temperatures at which determinations were made. for K, R=CH$_3$(CH$_2$)$_6$-; and for X, R=HO-⟨⟩-CH$_2$-

1 **ACTINOMYCIN(S):** IN VITRO: Inhibit some Gram-pos. and Gram-neg. bacteria, and certain fungi. IN VIVO: A inactive against Diplococcus pneumoniae and Streptococcus pyogenes infections in mice. Actinomycin C shows cytostatic activity against malignant tumors: Crocker sarcoma 180, Walker-carcinoma, mouse RC carcinoma. CLINICAL: C gave encouraging results in a few patients with lymphogranulomatosis. Inconclusive results in patients with a variety of inoperable malignant conditions.

2 **AMICETIN:** IN VITRO: Active against mycobacteria and Gram-pos. bacteria. IN VIVO: Active against Mycobacterium tuberculosis H37Rv in infected mice and against certain animal tumors. CLINICAL: Preliminary studies indicate that it is well tolerated in man when administered intramuscularly or intravenously.

3 **AMIMYCIN:** IN VITRO: Active against Gram-pos. bacteria, including mycobacteria. Active against some Gram-neg. bacteria (Hemophilus, Neisseria and Brucella), rickettsiae, large viruses and protozoa. CLINICAL: Effective in bacterial pneumonia and staphylococcal enteritis, especially in types resistant to other antibiotics. No serious side effects reported.

4 **AMPHOTERICINS A and B:** IN VITRO: Inhibits many pathogenic and saprophytic fungi. IN VIVO: B protected mice against systemic infection by Candida albicans, Histoplasma capsulatum, and Cryptococcus neoformans. Active against topical infection by Trichophyton mentagrophytes.

5 **ANISOMYCIN:** IN VITRO: Little or no antibacterial activity. Inhibits certain fungi, protozoa. IN VIVO: Active in Trichomonas foetus infection in mice. Protects guinea pigs from Entamoeba histolytica infection. CLINICAL: Favorable results vs Tr. vaginalis.

6 **AUREOTHRICIN:** IN VITRO: Active against Gram-pos. and Gram-neg. bacteria, mycobacteria and fungi. IN VIVO: Promoted growth of chicks with low concentration in diet; diet refused with increased concentration.

7 **AZASERINE:** IN VITRO: Inhibits Gram-pos. and Gram-neg. bacteria, fungi and protozoa. IN VIVO: Active against Plasmodium lophurae in chicks, meningopneumonitis virus and Rickettsia prowazekii in chick embryos. Cytostatic activity against mouse leukemia, Crocker mouse sarcoma, carcinomas. No protection against Mycobacterium tuberculosis or viruses.

8 **BACITRACIN(S):** IN VITRO: In general, active against Gram-pos. bacteria with little or no activity against Gram-neg. organisms or fungi. IN VIVO: Protects against Clostridia, Micrococcus pyogenes var. aureus and Streptococcus pyogenes infections. Active against Borrelia duttoni in mice, Treponema pallidum in rabbits. Inhibited Plasmodium lophurae in chicks. Active against pinworms in mice. Promotes growth in chickens, turkeys, some plants. Increases fertility and egg production in hens.

9 **CARBOMYCIN:** IN VITRO: Active mainly against Gram-pos. and a few Gram-neg. bacteria, large viruses, rickettsiae, and certain protozoa. IN VIVO: Good protection against Diplococcus pneumoniae, Micrococcus pyogenes var. aureus, Pasteurella multocida, Clostridium tetani, many rickettsiae, viruses of psittacosis, ornithosis, lymphogranuloma venereum, human and feline pneumonitis, and sporadic encephalomyelitis. Inactive against Bacillus anthracis, Entamoeba histolytica, and Mycobacterium tuberculosis. CLINICAL: Useful vs infections, particularly from Gram-pos. organisms resistant to penicillin and other antibiotics. Good response in M. pyogenes var. aureus and Streptococcus pyogenes infections; also in pneumonia caused by D. pneumoniae and Str. pyogenes. Promptly cleared lesions of Treponema pallidum. Good response in amebic dysentery; may be of value in granuloma inguinale.

10 **CELESTICETIN:** IN VITRO: Active against Gram-pos. bacteria. Only slight activity against Gram-neg. bacteria and fungi. IN VIVO: Provides complete protection vs Streptococcus hemolyticus and Micrococcus aureus in mice; increased survival time of mice infected with Diplococcus pneumoniae (mortality ratio unaffected). CLINICAL: Preliminary trials indicate it is well tolerated and relatively non-toxic.

11 **CEPHALOSPORIN N:** IN VITRO: Inhibits Gram-pos. and Gram-neg. bacteria; weakly active against Mycobacterium tuberculosis.

12 **CHLORAMPHENICOL:** IN VITRO: Active against Gram-pos. and Gram-neg. bacteria (including Mycobacterium tuberculosis), rickettsiae and larger viruses; no activity against fungi. Active against Entamoeba histolytica, Borrelia sp, Trypanosoma cruzi. IN VIVO: Protection in one or more laboratory animals against Borrelia anserina, B. novyi, Klebsiella pneumoniae, Pasteurella multocida, Past. pestis, Plasmodium berghei, P. gallinaceum, Salmonella gallinarum, Shigella paradysenteriae, Vibrio comma, many rickettsiae, and the viruses of lymphogranuloma venereum and psittacosis. Only slight protection against Bacillus anthracis, Diplococcus pneumoniae, Erysipelothrix rhusiopathiae, Listeria monocytogenes, Mycobacterium tuberculosis, Streptococcus pyogenes, Str. viridans and most viruses. Showed an effect vs experimental pinworm infestation. CLINICAL: Useful in a wide variety of infections by susceptible microorganisms; especially valuable against Gram-neg. infections and the rickettsioses. Favorable results in typhoid fever, bacillary dysentery, cholera, gonorrhea, chancroid, lymphogranuloma venereum, granuloma inguinale, urinary and intestinal tract infections, bacterial pneumonia, epidemic and scrub typhus, Rocky Mt. spotted fever, Q fever, psittacosis, brucellosis, tularemia, primary atypical pneumonia, syphilis, relapsing fever, bartonellosis (Carrion's disease), non-specific urethritis, smallpox, yaws, and tropical ulcer. VETERINARY: Useful in a wide variety of infections, e.g., diarrhea of calves, colts and lambs; conjunctivitis, keratitis, and gastroenteritis in dogs. MISCELLANEOUS: Inhibited stone fruit virus in cucumber plants, and tobacco mosaic virus in tomato seedlings.

13 **CHLORTETRACYCLINE:** IN VITRO: Active against many Gram-pos. and Gram-neg. bacteria, rickettsiae, some viruses, and certain protozoa. Active against Actinomyces bovis, Histoplasma capsulatum. IN VIVO: Good protection in one or more laboratory animals against Bacillus anthracis, Bartonella muris, Borrelia duttoni, B. novyi, Diplococcus pneumoniae, Erysipelothrix rhusiopathiae, Escherichia coli, Hemophilus influenzae, Klebsiella pneumoniae, Listeria monocytogenes; Pasteurella multocida, Plasmodium gallinaceum, Proteus vulgaris, Salmonella typhi, Streptococcus pyogenes, and several spp of Clostridium; active in experimental leptospirosis, plague and histoplasmosis; also in most rickettsial infections, and viruses of psittacosis, Herpes zoster, rabies virus in mice, and lymphogranuloma venereum. No effect on Mycobacterium tuberculosis, or viruses of H. influenzae B, canine distemper, Newcastle disease, poliomyelitis, mumps, or foot and mouth disease. Inhibits development of Yoshida ascites in rats. CLINICAL: Good response in bacillary infections by Aerobacter aerogenes, E. coli, Kleb. pneumoniae, Neisseria gonorrhoeae, Shigella spp; also in chancroid, granuloma inguinale, brucellosis, tularemia, streptococcal and D. pneumoniae infections, and sub-acute bacterial endocarditis. Highly effective in infections by most rickettsiae and larger viruses; also in primary atypical pneumonia. Useful in amebic and urinary tract infections, and in acute bronchitis, anthrax and otitis media. As effective as penicillin in secondary syphilis, yaws, and tropical ulcer. VETERINARY: Of value in bovine infections, e.g., calf scours, pneumonia, foot rot, vibriosis, chronic bloat, heartwater and mastitis; equine infections: strangles and septicemia; swine infections: dysentery, salmonellosis, baby-pig diarrhea and pneumonia; smaller animals: leptospirosis, coccidiosis, feline distemper, fowl typhoid, and topically for skin, eye, and ear infections. RESISTANCE: A considerable number of resistant strains of Micrococcus pyogenes var. aureus have emerged; in clinical experience this has not been a problem with other bacteria, e.g., Streptococcus spp, D. pneumoniae, Neisseria meningitidis and N. gonorrhoeae. MISCELLANEOUS: Wide usage as a growth stimulant for domestic and laboratory animals. Used as preservative for fish and poultry. Effective in control of crown gall tumor of tomato and other plants, and in many bacterial diseases of plants.

14 **CYCLOHEXIMIDE:** IN VITRO: Little or no effect on bacteria. Affects some phytopathogenic fungi, particularly yeasts, but most fungi pathogenic to animals are not susceptible, although Cryptococcus neoformans, Blastomyces dermatitidis, and Histoplasma capsulatum are inhibited. Active against Trypanosoma cruzi and Trichomonas sp. IN VIVO: Effective in control of some experimental amebiasis (Entamoeba histolytica). CLINICAL: Good response in a single patient with meningitis caused by Coccidioides immitis, and in a case of Cryptococcus neoformans meningitis. MISCELLANEOUS: Good control of powdery mildew and cherry leaf spot, but toxic for some plants. Effective as a rat repellant.

15 **CYCLOSERINE:** IN VITRO: Inhibits Mycobacterium tuberculosis (including strains resistant to isoniazid, pyrazinamide, and p-aminosalicylic acid); Gram-pos. and some Gram-neg. bacteria are inhibited only with high concentrations which also inhibit some fungi. IN VIVO: Relatively inactive against Myco. tuberculosis infection in mice; synergistic with dihydrostreptomycin. Good protection against Diplococcus pneumoniae, Escherichia coli, Klebsiella pneumoniae, Micrococcus pyogenes var. aureus, Pseudomonas aeruginosa, Salmonella schottmuelleri, and Streptococcus pyogenes. Suppressed murine typhus infection in chick embryos, and Borrelia novyi infection in mice. CLINICAL: Favorable responses in preliminary trials vs advanced pulmonary tuberculosis refractory to other agents. Good response in urinary infections by Aerobacter aerogenes, E. coli, Proteus, and Pseudomonas.

16 **ERYTHROMYCIN:** IN VITRO: Active primarily against Gram-pos. bacteria, but a few Gram-neg. organisms, certain rickettsiae and larger viruses are susceptible. Active against Entamoeba histolytica, Borrelia novyi and Trichomonas vaginalis. IN VIVO: Good protection against Corynebacterium diphtheriae, Diplococcus pneumoniae, Entamoeba histolytica, Streptococcus pyogenes; moderate protection against Hemophilus pertussis, Micrococcus pyogenes var. aureus, Listeria monocytogenes, Trypanosoma equiperdum. Not effective against Bacillus anthracis, Erysipelothrix rhusiopathiae, Klebsiella pneumoniae, Salmonella gallinarum, Trypanosoma cruzi, or rabies, poliomyelitis, lymphocytic choriomeningitis, influenza viruses. CLINICAL: Useful in infections by organisms resistant to penicillin and tetracycline. Highly effective in pneumococcus pneumonia and in infections by micrococci and streptococci, including pharyngitis, tonsilitis, scarlet fever and cellulitis. Favorable as well as indifferent results in gonorrhea, lymphogranuloma venereum, chancroid and donovanosis. Good responses in primary and secondary syphilis, trachoma, surgical infections and infections by E. histolytica. Topical therapy useful in acute pyoderma and acne vulgaris. VETERINARY: Effective in control of canine pneumonia, bronchitis, pyogenic surgical infections, otitis media and early cases of distemper. RESISTANCE: No significant cross-resistance between erythromycin and penicillin or most other antibiotics except carbomycin.

17 **ERYTHROMYCIN B:** IN VITRO: Antimicrobial spectrum similar to erythromycin.

18 **FRAMYCETIN:** IN VITRO: Active against Gram-pos. and Gram-neg. bacteria (including mycobacteria); low activity against fungi. CLINICAL: Topical therapy effective against staphylococcal infections.

19 **FUMAGILLIN:** Little or no activity against bacteria and fungi; active against certain protozoa and viruses. IN VITRO: Inhibits Entamoeba histolytica and Trichomonas vaginalis. Active against bacteriophages. In tissue cultures virucidal to eastern and western equine encephalitis, slightly active against influenza PR8, inhibits poliomyelitis (Lansing strain). IN VIVO: Highly active in experimental amebiasis; inactive against Borrelia novyi, Trypanosoma cruzi, T. equiperdum, and T. gambiense. No antiviral activity in mice with poliomyelitis (MM strain), influenza A, or swine influenza viruses. CLINICAL: Cleared majority of human E. histolytica cyst passers. Generally favorable results vs chronic intestinal amebiasis.

20 **GLIOTOXIN:** IN VITRO: Inhibits Gram-pos. and Gram-neg. bacteria and some fungi. Inactivates Gardner lymphosarcoma and various transplantable carcinomas of mice and rabbits. Sarcoma 180 implants rendered innocuous in mice. IN VIVO: No protection in mice against Streptococcus pyogenes, nor in experimental mouse tuberculosis. Post-treatment in mice failed to suppress implants of Sarcoma 180. MISCELLANEOUS: Good control in covered barley smut and wheat bunt; seed protective.

21 **GRAMICIDIN:** Primarily active against Gram-pos. bacteria. IN VITRO: Active in low concentrations against a wide variety of Gram-pos. bacteria; some Gram-neg. organisms inhibited at higher concentrations. IN VIVO: Small intraperitoneal injections gave high protection against Bacillus anthracis, Clostridium perfringens, Diplococcus pneumoniae, Micrococcus pyogenes var. aureus and Plasmodium gallinaceum. CLINICAL: Parenteral toxicity of gramicidin (or tyrothricin q.v.) precludes use in systemic infections. Topical therapy may be beneficial.

22 **GRAMICIDIN S:** IN VITRO: Antimicrobial spectrum similar to that of gramicidin. IN VIVO: Good protection against Clostridium perfringens infections. CLINICAL: Used topically in skin infections, empyema, with favorable results.

23 **GRISEOFULVIN:** IN VITRO: Antifungal. Inhibits numerous spp of zygomycetes, ascomycetes, basidiomycetes and fungi imperfecti. UTILIZATION: Protects plants against several phytopathogenic fungi.

24 **NEOMYCIN:** IN VITRO: Active primarily against Gram-pos. (including mycobacteria) and Gram-neg. bacteria and actinomycetes; little activity against fungi, viruses, or protozoa. IN VIVO: Good protection in experimental murine tuberculosis and against streptomycin-resistant strains of Mycobacterium tuberculosis. High protection against Bacillus anthracis, Hemophilus influenzae, Klebsiella pneumoniae, Micrococcus pyogenes var. aureus, Pasteurella multocida, Proteus vulgaris, Salmonella cholerasuis, S. gallinarum, S. schottmuelleri, S. typhi, S. typhimurium, Vibrio comma, and in experimental bubonic and pneumonic plague. Active against Hemophilus pertussis and Salmonella pullorum in embryonated eggs. CLINICAL: Effective pre-operative intestinal antiseptic. Of value in bacillary dysentery, amebiasis, and epidemic infantile diarrhea. Favorable results following topical therapy for many skin and ocular infections. Instillation favorable in cervicitis and vaginitis by Proteus spp, in non-gonococcal urethritis, peritonitis. Beneficial results in tuberculosis; nephro- and ototoxicity after prolonged parenteral administration limit usefulness. VETERINARY: A variety of gastrointestinal infections in domestic animals respond to oral therapy.

25 **NOVOBIOCIN:** IN VITRO: Active primarily against Gram-pos. bacteria, although a few Gram-neg. bacteria are inhibited. Active against strains resistant to commercially available antibiotics including penicillin. IN VIVO: Good protection against Micrococcus pyogenes var. aureus, Streptococcus pyogenes, Diplococcus pneumoniae, Hemophilus pertussis, Proteus vulgaris, Pasteurella avicida, Neisseria meningitidis. No protection against Klebsiella pneumoniae, Escherichia coli, Salmonella typhi, S. schottmuelleri, Shigella dysenteriae. No evidence of antituberculosis or antifungal activity in experimentally infected mice. No demonstrable activity against rickettsiae, viruses or protozoa in mice. Equally active orally or subcutaneously.

26 **FUNGICIDIN:** Active against fungi. IN VITRO: Inhibits many fungi. IN VIVO: Protects mice against Candida albicans, Coccidioides immitis, Cryptococcus neoformans, Histoplasma capsulatum and Sporotrichum schenckii. CLINICAL: Reduced number of C. albicans in fecal flora. Counteracts increase in gastrointestinal yeast flora accompanying oral tetracycline therapy. Oral doses effective against a variety of monilial infections.

27 **OXYTETRACYCLINE:** IN VITRO: Active against many Gram-pos. and Gram-neg. bacteria, actinomycetes, rickettsiae, larger viruses, and certain protozoa; no activity against fungi. IN VIVO: High protection in one or more laboratory animals against Bacillus anthracis, Borrelia anserina, B. duttoni, B. novyi, most Clostridium spp, Diplococcus pneumoniae, Hemophilus influenzae, Klebsiella pneumoniae, Micrococcus pyogenes var. aureus, Pasteurella multocida, Past. tularensis, Salmonella cholerasuis, S. enteritidis, S. typhi, S. typhimurium, Streptococcus pyogenes, and Vibrio comma. Active against Bartonella muris, Plasmodium spp. Suppressive effect against Brucella melitensis. Highly active against most rickettsiae, gray lung virus in mice and experimental feline pneumonitis virus. Effective in experimental rabbit syphilis, but less active on weight basis than penicillin. CLINICAL: Highly effective in treatment of infections by streptococci, micrococci, bacterioides, brucellae, D. pneumoniae, and in urinary tract infections. Useful for pre- and post-operative prophylaxis in bowel surgery, peritonitis, respiratory infections. Highly effective in most rickettsial diseases, psittacosis, lymphogranuloma venereum, granuloma inguinale and in amebic dysentery. Very effective in gonorrhea; preliminary trials in syphilis gave variable results. Favorable response in yaws, primary atypical pneumonia, Plasmodium falciparum malaria and P. vivax. Excellent response in pinworm infestation (Enterobius vermicularis); Balantidium coli infection and non-gonococcal urethritis have been treated with good results. Meningitis caused by H. influenzae or Neisseria meningitidis responded favorably. Topical therapy is effective in skin and ocular infections, including trachoma. VETERINARY: Good results vs mastitis, anaplasmosis, pneumoenteritis and metritis in cattle; necrotic enteritis in swine; chronic respiratory disease, infectious sinusitis and salmonellosis in poultry; pneumonia, wound infections, in dogs; pleuropneumonia in goats. RESISTANCE: Clinically, resistance strains of M. pyogenes var. aureus have emerged, but this has not become a problem with other bacteria. Organisms developing resistance generally exhibit cross-resistance to other tetracycline antibiotics. MISCELLANEOUS: Useful vs many bacterial diseases of plants. Growth stimulant for domestic and laboratory animals. Preservative for fish, poultry, vegetables and fruits.

28 **PA 114, A and B:** IN VITRO: A and B show independent activity against Gram-pos. bacteria including a wide variety of Micrococcus pyogenes var. aureus strains resistant to penicillin and other antibiotics. A and B synergise when combined in appropriate percentage combinations. IN VIVO: A and B separately showed little protection against Streptococcus pyogenes infections in mice. Mixtures, ranging from 1% of one to 99% of the other, showed a marked increase in activity. A partly purified product containing A and B in ratios produced during fermentation showed good protection against Streptococcus pyogenes, Diplococcus pneumoniae, and both normal and resistant strains of Micrococcus pyogenes var. aureus. No activity against yeasts or filamentous fungi. RESISTANCE: Similar to that shown by penicillin.

29 **PATULIN:** IN VITRO: Active against Gram-pos. and Gram-neg. bacteria, fungi. IN VIVO: Inactive against all bacteria and viruses tested. CLINICAL: Ointment of slight value in skin infections.

30 **PENICILLIC ACID:** IN VITRO: Active against some Gram-pos. and Gram-neg. bacteria, plant pathogenes and fungi.

31 **PENICILLIN:** IN VITRO: In general, highly active against Gram-pos. bacteria. Although some resistant strains are encountered, most strains of the following genera are sensitive to low concentrations: Bacillus, Clostridium, Corynebacterium, Diplococcus, Micrococcus, Streptococcus and Actinomyces. Spp of Borrelia, Leptospira and Treponema are highly sensitive. Excepting strains of Hemophilus and Neisseria, many of Gram-neg. strains are not sensitive, e.g., Aerobacter, Escherichia, Klebsiella, Pasteurella, Proteus, Pseudomonas, Salmonella, Shigella and Vibrio spp. Inactive against Mycobacterium spp, pleuropneumonia-like organisms, yeasts, fungi, viruses, rickettsiae and protozoa. IN VIVO: Activity in experimental infections similar to that of the IN VITRO antimicrobial spectrum. CLINICAL: Indicated in a wide variety of infections by susceptible organisms. Value established in veterinary practice. RESISTANCE: Has taken on proportions of a serious clinical problem only with Micrococcus pyogenes. The clinically isolated resistant strains are generally penicillinase producers, in contrast to the temporary resistance produced IN VITRO.

32 **PENICILLIN V:** IN VITRO, IN VIVO: Activity similar to that of penicillin. CLINICAL: Free acid, when given orally, yields higher blood levels than does penicillin.

33 **POLYMYXIN(S):** IN VITRO: Active mainly against Gram-neg. bacteria, many of which are inhibited at low concentrations. At higher concentrations some Gram-pos. bacteria are sensitive. IN VIVO: Good protection against Hemophilus pertussis, Klebsiella pneumoniae, Pasteurella multocida, Salmonella gallinarum, S. typhi. CLINICAL: Promising results vs Aerobacter aerogenes bacteremia, pertussis, acute brucellosis, Kleb. pneumoniae infections. Nephro- and neurotoxicity probably caused by impurities; purified preparations of polymyxin B and E seem to be safe intramuscularly. Pseudomonas aeruginosa infections, especially of the urinary tract, respond to treatment with B when other antibiotics have been ineffective. Oral therapy is of value in certain gastrointestinal infections. MISCELLANEOUS: Skin histamine released at areas remote from site of subcutaneous injections of B or E in rats.

34 **PRODIGIOSIN:** IN VITRO: Active against certain fungi and protozoa; little or no activity against bacteria. IN VIVO. Slight activity in mice infected with Diplococcus pneumoniae and Micrococcus pyogenes var. aureus. Oral doses in rodents prevented Entamoeba histolytica, Trypanosoma brucei and T. equiperdum infections. CLINICAL: Encouraging results in a few patients having disseminated coccidioidomycosis.

35 PUROMYCIN: IN VITRO: Active against certain Gram-pos. and Gram neg. bacteria, and protozoa. IN VIVO: Suppressed Trypanosoma cruzi and T. equiperdum infections. Good protection against T. equinum, T. evansi, T. gambiense, T. rhodesiense; little or no activity against T. congolense. Effective against Entamoeba histolytica and Toxoplasma gondii. Highly effective against mouse oxyurids (Aspiculuris tetraptera and Syphacia obvelata); partly suppressed tapeworm (Hymenolepis nana var. fraterna) in mice. Active against transplanted mouse mammary adenocarcinoma. Slightly effective against mouse sarcoma 180. No effect vs mouse or rat leukemia. CLINICAL: Effectively controlled T. gambiense and E. histolytica infections. Slight to moderate tumor regression in a few patients with disseminated or advanced incurable neoplastic disease.

36 SARKOMYCIN: IN VITRO: Inhibits Bacillus anthracis, Micrococcus pyogenes var. aureus, Salmonella typhi, S. paratyphi, S. schottmuelleri, Proteus vulgaris, Pseudomonas aeruginosa, Mycobacterium spp, Nocardia asteroides. Antifungal activity vs Histoplasma capsulatum, Trichophyton mentagrophytes, Torula utilis, Cryptococcus neoformans, Saccharomyces sake, Aspergillus niger, Penicillium chrysogenum. IN VIVO: Prolonged survival time in rats with Yoshida sarcoma and in mice with Ehrlich carcinoma. CLINICAL: Clinical improvement in 26 of 78 cases with inoperable carcinoma; no serious side effects observed.

37 SPIRAMYCIN: Principally active against Gram-pos. bacteria, particularly staphylococci resistant to the usual antibiotics. Inhibits streptococci, corynebacteria, neisseria, and certain strains of clostridia. Also active against some rickettsiae. Little activity against myco- and enteric bacteria. CLINICAL: Effective against respiratory, staphylococcal, streptococcal and gonococcal infections, virus pneumonia and exanthematic typhus.

38 STREPTOLYDIGIN: IN VITRO: Active against Gram-pos. bacteria, particularly species of Clostridium, Diplococcus, Streptococcus, and Mycobacterium. Also active against Pasteurella multocida. Slight antifungal activity. IN VIVO: Effective both orally and subcutaneously in mice infected with Streptococcus hemolyticus, Diplococcus pneumoniae and Pasteurella multocida.

39 STREPTOMYCIN: IN VITRO: Active against Gram-pos. and Gram-neg. bacteria, including mycobacteria. No activity against fungi, rickettsiae, or viruses. IN VIVO: Excellent protection is afforded in a wide variety of experimental infections, including Bacillus anthracis, Brucella abortus, Diplococcus pneumoniae, Micrococcus pyogenes var. aureus, Mycobacterium tuberculosis, Neissaria meningitidis, Pasteurella pestis, Past. tularensis, Streptococcus pyogenes, and spp of Hemophilus, Klebsiella, Pseudomonas, Salmonella, Shigella. CLINICAL: Used with success in tuberculosis, bacteremia, meningitis, pneumonia caused by Klebsiella pneumoniae, empyema and other pulmonary conditions, chancroid, tularemia, plague, glanders, skin infections by Proteus vulgaris, peritonitis and enteritis, corneal ulcers from Pseudomonas aeruginosa. RESISTANCE: Strains of Myco. tuberculosis may develop resistance very rapidly. The emergence of resistant strains of other organisms has also been noted, e.g., the majority of strains now being clinically isolated of Aerobacter aerogenes, Pseudomonas aeruginosa, Proteus vulgaris, and Streptococcus fecalis are resistant. MISCELLANEOUS: Widely used in agriculture vs several diseases including fire blights.

40 STREPTOTHRICIN: Active against Gram-pos. and Gram-neg. bacteria and certain fungi. IN VIVO: Active against Brucella abortus, Escherichia coli, Pasteurella tularensis, Salmonella schottmuelleri, S. typhi, Shigella dysenteriae. No protection against Diplococcus pneumoniae, Pasteurella pestis, Proteus vulgaris, Pseudomonas aeruginosa, and Streptococcus pyogenes. No activity in experimental tuberculosis of guinea pigs or hamsters, Suppressed Blastomyces dermatitidis in chick embryos. RESISTANCE: IN VITRO: Resistance develops fairly rapidly. Resistant strains frequently display cross-resistance to streptomycin and neomycin.

41 SUBTILIN: IN VITRO: Active mainly against Gram-pos bacteria and some fungi. Also active against bacteriophages. IN VIVO: Active experimentally against Bacillus anthracis, Diplococcus pneumoniae, Micrococcus pyogenes var. aureus, Streptococcus pyogenes in mice. Inactivated influenza PR8 and Newcastle disease viruses in embryonated eggs. Activity against Rickettsia tsutsugamushi, but less effective against Rickettsia rickettsi in chick embryos. MISCELLANEOUS: Used as a feed supplement for enhanced growth of chicks. May prove useful as a food preservative.

42 TETRACYCLINE: IN VITRO: Active against many Gram-pos and Gram-neg. bacteria, certain protozoa. IN VIVO: Good protection against Diplococcus pneumoniae, Klebsiella pneumoniae, Micrococcus pyogenes var. aureus, Pasteurella multocida, Salmonella typhi, Streptococcus mitis, Str. pyogenes. Some protection vs experimental tuberculosis in mice. Large doses suppressed Bacillus anthracis and Listeria monocytogenes, as well as virus of primary atypical pneumonia. CLINICAL: Effective in a wide variety of diseases including pneumonia, scarlet fever, otitis media, acute pharyngitis, sinusitis, osteomyelitis, laryngotracheobronchitis, meningitis, and in surgical infections and infections of the urinary tract and soft tissues. Excellent results vs acute gonorrhea. Favorable response vs non-gonococcal urethritis, acute or chronic brucellosis, lymphogranuloma venereum, donovanosis, chancroid, psittacosis, exanthematic typhus, Rocky Mt. spotted fever, acute amebiasis, bartonellosis (Carrion's disease), and bacillary dysentery caused by Shigella sonnei. Successful vs a variety of skin infections, and in trachoma. Appeared to benefit 36 of 45 patients with infectious hepatitis. VETERINARY: Effective vs mastitis, shipping fever complex and pneumonia in cattle; pneumonia-enteritis complex, mastitis and listeriosis is sheep; infectious scours and pneumonia in swine; distemper in cats; pneumonia, bacillary enteritis and distemper complex in dogs; psittacosis in parakeets. RESISTANCE: IN VITRO: Resistance developed in Escherichia coli and M. pyogenes var. aureus; pattern similar to that of penicillin, and in contrast to that of streptomycin. Cross-resistance to other tetracyclines.

43 THIOLUTIN: IN VITRO: Active against some Gram-pos. and Gram-neg. bacteria, fungi, and protozoa. IN VIVO: Slight suppressive effect experimentally vs Trypanosoma cruzi in mice, but toxic at doses administered. No activity against Plasmodium gallinaceum in chicks. MISCELLANEOUS: Sprays useful in control of apple tree fire blight and late blight of potato. Controls tomato wilt by Bacterium lycopersici. Improved germination of oat grain infected with Helminthosporium sativum.

44 TYROCIDINE: IN VITRO: Principally inhibits Gram-pos. bacteria, some protozoa. IN VIVO: In mice, exhibits little or no effect vs Clostridium perfringens or Micrococcus pyogenes var. aureus infections, and no activity against Trypanosoma cruzi.

45 TYROTHRICIN: IN VITRO: Active against many Gram-pos. and some Gram-neg. bacteria, certain fungi, spirochetes and protozoa. IN VIVO: In experimental infections protects against Bacillus anthracis, Clostridium perfringens, Diplococcus pneumoniae, Micrococcus pyogenes var. aureus, Plasmodium gallinaceum, Streptococcus pyogenes. CLINICAL: Toxicity precludes parenteral use; is ineffective orally. Used topically with success vs superficial indolent ulcers, mastoiditis, empyema, and wound infections when the predominating organisms are susceptible Gram-pos. bacteria. Effective vs tonsillitis, otitis, dermatoses, infected ulcers and burns, and infections of the eye and conjunctiva. Inhalation of an aerosol beneficial in various forms of bronchitis, in rhinopharyngitis and allergic rhinitis. Favorable results reported in treatment of puerperal mastitis by M. pyogenes var. aureus. VETERINARY: Of value vs acute and chronic mastitis in cattle, in topical treatment of infected wounds, canine dermatoses, sarcoptic mange, ear mites of dogs, cats, and rabbits, and leg mange of birds.

46 VIOMYCIN: IN VITRO: Inhibits some Gram-pos. and Gram-neg. bacteria and Mycobacterium tuberculosis (including strains resistant to streptomycin and neomycin). IN VIVO: Good protection vs Myco. tuberculosis. Strains sensitive or resistant to streptomycin equally responsive to to viomycin. Protects vs Bacillus anthracis, Klebsiella pneumoniae, Pasteurella multocida, Proteus vulgaris, Salmonella gallinarum, S. typhi. Some activity vs mouse leprosy bacilli (Mycobacterium lepraemurium). Suppressed Rickettsia typhi in embryonated eggs. CLINICAL: Effective in treatment of tuberculosis, but usefulness limited as its activity is less impressive than that of streptomycin or isoniazid and because of its toxic potentialities. RESISTANCE: Myco. tuberculosis may develop resistance. Strains resistant to streptomycin or neomycin not cross-resistant to viomycin.

346. ANTIAMEBIC DRUGS: PHYSICAL, CHEMICAL, AND BIOLOGICAL CHARACTERISTICS

	Common Name and Synonyms	Empirical Formula, Melting Point °C	Solubility[1]	Structure	Acute Oral Toxicity mg/kg	Activity in vitro µg/ml	Activity against Amebiasis in Laboratory Animals — Intestinal	Hepatic	Side Effects
1	Diiodohydroxyquinoline (Diodoquin)[2]	$C_9H_5I_2NO$ MP = 200-215 d.	i. w.; sl. s. al., eth., acet.; s. pyr., dioxane	$R_1=I$ (quinoline, OH, I)	LD_{50} 5000 (mouse)	200-1000	Cat, dog, guinea pig, rabbit, rat.		Diarrhea.
2	Chiniofon (Yatren)[2]	$C_9H_6INO_4S$ MP = 244-250 d.	i. w.; al.; s. alk.	$R_1=SO_3H$ (+Na salt)	LD_{50} 900 (guinea pig)	100-3000	Cat, dog, guinea pig, hamster, monkey, rat.		Diarrhea, nausea and vomiting; skin rash.
3	Iodochlorohydroxyquinoline (Vioform)[2]	C_9H_5ClINO MP=172 d.	i. w.; s. al., chl., ac. a.	$R_1=Cl$	LD_{50} 175 (guinea pig), LD_{50} 400 (cat)	125	Cat, dog, guinea pig, monkey, rat.		Diarrhea and abdominal pain; agranulocytosis.
4	Carbarsone[2]	$C_7H_9AsN_2O_4$	sl. s. w., al.; i. eth., chl.; s. alk.	H_2O_3As; $R_1=H$, $R_2=NHCOCH_3$	MLD 200 (guinea pig, MLD 150 (rabbit)	125-3300	Cat, dog, guinea pig, hamster, monkey, rabbit, rat.		Arsenic reactions (rarely); diarrhea, nausea; skin rash.
5	Diaphetarsine[2]	$C_{14}H_{18}As_2N_2O_6$ MP=above 250	s. alk.	$R_2=NH(CH_2)_2NH$ ... AsO_3H_2; $R_1=H$	LD_{50} 5000 (mouse), LD_{50} 2500 (rat)		Rat.		
6	Thiocarbarsone (C.C. 914)	$C_{11}H_{13}AsS_2N_2O_5$ MP=83-84	sl. s. w.; s. alk.	$H_2N-CO-HN-$ $As(S-CH_2-COOH)_2$	LD_{50} 1000 (rat)	20-100	Monkey.	Hamster.	Gastrointestinal.
7	Bismuthoxy-glycolyl-arsanilate (Milibis; Glycobiarsol)[2]	$C_8H_9AsBiNO_6$ MP=d.	i. most solvents.	$BiHO_4As-$ $NH-CO-CH_2OH$	Tolerated at 10,000 (rat)	33	Cat, hamster.		Arsenic reactions (rarely); diarrhea and abdominal pain; skin rash.
8	Emetine[3]	$C_{29}H_{40}N_2O_4$ MP=233-255 (2HCl·7H2O), MP=68, MP=74 (base)	s. al., chl., eth.; sl. s. w. (base).	(structure)	LD_{50} 30 (mouse)	0.5-31	Guinea pig, monkey, rat.	Hamster.	Diarrhea, dizziness; weakness and tenderness of skeletal muscles; damage to heart muscle.
9	Conessine (Wrightine; Neviine)[2]	$C_{24}H_{40}N_2$ MP=340 (2HCl), MP=125 (base), MP=222-224 (picrate)	sl. s. w.; s. acet., al.	(structure)			Rat.		Central nervous system (tremors, hallucinations, nervousness).
10	Biallylamicol (Camoform)[2]	$C_{28}H_{40}N_2O_2$ MP=210-212 (2HCl)	s. w.	(structure)	LD_{50} 3840 (mouse), LD_{50} 1706 (rat)	40-134	Dog, rat.	Hamster.	Gastrointestinal; skin rash.
11	Chlorbetamide (Mantomide; Win 5047; Letrenol)[2]	$C_{11}H_{11}Cl_4NO_2$ MP=110-113	i. w., eth.; s. al.	(structure)	LD_{50} >16,000 (mouse)	6.25-7.8	Hamster, rat, monkey.		
12	Chlortetracycline (Aureomycin)[2,4]	See Table for physical and chemical properties.				29-250	Dog, guinea pig, monkey, rabbit, rat.	Hamster (slight).	Gastrointestinal; proctitis.
13	Erythromycin (Ilotycin; Erythrocin)[2,4]	See Table for physical and chemical properties.				1000->1000	Monkey, rat.		Gastrointestinal.
14	Fumagillin (Fumidil)[2]	$C_{26-27}H_{34-36}O_7$ MP=189-194	i. w.; s. organic solvents, alk.	$[C_{16-17}H_{25-27}O_3]-OCO(CH=CH)_4-COOH$		0.07-0.13	Dog, guinea pig, monkey, rabbit, rat.		Gastrointestinal; vertigo; leucopenia; skin rash.
15	Oxytetracycline (Terramycin)[2,4]	See Table for physical and chemical properties.				133-400	Dog, guinea pig, monkey, rabbit, rat.	Hamster (slight).	Gastrointestinal; proctitis.

/1/ Abbreviations: ac.a.=acetic acid; acet.=acetone; al.=ethyl alcohol (95%); alk.=alkali; chl.=chloroform; d.=decomposes; eth.=ether; i.=insoluble; pyr.=pyridine; s.=soluble; sl.=slightly; w.=water.
/2/ Active in intestinal amebiasis. /3/ Active in hepatic amebiasis. /4/ Probably active in an indirect manner.

347. ANTIMALARIAL DRUGS: PHYSICAL, CHEMICAL, AND BIOLOGICAL CHARACTERISTICS

	Common Name and Synonyms	Empirical Formula, Molecular Weight, Melting Point, °C	Structural Formula	Oral Toxicity Mouse LD50 mg/kg	Max. Tol. Dose Dog mg/kg/da	Max. Tol. Dose Monkey mg/kg/da	Max. Tol. Dose Man g/da	Prophylaxis P. vivax[1]	Prophylaxis P. falc.[2]	Suppression, Active Infection P. vivax[1]	Suppression, Active Infection P. falc.[2]	Control of Acute Attack P. vivax[1]	Control of Acute Attack P. falc.[2]	Eradication of Infection P. vivax[1]	Eradication of Infection P. falc.[2]
1	Amodiaquin (Camoquin, CAM-AQI, Miaquin, SN 10,751)	$C_{20}H_{22}Cl\,N_3O$ MW = 355.86 MP = 208	(structural formula)		40	25-50	0.3	-	-	++++	++++	++++	++++	-	++++
2	Chlorguanide (Guanatol, Paludrine, Palusil, Proguanil)	$C_{11}H_{16}Cl\,N_5$ MW = 253.7 MP = 135	(structural formula)	24-70[3]	10-20	40-80	1.0	± to -	+	++	++ to ±	++	+ to ±	-	+ to ±
3	Chloroquine (Aralen, Nivaquine B, Resochin, SN 7618)	$C_{18}H_{26}Cl\,N_3$ MW = 319.88 MP = 87	(structural formula)	752	12	25-50	0.3	-	-	++++	++++	++++	++++	-	++++
4	Pamaquine (Plasmochin, Plasmoquine, Praequine)	$C_{19}H_{29}N_3O$ MW = 305.4 MP = 187-189 boils 0.2 mm	(structural formula)	68	3	6	0.06[4]	+ to ±	+ to ±	-	-	-	-	+	-
5	Primaquine (SN 13,272)	$C_{15}H_{21}N_3O$ MW = 259.34 MP = 175-179 boils 0.2 mm	(structural formula)	51	3	12	0.09	++ to ±	?	?	?	-	-	++	-
6	Pyrimethamine (Daraprim, BW 50-63)	$C_{12}H_{13}Cl\,N_4$ MW = 248.7 MP = 233-234	(structural formula)	92	5± i.v.[5]	2.5	0.025	+	++	+++	+++ to ±	++	++ to ±	++ to ±	++ to ±
7	Quinacrine (Atebrin, Atebrine, Erion, Mepacrine)	$C_{23}H_{30}Cl\,N_3O$ MW = 399.77	(structural formula)	510-800[4]	40-80	50	0.2	-	-	++	++	++	++	-	++
8	Quinine	$C_{20}H_{24}N_2O_2$ MW = 324.41 MP = 175-177	(structural formula)	350-950[4]	80	480	2.0	-	-	+	+	+	++	-	+ to ±

/1/ Plasmodium vivax. /2/ Plasmodium falciparum. /3/ Range of means reported by different investigators. /4/ Three divided doses. /5/ Intravenously.

348. RODENTICIDES: PHYSICAL AND BIOLOGICAL CHARACTERISTICS

	Common Name	Chemical Name	Formula	Molecular Weight	Crystalline Form, Color, Density (d)	Melting Point °C	Solubility[1]	Lethal Dose (mg/kg)[2] and Relative Effectiveness[3]			
								Norway Rats	Roof Rats	House Mice	Other Rodents
1	ANTU	Urea, 1-(1-naphthyl)-2-thio-	$C_{11}H_{10}N_2S$	202.27	Gray prisms from al.	198	i.w., eth.;s. h.al.	6-8 (+++)[4]	(-)	25-130 (-)	100-400 (-)
2	Arsenic; white arsenic	Arsenic trioxide	As_2O_3	197.82	White crystals or amorphous; d = 3.71.	Sublimes	sl.s.w.;s.alk., HCl, carbonates	25-100 (++ to +++)[5]	25-100 (++ to +++)[5]	(-)	(-)
3	Barium carbonate	Barium carbonate	$BaCO_3$	197.37	White rhomboids; d = 4.43.	dec.: 1300	i.w.;s.HCl, HNO_3, NH_4Cl	750-1480 (+)	(-)	(-)	150+ (-)
4	Fumarin	Coumarin, 3-(1'-furyl-2'-acetyl)-ethyl-4-hydroxy-	$C_{17}H_{14}O_3$	298	White powder.	121-123	i.w.;s.org. solv., alk.	5[6] (+++)	5[6] (+++)	5[6] (+++)	
5	Phosphorus, yellow	Yellow phosphorus	P_4	124.08	White or yellowish cubic or waxy solid; d = 1.82.	44.1	i.w.;s.chl., bz., CS_2	1.7 (++)	1.7 (++)	(-)	(-)
6	Pival	1,3-Indandione, 2-pivaloyl-[7]	$C_{14}H_{14}O_3$	230.27	Yellow needles.	108-110	i.w.;s.org. solv., alk.	5[6] (+++)	5[6] (+++)	5[6] (+++)	
7	Red squill[8]				Red powder.		Sl.s.w., acet., chl.;glucoside extr. by al.	400-600 (++)[9]	(-)	(-)	(-)
8	Sodium fluoroacetate; compound 1080	Fluoacetic acid, sodium salt	FCH_2COONa	100.01	White powder.	dec.:201-204	s.w.	2-5 (+++)	2 (+++)	10 (+++)	1.4-2.2 (+++)
9	Strychnine	Strychnine	$C_{21}H_{22}N_2O_2$	334.40	Rhombic crystals from al.	268-290	i.w.;s.chl.	16 (-)	(-)	6 (++)	(++)
10	Strychnine sulfate	Strychnine sulfate	$(C_{21}H_{22}N_2O_2)_2 \cdot H_2SO_4 \cdot 5H_2O$	856.97	Colorless monoclinic crystals.	dec.: 200	sl.s.2.,al.; i.eth.;s.gly.	4.8 (-)	(-)	8 (++)	(++)
11	Thallium sulfate	Thallium or thallous sulfate	Tl_2SO_4	504.84	White rhombic crystals; d = 6.77.	632	sl.s.c.w.; s.h.w.	16-25 (+++)	25 (+++)	25 (+++)	
12	Warfarin	Coumarin, 3-(α-acetonylbenzyl)-4-hydroxy-[7]	$C_{19}H_{16}O_4$	308.32	Colorless needles from al.	159-161	i.w.;s.al., acet., alk.	5[6] (+++)	5-20[6] (+++)	5-10[6] (+++)	
13	Zinc phosphide	Zinc phosphide	Zn_3P_2	258.11	Dark gray cubic crystals; d = 4.55	420+	i.w.;dec.with evolution of PH_3 in acids.	40 (++)	40 (++)	40 (++)	(++)

	Common Name	Physiological Effects			Rate of Action	Relation to Man and Other Animals			
		Cumulation (Fatal)	Tolerance Developed	Cause of Death		Secondary Poisoning	Skin Absorption	Hazard in Use	Antidote[10]
1	ANTU	No	Yes	Pulmonary edema; pleural effusion.	Slow.	No	No	Moderate	None.
2	Arsenic; white arsenic	No	Yes	Kidney damage; gastro-enteritis; CNS affected.	Slow	No	No[11]	Moderate	Milk of magnesia, milk and H_2O, oxide of iron.
3	Barium carbonate	No	No	Intestinal spasm; digitalis-like action; CNS paralysis.	Slow.	No	No	Slight	Magnesium sulfate.
4	Fumarin	Yes	No	Blood loss from internal or external hemorrhage.	Very slow, 5-10 days exposure required.	No		Slight	Vitamin K, blood transfusions.
5	Phosphorus, yellow	No	No	Heart paralysis; liver and gastrointestinal damage.	Fast.	No	No	Moderate	Copper sulfate, followed with lavage or emetic; cathartic and water; avoid fats and oils.
6	Pival	Yes	No	Blood loss from internal or external hemorrhage.	Very slow, 5-10 days exposure required.	No		Slight	Vitamin K, blood transfusions.
7	Red squill[8]	No	No	Heart and respiratory paralysis.	Slow.	No	No	Slight	Acts as emetic in animals capable of vomiting. Treat as for digitalis poisoning.
8	Sodium fluoroacetate; compound 1080	No	No	Heart and CNS paralysis.	Fast.	Yes	No[11]	Extreme	None reliable; monacetin or ethyl alcohol and acetic acid recommended. Rapid i.m. injection of atropine salts (3 mg) effective.
9	Strychnine	No	No	Convulsions from hyperstimulation; asphyxia.	Very fast.	No	No	Moderate	No emetic after 10 min. or after onset of convulsions; sedative, charcoal in H_2O, orally.
10	Strychnine sulfate								
11	Thallium sulfate	Yes	No	Gastrointestinal hemorrhage; kidney and endocrine damage; respiratory failure.	Slow.	Yes	Yes	Extreme	None reliable; sodium iodide and sodium thiosulfate may help.
12	Warfarin	Yes	No	Internal and external hemorrhage.	Very slow;5-10 days exposure required.	See Fn 12	No	Slight	Vitamin K, blood transfusions.
13	Zinc phosphide	No	No	Heart paralysis; gastro-intestinal and liver damage.	Fast.	No	No	Moderate	Copper sulfate, followed with lavage or emetic; cathartic and water; avoid fats and oils.

/1/ Abbreviations: acet. = acetone; al. = alcohol; alk. = alkali; bz. = benzene; c. = cold; chl. = chloroform; dec. = decomposes; eth. = ether; gly. = glycerine; h. = hot; i. = insoluble; org. solv. = organic solvents; s. = soluble; sl.s. = slightly soluble; w. = water. /2/ Amount necessary to control rodents under conditions of use. /3/ (-) = ineffective; (+) = poor; (++) = fair; (+++) = good. /4/ On first exposure only; ingestion of sub-lethal doses results in increased tolerance and decreased effectiveness. /5/ Lethal dose and relative effectiveness vary with particle size. /6/ Successive doses of 1 mg/kg/da required for 5 or more days. Minimum lethal dose (acute oral toxicity): fumarin 400 mg/kg; pival 200-250 mg/kg; warfarin 160 mg/kg. /7/ Alkaline salts available for use in aqueous solutions. /8/ Crude drug consists of powdered inner scales of Urginea maritima, with or without fortification of alcoholic extracts. Active principle appears to be one or more glucosides, one of which (scilliroside) has the formula $C_{32}H_{44}O_{12}$. /9/ Toxicity of crude drug may be increased through addition of alcoholic extractives, such as scilliroside. /10/ Emetics are used as first aid, except as noted. One tablespoon of salt in warm water is usually effective; physician should be called immediately. /11/ May be absorbed through cuts or breaks in the skin, also by inhalation of dusts. /12/ Reported poisonings from ingestion of warfarin-poisoned animals.

	Common Name	Chemical Definition	Action
		Inorganic	
1	Borax	Sodium tetraborate, $Na_2B_4O_7 \cdot 10H_2O$.	Probably slow nerve poison.
2	Calcium arsenate	Mixture of $CaHAsO_4$, $Ca_5H_2(AsO_4)_4$, $Ca_3(AsO_4)_2$, $[Ca_3(AsO_4)_2]_3 Ca(OH)_2$, free $CaCO_3$ and unreacted $Ca(OH)_2$.	Destroys mid-gut epithelium.
3	Calomel	Mercurous chloride, $HgCl$.	Enzyme inhibitor.
4	Corrosive sublimate	Mercuric chloride, $HgCl_2$.	Enzyme inhibitor.
5	Cryolite	Sodium aluminum fluoride, Na_3AlF_6.	Produces flaccid paralysis.
6	Lead arsenate	Acid lead arsenate, $PbHAsO_4$.	Destroys mid-gut epithelium.
7	Paris green	Copper acetoarsenite, $(CuOAs_2O_3)_3 \cdot Cu(CH_3COO)_2$.	Inhibits enzymes with sulfhydryl groups.
8	Sodium arsenite	Mixture of Na_3AsO_3 and $NaAsO_2$.	Destroys mid-gut epithelium.
9	Sodium fluoride	Sodium fluoride, NaF.	Nerve, stomach poison.
10	Sodium fluosilicate	Sodium silicofluoride, Na_2SiF_6.	Nerve, stomach poison.
11	Sodium selenate	Sodium selenate, Na_2SeO_4.	Similar to H_2S; blocks cytochrome system(?).
12	Tartar emetic	Potassium antimonyl tartrate $K(SbO)C_4H_4O_6 \cdot 1/2H_2O$.	Similar to arsenic poisoning.
13	White arsenic	Arsenious oxide, As_2O_3.	Destroys mid-gut epithelium.
		Organic	
14	Aldrin	Not less than 95% of 1,2,3,4,10,10 -hexachloro-1,4,4a,5,8,8a-hexahydro-1,4-endo-exo-5,8-dimethanonaphthalene.	Delayed action on nerve.
15	Allethrin	dl-2-Allyl-4-hydroxy-3-methyl-2-cyclopenten-1-one ester of cis- and trans-dl-chrysanthemum monocarboxylic acid.	Rapid veratrine-like nerve poison.
16	Anabasine	l-3-(2'-Piperidyl)pyridine.	Rapid nicotinic nerve poison.
17	BHC	A mixture of several isomers of 1,2,3,4,5,6-hexachlorocyclohexane.	Potent stomach poison and persistent contact poison; fumigant.
18	Chlordane	1,2,4,5,6,7,8,8-Octachloro-2,3,3a,4,7,7a-hexahydro-4,7-methanoindene.	Delayed action on nerve.
19	Chlorthion	O,O-Dimethyl-O-(3-chloro-4-nitrophenyl) thiophosphate.	Probably anticholinesterase.
20	DDD	2,2-bis-(p-Chlorophenyl)-1,1-dichloroethane.	Repetitive nerve discharge.
21	DDT	2,2-bis-(p-Chlorophenyl)-1,1-trichloroethane.	Repetitive nerve discharge.
22	Diazinon	O,O-Diethyl-O-(2-isopropyl-4-methyl-6-pyrimidyl)thiophosphate.	Anticholinesterase (technical grade).
23	Dieldrin	Not less than 85% of 1,2,3,4,10,10-hexachloro-6,7-epoxy-1,4,4a,5,6,7,8,8a-octahydro-1,4-endo-exo-5,8-dimethanonaphthalene.	Delayed action on nerve.
24	Dilan	53% 2-Nitro-1,1-bis(p-chlorophenyl) butane and 27% 2-nitro-1,1-bis (p-chlorophenyl) propane, and 20% related compounds.	Probably similar to DDT.
25	DNBP	4,6-Dinitro-2-butylphenol.	Mordant stimulant nerve poison.
26	DNCHP	2,4-Dinitro-6-cyclohexylphenol.	Mordant stimulant nerve poison.
27	DNOC	4,6-Dinitro-o-cresol.	Mordant stimulant nerve poison.
28	Endrin	1,2,3,4,10,10-Hexachloro-6,7-epoxy-1,4,4a,5,6,7,8,8a-octahydro-1,4-endo-endo-5,8-dimethanonaphthalene.	Probably like its isomer, dieldrin.
29	EPN	Ethyl-p-nitrophenylthionobenzenephosphonate.	Impure samples have anticholinesterase activity.
30	Heptachlor	l(or 3a),4,5,6,7,8,8-Heptachloro-3a,4,7,7a-tetrahydro-4,7-methanoindene.	Delayed action on nerve.
31	Isodrin	1,2,3,4,10,10-Hexachloro-1,4,4a,5,8,8a-hexahydro-1,4-endo-endo-5,8-dimethanonaphthalene.	Delayed action on nerve, like aldrin.
32	Isopestox	bis-(Isopropylamino)fluophospine oxide.	Eventual anticholinesterase effect.
33	Lethane 60	Mixture of β-thiocyano ethyl esters of aliphatic fatty acids; av. C content is 10-18; $(CnH_{2n+1}COOCH_2CH_2SCN)$, with 50% petroleum distillate.	Depression of respiration, rapid knockdown.
34	Lethane 384	Mixture of β-butoxy-β-thiocyanodiethyl ether with 50% petroleum distillate.	Depression of respiration, rapid knockdown.
35	Lindane	Not less than 99% of gamma isomer of 1,2,3,4,5,6-hexachlorocyclohexane.	Rapid nerve stimulant.
36	Malathion	O,O-Dimethyl-S-(1,2-dicarbethoxyethyl) dithiophosphate.	Anticholinesterase enzyme inhibitor.
37	Methoxychlor	1,1,1-Trichloro-2,2-bis(p-methoxyphenyl)-ethane.	DDT-like action on nerve.
38	Methyl-parathion	O,O-Dimethyl-O-p-nitrophenyl thiophosphate.	Anticholinesterase.
39	Nicotine	l-3-(1-Methyl-2-pyrrolidyl)-pyridine.	Blocks ganglionic synapses.
40	Parathion	O,O-Diethyl-O-p-nitrophenyl thiophosphate.	Anticholinesterase.
41	PDB	p-Dichlorobenzene.	Stimulant, probably nervous.
42	PCP	Pentachlorophenol.	Repellent and fumigant.
43	Perthane	1,1-bis-(p-Ethylphenyl)-2,2-dichloroethane.	Probably similar to DDT.
44	Phenothiazine	Dibenzo-1,4-thiazine, thiodiphenylamine.	Slow flaccid paralysis.
45	Pyrolan	Dimethyl-5-(3-methyl-1-phenyl-pyrazolyl)carbamate.	Anticholinesterase.
46	Pyrethrins	Pyrethrolone and cinerolone esters of chrysanthemum monocarboxylic acid and chrysanthemum dicarboxylic acid methyl ester.	Rapid veratrine-like nerve poison.
47	Rotenone	$C_{23}H_{22}O_6$.	Depresses respiration and nerve.
48	Ryania	Powdered stems of R. speciosa, containing active principle ryanodine $(C_{25}H_{35}O_9N)$.	Ryanodine depresses muscle metabolism.
49	Sabadilla	Powdered seeds of sabadilla (Schoenocaulon spp), containing veratrine and veratridine.	Mild veratrine-like poison.
50	Schradan	Octamethylpyrophosphoramide.	Converted in vivo to anticholinesterase.
51	Strobane	Mixture of terpene polychlorinates containing about 66% chlorine.	
52	Systox	Mixture of O,O-diethyl-S-ethylmercaptoethyl thiophosphate and O,O-diethyl-O-ethylmercaptoethyl thiophosphate.	Probably similar to Schradan.
53	TEPP	Tetraethyl pyrophosphate, $(C_2H_5O)_2 PO \cdot O \cdot PO(OC_2H_5)_2$.	Anticholinesterase.
54	Thanite	Isobornyl thiocyanoacetate, plus 18% terpene esters.	Quick knockdown; synergist.
55	Toxaphene	Mixture of chlorinated camphene isomers containing 67-69% chlorine.	Delayed action on nerve.

/1/ Oral, principally to albino rats, milligrams per kilogram body weight. /2/ Also Blattella germanica. /3/ Also Boophilus microplus, Scleroracus vaccinii, Rhopobota naevana, Drosophila. /6/ Also Chromaphis juglandicola.

AND BIOLOGICAL CHARACTERISTICS

Method	Insects Especially Affected	Insects Developing Tolerance	Rats LD_{50}[1] mg/kg	
Inorganic				
Powders or aqueous solutions.	Housefly and blowfly maggot.			1
Crop and forest dusting.	Corn earworm, cotton leafworm.		50	2
Seed or seedling treatment.	Root maggot.		1-5	3
Seed or seedling treatment.	Root maggot.		1-5	4
Orchard and crop sprays and dusts.	Codling-moth, velvet bean caterpillar.	Rhagoletis completa.		5
Orchard sprays and dusts.	Codling-moth, peach moth.	Carpocapsa, Anarsia.	100	6
				7
Sprays, dusts, baits.	Potato beetle, anopheline larva, cutworm.		200	8
Livestock dips, baits.	Cutworm, grasshopper.	Boophilus decoloratus, australis.	200	9
Dry powders.	Cockroach, ant, Mallophaga.		150	10
Baits, powders, impregnants.	Grasshopper, ant, clothes moth.		5	11
Systemic, by watering soil.	Aphids, scale, thrips.	Tetranychus telarius.	6	12
Bait sprays, ant traps.	Thrips, caterpillar, ant.	Scirtothrips, Taeniothrips.	2-85	13
Ant traps, grasshopper baits.	Ant, grasshopper.			
Organic				
Baits, sprays, soil treatments.	Grasshopper, wireworm, ant, cutworm, root maggot, white grub.	Aedes, Culex, Musca.	50	14
Domestic aerosols, louse powders.	Housefly, louse, livestock insects.		1000	15
Contact and fumigant sprays.	Aphids.		10	16
Wettable powder, dispersible liquid or dust.	Field and garden insects, wireworm.	Musca, Boophilus decoloratus, B. microplus, Cimex, Drosophila.[2]	1200	17
Dusts and residual sprays.	Cockroach, ant, mosquito, plum curculio, cotton boll weevil.	Blattella, Musca, Culex tarsalis[3]	500	18
Wettable powder sprays.	Mosquito, housefly, grape berry moth.		1000	19
Orchard sprays.	Leaf-roller, corn earworm.	Musca, Aedes taeniorhynchus[4]	2500	20
Residual sprays and dusts, paints and resin coatings, domestic aerosols.	Caterpillar, sawfly, household insects, louse, cotton boll weevil, grasshopper, Mexican bean beetle; virtually all insects except resistant species.	Musca, Aedes, Culex, Pediculus, Psychoda, Cimex, Anopheles, Carpocapsa, Boophilus, Pieris, Leptinotarsa(?), Pulex, Plutella, Blatta, Triatoma.[5]	250	21
Wettable powder sprays.	Orchard insects, housefly.		100	22
Residual sprays.	Housefly, mosquito, ant, assassin bug, plum curculio, chinch bug, flea beetle.	Musca, Psychoda, Aedes nigromaculis, Boophilus microplus.	65-100	23
Residual emulsion sprays.	Housefly, Mexican bean beetle.	Musca.	1100	24
Dormant orchard sprays.	Aphid eggs, overwintering forms.		5-60	25
Summer orchard sprays.	Orchard mites.		30-180	26
Contact sprays and dusts.	Grasshopper, aphid eggs.		45	27
Baits and residual sprays.	Grasshopper, tobacco insects.		10	28
Orchard suspension sprays.	Aphids, psyllids, plum curculio, mosquito larva.		15-90	29
Dusts, wettable powder and emulsion sprays.	Cockroach, plum curculio, blackfly larva, cotton mite, cutworm, rootworm, wireworm.	Culex, Aedes nigromaculis	200	30
Baits and residual sprays.	Bark beetle, cutworm.		15	31
Systemic foliage sprays.	Aphids.		90	32
Aerosols and emulsion sprays.	Housefly, louse, livestock insects.		500	33
Aerosols and emulsion sprays.	Housefly, louse, livestock insects.		400	34
Contact and residual sprays, electric vaporizers, dusts.	Housefly, mosquito, louse, wireworm, household stored-products insects, orchard and field crop insects.	Musca, Blattella, Pediculus, Anopheles, Boophilus	125	35
Residual and orchard sprays, baits.	Aphids, scale, orchard mites, housefly, mosquito larva.		1250	36
Residual and livestock sprays.	Forage and truck-crop insects, Mexican bean beetle.	Musca, Pieris rapae, Drosophila.	6000+	37
Orchard sprays.	Aphids.			38
Contact sprays, fumigant vapors.	Aphids, psyllids.		10	39
Contact and residual sprays.	Aphids, most insects.	Tetranychus, Metatetranychus.[6]	3.5	40
Fumigant of soil and closed spaces.	Clothes moth, peach borer.		2000	41
Wood impregnant.	Powder-post beetle, termite.		210	42
Wettable powder, emulsion sprays.	Leafhopper nymph, forage-crop insects.		8000	43
Oral anthelmintic.	Bot and mosquito larva.	Callitroga americana (lab.).	1500+	44
Surface sprays.	Woolly apple aphid, housefly.		60-90	45
Domestic aerosols, sprays, dusts.	Housefly, mosquito, louse, truck-crop insects, livestock insects.	Musca, Blattella.	1500	46
Crop dusts, livestock sprays.	Caterpillar, sheep-ked.	Epilachna varivestis.	25-1000	47
Dusts or wettable powders.	European corn borer, codling moth.		1200	48
Dusts.	Leafhopper, squash bug.		2000+	49
Systemic application to plants.	Aphids, scale.		20	50
Liquid insecticide.	Acarids.		250	51
Systemic application to plants.	Cotton aphid.			52
Rapid contact sprays.	Aphids, scale.	Tetranychus.	2	53
Livestock sprays and aerosols.	Housefly, horn-fly, stable-fly.		1000	54
Residual sprays and dusts.	Cotton boll weevil, cutworm, grasshopper, salt-marsh caterpillar.	Musca, Culex.	60	55

Anopheles, Psychoda. /4/ Also A. sollicitans, Pieris rapae, Drosophila. /5/ Also Erythroneura variabilis, Trichoplusia Ni., Lygus bugs, Psychoda,

350. REPRESENTATIVE ARTHROPOD REPELLENTS: CHARACTERISTICS AND EFFECTIVENESS
Values in parentheses are ranges.

#	Chemical Designation	Empirical Formula	Physical Properties[1,2]	Solubility[1]	Anopheles quadrimaculatus Min to 1st Bite, Skin[3]	Anopheles Da to 5th Bite, Cloth[3]	Aedes aegypti Min to 1st Bite, Skin[3]	Aedes Da to 5th Bite, Cloth[3]	Amblyomma americanum Da Effective on Cloth[3]	Ctenocephalides felis Da Effective on Cloth[3]	Trombiculid (Chigger) Mites Min to 100% Knock-down[3]	Min Effective after Washes no.[3]
1	Benzyl benzoate (benzoic acid, benzyl ester)	C14H12O2	MW=212.24; needles, leaflets or clear oily liq.; MP=21; BP=323.4; den.=1.118[18]; sp gr = 1.114; n_D = 1.568[21]	i.w.;s.acet., al., eth.	23(2-97)	<1	99(2-347)	0-5	103	197	1	3
2	Butyl acetanilide (N-butylacetanilide)	C13H17ON	MW=203.27; clear liq., colorl. to light straw; MP (setting point)=22; BP=277-281; sp gr=0.992[25]	i.w.;s.acet. al.,eth.	116(14-374)	6	218(39-481)	8-36	54-139	29	0.5	2
3	2-Butyl-2-ethyl-1,3-propanediol(1,3-propanediol, 2-butyl-2-ethyl)	C9H20O2	MW=160.25; wh. cr.; MP=41.4; BP=178[50]; den.=0.929[50]	0.8% s.w. at 20°C;s.acet., al., eth.	18(11-25)	<1	63(21-104)	93-196	27	<1	15+	0
4	N-sec.-Butylphthalimide (phthalimide, N-sec.-butyl)[4]	C12H13O2N	MW=203.23; clear liq.; BP=114-116[3]; sp gr=1.112[26]	i.w.;s.acet., al., eth.	55(11-122)		198(11-511)	14	12	14	0.5	0
5	o-Chloro-N,N-diethylbenzamide (benzamide, o-chloro-N,N-diethyl)	C11H14ONCl	MW=211.69; colorl. prisms; MP=39-40; BP=125-128	i.w.;s.acet., al., eth.			470+(404-512+)	1-28	8	84	1.5	0
6	Citronella, Ceylon (oils, citronella, Ceylon)[4]		Pale, yel. liq.;sp gr=0.920[16]; n_D=1.479-1.485[20]	sl.s.w.;10 vol.80%al.	15(7-19)		74(30-148)	20-27		8	0.5	0
7	Citronella, Java (oils, citronella, Java)[4]		Pale, yel. liq.; den.=0.885-0.900; n_D=1.468-1.473[20]	sl.s.w.;10 vol.80%al.	26(10-41)		114(91-157)				15+	
8	Cyclohexyl acetoacetate (acetoacetic acid, cyclohexyl ester)[4]	C10H16O3	MW=184.23;colorl. liq.; BP=81-83[0.3]; sp gr=1.021[26], n_D=1.459[20]	i.w.;s.acet., al., eth.	57(15-226)		109(15-275)	5	49	<1	15+	0
9	Dibutyl adipate (adipic acid, dibutyl ester)	C14H26O4	MW=258.35; colorl. liq.; MP=-38; BP=183[14]; sp gr=0.965[20]/4	i.w.;misc.al., eth.	21(1-61)		36(12-66)	<1			2	3
10	Dibutyl phthalate (phthalic acid, dibutyl ester)	C16H22O4	MW=278.34; oily, colorl. liq.; BP=340; sp gr=1.045[21]	i.w.;misc.al., eth.	18(2-84)		12(1-86)		160		12.5	3
11	Diethyl cyclohexanedicarboxylate (1,2-cyclohexane dicarboxylic acid, diethyl ester)[4]	C12H20O4	MW=228.28; liq.; BP=83-87[0.5]; n_D = 1.453[25]	i.w.;s.acet., bz., al., eth.	57(15-176)		176(16-369)	27+	5		1	0
12	N,N-Diethyl-m-toluamide (tech.) (m-toluamide, N,N-diethyl)	C12H17ON	MW=191.26; colorl. liq.; BP=111[1]; sp gr=0.996[26], n_D=1.520[25]	i.w.;s.acet., al., eth.	40(8-94)		812(706-840)	11-63	54	30-56[5]	0.2	0
13	Diisopropyl tartrate (tartaric acid, diisopropyl ester)[4]	C10H18O6	MW=234.24; colorl. oily liq.; BP=275; sp gr=1.117[26]; n_D=1.437[25]	i.w.;s.acet., al., eth.			255(7-499)	1			5.5	0
14	Dimethyl carbate (Bicyclo[2,2,1]-5-heptene-2,3-dicarboxylic acid, cis-, dimethyl ester)[4]	C11H14O4	MW=210.22; cr. solid; MP>>35 (setting point); sp gr=1.162-1.167[35/4]	i.w.;misc. al.	66(9-270)	20	229(28-456)	21+	19		0.5-2.5	0
15	Dimethyl phthalate (phthalic acid, dimethyl ester)[4]	C10H10O4	MW=194.18; clear, oily liq.; BP=282; sp gr=1.190-1.194; n_D=1.515[21]	0.43% s. w.; s.acet., al., eth.	108(5-542+)	4-21+	247(5-1051)	11-27			1-2	0
16	2-Ethoxy-N,N-diethylbenzamide (benzamide, 2-ethoxy-N,N-diethyl)	C13H19O2N	MW=221.29; liq.; BP=115[0.1]; sp gr = 1.029[26]; n_D=1.515[25]	i.w., s.acet., al., eth.	53(2-312)	0-3	366(250-496)	16-63	15	92[5]	1.5	0
17	2-Ethyl-1,3-hexanediol (1,3-hexanediol, 2-ethyl)[4]	C8H18O2	MW=146.22; clear oily liq.; BP=244.2; sp gr=0.942[20]; n_D=1.4465-1.4515[25]	4.2% s.w.;s. hydrocarb.	42(19-73)		331(12-608)	27			3.5-10.5	0
18	Ethyl-β-phenyl hydracrylate (hydracrylic acid, β-phenyl-ester)[4]	C11H14O3	MW=194.22; oily liq.; BP=124-125[1]; sp gr=1.090[26]; n_D=1.508[22]	i.w.;s.acet., al., eth.			262(33-497)	36	119		0.5	0
19	Hexyl mandelate (mandelic acid, hexyl ester)[4]	C14H20O3	MW=226.30; liq.; BP=135[3]; sp gr=1.026[26], n_D=1.491[25]	i.w.;s.acet., al., eth.	80(49-165)		279(49-502)	154	83	28	2	0
20	Indalone (2H-pyran-6-carboxylic acid, 3,4-dihydro-2,2-dimethyl-4-oxo-butyl ester)[4]	C12H18O4	MW=226.26; light yel. liq.; BP=256-70; sp gr=1.058-1.062; n_D=1.4745-1.4755[25]	i.w.;misc.al., chl., eth.,	41(3-186)		141(24-411)	0-161	32	1	0.5-2	0
21	Navy 448 ingredients {2-cyclohexylcyclohexanol (cyclohexanol, 2-cyclohexyl)	C12H22O	MW=182.30; visc. liq.; BP=125-128[7], sp gr=0.975[26]	i.w.;misc.al., glac.ac.a. v.sl.s.w.;s. acet., al., eth.	44(1-115)		304(2-615)	18	29		0.5	0
22	phenylcyclohexanol (cyclohexanol, 2-phenyl)	C12H16O	MW=176.25; light amber liq.; sp gr=1.045[26]	v.sl.s.w.;s. acet., al., eth.	76(1-382)	1-4	368(3-1354)	27	14		0.5	0

412

No.	Insecticide	Formula	Physical constants[2]	Solubility							
23	Navy 448 (mixture of 30% 2-cyclo-hexylcyclohexanol and 70% phenylcyclohexanol)[4]				282		18	13	8-22	1-2	
24	1,5-Pentanediol, dipropionate (propionic acid, diester with 1,5-pentanediol)[4]	$C_{11}H_{20}O_4$	MW=216.27; clear, colorl. liq.; BP=110[2]; sp gr=0.991[26]; n_D=1.4274[25]	i.w.;s.acet., al, eth.	160(30-304)	89(21-281)	8-20			0.5	0
25	2-Phenoxyethanol, acetate (ethanol, 2-phenoxy-, acetate)[4]	$C_{10}H_{12}O_3$	MW=180.20; liq.; BP=147-150[23]; sp gr=1.1000[26]; n_D=1.5058[21]	i.w.;s.acet., al, eth.	164(10-363)	53(6-212)					
26	Propylcinnimate (cinnamic acid; propyl ester)[4]	$C_{12}H_{14}O_2$	MW=190.23; liq.; BP=122[11]; n_D=1.5467[28]	i.w.;s.acet., al, eth.	322(16-494)	61(8-273)	38	28	<1	1.5	0
27	Propyl N,N-diethyl succinnamate (succinamic acid, N,N-diethyl-, propyl ester)[4]	$C_{11}H_{21}O_3N$	MW=215.29; clear liq.; BP=107-108[0.5]; sp gr=1.006-1.011; n_D=1.4517[22]	i.w.;s.acet., al, eth.	237(40-362)	47(14-328)	0-63	21-123	133	2.5	0
28	Thiodiethanol, diacetate (ethanol, 2,2'-thiodi-, diacetate)[4]	$C_8H_{14}O_4S$	MW=206.26; colorl. liq.; BP=130[5]; sp gr=1.1380[26]; n_D=1.4684[25]	i.w.;s.acet., al, eth.	168(83-460)	128(83-277)	19+			2.5	0
29	Undecenoic acid (undecylenic acid)	$C_{11}H_{20}O_2$	MW=184.27; liq. or cr.; MP=24.5; BP=275 d.; den.=0.9102; n_D=1.4464[24]	i.w.;s.al., chl., eth.		<1				2-5	

/1/ Abbreviations and symbols: ac.a. = acetic acid; acet. = acetone; al. = alcohol; BP = boiling point; bz. = benzene; chl. = chloroform; colorl. = colorless; cr. = crystals, crystalline; d. = decomposes; den. = density; eth. = ether; glac. = glacial; hydrocarb. = hydrocarbon; i. = insoluble; liq. = liquid; MP = melting point; misc. = miscible; MW = molecular weight; n_D = refractive index; s. = soluble; sl. = slightly; sp gr = specific gravity; v. = very; w. = water; wh. = white; yel. = yellow; visc. = viscous. /2/ MP in °C; BP in °C at atmospheric pressure (760 mm of mercury) unless otherwise indicated by specific pressure in underlined superscript; sp gr and den. at temperature (°C) indicated by underlined superscript, except in Lines 9 and 14, where temperature is referred to water at 4°C; refractive index (n_D) at temperature of °C shown in subscript. /3/ For techniques, see U.S. Department of Agriculture Handbook No. 69, "Chemicals Evaluated as Insecticides and Repellents at Orlando, Fla.," U. S. Government Printing Office, May 1954. /4/ Deemed safe for use on skin. /5/ Tests conducted with oriental rat flea (Xenopsyll cheopis).

351. ORGANIC INSECTICIDES: LARVICIDAL, KNOCKDOWN, AND LD50 TESTS

Insecticide	Larvicide Test Results[1]			Knockdown Test Results[2]		Topical LD50[5]
	100% Effective Dose[3]	Lower Doses		100% Knockdown	100% Effective for:[4]	
	ppm	ppm	% kill	hr	da	μg/g
1 Aldrin	0.025	0.01	98	1	31+	1.6
2 Allethrin	0.2	0.1	76	1	31+	21.5
3 BHC	0.2	0.1	92	0.25	30-31	4.0
4 Chlordane	0.01	0.005	52	3	31+	1.65
5 DDT	0.01	0.005	66	6	31+	5.0
6 DFDT	0.025	0.01	85	3	31+	1.1
7 Dieldrin	0.005	0.0025	90	24	31+	4.75
8 Dilan	0.1	0.05	94	1	7-8	
9 DNOC	10.0	1.0	10	3	31+	
10 DNOCHP	10.0	1.0	50	3	31+	
11 DNOSBP	10.0	1.0	0	0.25	30-31	
12 Endrin	0.01	0.01	96	1	31+	
13 EPN	0.005	0.0025	96	24	31+	1.9
14 Heptachlor	0.025	0.01	79		31+	1.6
15 Isodrin	1.0		78	3	31+	
16 Lethane 606		10.0	20	0.5	16	120
17 Lethane 384[6]		10.0	20	1	31+	1.0
18 Lindane	0.05		62	0.5	31+	28
19 Malathion		0.025	96	3	31+	
20 Methoxychlor	0.1	0.05	45	24+	0	3.4
21 Methyl parathion	0.005	0.0025	67	0.25	31+	1.0
22 Nicotine		10.0	15			
23 Para-oxon	0.025	0.01	82	0.25	31+	0.5
24 Parathion	0.0025	0.001	80	0.25	31+	0.9
25 PDB		10.0	70	24+		
26 Pentachloro-phenol	10.0	1.0	45	1	30-31	
27 Phenothiazine	1.0	0.1	5	24+	0	
28 Potasan	0.1	0.01	18	0.5	31+	
29 Pyrolan		10.0	98	0.25	31+	1.0
30 Pyrethrins	0.1	0.05	78	24+	30-31	
31 Rotenone	10.0	1.0	60	3	31+	
32 Sabadilla				6	31+	
33 Schradan		10.0	42	0.5	31+	>500
34 Sulfotepp	0.0025	0.001	74	0.25	31+	5.0
35 Systox	0.1	0.01	6	6-24	31+	
36 TDE	0.005	0.0025	95	6-24	0-1	6.5
37 TEPP	10.0	1.0	42	3	3-7	
38 Thanite	10.0	1.0	5	3	31+	150
39 Toxaphene	0.01	0.005	80		31+	31.0

/1/ Fourth-instar larvae (Anopheles quadrimaculatus) exposed 48 hr in serial water-dilutions of test compound-acetone solution. /2/ Young adults (Pediculus humanis corporis) exposed 24 hr on dry woolen patches previously dipped in 1% solutions of insecticides in solvent. /3/ A measure of minimum lethal concentration. /4/ A measure of residual effectiveness. /5/ Musca domestica. /6/ Data on per cent active ingredients not available.

352. MEDICAL FUNGICIDES: PHYSICAL, CHEMICAL, AND BIOLOGICAL CHARACTERISTICS

	Common Name	Chemical Formula or Designation	MP °C[1]	BP °C[1]	Form, Color, Solubility[1]	Organisms Susceptible in Vitro[1,2,3]	Indications	Toxicity and Remarks
1	Benzoic acid	Benzene carboxylic acid.	122	249	Colorl. crys.; sl.s.w.; s. most org. solv.	Fungistatic. 2-6, 8, 10, 11, 14.	Dermatomycoses.	Used in combination with salicylic acid. Should not be used in acute phase.
2	Boric acid	H_3BO_3	160	300 (-1½ HOH)	Colorl. crys. or white granules or powder; s. w., al., gly.; sl.s.acet.	Fungistatic. 1, 2, 4-9, 11.	Tinea pedis, T. cruris.	Should not be used over extensive areas of unbroken skin. Poisoning from topical use has occured in infants.
3	Caprylic acid	$CH_3(CH_2)_6COOH$	16	237	Colorl. liq.; sl.s.w.; s.al., chl., eth., CS_2, pet.eth., glac.ac.a.	Fungistatic, weakly fungicidal. 1, 2, 4-6, 9-14.	Dermatomycoses.	Relatively non-toxic on local application. Unpleasant odor. Only suppressive efficacy.
4	Chloramphenicol	D(-)-Threo-1-p-nitro-phenyl-2-dichloro-acetamido-1, 3-propanediol.	150.5-151.5		Needles; sl.s.w.; s.al., acet., eth., ethyl acetate, me.alc., butyl alc., prop.glycol.	A, E, G.	Actinomycoses, cryptococcosis, nocar-diosis.	Occasional blood dyscrasias. May cause can-didiasis.
5	5-Chloro-salicylanilide	$C_{13}H_{10}O_2NCl$	214-216		Crys.; i.w.; sl.s.al., gly.; s.acet.	Fungistatic, weakly fungicidal. 2,4-6, 9, 10, 12.	Tinea capitis.	About 70% effective. Occasional dermatitis, folliculitis and kerion.
6	Chlorothymol	6-Chloro-4-isopropyl-1-methyl-3-phenol.	62-64		Crys.; sl.s.w.; s.al., bz., chl., eth., pet.eth.	Fungistatic, fungicidal. 2, 9-12, 14.	Tinea pedis.	Primary skin irritant. Effectivity reduced in presence of serum.
7	Chlortetracycline	$C_{22}H_{23}ClN_2O_8$	168-169		Yellow crys.; sl.s.w., alcohols, acet., bz.; s. cellosolves, dioxane, carbitol.	A, G.	Actinomycosis, nocardiosis.	Rare cases of hypersensitivity. Occasional diarrhea, skin eruptions. Candidiasis may result.
8	Diamthazole dihydrochloride	2-Dimethylamino-6-(β-diethylaminoethoxy)-benzothiazole dihydro-chloride.	269		Colorl. crys.; s.w., al., me.alc.	Fungistatic, weakly fungicidal. 1, 2, 4-6, 9-12, 14.	Dermatomycoses.	Reported to cause encephalopathy in children under 5 years. Not to be used in acute stage.
9	Dibrom-salicylaldehyde	3, 5-Dibromo-2-hy-droxybenzaldehyde.	86		Yellow prisms; sl.s.w.; s.eth., bz., chl., al., glac.ac.a.	Fungistatic, weakly fungicidal. 2, 4-6, 9-12, 14.	Tinea capitis.	20% effective. Occasional dermatitis, folliculitis, and kerion.
10	Ethyl vanillate	3-Methoxyethyl benzoate.	44	291-293	Colorl. crys. solid; i.w.; s.al., prop. glycol, carbowax, mod. conc. cold KOH.	D, F.	Coccidioidomycosis, histoplasmosis.	Low toxicity. 30-45 g/da for 3-18 mo produces occasional nausea, acidosis, hyperpnea, or shock. Liver and kidney damage from larger doses after a month or more.
11	Gentian violet	Methylrosaniline chloride.			Green powder; s.w., al., gly., chl.; i.eth.	Fungistatic. C, 1, 2, 4-6, 9, 10, 12, 14.	Candidiasis, Tinea corporris, T. cruris.	Usually non-toxic topically. Stains skin and clothing. Orally may cause nausea, vomiting, diarrhea, and lassitude.
12	8-Hydroxyquinoline	8-Quinolinol	76	267	White crys.; almost i.w., eth.; s.al., acet., chl., bz.	Fungicidal, fungistatic. 1, 2, 9-13.	Dermatomycoses.	Occasional local allergic-type reaction.
13	Iodine tincture U.S.P.	2% iodine, 2.4% sodium iodide, alcohol.			Transparent, reddish-brown liquid.	Fungistatic. H, 1, 2, 4-6, 9, 10.	Dermatomycoses, superficial lesions in sporotrichosis.	Iodism on chronic use. Not to be used in acute phase topically.
14	Methyl paraben	Methyl parahydroxy-benzoate.	125-128		Colorl. crys.; s. 1/400 w., al., eth.; sl.s.bz., CCl_4.	Fungistatic. C, 1.	Candidiasis.	Mixed with 4 parts propyl paraben to prevent candidiasis from antibiotic therapy. Less toxic than benzoic or salicylic acids.
15	Nystatin	Derived from cultures of Streptomyces noursei.			Yellow powder; sl.s.me. alc., prop. glycol.	Fungicidal. C, 1.	Candidiasis.	LD_{50} for crude nystatin i.p. in mice, 20-26 mg/kg. Too irritating for subcutaneous or intramuscu-lar injection. Combined with antibiotics to pre-vent candidiasis.
16	Oxytetracycline	$C_{22}H_{24}N_2O_9$	181-182 d.		Yellow crys. or powder; sl.s.w., al.; s.dil. HCl.	A, G.	Actinomycosis, nocardiosis.	Rare cases of hypersensitivity. Occasional diar-rhea, skin eruptions. Candidiasis may result.
17	Penicillin G sodium	Benzylpenicillin sodium.			White crys.; s.al., gly.; i.acet., eth., chl.	A, E, G.	Actinomycosis, cryptococcosis, nocardiosis.	Skin rashes and eruptions, serum sickness-like symptoms, anaphylaxis, id-like reactions, mucosal lesions, other systemic reactions in sensitive people. May produce candidiasis.
18	Phenyl mercuric acetate	$C_6H_5HgO_2C_2H_3$	149		White prisms; s.al., bz., 1/600 w.	Fungistatic, fungicidal. 2, 4-6, 9-12, 14.	Dermatomycoses.	Chronic use may produce mercury poisoning. Acrodynia in children from mercury sensitiza-tion. BAL helpful as an antagonist.

No.	Name	Formula	M.P.	Physical properties and solubility[1]	Effective[2][3]	Diseases	Remarks
19	Phenyl mercuric nitrate, N.F.	$C_6H_5HgOH \cdot C_6H_5HgNO_3$	178-184 d.	White or gray powder; sl. s.w., al.; mod.s.gly.	See phenyl mercuric acetate.		Must check for sensitivity in sensitive people.
20	Potassium iodide solution, N.F.	Saturated potassium iodide.		Clear, colorless solution.	A, B, C, D, E, H.	Actinomycosis (supplemental), candidiasis, coccidioidomycosis, cryptococcosis, N. Amer. blastomycosis.	Iodism in candidiasis, coccidioidomycosis, and N. Amer. blastomycosis as exacerbations of indolent infections have occurred.
21	Propionic acid	CH_3CH_2COOH	141	Colorl. liq.: misc. w., al., chl., eth.	Fungistatic. 1, 2, 4-6, 9-11, 13,14.	Dermatomycoses.	Relatively non-toxic on local application. Effect mostly suppressive.
22	Propyl paraben	Propyl parahydroxy-benzoate.	95-98	Color. crys.; s. 1/2000 w., al., eth., acet.	See Methyl paraben.		
23	Salicylanilide	$C_6H_5NHCOC_6H_4OH$	134-135	White leaflets; sl.s.w.; s. al., eth., chl., bz.	Fungistatic. 2,4-6,9-11, 14.	Tinea capitis, T. favosa.	26% effective. Occasional dermatitis, folliculitis, and kerion.
24	Salicylic acid	o-Hydroxybenzoic acid.	157-159 Sublimes at 20	White crys. or powder; sl. s.w.; s.al., eth., chl.	Fungistatic. 2-6,8-11,14.	Dermatomycoses.	Irritating to skin. Keratolytic effect more pronounced than fungistatic. Used in combination with benzoic acid in Whitfield's Ointment, U.S.P.
25	Sodium iodide	NaI	651	White crys.; s.w., al., gly., acet.	See Potassium iodide.		
26	Stilbamidine	4,4'-Stilbenedicarbox-amidine.	290 d.	White crys.; s.w.; sl. s. me. alc.	B, D, F.	Coccidioidomycosis, histoplasmosis, N. Amer. blastomy-cosis.	Local irritation, vascular reactions, kidney and liver damage, delayed facial neuropathy from trigeminal lesions.
27	Sulfadiazine	2-Sulfanilamidopyrim-idine.	252-256	White or yellow powder; sl.s.w., al., acet., serum; s.dil.mineral acids, KOH, NaOH, NH_4OH.	A, E, G.	Actinomycosis, nocardiosis.	May cause contact dermatitis, crystalluria, hematuria, drug fever, renal pathology, agranulocytosis, anemia, hepatic necrosis.
28	Tetracycline	$C_{22}H_{24}N_2O_8$	170-173 d.	Yellow crys. or powder; sl.s.w.; s. al. (1:50); dil. HCl, alk. hydroxide sol.	A, G.	Actinomycosis, nocardiosis.	Rare cases of hypersensitivity. Occasional diarrhea, skin eruptions. Candidiasis.
29	Undecylenic acid	10-Undecenoic acid.	24.5; 275 d.	Colorl. liq.; i.w.; s.al., chl., eth.	Fungistatic, weakly fungicidal. 1,2,4-6,9-14.	Dermatomycoses.	Usually well tolerated locally. Effect mostly suppressive.

/1/ ac. a. = acetic acid; acet. = acetone; al. = ethanol; alc. = alcohol; alk. = alkali; bz. = benzene; chl. = chloroform; colorl. = colorless; conc. = concentrated; crys. = crystals; d. = decomposes; eth. = ethyl ether; glac. = glacial; gly. = glycerol; i. = insoluble; i.p. = intraperitoneal; me. = methyl; mod. = moderately; org. solv. = organic solvents; pet. = petroleum; prop. = propylene; s = soluble; sl. = slightly; sol. = solution(s); w. = water. /2/ Deep mycoses: A = Actinomyces bovis; B = Blastomyces dermatitidis; C = Candida albicans; D = Coccidioides immitis; E = Cryptococcus neoformans; F = Histoplasma capsulatum; G = Nocardia asteroides; H = Sporotrichum schenckii. /3/ Superficial mycoses: 1 = Candida albicans; 2 = Epidermophyton floccosum; 3 = Malassezia furfur; 4 = Microsporum audouini; 5 = M. canis; 6 = M. gypseum; 7 = Nocardia minutissima; 8 = Trichophyton concentricum; 9 = T. mentagrophytes; 10 = T. rubrum; 11 = T. schoenleini; 12 = T. tonsurans; 13 = T. verrucosum; 14 = T. violaceum.

353. FUNGICIDES: PHYSICAL, CHEMICAL, AND BIOLOGICAL CHARACTERISTICS

	Common Name	Chemical Name or Formula	Molecular Weight	Melting Point °C [1]	Vapor Pressure mm Hg	Purity of Technical Product	Form and Color	Solubility g/100g at 25°C [1]	Toxicity Lethal Dose Rat	Relation to Human Health: Skin Absorption	Degree of Hazard [2]
1	Bordeaux mixture	Copper sulfate and lime			Non-volatile		Blue gelatinous precipitate; crystallizes on standing.	i. w.	Slightly toxic.	Poor.	Irritant.[2]
2	Captan; SR-406	N-Trichloromethyl-thio-tetrahydrophthalimide	300.6	172-173 (pure)[3]	Non-volatile		Colorless crys. (pure); yellow amorphous (technical).	i. w., hydrocarbons; sl. s. al., dioxane, chl.;s. acet., bz.	Oral LD50 10g/kg.	Poor.	Irritant.[4]
3	Captax	2-Mercaptobenzo-thiazole	167.2	179	Low; non-volatile		White needles or leaflets.	<0.005 w.;19.7 acet.;5.2 al.;0.52 bz.; s. alk., Cellosolve.			
4	Chloranil	Tetrachloroquinone	245.9	294-295		(?)	Yellow leaflets or prisms.	<0.008 w.;33 acet.;16 eth.	Oral LD50 4g/kg.	50% not toxic.	Irritant.[5]
5	p-Chloro-m-xylenol	p-Chloro-m-xylenol	156	112-115.5	Volatile in steam	(?)	White to creamy white crys.	0.0025 w.;6.1 bz.;86.6 al.;50 isopropyl alc.; s. eth.		Absorbed.	
6	Compound G-4	2,2'-Methylenebis-(4-chlorophenol)	269	179 (pure)	10^{-10}(200°C); 10^{-4}(100°C)	High	Almost white (pure);light pink to tan (technical).	1.7 mg/100 ml w.;76.5 acet.;1.4 bz.;42.3 butanol.	Oral LD50(?) 1g/kg.	None.	Low.
7	Copper naphthenate	Copper naphthenate	250-400		0.001 (100°C)	Usually 80%	Semiviscous green fluid or green plastic mass.	0.0015 w.;s. isopropyl alc., methyl ethyl ketone.			
8	Copper-3-phenyl-salicylate	Copper-3-phenyl-salicylate	490	148-152 d.	Non-volatile		Tan, crystalline.	i. w.;to 5% by wt. in acet., bz., linseed oil, xylene.	Oral LD50 0.52g/kg.	None.	Low.
9	Crag 974	3,5-Dimethyltetra-hydro-1,3,5,2H-thiadiazine-2-thione	152.2	100-103 d.	1 psi abso-lute(30°C)	95%	White crystalline powder.	0.12 w.(30°C);19.4 acet.(30°C);26 tri-chlorethane.	Oral LD50 0.5g/kg.	Slight when moist.	Slight.
10	Cresatin	Metacresyl acetate	150.2	212 (boil-ing point)	Volatile with steam	Close to 100%	Colorless, oily liquid.	i. c. w.;s. h. w.;miscible al., eth., chl., bz., pet. eth.		Absorbed.	Slight.
11	Dichlone; Phygon	2,3-Dichloro-1,4-naphthaquinone	227	193	Slightly volatile		Yellow crystalline solid.	sl. s. w., most org. solvents, acet., dioxane.	Oral LD50 1.5g/kg.	Poor.	Irritant.
12	Dowicide 1	o-Phenylphenol	170.2	57.2	Approx. 1 (100°C)	98% or higher	White or light buff to pink flakes.	<0.006 w.;>127 acet.;>110 ac. a.; 975 me. alc.;257 pine oil.	Oral LD50 2.4-3.1 g/kg	None.	Low.
13	Dowicide 6	Tetrachlorophenol (2,3,4,6)	231.9	56.0	Approx. 1 (100°C)	92%	Light brown flakes to a sublimed mass.	<0.1 w.;570 acet.;189 bz.,392 al.; 412 eth.319 me. alc.	Moderately toxic orally.	Absorbed.	Slight.
14	Dowicide 7; Santophen	Pentachlorophenol	266.3	190 (pure); 167-176 (technical)	1.1×10^{-4} (20°C);0.12 (100°C)	Usually 83%	White, needle-like crys. (pure); dark flakes and sublimed crys. (technical.)	14 ppm w. (20°C);21.5% acet. (20°C); 11.0 bz. (20°C); 57.0 me. alc. (20°C)	Oral LD50 80mg/kg.	Absorbed.	Low; irritant, dust & vapor.[2,5]
15	Glyodin	2-Heptadecylgly-oxalidine acetate	368.6	62-68		(?)	Light orange crystalline solid.	i. w., acet., toluene;s.(39%) isopropyl alc.	Oral LD50 1.34g/kg	Slight.	Irritant.[5]
16	Milmer I; Bioquin; Copper-8	Copper-8-quinolin-olate	351.8	Does not melt	Practically nil	85% or higher	Yellowish-green powder.	<0.002 w.;0.98 ac. a;<0.009 bz.; <0.01 al.; s. chl.	Large.	None.	Slight.
17	p-Nitrophenol	p-Nitrophenol	139.1	111.4-114	0.083(100°C)	(?)	Colorless or yellow prisms.	1.6 w.;21.2 h. w.;54.4h. tol.;189.5 al.	s.c. MLD 0.6 g/kg(rabbit).	None. 1g/L causes blistering.	Slight.[6]
18	Phenylmercuric acetate	Phenylmercuric acetate	336.7	149-153	Very low	(?)	Small white lustrous prisms.	0.5 w.;2.9 h. w.;5 al.;1.8 bz.;sl. s. pet. solvents.	S. c. LD50 27mg/kg.	Absorbed.	Irritant.[5]
19	Phenylmercuric oleate	Phenylmercuric oleate	558.9	212 d.	Non-volatile	10%	Amorphous solid.	i. w.; s. most hydrocarbon solvents.	MLD about 133mg/kg.	Absorbed.	
20	Pyridylmercuric stearate	Pyridylmercuric stearate	562.2	120-130 d. at 2000°C			White powder.	0.01 w.; 0.3 acet.;0.8% bz;1.5% gly.			
21	Semesan; Uspulun	2-Chloro-4-(hydroxy-mercuri)phenol	345.2		Low vola-tility.		Pink-white powder.	i. w., most org. solvents; s. a., alk.	Highly toxic.	Absorbed.	Irritant.[7]
22	Shirlan	Salicylanilide	213	134-140; d. at 142°C	Volatile with steam	High	White crys. (pure), cream powder (technical).	0.005 w.;47 acet.;11.6 al.;8.0 eth.; 49 ac. a.	MLD about 1g/kg.	Poor.	None(?).
23	Sorbic acid	2,4-Hexadienoic acid	112.1	134.5.	0.01(20°C)	Close to 100%	Colorless solid. Colorless needles from water.	0.6 gly.;5.8 propylene glycol; 9.2 acet. (20°C).	Oral LD50 10.5g/kg.	Poor.	Irritant.[8]
24	Sulphur, lime	Calcium polysulfides			Non-volatile		Orange-red liquid.	i. w.	Oral LD50 0.25-0.5g/kg.	Absorbed.	Slight; irritant, eye.
25	Thiram; Thirurad; Tuads	Tetramethylthiuram disulfide	240.4	155-156			White powder or grains.	<0.005 w.;3.1 acet.;5.0 bz.;15 chl.; 1.6 toluene.	Oral LD50 860mg/kg.	Absorbed.	Irritant.[5]
26	Zineb	Zinc ethylenebisdithio-carbamate	275		Negligible at 25°C		White solid.	i. w.; s. pyr.	Oral LD50 5.2g/kg.	Poor.	Slight.
27	Ziram; Milban; Zimate	Zinc dimethyldithio-carbamate	305.8	246(pure)[9]	Negligible at 25°C		White solid.	<0.008 w.;0.33 acet.;0.74 chl.; s. CS_2	Oral LD50 1.4‡ 0.1g/kg.‡	Poor.	Irritant.[5]

/1/ Abbreviations: a. =acid; ac. =acetic acid; acet. =acetone; al. =alcohol; ac. a. =acetic acid; al. =ethyl alcohol(95%); alc. =alcohol; bz. =benzene; c. =cold; chl. =chloroform; crys. =crystals; d. =decomposes; dil. =dilute; eth. =ether; gly. =glycerol; h. =hot; i. =insoluble; me. =methyl; MLD=minimum lethal dose; org. =organic; pet. =petroleum; ppm=parts per million; ppt. =precipitate; pyr. =pyridine; s. =soluble; s. c. =subcutaneous; sl. =slight; tol. =toluene; w. =water. /2/ To nose and throat. /3/ 158-171 (technical). /4/ To skin and respiratory tract. /5/ To skin. /6/ May cause dermatitis. /7/ Strongly irritant and sensitizing. /8/ Eye injury in rabbits. /9/ 240-244 (technical).

354. "ESSENTIAL" DRUGS

The question "If you were limited to the use of only 25 drugs in your practice, which would you choose?" was presented to several hundred clinicians, dentists, and veterinarians throughout the United States. The total response, entailing some 600 compounds, was statistically analyzed and the results are tabulated below -- 30 drugs in each professional category listed in order of preference. Biologicals were not included.

	Drug[1]	Use		Drug[1]	Use
CLINICIANS					
1	Atropine	Anti-parasympatholytic, antispasmodic, mydriatic.	16	Iron	In nutritional iron deficiencies.
			17	Ether, diethyl	Inhalation anesthetic.
2	Morphine	Analgesic, narcotic.	18	Sulfadiazine	Bacteriostat and bactericide.
3	Penicillin	Antibiotic.	19	Adrenocorticotropic hormone (ACTH)	In adrenal cortical insufficiency; see Item 4.
4	Adrenal cortical hormones (ACH)	In adrenal insufficiency, rheumatoid arthritis, rheumatic fever, allergies, hay fever, bronchial asthma.	20	Meperidine hydrochloride (Demerol HCl)	Analgesic, antispasmodic; similar to morphine.
5	Acetylsalicylic acid (Aspirin)	Analgesic, antipyretic.	21	Gantrisin (a sulfisoxazole)	Wide-spectrum antibacterial.
6	Digitalis	Myocardial stimulant in congestive heart failure.	22	Pentobarbital (Nembutal)	Hypnotic, sedative, antispasmodic.
7	Tetracycline	Antibiotic.	23	Alcohol, ethyl	CNS depressant, sedative, nutrient, antiseptic, solvent.
8	Epinephrine (Adrenalin)	Sympathomimetic, antispasmodic, vasoconstrictor.	24	Aminophylline	Diuretic, antispasmodic, cardiac and respiratory stimulant.
9	Vitamin B complex	In Vitamin B deficiencies.	25	Diphenylhydantoin sodium (Dilantin Na)	Anticonvulsant in epilepsy, chorea, and similar conditions.
10	Streptomycin	Antibiotic.			
11	Codeine	Analgesic, sedative, narcotic, antitussive.	26	Ephedrine	Sympathomimetic, vasoconstrictor, nasal decongestant.
12	Phenobarbital (Luminal)	Long-acting sedative, hypnotic, antispasmodic.	27	Ergot	Oxytocics.
13	Procaine (Novocaine)	Local anesthetic.	28	Chloramphenicol (Chloromycetin)	Wide-spectrum antibiotic.
14	Thyroid	In replacement therapy, obesity, myxedema, low BMR.	29	Oxygen	With inhalation anesthesia; treatment or prevention of hypoxia.
15	Insulin	In diabetes mellitus, hypoglycemic shock therapy.	30	Quinidine	In auricular fibrillation and tachycardia.
DENTISTS					
31	Procaine (Novocaine)	See Item 13.	46	Ammonia, aromatic spirit	Analeptic in syncope; antacid.
32	Eugenol (eugenic acid, allyl guaiacol)	Local anesthetic and antiseptic.	47	Pentobarbital (Nembutal)	See Item 22.
			48	Sodium fluoride	Inhibition of tooth decay.
33	Codeine	See Item 11.	49	Calcium hydroxide	Neutral base for temporary fillings and pulp capping.
34	Epinephrine (Adrenalin)	See Item 8.			
35	Acetylsalicylic acid (Aspirin)	See Item 5.	50	Benzalkonium chloride (Roccal)	Surface antiseptic.
36	Alcohol, ethyl	Aid in drying cavities; see also Item 23.	51	Silver nitrate	Antiseptic, astringent, caustic.
37	Iodine (tincture)	Local antiseptic.	52	Zinc chloride	Antiseptic, astringent, caustic.
38	Nitrous oxide (N₂O)	Inhalation anesthetic and analgesic.	53	Glycerol	Solvent, emollient, plasticizer.
39	Penicillin	See Item 3.	54	Ethylaminobenzoate (Benzocaine)	Local anesthetic.
40	Zinc oxide	In dental cements.			
41	Lidocaine (Xylocaine)	Infiltration anesthesia; nerve block.	55	Sodium bicarbonate	In mouth wash.
42	Oxygen	See Item 29.	56	Gentian violet	Local antiseptic.
43	Phenol	Local antiseptic and anesthetic.	57	Phenobarbital (Luminal)	See Item 12.
44	Hydrogen peroxide (H₂O₂)	Bleaching and disinfecting agent; used in dentrifices, mouthwashes.	58	Tetracycline	See Item 7.
			59	Nitromersol (Metaphen)	Local antiseptic.
45	Creosote, beechwood	Local antiseptic and anesthetic; in sterilization of root canals.	60	Petrolatum, liquid	Lubricant, solvent, vehicle.
VETERINARIANS					
61	Tetracycline	See Item 7.	77	Iron	See Item 16.
62	Penicillin	See Item 3.	78	Streptomycin	See Item 10.
63	Phenothiazine	Anthelmintic for pinworms, roundworms.	79	Petrolatum, liquid	See Item 60.
			80	Arecoline hydrobromide	Teniacide for dogs, cats; cathartic for horses.
64	Procaine (Novocaine)	See Item 13.			
65	Dextrose (glucose)	Parenteral nutrient solution.	81	Sodium fluoride	Insecticide, anthelmintic for roundworms of swine.
66	Iodine (tincture)	See Item 37.			
67	Pentobarbital (Nembutal)	See Item 22.	82	Benzalkonium chloride (Roccal)	See Item 50.
68	Calcium gluconate	In milk fever (cattle), preg. disease (sheep); in convulsions, eclampsia, paraplegia (cats, dogs); in Mg, Hg, Pb, CCl₄ poisonings.	83	Sulfamerazine	Bacteriostat.
			84	Sulfamethazine	Bacteriostat.
			85	Sulfaquinoxaline	Prevention and control of cecal and intestinal coccidiosis of fowl.
69	Chloral hydrate	Narcotic, anesthetic; in tetanus, colic (horses), convulsions, strychnine poisoning.	86	Tetrachloroethylene	Anthelmintic for hookworms.
			87	Adrenal cortical hormones (ACH)	See Item 4.
70	Ether, diethyl	See Item 17.			
71	Nemural (a diocarbyl)	Teniacide.	88	N-Butylchloride (Chlorobutane)	Anthelmintic.
72	Alcohol, ethyl	See Item 23.			
73	Magnesium sulfate	Cathartic.	89	Epinephrine (Adrenalin)	See Item 8.
74	Hexachlorocyclohexane (Lindane)	Insecticide.			
75	Morphine (salts)	See Item 2.	90	Acetylsalicylic acid (Aspirin)	See Item 5.
76	Posterior pituitary	Oxytocic, pressor, antidiuretic.			

/1/ Drugs listed may include, or be interpreted in terms of, salts, closely related derivatives, or preparations. The eight drugs or drug types unanimously selected in all categories are: codeine (or morphine), acetylsalicylic acid, procaine, alcohol, epinephrine, a barbiturate (either pheno- or pentobarbital), penicillin, and tetracycline.

355. COMMON POISONS: SYMPTOMS, PROCEDURES, AND ANTIDOTES

The symptoms indicated below may result from numerous pathological conditions or from exposure to many factors other than those given in the table. They may also vary in severity and order of appearance, according to the nature and amount of the toxic agent. This table lists examples of some common household poisons and therapeutic drugs which exert a toxic effect.

Part I: CHARACTERISTIC SYMPTOMS

	Symptom	Poison
	Circulatory	
1	Blood cell changes	Anemia: alcohol(chronic), arsenic, barbiturates(chronic), benzene(chronic), lead, morphine(addiction), naphthalene, sulfonamides; brown blood(Meth Hb): acetanilid, antipyrine, nitrites, nitrobenzene, nitroglycerin, phenacetin, potassium chlorate, sulfanilamide, sulfites; leucocytosis: chloral hydrate, pilocarpine, atropine; leucopenia: aminopyrine, aniline derivatives, arsenicals, benzene, sulfonamides; polycythemia: aniline derivatives(chronic), arsenic(dysentery); stippling: lead.
2	Bradycardia	Barium, digitalis, muscarine, physostigmine, pilocarpine, quinine, strophanthin, tetraethyl lead, veratrum.
3	Collapse(circulatory)	May be produced by practically any poison.
4	Hemorrhage, petechiae, purpura	Arsenic, benzene, corrosives, dicumarol, heparin, sedormid, warfarin.
5	Hypertension	Amphetamine, barium, ephedrine, epinephrine.
6	Hypotension	Apresoline, barbiturates(acute), chloroform, hexa-and pentamethonium compounds, histamine, muscarine, nitrites and nitroglycerin, tribromethanol, veratrum.
7	Tachycardia	Amphetamine, atropine, cocaine, ephedrine, epinephrine.
8	Vasoconstriction, gangrene	Amphetamine, ephedrine, epinephrine, ergot, lead, nicotine.
9	Coma or drowsiness	Alcohol, aniline, anesthetics, arsenic, antihistaminics, atropine, barbiturates, bromides, carbon disulfide, carbon monoxide, carbon tetrachloride, chloral hydrate, cyanides, gasoline, kerosene, methyl bromide, methylchloride, organic phosphate insecticides[1], opiates, synthetic morphine-like analgesics[2], phenol, sulfanilamide, sulfides.
10	Constipation	Calcium salts, dihydromorphinone, lead, opiates, synthetic morphine-like analgesics.[2]
	Convulsive	
11	Clonic	Abrin and castor beans, atropine, caffeine, camphor, carbon disulfide, ergot, insulin(inj.), phenol, picrotoxin, strychnine(early), theophylline.
12	Tonic or tetanic	Camphor, carbon monoxide, cocaine, cyanides, insulin(inj.), metrazol, nicotine, organic chloride insecticides[3], organic phosphate insecticides[1], procaine, strychnine.
13	Tremor	Alcohol, amphetamine, arsenic, barium, ergot, ephedrine, insulin(inj.), lead, manganese(chronic), mercury(chronic). nicotine, physostigmine.
14	Diarrhea	Abrin and castor beans, antimony, arsenic, barium, corrosives, croton oil, digitalin group, emetine, ergot, mercury, muscarine, nicotine, organic phosphate insecticides[1], physostigmine, pilocarpine.
15	Hyperthermia(fever)	Arsenicals, atropine, barbiturates(early), camphor, cocaine, dinitrophenols, phosphorus, sulfonamides, salicylates.
16	Hypothermia	Alcohol, anesthetics, aniline derivatives, chloral hydrate, coal tar analgesics and antipyretics, opiates and synthetic morphine-like analgesics(except demerol)[2], nitrites, phenol.
17	Mania or delirium	Alcohol(chronic), amphetamine, atropine, barbiturates(chronic), bromides, camphor, cannabis, cocaine, ephedrine, insulin(inj.), lead, mercury, phenol, physostigmine, scopolamine.
18	Odor of breath	Acetone(diabetes, ingestion, starvation), alcohol, ammonia, camphor, chloroform, cyanides, methylsalicylate, nitrobenzene, paraldehyde, phenols, phosphorus, sulfides, other odoriferous poisons.
19	Paralysis	Abrin and castor beans, alcohol, arsenic, barium, carbon disulfide, lead, nicotine, triorthocresyl phosphate.
	Pupillary	
20	Dilation	Alcohol, amphetamine, atropine, barbiturates, cocaine(early), ephedrine, homatropine, scopolamine.
21	Constriction	Codeine, ergot, opiates and synthetic morphine-like analgesics[2], muscarine, neostigmine, nicotine, organic phosphate insecticides[1], physostigmine, pilocarpine.
22	Fixation	Acetanilid, alcohol, anesthetics, chloral hydrate, coal tar analgesics, paraldehyde, somnifacients.
23	Respiratory depression	Alcohol, ANTU, barbiturates, barium, carbon disulfide, carbon tetrachloride, cyanides, opiates and synthetic morphine-like analgesics[2], organic phosphate insecticides[1].
	Sensory	
24	Abdominal pain and colic	Arsenic, barium, carbon disulfide, cathartics(drastic), corrosives, fluorides, lead, mercury, methyl alcohol, muscarine, nicotine, organic phosphate insecticides[1], oxalates, physostigmine, pilocarpine.
25	Blindness and deafness	Atropine, barium, cocaine, digitalis, ergot, methyl alcohol, nicotine, quinine, salicylates.
26	Color vision	Digitalis, santonin.
27	Paresthesia	Alcohol, arsenic, carbon disulfide, ergot, lead, mercury.
28	Vertigo	Alcohols, anesthetics, antihistaminics, barbiturates, carbon monoxide, cyanides, ergot, fluorides, gasoline, histamine, kerosene, methadione, nicotine, nitrites, opiates and synthetic morphine-like analgesics[2], quinine, salicylates.
	Dermal	
29	Corrosion(incl.mucosa)	Acids, alkalies, cresol, phenol.
30	Cyanosis	Acetanilid, alcohol, anesthetics, aniline, barbiturates, cyanides, gasoline, kerosene, nitrates, nitrobenzene, phenacetin, sulfanilamide, sulfides.
31	Discoloration (incl. tongue, oral mucosa)	Black: sulfuric acid; brown: bromine, iodine; greenish-blue: Paris green, other copper salts; white: alkalies, corrosive acids, metallic salts, phenol; yellow: nitric and picric acids; gingival line: bismuth, copper, lead, mercury, silver.
32	Dryness of mouth	Antihistaminics, atropine, ephedrine, scopolamine.
33	Edema	Arsenic, cortisone and derivatives, cresol, mercury, oxalates, phenol, turpentine.
34	Epilation	Alkali sulfides, radium, thallium.
35	Exfoliation	Arsenic, gold, sulfonamides.
36	Flush	Alcohol, anesthetics, arsenic, atropine, borates, carbon disulfide, carbon monoxide, cyanides, histamine, nicotinic acid, opium derivatives, pilocarpine.
37	Jaundice	Arsenic, bismuth, carbon tetrachloride, chloroform, cincophen, gold, phosphorus, sulfonamides.
38	Pallor	Arsenic, barbital, cocaine and other local anesthetics, ephedrine, lead.
39	Rash	Can be caused by almost any drug, the more common being: antihistaminics, arsenicals, atropine, barbiturates, bromides, dyes, iodides, mercurials, procaine, quinine, radioactive substances, salicylates, sulfonamides.
40	Sweating	Acetanilid, antipyrine, emetics, opiates, phenacetin, physostigmine, pilocarpine, sulfonal.
41	Urticaria	Bromides, organic chloride insecticides[3], histamine, phenobarbital, salicylates, sulfonamides.
	Urinary	
42	Albuminuria	Arsenic, carbon tetrachloride, chlorates, chloroform, mercury, phenols, sulfonamides.
43	Color changes	Brown to black: naphthalene, phenol, pyrogallol, quinine, resorcinol; green: anthraquinone, methylene blue; orange: santonin; red: anthraquinone dyes, phenolphthalein(alkaline), santonin(alkaline).
44	Glycosuria	Ephedrine, morphine and opiates.
45	Hematuria	Arsenic, cantharides, mercury, naphthalene, oxalates, phenols, sulfonamides.
46	Oliguria	Arsenic, carbon tetrachloride, chromate, mercury(late stages), oxalates, phenols, sulfonamides.
47	Odor	Turpentine.
48	Polyuria(early); anuria(later)	Mercurials.
	Vomiting	
49	Gastrointestinal irritation	Abrin and castor beans, alcohol, alkaline sulfides, antibiotics, antimony, arsenic, copper, cyanides, emetine and other ipecac alkaloids, gasoline, iodine, kerosene, mercury, naphthalene, phenol, strong acids and alkalies(also ammonia).
50	Systemic poisoning	Antihistaminics, apomorphine, atropine, camphor, carbon disulfide, cyanides, DDT(?), digitalis and other cardiotonic glycosides, emetine and other ipecac alkaloids, nicotine, organic chloride insecticides[3], organic phosphate insecticides, phenol, picrotoxin, quinine, salicylates, strychnine, sulfonamides.

/1/DFP, HETP, malathion, parathion, TEPP, etc.   /2/ Levorpan(dromoran), meperidine(demerol), methadone, etc.   /3/ Chlordane, lindane, etc.

355. COMMON POISONS: SYMPTOMS, PROCEDURES, AND ANTIDOTES (Concluded)

The symptoms indicated below may result from numerous pathological conditions or from exposure to many factors other than those given in the table. They may also vary in severity and order of appearance, according to the nature and amount of the toxic agent. This table lists examples of some common household poisons and therapeutic drugs which exert a toxic effect.

Part I: CHARACTERISTIC SYMPTOMS (concluded)

	Symptom	Poison
	Vomiting (concluded)	
51	Vomitus, colored	Blue: with iodine if starch is present; brown or "coffee grounds": alkaline or acid corrosives; green: copper sulfate, Paris green, Scheele's green.

Part II: GENERAL PROCEDURES

Poisons Taken Orally

1. If nature of poison is unknown, give 15g of "universal antidote" (finely divided activated charcoal, 2 parts; tannic acid, 1 part; magnesium oxide, 1 part) in half a glass of warm water; if this preparation is not available, give large amounts of water, tea, milk or eggs. If poison is known, give specific antidote. Caution: Never give anything by mouth to an unconscious person.
2. Induce vomiting by stroking back of tongue from side to side, or by giving plenty of warm salt water or soapy water; or wash stomach promptly by means of tube. Caution: Do not use these procedures (a) where corrosive poisons have been ingested >30 minutes (danger of perforation of stomach or esophagus), or (b) in strychnine poisoning (danger of convulsions). With infants, avoid aspiration of vomitus into trachea or lungs by placing child face down when first retching appears, with head at least 8-10 inches lower than hips. Apomorphine injected subcutaneously is very effective emetic, but should be avoided in coma or respiratory depression.
3. Give cathartic, 15g of sodium sulfate or 30g of magnesium sulfate in half a glass of water; flush bowel by high colonic irrigation with warm water.

Poisons Inhaled

4. Try to identify toxic vapor. In areas contaminated with ammonia, arsine, carbon monoxide, chlorine, bromine, fluorine, hydrogen cyanide, hydrogen sulfide, nitric vapors, or other highly toxic gases (i.e., CW agents), proper masks should be worn or the breath held.
5. Remove the victim promptly from exposure.
6. At first sign of difficult breathing begin artificial respiration, using approved method; oxygen should be administered only by trained personnel; continue artificial respiration until professional medical personnel arrive.

Poisons in Contact with the Skin

7. Try to identify the poison, avoiding personal contact with it.
8. Flood the contaminated area with successive increments of water for at least 15 minutes.
9. Remove all contaminated clothing, including gloves, headgear, shoes, watches, rings, jewelry.
10. Do not use oils, fats or pastes (sodium bicarbonate, etc.), or bandages, unless specifically indicated.

Poisons in Contact with the Eyes

11. Promptly flood both eyes with copious amount of water, with the eyelids open (eyelids can be opened and held apart by grasping the eyelashes and pulling the eyelids away from the eyeball). Using this method, continue washing for at least 15 minutes.

Other Precautions

12. Keep the patient warm and in a recumbent position; never leave him unattended.
13. If breathing is difficult or has stopped, give artificial respiration, and continue until voluntary respiration reappears or medical aid arrives.
14. Do not give alcoholic beverages except on proper medical advice; alcohol increases the absorption of some poisons.
15. Send for medical assistance as soon as possible, but do not interrupt the procedures outlined above.

Part III: SPECIFIC ANTIDOTES

The "General Procedures" (G. P.) referred to below are found in Part II above.

i. m. = intramuscular injection; i. v. = intravenous injection; s. c. = subcutaneous injection.

	Poison	Antidote
1	Acids, strong (CH_3COOH, HCl, HNO_3, H_2SO_4, H_3PO_4)	Use G. P. 1, or milk of magnesia; do not give carbonates or emetics.
2	Alcohol, methyl (wood alcohol)	Use G. P. 2, 3; 3-5% sodium bicarb. and 5% glucose, i. v., or orally if patient is conscious.
3	Alkalies, strong (NaOH, KOH, NH_4OH, K_2CO_3, Na_2CO_3)	Large amounts 1% acetic acid or vinegar (4 x dil.) orally, then milk, white of eggs; do not use stomach tube or induce vomiting.
4	Alkaloids	Use G. P. 1, 2, 3, or gastric lavage with 0.01% potassium permanganate.
5	Belladonna (atropine, hyoscyamine, solanine, stra-	Same as above, then pilocarpine i. v., and pentobarbital i. m. or i. v.
6	Cocaine monium)	Use G. P. 1, 2, 3; pentobarbital i. m. or i. v., to control convulsions.
7	Ergot (ergotoxine, etc.)	Use G. P. 1, 2, 3; amyl nitrite inhalation, nitroglycerin s. c., papaverin i. v.
8	Muscarine, physostigmine, pilocarpine	Atropine i. v. or s. c. immediately and until symptoms are controlled, then G. P. 1, 2.
9	Nicotine (tobacco, "Black Leaf 40")	Ephedrine i. m., or amphetamine i. v. Do not give strychnine. G. P. 1, 2.
10	Opium (codeine, heroin, laudanum, morphine), synthetic morphine-like analgesics.	Gastric lavage with 0.1% potassium permanganate; N-allyl morphine i. v.; caffeine, sodium benzoate s. c., to stimulate respiration.
11	Strychnine	Pentobarbital i. v. immediately, or inhalation anesthesia to control convulsions; gastric lavage with 0.1% potassium permanganate only after convulsions have ceased; keep quiet, in absolute darkness; no morphine.
12	Arsenicals (As_2O_3, Fowler's sol., Paris green, insecticides, rodenticides, Scheele's green)	G. P. 1, 2, 3; then BAL[1] i. m., repeated doses; 30-60g Na or Mg sulfate in warm water, orally.
13	Barbiturates (barbital, luminal, nembutal, pentobarbital, phenobarbital, veronal)	G. P. 1, 2; amphetamine, metrazol or picrotoxin i. v., repeated until muscle excitation or recovery.
14	Barium salts (acetate, chloride, carbonate, sulfide)	Sodium or magnesium sulfate in warm water, orally; G. P. 2, 3.
15	Chloral hydrate	Gastric lavage with tea or coffee; picrotoxin, amphetamine or ephedrine i. v. until conscious.
16	Cyanides (HCN, KCN, NaCn)	Amyl nitrite inhalation immediately, then 3% sodium nitrite i. v. and 25% sodium thiosulfate i. v.
17	Formaldehyde (ingested)	Milk, eggs, ammon. acetate (15g in glass of water), or 0.2% ammonia water freely by mouth; G. P. 2.
18	Fluorides [HF, NaF, NH_4F, Na fluoroacetate (1040)]	Ca gluconate i. v. immed.; glass of lime water or 1% of $CaCl_2$ orally, or as gastric lavage.
19	Halogens (bromate, bromine, chlorate, iodine)	Sodium thiosulfate 15g in glass of water or starch solution; G. P. 2 and 3.
20	Lead compounds	Acute: gastric lavage with magnesium, sodium or aluminum sulfate solution, followed with plain water to remove lead sulfate thus formed; milk, eggs. Chronic: sodium calcium versenate 3% in glucose solution, by slow intravenous drip.
21	Mercury compounds	Orally, glass of 5-10% sodium phosphite or sodium formaldehyde sulfoxalate solution; G. P. 2, 3; BAL[1] i. m.
22	Organic and fluorophosphates [diisopropyl fluoro-phosphate (DFP), hexaethyltetraphosphate (HETP), "nerve gas," parathion, tetraethylpyrophosphate, etc.]	Atropine sulfate i. m. or i. v. immediately, until symptoms subside; if poison swallowed, give milk, induce vomiting (G. P. 2); long-continued artificial respiration may be necessary.
23	Oxalic acid and oxalates	Orally or by stomach tube, lime water, magnesium oxide, chalk, or soluble calcium or magnesium salts; gastric lavage if mucosa not deeply corroded (burning pain, collapse); 10% calcium gluconate or 5% calcium chloride i. v. for tetany; later, magnesium sulfate purge.
24	Phenols (carbolic acid, creosote, cresol, etc.)	Give olive oil by mouth; carefully pass small, well-lubricated tube and wash out stomach with olive oil; if olive oil not available, give milk or egg white. Skin: wash with 50% alcohol, glycerine, vegetable oils, or soapy water.
25	Phosphorus, yellow (rat poisons)	Copious, repeated gastric lavage with 1-2% copper sulfate or 0.1-1% potassium permanganate solutions, or normal saline; G. P. 3; no oils, fats or milk in diet.
26	Salicylates [acetylsalicylic acid (aspirin), methyl salicylate (oil of wintergreen), phenyl salicylate (salol), salicylic acid, sodium salicylate]	Gastric lavage with sodium bicarbonate, saline catharsis, glucose i. v.; stimulants.
27	Silver salts ($AgNO_3$)	Sodium chloride or tannic acid in water; G. P. 2, followed with milk or other demulcents.
28	Thallium salts (insecticides, rodenticides)	Gastric lavage with 1% sodium or potassium iodide; G. P. 2; stimulants, demulcents; BAL[1] i. m.

/1/ BAL (British anti-lewisite): 2, 3-dimercapto-1-propanol; used as a 10% solution in peanut oil with 20% benzyl benzoate.

A = Bradykininogen; B = Carboxypolypeptidase; C = Catalase; D = Cephalinase; E = Cholinesterase; F = Desoxyribonuclease; G = Diaminoxidase; H = ithinase; P = Lipase; Q = 5-Nucleotidase; R = Ophio-ATP-ase; S = Phospholipase; T = Phosphodiesterase; U = Phosphomonesterase; V = Polypepti-

	Animal, Distribution	Adult Length ft	Fibrinogen Coagulate	Fibrinogen Destroy	Prothrombin Activate	Prothrombin Destroy	Enzyme Activity[1]	Mouse Toxicity[2] mg/kg
				Helodermatidae				
1	Gila monster (Heloderma suspectum), S.W.U.S.A., N.W. Mexico (chiefly Arizona and Sonora)	$1\frac{1}{2}$-2						LD_{50}(rat)20.18 lyophilized venom
			Colubridae[7] (Snakes)					
2	Boomslang[8] (Dispholidus typus), forested portions of Africa south of Sahara	$4\frac{1}{2}$-$5\frac{1}{2}$			+(?)		W	MLD 10.0
			Elapidae[9] (Snakes)					
3	Adder, death (Acanthophis antarcticus), most of Australia, parts of New Guinea, nearby islands	2-3	+(?)		+(?)		E, L, N, O, R	LD_{100} (0.5-0.7)
4	Black, red-bellied (Pseudechis porphyriacus), E. Australia	$4\frac{1}{2}$-$5\frac{1}{2}$	+(?)		+(?)		N, O	LD_{100} 3.5
5	Brown, Australian (Demansia textilis), most of Australia	4-5					E, N, R	LD_{100} 0.25
6	Brown, giant or Taipan[11] (Oxyuranus scutellatus), N. Australia	8-11	+(?)		+(?)			LD_{100} 0.17
7	Cobra, Indian (Naja naja), S. Asia to Indonesia, Formosa, Philippines	4-6	-	-	-	+	B, E, H, I, J, L, M, N, O, P, R, T, U, V, W	MLD 0.75 LD_{50} 0.5
8	Cobra, king[13] (Ophiophagus hannah), W. India, Burma, Philippines, Indonesia, S. China, Thailand	12-16					E, N, R	
9	Cobra, spitting (Naja nigricollis), Africa south of Sahara in savannah areas	5-6				+	E, L, N, R, W	MLD 0.5
10	Copperhead, Australian[14] (Denisonia superba), E. Australia	$4\frac{1}{2}$-$5\frac{1}{2}$	+(?)		+(?)		E, L, N, O, R	LD_{100} 1.2
11	Coral, Central American (Micrurus nigrocinctus), tropical Mexico through Panama	2-$3\frac{1}{2}$						
12	Coral, North American (M. fulvius), southern U.S.A. to N.E. Mexico	2-$3\frac{1}{2}$						LD(MLD?) 1.0
13	Coral, South American (M. frontalis), southern Brazil to northern Argentina	2-5	-	-	+	-	L, W	LD_{100} 2.5
14	Coral, subtropical (M. corallinus), subtropical South America	2-4					E, L, N, R	
15	Krait, common (Bungarus candidus coeruleus), India, Burma, Malay Peninsula, Java, Sumatra, Celebes	$3\frac{1}{2}$-$4\frac{1}{2}$					E, K, L, N, W	LD_{100} 3.0 LD_{50} 1.0
16	Krait, Formosan (B. multicinctus), S.E. China, Formosa	3-4	-(?)		-(?)			LD 0.1
17	Long-glanded[17] (Maticora intestinalis), Burma, Malay Peninsula, Java, Sumatra	$1\frac{1}{2}$-2						
18	Mamba, eastern green (Dendroaspis angusticeps), E. Africa, Ethiopia to Natal	6-13						MLD 0.75
19	Mamba, western green[18] (D. viridis), W. Africa	$6\frac{1}{2}$-8					E, L	LD_{100} 3.0
20	Ringhals (Hemachatus haemachates), S. Africa	3-4	+	-	±	-	E, N, R, T, U, W	LD_{50} 3.0
21	Tiger[19] (Notechis scutatus), most of Australia including Tasmania	4-$5\frac{1}{2}$	-	-	+	-	E, L, N, R, T, U, W	LD_{100} >0.24 LD_{50} (g. pig) 6.5 µg/kg
			Viperidae[20] (Snakes)					
22	Adder, night (Causus rhombeatus), most of Africa	2-3					W	MLD 15.0
23	Adder, puff (Bitis arietans), Africa, S. Arabia	$2\frac{1}{2}$-5	-	+	-	-	A, E, N, R, T, U, W	MLD 7.5
24	Viper, European (Vipera berus), British Isles, across N. Europe and Asia to Japan	$1\frac{1}{2}$-$2\frac{1}{2}$					A, N	Mean LD 6.5
25	Viper, gaboon[22] (V. gabonica), tropical Africa	4-$5\frac{1}{2}$	+	+			E, L, N, Q, R, S, W	MLD 20.0
26	Viper, horned or Sahara sand (Cerastes vipera), N. Africa, Arabia, S. Iraq[23]	$1\frac{1}{2}$-2					N	MLD 15.0
27	Viper, Jura (Vipera aspis), Central and S. Europe	2-3		+		+(?)	E, G, L, N, O, R, W	MLD 0.75
28	Viper, mountain (V. lebetina), S.E. Europe to Pakistan[24]	$3\frac{1}{2}$-5					E, N	Mean LD 22.0
29	Viper, Palestine (V. palestinae), Israel and surrounding area							
30	Viper, Russell's, Daboia, or Tic polonga (V. russellii), India, Burma, S. China, Formosa, Java[25]	4-$5\frac{1}{2}$	+	-	-	+	B, E, H, I, J, K, L, M, N, O, P, Q, R, T, U, V, W	MLD 1.0 LD_{50} 20.0
31	Viper, saw-scaled[26] (Echis carinata), India, Iraq, Arabia, Africa north of equator[27]	$1\frac{1}{2}$-$2\frac{1}{2}$	+				B, E, I, J, L, N, R, V, W	MLD 5.0 LD_{50} 7.5
32	Viper, Sudan mole[28] (Atractaspis microlepidota), eastern central Africa	$1\frac{1}{2}$-$2\frac{1}{2}$						
			Crotalidae[29] (Snakes)					
33	Boicotiara (Bothrops cotiara), southern Brazil, northern Argentina	$1\frac{1}{2}$-3					E, L, N	LD_{100} 15.0
34	Bushmaster[30] (Lachesis muta), Costa Rica to northern South America	8-11					L, W	LD_{100} 57.0

/1/ Implies characteristic activity for enzyme but not its specific isolation. /2/ Dry venom administered subcutaneously unless otherwise stated. rificus, C. atrox, C. horridus. /3/ GOOD implies a mortality of less than 1%; FAIR, 2-10% mortality; GUARDED, 11-40% mortality; POOR, mor- for crotalid envenomation believed effective. /7/ Fangs rear, immovable, grooved; over 1000 species (few poisonous, none dangerously). /8/ Ar- /11/ Large, aggressive; long fangs. /12/ Also Cape cobra (N. nivea), S.W. Africa and Cape Province; Egyptian cobra (N. haje), N.E. and S. Africa; /15/ Also banded krait (B. faciatus). Slightly lower mortality. /16/ Mortality 77%. /17/ Venom glands extend through anterior third of body. /18/ Ar- ammodytes), S.E. Europe and Asia Minor; fair prognosis; symptoms somewhat more severe. /22/ Heavy snake, very long fangs. /23/ In arid gressive; chiefly arid habitat. /28/ Small, burrowing snake; large fangs. /29/ Fangs front, movable, hollow; pit between eye and nostril; more than

CHEMICAL AND BIOLOGICAL CHARACTERISTICS

Diastase; I = Dipeptidase; J = Endopeptidase; K = Flavin adenine dinucleotide; L = Hyaluronidase; M = Invertase; N = L-Amino-acid oxidase; O = Lecdase; W = Protease. Slash mark (/) through letter indicates enzyme activity not known to be present.

Symptoms of Envenomation in Man	Prognosis[3]	Available Antiserum	
Helodermatidae			
Local pain, swelling, hyperemia, weakness, hyperpnea, tinnitis, nausea, vomiting. Death by respiratory paralysis and cardiac failure.[4]	(?)[5]	No[6]	1
Colubridae[7] (Snakes)			
Local pain, swelling and hemorrhage, ecchymoses, bleeding from nose and mouth, sometimes from all mucous membranes and skin, headache, vomiting, collapse; temperature normal or subnormal.	Good	No	2
Elapidae[9] (Snakes)			
Similar to poisoning by tiger except that peripheral circulatory failure is more common and hemorrhagic phenomena occur.	Guarded	Yes	3
Local pain and swelling, vomiting, hemorrhages from nose and mouth, prostration, hematuria.[10]	Good	Yes	4
Latent period to 12 hr followed by abdominal pain, vomiting, headache, dizziness, weakness, rapid pulse and subnormal temperature, respiratory and circulatory collapse, hemoglobinuria and peripheral thromboses.	Guarded	Yes	5
Similar to tiger. Flaccid paralysis of limbs, intercostal and bulbar paralysis, often rapidly fatal.	Poor	Yes	6
Pain radiating from bite, edema, numbness, tremors, ptosis, drooping of head, salivation, speech difficulty, giddiness, muscular incoordination and weakness, blindness, progressive depression of respiration, convulsions, incontinence of urine and feces. Pupils react to light and heart beats after respiration ceases.[12]	Guarded	Yes	7
Similar to poisoning by Naja spp. Symptoms develop rapidly, often death in 30-60 min.	Poor	Yes	8
Similar to poisoning by Naja spp. Frequently sprays venom at eyes. Contact produces acute, intense ophthalmia. Systemic poisoning does not occur by this route, and permanent damage to vision is rare.	Guarded	Yes	9
Similar to tiger. Rapid loss of muscle tone and consciousness, peripheral circulatory failure.	Guarded	Yes	10
Local numbness; minimal systemic symptoms. Few cases reported.	Fair (?)	No	11
Cyclic pains radiating from bite; somnolence, dyspnea, dysphagia, sweating; soreness of face, throat and eyes.	Guarded	No	12
Neurologic symptoms at site of bite; involvement of 3rd, 4th and 6th cranial nerves producing ptosis and diplopia. Prolonged coagulation time.	Guarded	Yes	13
Numbness without pain at bite. Early: headache, swelling of face and lips; hyperesthesia, sore throat, ptosis, photophobia, normal pupillary reflex, vomiting, cramps, dyspnea, loss of muscle tone, tachycardia. Later: backache, irritability, salivation, bradycardia, dysuria, albuminuria.	Guarded	Yes	14
Little immediate pain or local reaction. Latent period to 12 hr followed by abdominal pain, staggering gait, dysphagia, dyspnea, ptosis, stiffness of jaws, coma, respiratory paralysis, cardiac failure.[15]	Poor[16]	Yes	15
Poisoning similar to common krait.	Guarded	Yes	16
Minimal local pain and edema. Later: faintness, unsteady gait, periods of mental confusion, choking sensation with swelling and soreness of throat and mouth, salivation, vomiting, diarrhea, sweating, dyspnea.	Good (?)	No	17
Local pain and swelling, vomiting, restlessness, drowsiness or collapse followed by coma. Dyspnea and respiratory failure.	Poor	Yes	18
Poisoning similar to D. angusticeps.	Guarded	Yes	19
Pain; dyspnea; weak, thready pulse; cyanosis; collapse. Sprays venom at eyes. Effects resemble N. nigricollis.	Fair	Yes	20
Latent period 15-60 min followed by nausea, vomiting, faintness, drowsiness, sweating. Later: dullness of sensation, staggering, dysphagia, slurred speech, ptosis, pupils dilated and do not react to light; rapid, weak pulse and respiration, progressive dyspnea and death from respiratory failure.	Poor	Yes	21
Viperidae[20] (Snakes)			
Local hemorrhages, swelling.	Good	Yes	22
Severe local edema, necrosis and sloughing, restlessness, weak pulse, dyspnea, gastrointestinal hemorrhages.	Guarded	Yes	23
Local pain and edema of bitten extremity, sometimes extending into trunk; hemorrhages along lymphatics. Little systemic reaction, sometimes vomiting, sweating, abdominal pain, faintness, cyanosis, shock.[21]	Good	Yes	24
Pain, hemorrhagic edema, necrosis, severe shock, respiratory depression, pain in loins with hematuria, pupils dilated and do not react to light.	Guarded	Yes	25
Local pain, edema, fever, thromboses and cardiac collapse in severe cases.	Fair	Yes	26
Similar to V. berus but systemic symptoms prominent. Vomiting, diarrhea, dysuria, weakness, depression.	Good	Yes	27
Rapidly spreading edema and necrosis, cold sweat, thirst, nausea, vomiting. Severe cases show epistaxis and hematuria.	Fair	Yes	28
Local pain, edema, ecchymoses, abdominal pain, vomiting, diarrhea with bloody stools in severe cases, fever, peripheral vascular collapse and shock. Autopsy: serosanguineous transudate in subcutaneous tissue and muscles with degeneration of arteriole and capillary walls. Visceral hemorrhages especially under endocardium and in gastrointestinal mucosa.	Fair	Yes	29
Rapidly spreading edema with extravasation of blood, epistaxis and petechiae, abdominal pain, vomiting, paralytic ileus, collapse, shock, albuminuria, prolonged clotting time. Terminally: loss of consciousness, pupils fail to react to light, circulatory failure. Autopsy: subcutaneous hemorrhages especially near bite, meningeal congestion, blood in lungs.	Guarded	Yes	30
Local pain and edema, low platelet count with ecchymoses and hemorrhages from mucous membranes, profound anemia, abdominal pain, impaired liver function.	Guarded	Yes	31
Local pain followed by numbness, adenitis, tachycardia, sweating, salivation, vomiting, dyspnea and pulmonary congestion, microscopic hematuria.	Fair	No	32
Crotalidae[29] (Snakes)			
Inadequate information. Presumably similar to fer-de-lance.	Fair	Yes	33
Inadequate information. Rapid death preceded by a severe shock-like state.	Poor[31]	Yes	34

Considerable geographic and individual variation in toxicity exists, e.g., Ancistrodon contortrix, Bothrops jararacussu, B. neuweidii, Crotalus tertality in excess of 40%. /4/ Nonaggressive, bite sometimes ineffective. /5/ Prognosis from good to poor, literature conflicting. /6/ Antiserum boreal, timid. /9/ Fangs front, grooved though virtually fused for most of length; over 150 species. /10/ Also Mulga snake (P. australis). black cobra (N. melanoleuca), W., Central and E. Africa south of Zululand in forests. /13/ Highly aggressive. /14/ Sluggish, seldom bites. boreal, quick, aggressive. /19/ Active, aggressive; short fangs. /20/ Fangs front, movable, hollow; about 50 species. /21/ Also sand viper (V. habitat. /24/ Occurs in mountains to 8000 ft. /25/ Often common in thickly settled areas. /26/ Also called carpet viper or phoorsa. /27/ Ag-80 species. /30/ Very aggressive, jungle habitat. /31/ Mortality usually 100%.

A = Bradykininogen; B = Carboxypolypeptidase; C = Catalase; D = Cephalinase; E = Cholinesterase; F = Desoxyribonuclease; G = Diaminoxidase; H = ithinase; P = Lipase; Q = 5-Nucleotidase; R = Ophio-ATP-ase; S = Phospholipase; T = Phosphodiesterase; U = Phosphomonesterase; V = Polypeti-

	Animal, Distribution	Adult Length ft	Fibrinogen		Prothrombin		Enzyme Activity[1]	Mouse Toxicity[2] mg/kg
			Coagulate	Destroy	Activate	Destroy		
	Crotalidae[29] (concluded)							
35	Cascabel (Crotalus terrificus), southern Mexico to Uruguay and Argentina, mostly in highlands	4-5½	+	-	±	-	E, F, L, N, R, W	LD$_{100}$ 1.1 LD$_{50}$ 0.6
36	Copperhead, North American (Ancistrodon contortrix), eastern and southern U.S.A.	2-3½					E, N, T, V, W	LD$_{100}$ 53.0 LD$_{50}$ 25.6
37	Fer-de-lance[32] (Bothrops atrox), central Mexico to eastern Argentina, islands of Martinique, Tobago, Trinidad, and St. Lucia	4½-6½	+	-	-	+	E, F, L, N, R, W	LD$_{100}$ 31.0 LD$_{50}$ 22.0
38	Habu (Trimeresurus flavoviridis), Riu Kiu Islands	4-5					R, T, U, W	LD$_{100}$ 16.0
39	Jararaca (Bothrops jararaca), Brazil to northern Argentina and Paraguay	3½-4½	+	-	+	-	A, E, J, L, N, R, W	LD$_{100}$ 7.0
40	Jararaca, painted (B. neuwiedii), Brazil and Bolivia to Argentina	2-3					E, F, L, N, R, W	LD$_{100}$ 14.0[34]
41	Jararacussu (B. jararacussu), Bolivia, Brazil, Paraguay, Argentina	4-6					E, F, L, N, W	LD$_{100}$ 9.0
42	Massasauga or marsh rattlesnake (Sistrurus catenatus), southern Ontario, central and S.W. U.S.A.	2-3					E, N, R	LD$_{100}$ 9.0 LD$_{50}$ 5.2
43	Moccasin, water (Ancistrodon piscivorus), southern U.S.A. to central Texas	3-5	-	+	-	+	D, E, K, L, N, O, Q, T, V, W	LD$_{100}$ 45.0 LD$_{50}$ 25.8
44	Rattlesnake, eastern diamondback (Crotalus adamanteus), S.E. U.S.A. in lowlands	4½-6½	+	+	-	-	D, E, L, N, Q, T, V, W	LD$_{50}$ 14.5
45	Rattlesnake, Mexican diamondback (C. basiliscus), western Mexico	4½-6½	+	-	-	-	E, N, R, W	LD$_{100}$ 4.0
46	Rattlesnake, prairie or Pacific (C. viridis), western U.S.A., S.W. Canada, N. Mexico	2½-5					E, N	LD$_{50}$ 3.6
47	Rattlesnake, red[35] (C. ruber), extreme S.W. U.S.A., parts of California (Baja)	3-5					E, N	LD$_{50}$ 21.2
48	Rattlesnake, timber (C. horridus), eastern U.S.A.	3-5	+	-	-	+	E, N, R, W	LD$_{100}$ 9.2[36]
49	Rattlesnake, western diamondback[32] (C. atrox), S.W. U.S.A., northern Mexico	3½-5½	-	+	-	-	A, E, L, N, R, W	LD$_{100}$ 19.0 LD$_{50}$ 7.5[37]
50	Sidewinder or horned rattlesnake (C. cerastes), S.W. U.S.A. in deserts	1½-2½						LD$_{50}$ 4.2
51	Timbo or jumping viper (Bothrops mexicana), southern Mexico through Central America	2-3	+	-	-	-	E, N, W	
52	Urutu (B. alternata), southern Brazil to Argentina	3-5					E, F, L, N, O, W	LD$_{100}$ 23.0 LD$_{50}$ 13.0
53	Viper, Chinese pit (Trimeresurus mucrosquamatus), S. E. China, Formosa	3-4						MLD 7.6
54	Viper, hognosed (Bothrops lansbergii), Central America, Panama to El Salvador	1-1½						
55	Viper, Malay pit (Agkistrodon rhodostoma), Thailand, Java, Malay Peninsula, Sumatra	2-3						
56	Viper, palm[39] (Bothrops schlegelii), British Honduras to Ecuador and Columbia	1½-3	+				W	

/1/ Implies characteristic activity for enzyme but not its specific isolation. /2/ Dry venom administered subcutaneously unless otherwise stated. rificus, C. atrox, C. horridus. /3/ GOOD implies a mortality of less than 1%; FAIR, 2-10% mortality; GUARDED, 11-40% mortality; POOR, mor- 30%. /34/ 26 mg/kg also reported. /35/ Nonaggressive. /36/ 36 mg/kg also reported. /37/ 16.8 mg/kg also reported. /38/ Also Mamushi or

357. TOAD VENOMS: CHEMICAL

	Toad, Distribution	Bufagins[1]			Bufotoxins[2]
		Name (Proposed Formula)	Action or Effect[4]	Toxicity[5] mg/kg	Name (Proposed Formula)
1	Bufo alvarius, S.W. U.S.A.	Absent			Alvarobufotoxin
2	Bufo arenarum, Argentina	Arenobufagin ($C_{25}H_{34}O_6$)	Digitalis-like; emesis; systolic standstill of heart.	0.092 ±0.005	Arenobufotoxin ($C_{39}H_{60}O_{11}N_{14}$)
3	Bufo bufo bufo (B. vulgaris), Europe	Absent			Vulgarobufotoxin ($C_{38}H_{60}O_{11}N_4$)
4	Bufo bufo gargarizans, China	Cinobufagin ($C_{25}H_{31}O_5$)[7] Telecinobufagin ($C_{24}H_{34}O_5$)	Digitalis-like action on vagus, vagus center, myocardium; emesis; clonic or tonic convulsions after paralysis.	0.219 ±0.011 0.102 ±0.007	Cinobufotoxin ($C_{43}H_{64}O_{12}N_4$, or $C_{39}H_{58}O_{11}N_4$)
5	Bufo formosus (Bufo bufo japonicus), Japan	Gamabufagin ($C_{27}H_{38}O_6$)		0.101 ±0.005	Gamabufotoxin ($C_{41}H_{64}O_{11}N_4$)
6	Bufo marinus (B. aqua), circumtropical	Marinobufagin[8] ($C_{24}H_{32}O_5$)	Digitalis-like action; emesis; ventricular fibrillation.	0.555 ±0.028	Marinobufotoxin ($C_{38}H_{58}O_{10}N_4$, or $C_{42}H_{62}O_{11}N_4$)[9]
7	Bufo quercicus, S.E. U.S.A.	Quercicobufagin ($C_{23}H_{34}O_5$)		0.097 ±0.004	Quercicobufotoxin
8	Bufo regularis pardalis, South Africa	Regularobufagin ($C_{23}H_{34}O_5$)		0.153 ±0.006	Regularobufotoxin ($C_{37}H_{60}O_{10}N_4$)
9	Bufo terrestrius-americanus, E. U.S.A.	Americobufagin	Digitalis-like action.		Americobufotoxin
10	Bufo valliceps, eastern Mexico, Texas and Louisiana	Vallicepobufagin ($C_{23}H_{34}O_5$)	Nausea; emesis; A-V block and ventricular standstill.	0.201 ±0.017	Vallicepobufotoxin
11	Bufo viridis viridis, Europe	Viridobufagin ($C_{23}H_{34}O_5$)	Nausea, emesis, increased intestinal tone, ventricular fibrillation.	0.111 ±0.008	Viridobufotoxin ($C_{37}H_{60}O_{10}N_4$)
12	Bufo woodhousei, S.E. U.S.A.	Fowlerobufagin ($C_{23}H_{33}O_6$)	Digitalis-like action; emesis; ventricular fibrillation.	0.218 ±0.012	Fowlerobufotoxin

/1/ The bufagins are steroid-type compounds and possess a digitalis-like action. /2/ The bufotoxins are the conjugation product of the specific buf- lethal or average fatal dose for cat, intravenous. /6/ Frog heart; heart perfusion method. /7/ Also reported $C_{29}H_{38}O_7$. /8/ Also reported as oc-

Diastase; I = Dipeptidase; J = Endopeptidase; K = Flavin adenine dinucleotide; L = Hyaluronidase; M = Invertase; N = L-Amino-acid oxidase; O = Lecdase; W = Protease. Slash mark (/) through letter indicates enzyme activity not known to be present.

Symptoms of Envenomation in Man	Prognosis[3]	Available Anti-serum	
Crotalidae[29] (concluded)			
Little local reaction other than swelling, intense headache, nausea, dizziness, blindness, paralysis of neck and of eyelids (ptosis), collapse, albuminuria and hematuria followed by anuria. Death from respiratory paralysis or uremia. Autopsy: hyperemia of brain and meninges, sometimes with hemorrhages; intermediate nephron necrosis.	Poor	Yes	35
Local pain, swelling and necrosis, lymphangitis and lymphadenitis, sweating, nausea, vomiting. In severe cases: shock, petechiae, bloody stools.	Good	Yes	36
Local pain, edema and lymphadenopathy, bleeding from fang punctures, gums, nose and other body orifices, low prothrombin, prolonged clotting time, moderate to high leukocytosis, hematuria. In severe cases; shock, pupils do not react to light, respiration irregular. Autopsy: hemorrhagic necrosis at bite; hemorrhages into muscles, bowel, central nervous system; blood incoagulable.	Guarded[33]	Yes	37
Marked local and regional edema, ecchymoses, anesthesia at site of bite, nausea and vomiting.	Fair	Yes	38
Similar to fer-de-lance. Autopsy: generalized visceral hemorrhages, cerebral hemorrhage, hemoglobinuric nephrosis.	Guarded	Yes	39
Presumably similar to poisoning by fer-de-lance.	Fair	Yes	40
Clinical and autopsy findings similar to fer-de-lance.	Guarded	Yes	41
Pain, edema, ecchymoses, weakness, sweating, vomiting, hemolytic anemia in severe cases.	Good	Yes	42
Similar to poisoning by N.A. copperhead, but more severe. Local necrosis more marked.	Fair	Yes	43
Local pain, edema and ecchymoses, dryness of mouth, vomiting, shock, hemolytic anemia. In severe cases: muscular twitching, paresthesia, speech difficulty, sensation of yellow vision, unconsciousness.	Guarded	Yes	44
Similar to cascabel, but less severe. Inadequate information.	Guarded	Yes	45
Usual local symptoms of Crotalus. Also thirst, abdominal pain, vomiting, diarrhea, dyspnea. In severe cases: excitement, hypertonicity of muscles, paresthesia, convulsions, cyanosis, respiratory failure, clouding of consciousness.	Fair	Yes	46
Similar to western diamondback but less severe.	Fair	Yes	47
Local pain, edema, vesication, pallor, vomiting, fever, restlessness, shock, anemia.	Fair	Yes	48
Similar to eastern diamondback but neurotoxic symptoms less marked. Profound shock in severe cases.	Guarded	Yes	49
Inadequate information. Presumably similar to prairie rattlesnake but less severe.	Fair	Yes	50
Local pain, edema and necrosis, minimal systemic reaction. Information meager, possibly unreliable.	Good (?)	Yes	51
Similar to fer-de-lance. Late death from CNS hemorrhage. Autopsy: massive subdural hemorrhage, dilated left heart, renal hemorrhage, cerebral edema.	Guarded	Yes	52
Local pain, ecchymoses, blistering, little systemic reaction.	Fair	Yes	53
Local pain and edema, minimal systemic reaction.	Good	Yes	54
Local pain, swelling and necrosis, pallor, weakness, rapid pulse, prolonged clotting time.[38]	Good	Yes	55
Local symptoms as with other Bothrops spp. Also headache, faintness, bleeding from gums.	Good	Yes	56

Considerable geographic and individual variation in toxicity exists, e.g., Ancistrodon contortrix, Bothrops jararacussu, B. neuweidii, Crotalus tertality in excess of 40%. /29/ Fangs front, movable, hollow; pit between eye and nostril; more than 80 species. /32/ Aggressive. /33/ Mortality about Pallas' pit viper (A. halys), S.E. Europe, across Asia to Japan. /39/ Arboreal.

AND BIOLOGICAL CHARACTERISTICS

Bufotoxins[2]		Bufotenines[3]				
Action or Effect[4]	Toxicity[5] mg/kg	Name (Proposed Formula)	Action or Effect	Cardiac Arrest[6]	Remarks	
Digitalis-like; emesis; systolic standstill of heart.	0.756 ±0.075	Alvarobufotenine ($C_{12}H_{18}O_2N_2$)	Oxytocic; slight pressor action; diastolic standstill of heart.	1:5000 dil.	Cholesterol and ergosterol present.	1
Digitalis-like; emesis; ventricular fibrillation.	0.406 ±0.012	Arenobufotenine A ($C_{12}H_{20}O_3N_2$)	Oxytocic; slight pressor action.	1:5000 dil.	Cholesterol and epinephrine present.	2
		Arenobufotenine B ($C_{14}H_{18}O_2N_2$)		1:5000 dil.		
Emesis; ventricular fibrillation.	0.292 ±0.017	Vulgarobufotenine ($C_{12}H_{18}O_2N_2$)	Oxytocic; marked pressor action.		Cholesterol and ergosterol present.	3
Emesis; vasopressor effect, followed by cardiac collapse, death in systole; prolongation of P-R interval.	0.359 ±0.024	Cinobufotenine ($C_{12}H_{16}ON_2$)	Oxytocic; miotic; intense, short vasopressor action; contraction of smooth muscle not inhibited by atropine.	1:10,000 dil.	Cholesterol, epinephrine, norepinephrine and bufotenidine present.	4
Persistent action; slight pressor action; emesis; ventricular fibrillation.	0.374 ±0.027	Gamabufotenine ($C_{12}H_{18}O_2N_2$)	Oxytocic; marked pressor action.	1:5000 dil.	Cholesterol, epinephrine, and bufotenidine present.	5
More emetic than bufagin.	0.417[10] ±0.022	Marinobufotenine ($C_{12}H_{14}O_2N_2$)	Oxytocic; little or no pressor action.	1:5000 dil.	Epinephrine, cholesterol, ergosterol, 5-hydroxytryptamine also present.	6
Ventricular systolic standstill.		Quercicobufotenine ($C_{12}H_{18}O_2N_2$)	Oxytocic; slight pressor action.		Cholesterol present (?).	7
Emesis; ventricular fibrillation.	0.477 ±0.026	Regularobufotenine	Oxytocic; marked pressor action.		Epinephrine present (4.3-5% of whole venom, 10.7 mg per animal).	8
Digitalis-like action.		Americobufotenine. ($C_{12}H_{18}O_2N_2$)	Oxytocic; marked pressor action.			9
		Vallicepobufotenine ($C_{11}H_{12}O_2N_2$)	Oxytocic; slight pressor action; decreased amplitude and arrest of heart contractions.	1:1000 dil.		10
Action similar to, but weaker than, that of viridobufagin.	0.270 ±0.012	Viridobufotenine A ($C_{12}H_{18}O_2N_2$)	Oxytocic; marked pressor action.	1:5000 dil.	Cholesterol and ergosterol present.	11
		Viridobufotenine B ($C_{12}H_{20}O_3N_2$)	Oxytocic; slight pressor action.	1:5000 dil.		
Emesis.	0.792 ±0.054	Fowlerobufotenine ($C_{13}H_{20}O_2N_2$)	Oxytocic; marked pressor action; epinephrine-like action.	1:5000 dil.	Bufotenidine present.	12

ogin with one molecule of suberyl-arginine. /3/ The bufotenines are organic bases having an indole ring in the molecule. /4/ On cat. /5/ Mean curring in Bufo paracnemis (Argentina). /9/ Also reported as $C_{42}H_{64}O_{11}N_4$. /10/ Also reported as 0.43 and 0.49.

358. TOXIC MARINE ORGANISMS

Protozoa

1 PARALYTIC SHELLFISH POISONING caused by ingestion of mollusks which have fed on toxic dinoflagellates.

Animal, Distribution. Dinoflagellates: (Gymnodinium brevis), Florida coast; (Gonyaulax catenella), U.S. Pacific coast, Gulf of Mexico; (G. tamarensis), Nova Scotia, Canadian Atlantic coast; (Pyrodinium phoneus), Belgium.

Symptoms, Findings. Symptoms may appear within 10 min after ingestion. Gastrointestinal and mental symptoms variable. Paresthesia of lips, tongue and fingertips followed by ataxia and muscular incoordination. Ascending paralysis. Death may occur from cardiovascular collapse or respiratory failure in 2-12 hr. Aphasia also reported. (See also Mollusca.)

Chemistry, Toxicology. Toxin a potent alkaloid soluble in alcohol and water, insoluble in ether and chloroform. Loses stability but not necessarily toxicity in aqueous solution with pH and temperature increase. Poison not isolated; postulated empirical formula of hydrochloride: $C_9H_{17}N_6O_4(HCl)_2$. Purest preparation has toxicity of 4 mouse units per μg. MLD for man is probably 5-10 mg. Neurotoxin with both central and peripheral actions. Depresses cardio-inhibitory and vasomotor centers and conduction system of myocardium.

Porifera

2 SPONGE STING caused by contact.

Animal, Distribution. Brown sponge (Fibulia nolitangere), W. Indies; fire sponge (Tedania ignis), W. Indies; fire sponge (T. toxicalis), California coast.

Symptoms, Findings. Urticaria and pruritis with occasional swelling of affected areas.

Chemistry, Toxicology. Intraperitoneal injections of crude extracts of the animal lethal to mice. Kills aquarium animals.

Coelenterata

3 HYDROID STING caused by contact. Venom apparatus of cnidoblasts comprised of capsule, nematocyst and cnidocil. Toxin is introduced through the tubular filament of the nematocyst. Chemical and mechanical factors appear to be involved in the discharge of the nematocysts.

Animal, Distribution. False; or stinging; coral (Millepora alcicornis), eastern Florida, Malaya, tropical seas.

Symptoms, Findings. Acute burning sensation on contact. Erythema, pustule formation and desquamation reported.

Chemistry, Toxicology. Not known.

4 PHYSALIA STING caused by contact with nematocyst-bearing tentacles.

Animal, Distribution. Portuguese-man-of-war (Physalia physalis), Florida, Hawaii, Australia, warm seas.

Symptoms, Findings. Intense burning pain following contact. Erythematous wheals with occasional numbness. Gastrointestinal and mental symptoms reported, also muscular weakness and pain sometimes followed by clonic contractions. Respiratory distress in severe cases; secondary shock may develop. Skin lesions persist for weeks. Fatal cases reported.

Chemistry, Toxicology. Tentacles yield hypnotoxin, an anesthetizing substance, precipitated by alcohol, non-dialyzable, and destroyed by temperature above 55°C.

5 JELLYFISH STING caused by contact.

Animal, Distribution. Sea wasp (Chiropsalmus quadrigatus), Indian Ocean, Netherlands Indies, Australia; giant jellyfish (Cyanea capillata), north temperate and arctic seas; pink-fringed jellyfish (Dactylometra quinquecirrha), Florida coast, Philippines.

Symptoms, Findings. Symptoms similar to those provoked by Physalia; fatal cases reported from Chiropsalmus sting.

Chemistry, Toxicology. Meduso-congestin, an alcohol-precipitated toxin, has been isolated from certain jellyfish. Toxin has local effect on pilomotor muscles; causes spastic contractions. Hypersensitizes temperature perception organ in skin.

6 SEA ANEMONE STING caused by contact.

Animal, Distribution. Sea anemones: (Actinia equina), Black Sea; (Actinodendron alcyonoideum), Pacific coral reefs, Australia; (Sagartia elegans), Mediterranean and African Seas.

Symptoms, Findings. Stinging sensation on contact; may be followed by pruritis and edema. Severe cases may develop papules which occasionally ulcerate. Systemic symptoms and deaths reported. "Sponge fisherman's disease" thought to be caused by Sagartia.

Chemistry, Toxicology. Actinia toxin separated into two fractions: congestin and thalassin. Congestin is a water soluble, heat resistant, white crystalline substance that produces vomiting, diarrhea and visceral congestion. One-tenth g/kg animal produces death from respiratory paralysis. Thalassin is a water soluble, alcohol-precipitated crystal antagonistic to congestin. One-hundredth mg/kg animal causes intense scratching and sneezing in dogs. A curare-like fraction, tetramine, has been isolated from Actinia equina.

Mollusca

7 CONE SHELL STING caused by contact. Wounds inflicted by hollow teeth attached to long slender, tubular, fleshy proboscis connected to a venom gland.

Animal, Distribution. Cloth-of-gold shell (Conus auricus), S. Pacific; cone shell (C. geographus), S. Pacific, Japan, Australia; cone shell (C. marmoreus), S. Pacific; cone shell (C. tulipa), S. Pacific.

Symptoms, Findings. Sting results in intense burning pain often followed by numbness. Area about wound is cyanotic and swollen. Muscular incoordination, paresis or paralysis, mental confusion, visual disturbances and paresthesia reported. In severe cases, respiratory distress and cardiovascular collapse. Deaths reported in 3-5 hr.

Chemistry, Toxicology. Not known.

8 PARALYTIC SHELLFISH POISONING caused by ingestion of mollusks. (See Protozoa.)

Animal, Distribution. Razor clam (Ensis directus), New England coast; bar or surf clam (Mactra solidissima), New England coast; horse or red mussel (Modiolus modiolus), both N. American coasts, Europe; ocean mussel (Mytilus californianus), Pacific coast N. America; common or blue mussel (M. edulis), Europe, N. American coasts, New Zealand, S. Africa; butter clam (Saxidomus giganteus), Pacific coast N. America, Canada; butter clam (S. nuttalli), California coast.

Symptoms, Findings. (See Protozoa.)

Chemistry, Toxicology. (See Protozoa.)

9 VENERUPIN POISONING caused by ingestion.

Animal, Distribution. Venus shell (Tapes semidecussata), Japan.

Symptoms, Findings. Gastrointestinal upset.

Chemistry, Toxicology. Toxic principle, called venerupin, thought to be an amine. LD of purified poison is 0.25 mg for a 15 g mouse. Venerupin treated with acidulated ethanol becomes violently toxic to mice, resembling paralytic shellfish poisoning. Causes acute yellow or red atrophy of liver and hemorrhagic symptoms.

10 OCTOPUS BITE. Venom apparatus of anterior and posterior salivary glands, salivary ducts, buccal mass and beak. Bite is puncture-wound variety. Venom is secreted by posterior salivary gland.

Animal, Distribution. Octopuses: (Eledone moschata), Mediterranean Sea; (Octopus apollyon), Pacific coast N. America; (O. macropus), Europe, Mediterranean and Red Seas, Indian Ocean, Malaysia, China, Japan and Australia; (O. vulgaris), warm seas.

Symptoms, Findings. Symptoms variable. Bite usually produces sharp throbbing pain, tingling and edema lasting few hours to several days.

Chemistry, Toxicology. Not known.

Annelida

11 WORM BITE.

Animal, Distribution. Bloodworm (Glycera dibranchiata), Caribbean Sea, N. Carolina to Massachusetts, Pacific coasts of Mexico and S. California.

Symptoms, Findings. Stinging pain, edema, increase localized skin temperature, pruritis for several hours.

Chemistry, Toxicology. Not known.

Arthropoda

12 | KING CRAB POISONING caused by ingestion.

Animal, Distribution. King or horseshoe crabs: (Carcinoscorpius rotundicauda), estuaries of Malaya and Siam; (Tachypleus gigas), Japan, Malaya, India.[1]

Symptoms, Findings. Onset of symptoms in 10 min to $\frac{1}{2}$ hour. Dizziness, nausea, vomiting, weakness, headache, paresthesia of lips and mouth, cardiac arrhythmia, drowsiness, possible paralysis of muscles of mastication and limbs. Death may occur in 1-6 hr. In non-fatal cases, recovery is prolonged.

Chemistry, Toxicology. Tissues contain powerful toxic alkaloid. Flesh and eggs of Carcinoscorpius can be fatal.

Echinodermata

13 | STARFISH POISONING caused by contact.

Animal, Distribution. Common starfish (Crossaster papposus), N. Atlantic coasts of Europe and America.

Symptoms, Findings. All starfish are said to exude a poison which diffuses through water or alcohol; when large numbers are present, the liquid may cause a pruritic rash.

Chemistry, Toxicology. Nature of toxin unknown. Extracts injected into cats produce prostration and convulsions.

14 | SEA URCHIN STING caused by contact. Venom is injected by globiferous pedicellariae which are comprised of three spoon-shaped blades, each having a globular body and hook-like process. Venom glands are located under each of the blades.

Animal, Distribution. Sea urchins: (Toxopneustes pileolus), Malaya, Japan; (Sphaerechinus granularis), Mediterranean Sea, eastern Atlantic.[2]

Symptoms, Findings. Pedicellariae wounds produce severe pain, faintness, giddiness, dyspnea, paralysis of lips and tongue, relaxation of limbs. Drop in body temperature is usual in animals. Facial paralysis may persist 6 hr. Total paralysis and death from drowning reported.

Chemistry, Toxicology. Toxin resistant to high temperatures and evokes curare-like action. Depressed body temperature in animals. Exact nature of toxin unknown.

15 | SEA CUCUMBER POISONING caused by contact.

Animal, Distribution. Sea cucumbers: (Actinopyga agassizi), British W. Indies; (Holothuria argus), Netherlands Indies, Australia, Polynesia; (H. forskali), Mediterranean Sea, southern coast of England.

Symptoms, Findings. Injection of extracts kills mice; when added to water extracts kill fish. Contact with organ of Cuvier may produce inflammation of skin, intense pain, and loss of sight.

Chemistry, Toxicology. Active toxic agent holothurin, located in the organ of Cuvier, water soluble, non-volatile, and heat stable; decolorizes Lugol's solution but not methylene blue; cannot be extracted or inactivated with acetone, ether or chloroform. One ounce of crude extract per 750 gallons of water kills fish in 23 min. Intraperitoneal injection lethal to mice.

Chordata

16 | ELASMOBRANCH POISONING caused by ingestion.

Animal, Distribution. Cow shark (Hexanchus griseus), Atlantic and Pacific Oceans, Mediterranean Sea; cat shark (Scyliorhinus caniculus), Atlantic Ocean, Mediterranean Sea; smooth dogfish (Mustelus canis), Atlantic Ocean, Caribbean Sea; requiem or blue shark (Prionace glauca), warm and temperate seas; Greenland shark (Somniosus microcephalus), North Sea, North Atlantic Ocean; skate (Raja batis), S. Africa, Atlantic Ocean.

Symptoms, Findings. Onset may occur within $\frac{1}{2}$-1 hr. Nausea, vomiting, abdominal pain, oily stools, pallor, headache, burning and tingling sensation of lips, tongue and throat, visual disturbances, pain and heaviness in limbs, chest pain, and itching; primary shock reported. Coma and death may occur several days after ingestion.

Chemistry, Toxicology. Artificial immunity to Greenland shark; its poison water soluble and resistant to cooking temperatures (less than 100°C).

17 | BULLHEAD SHARK STING caused by contact. Venom secreted by the glandular epithelium in the posterior groove of the dorsal spines.

Animal, Distribution. Bullhead sharks: (Heterodontus francisci), California coast; (H. philippi), Australia, Japan.[3]

Symptoms, Findings. Intense pain, redness, edema, increase skin temperature.

Chemistry, Toxicology. Not known.

18 | STINGRAY STING caused by contact. Venom apparatus of a bilaterally serrated, dentinal caudal spine enveloped in an integumentary sheath. Venom contained within tissues of the two ventrolateral grooves.

Animal, Distribution. Common stingray (Dasyatis pastinacus), European coasts; round stingray (Urobatis halleri), Pacific coast of southern N. America; spotted stingray (Aetobatis narinari), tropical Pacific, Atlantic and Indian Oceans.

Symptoms, Findings. Sting followed by intense pain often involving entire affected extremity. Wound edges ragged, localized discoloration and edema. Primary shock common; convulsions and paresthesia reported; death infrequent.

Chemistry, Toxicology. Action of crude extract on peripheral vascular system may be diphasic, the principal response being vasoconstriction. Large doses provoke auricular and ventricular standstill; may damage sino-auricular node. Chemical properties unknown.

19 | RATFISH STING caused by contact. Venom secreted by epithelium of the integumentary sheath of the dorsal spine. Greatest concentration of venom tissue in the interdentate depression on posterior aspect of spine.

Animal, Distribution. Ratfish (Chimaera monstrosa), Atlantic Ocean off Portugal and northern U.S.; Pacific ratfish (Hydrolagus colliei), Pacific coast of N. America.

Symptoms, Findings. Intense pain and deaths reported for Chimaera. Erythema and mild, dull ache lasting several minutes reported for Hydrolagus.

Chemistry, Toxicology. One ml of crude extract kills mice in 24-54 hr.

20 | TETRAODON POISONING caused by ingestion.

Animal, Distribution. Sharp-nosed puffer (Canthigaster margaritatus), Red Sea, E. Africa, Netherlands Indies, China, Melanesia, Micronesia, Polynesia; sharp-nosed puffer (C. rivulatus), Japan, Hawaiian islands; puffer (Colomesus psittacus), rivers of Guiana, northern Brazil, W. Indies; puffer (Chilomycterus spinosus), W. Indies, Brazil, S. Africa; puffer (Diodon holacanthus), tropical Pacific, Atlantic and Indian Oceans; tetrodon of the Cape (Amblyrhynchotes honckenii), S. Africa, Indo-Pacific; puffer (Fugu basilevskianus), northern China, northwestern Korea; puffer (F. chrysops), Pacific coast of central Japan; puffer (F. niphobles), Japan; puffer (F. ocellatus), China, Japan, Philippine Islands; puffer (F. pardalis), China, Japan; puffer (F. pseudomus), East China Sea and Yellow Sea; puffer (F. rubripes), China to Korea, Sea of Japan, Pacific coast of Japan; puffer (F. stictonotus), southern Korea, East China Sea, Japan; puffer (F. vermicularis), East China Sea, Japan; puffer (F. xanthopterus), China, Korea, southern Japan; puffer (Lagocephalus laevigatus inermis), eastern Africa, tropical Indian Ocean, Australia, East China Sea, southern Japan; puffer (L. lunaris), Red Sea, southern and eastern Africa, India to Australia, China, Japan; puffer (L. sceleratus), east coast Africa to Philippine Islands, southern Japan, Australia, Tahiti; puffer (Sphoeroides annulatus), California to Peru, Galapagos Islands; puffer (S. maculatus), Atlantic coast, U.S. to Guiana; puffer (S. spengleri), Texas, Florida, W. Indies, Brazil, Canary Islands, west coast Africa; puffer (Torquigener hamiltoni), Australia, Melanesia, Polynesia; sunfish (Mola mola), temperate and tropical seas; puffer (Arothron aerostaticus), Red Sea, eastern Africa, Netherlands Indies, Australia, Guam, Japan, Tahiti; puffer (A. hispidus and immaculatus), Red Sea, S. Africa to southern Japan, Australia, Melanesia, Micronesia, Polynesia, Panama; puffer (Tetraodon lineatus), rivers of northern and western Africa.

Symptoms, Findings. Onset within 30 min after ingestion. Numbness of lips, tongue, fingertips and toes; nausea, vomiting, headache, dizziness, weakness, dyspnea; occasional complete paralysis and loss of speech reported; coma and death may occur within 1-24 hr as a result of respiratory paralysis.

Chemistry, Toxicology. Postulated formula for tetrodotoxin: $C_{16}H_{31}NO_{16}$; soluble in water; MLD for rabbits is 3.0-4.0 g/kg. Spheroidine: $C_{12}H_{17}O_{10}N_3$; insoluble in water; MLD for mice, 0.013-0.014 µg. Only a few Japanese puffers studied. It is assumed that all puffers contain same toxin.

/1/ Common sand crab (Emerita analoga), Pacific coast, Oregon to Mexico; contains paralytic shellfish poison varying in toxicity, depending on nearby mussels. /2/ Also sea urchins: (Asthenosoma varium, Diadema antillarum, D. setosum, Echinothrix spp, Echinus actus, Paracentrotus lividus, Salmacis sphaeroides); toxin in spines; nature unknown. /3/ Also DOGFISH STING. Spiny dogfish (Squalus acanthias), temperate waters of N. and S. hemispheres.

Chordata (concluded)

21 | CIGUATERA POISONING caused by ingestion.

  Animal, Distribution. Surgeonfish (Acanthurus triostegus), tropical Pacific; ladyfish (Albula vulpes), tropical Pacific; left-eyed flounder (Bothus mancus), tropical Pacific; pompano (Caranx latus), W. Indies, South Africa, Australia; pompano (C. melampygus), Red Sea, Indian Ocean, central Pacific; herring (Clupanodon thrissa), W. Indies, Indian Ocean, Japan; anchovy (Engraulis japonica), Japan; wrasse (Epibulus insidiator), tropical Pacific; wrasse (Cheilinus fasciatus), Red Sea to tropical Pacific, Japan; snapper (Lutjanus vaigiensis), Indian Ocean and tropical Pacific; snapper (L. bohar), Red Sea, Indian Ocean, tropical Pacific, Japan; goatfish(Mulloidichthys samoensis), tropical Pacific; damselfish (Abudefduf sexfasciatus), tropical Pacific; parrot fish (Scarus microrhinos), Indian Ocean, tropical Pacific; bass (Epinephelus fuscoguttatus), Red Sea, Indian Ocean, tropical Pacific; bass (Variola louti), Red Sea, Indian Ocean, tropical Pacific; squaretail (Tetragonurus cuvieri), Mediterranean Sea, Atlantic and Pacific Oceans.

  Symptoms, Findings. Onset may be immediate but usually within 30 hr. Tingling, numbness, malaise, chills, fever, headache, sweating, pruritus diarrhea, prostration, metallic taste, generalized motor incoordination, weakness and myalgia common. Sensory disturbances (perversion of heat and cold): convulsions and paralysis reported. About 2-3% of cases fatal. Complete recovery may take months.

  Chemistry, Toxicology. Not known.

22 | GYMNOTHORAX POISONING caused by ingestion.

  Animal, Distribution. Moray eels: (Gymnothorax eurostus, G. flavimarginatus, G. javanicus, G. meleagris, G. pictus, G. petelli, G. undulatus), Red Sea, Indian Ocean, tropical Pacific.

  Symptoms, Findings. Onset 20 min to 8 hr with tingling, numbness, vomiting, respiratory distress, laryngeal spasm and paralysis, motor incoordination, clonic and tonic convulsions; abnormal deep and superficial reflexes reported. Coma may develop, lasting 2-10 da; mortality about 10%. Acute symptoms usually subside within 10 da.

  Chemistry, Toxicology. May be small molecular substance. One ml of crude extract injected intraperitoneally into mice produces death in 16 min to 24 hr.

23 | SCOMBROID POISONING caused by ingestion.

  Animal, Distribution. Mackerel (Scomber japonicus), Pacific, Atlantic, Indian Oceans, Mediterranean and Red Seas; skipjack(Katsuwonus pelamis), cosmopolitan; tuna (Thunnus thynnus); cosmopolitan.

  Symptoms, Findings. Histamine-like symptoms: headache, flushing, congestion of soft tissues of eyes, nausea, vomiting, urticaria, and erythema. Recovery within 12 hr.

  Chemistry, Toxicology. Thought to be histamine or histamine-like substance. Exact mechanism of production and chemical structure unknown.

24 | SCORPION FISH STING caused by contact. Venom apparatus of the dorsal, ventral and anal stings. Primary sites of venom production in the glandular grooves of the stings.

  Animal, Distribution. Bullrout (Notesthes robusta), Australia; thread-finned zebrafish (Pterois antennata), all tropical and temperate seas; tiger fish (P. lunulata), Japan, Banka Islands; zebrafish (P. volitans), E. Africa to Australia, Japan; lionfish (Scorpaena grandicornis), all seas; hogfish (S. porcus), Mediterranean Sea, Atlantic Ocean; scorpion fish (S. scrofa), Mediterranean Sea, Atlantic Ocean; lumpfish (Inimicus didactylus), Philippines, Malaya, Johore Straits; stonefish (I. japonicus), Sea of Japan, China Sea; stonefish (Minous monodactylus), South Seas, China, Japan; stonefish (Synancea horrida), Red Sea, coasts of Africa, India, Malaya, Indo-Pacific, Australia, New Zealand; stonefish (S. verrucosa), Red Sea, coasts of Africa and India, Netherlands Indies, Australia, tropical Indo-Pacific, Marshalls, Polynesia.

  Symptoms, Findings. Localized pain, pallor about wound, diarrhea, vomiting. Dyspnea, coma and fatalities reported.

  Chemistry, Toxicology. Not known.

25 | WEEVERFISH STING caused by contact. Venom apparatus of opercular and dorsal stings. Venom gland located within glandular grooves of the sting.

  Animal, Distribution. Weever (Trachinus draco), European seas, Australia, Chilean seas; (T. radiatus), Mediterranean Sea; (T. vipera), European seas.

  Symptoms, Findings. Intense shooting pain, redness and edema of affected part, vomiting, diuresis and diarrhea.

  Chemistry, Toxicology. Two or three drops of venom injected intravenously into rabbit produce death in 4-10 min. Venom thought to contain both neurotoxic and hemotoxic fractions.

26 | TOADFISH STING caused by contact. Venom apparatus of the opercular and dorsal stings. Venom produced by sac-like glands at base of stings.

  Animal, Distribution. Grunting toadfish (Batrachus grunniens), W. Indies, tropical waters; toadfish (Opsanus tau), waters of N. America; toadfish (Thalassophryne dowi), Pacific coast of Panama, tropical and south temperate America; toadfish (T. maculosa), east coast of America; lumpfish (T. reticulata) Panama, Brazil.

  Symptoms, Findings. Severe localized pain; convulsions reported. Seldom serious.

  Chemistry, Toxicology. Not known.

27 | CATFISH STING caused by contact. Venom apparatus of dorsal and pectoral stings, and axillary venom glands. Venom glands in the integumentary sheaths surrounding the spines. Axillary gland located under skin beneath posthumeral process of cleithrum and opens to outside by pore.

  Animal, Distribution. Madtoms (Noturus spp), rivers of N. and S. America; Madtoms (Schilbeodes spp), rivers of N. and S. America; sea catfish (Galeichthys felis), coasts of southeastern U.S.; (Heteropneustes fossilis), India, Burma, Ceylon, Indo-China, swamps, marshes, muddy rivers; (Ictalurus catus), rivers of northestern America, Italy; (Plotosus lineatus), throughout Indo-Pacific region.

  Symptom, Findings. Stinging pain either localized or radiating through limb, usually subsides within 30 min. Area becomes ischemic, redness and edema may follow. In severe cases massive edema and numbness involving entire limb often accompanied by lymphadenopathy. Primary shock reported. Recovery may take weeks.

  Chemistry, Toxicology. Not known.

28 | SURGEONFISH STING caused by contact. Caudal penduncular spine inflicts wound.

  Animal, Distribution. Surgeonfish, lancet fish (Acanthurus hepatus), Atlantic Ocean to W. Indies.

  Symptoms, Findings. Sharp pain which may last several hours.

  Chemistry, Toxicology. Not known.

29 | DRAGONET STING caused by contact. Venom apparatus of venom glands in connection with spines. (See Weeverfish.)

  Animal, Distribution. Dragonet (Callionymus lyra), coast of France, tropical zones.

  Symptoms, Findings. Sharp stinging pain.

  Chemistry, Toxicology. Not known.

30 | TURTLE POISONING caused by ingestion.

  Animal, Distribution. Hawksbill sea turtle (Eretmochelys imbricata), Arabia, Malay Peninsula and Archipelago, Australia, Formosa, Samoa, Guiana, Bahamas, Guatemala; hawksbill (Chelonia japonica) Philippines; leatherback (Dermochelys coriacea), Cape of Good Hope, Indian Ocean, New Zealand, Solomons.

  Symptoms, Findings. Onset almost immediate to one week, with nausea, vomiting, diarrhea, weakness and sore lips and throat. Hallucinations, coma and death may occur within 12 hr after ingestion.

  Chemistry, Toxicology. Not known.

31 | PORPOISE POISONING caused by ingestion.

  Animal, Distribution. Porpoise (unidentified sp), Yangtze region of China, Chinese rivers. Not poisonous in open seas.

  Symptoms, Findings. Onset almost immediate. Severe pain, numbness and paralysis of extremities, cyanosis, swelling of abdomen, salivation, and rapid death. Many fatal cases reported, especially in spring. Blood, liver, fat and eyes are reported most toxic.

  Chemistry, Toxicology. Not known.

Plant [Toxic Portion] Geographic Distribution	Toxic Principle	Signs and Symptoms Produced	Remarks
1 Amanita, deadly (Amanita phalloides) [Entire fungus] Europe, N. America	Amanita-toxin (amanitin) formerly reported as phallin. Fungus also contains amanita-hemolysin, possibly a factor in poisoning by the raw mushroom.	After 6-15 hr: Abdominal pain; vomiting; diarrhea; intense thirst; recurrent drowsiness; respiratory, circulatory depression; delirium; sometimes convulsions; jaundice, hepatitis; renal disturbances; coma; death from heart failure.	One of the most deadly of fungi with a mortality of about 50%; cause of 90% of "mushroom deaths" in U.S. Genus contains other equally poisonous mushrooms and some edible species.
2 Autumn crocus (Colchicum autumnale) [Entire plant; principally corms, seeds] U.S., England, Europe, N. Africa	Colchicine.	Man: Burning in throat; 6-8 hr later a feeling of suffocation, oppression in chest, difficult swallowing; vomiting; diarrhea; colic; tenesmus; giddiness; weakness in legs; arthralgia; cyanosis; labored breathing; convulsions; death from respiratory exhaustion in 7-36 hr; consciousness preserved to end. Other animals: Nausea; vomiting; colic; diarrhea; hematuria; depression; unconsciousness; paralysis; mydriasis; profuse perspiration. Death in 1-3 days.	Colchicine arrests mitotic division of cells. Effects in relief of gout may be dramatic.
3 Belladonna[1] (Atropa belladonna) [Entire plant; especially seeds, roots, leaves] Europe, Asia, eastern U.S.	Chiefly hyoscyamine, atropine, other solanaceous alkaloids.	Man, acute: Dryness of skin, mouth, throat; difficulty in swallowing; flushing of face; cyanosis; mydriasis; nausea; vomiting; constipation. Slurred speech; giddiness; stupor; coma; rapid, weak pulse; fever; death from asphyxia, heart failure. Man, chronic: Erythema, urticaria, vesicular eruptions; slurred speech; mydriasis; glaucoma; muscular tremors or twitchings. Sudden withdrawal causes nausea, salivation, perspiration. Cattle: Mydriasis; constipation; rapid pulse; labored breathing; frenzy; paralysis.	Yields belladonna preparations. Fruits most often responsible for poisoning in man.
4 Castor bean (Ricinus communis) [Seeds] Primarily tropical Africa; U.S., tropics and subtropics	Ricin or phytotoxin; ricinine.	Man: Burning in mouth, throat and stomach; vomiting; diarrhea; thirst; rapid, then faint pulse; cramps of abdomen, legs; convulsions; shallow respirations. Other animals: Hemorrhagic enteritis; staggering; dulled vision; heart weakness; bloating; paralysis; convulsions; fever; shivering; coma; death in 1-3 days.	Seeds yield castor oil. 2 or 3 seeds may be fatal to child. Ricin not extracted in oil.
5 Chinaberry (Melia azedarach) [Fruit (pulp only), bark, flowers] S.W. Asia, South Africa, tropical America, southern U.S.	Azadarin (margosine), possibly an alkaloid, affecting central nervous system.	Man: Leaf poisoning produces stomatitis; decrease in urine formation; violent, bloody vomiting. Fruit poisoning results in irregular breathing; signs of suffocation; complete paralysis. Other animals (especially swine): Vomiting; colic; diarrhea; labored breathing; convulsions or paralysis; death by asphyxia.	Roots, bark, leaves, flowers and fruit used for stupefying fish. Seeds yield oil of azedarach.
6 Chokecherry and other wild cherries (Prunus spp) [Leaves, especially when wilted; bark, seeds] Primarily northern hemisphere; Orient	Hydrocyanic acid is formed by action of enzymes upon amygdalin (?) or prunasin.	Animals: Uneasiness; staggering; falling; convulsions; labored breathing; bloating; death.	Frequent cause of fatal poisoning of livestock.
7 Christmas rose (Helleborus niger) [Rootstock, leaves] Principally Europe	Helleborin, helleborein, hellebrin.	Man, externally: Severe dermatitis in some individuals. Man, internally: Violent inflammation of mucous membranes of stomach, intestines; vomiting; dizziness; convulsions; sometimes death. Digitalis-like effect on heart.	Cultivated in flower gardens. Rootstock formerly an official drug.
8 Coca (Erythroxylum coca) [Leaves] Northern S. America; tropics of both hemispheres	Cocaine, other alkaloids.	General central nervous system stimulation followed by depression; numbness of tongue, paralysis of respiratory centers; cyanosis; shallow, irregular breathing; often sudden death from asphyxia.	Leaves commonly chewed as a stimulant by Indians of Peru and Bolivia. Cocaine used as a local anesthetic.
9 Corn-cockle (Agrostemma githago) [Seeds] Europe, Canada, U.S.	Githagin, agrostemmic acid (saponins).	Man: Irritation of digestive tract; vomiting; headache; vertigo; diarrhea; depressed breathing; sharp pains in spine; difficult locomotion; sometimes coma, death. Horses and cattle: Colic; diarrhea; muscular tremors; rigidity; coma, death. 0.25-1 lb per 100 lb live weight fatal.	Milled seeds sometimes present in wheat flour. Frequent ingestion of small amounts results in chronic githagism.
10 Croton, purging (Croton tiglium) [Roots, leaves, bark, seeds] Southern Asia, East Indies, Pacific Islands, Africa	Crotin, croton resin.	Externally: Croton oil is a skin-irritant, causing reddening, swelling, pustules. Smoke from burning wood inflames the eyes. Internally: Vomiting, drastic purging; possibly collapse and death.	Yields croton oil, formerly a human and veterinary purgative, lubricant for fine machinery.
11 Curare (Strychnos toxifera) [Bark, roots; not extremely toxic by mouth] Central America, northern S. America	Tertiary bases: curine, D-chondrocurine, D-isochondrodendrine, and D-isochondrodendrine dimethylether. Quaternary salts: D-tubocurarine chloride, D-chondrocurine dimethiodide, and L-tubocurarine chloride and others.	Haziness of vision; relaxation of facial muscles; inability to raise head; loss of muscular contraction in arm and leg; depressant effects on the muscles of respiration; muscle nerve end-plate paralysis.	Source of curare, one of the most potent poisons known. Tubocurarine chloride (U.S.P.) now used as a skeletal muscle relaxant in shock therapy, and as a diagnostic aid.
12 Death camass (Zigadenus spp) [Leaves, stems, flowers, bulb] Northern hemisphere, especially western U.S.	Zygadenine, similar to veratrine and cevadine in action.	Animals: Salivation; vomiting; lowered temperature; staggering or collapse; labored breathing; paralysis; possibly coma, death.	Frequent cause of fatal poisoning of livestock. Children occasionally poisoned by eating bulb.

/1/ Henbane (Hyoscyamus niger), which yields scopolamine, hyoscyamine, atropine, and other alkaloids, has similar signs and symptoms.

	Plant [Toxic Portion] Geographic Distribution	Toxic Principle	Signs and Symptoms Produced	Remarks
13	Ergot (Claviceps purpurea) [Sclerotium] Europe, Asia, Australia, N. America	Ergotoxine, ergotamine, ergonovine, and others.	Man, acute: Vomiting; diarrhea; respiratory difficulties; visual, motor disturbances; followed by convulsions, lowered blood pressure, shallow respiration, unconsciousness. In pregnancy, possibly uterine hemorrhage, abortion, peripheral gangrene. Man, chronic: Convulsive type -- vomiting; itching; paresthesia; analgesia of extremities; anorexia or uncontrollable hunger; diarrhea; muscle contracture; delirium; sometimes a tabes-like complex. Gangrenous type -- pustules may form; limbs swell, become hot; gangrene may follow. Cattle: Gastrointestinal irritation; gangrene of extremities; uterine contractions; nervous disturbances.	Occurs on wheat, oats, barley, rye, and other grasses; cause of many cases of poisoning (ergotism) in man and livestock.
14	Foxglove (Digitalis purpurea, D. lanata) [Entire plant, especially seeds, leaves] From western Europe; widely distributed.	Diacetyldigilanid A and B in D. purpurea. Digilanid A, B, C, in D. lanata.	Anorexia; nausea; vomiting; slow, pronounced pulse in early stages; cardiac arrhythmias; diarrhea; abdominal pain; headache; fatigue; drowsiness; convulsions; rapid, irregular pulse; death in severe cases.	Digitalis and derivatives used in cardiovascular therapy. D. purpurea common in flower gardens.
15	Grass-pea (Lathyrus sativus) [Seeds, mature plant] Southern Europe, Asia, southern U.S.	Alkaloids.	Man: Sudden weakness in legs from effect on spinal cord. Further ingestion may cause leg paralysis. Animals: Similar, plus asphyxia. Cattle evidence constipation, weak pulse, numbness of skin.	Used as food and fodder but causes many cases of lathyrism in man and livestock.
16	Groundsel (Senecio spp) [Entire plant, especially seeds] World-wide.	Senecifoline, senecifolidine, retrorsine, seneciphyline, jacobine.	Man: Abdominal pain; vomiting; ascites; enlarged liver; emaciation; bloody diarrhea. Generally fatal in the absence of early treatment. If not immediately fatal, liver damage may bring about subsequent death. Grazing animals: Inappetence; emaciation; staggering; colic; unconcsiousness; death.	Seeds of various species in harvested grain considered responsible for "bread poisoning." Senecio poisoning common in livestock.
17	Hellebore, American white (Veratrum viride) [Entire plant] Canada, U.S.	Protoveratrine, germerine, jervine, and others.	Man: Vomiting; abdominal pain; muscular weakness; spasms; possibly convulsions; rapid pulse; shallow breathing; semiconsciousness; death from asphyxia.	This and related species yield veratrum, a therapeutic agent for hypertension.
18	Hemp, marijuana (Cannabis sativa) [Upper leaves, flower bracts of female plants] Temp. Asia, Europe, U.S., Mexico, Panama	Cannabinene, tenanocannabine, cannabinol.	Man: Exaltation; inebriety; confusion; followed by central nervous system depression. Prolonged addiction may produce dullness or mania; in rare cases death from cardiac depression.	Dried leaves and bracts smoked by marijuana addicts; seeds harmless.
19	Larkspur (Delphinium spp) [Seeds, leaves; to a lesser degree, roots] North temperate regions, including western U.S.	Delphinine, delphinoidine, delphisine, staphisagroine.	Man: Burning, inflammation of mouth and pharynx; lowered blood pressure; nausea; abdominal pain; labored respiration; itching; cyanosis. Animals: Inappetence; uneasiness; staggering; constipation; nausea; bloating.	Second to locoweed (q.v.) in causing fatalities among livestock.
20	Lead-tree (Leucaena glauca) [Leaves (especially immature), bark, roots] Southern U.S., tropics	Mimosine (leucenol).	Horses, mules and donkeys: Alopecia of manes and tails; possibly deformation, loss of hoofs. Swine: Total alopecia; impaired vision; emaciation; various degrees of paralysis; respiratory failure.	A fodder plant for cattle, sheep, goats (immune to toxic action). Seeds used as coffee substitute.
21	Locoweed (Astragalus spp) [Fresh plant] Northern hemisphere	Selenium; locoine in some species.	Horses and cattle: Dullness; weakness; irregularity in behavior; impaired vision; edema of eyelids; loss of muscular control; depraved appetite; emaciation; starvation; death. Sheep: Above symptoms, with possibly blindness.	Hazard to livestock industry of the U.S.; toxicity varies with locality.
22	Lupine (Lupinus spp) [Pods, leaves; especially seeds] Temperate regions.	European spp: Ictrogen (lupinotoxin); American spp: sparteine (lupinidine), lupinine.	European lupinosis, chronic: Anemia; cachexia. Acute: Fever; general icterus; coma; paralysis; constipation followed by hemorrhagic diarrhea; swelling of ears, eyelids, lips, nose. American lupinosis, sheep: Frothing at mouth; dyspnea; frenzied actions; nausea; bloating; coma, possibly death.	Toxicity of lupines varies with season and location; some species are harmless. Many livestock fatalities in Europe and U.S. attributed to lupines.
23	Manchineel (Hippomane mancinella) [Milky sap] Florida, W. Indies, Central America, northern S. America	Physostigmine or a similar alkaloid, plus a sapogenin.	Man, externally: Severe burning of skin, swelling; possibly hemorrhage in eyes; temporary blindness from sap. Man, internally: Fruit causes gastroenteritis which may be fatal. Ulceration of intestinal tract proceeds slowly.	Apparently more toxic in summer than in winter. Sap used as arrow poison. Smoke from burning wood toxic.
24	Manioc (Manihot esculenta) [Roots; mature leaves, stems, fruit] Tropics	Phaseolunatin	Man and livestock: Rapid, labored breathing; rapid, irregular, weak pulse; twitching; staggering; spasms of neck, legs; convulsions; mydriasis; coma; death from respiratory paralysis.	Cultivated for starch from which tapioca is made.
25	Metel (Datura metel) [Entire plant] India; tropics	Scopolamine, hyoscyamine, atropine.	Man: Mydriasis; drowsiness; thirst; bitter burning sensation in mouth; impaired vision; delirium. Exhaustion, coma, death, in extreme cases. Non-fatal poisoning usually results in loss of memory, mental confusion.	Used medicinally in Far East; employed criminally for narcotic effect on victims.
26	Monkshood (Aconitum napellus) [Roots, leaves, flowers, seeds] Europe, Asia, Canada, northeastern U.S.	Aconitine, picraconitine, aconine, napelline, and others.	Moderate doses: Tingling, burning sensation in tongue, throat, skin; great restlessness; dyspnea; slow pulse; muscular weakness; incoordination; cold, livid skin; pupillary constriction, followed by dilation; vomiting; diarrhea; convulsions; possibly death in 1-8 hr by respiratory or cardiac paralysis.	Young leaves have been eaten by mistake for parsley and the roots for horseradish.
27	Mountain-laurel (Kalmia latifolia) Sheep-laurel (K. angustifolia) [Entire plant, except wood] Canada, northeastern U.S., Pacific Coast	Andromedotoxin.	Animals (usually sheep): Salivation; flow of tears; secretions from nose; frothing at mouth; impaired vision or blindness; dizziness; irregular respiration; vomiting; convulsions, followed by paralysis of limbs, coma, death. Man: Similar to above, plus pain in head, sweating, tingling of skin.	Frequent cause of fatal poisoning of livestock, especially sheep.

	Plant [Toxic Portion] Geographic Distribution	Toxic Principle	Signs and Symptoms Produced	Remarks
28	Nightshade, black (Solanum nigrum) [Entire plant, unripe fruit] World-wide	Solanine, saponin.	Man: Vomiting; diarrhea; rapid pulse; fever; sweating; dizziness; mydriasis; disturbed speech, sight; hallucinations. Death from heart failure or respiratory paralysis. Other animals: Nervous form -- narcosis; paralysis. Gastric form -- salivation; vomiting; bloating; diarrhea. Exanthematous form -- vesicular exanthema on legs, udder, scrotum, neck; conjunctivitis.	
29	Oleander (Nerium oleander) [Leaves, bark, roots, flowers] Tropics, subtropics	Neriin, oleandrin.	Man: Vomiting; slow, irregular pulse; bloody diarrhea; death from cardiac or respiratory paralysis. Other animals: Similar to above, plus sweating, gnashing of teeth, groaning, sometimes polyuria.	Smoke from burning green plants can cause poisoning. Meat roasted on skewers of oleander wood, or food stirred with oleander sticks, becomes fatally poisonous. Honey made from the nectar possibly toxic.
30	Physic nut (Jatropha curcas) [Seeds, milky sap] Tropics	Curcin.	Man: Burning in throat; bloating; dizziness; vomiting; diarrhea; drowsiness; possibly dysuria, mydriasis; severe leg cramps; deafness. Violent purgative action often fatal to children. Other animals: Hemorrhagic enteritis; staggering; dull vision; mydriasis; bloating; paralysis; somnolence; convulsions; fever; shivering; coma; death in 1-3 days in acute cases.	Sap used as a fish poison.
31	Poison hemlock (Conium maculatum) [Fruit; stems, leaves, root] Europe, Asia, Africa, N. America	Coniine, conhydrine, methylconiine, coniceine.	Man: Muscular weakness; often blindness; paralysis of extremities; death from respiratory paralysis. Cattle: Inappetence; salivation; bloating; muscular weakness; coma. Horses: Nausea; grinding of teeth; rapid, labored respiration; paralysis; death from respiratory failure.	Leaves more toxic when plant is flowering; root less toxic in spring.
32	Poison ivy (Rhus toxicodendron)[2] [Entire plant] N. America	Urushiol, toxicodendrol, or toxicodendrin.	Man: Skin irritation, swelling, blisters, extreme discomfort. Sometimes fatal to children.	Smoke from burning plant toxic.
33	Poison wood (Metopium toxiferum) [Entire plant, especially sap] Southern Florida, W. Indies	Probably similar to poison ivy.	Externally: Dermatitis similar to that caused by poison ivy. Blistering may continue for weeks, readily spreading from one area to another; may be accompanied by intense itching, burning.	Smoke from burning wood highly irritating.
34	Pokeweed (Phytolaca americana) [Entire plant, especially root] Eastern and southern U.S.	Saponin and a toxic resin-like material.	Vomiting; purging; spasms, sometimes convulsions; death from respiratory paralysis.	Young shoots edible if well cooked.
35	Spurge (Euphorbia spp) [Milky sap] World-wide	Euphorbon, euphorboresene, and an acrid substance.	Man, externally: Dermatitis; eye-irritation, temporary blindness. Man, internally: Swelling around mouth, eyes; burning in mouth, throat; sneezing; vomiting; diarrhea; fainting; death. Other animals, externally: Blistering of skin, loss of hair. Other animals, internally: Weakness; collapse; scours; death.	Euphorbium derived from E. resinifera formerly used medicinally, now employed in paint as a protectant. Severe dermatitis observed from sap of poinsettia (E. pulcherrima).
36	Strophanthus (Strophanthus spp) [Seeds, bark] Tropical Africa, southern Florida, tropical America	Strophanthin.	Vomiting; slow, irregular pulse; blurred vision; delirium; death from circulatory failure of cardiac origin. Effect on heart similar to that of digitalis.	Arrow-poisons from several species. S. sarmentosus is a possible source of cortisone.
37	Strychnine tree (Strychnos nux-vomica) [Seeds, leaves, bark, wood, flowers] India, Hawaii	Strychnine, brucine.	Action on spinal cord causes excessive reflex irritability, followed by rapid tonic convulsions with intermissions of exhaustion and sweating; extreme muscular rigidity, asphyxia; death. Mind not affected.	Strychnine formerly used as stimulant and tonic.
38	Thevetia (Thevetia peruviana) [Leaves, seeds, bark, milky sap] Tropics	Thevetin.	Externally: Contact with sap may inflame and blister skin. Internally: Vomiting; high blood pressure; erratic heart beat; death from asphyxiation; sudden cardiac paralysis.	Seeds used as fish poison.
39	Thorn apple (cocklebur) (Datura stramonium) [Entire plant (including flowers, nectar), especially seeds] Tropics; N. America	Scopolamine, hyoscyamine, atropine.	Man: Headache; nausea; vertigo; thirst; dry, burning sensation in skin; mydriasis; loss of muscular control. Acute poisoning results in mania, convulsions, death. Cattle: Mydriasis; suspension of secretions or diarrhea; rapid heart action; paralysis; death from asphyxia. 10-15 oz of plant fatal. Swine: Convulsive twitching.	Children often poisoned by eating seeds and pods.
40	Upas tree (Antiaris toxicaria) [Milky sap] Southern Asia, E. Indies	Antiarin (α-, β-)	Externally: Skin irritation, blistering, swelling. Internally: Vomiting; convulsions; death. E. Indies, southern Asia. Cloth made from the bark causes intolerable itching if sap (latex) is not thoroughly eliminated. More potent than digitalis in effect on heart.	One of the principal arrow-poisons of natives of
41	Water hemlock (Cicuta maculata and related spp) [Primarily roots] North temperate regions	Cicutoxin.	Man and other animals: Abdominal pain; nausea; vomiting; diarrhea; mydriasis; labored breathing; foaming at mouth; weak, rapid pulse; epileptoid convulsions; death from respiratory failure.	Genus includes the most poisonous plants in the U.S.
42	Wild yam (Dioscorea hispida) [Entire plant, tubers] Southern Asia, E. Indies, Pacific Islands	Dioscoreine.	Discomfort, then burning, in throat; giddiness; vomiting of blood; suffocation; drowsiness; exhaustion.	Eating raw tubers a frequent cause of death in Philippines.

/2/ Data applicable also to poison sumac (R. vernix).

360. ALKALOIDS: OCCURRENCE, PHYSICAL, CHEMICAL, AND BIOLOGICAL CHARACTERISTICS

Information regarding properties of salts is enclosed in brackets. Remarks when not bracketed may refer to alkaloids (base or B) or to salts, or to both.

Alkaloids [Salts][1]	Botanical Source	Geographical Source	Properties[2]	Solubility[2]	Remarks[3]
1 Aconitine $C_{34}H_{49}NO_{11}$	Aconitum napellus (root).	Europe, Asia.	MP = 204; $(\alpha)_D$ =+17.3° in chl.	s. chl., bz., al., eth.; i.w.	One of several isomers in aconite root. Acts peripherally and centrally on nervous system; highly toxic; relieves neuralgia, toothache; depresses heart; lowers blood pressure; causes smarting, tingling of skin, prickling in throat.
2 Apomorphine $C_{17}H_{17}NO_2$ [B·HCl·1½ H_2O]	Morphine.	Pacific Islands, India, E.Africa.	[$(\alpha)_D$ = -48° in w.]	[s. w.1:50.]	B and salt oxidize readily in air. Stimulates medullary chemo-receptor trigger zone to produce emesis; CNS depressant.
3 Arecoline $C_8H_{13}NO_2$ [B·HBr]	Areca catechu (nut).		BP = 209; opt. inactive; [MP = 169-171].	s.w., al., eth., chl.; [s. w.1:1].	Parasympathetic stimulant; sialogogue diaphoretic; anthelmintic.
4 Atropine (DL-Hyoscyamine) $C_{17}H_{23}NO_3$ [$B_2·H_2SO_4·H_2O$]	Atropa belladonna (leaf, root), also synthetic.	Europe.	MP = 118; $(\alpha)_D$ = O°; [MP = 190-194; $(\alpha)_D$ =O°].	s. w. 1:455, al.1:2, glyc., eth., bz., chl.; [s.w.1:0.4, al.1:5, sl.s.chl., eth.].	Parasympatholytic: mydriatic, speeds heart, relaxes gut, causes vasodilation, inhibits secretions; also CNS stimulant.
5 Berberine $C_{20}H_{19}O_5N·5½ H_2O$ [$C_{20}H_{18}O_4N·HSO_4$]	Barberry (bark) (Berberis vulgaris, B. asiatica).	Europe, India, N. America.	Loses water above 100°C; d. about 160°C.	s.w., al.;sl.s.acet., bz., eth.,chl.; [s.w., sl.s.al.].	Effective against cutaneous leishmaniasis; bactericide; has very bitter taste; inhibits heart rate; excreted in urine.
6 Caffeine $C_8H_{10}N_4O_2$ [B + Na benzoate]	Coffee (Coffea arabica), tea (Thea sinensis).	Tropical, sub-tropical areas.	MP = 238; opt. inactive.	s.w.1:46, al.1:66, chl.1:5.5; sl.s.eth.,pet.eth; [s.w. 1: 1:1.1., al.1:30].	Causes mild CNS stimulation, particularly cortex and medullary centers. Relaxes vascular musculature, stimulates heart and skeletal muscle, causes diuresis. [Contains approx. 50% caffeine.]
7 Cevadine (Veratrine) $C_{32}H_{49}NO_9$	Hellebore (rhizome) (Veratrum spp).	Europe, U.S.	MP = 205; $(\alpha)_D$ = +12.5° in al.	s. al., eth. 1:15; i.w.	Action like veratramine.
8 Cinchonidine $C_{19}H_{22}N_2O$ [$B_2·H_2SO_4$]	Cinchona spp.	S. America, Java.	MP = 210; $(\alpha)_D$ = -109° in al.	s. al., chl.; mod. s. eth.; i.w.;[s.w.1:70].	Antimalarial, see quinine.
9 Cinchonine $C_{19}H_{22}N_2O$ [$B_2·H_2SO_4·2H_2O$]	Cinchona spp.	S. America, Java.	MP approx. 265; $(\alpha)_D$ = +229° in al.;[MP approx. 198].	s. al.1:60, chl. 1:110; sl.s. eth.;i.w.;[s.w.1:65, al.1:12].	Antimalarial, see quinine.
10 Cocaine $C_{17}H_{21}NO_4$ [B·HCl]	Erythroxylum coca (leaf).	S. America.	MP = 98; $(\alpha)_D$ = -16° in chl.; [MP approx 195; $(\alpha)_D$ = -72o in w.].	s. w. 1:600, al. 1:65; fats v.s. chl., eth.;[v.s.w., al.; i.eth.,fats].	Local anesthetic, absorbed both from mucous membrane or by injection; CNS stimulation, particularly cortex; potentiates sympathetic nervous system, causes vasoconstriction; habit-forming, but does not cause true addiction.
11 Codeine $C_{18}H_{21}NO_3·H_2O$ a[$B_2·H_2SO_4·5H_2O$] b[$B·H_3PO_4·1½ H_2O$]	Poppy, opium (Papaver somniferum), also from morphine.	Asia Minor, India.	MP = 155; $(\alpha)_D$ = -136° in al.; $(\alpha)_D$ = - 112° in chl.; a[$(\alpha)_D$ = -101° in w.].	s.w.1:120, al.1:2,bz.,chl.; i.pet.eth.; a[s.w.1:30, al. 1:1020]; b[s.w.1:2.3, in chl.;al.1:325].	Narcotic, analgesic, sedative, antitussive. Less potent than morphine. Causes true addiction.
12 Colchicine $C_{22}H_{25}NO_6$	Saffron (seed and corm) (Colchicum autumnale).	Europe, N.Africa.	MP = 157; $(\alpha)_D$ = -121° in chl.; $(\alpha)_D$ = -429° in w.	s. al., chl., w.1:22, bz.1:100.	Causes transient fall in number of leucocytes; appears to stimulate karyokinesis in bone marrow; arrests cell division in metaphase; causes bizarre mitotic figures; relieves acute gout.
13 Conessine $C_{24}H_{40}N_2$	Conessi (bark). (Holar-rhena antidysenterica)	India.	MP = 125; $(\alpha)_D$ = -25 in al.	s. al., chl.; sl. s.w.	Local anesthetic; causes necrosis; kills Entamoeba histolytica (effective orally).
14 Coniine $C_8H_{17}N$ [B·HBr]	Poison hemlock (Conium maculatum)	Europe.	MP = -2; BP 166; $(\alpha)_D$ = +16° (no solvent); [MP = 207].	s. al., eth., acet., bz.;sl.s.w.; [s.w., al., chl., eth.].	Paralyses motor nerve endings; first stimulates, then depresses CNS. [Has been used as sedative, antispasmodic.]
15 Emetine $C_{29}H_{40}N_2O_4$ [B·2HCl + 3 to 8H_2O]	Ipecac (root) (Cephaelis ipecacuanha).	Brazil.	MP = 74; $(\alpha)_D$ = -50° in chl.	s. al.,eth.,chl.; sl.s.w., pet. eth.;[s.w. approx. 1:7].	Kills Entamoeba histolytica; toxic to heart, skeletal muscles; concentrated in liver.
16 Ephedrine $C_{10}H_{15}NO·½ H_2O$ a[B·HCl] b[$B_2·H_2SO_4$]	Ephedra spp, also synthetic.	China, India.	MP approx. 40; $(\alpha)_D$ = +11° in w.; a[MP approx. 216; $(\alpha)_D$ = -34° in w.]; b[d.245; $(\alpha)_D$ = -30° in w.].	s. al., eth., chl., oils w.1:20; a[s.w.1:3, al. 1:14] ; b[s.w.1:2, al.1:95].	Sympathomimetic; stimulates CNS and heart mucle; raises blood pressure; constricts arterioles; relaxes smooth muscle of bronchi and gastrointestinal tract; dilates pupil; increases metabolic rate; readily absorbed from intestinal tract.
17 Ergonovine $C_{19}H_{23}N_3O_2$ [B·$C_4H_4O_4$ (maleate)]	Ergot (Claviceps purpurea).	Russia, Finland, Spain, Portugal, U.S. (Minnesota)	MP = 162; $(\alpha)_D$ = +44° in chl.; [d. 167; $(\alpha)_D$ = +48° to +57° in chl.].	s. al., acet., eth.ac.; mod. s.w.; [s.w.1:36, al.1:120].	Stimulates uterus, causing rapid contraction; absorbed from GI tract.
18 Ergotamine $C_{33}H_{35}N_5O_5$ [B_2·tartrate + 2CH_3OH]	Ergot (C. purpurea).		d. 212-214; $(\alpha)_D$ -160° in chl.; [$(\alpha)_D$ =-125° to -155° in chl.]	s.chl., pry., me.al. 1:70, acet.1:150; [s.w., al. 1:500].	B usually cryst. solvated, e.g., + 2 acet. + 2H_2O. Stimulates uterus: causes peripheral vasoconstriction; causes adrenergic blockage; stimulates and depresses CNS; depresses heart; causes vomiting.
19 β-Erythroidine $C_{16}H_{19}NO_3$	Coral tree (seed) (Erythrina americana).	N. America.	MP = 100; $(\alpha)_D$ = +89° in w.	s.w., chl., al., bz.; mod. s. eth.	Blocks myoneural junction, causing skeletal muscle paralysis; CNS depressant; absorbed from GI tract.
20 Heroin (diamorphine) ($C_{21}H_{23}NO_5$) [B·HCl·H_2O]	Morphine.		MP = 173; $(\alpha)_D$ = -166° in me. al.; [MP = 244; $(\alpha)_D$ = -156° in w.].	s.chl.1:1.5, al.1.31, eth.1:100;sl.s.w.; [s.w.1:2, al.1:11;i.eth.].	Narcotic, action similar to morphine, more potent but shorter duration. Causes euphoria and severe addiction; production illegal in most countries.
21 Hydrastine $C_{21}H_{21}O_6N$ [B·HCl]	Orange-root (root) (Hydrastis canadensis).	N. America.	MP = 132; $(\alpha)_D$ = -50 in al.; [$(\alpha)_D$ = +127 in dil. HCl].	s. chl., acet., bz.; sl.s.al., eth.; [s.w., al.].	Oxytocic; internal styptic in uterine hemorrhage; stimulates spinal center; excreted unchanged in urine.
22 Hyoscyamine $C_{17}H_{23}NO_3$ [B·HCl]	Solanaceae.	World-wide.	MP = 108.5; $(\alpha)_D$ = -21° in al.; [MP = 149-151].	s. al., chl., H_2O 1:150, w.1:280; [s.w., al.].	The levo-rotatory constituent of atropine. Action like that of atropine.
23 Lobeline $C_{22}H_{27}NO_2$ [B·HCl]	Indian tobacco, (Lobelia inflata), also synthetic.	N. America.	MP = 130-131; $(\alpha)_D$ = -43° in al.; [MP = 178-180].	s. chl., bz., hot al.; i.w.; pet.eth.;[s.w. 1:40, al. 1:12; v.s.chl.].	Action like that of nicotine, less potent.

#	Name / Formula [salt]	Source	Origin	Physical constants	Solubility	Physiological action
24	Mescaline $C_{11}H_{17}NO_3$ [B·HCl]	Mescal cactus (flesh) (Anhalonium Lewinii).	Southwestern U.S., Mexico.	MP = 35–36; opt. inactive; [MP = 181].	s. al, chl., bz.; s.l.s.w.; i.eth, pet. eth.;[s.w., al.].	Depresses CNS; produces psychic effects and visual color hallucinations.
25	Morphine $C_{17}H_{19}NO_3 \cdot H_2O$ [B·HCl·3H₂O] a [B·HCl·3H₂O] b [B₂·H₂SO₄ 5H₂O]	Opium, see codeine.		d. 254; $(a)_D = -132°$ in me.al.; a [d. approx. 200; (a) = −110° in w.]; b[$(a)_D = -95°$ in w.].	s.al,1:210, alkalies; me.al. 1:10, alkalies; a[s.,w. 1:17, al. 1:50]; b[s.,w. 1:15, al. 1:565].	Narcotic action in man; produces analgesia and sleep; depresses respiration; constricts pupils; relieves pain; contracts smooth muscles; effects constipation; retards secretion of HCl by stomach; little effect on blood pressure, heart rate or rhythm; readily absorbed from the GI tract; principally destroyed in body and excreted in urine. Causes true addiction.
26	Narcotine $C_{22}H_{23}NO_7$	Opium.		MP = 176; $(a)_D = -207°$ in chl.	s.chl. 1:2, bz. 1:30, al.1:250; sl.s.hot w.	Action like that of papaverine, but less potent. Has antitussive properties.
27	Nicotine $C_{10}H_{14}N_2$ [B₂·H₂SO₄]	Tobacco (leaf, stem) (Nicotiana spp).	World-wide.	BP = 247; $(a)_D = -169°$ in w.; $n_D = 1.5282$; [$(a)_D = +88°$ in w.].	s.w., oils, most organic solvents; [s.w., al.].	Causes initial and transient stimulation, then depression, paralysis of autonomic ganglia; mild CNS stimulation; paralyzes skeletal muscle; absorbed from skin and mucous membrane; rapidly detoxified. Insecticide.
28	Papaverine $C_{20}H_{21}NO_4$ [B·HCl]	Opium, also synthetic.		MP = 147; opt. inactive; [MP = 225].	s.al. 1:45, hot al. 1:4; sl.s.eth., bz., pet.eth.; i.w.;[s.al., chl., w. 1:40].	No narcotic action; paralyzes smooth muscle of intestines and blood vessels.
29	Pelletierine $C_8H_{15}NO$ [B·tannate]	Pomegranate (bark) (Punica granatum).	Subtropical lands.	BP = 195 (inert atmosphere); a D mixture; [tannic acid salt of several Punica alkaloids].		Easily oxidized, becoming resinous in air. Acts on central and peripheral nervous system, voluntary muscle; selectively acts on optic nerve; effective against tapeworm.
30	Physostigmine (Eserine) $C_{15}H_{21}N_3O_2$ [B·C₇H₆O₃ (salicylate)]	Calabar bean (Physostigma venenosum).	W. Africa, India, Brazil.	MP = 105; $(a)_D = -76°$ in chl., −120° in bz.;[MP = 185–187].	s.al., bz., chl., oils; [s.w. 1:75, al. 1:16, chl. 1:6].	Inhibits cholinesterase, acts to stimulate skeletal muscle and as parasympathomimetic; causes pupillary constriction and spasm of accommodation; readily absorbed from GI tract and increases tone and motility; eliminated through kidney.
31	Pilocarpine $C_{11}H_{16}N_2O_2$ [B·HNO₃]	Jaborandi (Pilocarpus spp).	S. America.	MP = 34; $(a)_D = +100°$ in chl.; [MP = 178; $(a)_D = +83°$ in w.].	s.w., al., chl.; i.eth.; [s.w. 1:6.4].	Parasympathomimetic; stimulates involuntary smooth muscle, gland cells, sweat, salivary and gastric glands; causes pupillary constriction; diaphoretic; depresses heart; partly destroyed in body; greater part excreted in urine.
32	Protoveratrine $C_{39}H_{61}O_{13}N$	Hellebore (root). (Veratrum viride)	N. America.	MP = 283; (a) = −9 in chl.	s.al., chl.; i.w., bz.	Slows heart rate; lowers systemic blood pressure; side effects include nausea, diarrhea.
33	Quinidine $C_{20}H_{24}N_2O_2 \cdot 2H_2O$ a [B₂·H₂SO₄·2H₂O] b [B·H₂SO₄·4H₂O]	Cinchona spp, also by isomerization of quinine.	S. America, Java.	MP = 175; $(a)_D = +230°$ in chl.; a[$(a)_D = +212°$ in al.].	s.al., chl., w. 1:36, eth.1:56; sl. s.w.; a [s.w. 1:90]; b [s.w. 1:8].	Stereoisomer of quinine. Acts on heart to increase excitability, slow conduction and increased refractory period; can stop auricular fibrillation; like quinine in other actions.
34	Quinine $C_{20}H_{24}N_2O_2$ (also + 3H₂O) a [B₂·H₂SO₄·2H₂O] b [B·H₂SO₄·7H₂O] c [B·HCl·2H₂O]	Cinchona spp (bark).	S. America, Java.	MP = 177; $(a)_D = -169°$ in al., −117° in chl.	s.al. 1:1, chl. 1:1.2, bz.1:80, eth.1:250; a[s.al.1:120, w.1:810]; b[s.w. 1:9]; c[s.w.1:16].	Lethal to asexual erythrocyte forms of malarial parasite; mildly stimulates uterus; antipyretic; local irritant; absorbed from GI tract; largely destroyed in body. Cardiac actions like that of quinidine but less pronounced.
35	Reserpine (Serpasil) $C_{33}H_{40}N_2O_9$	Rauwolfia serpentina.	India.	MP = 278; $(a)_D = -118°$ in chl.	s.chl., bz., eth.,ac.; sl.s. acet., me.al., eth., w.	Hypotensive, CNS sedative action.
36	Scopolamine (Hyoscine) $C_{17}H_{21}NO_4$	Datura, Hyoscyamus, and Scopolia spp.	World-wide.	Liquid; $(a)_D = -28°$ in w.; also cryst. + H₂O, MP = 54; [MP = 195 (anhydrous)]; $(a)_D = -26°$ in w.].	s.al., eth., chl., w. 1.95; sl. s.bz., pet.eth.; [s.w.1:1.5, al.1:20] .	Causes sedation, sleep, and amnesia; otherwise like atropine.
37	Sparteine $C_{15}H_{26}N_2$ [B·H₂SO₄·5H₂O]	Lupinus and Spartium spp.	Europe.	Liquid; BP = 173 at 8 mm Hg; $n_D=1.5312$; $(a)_D = -16.4°$ in al.;[d, 136].	s.al., chl., eth., w. 1:325; [s.w. 1:1, al. 1:3].	Paralyzes autonomic ganglia; slows heart rate; curare-like action.
38	Strychnine $C_{21}H_{22}N_2O_2$ [B₂·H₂SO₄·5H₂O, also 6H₂O]	Strychnos spp (seed), especially Strychnos nux-vomica.	India, Indo-China.	MP = 268–90, varies with rate of heating; $(a)_D = -139°$ in al.	s.chl. 1:5, al.1:150, bz.1:180; i.w.;[s.w.1:35, al.1:81, glyc.1:6].	Stimulates CNS; increases reflex excitability of spinal cord; sensitizes sensory cortex, medulla; readily absorbed from GI tract.
39	Thebaine $C_{19}H_{21}NO_3$	Opium.		MP = 193; $(a)_D = -219°$ in al.	s. hot al. 1:15, chl.1:13, bz.1:25, pyr. 1:12.	Violent tetanic poison, no med. use per se. Source material for valuable narcotics.
40	Theobromine $C_7H_8N_4O_2$	Cacao bean (Theobroma cacao).	S. and Central America.	Sublimes 290; opt. inactive.	sl. s.w., al.; s. alkali.	Action like that of caffeine.
41	Theophylline $C_7H_8N_4O_2$ [B·Na acetate]	Tea (Thea sinensis), also synthetic.	China, India.	MP = 270–274; opt. inactive.	s.w.1:120, al.1:80, chl. 1:110, alkali;[s.w.1:25].	Action like that of caffeine. [Contains 27% Na acetate]
42	Tubocurarine chloride $C_{38}H_{44}N_2O_6Cl_2 \cdot 5H_2O$	Curare (Chondrodendron tomentosum).	S. America	d. 268; $(a)_D = +190°$ in w.	s.w.1:20, al.; i.chl., bz.; pyr., acet.	Paralyzes skeletal muscles by blocking myoneural junction; blocks autonomic ganglia; not absorbed from GI tract.
43	Veratramine $C_{27}H_{39}NO_2$	Veratrum spp.	N. and S. America.	MP = 206; $(a)_D = -71°$ in al.	s.al., me.al.	Inhibits cardioacceleration of epinephrine, sympathomimetic amines; CNS stimulant.
44	Yohimbine $C_{21}H_{26}N_2O_2$ [B·HCl]	Corynanthe yohimbe.	Africa.	MP = 234; $(a)_D = +108°$ in pyr.; $(a)_D =+103°$ in w.;[s.w.1:120, al.1:400].	s.al.,chl.; sl.s.eth., w.; [s.w.1:120, al.1:400].	Adrenolytic; causes antidiuresis; mild local anesthetic.

/1/ in salt formula, B = base. /2/ Abbreviations: acet. = acetone; al. = alcohol (ethyl 95%); bz. = benzene; chl. = chloroform; d. = decomposes; dil. = dilute; eth. = ether; eth. ac. = ethyl acetate; glyc. = glycerol; i. = insoluble; me.al. = methyl alcohol; mod. = moderately; opt. = optically; pet. eth. = petroleum ether; pyr. = pyridine; s. = soluble; sl. = slightly; v. = very; w. = water. /3/ CNS = central nervous system; crys. = crystalline; GI = gastrointestinal; med. = medicinal.

Part I: IRRITANTS

Plant	Type or Class	Compound	Irritant Empirical Formula	Toxic Action or Effect
1 Anemone (Anemone japonica)	Oil	Protoanemonin	$C_5H_4O_2$	Local irritation.
2 Baneberry (Actaea spp)				Acrid juice an emeto-purgative; cardiotoxic.
3 Chaulmoogra oil (Hydnocarpus spp)	Cylic acid	Chaulmoogric acid	$C_{18}H_{22}O_2$	Irritation of digestive tract, liver, kidneys.
4 Christmas rose (Helleborus niger)	Glycoside	Helleborein	$C_{37}H_{56}O_{18}$	Intense irritation of mucous membranes.
5 Conringia (Conringia orientalis)	Volatile oil	Allyl isothiocyanate	C_3H_5CNS	Local irritation.
6 Crab's-eye vine (Abrus precatorius)	Toxalbumin	Abrin		Severe gastroenteritis.
7 Croton (Croton tiglium)		Croton resin		Severe local irritation.
8 Cyclamen (Cyclamen europaeum)	Glycosidal saponin	Cyclamin		Irritation of gastrointestinal tract.
9 Daphne (Daphne mezereum)	Glycoside	Daphnin	$C_{15}H_{16}O_9$	Irritation of gastrointestinal tract; convulsions.
10 Indian turnip (Arisaema triphyllum)	Saponin			Irritation of mucous membranes; gastroenteritis.
11 Juniper (Juniperus spp)	Volatile oil			Inflammation of gastrointestinal tract.
12 Milkweed (Calotropis spp)	Milky juice			Violent local irritation; fatal gastroenteritis.
13 Mustard (Brassica spp)	Volatile oil	Allyl isothiocyanate	C_3H_5CNS	Local irritation.
14 Pine (Pinus spp)	Volatile oil	Oil of turpentine		Irritation of skin, kidneys.
15 Pyrethrum flowers (Chrysanthemum		Pyrethrin I	$C_{21}H_{30}O_3$	
16 cinerariaefolium,		Pyrethrin II	$C_{22}H_{30}O_5$	Irritation of eyes and mucous membranes.
17 C. coccineum, or C. marschallii)		Cinerin I	$C_{20}H_{28}O_3$	
18		Cinerin II	$C_{21}H_{28}O_5$	
19 Radish (Raphanus raphanistrum)	Volatile oil	Allyl isothiocyanate	C_3H_5CNS	Local irritation.
20 Skunk cabbage (Symplocarpus foetidus)				Severe irritation of mucous membranes; violent gastroenteritis may be fatal.
21 Snakeroot (Aristolochia spp)	Volatile oil	Borneol ester, pinene		Irritation of gastrointestinal tract, kidneys.
22	Alkaloid	Aristolochine	$C_{17}H_{19}NO_3$	
23 Sneezeweed (Helenium autumnale)		Helenalin		Gastroenteritis, muscular paralysis.
24 Sneezeweed (H. hoopesii)	Glycoside	Dugaldin		Salivation, vomiting, diarrhea.
25 Snowberry (Chiococca racemosa)	Glycoside	Caincin	$C_{40}H_{64}O_{18}$	Emeto-cathartic; severe gastroenteritis.
26 Soap-bark tree (Quillaja saponaria)	Sapogenin	Quillaic acid	$C_{30}H_{46}O_5$	Severe local irritation.
27 Wood-fern (Dryopteris spp)		Aspidol	$C_{12}H_{16}O_4$	
28		Filicinic acid	$C_8H_{10}O_3$	Irritation of gastrointestinal tract.

Part II: REPELLENTS

Plant	Type or Class	Compound	Repellent Empirical Formula	Insects Repelled	Toxicity to Higher Animals[1]
1 Camphor tree (Cinnamomum camphora)	Ketone	Camphor	$C_{10}H_{16}O$	Mosquitoes	Increased sensibility; convulsions.
2 Cinnamon tree (Cinnamomum spp)	Volatile oil	Oil of cinnamon		Mosquitoes	Inflammation of gastrointestinal tract.
3 Citronella grass (Cymbogen nardus)	Oil	Citronella, geraniol		Mosquitoes	
4 Eucalyptus (Eucalyptus spp)	Oil	Eucalyptol	$C_{10}H_{18}O$		Inflammation of stomach; nausea; vomiting; dizziness; muscular weakness; fatal collapse.
5		Pinene	$C_{10}H_{16}$	Cockroaches	
6		Eudesmol	$C_{15}H_{26}O$		
7 Horse-radish (Radicula armoracia)	Glycoside	Sinigrin	$C_{10}H_{16}KNO_9S_2$	Cockroaches	Corrosive; inflammation, vesication of skin.
8 Juniper (Juniperus communis)	Oil	Camphene	$C_{10}H_{16}$		
9		α-Pinene	$C_{10}H_{16}$		
10		Terpineol	$C_{10}H_{18}O$	Cockroaches	Local irritation; may injure kidneys.
11		Cadinene	$C_{15}H_{24}$		
12 Sassafras (Sassafras albidum)	Oil	Camphor	$C_{10}H_{16}O$	Screw-worm flies	Paralysis of respiratory center; fatty degeneration of heart, liver, kidneys.
13		Safrol	$C_{10}H_{10}O_2$		
14		Eugenol	$C_{10}H_{12}O_2$		
15 Thyme (Thymus vulgaris)	Volatile oil	Cymene, pinene, thymol		Mosquitoes	Excitement.
16 Wormseed (Chenopodium ambrosioides anthelminticum)	Volatile oil	Ascaridole	$C_{10}H_{16}O_2$		Temporary deafness; convulsions; gastric irritation; nephritis.
17		Cymene	$C_{10}H_{14}$	Mosquitoes	

/1/ When ingested or applied locally in high concentrations.

Part III: MISCELLANEOUS

Plant	Type or Class	Compound	Toxic Component Empirical Formula	Toxic Action or Effect
1 Anamirta (Anamirta cocculus)	Neutral principle	Picrotoxin	$C_{30}H_{34}O_{13}$	Convulsions; paralysis; death by asphyxia.
2 Andromeda (Andromeda spp)	Neutral principle	Andromedotoxin	$C_{31}H_{50}O_{10}$	Vomiting; paralysis of motor nerve endings; cardiotoxin.
3 Aster (Aster xylorrhiza)	Resinous			Impaired vision; depraved appetite; abdominal pain.
4 Beet (Beta vulgaris), leaf only	Inorganic	Oxalic acid, nitrates	$C_2H_2O_4$	Inability to stand; muscular tremors, tetany.
5 Buckwheat (Fagopyrum esculentum)	Photodynamic	Porphyrin		Photosensitization.
6 Carissa (Carissa ovata)	Glycoside	Carissin	$C_{32}H_{50}O_{12}$	Heart derangement.
7 Cocklebur (Xanthium spp)	Glycoside	Xanthostrumarin		Depression; nausea; vomiting; labored respiration.
8 Coriaria (Coriaria myrtifolia)	Glycoside	Coriamyrtin	$C_{15}H_{18}O_5$	Convulsions; paralysis; death by asphyxia.
9 Cotton (Gossypium hirsutum), seed only		Gossypol	$C_{30}H_{30}O_5$	Edema of lungs; irritation of kidneys, gastrointestinal tract.
10 Dogbane (Acokanthera venenata)	Glycoside	Abyssinin (ouabain)	$C_{32}H_{50}O_{12}$	Inflammation, gastrointestinal tract; cardiotoxin.
11 Flax (Linum usitatissimum)	Glycoside	Phaseolunatin	$C_{10}H_{17}O_6N$	Asphyxia.
12 Hyena poison (Hyaenanche capenis)		Hyaenanchin	$C_{15}H_{18}O_7$	Convulsions; paralysis; death by asphyxia.
13 Laurel (Kalmia spp)		Andromedotoxin	$C_{31}H_{50}O_{10}$	See Andromeda, Line 2.
14 Lippia (Lippia rehmanni)	Photodynamic	Icterogenin	$C_{34}H_{52}O_6$	Photosensitization.
15 Marsdenia (Marsdenia cundurango)	Glycoside	Condurangin	$C_{35}H_{54}O(OCH_3)_2$	Convulsions followed by paralysis.
16 Oleander (Nerium oleander)	Glycoside	Oleandrin	$C_{31}H_{48}O_9$	Digitalis-like action.
17 Rhubarb (Rheum spp), leaf only	Inorganic	Oxalic acid	$C_2H_2O_4$	Weakness; muscular tremors; tetany.
18 Sorghum (Sorghum halepense)	Cyanogenetic glycoside	Dhurrin	$C_{14}H_{17}O_7N \cdot H_2O$	Asphyxia.
19 Strophanthus (Strophanthus spp)	Glycoside	Ouabain	$C_{29}H_{44}O_{12} \cdot 8H_2O$	Digitalis-like action.
20 Sweetclover (Melilotus spp), spoiled	Anticoagulant	Dicoumarin	$C_{19}H_{12}O_6$	Hemorrhages; retards blood coagulation.
21 Veronia (Veronia nigritiana)	Glycoside	Vernonin	$C_{10}H_{24}O_7$	Digitalis-like action.
22 Water hemlock (Cicuta spp)	Neutral principle	Cicutoxin	$C_{19}H_{26}O_3$	Violent convulsions.
23 Wild cherry (Prunus spp)	Cyanogenetic glycoside	Prunasin		Asphyxia.

The following abbreviations for sites of temperature measurement are used in this table: A = air; B = body; C = cloaca; G = gullet; I = intestine; R = rectum; S = stomach; T = throat; U = underground; W = water.

Part I: MAMMALS

	Mammal	Specification	Site	Temperature °C (°F)	Duration	Humidity %	Survival n/n'[1]
1	Man (Homo sapiens)	Adult	R	25-29(77-84.2)	1 hr		0/7[2]
2			W	15(59)	50-70 min		6/6[3]
3			A	29-36(84.2-96.8)		36-84[4]	
4			A	43-48(109.4-118.4)		11-21[5]	
5	Anteater, spiny (Tachyglossus aculeatus)	2.36 kg	I[6]	26-29(78.8-84.2)[7]	77-102 min		3/3
6		1.67 kg	I[6]	40(104)[8]	70 min		0/1
7	Armadillo (Dasypus novemcinctus)	Adult	I[6]	29-33(84.2-91.4)[9]	3-6 hr		6/6
8	Bat (Myotis lucifugus)	5.2 g	A	0.5(32.9)[10]	2 hr		5/5
9		6.4 g	A	44(111.2)[11]	30 min		0/5
10	Cat (Felis catus)	Adult	I[6]	43(109.4)[12]	Few min	Dry air	50%
11			A	41-43(105.8-109.4)[13]	7 hr	35-65[13]	100%
12	Cattle (Bos indicus, B. taurus)	Adult	A	-13(8.6)[14]	2 wk	66	6/6
13		195-300 kg	A	41(105.8)[14]	24 hr	51	3/3
14	Dog (Canis familiaris)	Adult	I[6]	17(62.6)[15]	65-118 min		0/6
15		Adult	I[6]	22-26(71.6-78.8)[16]	15 min-26 hr		3/11
16		Adult	I[6]	42(107.6)[12]	Few min	Dry air	50%
17		27.6 kg	W	0(32)[17]	1-5 hr		4/4
18	Guinea pig (Cavia porcellus)	Adult	I[6]	41-42(105.8-107.6)[18]	7 hr		2/2
19			A	48(118.4)	100 ± 4 min	15	0/11
20	Hamster, golden (Mesocricetus auratus)	Adult	I[6]	2-4(35.6-39.2)[19]			8/20
21			A	4-6(39.2-42.8)	6 da		22/45
22	Mouse (Mus musculus)	45-109 g	I[6]	9-15(48.2-59)[20]	25-65 min		20/20
23		Adult	A	38(100.4)[12]	3 hr		50%
24	Rabbit (Oryctolagus cuniculus)	Adult	I[6]	19-25(66.2-77)[21]	30 min		87/103
25		1.76 kg	A	-35(-31)[22]	3½-6½ hr		0/9
26		Adult	W	3.5 av (38.3)[23]	21 min (av)		16/24
27		3.95 kg	W	10(50)[24]	30 min		4/4
28		Adult	A	35(95)[25]	7 hr	95[25]	2/2
29		Adult	A	38(100.4)[25]	7 hr	35[25]	2/2
30	Rat (Rattus rattus)	235 g	A	-35(-31)[22]	45-120 min		0/12
31		237 g	W	10(50)[24]	10 min		3/3
32		Adult	A	40(104)[26]	213 ± 36 min	15	0/16
33		Adult	A	49-51(120.2-123.8)[26]	31 ± 1 min		0/36
34	Sheep (Ovis aries)	Adult	I[6]	42(107.6)[27]	7 hr		100%
35			A	43(109.4)[27, 28]	7 hr	65	100%
36	Sloth (Bradypus griseus and/or Choloepus hoffmani)	Adult	I[6]	24(75.2)[29]			1/2
37			I[6]	40 ± (104±)[30]			
38	Squirrel (Citellus pygmaeus)	120-265 g	B	2-6(35.6-42.8)[31]			11/19
39	Swine, Berkshire (Sus scrofa)	59 kg	I	42(107.6)[27]			100%
40			A	38-41(100.4-105.8)[32]			

/1/ n = number survived; n' = number in test. Percentages are per cent survived. /2/ WW II concentration camp; subjects cooled rapidly in water. /3/ Subjects refused to continue, or investigator considered continuance detrimental. /4/ Range at onset of heat exhaustion in humid climates. /5/ Range at onset of heat exhaustion in desert climates. /6/ May include rectum and colon. /7/ In metabolic chamber placed in water bath at 4-8°C (39.2-46.4°F). /8/ In metabolic chamber placed in water bath at 35-37°C (95-98.6°F). /9/ In cold room at 0-21°C (32-69.8°F). /10/ In metabolic chamber; -5°C (23°F) fatal to hibernating bats. /11/ In metabolic chamber at high humidity. /12/ Temperature for 50% mortality estimated from curve. /13/ Upper limits of temperature and humidity cats can withstand for 7 hr. /14/ Indoors; air flow 22.9 cm/sec. /15/ In ice water at 1.5-6°C (34.7-42.8°F); dogs etherized during initial cooling stages. /16/ Anesthetized and cooled with ice for 1 1/4 to 27 hr. /17/ Serious impairment in 3 dogs in 1 hr; 4th not markedly affected. /18/ 7 hr exposure to environmental temperature of 41°C (105.8°F). /19/ In cold water at 3°C (37.4°F), or in cold air. /20/ In cold air, about -10°C (14°F). /21/ Immersed in cold water, then exposed to cold air (total ½ hr). /22/ In controlled temperature room, air flow 89.4 cm/sec. /23/ Body temperature in all but three fell below 19°C (66.2°F). /24/ Serious impairment, approaching unconsciousness. /25/ Upper limits tolerated for 7 hr in controlled temperature room. /26/ In heated room. /27/ In controlled temperature room; near heat tolerance limit. /28/ Merino wethers sheep. /29/ In cold room, 10-16°C (50-60.8°F); rectal temperature of 23-25°C (73.4-77°F) for 7 hr for animal that died and for 9 hr for survivor. /30/ Outdoor exposure at 35-40°C (95-104°F) in sunlight; several died. /31/ In refrigerator 2-4 hr at -13 to -19°C (8.6 to -2.2°F); all but one of eight that died had body temperature of 0°C (32°F) or less. /32/ In controlled temperature room; withstood 38°C (100.4°F) at 65 relative humidity, but could not tolerate 41°C (105.8°F) at any humidity.

Part II: BIRDS

	Bird	Specification	Body Temperature Site	Body Temperature °C (°F)	Ambient Temperature Site	Ambient Temperature °C (°F)	Duration hr	Survival n/n'[1]
1	Canary (Serinus serinus canaria)	20 g			A	-35 (-31)	0.6	0/2
2	Duck (Anas platyrhynchos)	1.45-1.8 kg			A	-40 (-40)	168-264	0/3
3	var. domesticus	2 kg			A	-40 (-40)	384	1/1
4	wild mallard	1 kg			A	-18 (-0.4)	225	0/8
5	Fowl (Gallus gallus) var. domesticus	♂	C	19.4-22.2 (68.9-72)	W	6-10 (42.8-50)	1.1-1.5	0/4
6		♀	C	22.8-23.6(73-74.5)	W	9-11.7(48.2-53.1)	1.1-1.5	0/5
7		♀	C	27.8-29.4(68-84.9)	W	20-27.8 (68-82)	35-44	0/5
8		♀	C	27.8-31.1(68-88)	W	20-27.8 (68-82)	23-37	5/5
9		1.6 kg	C	21-41(69.8-105.8)	A	-35 (-31)	3.3-16	0/8
10		1.5 kg	C	21-41(69.8-105.8)	A	-35 (-31)	16-29.5	0/3
11		Embryo (0 da)			A	-5(23)	48	50%
12		Embryo (5 da)			A	0(32)	38	49%
13		Embryo (17 da)			A	10(50)	144	60%
14		Embryo (0-5 da)			A	21(69.8)	120	50%
15		Embryo (0-21 da)			A	28(82.4)	504	50%
16		Embryo (0-21 da)			A	43(109.4)	504	50%
17	Junco, slate-colored (Junco hyemalis)	21.8 g			A	-14(6.8)	37	0/12
18		20.7 g			A	37(98.6)	12	0/3
19	Pheasant, ring-neck (Phasianus colchicus)	1.05 kg			A	-9 (15.8)	336	0/16
20		1.15 kg			A	-1 ± (30.2±)	340	0/24
21	Pigeon (Columba livia)		R	46(114.8)			<1	50%
22		300-400 g			A	-40(-40)	0.3-0.5	0/7[2]
23		300-400 g			A[3]	-40(-40)	24	4/6

/1/ n = number survived; n' = number in test. Percentages are per cent survived. /2/ Plucked birds. /3/ In path of 5 mph breeze.

362. TOLERANCES TO EXTREMES OF HEAT AND COLD: ANIMALS (Continued)

The following abbreviations for sites of temperature measurement are used in this table: A = air; B = body; C = cloaca; G = gullet; I = intestine; R = rectum; S = stomach; T = throat; U = underground; W = water.

Part II: BIRDS (Concluded)

	Bird	Specification	Body Temperature Site	Body Temperature °C (°F)	Ambient Temperature Site	Ambient Temperature °C (°F)	Duration hr	Survival n/n'[1]
24	Pigeon (Columba livia)	300-400 g			A[3]	-40(-40)	48	0/6
25	(concluded)	300-400 g			A	-40(-40)	96-120	11/25
26		300-400 g			A	-40(-40)	144	4/25
27	Quail, bob white (Colinus virginianus)	165 g			A	-18 (0.4)	60	0/10
28	Grouse, ruffed (Bonasa umbellus)	615 g			A	-18(-0.4)	185	0/2
29		29 ± g			A	-39 to -30(-38.2 to -22)	3.7-5.3	0/10
30					A	-29 to -20(-20.2 to -4)	3.2-4.4	0/8
31	Sparrow, house (Passer domesticus)				A	-19 to -10(-2.2 to 14)	11.3-21.4	0/37
32					A	38-39(100.4-102.2)	9.9-13.6	0/19
33					A	41-45(105.8-113)	0.5-1	0/7
34	Sparrow, tree (Spizella arborea)	21.1 g			A	-13(8.6)	31	0/3
35		20.5 g			A	38(100.4)	7	0/4
36	Sparrow, white-crowned (Zonotrichia	37.5 g			A	-18(0.4)	19	0/4
37	leucophrys)	32.4 g			A	38(100.4)	5	0/3
38	Sparrow, white-throated	26.6 g			A	-17(1.4)	16	0/3
39	(Zonotrichia albicollis)	27.8 g			A	-37(98.6)	7	0/20
40	Turkey, wild (Meleagris gallopao)	4.9 kg			A	-18(0.4)	324	0/2
41					A	-13.9(7)	4	1/1
42			T	6.8-11.3(44.2-52.3)	A	6.4-10.1(43.5-50.2)	<1	5/9
43	Wren, house (Troglodytes aedon)		T	21.7(71.1)	A[4]	10 ± 1(50±)	<1	0/1
44			T	23.7(74.7)	A[4]	10 ± (50±)	<1	1/1
45			T	45.3(113.5)	A[5]	37.9±(100.2)	<1	2/2
46			T	46.6(115.9)	A	45.2(113.2)	<1.5	1/11
47			T	46.8(116.2)	A[5]	37.9 ± (100.2)	<1	0/4

/1/ n = number survived; n' = number in test. Percentages are per cent survived. /3/ In path of 5 mph breeze. /4/ Low and falling air temps. /5/ High and rising air temps.

Part III: REPTILES

Values are LD$_{50}$ temperature tolerance limits, i.e., temperatures survived by 50% of test animals. Counts were made after animals regained "normal" temperature and behavior. Information on site of measurement, if available, is given in brackets.

	Reptile	Lower Limit °C (°F)	Upper Limit °C (°F)		Reptile	Lower Limit °C (°F)	Upper Limit °C (°F)
1	Alligator (Alligator mississippiensis)	4(39.2)[C]	39(102.2)[C]	13	Snake, garter (Thamnophis radix)	-2(28.4)[U]	
2	Lizard, chuckwalla (Sauromalus obesus)		44(111.2)[C]	14	Snake, garter (T. radix)	0(32)[A]	41(105.8)[A]
3	Lizard, collared (Crotaphytus collaris)		46(114.8)[C]	15	Snake, glossy (Arizona elegans)		42(107.6)[C]
4	Lizard, crested (Dipsosaurus dorsalis)		47.5(117.5)[C]	16	Snake, leaf-nosed (Phyllorhynchus decurtatus)		38(100.4)[C]
5	Lizard, European (Lacerta agilis)	-4(24.8)	44(111.2)[B]	17	Snake, shovelnose (Sonora occipitalis)		37(98.6)[C]
6	Lizard, fringe-footed (Uma notata)		45(113)[C]	18	Snake, sidewinder (Crotalus cerastes)		41(105.8)[C]
7	Lizard, ground (Uta stansburiana)		48(118.4)[C]	19	Snake, water (Natrix sipedon)	0(32)[A]	43(109.4)[A]
8	Lizard, horned (Phrynosoma platyrhinos)		46(114.8)[C]	20	Turtle, central painted (Chrysemys bellii marginata)		
9	Lizard, night (Xantusia vigilis)		38(100.4)[C]				40(104)[C]
10	Lizard, slowworm (Anguis fragilis)		37(98.6)[A]	21	Turtle, land (Testudo norsefieldi)	-1(30.2)[B]	
11	Lizard, swift (Sceleporus graciosus)		43.6(110.5)[C]	22	Turtle, painted (Pseudemys elegans)	1(33.8)[C]	46(114.8)[C]
12	Lizard, whiptail (Cnemidophorus tessellatus)		46(114.8)[C]	23	Turtle, snapping (Chelydra serpentina)	<4(<39.2)[C]	40(104)[C]

Part IV: AMPHIBIANS

Values are LD$_{50}$ temperature tolerance limits, i.e., temperatures survived by 50% of test animals. Counts were made after animals regained "normal" temperature and behavior. Information on site of measurement, if available, is given in brackets.

	Amphibian	Lower Limit °C (°F)	Upper Limit °C (°F)		Amphibian	Lower Limit °C (°F)	Upper Limit °C (°F)
1	Bullfrog (Rana catesbeiana), embryo	15(59)[W]	32(89.6)[W]	10	Frog, water (Rana esculenta)	-0.5(31.1)[C]	
2	Bullfrog (R. catesbeiana), large tadpoles[1]		36(96.8)[W]	11	Frog, wood (R. sylvatica), embryo	2.5(36.5)[W]	24(75.2)[W]
3	Frog, green (R. clamitans)	-0.5(31.1)[S]	22(71.6)[A][2]	12	Frog, European wood (R. temporaria), embryo	-1.4(29.5)[G]	32.5(90.5)[W][5]
4	Frog, green (R. clamitans), embryo	12(53.6)[W]		13	Salamander, European spotted (Salamandra maculosa)	-3(26.6)[W]	
5	Frog, leopard (R. pipiens), embryo[3]	11(51.8)[W]	34(93.2)[W]	14	Toad, American (Bufo americanus), embryo	11(51.8)[W]	31(87.8)[W]
6	Frog, leopard (R. pipiens), embryo[4]	5(41)[W]	28(82.4)[W]	15	Toad, clawed (Xenopus laevis)	0(32)[C]	33(91.4)[C]
7	Frog, pickerel (R. palustris), embryo	7(44.6)[W]	30(86)[W]	16	Toad, common (Bufo bufo)	-1(30.2)[W]	33(91.4)[W][5]
8	Frog, spring peeper (Hyla crucifer), embryo	<6(<42.8)[W]	28(82.4)[W]	17	Toad, fire-bellied (Bombinator igneus)	-0.5(31.1)[C]	
9	Frog, tree (H. arborea)	-0.5(31.1)[C]					

/1/ Tadpoles of known ages, for brief exposures. /2/ 12 hr exposure. /3/ From Florida. /4/ From Vermont. /5/ 1 hr exposure.

Part V: FISHES

Values are LD$_{50}$ temperature tolerance limits, i.e., water temperatures survived by 50% of test animals. Counts were made by observing or estimating the number killed during exposure, or within a reasonable time thereafter in which it could be safely assumed that all deaths were attributable to the temperature effects. Exposure periods, in hours, are given in brackets.

	Fish	Acclimated to °C (°F)	Lower Limit °C (°F) [hr]	Upper Limit °C (°F) [hr]		Fish	Acclimated to °C (°F)	Lower Limit °C (°F) [hr]	Upper Limit °C (°F) [hr]
1	Bass, large mouth (Microp-	20(68)	5(41)[24]	32(89.6)[72]	13	Dace, blacknose (Rhinich-	5(41)		27(80.6)[340]
2	terus salmoides floridanus)[1]	30(86)	11(51.8)[24]	34(93.2)[72]	14	thys a. atratulus, R. a. meleagris)[1]	25(77)	5(41)[24]	29(84.2)[2][340]
3	Bluegill (Lepomis machro-	10(50)		28(82.4)[24]	15	Eelpont (Zoarces anguillaris)[3]		-2(28.4)[12][4]	28(82.4)[2]
4	chirus machrochirus)[1]	30(86)		36(96.8)[24]	16	Flounder, winter (Pseudo-	-2(28.4)	16(60.8)	29(84.2)[2]
5	Bluegill (L. machrochirus	15(59)	3(37.4)[24]	31(87.8)[>60]		pleuronectes americanus)[3]			
6	purpurescens)[1]	30(86)	11(51.8)[24]	34(93.2)[>60]	17	Goldfish (Carassius	2(35.6)		28(82.4)[14]
7	Bullhead (Ameiurus n. neb-	20(68)	1(33.8)[24]	32(89.6)[96]	18	auratus)[1]	17(62.6)	<0(32)[14]	34(93.2)[14]
8	ulosus, A. n. marmoratus)[1]	30(86)	7(44.6)[24]	35(95)[96]	19		24(75.2)	5(41)[14]	36(96.8)[14]
9	Catfish, channel (Ictalurns	15(59)	0(32)[24]	30(86)[>24]	20		37(98.6)	15(59)[14]	42(107.6)[14]
10	lacustris lacustris, I. l. punctatus)[1]	25(77)	6(42.8)[24]	34(93.2)[>24]	21	Greenfish (Girella	12(53.6)	5(41)[120]	30(86)[120]
11	Chub, creek (Semotilus a.	5(41)		25(77)[>96]	22	nigricans)[3]	18(64.4)	13(55.4)[72]	31(87.8)[120]
12	atromaculatus)[1]	25(77)		32(89.6)[>96]	23	Killifish (Fundulus	14(57.2)	1(33.8)[48]	32(89.6)
					24	heteroclitus)[3]	20(68)	2(35.6)[48]	34(93.2)

/1/ Fresh-water fish. /2/ Upper limit in gradually rising temperatures. /3/ Marine fish. /4/ Approximate average survival time.

434

362. TOLERANCES TO EXTREMES OF HEAT AND COLD: ANIMALS (Continued)

The following abbreviations for sites of temperature measurement are used in this table: A = air; B = body; C = cloaca; G = gullet; I = intestine; R = rectum; S = stomach; T = throat; U = underground; W = water.

Part V: FISHES (Concluded)

Values are LD$_{50}$ temperature tolerance limits, i.e., water temperatures survived by 50% of test animals. Counts were made by observing or estimating the number killed during exposure, or within a reasonable time thereafter in which it could be safely assumed that all deaths were attributable to the temperature effects. Exposure periods, in hours, are given in brackets.

	Fish	Acclimated to °C (°F)	Lower Limit °C (°F) [hr]	Upper Limit °C (°F) [hr]		Fish	Acclimated to °C (°F)	Lower Limit °C (°F) [hr]	Upper Limit °C (°F) [hr]
25	Minnow, fathead	20(68)	2(35.6)[24]	32(89.6)[133]	44	Shiner, common	5(41)		27(80.6)[133]
26	(Pimephales promelas)[3]	30(86)	11(51.8)[24]	33(91.4)[133]	45	(Notropis cornutus	25(77)	4(39.2)[24]	31(87.8)[133]
27	Minnow, blunt-nose	15(59)	1(33.8)[24]	31(87.8)[133]	46	frontalis)[1]	30(86)	8(46.4)[24]	31(87.8)[133]
28	(Hyborhynchus notatus)[1]	25(77)	8(46.4)[24]	33(91.4)[133]	47	Shiner, common (N.	25(77)[5]		32(89.6)[133][5]
29	Mosquito fish (Grambusia	15(59)	2(35.6)[24]	35(95)[>66]	48	cornutus chrysocephalus)[1]	30(86)[6]		34(93.2)[133][6]
30	affinis affinis, G.a.holbroki)[1]	35(95)	15(59)[24]	37(98.6)[>66]	49	Shiner, lake	5(41)		23(73.4)[133]
31	Perch (Perca flavescens)[1]	5(41)		21(69.8)[96]	50	(N. atherinoides)[1]	15(59)	2(35.6)[24]	29(84.2)[133]
32	Winter	25(77)	4(39.2)[24]	30(86)[>96]	51		25(77)	8(46.4)[24]	31(87.8)[133]
33	Summer	25(77)	9(48.2)[24]	32(89.6)[>96]	52	Shiner, golden	20(68)	8(46.4)[24]	32(89.6)[133]
34	Salmon, spring (On-	5(41)		21.5(70.7)[168]	53	(Notemigonus c. cryso-	30(86	11(51.8)[24]	35(95)[>66]
35	corhynchus tschawytscha)	20(68)	4.5(40.1)[92]	25.1(77.2)[168]		leucas, N. c. auratus)[1]			
36	Salmon, sockeye	5(41)	0(32)[92]	22.2(72)[168]	54	Sucker, common (Catosto-	15(59)		29(84.2)[133]
37	(O. nerka)	20(68)	4.7(40.9)[92]	24.8(76.6)[168]	55	mus commersoni)[1]	25(77)	5(41)[24]	29(84.2)[133]
38	Salmon, chum	5(41)		21.8(71.2)[168]	56	Sunfish	10(50)		28(82.4)[24]
39	(O. keta)	20(68)	6.5(43.7)[92]	23.7(74.7)[168]	57	(Lepomis gibbosus)[1]	30(86)		24(75.2)[24]
40	Salmon, coho	5(41)	0.2(32.4)[92]	22.9(73.2)[168]	58	Trout, brook	3(37.4)		23(73.4)[133]
41	(O. kisutch)	20(68)	4.5(40.1)[92]	25(77)[168]	59	(Salvelinus fontinalis)[1]	20(68)		25(77)[133]
42	Shad, gizzard (Dorosoma	25(77)	11(51.8)[24]	34(93.2)[48]	60		25(77)		25(77)[133]
43	cepedianum)[1]	35(95)	20(68)[24]	37(98.6)[48]					

/1/ Fresh water fish. /3/ Marine fish. /5/ Summer. /6/ Winter.

Part VI: INSECTS
Exposure periods, in hours, are given in brackets.

	Insect	Specifications	Activity Range °C (°F)	Biological Zero[1] °C (°F)	Heat Death °C (°F) [hr]	R.H. %[2]	Cold Death Temperature °C (°F) [hr]
					Anoplura		
1	Louse, human (Pediculus	Adult	20-39(68-102.2)[3]		50-55(122-131)[0.25-0.42]		
2	humanus)	Adult			46-47(114.8-116.6)[1]	0-90	
3		Adult			33-38(91.4-100.4)[24]	0-90	
					Coleoptera		
4	Beetle, diving	Egg	10-27(50-80.6)	0(32)	31(87.8)		
5	(Dysticus marginalis)	Larva		1.38(34.5)[4]			
6	Beetle, furniture (Anobium striatum)	Adult			42-46(107.6-114.8) [0.01-0.02]		
7	Beetle, Mexican bean (Epilachna varivestis)	Larva; adult			42.5(108.5)[3]	1-100	
8	Beetle, western pine (Dendroctonus						
8	brevicomis)	Larva	12.8-32(55-89.6)	4-7(39.2-44.6)[5]	37.8-40.6(100-105.1)[0.5]		5-10(41-50)
9	Mealworm, yellow (Tenebrio	Larva	12-20(53.6-68)[6]		42-43(107.6-109.4)[1-3]	0-90	
10	molitor)	Larva			38.5(101.3)[24]	0-90	
11	Tree borer, flat-headed apple- (Chrysobothris femorata)	Larva			53(127.4)[2]	10-15;95-100	
12	Weevil, bean (Acanthoscelides	Egg			52(125.6)[0.17]		-8(17.6)
13	obtectus)	Larva		-2(28.4)	55(131)[0.35]		-8(17.6)
14		Pupa		-2(28.4)	55(131)[0.42]		-9(15.8)
15		Adult		-2(28.4)	55(131)[0.06]		-8(17.6)
16	Weevil, boll (Anthonomus grandis)	Adult	13.3-35(55.9-95)	3 to -4(37.4-24.8)[7,8]	50-60(122-140)		
17	Weevil, granary (Sitophilus granarius)	Adult	25(77)[6]	9.5(49.1)[9,10]	49(120.2)[3]	20-60	-4 to -1(24.8-30.2) [1104]
					Diptera		
18	Cheese skipper (Piophila casei)	Larva			46-48(114.8-118.4)[11][24]	0-100	
19	Fly, green bottle (Phaenicia	Egg	10-30(50-86)	5-6(41-42.8)			
20	sericata)	Larva	10-30(50-86)	4.2-10(39.6-50)[12]			
21		Adult	20-38(68-100.4)	6.7-7.2(44.1-45)[5]			
22	Fly, house (Musca domestica)	Egg			42.8-43(109-109.4)		
23		Larva	44-48(111.2-118.4)[13]	5(41)	49(120.2)		
24		Pupa	>7.8(>46)	10(50)			0-1(32-33.8)[168]
25		Adult	>15.6(>60.1)[6]	6.7-7.2(44.1-45)[5]	44.6(112.3)		0(32)[72]
26	Fly, tsetse (Glossina morsitans)	Adult			44-46(11.2-114.8)[0.08]		-12(10.4)[0.2]
27	Mosquito, malarial (Anopheles	Larva			42(107.6)[0.12-0.3]		
28	quadrimaculatus)	Pupa			42(107.6)[0.08]		
29	Mosquito, northern house (Culex	Egg					5
30	pipiens)	Adult			44.5-45.6(112.1-114.1)		-17(1.4)
					Hemiptera		
31	Aphid, potato (Macrosiphum						
31	solanifolii)	Adult			38.5(101.3)[1]	60	
32	Bedbug (Cimex lectularis)	Adult	12-22(53.6-71.6)[14]	7.5(45.5)[5]			
33		Adult			34-43.5(93.2-110.3)[15] [1-24]	0-90	
34	Greenbug (Toxoptera graminum)	Adult		1.7-4.5(35.1-40.1)[14]	37.5-40(99.5-104.2)		-8.3(46.9)
					Heteroptera		
35	Bug, assassin (Rhodnius prolixus)	Nymph			40-43(104-109.4)[15][1-24]	0-90	

/1/ Temperature at which all vital processes are arrested by cold. /2/ R.H. = relative humidity. /3/ Temp "preferred" by insect is 24-32°C (75.2-89.6°F). /4/ Cold stupor at 6°C (42.8°F). /5/ Cold stupor. /6/ Temp "preferred" by organism. /7/ Cold stupor at 13.3°C (55.9°F). /8/ Heat stupor at 35-50°C (95-122°F). /9/ Cold stupor at 13-15°C (55.4-59°F). /10/ Heat stupor at 28°C (82.4°F). /11/ The higher temp corresponds to a relative humidity of 60%. /12/ Cold stupor at 2°C (35.6°F). /13/ Temp "preferred" by larva is 30-37°C (86-98.6°F)./14/ Temp "preferred" by adult; relative humidity 24-44%. /15/ The higher temperature kills in 1 hr, the lower in 24 hr.

The following abbreviations for sites of temperature measurement are used in this table: A = air; B = body; C = cloaca; G = gullet; I = intestine; R = rectum; S = stomach; T = throat; U = underground; W = water.

Part VI: INSECTS (Concluded)
Exposure periods, in hours, are given in brackets.

Insect	Speci-fica-tions	Activity Range °C (°F)	Biological Zero[1] °C (°F)	Heat Death °C (°F) [hr]	R.H. %[2]	Cold Death Temperature °C (°F) [hr]
			Hymenoptera			
36 Bee, honey (Apis mellifera)	Adult	10-35(50-95)		46-48(114.8-118.4)[0.5]		-2 to -1(28.4-30.2)
			Lepidoptera			
37 Borer, European corn- 37 (Pyrausta nubilalis)	Larva			58(136.4)[0.18]		-31.7(-25.1)[0.17]
38 Moth, codling	Egg	6.7-9.4(44.1-48.9)				
39 (Carpocapsa pomonella)	Larva	6.1-8.8(43-47.8)				
			Orthoptera			
40 Cockroach, American (Periplaneta 41 americana)	Adult			42-45(107.6-113)[1] 37-49(98.6-120.2)[24]	0-90 0-90	
42 Cockroach, German (Blattella 42 germanica)	Adult			43-45(109.4-113)[1]	0-90	
			Siphonaptera			
43 Flea, oriental rat (Xenopsylla 44 cheopis)	Larva Adult			40(104)[1] 38-40.7(100.4-105.3)[15] [1-24]	0-90 0-90	

/1/ Temperature at which all vital processes are arrested by cold. /2/ R.H. = relative humidity. /15/ The higher temperature kills in 1 hr, the lower in 24 hr.

363. OPTIMAL TEMPERATURES AND HUMIDITIES FOR PHYSIOLOGICAL FUNCTIONS: ARTHROPODS
Several ranges represent extremes reported by different investigators.

Arthropod	Temperature °C	Optimal Humidity %	Function	Arthropod	Temperature °C	Optimal Humidity %	Function
Isopoda				Collembola			
1 Armadillium vulgare, adult	14-35	100	Survival	44 Dicyrtomia minuta, adult	25	100	Survival
2 Ligia occidentalis, adult	20-35	100	Survival	45 Entomobrya multifasciata, adult	25	100	Survival
3 L. pallasii, adult	20-35	100	Survival	46 Isotoma viridis, adult	25	100	Survival
4 Ligidium gracili, adult	20-35	100	Survival	47 Sminthurus viridis, nymph	30	100	Survival
5 Oniscus asellus, adult	14-18	100	Survival	48 adult	7	80-90	Oviposition
6 Porcellio laevis, adult	20-35	100	Survival	49	25	100	Survival
7 Porcellionides pruinosus, adult	20-35	100	Survival	50 Tomocerus vulgaris, adult	25	100	Survival
8 P. scaber, adult	14-35	100	Survival	Diptera			
9 P. spinacornis occidentalis, adult	20-35	100	Survival	51 Fly, green-bottle (Phaenicia	22	100	Development
Acarina				52 sericata), egg	37	90-100	Survival
10 Halotydeus destructor, adult	18-26	100	Survival	53 Fly, heel (Hypoderma lineatum) pupa	20-25	0-76	Survival, development
11 Ixodes ricinus, nymph	25-30	90-100	Development	54 Fly, tachinid (Winthemia			
12 I. ricinus, adult	25	100	Oviposition	quadripustulata), pupa	27	73.4	Development
Anoplura				55 Fly, vinegar (Drosophila			
13 Louse, horse-sucking (Hematopinus asini), egg	37.8	100	Survival	melanogaster), pupa	18-19	100	Development
Coleoptera				Heteroptera			
14 Acilius sulcatus, adult	19	100	Survival	56 Bedbug (Cimex lectularius), egg	13-35	75-90	Survival
15 Beetle, capricorn (Hylotrupes	16.6	50-60	Development	57 nymph	18	44-77	Development
16 bajalus), egg	31.5	90-100	Survival, development	58 Bedbug (C. rotunda), egg	18	93	Survival
				59 nymph	18	77-93	Development
17 Beetle, caraboides (Hydrous caraboides), adult	18-20	100	Survival	60 Cone nose bug (Rhodnius prolixus), egg	17-33	70-90	Survival
18 Beetle, cigarette (Lasioderma serricorne), egg	32	75	Development	61 Cotton stainer (Dysdercus cingulatus), egg	35	82-100	Survival
19 Beetle, clavicorn (Hydrophilus piceus), adult	18-20	100	Survival	62 Eurygaster mauro, nymph	24-30	80-100	Survival
20 Beetle, confused flour (Tribolium confusum), egg	27	1-75	Survival	63 Palomena prasina, nymph	24-30	80-100	Survival
21 pupa	27	0-25	Survival	Hymenoptera			
22 Beetle, ladybird (Epilachna	27	76-81	Survival	64 Wasp, parasitic (Habrobracon juglandis), egg	16-35	80	Survival
23 corrupta), egg	27	81-100	Development	65 Wasp, parasitic (Macrocentrus ancylivorus), adult	26.7	80	Oviposition
24 Beetle, oriental (Anomala orientalis), egg	25.5	100	Survival	Lepidoptera			
25 Beetle, spider (Ptinus tectus), egg	25	70	Development	66 Araschnia levana, pupa	18-20	55-85	Survival
26 larva	24.7	70	Development	67	18-20	100	Development
27 pupa	27	90	Development	68 Armyworm (Prodenia littoralis), egg	29	90-95	Survival
28 Borer, grain (Rhyzopertha dominica), egg	18.3-38.2	90	Survival	69 Cutworm, grain (Agrotis segetum) pupa	17-21	65-85	Development
29 Colymbetes fuscus, adult	15-20	100	Survival	70 Dendrolimus pini, egg	24	80-85	Survival
30 Eurostus hilleri, egg	20	90	Development	71 Hoffmannophila pseudospretella,			
31 Geotrupes stercorosus, adult	15-19	100	Survival	egg	15-25	90	Development
32 Laemophloeus minutes, adult	21-25	90	Survival	72	13-27	8.5-90	Survival
33	21-25	55-90	Oviposition	73 Hornworm, tomato (Protoparce quinquemaculata), pupa	27	0-73.4	Development
34 Melasoma populi, egg	17-21	100	Development	74 Moth, cecropia (Hyalophora cecropia), egg	25-21	56-76	Survival
35 adult	19-25	100	Survival	75 Moth, lackey (Malacosoma neustria), egg	11-21	90	Survival
36 Weevil (Acanthoscelides obtectus) adult	26.6	100	Oviposition	76 Moth, promethea (Callosamia promethea), egg	20-30	76	Survival
37 egg	25.2	50-90	Development	77 Moth, webbing (Tineola bisselliella), larva	23.9	75	Development
38 Weevil, cowpea (Callosobruchus chinensis), larva	30.4	76	Survival, development	78 Panolis flammea, egg	12-22	65-85	Survival
39 Weevil, cowpea (C. maculatus), egg	30	63	Survival, development	79 Samia walkeri, egg	15-25	56-100	Survival
40 Weevil, granary (Sitophilus granarium), adult	20-27.5	60-100	Oviposition	80 Silkworm (Bombyx mori), pre-pupa + pupa	25	7-100	Development
41 Weevil, rice (Calandra oryza), egg	15-32	90	Survival	81 Tlea polyphemus, egg	30	53-76	Survival
42 Wireworm (Agriotes lineatus), egg	19	100	Survival				
43 larva	20	98-100	Survival				

363. OPTIMAL TEMPERATURES AND HUMIDITIES FOR PHYSIOLOGICAL FUNCTIONS: ARTHROPODS (Concluded)
Several ranges represent extremes reported by different investigators.

	Arthropod	Temperature °C	Optimal Humidity %	Function		Arthropod	Temperature °C	Optimal Humidity %	Function
	Orthoptera					**Siphonaptera**			
82	Carausius morosus, egg	15-21	100	Development	90	Flea, oriental rat (Xenopsylla astia), larva	17-35	80-94.8	Survival
83	Grasshopper, clear-winged (Camnula pellucida), egg	27	60-90	Development	91	Flea, oriental rat (X. cheopis), larva	22-35	80-90	Survival
84	Grasshopper, Rocky Mountain (Melanoplus mexicanus), egg	22-37	80-90	Survival	92	Flea (X. brasiliensis), larva	22-27	80-95	Survival
85	Locust, desert (Schistocerca gregaria), egg	30	100	Survival		**Thysanoptera**			
86	nymph	37.8	55-70	Development	93	Thrips, onion (Thrips tabaci), larva	10-35	75-85	Survival
87	adult	37.8	50-60	Oviposition		**Thysanura**			
88	Locust, migratory (Locusta migratoria), nymph	32.2-37.8	60-70	Development	94	Firebrat (Thermobia domestica) egg	37	76-85	Survival
89	adult	37.8	60-75	Oviposition	95	nymph	37	84	Development
					96	adult	37	84	Oviposition

364. HEAT EXCHANGES AND ACTIVITY LIMITS IN HOT ENVIRONMENTS: MAN

Basic equation for maximum energy expenditure with heat balance is $M=R+C+E_{max}$, where values are in Cal/sq m body surface per hour; M = body heat production (metabolic rate); R = radiation heat exchange; C = convective heat exchange; E_{max} = maximum evaporative exchange from wet skin. E_{max} is always negative; R and C are positive when heat moves toward the body, and negative when away from the body.

	Environment	Wind Velocity km/hr	Dry Bulb °C	Relative Humidity %	Vapor Pressure[1] mm/Hg	Clothing Type[2]	Convection (C)[3] Cal/sq m/hr	Radiation (R)[4] Cal/sq m/hr	Evaporation (E max)[5] Cal/sq m/hr	Metabolic Rate Limit (M)[6] Cal/sq m/hr
1	Wet tropics, shade	0.9	31	90	11	None	-13	-18	-72	105
2	Wet tropics, shade	0.9	31	90	11	Light	-7	9	-54	52
3	Wet tropics, shade	8.0	31	90	11	None	-42	-18	-150	210
4	Wet tropics, shade	8.0	31	90	11	Light	-21	9	-113	125
5	Wet tropics, sun	0.9	31	90	11	None	-13	112	-72	0
6	Wet tropics, sun	0.9	31	90	11	Light	-7	45	-54	16
7	Wet tropics, sun	8.0	31	90	11	None	-42	112	-150	80
8	Wet tropics, sun	8.0	31	90	11	Light	-21	45	-113	89
9	Desert, sun	0.9	44	10	35	None	32	172	-230	26
10	Desert, sun	0.9	44	10	35	Light	16	69	-172	87
11	Desert, shade	0.9	44	10	35	None	32	42	-230	155
12	Desert, shade	0.9	44	10	35	Light	16	21	-172	135
13	Desert, sun	8.0	44	10	35	None	94	172	-476	210
14	Desert, sun	8.0	44	10	35	Light	47	69	-357	240
15	Desert, shade	8.0	44	10	35	None	94	42	-476	340
16	Desert, shade	8.0	44	10	35	Light	47	21	-357	390
17	Glass forming[7]	3.7	38	42	21	None	21	255	-220	0
18	Glass forming[7]	3.7	38	42	21	Light	11	128	-165	26
19	Heated chamber	0.9	115	3	19	Light	267	530	-124	0

/1/ Vapor pressure of skin assumed to be saturated at 35°C (42 mm Hg), minus ambient vapor pressure under prevailing conditions of exposure. /2/ Clothing type: light = underwear shorts, cotton shirt with sleeves, cotton trousers, shoes and stockings or equivalent, offering 0.5 clo protection (1 clo = insulation maintaining difference of 0.18°C for flow of 1 Cal/sq m/hr; a business suit = 1 clo). /3/ For the nude body, $C=3.7\sqrt{V}$ (Ta-35 where V is wind speed in km/hr, 35 is assumed skin temperature, and Ta is ambient temperature in °C. Light clothing is assumed to reduce convective exchange by 50%. /4/ For the nude body, $R=3.9\times10^{-8}(T_w^4-T_s^4)$ when T_w and T_s are in degrees absolute and T_s is assumed 308°A. Solar heat load on nude skin is taken as 130 Cal/sq m/hr. Light clothing is assumed to decrease nominal solar heat load by 60% and radiant exchange with hot or cool walls by 50%. /5/ For the nude body $E_{max}=6.3V^{0.37}.\Delta VP$, where V is air movement in km/hr; VP=vapor pressure. For the lightly-clad body, it is assumed that evaporation from the skin is reduced by 50%, but this half is, nevertheless, evaporated from the clothing surface where the heat removed is 50% efficient for skin cooling; this gives an assumed net efficiency of sweating equal to 0.75xE_{max} determined for the nude body. /6/ Limit for sustained activity. Expenditure of 50-70 Cal/sq m/hr is involved in sedentary activities; 80-110, light physical work; 120-190, moderate work; 200-290, moderately hard work; 300-390, hard work; 400 and above, very hard work tolerated for prolonged periods only by fit, trained subjects. /7/ Radiant heat.

365. TEMPERATURE CHARACTERISTICS: VARIOUS HOMEOTHERMIC ANIMALS
+ = present; - = absent.

	Animal	Rectal Temperature Normal °C	Min °C	Max °C	Critical Air Temperature[1] Low °C	High °C	Temperature Regulating Mechanisms Sweating	Shivering	Panting	Thermo-neutrality Zone[2] °C
1	Man	37	22	44	17-22	32	+	+		23-34.5
2	Cat	37.2-39	17	42		32.2	-	+	+	10-30
3	Cow, Brahman	38		41.1		32			+	10-27
4	Cow, dairy	38-39		42.8	-40	21-27			+	4.4-15.6
5	Dasyurus	36.3		40		35-40	-	+	-	24-30
6	Dog	39	17	42.8	-40	29	-	+	+	-40 to 30
7	Donkey	36-38					+			
8	Echidna	28-29	25.5	39-40		35	-	+	-	26-37
9	Elephant	35.9-36.7					-	+		
10	Goat	40								13-21
11	Guinea pig	38.5-39.9	21		-15	29.5			+	30-31
12	Hamster	37	2.2					+		
13	Horse	38					+	+		
14	Marmot	34-39	3	42.1	27.5	30	-	-		28
15	Monkey	38	20	42.7		30-32	+		+	27-30
16	Mouse	35.2-37.8	12.5		13.14	31.5				30-33
17	Platypus	32.5	25.5	35.3	15	35-40	-	+	-	22-35
18	Rabbit	39.6	20	41.7	-7	28-30	-		+	-5 to 30
19	Rat	35.8-37.6	15-16	43	-7	28.5	-	+	-	28-29
20	Sheep	38		42		41-43	+		+	25-27
21	Sloth	33-34.4	20	40	15	35				
22	Squirrel	35.5-38.4	0-2	42.3						7-37
23	Swine	38-39.6		41.7		29.5	-		+	
24	Chicken	40-42	25-27	45	-34	32.2	-	+	+	16-35
25	Pigeon	42-43	20	47	-40					26-37

/1/ Air temperature at which the first indication of a change in rectal temperature occurs in the unanesthetized animal. /2/ Range of air temperature over which the metabolic rate is lowest and constant in the unanesthetized animal.

366. HEAT PRODUCTION UNDER CONTROLLED ENVIRONMENTAL CONDITIONS: VARIOUS ANIMALS

	Animal	Temperature °C	Heat Production Cal/sq m/24hr[1]
1		15.3	1254
2		19.7	1043
3	Rat	25.0	826
4		30.0	744
5		34.0	1178
6		15.1	1050
7		20.0	913
8	Guinea pig	24.8	784
9		29.8	601
10		35.3	716
11		14.6	1741
12		20.0	1037
13	Mouse	24.9	953
14		29.9	879
15		35.3	1009
16		18.0	1.2[2]
17	Reptile	26.0	2.3[2]
18		32.0	3.2[2]

/1/ Lines 1-15. /2/ Cal/kg/24 hr.

367. EFFECTS OF ENVIRONMENTAL TEMPERATURE CHANGE: MAN, DOMESTIC ANIMALS

Values are for resting state.

	Animal	Variable	Increase of Environmental Temperature			Decrease of Environmental Temperature		
			Single Exposure Response		Repeated or	Single Exposure Response		Repeated or
			General	15-20°C Inc.	Continued Exposure	General	15-20°C Dec.	Continued Exposure
1		Blood volume	Increase		Increase			Decrease
2		Cardiac output	Increase		Return toward normal	Decrease		Return toward normal
3		Food intake	Decrease	Variable	Decrease	Increase	Variable	Increase
4		Heart rate	Increase	5/min[1]	Return toward normal	Decrease	-5/min	Return toward normal
5		Heat production	0 or slight +[1]		Some decrease	Increase	50 to 100 Cal[2]	Increase
6	Man	Manual skill	Deteriorates		Return toward normal	Deteriorates		Return toward normal
7		Packed cell volume	Slight decrease	-2 to 3%	Decrease	Slight increase	2 to 3%	Increase
8		Rectal temperature	Increase	0.5 to 1°C	Return toward normal	Decrease	-1 to 2°C	Return toward normal
9		Skin temperature	Increase	10 to 15°C	Return toward normal	Decrease	-10 to 15°C	Return toward normal
10		Output of urine	Decrease	-200 to 500[3]	Sustain low level	Increase	200 to 500[3]	Sustain high level
11		Blood flow[4]	Decrease		Return toward normal	Increase		Return toward normal
12		Water intake	Increase	400[3]	Sustain high level	Decrease	-400[3]	Sustain low level
13		Food intake	Decrease	to 60% normal		Increase		Sustain high level
14		Heart rate	Decrease	-15/min	Sustain low level	Increase	5 to 10/min	Sustain high level
15	Cattle	Heat production	Decrease		Lasting decrease	Increase	10 Cal/kg/da	Sustain high level
16		Rectal temperature	Increase	-1 to 2°C	Return toward normal	0 or slight ±[5]		Normal level
17		Respiration rate	Increase	20 to 30/min	Sustain high level	Decrease	-10 to 20/min	Sustain low level
18		Food intake	Decrease	-15 to 30%	Return toward normal	Increase		
19	Horse	Rectal temperature	0 or slight ±[5]		Normal level	0 or slight ±[5]		
20		Respiration rate	0 or slight ±[5]		Normal level	0 or slight ±[5]		
21		Heart rate	Increase	8/min				
22	Sheep	Rectal temperature	Increase	1°C				
23		Respiration rate	Increase	100-150/min				
24		Food intake	Decrease		Continued low level			
25		Heart rate	Increase	10/min				
26	Swine	Rectal temperature	Increase 2	2 to 3°C				
27		Respiration rate	Increase	150-200/min				
28		Water intake	Increase		Continued high level			

/1/ No change or slight increase. /2/ Per sq m/hr. /3/ ml/da. /4/ Visceral. /5/ Little or not change.

368. EFFECTS OF HYPOTHERMIA: MAMMALS

Part I: PHYSIOLOGICAL VALUES

A = anesthetized; N = unanesthetized; C = curarized; R = restrained.

	State	Variable	Body Temperature, °C						State	Variable	Body Temperature, °C				
			20	25	30	35	37-39				20	25	30	35	37-39
		Man								**Guinea pig (concluded)**					
1	N	Metabolic rate, Cal/sq m/hr				200	60	33	R	O$_2$ consumption, cu mm/min/g		13	25	35	20.8
2	A	Metabolic rate, Obs/Est		1.58	1.46	2.82	1.00	34	R	Ventilation rate, % of normal		75	125	170	100
3	A	Respiratory volume, L/min		9.6	12.7	19.4	8.7			**Hamster**					
4	A	Respiratory quotient		0.68	0.75	0.77	0.88	35	N	Heart rate, min		190	260	330	380
5	A	Blood HbO$_2$ capacity, mM/L		10.8	9.73	9.2	8.0	36	N	O$_2$ consumption, ml/kg/min		38	50	56	
6	A	Blood HbO$_2$ content, %		93.0	96.7	95.9	97.2	37	N	Respiratory rate, min		120	122	110	90
7	A	Blood total CO$_2$, mM/L		20.0	13.5	18.6	21.5	38		Perfused heart rate, min		47	73	105	155
8	A	Blood pH		7.22	7.31	7.29	7.39			**Rabbit**					
9	A	Blood pCO$_2$, mm Hg		45.2	27.4	42.2	40.7	39	C	O$_2$ consumption, ml/kg/hr			200	300	600
10		Heart rate, sinus-atrium, min[1]	40	70	100	145	157	40	N	Respiratory rate, min	60	20-40[5]			200
11		Ventricle, min[1]	10	20	40			41	N	Heart rate, min	20-40	40-70			200
		Cat						42	A	Plasma volume, ml/kg			28		44
12	N	Heart rate, min	50	117	180	220		43	A	Hematocrit, %			44		41
13	N	Respiratory rate, min	0	47	55	60		44	A	Blood volume, ml/kg			50		73
14		Perfused heart rate, min	53	100	145			45	A	Plasma protein, g/100 ml			6.0		4.9
		Dog						46	A	Thiocyanate space, ml/kg			170		245
15	A	O$_2$ consumption, ml/kg/hr[2]	90	160	270	390	430	47	A	Circulating RBC volume, ml/kg			22		29
16	A	O$_2$ consumption, ml/kg/hr[3]	72	325	480	340	380	48	A	Total circulating plasma protein, g/kg			1.7		2.1
17	A	Heart rate, min	30	70	125	170	155	49	A	Extravascular CNS space, ml/kg			140		200
18	A	Cardiac output, ml/kg/min	18				135	50		Isolated atrium rate, min	30	65	100	145	
19	A	Mean arterial pressure, mm Hg	70	110	120	130	125			**Rat**					
20	A	Blood viscosity[4]	8.78	7.23	5.52	4.42	3.50	51	N	O$_2$ consumption, ml/kg/min	8	17	25		
21	A	Hematocrit, %[4]	60.6	56.9	54.2	54.1	43.9	52	A	Heart rate, min	120	195	270	350	
22	A	Arterial O$_2$ content, vol %[4]	21.0				18.6	53	R	Heart rate, min	110	200	300	420	460
23	A	Coronary vein saturation, %[4]	29.0				28.4	54	R	A-V conduction time, sec	0.08	0.06	0.045	0.04	
24	A	Coronary vein, O$_2$ content, vol %[4]	8.3				4.8	55	A	Respiratory rate, min	18	48	68	66	
25	A	Coronary vein, pO$_2$, mm Hg[4]	8.6				22.2	56	A	Mean arterial pressure, mm Hg	50	130	140	140	
26	A	Coronary artery-vein diff., vol %[4]	12.7				13.8	57	A	Liver, glycogen, %					4.10
27	A	Duration of systole, sec	0.60	0.33	0.20	0.16	0.15	58	A	Blood glucose, mg %					138
28	A	P-R interval, sec	0.22				0.10	59		Perfused heart rate, min	73	120	165	225	
29	A	Q R S duration, sec	0.09				0.05			Tissue slices, dry					
30	A	Q-T interval, sec	1.04				0.25	60		Cerebral cortex, ml/g/hr	2.7	3.8	5.4	7.9	10.2
31		Perfused heart rate, min			53	167		61		Liver, ml/g/hr	2.3	4.0	5.9	8.3	9.8
		Guinea pig						62		Heart ventricle, ml/g/hr	3.3	5.1	7.2	8.3	10.0
32	R	Heart rate, min		125	215	300		63		Skeletal muscle, ml/g/hr	1.2	1.50	1.9	2.4	3.1

/1/ Embryo. /2/ Shivering absent; arterial O$_2$ saturation 90-100%. /3/ Pattern varies in different animals. /4/ Arterial O$_2$ saturation 95% and above. /5/ "Pseudo-hibernating" state.

Part II: LOCAL COLD INJURY

	Mammals	Medium	Exposure Conditions $^{\circ}$C; min	Results		Mammal	Medium	Exposure Conditions $^{\circ}$C; min	Results
1	Man, face	Air	-32.5	Cooling rate 2000 Cal/sq m/hr. Average time to freeze: 102 sec.	9	Rabbit, foot[4]	Liquid[2]	-55; 2	Edema and gangrene; 80% lost all toes.
2	forearm	Copper bar		Highest temp at which freezing occurred: -2.2 to -4.6°C. Supercooling to -20.4°C observed without freezing.	10	(concluded)		-55; 3	Edema and gangrene; 69% lost complete exposed area.
3	Rat, foot[1]	Liquid[2]	-22	Average time to freeze: 38 sec.	11	leg[5]	Alcohol	+5; 30	No edema; slight atrophy.
4			-25	Average time to freeze: 11 sec.	12			0; 30	Little edema; moderate atrophy and temporary paralysis.
5	Rabbit, ear[3]	Liquid[2]	-55; 0.25	Gangrene, loss of 80% exposed area.	13			-5; 30	Edema, atrophy, temporary paralysis.
6			-55; 0.5	Gangrene, loss of 80% exposed area.	14			-10; 30	Edema, atrophy, paralysis, loss of sensation. Muscle necrosis in 50%.
7			-55; 1+	Edema, gangrene, complete loss of exposed area.	15			-12; 30	Edema, marked muscle necrosis.
8	foot[4]	Liquid[2]	-55; 1	Edema, no gangrene; 92% of animals showed no loss of tissue, but moderate induration.	16			-15; 30	Edema, muscle and skin necrosis.
					17			<-15; 30	Usually complete loss of exposed part.

/1/ Pentobarbital anesthesia; no hair removed. /2/ 150 ml 95% alcohol added to one liter 50% ethylene glycol. /3/ Dial anesthesia; no hair removed. /4/ Dial anesthesia; hair removed by close clipping; immersed to tuberosity at base of 5th metatarsal. /5/ Chemical depilation; no anesthesia; covered with layer of wool fat and rubber boot; immersed to knee.

369. EFFECTS OF HYPOTHERMIA: MAN

Part I: EFFECTS OF BRIEF EXPOSURES TO LOW TEMPERATURES

	Variable	Before Exposure, Air 24°C	After Exposure[1], Air -40°C	Before Exposure, Air 23°C	After Exposure[2], Water 6°C
1	Rectal temperature, $^{\circ}$C			37.5	36.5
2	Skin temperature, $^{\circ}$C			29.4[3]	8.3[3]
3	Respiratory volume, L/min			9	38.2
4	Oxygen consumption, L/min			0.34	1.74
5	Respiratory quotient			0.81	1.01
6	Metabolic rate, Cal/hr			97	523
7	Heart rate, per min			75	95
8	Systolic pressure, mm Hg			125	144
9	Diastolic pressure, mm Hg			80	93
10	Leucocytes, per cu mm	7000	8300	6600	7950
11	Neutrophils, per cu mm	3500	5000	3370	5720
12	Lymphocytes, per cu mm	2500	2700	2570	1270
13	Monocytes, per cu mm	520	530	265	795
14	Eosinophils, per cu mm	120	105	265	160
15	Basophils, per cu mm	42	40	130	0
16	Hematocrit, %	47.5	49.5	52	50
17	Hemoglobin, g/100 ml blood	16.3	17		
18	Blood, specific gravity	1.057	1.059		
19	Serum protein, g/100 ml	6.8	7.4	5.9	5.9
20	Ascorbic acid, RBC, mg/100 ml	1.7	2		
21	Ascorbic acid, serum, mg/100 ml	1	1.6		
22	Serum chloride, mEq/L	109	100		
23	Serum sodium, mEq/L	144	140		
24	Serum potassium, mEq/L	6.8	8.2		
25	Urine volume, ml/hr	40	100		

/1/ 4 hours exposure. Clothing: U.S. Army Quatermaster winter issue.
/2/ 32-49 minutes after immersion to neck. /3/ Mean temp of immersed parts.

Part II: SURVIVAL TIME FOR IMMERSION IN COLD WATER

	Probability of Survival		Duration of Immersion and Range of Water Temperature						
			hr	$^{\circ}$F	$^{\circ}$C		hr	$^{\circ}$F	$^{\circ}$C
1	Few, if any survivors	From	1.2	30	-1.1	To	3.0	46	7.8
2	50% survive		0.5	35	1.7		2.3	52	11.1
3	All survive		0.7	50	10.0		2.0	70	21.1

Part III: ESTIMATES OF TIME (HOURS) FOR MAXIMUM SAFE LOSS OF STORED BODY HEAT UNDER COLD CONDITIONS

80 calories is estimated safe loss of stored body heat by an adult. Effectiveness of clothing insulation, measured under static conditions, is reduced by penetrating force of wind.

	Air Movement ft/min	Effective Insulation clo[1]	Air at 0°C Body at:			Air at -40°C Body at:		
			Rest	3 mi/hr	4 mi/hr	Rest	3 mi/hr	4 mi/hr
1	100	1	0.73	1.90	Infant[2]	0.27	0.34	0.44
2	4000	1	0.58	1.10	11.20	0.22	0.27	0.34
3	100	2	1.17	Infant[3]	Infant[2]	0.53	0.90	2.10
4	4000	2	1.15	Infant[3]	Infant[2]	0.48	0.78	1.60
5	100	3	3.80	Infant[3]	Infant[2]	0.85	2.50	Infant[4]
6	4000	3	3.30	Infant[3]	Infant[2]	0.80	2.20	Infant[4]
7	100	4	10.80	Infant[3]	Infant[2]	1.30	57.0	Infant[4]
8	4000	4	8.80	Infant[3]	Infant[2]	1.20	21.0	Infant[4]

/1/ 1 clo = insulation maintaining difference of 0.18°C for flow of 1 Cal/sq m/hr. /2/ Complete protection given by 0.6-1.1 clo. /3/ Complete protection given by 1.2-1.7 clo. /4/ Complete protection given by 2.6-2.7 clo.

Part IV: PREDICTED LOWEST AMBIENT TEMPERATURES FOR PROLONGED THERMAL EQUILIBRIUM AND TOLERABLE EXPOSURE

Values are approximations for young adult males and, except where indicated by an asterisk, are from actual observations at Harvard Fatigue Laboratory or Quartermaster Climatic Research Laboratory. Ambient temperature, $T_a = \dfrac{5.56 T_s - (I \times H)}{5.56}$, where 5.56 is applicable constant for the units of choice; T_s is mean skin temperature, assumed to be 32°C; I is total insulation against heat loss by convection and radiation in clo units (1 clo = insulation maintaining difference of 0.18°C for flow of 1 Cal/sq m/hr); H is total heat available for loss from body by convection and radiation.

	Activity	Environment	Nude Equilibrium[1] $^{\circ}$C	1 hr[2] $^{\circ}$C	Business Suit (1 clo) Equilibrium $^{\circ}$C	1 hr[2] $^{\circ}$C	Arctic Clothing (4 clo) Equilibrium $^{\circ}$C	1 hr[2] $^{\circ}$C
1	Sitting[3]	Calm, shade, sea level	27	17	21	-4	0	-67
2		Wind, 8 km/hr (5 mi/hr); shade, sea level	30	26	24	4	4	-55
3		Wind, 40 kg/hr (25 mi/hr); shade, sea level	31	28	26	12	10	-36
4		Wind, 8 km/hr (5 mi/hr); sunshine[4], sea level	23	19	17	-1	-7	-48
5		Wind, 8 km/hr (5 mi/hr); sunshine, 6 km (20,000 ft) above sea[5]	13*	8*	4*	-19*	-32*	-111*
6	Standing, light work[6]	Wind, 8 km/hr (5 mi/hr); shade, sea level	29	25	20	4	-6	-56
7	Walking, 6 km/hr[7]	Wind, 8 km/hr (5 mi/hr); shade, sea level	25	20	10	-3	-34	-72*
8	Running, 10 km/hr[8]	Wind, 8 km/hr (5 mi/hr); shade, sea level	14	10	-15	-27	-104*	-138*

/1/ In simplest equilibrium state, H is taken as 0.75 M, where M is limit of metabolic rate for sustained activity, expressed as Cal/sq m/hr. (Approximately three-quarters of the heat produced is available for loss by convection and radiation.) /2/ Heat available for loss is 0.75 M+80. (Withdrawal of 80 Cal/sq m from the total body mass can be tolerated with discomfort.) /3/ M=50. /4/ Absorbed solar heat (S) becomes part of H in basic formula. S=130 for nude body, 13.75 for business suit, and 16 for arctic suit. /5/ S increased 70% over values of Fn 4 (greater intensity of solar radiation at altitude). /6/ M=80. /7/ N=180. /8/ M=440.

370. TEMPERATURE RANGES FOR EGG-LARVA DEVELOPMENT: HELMINTHS

Part I: TREMATODES

	Helminth	Stage	Medium	Optimum	Maximum	Minimum	Development
				Temperature, °C			
1	Clonorchis sinensis	Metacercaria	Tyrode's solution, plus rabbit serum.	37			Survived 2 weeks. No development.
2	Diplostomum flexicaudum		Tyrode's solution, plus lenses from eyes of vertebrates.	Room			Survived and active 52 days. No growth.
3	Fasciola hepatica	Egg	Water.	25	37	5-13	Hatched in 14 days at optimum temperature.
4		Larval stages	In snail.	25			Infection to mature cercariae 38-42 days.
5						16-19	Infection to mature cercariae 57 days.
6	Gynaecotyla adunca	Metacercaria	1% sea water.	40			Matured sexually within 80 hours. Survived 8 days.
7	Microphallus opacus		Ringer's solution and normal saline.	37			Eggs in uterus within 12 hours. Survived 4-5 days.
8						12	Developed slowly.
9	Posthodiplostomum minimum		Dilute Tyrode's solution, plus chicken serum, plus yeast extract.	39			Matured but eggs infertile.
10						5-7	Survived 1 month. No growth.
11	Schistosoma japonicum	Egg	Water.	10-30	37	2	Range for hatching.
12	Zygocotyle lunata	Metacercaria	Water and a wide variety of hosts.			-13 to 7	Metacercariae withstood freezing and thawing 15 hours to 10 days.
13				Body			Matured in bird, mammal.

Part II: CESTODES

	Helminth	Stage	Medium	Optimum	Maximum	Minimum	Development
				Temperature, °C			
1	Crepidobothrium lönnbergi	Immature worm	Hottinger's broth (modified).	Room			Increased length. Survived 32 days.
2	Diphyllobothrium latum	Egg	Washed feces and tap water.			-10	Eggs non-viable after 48 hours.
3						15	Eggs remained viable 8 months.
4		Plerocercoid	Nutrient agar, plus hog serum.	37.5			Increased size.
5	Echinococcus granulosus	Scolex	Hydatid fluid, plus horse or ox serum.	37-39	42-44	-4 to 0	Volume of bladder increased. Survived 31 days.
6	Ligula intestinalis					Room	Little activity. Did not mature.
7				40			Matured sexually within 7 days. Survived 7 days.
8	Schistocephalus solidus	Plerocercoid	Peptone broth.	16-19			Active. Normal appearance for 300 days. No eggs.
9				40			Matured sexually within 48-60 hours. Survived 4-6 days.
10	Taenia crassicollis	Blastocyst	Locke's solution, plus chick embryo extract, plus horse serum.	37.5			Developed to invagination of scolex. Survived 35 days.
11	T. saginata	Egg	Sodium hypochlorite or pepsin-pancreatin, physiological saline.	39			Eggs hatched within 4½ hours.
12						2-5	Remained viable for 13½ weeks.

Part III: NEMATODES

	Helminth	Stage	Medium	Optimum	Maximum	Minimum	Development
				Temperature, °C			
1	Ancylostoma caninum	Egg	Bacteriological agar, plus Bacillus coli.	30	40	12	Range of hatching.
2		Larva		30	37	15	Development range.
3	Ascaris lumbricoides var. suis	Egg	Tyrode's solution.	38-40			Hatched.
4		Larva	Distilled water.	Room			Matured 5 weeks.
5	Dirofilaria immitis	Larva	Dextrose dog serum.	37			Little development. Survived 3-8 days.
6						12	Increased size 2½ times. Survived 2 weeks in ice chest.
7	Eustrongylides ignotus		Bacto-proteose-peptone 1.0%; NaCl, 0.85%; glucose, 0.5%.	20			Survived 30 months. Infectivity not established.
8	Haemonchus contortus	Egg Larva	Rabbit kidney, plus liver extract agar, plus ground yeast.	22-27			Eggs hatched 14 days; infective larvae within 26 days.
9	Necator americanus	Egg Larva	"Most favorable conditions."	25-30	37-40	8-10	Range for egg-larvae development.
10	Neoaplectana glaseri	Egg Larva Adult	Veal infusion broth, plus raw liver extract.	21-26	31.8	0	Cycle completed. Survived 44 months.
11	Nippostrongylus muris	Egg	Water.	22-30	35	0-5	Hatched at optimum within 24 hours.
12	Trichinella spiralis	Larva	Simm's solution, plus chicken plasma, plus chick embryo extract.	37			Several molts completed. Few survived 9 days.
13	Trichuris trichiura	Egg	Water.	30	54	-9 to -12	Development range.

371. TEMPERATURES FOR INACTIVATION AND SURVIVAL: ANIMAL VIRUSES

The capacity of animal viruses to infect susceptible cells is destroyed more and more rapidly as the environmental temperature is increased. Thermal inactivation of the infectivity of a virus may be expressed in several ways, as the highest temperature at which there is detectable virus after a selected interval of time, as the longest time at which virus is detectable at a given temperature, or as the number of entropy units. The first two values are dependent on the quantity of virus (number of LD_{50} per ml) in the initial preparation and all three measurements of inactivation depend upon the inherent resistance of the virus particles in the preparation. Substrains composed of heat resistant mutants have been selected for several viruses, and heat resistant and susceptible wild strains are recognized for these and other viruses. Many factors, some well known, modify the thermal inactivation of a virus, e.g., condition of the virus whether wet (inactivation being rapid in a fluid medium) or dry (inactivation of lyophilized virus being slow), the amount of available oxygen (reducing agents increasing stability), the pH of the suspending medium (inactivation being more rapid in basic or acidic preparation than in those in the neutral range), the presence of divalent and monovalent ions (the sodium ion decreasing stability), and admixture with or adsorption to proteins. Most available information has been obtained by using crude preparations in which the contributions of modifying factors are unknown. Tabulation of such data may not, therefore, be meaningful. A figure, therefore, depicting the stability of representative animal viruses in a crude preparation at several temperatures and for varying periods, may be of use to investigators concerned with virus storage, insofar as it suggests the pattern of time-temperature points at which inactivation may occur. On the basis of studies with reasonably pure preparations heat inactivation of virus follows a first order of kinetics.

B = bronchitis; D = distemper; I = influenza A; M = myxomatosis; N = Newcastle disease; P = poliomyelitis; V = vesicular stomatitis.

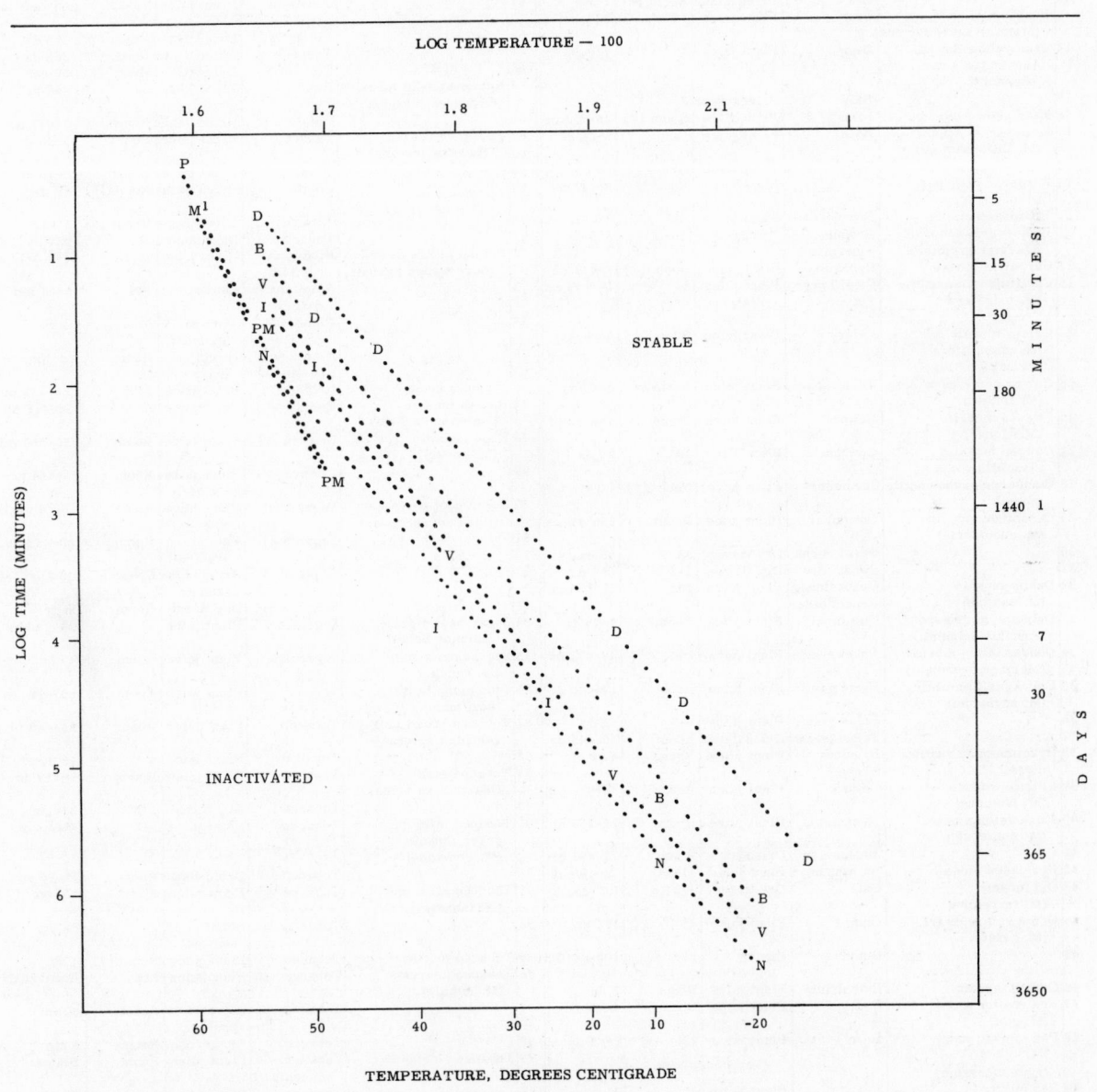

Common names of viruses are taken largely, but not exclusively, from "Common Names of Viruses Used in The Review of Applied Mycology," Rev. Appl. Mycol. 24:513, 1946. Latin names follow the system of virus nomenclature used by Holmes, "The Filterable Viruses," Williams and Wilkens, Baltimore, 1948.

#	Virus	Plant Source of Virus	Medium	Temp °C	Survival Time
1	Alfalfa mosaic (Marmor medicaginis)		Plant juice	Room	8-<9 da
2		Tobacco	Plant juice	4	7 da
3		Tobacco	Buffer	4	28 da
4		Cucumber	Dry tissue	1-2	303 da
5	Alsike clover mosaic (M. fastidiens)	Pea (?)	Plant juice	20	24-<48 hr
6	Aster yellows (Chlorogenus callistephi)	Vector	Insect juice	0	24-<48 hr
7		Vector	Insect juice	25	2-<3 hr
8	Bean mosaic (Marmor phaseoli)	Bean	Plant juice	Room	14-<24 hr
9	Bean pod mottle (M. valvolarum)	Bean	Plant juice	18	62-<93 da
10	Bean red node (Annulus orae var. phaseoli)	Bean	Plant juice	18	24-<48 hr
11		Bean	Plant juice	20-25	30-<90 da
12		Bean	Dried tissue	Room (?)	7 mo
13	Bean southern mosaic (Marmor laesiofaciens)	Bean	Plant juice	18	32 wk
14	Bean yellow dot (M. medicaginis var. phaseoli)	Bean	Plant juice	18	72-<96 hr
15		Bean	Dried tissue	8	1 yr
16	Bean yellow mosaic	Bean	Plant juice	Room (?)	28-<32 da
17	Bean yellow stipple (M. flavopunctum)	Bean	Plant juice	18	5-<6 da
18		Bean	Dried tissue	18	80 da
19	Bergerac ringspot (Annulus bergerac)		Plant juice	Room	9-<12 da
20	Broadbean mottle	Broadbean	Plant juice	15	<20 da
21	Brome-grass mosaic (Marmor graminis)	Bromus inermis	Dried tissue	Room	306 da
22	Carnation mosaic	Carnation	Plant juice	Room (?)	7-<42 da
23	Cauliflower mosaic (M. cruciferarum)	Cauliflower	Plant juice	22	14-<15 da
24	Celery mosaic (M. umbelliferarum)	Celery	Plant juice	Room	6-<7 da
25	Clover red vein mosaic (M. trifolii)	Vicia faba	Plant juice	Room	2-<3 da
26	Cowpea mosaic (M. vignae)	Cowpea	Plant juice	20-25	48-<72 hr
27	Cowpea mosaic (Trinidad)	Cowpea	Plant juice	20	20 da
28	Cucumber green-mottle mosaic	Cucumber	Plant juice	Room (?)	1 yr
29	Cucumber mosaic (M. cucumeris)	Cucumber	Plant juice	Room	2-5 da
30		Sweet corn	Dry tissue	23	58 da
31		Sweet corn	Dry tissue	1-2	669 da
32	Dahlia mosaic (M. dahliae)	Verbesina encelioides	Plant juice	18	28-<35 da
33	Delphinium ringspot (Annulus delphinii)	Cucumber	Plant juice	Room	4-<5 da
34	Dodder latent mosaic (Marmor secretum)	Pokeweed	Plant juice	24	48-<72 hr
35	False garlic mosaic (M. angustum)	False garlic	Plant juice	Room	17-<20 da
36		False garlic	Plant juice	4-5	52 da
37		False garlic	Dried tissue	Room	40-<43 da
38	Hyacinth bean enation mosaic	Hyacinth bean	Plant juice	Room	6 yr
39	Lettuce mosaic (M. lactucae)	Lettuce	Plant juice	Room	48-<72 hr
40	Muskmelon mosaic (M. melonis)	Muskmelon	Plant juice	Room	74-250 hr
41		Muskmelon	Dried juice	Room	72-298 hr
42	Narcissus mosaic	Narcissus	Plant juice	21-24	72-<96 hr
43	Oat mosaic (M. terrestre)	Oat	Dry tissue	1-2	177 da
44	Onion yellow dwarf (M. cepae)	Onion	Plant juice	29	112 hr
45		Onion	Drying leaves	29	100-<110 hr
46	Orchid mosaic	Cymbidium	Plant juice	Room	7 da
47	Pea enation mosaic (M. pisi)	Pea	Plant juice	Room	4-<5 da
48	Pea mosaic virus (M. leguminosarum)	Bean	Plant juice	22	2-<3 da
49	Pea mottle (M. efficiens)	Pea	Plant juice	25	31 da
50	Pea, mottle (concluded)	Pea	Dried tissue	25	31 da
51	Pea streak, American	Pea	Plant juice	20	24-<48 hr
52	Pea streak, New Zealand (Marmoriners)	Pea	Plant juice	Room (?)	41 da
53	Pea streak, Wisconsin	Pea	Plant juice	22	16-<32 da
54		Pea	Plant tissue	<0	10-40 da
55	Pea stunt	Pea	Plant juice	22	24-<48 hr
56	Pea wilt (M. repens)	Pea	Plant juice	25	31 da
57		Pea	Dried tissue	25	31 da
58	Potato aucuba mosaic (M. aucuba)	Potato	Plant juice	15	3-<4 da
59	Potato mild mosaic (M. solani)	Potato	Plant juice	Room	2-4 hr
60	Potato mottle (Annulus dubius)	Potato	Plant juice	Room	4-5 mo
61		Nicotiana rustica	Plant juice	16-20	60-360 da
62		Potato	Dried tissue	Room (?)	363 da
63		Tobacco	Dried tissue	Room (?)	386 da
64		Tomato	Dried tissue	Room (?)	50 da
65	Potato spindle tuber (Acrogenus solani)	Potato	Plant juice	10	<48 hr
66		Potato	Dried tissue	Room	7-<17 da
67	Potato vein banding (Marmor upsilon)	Tobacco	Plant juice	Room (?)	5-<6 da
68		Tobacco	Plant juice	20-22	6-18 da
69		Potato	Dried tissue	Room (?)	50 da
70		Tomato	Dried tissue	Room (?)	17 da
71		Tobacco	Dry tissue	1-2	420 da
72	Potato yellow dwarf (Aureogenus vastans)	Nicotiana rustica	Plant juice	25	2-1/2-12 hr
73		Nicotiana rustica	Leaves	-14	1-<7 mo
74		Nicotiana rustica	Partly purified	0	4 wk
75		Nicotiana rustica	Dried leaves	Room	<1 wk
76	Primula mosaic	Primula	Plant juice	22	24-<48 hr
77	Radish mosaic (Marmor raphani)	Radish	Plant juice	22	14-<16 da
78	Rose mosaic (M. rosae)	Cowpea	Plant juice	Room	30-<60 min
79		Cowpea	Plant juice + buffer	Room	6-<24 hr
80	Sugar beet curly top (Ruga verrucosans)	Sugar beet	Plant juice	Room	7-14 da
81		Sugar beet	Ext. alc. precip.	Room	28-<35 da
82		Sugar beet	Dried phloem exudate	Room	10 mo
83		Sugar beet	Dry tissue	Room	8 yr
84	Sugar beet mosaic (Marmor betae)	Sugar beet	Plant juice	21	24-<48 hr
85	Sugarcane mosaic (M. sacchari)	Sugarcane	Plant juice	Room	<7 hr
86	Sunn hemp mosaic, southern		Plant juice	Room (?)	557 da
87	Tobacco broad ringspot (Annulus apterus)	Tobacco	Plant juice	Room	42-<48 hr
88		Tobacco	Plant juice	4	16 da
89	Tobacco etch (Marmor erodens)	Tobacco	Plant juice	Room	5-<13 da
90		Tobacco	Dry tissue	1-2	301 da
91	Tobacco mild dark-green mosaic (M. constans)	Tobacco	Plant juice	5±2	Many yr
92		Tobacco	Dried tissue	Room	Many yr
93	Tobacco mosaic (M. tabaci)	Tobacco	Plant juice	Room	15 mo
94		Tobacco	Dried leaves		52 yr
95	Tobacco mottle	Tobacco	Plant juice	Room (?)	2 da
96	Tobacco necrosis (M. lethale)	Tobacco	Plant juice	21±	About 20 da
97		Tobacco	Dry alc. precip.	Room	6 mo
98		Tobacco	Ab. alcohol	Room	6 mo
99	Tobacco ringspot (Annulus tabaci)	Various suscepts	Plant juice	Room	1-6 da
100		Tobacco	Dry tissue	1-2	393 da

Common names of viruses are taken largely, but not exclusively, from "Common Names of Viruses Used in The Review of Applied Mycology," Rev. Appl. Mycol. 24:513, 1946. Latin names follow the system of virus nomenclature used by Holmes,"The Filterable Viruses," Williams and Wilkens, Baltimore, 1948.

	Virus	Plant Source of Virus	Conditions of Survival		Survival Time		Virus	Plant Source of Virus	Conditions of Survival		Survival Time
			Medium	Temp ^{o}C					Medium	Temp ^{o}C	
101	Tobacco ringspot (Annulus tabaci var. cyamopsidis)	Guar	Plant tissue	5	2-<4 mo	106	Tomato spotted wilt (Lethum australiense)	Tobacco	Plant juice	Room	3-1/2-<4 hr
102	Tobacco streak (A. orae)	Tobacco	Plant juice	22	24-<36 da	107	Tulip breaking (Marmor tulipae)	Lily	Plant tissue	Room (?)	2-6 da
103	Tomato aspermy	Tomato	Plant juice	20.5-21.5	24-<48 hr	108	Turnip mosaic virus (M. brassicae)		Plant juice	20	3-8 da
104	Tomato black ring	Tomato	Plant juice	Room	7 da	109	Vigna catjang mosaic	Vigna	Plant juice	24	9-<15 da
105	Tomato bushy stunt (Marmor dodecahedron)		Plant juice	Room	28-<33 hr	110	Wheat mosaic (M. tritici)	Wheat	Dry tissue	1-2	290 da
						111	Wheat streak (M. virgatum)	Wheat	Dried tissue	Room	34-40 da

373. EFFECT OF TEMPERATURE ON GROWTH AND SURVIVAL: BACTERIA, RICKETTSIAE, AND COXIELLA

Values are approximate, representing data obtained under widely varying conditions by many investigators. Data may differ from species to species within the same genus, and even with various cultures of the same species. Temperatures given under thermal death time are assumed to be moist heat, but in some cases this has not been specified in the literature source. Values in parentheses are ranges, probably estimate "c" of the 95% range (cf Introduction).

	Organism	Temperature for Growth[1] ^{o}C	Thermal Death			Organism	Temperature for Growth[1] ^{o}C	Thermal Death	
			^{o}C	min				^{o}C	min
1	Acetobacter roseum	30-35(10-41)	50	5	48	Methanococcus mazei	30-37		
2	Achromobacter ichthyodermis	25(-2 to 30)			49	Micrococcus luteus	25		
3	Actinobacillus lignieresi	37	60	15	50	M. pyogenes var. albus	37	62	10
4	Actinomyces bovis	37	60	10	51	M. pyogenes var. aureus	37(15-40)	60	20
5	A. thermophilus	50(28-65)			52	Micromonospora chalcea	30-35	70	5
6	Aerobacter aerogenes	30(to 42-44)	60	30	53	Miyagawanella lymphogranulomatis	35-37	56	10
7	Agrobacterium tumefaciens	25-28(0-37)			54	Mycobacterium avium	40(30-44)		
8	Alkaligenes faecalis	37			55	M. phlei	37(20-58)	60[3]	60[4]
9	Azobacter chroococcum	25-28			56	M. tuberculosis	37(30-42)	65	15
10	Azotomonas indicum	30			57	Mycoplana dimorpha	30		
11	Bacillus anthracis	35(to 43)	100[2]	10[2]	58	Neisseria gonorrhoeae	37(25-40)	55	<5
12	B. subtilis	30-37(15-55)	100[2]	14	59	N. meningitidis	37(25-42)	50	<5
13	B. thermodiastaticus	65(50-75)[3]			60	Nitrobacter winogradskyi	25-28	50	5
14	Bacteroides fragilis	37			61	Nitrosococcus nitrosus	20-25		
15	Bacterium erythrogenes	28-35			62	Nitrosomonas monocella	28		
16	B. phosphoreum	10(5-25)			63	Nocardia asteroides	37	60	60
17	Bartonella bacilliformis	28			64	Noguchia granulosis	30(15-37)	57	10
18	Brucella spp	37(20-40)	60	10	65	Pasteurella multocida	37	60	10
19	Cellfacicula viridis	20			66	P. pestis	25-30(0-45)	55	5
20	Cellulomonas biazotea	20			67	P. tularensis	37(24-39)	56	10
21	Cellvibrio ochraceus	20			68	Pediococcus cerevisiae	30		
22	Chromobacterium violaceum	25-30			69	Propionibacterium freudenreichii	30		
23	Clostridium botulinum	20-35(18-55)	120[2]	5[2]	70	Proteus vulgaris	37(10-43)	55	60
24	C. perfringens	38	100[2]	20[2]	71	Protaminobacter alboflavum	30		
25	C. tetani	37-38(14-50)	105[2]	10[2]	72	Pseudomonas aeruginosa	37(0-42)	62	10
26	Coliforms (various)		60-63	30	73	Rhizobium leguminosarum	25		
27	Corynebacterium diphtheriae	34-36(15-40)	54	10	74	Rickettsia prowazekii	32-35	56	30
28	Coxiella burnetii	37	62	30	75	Rhodopseudomonas palustris	37		
29	Cytophaga hutchinsonii	28-30			76	Rhodospirillum rubrum	30-37		
30	Desulfovibrio desulfuricans	25-30(to 40)			77	Saccharobacterium ovale	34-35(20-37)	54	10
31	Diplococcus pneumoniae	37(18-42)	56	5-7	78	Salmonella typhimurium	37(4-46)	55	24
32	Erwinia carotovora	25-30(4-39)			79	S. typhosa	37(4-46)	60	2
33	Erysipelothrix rhusiopathiae	37(15-44)	55	10	80	Sarcina ventriculi	30(10-45)	65	10
34	Escherichia coli	30-37(10-45)	60	10	81	Serratia marcescens	25-30(to <37)	55	60
35	Flavobacterium aquatile	25			82	Shigella dysenteriae	37(10-40)	60	10
36	Gaffkya tetragena	37(15-39)			83	S. equuli	37	60	15
37	Hemophilus influenzae	37(26-43)	50-55	30	84	Spirochaeta daxensis	42-52	60	30
38	H. pertussis	37	56	60	85	S. plicatilis	20-25		
39	H. suis	37	60	20	86	Sporocytophaga mycococcoides	28-30		
40	Hydrogenomonas pantotropha	28-30			87	Streptococcus pyogenes	37(15-40)	60	15
41	Klebsiella pneumoniae	37(12-43)	55	30	88	Streptomyces thermophilus	40-45(20-<53)	72-74	10
42	Lactobacillus casei	30(10-40)			89	S. griseus	37		
43	L. thermophilus	50-63(30-65)	71	30	90	Thiobacillus thiooxidans	28-30		
44	Leptospira icterohemorrhagiae	25-30(25-37)	56	20	91	Treponema pallidum	37[5]	40	60-180
45	Listeria monocytogenes	37	59	10	92	Veillonella parvula	37	55	60
46	Malleomyces mallei	37(15-43)	55	10	93	Vibrio comma	37(14-42)	55-60	2
47	Methanobacterium omelianskii	37-40(to 48)			94	Xanthomonas campestris	28-30(5-38)		

/1/ In this column optimal values are given first, followed in parentheses by a range in which growth occurs but diminishes rapidly as either extreme is approached. /2/ Applies to spores and is an experimental minimum. It is customary to rely only on autoclaving at 121°C for at least 20 minutes to kill these and related spores. /3/ No growth at 50° but growth at 75°. /4/ Survives. /5/ Has never been cultivated in artificial medium.

	Organism	Thermal Death Point °C	Survival Duration, Various Conditions (W = overwinters)[1]		Organism	Thermal Death Point °C	Survival Duration, Various Conditions (W = overwinters)[1]
1	Agrobacterium tumefaciens	51	24 mo in soil debris[2], hosts[3]	21	Pseudomonas pisi	50	W in or on seeds
2	Corynebacterium agropyri	50	12 mo in dried exudate	22	P. savastanoi	43-46	W in insect body, hosts[3]
3	C. fascians	50-57	W in or on seeds	23	P. solanacearum	52	>2 yr in soil
4	C. flaccumfaciens	57.5-60	2.5 yr in seed	24	P. syringae	51	W in or on seeds[5], hosts[3]
5	C. insidiosum	51-52	W in soil debris, hosts[3]	25	P. tabaci	49-51	W in soil debris
6	C. Michiganense	53	W in or on seeds, soil	26	P. viridiflava	48-50	W in or on seeds
7	C. sepedonicum		W in soil[4, 5, 6]	27	Xanthomonas begoniae	49-50	W in hosts[3]
8	Erwinia amylovora	45.1-49.5	W[7] in soil, insect body, hosts[3]	28	X. campestris	51	W in or on seeds[3,5]
9	E. atroseptica	48-51	W in soil, insect body[4]	29	X. carotae	49	W in or on seeds[3,5]
10	E. carotovora	48-51	W in soil, insect body[4]	30	X. citri		W in hosts[3]
11	E. tracheiphila	43	W in insect body	31	X. hyacinthi	47.5-49	W in tubers, corms
12	Pseudomonas caryophylli		W in soil	32	X. juglandis	53-55	W in hosts[3]
13	P. coronafaciens	48	W in or on seeds	33	X. malvacearum	50-51	W in or on seed
14	P. gladioli	47	W in tubers, corms	34	X. papavericola	52	W in soil debris, hosts[3]
15	P. glycinea	48-49	W in or on seeds	35	X. phaseoli	48-50	W in or on seeds, soil[6]
16	P. lachrymans	49-50	24 mo in or on seeds	36	X. pruni	51-52	W in hosts[3]
17	P. maculicola	46	W in or on seeds	37	X. rubrilineans	51-52	W in hosts[3, 4]
18	P. marginata	53	W in tubers, corms	38	X. stewartii	53	W in insect body, seeds
19	P. mori	51.5	W in hosts[3]	39	X. translucens hordei	50	W in or on seeds
20	P. phaseolicola		W in or on seeds	40	X. vesicatoria	56	W in seeds, soil[8]

/1/ Organism in specified condition survives the winter. /2/ W on plant roots. /3/ In perennial or biennial hosts. /4/ W also in tubers, corms, bulbs, etc. /5/ W also in soil debris. /6/ W also in dried exudate. /7/ In beeswax 1.8 mo. /8/ Associated with wheat roots.

375. EFFECTS OF TEMPERATURE ON GROWTH AND SURVIVAL: FUNGI

Part I: PLANT PATHOGENS

	Species	Temp for Growth[1] °C	Method of Overwintering
		Phycomycetes	
1	Albugo candida	10(1-20)S	Soil; crucifers
2	Peronospora effusa	8-10(3-30)S	Soil; spinach
3	P. parasitica	8-12(to 29)S	
4	P. tabacina	15-23(1-29)S	Plant debris
5	Physoderma zeae-maydis	28-29(23-30)S	Soil; plant debris
6	Phytophthora infestans	20(7-30)C	Soil; tubers
7	Plasmodiophora brassicae	25-27(10-30)S	Soil
8	Plasmopara vitacola	25-28(8-35)S	Buds; leaves
9	Pseudoperonospora cubensis	20	
10	Phythium debaryanum	27-30(5-35)C	Soil
11	Rhizopus nigricans	25-30(7-35)C	Soil
12	Spongospora subterranea	20-23(12-35)	Soil
		Ascomycetes	
13	Ceratostomella ulmi	22-27(5-40)C	
14	Claviceps purpurea	22-26C	Soil; among seeds
15	Dibotryon morbosum	37(?)	Twig knots
16	Diplocarpon rosae	16-21	Plant debris
17	Endothia parasitica	25-30(4-40)C	Cankers
18	Erysiphe graminis	15-20(5-29)S	Plant debris
19	Gibberella zeae	20-30(3-37)C	Plant debris; soil
20	Glomerella gossypii	25(18-33)	Soil; seed coat
21	Monilinia fructicola	24(0-32)C	Mummy
22	Physalospora malorum	20(10-30)	Cankers; plant debris
23	Podosphaera leucotricha	19-20(10-28)S	Leaf and flower buds
24	Sphaerotheca humuli	37(?)	Plant debris
25	Taphrina deformans	20(10-30)C	Plant debris; bark
26	Venturia inaequalis	20(4-32)C	Plant debris
		Basidiomycetes	
27	Armillaria mellea	25(15-30)C	Soil
28	Cronartium ribicola	12-18(5-25)S	Pine; Ribes
29	Fomes igniarius	30-32(to 42)C	Wood
30	Gymnosporangium juniperi-virginianae	20-25(6-32)S	Redcedar
31	Puccinia antirrhini	10(5-30)S	Plant debris
32	P. coronata	17-22(2-35)S	Plant debris
33	P. graminis	12-20(2-35)S	Wheat
34	P. triticina	16-20(2-31)S	Wheat
35	Tilletia caries	15-20(4-29)S	Soil; seed coat
36		(1-25)C	Soil; seed coat
37	Uromyces cariophyllinus	14(4-29)S	Plant debris
38	Ustilago avenae	20-28(4-35)S	Soil; within seed
39		18-26(6-34)C	Soil; within seed
40	U. tritici	20-25(5-35)S	Within seed
41		20-25(8-34)C	Within seed
42	U. zeae	25-30(8-40)S	Soil; plant debris
		Fungi imperfecti	
43	Alternaria solani	26-28(1.5-45)C	Soil; plant debris
44	Botrytis cinerea	25-25(0-30)C	Apple fruit
45	Cercospora beticola	25-30(6-34)C	Plant debris
46	Cladosporium carpophilum	19-28(2-33)C	Cankers
	(continued on next page)		

/1/ Desirable temperature for growth, with range (where known) in parentheses, followed by a symbol for the type of growth: C = in culture; S = spore germination.

Part II: ANIMAL PATHOGENS AND RELATED SAPROPHYTES

Data are for artificial culture, under humidity conditions favoring growth.

	Species	Temp for Growth[1] °C	Thermal Death °C	min
1	Absidia corymbifera	28-40(20-46)[37]		
2	Achorion castellani	[20]		
3	Actinobacillus lignieresi	37(min 20)[37]	62	10
4	Allescheria boydii	25-30(15-45)[30]	56	80
5	Aspergillus bronchialis	[34]		
6	A. fumigatus	25-45(max >50)[40]		
7	A. nidulans	25-37[36-38]		
8	A. niger	25-37(max <60)[37]		
9	Blastomyces brasiliensis	25-30[25-30]	60	60
10	Yeast phase	37	60	60
11	B. dermatitidis	25-33(8-40)[31]	56	60
12	Yeast phase	35-37[35]	56	60
13	Candida albicans	24-40(<20->40)[30-37]	60	10
14	C. guilliermondi	25-37[30-37]		
15	C. krusei	25-37[30-37]		
16	C. tropicalis	25-37[30-37]	60	10
17	Castellania hashimotoi	[22-25]		
18	Cephalosporium granulomatis	Room to 37	53	5
19	C. recifei	Room [25-30]		
20	Cladosporium gougerotii	25-37		
21	C. sphaerospermum	Room (min <18)		
22	C. trichoides	Room to 30[30]		
23	C. mansoni	25-35[30-32]		
24	Coccidioides immitis	25-37(max <42)[30-37]	60	4
25	Corynebacterium acnes	37(30-<45)[37]	60	10
26	C. tenuis	30-37[about 37]		
27	Cryptococcus neoformans	25-37 (<17-40)[25-30]	50	10
28	Debaryomyces kloeckeri	30-35(3-37)		
29	D. laedegaardi (D. hildegaardi)	25(5-37)		
30	Endomyces pulmonalis	33-37(>5-<41)		
31	Epidermophyton floccosum	25-30(min <18)[27±]	50	10
32	Geotrichum candidum	25-37	56	60
33	G. issavi	22-25		
34	Hansenula anomala	(0.5-38)		
35	Histoplasma capsulatum	22-30(10-40)[25-30]	55	15
36	Yeast phase	34-37(<34->43)[37±]	55	30
37	H. farciminosum	25-37(15-40)[37]		
38	Hormodendrum compactum	25-37[37]	100	15
39	H. dermatitidis	Room to 30 (max <43)[20-30]		
40	H. pedrosoi	25-37[37]	100	15
41	Madurella grisea	Room to 37[30]		
42	Microsporum audouini	25-30(max 38)[25-30]	60	60
43	M. canis	25-32(max 40)[30-32]	70	10
44	M. gypseum	25-30(max 38)[25-30]	60	60
45	Nocardia asteroides	25-37[37]	70	5
46	N. brasiliensis	Room to 37	60	60
47	N. caprae	Room to 37[33-37]		
48	N. farcinica	30-40(min >24)[37]	70	10
49	N. intracellularis	37[37.5]	60	10
	(continued on next page)			

/1/ Desirable temperature for growth, with range (where known) in parentheses, and optimum growth temperature in brackets.

Part I: PLANT PATHOGENS (Concluded)

	Species	Temp for Growth[1] °C	Method of Overwintering
	Fungi imperfecti (concluded)		
47	Colletotrichum lagenarium	22-24(6-35)C	Soil
48	C. lindemuthianum	20-23(4-35)C	Within seed
49	Diplodia zeae	30(10-35)C	Soil; within seed
50	Fusarium cubense var. oxysporium	20-30(5-37.5)C	Soil
51	F. lycopersici	24-30(5-38)C	Soil
52	F. vasinfectum	28-30(10-38)C	Soil
53	Helminthosporium gramineum	15-20 C	Seed coat
54	Phomopsis citri	24-28(9-34)C	Plant debris
55	Phyllosticta solitaria	25-30(5-35)C	Soil debris
56	Phymatotrichum omnivorum	29(18-36)C	Soil; roots
57	Septoria apii-graveolentis	22-24(14-25)C	Plant debris; seed coat
58	Thielaviopsis basicola	17-33	Soil
59	Verticillium albo-atrum	21-26(8-31)C	Soil
	Mycelia sterilia		
60	Rhizoctonia solani	31(8-40)C	Soil
61	Sclerotium cepivorum	20-24(5-29)C	Soil

Part II: ANIMAL PATHOGENS AND RELATED SAPROPHYTES (Concluded)

	Species	Temp for Growth[1] °C	Thermal Death °C	min
50	N. madurae	Room to 37(<20-40)[37]	60	5
51	N. paraguayensis	Room to 37	60	60
52	Phialophora jeanselmei	Room to 37[30]		
53	P. verrucosa	25-37[37]	100	15
54	Pityrosporum ovale	30-37(min <22)[37]	60	30
55	Rhizopus arrhizus	(6-43±)[32.5-35.5]		
56	R. equinus	(min >5)[37-39]	100	20
57	R. oryzae	(7.5-45.5)[31-34]		
58	Schizophyllum commune	(<16->40)[30±]		
59	Scopulariopsis brevicaulis	Room to (<6-37)[20-25]		
60	Sporotrichum schenckii	Room to 37[30-37]	59	5
61	Trichophyton concentricum	25-37[37±]		
62	T. ferrugineum	25	60	10
63	T. megnini	25	55	10
64	T. mentagrophytes	25-30(8-40)[30]	60-70	10
65	T. schoenleini	25-37(min <15)[33]	60	10
66	T. tonsurans	25-37[30]		
67	T. violaceum	25-37[25-30]		
68	Trichosporon beigelii	Room to 37 (max <43)[30-37]		

/1/ Desirable temperature for growth, with range (where known) in parentheses, followed by a symbol for the type of growth: C = in culture; S = spore germination.

/1/ Desirable temperature for growth, with range (where known) in parentheses, and optimum growth temperature in brackets.

376. EFFECTS OF TEMPERATURE: PLANT PATHOGENIC FUNGI

Values not in parentheses are "optimum" values in °C; values in parentheses are minimum-maximum values in °C. The following symbols, in brackets, identify, where known, the part or stage studied: ae = aeciospores; as = ascospores; b = basidiospores; c = conidia; m = mycelium; o = oospores; p = pycnidia, pycnospores; s = spores (not specified); sa = sporangia; sc = sclerotia; t = teliospores; u = uredospores; z = zoospores.

	Fungus	Germination	Development in Culture	Fructification and/or Sporulation	Infection	Disease Development	Infection and Disease Development	Thermal Death Point[1]
1	Actinomyces scabies[2]	16-37	25-32(8-40)			14-22(11-31)		
2	Albugo candida[2]	14-20(0-25)[c]	10-13(0-25)					
3	Alternaria brassicae	33-35(1-46)	25-27(2-36)				25-31(2-36)	55
4	A. citri[2]		25				25-30	
5	A. solani[2]	26-28(1-45)	26-28(1-45)				24-25	
6	Aphanomyces euteiches		15-34(9-37)	(9-35)			15-30(10-30)	
7	Armillaria mellea[2]		25(15-30)	18-22				65[m]
8	Ascochyta pisi	20(10-35)	20-28(0-35)					
9	Aspergillus niger[2]		30-39(7-46)					99[3]; 62[4][s]
10	Basisporium gallarum[2]	20-35(9-35)	25-35(10-40)					
11	Botryosphaeria ribis[2]		28-30(10-35)			18-28(13-33)		
12	Botrytis allii[2]	19-27(3-27)	20-25(3-33)	4-25(4-25+)			15-20(2-40)	
13	B. cinerea[5]	17-25(1-35)	15-25(0-35)	16-30(4-37)			7-25(0-35)	55
14	Calonectria graminicola[2]		20-22(0-33)		0-10(to 20)			
15	Cephalothecium rosae[2]	19-33(9-35)	20-25(5-35)			25(0 to)		
16	Ceratostomella fimbriata		23-29(9-36)				23-27(9-36)	
17	C. ips		27-29(6-35)	27-31(6-35)				52
18	C. ulmi		19-28(5-40)				51-57[s]	
19	Cercospora beticola	26-33(2-35)	24-30(5-40)	24-32(17-34)	21-32			95[3]; 46[4]
20	Cercosporella herpotrichoides		20-23(-5 to 30)			5-9		
21	Choanephoridea cucurbitae	15-20	30(9-35)	20(10-25)				
22	Cladosporium carpophilum		19-28(2-33)					
23	C. cucumerinum		20-21(0-32)		20(to 35)			
24	C. fulvum[2]	18-26(0-33)	16-26(0-34)	20-26(2-35)			21-25(7-29)	70[3]
25	C. malorum		25			20-25		
26	Claviceps purpurea	18-22[sc]	22-30	17-21				
27	Coccomyces hiemalis		20-24(4-28)	12-16(4-28)	8-28			
28	Colletotrichum circinans	20-26(4-32)	26(2-32)				20-30	
29	C. lagenarium	22-32(4 to)	22-23(6-35)		20-28			
30	C. lindemuthianum[2]	20-32(0-42)	18-30(0-42)	12-15(4-28)			25(6-33)	
31	Coniothyrium wernsdorffiae	16-17(0-27)	20-21(-1 to 26)				10-16(to 27)	
32	Corticium vagum[5]	20-32(8-36)[sc]	20-33(0-44)	18-21			9-30(1-36)	60[sc]
33	Cronartium ribicola	12(5-19)[ae]; 10-18(0-21)[b]; 12-18(0-21)[t]; 14(8-25)[u]						
34	Dasyscypha willkommii	15-27(<13-31)	18-23					
35	Deuterophoma tracheiphila	18-20(15 to)	(10-28)	12-28[c]; 12-24[p]			21-32(15 to)	
36	Diplodia zeae	30[p]	24-32(10-36)	25-30[p]				
37	Endothia parasitica[2]	21[as]; 15-32[p]	18-30(4-40)	16-27(2-38)[as]; 30[p]				
38	Erysiphe graminis	18[as]; 12-21(<5-29)[c]	10(0-25)		20			
39	E. polygoni[5]			15-24(<8-30)[c]	15-25 or 24-32[3][p]			65[m]
40	Fomes applanatus[2]		27-30(15-35)					
41	Fusarium conglutinans		20-30(5-35)				16-28(12-34)	
42	F. lini[2]	12-30(7-35)	18-30(5-37)				15-21(12-38)	
43	F. lycopersici[2]		24-30(5-38)				27-29(21-33)	
44	F. oxysporum[5]		15-32(4-40)				14-32(>5 to >38)	57

/1/ Usually at 10 min exposure. /2/ Fungus exhibits variability among different strains or in different hosts. /3/ Dry state. /4/ Wet state.
/5/ Fungus exhibits extreme variability among different strains or in different hosts.

376. EFFECTS OF TEMPERATURE: PLANT PATHOGENIC FUNGI (Continued)

Values not in parentheses are "optimum" values in $^\circ$C; values in parentheses are minimum-maximum values in $^\circ$C. The following symbols, in brackets, identify, where known, the part or stage studied: ae = aeciospores; as = ascospores; b = basidiospores; c = conidia; m = mycelium; o = oospores; p = pycnidia, pycnospores; s = spores (not specified); sa = sporangia; sc = sclerotia; t = teliospores; u = uredospores; z = zoospores.

	Fungus	Germination	Development in Culture	Fructification and/or Sporulation	Infection	Disease Development	Infection and Disease Development	Thermal Death Point[1]
45	Fusarium solani martii[2]	13-25(5-37)	18-34(5-39)			21-34		
46	F. vasinfectum[2]		25-35(5-40)	27-38			17-33(10-35)	
47	Gibberella zeae[5]	30(5-32)[as]; 24-28(4-32)[c]	20-30(3-37)	20-27(to 37[as]; 20-28(4-34)[c]			24-28(8-39)[6]	>65[as]
48	Gloeosporium venetum	22-26(11-32)	20-26(11-31)					
49	Glomerella gossypii		25-29(10-38)			<24		>95[3]; 51[4][c]
50	G. rufomaculans	19-36(3-26)	33-38(9-38)			38		
51	Guignardia bidwellii		20-30	20-25(9-35)[p]				>60[s]
52	Gymnosporangium juniperi-virginianae[2]	24(6-32)[ae]; 16(8-28)[b]; 22-25(4-32)[t]					16-19(10 to)	
53	Helminthosporium turcicum		28-30(7-35)	20-28(11-33)		<30		
54	Hypochnus centrifugus[2]		28-35(8-41)	27-35			20-35(2 to)	
55	Lentinus lepideus		27-28(<9-40)			<24		>105[3]; >60[4][m]
56	Macrophomina phaseoli[2]		31(8-42)				20-40(12 to)	55
57	Merulius lacrymans[2]	22-25	20-26(4-32)					50-55[m]
58	Monilinia fructicola		24-27(0-32)					
59	Mycogone perniciosa		21-28(8-32)				15-21	
60	Mycosphaerella rubi	23(2-32)[as]; 23(2-32)[p]	20-23(2-32)					>42
61	Nectria cinnabarina	17-20(5-30)[as]; 20-25(>0-35)[c]	21(3-33)					
62	Neofabraea malicorticis	15-25(0-30)	20(0 to <30)			20(0 to)		
63	Nigrospora oryzae	30(10-47)	30(10-35)					
64	Ophiobolus graminis[2]		19-30(3-35)				12-24(9-32)	>67[3], 56[4][s]
65	O. miyabeanus[2]	25[as]; 25-30(2-41)[c]	24-32(5-40)	25-28[as]; 20-30(5-38)[c]			25-30(16-40)	
66	O. sativus[2]	22-32(6-39)[c]	25-33(1-37)	15-28(10-30)[c]			22-30(8-35)	54
67	Penicillium expansum		25-27(0-30)			25(0 to)		
68	Peronoplasmopara cubensis[2]	15-22(1-32)[c]		15-22(7-30)			16-22(10-30)	
69	P. humuli	17-20[c]; 20-22[o]		15-20(0-28)[c]; 17-20[z]	18-22(4-30)			
70	Peronospora parasitica	8-12(to <29)[c]	8-12(to 29)		3-8			
71	P. tabacina	15-23(1-29)	to 20	21-22(to 26)	11-25(5-30)			
72	Phomopsis citri	20-27(16-33)	24-38(4 to <40)	20(10 to <28)	20-25(15-30)			
73	Phyllosticta solitaria	25-30(5-39)	25-30(5-35)	19-30				
74	Phymatotrichum omnivorum		30	21-32(18-36)				46-51
75	Physoderma zeae-maydis	28-29(23-30)						>80
76	Phytophthora cactorum	25-27[c]	20-36(5-38)				20-25(9-30)	
77	P. cinnamoni[2]		20-30(5-33)	21-29(to 35)				
78	P. citrophthora[2]	28-30; 15-18	25-38(5-37)		20-21			
79	P. infestans[5]	4-20(1-30)	15-25(2-35)	16-23			10-13[7]	45[m]; 25[s]
80	P. parasitica[5]	25-27	20-35(5-44)				21-25	
81	Piricularia oryzae	25-30(16-35)[c]	25-30(8-40)	18-30(10-35)			24-28(to 34)	51[c]; 52-55[m]
82	Plasmodiophora brassicae	25-30(6-27)					25(9-30)	
83	Plasmopara viticola[2]	25-35(5-35)[8][c]; 23-35(11-33)[o]		18-22(8-30)			18-25(9 to <30)	
84	Polystictus versicolor[2]		25-32[9]			27-32		>70[m]
85	Pseudopeziza ribis	12[as]; 20[c]	20(<4 to 32)	(1-32)[as]; 8-24(<4 to <32)[c]				
86	Puccinia coronata[2]	12-22(0-35)				12-17(7-30)		
87	P. glumarum[2]	10-20(2-29)[u]		10-16(0-20)[u]			10-15	
88	P. graminis[5]	5-20(<5 to >30)[ae]; 15-20[b]; 12-20(5-30)[t]; 5-25(2-35)[u]		12-18[p]			12-21(to 26); 20-25(10-30)[u]	
89	P. helianthi	18(6-28)[t]; 18(<6 to >28)[u]					(10 to)	
90	P. sorghi	15-18(4-32)[u]					18-20(<8 to 32)[u]	
91	P. triticina[2]	10-26(2-32)[u]			20(2-31)[u]	15-22[u]		
92	Pyrenophora graminea		18-30(3-35)				10-18(to 24)	52[c]; 55[m]
93	P. teres	20[as]; 20-25[c]	23-30(3-33)	5-30[c]; 10-30[p]	15-35			45[c]; 55[m]
94	Pythiacystis citrophthora		25-27(9-32)			18-28(6-32)		46[s]
95	Pythium debaryanum[5]		24-33(5-40)				30-35[10]	
96	P. ultimum		25-35(2-42)				12-21(2-35)	
97	Rhizopus nigricans[2]	19-41(2-41)	20-36(2-40)	16-30(7-32)			6-28(0-36)	55[s]
98	Sclerospora graminicola	18-30(5-35)[c]; 20-34(10-38)[o]; 14-18[sa]; 25-27(8-30)[z]		17-27(5-35)[sa]	17-20(11-34)[o]			40[c]; 118[3], 53[4][o]
99	Sclerotinia americana	23[c]	24[27(3-33)					
100	S. fructigena	21-25(10 to)[c]	18-25(0-33)	28-33(5-30)			(5 to <35)	52
101	S. libertiana	(3-31); (to 30)[as]	22-25(0-33)	20-25		18-23(0 to >33)		60[sc]
102	S. sclerotiorum[2]	25(3-30)[as]	22-25(0-33)				17-24(0-28)	50[4][sc]
103	Septoria apii		16-27(10-27)	16-25				

/1/ Usually at 10 min exposure. /2/ Fungus exhibits variability among different strains or in different hosts. /3/ Dry state. /4/ Wet state. /5/ Fungus exhibits extreme variability among different strains or in different hosts. /6/ Value also reported as 8-16 (to 28). /7/ Also 18-32(3-37). /8/ Also 10-16(2-27). /9/ Also 15(0-40). /10/ Also 15-30, or 5-8.

376. EFFECTS OF TEMPERATURE: PLANT PATHOGENIC FUNGI (Concluded)

Values not in parentheses are "optimum" values in °C; values in parentheses are minimum-maximum values in °C. The following symbols, in brackets, identify, where known, the part or stage studied: ae = aeciospores; as = ascospores; b = basidiospores; c = conidia; m = mycelium; o = oospores; p = pycnidia, pycnospores; s = spores (not specified); sa = sporangia; sc = sclerotia; t = teliospores; u = uredospores; z = zoospores.

	Fungus	Germination	Development in Culture	Fructification and/or Sporulation	Infection	Disease Development	Infection and Disease Development	Thermal Death Point[1]
104	Septoria lycopersici		25(2-34)	25(15-27)				53[s]
105	S. tritici	2-32	20-24(3-32)					85[4][sa]
106	Synchytrium endobioticum	12-20(5-30)			16-18(0-30)		13-17(10-21)	46[m]
107	Taphrina deformans		<20-20(10-30)				17-23(15-32)	
108	Thielaviopsis basicola		23-32(7-37)					
109	Tilletia laevis	16-20(4-36)	20		5-10(to 25)			
110	T. tritici	15-20(0-36)	20(>1 to <25)		6-12(4-22)			65-70[m]
111	Trametes pini		20-25(10-40)					
112	Urocystis cepulae	15(4-28)[m]; 15-20(9 to >32)[s]	>18(>9 to 28)				10-25(10-28)	
113	Uromyces trifolii	15-20(6-30)[ae] 17(7 to <30)[t];9-25(<3 to >33)[u]						
114	Ustilago avenae	15-30(4-35)[u]; 15-28(0-35)[t]	18-26[6-34]		18-22(7-32)			45-53
115	U. hordei[2]	10-30(0-35)	16-26(<-1 to <35)					43-48
116	U. nuda[2]	20-29(0-34)	20-25(<10-35)					>42[s]
117	U. tritici[2]	22-30(0-35)	24-30(6 to >35)	19-24	23-25(10-30)			45-48
118	U. zeae	25-34(5-40)[t]; 20-26 (to 40)[u]	18-26(10-34)		27-35			106[3];52[4][s]
119	Venturia inaequalis	13-22(0-35)[as]; 14-25(2-31)[c]	20(<4 to <32)				19(6-24)	
120	Verticillium albo-atrum		16-31(4-37)	23(8-31)		21-25		

/1/ Usually at 10 min exposure. /2/ Fungus exhibits variability among different strains or in different hosts. /3/ Dry state. /4/ Wet state.

377. TEMPERATURE CHARACTERISTICS: PLANTS

Part I: TEMPERATURE TOLERANCE EXTREMES: ALGAE

Most values in this table are based on observations of algae growing under natural conditions where it is difficult to determine the true temperature of the habitat. Moreover, light absorption may raise the temperature of an algal mass above that of its surroundings. Values, therefore, should be interpreted with caution. * = temperature for maximum growth rate. Where values are given for general groups it is implied that these hold for some but not necessarily all species in that group.

	Species	Maximum for Habitat[1]	Maximum Tolerated	Minimum Tolerated
		Temperature, °C		
1	Cyanophyta (blue-green)		85	
2	40 non-thermal spp		40	
3	Anabaena sp	40		
4	A. variabilis	35*		
5	Anacystis nidulans	41*		
6	A. thermalis	42*		
7	Chroococcus sp	57		
8	C. minutis fuscus	46		
9	C. yellowstonensis	41		
10	Cylindrospermum stagnate	44.1		
11	Gleocapsa stegophalia	38		
12	Lyngbya sp	65		
13	L. cutealis			Below -17
14	Mastigocladus laminosus	65		-19
15	Microcystis elabens			Below -17
16	Nostoc kihlmani			Below -17
17	N. muscorum	32.5*		
18	N. sphaericum	30		
19	Oscillatoria amphibia	50		
20	O. filiformis	85.2[2]	85.2[3]	59
21	O. formosa	50		
22	O. geminata	45		
23	O. okeni	44		
24	O. proboscidea	47		
25	O. tennis tergestina	44		
26	Phormidium bijahensis	60-62*	85.2[3]	38
27	P. geysericola	75*	85	58
28	P. laminosum	75*	85	58
29	P. tenue	47.2		
30	Rivularia globiceps	26.4		

	Species	Maximum for Habitat[1]	Maximum Tolerated	Minimum Tolerated
		Temperature, °C		
	Cyanophyta (blue-green) (concluded)			
31	Scytonema mirabile			Below -17
32	Synechocystis thermalis	62.2		
33	Synechococcus eximius	79*	84	70
34	S. vulcanus	70*	85	46
35	S. vulcanus bacillarioides	64*	70	57
36	Chlorophyceae (green)		50	-18 to -20[4]
37	Ankistrodesmus falcatus			Below -17
38	Chaetomorpha linum		35	-2 to -7
39	Chlamydomonas nivalis		10	-36
40	Chlamydothris thermalis	72-74		
41	Cladophora hamosa		35	Below -7
42	C. laetevirens		35	Below -7
43	C. prolifera	30-35		-2 to -7
44	C. rupestris			-16.8 to -20
45	Cosmarium conspersum			Below -17
46	Desmidium quadratum			-18 to -20[4]
47	Enteromorpha intestinalis			Below -17
48	Euastrum sublobatum			Below -17
49	Protococcus botyroides	80		
50	Ulothrix sp		17	
	Chrysophyta			
51	Bacillariophyceae (diatoms)		50.7	-11
52	Nitzschia putrida		30	-11
53	Chrysophyceae (golden brown)	40.2		
54	Xanthophyceae (yellow-green)	32.5		
55	Phaeophyta (brown)		30	-18 to -20[4]
56	Fucus vesiculosus		30	-18 to -20[4]
57	Rhodophyta (red)			-18 to -20[4]
58	Bangia fuscopurpurea			-18 to -20[4]
59	Porphyra hiemalis			-18 to -20[4]

/1/ Highest temperature reported for natural habitats. /2/ Optimum temperature, 79°C. /3/ Highest recorded temperature for algal growth.
/4/ Based on observations of algae in polar seas; not certain that algae were actually growing.

Part II: COLD TOLERANCE: MARINE ALGAE

After 10 hr controlled exposure recorded in western Sweden. + = living; - = dead.

Species	Temperature, °C						
	-2.9	-4.0	-5.7	-7.8	-10.7	-16.8	-18 to -20
Red Algae							
1 Trailella intricata	-						→
2 Laurencia pinnatifida	+	-					→
3 Delesseria sanguinea	+	-					→
4 D. sinuosa	←	+	-				→
5 Ceramium rubrum		+	-				→
6 Chondrus crispus	←				+		→
7 Nemalion multifidum[1]	←					+	+
8 Bangia fuscopurpurea	←					+	+
9 Porphyra hiemalis	←					+	+
Brown Algae							
10 Laminaria saccharina[2]	←	+	-				→
11 L. digitata[3]	←		+	+	-		→
12 L. saccharina[4]	←			+	+		→
13 Pylaiella litoralis	←				+		→
14 Fucus vesiculosus	←						+
15 F. serratus	←						+
16 Ascophyllum nodosum	←						+
Green Algae							
17 Cladophora rupestris	←					+	-
18 Enteromorpha intestinalis							+

/1/ Prostrate protonematal stage in winter. /2/ One year old.
/3/ Young thallus. /4/ Old thallus; plant several years old.

Part III: TEMPERATURE TOLERANCES: MARINE ALGAE

After 12 hr controlled exposure recorded at Naples. + = living; - = dead; O = not examined.

Algae	Temperature, °C						
	-7	-2	1 to 2	27	30	35	42
Intertidal Zone							
1 Bangia fuscopurpurea	+	+	+	+	+	+	-
2 Cladophora bertolinii	+	+	+	+	+	+	
3 C. hamosa	+	+	+	+	+	+	
4 C. laetevirens	+	+	+	+	+	+	
5 C. spinulosa	O	+	+	+	+	+	
6 Polysiphonia pulvinata	+	+	+	+	+	+	
7 Porphyra leucosticta		+	+	+	+	-	
Low Water Level							
8 Antithamnion cruciatum	-	+		+	+		
9 Callithamnion granulatum	-	O	O	+	-		
10 Ceramium berneri	-	-	-	+	+		
11 Chaetomorpha linum	-	+	+	+	+		
Depth							
12 Acrosorium uncinatum	-		+	+			
13 Callithamnion scopulorum	-	-	-	+			
14 Ceramium strictum	-	+	+	+	+		
15 Cladophora prolifera	-	+	+	+	+		
16 C. ramellosa	-	O	O	-	-		
17 C. utriculosa	-	+	+	+	-		
18 Griffithsia furcellata	-	-		+	-		
19 G. schousboei	O	O	O	+	+		
20 G. setacea	-	-		+	-		
21 Nitophyllum punctatum	-		+	+	-		
22 Pleonosporium borreri	-		+	+	-		
23 Plocamium coccineum	-		+	+	-		
24 Taonia atomaria	-	O	O	+	+	-	

Part IV: WORLD-WIDE DISTRIBUTION: THERMAL ALGAE

	Temp °C	Cyano-phyceae	Chloro-phyceae	Conju-gatae	Rhodo-phyceae
		Number of Species			
1	17-30	41	9	4	1
2	30-35	38	7	2	0
3	35-40	62	8	6	0
4	40-45	37	5	1	1
5	45-50	35	4	0	0
6	50-60	37	3	2	0
7	60-75	10	0	0	0

Part V: MAXIMUM TEMPERATURE TOLERANCE: LICHENS

Values are for air-dry tissue. Those in parentheses are for water-soaked tissue. After treatment of air-dry tissue for 30 min, a 50% decrease in respiration was observed.

	Lichen	Temp °C		Lichen	Temp °C
	Hygrophilic			Xerophytic	
1	Alectoria implexa	72-73	7	Cladonia foliacea convoluta	92-96
2	A. ochroleuca	72	8	C. pocillum, C. pyxidata	101
3	A. sarmentosa	70-74	9	C. rangiformis pungens	99(46.5)
4	Lobaria pulmonaria	73(36.5)	10	Umbilicaria cylindrica	95
5	Usnea dasypoga	71-74(<35)	11	U. hirsuta	100
6	U. florida	70	12	U. pustulata	98(45.5)
			13	U. vellea	98-100(44)

Part VI: TOLERANCE TO EXTREMES OF HEAT AND COLD: MOSSES

	Moss	Temp °C		Moss	Temp °C		Moss	Temp °C
	Maximum Temperature[1]			Maximum Temperature[1] (continued)			Maximum Temperature[1] (concluded)	
	Most sensitive of 50 spp tested			Least sensitive of 50 spp tested		9	Pleurochaete squarrosa, Montpellier	105-110
1	Frullania dilatata, Lake Garda	70-75	5	Barbula gracilis, Montpellier	110-115		Minimum Temperature[2]	
2	Gymnomitrium obtusum	65-70	6	Ceratodon purpureus	100-105	10	Majority of 30 spp tested	-10 to -20
3	Plagiothecium curvifolium	65-70	7	Grimmia trichophylla	105-110	11	Least sensitive of 30 spp tested[3]	-20 to -30
4	P. denticulatum	70-75	8	Pleurochaete squarrosa, Lake Garda	100-105			

/1/ Injury observed after 30 min heating in dry state over phosphorus pentoxide. /2/ Duration, 18 hr in turgescent state during winter. /3/ Species include: Ceratodon purpureus, Dicranum scoparium, Grimmia pulvinata, Plagiothecium denticulatum, P. undulatum.

Part VII: TOLERANCE TO EXTREMES OF HEAT AND COLD: FLOWERING PLANTS

Plant	Temperature °C		Plant	Temperature °C
Maximum Temperature[1]			**Winter-conditioned Plants[4] (concluded)**	
Hydrophytes			29 Oat (Avena sativa)	-9 to -12
1 Elodea (Elodea callitrichoides)	38.5		30 Potato (Solanum tuberosum)	-2 to -3
2 Elodea (E. canadensis)	39-39.5		31 Rape (Brassica napus)	-9
3 Parrot's feather (Myriophyllum			32 Rye (Secale cereale)	-15 to -25
verticilatum)	40		33 Wheat (Triticum aestivum)	-10 to -22
4 Vallisneria (Vallisneria spiralis)	41.5		Tree fruits: flowers[6]	
Shade plants			34 Apple (Pyrus malus)	-1.7 to -2.2
5 Oxalis (Oxalis acetosella)	40.5		35 Apricot (Prunus armeniaca)	-0.6 to -2.9
6 Impatiens (Impatiens parviflora)	41.5		36 Cherry (Prunus sp)	-1.1 to -2.2
Herbaceous plants: xerophytic habitat			37 Peach (P. persica)	-1.1 to -2.8
7 Ceterach (Ceterach officinarum)	48		38 Pear (Pyrus communis)	-1.1 to -2.2
8 Fescue (Festuca glauca)	50.5		39 Plum (Prunus sp)	-0.6 to -2.2
9 Germander (Teucrium chamaedrys)	48		Tree fruits: fruit set	
10 Germander (T. montanum)	48.5		40 Apple (Pyrus malus)	-1.1 to -2.2
11 Hawkweed (Hieracium pilosella)	50.5		41 Apricot (Prunus armeniaca)	0 to -2.2
12 Iris (Iris chamaeiris)	49.5		42 Cherry (Prunus sp)	-1.1 to -2.2
13 Mullein (Verbascum thapsus)	48.5		43 Peach (P. persica)	-1.1 to -2.8
14 Opuntia (Opuntia sp)	63		44 Pear (Pyrus communis)	-1.1 to -2.2
15 Pink (Dianthus carthusianorum)	48		45 Plum (Prunus sp)	-0.6 to -2.2
16 Sedum (Sedum acre)	48.5-49.5		Trunk cortex	
17 Sedum (S. reflexum)	49.5-50		Apple (Pyrus malus)	
18 Sedum (S. spurium)	48.5		46 In January	-29
19 Thorn apple (Datura stramonium)	47		47 Flowering period	-8
Minimum Temperature			Apricot (Prunus armeniaca)	
20 Achimene (Achimenes patens)[2]	1-5		48 In January	-21
21 Coleus (Coleus spp)[3]	>1		49 Flowering period	-6 to -7
22 Episcia (Episcia cupreata)[2]	1-5		Cherry (Prunus sp)	
23 Gloxinia (Gloxinia grandiflora)[2]	1-5		50 In January	-23
24 Peperomia (Peperomia arifolia)[3]	>1		51 Flowering period	-8
25 Sultana (Impatiens sultani)[3]	>1		Deciduous trees (29 species)[7]	
Winter-conditioned Plants[4]			52 Buds opening (May 15)	-3 to -4
Cereal and field crops[5]			Resting buds (January)	
26 Barley (Hordeum vulgare)	-10 to -15		53 Majority of spp tested	-20 to -22
27 Beet (Beta vulgaris)	-5 to -7		54 Filbert (Corylus avellana)	Below -20
28 Cabbage (Brassica oleracea capitata)	-8 to -11		55 Walnut (Juglans regia)	Below -20

/1/ More than 50% of test plants (50+ species) uninjured after 30 min heating in an atmosphere of saturated humidity. In dry atmosphere maximum tolerated temp is 2-5°C greater. /2/ Endures exposure up to 24 hr in an atmosphere of saturated humidity. Further exposure results in injury to leaves and, later, shoot apex. /3/ Injury observed after 28 hr at 0.3-1°C. /4/ Plants previously conditioned to low temp. /5/ Experimental temp for conditioned tissues. Data may be useful for estimating winter-cold resistance. /6/ Reported to endure -2.3 to 2.7°C for 30 min. /7/ 12-hr exposure.

Part VIII: LOW TEMPERATURE TOLERANCE: FLOWERING PLANTS

Winter-conditioned plants were exposed to experimental temperatures indicated in winter column; actively growing plants (in summer season) were observed under experimental temperatures shown in summer column.[1]

Plant	Winter °C	Summer °C		Plant	Winter °C	Summer °C
Evergreen species (Riva-Gardasee)				Evergreen dwarf Alpine shrubs (Innsbruck) (concluded)		
1 Chamaerops (Chamaerops humilis)	-12 to -14	-10 to -12	15	Heather (Calluna vulgaris)	-28	-5
2 Fortune's palm (Trachycarpus fortunei)	-12.5 to -15	-10 to -13	16	Loiseleuria (Loiseleuria procumbens)	-35	-9
3 Laurel (Laurus nobilis)	-10 to -10.5	-6		Rhododendron (Rhododendron ferrugineum)		
4 Oak (Quercus ilex)	-13 to 13.5	-6	17	In protected position	-15	-5
5 Oleander (Nerium oleander)	-9	-4 to -6	18	In exposed position	-25	-5
6 Olive (Olea europaea)	-12	-6.5	19	Rhododendron (R. hirsutum)	-28.5	-5.5
7 Strawberry-tree (Arbutus unedo)	-10	-5 to -8		Conifers of Alpine Timberline (Innsbruck)		
8 Trifoliate-orange (Poncirus trifoliata)	-18 to -22	-12 to -16	20	Pine (Pinus cembra)	below -39	-10
9 Viburnum (Viburnum tinus)	-11 to -12	-4 to -7	21	Pine (P. montana)	-35	-6
Conifers (Riva-Gardasee)			22	Spruce (Picea excelsa)	-38	-8 to -9
10 Cedar (Cedrus atlantica, C. deodara)	-15 to -17	-6 to -8		Conifers of Moscow Mountains (Idaho)[2]		
11 Cypress (Cupressus sempervirens)	-14 to -18	-7 to -9	23	Fir (Abies grandis)	-45 to -55	-15
12 Pine (Pinus pinea)	-11 to -14	-5 to -7	24	Pine (Pinus ponderosa)	-50 to -60	-15
Evergreen dwarf Alpine shrubs (Innsbruck)				Field weeds		
13 Bear-berry (Arctostaphylos uva-ursi)	-29	-9	25	Chickweed (Stellaria media)	-9.7	-2.5
14 Heath (Erica carnea)	-18.5	-4.5	26	Ironweed (Veronia tournefortii)	-10.8	-4.3

/1/ 15-20% injury observed after 2-3 hr at indicated temp, and slow freezing and thawing for several hr with mature 1-2 yr old leaves of adult plants. No injury observed at 1-2°C higher temp. Resting buds reported to be more tolerant to low temp than leaves. /2/ Slight injury observed after exposure of a few min.

Part IX: TEMPERATURE RANGE OF METABOLIC ACTIVITY: PLANTS

Temperature values, unless otherwise specified, are lower and upper limits within which the specified activity was observed.

Plant	Activity	Temp °C		Plant	Activity	Temp °C
Algae				**Flowering Plants (concluded)**		
1 Chlamydomonas nivalis	Photosynthesis	-10 to 10	14	Bean, kidney (Phaseolus multiflorus)	Carbohydrate translocation	1 to 6[5]
Chlorella (Chlorella pyrenoidosa)			15	Cherrylaurel (Prunus laurocerasus)	Photosynthesis	-6 to 37
2 Strain Emerson	Growth	25[1], 29[2]	16	Chickweed (Stellaria media)	Photosynthesis	-10 to 35
3 Strain Tx 71105	Growth	39[1], 41[2]	17	Coconut (Cocos nucifera)	Growth	10 to 30
4 Strain Emerson	Photosynthesis	32[3], 39[4]	18	Corn (Zea mays)	Growth	9.5 to 46
5 Strain Tx 71105	Photosynthesis	41[3], 45[4]	19		Chlorophyll formation	13 to 14[5]
6 Strain Emerson	Respiration	30[3], >45[4]	20	Date (Phoenix dactylifera)	Photosynthesis	10 to 54
7 Strain Tx 71105	Respiration	41[3], >50[4]	21	Fir, arctic (Abies excelsa)	Photosynthesis	-40 to 30
8 Dunaliella salina	Protoplasmic streaming	-19 to 40	22	Morning glory (Ipomoea spp)	Respiration	10 to 60
9 Mastigocladus laminosus	Growth	5 to 60	23	Pea (Pisum sativum)	Growth	-2 to 40
10 Nitella syncarpa	Protoplasmic streaming	0[5]	24	Pumpkin (Cucurbita pepo)	Growth	14 to 46
11 Phaeosphaera perforata	Growth	4 to 10	25		Protoplasmic streaming	11 to 12[5]
Lichens			26	Wheat (Triticum aestivum)	Growth	5 to 42
12 Reindeer (Cladonia rangiferina)	Photosynthesis	-20 to 38	27	Wheat (T. ferruginum)	Chlorophyll formation	2[5]
Flowering Plants						
13 Barley (Hordeum vulgare)	Growth	5[5]				

/1/ Optimum temperature for continuous growth. /2/ Maximum temperature for continuous growth. /3/ Optimum temperature in experiments of short duration. /4/ Maximum temperature in experiments of short duration. /5/ Minimum temperature.

377. TEMPERATURE CHARACTERISTICS: PLANTS (Concluded)

Part X: LOWER TEMPERATURE LIMITS OF PHOTOSYNTHESIS

Lines 1, 2, and 4 apply to the Alpine timberline (1900 m), Innsbruck in May; all others at 600 m in April.

Plant	Temperature, °C							Plant	Temperature, °C						
	1	-1	-2	-3	-4	-5	-6		1	-1	-2	-3	-4	-5	-6
1 Pinus cembra	+	-					→	6 Pinus silvestris	+	+	+	-			→
2 Arctostaphylos uva ursi	+	+	-				→	7 Taxus baccata	+	+	+	50%	-		→
3 Buxus japonica	+	+	50%	-			→	8 Veronica persica	+	+	+	50%	-		→
4 Picea excelsa	+	+	-				→	9 Picea excelsa	+	+	+	+	-		→
5 Erica carnea	+	+	50%	-			→	10 Viscum album	+	+	+	50%	-		→
								11 Hedera helix	+	+	+	+	67%	50%	- →

Part XI: TEMPERATURE REQUIREMENTS FOR SPECIFIC CROPS

Data adapted from "Climate and Man," Yearbook of Agriculture, 1941. Values are broad generalizations and do not take into account such variables as day-night temperature differentiation, variety differences, physiological responses for which the optima are different from those for growth, and, in some instances, length of time during which temperatures above or below tolerance limit may persist. However, in many cases, data in this part may be correlated with that in other parts of this table and in other tables in this series.

Plant	Specification
	Very Hardy Cool-season Crops
1 Beet, garden (Beta vulgaris)[1]	Optimum vegetative growth at 16-21°C (60-70°F); tolerates repeated mild freezing temperatures at market stage. At >21°C (>70°F) growth is retarded.
2 Broccoli, sprouting (Brassica oleracea botrytis)	Similar to cabbage. Yield and quality reduced at mean temperature of >16°C (>60°F).
3 Brussels sprouts (B. oleracea gemmifera); collards, kale (B. oleracea acephala)	Tolerant to freezing temperatures at market stage; cool temperatures improve quality. Intolerant to monthly means of >21°C (>70°F).
4 Cabbage (B. oleracea capitata)[2]	Optimum vegetative growth at 16-21°C (60-70°F). At >21°C (>70°F) plants remain vegetative, with slow, abnormal growth. Plants in head-stage are tolerant to frost, intolerant to freezing temperatures. Young, stocky, well-hardened plants, with stem 5-8 mm in diameter, survive winter temperature of -18°C (0°F) for short periods; larger or smaller plants are less hardy; larger surviving plants are likely to produce flowering stalks, instead of heading, in spring. Plants in active growing condition are intolerant to sudden freezing temperatures.
5 Spinach (Spinacia oleracea)	Optimum vegetative growth at 10-16°C (50-60°F). Fall-sown plants having a few well-developed leaves at the onset of cold weather are tolerant to subfreezing temperatures for many weeks; small seedlings and plants approaching maturity are less hardy. Sudden warm temperatures in spring terminate vegetative growth of plants overwintered or spring planted. At 21-27°C (70-80°F) crinkling and sturdy leaf growth reduced.
6 Turnip (Brassica rapa); rutabaga (B. napus napobrassica)	Optimum temperature similar to cabbage. Immature plants are more tolerant than cabbage to short periods at 4°C (40°F); mature plants more tolerant to mild freezing temperatures. At 24°C (75°F) growth rate is reduced, leaves injured.
	Less Hardy Cool-season Crops
7 Carrot (Daucus carota)	Optimum temperature 16-21°C (60-70°F); in seeding stage is more sensitive to temperature extremes. Leaves are damaged at freezing temperatures. Best color and highest carotene content occur at 10-16°C (50-60°F) (crop yield low). Normal growth does not occur between <10 (<50°F) and >21°C (>70°F).
8 Cauliflower, heading broccoli (Brassica oleracea botrytis)	Optimum temperature 16-21°C (60-70°F); less tolerant to temperature extremes than cabbage. Above 21°C (70°F) leafy, loose, or yellowed curds develop.
9 Celery (Apium graveolens dulce)	Optimum temperature 16-21°C (60-70°F). Treatment at 4-10°C (40-50°F) for 10 days conducive to flowering instead of normal growth. Prompt flowering (under chilled conditions) proportional to age of plant.
10 Lettuce (Lactuca sativa)	Optimum temperature 13-18°C (55-65°F). At 21-27°C (70-80°F) heading is prevented, plants flower. At constant temperature of 21°C (70°F) tip-burn is serious. High temperature conducive to development of bitter flavor. Small immature plants tolerant to mild freezing temperatures but mature plants are injured.
11 Pea, garden (Pisum sativum)	Optimum temperature 13-18°C (55-65°F); more seriously injured by frost than cabbage; slight freezing temperatures may injure or destroy flowers and fruits. At >27°C (>80°F) premature ripening of fruit occurs.
12 Potato (Solanum tuberosum)	Most rapid development of young sprouts at constant temperature of 24°C (75°F), later growth best at 18°C (64°F). At soil temperature of >24°C (>75°F), there occurs excessive branching of young sprouts, shortening of internodes, decrease in segmentation of leaves, diminution in stem diameter. At constant temperature of 20°C (68°F) tuber production is decreased with complete inhibition at 29°C (84°F). Below -1°C (30.2°F) tubers are injured.
	Adapted to a Wide Range of Temperature and Tolerant to Frost
13 Onion (Allium cepa)	Fairly low temperatures best for early stages of growth; for bulbing, fairly high temperatures, 16-21°C (60-70°F). Bulbing is influenced by day length. At 10-16°C (50-60°F) flowers are initiated; at 21-27°C (70-80°F), no flowering.
	Adapted to a Wide Range of Conditions but not Tolerant to Frost[1]
14 Bean (Phaseolus spp)[3]	Optimum temperature 16-21°C (60-70°F).
15 Corn (Zea mays)	Optimum: mean summer temperature 21-27°C (70-80°F), night temperature, >14°C (>58°F). Date of flowering much earlier at 27°C (80°F) than at 21°C (70°F); retarded flowering at 16°C (60°F).
16 Cucumber (Cucumis sativus), Muskmelon (C. melo)	Optimum temperature 18-24°C (65-75°F).
17 Pepper, hot (Capsicum sp)	Tolerates higher temperature than sweet pepper.
18 Pepper, sweet (Capsicum sp)	Temperature requirements are a little higher than those for tomato, but more sensitive to chilly, wet weather in the spring and more tolerant to high summer temperatures. At 27°C (80°F) fruit set poor; constant temperature below 16°C (60°F) or above 32°C (90°F), complete barrenness.
19 Tomato (Lycopersicon esculentum)	Optimum temperature 21-24°C (70-75°F); tolerance extremes, 18-27°C (65-80°F). A constant temperature of 24°C (75°F), almost complete barrenness.
	Warm Region Crops
20 Eggplant (Solanum melongena esculentum)	Minimum temperature 18-21°C (65-70°F).
21 Sweetpotato (Ipomoea batatas)	Very sensitive to frost; minimum temperature 21°C (70°F).
22 Watermelon (Citrullus vulgaris)	Long growing season with high temperatures required.
	Perennial Crops
23 Asparagus (Asparagus officinalis)	Stem elongation rapid at 25°C (78°F), greatly retarded at 11°C (52°F). Early development of lateral branches at 35-40°C (95-105°F).
24 Rhubarb (Rheum rhaponticum)	Injured at -3 to -4°C (25-27°F), but intolerant to high temperatures of southern U.S.A. Development of pink color occurs at low temperatures and green color at high temperatures.

/1/ Cold, wet weather, even though frost-free, is harmful. Should not be planted until monthly means have reached 16-18°C (60-65°F). /2/ Biennial; after first growing period requires a dormant period at low temperature for initiation of flower stalk and flowers. /3/ Includes lima, string and many others.

450

	Test	Seeds	Specification	Interpretation or Results
			Biochemical Tests	
1	Indigo carmine, 0.05%	Pine	Stain for 2 hr, 20°C.	Embryo uncolored to 1/4 colored = viable.
2	Phenol, 1%	Wheat	Stain for 25 hr, 15°C.	
3	Tetrazolium, 1%	Various spp.	Stain for 24 hr (in dark), 20°C.	Embryo red = viable.
4	NaHSeO$_3$, 2%	Agricultural spp.	Stain for 16 hr + 8 hr with aeration.	
5,6	Na$_2$TeO$_4$	Various spp.	Treat in H$_2$O for 24 hr, 20°C; remove seed coat; stain for 48 hr.	Embryo black = viable.
7	Meta-dinitrobenzene	Rye, wheat	Oxidation-reduction: treat for 5 hr, 20°C.	Seed purple in NH$_3$ = viable.
8	KOH	Tropical spp.		Seed discolored = dead.
9	KI, 1.3%	Spruce	Treat for 8 hr, 20°C; then incubate for 24 hr.	Seed deep purple = viable.
10	I, 0.3%	Pine		Seed blue or violet = viable.
11	Oxidase activity	Various spp.	Crush and treat in 0.1% guaiac resin.	
			Embryo Culture	
12	Nutrient culture	Various spp.	Knop's medium + glucose, agar; for 7 da, 20°C.	Growth of embryo directly proportional to actual germination.
13	Filter paper		Moisten with H$_2$O, 5-10 da, 21-23°C.	
			Physical Tests	
14	Cutting and crushing	Thin, soft coated	Cutting: treat in water.	Seed firm, free from discoloration = viable.
15		Heavy coated	Crushing: stratify for 4 wk.	
16	Visual	Birch	Transparency.	Embryo undeveloped, shrunken = immature.
17		Pine, spruce	Embryo-ratio.	Embryo length-seed length ratio <0.8 = immature.
18	Specific gravity	Pine	In water.	Floating seed = dead.[1]
19		Spruce	In alcohol	
20	Electric conductivity	Grasses	"Blaze current" proportional to viability; rise in conductivity proportional to % dead seed.	
21	Heat of respiration	All species	Aseptic incubation.	Temp. increase proportional to germinative energy.

/1/ Floating seeds are almost invariably non-viable; however, sinking is not necessarily an indication of viability.

379. CONDITIONS FOR SEED GERMINATION: HERBACEOUS PLANTS

	Species	Temp[1] °C	Dura-tion[2] da	Specifications[3]		Species	Temp[1] °C	Dura-tion[2] da	Specifications[3]
	Agricultural Crops					Vegetable Crops (concluded)			
1	Alfalfa (Medicago sativa)	20	4-7	B, S	46	Celery (Apium graveolens dulce)	20-30	10-21	P, TB; light, KNO$_3$[9]
2	Barley (Hordeum vulgare)	20	4-7	T, S; prechill[4]	47	Cucumber (Cucumis sativus)	20-30	3-7	T, S, B
3	Bean, field (Phaseolus vulgaris)	20-30	5-8	R, S	48	Dandelion (Taraxacum officinale)	20-30	7-21	P, TB; light
4	Beet (Beta vulgaris)	20-30	3-14	B;H$_2$O soak[5]	49	Eggplant (Solanum melongena escul.)	20-30	7-14	TB
5	Bentgrass (Agrostis tenuis)	20-30	7-28	P; light, KNO$_3$	50	Endive (Cichorium endiva)	20-30	5-14	P, TS
6	Bermuda grass (Cynodon dactylon)	20-35	7-21	P; light, KNO$_3$	51	Kale (Brassica oleracea acephala)	20-30	3-10	B, P[11]
7	Bluegrass (Poa pratensis)	15-30	10-28	P; light, KNO$_3$[6]	52	Lettuce (Lactuca sativa)	20	7	P; light, prechill[12]
8	Buckwheat (Fagopyrum esculentum)	20-30	3-6	B, T	53	Muskmelon (Cucumis melo)	20-30	4-10	B, T, S[13]
9	Canary grass (Phalaris canariensis)	20-30	3-7	B	54	Okra (Hibiscus esculentus)	20-30	4-21	R
10	Clover (Trifolium spp)[7]	17-18[8]	4-7	B, S	55	Onion (Allium cepa)	20	6-12	B, S
11	Corn (Zea mays)	20-30	4-7	R, S	56	Parsley (Petroselinum hortense)	20-30	11-28	B
12	Cotton (Gossypium spp)	20-30	4-12	R, S	57	Parsnip (Pastinaca sativa)	20-30	6-28	B
13	Cowpea (Vigna sinensis)	20-30	5-8	R, S	58	Pea, garden (Pisum sativum)	20	5-8	R, S
14	Crotalaria (Crotalaria spp)	20-30	4-10	B, S	59	Pepper (Capsicum spp)	20-30	6-14	TB
15	Dallis grass (Paspalum dilatatum)	20-35	7-21	P; light, KNO$_3$	60	Pumpkin (Cucurbita spp)	20-30	4-7	T, S[13]
16	Festuca (Festuca arundinacea)	20-30	5-14	P; light	61	Radish (Raphanus sativus)	20	4-6	B
17	Fescue (F. elatior)	20-30	5-14	P; light	62	Rhubarb (Rheum rhaponticum)	20-30	7-21	TS; light
18	Flax (Linum usitatissimum)	20-30	3-7	B, S	63	Rutabaga (Brassica napus napob.)	20-30	3-14	B
19	Hemp (Cannabis sativa)	20-30	3-7	B	64	Spinach (Spinacia oleracea)	10	7-21	TB[13]
20	Johnson grass (Sorghum halepense)	20-35	7-35	P; light, KNO$_3$	65	Squash (Cucurbita spp)	20-30	4-7	T, S[13]
21	Lespedeza (Lespedeza stipulacea)	20-35	5-14	B	66	Tomato (Lycopersicon esculentum)	20-30	5-14	B[14]
22	Lupine (Lupinus angustifolius)	20	4-10	R, S	67	Turnip (Brassica rapa)	20-30	3-7	B
23	Mustard (Brassica nigra)	20-30	3-7	P; light, KNO$_3$[9]	68	Watermelon (Citrullus vulgaris)	20-30	4-14	T, S[13]
24	Oat (Avena sativa)	20	5-10	T, S; prechill[4]		Flowers			
25	Orchardgrass (Dactylis glomerata)	20-30	7-21	P, S; light	69	Aster, annual (Aster sp)	20	8	TB
26	Pea, field (Pisum sativum arvense)	20	3-8	R, S	70	Balsam (Impatiens balsamina)	20	8	TB; light, KNO$_3$
27	Peanut (Arachis hypogaea)	20-30	5-10	R, S	71	Canterbury bell (Campanula spp)	20-30	6-12	TB
28	Redtop (Agrostis alba)	20-30	5-10	TB, P; light	72	Carnation (Dianthus caryophyllus)	20	8	TB
29	Rice (Oryza sativa)	20-30	5-14	B, T	73	Cornflower (Centaurea cyanus)	15	4-8	TB
30	Rye (Secale cereale)	20	4-7	T, S; prechill[4]	74	Cosmos (Cosmos spp)	20-30	3-8	TB; light, KNO$_3$
31	Ryegrass (Lolium multiflorum)	20-30	5-14	P, TB; light, KNO$_3$	75	Dahlia (Dahlia spp)	20-30	4-10	TB
32	Sesame (Sesamum orientale)	20-30	3-6	P	76	Daisy (Chrysanthemum maximum)	20-30	8	TB; light
33	Sorghum (Sorghum vulgare)	20-30	4-10	B, S; prechill[4]	77	Forget-me-not (Myosotis sp)	20	5-12	TB
34	Soybean (Glycine soja)	20-30	5-8	R, S	78	Hollyhock (Althaea rosea)	20	5-18	B
35	Sunflower (Helianthus annuus)	20-30	3-7	T, B	79	Larkspur (Delphinium spp)	15	10-21	TB
36	Timothy (Phleum pratense)	20-30	5-10	P, TB; light, KNO$_3$	80	Marigold (Tagetes spp)	20-30	7	R
37	Tobacco (Nicotiana tabacum)	20-30	7-14	P, TB; light	81	Nasturtium (Tropaeolum spp)	18	14	R
38	Wheat (Triticum spp)	20	4-7	T, S; prechill[4]	82	Pansy (Viola tricolor)	20	12	TB
39	Wheatgrass (Agropyron cristatum)	20-30	5-14	P, TB; light, KNO$_3$[10]	83	Petunia (Petunia spp)	20-30	6-10	P; light
	Vegetable Crops				84	Poppy (Papaver orientale)	20	6-12	TB
40	Asparagus (Asparagus officinalis)	20-30	7-21	T	85	Salvia (Salvia splendens)	20-30	4-12	TB; light
41	Bean (Phaseolus coccineus)	20-30	5-9	R, S	86	Snapdragon (Antirrhinum spp)	20-30	5-12	P; light[15]
42	Bean (P. lunatus macrocarpus)	20-30	5-9	R, S, C	87	Stock (Matthiola incana)	20-30	7	TB; light
43	Broadbean (Vicia faba)	17-18	4-14	S, C[9]	88	Sweetpea (Lathyrus odoratus)	18	12	R
44	Cabbage (Brassica oleracea cap.)	20-30	3-10	B, P[11]	89	Wallflower (Cheiranthus allioni)	20-30	4-10	TB; KNO$_3$
45	Carrot (Daucus carota)	20-30	6-28	B	90	Zinnia (Zinnia spp)	20-30	3-7	TB; light

/1/ When a range is given, a daily fluctuating temperature is preferred, viz: 16 hours at lower temperature and 8 hours at higher temperature.
/2/ Maximum germination is usually obtained during the time limits as specified; for hard coated seeds an additional 5 days is recommended.
/3/ Substrata: B = between blotters; TB = top of blotters; T = between folded paper toweling; R = rolled towel; S = soil or sand; P = closed petri dish with cotton, blotter or filter paper; C = creped cellulose paper wadding. For KNO$_3$ treatment, a 0.2% solution, unless otherwise specified, is used to moisten substrata. /4/ Prechill at 5 or 10°C for 5 days. /5/ Soak in water for 2 hours, rinse, blot surface dry. /6/ Use 0.1% KNO$_3$. Prechill dormant seeds at 10°C for days. /7/ Species include: T. hybridum, T. incarnatum, T. pratense; T. repens, duration of 3-7 days. /8/ Dormant seed: 15°C. /9/ Prechill at 10°C for 3 days. /10/ Prechill at 5 or 10°C for 7 days. /11/ Dormant seed: light, KNO$_3$; prechill at 5 or 10°C for 3 days. /12/ Prechill at 10 or 15°C for 3 days. /13/ Substrata held somewhat drier than for the average kind of seed. /14/ Dormant seed: light, KNO$_3$. /15/ Fresh and hybrid seed may require prechilling at 3 or 5°C for 10-20 days.

380. EFFECTIVE PRETREATMENT AND GERMINATION CONDITIONS, SEEDS: WOODY PLANTS

When shed by the plant, seeds of certain species normally undergo a dormant period before onset of germination. Dormancy may be broken by various appropriate treatments prior to planting. Pretreatments usually include exposure to cold and to moisture, and may also include partial or complete rupture of the seed coat by scarification. If, following pretreatments, conditions for germination are established, maximum germination occurs within the indicated interval.

Species	Pretreatment[1] Temp[2] °C	Duration da	Germination Temp[3] °C	Duration da
Fruit and Nut Crops				
1 Apple (Pyrus malus)	5	75	20-30	60
2 Butternut (Juglans cinerea)	2-7	90-120	20-30	45-60
3 Cherry (Prunus avium and cerasus)	0-5	90-120	20-30[4]	60
4 Chestnut (Castanea dentata)	0-5	90	15-26[4]	30-45
5 Hickory (Carya spp)	-1 to 7	90-150	20-30	30-60
6 Mulberry (Morus rubra)	5	90-120	20-30	30-45
7 Peach (Prunus persica)	2-7	45-90	20-30[4]	60
8 Pear (Pyrus communis)	0-7	60-90	10	45
9 Pecan (Carya illinoensis)	2-7	30-90	20-30	45-60
10 Persimmon (Diospyros virg.)	10	60-90	20-30	40-60
11 Plum (Prunus americana)	5	150	10[5]	60
12 Raspberry (Rubus idaeus)	20-30;	90		
13	then 5[6]	90	20-30	30
14 Walnut (Juglans nigra)	3	60-120	20-30	15-40
Broadleaf Trees and Shrubs				
15 Alder (Alnus rubra)	5[4]	30-60	20-30[4,7]	30-40
16 Ash (Fraxinus spp)[8]	5	30-90	20-30	40-60
17 Ash (F. excelsior, F. nigra)	20;	60-90		
18	then 5[6]	60-90	20-30	30-40
19 Aspen (Populus tremuloides)			20-40	7
20 Barberry (Berberis spp)	0-5	15-40	12-24	40
21 Basswood (Tilia americana)	2-5[9]	110-130	18-29	30-60
22 Beech (Fagus spp)	5	90	20-30	60
23 Birch (Betula pendula)	0-10	30-60	20-30	30-40
24 Birch (B. populifolia)	0-10	60-90	20-30	40
25 Birch (B. papyrifera)	5	60-75	15-32	30-40
26 Birch (B. lenta)	0-5	40-70	15-32	30
27 Birch (B. alleghaniensis)	5	60-90	15-32	30-40
28 Boxelder (Acer negundo)	5	90	10-25	50-60
29 Catalpa (Catalpa spp)			20-30	30-60
30 Cherry (Prunus serotina)	5	90-120	20-30	30
31 Coffeetree (Gymnocladus dioica)	18-30;	60-120		
32	then 1-5[6]	60-90	20-30	60-90
33 Cottonwood (Populus deltoides)			20-30	2-6
34 Crabapple (Malus baccata)	5	30	20-30	30
35 Crabapple (M. coronaria)	5	120	10	30
36 Dogwood (Cornus florida)	5	100-130	20-30	20-25
37 Dogwood (C. nuttallii)	0-5	120-200	20-30	40
38 Elaeagnus (Elaeagnus spp)	5	90	20-30	20-40
39 Elm (Ulmus americana)	5	60	20-30	13-60
40 Elm (U. thomasii)			20-30	4-10
41 Elm (U. rubra)	5	60-90[4]	20-30	50-70
42 Eucalyptus (Eucalyptus globulus)			16-21[10]	10-15
43 Hackberry (Celtis spp)	5	60-90	20-30	60
44 Hawthorn (Crataegus mollis)	21-27;	60		
45	then 5[6]	75-90	16-27	
46 Honeylocust (Gleditsia triacanthos)	Scarification[11]		20-30	15-40
47 Honeysuckle (Lonicera		60		
48 tatarica)	5	30-60	20-30	60-90
49 Hornbeam (Carpinus caroliniana)	2-7	100-120	16-27	45
50 Locust (Robinia pseudoacacia)	Scarification[12]		15-27	10-25
51 Magnolia (Magnolia grandiflora)	5	90-120	15-26[4]	60
52 Maple (Acer macrophyllum)	5	60	20-30[4]	60[4]
53 Maple (A. rubrum)	5	60-75	10-25	30-40
54 Maple (A. saccharinum)			25-30	20-30
55 Maple (A. saccharum)	3-5	60-90	20-30	30
56 Oak (Quercus velutina)	1-5	30-60	18-27	30-50
57 Oak (Q. macrocarpa)	5	30-45	20-30	40
58 Oak (Q. prinus)			18-27	60
59 Oak (Q. robur)			16-25	30-60
60 Oak (Q. rubra)	0-4	30-45	20-30	40-60
61 Oak (Q. coccinea)	0-5	30-60	20-30	60

Species	Pretreatment[1] Temp[2] °C	Duration da	Germination Temp[3] °C	Duration da
Broadleaf Trees and Shrubs (concluded)				
62 Oak (Quercus imbricaria)	0-5	30-60	16-24	30
63 Oak (Q. alba)			20-30	30-50
64 Peashrub (Caragana spp)	Water soaking[13]		20-30	30-60
65 Poplar (Populus spp)			20-30	4-7
66 Rhododendron (Rhododendron spp)			20-30	30-90
67 Rose (Rosa spp)	5[14]	120	20-30[4]	30[4]
68 Serviceberry (Amelanchier spp)	2-5	90-180	20-30	40
69 Sumac (Rhus glabra)	Scarification[15]		20-30	30-60
70 Sweetgum (Liquidambar styraciflua)	5	30-90	20-30	20-60
71 Sycamore (Platanus occidentalis)	2-5	45-60	20-30	15-20
72 Tupelo (Nyssa sylvatica)	-1 to 10	60-90	20-30	30-60
73 Yellow-poplar (Liriodendron tulipifera)	0-10	70	20-30	50-70
Conifers				
74 Alaska-cedar (Chamaecyparis nootkatensis)	5[4]	60-90[4]	20-30	60
75 Baldcypress (Taxodium distichum)	5	30-60	20-30	30-50
76 Cedar (Cedrus spp)			20-30	30-40
77 Cypress (Cupressus arizonica)	5	60	20-30	30
78 Douglas-fir (Pseudotsuga menziesii)	1-5	30-60	16-30	15-30
79 Fir (Abies spp)[16]	5	60-90	20-30	30-45
80 Fir (A. balsamea)	5	90	20-30	60-120
81 Fir (A. grandis)[17]	5	30-40	20-30	30-45
82 Fir (A. procera)	1-5[4]	40-60	20-30	15-30
83 Hemlock (Tsuga canadensis)	5	60-120	20-30	60
84 Hemlock (T. heterophylla)	1-5	90	11-16	25-30
85 Incense-cedar (Libocedrus decurrens)	2-5	60-90	15-27	40-60
86 Juniper (Juniperus scopularum)	20-30;	120		
87	then 5[6]	120	20-30	20-30
88 Larch (Larix laricina)	5	30-60	20-30	30-50
89 Larch (L. decidua)	5	60	20-30	35
90 Larch (L. occidentalis)	5	30	20-30	20-30[4]
91 Pine (Pinus spp)[18]			20-30	30-40
92 Pine (P. strobus)	10	30	20-30	30-40
93 Pine (P. jeffreyi)			15-27	60-90
94 Pine (P. taeda)	2-4	30-90	20-30	35-45
95 Pine (P. contorta)			15-27	30
96 Pine (P. palustris)			13-24	35
97 Pine (P. rigida)	5	30	18-27	30
98 Pine (P. echinata)	2-4	30-45	15-27	35-45
99 Pine (P. elliottii)	2-5	15-45	18-30	20-45
100 Pine (P. lambertiana)	2-10	90	16-21	40
101 Pine (P. monticola)	0-5	90	16-27	60-90
102 Port-Orford-cedar (Chamaecyparis lawsoniana)	5[4]	30-60[4]	20-30	60
103 Redcedar (Juniperus virginiana)	25;	30		
104	then 5[6]	90	10-25	20-30
105 Redcedar (Thuja plicata)	0-10	30-60	20-30	20
106 Sequoia (Sequoia spp)			15-20	40-60
107 Spruce (Picea mariana)	5	30-60	20-30	20-30
108 Spruce (P. engelmannii)			20-27	50
109 Spruce (P. abies)			20-30	20-30
110 Spruce (P. rubens)	5	30-45	20-30	20-30
111 Spruce (P. sitchensis)	1-5	40	25	15
112 Spruce (P. glauca)	5	60-90	20-30	30-45
113 White-cedar (Chamaecyparis thyoides)	5[4]	30-60	20-30	60
114 White-cedar (Thuja occidentalis)	0-10	30-60	20-30	30

/1/ When no treatment is specified, pretreatment is not required. /2/ When a range is given, the temperature may vary between the limits. /3/ When a range is given, a daily fluctuating temperature, 16 hr at lower temperature and 8 hr at higher temperature, is preferred. /4/ Suggested treatment, experimental data incomplete. /5/ Seeds from southern USA germinate best at 21-27°C. /6/ Treatment at high temperature is followed by treatment at low temperature. /7/ Germination data also applicable to European alder (A. glutinosa), pretreatment not required. /8/ Species include: green ash (F. pennsylvanica), white ash (F. americana). /9/ Prior to stratification soak 3 da in water, surface dry, then digest 40 min in concentrated H_2SO_4 (below 55°C), wash and extract seeds. Place dry seed in concentrated H_2SO_4 for 10-15 min. /10/ Constant temperature between these limits is preferred. /11/ Scarify with concentrated H_2SO_4 (25-36°C) for 1-2 hr prior to planting. /12/ Scarify with concentrated H_2SO_4 (16-27°C) for 20-120 min prior to planting. /13/ Soak seed in water at 21°C for 12 hr prior to planting. /14/ Scarify with concentrated H_2SO_4 for 60-80 min prior to planting. /15/ Scarify with concentrated H_2SO_4 for 1-4 hr prior to planting. /16/ Data applicable to Pacific silver fir (A. amabilis), white fir (A. concolor); for California red fir (A. magnifica), with a duration of pretreatment modified to 60 days. /17/ Data also applicable to Fraser fir (A. fraseri), cf Fn 4. /18/ Species include: ponderosa pine (P. ponderosa), red pine (P. resinosa), Scotch pine (P. sylvestris); jack pine (P. banksiana), with duration of germination modified to 15-60 days.

381. RESISTANCE TO WILTING

Plants may grow within a wide range of soil moisture conditions, but at a definite moisture limit, known as the wilting coefficient (permanent wilting percentage), the plant is unable to overcome the resistance of soil to water removal. The wilting coefficient is the moisture content of the soil, expressed as a percentage of dry weight, at the time when the leaves of the plant first undergo a permanent reduction in moisture content (resulting from soil moisture deficiency). At this condition the leaves cannot recover in an approximately saturated atmosphere without the addition of water to the soil. In Part I, free energy values indicate soil's resistance(to removal of water) that plants would have to overcome at various moisture levels. Part II shows that all plants wilt at relatively the same moisture content in a given soil. Sampling error varies with completeness with which the roots contact the soil mass. Cocklebur, for example, may have relatively few coarse roots whereas alfalfa has very many fine absorbing-roots. Part III gives wilting coefficients as determined from small or large soil containers. Part IV demonstrates that repeated wiltings do not increase the ability of plants to take more water from soil. Part V reveals the constancy and recurrence of wilting coefficient in the field; determinations were made in the same orchard for many years. Soil moisture is reduced to essentially the same per cent annually, and plants do not become more resistant to wilting with increase in age. Differences in root distribution influence wilting percentages. Part VI denotes that wilting coefficient is not affected by evaporation conditions antecedent to wilting, or by soil temperature within the minimum and maximum range likely to be encountered during the growing season. Part VII gives the depths to which the roots of mature crops might exhaust the water supply when grown in a deep, permeable, well-drained soil, having little horizon formation. The survival of certain plants under severe conditions of drought may depend, in part, on the depth of rooting and thoroughness with which the roots permeate soil and not on the capacity to extract more water from soil than other plants.

Part I: FREE ENERGY PER GRAM OF WATER: VARIOUS SOIL MOISTURE CONTENTS AT 30°C

	Soil Moisture[1]	Vapor Pressure mm Hg	Relative Humidity %	Energy[2] ergs
	Fine Sandy Loam			
1	10.5	31.7	99.7	4.40
2	9.3	31.7	99.7	4.40
3	5.9	31.6	99.4	8.82
4	5.4	31.4	98.7	17.70
5	4.6	31.4	98.7	17.70
6	3.0	31.4	98.7	17.70
7	1.7	30.8	96.7	44.68
8	1.6	30.3	95.3	67.55
9	1.2	27.5	86.5	203.12
10	0.9	24.9	78.3	341.95
11	0.8	23.3	73.3	434.78
12	0.7	17.9	56.3	803.43
	Clay Soil			
13	27.0	31.6	99.4	8.82
14	21.6	31.5	99.1	13.25
15	18.6	31.3	98.4	22.16
16	13.1	31.3	98.4	22.16
17	10.9	31.1	97.8	31.12
18	10.8	30.6	96.2	53.78
19	10.1	29.3	92.1	114.47
20	9.6	28.1	88.4	172.93
21	9.0	26.5	83.1	268.83
22	8.7	25.3	79.6	319.72
23	8.5	24.0	75.5	393.40
24	8.4	22.9	72.0	458.96
25	7.9	18.2	57.2	780.22
26	7.8	17.0	53.5	875.57

/1/ Grams water per 100 g soil. /2/ Free energy per g water x 10^6.

Part III: WILTING COEFFICIENT: VARIOUS SOIL CONTAINERS

	Plants	Soil Container	Wilting %	Availability Ratio[1]
	Oakley Fine Sand (3.29)[2]			
1	Sunflower	10-quart	1.41	2.33
2	Corn	10-quart	1.35	2.44
3	Sunflower	Small[3]	1.24	2.65
4	Corn	Small[3]	1.36	2.42
5	Miscellaneous[4]	10-quart	1.29	2.55
	Yolo Fine Sandy Loam (16.80)[2]			
6	Miscellaneous[4]	10-quart	8.67	1.98
7	Miscellaneous[4]	Tank[5]	9.88	1.74
	Yolo Fine Sandy Loam (18.49)[2]			
8	Sunflower	10-quart	9.78	1.89
9	Corn	10-quart	9.67	1.91
10	Sunflower	Small[3]	10.06	1.84
11	Corn	Small[3]	10.33	1.79
	Yolo Silt Loam (21.35)[2]			
12	Sunflower	10-quart	10.25	2.08
13	Corn	10-quart	10.28	2.08
14	Sunflower	Small[3]	10.38	2.05
15	Corn	Small[3]	10.71	2.00
16	Miscellaneous[4]	10-quart	9.95	2.15
	Yolo Clay (28.03)[2]			
17	Sunflower	10-quart	13.35	2.10
18	Corn	10-quart	13.13	2.13
19	Sunflower	Small[3]	14.48	1.94
20	Corn	Small[3]	14.46	1.94
21	Miscellaneous[4]	10-quart	12.65	2.22

/1/ Ratio of moisture equivalent, cf Fn 2, and permanent wilting; indicates the range of available water. /2/ Moisture equivalent, i.e., percentage water content that a soil can retain in opposition to a force 1000 times that of gravity, is enclosed in parentheses. /3/ Cannery cans containing about 550 g soil. /4/ Include cotton, sorghum, guar, mustard, black-eye and mung beans. /5/ Tanks contained 1000 to 2000 lbs soil.

Part VI: WILTING COEFFICIENT: SHADE AND FULL SUNLIGHT

	Soil	Plant	Wilting % In Shade	Wilting % In Sun
1	Oakley fine sand	Sunflower	1.3	1.4
2		Corn	1.3	1.4
3	Yolo clay	Sunflower	14	13.7
4		Corn	13.5	14.1
5	Yolo fine sandy loam	Sunflower	11	9.5
6		Corn	9.8	9.9
7	Yolo silt loam	Sunflower	10.4	10.4
8		Corn	10.7	10.6
9	Placentia loam	Sunflower	3.7	4.3
10		Corn	4.6	3.8
11	Sierra sandy loam	Corn	6	6.5
12	Columbia sand	Sunflower	6.3	7.2
13		Corn	6.7	6.5

Part VII: DEPTH OF WATER EXTRACTION: MATURE PLANT ROOTS

	Species	Root Depth Ft
1	Alfalfa (Medicago sativa)	10-15
2	Almond (Prunus amygdalus)	6-9
3	Apricot (P. armeniaca)	6-9
4	Artichoke (Helianthus tuberosus)	4.5
5	Asparagus (Asparagus officinalis)	10
6	Bean (Phaseolus lunatus macrocarpus)	4
7	Beet, garden (Beta vulgaris)	3
8	Beet, sugar (B. vulgaris)	5-6
9	Broccoli (Brassica oleracea botrytis)	2
10	Cabbage (B. oleracea capitata)	2
11	Cantaloupe (Cucumis melo cantalupensis)	4-6
12	Carrot (Daucus carota)	3
13	Cauliflower (Brassica oleracea bot.)	2
14	Celery (Apium graveolens)	2
15	Cherry (Prunus spp)	6-9
16	Citrus (Citrus spp)	6
17	Corn, field (Zea mays)	6
18	Corn, sweet (Z. mays)	3
19	Cotton (Gossypium spp)	6
20	Cucumber (Cucumis sativus)	3.5
21	Eggplant (Solanum melongena)	3
22	Fig (Ficus carica)	5
23	Flax (Linium usitatissimum)	6
24	Grape (Vitis vinifera)	8
25	Hop (Humulus lupulus)	4-6
26	Lettuce (Lactuca sativa)	1.5
27	Milo (Sorghum vulgare)	6
28	Mustard (Brassica juncea)	3.5
29	Olive (Oleo europaeo)	6-9
30	Onion (Allium cepa)	1
31	Parsnip (Pastinaca sativa)	4
32	Pea (Pisum sativum)	3.5
33	Peach (Prunus persica)	6-9
34	Pear (Pyrus communis)	6-9
35	Prune (Prunus americana)	6-9
36	Pepper (Capsicum frutescens)	3
37	Potato (Solanum tuberosum)	3
38	Pumpkin (Cucurbita pepo)	6
39	Radish (Raphanus sativus)	1.5
40	Spinach (Spinacia oleracea)	2
41	Squash (Cucurbita pepo)	3
42	Sudan grass (Sorghum sudanense)	>6
43	Tomato (Lycopersicon esculentum)	6-10
44	Turnip (Brassica rapa)	3
45	Strawberry (Fragaria spp)	3-4
46	Sweet potato (Ipomoea batatus)	4-6
47	Walnut (Juglans spp)	12-18
48	Watermelon (Citrullus vulgaris)	6

Part II: WILTING COEFFICIENT: CLAY SOIL

	Species	Wilting %
1	Alfalfa (Medicago sativa)	13
2	Castor bean (Ricinus communis)	15
3	Cocklebur (Xanthium canadense)	15.6
4	Coleus (Coleus blumei)	14.2
5	Corn (Zea mays)	15
6	Fenugreek (Trigonella foenum-graecum)	15
7	Hollyhock (Althaea rosea)	14.2
8	Jimson-weed (Datura tatula)	15
9	Lettuce (Lactuca sativa)	14.6
10	Mallow (Malva parviflora)	13.4
11	Marigold (Tagetes locida)	13.6
12	Mung-bean (Phaseolus aureus)	14.7
13	Mustard (Brassica alba)	13.8
14	Okra (Hibiscus esculentus)	14.7
15	Pepper (Piper capsicum)	14.6
16	Petunia (Petunia hybrida)	13.5
17	Pigweed (Amaranthus retroflexus)	14.5
18	Salvia (Salvia splendens)	14.4
19	Sorghum (Sorghum vulgare)	14.2
20	Soybean (Glycine soja)	14
21	Spinach (Spinacia oleracea)	13.7
22	Sunflower (Helianthus annuus)	14
23	Thistle (Silybum marianum)	15
24	Wheat (Triticum aestivum)	13.6

Part IV: WILTING COEFFICIENT: SUNFLOWER

	Soil	1st	2nd	3rd	4th	5th	6th
		Percentages for Successive Wiltings					
1	Oakley fine sand	1.6	1.5	1.5	1.5	1.5	1.5
2	Yolo fine sandy loam	9.5	9.4	9.4	9.3	9.2	9
3	Yolo silt loam	10.7	10.5	10.8	10.7	10.6	11
4	Yolo clay	13.4	13.8	13.8	14	14.3	
5	Plainfield fine sand	1.4	1.4				
6	Fresno sandy loam	3.1	3.1	3.1	3	3	
7	Tehama loam	4.5	4.5	4.4			
8	Placentia loam	5.8	6	6.1			
9	Wooster silt loam	6.2	6	5.8			
10	Madera & Gridley loam	10.5	10.5	10.4	10.5		
11	Brockton clay loam	11.6	11.4	11.6			

Part V: PERMANENT WILTING PERCENTAGE: END OF GROWING SEASON

	Soil Depth ft	1 yr	2 yr	3 yr	4 yr	5 yr	6 yr	7 yr	8 yr	9 yr	10 yr
		Peach (Prunus persica)									
1	0-3	9.9	8.0	8.7	8.8	8.6	9.2	10.5	10.3	9.8	9.7
2	3-6	8.6	8.0	8.4	7.8	8.0	8.3	9.4	9.6	9.1	8.6
3	6-9	7.9	7.4	7.6	7.7	7.6	7.6	9.1	8.8	7.7	7.4
4	9-12	8.8	7.4	8.3	8.3	7.7					
		Plum (Prunus americana)									
5	0-3	8.4	8.0	8.5	8.5	8.4	8.8	8.9	8.8	8.9	
6	3-6	7.9	7.8	8.0	7.8	8.0	8.2	8.6	7.8	7.6	8.4
7	6-9	9.8	10.2	9.7	9.9	10.3	9.6	10.6			
		Walnut (Juglans sp)									
8	0-3	10.5	10.8	11.1	11.1	10.1	10.8	11.3	11.0	10.4	11.1
9	3-6	11.3	11.2	11.1	10.5	10.7	11.1	11.2	11.1	10.9	11.4
10	6-9	8.4	8.9	9.1	8.7	7.9	8.7	8.8	9.0	9.5	9.5

453

382. SOIL pH ADAPTATIONS: PLANTS

Plant growth is best at the pH indicated and only fair at the limits of the ranges shown in parentheses - estimates "c" of the 95% range (cf Introduction).

	Species	Soil pH
	Field and Forage Crops	
1	Alfalfa (Medicago sativa)	6.0-7.5(5.5-8.5)
2	Barley (Hordeum vulgare)	6.0-7.5(5.5-8.5)
3	Beet, sugar (Beta vulgaris)	6.5-8.0(5.5-8.5)
4	Bluegrass, Kentucky (Poa pratensis)	5.5-7.5
5	Buckwheat (Fagopyrum esculentum)	5.5-7.0(4.5-8.0)
6	Clover, red (Trifolium pratense)	6.0-7.5
7	Clover, white (T. repens)	6.0-7.5
8	Cotton (Gossypium hirsutum)	5.0-6.5(to 8.5)
9	Flax (Linum usitatissimum)	5.0-7.0(to 8.5)
10	Hemp (Cannabis sativa)	6.0-7.5
11	Oat (Avena sativa)	5.0-7.5(4.5-8.0)
12	Peanut (Arachis hypogaea)	5.0-6.5(to 8.0)
13	Redtop (Agrostis alba)	5.0-6.5
14	Rice (Oryza sativa)	5.0-6.5
15	Rye (Secale cereale)	5.0-7.0(4.5-8.0)
16	Sorghum (Sorghum vulgare)	5.5-7.5(4.5-8.0)
17	Soybean (Glycine soja)	6.0-7.5
18	Sugar cane (Saccharum officinarum)	6.0-8.0(5.0-
19	Sunflower (Helianthus annuus)	6.0-7.5
20	Sweetclover (Melilotus alba)	6.5-8.0
21	Tobacco (Nicotiana tabacum)	5.5-7.5(4.5-
22	Wheat (Triticum aestivum)	5.5-7.5(5.0-8.5)
	Fruit and Vegetable Crops	
23	Apple (Pyrus malus)	5.0-6.5(to 8.0)
24	Bean, lima (Phaseolus lunatus macrocarpus)	6.0-7.5
25	Bean, string (P. vulgaris)	6.0-7.5
26	Beet, garden (Beta vulgaris)	6.0-7.5
27	Blueberry (Vaccinium spp)	4.5-6.0
28	Cabbage (Brassica oleracea capitata)	6.0-7.5(to 8.5)
29	Cantaloupe (Cucumis melo)	6.0-8.0
30	Carrot (Daucus carota)	5.5-7.0(5.0-8.5)
31	Celery (Apium graveolens dulce)	6.0-7.5(to 8.5)
32	Corn (Zea mays)	5.5-7.5(5.0-8.0)
33	Cucumber (Cucumis sativus)	5.5-7.0(to 8.0)
34	Lemon (Citrus limonia)	6.0-7.5(to 8.5)
35	Lettuce (Lactuca sativa)	6.0-7.5(5.5-8.0)
36	Onion (Allium cepa)	6.0-7.5(5.0)
37	Orange, sweet (Citrus sinensis)	6.0-7.5
38	Parsley (Petroselinum hortense)	5.0-7.0
39	Pea, garden (Pisum sativum)	6.0-8.0
40	Peach (Prunus persica)	6.0-7.5
41	Pear (Pyrus communis)	6.0-7.5
42	Pepper (Capsicum annuum)	5.5-7.0
43	Pineapple (Ananas sativus)	5.0-6.5
44	Potato (Solanum tuberosum)	5.0-6.5(7.0-8.0)
45	Radish (Raphanus sativus)	5.5-7.0(5.0-8.0)
46	Spinach (Spinacia oleracea)	6.0-7.5(5.5-8.5)
47	Squash, winter (Cucurbita maxima)	5.5-7.0
48	Strawberry (Fragaria spp)	5.0-6.5(4.5-8.0)
49	Sweetpotato (Ipomoea batatas)	5.0-6.5(to 7.5)
50	Tomato (Lycopersicon esculentum)	5.5-7.5(4.5-
51	Turnip (Brassica napus)	5.5-7.0
52	Watermelon (Citrullus vulgaris)	5.0-6.5(5.0-8.0)
	Ornamental Plants	
53	African-violet (Saintpaulia ionantha)	5.5-7.0
54	Almond, flowering (Prunus glandulosa)	6.0-7.5
55	Aster, China (Callistephus chinensis)	6.0-7.5(5.5-)
56	Balsam, garden (Impatiens balsamina)	6.0-7.5(5.5-)
57	Begonia (Begonia spp)	5.5-7.0
58	Boxwood (Buxus sempervirens)	6.0-7.5
59	Camellia (Camellia japonica)	4.5-6.0
60	Canna (Canna indica)	6.0-8.0
61	Carnation (Dianthus caryophyllus)	6.0-7.5(5.0-)
62	Chrysanthemum (Chrysanthemum morifolium)	6.0-7.5(5.0-8.0)
63	Coleus (Coleus blumei)	6.0-7.5
64	Dahlia (Dahlia spp)	6.0-8.0
65	Gardenia (Gardenia jasminoides)	5.0-7.0
66	Geranium (Pelargonium domesticum)	6.0-8.0(5.0-)
67	Gladiolus (Gladiolus spp)	6.0-8.0
68	Hibiscus, Chinese (Hibiscus rosa-sinensis)	6.0-8.0
69	Hyacinth (Hyacinthus orientalis)	6.0-7.5
70	Iris, bearded (Iris spp)	6.0-8.0
71	Ivy, English (Hedera helix)	6.0-8.0
72	Kalanchoe (Kalanchoe blossfeldiana)	6.0-7.5
73	Lily, Easter (Lilium longiflorum)	6.0-7.5
74	Nasturtium (Tropaeolum majus)	5.5-7.5
75	Narcissus (Narcissus spp)	5.0-7.0

	Species	Soil pH
	Ornamental Plants (concluded)	
76	Primrose, evening (Oenothera biennis)	6.0-8.0
77	Rose (Rosa hybrida)	5.5-7.0(5.0-7.5)
78	Snapdragon (Antirrhinum majus)	6.0-7.5(5.0-8.0)
79	Spiderwort (Tradescantia virginiana)	5.0-7.5
80	Stock (Matthiola incana)	6.0-7.5
81	Tulip (Tulipa gesneriana)	6.0-7.5
	Trees and Shrubs	
82	Acacia (Acacia spp)	6.5-8.0
83	Ailanthus (Ailanthus altissima)	6.0-8.0
84	Alder (Alnus spp)	6.0-7.5
85	Aspen, quaking (Populus tremuloides)	4.0-5.5
86	Baldcypress (Taxodium distichum)	6.0-7.5
87	Basswood (Tilia spp)	6.0-7.5
88	Beech, European (Fagus sylvatica)	6.0-7.5
89	Beech, American (F. grandifolia)	5.0-6.5
90	Birch, sweet (Betula lenta)	4.5-6.0
91	Buckeye, Ohio (Aesculus glabra)	6.0-7.5
92	Buckeye, red (A. pavia)	5.0-6.5
93	Catalpa (Catalpa spp)	6.0-7.5
94	Cherry, choke (Prunus virginiana)	6.0-7.5
95	Chestnut, American (Castanea dentata)	4.0-6.5
96	Chinkapin, Allegheny (C. pumila)	4.0-6.5
97	Dogwood, flowering (Cornus florida)	5.0-6.5
98	Douglas-fir (Pseudotsuga taxifolia)	5.0-6.5
99	Elm (Ulmus spp)[1]	6.0-8.0
100	Eucalyptus (Eucalyptus spp)	6.5-8.0
101	Fir (Abies spp)	4.0-6.5
102	Ginkgo (Ginkgo biloba)	5.5-7.0
103	Hackberry (Celtis spp)	6.0-7.5
104	Hemlock, eastern (Tsuga canadensis)	4.5-6.0
105	Hickory, shagbark (Carya ovata)	6.0-6.5
106	Holly, American (Ilex opaca)	4.5-6.0
107	Holly, English (I. aquifolium)	5.0-6.5
108	Honeylocust (Gleditsia triacanthos)	6.0-7.5
109	Hophornbeam, eastern (Ostrya virginiana)	6.0-7.0
110	Hornbeam (Carpinus spp)	6.0-7.5
111	Horsechestnut (Aesculus hippocastanum)	5.5-7.0
112	Juniper (Juniperus spp)	5.5-7.5
113	Juniper, common (J. communis)	5.0-6.5
114	Juniper, mountain (J. communis saxatilis)	4.0-5.5
115	Coffeetree, Kentucky (Gymnocladus dioica)	6.0-7.5
116	Larch (Larix spp)	4.5-7.5
117	Locust (Robinia spp)	5.5-7.5
118	Magnolia, southern (Magnolia grandiflora)	5.0-7.0
119	Maple (Acer spp)	5.5-7.5
120	Maple, mountain (A. spicatum)	4.5-6.0
121	Mountain-ash, American (Sorbus americana)	4.5-6.5
122	Mountain-ash, European (S. aucuparia)	5.5-7.5
123	Mountain-laurel (Kalmia latifolia)	4.0-6.0
124	Mulberry (Morus spp)	6.0-7.5
125	Oak (Quercus spp)[2]	4.5-6.5
126	Oak (Quercus spp)[3]	4.0-5.0
127	Oak, English (Q. robur)	6.0-7.5
128	Oak, white (Q. alba)	6.5-7.5
129	Oak, willow (Q. phellos)	4.5-6.5
130	Paulownia, royal (Paulownia tomentosa)	5.5-7.5
131	Pine (Pinus spp)	4.0-6.5
132	Pine, longleaf (P. palustris)	4.0-6.0
133	Pine, red (P. resinosa)	5.0-6.0
134	Poplar (Populus spp)	5.5-7.5
135	Redbud, eastern (Cercis canadensis)	6.0-7.5
136	Redcedar, eastern (Juniperus virginiana)	5.0-8.0
137	Rhododendron (Rhododendron spp)	4.0-6.0
138	Service berry (Amelanchier spp)	5.0-7.5
139	Spruce (Picea spp)	4.0-6.5
140	Spruce, blue (P. pungens)	5.0-6.5
141	Spruce, Sitka (P. sitchensis)	5.0-6.5
142	Sweetgum (Liquidambar styraciflua)	5.0-6.5
143	Sycamore (Platanus spp)	5.5-7.5
144	Tupelo, black (Nyssa sylvatica)	4.5-6.0
145	Walnut (Juglans spp)	6.0-7.5
146	White-cedar, Atlantic (Chamaecyparis thyoides)	4.0-6.0
147	White-cedar, northern (Thuja occidentalis)	6.0-7.5(5.5-8.5)
148	Willow (Salix spp)	5.5-7.5
149	Willow, creeping (S. repens)	4.5-6.0
150	Yellow-poplar (Liriodendron tulipifera)	5.5-7.5
151	Yew (Taxus spp)	5.0-7.5

/1/ Species include: American elm (U. americana), Chinese elm (U. parvifolia). /2/ Species include: black oak (Q. velutina), northern red oak (Q. rubra), scarlet oak (Q. coccinea). /3/ Species include: blackjack oak (Q. marilandica), post oak (Q. stellata), turkey oak (Q. laevis), southern red oak (Q. falcata). For pin oak (Q. palustris) and chestnut oak (Q. prinus), 6.0-7.0.

383. BORON TOLERANCE: PLANTS

For each tolerance group, plants are listed in order of decreasing tolerance to boron present in nutrient solutions. Differences of a few places in position may not be significant, and there is no sharp division between successive groups. Boron concentrations indicate the range within which injury was observed at the time of harvest.

High Tolerance (Boron 25-10 ppm)	Median Tolerance (Boron 10-5 ppm((concluded)	Low Tolerance (5-1 ppm) (concluded)
1 Athel (Tamarix aphylla)	18 Cotton, Acala (Gossypium hirsutum)	36 Walnut (Juglans nigra)
2 Asparagus (Asparagus officinalis)	19 Cotton, Pima (G. barbadense)	37 Walnut (J. regia)
3 Palm (Phoenix canariensis)	20 Tomato (Lycopersicon esculentum)	38 Artichoke (Helianthus tuberosus)
4 Date (P. dactylifera)	21 Sweet pea (Lathyrus odoratus)	39 Bean, navy (Phaseolus vulgaris)
5 Beet, sugar (Beta vulgaris)	22 Radish (Raphanus sativus)	40 Elm (Ulmus americana)
6 Beet, mangel (B. vulgaris)	23 Pea, field (Pisum sp)	41 Plum (Prunus sp)
7 Beet, garden (B. vulgaris)	24 Olive (Oleo europaea)	42 Pear (Pyrus communis)
8 Alfalfa (Medicago sativa)	25 Barley (Hordeum vulgare)	43 Apple (P. malus)
9 Gladiolus (Gladiolus spp)	26 Wheat (Triticum aestivum)	44 Grape, Malaga and Sultanina (Vitis vinifera)
10 Broadbean (Vicia faba)	27 Corn (Zea mays)	45 Fig, Kadota (Ficus carica)
11 Onion (Allium cepa)	28 Milo (Sorghum vulgare)	46 Persimmon (Diospyros virginiana)
12 Turnip (Brassica rapa)	29 Oat (Avena sativa)	47 Cherry (Prunus spp)
13 Cabbage (B. oleraceae cap.)	30 Zinnia (Zinnia sp)	48 Peach (P. persica)
14 Lettuce (Lactuca sativa)	31 Pumpkin (Cucurbita pepo)	49 Apricot (P. armeniaca)
15 Carrot (Daucus carota)	32 Pepper, bell (Capsicum sp)	50 Blackberry, thornless (Rubus sp)
Medium Tolerance (Boron 10-5 ppm)	33 Sweetpotato (Ipomoea batatas)	51 Orange (Citrus spp)
16 Sunflower (Helianthus annuus)	34 Bean (Phaseolus lunatus mac.)	52 Avocado (Persea gratissima)
17 Potato (Solanum tuberosum)	**Low Tolerance (5-1 ppm)**	53 Grapefruit (Citrus paradisi)
	35 Pecan (Carya illinoensis)	54 Lemon (C. limonia)

384. SALT TOLERANCE: PLANTS

Salinity values are expressed in terms of electrical conductivity (EC_e) of the saturation extract of active root-zone soil, and are for total soluble salts. Units of conductivity measurement are millimhos per cm at 25°C. In each tolerance group, plants are listed in order of decreasing salt tolerance; however, individual differences fron one place to the next may not be significant.

Part I: EFFECT ON CROP YIELD

Data correlate soil salinity with crop yield. Plants listed at the beginning and at the end of each tolerance group may be expected to produce only 50% of a normal yield when grown in soils of salinity represented in upper and lower ranges.

Fruit Crops	Vegetable Crops (concluded)	Forage Crops (concluded)
High Tolerance	**Medium Tolerance (EC_ex1000=10-4) (concl'd)**	**High Tolerance (EC_ex 1000 = 18-12) (concluded)**
1 Date (Phoenix dactylifera)	30 Squash (Cucurbita spp)	57 Wheatgrass (Agropyron smithii)
Medium Tolerance	31 Cucumber (Cucumis sativus)	58 Barley (Hordeum vulgare)[2]
2 Pomegranate (Punica granatum)	**Low Tolerance (EC_ex1000=4-3)**	59 Trefoil (Lotus corniculatus)
3 Fig (Ficus carica)	32 Radish (Raphanus sativus)	**Medium Tolerance (EC_ex1000=12-4)**
4 Olive (Olea europaea)	33 Celery (Apium graveolens)	60 Sweetclover (Melilotus alba)
5 Grape (Vitis vinifera)	34 Bean, garden (Phaseolus vulgaris)	61 Sweetclover (M. officinalis)
6 Cantaloupe (Cucumis melo canta.)	**Field Crops**	62 Ryegrass (Lolium perenne)
Low Tolerance	**High Tolerance (EC_ex1000=16-10)**	63 Brome (Bromus marginatus)
7 Pear (Pyrus communis)	35 Barley (Hordeum vulgare)[1]	64 Clover (Trifolium fragiferum)
8 Apple (P. malus)	36 Beet, sugar (Beta vulgaris)	65 Dallis grass (Paspalum dilatatum)
9 Prune (Prunus sp)	37 Rape (Brassica napus)	66 Sudan grass (Sorghum sudanense)
10 Plum (P. americana)	38 Cotton (Gossypium sp)	67 Sweetclover, hubam (Melilotus alba)
11 Almond (Amygdalus communis)	**Medium Tolerance (EC_ex1000=10-6)**	68 Alfalfa (Medicago sativa)
12 Apricot (Prunus armeniaca)	39 Rye (Secale cereale)[1]	69 Fescue (Festuca elatior arundinacea)
13 Peach (P. persica)	40 Wheat (Triticum aestivum)[1]	70 Rye (Secale cereale)[2]
14 Strawberry (Fragaria sp)	41 Oat (Avena sativa)[1]	71 Wheat (Triticum aestivum)[2]
Vegetable Crops	42 Rice (Oryza sativa)	72 Oat (Avena sativa)[2]
High Tolerance (EC_ex1000=12-10)	43 Sorghum (Sorghum vulgare)[1]	73 Orchard grass (Dactylis glomerata)
15 Beet, garden (Beta vulgaris)	44 Corn (Zea mays)	74 Bluegrama (Bouteloua gracilis)
16 Kale (Brassica oleracea acephala)	45 Flax (Linum usitatissimum)	75 Fescue (Festuca elatior)
17 Asparagus (Asparagus officinalis)	46 Sunflower (Helianthus annuus)	76 Canary grass (Phalaris arundinacea)
18 Spinach (Spinacia oleracea)	47 Castor bean (Ricinus communis)	77 Trefoil (Lotus uliginosus)
Medium Tolerance (EC_ex1000=10-4)	**Low Tolerance (EC_ex1000=4)**	78 Brome (Bromus inermis)
19 Tomato (Lycopersicon esculentum)	48 Bean, field (Phaseolus sp)	79 Oatgrass (Arrhenatherum elatius)
20 Broccoli (Brassica oleracea italica)	**Forage Crops**	80 Milk vetch (Astragalus cicer)
21 Cabbage (B. oleracea capitata)	**High Tolerance (EC_ex 1000 = 18-12)**	81 Sourclover (Melilotus indica)
22 Pepper, bell (Capsicum sp)	49 Sacaton (Sporobolus airoides)	82 Milk vetch (Astragalus falcatus)
23 Cauliflower (Brassica oleracea bot.)	50 Saltgrass (Distichlis stricta)	**Low Tolerance (EC_ex1000=4-2)**
24 Lettuce (Lactuca sativa)	51 Nuttall alkali grass (Puccinellia nuttallians)	83 Whiteclover (Trifolium repens)
25 Corn, sweet (Zea mays)	52 Bermuda grass (Cynodon dactylon)	84 Foxtail (Alopecurus pratensis)
26 Potato (Solanum tuberosum)	53 Rhodes grass (Chloris gayana)	85 Clover (Trifolium hybridum)
27 Carrot (Daucus carota)	54 Rescue grass (Bromus catharticus)	86 Clover (T. pratense)
28 Onion (Allium cepa)	55 Wild rye (Elymus canadensis)	87 Clover, Ladino (T. repens)
29 Pea (Pisum sativum)	56 Wild rye (E. triticoides)	88 Burnet (Sanguisorba minor)

/1/ Tolerance determined on basis of yield of grain. /2/ Determined as yield in hay.

Part II: EFFECT ON PLANT

Data are based on soil salinity values at which no evidence of toxicity is generally observed. For citrus and avocados the salts present in the soil were predominantly chlorides; for other plants, a mixture of chlorides and sulfates.

Medium Tolerance (EC_ex1000=8-4)	Poor Tolerance (EC_ex 1000 = 4-2) (concluded)	Very Poor Tolerance (EC_ex 1000 = 2-1) (concluded)
	Grapefruit (Citrus paradisi)(concluded)	Avocado, Mexican
1 Grapefruit (Citrus paradisi) on Rangpur lime	8 on Sampson tangelo	17 on West Indian
	9 on sweet orange	Grapefruit (Citrus Paradisi)
2 Orange (Citrus spp) on Cleopatra mandarin	Lemon (C. limonia)	18 on trifoliate-orange
3 Grapefruit (C. paradisi) on Cleopatra mandarin	10 on sour orange	19 on Troyer citrange
4 on Timkat mandarin	11 Plum, Natal (Prunus americana)	20 on Kara mandarin
Poor Tolerance (EC_ex1000=4-2)	Avocado, West Indian (Persea gratissima)	21 on king orange
5 Orange (Citrus spp) on sour lime	12 on West Indian	22 Sapote, white
	13 Cherry, Surinam (Prunus sp)	23 Mango, Saigon (Mangifera indica)
6 Grapefruit (C. paradisi) on rough lemon	14 Cherry, haden (Prunus sp)	24 Mango, Brooks (M. indica)
	Very Poor Tolerance (EC_ex1000=2-1)	Avocado, Mexican (Persea gratissima)
7 on sour orange	15 Papaya (Carya papaya)	25 on Mexican
	Avocado, Lula (Persea gratissima)	26 Cherimoya (Annona cherimola)
	16 on West Indian	

Data are based on field observations unless otherwise indicated in footnotes. Tolerance to salinity alone is often not the most critical factor, as it differs with the age of the individual, temperature and hydrogen ion concentration of the water, previous conditioning, length of exposure, and other variables. Values represent lower and upper limits of salinity at which these animals have been found to survive. Salinity is defined as the total weight of dissolved solids in 1 kg of water at $27^{\circ}C$ ($80.6^{\circ}F$), expressed as g/kg or o/oo.

FW = fresh water; BW = brackish water; MW = marine water; SLW = highly saline lake water.

	Animal	Normal Habitat[1]	Salinity Tolerance g/kg or o/oo		Animal	Normal Habitat[1]	Salinity Tolerance g/kg or o/oo
	Porifera				**Teleostomi (concluded)**		
1	Sponge, boring or sulfur (Cliona celata)	MW	15-36	58	Flounder, fringed (Etropus crossotus)	MW	4.4-37
	Coelenterata			59	Flounder, gulf (Paralichthys lethostigma)	MW, BW[13]	0-36
2	Hydra (Chlorohydra and Pelmatohydra)	FW	0-2.5	60	Flounder, Gunter's (Syacium gunteri)	MW	31-35
3	Hydroid (Clava)	BW	10-30	61	Gaff-topsail (Bagre marina)	MW, BW[13]	0-34
4	Moon jelly (Aurelia aurita)	MW	16-35	62	Gar, alligator (Lepisosteus spatula)	BW	0-31
5	Sea nettle (Dactylometra quinquecirrha)	MW	16-35	63	Goby, darting (Gobionellus boleosoma)	MW	15-30
6	Sea pansy (Renilla muelleri)	MW	27-37	64	Goby, naked (Gobiosoma bosci)[13]	BW	0-20
	Turbellaria			65	Goldfish (Carassius auratus)	FW	0-15
7	Flatworm (Procerodes littoralis)	BW	3.5-35[2]	66	Green chromide (Etroplus suratensis)	BW	0-35
	Annelida			67	Grouper, high-finned (Cromileptes altivelis)	MW[13]	0-35
8	Clamworm (Nereis diversicolor)	BW	4-32[3]	68	Hake, southern (Urophycis floridanus)	MW	13-34
	Mollusca			69	Jack (Caranx ignobilis)	MW[13]	0-35
9	Octopus (Octopus vulgaris)	MW	30-35	70	Jack (C. sexfasciatus)	MW[13]	0-35
10	Oyster, eastern (Crassostrea virginica)	MW, BW	7-27[4]	71	Jack, common (C. hippos)	MW[13]	0-36
11	Oyster, horse (Ostrea equestris)	MW	27-35	72	Jarbua (Therapon jarbua)	MW, BW	0-35
12	Squid, common (Loligo pealii)	MW	31-36	73	Killifish, California (Fundulus parvipinnis)	MW[15]	0-35[16]
13	Squid, short (Lolligunculus brevis)	MW	18-37	74	Killifish, gulf (F.grandis and F.similis)	BW	2-37[16]
14	Tun, giant (Tonna galea)	MW	30-38	75	Killifish, mummichog (F. heteroclitus)	MW[17]	0-35[16]
15	Whelk, lightning (Busycon contrarium)	MW	20-37	76	Langaray (Ambassis lala)	MW, BW, FW	0-35
	Crustacea			77	Menhaden (Brevoortia smithi)	BW	2-34
16	Crab (Heloecius cordiformis)	BW, MW	0.7-53	78	Milkfish (Chanos chanos)	MW	0-35
17	Crab, blue (Callinectes sapidus)[5]	BW, MW	0-37	79	Minnow, variegated (Cyprinodon variegatus)	BW[13]	0-71
18	Crab, gulf (C. danae)	MW	17-37	80	Mojarra (Eucinostomus argenteus)	MW[13]	0-37
19	Crab, mitten (Eriocheir sinensis)[6]	FW, BW, MW	0-47	81	Moonfish (Vomer setapinnis)	MW	17-37
20	Crab, stone (Menippe mercenaria)[7]	BW, MW	12-34	82	Mouthbreeder (Tilapia mossambica)	FW[18]	0-69
21	Sea bob (Xiphopeneus kryeri)	MW	22-36	83	Mudskipper (Periophthalmus barbarus)	BW	0-35
22	Shrimp (Crago franciscorum)	MW	12-35	84	Mullet, striped (Mugil cephalus)	MW, BW[13]	0-35[16]
23	Shrimp (Palaemon longirostris)	MW	0-35	85	Needlefish (Strongylura marina)	MW, BW[13]	0-37
24	Shrimp, brine (Artemia salina)	SLW	<35-220[8]	86	Paradise fish (Macropodus opercularis)	FW	0-30
25	Shrimp, grass (Palaemonetes vulgaris)[9]	BW, MW	2-34	87	Pigfish (Orthopristis chrysopterus)	MW	10-37
26	Shrimp, white (Peneus setiferus)[10]	BW, MW	0.8-35	88	Pinfish (Lagodon rhomboides)	MW, BW[13]	0-37
	Echinodermata			89	Pipefish (Syngnathus scovelli)	BW	0-26
27	Sand dollar (Mellita quinquiesperforata)	MW	30-35	90	Pompano, common (Trachinotus carolinus)	MW	28-37
28	Star, brittle or serpent (Amphioda limbata)[11]	BW, MW	8.9-36	91	Rain-water fish (Lucania parva venusta)	BW[13]	0-24
	Elasmobranchii[12]			92	Sailfin molly (Mollienesia latipinna)	FW, BW[13]	0-87
29	Sawfish, Pacific (Pristis microdon)	MW[13]	0-35	93	Salmon, chum (Oncorhynchus keta), fry	FW	0-30
30	Shark, blacknose (Carcharhinus limbatus)	MW	11-35	94	Salmon, king (O. tshawytscha)	FW, MW	0-35
31	Shark, bonnethead (Sphyrna tiburo)	MW	23-36	95	Salmon, silver (O. kisutch), fry	FW	0-15
32	Shark, Ganges (Carcharhinus gangeticus)	MW[13]	0-35	96	Sardine, silver (Harengula pensacolae)	BW	4.8-37
33	Stingray (Dasyatis americana)	MW	29-36	97	Scatfish (Scatophagus argus)	MW, BW, FW	0-35
34	Stingray (D. sabina)	MW[13]	0-37	98	Scatfish (Selenotoca papuensis)	MW, BW	0-35
35	Torpedo fish (Narcine brasiliensis)	MW	31-37	99	Sea perch, silver (Lates calcarifer)	MW	0-35
	Teleostomi[14]			100	Sea robin (Prionotus tribulus)	MW	10-37
36	Anchovy (Anchoa hepsetus)	BW	2.5-37	101	Shad, gizzard (Dorosoma cepedianum)	BW	0-34
37	Anchovy, bay (A. mitchilli diaphana)	BW[13]	0-37	102	Sheepshead (Archosargus probatocephalus)	BW	2.2-30
38	Archerfish (Toxotes jaculator)	MW, BW, FW	0-35	103	Silverside, common (Menidia beryllina)	BW[13]	0 to >80
39	Bararog (Leiognathus caballus)	MW	0-35	104	Sleeper, striped (Dormitator maculatus)	BW[13]	0-35
40	Barb (Puntius javanacus)	FW	0-8	105	Snapper (Lutianus argentiventris)	MW[13]	0-35
41	Bass, mountain (Kuhlia sandvichensis)	MW, BW[13]	0-35	106	Sole, broad (Trinectes fasciatus)	MW, BW[13]	0-35
42	Batfish, silver (Monodactylus argenteus)	MW, BW	0-35	107	Sole, lined (Achirus lineatus)	MW	2.5-36
43	Blowfish (Sphoeroides marmoratus)	MW	4.4-36	108	Spadefish (Chaetodipterus faber)	MW	11-36
44	Bumper (Chloroscombrus chrysurus)	MW	17-37	109	Squeteague, sand (Cynoscion arenarius)	BW	4.9-30
45	Carp (Cyprinus carpio)	FW	0-10	110	Squeteague, sand (C. nothus)	MW	18-37
46	Catfish, blue (Ictalurus furcatus)	FW	0-6.9	111	Squeteague, speckled (C. nebulosus)	BW[13]	0-75
47	Catfish, sea (Galeichthys felis)	MW, BW[13]	0-60	112	Stickleback, 3-spine (Gasterosteus aculeatus)	FW, MW	0-55
48	Croaker (Micropogon undulatus)	MW, BW	0-37	113	Tarpon (Tarpon atlanticus)	MW[13]	0-35
49	Croaker, spot (Leiostomus xanthurus)	MW, BW[13]	0-37	114	Tarpon, Asiatic (Megalops cyprinoides)	MW[13]	0-35
50	Cutlassfish (Trichiurus lepturus)	MW	13-37	115	Tenpounder (Elops saurus)	MW, BW[13]	0-35
51	Damselfish (Pomacentrus fuscus)	MW	0-35	116	Threadfin (Polydactylus octonemus)	BW	2.1-37
52	Drum, black (Pogonias cromis)	MW, BW	0-50	117	Tonguefish (Symphurus plagiusa)	MW	17-37
53	Drum, channel (Sciaenops ocellata)	MW, BW	0-32	118	Trout, steelhead (Salmo gairdneri)	FW, MW	0-35
54	Drum, star (Stellifer lanceolatus)	MW	8.9-37	119	Whiff (Citharichthys spilopterus)	BW[13]	0-36.7
55	Eel, European (Anguilla vulgaris)	FW, MW	0-35	120	Whiting (Menticirrhus americanus)	MW	14-37
56	Faguito (Limia vittata)	FW, BW	0-35	121	Whiting, surf (M. littoralis)	MW	18-37
57	Flounder, European (Pleuronectes flesus)	MW	0-35	122	Yellowtail (Bairdiella chrysura)	BW	2.1-34

/1/ Brackish water species are usually euryhaline, i.e., able to live in waters of a wide range of salinity. Calcium ions aid fishes to withstand low salinities; field observations indicate that all marine animals invade fresh water of high Ca concentration much more than they do Ca-deficient fresh waters. /2/ Can undergo these changes with the tidal cycle. /3/ Has been adapted to chlorinities of about 0.25, and also observed in nearly fresh water in Denmark. /4/ Oysters withstand short-time salinity changes of 0-42 in the laboratory. /5/ May live in fresh water, but normal habitat is in estuarine waters of high salinity. /6/ Normally lives in fresh or brackish water, migrating to sea only to release larvae. /7/ Probably occurs more commonly in marine than brackish water. /8/ Occurs only in highly saline lakes; will tolerate sea water of <35 salinity (laboratory), but is not found in sea water of this salinity or other waters where there are predatory fish (Laguna Madre, Suez Canal). /9/ Recently split into 3 spp: P. vulgaris, P. intermedius, and P. pugio; it is possible that P. vulgaris does not occur in waters of low salinity. /10/ Only immature stages occur in brackish water. /11/ The common sea star (Asterias forbesi) can tolerate salinities down to 16 for short periods, and 18 regularly; A. rubens of Europe lives in a salinity of 18. /12/ Field observations; listed species where discovered in waters of known salinities; this constitutes a measure of tolerance, but does not indicate what are the physiological limits of tolerance to changes in salinity. /13/ Migrates into fresh water. /14/ Many marine teleosts can tolerate reduced salinity or fresh water if the change is not sudden. /15/ Abrupt transfer to fresh water causes 5-80% mortality. /16/ Salinity tolerance of 80-100 also reported. /17/ Gradual transfer to fresh water causes 11.5-56% mortality; abrupt transfer to fresh water causes 100% mortality. /18/ Will spawn in both fresh and salt water.

386. pH RANGE FOR GROWTH: REPRESENTATIVE MICROORGANISMS

Organism	Medium[1]	Temp °C	pH Optimum	pH Range		Organism	Medium[1]	Temp °C	pH Optimum	pH Range
1 Bacteria			6.5-7.5	3.8-12.0	20	Colpoda cucullus			6.5; 7.5	5.5-9.5
2 Molds			4.0-5.8	1.5-8.5	21	Didinium sp	S		6.4-8.4	5.2-9.4
3 Yeasts			3.8-6.0	2.5-8.0	22	Gastrostyla sp				6.0-8.5
Protozoa[2]					23	Glaucoma scintillans	B		5.6-6.8	
Flagellates					24	Holophrya sp				6.5-7.4
4 Astasia klebsii	P	25	4.2-6.0	3.2-8.2	25	Paramecium aurelia	HF	25	7.0	5.7-7.8
5 A. longa	TR	25	6.0	3.3-9.6	26	P. bursaria	MS + P	19-26	6.7-6.8	4.9-8.0
6 Chilomonas paramecium	P	28	4.8-5.1	4.1-8.4	27	P. calkinsi	L		7.1-7.4	6.5-7.8
7 Chlorogonium elongatum	P	28	7.8	4.9-8.7	28	P. caudatum	HT	24	6.9-7.1	6.0-9.5
8 C. euchlorum	P	28	7.4	4.8-8.7	29	P. multimicronucleatum	HT	27	7.0	4.8-8.3
9 C. tetragonium	T + MS	28	8.6	4.2-8.8	30	P. polycaryum	LT		6.9-7.3	5.0-7.5
10 Euglena anabaena	P	29.5	6.9	4.5-8.3	31	P. trichium	HT		6.7-7.1	6.2-7.1
11 E. deses	P	29.5	7.0	5.3-8.0	32	P. woodruffi	L		7.0-7.5	6.5-7.5
12 E. gracilis	P	28.3	6.6	3.9-9.9	33	Plagiopyla sp				6.9-7.5
13 E. klebsii			6.5	5.5-7.5	34	Spirostomum ambiguum			7.4	6.8-7.5
14 E. mutabilis			3.4-5.4	2.1-7.7	35	Stentor coeruleus	MP	18-20	7.7-8.0	
15 E. pisciformis				6.0-8.0	36	Stylonychia pustulata	HT	25	6.7; 8.0	6.0-8.0
16 E. stellata	P		5.5	4.5-8.0	37	Tetrahymena pyriformis E	T	25	5.5; 7.4	4.5-8.5
17 E. viridis	MS			4.0-7.2	38	T. pyriformis Gf-J	T	28	5.1-6.0	4.9-9.5
18 Polytomella caeca	P			2.2-9.2	39	T. pyriformis GL	T	28	4.8-5.3	4.0-8.9
Ciliates					40	T. pyriformis T-P	PH	24	7.0; 9.0	
19 Amphileptus sp			7.1-7.3		41	T. vorax D	P			6.2-7.6

/1/ A = acetate; B = brewers yeast-Harris; HF = hay + flour; HT = hay tea; L = lettuce-sea water; LT = lettuce tea; MP = modified peters + ciliates; MS = mineral salts; P = peptone; PH = phelps; S = spring water + paramecium; T = tryptone; TR = tryptophan. /2/ Exclusive of all parasitic forms.

387. FACTORS AFFECTING POND FISH CULTURE

Part I: TEMPERATURE, DISSOLVED OXYGEN AND CARBON DIOXIDE: FERTILIZED AND UNFERTILIZED PONDS (SOUTHERN U.S.A)

F = fertilized pond, area 1.3 acres, maximum depth 9 ft, bottom sample taken at 5 ft., 11 applications of 100 lb of 8-8-2 (N-K-P) per acre; U = unfertilized pond, 1.8 acres, maximum depth 9 ft, bottom sample taken at 7.5 ft. Averages are from 4 depths.

Month	Temperature, °C Surface U	F	Bottom U	F	Average U	F	Oxygen, ppm Surface U	F	Bottom U	F	Average U	F	Carbon Dioxide, ppm Surface U	F	Bottom U	F	Average U	F
1 April	21.0	23.5	17.0	15.5	18.9	19.0	4.1	9.0	1.9	1.3	4.3	4.4	3.3	2.2	4.4	3.3	4.7	3.0
2 May	23.8	26.2	20.5	22.3	22.5	25.5	5.6	7.5	0.6	0.5	3.8	2.1	3.9	8.8	20.9	58.4	13.2	28.0
3 June	23.0	28.0	22.0	24.0	22.8	26.2	4.9	3.4	3.1	0.6	4.1	1.5	3.8	3.7	9.9	70.9	6.5	28.3
4 July	27.2	29.0	25.2	26.0	26.2	27.7	4.2	4.2	0.9	1.0	2.7	2.2	3.8	3.7	11.0	18.1	6.6	10.4
5 August	29.0	30.0	26.5	28.5	23.1	29.2	3.0	2.2	1.0	0.5	2.2	1.2	6.5	11.0	11.0	52.2	15.1	24.1
6 September	24.5	26.0	23.7	24.7	24.2	25.3	4.2	3.4	2.1	1.9	2.7	2.8	4.9	7.7	13.7	20.9	8.4	11.9
7 October	20.5	21.0	20.5	20.0	20.6	20.5	4.3	3.7	4.5	3.7	4.8	3.6	3.7	6.9	7.7	8.7	4.8	7.3
8 November	17.0	17.0	17.0	17.0	17.0	17.0	4.9	4.1	5.1	4.7	5.0	4.5	2.2	3.3	2.2	4.4	2.7	4.4

Part II: RELATION OF POND WATER OXYGEN CONTENT TO FISH CULTURE

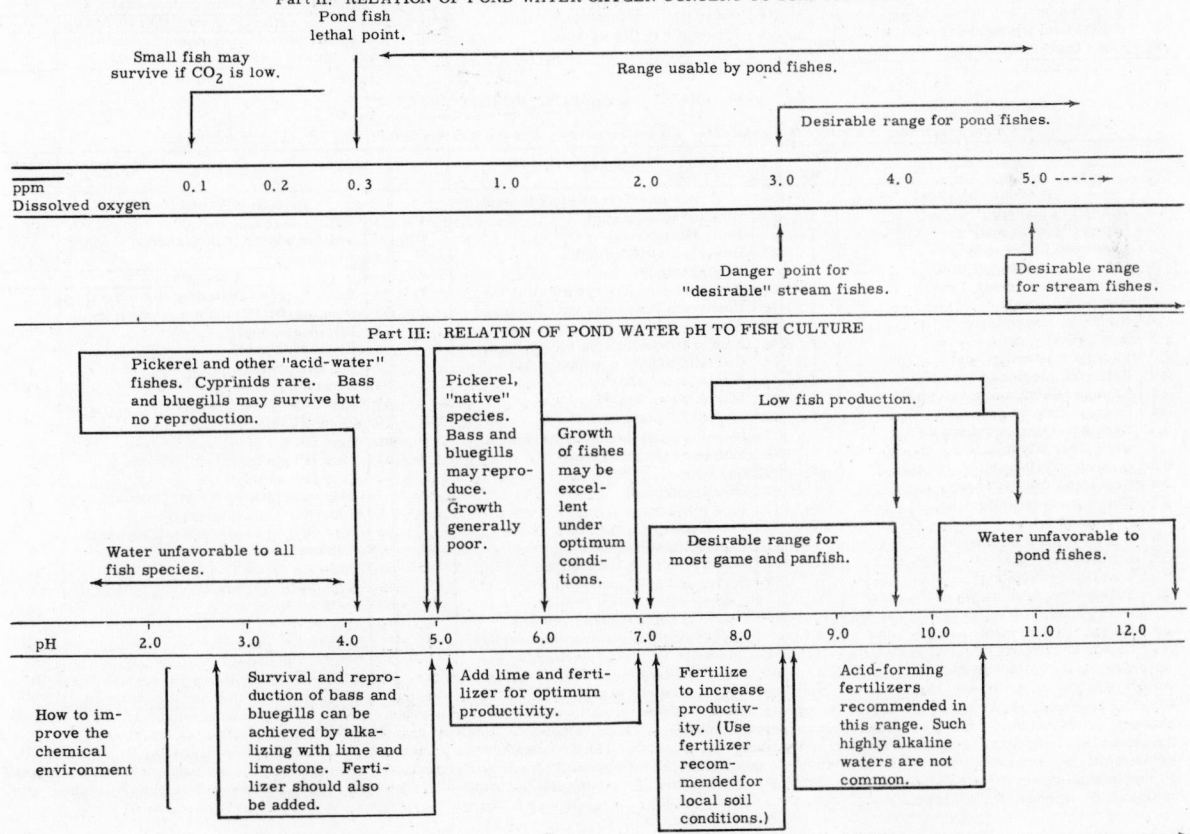

388. SHADE TOLERANCE: SHRUBS AND HERBACEOUS PLANTS

T = highly tolerant; t = moderately tolerant; I = intermediate; ¥ = moderately intolerant; T̶ = highly intolerant.

	Species	Tolerance		Species	Tolerance		Species	Tolerance
	Shrubs			Herbaceous Flowers			Herbaceous Flowers (concluded)	
1	Abelia (Abelia grandiflora)	I	39	Ageratum (Ageratum spp)	I	77	Spiderwort (Tradescantia virginiana)	T
2	Barberry (Berberis thunbergi)	¥	40	Alyssum (Alyssum spp)	I	78	Squill (Scilla siberica)	T
3	Beauty bush (Kolkwitzia amabilis)	I	41	Anemone (Anemone quinquefolia)	t	79	Trillium (Trillium grandiflorum)	t
4	Blueberry (Vaccinium corymbosum)	I	42	Arbutus (Epigaea repens)	t	80	Trillium (T. undulatum)	T
5	Boxwood (Buxus microphylla)	I	43	Aster (Aster spp)	I	81	Twin flower (Linnaea borealis)	T
6	Buckthorn (Rhamnus cathartica)	t	44	Baneberry (Actaea spp)	t	82	Violet (Viola papilionacea)	T
7	Burning bush (Evonymus atropurpurea)	I	45	Blood root (Sanguinaria canadensis)	t	83	Zinnia (Zinnia spp)	I
8	Chokeberry (Aronia atropurpurea)	¥	46	Blue bead (Clintonia borealis)	T		Grasses	
9	Coralberry (Symphoricarpos orbiculatus)	I	47	Bluebell (Polemonium reptans)	I	84	Bluegrama (Bouteloua gracilis)	¥
10	Cranberry (Viburnum opulus)	T	48	Calendula (Calendula spp)	I	85	Bluegrass (Poa trivialis)	t
11	Currant (Ribes americanum)	T	49	Cardinal flower (Lobelia cardinalis)	I	86	Fescue (Festuca rubra)	t
12	Dogwood (Cornus racemosa)	I	50	Chrysanthemum (Chrysanthemum spp)	I	87	Wheatgrass (Agropyrum cristatum)	I
13	Dogwood (C. stolonifera)	¥	51	Columbine (Aquilegia canadensis)	I		Vegetable Crops	
14	Elderberry (Sambucus canadensis)	I	52	Cone-flower (Rudbeckia triloba)	t	88	Beet (Beta vulgaris)	I
15	Elderberry (S. racemosa)	t	53	Coral bells (Heuchera sanguinea)	I	89	Cauliflower (Brassica oleracea botrytis)	T
16	Firethorn (Pyracantha coccinea)	t	54	Coral root (Corallorhiza maculata)	T	90	Celery (Apium graveolens dulce)	I
17	Forsythia (Forsythia suspensa)	I	55	Cowslip (Mertensia virginica)	I	91	Eggplant (Solanum melongena esculentum)	I
18	Gooseberry (Ribes cynosbati)	T	56	Day lily (Hemerocallis spp)	¥	92	Lettuce (Lactuca sativa)	¥
19	Holly, Japanese (Ilex crenata)	t	57	Foxglove (Digitalis purpurea)	t	93	Tomato (Lycopersicon esculentum)	I
20	Honeysuckle (Lonicera japonica)	t	58	Goldthread (Coptis trifolia)	T		Pteridophytes - Ferns	
21	Honeysuckle (L. sempervirens)	¥	59	Grape-hyacinth (Muscari azureum)	I	94	Beech (Phegopteris polypodioides)	T
22	Honeysuckle (L. tatarica)	t	60	Hepatica (Hepatica triloba)	I	95	Bladder (Cystopteris bulbifera)	t
23	Laurel (Kalmia latifolia)	¥	61	Iris (Iris cristata and verna)	I	96	Brake (Pteridium aquilinum)	t
24	Lilac (Syringa vulgaris)	I	62	Jack-in-the-pulpit (Arisaema triphyllum)	T	97	Christmas (Polystichum acrostichoides)	T
25	Mahonia (Mahonia aquifolium)	I	63	Lady's slipper (Cypripedium hirsutum)	t	98	Cinnamon (Osmunda cinnamomea)	t
26	Maple (Acer pennsylvanicum)	t	64	Lady's slipper (C. pubescens)	T	99	Hartford (Lygodium palmatum)	t
27	Mockorange (Philadelphus coronarius)	I	65	Lily (Lilium spp)	¥	100	Hayscented (Dennstaedtia punctilobula)	t
28	Peashrub (Caragana arborescens)	I	66	Monkshood (Aconitum fisheri)	t	101	Interrupted (Osmunda claytoniana)	t
29	Photinia (Photinia villosa)	t	67	Narcissus (Narcissus spp)	t	102	Lady (Asplenium filix-foemina)	T
30	Prickly-ash (Zanthoxylum americanum)	T	68	Oxalis (Oxalis corniculata)	T	103	Maidenhair (Adiantum pedatum)	T
31	Privet (Ligustrum amurense)	t	69	Oxalis (O. violacea)	t	104	Ostrich (Pteris pennsylvanica)	T
32	Rhododendron (Rhododendron spp)	T	70	Periwinkle (Vinca minor)	t	105	Polypody (Polypodium virginianum)	T
33	Spice bush (Lindera benzoin)	t	71	Petunia (Petunia hybrida)	¥	106	Walking (Camptosorus rhizophyllus)	T
34	Viburnum (Viburnum acerifolium)	T	72	Phlox (Phlox divaricata)	T	107	Wood (Dryopteris marginalis)	t
35	Viburnum (V. dentatum)	t	73	Phlox (P. maculata)	t		Pteridophytes - Fern Allies	
36	Winterberry (Ilex verticillata)	t	74	Phlox (P. paniculata)	I	108	Clubmoss (Lycopodium lucidulum)	T
37	Witch hazel (Hamamelis mollis)	t	75	Plantain lily (Hosta spp)	T	109	Horsetail (Equisetum hyemale)	T
38	Yew (Taxus canadensis)	T	76	Primrose (Primula vulgaris)	I			

389. SHADE TOLERANCE: FOREST TREES

T = highly tolerant; t = moderately tolerant; I = intermediate; ¥ = moderately intolerant; T̶ = highly intolerant.

	Species	Tolerance		Species	Tolerance		Species	Tolerance
	Broadleaf Trees			Broadleaf Trees (continued)			Broadleaf Trees (concluded)	
1	Ash (Fraxinus spp)[1]	I	26	Hickory (Carya spp)	¥	51	Willow (Salix spp)	T̶
2	Aspen (Populus spp)[2]	T̶	27	Holly (Ilex opaca)	T	52	Yellow-poplar (Liriodendron tulipifera)	¥
3	Basswood (Tilia spp)	t	28	Honeylocust (Gleditsia triacanthos)	¥		Conifers	
4	Beech (Fagus grandifolia)	T	29	Hophornbeam (Ostrya virginiana)	T	53	Baldcypress (Taxodium distichum)	I
5	Birch (Betula lenta)	I	30	Hornbeam (Carpinus caroliniana)	T	54	Douglas-fir (Pseudotsuga menziesii)	I
6	Birch (B. lutea)	I	31	Horsechestnut (Aesculus hippocastanum)	¥	55	Fir (Abies spp)[7]	T
7	Birch (B. papyrifera)	¥	32	Laurel (Umbellularia californica)	t	56	Fir (Abies spp)[8]	t
8	Birch (B. pendula)	T̶	33	Locust (Robinia pseudoacacia)	T̶	57	Fir (A. procera)	¥
9	Buckeye (Aesculus spp)	t	34	Maple (Acer spp)[4]	T	58	Hemlock (Tsuga spp)[9]	T
10	Butternut (Juglans cinerea)	¥	35	Maple (Acer spp)[5]	t	59	Hemlock (T. mertensiana)	t
11	Catalpa (Catalpa bignonioides)	¥	36	Maple (A. platanoides)	¥	60	Larch (Larix spp)	T̶
12	Cherry (Prunus serotina)	¥	37	Mountain-ash (Sorbus americana)	I	61	Pine (Pinus spp)[10]	¥
13	Chestnut (Castanea dentata)	I	38	Mulberry (Morus rubra)	I	62	Pine (Pinus spp)[11]	T̶
14	Coffeetree (Gymnocladus dioica)	¥	39	Oak (Quercus spp)[6]	I	63	Pine (Pinus spp)[12]	I
15	Cottonwood (Populus deltoides)	T̶	40	Oak (Q. prinus)	¥	64	Redcedar (Juniperus virginiana)	¥
16	Crabapple (Malus coronaria)	I	41	Papaw (Asimina triloba)	¥	65	Redcedar (Thuja plicata)	T
17	Cucumbertree (Magnolia acuminata)	T̶	42	Pecan (Carya illinoensis)	¥	66	Port Orford cedar (Chamaecyparis lawsoniana)	t
18	Dogwood (Cornus florida)	T	43	Poplar (Populus nigra)	T̶	67	Redwood (Sequoia sempervirens)	t
19	Elm (Ulmus spp)[3]	I	44	Redbud (Cercis canadensis)	I	68	Sequoia (S. gigantea)	I
20	Elm (U. campestris)	t	45	Serviceberry (Amelanchier arborea)	I	69	Spruce (Picea spp)[13]	t
21	Fringe-tree (Chionanthus virginica)	I	46	Sumac (Toxicodendron vernix)	t	70	Spruce (P. abies)	T̶
22	Ginkgo (Ginkgo biloba)	¥	47	Sweetgum (Liquidambar styraciflua)	¥	71	Spruce (P. pungens)	I
23	Hackberry (Celtis occidentalis)	I	48	Sycamore (Platanus occidentalis)	¥	72	Torreya (Torreya californica)	T
24	Hawthorn (Crataegus spp)	¥	49	Tupelo (Nyssa sylvatica)	I	73	White-cedar (Chamaecyparis thyoides)	T
25	Hawthorn (C. oxyacantha)	I	50	Walnut (Juglans nigra)	¥	74	White-cedar (Thuja occidentalis)	t

/1/ F. americana, F. latifolia, F. nigra, F. pennsylvanica. /2/ P. grandidentata, P. tremuloides. /3/ U. americana, U. thomasii. /4/ A. saccharum, A. spicatum. /5/ A. rubrum, A. saccharinum. /6/ Q. alba, Q. lobata, Q. macrocarpa, Q. palustris, Q. rubra, Q. velutina. /7/ A. balsamea, A. lasiocarpa. /8/ A. amabilis, A. grandis, A. concolor. /9/ T. canadensis, T. heterophylla. /10/ Pinus attenuata, P. contorta, P. coulteri, P. echinata, P. jeffreyi, P. muricata, P. ponderosa, P. resinosa, P. rigida, P. taeda, P. virginiana. /11/ P. banksiana, P. palustris, P. sabiniana, P. sylvestris. /12/ Pinus elliottii, P. lambertiana, P. monticola, P. radiata, P. strobus. /13/ Picea engelmannii, P. glauca, P. mariana, P. rubens, P. sitchensis.

390. EFFECT OF LIGHT ON VARIOUS PROCESSES: PLANTS

Part I: EFFECT OF WAVE LENGTH

Data present the effectiveness of brief dark-period interruption for control of flowering and certain vegetative expressions. For studies of the inhibition or promotion of flowering, plants growing under radiation from carbon arc and incandescent filament lamps for a daily period of about 12 hrs were subjected, at the midpoint of the dark-period, to radiation of known energy and wave length. Values represent relative energy and may be converted to kiloergs per sq cm by multiplying the values in this table by the following factors: cocklebur, 40; soybean, 30; barley (flowering) 35; henbane, 300; lettuce, 2; pea, 160; barley (elongation), 100; tomato, 200.

Effect	Relative Energy Normalized to Maximum Response at Wave Length											
	4400 Å	4800 Å	5000 Å	5200 Å	5400 Å	5600 Å	5800 Å	6200 Å	6600 Å	6800 Å	7000 Å	7200-7600 Å
Inhibition of flowering												reverses
1 Cocklebur (Xanthium pensylvanicum)	125	173	92	40	8	5.4	2.6	1	1.5	3.1	7	the
2 Soybean, Biloxi (Glycine soja)	18	27	17	6	3.7	2	1.3	1	1.3	1.6	3.5	response
Promotion of flowering												caused
3 Barley, Wintex (Hordeum vulgare)	218	185	85	35	4	1.8	1.3	1	1.5	4	7	by
4 Henbane (Hyoscyamus niger)					4	1.8	1.3	1	1.5	4	7	red
Promotion of germination												(6200-
5 Lettuce, Grand Rapids (Lactuca sativa)						18	10	3	1	1.2	50	6600 Å)
Promotion of leaf elongation												for Items
6 Pea, Little Marvel (Pisum sativum)	100	190	200	95	24	10	6.5	1	1	1	1.3	1, 3, 4,
Inhibition of stem elongation												5, 7, and
7 Barley, Colsess I (Hordeum vulgare)	250		200	40	20	5	2	1.3	1	2	6	8.
Production of pigmentation (fruit cuticle)												
8 Tomato, Rutgers (Lycopersicon esculentum)	30	30	30	30	20	10	3	1	1	1.2	7	

Part II: EFFECT OF DAY LENGTH ON DEVELOPMENT, EXCLUSIVE OF FLOWER INITIATION

	Process Affected	Day Length		Process Affected	Day Length		Process Affected	Day Length
	Winter hardening			Root thickening			Bud elongation	
1	Abelia (Abelia grandiflora)	Short	8	Radish (Raphanus sativus)	Short	15	Orchid (Cattleya trianae)	Short
2	Alfalfa (Medicago sativa)	Short		Bulb development			Pistillate flowers increased	
	Tuber development		9	Onion (Allium cepa)	Long	16	Cucumber (Cucumis sativus)	Short
3	Artichoke (Helianthus tuberosus)	Short		Runner development			Staminate flowers increased	
4	Potato (Solanum tuberosum)	Short	10	Strawberry (Fragaria chiloensis)	Long	17	Cucumber (C. sativus)	Long
5	Yam (Dioscorea alata)	Short		Stem elongation			Seed development	
	Storage root development		11	Coneflower (Rudbeckia spp)	Long	18	Hemp, staminate (Cannabis sativa)	Short
6	Dahlia (Dahlia spp)	Short	12	Henbane, biennial (Hyoscyamus niger)	Long		Plantlet development	
	Fibrous root development		13	Rye, winter (Secale cereale)	Long	19	Bryophyllum (Bryophyllum pinnatum)	Long
7	Dahlia (Dahlia spp)	Long	14	Spinach (Spinacia oleracea)	Long			

Part III: EFFECT OF VARIOUS DAY LENGTHS

	Species	Beginning of Test	10 hr			12 hr			12.5 hr			13 hr			Photoperiodic Class
			Buds	Fls	Height	Buds	Fls	Height	Buds	Fls	Height	Buds	Fls	Height	
			da		in	da		in	da		in	da		in	
1	Althea (Hibiscus syriacus)	Mar 27							95	117	30	96	123	48	Long day
2	Amaranth (Gomphrena globosa)	May 13	21	33	8	21	33	10	21	36	11	23	32	8	Day neutral
3	Balsam (Impatiens balsamina)	June 23	20	28	14	20	28	18				20	29	19	Day neutral
4	Bindweed (Convolvulus sepium)	May 19													Long day
5	Bougainvillea (Bougainvillea glabra)	May 24	28	45	38	36	57	40	69	88	56	96	157	60	Short day
6	Calendula (Calendula officinalis)	May 9	26	42	9	26	41	13	26	41	15	26	41	15	Day neutral
7	Caryopteris (Caryopteris incana)	June 5	26	38	13	26	38	16				24	35	16	Short day
8	Cloud grass (Agrostis nebulosa)	May 14										49	58	10	Long day
9	Cobaea (Cobaea scandens)	May 26	24	53	46	36	91	41				55	91	46	Short day
10	Columbine (Aquilegia car.adensis)	Mar 27	4	25	19	4	28	19				4	36	30	Short day
11	Cosmos (Cosmos bipinnatus)	May 7	10	17	19	10	24	36	10	17	19	10	19	20	Day neutral
12	Gama-grass (Tripsacum dactyloides)	Mar 31	63	72	64	65	74	56	68	75	45	68	75	67	Short day
13	Goldenrod (Solidago ulmifolia)	Apr 23	39	73	25	45	73	22	69	88	14	49	77	19	Short day
14	Kalanchoe (Kalanchoe laxiflora)	May 8							173	239	38	173	199	47	Day neutral
15	Loosestrife (Steironema ciliatum)	Apr 15							56	65	21	87	93	24	Long day
16	Perilla (Perilla frutescens)	May 17	25	39	22	37	47	27	39	58	30	39	50	25	Short day
17	Periwinkle (Vinca minor)	June 7	18	26	16	18	23	12							Day Neutral
18	Poinsettia (Euphorbia pulcherrima)	May 16	32	65	47	39	44	53	48	180	66	107	179	76	Short day
19	Purpletop (Triodia flava)	May 20	29	38	26	39	44	25	39	46	37	42	47	30	Short day
20	Reed grass (Calamagrostis cinnoides)	Mar 30				58	76	41	63	88	42	70	98	35	Day neutral
21	Rosinweed (Silphium trifoliatum)	Apr 18	89	107	38	89	110	56	68	90	56	68	89	70	Long day
22	Soybean, Biloxi (Glycine soja)	May 25	20	23	9	21	27	14	24	27	18	25	31	16	Short day
23	Spider-flower (Cleome spinosa)	May 31	26	38	28	27	35	28				27	36	34	Day neutral

	Species	Beginning of Test	13.5 hr			14 hr			14.5 hr			24 hr			Photoperiodic Class
			Buds	Fls	Height	Buds	Fls	Height	Buds	Fls	Height	Buds	Fls	Height	
1	Althea (Hibiscus syriacus)	Mar 27	95	126	46	103	136	44	106	144	52	103	130	44	Long day
2	Amaranth (Gomphrena globosa)	May 13	21	33	9	21	41	15	21	35	12	18	32	10	Day neutral
3	Balsam (Impatiens balsamina)	June 23	20	28	17							30	38	21	Day neutral
4	Bindweed (Convolvulus sepium)	May 19	44	59	40							35	49	45	Long day
5	Bougainvillea (Bougainvillea glabra)	May 24	145	164	75	103	153	50	143	157	53	131	157		Short day
6	Calendula (Calendula officinalis)	May 9	26	47	20	26	41	18	26	44	20	26	41	17	Day neutral
7	Caryopteris (Caryopteris incana)	June 5				54	71	28				59	71	28	Short day
8	Cloud grass (Agrostis nebulosa)	May 14	48	58	13	37	45	11	35	41	16	34	48	11	Long day
9	Cobaea (Cobaea scandens)	May 26				60	92	60				64	97	60	Short day
10	Columbine (Aquilegia canadensis)	Mar 27				14	36	30				4	36	30	Short day
11	Cosmos (Cosmos bipinnatus)	May 7	10	15		10	21	19	10	24	26	10	19	17	Day neutral
12	Gama-grass (Tripsacum dactyloides)	Mar 31	68	76	58	81	89	56	82	89	60	82	89	65	Short day
13	Goldenrod (Solidago ulmifolia)	Apr 23	58	82	32	57	88	36	85	108	30	67	114	36	Short day
14	Kalanchoe (Kalanchoe laxiflora)	May 8				173	192	51	173	204	50	173	192	51	Day neutral
15	Loosestrife (Steironema ciliatum)	Apr 15	49	61	19	48	65	25	49	68	23	49	68	20	Long day
16	Perilla (Perilla frutescens)	May 17	49	70	38	53	83	41	62	96	47	93	114	50	Short day
17	Periwinkle (Vinca minor)	June 7										18	23	12	Day neutral
18	Poinsettia (Euphorbia pulcherrima)	May 16	162	191	74	163	193	76	163	195	91	158	197	70	Short day
19	Purpletop (Triodia flava)	May 20	43	51	45	50	56	25	69	87	51	92	103	42	Short day
20	Reed grass (Calamagrostis cinnoides)	Mar 30	63	84	41	57	84	46	67	91	45	60	84	37	Day neutral
21	Rosinweed (Silphium trifoliatum)	Apr 18	65	89	83	65	89	76	54	79	54	54	78	57	Long day
22	Soybean, Biloxi (Glycine soja)	May 25	34	37	19	42	48	27	50	60	30	81	90	38	Short day
23	Spider-flower (Cleome spinosa)	May 31				28	40	36				28	38	65	Day neutral

459

391. EFFECT OF LIGHT, WITH TEMPERATURE INTERACTIONS, ON FLOWERING OF PLANTS

Temperature interactions and effects on photoperiodic classification are incomplete. Upon further investigations these data may become modified.

Species	Photoperiodic Class and Light Period[1]	Temperature Interactions and Effects[2]	Species	Photoperiodic Class and Light Period[1]	Temperature Interactions and Effects[2]
Fruit and Vegetable Crops			**Legumes and Other Field Crops (concluded)**		
1 Artichoke (Helianthus tuberosus)	s, N		60 Lespedeza (Lespedeza stipulacea)	S(<13.5 hr)	
2 Bean, lima (Phaseolus lunatus)	N, S		61 Soybean, Biloxi and Mandarin (Glycine soja)	S-s	Th;Tq
3 Bean, string (P. vulgaris)	N, S[3]		62 Soybean, Mandell (G. soja)	s	Th;Tq
4 Beet, garden (Beta vulgaris)	l	Th;Tl, L	63 Sweetclover (Melilotus alba)	L	
5 Cabbage (Brassica pekinensis)	l	Th;Tl, L	64 Tobacco (Nicotiana tabacum)[5]	N	
6 Chicory (Cichorium intybus)	L	Th;Tl, N	65 Tobacco, Havana (N. tabacum)	l	
7 Carrot (Daucus carota)	N	Ve(4-10°C)	66 Tobacco, Md. Mammoth (N. tabacum)	S(<14 hr)	Th;<13°C, N
8 Celery (Apium graveolens)	N	Ve(4-10°C)	67 Vetch, spring (Vicia sativa)	l	Th;Tl, N
9 Cucumber (Cucumis sativus)	N		**Ornamental Plants**		
10 Dill (Anethum graveolens)	L(>11 hr)		68 Althea (Hibiscus syriacus)	L(>12 hr)	
11 Lettuce (Lactuca sativa)	l	Th;Tl, N	69 Aster (Callistephus chinensis)	l	Th
12 Onion (Allium cepa)	l, s, N	Tl	70 Azalea, coral bell (Rhododendron sp)	N	
13 Pea (Pisum sativum)	N, l		71 Balsam (Impatiens balsamina)	N	
14 Pepper (Capsicum annuum)	N, s	TP	72 Begonia (Begonia semperflorens)	N	Tl;Th, l
15 Potato (Solanum tuberosum)	l, s, N		73 Bryophyllum (Bryophyllum pinnatum)	S(<12 hr)	
16 Radish (Raphanus sativus)	L		74 Cactus (Zygocactus truncatus)	s	Tl(18°C);13°C, N
17 Spinach (Spinacia oleracea)	L(>13 hr)	Ve[4]	75 Chrysanthemum (Chrysanthemum frutescens)	L	
18 Strawberry (Fragaria chiloensis)[5]	S(<10 hr)	Tq	76 Chrysanthemum (C. indicum)	S(<15 hr)	Tq
19 Strawberry, everbearing (F. chiloensis)	l, N		77 Cineraria (Senecio cruentus)	s	
20 Sweetpotato (Ipomoea batatas)	S		78 Cornflower (Centaurea cyanus)	l	Th;Tl, N
21 Tomato (Lycopersicon esculentum)	N, l, s	TP	79 Cosmos (Cosmos bipinnatus)[5]	s	
22 Turnip (Brassica rapa)	l		80 Cosmos, Klondyke (C. sulphureus)	S(<14 hr)	Th and Tl
Grasses			81 Cosmos, orange flare (C. sulphureus)	N	Th;Tl, S
23 Barley, spring (Hordeum vulgare)		Vo	82 Foxglove (Digitalis purpurea)	l	Ve
24 Barley, winter (H. vulgare)	L(>12 hr)	Va(7-9°C)	83 Fuchsia (Fuchsia hybrida)	N	Th
25 Beardgrass (Andropogon gerardii)	S(<18 hr)		84 Gardenia (Gardenia jasminoides fort.)	N	
26 Bentgrass (Agrostis palustris)	L(>16 hr)		85 Geranium (Pelargonium hortorum)	N	Tl
27 Bluegrass, annual (Poa annua)	N	Vo	86 Holly, English (Ilex aquifolium)	N	
28 Bluegrass, Kentucky (P. pratensis)	l	Th;Tl, N or s;Ve	87 Hydrangea (Hydrangea macrophylla)	N(?)	Ve
29 Bromegrass (Bromus inermis)	L(>12.5 hr)	Va	88 Kalanchoe (Kalanchoe blossfeldiana)	S(<12 hr)	
30 Broomsedge (Andropogon virginicus)	s(12-14.5 hr)		89 Larkspur (Delphinium cultorum)	L	Tl;Th, N
31 Canary-grass (Phalaris arundinacea)	L(>12.5 hr)		90 Morning glory (Ipomoea hederacea)	S	
32 Cloudgrass (Agrostis nebulosa)	L(>13 hr)		91 Morning glory (I. purpurea)	s[11]	
33 Corn (Zea mays)	N, S		92 Orchid (Cattleya trianae)	S	
34 Fescue (Festuca elatior)	L		93 Pansy (Viola tricolor)	N	Tl
35 Foxtail (Alopecurus pratensis)	L(>9 hr)		94 Petunia (Petunia hybrida)	l	Th;Tl, N
36 Oat (Avena sativa)	L(>9 hr)	Tl;Va, Vo[6]	95 Phlox (Phlox paniculata)	L	Th
37 Orchardgrass (Dactylis glomerata)	L(>12 hr)	Ve	96 Poinsettia (Euphorbia pulcherrima)	S(<12.5 hr)	Tl[12]
38 Rice, summer (Oryza sativa)	N	Th	97 Salvia (Salvia splendens)	s	Th;Tl, N
39 Rice, winter (O. sativa)	S(<12 hr)	Th	98 Sedum (Sedum spectabile)	L(>13 hr)	
40 Rye, spring (Secale cereale)	l	Tl;Vo	99 Snapdragon (Antirrhinum majus)	l	Th;Tl, N
41 Rye, winter (S. cereale)	l	Va	100 Stock, German (Matthiola incana)	l	Th;Tl, N
42 Ryegrass, Italian (Lolium italicum)	L(>11 hr)	Va	101 Tephrosia (Tephrosia candida)	IM(10-13.2 hr)	
43 Ryegrass, early perennial (L. perenne)	L(>9 hr)	Ve	102 Violet (Viola papilionacea)	S(<11 hr)[13]	Th;Tq
44 Ryegrass, late perennial (L. perenne)	L(>13 hr)	Ve	**Field Weeds**		
45 Sorghum (Sorghum vulgare)	l		103 Cocklebur (Xanthium pennsylvanicum)	S(<15.5 hr)	Tq
46 Sudan (Holcus sudanensis)	s	Th;Tl, N	104 Coneflower (Rudbeckia bicolor)	L(>10 hr)	Th
47 Sugar cane (Saccharum officinarum)[5]	s		105 Coneflower (R. hirta)	L(>12 hr)	
48 Sugar cane, var. 28 NG 292	IM(12-14 hr)		106 Daisy (Chrysanthemum leucanthemum)	L	
49 Timothy, hay (Phleum pratensis)	L(>12 hr)		107 Dog fennel (Anthemis cotula)	l	Th;Tl, N
50 Timothy, pasture (P. nodosum)	L(>14.5 hr)		108 Goldenrod (Solidago spp)[14]	S	
51 Wheat, spring (Triticum aestivum)	l	Vo	109 Henbane, annual (Hyoscyamus niger)	L(>10 hr)	Tq
52 Wheat, winter (T. aestivum)[5]	L(>12 hr)	Va	110 Henbane, biennial (H. niger)	L	Tq;Ve
53 Wheatgrass (Agropyron smithii)	L(>10 hr)		111 Jimson weed (Datura stramonium)	s[15]	
Legumes and Other Field Crops			112 Lamb's-quarters (Chenopodium album)	S	
54 Alfalfa (Medicago sativa)	l	Th;Tl, N[7]	113 Mallow (Malva verticillata)	s	Th(23°C);18°C, N
55 Beet, sugar (Beta vulgaris)	L	Tl(7-9°C);Ve	114 Nightshade (Solanum nigrum)	N	Tl;Th, l
56 Clover (Trifolium spp)[8]	L		115 Primrose, evening (Oenothera biennis)	l	Tl
57 Clover (Trifolium spp)[9]	l	Tl	116 Ragweed (Ambrosia artemisiifolia)	S	
58 Clover, red (T. pratense)[10]	L(>12 hr)		117 Sow-thistle (Sonchus oleraceus)	l	
59 Cotton (Gossypium hirsutum)	N, s	Tq	118 Tumbleweed (Amaranthus graecizans)	s	Th

/1/ L=long day required; l=long day favorable; S=short day required; s=short day favorable; N=day neutral; IM=intermediate. Where there is more than one symbol of classification, varietal differences occur, the most common class being entered first. Classification is followed in parentheses by light period for flowering (>12 hr should be interpreted as 12 hr or more; <12 hr, as 12 hr or less). /2/ Tl=indicated photoperiodic response occurs at relatively low temperatures (plant may also flower at other day lengths at higher temperatures), or reproductive development is promoted by low temperatures during photoperiodic induction; Th=indicated response occurs at relatively high temperatures (plant may also flower at other day lengths at lower temperatures), or reproductive development is promoted by high temperatures during photoperiodic induction; Tq=temperature has a quantitative effect on the critical day length, i.e., an increase in temperature lowers the minimum limits for long day plants and raises the maximum limits for short day plants, or on the degree of photoperiodic response; Ve=vernalization or other low temperature preconditioning of embryo plants, seedlings, buds, or plants, previous to photoperiodic induction, is essential for complete reproduction development; Va=vernalization promotes reproductive development but is not essential; Vo=vernalization not effective; TP=thermoperiodic, i.e., development affected by alternation of temperature between day and night periods. /3/ Photoperiod influences fruit development but floral initiation is not affected. /4/ For some varieties. /5/ Data applicable to most varieties. /6/ Winter varieties, Va; spring varieties, Vo. /7/ Vegetative in warm nights. /8/ Species include crimson clover (T. incarnatum), Ladino clover (T. repens). /9/ Species include red clover (T. pratense), white clover (T. repens). /10/ Variety English Montgomery; for American Medium, l(>9 hr). /11/ Night temperature, 22°C. At 18°C, N; at 13°C, L. /12/ Night temperature, <21°C. At 13-14°C, L. /13/ Production of blue petaliferous flowers; formation of fertile, cleistogamous flowers, L. /14/ Species include: S. altissima, S. fistulosa, S. juncea. For S. cutleri, L. /15/ Becomes N with aging of plant.

Part I: SUMMATION OF DAY LENGTHS IN NORTHERN AND SOUTHERN LATITUDES, BEGINNING DECEMBER 21

Values for northern latitudes are followed in parentheses by those for southern latitudes.

#	Date	Latitude	Daylight[1] min	Twilight[2] min	Total min	Percentage Change vs Equator	Percentage Change vs Preceding Latitudes
1	Jan 1	0°	8729(8729)	552(552)	9281(9281)		
2		10°	8312(9148)	552(552)	8864(9700)	-4.5(+4.5)	-4.5(+4.5)
3		20°	7870(9602)	576(600)	8446(10,202)	-9.0(+9.9)	-4.7(+5.2)
4		30°	7362(10,129)	624(662)	7986(10,791)	-14.0(+16.3)	-5.4(+5.8)
5		40°	6730(10,796)	738(792)	7468(11,588)	-19.5(+24.8)	-6.5(+7.4)
6		50°	5934(11,767)	922(1072)	6856(12,839)	-26.1(+38.3)	-8.2(+10.8)
7	Jan 15	0°	18,913(18,913)	1168(1168)	20,081(20,081)		
8		10°	18,039(19,793)	1192(1196)	19,231(20,989)	-4.2(+4.5)	-4.2(+4.5)
9		20°	17,109(20,748)	1248(1276)	18,357(22,024)	-8.6(+9.7)	-4.5(+4.9)
10		30°	16,047(21,857)	1352(1418)	17,399(23,275)	-13.4(+15.9)	-5.2(+5.7)
11		40°	14,722(23,263)	1578(1696)	16,300(24,959)	-18.8(+24.3)	-6.3(+7.2)
12		50°	12,850(25,293)	1974(2282)	14,824(27,575)	-26.2(+37.3)	-9.0(+10.5)
13	Feb 1	0°	31,275(31,275)	1916(1916)	33,191(33,191)		
14		10°	29,925(32,642)	1940(1962)	31,865(34,604)	-4.0(+4.2)	-4.0(+4.2)
15		20°	28,494(34,126)	2038(2086)	30,532(36,212)	-8.0(+9.1)	-4.2(+4.6)
16		30°	26,859(35,847)	2220(2316)	29,079(38,163)	-12.4(+15.0)	-4.8(+5.4)
17		40°	24,828(38,021)	2572(2752)	27,400(40,773)	-17.4(+22.8)	-5.8(+6.8)
18		50°	21,974(41,141)	3196(3654)	25,170(44,795)	-24.2(+35.0)	-8.1(+9.9)
19	Feb 15	0°	41,453(41,453)	2514(2514)	43,967(43,967)		
20		10°	39,805(43,135)	2556(2578)	42,363(45,713)	-3.7(+4.0)	-3.7(+4.0)
21		20°	38,060(44,959)	2682(2730)	40,742(47,689)	-7.3(+8.5)	-3.8(+4.3)
22		30°	36,071(47,074)	2920(3032)	38,991(50,106)	-11.3(+14.0)	-4.3(+5.1)
23		40°	33,605(49,736)	3360(3580)	36,965(53,316)	-15.9(+21.3)	-5.2(+6.4)
24		50°	30,159(53,543)	4152(4694)	34,311(58,237)	-22.0(+32.4)	-7.2(+9.2)
25	Mar 1	0°	52,355(52,355)	3144(3144)	55,499(55,499)		
26		10°	50,499(54,273)	3188(3244)	53,687(57,497)	-3.3(+3.6)	-3.3(+3.6)
27		20°	48,536(56,344)	3344(3412)	51,880(59,756)	-6.5(+7.7)	-3.4(+3.9)
28		30°	46,299(58,752)	3642(3780)	49,941(62,532)	-10.0(+12.7)	-3.7(+5.1)
29		40°	43,539(61,775)	4184(4432)	47,723(66,207)	-14.0(+19.3)	-4.4(+5.9)
30		50°	39,693(66,070)	5142(5738)	44,835(71,808)	-19.2(+29.4)	-6.0(+8.4)
31	Mar 15	0°	62,527(62,527)	3732(3732)	66,259(66,259)		
32		10°	60,581(64,561)	3776(3812)	64,357(68,373)	-2.9(+3.2)	-2.9(+3.2)
33		20°	58,523(66,750)	3960(4028)	62,483(70,778)	-5.7(+6.8)	-2.9(+3.5)
34		30°	56,184(69,297)	4314(4452)	60,498(73,749)	-8.7(+11.3)	-3.2(+4.2)
35		40°	53,303(72,497)	4940(5202)	58,243(77,699)	-12.1(+17.3)	-3.7(+5.4)
36		50°	49,293(77,034)	6038(6668)	55,331(83,702)	-16.5(+26.3)	-5.0(+7.7)
37	Apr 1	0°	74,877(74,877)	4446(4446)	79,323(79,323)		
38		10°	72,972(76,903)	4490(4526)	77,462(81,429)	-2.3(+2.6)	-2.3(+2.6)
39		20°	70,954(79,084)	4708(4776)	75,662(83,860)	-4.6(+5.7)	-2.3(+3.0)
40		30°	68,668(81,626)	5130(5268)	73,798(86,894)	-7.0(+9.5)	-2.5(+3.6)
41		40°	65,856(84,826)	5858(6120)	71,714(90,946)	-9.6(+14.6)	-2.8(+4.7)
42		50°	61,943(89,364)	7144(7764)	69,087(97,128)	-12.9(+22.4)	-3.7(+6.8)
43	Apr 15	0°	85,050(85,050)	5034(5034)	90,084(90,084)		
44		10°	83,297(86,949)	5078(5114)	88,375(92,063)	-1.9(+2.2)	-1.9(+2.2)
45		20°	81,438(88,996)	5324(5392)	86,762(94,388)	-3.7(+4.8)	-1.8(+2.5)
46		30°	79,336(91,396)	5810(5940)	85,146(97,333)	-5.5(+8.0)	-1.9(+3.1)
47		40°	76,758(94,417)	6638(6876)	83,396(101,293)	-7.4(+12.4)	-2.0(+4.0)
48		50°	73,160(98,718)	8084(8670)	81,244(107,388)	-9.8(+19.2)	-2.6(+6.0)
49	May 1	0°	96,678(96,678)	5708(5708)	102,386(102,386)		
50		10°	95,221(98,311)	5778(5800)	100,999(104,111)	-1.4(+1.7)	-1.4(+1.7)
51		20°	93,674(100,077)	6062(6110)	99,736(106,187)	-2.6(+3.7)	-1.2(+2.0)
52		30°	91,942(102,154)	6610(6722)	98,552(108,876)	-3.7(+6.3)	-1.2(+2.5)
53		40°	89,813(104,795)	7558(7766)	97,371(112,561)	-4.9(+9.9)	-1.2(+3.1)
54		50°	86,836(108,570)	9224(9734)	96,060(118,304)	-6.2(+15.5)	-1.3(+5.1)
55	May 15	0°	106,855(106,855)	6322(6322)	113,177(113,177)		
56		10°	105,752(108,153)	6394(6416)	112,146(114,569)	-0.9(+1.2)	-0.9(+1.2)
57		20°	104,585(109,564)	6712(6754)	111,297(116,318)	-1.7(+2.8)	-0.8(+1.5)
58		30°	103,290(111,238)	7338(7422)	110,628(118,660)	-2.3(+4.8)	-0.6(+2.1)
59		40°	101,709(113,383)	8406(8566)	110,115(121,949)	-2.7(+7.8)	-0.5(+2.8)
60		50°	99,507(116,484)	10,300(10,708)	109,807(127,192)	-3.0(+12.4)	-0.3(+4.3)
61	June 1	0°	119,216(119,216)	7070(7070)	126,286(126,286)		
62		10°	118,634(120,007)	7172(7172)	125,806(127,179)	-0.4(+0.7)	-0.4(+0.7)
63		20°	118,033(120,876)	7528(7556)	125,561(128,432)	-0.6(+1.7)	-0.2(+1.0)
64		30°	117,391(121,932)	8248(8302)	125,639(130,234)	-0.5(+3.1)	+0.1(+1.4)
65		40°	116,636(123,312)	9478(9572)	126,114(132,884)	-0.1(+5.2)	+0.4(+2.0)
66		50°	115,608(125,343)	11,710(11,952)	127,318(137,295)	+0.8(+8.7)	+1.0(+3.3)
67	June 15	0°	133,762(133,762)	7978(7978)	141,740(141,740)		
68		10°	133,871(133,871)	8092(8092)	141,963(141,963)	+0.2(+0.2)	+0.2(+0.2)
69		20°	134,014(134,014)	8516(8516)	142,530(142,530)	+0.6(+0.6)	+0.4(+0.4)
70		30°	134,239(134,239)	9342(9342)	143,581(143,581)	+1.3(+1.3)	+0.7(+0.7)
71		40°	134,582(134,582)	10,790(10,790)	145,372(145,372)	+2.6(+2.6)	+1.2(+1.2)
72		50°	135,144(135,144)	13,482(13,482)	148,626(148,626)	+4.8(+4.8)	+2.2(+2.2)

/1/ Computed from time of sunrise to time of sunset. /2/ Civil twilight.

Part II: PERCENTAGE DIFFERENCE IN SUMMATION OF DAY LENGTH BETWEEN NORTHERN AND SOUTHERN LATITUDES, BEGINNING DECEMBER 21

Percentage difference is presented in terms of southern latitudes.

Southern Latitude	Date	Northern Latitude 10° %	20° %	30° %	40° %	50° %
10°	Jan 1	-8.6	-12.9	-17.7	-23.0	-29.3
	Feb 1	-7.9	-11.8	-16.0	-20.8	-27.3
	Mar 1	-6.6	-9.8	-13.1	-17.0	-22.0
	Apr 1	-4.9	-7.1	-9.4	-11.9	-15.2
	May 1	-3.0	-4.2	-5.3	-6.5	-7.7
	June 1	-1.1	-1.3	-1.2	-0.8	+0.1
20°	Jan 1	-13.1	-17.2	-21.7	-26.8	-32.8
	Feb 1	-12.0	-15.7	-19.7	-24.3	-30.5
	Mar 1	-10.2	-13.2	-16.4	-20.1	-25.0
	Apr 1	-7.6	-9.8	-12.0	-14.5	-17.6
	May 1	-4.9	-6.1	-7.2	-8.3	-9.5
	June 1	-2.0	-2.2	-2.2	-1.8	-0.9
30°	Jan 1	-17.9	-21.7	-26.0	-30.8	-36.5
	Feb 1	-16.5	-20.0	-23.8	-28.2	-34.0
	Mar 1	-14.1	-17.0	-20.1	-23.7	-28.3
	Apr 1	-10.9	-12.9	-15.1	-17.5	-20.5
	May 1	-7.2	-8.4	-9.5	-10.6	-11.8
	June 1	-3.4	-3.6	-3.5	-3.2	-2.2
40°	Jan 1	-23.5	-27.1	-31.1	-35.6	-40.8
	Feb 1	-21.8	-25.1	-28.7	-32.8	-38.3
	Mar 1	-18.9	-21.6	-24.6	-27.9	-32.3
	Apr 1	-14.8	-16.8	-18.9	-21.1	-24.0
	May 1	-10.3	-11.4	-12.4	-13.5	-14.7
	June 1	-5.3	-5.5	-5.5	-5.1	-4.2
50°	Jan 1	-31.0	-34.2	-37.8	-41.8	-46.6
	Feb 1	-28.9	-31.8	-35.1	-38.8	-43.8
	Mar 1	-25.2	-27.8	-30.5	-33.5	-37.6
	Apr 1	-20.2	-22.1	-24.0	-26.2	-28.9
	May 1	-14.7	-15.7	-16.7	-17.7	-18.8
	June 1	-8.4	-8.5	-8.5	-8.1	-7.3

Part III: SEASONAL TIME SCALE OF DAY AND NIGHT HOURS

#	Northern Hemisphere Parallel	Period	Dec 21	Jan 21 Nov 21	Feb 21 Oct 21	Mar 21 Sept 21	Apr 21 Aug 21	May 21 July 21	June 21
1	0°	Day	12.0	12.0	12.0	12.0	12.0	12.0	12.0
2		Night	12.0	12.0	12.0	12.0	12.0	12.0	12.0
3	10°	Day	11.5	11.6	11.7	12.0	12.4	12.5	12.5
4		Night	12.5	12.4	12.3	12.0	11.7	11.6	11.5
5	20°	Day	10.8	11.0	11.4	12.0	12.6	13.0	13.2
6		Night	13.2	13.0	12.6	12.0	11.4	11.0	10.8
7	30°	Day	10.2	10.4	11.1	12.0	12.9	13.6	13.8
8		Night	13.8	13.6	12.9	12.0	11.1	10.4	10.2
9	40°	Day	9.3	9.7	10.6	12.0	13.4	14.3	14.7
10		Night	14.7	14.3	13.4	12.0	10.6	9.7	9.3
11	50°	Day	8.0	8.6	10.1	12.0	13.9	15.4	16.0
12		Night	16.0	15.4	13.9	12.0	10.1	8.6	8.0
13	60°	Day	5.9	6.9	9.2	12.0	14.8	17.1	18.1
14		Night	18.1	17.1	14.8	12.0	9.2	6.9	5.9
15	70°	Day	0	1.5	7.4	12.0	16.6	22.5	24.0
16		Night	24.0	22.5	16.6	12.0	7.4	1.5	0
17	80°	Day	0	0	0	12.0	24.0	24.0	24.0
18		Night	24.0	24.0	24.0	12.0	0	0	0
19	90°	Day	0	0	0	12.0	24.0	24.0	24.0
20		Night	24.0	24.0	24.0	12.0	0	0	0
	Southern Hemisphere		June 21	May 21 July 21	Apr 21 Aug 21	Mar 21 Sept 21	Feb 21 Oct 21	Jan 21 Nov 21	Dec 21

Part IV: MEAN TEMPERATURES OF THE PARALLELS

#		Parallel	Annual °C	January °C	July °C
1	Northern	90°	-22.7	-41	-1
2		75	-14.7	-29.0	3.4
3		60	-1.1	-16.1	14.1
4		45	9.8	-1.7	20.9
5		30	20.4	14.5	27.3
6		15	26.3	24.0	27.9
7	Equator		26.2	26.4	25.6
8	Southern	15	24.4	25.9	22.3
9		30	18.4	21.9	14.7
10		45	8.8	12.3	6.2
11		60	-4.1	1.2	-10.3
12		75	-18.0	-3.5	-29.7
13		90	-30.0	-11.0	-42

The term "galvanotaxis" is applied to the physiological response toward an electrode exhibited by an organism placed in a direct current field. If the organism aligns itself parallel to the current lines, and faces and migrates toward the anode, the response is termed "anodal galvanotaxis." Similarly, if the organism reacts in a like manner to stimulation from the cathode, the action is called "cathodal galvanotaxis." When a movement is started in one direction and then is reversed, the response is "biphasic." When an organism in an alternating current field takes a position at right angles to the current lines, and moves parallel to the electrode, the term "oscillotaxis" is used. A=anode; AG=anodal galvanotaxis; CG=cathodal galvanotaxis; BP=biphasic; OT=oscillotaxis; NR=no response; R=response (described in footnotes) not defined by other symbols.

Part I: GAVANOTAXIS

#	Organism	Response	#	Organism	Response	#	Organism	Response
	Protozoa			**Platyhelminthes**			**Arthropoda (concluded)**	
	Rhizopoda			*Turbellaria*		88	Astacus fluviatilis	AG[21,22]
1	Ameba diffluens	CG[1]	48	Dendrocoelum lacteum	CG	89	Bosmina longispina	AG or CG
2	A. limax	CG[1]	49	Leptoplana variabilis	CG	90	Chydorus sphaericus	AG or CG
3	A. proteus	CG[1]	50	Planaria agilis	CG[13,14]	91	Cyclops viridis	AG or CG
4	A. verrucosa	CG[1]	51	P. dorotocephala	CG[13,14]	92	C. strenuus	AG or CG
5	A. dofleini	NR	52	P. gonocephala	CG[13,14]	93	Cyclocypris ovum	CG
	Flagellata		53	P. maculata	CG[13,14]	94	Cyprinotus incongruens	CG
6	Chilomonas paramecium	CG-AG[2]	54	P. polychroa	CG[13,14]	95	Daphnia longissima	AG or CG
7	Euglena viridis	NR[3]	55	P. simplissima	CG[13,14]	96	D. magna	AG or CG
8	Gonium pectorale	CG-AG[4]	56	P. velata	CG[13,14]	97	D. pulex obtusa	AG or CG
9	Peridinium tabulatum	CG	57	Polycelis nigra	CG[14]	98	Diaptomus denticornis	CG
10	Polytoma uvella	AG	58	Stenostoma leucops	CG[15]	99	D. gracilis	CG
11	Trachelomonas hispida	CG		*Nemertea*		100	D. tatricus	CG
12	Volvox aureus	CG-AG[4,5]	59	Lineus socialis	CG[15]	101	Galathea squamifera	AG[22]
13	V. globator	CG-AG[4,5]	60	L. viridis	CG[13]	102	Gammarus spp	CG-AG[2,23]
	Ciliata			**Echinodermata**		103	Homarus americanus	R[24]
14	Balantidium duodeni	CG[6]		*Asteroidea*		104	Moina macrocopa	CG
15	B. elongatum	CG[6]	61	Asterina gibbosa	BP-CG[16]	105	Notodromas monacha	CG
16	B. entozoon	CG[6]	62	Asterias glacialis	BP	106	Palaemonetes vulgaris	AG[22]
17	Bursaria truncatella	CG[7]	63	A. rubens	BP	107	Simocephalus vetulus	AG or CG
18	Chilodon cucullulus	CG[7]	64	A. tenuispina	BP		*Myriopoda*	
19	Coleps hirtus	CG	65	Astropecten bispinosus	BP	108	Isobates varicornis	AG
20	Colpidium colpoda	CG[7]	66	A. mülleri	BP	109	Lithobius validus	AG
21	Colpoda cucullus	CG	67	A. spinulosus	BP	110	Polydesmus complanatus	AG
22	Condylostoma patens	CG	68	Echinaster sepositus	BP		*Insecta*	
23	Glaucoma pyriformis	CG	69	Ophiotrix fragilis	AG[17]	111	Corixa striata	AG
24	Halteria grandinella	CG	70	Ophiura albida	AG	112	Dytiscus marginalis	AG
25	Leucophrys spatula	NR	71	O. texturata	AG		**Mollusca**	
26	Nyctotherus cordiformis	CG[8]	72	Solaster papposus	BP-CG[16]	113	Limnaea stagnalis	CG
27	Opalina ranarum	CG-AG[2,8]		*Echinoidea*		114	Planorbis corneus	CG
28	Oxytricha fallax	CG-AG[2]	73	Echinus milaris	NR[18]		**Vertebrata**	
29	Paramecium aurelia	CG[9]	74	Sphaerechinus granularis	CG[17]		*Cyclostomata*	
30	P. bursaria	CG[9]	75	Strongylocentrotus lividus	AG[17,18]	115	Petromyzon fluviatilis	AG
31	P. caudatum	CG[9]	76	S. drobachiensis	AG[17,18]		*Pisces*	
32	P. marinum	CG[9]		**Echiuroidea**		116	Acerina cernua	AG
33	P. putrinum	CG[9]	77	Echiurus crysocanthophorus	AG[13]	117	Apodes spp	AG
34	Pleuronema chrysalis	CG		**Annelida**		118	Cyprinus auratus	AG[25]
35	Spirostomum ambiguum	CG[7]		*Chaetopoda*		119	Esox spp	AG
36	Stentor coeruleus	CG	78	Dasychone lucullana, larva	CG	120	Gastrosteus aculeatus	AG
37	S. polymorphus	CG	79	Dero limosa	CG	121	Gobio fluviatilis	AG[25]
38	S. roeseli	CG	80	Lumbriculus inconstans	CG	122	Leuciscus idus	AG
39	Stylonychia mytilus	CG[7]	81	Lumbricus terrestria	CG[14]	123	L. rutilus	AG
40	Urocentrum turbo	CG	82	Nereis spp	R[14,19]	124	Phoxinus laevis	AG
41	Uronema marina	CG	83	Tubifex rivulorum	CG	125	Salmo, embryo	AG
42	Urostyla grandis	CG[7]		*Hirudinea*		126	Sardinops caerulae	AG
	Coelenterata		84	Hirudo medicinalis	R[20]	127	Tinca spp	AG
43	Hydra fusca	R[10,11]		**Arthropoda**			*Amphibia*	
44	H. viridis	R[10,11]		*Crustacea*		128	Ambystoma larvae	R[25,26]
45	Pelmatohydra oligactis	R[11,12]	85	Apus cancriformis	AG	129	Rana, adult	NR
46	Pennaria tiarella	R[12]	86	Asellus aquaticus	AG	130	Rana, tadpole	CG-AG[2]
47	Polyorchis penicillata	R[12]	87	A. communis	AG	131	Triton spp	NR
						132	Triturus torosus	R[25,26]

/1/ AG after treatment with NH$_3$OH or NH$_3$ salts. AG when free from substrate. /2/ CG in weak (or medium) fields. AG in strong fields. /3/ Or CG or AG, depending upon culture. /4/ CG in light; AG in dark. /5/ AG after duration in current field. /6/ AG in moderately alkaline field. /7/ When fixed to substrate turns at right angles with current lines, peristome toward C. /8/ Fresh from frog intestine or with acid treatment. AG out of intestine or with alkali treatment. /9/ In strong field, after moderate currents of long duration, growth in 1/20 M NaCl, suspension in NaCl solution above 0.01-0.1 N, suspension in salt solutions at high concentration, organism may move towards A electrophoretically with anterior end directed towards C. True AG in medium with low calcium concentration. /10/ When fixed bends toward A. /11/ When not fixed bends toward C. /12/ When fixed bends toward C. /13/ Reversed by strychnine. /14/ Bends concavely toward C when at right angles with field. /15/ Reversed by barium salts. /16/ BP, strong fields; CG, weak fields. /17/ Older larvae CG. /18/ Spines and tube feet AG. /19/ After long period in laboratory bends concavely toward A. /20/ Bends anteriorly toward C. /21/ CG in hypertonic salt solutions. /22/ At right angles with field, extremities facing A flexed, facing C extended. /23/ Acid promotes AG, alkali CG. /24/ Gather at, but not directed toward, A. /25/ Bends concavely toward A when at right angles with field. /26/ Bends ventrally concave facing A, dorsally concave facing C, when parallel with field.

Part II: OSCILLOTAXIS

#	Organism	Response	#	Organism	Response	#	Organism	Response
	Protozoa			**Protozoa (concluded)**			**Arthropoda (concluded)**	
	Rhizopoda		12	Vorticella campanulata	NR[7]		*Insecta*	
1	Ameba dolfeini	NR		**Platyhelminthes**		21	Aeschna larvae	OT
2	A. proteus	OT	13	Dendrocoelum lacteum	OT	22	Dytiscus marginalis	OT
	Flagellata			**Annelida**			**Vertebrata**	
3	Peridinium umbonatum	R[1]	14	Hirudo medicinalis	OT		*Pisces*	
	Ciliata			**Arthropoda**		23	Cyprinus auratus	OT
4	Aspidisca spp	R[2]		*Crustacea*		24	Esox lucius	OT
5	Chilodon spp	OT[3]	15	Asellus aquaticus	OT	25	Gastrosteus aculeatus	OT
6	Colpidium colpoda	OT[3]	16	Gammarus pulex	OT	26	Perca fluviatilis	OT
7	Euplotes spp	OT[4]	17	Palaemon serratus	OT	27	Phoxinus laevis	OT
8	Onychodromus grandis	R[2]	18	Peneus caramote	OT	28	Rhodeus amarus	OT
9	Paramecium caudatum	OT[5]	19	Portunus olsatus	OT	29	Salmo lacustris	OT
10	Stentor polymorphus	NR[6]	20	Potamobius leptodactylus	OT		*Amphibia*	
11	Stylonychia mytilus	OT[2]				30	Rana esculenta, tadpole	OT

/1/ Swims in elipses with long axes at right angles with current. /2/ Swims backwards in circles. /3/ Anterior part describes circle around point in posterior part of organism. /4/ Strong field. Swims in direction of current in weak field. /5/ May make rotary movements with anterior end; posterior end stationary with body describing cone (double cone in stronger field); middle of organism stationary. /6/ Rotation around longitudinal axis accelerated. /7/ When unattached swims in circles.

394. EFFECTS OF HYDROSTATIC PRESSURE

Part I: EFFECTS ON BIOLOGICAL MATERIALS AT PRESSURES IN EXCESS OF 1000 ATMOSPHERES

Material	Approximate Pressure, Atmospheres	Results of Compression	Material	Approximate Pressure, Atmospheres	Results of Compression
Tissues and Tumors			**Antigens and Antibodies**		
1 Carcinoma, Brown-Pearce	1000[1]	Resistant.	33 Antigen, equine serum	4000	Specificity may be changed or unchanged.
2 Chick heart, embryonic	1000-1850	Reduction of subsequent growth in culture.	34 Antitoxin, tetanus, equine	13,500	Gelated, partially inactivated.
3 Erythrocytes	500-3000	Rounded.	35 Filtrate, S. typhi	6000	Superior to cells as immunizing antigen.
4	5000	Disintegrated.	36 Toxin, diphtheria	13,500	Partially destroyed.
5 Sarcoma transplants, rat	1800	Inactivated.	37	17,600	Mostly destroyed.
Bacteria and Fungi			38 Toxin, tetanus	13,500	Greatly attenuated or inactivated.
6 Bacillus anthracis	3000	Partial loss of virulence; death of vegetative cells.	39 Tuberculin	13,500	Not destroyed.
7 Bacteria, colon	3000	Unaffected.	40 Venom, cobra	13,500	Lethality unchanged.
8 Bacteria, various spp	5000	Vegetative cells killed.	**Enzymes**		
9 Spores, bacterial	12,000	Killed.	41 Amylase, laccase, lipase, sucrase(yeast), trypsin (pancreatic), trypsinogen	8,000-15,000	Some completely, others partially inactivated.
10 Staphylococci	3000	Unaffected.	42 Chymotrypsinogen	7600	pH 3.1-7.6: partly inactivated.
11 Streptococci	3000	Killed or retarded in growth.	43 Chymotrypsin, trypsin	7600	pH 3: scarcely affected; pH 7.6: partially inactivated.
12 Yeast cells	4000-6000	Death, preceded by cytoplasmic flocculation or coagulation.	44 Pepsin	7600	pH 2-5.2: largely inactivated.
Viruses			45 Pepsin, rennin	6000	Inactivated.
13 Avian pest (fowl plague)	4000	Inactivated, but retained antigenicity.	46 Ribonucleode-polymerase	6000	Reversible diminution in activity under pressure (pressure also affects polymerization of ribonucleic acid alone).
Bacteriophage vs.:			**Proteins**		
14 Bacillus megatherium	7000	Inactivated.	47 Albumin, egg	5000	Slight stiffening.
15 B. subtilis	7000	Inactivated.	48	7000	Completely coagulated.
16 Salmonella typhosa	7000	Inactivated.	49	7500	Denatured, coagulated; SH groups exposed.
17 Staphylococci	2000	Inactivated.	50 Amylase (active) plus its starch digest	6000	Resynthesis of product resembling initial undigested material.
18 Encephalomyelitis (rabbit)	7000	Inactivated.	51 Carboxyhemoglobin	9000	Coagulated.
19 Foot and mouth disease	4000	Inactivated.	52 Gelatin	2000	Gelation accelerated.
20 (in guinea pig)	3000	Attenuated.	53 Gelatin gel	3000	Water squeezed out.
21 Herpes (rabbit)	3000	Inactivated.	54 Globulin, serum (equine)	3,000-13,000	Gelated.
22 Papilloma	4000	No tumors.	55 Insulin	10,000	Coagulated, but not physiologically inactivated.
23 Rabies (rabbit)	4000	Attenuated.	56 Trypsin (active) plus its gelatin or serum albumin digest	6000	Resynthesis of product resembling initial undigested material.
24	5000	Inactivated.			
25 Rous sarcoma	1800	Tumors delayed.			
26 Sarcoma filtrate	4000	No tumors.			
27 Shope papilloma	1800	Tumors delayed.			
28 Tobacco mosaic	7500	Inactivated; coagulated.			
29	8000-8700	Inactivated.			
30 Tobacco necrosis	3000-5000	Inactivated.			
31 Vaccinia (rabbit)	4500	Inactivated.			
32 Yellow fever (monkey)	3000	Slightly attenuated.			

/1/ Transplantability destroyed by pressure of 1800 atmospheres.

Part II: PHYSIOLOGICAL EFFECTS ON BIOLOGICAL MATERIALS AT PRESSURES NOT EXCEEDING 1000 ATMOSPHERES

	Material or Activity	Pressure, Atmospheres	Results of Compression
	Cell Division		
1	Eggs (Arbacia)	100-400	Progressive reversible solation of gelated cortical cytoplasm.
2		400	Reversible regression of cleavage furrows; reversible solation of cortical plasmagel.
3	Eggs (annelid, echinoderm, and vertebrate)	100-500	Cleavage-inhibiting pressure increases with temperature (5-30°C).
4	Eggs (Ascaris)	800	Exceptionally resistant to pressure; division not inhibited.
5	Eggs, marine (miscellaneous)	200-400	Reversible inhibition of cleavage.
6	Eggs (Urechis)	300-400	Reversible solation of spindles and asters; movements of chromosomes stopped.
	Other Cellular Activities		
7	Ameboid movement (A. proteus, A. dubia)	200-500	Reversible solation of plasmagel; collapsing of pseudopodia; stopping of movement. At higher temperatures greater pressures required to produce effects.
8	Bioluminescence (bacterial)	200-400	Effect depends on temperature. Light intensity decreases at lower, increases at higher, temperature.
9	Ciliary movement	200-400	Temporary increase in beat frequency with each increase of pressure; reverse effect with pressure decrements.
10	"Contraction" of pigment cells (fish)	200-400	"Contraction" phase reversibly inhibited; totally inhibited at higher level.
11	Heart rate, tissue cultured fragments (frog heart)	300	Effect depends on temperature; retardation at lower temperatures, acceleration at higher temperatures.
12	Muscular contraction	200-400	Effect depends on temperature. Tension decreases at lower, increases at higher, temperatures.
13	Protoplasmic streaming (Elodea)	200-400	Solation of cytoplasm; streaming slowed; stopped at 400 atmospheres; reversible.
14	(Pelomyxa)	200-400	Solation of plasmagel; streaming stopped.

Part III: EFFECTS ON RATE OF SPECIFIC ENZYME REACTIONS AT PRESSURES LESS THAN 680 ATMOSPHERES

Net volume changes of activation computed according to observed influences of pressure.

#	Enzyme Kind	Conc mg/ml	Substrate Kind	Conc	pH	Temp °C	Observed Volume Change ml/mol	#	Enzyme Kind	Conc mg/ml	Substrate Kind	Conc	pH	Temp °C	Observed Volume Change ml/mol
1	Amylase, pancreatic	Commercial	Starch	2%		22-23	-28	10	Lysozyme	0.0015	Micrococcus lysodeikticus (whole cells)	± 10^9 cells per ml	6.2-8.7	25	-10 to -24
2	Amylase, salivary	Commercial	Starch	1%		22-23	-22	11	Pepsin	Commercial	Gelatin	0.83%		22-23	-22
3	Chymotrypsin, crystal	0.00154	Casein	1%	7.7	14.5	-13.5	12	Trypsin, crystal	0.062	α-Benzoyl-l-argininamide	0.04 M	7.76	84.5	-1
4		0.0148	L-Tyrosine, ethyl ester	0.02 M	7.8	25.1	-13.5	13		0.076	α-Benzoyl-l-argininamide isopropyl ester				
5	Dehydrogenase, formic		Na formate		5.6-9.5	30	0					0.011 M	8.1	25.2	0
6	Invertase	Commercial	Sucrose	10%	4.8	30	-3	14		0.076		0.04 M	7.76	25.1	0
7			Sucrose	10%	7.04	30	-5	15			β-Lactoglobulin	0.5%	8.1	25.1	-36
8			Sucrose	10%	7.03-70.7	35-45	-69+	16		0.5	Casein	0.68%	7.3	55	-1
9	Lipase, pancreatic	Commercial	Tributyrin	Very low		22-23	-13	17				0.66%	7.3	25-35	-5 to -10

/1/ Acceleration in observed rate under pressure at these temperatures attributed to retardation by pressure of enzyme dehydration, proceeding with a large volume increase.

395. EFFECTS OF ACCELERATION: MAN

"G" denotes accelerative force in terms of the magnitude of force of gravity at the earth's surface. "Positive G" designates that the force vector acts parallel to the long axis of the body, from foot to head; "transverse G", that force vector acts transverse (perpendicular) to the long axis of the body, and may be (a) prone (from chest to back),or (b) supine (from back to chest). "Negative G" refers to a force vector acting parallel to the long axis of the body from head to foot.

Part I: TOLERANCE TO POSITIVE G

Data are for relaxed young healthy males exposed for 10 seconds. Values in parentheses are ranges, estimate "b" of the 95% range (cf Introduction).

#	Reaction	G
1	Grayout (Loss of peripheral vision)[1]	4.3(3-5.6)
2	Blackout (Loss of central vision)[1]	4.9(3.4-6.4)
3	Unconsciousness	5.5(3.7-7.3)

/1/ Grayout and blackout for at least 5 sec of 10 sec period.

Part II: G-TOLERANCE TIME LIMITS

Data are for young healthy males actively resisting G. Tolerance limit is unconsciousness. Values in parentheses are ranges of estimates.

#	Direction of Force	.001	.01	0.1	1.0	10	100	1000
1	Positive G	70	(30-40)	(19-22.5)	12.5	(6.5-8.2)	(3.5-5.5)	3.5
2	Transverse G	200	(60-100)	(38-55)	(25-27.5)	(15-17.5)	(7.2-12.5)	8.5
3	Negative G	15	(9.5-16.5)	(6.5-10)	(4.5-6.5)	(3.2-3.8)	(2.2-2.5)	1.5

Part III: G-FORCES ACTING UPON MAN AND AIRCRAFT IN FLIGHT

Section 1: Various Turns
Values in parentheses indicate time in seconds required for a 360° turn.

#	Speed mi/hr	Radius of Turn (Statute Miles) 0.5	1.0	2.0	5.0	10.0	#	Speed knots/hr	Radius of Turn (Nautical Miles) 0.5	1.0	2.0	5.0	10.0
1	100	1.03 (113)	1.00 (226)	1.00 (452)	1.00 (1131)	1.00 (2262)	13	100	1.04 (113)	1.01 (226)	1.00 (452)	1.00 (1131)	1.00 (2262)
2	200	1.42 (56)	1.12 (113)	1.03 (226)	1.01 (565)	1.00 (1131)	14	200	1.53 (56)	1.16 (113)	1.04 (226)	1.01 (565)	1.00 (1131)
3	300	2.49 (38)	1.52 (75)	1.15 (151)	1.03 (377)	1.01 (754)	15	300	2.80 (38)	1.65 (75)	1.20 (151)	1.03 (377)	1.01 (754)
4	400	4.17 (28)	2.26 (57)	1.42 (114)	1.08 (283)	1.02 (565)	16	400	4.76 (28)	2.54 (57)	1.53 (114)	1.10 (283)	1.02 (565)
5	500	6.41 (23)	3.32 (45)	1.87 (90)	1.18 (225)	1.05 (452)	17	500	7.36 (23)	3.78 (45)	2.08 (90)	1.23 (225)	1.07 (452)
6	600	9.18 (19)	4.67 (38)	2.49 (76)	1.35 (188)	1.10 (377)	18	600	10.55 (19)	5.35 (38)	2.81 (76)	1.45 (188)	1.13 (377)
7	700	12.50 (16)	6.28 (32)	3.26 (64)	1.60 (161)	1.18 (323)	19	700	14.30 (16)	7.21 (32)	3.70 (64)	1.74 (161)	1.23 (323)
8	800	16.25 (14)	8.15 (28)	4.17 (56)	1.91 (141)	1.29 (283)	20	800	18.70 (14)	9.39 (28)	4.76 (56)	2.11 (141)	1.36 (283)
9	900	20.60 (13)	10.28 (25)	5.24 (50)	2.28 (126)	1.43 (251)	21	900	23.61 (13)	11.85 (25)	6.00 (50)	2.56 (126)	1.54 (251)
10	1000	25.35 (11)	12.70 (23)	6.41 (46)	2.72 (113)	1.61 (226)	22	1000	29.21 (11)	14.60 (23)	7.35 (46)	3.08 (113)	1.76 (226)
11	1500	57.00 (7)	28.55 (15)	14.30 (30)	5.80 (75)	3.02 (151)	23	1500	65.80 (7)	32.90 (15)	16.45 (30)	6.64 (75)	3.43 (151)
12	2000	101.30 (6)	50.70 (11)	25.40 (23)	10.20 (57)	5.16 (113)	24	2000	117.00 (6)	58.40 (11)	29.20 (23)	11.70 (57)	5.91 (113)

Section 2: Standard 3°/sec Turn
Full turn requires 120 seconds.

#	Speed mi/hr	Radius, Statute Miles	G	#	Speed knots/hr	Radius, Nautical Miles	G
1	100	0.53	1.03	13	100	0.53	1.03
2	200	1.06	1.11	14	200	1.06	1.14
3	300	1.59	1.23	15	300	1.59	1.29
4	400	2.12	1.38	16	400	2.12	1.49
5	500	2.65	1.56	17	500	2.65	1.70
6	600	3.18	1.75	18	600	3.18	1.93
7	700	3.71	1.95	19	700	3.71	2.16
8	800	4.24	2.16	20	800	4.24	2.42
9	900	4.77	2.48	21	900	4.77	2.67
10	1000	5.31	2.59	22	1000	5.31	2.93
11	1500	7.96	3.72	23	1500	7.96	4.25
12	2000	10.61	4.88	24	2000	10.61	5.57

A = mass number; α = alpha particle; β⁺ = positive beta particle from nucleus; β⁻ = negative beta particle from nucleus; γ = gamma ray; EC = electron capture; Mev = million electron volts; n = neutron; Z = atomic number.

#	Z	Symbol	A	Half-life	%[1]	Type	Mev	Average β-Energy[2] Mev
1	0	n	1	13 min	100	β⁻	0.78	
2	1	H	3	12.4 yr	100	β⁻	0.018	0.0057
3	4	Be	7	53.6 da	100	EC[3]		
4	6	C	14	5570 yr	100	β⁻	0.155	0.050
5	11	Na	22	2.6 yr	90	β⁺	0.541	0.225
6					10	EC[3]		
7					100	γ	1.28	
8	11	Na	24	15.1 hr	100	β⁻	1.39	0.540
9					100	γ	1.37	
10					100	γ	2.75	
11	15	P	32	14.3 da	100	β⁻	1.71	0.70
12	16	S	35	87.1 da	100	β⁻	0.167	0.055
13	17	Cl	36	$\sim 3 \times 10^5$ yr	100	β⁻	0.714	0.24
14	19	K	42	12.52 hr	18	β⁻	1.99	
15					82	β⁻	3.55	1.395
16					18	γ	1.53	
17	20	Ca	45	164 da	100	β⁻	0.254	0.075
18	20	Ca	47	4.8 da	83	β⁻	0.66	
19					17	β⁻	1.94	
20					~17	γ	1.31	
21	21	Sc	46	85 da	~100	β⁻	0.36	0.117
22					~100	γ	0.89	
23					~100	γ	1.12	
24	24	Cr	51	27.7 da	100	EC[3]		
25					~10	γ	0.32	
26	25	Mn	52	5.7 da	33	β⁺	0.58	0.084
27					67	EC[3]		
28					100	γ	0.73	
29					100	γ	0.94	
30					100	γ	1.45	
31	25	Mn	54	291 da	100	EC[3]		
32					100	γ	0.84	
33	26	Fe	55	2.94 yr	100	EC[3]		
34						γ	cont[4]	
35	26	Fe	59	45 da	~46	β⁻	0.271	
36					~54	β⁻	0.462	0.120
37					3	γ	0.191	
38					57	γ	1.10	
39					43	γ	1.29	
40	27	Co	57	270 da	100	EC[3]		
41					~90	γ	0.014	
42					~90	γ	0.123	
43					~10	γ	0.137	
44	27	Co	60	5.38 yr	~100	β⁻	0.306	0.099
45					~100	γ	1.17	
46					100	γ	1.33	
47	28	Ni	63	85 yr	100	β⁻	0.063	0.022
48	29	Cu	64	12.84 hr	38	β⁻	0.573	0.12
49					19	β⁺	0.656	
50					43	EC[3]		
51					0.4	γ	1.34	
52	30	Zn	65	245 da	1.5	β⁺	0.325	0.003
53					98.5	EC[3]		
54					46	γ	1.11	
55	33	As	77	38.7 hr	2	β⁻	0.43	
56					98	β⁻	0.68	
57						γ 1-7[5]	0.023-0.53	
58	34	Se	75	127 da	100	β⁻	0.467	
59						γ	0.136	
60						γ 1-11[5]	0.025-0.40	
61	35	Br	82	35.9 hr	100	β⁻	0.45	0.150
62						γ	0.55-2.0	
63	37	Rb	86	18.6 da	10	β⁻	0.68	
64					90	β⁻	1.77	
65					10	γ	1.08	
66	38	Sr	89	50.5 da	100	β⁻	1.46	0.49
67	38	Sr	90	28 yr	100	β⁻	0.53	
68	42	Mo	99	68 hr	14	β⁻	0.45	
69					~1	β⁻	0.87	
70					85	β⁻	1.23	
71						γ 1-6[5]	0.041-0.780	
72	47	Ag	110	270 da	35	β⁻	0.09	
73					10	β⁻	0.31	
74					50	β⁻	0.57	
75					5	β⁻	2.86	
76						γ 1-14[5]	0.116-1.51	
77	47	Ag	111	7.5 da	8	β⁻	0.70	0.36
78					1	β⁻	0.80	
79					91	β⁻	1.04	
80					1	γ	0.247	
81					8	γ	0.340	
82	50	Sn	113	112 da	100	EC[3]		
83					100		0.393	
84	51	Sb	124	60 da	10	β⁻	0.22	
85					53	β⁻	0.61	
86					6	β⁻	0.87	
87					5	β⁻	1.58	
88					5	β⁻	1.66	
89					21	β⁻	2.31	
90						γ 1-6[5]	0.603-2.07	
91	53	I	131	8.05 da	2.8	β⁻	0.250	
92					9.3	β⁻	0.335	0.189
93					87.2	β⁻	0.606	
94					0.7	β⁻	0.807	
95					6.3	γ	0.080	
96					0.7	γ	0.163	
97					6.3	γ	0.284	
98					80.9	γ	0.364	
99					9.3	γ	0.638	
100					2.8	γ	0.723	
101	55	Cs	134	2.3 yr	32	β⁻	0.083	
102					5	β⁻	0.31	
103					50	β⁻	0.655	
104					13	β⁻	0.683	
105						γ 1-12[5]	0.200-1.37	
106	55	Cs	137	30 ± 3 yr	92	β⁻	0.518	0.19
107					8	β⁻	1.18	
108					92	γ	0.662	
109	56	Ba	140	13 da	40	β⁻	0.48	
110					60	β⁻	1.02	0.25
111						γ 1-4[5]	0.03-0.54	
112	58	Ce	144	282 da	20	β⁻	0.16	
113					5	β⁻	0.26	
114					75	β⁻	0.33	
115						γ 1-8[5]	0.03-0.15	
116	59	Pr	143	13.8 da	100	β⁻	0.93	
117	63	Eu	152	13 yr		β⁻	0.70	
118						EC[3]		
119						γ 1-7[5]	0.12-1.09	
120	63	Eu	154	16 yr		β⁻	1.45	
121						EC[3]		
122						γ	0.12	
123						γ	1.12	
124						γ	1.42	
125	77	Ir	192	74.4 da	44	β⁻	<0.6	
126					50	β⁻	0.67	
127					6	EC[3]		
128						γ 1-20[5]	0.14-1.16	
129	79	Au	198	2.70 da	99	β⁻	0.958	
130					100	γ	0.411	
131	79	Au	199	3.16 da	20	β⁻	0.25	
132					73	β⁻	0.30	0.098
133					7	β⁻	0.46	
134					5	γ	0.05	
135					78	γ	0.16	
136					15	γ	0.21	
137	80	Hg	203	47 da	100	β⁻	0.210	0.07
138					100	γ	0.279	
139	82	Pb	210	19 yr	100	β⁻	0.018	0.006
140					100	γ	0.047	
141	83	Bi	210	5.0 da	100	β⁻	1.17	0.33
142	88	Ra	226	1620 yr	6	α	4.61	
143					94	α	4.79	
144					6	γ	0.18	
145	90	Th	232	1.39×10^{10} yr	25	α	3.95	
146					75	α	4.00	
147					25	γ	0.05	
148	92	U	232	74 yr	~32	α	5.261	
149					68	α	5.318	
150					32	γ	0.06	
151	92	U	233	1.62×10^5 yr	2	α	4.72	
152					15	α	4.77	
153					83	α	4.82	
154						γ 1-3[5]	0.04-0.09	
155	92	U	238	4.51×10^9 yr	22	α	4.13	
156					78	α	4.18	
157					22	γ	0.05	
158	94	Pu	238	90 yr	0.1	α	5.35	
159					~28	α	5.45	
160					72	α	5.50	
161						γ 1-3[5]	0.04-0.15	
162	94	Pu	239	2.44×10^4 yr	11	α	5.10	
163					89	α	5.15	
164						γ 1-5[5]	0.04-0.38	

/1/ Per cent disintegration in which radiation is emitted. /2/ Average energy of all β particles per disintegration. /3/ Electron capture, accompanied by X-rays characteristic of the daughter element. /4/ Continuous X-ray spectrum. /5/ Multiple γ rays with energies in the range indicated; branching ratios not established.

397. RADIOISOTOPES: METABOLIC FEATURES

A = mass number; α = alpha particles; β = beta particles; γ = gamma rays; Z = atomic number.

	Z	Symbol	A	Half-life	Radiation	Absorption	Localization	Elimination
1	11	Na	24	15.1 hr	β, γ	Complete	General	Rapid
2	15	P	32	14.3 da	β	Excellent	Bone; general	Few weeks[1]
3	20	Ca	45	164 da	β	Moderate	Bone	Slow[1]
4	38	Sr	89	50.5 da	β	Excellent	Bone	Slow[1]
5	38	Sr	90	28 yr	β	Excellent	Bone	Very slow[1]
6	39	Y	91	57 da	β, γ	Poor[2]	Bone	Very slow[1]
7	40	Zr	95	65 da	β, γ	Poor[2]	Bone	Slow[1]
8	41	Nb	95	35 da	β, γ	Slight	Bone	Slow[1]
9	44	Ru	103	42 da	β, γ	Poor[2]	Kidney	Few weeks
10	44	Ru	106	1 yr	β	Poor[2]	Kidney	Few weeks
11	52	Te	127	90 da	γ	Moderate	Kidney	Few weeks
12	52	Te	129	32 da	γ	Moderate	Kidney	Few weeks
13	53	I	131	8.05 da	β, γ	Complete	Thyroid	Month
14	55	Cs	134	2.3 yr	β, γ	Complete	Muscle; general	Fairly rapid
15	55	Cs	137	30 ± 3 yr	β, γ	Complete	Muscle; general	Fairly rapid
16	56	Ba	140	13 da	β, γ	Good	Bone	Very slow[1]
17	57	La	140	40 hr	β, γ	Poor[2]	Bone; liver	Few weeks[1,3]
18	58	Ce	139	140 da	γ (soft)	Poor[2]	Bone; liver	Slow[1,3]
19	58	Ce	141	32.5 da	β, γ	Poor[2]	Bone; liver	Slow[1,3]
20	58	Ce	144	282 da	β, γ	Poor[2]	Bone; liver	Slow[1,3]
21	59	Pr	143	13.8 da	β	Slight	Bone; liver	Slow[1,3]
22	61	Pm	147	2.6 yr	β	Poor[2]	Bone; liver	Slow[1,3]
23	84	Po	210	138.3 da	α, γ	Good	Kidney	Slow
24	88	Ra	226	1620 yr	α, γ	Good	Bone	Almost nil[1]
25	92	U	238	4.51×10^9 yr	α	Poor[2]	Lung; kidney	Slow
26	94	Pu	239	2.44×10^4 yr	α, γ	Very poor[2]	Lung; bone	Almost nil[1]

/1/ Retention in bones is usually a matter of months, approaching a year or more in the case of Sr and Y, and becoming virtually permanent in case of Ra and Pu. /2/ Poorly absorbed isotopes, if in sufficient concentration, may damage the gastrointestinal tract during passage; they also tend to be retained in the lung if and when they gain access. /3/ Liver retention is about 10 days in experimental animals, and kidney retention about 20 days.

398. RADIOISOTOPES: POSSIBLE TELETHERAPY SOURCES

Teletherapy refers to therapeutic irradiation with collimated (parallel) gamma rays.

c = curie; Mev = million electron volts; n = neutron; r = roentgen.

	Z	Symbol	A	Half-life	Gamma Energy (Mev)	Practical Clinical Form	Production	Highest Practical-Volume Specific Activity[1] (c/ml)	Specific Gamma Exposure Rate[2] (r/c-hr at 1 m)
1	88	Ra	226	1620 yr	0.2-2.2	Sulfate	Natural	4	0.84[3]
2	55	Cs	137	30 ± 3 yr	0.661	Sulfate	Fission	100	0.39
3	63	Eu	152, 154	13, 16 yr	1.0[4]	Oxide	Nuclear reactor	5000	0.70
4	27	Co	60	5.38 yr	1.17, 1.33	Metal	Nuclear reactor	1000	1.35
5	55	Cs	134	2.3 yr	0.5-1.3	Sulfate	Nuclear reactor	1000	1.20
6	58	Ce	144	282 da	0.6-2.6[5]	Oxide	Fission	2000	0.20
7	47	Ag	110	270 da	0.6-1.5	Metal	Nuclear reactor	250	1.40
8	69	Tm	170	129 da	0.08	Oxide	Nuclear reactor	500	0.01
9	73	Ta	182	115 da	0.04-1.2	Metal	Nuclear reactor	1500	0.6
10	21	Sc	46	85 da	0.9-1.1	Oxide	Nuclear reactor	500	1.1
11	65	Tb	160	72.5 da	0.1-1.1	Chloride	Nuclear reactor	50	0.3
12	77	Ir	192	74.4 da	0.1-0.6	Metal	Nuclear reactor	1000	0.3

/1/ One year irradiation in 5×10^{13} n/cm^2/sec, 1 yr after removal from reactor, ideal geometry, for neutron reactions. /2/ Assuming that gamma absorption in the source is negligible. /3/ Assuming the source is sealed within a 0.5 mm-thick platinum capsule. /4/ Following filtration with 3 mm lead, 83% of total radiation appears to be from four high-energy photons averaging 1.08 mev. /5/ Gamma activity from 17 min praseodymium daughter; energy levels are doubtful.

399. RADIOISOTOPES PRODUCED BY THE CYCLOTRON

Adapted from National Bureau of Standards Handbook 52 "Maximum Permissible Amounts of Radioisotopes in the Human Body and Maximum Permissible Concentrations in Air and Water," and from Nuclear Science & Engineering Corp. Catalogue.

	Radioisotope	Half-life	Mode of Disintegration	Maximum Energy Beta, Mev	Maximum Energy Gamma, Mev[1]	Critical Organ weight, kg	Element Concentration g/kg	Daily Intake of Element	Use
1	Arsenic 73	76 da	K		0.011(X), 0.014, 0.052	Kidneys, 0.3			
2	Arsenic 74	17.5 da	β- (30%); β+ (35%); K (35%)	0.7, 1.4, 0.92, 1.53	0.011(X), 0.511, 0.59, 0.64	Kidneys, 0.3			
3	Beryllium 7	54.5 da	K		0.00011(X), 0.48 (~11%)	Bone, 7.0			
4	Cobalt 56	80 da	β+; K	1.5	0.0069(X), 0.511, 0.845, 1.26, 1.74, 2.01, 2.55, 3.25	Liver, 1.7	2.0×10^{-4}		Tracer studies.
5						Spleen, 0.15	4.7×10^{-4}		
6	Cobalt 57	270 da	β+	0.26	0.014, 0.119, 0.131, 0.511	Liver, 1.7	2.0×10^{-4}	Trace	
7						Spleen, 0.15	4.7×10^{-4}		
8	Cobalt 58	70 da	β+ (14.5%), K	0.47	0.0069(X), 0.511, 0.81	Liver, 1.7	2.0×10^{-4}		
9						Spleen, 0.15	4.7×10^{-4}		
10	Gold 195	180 da	K		0.067(X)	Kidneys, 0.3	Trace		
11	Iron 55	2.94 yr	K		0.0064(X)	Blood, 5.0	0.5	12 mg	Blood studies; iron turn-over.
12	Manganese 52	6 da	β+ (35%); K (65%)	0.582	0.0059(X), 0.511, 0.73, 0.94, 1.46	Kidneys, 0.3	6.0×10^{-4}		Tracer studies.
13						Liver, 1.7	1.7×10^{-3}		
14	Manganese 54	310 da	K		0.0059(X), 0.835	Kidneys, 0.3	6.0×10^{-4}	4 mg	
15						Liver, 1.7	1.7×10^{-3}		
16	Sodium 22	2.6 yr	β+	0.58	0.511, 1.28	Total body, 70.0	1.5	4.0 g	Circulatory studies.
17	Strontium 85	65 da	K		0.014(X), 0.513	Bone, 7.0	6×10^{-2}	0.3 mg	
18	Tungsten 181	140 da	K		0.058(X)	Bone, 7.0			
19	Zinc 65	250 da	β+ (3%); K (97%)	0.32	0.0086(X), 0.511, 1.11	Bone, 7.0	0.1	17 mg	Tracer studies.

/1/ (X) indicates K X-rays.

β^- = nuclear negatron; β^+ = nuclear positron; e^- = electron; K = electron capture from K ring; Mev = million electron volts; EC = electron capture.

Isotope	Half-life	Maximum Energy of Radiation Beta Mev	Maximum Energy of Radiation Gamma Mev	Internal Dosages Determination Effective Energy per Disintegration Mev	Highest Isotope Concentration Tissue wt, kg[1]	Highest Isotope Concentration Isotope, g/kg tissue	Isotope Intake, per da	Investigative or Therapeutic Use
1 Arsenic-76	26.8 hr	1.29, 2.49, 3.04	0.55, 1.20, 1.70	1.1	Kidneys, 0.3			Trace element metabolism.
2 Calcium-45	164 da	0.254		0.085	Bone, 7.0	150	800 mg	Muscle, bone metabolism.
3 Carbon-14	5570 yr	0.155		0.053	Adipose, 10	750	300 g	Protein, fat, carbohydrate, drug metabolism.
4 Chlorine-36	3.08×10^5 yr	0.714		0.260	Total body, 70	1.5	6.7 g	Electrolyte balance.
5 Cobalt-60	5.38 yr	0.306	1.17, 1.33	0.72, 0.55	Liver, 1.7	2×10^{-4}		External and interstitial radiotherapy.
6					Spleen, 0.15	4.7×10^{-4}	Trace	Trace element metabolism.
7 Copper-64	12.84 hr	$0.571\beta^-$, $0.657\beta^+$	1.35	0.11	Liver, 1.7	6×10^{-3}	2 mg	Trace element metabolism.
8 Iodine-131	8.05 da	0.34, 0.61, 0.81, 0.25	0.64, 0.72, 0.36, 0.16, 0.28, 0.08	0.224	Thyroid, 0.02	0.52	0.2 mg	Thyroid function, iodine metabolism, determination of blood volume and brain tumors.
9 Iron-55	2.94 yr	EC		0.006	Blood, 5.0	0.5	12 mg }	Iron, hemoglobin metabolism.
10 Iron-59	45 da	0.26, 0.46	1.10, 1.30	0.54	Blood, 5.0	0.5	12 mg }	
11 Mercury-197	2.71 da	EC	0.08, 0.191					Distribution of mercurial diuretics.
12 Mercury-203	47 da	0.208	0.279					
13 Phosphorus-32	14.3 da	1.701		0.68	Bone, 7.0	69	1.4 g }	Therapy, diagnosis of blood dyscrasias; metabolism of nucleoproteins, phospholipids; phosphate tracers.
14 Potassium-42	12.52 hr	2.04, 3.58	1.51	1.59	Muscle, 30.0	3	2.8 g	Mineral metabolism, electrolyte balance.
15 Sodium-24	15.1 hr	1.39	1.37, 2.75	2.7	Total body, 70	1.5	4.0 g	Hemodynamic function, mineral metabolism, and electrolyte balance.
16 Strontium-89	50.5 da	1.46		0.55	Bone, 7.0	0.06	0.3 mg	Metabolism and toxicity.
17 Strontium-90	28 yr	0.61		1.0	Bone, 7.0	0.06	0.3 mg	External radiotherapy.
18 Sulfur-35	87.1 da	0.167		0.055	Skin, 2.0	9	1.3 g	Metabolism of S-containing compounds.
19 Tritium (H-3)	12.4 yr	0.018		0.006	Total body, 70	100	250 g	Protein, carbohydrate, fat metabolism.
20 Zinc-65	245 da	EC, $0325\beta^+$	1.12	0.085	Bone, 7.0	0.1	17 mg	Trace element metabolism.

/1/ Values for standard 70 kg man, determined at Chalk River Conference, Chalk River, Canada, September 29-30, 1949.

401. RADIATIONS: PHYSICAL PROPERTIES AND RELATIVE BIOLOGICAL EFFECTIVENESS

Radiation	Corpuscular[1] Physical Atomic Wt.	Mass g	Charge[2]	Composition	RBE[3]	Radiation	Electromagnetic Wave Length[9] cm	RBE[3]
1 Alpha (α)[4]	4.00275	6.6442×10^{-24}	2^+	2 neutrons, 2 protons	20	9 Electric waves	6×10^{12} to 1×10^6	
2 Beta $(\beta^-$ or $\beta^+)$[5]	0.0005486	9.11×10^{-28}	1^- or 1^+	Fundamental particle	1	10 Radio waves	5×10^6 to 8×10^{-2}	
3 Deuteron (d)[6]	2.01418	3.3433×1	1^+	1 neutron, 1 proton	~1	11 Infrared rays	3×10^{-2} to 8×10^{-5}	
4 Electron or negatron (e^-)[7]	0.0005486	9.11×10^{-28}	1^-	Fundamental particle	1	12 Visible light rays	8×10^{-5} to 4×10^{-5}	
						13 Ultraviolet rays	4×10^{-5} to 8×10^{-7}	
5 Positron (e^+)	0.0005486	9.11×10^{-28}	1^+	Fundamental particle	1	14 X-rays[10] (0.1 - 3.0 Mev)	2×10^{-6} to 3×10^{-10}	1
6 Proton (p)[8]	1.00758	1.67×10^{-24}	1^+	Fundamental particle	10	15 Gamma rays (γ)[10]	2×10^{-8} to 6×10^{-11}	0.6-1
7 Neutron (n), fast	1.00894	1.67×10^{-24}	Neutral	Fundamental particle	10	16 Cosmic rays[11]	Variable	~1-10
8 Neutron (n), slow	1.00894	1.67×10^{-24}	Neutral	Fundamental particle	5			

/1/ Meson and neutrino are not included as they probably are unimportant biologically. /2/ Unit charge = 4.8025×10^{-10} electrostatic units (esu), 1.60203×10^{-20} electromagnetic units (emu). /3/ Relative biological effectiveness, calculated as ratios of rep (roentgen equivalent physical), the amount of ionizing radiation from which tissue will absorb energy to the extent of 95 ergs/g (x-radiation = 1). /4/ Helium nuclei. /5/ The term "beta" (β) is reserved for electrons [negatrons (β^-) and positrons (β^+)] of nuclear origin. /6/ Deuterium nuclei. /7/ Electrons [negatrons (e^-)] of extra-nuclear origin, and cathode rays. /8/ Hydrogen nuclei. /9/ Approximate; some overlapping occurs. /10/ x- and gamma ray (photons) mass units equal (0.00107 for 1 Mev). /11/ Consist of electrons, protons, mesons, secondary pair production; below altitudes of 70,000 ft biological significance is questionable.

402. RADIUM, COBALT-60, AND CESIUM-137 TELETHERAPY: PROTECTION REQUIREMENTS
For additional information, see National Bureau of Standards Handbook 54.
Part I: LEAD PRIMARY PROTECTIVE BARRIER REQUIREMENTS[1]
r/hr/m = roentgens per hour at 1 meter

	Radium mg	Lead, in cm, Required at a Distance of: 30 cm	Lead, in cm, Required at a Distance of: 1 m	Lead, in cm, Required at a Distance of: 2 m	Cobalt-60 r/hr/m	Lead, in cm, Required at a Distance of: 30 cm	Lead, in cm, Required at a Distance of: 1 m	Lead, in cm, Required at a Distance of: 2 m	Cesium-137 r/hr/m	Lead, in cm, Required at a Distance of: 30 cm	Lead, in cm, Required at a Distance of: 1 m	Lead, in cm, Required at a Distance of: 2 m
						48 hr/wk						
1	25	6.6	1.9	0	0.1	9.4	5.5	3.0	0.01	2.7	0.7	0
2	50	8.1	3.3	0.7	0.3	11.3	7.5	5.0	0.03	3.7	1.65	0.35
3	75	9.0	4.0	1.3	1.0	13.4	9.5	7.1	0.1	4.85	2.8	
4	100	9.6	4.6	1.9	3.0	15.4	11.4	9.0	0.3	5.9	3.8	
5	200	11.1	6.0	3.3	10.0	17.7	13.6	11.1	1.0	7.0	4.95	
						12 hr/wk						
6	25	3.8	0	0	0.1	7.0	3.0	0.6	0.01	1.4	0	0
7	50	5.2	0.7	0	0.3	8.9	5.0	2.6	0.03	2.4	0.35	0
8	75	6.1	1.3	0	1.0	11.0	7.2	4.7	0.1	3.55	1.5	0.15
9	100	6.6	1.9	0	3.0	13.0	9.1	6.6	0.3	4.6	2.55	1.2
10	200	8.1	3.3	0.7	10.0	15.1	11.1	8.6	1.0	5.75	3.65	2.35
						6 hr/wk						
11	25	2.5	0	0	0.1	5.8	1.8	0	0.01	0.8	0	0
12	50	3.8	0	0	0.3	7.7	3.9	1.3	0.03	1.75	0	0
13	75	4.6	0.3	0	1.0	9.7	5.9	3.5	0.1	2.95	0.9	0
14	100	5.2	0.7	0	3.0	11.7	7.8	5.4	0.3	3.95	1.9	0.55
15	200	6.6	1.9	0	10.0	13.9	10.0	7.5	1.0	5.05	3.0	1.7

/1/ Shielding required to reduce radiation exposure to 0.3 r/wk.

402. RADIUM, COBALT-60, AND CESIUM-137 TELETHERAPY: PROTECTION REQUIREMENTS (Concluded)

For additional information see National Bureau of Standards Handbook 54.

Part II: PROTECTIVE BARRIER REQUIREMENTS

Work load equal to 80,000 roentgens per week at 1 meter. r = roentgen; HVL = half-value layer.

	Distance (Source to Occupied Space)		For Primary-Protective Barrier									Distance (Scatterer to Occupied Space)		For Scattered Radiation[1]			
			Radium			Cobalt-60			Cesium-137					Radium and Cobalt-60		Cesium-137	
	m	ft	Concrete cm	Steel cm	Lead cm	Concrete cm	Steel cm	Lead cm	Concrete cm	Steel cm	Lead cm	m	ft	Concrete cm	Lead cm	Concrete cm	Lead cm
1	3	9.8	108	34	23.1	96.5	32	19.2	76.2	27.7	9.6	3	9.8	30.2	1.8	24.9	0.9
2	3.1	10	106.7	34	23.1	96.5	32	19.2	76.2	27.7	9.5	3.1	10	27.4	1.8	24.6	0.9
3	4	13.1	101.6	32	21.6	91.4	30	18.2	73.7	33.6	9.0	4	13.1	24.4	1.5	21.8	0.7
4	4.6	15	99.1	31	20.9	88.9	29.5	17.6	71.1	23.1	8.8	4.6	15	22.9	1.4	20.3	0.7
5	5	16.4	96.5	30.5	20.4	87.6	29	17.4	69.9	22.6	8.6	5	16.4	21.8	1.3	19.3	0.6
6	6.1	20	92.7	29	19.3	83.8	27.4	16.6	66	21.6	8.2	6.1	20	19.8	1.1	17.5	0.5
7	7	23	90.2	27.9	18.6	81.3	26.4	16.1	64.8	21.1	7.9	7	23	18	1.1	16	0.5
8	7.6	25	87.6	27.4	18.1	80	25.9	15.7	63.5	20.8	7.8	7.6	25	17.3	0.9	15.2	0.4
9	8	26.3	87.6	27.4	17.9	78.7	25.9	15.6	63.5	20.1	7.7	8	26.3	16.5	0.8	14.5	0.4
10	9.2	30	85.1	26.4	17.2	77.5	24.9	15.1	58.4	19.8	7.5	9.2	30	15	0.7	13	0.3
11	10	32.8	82.6	25.9	16.8	74.9	24.4	14.8	57.2	19.3	7.3	10	32.8	14	0.7	12.2	0.3
12	Approximate HVL thickness		6.6	2.3	1.3	6.4	2.3	1.2	4.8	1.7	0.6	Approximate HVL thickness		4.1	3.3[2]	3.6	1.9[2]

/1/ Shielding required to reduce the 90° scattered radiation to 0.3 r/wk for a work load of 80,000 r/wk at 1 m and occupancy factor of 1 (full occupancy); the barrier for leakage radiation will depend upon the leakage permitted by the source housing. /2/ Values only for estimating purposes, since they vary considerably over the range of attenuations.

Part III: DISTANCE-EXPOSURE RELATIONSHIPS

Relation between distance and millicurie-hour for an exposure of 0.3 roentgen from an unshielded source.

	Milli-curie hr	Distance to Source							Milli-curie hr	Distance to Source					
		Radium		Cobalt-60		Cesium-137				Radium		Cobalt-60		Cesium-137	
		ft	m	ft	m	ft	m			ft	m	ft	m	ft	m
1	10	0.5	0.15	0.7	0.21	0.4	0.12	5	1000	5.5	1.68	7.0	2.13	3.7	1.13
2	30	1.0	0.30	1.2	0.37	0.6	0.18	6	3000	9.5	2.90	12	3.66	6.5	1.98
3	100	1.8	0.55	2.2	0.67	1.2	0.37	7	10,000	18.0	5.48	22	6.71	12	3.66
4	300	3.0	0.91	3.8	1.16	2.1	0.64								

403. X-RADIATION: PROTECTION

For additional information, see National Bureau of Standards Handbooks 50 and 60.

concr = concrete; kv = kilovolt; kvp = kilovolt peak; ma = milliampere.

Part I: PRIMARY PROTECTIVE BARRIER REQUIREMENTS

	Target Distance		For 10 ma at Pulsating Potentials[1] and Distances Indicated			For 400 kvp Pulsating Potential with Reflection Target			For 500 kv Constant Potential with Transmission Target				For 1000 kv Constant Potential with Transmission Target				For 2000 kvp Pulsating Potential with Transmission Target		
			75 kv	150 kv	250 kv	1 ma	3 ma	5 ma	1 ma		5 ma		1 ma		5 ma		0.5 ma	1.0 ma	1.5 ma
													Barrier Thickness						
	ft	m	Lead mm	Lead mm	Lead mm	Lead mm	Lead mm	Lead mm	Lead mm	Concr[2] cm	Lead mm	Concr[2] cm	Lead mm	Concr[2] cm	Lead mm	Concr[2] cm	Concrete[2] cm	Concrete[2] cm	Concrete[2] cm
1	2	0.61	2.2	4.3	11.8														
2	3	0.91	2.0	4.0	10.9														
3	5	1.52	1.7	3.6	9.6	16.5	20.0	22.0	36	45.7	44	54.6	123	77.5	136	85.1	108.0	114.3	118.1
4	8	2.44	1.5	3.2	8.5	14.0	17.0	18.5	31	40.6	39	49.5	113	71.1	125	77.5	100.3	106.7	110.5
5	10	3.05	1.3	3.0	8.1	12.5	15.5	17.0	29	38.1	37	47.0	107	68.6	120	74.9	97.8	102.9	106.7
6	15	4.57	1.1	2.6	7.1	11.0	13.5	14.5	25	34.3	33	43.2	97	62.2	110	69.9	90.2	96.5	100.3
7	20	6.10	1.0	2.4	6.4	9.5	11.5	13.0	22	31.8	30	40.6	91	58.4	103	66.0	86.4	91.4	95.3
8	50	15.24	0.5	1.7	4.3	5.5	8.0	9.0	14	21.6	21	30.5	69	47.0	82	53.3	71.1	76.2	80.0
9	100	30.48							8	15.2	15	24.1	53	38.1	66	45.7	59.7	64.8	68.6
10	Approximate HVL thickness[3]		1.8	0.3	0.8	2.0												5.8	
11	Radiation filter		0.5mm of Al	3.0mm of Al	3.0mm of Al	0.4mm of Sn, plus 0.75mm Cu and 2mm Al			2mm of W, plus 2.8mm Cu, 2.1mm brass, and 1.87mm of H_2O				2.8mm of W, plus 2.8mm Cu, 2.1mm of brass, and 18.7mm pf H_2O				1.6mm of W, plus 5.1mm Cu and 6.8mm of H_2O		

/1/ X-rays excited by direct current potentials require approximately 10% greater thickness. /2/ Density, 147 lb/cu ft. /3/ HVL = half value layer.

Part II: DISTANCE PROTECTION

Values are distances at which no shielding is necessary.

	Target Current ma	50 kvp		75 kvp		100 kvp		150 kvp		200 kvp		250 kvp		400 kvp		500 kvp		1000 kvp		2000 kvp	
		ft	m	ft	m	ft	m	ft	m	ft	m	ft	m	ft	m	ft	m	ft	m	ft	m
1	0.005	15	4.57	20	6.10	25	7.62	20	6.10	25	7.62	25	7.62	25	7.62	30	9.14	90	27.43	195	59.44
2	0.01	20	6.10	25	7.62	30	9.14	30	9.14	35	10.67	35	10.67	40	12.19	115	35.05	240	73.15		
3	0.025	30	9.14	40	12.19	45	13.72	45	13.72	55	16.76	55	16.76	60	18.29	175	53.34	370	112.78		
4	0.05	40	12.19	50	15.24	60	18.29	60	18.29	65	19.81	70	21.34	70	21.34	75	22.86	220	67.06	460	140.21
5	0.1	50	15.24	70	21.34	80	24.38	80	24.38	90	27.43	95	28.96	95	28.96	110	33.53	275	83.82	540	164.39
6	0.25	70	21.34	95	25.91	115	35.05	115	35.05	125	38.10	135	41.45	135	41.45	155	47.24	380	115.82	720	219.46
7	0.5	85	25.91	115	35.05	145	44.20	145	44.20	165	50.29	170	51.82	170	51.82	200	60.96	460	140.21	850	259.08
8	1.0	100	30.48	145	44.20	180	54.86	185	56.39	205	62.48	215	65.53	215	65.53	255	77.72	550	167.64	980	298.70
9	2.0	115	35.05	175	53.34	220	67.06	225	68.58	255	77.72	270	82.30	270	82.30	320	97.54	640	195.07	1080	329.18
10	2.5	120	36.58	185	56.39	235	71.63	245	74.68	270	82.30	285	86.87	295	89.92	340	103.63	690	210.31		
11	5.0	140	42.67	220	67.06	280	85.34	295	89.92	330	100.58	350	106.68	360	109.73	410	124.97				
12	10.0	160	48.77	250	76.20	330	100.58	350	106.68	390	118.87	420	128.02								
13	15.0	175	53.34	270	82.30	355	108.20	390	118.37	430	131.06	460	140.21								
14	20.0	185	56.39	290	88.39	380	115.82	410	124.97	460	140.21	490	149.35								
15	25.0	195	59.94	300	91.44	390	118.87	420	128.02	480	146.30	510	155.45								

404. MAXIMUM PERMISSIBLE QUANTITY OF RADIOISOTOPES IN TOTAL BODY, AIR, AND WATER FOR CONTINUOUS EXPOSURE

Body intake is by ingestion and inhalation only. It is considered that any mixture of the radioisotopes listed is permissible, if the accumulated body burden in any organ, or the concentration in the contents of the gastrointestinal tract, does not reach a value that delivers a dose exceeding the maximum permissible dose-rate of 0.3 rem/wk. Explanations of the formulae and their use in calculating the values presented in this table may be obtained from Report of Subcommittee II on Permissible Dose For Internal Radiation, International Committee on Radiation Protection, and from Handbook 52 of the National Bureau of Standards.

A = mass number; α = alpha particles; dr = daughter element; β = beta particles; K = K type disintegration with α-ray emission; μc = microcurie; rem = roentgen equivalent man; Z = atomic number; s. = soluble; i. = insoluble.

#	Z Symbol A	Type of Decay	Critical Organ [1] Organ	wt, kg	Max Permissible Total Body Burden [2] μc	Max Permissible Conc. In H_2O μc/ml	Max Permissible Conc. In Air μc/ml
1	1 H3 (HTO or H2O)3	β-	Total body	70	10,000	0.2	1×10^{-5}
2	4 Be7	K, γ	Bone	7	725	1.0	5×10^{-6}
3	6 C14 ≡ (CO2)3	β-	Fat	10	260	3×10^{-3}	1×10^{-5}
4	9 F18	β+	Bone	5	5	0.2	3×10^{-5}
5	11 Na24 3	β-, γ	Total body	70	15	8×10^{-3}	2×10^{-6}
6	15 P32	β-	Bone	10	10	2×10^{-3}	1×10^{-7}
7	16 S35 3	β-	Skin	2	300	5×10^{-3}	1×10^{-6}
8	17 Cl36 3	β-	Total body	70	230	4×10^{-3}	6×10^{-7}
9	18 A41	β-, γ	Total body	70	33	5×10^{-4}	6×10^{-7}
10	19 K42 3	β-, γ	Muscle	30	21	1×10^{-2}	2×10^{-6}
11	20 Ca45 3	β-	Bone	14	14	1×10^{-4}	8×10^{-9}
12	21 Sc46	β-, γ	Spleen	0.15	5	0.4	7×10^{-8}
13	21 Sc47	β-	Liver	1.7	15	4.0	5×10^{-8}
14	21 Sc48	β-, γ	Spleen	0.15	11	3.0	6×10^{-7}
15	23 V48	β-, γ	Liver	1.7	5	3.0	6×10^{-7}
16	24 Cr51	K	Spleen	0.15	10	1.0	6×10^{-7}
17	25 Mn56 3	β-, γ	Liver	1.7	600	0.3	6×10^{-7}
18	26 Fe55 3	K, β+, γ	Bone	7	25	0.7	6×10^{-7}
19	26 Fe59 3	K, γ	Kidneys	0.3	8	0.15	4×10^{-6}
20	27 Co60	β-, γ	Blood	5.4	1000	5×10^{-3}	4×10^{-7}
21	28 Ni59	K	Liver	1.7	13	1×10^{-4}	2×10^{-8}
22	29 Cu64 3	K, β-, β+, γ	Blood	5.4	3	2×10^{-2}	1×10^{-6}
23	30 Zn65	K, β+, γ	Liver	1.7	42	0.3	5×10^{-6}
24	31 Ga72	β-, γ	Liver	7	120	6×10^{-2}	6×10^{-6}
25	32 Ge71	K	Bone	1.7	400	6×10^{-2}	1×10^{-6}
26	33 As76	β-, γ	Bone	7	72	10	4×10^{-5}
27	37 Rb86	β-, γ	Kidneys	0.3	11	0.2	4×10^{-7}
28	38 Sr89	β-	Kidneys	0.3	64	3×10^{-3}	2×10^{-8}
29	38 Sr90 + Y90 4	β-	Muscle	30	2	0.1	1×10^{-10}
30	39 Y91	β-, γ	Bone	7	1	0.4	3×10^{-8}
31	40 Zr95 + Nb95	β-, γ	Bone	7	10	8×10^{-2}	2×10^{-6}
32	41 Nb95	β-, γ	Bone	7	44	2	8×10^{-8}
33	42 Mo99	β-, γ	Bone	7	17	1×10^{-2}	6×10^{-4}
34	43 Tc96	β-, γ	Bone	7	5	5	3×10^{-8}
35	44 Ru106 + Rh106 4	β-	Bone	7	4	7×10^{-2}	1×10^{-6}
36	45 Rh105	β-, γ	Kidneys	0.3	9	0.2	8×10^{-6}
37	46 Pd103 + Rh103 4	K, γ	Kidneys	0.3	2	3×10^{-2}	1×10^{-6}
38	47 Ag105	K, e-	Kidneys	0.3	19	1×10^{-2}	8×10^{-7}
39	47 Ag111	β-, γ	Kidneys	0.3	39	4×10^{-2}	2×10^{-6}
40	48 Cd109 + Ag109 4	K, γ	Liver	1.7	45	2	1×10^{-5}
41	50 Sn113	β-	Liver	1.7	84	5	7×10^{-6}
42	52 Te127	β-, γ	Bone	7	1.4	0.2	7×10^{-7}
43	52 Te129	γ, K	Liver	7	0.6	3×10^{-2}	6×10^{-7}
44	53 I131 3	β-, γ	Thyroid	0.02	320	1×10^{-2}	6×10^{-9}
45	54 Xe133	β-, γ	Total body	70	100	6×10^{-3}	4×10^{-6}
46	54 Xe135	β-, γ	Total body	70	98	1×10^{-3}	4×10^{-6}
47	55 Cs137 + Ba137 4	β-, γ	Muscle	30	1	2×10^{-4}	2×10^{-6}
48	56 Ba140 + La140 4	β-, γ	Bone	7	1	5×10^{-4}	2×10^{-7}

#	Z Symbol A	Type of Decay	Critical Organ [1] Organ	wt, kg	Max Permissible Total Body Burden [2] μc	Max Permissible Conc. In H_2O μc/ml	Max Permissible Conc. In Air μc/ml
53	57 La140	β-, γ	Bone	7	7	0.3	4×10^{-7}
54	58 Ce144 + Pr144 4	β-, γ	Bone	7	6	8×10^{-3}	2×10^{-9}
55	59 Pr143	β-	Bone	7	6	8×10^{-3}	2×10^{-8}
56	61 Pm147	β-	Bone	7	25	0.2	4×10^{-8}
57	62 Sm151	β-	Bone	7	90	5×10^{-2}	2×10^{-9}
58	63 Eu154	β-, γ	Bone	7	4	1×10^{-2}	1×10^{-8}
59	63 Eu155	β-, γ	Bone	7	5	5	8×10^{-8}
60	67 Ho166	β-, γ	Bone	7	4	6×10^{-2}	1×10^{-8}
61	69 Tm170	β-, γ	Bone	7	18	6	1×10^{-6}
62	71 Lu177	β-, γ	Bone	7	6	1×10^{-1}	2×10^{-8}
63	73 Ta182	β-, γ	Liver	1.7	24	0.1	5×10^{-6}
64	74 W181	K, γ, e-	Bone	7	37	9×10^{-2}	9×10^{-6}
65	75 Re183	K, γ	Thyroid	2	650	0.3	3×10^{-5}
66	77 Ir190	β-, γ	Kidneys	0.15	23	1×10^{-2}	8×10^{-7}
67	77 Ir192	β-, γ	Spleen	0.3	21	0.2	1×10^{-6}
68	78 Pt191	K, γ	Kidneys	0.3	3	9×10^{-4}	3×10^{-8}
69	78 Pt193	K, γ, e-	Kidneys	0.3	3	6×10^{-3}	2×10^{-7}
70	79 Au196	K, β-, γ	Kidneys	0.3	2	5×10^{-3}	2×10^{-7}
71	79 Au198	β-, γ	Liver	1.7	8	5×10^{-3}	2×10^{-7}
72	79 Au198	β-	Kidneys	0.3	32	5×10^{-2}	2×10^{-7}
73	79 Au199	β-, γ	Kidneys	0.3	10	4×10^{-2}	4×10^{-7}
74	79 Au199	β-, γ	Liver	1.7	10	3×10^{-2}	1×10^{-7}
75	79 Au199	β-, γ	Kidneys	0.3	30	8×10^{-3}	3×10^{-7}
76	81 Tl200	K, γ, e-	Kidneys	0.3	40	2×10^{-2}	7×10^{-6}
77	81 Tl201	K, γ	Muscle	30	310	2×10^{-2}	2×10^{-6}
78	81 Tl202	K, γ, e-	Muscle	30	230	8×10^{-3}	2×10^{-7}
79	81 Tl204	β-	Muscle	30	200	10	8×10^{-7}
80	82 Pb203	K, γ	Bone	7	61	0.2	7×10^{-7}
81	82 Pb210 + dr 4	β-, γ	Bone	7	0.2	2×10^{-6}	8×10^{-11}
82	84 Po210 (s.)	α, γ	Spleen	0.15	0.04	3×10^{-5}	1×10^{-10}
83	84 Po210 (i.)	α, γ	Lungs	1	0.02	—	5×10^{-10}
84	85 At211	α, K	Thyroid	0.02	0.001	3×10^{-6}	1×10^{-7}
85	86 Ra222 + dr	α, β-, γ	Lungs	1	0.1	4×10^{-8}	4×10^{-12}
86	86 Ra226 + dr	α, β-, γ	Lungs	1	0.01	4×10^{-6}	3×10^{-11}
87	88 Ra226 + 55% dr 4	α, β-, γ	Bone	7	0.01	5×10^{-7}	5×10^{-11}
88	89 Ac227 + dr 4	α, β-, γ	Bone	7	0.002	—	3×10^{-11}
89	90 Th-natural (i.)	α, β-, γ	Lungs	1	2	5×10^{-2}	5×10^{-11}
90	90 Th234 (Pa234) 4	α, β-, γ	Kidneys	0.3	0.04	1×10^{-4}	1×10^{-8}
91	92 U-natural (s.)	α, β-, γ	Lungs	1	0.04	5×10^{-2}	3×10^{-11}
92	92 U-natural (i.)	α, β-, γ	Bone	7	0.04	1×10^{-4}	3×10^{-11}
93	92 U233 (s.)	α, γ	Bone	7	0.016	—	3×10^{-11}
94	92 U233 (i.)	α, γ	Lungs	1	—	1.5×10^{-4}	2×10^{-11}
95	94 Pu239 (s.)	α, γ	Lungs	1	0.04	6×10^{-6}	2×10^{-12}
96	94 Pu239 (i.)	α, γ	Bone	7	0.02	—	2×10^{-12}
97	95 Am241	α, γ	Bone	7	0.06	2×10^{-4}	2×10^{-12}
98	96 Cm242	α	Bone	7	0.06	1×10^{-3}	4×10^{-10}
102	Any fission mixture (β, γ) [5]		Bone	7	1	1×10^{-7}	1×10^{-9}
103	Any mixture of α-emitters [5]		Bone	7		5×10^{-7}	5×10^{-12}

[1] Organ or tissue of body receiving the radioisotope that results in the greatest body damage. [2] Exclusive of the amount in the gastrointestinal tract. [3] Common body element. [4] Values in μc and μc/ml given for parent element; daughter elements assumed to reach appropriate fraction of equilibrium with the parent after being taken into the body. [5] Values for unidentified β-, γ-, and α-emitters for short periods of time (a few months). [6] Safe for any mixture of β- and γ-emitters and all α-emitters except Ra226. [7] Safe for any mixture of β- and γ-emitters except Sr90 [8] Safe for any mixture of α-emitters except Pu239 and Ac227.

405. MAXIMUM PERMISSIBLE EXTERNAL EXPOSURE OF BODY ORGANS TO IONIZING RADIATIONS: MAN, ADULT[1]

Values may be converted from units of mrem/wk to mrad/wk by dividing by appropriate values of RBE (relative biological effectiveness). Commonly assumed average RBE values are: 1 for X, γ, β, e⁻ and e⁺; 10 for p and α, and 20 for heavy ions (oxygen, carbon, nitrogen). Values in parentheses apply to persons over 45.

Mev = million electron volt; mr = milliroentgen, mrad = millirad; mrem = milliroentgen equivalent, man or mammal; rad = unit of energy absorption.

Type of Radiation	At Surface of Body Trunk	In Skin[2,3] Total Body mrem/wk	In Skin[2,3] Body Appendages[4] mrem/wk	In Eye Lenses[5] mrem/wk	In Gonads[5] mrem/wk	In Blood-forming Organs[5] mrem/wk	In Intermediate Tissue[3,6] mrem/wk
1 Low, penetrating[7]	1500 mrad/wk	1500	1500	300	300	300	300-1500
2	(1500 mrad/wk)	(1500)	(1500)	(600)	(600)	(600)	(600-1500)
3 Roentgen (X) and	450 mr/wk	450	1500	450	300	400	400-450
4 gamma (γ) of <3 Mev	(900 mr/wk)	(900)	(1500)	(600)	(300)	(800)	(800-900)
5 Electrons (β⁻,	600 mrad/wk	600	1500	300	300	300	300-600
6 e⁻, e⁺)	(1200 mrad/wk)	(1200)	(1500)	(600)	(600)	(600)	(600-1200)
7 Protons (p)	60 mrad/wk	600	1500	300	300	300	300-600
8	(120 mrad/wk)	(1200)	(1500)	(300)	(600)	(600)	(600-1200)
9 Fast neutrons	30-2000 n_f/sq cm/sec	300-600[8]	750-1500[8]	300	300	300	300-600
10 (n_f)	(60-4000 n_f/sq cm/sec)	(600-1200)[8]	(750-1500)[8]	(300-600)[8]	(600)	(600)	(600-1200)
11 Thermal neutrons	3000 n_t/sq cm/sec	500[8]	1200[8]	300	100,300[8,9]	170[8]	170-500
12 (n_t)	(6000 n_t/sq cm/sec)	(1000)[8]	(1200)[8]	(420)[8]	(200,600)[8,9]	(340)[8]	(340-1000)
13 Alpha particles	Exposure from internally	1500	1500	300	300	300	300-1500
14 (α)	deposited isotopes	(1500)	(1500)	(300)	(600)	(600)	(600-1500)
15 Oxygen, carbon,	Generated in body by	1500	1500	300	300	300	300-1500
16 nitrogen, etc.	fast neutrons	(1500)	(1500)	(300)	(600)	(600)	(600-1500)

/1/ Further information concerning data in this table may be obtained from Subcommittee 1, "Permissible Dose from External Sources," and Subcommittee 2, "Permissible Internal Dose," National Committee on Radiological Protection; also from Handbooks 52 and 59, National Bureau of Standards. /2/ Minimum thickness of epidermis taken as 0.07 mm. /3/ Values must not be used unless radiation is shielded or localized so that exposure limits to other critical tissues are not exceeded. /4/ Appendages include head, neck, hands, forearms, feet, and ankles. /5/ Average depths of lens, ovaries, testes, and blood-forming organs considered to be 3 mm, 7 cm, 1 cm, and 5 cm respectively. /6/ "Intermediate" tissue considered to be that of body trunk 0.07 mm-5 cm in depth (excluding testes and lens of eye). /7/ Low penetrating radiation (X, γ, β, e, α or p) with a half-value layer of less than 1 mm of soft tissue; does not apply to neutron radiation. /8/ Values for neutron surface dose determined by pattern of distribution in body; values used decrease with energy of neutrons. /9/ Smaller value applies to ovaries at 7 cm depth, and larger value to testes at 1 cm depth.

406. BACKGROUND AND NON-OCCUPATIONAL EXPOSURES TO IONIZING RADIATION: MAN

β = beta ray; c = curie; μc = microcurie; r = roentgen; mr = milliroentgen; mrep = milliroentgen equivalent physical; μg = microgram; γ = gamma ray.

Source	Amount or Rate	Source	Amount or Rate
1 Air, radon (incl. thoron)	~10^{-10} μc/ml	18 Shoe fitting (20 sec exposure)	av. 10-15 r to feet
Airplane instruments (10-100 μg per dial)		19 Spectacle lenses containing U	1-8 mr/hr β to eyes
2 At face of each dial	5-10 mr/hr	20 Water, drinking	10^{-16}-10^{-12} c/ml
3 At pilot's position	<1 mr/hr	Water, sea	
4 "Background" exposure, average	0.4 mrep/da	21 K⁴⁰	0.33 μc/cu m
5 natural[1]	0.01-0.1 mr/hr	22 U	0.0015 mg/kg
6 C¹⁴ (isotopic abundance 1.6 x 10^{-12})	16 dis./min/g carbon[2]	23 Watch dial, wrist (~1 μg Ra)	~1 mr/hr, γ, wrist
Cosmic rays		X-ray, diagnostic[4]	
7 Sea level	~0.1 mr/da	24 Abdomen[5]	1.3 r
8 15,000 ft altitude	0.5 mr/da	25 Chest, photofluorographic	0.7-1.2 r
9 55,000 ft altitude	7.5 mr/da	26 Chest, plate 14 x 17 in.	0.05-0.25 r
10 Top of atmosphere	70.0 mr/da	27 Dental	0.5 r/film
11 Cow's milk	10^{-14} c/ml	28 Extremities	0.25-1.0 r
Earth's outer crust		29 Fluoroscopy	0.28 r/sec
12 Radium by weight	2 x 10^{-6}	30 Gastrointestinal series	0.65 r/plate
13 Thorium by weight	12 ppm	31 Lumbar spine, lateral[6]	5.7 r
14 Uranium by weight	6 ppm	32 Pelvimetry, central area, anterio-posterior films	0.2-0.4 r/film
Human body		33 Pregnancy, lateral	9.0 r
15 C¹⁴, total	0.0068 μc	34 Skull	1.3 r[7]
16 K⁴⁰, total	0.12 μc	35 Urographic series, center of abdomen	1.3 r
17 Residual activity, all A-bomb detonations[3] calculated to July 15, 1952	8.8 x 10^6 c		

/1/ Approximate total of cosmic ray and natural "background" 0.3 mr/24 hr. /2/ 16 disintegrations per min/g carbon. /3/ Includes suspended and deposited particles. /4/ Considerable variation depending on filtration distance and techniques. /5/ Abdominal fluoroscopy plus spot and serial films; 3 r in center of abdomen (may be higher). /6/ Up to 8 r in center of abdomen. /7/ Considerable variation depending on scope and type of examination.

407. HEAVY IONIZING PARTICLES: RELATIVE BIOLOGICAL EFFECTIVENESS VALUES

The following RBE values for all the critical organs, according to the value of the average specific ionizations (occurring in the critical organ in which it is highest) are recommended for determination of permissible tissue doses in rads from external sources by the relation: Permissible dose in rads = permissible dose in rems divided by RBE.[1]

	Average Specific Ionization ion pairs/μ[2]	RBE	Average Linear Energy Transfer to H₂O kev/μ
1	100 or less	1	3.5 or less
2	100-200	1-2	3.5-7
3	200-650	2-5	7-23
4	650-1500	5-10	23-53
5	1500-5000	10-20	53-175

/1/ International Commission on Radiological Protection (1955). /2/ i.e., μ of path of H₂O.

408. RADIOISOTOPES, BODY ABSORPTION HAZARDS: MAN

These selected radioisotopes are grouped according to relative radiotoxicity, with the amounts considered as low, intermediate, or high level, in laboratory practice. The slant boundaries between levels indicate borderline zones and emphasize that there is no sharp transition between the levels and the associated protection techniques. This activity scale system does not apply to the hazards of external radiation.

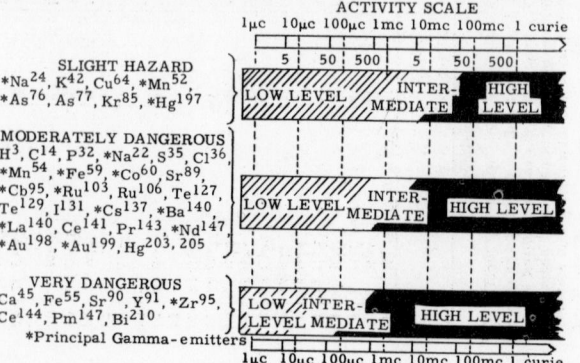

SLIGHT HAZARD
*Na²⁴, K⁴², Cu⁶⁴, *Mn⁵², *As⁷⁶, As⁷⁷, Kr⁸⁵, *Hg¹⁹⁷

MODERATELY DANGEROUS
H³, C¹⁴, P³², *Na²², S³⁵, Cl³⁶, *Mn⁵⁴, *Fe⁵⁹, *Co⁶⁰, Sr⁸⁹, *Cb⁹⁵, *Ru¹⁰³, Ru¹⁰⁶, Te¹²⁷, Te¹²⁹, I¹³¹, *Cs¹³⁷, *Ba¹⁴⁰, *La¹⁴⁰, Ce¹⁴¹, Pr¹⁴³, *Nd¹⁴⁷, *Au¹⁹⁸, *Au¹⁹⁹, Hg²⁰³, 205

VERY DANGEROUS
Ca⁴⁵, Fe⁵⁵, Sr⁹⁰, Y⁹¹, *Zr⁹⁵, Ce¹⁴⁴, Pm¹⁴⁷, Bi²¹⁰

*Principal Gamma-emitters

ACTIVITY SCALE

409. IONIZING RADIATION EFFECTS: BIOLOGICAL TESTS

Data are approximate exposures for various biological effects. Exposure required for a specific test may vary with such biological factors as **species**, age, metabolic state, and with certain physical factors including temperature and oxygen tension.

α = alpha rays; β = beta rays; γ = gamma rays; n = n unit[1]; x = roentgen- or X-rays

	Exposure Level[2]					Test Period[3]	Test Material	Effect Observed
	x	γ	α	β	n			
1	8					24 hr	Grasshopper (neuroblast)	Reduced rate of mitosis.
2	15-500					10 da	Frog (sperm)	Abnormal development (5-100%).
3	20-600	20-600				1-28 da	Mouse (testis)	Damage to germinal cells.
4	30-800					5 da	Mouse (thymus)	Weight loss.
5	35-225					2 hr-4 da	Mouse (skin)	Cells in mitosis decreased.
6		36-540			6-150	1.5-48 hr	Rat (retina)	Inhibition of mitosis.
7	50					10 min	Carboxypeptidase (dilute)	30% inactivation.
8	50					12 da	Salamander (eggs)	LD$_{50}$.
9	50					21 da	Grasshopper (eggs, 6 da old)	LD$_{50}$ (or abnormal development, 50%).
10	50-110					18 hr	Bluebottle fly (eggs)	LD$_{50}$.
11	100					24 hr	Chick (fibroblast culture)	Death of cells at next division.
12	100-600					3-10 da	Mouse (blood)	Decreased number of cells.
13	100-1000					7 da	Frog (eggs, fertilized)	Inhibition or abnormality of development.
14	125					21 da	Grasshopper (eggs, 1 da old)	LD$_{50}$ (or abnormal development, 50%).
15	140	250	36			1-14 da	Broad bean (root)	Inhibition of growth (cell division).
16	175-250	310		7750		14 da	Guinea pig[4]	LD$_{50}$.
17	190	240		275	85	48 hr	Fruit fly (eggs)	LD$_{50}$ (failure to hatch).
18	200					24 hr	Thymus (cell suspension)	Death of cells (eosin staining).
19	300-350					30 da	Dog	LD$_{50}$.
20	320					5 da	Tradescantia (microspores)	Chromosome breaks (17.3%).
21	350					30 da	Goat	LD$_{50}$.
22	350					2 wk	Fruit fly (adult)	1% increase in sex-linked mutations.
23		375-3600				2 wk	Fruit fly	Increased recessive mutation rate.
24	400[5]					30 da	Man	LD$_{50}$ (estimated).
25	400					24 hr	Spleen (cell suspension)	Death of cells (eosin staining).
26	400					15 da	Chick embryo (50 hr incubation)	Death of embryo.
27	400-500[6]					30 da	Swine	LD$_{50}$.
28	400-600[7]	850-950		4700	200-400	30 da	Mouse	LD$_{50}$.
29	500					100 hr	Wheat seedling (root, 18 hr old)	50% decrease in growth rate (longitudinal).
30	500					30 da	Monkey	LD$_{50}$.
31	600-900	1270		7500	200-300	30 da	Rat	LD$_{50}$.
32	670					30 da	Goldfish	LD$_{50}$.
33	700					6 wk	Frog	LD$_{50}$.
34	725[8]					30 da	Hamster	LD$_{50}$.
35	800				175-400	30 da	Rabbit	LD$_{50}$.
36	800[9]					12 da	Chicken	LD$_{50}$.
37	1000					4 da	Ascaris (eggs)	LD$_{50}$.
38	1000					3 wk	Duckweed	50% decrease in growth rate of fronds.
39	1000-2000					100 hr	Tomato, lettuce (germinated)	Inhibition of linear growth of shoot.
40	1000-2000					1 yr	Pigeon (<15 da old)	Inhibition of growth of wing bone.
41	1100					70 hr	Wheat seedling (primary leaf)	50% decrease in growth rate (longitudinal).
42	1500					30 da	Turtle	LD$_{50}$ (estimated).
43	2000					1 wk	Fundulus (eggs, gametes, embryo)	Abnormal development of embryo.
44	2500					100 da	Salpiglossis	50% decrease in growth rate; repression of flowering.
45	2,500-10,000					3 hr	Chick (fibroblast culture)	Immediate death of cells.
46	3000					30 da	Triton (salamander)	LD$_{50}$ (estimated).
47	3,000-50,000					2 wk	Neurospora (ascospores)	Production of biochemical mutants.
48	5,000-60,000					10 da	Mouse sarcoma 180	Inhibition of growth in transplants.
49	5600				2500	24 hr	Escherichia coli	LD$_{50}$.
50	10,000-100,000					10-40 da	Trypanosoma cruzi	Decreased infective power.
51	10,000-120,000					3-10 da	Tobacco callus (tissue culture)	Inhibition of growth.
52	15,000					32 da	Rabbit (mesenteric lymph node)	Inhibition of cell migration.
53	30,000					2 hr	Arbacia (eggs)	Delay of cleavage.
54	30,000					1 hr	Yeast cells	Immediate death.
55	40,000					5 hr	Frog (sperm)	Incomplete inactivation.[10]
56	50,000					24 hr	Rhizopus nigricans (spores)	50% less germination than controls.
57	94,000					3 wk	Chaetomium globosum (spores)	Lethal mutants in 50%.
58	100,000					10 min	Carboxypeptidase (concentrated)	30% inactivation.
59	150,000				37,000	24 hr	Bacillus mesentericus (spores)	LD$_{50}$.
60	180,000					30 hr	Penicillium (spores)	50% less germination than control.
61	200,000					40 da	Grasshopper embryo	Depression of respiration.
62	200,000					18 hr	Escherichia coli (phage C36)	37% inactivation.
63	210,000					18 hr	Lily (pollen grains)	50% less germination than control.
64	300,000-600,000					45 min	Pandorina	Immediate death.
65	330,000					2 hr	Colpidium colpoda	LD$_{50}$.
66	350,000	370,000	1900			10-15 min	Paramecium caudatum	Immediate loss of motility.
67	430,000					5 da	Tobacco mosaic virus	37% inactivation.

/1/ One n unit = quantity of fast neutron radiation that will discharge a particular Victoreen ionizing chamber in the same magnitude as will one r of X-rays. Measurements have indicated that one n unit is approximately equivalent to 2.5 rep. /2/ Exposure levels for x- or gamma (γ) radiation in r (roentgens); all other exposures in rep (roentgen equivalent physical). /3/ Test period = time after irradiation when effect was observed. /4/ Hybrids are more radio-resistant. /5/ Whole body, hard X-rays. However, detectable biological changes occur at levels of 25r-35r. /6/ LD$_{50}$ also reported as 400-450r. /7/ LD$_{50}$ also reported as about 625r, with range of 400-700r. /8/ LD$_{50}$ also reported as 800r. /9/ LD$_{50}$ for 30-da exposure for chicken depends upon age, but is estimated at 800-1000r. /10/ Sperm in testes can be used to fertilize eggs, even after testes have been exposed to 120,000r.

d = deuterons; e = electrons; n = neutrons; r = roentgens; α = alpha particles; β = beta particles; γ = gamma rays.

	Material	Radiation	Dose	Intensity	Effect or Product	Molecules/100 ev
				Acids		
1	C_nH_{2n+1} COOH (n = 1-29)	α (Rn)			CO_2.	0 5-2.8
2					CO.	<0.5
3					H_2.	<0.4
4					H_2O.	0.9-2.5
5					$C_n H_{2n+2}$.	0.4-1.1
6	Formic (aqueous)	e (1.4 Mev)			Loss of acid function.	2.5
7		d (4 Mev)			Loss of acid function.	1.7
8		γ (Co^{60})		5 x 10^4 r/hr	CO_2.	4.1
9					H_2.	0.5
10					H_2O_2.	4.6
11	Acetic (aqueous, deaerated, 1 M)[2]	He^{++} (35 Mev)[3]	3.8 x 10^{20} ev/ml	0.2 μa	CO_2.	0.28
12					Succinic acid.	0.32
13					CH_4.	0.08
14		d (18 Mev)	3.8 x 10^{20} ev/ml	0.2 μa	CO_2.	0.39
15					Succinic acid.	0.59
16					CH_4.	0.11
17	Caprylic (liquid)	α (Rn)			$H_2, CO_2, CO, H_2O, CH_4, C_2H_6, C_3H_8, C_4H_{10}$.	
18	Lauric (solid)	α (Rn)			$H_2, CO_2, CO, H_2O, n\text{-}C_{11}H_{24}$.	
19	Palmitic (solid)	α (Rn)			$H_2, CO_2, CO, H_2O, n\text{-}C_{15}H_{32}$.	
20	Glycolic, Ca salt (solid)	β (C^{14})	1.75-2.54 x 10^7 r		Decomposition.	31-77
21	Oxalic (aqueous)	X (2.5 Mev)	~ 10^6 r		Loss of acid function.	4-6
22	Lactic (aqueous)	X	1.2 x 10^4 r		Pyruvic acid.	
23	Benzoic (aqueous)	X (220 kv)	10^4-10^5 r	2350 r/min	o-C_6H_4(OH) COOH.	1.0
24					m-C_6H_4(OH) COOH.	
25					p-C_6H_4(OH) COOH.	
				Alcohols, Thiols		
26	Methanol (liquid)	β (C^{14})	5.94 x 10^8 r		Decomposition.	12
27		He^{++} (27 Mev)[3]		1.9-3.9 x 10^{21} ev/sec	H_2.	3.4-4.1
28		He^{++} (27 Mev)[3]		1.9-3.9 x 10^{21} ev/sec	HCHO.	1.7
29	Ethanol (liquid)	He^{++} (27 Mev)[3]		1.3-5.1 x 10^{21} ev/sec	H_2.	1.8-3.2
30					CH_3CHO.	0.7-1.7
31					$(CH_2OH)_2$.	0.7-1.1
32	Sucrose (solid)	X			Inversion, red color.	
33	Sucrose (aqueous)	X			Inversion.	
34	Propane-1,3-dithiol (aqueous)	X (250 kv)	500-5000 r		Oxidation.	11
35	2,3-Dimercapto-1-propanol (BAL)(liquid)	X (250 kv)	500-5000 r		Oxidation.	11
				Vitamins and Related Compounds		
36	o-Aminobenzoic acid (aqueous)	e (3 Mev)			Decarboxylation, loss of amine function.	
37	p-Aminobenzoic acid (aqueous)	e (3 Mev)			Decarboxylation, loss of amine function.	
38	β-Carotene (petroleum ether)	X (3 Mev)	0.66 x 10^6 r		Decomposition.	0.16
39	Choline chloride (solid)	β (C^{14})	1.07 x 10^7 r		Decomposition.	490
40	Niacin (aqueous)	e (3 Mev)	0.17-5.28 x 10^6 r		Decarboxylation.	1.6
				Amino Acids		
41	Glycine (aqueous)	X (200 kv)		3500 r/min	H_2, NH_3, HCHO(trace).	Non-linear
42		X (500 kv)	1.66 x 10^5 r		NH_3.	< 9.1
43		β (n α) Li	8-20 x 10^{20} ev/ml		NH_3.	≤ 1.7
44	Alanine (aqueous)	X (220 kv)		3500 r/min	H_2, NH_3, CH_3CHO (trace).	Non-linear
45	Serine (aqueous)	X (200 kv)		3500 r/min	$H_2, NH_3, (CHO)_2, HOCH_2$CHO.	Non-linear
46	L-Serine (aqueous)	X	1.66 x 10^5 r		NH_3.	1-13
47	Valine·HCl (solid)	β (C^{14})	8.2 x 10^6 r		Decomposition.	0.3
48	Norvaline·HCl (solid)	β (C^{14})	4.03 x 10^7 r		Decomposition.	1.7
49	Norleucine (solid)	β (C^{14})	3.2 x 10^6 r		Decomposition.	10
50	Cysteine (aqueous)	X (250 kv)		10^3 r/min	Loss of thiol function.	6-26
51					H_2O_2.	0-7
52					H_2S.	~1 (aerated)
53					H_2S.	2.5-5 (deaerated)
54	Histidine·HCl (aqueous)	e (3 Mev)	10^5 - 10^6 r		Decomposition.	1.0-10
				Steroids		
55	Cholesterol (aqueous)	X (200 kv)		3000 r/min	Cholestane-3(β), 5(α), 6(β)-triol; 3(β)-hydroxycholest-5-en-7-one.	
56	Δ^5-Pregnen-3-(β)-ol-20-one (aqueous)	X (200 kv)		3000 r/min	3(β),5(α), 6(β)-Trihydroxyallo-pregnan-20-one.	
57	Cholic acid (aqueous)	X (220 kv)	1.8 x 10^6 r		3(α), 12(α)-Dihydroxy-7-ketocholanic acid.	
58	(+)-Estrone-b (aqueous)	X (200 kv)	10^6 r		A lactone.	
				Miscellaneous		
59	Desoxyribonucleic acid (aqueous)	X (200 kv)		3000 r/min	NH_3.	0.4
60					Inorganic phosphate.	0.003
61	Yeast ribonucleic acid (aqueous)	X (200 kv)		3000 r/min	NH_3.	0.4
62					Inorganic phosphate.	0.01
63	Sodium thymonucleate (aqueous)	X (0.2, 2 Mev)			Decomposition.	
64		γ (Ra, Co^{60})			Decomposition.	~0.06
65	Carboxypeptidase (aqueous)	α (Rn)			Inactivation.	0.03
66		X (500 kv)			Inactivation.	0.55
67	Ferricytochrome c (aqueous)	X (180-200 kv)		439-1700 r/min	Oxidation.	1.7
68	Glutathione (aqueous)	X (250 kv)	500-5000 r		Oxidation.	10

/1/ In all aqueous media radiolysis may yield H_2, H_2O_2, and O_2, dependent on conditions; such data are not included here. /2/ Data for aerated solution are more complex. /3/ Rays of artificial (cyclotron) origin.

	Substance[1]	Irradiation	Products or Results of Irradiation	Quantum Efficiency moles/Einstein[2]
			Amino Acids and Amines	
1	L-Alanine	Hg-lamp	L-Lactic acid, pyruvic acid, NH_3.	0.027
2	Aminoisobutyric acid	Hg-lamp	NH_3 + (?).	
3	L-Aspartic acid	Hg-lamp	L-Malic acid.	
4	Betaine	Hg-lamp	Trimethylamine.	0.02
5	Cysteine	Hg-lamp	Cystine + (?).	
6	Cystine	2250Å	Cysteine + (?).	0.02
7	Dihydroxyphenylalanine (dopa)	Hg-lamp	Unknown.	
8	Glycine	2265Å	Glycolic acid, NH_3, CO.	0.033
9	Histamine	Hg-lamp	Unknown.	
10	Histidine		Imidazol-acetaldehyde, NH_3, hydroxy acid, histamine (?).	
11	Homocystine	Hg-lamp	S-Benzylhomocysteine.	
12	Leucine	Hg-lamp	NH_3 + (?).	
13	Methionine	2250Å	Methylmercaptan.	
14	Phenylalanine	Hg-lamp	NH_3, modified phenyl group, tyrosine.	
15	Proline, hydroxyproline	Hg-lamp	Destruction.	
16	Tryptophan	Hg-lamp	Indole-3-acetic acid + (?); change in absorption spectrum.	
17	Tyrosine	Hg-lamp	Unknown; some dopa; change in absorption spectrum.	
18	Valine	Hg-lamp	NH_3 + (?).	
			Hemipeptides[3]	
19	Acetylalanine	2537Å	NH_3 + (?).	0.072
20	Acetyltryptophan	2537Å	Modified indole group; no tryptophan.	0.0027
21	Benzoylalanine	2537Å	Alanine, modified phenyl group.	
22	Benzylstearylamine	2483Å, 2537Å	Stearic acid, benzylamine.	0.0064
23	Phenylacetylalanine	2537Å	Alanine, modified phenyl group.	0.055
24	Phenylbutyrylalanine	2537Å	Alanine, modified phenyl group.	
25	β-Phenylethylstearylamine	2483Å, 2537Å	Stearic acid, β-phenylethylamine.	0.0041
26	Phenylpropionylalanine	2537Å	Alanine, modified phenyl group.	0.0034
27	Phenylvalerylalanine	2537Å	Alanine, modified phenyl group.	0.005
28	Propionylphenylalanine	2537Å	NH_3, modified phenyl group.	0.26
29	Stearic anilide	2350Å, 2400Å	Stearic acid, aniline.	
			Peptides	
30	Acetylalanylglycine	Hg-lamp	NH_3 + (?).	
31	Alanylglycine	Hg-lamp	NH_3 + (?).	
32	Glycylleucine	Hg-lamp	NH_3 + (?).	
33	Glycyltryptophan		Modified indole group; no amino acids.	
34	Glycyltyrosine	2537Å	Modified phenyl group; no amino acids.	0.0034
35	Gramicidin		Destruction.	
36	Leucyltyrosine		Modified phenyl group; no amino acids.	
			Purines and Derivatives	
37	Adenine	2537Å	NH_3, urea; loss of characteristic absorption spectrum.	
38	Adenosine	2537Å	NH_3, urea; loss of characteristic absorption spectrum.	
39	Adenosinetriphosphate	<3000	Adenine.	
40	Adenylic acid	2537Å	NH_3, urea; pentose destruction; loss of characteristic absorption spectrum.	
41	Diphosphopyridine nucleotide(DPN)	<3000	Adenine; adenylic acid, adenosine diphosphate, nicotinamide; loss of coenzyme function.	
42	Triphosphopyridine nucleotide(TPN)	2537	Adenosine 2', 5'-diphosphate, 2'-phospho-adenosine diphosphate, nicotinamide.	
43	Guanine, guanosine, guanylic acid, hypoxanthine, inosine, uric acid, xanthine, xanthosine	2537Å	NH_3, urea; loss of characteristic absorption spectra; uric acid also yields triuret.	
			Pyrimidines and Derivatives	
44	Cytidine		NH_3, urea; loss of characteristic absorption spectrum; pentose of cytidylic acid destroyed.	
45	Cytidylic acid			
46	Cytosine			
47	1, 3-Dimethyluracil		6- or 5-Hydroxy-1, 3-dimethylhydrouracil.	
48	Thymine	2537Å	NH_3, urea; loss of characteristic absorption spectrum.	
49	Uracil		NH_3, urea; loss of characteristic absorption spectrum. (Primary product reverts to uracil in acid. Change in absorption spectrum, oxamide and parabanic acid.)	
50	Uridine		NH_3, urea; loss of characteristic absorption spectrum. (Primary product reverts to uridine in acid.)	
51	Uridylic acid		Unknown product which reverts to uridylic acid in acid solution.	0.0216
			Nucleic Acids	
52	Desoxyribonucleic acid	2537Å	Depolymerization and destruction of pyrimidine bases; loss of characteristic absorption spectrum and liberation of inorganic phosphate.	10^{-6}(depolymerization)
53	Desoxyribonucleic acid	2650Å	Gel formation.	0.01-0.04(dry)
54	DNA (transforming principle)		Inactivated by 500 ergs/sq mm per 200 µg DNA.	
55	Ribonucleic acid	2537Å	Depolymerization; loss of characteristic absorption spectrum.	0.1 (depolymerization)
			Vitamins	
56	B₁ (2-methyl-5-ethoxymethyl-6-aminopyrimidine component)	2537Å	Loss of selective absorption and ability to support growth of Phycomyces blakesleeanus.	0.0184
57	B₁ (4-methyl-5-β-hydroxyethyl-thiazole component)	2537Å	Loss of ability to support growth of Phycomyces; changes in side groups, breakdown of ring.	0.347
58	Ergosterol	2536Å, 2800Å	Vitamin D.	0.2-0.3
			Enzymes and Related Proteins[3]	
59	Aldolase		Loss of hexose diphosphate activity.	0.0019
60	Antibody, bushy stunt virus		Reduction in flocculation of antigen.	0.00096
61	Antibody, clover nodule bacteria	2537Å		0.0024
62	Antibody, tobacco mosaic virus			0.00096
63	Carboxypeptidase		Loss of chloroacetyltyrosinase activity.	0.001
64	Catalase		Loss of hydrogen peroxidase activity.	0.0011(dry)

/1/ In aqueous solution, unless otherwise indicated. /2/ Equivalent to number of molecules reacting per number of quanta absorbed. /3/ Values are representative and usually vary with pH. Absolute value depends on assumed molecular weight.

	Substance[1]	Irradiation	Products or Results of Irradiation	Quantum Efficiency moles/Einstein[2]
			Enzymes and Related Proteins[3] (concluded)	
65	Chymotrypsin	2537Å	Loss of activity on casein.	0.0065
66	Chymotrypsin	2967Å-2301Å		0.008-0.002(dry)
67	Chymotrypsinogen		Inability to convert to chymotrypsin.	0.0011(dry)
68	Desoxyribonuclease		Loss of nuclease activity.	0.0039(dry)
69	Insulin		Inability to produce hypoglycemic convulsions in mice.	0.015
70	Lysozyme		Loss of Micrococcus lysodeicticus activity.	0.24
71	Pancreatic trypsin inhibitor		Loss of trypsin-inhibiting power.	0.031
72	Pepsin	2537Å	Loss of hemoglobinase activity.	0.0024
73	Ribonuclease		Loss of nuclease activity.	0.03
74	Triosephosphate dehydrogenase		Loss of effect on diphosphopyridine nucleotide.	0.003
75	Trypsin		Loss of caseinase activity.	0.018
76	Trypsin			0.02-0.1(dry, 90°-450°K)
77	Trypsin inibitor, soybean		Loss of trypsin-inhibiting activity.	0.0088
78	Urease	1860Å	Loss of urease activity	0.00938
79	Urease	2537Å		0.00093
80	Urease	3130Å		0.00816
			Viruses and Phages[3]	
81	Tobacco mosaic virus	2537Å	Virus sensitized to heat, suffers loss of infectivity for Nicotiana glutinosa.	4.3×10^{-5}
82	T₁ phage	2220Å	Loss of activity on Escherichia coli, strain B.	5.0×10^{-4}
83	T₁ phage	2537Å		6.3×10^{-4}
84	T₁ phage	3022Å		7.3×10^{-4}
85	T₂ phage	2220Å		2.7×10^{-4}
86	T₂ phage	2537Å		3.1×10^{-4}
87	T₂ phage	3022Å		1.8×10^{-4}

/1/ In aqueous solution, unless otherwise indicated. /2/ Equivalent to number of molecules reacting per number of quanta absorbed. /3/ Values are representative and usually vary with pH. Absolute value depends on assumed molecular weight.

412. ULTRAVIOLET RADIATION: LD₅₀ FOR SOME UNICELLULAR ORGANISMS

Values in parentheses are ultraviolet wave lengths in mμ.

	Organism	Ultraviolet Wave Length, mμ								
		(310)	(302)	(297)	(290)	(280)	(265)	(254)	(248)	Other
		LD₅₀ Dose, ergs/sq mm								
	Bacteria[2]									
1	Escherichia coli	4580		2965	339	181-225	104	44-208		172(270)
2	Micrococcus candicans		11,375	3775		295	212	341		
3	Pseudomonas pyocyanea			7150		320	234	291		
4	Staphylococcus aureus		3000	500	200	110-440	90-206	86-275	96	150(238)
5	Serratia marcescens	5556		677		47	49	57		73(240)
6	Salmonella typhi-murium					237				
	Fungi									
	Saccharomyces cereviseae,									
7	in dark		23,500			556-1260	457-863	503-900	696	1 156(238)
8	in light							1400		
	Neurospora crassa, microconidia,									
9	in dark		1050			496	300	370		585(238)
10	in light							1020		
	Neurospora crassa, macroconidia,									
11	in dark					1700	1120	1440		
12	in light							3000		
	Protozoa									
13	Amoeba proteus, in dark							2160		
	Paramecium aurelia,									
14	in dark					3000				
15	in light					6000				
	Protophyta									
16	Chlorella pyrenoidosa, in dark							30,000		

/1/ Sterilizing dose, or dose which prevents colony formation under the usual conditions for culture of the organism. /2/ Not specified whether bacteria were handled in the light or dark.

Ranges, when preceded by average values, are given in parentheses.

c = curie; mc = millicurie; μc = microcurie; ev = electron volt; Mev = million electron volts; kv = 1000 volts; n = n unit[1]; r = roentgen; rep = roentgen equivalent physical; rem = roentgen equivalent mammals; α = alpha rays; γ = gamma rays.

	Radiation		Latent Period	Late Effects
	Type	Amount		
			Man	
1	A-bomb	Epilation dose	2 yr	10 cases of A-bomb cataract Japan, 1 case USA.
2	Hiroshima	Irradiated in utero, 1st half of pregnancy	5 yr	Microcephaly and mental retardation were present in 7 of 11 children within 1200 m of hypocenter.
3	Japan	Area within 2000 m of hypocenter	3-5 yr	Leukemia incidence 9.3 times that of non-exposed population of Hiroshima and Nagaski (only 1948-50 incl.).
4		Area within 1000 m of hypocenter	3-5 yr	Leukemia incidence 32 times that of non-exposed population (only 1948-50 incl.).
5	Cyclotron	Epilation dose	2 yr	2 cases of cyclotron-induced cataract.
6	16 Mev neutrons, fast	400-500 n	2 mo-5 yr	Severe epidermolytic reaction (13/16), skin atrophy and fibrosis, persistent ulcerations, and diminished repair by normal tissues; radiation osteitis; severe bowel reactions.
7	0-20 Mev neutrons, fast (small γ components)	10-135 n	2-10 yr	Cataracts: severe (3/10), slight to moderate (4/10), minimal (3/10); chronic irradiation: no blood changes; 2 cases mild epilation.
8	Radium-226 (external)	1000-1500 mg-hr		Cessation of ovarian function, 77% (63/82).
9		1500-2000 mg-hr		Cessation of ovarian function (6/7).
10	Radium[2]	0.02-0.5 μg	14-48 yr	Radiation osteitis (25%).
11		0.5-2.0 μg	23.6 yr (1-32) yr	Osteomyelitis and loss of teeth (5/9); radiation osteitis (8/9); pathol. fractures (3/9); giant cell tumor (1/9); osteogenic sarcoma (1/9); epidermoid carcinoma nasopharynx (1/9); high incidence of deafness and arthritis.
12		2.7 μg	24.6 (8-32) yr	Osteomyelitis of jaw and loss of teeth (5/9); radiation osteitis (8/9); pathol. fracture (1/9); fibrosarcoma (1/9); epidermoid carcinoma nasopharynx (1/9).
13		2-20 μg	6-8 yr	Radiation osteitis (osteosclerosis); osteogenic sarcoma (5/18 deaths); pathological fractures.
14		8-23 μg	19.5 (7-21) yr	Osteomyelitis of jaw and loss of teeth (6/8); radiation osteitis (7/8); epidermoid carcinoma nasopharynx (1/8); osteogenic carcinoma (1/8); pathol. fractures (3/8); leukemia (1/8).
15		10-180 μg	1-8 yr	Anemia with hyperplastic marrow, jaw necrosis (13 cases).
16		100-800 μg orig. dose, 1.0-10 μg residual radium	20-30 yr post treatment	Changes in bone density, similar to those in dead or dying bone, in all patients having at least 1 μg residual Ra; minimal changes with 0.5 μg (24 cases); dental changes in all with at least 4 μg residual Ra. Greatly enlarged haversian canals; distortion of normal bone configuration (7/24), edentia, mandibular lesions (3/19), aseptic necrosis of bone (7/24), fibrosarcoma, honey-combed teeth, "pink tooth."
17	Uranium, radium ores	Variable doses	13-23 yr	Lung cancer in uranium miners of Joachimsthal and Schneeberg.
18	X-ray	Variable doses	months to years	Skin atrophy, telangiectasis, sclerosis, pigmentation, alopecia and altered vasomotion, diminished sweat and sebaceous function; loss of cutaneous ridges and finger prints; ulcers and keratoses; malignancies; hyperkeratotic, warty growths; deformed and brittle, dry nails, loss of nails, fissures, subungual hyperkeratoses.
19		100-300 r (200 and 1000 kv)	60-680 da / 100-600 da	Temporary drop in white blood cell count. Temporary macrocytic anemia.
20		500-624 hr		94% castrated.
21		625 r (to ovaries)		Permanent cessation of menstruation, 72 patients.
22		≤ 1000 r (to center of vertebrae)	Followed 13 yr post-treatment	Vertebrae normal (irrespective of child's age); determined on 45 individuals, 34 living patients, 11 at autopsy.
23		1000-2000 r (to spine)	Followed 3-7 yr	"Transverse-line" growth disturbance of vertebrae (irrespective of child's age up to 6 yr).
24		1500-8500 r, therapeutic dose, eye tumor	2 yr	7 cases of cataract.
25		1500-25,000 r (130-200 kv)	6-22 yr	11 cases osteogenic sarcoma.
26		1700-3000 r (half value layer 1.5 mm Cu), lower abdomen	6-18 mo	Nephlosclerosis; hypertension; elevated albuminuria (22/55); edema; anuria. Death from congestive heart failure and/or uremia (7/55); (over 2300 r there is high risk of renal failure).
27		About 2000 r (to spine)	Followed 2-13 yr	Contour irregularity of vertebrae (all children, except one 1 yr old).
28		3500-5000 r	8-28 mo	Lens opacities (4 cases).
29	X-ray, radium	4000-6700 r	8.6 (5-20) yr	Sarcoma; osteogenic sarcoma. Therapy for lupus vulgaris, papillomata of bladder, actinomycosis, tubercular psoriasis.
30	X-ray and radium equipment	Unknown		Leukemia in radiologists (4.68%), 9 times the incidence in non-radiological physicians (0.51%).

/1/ One n unit defined as the quantity of fast neutron radiation that discharges a particular 100 r Victoreen ionizing chamber in the same magnitude as does one γ of X-radiation. Measurements have indicated that one n unit is the approximate equivalent of 2.5 rep. /2/ Variable amounts of mesothorium also present with the radium in some instances.

Ranges, when preceded by average values, are given in parentheses.

c = curie; mc = millicurie; µc = microcurie; ev = electron volt; Mev = million electron volts; kv = 1000 volts; n = n unit[1]; r = roentgen; rep = roentgen equivalent physical; rem = roentgen equivalent mammals; α = alpha rays; γ = gamma rays.

	Radiation Type	Amount	Latent Period	Late Effects
	Dog			
31	Neutrons	0.012, 0.06, 0.11 n/day	1 yr	Reduction of lymphocytes only observed effect (6 doses/wk).
32		1.7 n/da	1 yr	Mucoid conjunctivitis, keratoconjunctivitis and corneal opacities; reduced size of spleen and testes; increased incidence of infection; hypoplasia of bone marrow and regional lymph nodes; hemorrhage of lymph nodes, heart, stomach, small bowel and kidney; reduction of lymphocytes, neutrophils and erythrocytes.
33	Neutrons, fast	150 n	2 yr	Destruction and chronic inflammation of cornea and changes in lens capsules and fibers, but no cataracts.
34		800-900 n	2 yr	Cataracts in 65-75% of animals.
35	X-ray	0.1 r/da (6 times/wk)	2 yr	Lowered sperm count, increase in abnormal sperm.
36		0.5 r/da	11 mo	Lowered sperm count, increase in abnormal sperm.
37		0.5 r/da	2 yr	Partial testicular atrophy; slight reduction of leucocytes;
38		1.0 r/da	6 mo	Lymphopenia.
39		1.0 r/da	9 mo	50% aspermic.
40		1.0 r/da	1 yr	100% aspermic; neutrophil dec.
41		1.0 r/da	2 yr	Severe injury of testes.
42		3.0 r/da	2 mo	Lymphocyte and platelet reduction.
43		6.0 r/da	9 mo	50% aspermic.
44		6.0 r/da	1.5 yr	Severe injury of testes.
45		10.0 r/da	2 mo	Lymphocyte, platelet, and erythrocyte depression.
46		10.0 r/da	3.5 mo	50% aspermic.
47		10.0 r/da	1.5 yr	Bone marrow hypoplasia; focal bowel and lymph node hemorrhages.
48		10.0 r/da	6 mo	50% survival.
	Guinea Pig			
49	Cobalt-60 (γ-rays), external	15 r/da	106 da	50% survival.
50		30 r/da	63 da	50% survival.
51		60 r/da	41 da	50% survival.
52		90 r/da	20 da	50% survival.
53		120 r/da	18 da	50% survival.
54	Phosphorus-32	7750 rep (external)	2 mo	Alopecia.
55	Radium, filtered (γ-rays), repeated low dose	Non-radiated (controls)	38 mo	75% survival.
56		0.11 r/da	38 mo	75% survival.
57		1.1 r/da (1050 r)	32 mo	50% survival.
58		2.2 r/da (2100 r)	32 mo	50% survival.
59		4.4 r/da (2400 r)	18 mo	50% survival; reduction white blood cells.
60		8.8 r/da (2300 r)	5 mo	50% survival; recurrent anemia.
	Mouse			
61	Cobalt-60 (γ-rays), external	90 r/da	52 da	50% survival.
62		115 r/da	37 da	50% survival.
63		140 r/da	22 da	50% survival.
64	Neutrons, fast, 10^3 ev to ≥ 4 Mev, and γ-rays (divided doses)	Non-radiated (controls)	51 wk	
65		1 r/da	61 wk	50% survival for controls and each dosage increment. With respect to shortening life span, 1 n (divided small doses) is equivalent to 35 r. (For acute killing 1 n is equivalent to 9 r). Threshold for shortening life span is about 1 r/da and less than 0.1 n.
66		8.6 r/da	48 wk	
67		Non-radiated (controls)	70 wk	
68		0.115 n/da (total 32.2 n)	40 wk	
69		1.15 n/da (total 241.5 n)	30 wk	
70		4.3 n/da (total 301 n)	10 wk	
71		13 n/da (total 273 n)	3 wk	
72	Neutrons, fast, and X-rays (single exposure)	Non-radiated (controls)	64 wk	
73		500 r	58 wk	
74		700 r	39 wk	50% survival for controls and each dosage increment. Terminal changes are generalized; atrophy and an increased incidence of mediastinal lymphonatosis.
75		26 n	52 wk	
76		50 n	48 wk	
77		78 n	42 wk	
78		90 n	6 wk	
79	Neutrons, thermal	51 rem	14 wk	Lens opacities, 92% at 22 wk[3].
80		196.6 rem	14 wk	Lens opacities, 91% at 18 wk[3].
81		477 rem	6 wk	Lens opacities, 100% at 11 wk[3].
82	Phosphorus-32	3000-4000 rep (external)	30 da	General epilation, skin atrophy, loss of ear tips, ulcerations, keratosis.
83		3000-4000 rep (external)	3-4 mo	Lens opacities (4000 r).
84		3000-4000 rep (external)	8 mo	Lens opacities (3000 r).
85		3000-4000 rep (external)	6-8 mo	Tumors; shortening of life span.
86	Plutonium-239	3.1-15.6 µc/kg (i.v.)	190-250 da	Osteogenic sarcoma.
87		> 6.1 µc/kg (i.v.)		Marked shortening of life span.
88	Radium-226	> 12 µc/kg (i.v.)	250-300 da	Increased osteogenic sarcoma.
89		> 50 µc/kg (0.6-4170 µc/kg, i.v.)		Marked shortening of life span; debilitation and increased incidence of infection.

Note (rows 38-41): If irradiation is stopped after 1 yr, there is partial recovery of sperm 4 mo later in the 1 r/da group.

/1/ One n unit defined as the quantity of fast neutron radiation that discharges a particular 100 r Victoreen ionizing chamber in the same magnitude as does one r of X-radiation. Measurements have indicated that one n unit is the approximate equivalent of 2.5 rep. /3/ n/X-ray relative biological effectiveness (RBE) for production of opacities is 9 times the n/X-ray RBE for 30 da lethality.

Ranges, when preceded by average values, are given in parentheses.

c = curie; mc = millicurie; μc = microcurie; ev = electron volt; Mev = million electron volts; kv = 1000 volts; n = n unit[1]; r = roentgen; rep = roentgen equivalent physical; rem = roentgen equivalent mammals; α = alpha rays; γ = gamma rays.

	Radiation Type	Amount	Latent Period	Late Effects
				Mouse (concluded)
90	Radium filtered (γ-rays), repeated low dose	Non-radiated (controls)		50% survival for controls and each dosage increment; increase in lymphatic leukemia, mammary and ovarian carcinoma.
91		1.1 r/da (760 r)		
92		2.2 r/da (1390 r)		
93		4.4 r/da (2640 r)		
94		8.8 r/da (4400 r)		
	Strontium-89 (β-rays)			
95	Monthly injections	0.05 μc/g	500 da	Bone tumors begin to develop.
96		0.1 μc/g	425 da	
97		0.2 μc/g	350 da	
98		0.5 μc/g	220 da	
99		0.1 μc/g	160 da	
100	Single injection	2.5 μc/g	200 da	
101		5.0 μc/g	150 da	
102	Uranium-232	0.1-1.0 μc/kg (i.v.)	575 da	Osteogenic sarcoma (probably significant); used 0.1-10.0 μc/kg.
103		> 1.0 μc/kg (i.v.)	575 da	
104	Uranium-233	2.5 μc/kg (i.v.)	575 da	Osteogenic sarcoma (probably significant); used 0.1-100 μc/kg.
105		> 5 μc/kg (i.v.)	575 da	Osteogenic sarcoma.
106		> 53 μc/kg (i.v.)	575 da	Shortening of life span.
107	Uranium-238	> 3.6 x 10⁻⁷ μc/kg (i.v.)	575 da	Possibly significant increase in osteogenic sarcoma.
108	X-ray	25-200 r to fetus early in pregnancy (equivalent to 2-6 wk, human)	Until birth	At birth severe skeletal and other abnormalities, with clearly defined critical periods.
109		Irradiation of fetus late in pregnancy (equivalent to after 6 wk, human)	Until birth	Several weeks after birth: cataracts, hydrocephalus; behavior disturbances; skin lesions.
110		50 r (250 kv)	17 wk	Lens opacities, 92% at 22 wk[3].
111		200 r (250 kv)	14 wk	Lens opacities, 91% at 18 wk[3].
112		500 r (250 kv)	6 wk	Lens opacities, 100% at 11 wk[3].
113		400 r (single dose)	15-23 mo	Ovarian tumors 15 times that of controls.
114		600-1200 r (divided doses)	9-14 mo	Myelosis 8 times that of controls.
115		600-1200 r (divided doses)	6-12 mo	Mediastinal lymphosarcoma 7 times that of controls.
116		600 r (120 kv, 150 r alternate wks, to whole body)	420-580 da	Lymphomas (33/63).
117		600 r (120 kv, 150 r alternate wks, to whole body, mediastinum shielded)	118-525 da	No lymphomas.
118		1200 r (120 kv, 300 r alternate wks, to upper half of body)	324-365 da	Lymphomas (3/40).
119		1200 r (120 kv, 300 alternate wks, to alternate halves of body)	420-508 da	Lymphomas (3/37).
120		Non-radiated (controls)	526-570 da	Lymphomas (3/36).
				Rabbit
121	Neutrons	0.012 n/da, 6 doses/wk	1 yr	No observed effects.
122		0.06 n/da, 6 doses/wk	1 yr	No observed effects.
123		0.11 n/da, 6 doses/wk	1 yr	No observed effects.
124		1.7 n/da	1 yr	Increased incidence of infection; hypoplasia of bone marrow; atrophy of testes; reduction of lymphocytes; neutrophils depressed after 2 wk; erythrocytes after 32-35 wk.
125		3.7 n/wk (52.7-83.7 n, total)	4-12 mo	No lens changes.
126		33-100 n (single doses)	2-5 mo	Cataracts of posterior lens.
127	Fission	3 x 10¹⁰ particles/ml	125 da	Cataracts. 2 x 10⁹ particles/ml (or less) is threshold for lens opacities.
128	14 Mev	8 x 10⁹ particles/ml	125 da	Cataracts.
129	Phosphorus-32 (external)	2500-3000 rep	2 mo	Graying of fur.
130		5000 rep		Epilation, recovery by 10 wk.
131		7500 rep		Permanent epilation; ulcerations.
132		15000 rep		Emaciation.
133	Radium	100 μg in 90 da (RaSO₄ in glycerine, orally)	2 mo	Mottling and shortening of incisors.
134			5-18 mo	Pathological fractures; alopecia.
135			9 mo	Jaw abscesses, rarefaction of mandible and other bones (generalized osteoporosis and necrosis); weight loss; mild progressive regenerative anemia with hyperplasia and fibrosis of marrow, lymph nodes, and spleen.
136	Thorium dioxide ("thorotrast"), 20% colloidal suspension (α- and γ-rays)	I.v. injection		Osteosarcoma; hemopoietic depression and damage to liver and spleen. Deposited in reticulo-endothelial system.
137	X-ray	0.1-0.5 r/da	1 yr	No changes detected.
138		1.0 r/da	1 yr	Possible testicular injury.
139		10 r/da	8 wk	Lymphocytes significantly decreased.
140			3 mo	Platelets decreased.
141			1 yr	Erythrocytes decreased; testicular injury; ovarian follicles disappear.
142		250 r or less (1.2 Mev)	150 da	Threshold for production of lens opacities.
143		500 r	125 da	Cataracts, greatly affected by age, earlier in young rabbits.

/1/ One n unit defined as the quantity of fast neutron radiation that discharges a particular 100 r Victoreen ionizing chamber in the same magnitude as does one r of X-radiation. Measurements have indicated that one n unit is the approximate equivalent of 2.5 rep. /3/ n/X-ray relative biological effectiveness (RBE) for production of opacities is 9 times the n/X-ray RBE for 30 da lethality.

Ranges, when preceded by average values, are given in parentheses. c=curie; mc=millicurie; μc=microcurie; ev=electron volt; Mev=million electron volts; kv=1000 volts; n=n unit[1]; r=roentgen; rep=roentgen equivalent physical; rem=roentgen equivalent mammals; α=alpha rays; γ=gamma rays.

	Radiation		Latent Period	Late Effects
	Type	Amount		
			Rat (concluded)	
144	Cerium-144	1-3 mc/kg	200 da	Osteogenic sarcoma; liver atrophy with ascites and jaundice.
145	Cobalt-60 (γ-rays),	20 r/da	332 da	50% survival; increased tumor frequency.
146	external	60 r/da	236 da	50% survival; increased tumor frequency.
147		70 r/da	72 da	50% survival; increased tumor frequency.
148		80 r/da	53 da	50% survival; increased tumor frequency.
149		90 r/da	48 da	50% survival; increased tumor frequency.
150		120 r/da	38 da	50% survival; increased tumor frequency.
151	Neutrons	0.012-0.06 n/da	1 yr	No effects observed.
152		0.11 n/da	1 yr	Number of neoplasms three times that of controls (including leukemias).
153		1.7 n/da	1 yr	Incr. infection and incidence of neoplasms (high leukemia incidence); bilateral cataracts; hypoplasia of spleen; atrophy of testes and ovarian follicles; early reduction of lymphocytes; reduction of erythrocytes.
154	Phosphorus-32	4000-5000 rep (external)	4-5 mo	Tumors; keratoses; lens opacities (low incidence); ulceration of scrotum and base of tail; alopecia.
155	Praesodymium-144	1-3 mc/kg	200 da	Osteogenic sarcoma; liver atrophy with ascites and jaundice.
156	Plutonium-239	0.02 μg/g (0.0031-0.0062 c/g)	300-400 da	Osteogenic sarcomas.
157		0.03 μc/g	3-7 mo	Areas of dead bone and calcified cartilage, resumption of normal bone growth at epiphysis; destruction of spermatogenic cells; atrophy of ovary.
158	Radium	0.125 μc/g	5 mo	Damage to epiphyseal cartilage, overgrowth with atypical bone, loss of normal bone cells; atrophy of ovary.
159		0.5 μc/g	3-6 mo	Degenerative changes in ovary; damage to blood vessels.
160		0.6 μc/g	5 mo	Damage to epiphyseal cartilage and marrow, production of abnormal bone.
161	Strontium-89	0.05 μc/g	500 da	
162		0.1 μc/g	400 da	
163		0.5 μc/g (single injection)	400 da	Osteogenic sarcomas.
164		1.0 μc/g level (monthly injections)	250 da	
165		5.0 μc/g (single injection)	200 da	
166	Thorium dioxide ("thoro-	0.3 ml	14 mo	Produced fibroblastic tumors (14/60).
167	trast"),20% colloidal sus-	2.5 ml	10-17 mo	Produced sarcoma (33/60).
168	pension (α- and γ-rays)	5.0 ml	10-17 mo	Produced sarcoma (50/50).
169	X-ray	0.1 r/da (total 49 r)	81.7 wk	50% survival.
170		0.5 r/da (total 230 r)	76.7 wk	50% survival; incr. infibro-adenomata of mammary gland.
171		1.0 r/da (total 460 r)	76.9 wk	50% survival.
172		10.0 r/da (total 3500 r)	58.3 wk	50% survival; increase in leukemia.
173		12.5-100 r (8th da of gestation)		Retardation of growth.
174		12.5-100 r (9th and 10th da of gestation)		Malformations; increased mortality; growth retardation.
175		375 r (and above, whole body)		Enamel hypoplasia, retarded enamel dentin formation
176		500 r (whole body)		5 mo. required for complete restoration of epithelium in testes (Vanderbilt's strain adult males).
177		2000 r (and above, locally)		Retardation of eruption of incisors.
178		4000 r (locally to teeth)		Stoppage of growth of dentin (lengthwise) in incisors.
179	Yttrium-91	2.0 μc/g	1-3 mo	Damage to epiphyseal cartilage and production of atypical bone; increase in spleen hematopoesis.
180		20-30 mc/kg (1 dose orally), or 1-2 mc/kg/da, 6 da/wk for 3 mo		A variety of intestinal lesions with obstruction. Y is essentially non-absorbed from the intestinal tract.

/1/ One unit defined as the quantity of fast neutron radiation which will discharge a particular 100 r Victoreen ionizing chamber by the same amount as will one r of X-rays. Measurements have indicated that one n unit equals approximately 2.5 rep.

414. RADIATION: SUMMARY OF SOME PHYSICAL CHARACTERISTICS
Adapted from "Radiation Handbook for Biologists," by H. E. Kubitschek et al., Argonne National Laboratory, 1952.

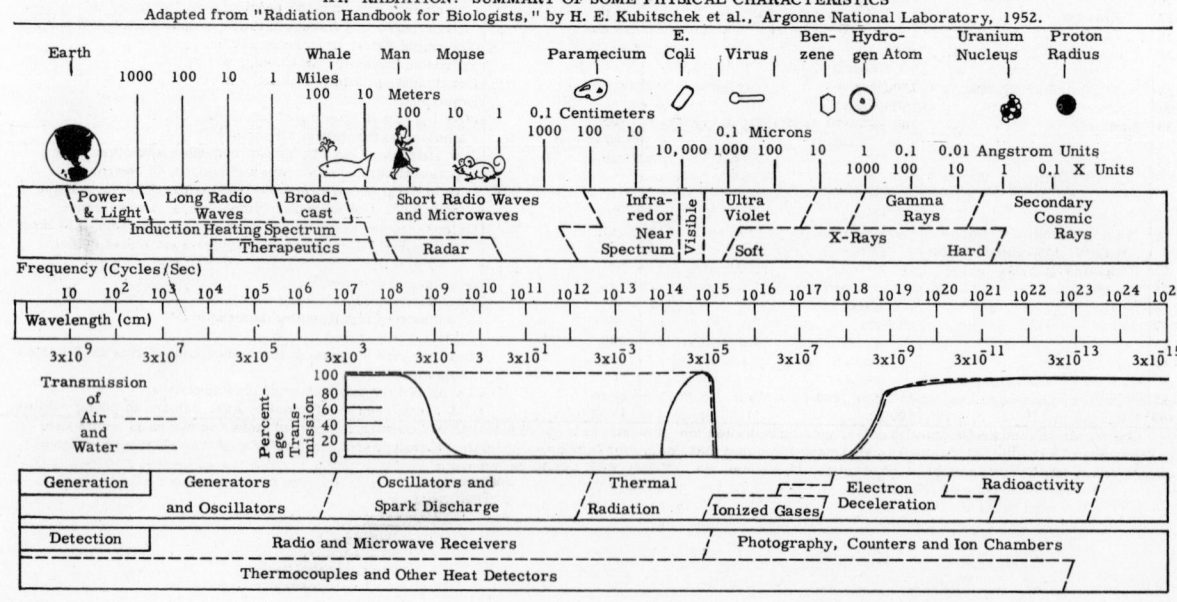

415. FACTORS AFFECTING RESPONSE TO X- AND GAMMA RADIATION

+ = increased; - = decreased; ± = no effect; i.p. = intraperitoneal; i.v. = intravenous.

Part I: PROPHYLACTIC FACTORS

Grouping of agents or measures is tentative and arbitrary as there is no general agreement concerning mechanism of action. Contradictory or conflicting results under similar conditions represent data reported by different investigators. Although there may be differences in the efficacy of the agents, it is not always possible to grade their effects on survival.

	Agent or Condition[1]	Animal	Time of Administration[2] (With Respect to Irradiation)	Survival	Other Effects
			Hypoxia (Physical)		
1	Anemia, bleeding-induced	Rat	Immediately before.		- sensitivity of skin and of Jensen rat sarcoma.
2	Anemia, bleeding-induced	Dog, rat	Immediately before or after.		Stimulation of erythropoiesis.
3	Carbon dioxide atmosphere	Mouse(newborn)	Immediately before and during.	+	
4	Hypothermia	Mouse(newborn)	Immediately before and during.	+	
5	Hypothermia	Rat (newborn)	Immediately before and during.		- skin sensitivity.
6	Interference with respiration[3]	Rat (newborn)	Immediately before and during.		
7	Lowered ambient oxygen tension	Mouse	Immediately before and during.	+	- incidence of abnormal mitoses in bone marrow.
8	Lowered ambient oxygen tension	Mouse	Immediately before and during.		No protection vs induction of dominant lethal mutations.
9	Lowered ambient oxygen tension	Rat	Immediately before and during.	+	
10	Lowered ambient oxygen tension	Mouse(in utero)	Immediately before and during.		- developmental abnormalities.
11	Nitrogen atmosphere	Mouse(newborn)	Immediately before and during.	+	
			Hypoxia (Chemical)		
12	p-Aminopropiophenone	Rat, mouse	Immediately before.	+	
13	p-Aminopropiophenone	Rat	Immediately before or after.		Stimulation of erythropoiesis.
14	Carbon monoxide (inhalation)	Mouse	Immediately before and during.	+	
15	Epinephrine	Rat	Immediately before.	+	
16	Hydrogen sulfide (inhalation)	Mouse	Immediately before and during.	+	
17	Methylene blue	Mouse	Immediately before.	+	
18	Morphine	Mouse	Immediately before.	+	
19	Pitressin	Rat	Immediately before.	+	
20	Sodium nitrite	Mouse	Immediately before.	+	
			Bone Marrow Hyperplasia		
21	Bleeding	Rabbit	Several da before.		+ resistance of erythropoietic tissue.
22	Cobalt	Mouse	Fed in diet several da before.	+	
23	Estrogens	Mouse	5 to 15 da before.	+	
24	High altitude (simulated)	Mouse	Repeatedly several da before.		+ resistance of erythropoietic tissue.
25	High altitude (simulated)	Rat	Repeatedly several da before.	-	- protection of DNA synthesis in bone marrow and spleen.
26	Phenylhydrazine	Rabbit	Repeatedly several da before.		+ resistance of erythropoietic tissue.
			Amines[4]		
27	Glucosamine	Mouse	Immediately before.	+	
28	Hydroxylamine	Mouse	Immediately before.	+	
29	5-Hydroxytryptamine	Rat	Immediately before.	+	
30	Isopropylamine	Mouse	Immediately before.	+	
31	Methylamine	Mouse	Immediately before.	+	
			Sulfhydryl Compounds[5]		
32	2-Aminoethyl disulfide	Mouse	Immediately before.	+	
33	Cysteine	Mouse	Immediately before.	+	- leukopenia, - splenic atrophy.
34	Cysteine	Mouse	Immediately before.		Additive with hypoxia in reducing incidence of abnormal mitoses in marrow.
35	Cysteine	Rat	Immediately before.	+	- depression and more rapid recovery of WBC and RBC.
36	Cysteine	Rabbit	Immediately before.		- incidence of nuclear fragmentation in ocular lens epithelium.
37	Cysteine	Rabbit	Immediately before[6]		- histological damage to cornea following beta radiation.
38	2,3-Dimercapto-1-propanol(BAL)	Rat, mouse	Immediately before.	+	
39	Glutathione	Mouse, rat	Immediately before.	+	No difference in initial destructive effects of radiation but more rapid recovery of hematopoietic and lymphopoietic tissues.
40	β-Mercaptoethylamine[7]	Mouse	Immediately before.	+	More rapid recovery of white blood cell count; no protection against mutagenic effects.
41	β-Mercaptoethylamine	Rat	Immediately before.	+	Prevented radiation-induced increase in adrenal weight and late fall in adrenal cholesterol.
42	Monothiol glycerol	Mouse	Immediately before.	+	
43	Sodium ethanedithiophosphonate	Mouse	Immediately before.	+	
44	Thiosorbitol	Mouse	Immediately before.	+	
45	Thiourea	Mouse	Immediately before.	+	
			Miscellaneous		
46	Atropine	Mouse	Daily before and after.	+	
47	Carbamoylcholine chloride	Mouse	Immediately before.	+	
48	Ethanol	Mouse	Immediately before.	+	
49	Glycerol	Mouse	Immediately before.	+	
50	Malononitrile	Mouse	Immediately before	+	
51	Mecholyl bromide or chloride	Mouse	Immediately before.	+	
52	Propylene glycol	Mouse	Immediately before.	+	
53	Serum, foreign	Mouse	10 days before.	±	
54	Serum, foreign	Rabbit	10 days before.		- severity of skin reaction.
55	Serum, foreign	Dog	7 days before.		- leukopenia, + general health.
56	Serum or plasma[8]	Mouse	Immediately before.	±	
57	Sodium azide	Mouse	Immediately before.	+	
58	Sodium or potassium cyanide	Mouse	Immediately before.	+	
59	Sodium or potassium cyanide	Rat	Immediately before.	±	
60	Terramycin	Rat	Repeatedly for 48-72 hr before.	+	

/1/ Unless otherwise indicated, chemical agents given by parenteral injection. /2/ "Immediately before" indicates a few minutes to 1 hour previous to radiation exposure. /3/ Taping of chest. /4/ Do not contain sulfhydryl groups. /5/ Some of these agents do not contain the sulfhydryl group, but it is believed that in vivo a sulfhydryl linkage is encountered; for instance, 2-aminoethyl disulfide (cystinamine) is converted in vivo to β-mercaptoethylamine (cysteamine). /6/ Local administration. /7/ The mercaptoethylamine derivative β-aminoethylisothiouranium is somewhat less toxic to mice, and more stable than its parent compound. /8/ Homologous or heterologous.

+ = increased; - = decreased; ± = no effect; i.p. = intraperitoneal; i.v. = intravenous.

Part II: THERAPEUTIC FACTORS

	Agent	Animal[1]	Method of Administration	Effect on Survival
			Antibiotics	
1	Aureomycin	Mouse, rat, guinea pig, dog	Daily by various routes and dosage schedules.	± to slight +.
2	Streptomycin	Mouse	Daily injections, various dosages.	Significant +.
3	Streptomycin	Swine	Daily injections after combined X-ray exposure and thermal burns.	+.
4	Terramycin	Mouse, rat	Various dosages, dosage schedules, methods of administration.	± to slight +.
5	Terramycin	Dog	Orally, 100 mg/kg/da for 28 da.	+.
6	Antibiotics, wide variety, various combinations	Mouse, rat, guinea pig	Various routes, dosages, dosage schedules.	± to slight +.
			Transfusion of Blood and Various Blood Components	
7	Blood, whole	Dog	Exchange transfusion[3] within a few hr.	± to slight +.
8	Blood, whole	Dog	Repeated transfusions.	±.
9	Blood, whole, plus aureomycin	Dog	Repeated transfusions plus aureomycin in various dosage schedules.	±.
10	Leukocytes	Dog	Daily transfusion of leukocyte suspensions.	Survival data inadequate; leukocytes migrate to foci of infections.
11	Platelets	Dog	Repeated transfusions of platelet suspensions	Survival data inadequate; control of hemorrhages.
			Spleen and Bone Marrow Inoculations	
12	Spleen	Mouse, rat	Implant, or i.p. injection of homologous homogenate within a few min to 2 da.[4]	Marked + (mouse spleen); ± (rat spleen).
13	Spleen	Mouse	Implants to anterior chamber of eye.	+.
14	Marrow, bone	Mouse, rat	I. p. inoculation of homologous marrow within a few min to 2 da.	Marked +.
			Miscellaneous	
15	Bone	Mouse	I. p. inoculation of ground bone 1-2 hr.	+.
16	Parabiosis	Rat	Para-biotic union of normal and irradiated rats within a few hr to several da.	+.
17	Properdin	Mouse, rat	I. v. injection.	+, if any.

/1/ Animals exposed to total-body radiation. /2/ Combined penicillin and streptomycin increased survival in dog. /3/ Cross circulation. /4/ Homologous rat spleen implants or intraperitoneal injections into X-irradiated rats is far less effective than similar mouse spleen therapy in irradiated mice.

416. RADIATION BIOLOGY: GLOSSARY

ALPHA PARTICLE (α): Positively charged particle emitted by radioactive atomic nuclei; usually travelling at high speed, and having a mass number 4 and atomic number 2. ALPHA RAY (α): Stream of alpha particles. ANGSTROM (Å): A unit of length, used chiefly in expressing short wave lengths; it equals 10^{-8} cm. ATOM: Smallest particle of an element which is capable of entering into a chemical reaction. ATOMIC MASS UNIT (amu): Exactly 1/16 of the mass of a neutral atom of the most abundant isotope of oxygen, 0^{16}. One amu = 1.660×10^{-24} g = 931 mev = 0.999728 awu: ATOMIC NUMBER (Z): Number of orbital electrons in a neutral atom, or the electric charge on the nucleus of an atom, or the number of protons in the nucleus of an atom. ATOMIC WEIGHT: Relative weight of an atom compared with the weight of 1 atom of oxygen taken at 16. ATOMIC WEIGHT (chemical scale): Average weight of the atoms of an element (of isotope distribution found in nature) referred to the weight of exactly 16 for the average weight of the atoms of oxygen of isotope distribution found in fresh lake or rain water. Atomic weights on the chemical scale are expressed as atomic weight units (awu). The value may be computed from atomic weights on the physical scale by: atomic weight ÷ 1.000272. ATOMIC WEIGHT (physical scale): Weight of an atom or the average weight of a mixture of atoms of an element referred to the exact value 16 for the principal isotope of oxygen, 0^{16}. Atomic weights on the physical scale are expressed in atomic mass units (amu). They may be computed from atomic weights on the chemical scale by atomic weight x 1.000272. ATOMIC WEIGHT UNIT (awu): Exactly 1/16 of the weighted mean of the masses of the neutral atoms of oxygen of isotopic composition found in fresh lake or rain water. 1 awu = 1.660×10^{-24} g = 1.000272 amu. ATTENUATION: Term often used to indicate the decrease in number of particles as a function of thickness of the absorbing medium, and this number of particles may or may not be proportional to the dose because specific ionization changes with the velocity of the particles. BETA PARTICLE (β): Electron, negative or positive (positron), emitted from the nucleus during radioactive disintegration. (Symbols β, β⁻, β⁺ are reserved for electrons of nuclear origin.) BETA RAY (β): Stream of beta particles. COLLIMATED: Beam of radiation limited to the required dimensions. COSMIC RAYS: Ionizing rays entering the earth's atmosphere from unidentified extra-terrestrial space and resulting in the presence of photons, electrons, neutrons, protons, mesons, etc., by collisions with atoms in the atmosphere and by radioactive decay. Most penetrating of all radiations. COULOMB: Practical unit of electrical charge. CURIE (c): A unit of radioactivity defined as the quantity of any radioactive nuclide in which the number of disintegrations per second is 3.7×10^{10}. DECAY, RADIOACTIVE: The spontaneous transformation with a measurable life-time of a nuclide into one or more different nuclides. The process involves the emission from the nucleus of alpha particles, electrons, positrons, gamma rays, neutrons or the nuclear capture or ejection of orbital electrons. Rate of decay is usually expressed in terms of half-life. DEUTERIUM (H^2): The hydrogen isotope of mass number 2 (1 proton, 1 neutron, 1 electron). It has an amu of 2.01474 ± 0.00002. DEUTERON: The nucleus of deuterium (1 proton, 1 neutron). It has an amu of 2.01419 ± 0.00002. DISINTEGRATION: Process of spontaneous breakdown of a nucleus of an atom resulting in the emission of a particle and/or a photon. DOSE: A quantity of radiation as defined in the definition of the unit "roentgen." DOSE ABSORBED (any ionizing radiation): Amount of energy imparted to matter by ionizing particles per unit mass of irradiated material at the place of interest. It shall be expressed in rads (I.C.R.U., 1953). Absorbed dose rate is the absorbed dose per unit of time. DOSE, AIR (free air dose): A dose of radiation measured in air at the point of interest, or in the absence of patient (or phantom) or other object, thus excluding secondary radiation, apart from that arising from the air or associated with the source. DOSE, PERMISSIBLE: Dose of ionizing radiation (within a specified period) that, in the light of present knowledge, is not expected to cause appreciable bodily injury to a person at any time during his lifetime. DOSE, PERMISSIBLE WEEKLY: Dose of ionizing radiation accumulated in one week of such magnitude that, in the light of present knowledge, exposure at this weekly rate for an indefinite period of time is not expected to cause appreciable bodily injury to a person at any time during his lifetime. (For long-continued X- or gamma ray exposure of the whole body it is 0.3 r/wk measured in air.) DOSE RATE: Radiation dose received per unit of time.

DYNE: Unit of force capable of producing an acceleration of 1 cm/sec/sec to 1 g. ELECTROMAGNETIC UNIT (emu): Relates magnetic field to electric current. 3×10^{10} esu of charge = 10 coulombs (the practical unit of charge) = 1 emu. ELECTRON (e^- or β^-): Subatomic particle having a rest mass of $(9.1086 \pm 0.0003) \times 10^{-28}$ g, or 1/1836 x mass of a proton, and a charge of negative electricity of $(4.80294 \pm 0.00008) \times 10^{-10}$ esu. (Synonym is "negatron.") ELECTRON CAPTURE (EC): Radioactive transformation occurring when a bound electron merges with the nucleus, converting a proton to a neutron, with liberation of energy in the form of a monoenergetic neutrino plus a photon of X-ray characteristic of the new substance. It is a type of beta decay. Electron capture, identified with a literal prefix (e.g., K-electron capture), refers to capture of electrons initially in the designated atomic shell. ELECTRON VOLT (ev): Unit of energy. The change in kinetic energy of an electron when it is accelerated through a potential difference of 1 volt. One ev is equivalent to 1.602×10^{12} erg. 100 ELECTRON VOLT YIELD (100 ev yield): Yield of molecules converted or produced per 100 ev of radiant energy input. ELECTROSTATIC UNIT OF CHARGE (esu): The amount of electrical charge which, in a vacuum, will repel a like charge with a force of 1 dyne at a distance of 1 cm. FISSION, NUCLEAR: The splitting of a nucleus into more-or-less equal fragments. Fission may occur spontaneously or may be induced by capture of bombarding particles. In addition to the fission fragments, neutrons and gamma rays are usually produced during fission. GAMMA RAY (γ): Electromagnetic radiation of short wave length and correspondingly high frequency, emitted by the nucleus of an atom in the course of radioactive decay. (There is no distinction between X-ray photons and gamma ray photons of the same energy.) HALF-LIFE, RADIOACTIVE: Time taken for the amount of a radioactive nuclide to decay to half its initial value. HALF-VALUE LAYER (HVL): The thickness of a specified absorbing material which, when introduced into the path of an X-ray beam, reduces the dose rate to 1/2 its original value. Also, half-value layer is applied to that layer which reduces the number of radioactive particles, and in many cases the absorbed dose rate, to the half-value. ISOTOPE: One of several nuclides having the same number of protons in their nuclei, hence belonging to the same element and having the same atomic number Z, but differing in the number of neutrons and therefore in mass number A. KILO-ELECTRON-VOLT (kev): 1000 electron volts. KILO-ROENTGEN (kr): 1000 roentgens. KILOVOLT (kv): A unit of electrical potential equal to 1000 volts. KILOVOLT PEAK (kvp): The crest value of the potential wave in kilovolts. MASS: Quantity of matter. MASS or NUCLEON NUMBER (A): Total number of nucleons (protons and neutrons) in the nucleus of an atom or nuclide. MEGA- or MILLION ELECTRON VOLT (Mev): 1,000,000 electron volts (unit of energy equal to 1.6×10^{-6} ergs). MESON: An elementary particle having a rest mass intermediate between the mass of an electron and that of a proton. All of the known mesons are unstable and short-lived. The meson is a quantum of the nuclear field. MICROCURIE (μc): 1/1,000,000 of a curie (3.7×10^4 disintegrations per second). MICROROENTGEN (μr): 1/1,000,000 of a roentgen. MILLIAMPERE (ma): 1/1000 of an ampere. MILLICURIE (mc): 1/1000 of a curie (3.7×10^7 disintegrations per second). MILLIRAD (mrad): 1/1000 of a rad. MILLIROENTGEN (mr): 1/1000 of a roentgen. MILLIROENTGEN EQUIVALENT PHYSICAL (mrep): Amount of energy absorption in soft tissue corresponding to 0.093 ergs per gram. MOLECULE: Ultimate unit quantity of a compound which can exist by itself and retain all the properties of the original substance. NEGATRON (β^-, or e^-): A negative electron (a term sometimes used when necessary to distinguish between positive and negative electrons). NEUTRINO: A theoretical particle of very small rest mass very nearly equal to zero, emitted in beta decay and other nuclear reactions. NEUTRON (n): A nuclear particle of zero charge and mass number 1; the mass is 1.008984 ± 0.000002 amu. (Neutrons are a constituent of all nuclei except H^1.) The neutron has a mass slightly greater than that of the proton. NEUTRON, FAST: A neutron possessing high kinetic energy. NEUTRON, SLOW: A neutron slowed in passage through a scattering material. NEUTRON, THERMAL: Neutron with kinetic energy distribution comparable with the kinetic energy distribution caused by thermal agitation of the nuclei composing the medium. NUCLEON: A constituent particle of the atomic nucleus (proton, neutron). NUCLIDE: A species of atom having a specific mass number (A), atomic number (Z), and atomic mass. PHOTON: Corpuscular (quantum) manifestation of electromagnetic radiation. POSITRON (β^+, or e^+): A subatomic particle having a rest mass of $(9.1086 \pm 0.003) \times 10^{-28}$ g, and a charge of positive electricity of $(4.80294 \pm 0.00008) \times 10^{-10}$ esu; a positive electron. PROTECTIVE BARRIER: Barrier of radiation-absorbing material, such as lead, concrete, etc., used to reduce radiation hazards. PROTECTIVE BARRIER, PRIMARY: Barrier sufficient to reduce the useful beam to the maximum permissible weekly dose. PROTIUM (H^1): Hydrogen isotope of mass 1. PROTON: An elementary nuclear particle of mass 1 having a charge equal and opposite to that of an electron. The rest mass is $(1.67245 \pm 0.00005) \times 10^{-24}$ g, or 1.0076 amu. (The nucleus of H^1 is a proton; the proton is one of the constituents of every nucleus.) PULSATING POTENTIAL (or VOLTAGE): A potential (or voltage) which undergoes large periodic variations in magnitude at a frequency related to that of the main supply. QUANTUM: The smallest quantity of energy constituting a photon of electromagnetic radiation which can be associated with a given phenomenon. (Electromagnetic radiation sometimes appears to consist of waves and of particles.) QUANTUM ENERGY: Energy contained in a quantum of radiation and proportional to the frequency of the radiation waves. RAD (rad): Unit of absorbed dose; it is the energy absorption of 100 ergs/g of any medium. RADIATION: Emission and propagation of energy through space or through a material medium as (a) electromagnetic or elastic waves (X-, gamma, infrared, visible, and ultraviolet rays), and (b) by extension, corpuscular emissions such as alpha, beta, neutron and proton radiation, and mixed or unknown rays such as cosmic rays. RADIATION, BACKGROUND: Undesired radiation arising from radioactive material other than that directly under consideration, i.e., cosmic rays, natural radioactivity, insulator leakage, power-line fluctuations, etc. RADIATION HEAVY PARTICLE: Particulate ionizing radiation consisting of atomic nuclei of any mass travelling at high speed. Alpha particles or rays constitute a special kind of heavy particle radiation. RADIATION, IONIZING: Electromagnetic ionizing radiation (X- or gamma ray photons or quanta), or corpuscular radiation (alpha particles, beta particles, electrons, positrons, protons, neutrons and heavy particles) capable of producing ions directly or by secondary processes. RADIATION, LEAKAGE: In the case of X-rays all radiation, except the useful beam, coming from within the X-ray tube and tube housing. RADIATION, PRIMARY: Radiation coming directly from the source, i.e., target of the X-ray tube ("useful beam" and leakage radiation), or radioactive material (beta and gamma rays). RADIATION, SCATTERED: Radiation which, during passage through a substance, has been deviated in direction, and may also have been modified by increase in wave length (Compton effect) and have had its energy diminished. It is one form of secondary radiation. RADIATION, SECONDARY: Radiation, other than primary radiation, emitted by any matter irradiated with X-rays, gamma rays, electrons, neutrons, etc.; it may consist of X-rays, gamma rays, electrons, protons, neutrons, etc., or ultraviolet or visible radiation. RADIATION, STRAY: Radiation not serving any useful purpose. It includes leakage radiation, and secondary radiation from irradiated objects, and represents the portion of the radiation against which special protective measures have to be taken. RADIATION, USEFUL BEAM: That part of the primary and secondary radiation which passes through the aperture, cone, or other device for collimating the X-ray beam. RADIATION HAZARD: The danger to health arising from exposure to ionizing radiation. It may be caused by external radiation or by radiation from radioactive materials within the body. RADIOACTIVITY: Spontaneous disintegration of an unstable nuclide with the emission of a particle or a photon to form a different nuclide. RADIOISOTOPE: Any radioactive isotope of an element. (Also loosely used as a synonym for radionuclide.) RELATIVE BIOLOGICAL EFFECTIVENESS (RBE): The appropriate value of the biological effectiveness of the radiation in question relative to that of X-radiation with an average specific ionization of 100 ion pairs per micron of water, for the particular biological system and biological effect under consideration, and for the condition under which the radiation is received. The RBE is expressed in terms of the pertinent biological effectiveness of ordinary X-rays taken as 1. ROENTGEN (r): The quantity of X- or gamma radiation such that the associated corpuscular emission per 0.001293 g of air produces, in air, ions carrying one electrostatic unit of electricity of either sign. ROENTGEN EQUIVALENT MAN (OR MAMMAL) (rem): The absorbed dose of any ionizing radiation which has the same biological effectiveness as one rad of X-radiation with average specific ionization of 100 ion pairs per micron of water, in terms of its air equivalent, in the same region. A dose in rem is equal to the dose in rads multiplied by the RBE. ROENTGEN EQUIVALENT PHYSICAL (rep): The dose of ionizing radiation which produces energy absorption of 93 ergs per gram of soft tissue (rep is being superseded by rad). ROENTGEN RAYS: X-rays, usually produced by bombarding a metallic target with high-speed electrons in a suitable device. TELETHERAPY: Therapeutic irradiation with collimated gamma rays. TRITIUM (H^3, or T): The hydrogen isotope of mass number 3 (1 proton, 2 neutrons, 1 electron). It has an amu of 3.01695, and half-life of 12.5 yr. VOLT (v): Practical unit of electric potential, i.e., that potential difference against which 1 joule of work is done in the transfer of 1 coulomb. One volt is equivalent to 10^8 electromagnetic units of potential. X-RAY: Electromagnetic ionizing radiation which originates outside the nucleus of the atom, and results from loss of energy of charged particles, e.g., electrons. It is of shorter wave length (less than about 100 Å) than ultraviolet radiation.

Part-I: NORMALLY OCCURRING: MAN

Organism	Mouth	Ileum	Cecum	Appendix	Colon
Bacteria					
1 Aerobacter aerogenes		+	+	+	+
2 A. cloacae		+	+	+	+
3 Alcaligenes faecalis		+	+	+	+
4 Bacteroides spp		+	+	+	+
5 Clostridium alcaligenes		+	+	+	+
6 C. angulosum		+	+	+	+
7 C. bifermentans		+	+	+	+
8 C. filamentosum		+	+	+	+
9 C. perfringens		+	+	+	+
10 C. tertium		+	+	+	+
11 C. tetani		+	+	+	+
12 Dialister granuliformans	+				
13 D. pneumosintes	+				
14 Diplococcus pneumoniae	+				
15 Escherichia coli		+	+	+	+
16 E. freundii		+	+	+	+
17 Fusobacterium plautivincenti	+				
18 Gaffkya anaerobia		+	+	+	+
19 G. tetragena	+	+	+	+	+
20 Klebsiella pneumoniae	+	+	+	+	+
21 Lactobacillus spp	+	+	+	+	+
22 Micrococcus pyogenes var. albus	+	+	+	+	+
23 M. pyogenes var. aureus	+	+	+	+	+
24 Neisseria catarrhalis	+				
25 N. sicca	+				

Organism	Mouth	Ileum	Cecum	Appendix	Colon
Bacteria (concluded)					
26 Proteus mirabilis		+	+	+	+
27 P. morganii		+	+	+	+
28 P. rettgeri		+	+	+	+
29 P. vulgaris		+	+	+	+
30 Streptococcus anaerobius	+	+	+	+	+
31 S. durans		+	+	+	+
32 S. faecalis		+	+	+	+
33 S. foetidus	+	+	+	+	+
34 S. liquefaciens		+	+	+	+
35 S. mitis	+				
36 S. pyogenes	+				
37 S. salivarius	+				
38 S. zymogenes		+	+	+	+
39 Veillonella gazogenes	+				
40 V. parvula	+				
Fungi					
41 Candida albicans	+	+	+	+	+
42 C. krusei		+	+	+	+
43 C. tropicalis		+	+	+	+
44 Cryptococcus spp		+	+	+	+
45 Debaryomyces klocheri	+				
46 Geotrichum brasiliensis		+	+	+	+
47 Mycoderma pulmoneum		+	+	+	+
48 Saccharomyces spp		+	+	+	+
49 S. tumefaciens albus	+				

/1/ Bacteria and fungi are not normally present in the stomach, duodenum and jejunum.

Part II: FECAL CONTENT: MAN

Values are on a dry weight of feces basis, unless otherwise indicated; those in parentheses are ranges. Superscripts after numerical values are exponents, not footnotes.

	Species or Group of Organisms	Units	Value
1	Bacterial content, total	grams per day	8.3
2	(living and dead)	% of feces	28(20-35)
3		No./g feces[1]	$(10-80 \times 10^{10})$
4		Total no.	30×10^{12}
5	Living bacteria: aerobic agar	No./g feces	$(14 \times 10^5 - 15 \times 10^8)$
6	Living bacteria: anaerobic agar	No./g feces	$(30 \times 10^5 - 12 \times 10^8)$
7	Gram-neg. bacteria, total	% of all bact.	81(63-97)
8	Gram-neg. rods		71(55-91)
9	Gram-neg. cocci	% of all bacteria	8(1-37)
10	Gram-neg. spirilla		0.1(0-0.2)
11	Gram-neg. spirochetes		1.1(0-11)
12	Gram-pos. bacteria, total	% of all bact.	17(1-34)
13	Gram-pos. cocci	% of all bacteria	11(0.4-32)
14	Gram-pos. rods		6(1-13)
15	Gram-pos. rods with spores	% of all bacteria	0.4(0-0.8)
16	Free spores		2(0-14)
	Microbial flora, living[2]		
17	Escherichia coli[3]	No./g feces	(10^4-10^9)
18		% of gram-neg.	65
19		% of subjects[4]	93
20	Aerobacter aerogenes	% of gram-neg.	0.2
21		% of subjects[4]	47
22	Intermediates (gram-neg.)	% of gram-neg.	34.8
23	Bacilli, anaerobic[5]	No./g feces[1]	(10^6-10^{12})
24	Lactobacilli[6]	No./g feces	(10^6-10^{10})
25	Monilia	% of subjects[4]	Few in 33%
26	Other fungi	% of subjects[4]	Few in 3-29%
27	Streptococci (S. faecalis)	No./g feces	(10^2-10^7)

/1/ Wet. /2/ In addition to organisms listed, Clostridia (mainly C. perfringens and C.lentoputrescens), Micrococci, Proteus and Pseudomonas spp, and various Bacterioides are frequently found in feces. /3/ Various sero- and bio-types, transient and resident. /4/ Present in feces in this percentage of adults. /5/ Non-sporulating. /6/ Non-sporulating, including Lactobacilli and Bacteroides.

Part III: ALIMENTARY TRACT: MAMMALS AND BIRDS

Values in parentheses are ranges. Superscripts after numerical values are exponents, not footnotes. Values are on wet weight basis.

	Animal	Source of Organisms	Species or Group of Organisms	Organisms per g wet wt
1	Calf[1]	Feces	Aerobes	$(2-940 \times 10^7)$
2			Anaerobes	$(150-950 \times 10^7)$
3			Coliforms	$(2-280 \times 10^7)$
4			Enterococci	$(10-700 \times 10^3)$
5	Guinea pig[2]	Stomach	Anaerobic sporing rods	10^3
6			L. acidophilus var. caviae	(10^5-10^6)
7			Yeast-like organisms	(10^3-10^4)
8		Duodenum-jejunum	Anaerobic sporing rods	10^3
9			Enterococci	10^3
10			L. acidophilus var. caviae	(10^5-10^6)
11			Yeast-like organisms	(10^4-10^5)
12		Ileum	Anaerobic sporing rods	10^3
13			Enterococci	10^3
14			L. acidophilus var. caviae	(10^6-10^7)
15			Yeast-like organisms	(10^4-10^5)
16		Cecum	Anaerobic sporing rods	10^3
17			Enterococci	(10^3-10^7)
18			L. acidophilus var. caviae	(10^5-10^8)
19			Yeast-like organisms	(10^4-10^5)
20		Colon	Anaerobic sporing rods	10^3
21			Enterococci	(10^3-10^7)
22			L. acidophilus var. caviae	(10^5-10^8)
23			Yeast-like organisms	(10^3-10^5)
24		Rectum	Anaerobic sporing rods	10^3
25			Enterococci	(10^3-10^5)
26			L. acidophilus var. caviae	(10^6-10^7)
27			Yeast-like organisms	(10^4-10^5)
28	White rat	Pooled feces	Aerobic flora, total	$(20-95 \times 10^8)$
29			Anaerobic flora, total	$(45-200 \times 10^8)$
30			Coliform bacteria	$(25 \times 10^3-95 \times 10^6)$
31			Lactobacilli	$(6-34 \times 10^8)$
32			Spore-formers, anaerobic	$(2-85 \times 10^4)$
33	Chicken	Duodenum	Coliform bacteria	(10^3-10^7)
34			Enterococci	(10^3-10^8)
35			Lactic acid bacteria	(10^5-10^9)
36		Ileum	Coliform bacteria	(10^4-10^7)
37			Enterococci	(10^5-10^8)
38			Lactic acid bacteria	(10^6-10^{10})
39		Cecal pouch	Coliform bacteria	(10^8-10^{11})
40			Enterococci	(10^7-10^{10})
41			Lactic acid bacteria	(10^9-10^{11})
42		Colon	Coliform bacteria	(10^6-10^9)
43			Enterococci	(10^6-10^8)
44			Lactic acid bacteria	(10^8-10^{11})
45	Turkey	Cecal feces	Bacterium spp, other misc. Gram-pos. rods (L. bifidus types)	$(0.7-10 \times 10^9)$
46			Coliform types	(10^6-10^8)
47			Corynebacterium spp	$(0.2-10 \times 10^9)$
48			Enterococci	$(10^4-30 \times 10^9)$
49			Lactobacilli, facultative anaerobic (L. acidophilus types)	$(2 \times 10^5-10^8)$
50			Micrococci (Pediococcus types)[3]	$(10^6-30 \times 10^9)$
51			Streptococci, anaerobic	(10^6-10^8)

/1/ Values are per gram dry weight of samples from calves 1-12 weeks old. /2/ Results with 4 different diets or under starvation conditions.
/3/ Aerobic and faculative anaerobic.

Organisms listed are only those which have been given scientific names, plus unnamed organisms appearing frequently in current literature. They account for only a few of the numerous bacteria that can be isolated from rumen fluid, and do not include many of the important fiber digesters.

	Organism	No. per ml of Rumen Contents	Morphology	Oxygen Relations	Principal End Products of Fermentation	Possible Role in the Rumen
1	Bacteroides succinogenes	$4 \times 10^7 - 4 \times 10^8$	Gram-neg., non-motile, slightly curved, small rods with pointed ends on cellulose agar.[1]	Anaerobic.	Acetic and succinic acids, and uptake of CO_2 from cellulose.	Vigorous cellulose digesters.
2	Borrelia sp	to 10^8	Gram-neg., small, slender, irregular coiled spirochete with pointed end. Not double contoured.	Anaerobic.	Acetic and succinic acids, with smaller amounts of CO_2, ethanol, formic and lactic acids from glucose.	Fermenter of readily available carbohydrates such as hydrolytic products of starch and cellulose.
3	Butyrivibrio fibrisolvens[2]	to 5×10^8	Gram-neg., curved, anaerobic rods with monotrichous flagella.	Anaerobic.	CO_2, H_2, and butyric, lactic and formic acids from glucose. Acetic acid produced or used.	Fermenter of fiber and readily available carbohydrates.
4	"Cellulolytic cocci"[3]	$10^8 - 4 \times 10^8$	Gram-pos. to gram-neg., iodophilic cocci; diplococci to long chains.	Anaerobic.	CO_2, H_2, ethanol, lactic, acetic, formic, succinic acids from cellulose (Hungate). Acetic, formic and succinic acids (Sijpesteijn).	Vigorous digesters of cellulose and xylan.
5	Escherichia coli[4]	to 10^6	Small, gram-neg. rods.	Facultative anaerobe.	Lactic, acetic, formic, succinic acids, ethanol, CO_2 and H_2 from glucose.	Possibly none.
6	Lachnospira multiparus	to 10^8	Weakly gram-pos., curved rods with monotrichous flagella.	Anaerobic.	CO_2, H_2, ethanol and acetic, formic and lactic acids.	Fermenter of readily available carbohydrates.
7	Anaerobic lactobacilli[5]	to 10^9	Gram-pos. rods of various sizes and shapes, including branched rods.	Anaerobic; some revert to facultative anaerobes.	Lactic acid from glucose.	Fermenters of readily available carbohydrates.
8	Lactobacillus brevis[6]	to 3×10^6	Gram-pos. rods with rounded ends; short in length to long filaments.	Facultative anaerobe.	Lactic acid from glucose.	Fermenter of readily available carbohydrates.
9	LC[7]	to 10^9	Gram-variable large diplococci.	Anaerobic.	CO_2, H_2, acetic, butyric, caproic, and small amount of propionic and valeric acids from glucose.	Fermenter of lactate, readily available carbohydrates and amino acids.
10	Propionibacterium acnes[8]	$2 \times 10^5 - 7 \times 10^9$	Gram-pos., short rods, metachromatic granules, some branching and longer under acid conditions.	Prefer anaerobic conditions.	Acetic and propionic acids and CO_2 from glucose or lactate.	Fermenter of lactate and readily available carbohydrates; also proteolysis.
11	Sarcina bakeri	to 1.4×10^6	Large, gram-neg. cocci in pairs, tetrods and larger groups.	Facultative anaerobe.		
12	Selenomonas ruminantum[9]	to 10^8	Gram-neg., large, crescentic rods; tuft of flagella usually attached to concave side of cell.	Anaerobic.	Propionic, acetic and lactic acids from glucose. Propionic and acetic acids from lactate.	Fermenter of readily available carbohydrates. Some strains ferment lactate.
13	Streptococcus bovis[10]	$10^5 - 6 \times 10^9$	Gram-pos. cocci in pairs; occasionally short chains.	Facultative anaerobe.	Lactic acid from glucose.	Active starch hydrolyzer; fermenter of readily available carbohydrates.
14	Succinivibrio dextrinosolvens[11]	to 10^9	Gram-neg., curved rods with monotrichous flagella.	Anaerobic.	Succinic and acetic acids from glucose.	Fermenter of the hydrolytic products of starch and other readily available carbohydrates.
15	Veillonella gasogenes	to 10^5	Gram-neg. to gram-variable masses of cocci.	Anaerobic.	Acetic and propionic acids, CO_2 and H_2 from lactate.	Fermenter of lactate and other organic acids and purines.

/1/ In sugar media, organisms may be larger, swollen, and exhibit bipolar staining. /2/ Similar to RO-H types of Huhtanen and Gall. /3/ A heterogeneous group requiring more study before species are designated. /4/ In large numbers only in sheep and very young calves. /5/ Predominantly in young calves and mature ruminants on rations with large amounts of readily available carbohydrates. /6/ These organisms have been isolated only from calves. /7/ Similar to RO-C8 of Huhtanen and Gall. /8/ Similar to RO-C1 of Huhtanen and Gall. /9/ Includes RO-HD types of Huhtanen and Gall. /10/ In large numbers only in animals receiving large amounts of readily available carbohydrates. /11/ Present in large numbers only in animals fed high grain ration.

Part I: DISEASE VECTORS

Unless otherwise indicated in the right-hand column ("Relationship"), infection or infestation is transmitted to man when bitten by the arthropod vector or host.

	Vector	Etiologic Agent	Disease or Infestation	Arthropod-Pathogen-Infection Relationship
			Crustacea (Crabs, Lobsters)	
1	Crabs and crayfish, fresh-water	Paragonimus westermani.	Paragonimiasis (pulmonary distomiasis, endemic hemoptysis).	Second intermediate host (snail first intermediate host); no multiplication of pathogen; man infested by ingestion of inadequately cooked host.
2	Flea, water (Cyclops spp)	Diphyllobothrium (subgenus Spirometra).	Sparganosis.	First intermediate host; no multiplication of pathogen; man infested by swallowing host Cyclops.
3	Flea, water (Cyclops, Diaptomus spp)	D. latum.	Diphyllobothriasis (fish tapeworm).	First intermediate host; no multiplication of pathogen; man infested by swallowing infested fish.
4	Flea, water (Cyclops spp).	Dracunculus medinensis.	Dracontiasis (Medina worm).	First intermediate host; no multiplication of pathogen; man infested by swallowing host Cyclops.
			Diplopoda (Millipedes)	
5	Fontaria virginiensis	Hymenolepis diminuta[1].	Rat tapeworm.	Pathogen develops from embryo to larva in arthropod hemocoel; definitive host infested by swallowing adult arthropod host.
6	Julus sp			
			Arachnida (Mites and Ticks)	
7	Mite, mouse (Allodermanyssus sanguineus)	Rickettsia akari.	Rickettsial pox.	Pathogen multiplies in mite; congenital transmission not demonstrated.
8	Mite, oribatid (Oribatidae)	Bertiella studeri, Inermicapsifer arvicanthidis.	Anoplocephaline tapeworm.	Pathogen matures from embryo to larva, without multiplication, in mite hemocoel. Man infested by swallowing host.
9	Mite, rat (Bdellonyssus bacoti)	Rickettsia typhi.	Murine typhus fever (experimental)	Pathogen multiplies in mite gut; experimental animal infected by mite bite.[2]
10	Mite, red chigger (Trombicula spp)	Rickettsia tsutsugamushi.	Scrub typhus (Japanese river fever).	Congenitally transmitted in mite.
11	Tick (Amblyomma spp, Dermacentor spp, Haemaphysalis spp, Hyalomma sp, Ornithodoros spp, Rhipicephalus spp)	Rickettsia australis, R. conori, R. rickettsi.	Spotted fever.	Pathogen multiplies in wall of tick midgut; congenitally transmitted in tick.
12	Tick (Amblyomma americanum, Dermacentor spp); many other ticks	Pasteurella tularensis.	Tularemia.	Pathogen multiplies in tick gut and hemocoel; congenitally transmitted in some ticks.
13	Tick (Dermacentor andersoni, Haemaphysalis humerosa, Rhipicephalus sanguineus)	Coxiella burneti.	Q fever[3], Rocky Mt. spotted fever, tularemia.	Pathogen multiplies in wall of tick midgut.
14	Tick (Ornithodoros spp)	Borrelia spp.	Enzootic-endemic relapsing fever.	Pathogen multiplies in tissues of tick outside gut.
			Insecta (True Insects)[4]	
15	Bug, cone nose (Panstrongylus, Triatoma spp)	Trypanosoma cruzi.	Chagas' disease.	Pathogen multiplies in bug midgut; infection by fresh bug feces in contact with mucous membranes or scarified skin.
16	Flea, cat (Ctenocephalides felis)			Pathogen develops from embryo to larva in flea hemocoel; swallowing flea causes infestation.
17	Flea, dog (C. canis)	Dipylidium caninum.	Dog tapeworm.	
18	Flea, human (Pulex irritans)			
19	Flea, rodent (Xenopsylla cheopis and egg); other rat fleas	Hymenolepis diminuta[1].	Rat tapeworm	Pathogen develops from embryo to larva in flea hemocoel; swallowing flea causes infection.
20	Flea (X. cheopis, possibly Pulex irritans)	Pasteurella pestis.	Plague.	Pathogen multiplies in flea gut.
21	Flea (X. cheopis); occasionally other fleas	Rickettsia typhi.	Murine typhus fever.	Pathogen multiplies in flea midgut epithelium; man infected by flea feces or crushed flea rubbed into skin.
22	Fly, horse (Chrysops, Tabanus spp)	Pasteurella tularensis.	Tularemia.	Mechanical transmission from mouth parts of fly to man (usually via food).
23	Fly, house (Musca domestica); and other spp of Muscidae	Salmonella typhosa, S. paratyphi A, other Salmonella and Shigella spp, Vibrio cholerae, other enteric diseases.	Typhoid and paratyphoid fevers, dysenteries, cholera.	Mechanical "filth-borne" transmission by setae, feet, regurgitation and defecation into food or drinking water.
24	Fly, mango (Chrysops spp)	Loa loa.	Loaiasis (filariasis).	Pathogen matures from embryo to larva without multiplication in fly tissues.
25		Bartonella bacilliformis.	Bartonellosis (Carrion's disease, Verruga peruana).	Pathogen multiplies in fly midgut.
26	Fly, sand (Phlebotomus spp)	Charon sp.	Sand-fly fever.	Pathogen multiplies in fly tissues.
27		Leishmania donovani, L. tropica, L. brasiliensis.	Visceral and cutaneous leishmaniasis, mucocutaneous leishmaniasis.	Pathogen multiplies in fly midgut.
28	Fly, tsetse (Glossina spp)	Trypanosoma gambiense, T. rhodesiense.	African trypanosomiasis.	Pathogen multiplies in midgut and salivary glands of fly.
29	Gnat (Culicoides spp)	Acanthocheilonema perstans, A. streptocerca, Mansonella ozzardi.	Acanthocheilonematiasis, Ozzard's filariasis.	Pathogen matures from embryo to larva, without multiplication in gnat tissues.
30	Gnat (Simulium spp); black flies, buffalo flies, coffee flies	Onchocerca volvulus.	Onchocerciasis (filariasis).	
31	Gnat, eye (Hippelates pusio)	Various bacteria, etc.	Conjunctivitis, pink eye.	Mechanical transmission.

/1/ Hymenolepis diminuta not commonly regarded as pathogenic to man. /2/ Reported experimental transmission not confirmed, nor has rat mite ever been shown to transmit murine typhus to man. /3/ Ticks of negligible or no significance in actual transmission of Q fever in the United States, the usual mode of transmission being via the respiratory route. /4/ The ear wig (Anisolabis annulipes), dung beetles (many spp), roaches (Blattella and Periplaneta spp), and moth larvae (a few spp) are not included in the table, as they either transmit pathogens to man so rarely as to be medical curiosities, or they transmit parasites not generally regarded as pathogenic to man. /5/ Human infestation with the dog tapeworm in this manner extremely rare.

Part I: DISEASE VECTORS (Concluded)

Unless otherwise indicated in the right-hand column ("Relationship"), infection or infestation is transmitted to man when bitten by the arthropod vector or host.

	Vector	Etiologic Agent	Disease or Infestation	Arthropod-Pathogen-Infection Relationship
			Insecta (True Insecta)[4] (concluded)	
32	Louse, body (Pediculus humanus)	Rickettsia prowazeki.	Epidemic typhus fever.	Pathogen multiplies in epithelium of louse midgut; man infected by feces, or crushing on skin.
33		Rickettsia quintana.	Trench fever.	Pathogen probably multiplies in lumen of louse midgut; man infected by feces, or crushing on skin.
34		Borrelia recurrentis.	Epidemic relapsing fever.	Pathogen multiplies in tissues of louse outside gut; man infected by crushing on skin.
35	Louse, dog (Trichodectes canis)	Dipylidium caninum.	Dog tapeworm.	Pathogen develops from embryo to larva, without multiplication in louse hemocoel; man possibly infested by swallowing louse.[5]
36	Mosquito (Aedes spp)	Charon evagatus.	Yellow fever.	Pathogen multiplies in mosquito tissues.
37	Mosquito (Aedes spp, Armigeres obturans)	Dengue virus.	Dengue.	
38	Mosquito (Aedes spp, Culex spp, Mansonia titillans)	Erro spp.	Certain encephalitides.	
39	Mosquito (Anopheles spp)	Plasmodium falciparum, P. malariae, P. ovale, P. vivax.	Malaria fever.	Pathogen completes sexual cycle, then multiplies by sporogony in mosquito.
40	Mosquito (Anopheles spp, Aedes spp, Culex spp)	Wuchereria bancrofti.	Bancroft's filariasis.	Pathogen matures from embryo to larva without multiplication in mosquito tissues.
41	Mosquito (Anopheles spp, Mansonia spp)	Wuchereria malayi.	Malayan filariasis.	

/4/ The earwig (Anisolabis annulipes), dung beetles (many spp), roaches (Blattella and Periplaneta spp), and moth larvae (a few spp) are not included in the table, as they either transmit pathogens to man so rarely as to be medical curiosities, or they transmit parasites not generally regarded as pathogenic to man.   /5/ Human infestation with the dog tapeworm in this manner extremely rare.

Part II: AGENTS OF DIRECT INJURY

	Arthropod	Geographical Distribution	Reservoir or Source	Injury
			Chilopoda (Centipedes)	
1	Centipede (Scolopendra spp)	World-wide.	Hidden under various objects.	Envenomization.
			Arachnida (Mites, Ticks, Scorpions, Spiders)	
2	Mite, follicle (Demodex folliculorum)[1]		Mammals.	Mild prurits; follicular mange.
3	Mite, cheese (Tyroglyphus spp)		Cheese, grain, cereals, fruits.	Dermatitis.
4	Mite, grain (Glyciphagus spp)			Intestinal acariasis, grocer's itch, tropical eosinophilia, dermatitis.
5	Mite, grain itch (Pyemotes ventricosus)	World-wide.	Grain, seeds, straw.	Dermatitis, prurits.
6	Mite, harvest, or chigger (Eutrombicula spp)		Weeds, grass, scrub.	Dermatitis, sucking of tissue fluids, allergy to arthropod saliva.
7	Mite, itch (Sarcoptes scabiei)		Man.	Sarcoptic acariasis, scabies.
8	Scorpion (Centruroides, Buthus, Tityus spp)	Tropics.	Under well-protected objects.	Envenomization.
9	Spider, black widow (Latrodectus mactans, other spp)	World-wide.	Protected dark places, latrines.	Arachnidism, envenomization.
10	Tick (Dermacentor, Ornithodoros, Ixodes spp)	N. America, Africa, Europe.	Mammals.	Tick paralysis, poisons in tick saliva. Vector organisms causing Rocky Mt. spotted fever.
			Pentastomida (Tongueworms)	
11	Worm, tongue (Armillifer, Linguatula, Porocephalus spp)	World-wide.	Reptiles, birds, mammals.	Linguatulosis, porocephaliasis, endoparasites of mouth, throat, lung.
			Insecta (True Insects)[2]	
12	Ant (Solenopsis)		Hives, nests.	Envenomization.
13	Bedbug (Cimex spp)	World-wide.	Dwellings, public conveyances.	Bites, allergic reactions to saliva of bedbug.
14	Botfly (Gasterophilus spp) larva		Horse.	Irritation of skin, mucous membranes, eyes.
15	Botfly, human (Dermatobia hominis), larva	S. America, W. Indies, tropical N. America.	Forests (eggs transported by certain mosquitoes, ticks, assassin bugs).	Burrows into exposed skin, causes painful furuncular skin lesions.
16	Botfly, sheep (Oestrus ovis), larva	World-wide.	Sheep.	Inflammation of eyes, nose, mouth, ears, sinuses; skin lesions.
17	Bug, assassin (Reduvius, Rasahus spp)	N. and S. America.	On plants, lights, house walls, under rocks.	Stinging bites, allergic reactions to saliva of bug.
18	Bug, conenose (Panstrongylus, Triatoma, Rhodnius spp)	World-wide.	Dwellings, dark hiding places, rodent harborages.	Allergic reactions to saliva of bug.
19	Chigoe or jigger, sand flea (Tunga penetrans)	S. America, W. Indies, Africa.	Homes, buildings, dwellings.	Cutaneous invasion, infection.
20	Flea, cat and dog (Ctenocephalides felis, C. canis)		Breeding areas or mammalian hosts.	Severe bites, allergic reactions, extreme annoyance.
21	Flea, human (Pulex irritans)			Vector of organisms causing epidemic typhus.
22	Flea, rat (Xenopsylla spp)			
23	Fly, black (Simulium spp)	World-wide.	Breeding areas.	Bites, allergic reactions.
24	Fly, deer (Chrysops spp), adult		Mammalian hosts.	Severe bites, allergic reactions, extreme annoyance.
25	Fly, heel, or cattle grub (Hypoderma spp), larva		Cattle.	Cutaneous or ocular invasion, furuncular lesions, pain, inflammation.
26	Fly, horse (Tabanus spp), adult		Mammalian hosts.	Severe bites, allergic reactions.
27	Fly, primary screwworm (Callitroga hominivoras), larva	W. Hemisphere (tropical, subtropical areas).	Adults: manure, meat, serous exudates; maggots: clean flesh.	Painful lesions of sinuses, ears, nose, anus, skin.

/1/ Now believed to be of little importance in man.   /2/ Includes blister beetles and caterpillars of the genus Megalopyge which have stinging hairs.

Part II: AGENTS OF DIRECT INJURY (Concluded)

	Vector	Geographical Distribution	Reservoir or Source	Injury
			Insects (True Insects)[2] (concluded)	
28	Fly, tumbu (Cordylobia anthropophaga), larva	Arica.	Dog, rat.	Cutaneous invasion, furuncular lesions, myiasis.
29	Fly (Wohlfahrtia spp)[3], larva	World-wide.	Various mammals.	Larvae penetrate tender areas of unbroken skin causing inflammation, furuncles.
30	Gadfly, Russian (Rhinoestrus purpureus), larva	N. Europe, Asia.	Host organisms.	Inflammation of eyes, nose, mouth, ears, sinuses and and skin by tissue penetration.
31	Honey-bee (Apis mellifera), wasp (Vespula spp); other bees		Hives, nests, flowers, tunnels.	Envenomization; allergy.
32	Louse, body (Pediculus humanus)	World-wide.		Pediculosis, skin irritation.
33	Louse, pubic or "crab" (Phthirus pubis)		Man.	Pediculosis, skin irritation.
34	Maggot, Congo floor (Auchmeromyia luteola)	Africa.	Shady places, native huts.	Blood loss from bloodsucking larvae.
35	Mosquitoes (several genera)			Severe bites, secondary infections, allergic reactions. Vectors of organisms causing dengue, malaria and yellow fever.
36	Punkies (Culicoides spp)	World-wide.	Water, moist places.	Skin bites, eye irritation.

/2/ Includes blister beetles and caterpillars of the genus Megalopyge which have stinging hairs. /3/ A "flesh fly" of the order Sarcophagidae (Sarcophaga, Wohlfahrtia).

420. SELECTED ARTHROPOD PARASITES: MAMMALS, BIRDS
Many of the arthropods listed are known to be parasites of man. Some of these are identified by an asterisk (*).

	Arthropod	Geographic Distribution	Location, Free Stage	Host	Location in Host	Effect on Host
				Arachnida (Mites, Ticks)		
1	Chigger (Eutrombicula alfreddugesi)	N. and S. America, West Indies.	Active forms, in grasses, shrubs, brambles.	Domestic and wild vertebrates.		Injection and toxins, sometimes death (small poultry); larvae are bloodsuckers.
2	Mite, chicken (Dermanyssus gallinae)		Eggs, non-feeding larvae, nymphs, adults in crevices of coops, roosts.	Poultry, other birds.	External	Decreased egg production, retarded growth, anemia, sometimes death. Vector of organisms causing spirochetosis, fowl cholera. Larvae, nymphs, adults bloodsuckers; nocturnal feeders only.
3	Mite, dog follicle (Demodex canis)	World-wide.		Dog.	Eggs, nymphs, adults in hair follicles and sebaceous glands.	Follicle inflammation; mange; thickened skin, alopecia, emaciation, sometimes death.
4	Mite, ear (Otodectes cyanotis)		None.	Dog, cat, ferret.	All stages in ears; sometimes external.	Inflammation, ear scabs, head-shaking, scratching, droopy ears with discharge; epileptiform fits (severe cases).
5	Mite, itch (Sarcoptes scabiei)*			Most mammals, sheep (on head).	External; all active stages in skin tunnels.	Scratching, papules, vesicles, keratinization, alopecia, mange, emaciation, sometimes death.
6	Mite, northern fowl- (Bdellonyssus sylviarum)	United States, Canada, Mexico, Europe, S. Africa.	Eggs on feathers, in nests; other stages on surroundings.	Poultry, wild birds.	External; on body and feathers.	Skin lesions, egg reduction, retarded growth, anemia. Harbors neurotropic viruses. Larvae, nymphs, adults bloodsuckers.
7	Mite, scab (Psoroptes equi v. ovis)		None.	Sheep (other varieties on various domestic animals).	External; all active stages on skin around edge of lesions.	Scabbing; wool loss from biting, scratching; emaciation, sometimes death.
8	Mite, scaly leg (Knemidokoptes mutans)	World-wide.		Chicken, turkey, other domestic birds.	External; all active stages in tunnels between scales of feet, legs, neck, comb.	Inflammation, keratinization between scales, feet, legs; lameness.
9	Tick, American dog- (Dermacentor variabilis)	N. America.	Eggs on soil; unfed larvae, nymphs, adults on vegetation until host is found.	Principally dog; other domestic and wild animals. mainly attack rodents and other small animals.	External; on host only, while feeding. Larvae, nymphs	Skin damage. Vector of organisms causing bovine anaplasmosis, tularemia, Rocky Mt. spotted fever. Larvae, nymphs, adults bloodsuckers.
10	Tick, black-legged (Ixodes ricinus scapularis)	Europe, some other countries.	Eggs on soil; larvae, nymphs, adults on grass and shrubbery until host is found.	Principally dog; other domestic and wild animals.	External; adults on head, neck of dog; on flank, leg, under tail of other animals. On host only while feeding.	Anemia. Vector of cattle red water fever, louping-ill virus, tick-borne fever virus of sheep. Larvae, nymphs blood suckers in ear, eyelid, head, rarely body.
11	Tick, brown dog- (Rhipicephalus sanguineus)*	World-wide.	Active forms near habitat of dog.	Dog mainly; occasionally other animals.	External. ness. Larvae, nymphs, adults bloodsuckers.	Vector of organisms causing canine piroplasmosis, cattle gall sickness. Larvae, nymphs, adults bloodsuckers.
12	Tick, cattle (Boophilus annulatus)*	N. America.	Eggs on soil; unfed larvae on grass.	Principally ungulates; other animals.	External.	Damage to hide; reduction of milk output. Vector of organisms causing Texas cattle fever. Larvae, nymphs, adults blood suckers.
13	Tick, ear (Otobius megnini)*	United States, Mexico, S. America, S. Africa.	Eggs on ground, in cracks; adults and unattached larvae in out-buildings.	Domestic animals.	Inside ears.	Ear inflammation, anorexia, dullness, sometimes death. Larvae, nymphs bloodsuckers.

420. SELECTED ARTHROPOD PARASITES: MAMMALS, BIRDS (Continued)

Many of the arthropods listed are known to be parasites of man. Some of these are identified by an asterisk (*).

	Arthropod	Geographic Distribution	Location, Free Stage	Host	Location in Host	Effect on Host
				Arachnida (Mites, Ticks) (concluded)		
14	Tick, fowl (Argas persicus)	Warm and temperate semi-arid regions of world.	All stages in crevices, cracks of housing and under bark of trees.	Domestic fowl; occasionally wild birds.	External; on host only while feeding.	Anemia, leg weakness, egg reduction, occasionally death. Vector of organisms causing fowl spirochaetosis, spiroplasmosis. Nymphs, adults bloodsuckers.
15	Tick, lone star (Amblyomma americanum)*	North, Central, and South America.	Eggs in soil; unfed larvae, nymphs, adults on grass.	Cattle, dog, horse, goat, sheep; occasionally birds.	External; on host only while feeding.	Damage to hide; milk reduction. Vector of organisms causing Rocky Mt. spotted fever, Q fever. Larvae, nymphs, adults bloodsuckers.
16	Tick, Rocky Mountain wood- (Dermacentor andersoni)*	Western N. America.	Eggs on soil.	Most mammals.	External; larvae, nymphs on most small animals; adults usually on larger animals during feeding periods.	Paralysis, particularly in sheep. Vector of organisms causing Rocky Mt. spotted fever, tularemia, equine encephalomyelitis, anaplasmosis. Larvae, nymphs, adults bloodsuckers.
				Pentastomida (Tongueworms)		
17	Worm, tongue (Linguatula serrata)	World-wide.	Eggs swallowed, hatched in alimentary tract of herbivores; larvae, nymphs develop in mesenteries.	Mammals, birds, reptiles.	Eggs expelled in respiratory tract; adults in nasal passages.	Severe irritation and blocking of nasal passages.
				Insecta (True Insects)		
18	Bedbug (Cimex lectularius)*		All stages in cracks, crevices, similar hiding places.	Domestic animals, poultry.	External.	Nymphs, adults bloodsuckers; irritate skin, cause welts.
19	Blowfly, black (Phormia regina)[1]	World-wide.	Pupae in soil; adults in pastures.	Sheep, other mammals.	Eggs in hair or wool; larvae in wounds; eggs and larvae also in carcasses.	Extension and infection of wounds, marring of wool, emaciation.
20	Botfly, horse (Gasterophilus intestinalis)[2]		Pupae in soil; adults attack animals only in daytime.	Ass, horse, mule, rarely other animals.	Eggs on foreleg fetlock hairs, larvae (maggots) in mouth, pharynx, stomach.	Extension and infection of wounds.
21	Botfly, human (Dermatobia hominis)*	S. America, West Indies, tropical N. America.	Eggs glued to other arthropods, and hatch when reach suitable host.	Dog, swine, mule, cattle, wild animals.	Larvae leave transport arthropod on contact with host; penetrate skin.	Boil-like skin lesions; reduced milk production, damage to hide; decreased growth rate.
22	Botfly, sheep (Oestrus ovis)		Pupae on ground; adults in warm corners, crevices.	Sheep, rarely goat.	Larvae in nasal cavities, sinuses.	Mucosal irritation, nasal discharge, emaciation, sometimes death.
23	Bug, cone nose (Triatoma sanguisuga)[3]	World-wide.	All stages commonly found in or close to rodent nests or habitats.	All domestic animals, poultry; wood rat normal host.		Nymphs and adults bloodsuckers, cause swelling, anemia.
24	Flea, cat (Ctenocephalides felis)*		Immature forms associated with nest or sleeping area of host; adults on ground part of time.	Cat, dog, other animals.	External	Coat damaged from biting, scratching. C. canis and C. felis vectors of dog- and dwarf tapeworms, heart-worm, plague, epidemic typhus. Adults are bloodsuckers.
25	Flea, dog (C. canis)					
26	Flea, human (Pulex irritans)*			Dog, swine, other animals.		
27	Flea, sticktight (Echidnophaga gallinacea)*	World-wide, especially warm climates.	Immature forms associated with nest or sleeping area of host.	Poultry, domestic animals, rodents.	External; skin, comb, wattles, around eyes and ears.	Anemia, sometimes death. Adults are bloodsuckers.
28	Fly, black (Simulium spp)[4]	World-wide in temperate to subarctic climates.	Immature forms on under sides of stones in moderate running streams.	All warm-blooded animals.	External; on bare parts of head, body, legs, under wings.	Vesicles, red swelling, anemia, toxemia, death. S. occidentale and S. slossonae are vectors of turkey leucocytozoan disease; some spp are vectors of onchocerciasis of man and cattle. Adults bloodsuckers.
29	Fly, black horse- (Tabanus atratus)	N. America.	Immature forms in leaves and mud in and near streams, ponds.	Most warm-blooded animals.	External.	Adults bloodsuckers during day; vector of organisms causing anaplasmosis.
30	Fly, deer (Chrysops discalis)	Western N. America.	Eggs near water; larvae in water; pupae in mud.	Principally horse, cattle.	External, mainly on underside of abdomen, neck, withers.	Vector of tularemia, surra. Adults bloodsuckers.
31	Fly, flesh (Wohlfahrtia vigil)*	N. America.	Pupae on ground; larvae in woods.	Rabbit, mink, guinea pig, young of domestic and wild animals.	Larvae in wounds.	Mild to extensive subcutaneous pustular lesions; occasionally death.
32	Fly, greenbottle (Phaenicia sericata)	World-wide, except S. America and Pacific Islands.	Adults free-living; deposit eggs on flesh, soiled wool; pupae in soil.	Sheep, goat, other animals.	Larvae on skin, in wounds.	Invasion of wounds, suppuration.
33	Fly, horn (Siphona irritans)	Europe, America.	Eggs, maggots in fresh dung; pupae in dung or soil.	Cattle, other animals.	External.	Weight loss; milk reduction. Adults bloodsuckers.
34	Fly, house (Musca domestica)	World-wide.	Immature forms in manure and decayed matter; adults in buildings.	Any larger animal with lesions or secretions.	External; adults accidently ingested by host.	Adults cause decreased productivity of livestock. Vector of several tapeworm species, mechanical vector of many bacterial and protozoan pathogens and helminth eggs.

/1/ The blowfly (Chrysomyia chloropyga) of Africa is similar to the black blowfly in its parasitism of sheep. /2/ The nose botfly (Gasterophilus haemorrhoidalis) and throat botfly (G. nasalis) are similar in many respects to the horse botfly. /3/ Sixteen spp of Triatoma found in Western Hemisphere, some of which are as important and as widely distributed as T. sanguisuga. /4/ Other Simulium spp that are important blackfly pests of livestock are S. articum, S. occidentale, S. ornatum, S. vittalum.

Many of the arthropods listed are known to be parasites of man. Some of these are identified by an asterisk (*).

	Arthropod	Geographic Distribution	Location, Free Stage	Host	Location in Host	Effect on Host
			Insecta (True Insects) (concluded)			
35	Fly, louse or tick; ked (Hippobosca equina, Melophagus ovinus)	Most parts of world.	Larvae retained in female until mature; pupae on wool and feathers.	Horse, cattle, dog, sheep and birds, occasionally goat.	External; pupae attached to wool or feathers.	Anemia; wool stained, damaged from rubbing. Adults bloodsuckers. H. equina is mechanical vector of anthrax.
36	Fly, primary screw-worm (Callitroga hominivorax)*[5]	W. Hemisphere (tropical, sub-tropical areas).	Pupae in soil; adults in pastures.	Obligatory parasite of warm-blooded animals including livestock, wild mammals, dog, cat.	Eggs deposited on edges of wounds.	Infect, extend wounds, prevent healing, invariably kill untreated host.
37	Fly, sand (Phlebotomus papatasii)*	Mediterranean region, southern Europe, Asia.	Immature forms in dark moist places, manure.	Warm-blooded animals.		Swelling at site of bite; vector of organisms causing pappataci fever. Adults nocturnal bloodsuckers.
38	Fly, stable (Stomoxys calcitrans)*	World-wide.	Immature forms in manure and other moist organic waste.	Most mammals and birds.	External.	Weight loss; milk reduction. Vector of poultry tapeworms, filariae, spiruoids; mechanical vector of surra. Adults bloodsuckers.
39	Fly, tsetse (Glossina morsitans)*	Central Africa.	Larvae pass from female when ready to pupate in soil.	Cattle, other animals.		Vector of organisms causing cattle and horse nangana, sleeping sickness to man. Adults bloodsuckers.
40	Grub, common cattle- (Hypoderma lineatum)	Prevalent in America, Europe, India, N. Asia.	Pupae in soil; adults in pastures.	Cattle, rarely horse.	Eggs on hair of legs, body; larger larvae form tumor under skin of back.	Skin perforation, hide and flesh damage, milk reduction.
41	Grub, northern cattle- (H. bovis)					
42	Louse, cattle biting (Bovicola bovis)	N. America.		Cattle.	External; eggs hairs; nymphs, adults feed on skin.	Reduced vigor, weight gains; irritation, scaly skin.
43	Louse, chicken body- (Menacanthus stramineus)	World-wide.		All domestic fowl.	External; nymphs, adults on skin around vent; eggs attached to feathers.	Scabbing of skin, wasting; loss in egg production.
44	Louse, chicken head- (Cuclotogaster heterographus)			Chicken, partridge.	External; nymphs, adults on skin and feathers of head, neck; eggs on feathers.	Unthriftiness.
45	Louse, dog biting (Trichodectes canis)	N. America.	None.	Dog.	External; eggs on hair; nymphs and adults feed on skin.	Scaly skin from rubbing, scratching.
46	Louse, hog (Haematopinus suis)			Swine.	External; eggs on hair.	Dermatitis, skin sores, retarded growth. Nymphs, adults bloodsuckers. Vector of organisms causing swine pox.
47	Louse, shaft (Menopon gallinae)	World-wide.		Chicken, duck, pigeon, turkey.	External; eggs, nymphs, adults feed on scales, scabs, feathers.	Scaling and scabbing.
48	Louse, short-nosed cattle- (Haematopinus eurysternus)[6]			Cattle.	External; eggs on shaft or at base of hairs.	Hair damage from rubbing; stunting; reduction of milk output. Nymphs, adults bloodsuckers.
49	Mosquito (Aedes dorsalis)*	N. America, Europe, northern Africa.	Immature forms in moist soil; eggs survive long periods of drying in soil.	Warm-blooded animals.	External.	Adult females bloodsuckers. Vector of organisms causing equine encephalomyelitis.
50	Mosquito (Anopheles puncti pennis)*	N. America.	Immature forms in streams, ponds of hilly country.		External, where hair or feathers are thinnest.	A. punctipennis is vector of organisms causing dog heartworm. C. quinquefasciatus is vector of organisms causing avian malaria, fowl pox. Adult females bloodsuckers.
51	Mosquito, southern house- (Culex quinquefasciatus)*	World-wide from 60°N to 50°S latitudes.	Immature forms in stagnant water, ponds and ditches.	Warm-blooded animals, especially birds.		

/5/ Adult stage of the secondary screwworm fly (C. macellaria) resembles the primary screwworm fly in appearance, but differs from the latter in being a secondary invader (facultative parasite), and breeding in carcasses; the larvae occasionally infest wool or necrotic wounds. /6/ Also applies to the long-nosed cattle louse (Linognathus vituli).

421. SELECTED ARTHROPOD PESTS: PLANTS AND PLANT PRODUCTS

Destructive stages of arthropods are indicated by the following symbols associated with the arthropod nomenclature: [A] = adult; [I] = immature; [N] = nymph; [L] = larva. Control measures, described in footnotes, should be used with great caution as many of these pesticides are extremely hazardous.

	Arthropod	General Distribution	Host	Destructive Activity
			Crustacea	
1	Sowbug or pillbug (Porcellio laevis), [A, I]	World-wide.	Vegetables, ornamentals.	Chews roots, growths near ground.[1]
2	Sowbug (Cylisticus convexus), [A, I]		Greenhouse seedlings.	Chews tender roots.[2]
			Arachnida	
3	Mite, bulb (Rhizoglyphus echinopus), [A, I]	N. America, Europe, Asia.	Ornamental bulbs, onion.	Bores into bulbs.
4	Mite, clover (Bryobia praetosia), [A, I]	N. America.	Trees, grasses, legumes.	Sucks plant juices.[3]
5	Mite, cyclamen (Steneotarsonemus pallidus), [A, I]	N. America, Europe.	Greenhouse ornamentals, strawberry.	Sucks plant juices, distorts buds and leaves.
6	Mite, fig (Aceria ficus), [A, I]		Fig.	Sucks plant juices.
7	Mite, pear leaf blister (Eriophyes pyri), [A, I]	All pear-growing regions.	Pear, apple.	Sucking causes blisters underside of leaves.
8	Mite, 2-spotted spider- (Tetranychus telarius), [A, I]	U.S.A., Europe, Africa, Asia, Australia.	Cultivated plants.	Sucks plant juices, causing loss of vigor, dropping of leaves.[3]
9	Mite, spider (Tetranychus, other spp), [A, I]	World-wide.	Cultivated plants.	Sucks sap causing whitish blotches on plant tissues, webbing of leaves.[3]

/1/ Nocturnal feeder, dependent on moist conditions. /2/ Control with DDT spray or dust. /3/ Control with phosphate and other insecticides.

Destructive stages of arthropods are indicated by the following symbols associated with the arthropod nomenclature: [A] = adult; [I] = immature; [N] = nymph; [L] = larva. Control measures, described in footnotes, should be used with great caution as many of these pesticides are extremely hazardous.

Arthropod	General Distribution	Host	Destructive Activity
Diplopoda			
10 Millipede, common (Julus heserus), [A, I]	World-wide.	Vegetables, ornamentals.	Chews young roots, stems.
11 Millipede (Orthomorpha spp), [A, I]		Young plants.	Chews young roots, stems.
Symphyla			
12 Centipede, garden (Scutigerella immaculata), [A, I]	N. and S. America, Europe, Africa.	Garden plants, flowers.	Chews tender plants, rootlets.[4]
Insecta			
13 Ant, cornfield (Lasius alienus americanus) [A]	U.S.A.	Corn.	Symbiotic with aphids attacking corn roots.
14 Aphid, apple (Aphis pomi), [A, N]	N. America.	Apple.	Causes wilting.[3, 5]
15 Aphid, cotton (A. gossypii), [A, N]	U.S.A.	Cotton, melons, other plants.	Causes shedding of leaves, fruit.
16 Aphid, green peach (Myzus persicae), [A, N]	Warm regions of world.	Many trees, shrubs.	Sucks sap from leaves, causing curling, distortion; honeydew excreted.
17 Aphid, pea (Macrosiphum pisi), [A, N]		Peas, clovers, alfalfa.	Transmits pea mosaic virus; sucks plant juices.[2, 3]
18 Aphid, woolly apple (Eriosoma lanigerum), [A, N]	N. and S. America, Europe, S. Africa, Asia, Australia.	Apple, pear, elm.	Sucks sap from roots, branches, causing deformed twigs, knotty roots, stunting.[5]
19 Appleworm or codling moth (Carpocapsa pomonella), [L]	All apple areas.	Apple, pear, walnut, others.	Burrows into fruit, destroying or reducing value.[2]
20 Armyworm (Pseudoletia unipuncta), [L]	World-wide.	Grains, grasses, some legumes.	Devours foliage.
21 Bagworm (Thyridopteryx ephemeraeformis), [L]	Eastern U.S.A.	Cedar, other trees.	Devours foliage.[6]
22 Bee, leaf-cutter (Megachile latimanus), [A]	World-wide.	Various trees.	Cuts off leaf fragments for nests.[2]
23 Beetle, Black Hills (Dendroctonus ponderosae), [A, L]	Rocky Mountain regions.	Ponderosa, lodgepole, limber and white bark pines.	Bores into bark and cambial region; may girdle and kill tree.
24 Beetle, blister (Epicauta vittata), [A]	World-wide.	Potato, legumes.	Devours plants.[2]
25 Beetle, Colorado potato- (Leptinotarsa decemlineata), [A, L]	N. America, Europe.	Potato, tomato, tobacco, eggplant, solanaceous plants.	Devours leaves, terminal growth.[2]
26 Beetle, confused flour- (Tribolium confusum), [A, L][7]	World-wide.	Flour, grain products.	Infests and contaminates flour, mixes, bread.
27 Beetle, dried fruit (Carpophilus hemipterus), [L]		Dried fruit.	Destroys dried fruit.
28 Beetle, drugstore (Stegobium paniceum), [A, L]		Dried vegetables.	Destroys dried vegetables.
29 Beetle, Engelmann spruce (Dendroctonus engelmanii), [L]	Western U.S.A.	Engelmann spruce, Colorado blue spruce, lodgepole pine.	Bores into bark and cambial region; may girdle and kill tree.
30 Beetle, flea (Altica, Epitrix, Phyllotrata spp) [A, L][8]	World-wide.	Vegetable crops.	Adult holes leaves; larva often feeds on roots.
31 Beetle, grain (Caulophilus latinasus), [A, L]		Stored grain.	Destroys grain.
32 Beetle, green June- (Cotinis nitidal), [A, L]		Cultivated plants (sap, fruit juices).	Destroys certain fruits; larva feeds on roots.
33 Beetle, Japanese (Popillia japonica), [A, L][9]	Eastern U.S.A., Japan, China.	Fruit trees, ornamentals, vegetables, grasses.	Destroys turf, foliage, blossoms, fruit.[2]
34 Beetle, lesser grain borer (Rhyzopertha dominica), [A, L]		Grain flour, wood-pulp paper.	Destroys.
35 Beetle, Mexican bean- (Epilachna varivestis), [A, L]	U.S.A., Mexico.	Bean, soybean, cowpea, other legumes.	Devours leaves, pods, stems.[10]
36 Beetle, mountain pine (Dendroctonus monticolae), [A, L]	Western U.S.A.	Western, lodgepole, sugar, ponderosa, white bark, and limber pines.	Bores into bark and cambial region; may girdle and kill tree.
37 Beetle, rhinoceros (Dynastes tityus), [A]		Ash.	Shreds bark.
38 Beetle, saw-toothed grain- (Oryzaephilus surinamensis), [A, L]	World-wide.	Grain, grain products, dried fruit.	Infests and devours grain, grain products, dried fruit.
39 Beetle, smaller European elm bark- (Scolytus multistriatus), [A]		Elm.	Vector of Dutch elm disease fungus.
40 Beetle, snout, or plum curculio (Conotrachelus nenuphar), [A, L]	Eastern U.S.A., and Canada.	Plum, apple, peach, cherry, deciduous stone fruits.	Adult punctures; larva feeds within and destroys fruit.[3, 11]
41 Beetle, southern pine (Dendroctonus frontalis), [A, L]		Pine.	Bores into bark and cambial region; may girdle and kill tree.
42 Beetle, spotted cucumber- (Diabrotica undecimpunctata), [A, L]		Corn, cucurbits, weeds, grasses, other plants.	Larva feeds on roots, adult devours foliage.[12]
43 Beetle, striped cucumber- (Acalymma vittata), [A, L]	N. America.	Cucurbits.	Adult devours leaves, shoots, blossoms, damages fruit; larva attacks underground parts.[13]
44 Beetle, tobacco flea- (Epitrix hirtipennis), [A]	World-wide.	Tobacco.	Devours leaves especially of young plants.[2]
45 Beetle, tuber flea- (E. tuberis), [A, L]		Potato.	Adult devours foliage; larva feeds on roots, tubers.
46 Beetle, western pine (Dendroctonus brevicomis), [A, L]	Western U.S.A.	Ponderosa and coulter pines.	Kills pine trees.
47 Bollworm, cotton, or corn earworm. (Heliothis zea), [L]	World-wide.	Cotton, corn, tomato, alfalfa, other plants.	Bores into and feeds on bolls, ears, buds; stunts plants, reduces yield.[2]
48 Bollworm, pink (Pectinophora gossypiella), [L]	Southern U.S.A., S. America, Africa, Europe, Asia, Australia.	Cotton, okra, other malvaceous plants.	Bores into and feeds on squares and bolls, cutting fiber, reducing yield.
49 Borer, currant (Ramosia tulipiformis), [L]	N. America, Asia, Europe, Australia.	Currant, gooseberry, black elder, sumac.	Burrows through canes.

/2/ Control with DDT spray or dust. /3/ Control with phosphate and other insecticides. /4/ Control by treating soil with DDT, chlordane. /5/ Control with demeton, malathion, or nicotine sprays. /6/ Remove bags by hand in winter; control with lead arsenate sprays. /7/ Another important species is the red flour beetle (T. castaneum). /8/ Overwinters as adult. /9/ Other important June beetles belong to Melolontha, Polyphylla and Phyllophaga spp. /10/ Control with malathion or rotenone dusts, sprays. /11/ Control with dieldrin sprays. /12/ Vector of (a) bacterial wilt of cucurbits, (b) virus of yellow disease of asters. /13/ Vector of bacterial wilt of cucurbits; control with methoxychlor.

Destructive stages of arthropods are indicated by the following symbols associated with the arthropod nomenclature: [A] = adult; [I] = immature; [N] = nymph; [L] = larva. Control measures, described in footnotes, should be used with great caution as many of these pesticides are extremely hazardous.

	Arthropod	General Distribution	Host	Destructive Activity
			Insecta (continued)	
50	Borer, flat-headed apple tree- (Chrysobothris femorata), [L]	U.S.A., Canadian fruit-growing areas.	Fruit trees, many shade trees.	Bores into trunk of weakened trees, branches, twigs; kills trees.[14]
51	Borer, peach tree (Sanninoidea exitiosa), [L]	All peach-growing areas.	Peach, other stone-fruit trees.	Bores in trunk at ground-level roots, girdles tree trunk, kills trees.[2]
52	Borer, round-headed apple tree- (Saperda candida), [L]	Eastern U.S.A., Canada.	Apple, pear, quince trees.	Bores into trunk.
53	Borer, squash vine (Melittia cucurbitae), [L]		Squash, pumpkin, cucumber, melons.	Bores into and may girdle vine.
54	Borer, sugar cane (Diatraea saccharalis), [L]		Sugarcane, rice, corn, sorghums, wild grasses.	Causes dead hearts in young plants, dead tops in older plants, broken-over stalks, loss in weight and sucrose, injury to seed cane.
55	Budworm, spruce (Choristoneura fumiferana), [L]	Northern U.S.A., Canada.	Fir, spruce, hemlock, larch, white pine.	Causes partial to complete defoliation.
56	Bug, box elder (Leptocoris trivittatus), [A, I, N, L]		Box elder.	Sucks plant juices.
57	Bug, chinch (Blissus leucopterus), [A, N]	N. America.	Corn, grains, grasses.	Sap sucking causes wilting, death.[15]
58	Bug, 3-cornered alfalfa- (Spississtilus festinus), [A]	World-wide.	Alfalfa.	Stunting.[16]
59	Bug, harlequin cabbage- (Murgantia histrionica), [A, N]	Southern U.S.A., Mexico, C. America.	Cabbage, related crops, other plants.	Sap sucking causes plants to wilt, brown, and die.
60	Bug, lace (Corythucha arcuata)	World-wide.	Various trees, shrubs.	Speckling of leaves, stunting.[17]
61	Bug, squash (Anasa tristis), [A, N]	N. and C. America.	Squash, other cucurbits.	Sap sucking causes plants to wilt and die.
62	Bug, tarnished plant (Lygus lineolaris), [A, N]	N. America.	Many plants, trees.	Leaf sucking and toxins cause bud drop, distortion, stunting.[17]
63	Butterfly, monarch (Danaus plexippus), [L]		Milkweeds.	Feeds on host.
64	Cabbageworm, imported (Pieris rapae), [L]	N. America, Asia, Australia, Europe.	Cabbage, other crucifers.	Devours foliage.[10,17]
65	Cadelle (Tenebroides mauritanicus), [A, L]	World-wide.	Stored grain, grain products.	Infests, destroys grain, grain products.
66	Cankerworm, spring (Paleacrita vernata), [L]	Eastern U.S.A., Canada.	Fruit and shade trees.	Defoliates trees in spring.[2]
67	Caterpillar, eastern tent- (Malacosoma americanum), [L]	U.S.A. east of Rocky mountains.	Wildcherry, apple trees.	Defoliates trees in spring, early summer.[2]
68	Caterpillar, forest tent- (M. disstria), [L]	N. America.	Aspen, sugar maple, oak, birch, basswood, ash, gum, other trees.	Defoliates trees in summer.[2]
69	Chafer, rose (Macrodactylus subspinosus), [A]		Rose, grape, other bushes, vines.	Destroys blossoms, leaves, fruit.[2]
70	Cicada, periodical (Magicicada septendecium), [A]	Eastern and southern U.S.A.	Many deciduous trees, shrubs.	Oviposition punctures injure or kill twigs.[18]
71	Cornborer, European (Pyrausta nubilalis), [L]	Eastern U.S.A., Europe, Asia.	Corn main host; also many vegetables, weeds, ornamentals.	Bores into stalks, ears, causing breakage, reduced yield and quality.[19]
72	Cricket, field (Gryllus spp), [A, N]	N., C., and S. America.	Hay crops, cotton, linen.	Devours hay, plants, cotton, linen.[20]
73	Cricket, Mormon (Anabrus simplex), [A, N]	Western U.S.A.	Hay, grain, many plants.	Devours hay, grain, leaves, of plants.[20]
74	Cutworm, variegated (Peridroma margaritosa), [L]	World-wide.	Many plants.	Cuts down seedlings, transplants.[21]
75	Earwig, European (Forficula auricularia)	World-wide.	Growing plants, stored grain, decayed vegetation.	Chewing.
76	Flea, Lucerne (Sminthurus viridis), [A, I]	Europe, Australia.	Legumes.	Surface feeding causes scorching of leaves.
77	Fly, bulb (Lampetia equestris), [L]	Europe, N. America.	Narcissus, other bulbs.	Bores into bulbs.
78	Fly, carrot rust (Psila rosae), [L]	Europe, northern N. America.	Carrot, celery, umbelliferous plants.	Bores into and eats fibrous roots.[22]
79	Fly, frit (Oscinella frit), [L]	N. America, Europe, Asia.	Cereals, grasses.	Bores into stems, eats central shoots.
80	Fly, hessian (Phytophaga destructor), [L]	Europe, Asia, N. America, New Zealand.	Wheat, barley, rye.	Feeds on stems, causing breaking and stunting.[23]
81	Fly, Mediterranean fruit (Ceratitis capitata), [A, L]	Mediterranean region, Hawaii, S. Africa, S. America, western Australia.	Fruits, vegetables.	Adult makes egg punctures, larva burrows through fruit.[24]
82	Fly, vinegar fruit- or vinegar gnat (Drosophila melanogaster), [L]	World-wide.	Ripe or decaying fruit.	Larva breeds in ripe fruit.
83	Fruitworm, tomato (Heliothis zea) [L]		Tomato, corn, cotton, bean.	Feeds in fruit. (See Bollworm, cotton.)
84	Grasshopper, red-legged (Melanoplus femur-rubrum), [A, N]	World-wide.	Hay crops, range, pasture.	Devours hay, grasses, vegetation.[25]
85	Grasshopper, migratory- (M. mexicanus), [A, N]	Western N. America.	Crops, grasses.	Devours hay, grasses, legumes, cotton.[25]
86	Greenbug (Toxoptera graminum), [A, N]		Barley, oats, wheat, small grains.	Sap sucking causes leaves to wither, yellow; plants die.[26]
87	Hornworm, tobacco (Protoparce sexta), [L]	U.S.A., Canada.	Tobacco, tomato, eggplant, pepper, potato.	Devours foliage.[27]

/2/ Control with DDT spray or dust. /10/ Control with malathion or rotenone dusts, sprays. /13/ Vector of bacterial wilt of cucurbits; control with methoxychlor. /14/ Control by wrapping trunks of young trees with paper for first year. /15/ Control with dieldrin barriers. /16/ Control with methoxychlor. /17/ Control with DDT, aldrin, dieldrin, toxaphene, heptachlor. /18/ Control with TEPP. /19/ Control with DDT, Ryania, culture methods. /20/ Control with poison bran bait containing fluosilicate, aldrin, chlordane, heptachlor, or toxaphene. /21/ Control with toxaphene. /22/ Control by treating soil with aldrin, dieldrin, etc. /23/ Control by planting after "free fly" dates, and by planting resistant varieties. /24/ Control with malathion bait or spray. /25/ Control with aldrin, chlordane, heptachlor in dusts, sprays, baits. /26/ Control with parathion spray. /27/ Control with TDE, endrin.

Destructive stages of arthropods are indicated by the following symbols associated with the arthropod nomenclature: [A] = adult; [I] = immature; [N] = nymph; [L] = larva. Control measures, described in footnotes, should be used with great caution as many of these pesticides are extremely hazardous.

	Arthropod	General Distribution	Host	Destructive Activity
			Insecta (continued)	
88	Hornworm, tomato (Protoparce quinquemaculata), [L]	N. and S. America, Europe, Hawaii.	Tomato, tobacco, other solanaceae.	Devours foliage.
89	Jointworm, wheat (Harmolita tritici), [L]	Eastern and central U.S.A.	Wheat, some grasses.	Causes galls in wheat, breaking of stems.[28]
90	Katydid, broad-winged (Microcentrum rhombifolium), [A, N]	N. America.	Many broad-leaved trees, shrubs.	Chews leaves.
91	Leafhopper, beet (Circulifer tenellus), [A]		Sugar beet, bean.	Vector of curly top disease of beets (virus).
92	Leafhopper, potato (Empoasca fabae), [A, N]	N. and S. America.	Potato, alfalfa, bean, celery, other plants.	Leaf sucking causes wilting, drying of leaves, stunting.[2, 29]
93	Leafworm, cotton (Alabama argillacea), [L]	N. and S. America.	Cotton only.	Devours leaves.[2]
94	Locust, desert (Schistocerca gregaria), [A, N] [30]	India, Iran, Arabia, N. Africa.	Many plants.	Chews leaves.
95	Louse, book (Liposcelis divinatorius), [A, I]	World-wide.	Cereals, vegetables.	Contaminates food, destroys book bindings.
96	Maggot, apple (Rhagoletis pomonella), [L]	North eastern and north central U.S.A.	Apple, blueberry.	Bores into and destroys fruit.[2]
97	Maggot, cabbage root (Hylemya brassicae), [L]	Northern U.S.A.	Cabbage, many other plants.	Bores into roots.[22]
98	Maggot, onion (H. antiqua), [L]	Europe, N. America.	Onion, garlic.	Mines out bulbs.[31]
99	Maggot, seed-corn (H. cilicrura), [L]		Corn, bean, other plants.	Devours seed.
100	Mealworm (Tenebrio molitor), [L]		Grain products and refuse.	Destroys grain, grain products.
101	Mealworm, dark (T. obscurus), [L]		Grain products and refuse.	Destroys grain, grain products.
102	Mealybug (Pseudococcus citri), [A, N]	Tropical and subtropical areas.	Citrus, ornamental plants.	Sap sucking causes plants to die back.[32]
103	Moth, Angumois grain (Sitotroga cerealella), [L]		Grain feed.	Destroys grain feed in storage.
104	Moth, codling (Carpocapsa pomonella), [L]	Apple growing regions of N. and S. America, Europe, Asia, S. Africa, S. Australia.	Apple, pear, quince, walnut, apricot, similar fruits.	Bores into and destroys fruit, or reduces its value.[2]
105	Moth, diamondback (Plutella maculipennis), [L]	World-wide.	All cruciferous plants.	Eats small holes in outer leaves.
106	Moth, European pine shoot- (Rhyacionia buoliana), [L]		Red, Scotch, mugho pines.	Kills buds, twigs.
107	Moth, grape berry (Paralobesia viteana), [L]	Eastern half U.S.A.	Grape.	Destroys berries.[2, 26]
108	Moth, gypsy (Porthetria dispar), [L]	Northeastern U.S.A., Europe, Asia.	Most deciduous and evergreen trees, shrubs.	Devours leaves.
109	Moth, Indian meal- (Plodia interpunctella), [L]	World-wide.	Grain, grain products, dried fruit, nuts.	Destroys and webs grain, grain products; infests fruit, nuts.
110	Moth, Mediterranean flour (Anagasta kuhniella), [L]		Mill products.	Destroys grain products.[2, 26]
111	Moth, Oriental fruit (Grapholitha molesta), [L]	N. America, Europe, Asia.	Peach, quince, apple.	Tunnels twigs, destroys fruit value.
112	Phylloxera, grape (Phylloxera vitifoliae), [A, N]	N. America, Europe.	Grape vines.	Root and leaf sucking causes galls, eventual death of vines.[33]
113	Pickleworm (Diaphania nitidalis), [L]	Southern U.S.A., West Indies.	Cucumber, squash, melons.	Feeds on surface, bores into flowers, buds, fruit, stalks, vines.
114	Psylla, pear (Psylla pyricola), [A, N]	Europe, U.S.A.	Pear.	Leaf sucking, causing leaf drop.[32, 26]
115	Roller, red-banded leaf- (Argyrotaenia velutiana), [L]	U.S.A.	Apple, peach; other trees, shrubs.	Devours foliage, scars fruit.
116	Sawfly, European spruce (Diprion hercyniae), [L]	Europe, northeastern U.S.A., Canada.	Spruce.	Devours leaves.
117	Sawfly, European wheat stem (Cephus pygmaeus), [L]	Northeastern U.S.A., Europe, Near East.	Wheat, rye, barley, timothy, other grasses.	Larva mines stems; causing breakage.
118	Sawfly, wheat stem (C. cinctus), [L]		Wheat, grasses.	Larva tunnels stems, cause breaking, reduced grain yield.
119	Scale, San Jose (Aspidiotus perniciosus), [A, N]	World-wide	Deciduous fruit trees, ornamentals.	Secreted toxins cause wilting, kill infested trees.[34]
120	Scale, soft brown (Coccus hesperidum), [A, N]	World-wide in greenhouses (subtropical spp).	Citrus, ornamentals.	Sap sucking causes plants to die back.[32]
121	Silverfish (Lepisma saccharina), [A, I] [35]	World-wide.	Starchy substances.	Devours book bindings, fabrics, wallpaper.
122	Slug, rose (Cladius isomerus), [L]	World-wide.	Rosebush.	Skeletonizes and causes browning of leaves.[36]
123	Spittlebug, meadow (Philaenus leucopthalmus), [N]	Eastern U.S.A.	Legumes, hay crops.	Sucks plant juices, causing wilting, stunting, reduced forage yield.[37]
124	Termite, eastern subterranean- (Reticulitermes flavipes), [A, N]	Eastern U.S.A.	Wood, dead wood, cellulose products.	Riddles, weakens, destroys wood and cellulose materials.[38]
125	Thrips, gladiolus (Taeniothrips simplex), [A, N]		Gladiolus, iris, lily.	Attacks flowers, foliage, causing silvering, browning, and distortion of leaves.
126	Thrips, onion (Thrips tabaci), [A, N, L]	N. and S. America, Europe, Asia, S. Africa, Australia.	Onion, bean, cabbage, tomato, cotton.	Sucks plant juices, causing leaves and buds to pucker and silver.[17]
127	Thrips, pear (Taeniothrips inconsequens), [A, N]		Pear, plum, prune.	Deforms buds, scars fruit, injures foliage.
128	Wasp, oak gall or apple (Amphibolips confluenta) [L]	World-wide.	Oak.	Causes galls on oak leaves.[39]

/2/ Control with DDT spray or dust. /17/ Control with DDT, aldrin, dieldrin, toxaphene, heptachlor. /22/ Control by treating soil with aldrin, dieldrin, etc. /26/ Control with parathion spray. /28/ Control by burning stubble, crop rotation. /29/ Transmits hopperburn disease. /30/ Has a migratory phase. /31/ More serious under wet and cool conditions. /32/ Honeydew is formed or excreted. /33/ Control by using resistant root stocks. /34/ Control by oil emulsion sprays in dormant stage, malathion sprays in summer. /35/ Another species is the firebrat (Thermobia domestica). /36/ Control by spraying undersides of leaves with malathion. /37/ Control with lindane, methoxychlor sprays. /38/ For protection of new structures, control by treating adjacent infested soil with DDT, chlordane, dieldrin. /39/ Control by burning leaves in winter.

421. SELECTED ARTHROPOD PESTS: PLANTS AND PLANT PRODUCTS (Concluded)

Destructive stages of arthropods are indicated by the following symbols associated with the arthropod nomenclature: [A] = adult; [I] = immature; [N] = nymph; [L] = larva. Control measures, described in footnotes, should be used with great caution as many of these pesticides are extremely hazardous.

	Arthropod	General Distribution	Host	Destructive Activity
			Insecta (concluded)	
129	Webworm, fall (Hyphantria cunea), [L]	U.S.A., southern Canada.	Broad leaf fruit, shade and nut trees.	Webs branches, devours foliage.[2]
130	Weevil, alfalfa (Hypera postica), [L]		Alfalfa.	Skeletonizes growing plant tips and leaves, making hay unpalatable as livestock feed.
131	Weevil, bean (Acanthoscelides obtectus), [L]	World-wide	Bean, pea, cowpea.	Devours inside of bean in field and storage.
132	Weevil, boll (Anthonomus grandis), [A, L]	Southern U.S.A., Mexico.	Cotton	Destroys buds, devours squares and bolls.[40]
133	Weevil, cowpea (Callosobruchus maculatus), [L]		Dried peas.	Destroys peas.
134	Weevil, pea (Bruchus pisorum), [L]	World-wide.	Pea.	Feeds within pea seeds.
135	Weevil, granary (Sitophilus granarius), [A, L]		Grain, grain products.	Destroys grain.
136	Weevil, rice (S. oryza), [A, L]	World-wide.	Stored grains, cereal products.	Larva grows in kernels, destroys stored grain.
137	Weevil, sweetpotato (Cylas formicarius elegantulus), [A, L]	Southern U.S.A., other areas.	Sweetpotato, morning glory.	Adult feeds on leaves, vines, roots; larva in stems, roots, potato.
138	Weevil, white pine (Pissodes strobi), [L]	U.S.A., southern Canada.	Pine, Norway spruce.	Kills terminal growth; degrades lumber.
139	Whitefly, greenhouse (Trialeurodes vaporariorum), [N]	World-wide.	Most plants.	Leaf sucking causes wilting.[32]
140	Wireworm, Pacific Coast (Limonius canus), [L]	Rocky Mountains.	All vegetables and feed crops.	Destroys seeds, cuts underground stems, bores into roots, stems, tubers.
141	Wireworms (Agriotes, Limonius, Melanotus, Horistonotus spp), [L]	World-wide.	Truck, cereal and forage crops.	Devours or bores into roots, seeds.[41]
142	White grubs, or June beetles (Phyllophaga fusca, other Phyllophaga spp), [A, L]		Most plants.	Devours roots, underground parts; adult defoliates trees.[17]

/2/ Control with DDT spray or dust. /17/ Control with DDT, aldrin, dieldrin, toxaphene, heptachlor. /32/ Honeydew is formed or excreted. /40/ Control by spraying or dusting with calcium arsenate, BHC, toxaphene, endrin, dieldrin, aldrin. /41/ Control corn wireworm (Melanotus sp) of U.S.A. by treating soil with DDT, chlordane, dieldrin, heptachlor.

422. SELECTED DISEASE VIRUSES: ANIMALS AND BACTERIA

Entries in parentheses include either scientific equivalents of common names, or questionable or unconfirmed reports. Abbreviations: Agglut.=agglutinates; antig.=antigenically; c=centrifugation; CNS=central nervous system; CSF=cerebrospinal fluid; dm=direct microscopy; em=electron microscopy; enceph.=encephalitis; g.pig=guinea pig; l.n.=lymph node(s); mf=membrane filtration; NP=nasopharyngeal; RBC=red blood cells; resp.=respiratory.

	Common Name	Scientific Name	Natural Host	Location in Body in Natural Infection	Natural Transmission	Experimental Host	Growth in Egg	Tissue Culture	Estimated Size mμ	Remarks
1	Abortion, equine	Tortor equae	Horse.	Fetus; fetal membranes.	Contact; lining from contaminated stalls.	Pregnant g.pig, hamster, equine fetus.	+	Fetal equine spleen; cat lung.	Passes Seitz.	Antig. related to equine influenza.
2	Abortion, sheep		Sheep.	Fetal membranes, uterine discharge.	(Ingestion).	Cattle, mouse, g. pig.	+		(Over 400 [mf]).	Psittacosis group.
3	Adenoidal-pharyngeal-conjunctivitis		Man.	Pharynx; NP discharges; conjunctiva.	Conjunctival and NP discharges.			Human adenoid, tumor; monkey kidney.		Several antigenic types.
4	Anemia, equine, infectious	Trifur equorum.	Man, horse, donkey.	Blood, (all secretions, excretions).	Contact (ingestion, milk, flies).	Rabbit, swine, rat, mouse			11-59[em].	

Entries in parentheses include either scientific equivalents of common names, or questionable or unconfirmed reports. Abbreviations: Agglut.=agglutinates; antig.=antigenically; c=centrifugation; CNS=central nervous system; CSF=cerebrospinal fluid; dm=direct microscopy; em=electron microscopy; enceph.=encephalitis; g. pig=guinea pig; l.n.=lymph node(s); mf=membrane filtration; NP=nasopharyngeal; RBC=red blood cells; resp.=respiratory.

	Common Name	Scientific Name	Natural Host	Location in Body in Natural Infection	Natural Transmission	Experimental Host	Growth in Egg	Tissue Culture	Estimated Size mμ	Remarks
5	Bacteriophages: Coli (T)	Escherichia coli, strain B.							15-150[em].	4 antigenic groups, 7 phages.
6	Coli-dysentery group	E. coli, Shigella dysenteriae.				Mutants of Bacillus megatherium.			8-75[mf].	Several antigenic types, plaques.
7	Megatherium	Bacillus megatherium.							30-45[mf]; 30-37[c].	
8	Staphylococcus (Kreuger)	Micrococcus pyogenes var. aureus.							50-75[mf]; 60-70[c].	3 antigenic types, plaques.
9	Typhoid V (Q151)	Salmonella typhosa.							Passes EK Seitz.	Acts on V component of cells.
10	B virus	Scelus beta.	Monkey, (man[1]).	CNS, spleen, saliva.	Bite.	Rabbit, g. pig.	+	Monkey, kidney	125[mf].	Herpes-pseudorabies group.
11	Blue tongue	Tortor ovis.	Sheep, cattle.	Blood, all organs.	Midges (Culicoides).	Goat, hamster[2], mouse[2].	+		100-150[mf].	(Several antigenic types).
12	Borna disease	Erro bornensis.	Horse, sheep, cattle.	CNS, pancreas, saliva, nasal secretions.	Ingestion, contact.	Rabbit, g. pig, rat, mouse, monkey, chicken.			85-125[mf].	Reddish intranuclear inclusions--Type B.
13	Bwamba fever	Smithburnia bwamba.	Man.	Blood.		Monkey, mouse.	+		75-113[mf].	
14	Chickenpox (varicella)	Briareus varicellae.	Man.	Fluid, crusts of cutaneous lesions.	Air-borne, contact.			Human foreskin, embryo.	210-243[em].	Antig. related to herpes zoster.
15	Choriomeningitis, lymphocytic	Armlillia erebea.	Man, "house mouse."	Blood, CSF, urine, NP secretions, CNS.	(Urine of infected mice).	Mouse, g. pig, monkey.	+	Mouse brain, chick embryo.	37-55[c]; 40-60[mf].	
16	Colorado tick fever	Sabinia coloradensis.	Man, tick.	Blood.	Tick (Dermacentor).	Hamster, mouse.	+		35-50[mf].	
17	Common cold	Tarpeia premens.	Man.	Respiratory tract.	NP discharges.	Chimpanzee, (man).		Human embryo lung.	30-70[mf].	
18	Contagious ecthyma	Hostis ecthymatis.	Man, sheep, goat.	Lesions of lips, eyelids, nose, mouth.	Contact, through abraded epith.				Passes V Berkefeld.	
19	Coxsackie	Daldorfia coxsackie.	Man, rabbit (cottontail).	Intestinal contents. Blood, pharynx, saliva, CNS.	Ingestion.	Mouse[2], hamster, monkey, chimpanzee.	+	Newborn, embryonic mouse[3].	37[em].	16 or more antigenic types.
20	Dengue	Sabinia ashburnii.	Man, monkey.	Blood.	Mosquito (Aedes).	Mouse, hamster[2].	+		17-25[mf].	2 antigenic types.
21	Distemper, canine	Tarpeia canis.	Dog, ferret, other carnivores.	Blood, secretions, excretions.	Contact, secretions, excretions.	Ferret; mouse[2], hamster.	+	Dog kidney.	20-22[em].	Classical, neurotrophic, hard pad types.
22	Distemper, feline	Tarpeia felis.	Cat, other Felidae.	All tissues, secretions, excretions.	Same as dog distemper.	(Cat).			Passes N Berkefeld.	Antig. diff. from dog distemper.
23	Durand disease		Man.	Blood, spleen, urine, CSF, intestinal contents.		Hamster, g.pig, dog, monkey, cat.	+	Chick embryo.	40-80[mf].	
24	Encephalitis, California	Rocaea hammonii.	(Man, horse, ground squirrel).		(Mosquito (Aedes, Culex).	Mouse, cotton rat, hamster.	+		60-125[mf].	Antig. related to St. Louis enceph. group.
25	Encephalitis, eastern equine	Erro tenbroeckii.	Man, horse, birds.	CNS, blood, spleen.	Mosquito (Mansonia), (mites).	Mouse, many domestic and wild animals, birds.	+	Chick embryo, rat.	25[mf]; 40[c, em].	Antigenically distinct.
26	Encephalitis, Venezuelan equine	Erro venezuelensis.	Man, horse, mule.	CNS, blood, nasopharynx.	Mosquito (Aedes, Mansonella).	Mouse, g.pig, rabbit, rat, dog, sheep, goat.	+	Mouse, human embryo	Passes N Berkefeld.	
27	Encephalitis, western equine	Erro equinus.	Man, horse, mule; wild, domestic birds.	CNS, blood, spleen.	Mosquito (Culex) (mites).	Mouse, many domestic and wild animals.	+	Chick embryo.	25[mf]; 40[c, em].	Antigenically distinct.
28	Encephalitis, Japanese	Erro japonicus.	Man, horse, cattle, goat, (some wild birds).	CNS, blood.	Mosquito (Culex).	Mouse, hamster, monkey, domestic animals.	+	Chick embryo, mouse, rabbit.	20-30[mf]; 10 or less [c].	Antig. related to St. Louis enceph. group; agglut. RBC.
29	Encephalitis, Russian Far East[4]	Erro silvestris.	Man, squirrel, hedgehog.	CNS, blood, CSF, NP secretions, urine.	Tick (Ixodes persulcatus).	Mouse, hamster, monkey, sheep, wild birds.		Mouse, chick embryo, mouse tumor.	15-25[mf].	Antig. related to louping-ill; agglut. RBC.
30	Encephalitis, St. Louis	Erro scelestus.	Man, chicken, other birds.	CNS, blood.	Mosquito, (Culex), (mites).	Mouse, monkey.	+	Mouse, chick embryo.	22-33[mf].	Antig. related to Japanese-West Nile group; agglut. RBC.
31	Encephalomyelitis, avian	Erro gallinae.	Chicken, pheasant.	Brain, liver, spleen.	Possibly by contact and through egg).	Young turkey, pigeon, duck.		Chick embryo.	20-30[mf].	
32	Encephalomyelitis, mouse, (Theiler)	Legio muris.	Mouse.	CNS, blood, intestinal contents.	Ingestion of feces.	Cotton rat, virus-free mice.	+	Chick, mouse embryo.	9-13[mf]; 15x115[em].	2 antigenic types; agglut. RBC.
33	Encephalomyocarditis		Monkey, mongoose, wild rodents.	CNS, blood.	(Mosquito (Taeniorrhynchus).	Mouse, hamster, g. pig, monkey, cotton rat.	+	Mouse, chick embryo.	8-15[mf]; 25-30[em].	4 antig. types; agglut. RBC.
34	Exanthema subitum[5]	Morbillifex subitus.	Man.	Blood, upper resp. tract (feces).		Monkey.		(Human embryo).	Passes Seitz.	

/1/ Only by laboratory infection. /2/ Suckling. /3/ Also chick, human, monkey embryo. /4/ Spring-summer encephalitis. /5/ Roseola infantum.

Entries in parentheses include either scientific equivalents of common names, or questionable or unconfirmed reports. Abbreviations: Agglut.=agglutinates; antig.=antigenically; c=centrifugation; CNS= central nervous system; CSF=cerebrospinal fluid; dm=direct microscopy; em=electron microscopy; enceph.=encephalitis; g. pig=guinea pig; l.n.=lymph node(s); mf=membrane filtration; NP=nasopharyngeal; RBC=red blood cells; resp.=respiratory.

	Common Name	Scientific Name	Natural Host	Location in Body in Natural Infection	Natural Transmission	Experimental Host	Growth in Egg	Tissue Culture	Estimated Size $m\mu$	Remarks
35	Fibroma, rabbit (Shope)	Molitor fibromatis.	Rabbit (cottontail), squirrel.	Subcutaneous nodules, skin; (blood, spleen).		Domestic rabbit, woodchuck.	+	Rabbit testis (variant).	125-175 [mf].	Antig. related to myxoma, inflammatory variant.
36	Foot and mouth disease	Hostis pecoris.	Man, cattle, goat, sheep, swine.	Blood, saliva, milk, urine.	Contact, secretions, excretions, garbage[6].	Rabbit, g.pig, puppy, mouse, rat, baby chick.	+	G. pig, bovine epithelium.	8-12[mf].	3 or more antigenic types, agglut. RBC.
37	Fowl plague	Tortor galli.	Domestic fowl, some wild birds.	Blood, secretions, excretions.	Ingestion.	Starling, canary, mouse, rat, rabbit, ferret.	+ and pigeon	Chick embryo.	60-140[mf, c, em].	Antig. variants, agglut. RBC.
	Fowl tumors									
38	Chicken tumor I (Rous sarcoma)	Molitor tumoris.	Chicken.	Any mesodermal tissue, sometimes in blood.	(Early life: upper resp.-digestive tract.)	Domestic fowl (age limitations).	+	Chick embryo, chick.	100[mf]; 60-70[mf, dm].	Antig. related to lymphomatosis viruses.
39	Fowl leucosis (leukemia)	Trifur gallinarum.	Chicken.	Blood, viscera.		(Chicken, turkey, pheasant, guinea fowl).			20-120[mf]; 120[dm].	
40	Lymphomatosis (Marek paralysis)		Chicken.	Viscera, bones, eye tissues, nasopharynx.	Through egg, in early life after hatching.	(Chicken).				
41	Gastroenteritis, human (Marcy)		Man.	Intestinal tract, resp. droplets.	Ingestion.	(Man).		Passes UF sintered glass.		Produces febrile disease.
42	Hepatitis, canine	Tortor vulpis.	Dog, fox, wolf, coyote, bear.	Blood, secretions, excretions.	Ingestion, secretions, excretions.	Ferret, other carnivores	+	Dog kidney.	Passes N Berkefeld.	
43	Hepatitis, human, (infectious)	Reedella triginta.	Man.	Blood, intestinal contents.	Ingestion of infected materials.	(Man).	+	(Rabbit, chick embryo).	Passes Seitz.	Antig. distinct. Type A.
44	Hepatitis, human, (serum)	Reedella centum.	Man.	Blood.	Injection, contact with blood or derivatives.	(Man).	(+)		26 or less [mf].	Antig. distinct. Type B.
45	Hepatitis, mouse		Mouse	Blood, liver, urine, spleen, kidney, feces.		Mouse[2].		Mouse embryo.	130-180[mf].	Several antigenic types.
46	Herpes simplex	Scelus recurrens.	Man.	Skin, cornea, blood, mucosa, CNS.	(Contact).	Rabbit, mouse.	+	Rabbit, chick embryo.	100-150[mf].	Antig. related to B. pseudorabies.
47	Herpes zoster	Briareus zosticus.	Man.	Skin, sensory nerves, ganglia.		(Man)		Human skin.	210-250[em].	Antig. related to chickenpox.
48	Hog cholera	Tortor suis.	Swine.	Blood, all secretions, excretions.	Contact, secretions, excretions, garbage[6].	Rabbit, g.pig.		Swine testis, marrow, spleen.	5[em]; 27[em].	Antig., neurotrophic variants.
49	Inclusion conjunctivitis	Chlamydozoon oculogenitale.	Man.	Conjunctiva, (cervix, urethra).	Contact, genitalia secretions.	Baboon.			250[dm].	
50	Influenza	Tarpeia alpha, beta, taylorii.	Man.	Respiratory tract.	Contact, NP secretions.	Ferret, mouse.	+	Chick embryo, mouse tumor.	80-120[mf, c, em].	Antig. types A-C, agglut. RBC.
51	Influenza, equine	Tarpeia caballi.	Horse, mule.	Respiratory tract, blood, semen.	Inhalation, ingestion, contact.	(Horse).	+		Passes N Berkefeld.	Antig. related to equine abortion.
52	Influenza, swine	Tarpeia shopei.	Swine	Respiratory tract, blood.	Contact, secretions, ingestion of lungworm ova, larvae.	Ferret, mouse.	+		80-120[mf, c].	Antig. related to type A influenza. Virus and H. suis elicit clinical disease.
	Insect viruses:									
53	Bergoldia calypta (Steinhaus)		Fir-shoot roller[7]	Blood cells, (fat tissue).	Oral, (egg).				50x262 [em].	Inclusion bodies: capsular.
54	Morator nudus (Wasser)		Armyworm[8]		Oral.				25[em].	Inclusion bodies: none.
55	Polyhedral of Arctia villica		Cream spot tiger moth.	Hypodermis.	Oral, (egg).					Inclusion bodies: polyhedral.
56	Polyhedral of Diprion hercyniae		European spruce sawfly.	Midgut, epithelium.	Oral, (egg).				50x250[em].	Inclusion bodies: polyhedral.
57	Silkworm jaundice	Borrelina bombycis.	Silkworm (Bombyx mori).	Fat, hypodermis, blood cells, (other tissues).	Oral, (egg).	(Gypsy moth; nun moth).			40x288[em].	Inclusion bodies: polyhedral.
58	Laryngotracheitis, avian, infectious	Tarpeia avium.	Chicken, pheasant.	Larynx, trachea, bronchi.	Contact.		+ and turkey		45-85[mf]; 100[em].	
59	Louping ill	Erro scoticus.	Man, sheep.	CNS, blood, CSF (man).	Tick (Ixodes ricinus), contact (man).	Mouse, vole, swine, hamster, cattle, (horse).	+	Chick embryo.	15-20[mf]; 22-27[c].	Antig. related to Russian Far East virus.
60	Lumpy skin disease		Cattle.	Cutaneous nodules, l.n., blood, other tissues.			+		10-25[mf].	
61	Lymphogranuloma venereum.	Miyagawanella lymphogranulomatis.	Man.	Genital lesion, CSF, inguinal l.n.	Direct contact.	Mouse, g.pig, monkey.	+	Chick, mouse embryo, g. pig, mouse testis.	300[dm]; 438[em].	Antig. related to psittacosis, produces toxin.
62	Measles (rubeola)	Morbillifex morbillorum.	Man.	Blood, skin, respiratory tract.	Contact, NP discharges.	Monkey.		Chick embryo, human, monkey kidney.	Passes Seitz.	
63	Measles, German (rubella)	Morbillifex embryorum.	Man.	Blood, nasopharynx.	Contact, NP discharges.	(Man).			Less than 800[mf].	

/2/ Suckling. /5/ Roseola infantum. /6/ Raw. /7/ Cacoecia murinana. /8/ Cirphis unipuncta.

Entries in parentheses include either scientific equivalents of common names, or questionable or unconfirmed reports. Abbreviations: Agglut.=agglutinates; antig.=antigenically; c=centrifugations; CNS=central nervous system; CSF=cerebrospinal fluid; dm=direct microscopy; em=electron microscopy; enceph.=encephalitis; g. pig=guinea pig; l.n.=lymph node(s); mf=membrane filtration; NP=nasopharyngeal; RBC=red blood cells; resp.=respiratory.

	Common Name	Scientific Name	Natural Host	Location in Body in Natural Infection	Natural Transmission	Experimental Host	Growth in Egg	Tissue Culture	Estimated Size mμ	Remarks
64	Meningo-pneumonitis	(Man, ferret)	Respiratory tract.			Mouse, ferret, monkey.	+		300-400[mf]; 354[em].	Antig. related to psittacosis; produces toxin. agglut. RBC.
65	Molluscum contagiosum	Molitor hominis.	Man.	Skin.	Direct contact.				190-250[em].	
66	Mumps	Rabula inflans.	Man.	Salivary glands, blood, gonads, CSF.	Droplets of saliva.	Monkey, hamster.	+	Chick, mouse embryo.	90-135[mf]; 140-268 [em].	Agglut. RBC, produces hemolysin.
67	Myxomatosis, infectious	Borreliota myxomatis.	Domestic, wild rabbit.	Skin, mucosa, blood.	Contact, arthropods (mechanical).	Domestic, wild rabbit.	+ (and duck.	Rabbit, chick embryo.	286x230x 75[em].	Antig. related to Fibroma (Shope).
68	Newcastle disease	Tortor furens.	Man, domestic fowl, some wild birds.	Blood, secretions, excretions (ovipara), lungs (calf).	Contact, garbage[6], (poultry scraps).	Common lab. animals, cattle, quail, sparrow[9].	+ (and duck).	Chick embryo.	80-100[mf].	Neural, pneumonic visceral strains, agglut. RBC.
69	Papilloma, rabbit (oral)	Molitor gingivalis.	Domestic rabbit.	Tongue.	(Suckling).	Wild rabbit.			Passes Berkefeld.	Differs antig. from papilloma (Shope).
70	Papilloma, rabbit (Shope	Molitor sylvilagi.	Rabbit (cottontail).	Skin.		Domestic rabbit, hamster.			22-35[mf]; 32-50[c].	Malignancy becomes carcinomatous.
71	Phlebotomus fever sand-fly, (pappataci fever)	Sabinia doerrii.	Man.	Blood.	Midge (Phlebotomus papatasii).	Man.			40-60[mf].	2 or more antig. types.
72	Pneumo-enteritis, bovine.	Tarpeia vitulae.	Calf.	Lungs, intestinal tract, blood.	(Contact, resp., intestinal discharges).	Mouse.			Passes N Berkefeld.	
73	Pneumonia of mice, virus		Mouse.	Lungs.	Contact, resp. excretions.	(Mouse).		Chick embryo.	100-150[mf].	Agglut. RBC.
74	Pneumonia, swine, virus		Swine.	Lungs.	Contact, resp. excretions.	(Swine).		Swine lung, kidney.	Over 200[f].	
75	Pneumonitis, feline	Miyagawanella felis.	Cat.	Respiratory tract.	Inhalation, resp. excretions.	Mouse, g. pig, rabbit, hamster.	+		423x161[em].	Antig. related psittacosis, produces toxin.
76	Pneumonitis, mouse (Nigg)		Mouse.	Lung.		(Mouse).	+		497[em].	Member of psittacosis group.
77	Poliomyelitis	Legio debilitans.	Man.	CNS, intestinal tract, blood.	monkey, mouse, cotton rat, hamster.	Chimpanzee,	+	Human, monkey.	28[em].	3 or more antig. types.
78	Pox, cow	Borreliota jenneri	Man, cattle.	Cutaneous lesions, teat, udder.	Contact.	Rabbit, g. pig.	+	Bovine fetus, skin.		Antig. related to vaccinia.
79	Pox, fowl	Borreliota avium.	Domestic fowl, some wild birds.	Skin lesions, blood, mucosa, viscera.	Contact, (mosquito).		+ and duck, turkey.	Chick embryo.	125[mf, m]; 264-322[em].	Differs antig. from vaccinia.
80	Pox, mouse (ectromelia)	Borreliota marmorans	Mouse (domestic).	Skin, blood, liver, spleen.	Contact.	(Mouse).	+ (and duck).	Mouse embryo.	210-300[em].	Antig. related vaccinia, agglut. RBC.
81	Pseudorabies (D'Aujezky's disease)	Formido aujeszkyii	Cattle, sheep, swine, dog, cat, rat.	Cutaneous lesions, CNS, nasal secretions (swine).	Ingestion, contact.	Rabbit, g. pig, bat, monkey, mouse, hamster.	+	Chick embryo, rabbit, g. pig.	90-100[em].	Antig. related to herpes.
82	Psittacosis (ornithosis, parrot fever)	Miyagawanella psittaci.	Man, psittacine birds, duck, chicken.	Lung, spleen, liver, resp. secretions, cloacal contents.	Inhalation, dried secretions, droppings, contact.	Mouse, g. pig, monkey.	+	Chick embryo, mouse.	455[em].	Produces toxin.
83	Rabies	Formido inexorabilis.	All mammals.	CNS, salivary, lacrimal glands, kidney, pancreas, saliva.	Saliva, through broken epithelium.	Mammals, domestic fowl.	+ (and duck).	Rabbit, rat, mouse, chick embryo.	100-150[mf].	
84	Rift Valley fever	Reedella vallis.	Man, sheep.	Blood, liver.	(Mosquito).	Cattle, goat, rat, monkey, mouse.	+	Chick embryo[10].	23-35[mf]	
85	Rinderpest	Tortor bovis.	Domestic animals, deer.	Blood, secretions, excretions.	Ingestion.	Rabbit, g. pig, Chinese pig.	+	Chick embryo.	Passes V Berkefeld.	
86	Smallpox variola	Briareus variolae (hominis).	Man, (monkey).	Lesions of skin, NP secretions, mucosa, scales.	Inhalation, secretions, scales.	Monkey, rabbit.	+		244-302[em].	Antig. related to vaccinia, agglut. RBC.
87	Stomatitis, vesicular	Hostis equinus.	Man, horse, cattle, swine.	Lesions of feet, nose, udder.	Contact.	Rat, g. pig, mouse, monkey.	+	Mouse, g. pig embryo.	70-100[mf].	2 antig. types.
88	Trachoma	Chlamydozoon trachomatis.	Man.	Conjunctiva, conjunctival exudate.	Contact, conjunctival exudate.	Ape, (man).	+		250[dm].	
89	Vaccinia		(Cutaneous lesions in man, rabbit, cattle).			Man, cattle, monkey, rabbit, mouse.	3 (and turtle).	Rabbit, g. pig, chick adult, embryo.	236-252[mf].	Antig. related to smallpox, agglut. RBC.
90	Vesicular exanthema, swine.	Hostis exanthematis.	Swine.	Lesions of nose, lip, mouth, feet, udder.	Contact, ingestion.	Horse, dog, hamster.		Swine embryo.	Passes N Berkefeld.	Several antig. types.
91	Wart, human (verruca)	Molitor verrucae.	Man.	Cutaneous lesions.	(Contact).	(Man).			Passes N Berkefeld.	
92	West Nile	Erro nili.	Man, pigeon.	Blood.	(Mosquito).	Mouse, g. pig, monkey, hamster, (man).	+	Mouse, chick embryo.	20-30[mf].	Antig. related to St. Louis, agglut. RBC.
93	Yellow fever	Reedella evagatus.	Man, monkey, galago.	Blood, liver, CNS, spleen, l.n.	Mosquito (Aedes, possibly others).	Mouse, monkey, hedgehog.	+	Chick, mouse embryo.	12-19[c].	
94	Zika	Rocaea zika.	Man, monkey.	Blood.	(Isolated from Aedes mosquito).	Mouse.	+		18-26[mf].	

/6/ Raw. /9/ Also dog, fox, hedgehog (N. African). /10/ Also ascites tumor cells (man).

423. SELECTED RICKETTSIALES PARASITES: MAN AND DOMESTIC ANIMALS

	Organism	Host[1]	Disease	Method of Transmission
1	Anaplasma centrale	Cattle.	Benign anaplasmosis.	Tick to host.
2	A. marginale	Cattle.	Malignant anaplasmosis.	Tick to host.
3	A. ovis	Sheep, goats.	Ovine anaplasmosis.	Tick to host.
4	Bartonella bacilliformis	Man.	Oroya fever.	Sand fly to man.
5	Chlamydia trachomae	Man, ape, monkey.	Trachoma.	Contact.
6	C. oculogenitale	Man.	Inclusion blennorrhea, inclusion conjunctivitis, neonatal conjunctivitis.	Contact. Contaminated swimming pools.
7	Colesiota conjunctivae	Cattle, goat, sheep.	Ophthalmia.	
8	C. conjunctivae gallii	Birds.	Conjunctivitis, keratitis.	
9	Cowdria ruminantium	Goat, sheep, cattle.	"Heartwater."	Tick feces. Tick to host.
10	Coxiella burnetti	Man, cattle, sheep, goat.	Q fever.	Tick feces. Host to tick to host. Contact domestic animals. Inhalation infected dust. Contaminated milk.
11	Ehrlichia canis	Dog.	Canine rickettsiosis.	Tick to host.
12	E. bovis	Cattle.	Bovine rickettsiosis.	Tick to host.
13	E. ovina	Sheep.	Ovine rickettsiosis.	Presumed tick to host.
14	Eperythrozoon spp	Cattle, mouse, sheep, swine.	Eperythrozoonsis, anemia (parasite of erythrocyte).	Mouse louse to louse. Other arthropods suspected.
15	Grahamella talpae	Mole.	Grahamellosis, anemia (parasite of erythrocyte).	
16	Haemobartonella spp	Animals.	Haemobartonellosis, anemia (parasite of erythrocyte).	Flea to host.
17	Miyagawanella bronchopneumoniae	Mouse.	Mouse pneumonitis.	Contact.
18	M. felis	Cat.	Feline pneumonitis.	Contact.
19	M. lymphogranulomatosis	Man.	Lymphogranuloma venereum, lymphogranuloma inguinale.	Venereal contact.
20	M. ornithosis	Man, non-psittacine birds.	Ornithosis.	Similar to psittacosis (see below).
21	M. psittacii	Man, psittacine birds.	Psittacosis.	Inhalation infected dust. Bird to man, man to man.
22	Neorickettsia helminthoeca	Dog, fox, coyote.	"Salmon poisoning disease."	Intestinal parasitic fluke to man.
23	Rickettsia akari	Man.	Rickettsial pox.	Mite to man.
24	R. conorii	Man; dog as reservoir host.	Boutonneuse, Marseilles, Mediterranean fever.	Tick to man.
25	R. prowazekii	Man.	Epidemic typhus ("classic, Old World").	Louse feces. Man to louse to man.
26	R. quintana	Man.	Trench fever.	Body louse to man.
27	R. rickettsii	Man, rabbit, squirrel.	Rocky Mountain spotted fever.	Tick to man.
28	R. siberica	Man, rodents.	Siberian tick typhus.	Tick to man.
29	R. tsutsugamushi	Man, monkey, rodents.	Tsutsugamushi fever, scrub typhus.	Mite to man.
30	R. typhi	Man, rodents.	Murine or endemic typhus	Flea feces. Rat to flea to man.
31	Ricolesia spp	Domestic ruminants and fowl.	Conjunctivitis.	Uncertain.

/1/ Animals listed in order of decreasing susceptibility.

424. SELECTED BACTERIAL PARASITES: MAN AND DOMESTIC ANIMALS

	Bacterial Organism	Host[1]	Disease	Method of Transmission
1	Actinobacillus lignieresi	Cattle, swine.	Actinobacillosis, "wooden tongue."	(Not definitely known.)
2	Actinomyces bovis	Cattle, swine, horse, man.	Actinomycosis, "lumpy jaw."	Buccal cavity. (Not definitely known.)
3	Bacillus anthracis	Man.	Anthrax.	Soil-borne. Contact, infected animal by-products, carcasses.
4		Cattle, sheep, horse, mule, swine.	Anthrax, "splenic fever," "charbon," "milzbrand."	Soil-borne. Infected feed, water, carcasses.
5	Borrelia anserina	Fowl.	Spirochetosis.	Arthropod vector. Feces-borne.
6	B. recurrentis	Man.	European relapsing fever.	Arthropod vector.
7	B. theileri	Cattle.	Spirochetosis.	Arthropod vector.
8	B. vincentii	Man.	Associated with Fusobacterium plauti-vincenti in Vincent's angina.	Buccal cavity. (Not definitely known.)
9	Brucella abortus	Cattle, man.	Brucellosis, undulant fever.	Ingestion infected milk. Contact.
10	B. melitensis	Goat, sheep, man.	Brucellosis, undulant fever.	Ingestion infected milk. Contact.
11	B. suis	Swine, man.	Brucellosis, undulant fever.	Contact.
12	Clostridium botulinum	Man, chicken, duck, horse, mule, cattle.	Botulism, food intoxication, limber-neck of fowl.	Ingestion of toxin in food.
13	C. feseri	Cattle.	Black leg, symptomatic anthrax.	Soil-borne. Wound infection.
14	C. hemolyticum	Cattle, sheep.	Icterohemoglobinuria.	Soil-borne. Contaminated feed, water.
15	C. novyi	Sheep.	Infectious necrotic hepatitis.	Soil-borne. Associated with liver fluke infection.
16	C. perfringens	Man.	Gas gangrene.	} Soil-borne. Wound infection.
17		Sheep.	Lamb dysentery, infectious enterotoxemia.	
18	C. septicum	Horse, sheep, cattle.	Malignant edema.	Soil-borne. Wound infection.
19	C. tetani	Man, sheep, cattle, goat, swine, horse.	Tetanus, lockjaw.	Soil-borne. Wound infection.
20	Corynebacterium diphtheriae	Man.	Diphtheria.	Carrier contact.
21	C. equi	Horse.	Pneumonia of foal.	Possible in utero.
22		Swine.	Submaxillary gland infection.	Contaminated soil, feed.
23	C. pseudotuberculosis	Sheep, goat.	Gaseous lymphadenitis.	Contaminated feed, water.
24		Horse.	Ulcerative lymphangitis, pseudoglanders.	Contact, wound infection.
25		Cattle.	Pseudotuberculosis.	
26	C. pyogenes	Cattle, swine, sheep, goat.	Mastitis, purulent infections, arthritis.	Inhabitant mucous membranes. Contact, wound infection.
27	C. renale	Cattle, swine.	Pyelonephritis.	Inhabitant mucous membranes. (Not definitely known.)

/1/ Animals are listed in order of decreasing susceptibility.

	Bacterial Organism	Host[1]	Disease	Method of Transmission
28	Diplococcus pneumoniae	Man.	Lobar pneumonia, meningitis, endocarditis.	Carrier contact.
29	Erysipelothrix rhusiopathiae	Man.	Erysipeloid.	Wound infection, contact infected carcasses.
30		Swine, sheep, fowl.	Erysipelas.	Feces-borne. Contaminated soil, feed, water.
31	Escherichia coli	Man, domestic animals.	Genito-urinary and intestinal infections.	Feces-borne. Normal flora of intestinal tract.
32	Fusobacterium plauti-vincenti	Man.	Associated with ulcerative stomatitis, Vincent's angina.	Buccal cavity. (Not definitely known.)
33	Hemophilus ducreyi	Man.	Soft chancre, chancroid.	Direct genital contact.
34	H. gallinarum	Chicken.	Infectious coryza.	Contact.
35	H. hemoglobinophilus	Dog.	Prepucial infection.	Direct sexual contact.
36	H. influenzae	Man.	Meningitis, obstructive respiratory infections.	Flora of respiratory tract. Droplet infection.
37	H. pertussis	Man.	Whooping cough.	Flora of respiratory tract. Droplet infection. Contact.
38	H. suis	Swine.	Associated with viral influenza.	Flora of respiratory tract. Droplet infection.
39	Klebsiella pneumoniae	Man, horse, cattle.	Respiratory infection; mastitis (cattle).	Contact. Flora of respiratory tract.
40	Leptospira canicola	Dog, man, swine, cattle.	Leptospirosis, Stuttgart's disease (dog).	Direct contact. Contamination of water by infected urine.
41	L. icterohemorrhagiae	Man, dog, swine, cattle, rodent.	Leptospirosis, Weil's disease.	Direct contact. Contamination of water by infected urine.
42	L. pomona	Cattle, swine, man.	Leptospirosis, swineherd's disease.	Direct contact. Contamination of water by infected urine.
43	Listeria monocytogenes	Man, domestic animals, fowl.	Listeriosis, meningoencephalitis.	(Not definitely known.)
44	Malleomyces mallei	Horse, man.	Glanders.	Contact. Contaminated feed, water.
45	Micrococcus pyogenes	Man, animals.	Abcesses, suppurative processes, food poisoning, septicemia.	Wound infection, ingestion contaminated food. Flora of skin and mucous membranes.
46	Moraxella bovis	Cattle.	Infectious keratitis.	Contact.
47	M. lacunata	Man.	Conjunctivitis.	(Not definitely known.)
48	Mycobacterium avium	Fowl, swine.	Tuberculosis.	Contact. Feces-borne. Contaminated feed, water.
49	M. leprae	Man.	Hansen's disease, leprosy.	(Not definitely known.)
50	M. paratuberculosis	Cattle, sheep.	Johne's disease.	Contact. Feces-borne. Contaminated feed, water.
51	M. tuberculosis var. bovis	Cattle, man, swine.	Tuberculosis.	Contact. Feces-borne. Contaminated feed, water. Milk-borne.
52	M. tuberculosis var. hominis	Man.	Tuberculosis.	Contact. Via respiratory or alimentary tract.
53	Neiserria catarrhalis	Man.	Catarrhal inflammations.	Flora of respiratory tract.
54	N. gonorrheae	Man.	Gonorrhea.	Direct sexual contact.
55	N. meningitidis	Man.	Epidemic cerebrospinal meningitis.	Infection from respiratory tract of carrier.
56	Pasteurella multocida	Domestic animals, fowl, man.	Hemorrhagic septicemia, bronchiectasis, conjunctivitis.	Contact. Contaminated feed, water. Bites.
57	P. pestis	Man, rodent.	Bubonic and pneumonic plague.	Flea bite from infected rat. Droplet infection.
58	P. tularensis	Man, rodent.	Tularemia.	Contact contaminated carcasses. Insect vector.
59	Proteus vulgaris	Man.	Genito-urinary and intestinal (?) infection.	Feces-borne.
60	Pseudomonas aeruginosa	Man, animals.	Suppurative processes, septicemia, meningitis, genito-urinary infections.	Contaminated water, soil, feces, wound infection.
61	Salmonella enteritidis	Man, rodents.	Food poisoning, gastroenteritis.	Feces-borne.
62	S. gallinarum	Fowl.	Fowl typhoid.	Feces-borne. Ovarian transmission.
63	S. hirschfeldii	Man.	Paratyphoid fever.	Feces-borne.
64	S. paratyphi A	Man.	Paratyphoid fever.	Feces-borne.
65	S. paratyphi B	Man.	Paratyphoid fever.	Feces-borne.
66	S. pullorum	Fowl.	Pullorum disease, bacillary white diarrhea.	Feces-borne. Ovarian transmission.
67	S. typhimurium[2]	Man, rodents.	Food poisoning, gastroenteritis.	Feces-borne.
68	S. typhosa	Man.	Typhoid fever.	Feces-borne.
69	Shigella dysenteriae	Man.	Dysentery.	Feces-borne. Contaminated food, water. Contact. Fly-borne.
70	S. equuli	Horse.	Joint infection, nephritis.	Possible in utero.
71	Spherophorus necrophorus	Man (?).	Associated with ulcerative colitis(?).	Feces-borne. Associated with unsanitary conditions.
72		Horse.	Gangrenous dermatitis, "scratches."	Feces-borne. Associated with unsanitary conditions.
73		Cattle	Calf diphtheria.	Feces-borne. Associated with unsanitary conditions.
74		Sheep, goat	Lip-and-leg ulceration, ulcerative stomatitis, food rot.	Feces-borne. Associated with unsanitary conditions.
75		Swine.	Ulcerative stomatitis, enteritis.	Feces-borne. Associated with unsanitary conditions.
76	Spirillum minus	Man, rodents.	Rat-bite fever.	Rat bite.
77	Streptococcus agalactiae	Cattle.	Mastitis.	Contaminated milking equipment.
78	S. dysgalactiae	Cattle.	Mastitis.	Contaminated milking equipment.
79	S. equi	Horse.	Strangles.	Contact. Contaminated water, feed.
80	S. pyogenes	Man.	Scarlet fever, septic sore throat.	Direct personal contact, contaminated milk.
81	S. uberis	Cattle.	Mastitis.	Contaminated milking equipment.
82	Treponema pallidum	Man.	Syphilis.	Direct sexual contact.
83	Vibrio comma	Man.	Cholera.	Feces-borne from carrier. Contaminated food, water.
84	V. fetus	Cattle, sheep.	Vibrionic abortion, sterility.	Direct sexual contact.
85	V. jejuni	Cattle.	Dysentery.	Feces-borne. Contaminated feed and water.

/1/ Animals are listed in order of decreasing susceptibility.   /2/ All warm-blooded animals.

	Host Plant and Pathogen	Disease		Host Plant and Pathogen	Disease
	Amaranth (Amaranthus viridis)			Cherry, sweet (Prunus avium)	
1	Xanthomonus amaranthicola	Leaf spot.	57	Pseudomonas syringae	Gummosis and blight.
	Apple (Pyrus malus)			Chicory, Witloof (Cichorium intybus)	
2	Erwinia amylovora	Fire blight.	58	Pseudomonas marginalis	Rot.
3	Pseudomonas papulans	Blister spot.		Chrysanthemum (Chrysanthemum morifolium)	
4	P. syringae	Twig blight.	59	Erwinia chrysanthemi	Bacterial blight.
5	P. melophthora	Brown rot of fruit.		Chestnut (Castanea spp)	
	Alfalfa (Medicago sativa)		60	Pseudomonas castaneae	Bacterial blight.
6	Corynebacterium insidiosum	Wilt and root rot.		Citrus (Citrus spp)	
7	Pseudomonas medicaginis	Stem blight.	61	Erwinia citrimaculans	Fruit spot.
	Ash (Fraxinus spp)		62	Pseudomonas syringae	Blast and black pit.
8	Pseudomonas savastonoi var. fraxini	Canker.	63	Xanthomonas bilvae	Shot hole and fruit canker.
	Banana (Musa paridisi)		64	X. citri	Canker.
9	Pseudomonas celebensis	Blood disease.		Clover (Trifolium spp)	
10	P. solanacearum	Brown rot.	65	Pseudomonas radiciperda	Root rot.
11	P. maublancii	Bud rot and stunt.	66	P. stizolobii	Leaf spot.
	Barley (Hordeum vulgare)		67	P. syringae	Leaf spot.
12	Pseudomonas coronafaciens	Leaf spot.		Cocklebur (Xanthium sp)	
13	P. striafaciens	Stripe.	68	Xanthomonas badrii	Blight.
14	Xanthomonas translucens (f. sp)	Blight.		Corn (Zea mays)	
	Barberry (Berberis spp)		69	Bacterium stewartii	Wilt.
15	Pseudomonas berberidis	Leaf spot.	70	Erwinia dissolvens	Stock rot.
	Bean (Phaseolus vulgaris)		71	Pseudomonas desaiana	Stinking rot.
16	Corynebacterium flaccumfaciens	Wilt.	72	P. lapsa	Leaf and stock rot.
17	Pseudomonas phaseolicola	Halo blight.		Cosmos (Cosmos spp)	
18	P. stizolobii	Leaf spot.	73	Erwinia cosmovora	Fire blight.
19	P. syringae	Lilac blight.		Cotton (Gossypium spp)	
20	P. viridiflava	Leaf spot and blight.	74	Xanthomonas malvacearum	Angular leaf spot.
21	Xanthomonas phaseoli	Common blight.		Cowpea (Vigna sinensis)	
22	X. phaseoli var. fuscans	Fuscous blight.	75	Pseudomonas syringae	Bacterial leaf spot.
	Beet, sugar (Beta vulgaris)		76	Xanthomonas vignicola	Canker.
23	Pseudomonas wieringae	Ring rot.		Crucifers: cabbage, cauliflower, turnips, radish	
24	Xanthomonas beticola	Bacterial pocket.	77	Xanthomonas campestris	Black rot.
	Betle pepper (Piper betle)		78	X. vesicatoria var. raphani	Blight.
25	Pseudomonas betlis	Leaf blight.		Cucumber (Cucumis sativus)	
26	Xanthomonas betlicola	Blight.	79	Pseudomonas lachyrmans	Angular leaf spot.
	Bindweed (Polygonum convolvulus)			Cucurbits: cucumber, squash, cantalopes	
27	Pseudomonas polygoni	Leaf spot.	80	Erwinia tracheiphila	Wilt.
28	Xanthomonas uppalii	Wilt.	81	Xanthomonas cucurbitae	Leaf spot.
	Bowlesia (Bowlesia septentrionalis			Cumin (Cuminum spp)	
29	Pseudomonas bowlesiae	Blight.	82	Pseudomonas cumini	Blight.
	Broom grass (Bromus spp)			Currant (Ribes aureum)	
30	Pseudomonas coronafaciens		83	Pseudomonas ribicola	Leaf spot.
	var. stropurpurea	Leaf spot.		Dandelion, Russian (Taraxacum	
31	Xanthomonas translucens (f. sp)	Blight.		kok-saghyz)	
	Begonia, tuberous (Begonia spp and		84	Xanthomonas taraxaci	Leaf blight.
	hybrids)			Delphinium (Delphinium spp)	
32	Xanthomonas begoniae	Leaf spot.	85	Pseudomonas delphinii	Black spot.
	Broad bean (Vicia faba)			Dianthus, Carnations, pinks	
33	Pseudomonas fabae	Blight.		(Dianthus spp)	
34	P. viciae	Leaf and stem spot.	86	Pseudomonas caryophylli	Root rot and wilt.
	Burdock (Arctium lappa)		87	P. woodsii	Leaf spot.
35	Xanthomonas nigromaculans	Black spot.		Dieffenbachia (Dieffenbachia picta)	
	Cabbage (Brassica oleraceae var. capitata)		88	Xanthomonas diffenbachiae	Leaf spot.
36	Pseudomonas cichorii	Zonate spot.		Dysoxylum sectabile	
37	Xanthomonas campestris	Black rot.	89	Pseudomonas dysoxyli	Leaf spot.
	Cactus (Opuntia spp)			Elder (Sambucus edulis)	
38	Erwinia sp	Soft rot.	90	Xanthomonas sambuci	Blight.
	Cactus, giant (Carnegiea gigantea)			Elm (Ulmus spp)	
39	Erwinia carnegieana	Rot or decay.	91	Erwinia nimipressuralis	Wetwood.
	Calendula (Calendula officinalis)		92	Pseudomonas lignicola	Black streak of wood.
40	Pseudomonas calendulae	Leaf and stem spot.		Fern, bird's nest (Asplenium nidus)	
	Canna (Canna indica)		93	Pseudomonas asplenii	Leaf blight.
41	Xanthomonas cannae	Blight.		Filbert (Corylina spp)	
	Carpet grass (Axonopus scoparius)		94	Pseudomonas colurnae	Leaf spot.
42	Xanthomonas axonoperis	Blight.	95	Xanthomonas corylina	Blight.
	Carrot (Daucus carota var. sativa)			Fir, Douglas (Pseudotsuga taxifolia)	
43	Erwinia carotovora	Soft rot.	96	Bacterium pseudotsugae	Gall.
44	Xanthomonas carotae	Leaf blight.		Flax, New Zealand (Phormium tenax)	
	Cassava (Manihot spp)		97	Xanthomonas phormicola	Leaf stripe.
45	Erwinia cassavae	Blight.		Fruit trees	
46	Xanthomonas cassavae	Leaf spot.	98	Agrobacterium rhizogenes	Hairy root.
47	X. manihotis	Wilt and gummosis.	99	A. tumefaciens	Crown gall.
	Castor bean (Ricinus communis)			Geranium (Geranium spp)	
48	Xanthomonas ricinicola	Leaf spot.	100	Xanthomonas geranii	Leaf spot.
	Cauliflower (Brassica oleraceae var.		101	X. pelargonii	Leaf spot.
	botrytis)			Gardenia (Gardenia jasminoides)	
49	Pseudomonas maculicola	Peppery spot.	102	Pseudomonas gardiniae	Leaf spot.
	Celery (Apium graveolens)		103	Xanthomonas maculifolium-gardeniae	Leaf spot.
50	Pseudomonas apii	Leaf spot.		Ginseng (Panax quinquefolium)	
	Cereals and grasses		104	Pseudomonas panacis	Root and stem rot.
51	Corynebacterium agropyri	Yellow gum disease.		Gladiolus (Gladiolus spp)	
52	C. rathayi	Yellow gum disease.	105	Pseudomonas marginata	Corm scab and leaf blight.
53	C. tritici	Yellow gum disease.	106	P. gladioli	Rot.
54	Pseudomonas alboprecipitans	Streak.	107	Xanthomonas gummisudans	Blight.
55	P. coronafaciens	Streak.		Glorybower (Clerodendron phlomoides)	
56	Xanthomonas translucens various f. sp	Blight.	108	Xanthomonas clerodendroni	Leaf spot.

	Host Plant and Pathogen	Disease
	Grape (Vitis vinifera)	
109	Erwinia vitivora	Dead arm.
110	Pseudomonas tumefaciens	Black knot.
	Guayule (Parthenium argentatum)	
111	Erwinia carotovora f. sp parthenii	Root and stem rot.
	Gypsophila (Gypsophila sp)	
112	Agrobacterium gypsophilae	Gall.
	Henna (Lawsonia inermis)	
113	Xanthomonas lawsoniae	Leaf spot.
	Heronsbill (Erodium texanum)	
114	Pseudomonas erodii	Leaf spot.
	Horseradish (Armoracia lapathifolia)	
115	Xanthomonas campestris var. armoraciae	Leaf spot.
	Hyacinth (Hyacinthus orientalis)	
116	Xanthomonas hyacinthi	Yellow disease.
117	Erwinia spp	Soft rot.
	Iris (Iris spp)	
118	Bacterium tardicrescens	Leaf blight.
119	Pseudomonas cichorii	Leaf blight.
120	P. iridicola	Leaf blight.
	Ivy (Hedera helix)	
121	Xanthomonas hederae	Leaf spot.
	Ivy, Japanese (Cissus japonica)	
122	Pseudomonas cissicola	Black spot.
	Jimson weed (Datura spp)	
123	Xanthomonas hemmiana	Leaf spot.
	Jute (Corchorus capsularis)	
124	Xanthomonas nakatae	Leaf spot.
	Larkspur (Delphinium spp)	
125	Erwinia atroseptica	Black leg.
	Laurel, California (Umbellularia californica)	
126	Pseudomonas lauracearum	Leaf spot.
	Lespedeza (Lespedeza spp)	
127	Xanthomonas lespedezae	Wilt.
	Lettuce (Lactuca sativa)	
128	Pseudomonas cichorii	Head rot.
129	P. marginalis	Marginal blight and rot.
130	P. viridilivida	Leaf spot and blight.
131	Xanthomonas vitians	Wilt and rot.
	Lilac (Syringa vulgaris)	
132	Pseudomonas syringae	Blight.
	Loquat (Eriobotrya japonica)	
133	Pseudomonas erobotryae	Bud rot.
	Lovage (Levisticum officinale)	
134	Pseudomonas levistica	Leaf blight.
	Lupine (Lupinus spp)	
135	Erwinia lupini	Brown blight.
136	Xanthomonas phaseoli	Blight.
	Mango (Mangifera indica)	
137	Bacillus subtilis	Soft rot.
138	Erwinia mangiferae	Leaf, stem and fruit blight.
139	Pseudomonas mangiferae-indicae	Leaf spot.
	Maple (Acer spp)	
140	Pseudomonas aceris	Leaf spot.
141	Xanthomonas acernea	Leaf blight.
	Marigold, African (Tagetes erecta)	
142	Pseudomonas tagetes	Leaf spot.
	Morning glory (Ipomoea musicata)	
143	Xanthomonas uppalii	Blight.
	Mulberry (Morus spp)	
144	Pseudomonas mori	Blight.
	Millet, foxtail (Setaria italica)	
145	Pseudomonas setariae	Brown stripe.
	Millet, broom corn (Panicum miliaceum)	
146	Pseudomonas panici-miliacei	Leaf stripe.
147	Xanthomonas panici	Streak.
	Mushroom (Agaricus campestris)	
148	Pseudomonas tolaasi	Spot.
	Oat (Avena sativa)	
149	Pseudomonas coronafaciens	Halo blight.
150	P. coronafaciens var. atropurpurea	Purple spot.
151	Xanthomonas translucens (f. sp)	Blight.
	Oleander (Nerium oleander)	
152	Pseudomonas tonelliana	Gall.
	Olive (Olea spp)	
153	Pseudomonas savastanoi	Knott.
	Onion (Alium cepa)	
154	Pseudomonas alliicola	Scale rot.
155	P. cepacia	Sour skin.
156	P. cichorii and P. marginalis	Soft rot.
157	Xanthomonas striaformans	Stripe.
	Orchids	
158	Pseudomonas cattleyae	Leaf spot.
	Palm, Washington (Washingtonia filifera)	
159	Pseudomonas washingtoniae	Leaf blight.

	Host Plant and Pathogen	Disease
	Pangara tree (Erythrina indica)	
160	Xanthomonas erythrinae	Leaf spot.
	Passion-flower (Passiflora edulis)	
161	Pseudomonas passiflorae	Grease spot.
	Pea (Pisum sativum)	
162	Pseudomonas pisi	Blight.
	Pea, pigeon (Cajanus cajan)	
163	Xanthomonas cajani	Blight.
	Peach (Prunus persica)	
164	Xanthomonas pruni	Spot of leaf and fruit.
	Pear (Pyrus communis)	
165	Erwinia amylovora	Fire blight.
166	Pseudomonas syringae	Twig and blossom blight.
167	P. barkeri	Blossom blight.
168	P. nectarophila	Blossom blight.
	Pelargonium (Pelargonium spp)	
169	Pseudomonas erodii	Leaf spot.
170	Xanthomonas pelargonii	Leaf spot and stalk rot.
	Pineapple (Ananas comosus)	
171	Erwinia ananas	Brown rot.
172	Pseudomonas ananas	Black rot.
	Plantain (Plantago laceolata)	
173	Xanthomonas plantaginis	Leaf spot.
	Plum (Prunus spp)	
174	Pseudomonas mors-prunorum	Canker and stunt.
175	P. syringae	Blight and gummosis.
176	Xanthomonas pruni	Fruit and leaf spot.
	Poinsettia (Euphorbia pulcherrima)	
177	Corynebacterium poinsettiae	Leaf and stem streak.
178	Xanthomonas poinsettiaecola	Leaf spot.
	Poplar (Populus spp)	
179	Corynebacterium humiferum	Wet wood.
180	Pseudomonas rimaefaciens	Canker.
	Poppy (Papaver spp)	
181	Pseudomonas papaveris	Black streak.
182	Xanthomonas papavericola	Black spot.
	Potato (Solanum tuberosum)	
183	Bacillus spp	Storage rots.
184	Corynebacterium sepedonicum	Ring rot.
185	Erwinia atroseptica	Black leg.
186	Erwinia spp	Soft rot.
187	Streptomyces scabies	Scab.
	Primrose (Primula spp)	
188	Pseudomonas primulae	Leaf spot.
	Privet (Ligustrum japonicum)	
189	Pseudomonas ligustri	Leaf spot.
	Solanaceae: eggplant, pepper, tomato, potato	
190	Pseudomonas solanacearum	Southern wilt or brown rot.
	Rhubarb (Rheum rhaponticum)	
191	Erwinia rhapontici	Crown rot.
	Rice (Oryza sativa)	
192	Xanthomonas oryzae	Leaf blotch.
193	X. kresek	Kresek disease.
	Rose-mallow (Hibiscus spp)	
194	Pseudomonas syringae	Blight.
	Rubus	
195	Agrobacterium rubi	Gall.
196	Erwinia amylovora f. sp rubi	Blight.
	Senna (Cassia tora)	
197	Xanthomonas cassiae	Blight.
	Sesbania (Sesbania sp)	
198	Xanthomonas sesbaniae	Leaf spot.
	Sesame (Sesamum orientale)	
199	Pseudomonas sesami	Blight.
	Snapdragon (Antirrhinum majus)	
200	Xanthomonas antirrhini	Leaf spot.
	Sorghum (Sorghum spp)	
201	Pseudomonas andropogoni	Leaf blotch and streak.
202	Xanthomonas holcicola	Leaf spot.
	Soybean (Glycine max)	
203	Pseudomonas glycenea	Leaf spot.
204	P. tabaci	Wildfire.
205	Xanthomonas phaseoli var. sojensis	Pustule.
	Stock (Matthiola incana)	
206	Pseudomonas matthiolae	Blight.
207	P. syringae	Blight.
208	Xanthomonas incanae	Blight.
	Sugar cane (Saccharum officinarum)	
209	Bacterium albilineans	White streak and wilt.
210	Xanthomonas rubilineans	Red streak.
211	X. rubrisubalbicans	Mottled stripe.
212	X. vasculocum	Gummosis.
	Sunflower (Helianthus spp)	
213	Pseudomonas helianthi	Leaf spot.
	Sweet coltsfoot (Petasites japonica)	
214	Pseudomonas petasites	Black spot.

425. SELECTED BACTERIAL PARASITES: PLANTS (Concluded)

	Host Plant and Pathogen	Disease		Host Plant and Pathogen	Disease
	Tamarind (Tamarindus indica)			Velvet bean (Stizolobium deeringianum)	
215	Xanthomonas tamarindi	Leaf spot.	239	Pseudomonas stizolobii	Leaf spot.
	Sweetpea and numerous other plants		240	Xanthomonas stizolobiicola	Blight.
216	Corynebacterium fascians	Fasciation.		Vetch, milk (Astragalus sp)	
	Teakwood (Tectona grandis)		241	Pseudomonas astragali	Black spot.
217	Pseudomonas tectonae	Seedling wilt.		Viburnum (Viburnum spp)	
218	Xanthomonas melhusii	Leaf spot.	242	Pseudomonas viburni	Leaf spot.
	Tick-trefoil (Desmodium diffusum, D. gangeticum)			Walnut (Juglans spp)	
219	Xanthomonas desmodii	Blight.	243	Xanthomonas juglandis	Blight.
220	X. desmodii-gangetica	Blight.		Wheat (Triticum aestivum)	
	Tobacco (Nicotiana spp)		244	Pseudomonas atrofaciens	Basal glume rot.
221	Erwinia aroideae	Hollow stalk and barn rot.	245	Xanthomonas translucens f. sp undulosa	Black chaff.
222	Pseudomonas angulata	Angular leaf spot.		Willow (Salix spp)	
223	P. mellea	Rust.	246	Erwinia salicis	Blight.
224	P. polycolor	Leaf spot and wet rot.	247	Pseudomonas saliciperda	Blight.
225	P. pseudozooglaeae	Black rust.		Winter cress (Barbarea vulgaris)	
226	P. solanacearum	Granville disease.	248	Xanthomonas barbareae	Leaf blight.
227	P. tabaci	Wildfire.		Wisteria, Japanese (Milletia floribunda)	
228	Xanthomonas heteroceae	Rust.	249	Erwinia milletiae	Galls.
	Tomato (Lycopersicon esculentum)			Zinnia (Zinnia elegans)	
229	Corynebacterum michiganense	Canker and wilt.	250	Xanthomonas nigromaculans f. sp zinniae	Angular leaf spot.
230	Pseudomonas tomato	Bacterial speck.		Numerous plants	
231	Xanthomonas vesicatoria	Pustule.	251	Agrobacterium tumefaciens	Crown gall.
	Trichrodesma zeylanicum		252	Corynebacterium fascians	Fasciation.
232	Xanthomonas trichodesmae	Leaf spot.	253	Erwinia amylovora	Fire blight of Rosaceae.
	Tung-oil tree (Aleurites fordii)		254	E. aroideae	Soft rot.
233	Pseudomonas aleuritidis	Angular leaf spot.	255	E. atroseptica	Soft rot.
	Unicorn-plant (Martynia louisiana)		256	E. carotovora	Soft rot.
234	Pseudomonas martyniae	Blight.	257	E. chrysanthemi	Soft rot.
	Vegetables (fleshy), plants of tuberous and fleshy roots		258	Pseudomonas solanacearum	Brown rot.
235	Erwinia aroideae	Soft rots.	259	P. syringae	Blight.
236	E. atroseptica	Soft rots.			
237	E. carotovora	Soft rots.			
238	E. chrysanthemi	Soft rots.			

426. SELECTED FUNGAL PARASITES: FIELD, FRUIT, VEGETABLE CROPS

	Host Plant and Pathogen	Disease		Host Plant and Pathogen	Disease
	Field Crops: Cereals			Field Crops: Cereals (concluded)	
	Barley (Hordeum vulgare)			Sorghum (Sorghum spp)	
1	Erysiphe graminis	Powdery mildew.	36	Ascochyta sorghina	Rough spot.
2	Gibberella zeae	Fusarium blight, scab.	37	Cercospora sorghina	Gray leaf spot.
3	Helminthosporium gramineum	Stripe disease.	38	Colletotrichum graminicola	Anthracnose.
4	H. sativum	Spot blotch, root rot, foot rot, kernel blight.	39	Gloeocercospora sorghi	Zonate leaf spot.
			40	Helminthosporium sorghicola	Target spot.
5	Puccinia graminis, P. tritici	Stem rust.	41	H. turcicum	Leaf blight.
6	P. hordei	Leaf rust.	42	Macrophomina phaseolina	Charcoal or stalk rot.
7	Pyrenophora teres	Net blotch.	43	Periconia circinata	Milo disease, root rot.
8	Rhynchosporium secalis	Scald.	44	Ramulispora sorghi	Sooty stripe.
9	Typhula itoana	Snow mold.	45	Sphacelotheca cruenta	Loose kernel smut.
10	Ustilago hordei	Covered smut.	46	S. sorghi	Covered kernel smut.
11	U. nigra	Black or semi-loose smut.		Wheat (Triticum aestivum)	
12	U. nuda	Loose smut.	47	Erysiphe graminis tritici	Powdery mildew.
	Corn (Zea mays)		48	Gibberella zeae	Fusarium blight or scab.
13	Cochliobolus heterostrophus	Southern leaf blight, seedling blight.	49	Helminthosporium sativum	Crown rot, root rot.
			50	Leptosphaeria nodorum	Glume blotch, node canker.
14	Diplodia zeae, D. macrospora	Stalk rot, dry ear rot.	51	Ophiobolus graminis	Take-all.
15	Gibberella fujikuroi	Pink ear rot, seedling blight.	52	Puccinia glumarum	Stripe rust.
16	G. zeae	Stalk rot, red ear rot, seedling blight, root rot.	53	P. graminis tritici	Stem rust.
			54	P. rubigo-vera tritici	Leaf rust.
17	Helminthosporium carbonum	Northern leaf spot, charred ear, seedling blight.	55	Septoria tritici	Leaf blotch.
			56	Tilletia brevifaciens	Dwarf bunt.
18	H. turcicum	Northern leaf blight, seedling blight.	57	T. caries, T. foetida	Bunt or stinking smut.
			58	Urocystis tritici	Flag smut.
19	Physalospora zeae	Gray ear rot.	59	Ustilago tritici	Loose smut.
20	Puccinia sorghi	Rust.		Field Crops: Legumes	
21	Sclerospora graminicola	Downy mildew.		Alfalfa (Medicago sativa)	
22	Ustilago maydis	Smut.	60	Ascochyta medicaginis	Spring black stem.
	Oats (Avena sativa)		61	Leptosphaeria pratensis	Leaf spot, root rot, crown rot.
23	Leptosphaeria avenaria	Black stem.	62	Peronospora trifoliorum	Downy mildew.
24	Puccinia coronata avenae	Crown rust.	63	Pseudopeziza medicaginis	Common leaf spot.
25	P. graminis avenae	Stem rust.	64	P. jonesii	Yellow leaf blotch.
26	Ustilago avenae	Loose smut.	65	Sclerotinia trifoliorum	Crown rot, root rot.
27	U. kolleri	Covered smut.	66	Uromyces striatus medicaginis	Rust.
	Rice (Oryza sativa)		67	Urophlyctis alfalfae	Crown wart.
28	Cercospora oryzae	Cercospora spot.		Clover (Trifolium spp)	
29	Cochliobolus miyabeanus	Helminthosporium blight.	68	Colletotrichum trifolii	Southern anthracnose.
	Rye (Secale cereale)		69	Cymadothea trifolii	Sooty blotch (red, white and alsike clover).
30	Claviceps purpurea	Ergot.	70	Erysiphe polygoni	Powdery mildew (red clover).
31	Erysiphe graminis	Powdery mildew.	71	Kabatiella caulivora	Northern anthracnose (crimson and red clover).
32	Gibberella zeae	Fusarium blight, scab.			
33	Puccinia graminis secalis	Stem rust.	72	Phoma trifolii	Spring black stem (red clover).
34	P. rubigo-vera secalis	Leaf rust.	73	Pseudoplea trifolii	Leaf spot.
35	Urocystis occulta	Stem smut.			

#	Host Plant and Pathogen	Disease	#	Host Plant and Pathogen	Disease
	Field Crops: Legumes (concluded)			**Fruit Crops (continued)**	
	Clover (Trifolium spp) (concluded)			Avocado (Persea americana)	
74	Sclerotinia trifoliorum	Root rot, crown rot.	137	Botryosphaeria ribis chromogena	Branch canker, fruit rot.
75	Uromyces trifolii	Rust.	138	Cercospora purpurea	Cercospora spot or blotch.
	Lespedeza spp		139	Colletotrichum gloeosporioides	Anthracnose or black spot.
76	Microsphaera diffusa	Powdery mildew.	140	Diplodia theobromae	Stem-end rot.
	Soybean (Glycine soja)		141	Phomopsis sp	Stem-end rot.
77	Cephalosporium gregatum	Brown stem rot.	142	Phytophthora cinnamomi	Phytophthora root rot.
78	Cercospora sojina	Frog-eye leaf spot.	143	Sphaceloma perseae	Scab (fruit and foliage).
79	Colletotrichum truncatum	Anthracnose.	144	Verticillium albo-atrum	Verticillium wilt.
80	Corynespora cassiicola	Target spot.		Blackberry (Rubus spp)	
81	Diaporthe phaseolorum batatis	Stem canker.	145	Cercosporella rubi	Double blossom.
82	D. phaseolorum sojae	Pod and stem blight.	146	Elsinoë veneta	Anthracnose.
83	Fusarium oxysporum tracheiphilum	Fusarium wilt.	147	Kuehneola uredinis	Yellow leaf and cane rust.
84	Glomerella glycines	Anthracnose.	148	Septoria rubi	Leaf and cane spot.
85	Macrophomina phaseoli	Ashy stem blight.	149	Verticillium albo-atrum	Verticillium wilt.
86	Pellicularia rolfsii	Southern wilt.		Blueberry (Vaccinium spp)	
87	Peronospora manshurica	Downy mildew.	150	Botrytis cinerea	Blossom, fruit and twig blight.
88	Phyllosticta sojicola	Leaf spot.	151	Dothichiza caroliniana	Leaf spot.
89	Phymatotrichum omnivorum	Texas root rot.	152	Microsphaera alni vaccinii	Powdery mildew.
90	Sclerotinia sclerotiorum	Stem rot.	153	Monilinia vaccinii corymbosi	Mummy berry.
91	Septoria glycines	Brown spot.	154	Physalospora corticis	Stem canker.
	Sweetclover (Melilotus alba)			Cherry (Prunus spp)	
92	Ascochyta spp	Leaf, stem, and pod blight.	155	Botrytis cinerea	Gray mold.
93	Cercospora zebrina	Leaf spot.	156	Coccomyces hiemalis	Leaf spot.
94	Leptosphaeria pratensis	Leaf spot, crown rot, root rot.	157	Monilinia fructicola	Brown rot, blossom blight.
95	Mycosphaerella davisii	Leaf spot.	158	M. laxa	European brown rot, blossom and twig blight.
96	M. lethalis	Black stem.			
97	Phytophthora cactorum	Root rot.	159	Podosphaera oxyacanthae	Powdery mildew.
98	Pseudopeziza melilote	Common leaf spot.		Citrus (Citrus spp)	
	Field Crops: Miscellaneous		160	Clitocybe tabescens	Root rot.
	Cotton (Gossypium spp)		161	Diaporthe citri	Melanose, stem-end rot.
99	Fusarium oxysporum vasinfectum	Fusarium wilt.	162	Diplodia natalensis	Twig and branch dieback, stem-end rot.
100	Glomerella gossypii	Anthracnose.	163	Elsinoë fawcetti	Scab.
101	Pellicularia filamentosa	"Soreshin" seedling stem canker.	164	Glomerella cingulata	Withertip, anthracnose.
102	Phymatotrichum omnivorum	Root rot.	165	Phytophthora citrophthora	Foot rot, brown rot.
103	Puccinia stakmanii	Rust.		Cranberry (Vaccinium spp)	
104	Verticillium albo-atrum	Wilt.	166	Acanthorhyncus vaccinii	Blotch rot of berries.
	Flax (Linum usitatissimum)		167	Diplodia vaccinii	Twig blight.
105	Colletotrichum lini	Anthracnose.	168	Glomerella cingulata vaccinii	Bitter rot, leaf spot.
106	Fusarium oxysporum lini	Fusarium wilt.	169	Guignardia vaccinii	Early rot, scald, blast.
107	Melampsora lini	Rust.	170	Sporonema oxycocci	Leaf spot, berry rot.
108	Mycosphaerella linorum	Pasmo disease.		Fig (Ficus carica)	
	Peanut (Arachis hypogaea)		171	Glomerella cingulata	Anthracnose.
109	Macrophomina phaseoli	Seedling blight.	172	Physopella fici	Rust.
110	Mycosphaerella arachidicola	Early leaf spot.	173	Rhizoctonia microsclerotia	Leaf blight, web blight.
111	Pellicularia filamentosa	Dry rot.		Grape (Vitis spp)	
112	P. rolfsii	Southern blight.	174	Cryptosporella viticola	Dead arm.
	Sugar cane (Saccharum officinarum)		175	Elsinoë ampelina	Anthracnose.
113	Helminthosporium sacchari	Eyespot.	176	Guignardia bidwellii	Black rot.
114	Physalospora tucumanensis	Red rot.	177	Plasmopara viticola	Downy mildew.
	Peppermint, spearmint (Mentha spp)		178	Uncinula necator	Powdery mildew.
115	Puccinia menthae	Rust.		Olive (Olea europaea)	
116	Verticillium albo-atrum	Verticillium wilt.	179	Armillaria mellea	Root rot.
	Tobacco (Nicotiana tabacum)		180	Asterina oleina	Black leaf spot.
117	Cercospora nicotianae	Frog-eye leaf spot.	181	Cycloconium oleaginum	Leaf spot.
118	Fusarium oxysporum[1]	Fusarium wilt.	182	Gloeosporium olivarum	Anthracnose.
119	Macrophomina phaseoli	Charcoal rot.	183	Phymatotrichum omnivorum	Root rot.
120	Pellicularia filamentosa	Stem canker.		Peach (Prunus persica)	
121	Peronospora tabacina	Blue mold.	184	Armillaria mellea	Root rot.
122	Phytophthora parasitica[1]	Black shank.	185	Clitocybe tabescens	Root rot.
123	Thielaviopsis basicola	Black rot.	186	Coryneum carpophilum	Blight, shot-hole.
	Fruit Crops		187	Glomerella cingulata	Ripe rot, twig blight.
	Apple (Pyrus malus)		188	Monilinia fructicola	Brown rot, twig canker.
124	Clitocybe tabescens	Root rot.	189	Taphrina deformans	Leaf curl.
125	Corticium galactinum	White root rot.		Pear (Pyrus communis)	
126	Gloeodes pomigena	Sooty blotch.	190	Botrytis cinerea	Gray mold.
127	Glomerella cingulata	Bitter rot of fruit, stem canker.	191	Clitocybe tabescens	Root rot.
128	Gymnosporangium juniperi virginianae	Rust.	192	Neofabraea malicorticis	Black spot canker.
129	Phyllosticta solitaria	Blotch, leaf spot, canker.	193	N. perennans	Perennial canker.
130	Podosphaera leucotricha	Powdery mildew.	194	Podosphaera leucotricha	Powdery mildew.
131	Venturia inaequalis	Scab.	195	Venturia pyrina	Scab.
132	Xylaria mali	Black root rot.		Plum (Prunus domestica)	
	Apricot (Prunus armeniaca)		196	Armillaria mellea	Root rot.
133	Armillaria mellea	Root rot.	197	Monilinia fructicola	Brown rot, blossom blight.
134	Coryneum carpophilum	Coryneum blight.	198	M. laxa	European brown rot, blossom and twig blight.
135	Monilinia fructicola	Brown rot (ripe fruit)			
136	M. laxa	Brown rot (green and ripe fruit), blossom and twig blight.		Raspberry (Rubus spp)	
			199	Didymella applanata	Spur blight.
			200	Elsinoë veneta	Anthracnose.
			201	Phragmidium rubi-idaei	Rust.

/1/ Variety nicotianae.

426. SELECTED FUNGAL PARASITES: FIELD, FRUIT, VEGETABLE CROPS (Concluded)

	Host Plant and Pathogen	Disease
	Fruit Crops (concluded)	
	Raspberry (Rubus spp) (concluded)	
202	Septoria rubi	Leaf and cane spot.
	Strawberry (Fragaria chiloensis)	
203	Botrytis cinerea	Gray mold rot.
204	Dendrophoma obscurans	Leaf blight, stem-end rot.
205	Diplocarpon earliana	Leaf scorch.
206	Mycosphaerella fragariae	Leaf spot.
207	Phytophthora fragariae	Red stele.
	Nut Crops	
	Almond (Prunus amygdalus)	
208	Armillaria mellea	Root rot.
209	Coryneum carpophilum	Blight, shot-hole.
210	Monilinia fructicola	Peach brown rot.
211	M. laxa	Brown rot, blossom blight.
	Filbert (Corylus spp)	
212	Apioporthe anomala	Twig blight, canker.
213	Armillaria mellea	Root rot.
214	Phyllactinia corylea	Powdery mildew.
	Pecan (Carya illinoensis)	
215	Cercospora fusca	Brown leaf spot.
216	Cladosporium effusum	Scab.
217	Gnomonia caryae pecanae	Liver spot.
218	G. nerviseda	Vein spot.
219	Mycosphaerella caryigena	Downy spot.
220	M. dendroides	Leaf blotch.
221	Phymatotrichum omnivorum	Cotton root rot.
	Walnut (Juglans regia)	
222	Armillaria mellea	Root rot.
223	Ascochyta juglandis	Ring spot.
224	Dothiorella gregaria	Dieback, black sap.
225	Exosporina fawcetti	Branch wilt, canker.
226	Gnomonia leptostyla	Leaf blotch.
227	Phytophthora cactorum	Crown rot.
	Vegetable Crops	
	Asparagus (Asparagus officinalis)	
228	Fusarium oxysporum asparagi	Wilt, root rot.
229	Puccinia asparagi	Rust.
	Bean (Phaseolus vulgaris)	
230	Colletotrichum lindemuthianum	Anthracnose.
231	Erysiphe polygoni	Powdery mildew.
232	Fusarium solani	Root rot.
233	Macrophomina phaseoli	Ashy stem blight, charcoal rot, leaf spot, root rot.
234	Uromyces phaseoli typica	Rust.
	Bean (Phaseolus lunatus macrocarpus)	
235	Colletotrichum truncatum	Stem anthracnose.
236	Diaporthe phaseolorum	Pod blight, leaf spot.
237	Macrophomina phaseolina	Ashy stem blight, charcoal rot, leaf spot, root rot.
238	Phytophthora phaseoli	Downy mildew.
	Beet (Beta vulgaris)	
239	Aphanomyces cochlioides	Black root, tip rot.
240	Cercospora beticola	Cercospora leaf spot.
241	Fusarium spp	Root rot, storage rot, wilt.
242	Peronospora schachtii	Downy mildew.
243	Pleospora betae	Leaf spot, root rot.
244	Uromyces betae	Rust.
	Carrot (Daucus carota)	
245	Alternaria dauci	Leaf blight.
246	A. radicina	Black rot.
247	Cercospora carotae	Blight, leaf spot.
	Celery (Apium graveolens dulce)	
248	Cercospora apii	Early blight.
249	Fusarium oxysporum apii	Fusarium yellows.
250	Septoria apii	Late blight (large spot).
251	S. apii-graveolentis	Late blight (small spot).

	Host Plant and Pathogen	Disease
	Vegetable Crops (concluded)	
	Crucifer (Brassica spp)[2]	
252	Alternaria brassicae	Gray leaf spot.
253	Fusarium oxysporum conglutinans	Yellows.
254	Mycosphaerella brassicicola	Ring spot.
255	Peronospora parasitica	Downy mildew.
256	Phoma lingam	Blackleg.
257	Phytophthora megasperma	Root rot of cabbage, cauliflower, and brussel sprouts.
258	Plasmodiophora brassicae	Clubroot.
	Cucurbit (Cucurbita spp)[3]	
259	Alternaria cucumerina	Leaf blight.
260	Cladosporium cucumerinum	Scab.
261	Colletotrichum lagenarium	Anthracnose (except squash).
262	Erysiphe cichoracearum	Powdery mildew.
263	Fusarium oxysporum melonis	Fusarium wilt (muskmelon).
264	F. oxysporum niveum	Fusarium wilt (watermelon).
265	F. solani cucurbitae	Fusarium root rot.
266	Mycosphaerella melonis	Black rot.
267	Pseudoperonospora cubensis	Downy mildew.
268	Verticillium albo-atrum	Verticillium wilt.
	Lettuce (Lactuca sativa)	
269	Botrytis cinerea	Gray mold.
270	Bremia lactucae	Downy mildew.
	Onion (Allium spp)	
271	Botrytis spp	Neck rot.
272	Peronospora destructor	Downy mildew.
273	Pyrenochaeta terrestris	Pink rot.
274	Urocystis cepulae	Smut.
	Pea (Pisum sativum)	
275	Aphanomyces euteiches	Root rot.
276	Ascochyta pinodella	Ascochyta foot rot.
277	A. pisi	Ascochyta leaf and pod spot.
278	Colletotrichum pisi	Anthracnose.
279	Erysiphe polygoni	Powdery mildew.
280	Fusarium oxysporum pisi, strain 1	Fusarium wilt.
281	F. oxysporum pisi, strain 2	Near-wilt.
282	F. solani pisi	Root rot.
283	Mycosphaerella pinodes	Mycosphaerella blight.
284	Peronospora viciae	Downy mildew.
	Pepper (Capsicum frutescens)	
285	Cercospora capsici	Frog-eye leaf spot.
286	Gloeosporium piperatum	Anthracnose.
287	Phytophthora capsici	Phytophthora blight.
	Potato (Solanum tuberosum)	
288	Alternaria solani	Early blight.
289	Fusarium spp	Wilt and tuber rot.
290	Phytophthora infestans	Late blight.
291	Streptomyces scabies	Common scab.
292	Verticillium albo-atrum	Verticillium wilt.
	Spinach (Spinacia oleracea)	
293	Albugo occidentalis	White rust.
294	Peronospora effusa	Downy mildew.
	Sweetpotato (Ipomoea batatas)	
295	Endoconidiophora fimbriata	Black rot.
296	Fusarium oxysporum batatas	Wilt, stem rot.
297	Monilochaetes infuscans	Scurf.
298	Plenodomus destruens	Foot rot.
299	Streptomyces ipomoea	Pox or soil rot.
	Tomato (Lycopersicon esculentum)	
300	Alternaria solani	Early blight.
301	Colletotrichum phomoides	Anthracnose.
302	Fusarium oxysporum lycopersici	Fusarium wilt.
303	Phoma destructiva	Phoma rot.
304	Phytophthora infestans	Late blight.
305	Septoria lycopersici	Leaf spot.
306	Stemphylium solani	Gray leaf spot.

/2/ Cabbage, cauliflower. /3/ Cucumber, muskmelon, squash, watermelon.

427. SELECTED FUNGAL PARASITES: FOREST TREES

	Host Plant and Pathogen	Disease
	Alaska-cedar (Chamaecyparis nootkatensis)	
1	Gymnosporangium nootkatense	Mountain ash-Alaska cedar rust.
	Alder (Alnus spp)	
2	Cytospora pulcherrima	Cytospora canker.
3	Didymospaeria oregonensis	Didymospaeria canker.
4	Erysiphe aggregata	Powdery mildew.
5	Melampsoridium alni	Leaf rust.

	Host Plant and Pathogen	Disease
	Alder (Alnus spp) (concluded)	
6	Taphrina amentorum	Leaf blister.
7	T. macrophylla	Yellow leaf blister.
8	T. occidentalis	Leaf blister.
9	T. robinsoniana	Leaf blister.
10	T. rugosa	Leaf blister.
	Arborvitae (Thuja orientalis)	
11	Coryneum berckmanii	Berckman's blight.
12	Gymnosporangium kernianum	Witches'-broom rust.

	Host Plant and Pathogen	Disease		Host Plant and Pathogen	Disease
	Arborvitae (Thuja orientalis) (concluded)			**Fir (Abies spp) (concluded)**	
13	Gymnosporangium nelsoni	Hawthorne-western juniper rust.	82	Melampsora abieti-capraearum	Needle rot.
			83	Melampsorella cerastii	Witches'-broom.
	Ash (Fraxinus spp)		84	Melesia fructuosa, M. marginalis	Needle rot.
14	Armillaria mellea	Root rot.	85	M. polypodophila	Needle-witches'-broom rust.
15	Cytospora annularis	Cytospora canker.	86	Peridermium holwayi,	
16	Fomes fraxinophilus	White heart rot.		P. ornamentale, P. rugosum	Needle rust.
17	Marssonia fraxini	Leaf spot.	87	Phacidium infestans var. abietis	Needle blight.
18	Mycosphaerella fraxinicola	Leaf spot.	88	Phomopsis boycei	Phomopsis canker.
19	Phymatotrichum omnivorum	Phymatotrichum root rot.	89	Polyporus abietinus	White pitted sap rot.
20	Polyporus hispidus	Spongy white rot.	90	P. balsameus	Brown butt rot.
21	Puccinia peridermiospora	Leaf rust.	91	P. dryadeus	White root rot.
	Ash, mountain (Sorbus americana)		92	P. schweinitzii	Root and butt rot.
22	Gymnosporangium aurantiacum	Fusiforme rust of juniper.	93	Poria subacida	Butt rot.
23	G. juniperinum	Subglobose gall rust.	94	Rehmellopsis balsamiae	Tip blight.
24	G. nidus-avis	Witches'-broom and spindle shaped gall rust.	95	Scleroderris abieticola	Scleroderris canker.
			96	Spicaria anomala	Brown stain of fir.
	Basswood (Tilia spp)		97	Stereum chailleti	Patchy rot.
25	Collybia velutipes	Spongy white rot.	98	S. sanguinolentum	Red heart rot.
26	Pholiota squarrosa adiposa	Brown mottled rot.	99	Uredinopsis atkinosinii, U. cera-	
27	Uncinula clintonii	Powdery mildew.		tophora, U. longimucronata,	
	Beech (Fagus grandifolia)			U. macrosperma, U. mirabilis	Needle rust.
28	Fomes fomentarius	White mottled rot.		**Douglas-fir (Pseudotsuga menziesii)**	
29	F. igniarius nigricans	Heart rot.	100	Adelopus gaümanni	Needle cast.
30	Nectria coccinea faginata	Beech bark disease.	101	Armillaria mellea	Shoestring root rot.
31	Phytophthora cactorum	Phytophthora blight.	102	Botrytis douglasii	Gray mold blight.
32	Polyporus glomeratus	Light-brown spongy heart rot.	103	Caliciopsis pinea	Caliciopsis canker.
33	Poria obliqua	Canker.	104	Chondropodium pseudotsugae	Chondropodium canker.
	Birch (Betula spp)		105	Cytospora friesii	Cytospora canker.
34	Fomes fomentarius	White mottled rot.	106	Dasyscypha pseudotsugae	Dasyscypha canker.
35	F. igniarius laevigatus	Heart rot and canker.	107	Diplodia pinea	Top damping off.
36	Melampsoridium betulinum	Leaf rust.	108	Echinodontium tinctorium	Brown stringy rot.
37	Nectria galligena	Nectria canker.	109	Fomes applanatus	Mottle rot.
38	Pholiota squarrosa adiposa	Brown mottled rot.	110	F. laricis	Brown trunk rot.
39	Poria obliqua	Canker.	111	F. pini	Red ring rot.
40	Stereum murrayi	Rot and canker.	112	F. pinicola	Brown cubical rot.
41	Taphrina boycei, T. flava	Yellow leaf blister.	113	F. roseus	Yellow-brown tap rot.
	Chestnut (Castanea dentata)		114	Melampsora albertensis	Needle rust.
42	Endothia parasitica	Chestnut blight.	115	Phacidium infestans var. abietis	Needle blight.
43	Fistulina hepatica	Brown cubical rot.	116	Phomopsis lokoyae	Phomopsis canker.
44	Monochaetia desmazierii	Leaf spot.	117	P. pseudotsugae	Douglas-fir canker.
45	Marssonia ochrolerica	Small leaf spot.	118	Polyporus schweinitzii	Root and butt rot.
46	Polyporus spraguei	Brown friable rot.	119	Poria monticola	Brown cubical rot.
	Cypress, Arizona (Cupressus arizonica)		120	P. weirii	Laminated root rot.
47	Gymnosporangium cupressi	Fusiform gall rust.	121	Rhobdocline pseudosugae	Needle blight.
	Cypress, monterey (Cupressus macrocarpa)		122	Sparassis radicata	Sparassis root rot.
48	Coryneum cardinale	Coryneum canker.		**Hemlock, eastern (Tsuga canadensis)**	
49	Polyporus basilaris	Brown cubical rot.	123	Fomes robustus-tsugina	White heart rot.
	Elm (Ulmus spp)		124	Ganoderma lucidum	White rot.
50	Ceratostomella ulmi	Dutch elm disease.	125	Keithia tsugae	Cedar leaf blight.
51	Chalaropsis thievaloides	Chinese elm root rot.	126	Melampsora abietis canadensis,	
52	Cytospora ambiens	Cytospora canker.		M. farlowii	Needle rust.
53	C. porinaludibunda	Dieback.	127	Polyporus borealis	White mottled rot.
54	Dothiorella ulmi	Dieback.	128	Pucciniastrum hydrangeae,	
55	Gloeosporium ulmicolum	Leaf spot.		P. myrtilli	Needle rust.
56	Gnomonia ulmea	Leaf spot.	129	Rosellinia herpotrichoides	Brown felt blight.
57	Phleospora ulmi	Elm leaf spot.		**Hemlock, western (Tsuga heterophylla)**	
58	Phytopthora inflata	Pit canker.	130	Armillaria mellea	Shoestring root rot.
59	Pleurotus ulmaris	Brown rot.	131	Caecoma dubium	Needle rust.
60	Sphaeropsis ulmicola	Canker.	132	Echinodontium tinctorium	Brown string rot.
61	Tubercularia sp	Elm canker.	133	Fomes annosus	Root and butt rot.
62	Uncinula macrocarpa	Powdery mildew.	134	F. pinicola	Brown cubical rot.
63	Verticillium rhizophagum	Verticillium root disease.	135	F. robustus-tsugina	White heart rot.
64	Verticillium sp	Verticillium wilt.	136	Ganoderma oregonense	White rot.
	Fir (Abies spp)		137	Uraecium holwayi	Needle rust.
65	Adelopus gaumanni	Swiss needle cast.		**Hickory (Hicoria spp)**	
66	Aleurodiscus amorphus	Aleurodiscus canker.	138	Microstroma juglandis	Witches'-broom.
67	Armillaria mellea	Shoestring root rot.		**Incense-cedar (Libocedrus decuurens)**	
68	Bifusella abietis, B. faullii	Needle cast.	139	Gymnosporangium libocedri	Apple-incense cedar rust.
69	Caecoma faulliana	Needle rust.	140	Polyporus amarus	Pocket dry rot.
70	Calyptospora goeppertiana	Needle rust.		**Juniper (Juniperus spp)**	
71	Cephalosporium sp	Cephalosporium canker.	141	Fomes juniperinus	Juniper pocket rot.
72	Corticium gelactimum	Corticium rot.	142	F. subroseus	Brown pocket rot.
73	Cytospora abietis	Cytospora canker.	143	Gymnosporangium aurantiacum	Mountain ash, mountain juniper rust.
74	Dasyscypha resinaria	Dasyscypha canker.	144	G. bermudianum	Juniper rust.
75	Fomes annosus	Root and butt rot.	145	G. betheli	Elongate gall rust of juniper.
76	F. pini	Red ring rot.	146	G. clavariaeforme	Fusiform gall rust of juniper.
77	F. pinicola	Brown cubical rot.	147	G. clavipes	Fusiform gall rust.
78	Hyalospora aspidiotus	Needle cast.	148	G. corniculans	Serviceberry, juniper rust.
79	Hyperma robustum	Needle cast.	149	G. davisii	Chokeberry-mountain juniper rust.
80	Hypodermella abietis concoloris,		150	G. effusum	Fusiform gall rust.
	H. mirabilis, H. nervata	Needle cast.	151	G. exiguum	Hawthorne-alligator juniper rust.
81	Lophodermium abietis,				
	L. uncinatum	Needle cast.			

	Host Plant and Pathogen	Disease		Host Plant and Pathogen	Disease
	Juniper (Juniperus spp) (concluded)			Oak (Quercus spp) (concluded)	
152	Gymnosporangium externum	Porteranthus, fusiform gall rust of juniper.	225	Taphrina caerulescens	Oak leaf blister.
				Austrian pine (Pinus laricio-austriaca) [hard]	
153	G. floriforme	Hawthorne-juniper rust.	226	Cronartium cerebrum	Eastern gall rust.
154	G. globosum	Hawthorne-cedar rust.	227	C. comandrae	Comandra blister rust.
155	G. harnessianum	Serviceberry-western juniper rust.	228	Dothistroma pini	Needle blight.
				Jack pine (Pinus banksiana) [hard]	
156	G. inconspicuum	Serviceberry-Utah twig rust.	229	Chilonectria cucurbitula	Burn blight.
157	G. juniperi-virginianae	Apple cedar rust.	230	Coleosporium solidaginis	Needle rust.
158	G. kernianum	Witches'-broom rust.	231	Cronartium cerebrum	Eastern gall rust.
159	G. multiporum	Utah juniper rust.	232	C. comandrae	Comandra blister rust.
160	G. nelsoni	Hawthorne-western juniper rust.	233	Hypodermella ampla, H. concolo	Needle cast.
			234	Lenzites saepiaria	Brown cubical rot.
161	G. trachysorum	Fusiform gall rust of juniper.		Loblolly pine (Pinus taeda) [hard]	
162	G. tuberlatum	Globoid gall rust of mountain juniper.	235	Coleosporium apocynaceum, C. lacinariae, C. minutum	Needle rust.
163	G. vauqueliniae	Witches'-broom of vaulquelinia.	236	Cronartium comandrae	Comandra blister rust.
164	Keithia juniperi	Leaf blight.	237	Hypoderma lethale	Needle spot.
165	Phomopsis juniperovora	Juniper blight.	238	Lophodermium pinastri	Needle spot.
	Larch (Larix europora)			Lodgepole pine (Pinus contorta) [hard]	
166	Dasyscypha willkommi	European larch canker.	239	Atropellis pinicola, A. piniphila	Atropellis canker.
167	Fomes pini	Red ring rot.	240	Coleosporium solidaginis	Needle rust.
168	Melampsora bigelowii	Needle rust.	241	Cronartium comandrae	Comandra blister rust.
	Larch (Larix larincina)		242	C. comptoniae	Sweet fern blister rust.
169	Hypodermella laricis	Needle cast.	243	C. filamentosum	Paintbrush blister rust.
170	Melampsora bigelowii	Needle rust.	244	C. harknessii	Western gall rust.
171	M. medusae	Needle spot.	245	Elytroderma deformans	Needle cast.
	Larch (Larix occidentalis)		246	Fomes pini	Red ring rot.
172	Fomes laricis	Brown trunk rot.	247	Hypodermella concolor, H. medusa, H. montivaga, H. montana	Needle cast.
173	Hypodermella laricis	Needle cast.			
174	Melampsora bigelowii, M.medusae	Needle rust.			
175	Sparassis radicata	Sparassis root rot.	248	Peridermium weirii	Needle rust.
	Locust, black (Robinia pseudoacacia)			Longleaf pine (Pinus palustris) [hard]	
176	Fomes rimosus	Yellow heart rot.	249	Coleosporium apocynaceum C. inconspicuum, C. lacinariae	Needle rust.
177	Fusicladium robiniae	Leaf spot.	250	Cronartium strobilinum	Pine cone rust.
178	Polyporus robiniophilus	White heart rot.	251	Fomes pini	Red ring rot.
	Maple (Acer spp)		252	Peridermium gutamalense	Needle rust.
179	Cristulariella depraedens	Leaf spot and wilt.	253	Polyporus schweinitzii	Root and butt rot.
180	Daedalea unicolor	Rot and canker.		Red pine (Pinus resinosa) [hard]	
181	Daldinia concentrica	White rot.	254	Armillaria mellea	Shoestring root rot.
182	Endoconidiophora virescens	Sapstreak.	255	Atropellis tingens	Atropellis canker.
183	Eutypella parasitica	Eutypella canker.	256	Chilonectria cucurbitula	Burn blight.
184	Fomes connatus	Butt rot.	257	Coleosporium campanulae, C. soladiganis	Needle rust.
185	F. igniarius nigricans	Heart rot.	258	Dothistroma pini	Needle spot.
186	Hydnum septentrionale	Soft spongy white rot.	259	Fomes annosus	Butt rot.
187	Hymenochaete agglutinans	Hymenochaete canker.	260	Pellurlaria pullulans	Needle blight.
188	Hypoxylon blakei	Hypoxylon canker.	261	Polyporus schweinitzii	Root and butt rot.
189	Nectria cinnabarina	Nectria dieback.	262	Pythium irregulare	Damping off.
190	N. galligena	Nectria canker.	263	Rhizina inflata	Rhizina root rot.
191	Phleospora aceris	Leaf spot.	264	Rhizoctonia solania	Damping off.
192	Phytophthora cactorum	Bleeding canker.		Scotch pine (Pinus sylvestris) [hard]	
193	Polyporus glomeratus	Rot and canker.	265	Cronartium comandrae	Comandra blister rust.
194	Rhytisma acerinum	Tar spot.	266	Cronartium harknessii	Western gall rust.
195	Schizoxylon microsporum	Schizoxylon canker.	267	Sphaeropsis ellisii	Burn bright.
196	Stereum murrayi	Rot and canker.		Shortleaf pine (Pinus echinata) [hard]	
197	Uncinula circinata	Powdery mildew.	268	Caliciopsis pinea	Caliciopsis canker.
198	Venturia acerina	Red-brown spot.	269	Coleosporum helianthi, C. inconspicuum	Needle rust.
199	Verticillium albo-atrum	Verticillium wilt.	270	Cronartium cerebrum	Globose gall rust.
200	Xylaria digitata	Xylaria root rot.		Slash pine (Pinus elliottii) [hard]	
	Oak (Quercus spp)		271	Atropellis tingens	Atropellis canker.
201	Aleurodiscus oaksii	Smooth patch.	272	Coleosporum apocynaceum	Needle rust.
202	Armillaria mellea	Shoestring root rot.	273	Cronartium fusiforme	Fusiform gall rust.
203	Cronartium cerebrum	Globose gall rust.	274	C. strobilinum	Pine cone rust.
204	C. fusiforme	Southern fusiform rust.	275	Fomes annosus	Root rot.
205	C. strobilinum	Pine cone rust.	276	F. pini	Red ring rot.
206	Daedalea quercina	Brown cubical rot.	277	Hypoderma lethale	Needle spot.
207	Endoconidiophora fagacearum	Oak wilt.	278	Lophodermium pinastri	Needle spot.
208	Fistulina hepatica	Brown cubical rot.	279	Polyporus schweinitzii	Root and butt rot.
209	Fomes everhartii	White heart rot.		Virginia pine (Pinus virginiana) [hard]	
210	Gnomonia veneta	Anthracnose.	280	Atropellis piniphila	Atropellis canker.
211	Hydnum erinaceus	White rot.	281	Coleosporium inconspicuum	Needle rust.
212	Morenoella quercina	Leaf spot.	282	Fomes annosus	Root rot.
213	Polyporus berkeleyi	White butt rot.	283	F. pini	Red heart rot.
214	P. croceus	White pocket rot.	284	Peridermium appalacianum	Virginia pine rust.
215	P. dryophilus	Piped rot.		Western yellow pine (Pinus ponderosa) [hard]	
216	P. frondosus	Butt rot.	285	Atropellis arizonica, A. piniphila	Atropellis canker.
217	P. hispidus	Heart rot and canker.	286	Coleosporium solidaginis	Needle rust.
218	P. spraguei	White rot.	287	Cronartium comandrae	Comandra blister rust.
219	P. sulphureus	Brown cubical rot.	288	C. comptoniae	Sweet fern blister rust.
220	Sphaerotheca lanestris	Witches'-broom.	289	C. filamentosum	Paintbrush blister rust.
221	Sphaeropsis quercina	Sphaeropsis canker.	290	C. quercuum	Gall rust.
222	Stereum gausapatum	White mottled rot.			
223	S. subpileatum	White pocket rot.			
224	Strumella coryneoidea	Strumella canker.			

504

	Host Plant and Pathogen	Disease		Host Plant and Pathogen	Disease
	Western yellow pine (Pinus ponderosa) [hard] (concluded)			**Spruce, Engelmann (Picea engelmannii)**	
291	Cronartium harknessii	Western gall rust.	353	Chrysomyxa ledicola	Needle rust.
292	Dasyscypha ellisiana	Dasyscypha canker.	354	C. pyrolae	Spruce cone rust.
293	Elytroderma deformans	Witches'-broom and needle cast.	355	C. weirii	Needle rust.
			356	Echinodontium tinctorium	Brown string rot.
294	Fomes laricis	Brown cubical rot.	357	Peridermium coloradense	Witches'-broom.
295	F. pini	Red ring rot.	358	Sparassis radicata	Sparassis root rot.
296	Hypodermella medusa	Needle cast.		**Spruce, Norway (Picea abies)**	
297	Lentinus lepideus	Brown cubical rot.	359	Ascochyta piniperda	Needle spot.
	Eastern white pine (Pinus strobus), Sugar pine (P. lambertiana), Western pine (P. monticola) [soft]		360	Chrysomyxa cassandrae, C. ledi	Needle rust.
			361	C. pyrolae	Spruce cone rust.
298	Armillaria mellea	Shoestring root rot.	362	Hymenochaete agglutinans	Smothering disease.
299	Atropellis pinicola	Atropellis canker.	363	Peridermium coloradense	Witches'-broom.
300	Bifusella linearis	Needle cast.	364	Phoma piciena	Needle blight.
301	Caliciopsis pinae	Caliciopsis canker.		**Spruce, red (Picea rubra)**	
302	Cronartium ribicola	White pine blister rust.	365	Ascochyta piniperda	Needle spot.
303	Fomes annosus	Root and butt rot.	366	Chrysomyxa cassandrae, C. empetri, C. ledi, C. ledicola	Needle rust.
304	F. laricis	Brown cubical rot.			
305	F. pini	Red ring rot.	367	C. pyrolae	Spruce cone rust.
306	Hypoderma desmazierii	Needle cast.	368	C. weirii	Needle rust.
307	Lentinus lepideus	Brown cubical rot.	369	Corticium galactinum	Corticium rot.
308	Lophodermium pinastri	Needle cast.	370	Lophodermium filiforme, L. picea	Needle cast.
309	Neopeckia coulteris	Brown felt blight.	371	Phoma piceina	Needle blight.
310	Polyporus circinatus	Red root and butt rot.	372	Polyporus borealis	White mottled rot.
311	Phacidium planum	Needle blight.		**Spruce, Sitka (Picea sitchensis)**	
312	Sparassis radicata	Sparassis root rot.	373	Chrysomyxa empetri	Spruce rust.
	Poplar (Populus spp)		374	C. ledicola, C. piperiana	Needle rust.
313	Armillaria mellea	Shoestring root rot.	375	Fomes laricis	Brown cubical rot.
314	Ciborinia whetzieii	Ink spot.	376	F. pini	Red ring rot.
315	Cytospora chrysosperma	Cytospora canker.	377	F. pinicola	Brown cubical rot.
316	Dothichiza populea	Dothichiza canker.	378	Lentinus kauffmanii	Brown pocket rot.
317	Fomes applanatus	White butt rot.	379	Peridermium coloradense	Witches'-broom.
318	F. fomentarius	White mottled rot.	380	Poria monticola	Brown cubical rot.
319	F. igniarius	White heart rot.		**Spruce, white (Picea glauca)**	
320	Fusicaldium radiosum	Shoot blight.	381	Chrysomyxa cassandrae, C. chiogenis, C. empetri, C. ledi, C. ledicola	Needle rust.
321	Hypoxylon pruinatum	Hypoxylon canker.			
322	Limospora tetraspora	Leaf blight.			
323	Melampsora bigelowii, M. medusae, M. occidentalis	Leaf spot.	382	C. pyrolae	Spruce cone rust.
			383	Peridermium coloradense	Witches'-broom.
324	Marssonia populi	Leaf spot and shoot blight.	384	Pucciniastrum americanum, P. arctium	Needle rust.
325	Nectria galligena	Nectria canker.			
326	Neofabraea populi	Neofabraea canker.	385	Rhizina inflata	Rhizina root rot.
327	Schlerotinia bifrons	Ink spot.		**Sycamore (Platanus spp)**	
328	Septoria musiva	Septoria canker.	386	Endoconidiophora sp	London plane canker stain.
329	S. populicola	Leaf spot.	387	Gnomonia veneta	Anthracnose.
330	Taphrina aurea	Yellow leaf blister.		**Sweetgum (Liquidambar styracifula)**	
331	T. johansonii	Catkin blister.	388	Polyporus ludovicianus	White pocket rot.
332	Trametes suaveolens	Soft white rot.	389	P. fissilis	Butt rot.
333	Uncinula salicis	Powdery mildew.		**Walnut (Juglans nigra)**	
334	Valsa nivea, V. sordida	Valsa canker.	390	Armillaria mellea	Shoestring root rot.
335	Xylaria digitata	Xylaria root rot.	391	Fomes everhartii	White heart rot.
	Port-Orford-cedar (Chamaecyparis lawsoniana)		392	Phymatotrichum omnivorum	Phymatotrichum root rot.
336	Phytophthora lateralis	Chamaecyparis root rot.	393	Phytophthora cinnamomi	Root rot.
	Red cedar, western (Thuja plicata)			**White-cedar, Atlantic (Chamaecyparis thyoides)**	
337	Coryneum thujinum	Leaf blight.	394	Gymnosporangium biseptatum	Spindle-shaped gall rust.
338	Fomes nigrolimitatus	White pocket rot.	395	G. ellisii	Witches'-broom rust.
339	Keithia thujina	Cedar leaf blight.	396	G. hyalinum	Frisiforme gall rust.
340	Poria albipelleducia	White ring rot.	397	G. transformans	Chokeberry-southern white cedar rust.
341	P. asiatica	Brown cubical rot.			
342	P. wierii	Laminated root rot.		**White-cedar, northern (Thuja occidentalis)**	
	Redwood (Sequoia sempervirens)		398	Coniphora puteana	Brown cubial rot.
343	Poria albipelleducia	White ring rot.	399	Keithia thujina	Cedar leaf blight.
344	P. sequoia	Brown pocket rot.		**Willow (Salix spp)**	
	Spruce, black (Picea mariana)		400	Botryosphaeria ribis	Botryosphaeria canker.
345	Chrysomyxa cassandrae, C. chiogenis, C. ledi, C. ledicola	Needle rust.	401	Cytospora pulcherrima	Cytospora canker.
			402	Fomes igniarius	Heart rot.
346	C. pyrolae	Spruce cone rust.	403	Fusicladium saliciperdum	Willow scab.
347	Lophodermium filiforme, L. picea	Needle cast.	404	Melamspora abieti-capraearum	Leaf rust.
348	Peridermium coloradense	Witches'-broom.	405	Physalospora miyabeana	Black canker.
349	Phacidium expansum	Needle blight.	406	Polyporus squamosus	White rot.
	Spruce, blue (Picea pungens)		407	Trametes suaveolens	Soft white rot.
350	Chrysomyxa cassandrae, C. ledi, C. ledicola	Needle rust.	408	Uncinula salicis	Powdery mildew.
			409	Valsa nivea, V. sordida	Valsa canker.
351	C. pyrolae	Spruce cone rust.		**Yellow-poplar (Liriodendron tulipifera)**	
352	Peridermium colaradense	Witches'-broom.	410	Nectria magnoliae	Nectria canker.

428. SELECTED PROTOZOAN AND HELMINTHIC PARASITES: VERTEBRATES

Part I: PARASITES OF MAN

#	Parasite	Geographic Distribution	Infective Stage	Portal of Entry	Immature Stage	Location in Man — Definitive Stages: Primary Site	Secondary Site	Reservoir Host of Definitive Stage	Other Obligate Host or Vector	Identification: Stage	Source
						Protozoa					
1	Entamoeba coli					Lumen, large intestine.	None.	Monkey(?).			Feces.
2	E. histolytica	World-wide; most common in warm climates.	4-nucleate cyst.	Mouth[1].		Wall, large intestine.	Other viscera, skin.	Monkey, dog, rat(?).	None.	Trophozoite, cyst.	Feces, visceral or skin abscesses.
3	Balantidium coli				None described.	Wall, large intestine.	None.	Swine, monkey(?).	Sheep(?).		Feces.
4	Giardia lamblia					Duodenal crypts.	Gallbladder(?).	Rat(?).			Feces.
5	Leishmania brasiliensis	W. Hemisphere from S. Mexico to N. Argentina.				Skin.	Mucous membranes.	Dog, possibly other mammals.			Reticulo-endothelial cells, skin, viscera. Culture.
6	L. donovani	China, India, Africa, Mediterranean area, S. America.	Leptomonad.	Skin[2].		Skin.	Reticulo-endothelium (fundamental).	Dog, rodents.	Sandfly (Phlebotomus).	Leishmanial. Leptomonad.	
7	L. tropica	W. India, Middle East, Near East, N. Africa.				Skin.	Mucous membranes (rare).				
8	Trichomonas vaginalis	Relatively common, both sexes.	Trophozoite (only stage known).	Vulva[3] or urethra.		Vaginal folds.	Bladder.	None.	None.	Trophozoite.	Urine, vaginal smear.
9	Trypanosoma cruzi	Western Hemisphere, from U.S.A. to N. Argentina.	Metacyclic trypanosome.	Skin[3], conjunctiva.		Skin.	In tissues, blood.	Many mammals.	Triatomid bugs.	Trypanosomal. Leishmanial. Crithidial.	Trypanosomal. Blood, tissues. Culture.
10	T. gambiense	W. and Cent. Africa.	Metacyclic trypanosome.	Skin[2].		Skin.	Blood, lymph nodes, CNS.	Cattle(?).	Tsetse fly (Glossina).	Trypanosomal.	Blood, gland juice, spinal fluid.
11	T. rhodesiense	Cent. and E. Africa.						Wild game, mammals.			Blood.
12	Plasmodium falciparum	Temperate or warm climates.	Sporozoite.	Skin[2].	Schizonts in hepatic parenchyma.	Exo-erythrocytic foci.	Erythrocytes.	None.	Mosquito (Anopheles spp)	Trophozoites, schizonts, gametocytes.	Blood.
13	P. malariae										
14	P. vivax										
15	Toxoplasma gondii	World-wide.	Trophozoite.	Unknown.	None known.	Reticulo-endothelium, many parenchymal cells.	Brain, retina.	Many mammals and birds.	None known.	Trophozoite or pseudo-cyst.	Focal areas of necrosis.
						Platyhelminthes					
16	Diphyllobothrium latum	N. temperate zones; Argentinian, Chilean lakes.	Sparganum larva in fish flesh.	Mouth.	Develops in small intestine.	Attached to small intestine.	None known.	Dog, bear, cat.	Diaptomus, Cyclops; fresh-water fish.	Eggs.	Feces.
17	Dipylidium caninum	Warm climates.	Larva in hemocoel of dog flea.	Mouth.	Develops in small intestine.		None.	Dog, cat.	Dog, cat, human flea.	Proglottids.	Feces.
18	Echinococcus granulosus	World-wide; common in southern S. America.	Eggs in dog's excreta.		Develops in liver, lungs.		Hydatid cysts in human viscera.	Dog, wild relatives.	Sheep, cattle, swine (alternating with dog).	Hydatid cyst with scolices.	Aspiration. Exploratory operation.
19	Hymenolepis diminuta		Larva in hemocoel of insect.	Mouth.	Develops in duodenum, small intestine.	Attached to small intestine.	None.	Rat, mouse.	Rodent flea, grain beetles, meal moths, etc.	Eggs, proglottids.	Feces.
20	H. nana	Warm and temperate climates.	Egg.	Mouth[5].	Develops in duodenal villi.		None known.		None; may develop in grain beetles.	Eggs.	Feces.
21	Taenia saginata	World-wide.	Cysticercus larva in beef.		Develops in small intestine.		None known.		Cattle.	Proglottids, eggs.	Feces[4].
22	T. solium	World-wide.	Cysticercus larva in pork; egg.		Develops in small intestine.		(Cysticercus larvae in various viscera)	None.	Swine.	Proglottids, eggs.	Feces[4].
23	Clonorchis sinensis	Sino-Japanese and Indo-Chinese areas.	Larva encysted in flesh of fresh-water fish.	In transit from duodenum to bile ducts.		Distal bile ducts.	Pancreatic ducts (rare).	Many fish eating mammals.	Snail, fresh-water fish.	Eggs.	
24	Fasciola hepatica	Sheep-raising countries.	Larva encysted on water plants.		Develops in duodenum, jejunum.	Proximal bile ducts.	Abdominal wall(?), lungs, brain.	Herbivores.	Snail, moist vegetation.	Eggs.	
25	Fasciolopsis buski	Oriental countries.	Larva encysted on water plants.		Develops in duodenum, jejunum.	Attached to duodenum, jejunum.	None.	Swine.	Snail, water plants.	Eggs.	

No.	Parasite	Geographic Distribution	Infective stage	Portal of entry	Migration / transit	Location of adult	Aberrant / other location	Reservoir host	Intermediate host / vector	Diagnostic stage	Diagnostic specimen
26	Paragonimus westermani	Sino-Jap. areas, S.W. Pacific islands; northern S. America.	Larva encysted in soft tissues of crabs, crayfish.	Mouth[5].	In transit from duodenum to lungs.	Lungs, near bronchioles.	Abdominal viscera, brain.	Cat, dog, swine, other animals.	Snail, crab and crayfish; sputum of man.	Eggs.	Sputum, feces.
27	Schistosoma hematobium	Africa, Near East, Middle East, southern Portugal.			Migrates in blood vessels.	Vesical venous plexus.	Pelvic organs, rectum, lungs, CNS.	Gerbil.	Bulinid snail.	Eggs.	Urine, feces.
28	S. japonicum	China, Japan, Philippines, Formosa, Celebes.	Cercaria free in fresh water.	Skin[6].		Mesenteric venules.	Liver, lungs, brain.	Many mammals.	Oncomelaniid snail.		Feces.
29	S. mansoni	Africa, Arabia, Brazil, Guianas, Venezuela, West Indies.						Monkey (rarely).	Planorbid snail.		
						Nematoda					
30	Ancylostoma brasiliense	Limited distribution in warm climates.	Filariform larva.	Skin[1].	Larvae migrate from skin via blood, lungs to epiglottis, GI tract.	Attached to small intestine.	None.	Dog, cat.	None.	Eggs (larvae).	Feces (cutaneous tunnels.)
31	A. duodenale	Palearctic region[7], western S. America.						None.		Eggs.	Feces.
32	Ascaris lumbricoides	World-wide; more common in warm climates.	Fully embryonated egg.	Mouth[1].	Larvae migrate.	Lumen, small intestine.	Various viscera.	Swine(?).	None.	Eggs.	Feces.
33	Dracunculus medinensis	Warm climates Eastern Hemisphere.	3rd stage larva in Cyclops.	Mouth[5].	Larvae migrate.	In viscera.	None known.	Fur-bearing mammals.	Cyclops.	Gravid ♀.	Ruptured skin blister.
34	Enterobius vermicularis	World-wide; common in children.	Fully embryonated egg.	Mouth[1].	In transit down small intestine.	Attached to cecum, appendix.	Female genital tract, perianal folds.	None.	None.	Eggs, adults.	Anal swab, anus.
35	Loa loa	Tropical Africa.		Skin[2].	Migrates in subcutaneous tissues.	Migrates in subcutaneous tissues.	Orbit, conjunctiva of eye.	None.	Mango-fly (Chrysops).	Microfilariae (sheathed).	Diurnal blood.
36	Necator americanus	Warm climates.	Filariform larva.	Skin[1].	Larvae migrate.	Attached to small intestine.	None.		None.	Eggs.	Feces.
37	Onchocerca volvulus	Tropical Africa, Mexico, Guatemala, E. Venezuela, Dutch Guiana.		Skin[2].	Adults in subcutaneous nodules. Larvae in skin, may invade eye tissues.	None known.	None known.		Blackflies (Simulium).	Microfilariae (unsheathed).	Skin biopsy.
38	Strongyloides stercoralis	Warm, moist climates.		Skin[1].	Larvae migrate.	Within intestinal mucosa.	Lungs.	Dog, chimpanzee.	None	Larvae.	Feces, duodenal aspirate.
39	Wuchereria bancrofti	Warm climates.		Skin[2].	Migrate in lymphatics.	Lymphatics of lower trunk, legs.	Lymphatics of upper trunk.	None.	Mosquito (Aedes, Culex).	Microfilariae (sheathed).	Usually nocturnal blood.
40	Trichinella spiralis	World-wide; common in United States.	Larvae encysted in pork muscle.	Mouth[5].	Enter duodenal mucosa.	In duodenal mucosa.	Larvae migrate, encysted in striped muscle.	Swine, bear, walrus.	None.	Larvae.	Compressed or digested muscle.
41	Trichuris trichiuris	Warm, moist climates.	Fully embryonated egg.	Mouth[1].	In transit down small intestine.	Attached to cecum, appendix.	Colon, rectum.	Swine(?), ape, monkey.	None.	Eggs.	Feces.

/1/ By direct or indirect contact with body excreta containing the parasite. /2/ From proboscis of insect vector at time of skin puncture to obtain blood or tissue juice from host. /3/ From feces of insect vector while feeding on blood or tissue juice of host. /4/ Also in sputum for P. westermani. /5/ From infected food or contaminated water taken into the mouth. /6/ In contact with infested water. /7/ Tropical and subtropical: Africa, Asia, Europe, U.S.A.

Part II: PARASITES OF ANIMALS OTHER THAN MAN

	Parasite	Geographic Distribution	Definitive Host	Intermediate Host	Primary Location in Definitive Host	Disease; Type of Damage
				Protozoa		
1	Anaplasma marginale	N., S., and C. America, Asia, Africa, France.	Cattle.	None. Mechanical transfer by ticks, tabanid flies, instruments.	Erythrocytes.	Anemia, icterus, fever, extreme splenomegaly.
2	Babesia bigemina	N., S., and C. America, Africa, Europe, Asia, Pacific Islands, Australia.	Cattle.	Tick (Boophilus Rhipicephalus).	Erythrocytes.	Texas fever; anemia, hemoglobinuria.
3	Eimeria tenella	World-wide.	Chicken.	None.	Cecal cells.	Hemorrhagic enteritis.
4	E. zurnii	World-wide.	Cattle.	None.	Intestinal cells.	Enteritis, dysentery.
5	Histomonas meleagridis	World-wide.	Domestic fowl, ruffed grouse, quail, partridge.	None. Transmitted in Heterakis gallinae eggs.	Cecum, liver.	Entero-hepatitis, necrosis, ulceration.

428. SELECTED PROTOZOAN AND HELMINTHIC PARASITES: VERTEBRATES (Concluded)
Part II: PARASITES OF ANIMALS OTHER THAN MAN (Concluded)

	Parasite	Geographic Distribution	Definitive Host	Intermediate Host	Primary Location in Definitive Host	Disease; Type of Damage
				Protozoa (concluded)		
6	Trypanosoma congolense	Africa.	Cattle, other ruminants, dog.	Tsetse fly (Glossina)	Blood.	Anemia.
				Cestoidea		
7	Moniezia expansa		Sheep, goat, cattle, other ruminants.	Grass mite (several spp).	Small intestine.	Intestinal irritation, slight damage.
8	Taenia pisiformis	World-wide.	Dog, fox, wolf, cat.	Hare, rabbit, rat, squirrel.	Small intestine.	Slight enteritis, anal pruritus.
				Nematoda		
9	Ascaridia galli[1]		Chicken, guinea fowl, turkey, goose, wild birds.		Small intestine.	Emaciation.
10	Dictyocaulus viviparus[2]	World-wide.	Cattle, deer.	None.	Bronchus, bronchiole.	Catarrhal inflammation, coughing, emaciation.
11	Dirofilaria immitis[3]	Europe, India, China, Japan, Australia, N. and S. America, Pacific Islands.	Dog, cat, fox, wolf.	Mosquito (Aedes, Anopheles, Culex); flea (Ctenocephalides, Pulex).	Heart, pulmonary artery; microfilariae in blood.	Emaciation, dyspnea, cough, edema.
12	Haemonchus contortus[4]	World-wide.	Sheep, goat, cattle, other ruminants.		Abomasum, small intestine.	Anemia, emaciation.
13	Strongylus vulgaris	Warm climates.	Horse, other equines.	None.	Large intestine.	Anemia, edema, digestive disturbance, emaciation; larvae form aneurisms in mesenteric arteries.

/1/ Roundworm. /2/ Lungworm. /3/ Heartworm. /4/ Stomachworm.

Most of the nematode parasites of plants are found in largest numbers in close association with roots of plants, or in the upper 16 inches of soil formerly occupied by plant roots. In general, plant parasites can be distinguished from saprophagous or predaceous forms, also found in the soil, by the presence of a protrusile spear or stylet used to puncture and feed on plant cells. The soil is not the only habitat, however, for nematodes. Some live in fresh waters of rivers, lakes and ponds. Others live only in the ocean. Many are parasites of animals and of man.

429. SELECTED PARASITIC NEMATODES: PLANTS

	Nematode	Geographical Distribution[1]	Hosts[2]	Feeding Habits[3]	Symptoms[4]	Control
1	Awl nematode (Dolichodorus heterocephalus)	Florida, Georgia, Michigan.	Celery, corn, tomato, bean, Chinese water-chestnut; many other plants growing in wet locations.	Vagrant ectoparasites of root tips, sides of succulent roots.	Devitalized root tips, small lesions on sides of roots; sometimes extensive root destruction.	Soil fumigation.
2	Bulb and stem nematode (Ditylenchus spp and closely related forms)	Widespread; temperate zones.	Over 300 different plants, including narcissus, hyacinth, iris, onion, clover, alfalfa, oats, phlox, potato.	Vagrant endoparasites of bulbs, stems, leaves, occasionally roots.	Twisting, wrinkling, distortion of stems and flowers; necrosis and destruction of bulb tissues.	Hot-water treatment of bulbs, corms; crop rotation; field sanitation; methyl bromide fumigation of infected onion and clover seed.
3	Burrowing nematode (Radopholus similis)	India, Indonesia, Formosa, Philippines, Hawaii, Brazil, C. America, Jamaica, La., Fla.	About 50 different plants including citrus, canna, coffee, tea, banana, avocado, black pepper, sugarcane, rice.	Vagrant endoparasites of roots.	Root lesions and disintegration.	Hot water treatment of infected citrus nursery stock; pulling of affected trees, then soil fumigation.
4	Chrysanthemum nematode (Aphelenchoides ritzema-bosi)	N. America, Europe.	About 50 different plants including chrysanthemum, delphinium, phlox, verbena, zinnia, strawberry.	Vagrant endoparasites of buds and foliage.	Crinkled, distorted leaves and leaf spots.	Hot water treatment of dormant plants; parathion sprays.
5	Citrus nematode (Tylenchulus semi-penetrans)	Fla., Tex., Calif., most citrus fruit-growing regions.	Most Citrus spp and closely related genera; olive.	Females are sedentary parasites, partly external, of roots.	Extensive necrosis, discoloration of cortex of small roots.	Plant uninfected stock on clean land.
6	Coconut palm nematode (Aphelenchoides cocophilus)	W. Indies, Br. Guiana, Honduras, Panama, Venezuela.	Coconut, date, and oil palms.	Vagrant endoparasites of roots, trunk (near periphery), leaf petioles.	Disintegration of trunk tissues (causing "red ring") and of root cortex.	No established control measures.
7	Dagger nematodes (Xiphinema spp)	World-wide.	Many plants, trees, shrubs, including laurel oak, pecan, rose, clove, strawberry, corn, oats, some grasses.	Vagrant ectoparasites of root tips, sides of succulent roots.	Devitalized root tips, necrosis of small roots, gall-like swellings, clusters of small stubby branches.	Soil fumigation.
8	Golden nematode of potatoes (Heterodera rostochiensis)	Europe, Bolivia, Peru; in N. America on Long Island, N.Y.	Potato, tomato, several other solanaceous plants.	Sedentary parasites, internal in early stages, becoming largely external as adults; attack roots, other underground parts.	Stunting of plant, decrease in size of root system, but often increase in number of small branch rootlets.	Crop rotation; soil fumigation.
9	Grass nematode (Anguina spp)	Europe, N. America.	Several Agrostis species; other grasses and cereals.	Larvae, ectoparasites around growing point; adults, endoparasites of flower primordia.	Abnormal flowers developing into galls.	Crop rotation; planting gall-free seed.
10	Lance nematode (Hoplolaimus coronatus)	N. America, Philippines.	Many plants including corn, sugarcane, cotton, St. Augustine and other lawn grasses.	Vagrant internal or partly external parasites of roots.	Lesions leading to complete destruction and sloughing off of cortex.	Soil fumigation.

No.	Nematode	Geographical distribution[1]	Host plants[2]	Feeding habit[3]	Symptoms[4]	Control
11	Meadow or root lesion nematode (Pratylenchus spp)	World-wide.	Many plants, including tobacco, corn, small grains, cotton, alfalfa, strawberry, trees and shrubs.	Vagrant endoparasites of roots and tubers[5].	Small brown root lesions. Causes "brown root-rot" of tobacco.	Crop rotation, tobacco; row fumigation with D-D.
12	Pin nematodes (Paratylenchus spp)	Netherlands, Br. Isles, Hawaii, N. America.	Many plants, including pineapple, oat, wheat, cowpea, alfalfa, cabbage, cucumber, okra, radish, celery, fig trees.	Vagrant ectoparasites of roots and other underground structures.	Stunting of plants from root injury and retarded root growth.	Fumigation somewhat effective.
13	Potato rot nematode (Ditylenchus destructor)	Europe, Idaho, Wisconsin, Prince Edward Isl.	Potato, carrot, sweetpotato; tulip, iris.	Vagrant endoparasites of tubers, and to some extent of roots.	Destruction of tuber tissues, causing sunken areas, followed by rot.	Crop rotation; planting of clean seed; soil fumigation.
14	Rice root nematode (Radopholus oryzae)	Indonesia, Japan, rice-growing areas of S. E. Asia, Louisiana, Texas.	Rice, various grasses, and related monocotyledonous plants.	Vagrant endoparasites of roots.	Root lesions, destruction of cortex; root hairs; in Indonesia associated with "mentek," a rice root-rot.	No established control measures.
15	Ring nematodes (Criconemoides spp)	Widespread.	Many plants; reported as injuring peach trees and peanut vines.	Semi-sedentary ectoparasites of roots, other underground parts.	Small lesions, stunting of plant.	Soil fumigation.
16	Root knot nematodes (Meloidogyne spp)	World-wide; most common in warm climates.	Over 1800 plants; hosts of individual species more restricted.	Sedentary endoparasites of roots, other underground parts.	Swellings, galls, often local necrosis of tissues; increase or reduction of branch rootlets.	Annual crops: rotation and fumigation. Planting of resistant varieties; hot-water treatment of bulbs, corms, tubers.
17	Soybean cyst nematode (Heterodera glycines)	Japan, China, Wilmington area of N. Carolina.	Soybean, adzuki bean, kidney bean. Snapbeans, annual lespedeza vetch.	Sedentary parasites of roots, internal in early stages, external as adults.	General stunting of plants, reduction in size of root system. Causes a disease known as "yellow dwarf" in Japan and China.	Crop rotation; soil fumigation.
18	Spiral nematodes (Rotylenchus and Helicotylenchus spp)	Widespread, in tropical and subtropical regions.	Many kinds of plants: ornamental, grass, bean, cowpea, pineapple.	Vagrant ectoparasites, occasionally endoparasites of roots and other underground parts.	Stunting of plant from retarded root growth, lesions may occur.	Soil fumigation.
19	Spring crimp nematode of strawberries (Aphelenchoides fragariae)	Europe, Br. Isles, Massachusetts, Connecticut, Delaware, Maryland.	Strawberry.	Vagrant ectoparasites of buds between young developing leaves.	Small, crinkled, distorted foliage.	Set new beds with uninfested plants.
20	Sting nematode (Belonolaimus gracilis)	S. Atlantic states.	Bean, beet, cabbage, celery, citrus, corn, cotton, cowpea, grass, millet, okra, onion, peanut, pine seedling, soybean, strawberry.	Vagrant ectoparasites of root tips, sides of succulent roots, other underground parts.	Devitalized root tips, root lesions, causing many short stubby branched roots, severely stunted plants.	Soil fumigation.
21	Stubby root nematodes (Trichodorus spp)	Widespread; important in S. E. U.S.A., S. Calif.	Many plants, including beet, celery, cabbage, cauliflower, chayote, fig.	Vagrant ectoparasites of root tips.	Devitalized root tips causing numerous short, stubby branch rootlets.	No satisfactory control known.
22	Stunt nematodes (Tylenchorhynchus spp)	Apparently widespread.	Many plants including cotton, oats, tobacco, wheat, sugar cane.	Mostly external, occasionally internal vagrant parasites of roots.	Stunting of plant from retarded root growth.	Tobacco: row fumigation with ethylene dibromide.
23	Sugar beet nematode (Heterodera schachtii)	Europe, Australia, Canada, U.S.A.	Over 100 plants, including sugar beet, table beet, mangelwurzel, cabbage, cauliflower, kale, broccoli, turnip, rutabaga, mustard.	Sedentary parasites of roots, other underground parts; internal in early stages, external as adults.	Stunting of plant, overall decrease in size of root system, often increase in number of small branch rootlets.	Crop rotation; soil fumigation with D-D before planting (sugar beet).
24	Summer crimp nematode of strawberries (Aphelenchoides besseyi)	S.E. U. S. A., Maryland-Texas.	Strawberry, rice.	Vagrant ectoparasites of buds and growing points between young developing leaves.	Small, crinkled, distorted foliage.	Set new beds with uninfested plants. Hot-water treatment or methyl bromide fumigation for rice seed.
25	Wheat nematode (Anguina tritici)	S. and E. Asia, Egypt, Australia, Europe, S. Atlantic states.	Wheat, rye, emmer, spell.	Larvae, ectoparasites around growing point; adults, endoparasites of flower primordia.	Stunted plants, distorted foliage, galls instead of seed.	Plant gall-free seed (galls may be removed by salt brine flotation or mechanical separators).

1/ Information on the geographical distribution of plant parasitic nematodes is fragmentary and incomplete, even for the best known species. Undoubtedly distribution is far wider than indicated.
2/ Species of nematodes within a given genus vary in their ability to attack plants; some have a rather wide host range; others are highly host-specific, attacking only one or two crop plants.
3/ Although parasitic nematodes feed on all parts of plants, feeding habits and particular tissues attacked vary, depending on the species, host plant and stage of development of the host and parasite. 4/ Symptoms of nematode damage are often difficult to distinguish from those caused by other organisms or by poor growing conditions; hence it is important in making a diagnosis to find the nematode in the diseased tissues or soil adjacent to the roots of affected plants. 5/ All species in the genus Pratylenchus are root parasites except P. mahogani and P. scribneri, observed in diseased mahogany wood and potato tubers, respectively.

430. VIRAL AGENTS: PLANT DISEASE

Except where otherwise indicated, the common name of the disease is identical with that of the virus.

	Virus	Distribution	Principal Plant Host	Principal Insect Vector	Other Means of Transmission	Symptoms
1	Abacá bunchy-top (Marmor abacá)	Philippine Islands	Abacá (Musa textilis)	Aphid (Pentalonia nigronervosa)		Chlorotic spots; reduction in leaf size.
2	Abutilon-variegation (M. abutilon)	West Indies	Flowering maple (Abutilon striatum)		Grafting, except bark grafting; seeds.	Systemic chlorotic mottling.
3	Alfalfa-mosaic (M. medicaginis)	United States	Alfalfa (Medicago sativa)	Aphid (Macrosiphum pisi, M. solanifolii)	Leaf rubbing.	Systemic chlorotic mottling, often masked.
4	Aster-yellows (Chlorogenus callistephi)	United States, Bermuda	Aster (Callistephus chinensis)	Leafhopper (Macrosteles divisus and others)	Grafting; dodder.	Leaves chlorotic, small; shoots many, erect; flowers virescent.
5	Bean-mosaic (Marmor phaseoli)	Almost world-wide	Bean (Phaseolus vulgaris)	Aphid (including Aphis rumicis)	Leaf abrasion; seeds.	Systemic chlorotic mottling.
6	Bean-mosaic, southern (M. laesiofaciens)	Southern United States	Bean (P. vulgaris)		Leaf rubbing; seeds.	Some varieties mottle; others show localized or systemic necrosis.
7	Beet-yellows (Corium betae)	Belgium, Holland Denmark, England	Beet (Beta vulgaris)	Aphid (including Myzus persicae and Aphis fabae)		Leaves yellow, thick, brittle; necrosis in secondary phloem.
8	Cassava-mosaic (Ruga bemisiae)	Africa, Java	Cassava (Manihot utilissima)	White-fly (Bemisia nigeriensis, B. gossypiperda)		Leaves distorted, mottled; plants stunted; side-branches numerous.
9	Cauliflower-mosaic (Marmor crucifer-arum)	United States, England	Cauliflower (Brassica oleracea)	Aphid (including Brevicoryne brassicae)	Leaf abrasion.	Systemic chlorotic mottling; leaves distorted; plant dwarfed.
10	Clover club-leaf (Aureogenus clavifolium)[1]	United States, (New Jersey)	Clover, crimson (Trifolium incarnatum)	Leafhopper (Agalliopsis novella)		Plant dwarfed; leaves small, yellowed or reddened at margins.
11	Cotton leaf-curl (Ruga gossypii)	The Sudan, Nigeria	Cotton (Gossypium hirsutum)	White-fly (Bemisia gossypiperda)	Grafting.	Leaves pale-spotted, puckered, un-symmetrical; internodes shortened.
12	Cranberry false-blossom (Chlorogenus vaccinii)	Eastern United States, Canada	Cranberry (Vaccinium macrocarpon)	Leafhopper (Ophiola striatula)	Dodder.	Flowers small, erect, streaked; calyx enlarged; fruit small.
13	Cucumber-mosaic (Marmor cucumeris)	Almost world-wide	Cucumber (Cucumis sativus)	Aphid (including Myzus persicae, Aphis gossypii)	Leaf rubbing; dodder.	Leaves mottled, distorted, small; plant stunted; fruits mottled.
14	Cucurbit-mosaic (M. astrictum)[1]	England	Cucumber (C. sativus)		Leaf rubbing.	Chlorotic mottling and distortion of foliage; plant stunted.
15	Dahlia-mosaic (M. dahliae)	United States, Holland, Germany, England	Dahlia (Dahlia pinnata)	Aphid (M. persicae)	Grafting.	Systemic chlorotic mottling or masked symptoms.
16	Lettuce-mosaic (M. lactucae)	World-wide	Lettuce (Lactuca sativa)	Aphid (M. persicae, Macrosiphum gei)	Leaf abrasion; seeds.	Clearing of veins, followed by systemic chlorotic mottling.
17	Maize-streak (Fractilinea maidis)	Africa	Corn (Zea mays)	Leafhopper (Cicadulina mbila, C. zeae, C. storeyi)		Chlorotic spotting and streaking of leaves.
18	Onion yellow-dwarf (Marmor capae)	United States, Germany, New Zealand, U.S.S.R.	Onion (Allium cepae)	Aphid (including Aphis rumicis, A. maidis)	Leaf rubbing.	Leaves yellowed, crinkled; plants dwarfed; bulbs small; seeds few.
19	Peach phony-disease (Nanus mirabilis)	Southeastern United States	Peach (Prunus persica)	Leafhopper (including Homalodisca triquetra)	Root grafting.	Foliage abnormally green; tree dwarfed; fruit small.
20	Peach-rosette (Carpophthora rosettae)	United States	Peach (P. persica)		Budding; dodder.	Stems short with dwarfed leaves; veins thickened; tree dies soon.
21	Peach X-disease (C. lacerans)	United States	Peach (P. persica)	Leafhopper (including Colladonus spp)	Budding.	Leaves light green, tattered; old leaves drop; fruit bitter.
22	Peach-yellows (Chlorogenus persicae)	Eastern United States, Eastern Canada	Peach (P. persica)	Leafhopper (Macropsis trimaculata)	Budding.	Leaves chlorotic; shoots erect, thin, numerous; tree dies soon.
23	Peanut-rosette (Marmor arachidis)	Africa, Madagascar, Java	Peanut (Arachis hypogaea)	Aphid (Aphis laburni)	Grafting.	Leaves small, chlorotic or mottled; internodes short; seeds few.
24	Potato aucuba-mosaic (M. aucuba)	United States, Europe, British Isles	Potato (Solanum tuberosum)	Probably aphid (Myzus persicae)	Leaf rubbing.	Yellow mottling of foliage; some necrosis in tubers.
25	Potato leafroll (Corium solani)	Wherever potatoes are grown	Potato (S. tuberosum)	Aphid (especially M. persicae)	Grafting.	Leaves thick, leathery, rolled, starchy; plant small; tubers few.
26	Potato mild-mosaic (Marmor solani)	United States, England, Holland	Potato (S. tuberosum)	Aphid (Aphis abbreviata and M. persicae)	Leaf rubbing.	Mild chlorotic mottling or masked symptoms in most varieties.

No.	Disease (virus)	Distribution	Host	Vector	Transmission	Symptoms
27	Potato-mottle (Annulus dubius)	World-wide	Potato (Solanum tuberosum)		Leaf rubbing; root and leaf contacts.	No obvious disease, or very mild chlorotic mottling.
28	Potato spindle-tuber (Acrogenus solani)	United States, Canada	Potato (S. tuberosum)	Aphid (Myzus persicae, Macrosiphum solanifolii)	Leaf rubbing; seed-piece cutting.	Leaves small, erect, dark green; plant brittle; tubers tapered.
29	Potato-veinbanding (Marmor upsilon)	United States, Brazil, England, France	Potato (S. tuberosum)	Aphid (especially Myzus persicae)	Leaf rubbing.	Chlorotic mottling, necrotic stem-streak, or no obvious disease.
30	Potato witches'-broom (Chlorogenus solani)	United States, U.S.S.R.	Potato (S. tuberosum)		Tuber-core and stem grafts.	Leaves small, pale; branches numerous, spindly; tubers small.
31	Potato yellow-dwarf (Aureogenus vastans)	United States, Canada	Potato (S. tuberosum)	Leafhopper (Aceratagallia sanguinolenta)	Leaf abrasion in some hosts; grafting.	Leaves yellowed; plant dwarfed; tubers few, small, often cracked.
32	Rice-dwarf (Fractilinea oryzae)	Japan, Philippine Islands	Rice (Oryza sativa)	Leafhopper (including Nephotettix apicalis)	Grafting, except root grafting.	Leaves chlorotic, spotted, streaked; internodes and roots short.
33	Sandal-spike (Chlorogenus santali)	Southern India	Sandal (Santalum album)	Leafhopper (Jassus indicus)	Grafting.	Leaves small; internodes short; flowers eventually suppressed.
34	Strawberry yellow-edge (Marmor marginans)	United States, England, France, New Zealand	Strawberry (Fragaria hybrids)	Aphid (Aphis fragaefolii)	Grafting; dodder.	Central leaves dwarfed, yellow-edged, lacking red color.
35	Sugar beet curly-top (Ruga verrucosans)	Western North America	Sugar beet (Beta vulgaris)	Leafhopper (Eutettix tenellus)		Leaves curled; enations on veins; plant stunted; rootlets many.
36	Sugar cane chlorotic streak (Fractilinea quarta)	United States, Java, Queensland, Hawaii, Puerto Rico	Sugar cane (Saccharum officinarum)	Leafhopper (Draeculacephala portola)		Long, narrow, white longitudinal streaks in leaves; yield reduced.
37	Sugar cane Fiji-disease (Galla fijiensis)	Australia and islands of the Pacific	Sugar cane (S. officinarum)	Leafhopper (Perkinsiella saccharicida, P. vastatrix)	Sugar cane Fiji-disease.	Leaves short, crumpled, darkened; galls on veins; roots dwarfed.
38	Sugar cane mosaic (Marmor sacchari)	Nearly everywhere sugar cane is grown	Sugar cane (S. officinarum)	Aphid (including Aphis maidis)	Needle puncture.	Systemic chlorotic mottling; vacuolate intracellular bodies.
39	Tobacco-etch (M. erodens)	United States	Tobacco (Nicotiana tabacum)	Aphid (especially Myzus persicae)	Leaf rubbing.	Systemic chlorotic mottling with traces of whitish etching.
40	Tobacco leaf-curl (Ruga tabaci)	Africa, India, Sumatra, Formosa	Tobacco (N. tabacum)	White-fly (Bemisia gossypiperda)	Grafting.	Leaves curled, wrinkled; veins thick; enations; plant stunted.
41	Tobacco-mosaic (Marmor tabaci)	World-wide	Tobacco (N. tabacum)		Leaf rubbing; dodder; soil.	Systemic chlorotic mottling; some distortion of leaves.
42	Tobacco-necrosis (M. lethale)	England, Scotland, Australia	Tobacco (N. tabacum)		Leaf rubbing; soil.	Necrosis in mid-rib and veins of lower leaves in winter.
43	Tobacco-ringspot (Annulus tabaci)	United States	Tobacco (N. tabacum)		Leaf rubbing; seeds of petunia.	Necrotic ringlike primary and secondary lesions; later recovery.
44	Tomato bushy-stunt (Marmor dodecahedron)	British Isles	Tomato (Lycopersicon esculentum)		Leaf rubbing; dodder.	Foliage yellowed, plant stunted; axillary buds stimulated.
45	Tomato spotted-wilt (Lethum australiense)	Almost world-wide	Tomato (L. esculentum)	Thrips (Thrips tabaci, Frankliniella moultoni, F. schultzei)	Leaf abrasion.	Bronze-ring lesions; necrosis or mottling; fruit discolored.
46	Turnip-mosaic (Marmor brassicae)	United States, New Zealand, England	Turnip (Brassica rapa)	Aphid (Brevicoryne brassicae, Myzus persicae)	Leaf rubbing.	Leaves mottled and distorted; plant stunted.
47	Wheat-mosaic (M. tritici)	United States, Japan	Wheat (Triticum aestivum)		Leaf abrasion.	Systemic chlorotic mottling; dwarfing; vacuolate inclusions.
48	Wheat streak-mosaic (M. virgatum)	United States, Canada	Wheat (T. aestivum)	Mite (Aceria tulipae)	Leaf abrasion.	Systemic chlorotic mottling and streaking of leaves.
49	Winter-wheat mosaic (Fractilinea tritici)[2]	U.S.S.R.	Wheat (T. aestivum)	Leafhopper (Deltocephalus striatus)		Chlorotic mottling; phloem necrosis; vacuolate inclusions.
50	Wound-tumor (Aureogenus magnivena)	United States	Clover, crimson (Trifolium incarnatum)	Leafhopper (Agalliopsis novella, Agallia constricta)		Experimentally, veins thickened; enations; plant dwarfed.

/1/ Agent of "English cucumber-mosaic" disease.   /2/ Agent of "Russian winter-wheat mosaic" disease.

431. SELECTED FUNGAL PARASITES: MAN
Part I: SUPERFICIAL MYCOSES

	Fungus	Diseases Produced	Natural Occurrence	Microscopic Appearance in Skin	Microscopic Appearance in Nail	Microscopic Appearance in Hair	Microscopic Appearance of Culture on Sabouraud's Agar
1	Cladosporium wernecki	Tinea nigra palmaris		Pigmented, light brown to dark green, branching, septate hyphae which may develop closely septate, swollen cells and chlamydospores.	None.	None.	Pigmented hyphae which produce blastospores laterally and 1 to 3 septate conidia in clusters or in short chains from apiculi or short conidiophores.
2	Epidermophyton floccosum	Tinea pedis, T. cruris, T. unguium		Abundant, branching, septate hyphae which segment into chains of arthrospores.	Branching, septate hyphae which segment into chains of arthrospores.	None.	Macroconidia abundant, clavate, 2 to 6 cells, blunt-tip, smooth thin walls; occur in clusters of 2 or 3. No microconidia. Abundant chlamydospores.
3	Malassezia furfur	Tinea versicolor		Clusters of spherical, thick-walled, budding cells (3 to 8 μ) and short irregular hyphae.	None.	None.	No culture method available.
4	Microsporum audouini	Tinea capitis, T. corporis	Dog (rare), Monkey (rare)		None.	Ectothrix. Sheath of small spores (2-3μ).	Mycelium with chlamydospores. Microconidia infrequent, clavate, 2.5 to 4x3 to 6 μ. Macroconidia rare, rudimentary, and ill-formed.
5	Microsporum canis	Tinea capitis, T. corporis, T. barbae, T. unguium	Cat[1], Dog[1], Horse, Monkey	Branching, septate hyphae which segment into chains of arthrospores.	Rare.		Macroconidia numerous, 8 to 15 cells, spindle-shape, thick rough walls, 8 to 15 x 40 to 150 μ. Microconidia few, clavate, 2 to 4 x 3 to 6 μ.
6	Microsporum gypseum	Tinea capitis, T. corporis	Cat, Dog[1], Horse[1], Monkey, Mouse, Rat, Soil[1]		None.	May be as above; more commonly large-spored ectothrix (5-8μ).	Macroconidia numerous, ellipsoid, thin, rough walls, 4 to 6 cells, 8 to 12 x 30 to 50 μ. Microconidia few, clavate.
7	Nocardia minutissima	Erythrasma		Delicate, branching filaments (1 μ or less in diameter), readily fragment into coccoid and bacillary forms.	None.	None.	No culture method available.
8	Piedraia hortai	Black piedra		None.	None.	Nodule on hair shaft consists of brown, dichotomously branched, closely septate hyphae (4 to 8 μ in diameter) and asci containing 2 to 8 ascospores.	Dark, thick-walled, closely septate hyphae; chlamydospores, asci and ascospores are rare.
9	Trichophyton concentricum	Tinea imbricata		Abundant branching, septate hyphae which segment into chains of arthrospores.	None.	None.	Septate, branching irregular mycelium with chlamydospores, pectinate hyphae, and favic chandeliers.
10	Trichophyton ferrugineum	Tinea capitis, T. corporis		Branching, septate hyphae which segment into chains of arthrospores.	None.	Ectothrix. Sheath of small arthrospores (2-3μ).	Irregular mycelium with hyphal swellings and many chlamydospores.
11	Trichophyton gallinae	Favus of poultry[1] and wild birds, Tinea capitis, T. corporis	Primarily a disease of poultry	Branching, septate hyphae. (Rare in man.)	None.	None.	Macroconidia usually numerous, clavate, 2 to 10 cells, smooth, slightly thickened walls. Microconidia few, small, pyriform to elongate.
12	Trichophyton megnini	Tinea barbae, T. capitis, T. unguium	Cattle, Dog(?)	Branching, septate hyphae.	Branching, septate hyphae which may segment into chains of arthrospores.	Endothrix. Chains of large spherical arthrospores (6 to 8 μ).	Microconidia numerous, small, pyriform to elongate. Macroconidia rare, slightly clavate, 2 to 8 cells.
13	Trichophyton mentagrophytes	Tinea pedis, T. cruris, T. corporis, T. capitis, T. unguium, T. barbae	Cat, Cattle, Chinchilla, Dog[1], Guinea pig[1], Horse[1], Monkey, Mouse, Muskrat, Rabbit[1], Rat[1]	Branching, septate hyphae which may segment into chains of arthrospores.	Branching, septate hyphae which may segment into chains of arthrospores.	Ectothrix. Chains of small arthrospores (3-5μ).	Microconidia numerous, subspherical to pyriform, in terminal clusters or singly along the hyphae. Macroconidia clavate thick walls, 2 to 5 cells, 4 to 6 x 10 to 50 μ.

512

Part I (continued)

No.	Fungus	Disease (host or site)	Animal host	Microscopic appearance in tissue/hair	In hair	Culture characteristics
14	Trichophyton rubrum	Tinea pedis, T. unguium, T. cruris, T. corporis, T. barbae, T. capitis	Cow (rare), Dog (rare)	Branching, septate hyphae which may segment into chains of arthrospores.	Ectothrix. Chains of large arthrospores (about 5μ).	Microconidia numerous singly along the hyphae and in clusters. Macroconidia infrequent, pencil-shaped thin walls, 4 to 6 x 10 to 50μ.
15	Trichophyton schoenleini	Favus, Tinea capitis, T. corporis, T. unguium	Dog (rare)	Abundant hyphae which may segment into chains of arthrospores throughout cellular debris of scutulum.	Endothrix. Mycelium, occasional arthrospore and numerous air bubbles inside hair.	Irregular mycelium, chlamydospores, hyphal swellings, pectinate hyphae, and favic chandeliers.
16	Trichophyton tonsurans	Tinea capitis, T. corporis, T. unguium		Branching, septate hyphae which segment into chains of arthrospores.	Endothrix. Large spores in chains (4-7.5μ).	Microconidia numerous, clavate or on short conidiophores. Spore-bearing hyphae stains poorly with LPCB. Numerous chlamydospores.
17	Trichophyton verrucosum	Tinea corporis, T. capitis, T. barbae	Cattle[1]; rare in dog, donkey, dromedary, goat, horse, sheep	None.		Irregular mycelium. Abundant chlamydospores. Microconidia and macroconidia present on thiamine-enriched media. Best growth at 37°C.
18	Trichophyton violaceum	Tinea capitis, T. corporis, T. barbae, T. unguium		Branching, septate hyphae with segment into chains of arthrospores.	Endothrix. Chains of large arthrospores (4-7.5μ).	Irregular mycelium. Abundant chlamydospores and hyphal swellings. Microconidia rare.
19	Trichosporon beigelii	White piedra		Not affected.	Nodule on hair shaft consists of hyphae which segment into spherical to rectangular cells (2 to 8μ). Budding cells present.	Hyphae segment into rectangular to spherical arthrospores. Budding cells present.

/1/ Host or site of most common occurrence.

Part II: DEEP MYCOSES

No.	Fungus	Disease	Geographical Distribution	Occurrence In Nature — Animal Host	Occurrence In Nature — Saprophytic Occurrence	Organs and Tissues Frequently Attacked	Susceptible Laboratory Animals	Microscopic Appearance in Tissue	Culture at 25°C	Culture at 37°C
1	Actinomyces bovis (A. israeli)	Actinomycosis (Lumpy jaw)	World-wide	Cattle, Deer, Dog, Horse, Swine	Man (often); obligate parasite	Cervico-facial region, lung, bone, cecum, appendix, liver	Hamster, Mouse	Granules of filamentous, branching, Gram-positive hyphae (1μ or less in width). Club-shaped accretions on tips of hyphae may be present.	Grows slowly.	Anaerobic, filamentous, branching. Gram-positive hyphae (1μ or less in width).
2	Allescheria boydii (Monosporium apiospermum), Aspergillus spp(?), Madurella spp, Indiella spp, Cephalosporium spp, Glenospora spp(?), Penicillium spp(?), Sterigmatocystis sp(?), Phialophora jeanselmei	Mycetoma (Maduromycosis; Madura foot)	World-wide; more frequent in tropics	Dog	Soil (A. boydii, P. jeanselmei)	Feet, hands, cutaneous and subcutaneous tissue, bone	Mouse (A. boydii)	Oval, irregular shaped granules (0.5 to 2 mm) made up of segmented branched hyphae (2 to 4μ in diameter) and chlamydospores.	Allescheria boydii — mycelium with ovoid to pyriform conidia (5 to 7 x 8 to 10μ) borne singly at ends of long conidiophores. Dark brown, thin-walled perithecia (50 to 200μ in diameter) containing evanescent asci and elliptical ascospores. Coremia occasionally present.	Similar to cultures at 25°C.
3	Aspergillus spp (A. fumigatus)	Aspergillosis	World-wide	Birds	Grain, Soil	Ear, sinus, orbit, vagina, lung, brain	Birds, Guinea pig, Rabbit	Fragments of septate hyphae and spherical, green conidia.	Conidiophore forms vesicle at tip. Surface covered with sterigmata bearing long chains of conidia.	Similar to growth at 25°C.
4	Blastomyces brasiliensis (Paracoccidioides brasiliensis)	South American blastomycosis (Paracoccidioidal granuloma; Lutz-Splendore-de-Almeida's disease)	South America, Central America	Not known	Not known	Mouth, lung, lymph node, gastro-intestinal tract	Guinea pig, Hamster, Mouse	Multiple budding, thick-walled cells (10 to 60μ).	Mycelium with rare oval conidia (3 to 5μ).	Similar to the forms observed in tissue.
5	Blastomyces dermatitidis	North American blastomycosis	U.S.A., Canada, Mexico	Dog, Horse	Not known	Skin, lung, bone	Guinea pig, Mouse	Single budding, thick-walled cells (8 to 15μ).	Mycelium with oval to pyriform conidia (3 to 5μ) on conidiophores or attached directly to hyphae.	Similar to the forms observed in tissue.

431. SELECTED FUNGAL PARASITES: MAN (Concluded)

Part II: DEEP MYCOSES (Concluded)

Fungus	Disease	Geographical Distribution	Occurrence in Nature — Animal Host	Occurrence in Nature — Saprophytic Occurrence	Organs and Tissues Frequently Attacked	Susceptible Laboratory Animals	Microscopic Appearance in Tissue	Microscopic Appearance in Culture at 25°C	Culture at 37°C
6 Candida albicans (Monilia albicans)	Candidiasis (Moniliasis; thrush; mycotic vulvovaginitis)	World-wide	Poultry	Man (often) Soil (rare)	Mucous membranes, nail, skin, bronchus, lung	Guinea pig Mouse Rabbit Rat	Oval to spherical budding cells (2 to 4μ) and frequently pseudohyphae and hyphae which may show clusters of blastospores attached at septations.	Oval to spherical single budding cells (2 to 4μ). Pseudohyphae and hyphae. Clusters of budding cells often at septations. Thick-walled chlamydospores (6 to 9μ) on special medium.	Similar to growth at 25°C.
7 Coccidioides immitis	Coccidioidomycosis (Coccidioidal granuloma; valley fever; Posada-Wernicke's disease)	Arid S.W. U.S.A. Northern Mexico Chaco region, S. America	Cattle Dog Gorilla Monkey Rodents Sheep	Soil	Lung, skin, bone, meninges	Guinea pig Hamster Mouse Other rodents	Thick-walled spherules (20 to 60μ) containing endospores (2 to 5μ).	Mycelium with arthrospores (2.5 to 3 x 3 to 4μ).	Similar to growth at 25°C. Under special conditions with special media, tissue spherules obtained in vitro.
8 Cryptococcus neoformans (Torula histolytica)	Cryptococcosis (Torulosis; European blastomycosis; Busse-Buschke's disease)	World-wide	Cat Cattle Dog Horse	Soil Pigeon droppings	Central nervous system, lung, skin, bone	Mouse Rat	Spherical, single budding, thick-walled cells (5 to 20μ) surrounded by a wide, gelatinous capsule.	Similar to cells seen in tissue.[1] Abortive hyphae may be seen on primary isolation.	Similar to cells seen in tissue.
9 Geotrichum sp	Geotrichosis	World-wide	Rodents	Milk products	Mouth, intestinal tract, bronchus, lung	Not known	Oblong to rectangular cells with somewhat rounded ends (4 to 8μ).	Mycelium with segments into rectangular arthrospores. Germ tube forms at corners.	Similar to growth at 25°C.
10 Histoplasma capsulatum	Histoplasmosis (Recticulo-endothelial cytomycosis; Darling's disease)	At least 24 countries of the world	Cat Cattle Dog Horse Mouse Rat Skunk	Soil, especially from avian habitats	Lung, liver, spleen, lymph nodes, mucous membranes, adrenal, kidney	Guinea pig Hamster Mouse	Intracellular oval, budding cells (1 to 5μ).	Delicate mycelium with thin-walled, subspherical to pyriform conidia (2 to 5μ) and thick-walled, tuberculated conidia 8 to 20μ).	Budding cells (1 to 5μ); must be grown on enriched medium.
11 Hormodendrum pedrosoi H. compactum H. dermatitidis Phialophora verrucosa	Chromoblastomycosis (Chromomycosis; verrucous dermatitis)	World-wide; more frequent in tropics	Not known	Soil, wood (H. dermatidis, P. verrucosa)	Usually on lower extremities, cutaneous and subcutaneous tissue, lymphatics	Mouse Rat	Single or clustered, spherical, thick-walled, dark brown cells (6 to 12μ) which multiply by splitting not budding.	Three types of sporulation characterize this group of fungi: Hormodendrum type-conidia in branching chains arising terminally from conidiophore. Acrotheca type-conidia borne acropleurogenously on swollen, club-like conidiophore. Phialophora type-conidia borne within a terminal cup-like structure on a flask-shaped conidiophore.	Similar to cultures at 25°C.
12 Mucor spp (Rhizopus oryzae, R. arrhizus, Absidia corymbifera)	Mucormycosis	Probably world-wide	Birds Cattle Dog Horse Swine	Soil	Lung, brain, eye, intestinal tract	Diabetic rabbit	Nonseptate, coenocytic hyphae (6 to 15μ in width).	Broad, coenocytic mycelium with brown sporangiophores.	Similar to growth at 25°C.
13 Nocardia asteroides N. brasiliensis N. madurae N. pelletieri N. paraguayensis	Nocardiosis (Actinomycotic mycetoma; Madura foot)	World-wide; more frequent in tropics	Cattle Dog	Soil	Lung, brain, cutaneous and subcutaneous tissue (asteroides and N.brasiliensis	Guinea pig Mouse	Granules of Gram-positive, branching, delicate hyphae. Occasionally not in granule form. N. asteroides and N. brasiliensis are partially acid-fast.	Delicate, branching hyphae (1μ or less in width) which may or may not fragment into bacillary forms of varying length.	Similar to growth at 25°C.
14 Rhinosporidium seeberi	Rhinosporidiosis	World-wide; more frequent in India & Ceylon	Cow Horse Mule	Not known	Mucous membranes, nose, eye, vagina, penis, skin	Not known	Thick-walled spherule (50 to 350μ) with pore, containing up to 16,000 endospores (7 to 9μ).	No culture method available.	No culture method available.
15 Sporotrichum schenckii	Sporotrichosis	World-wide	Cat Cow Dog Horse Mouse Mule Rat	Mine timbers Plants Soil	Hands, feet, cutaneous and subcutaneous tissue, lymphatics	Hamster Mouse Rat	Rarely seen without special stains. Gram-positive, cigar-shaped or spherical to oval, usually intracellular, budding cells (3 to 5μ). Asteroid forms rare.	Delicate (2μ in width) hyphae. Pyriform to spherical conidia (2 to 4 x 2 to 6μ) borne in clusters on lateral branches or laterally along the hyphae.	Cigar-shaped, spherical or oval budding cells. Must be grown on enriched medium.

/1/ Not true of some strains which may be weakly encapsulated in vitro, giving culture a different gross appearance similar to many of the common yeasts.

432. POPULATION, REGISTERED DEATHS AND DEATH RATES, BY RACE AND SEX: U.S.A., 1906-1954

Population estimated as of July 1 for 1906-39, 1941-49 and 1951-54, and enumerated as of April 1 for 1940 and 1950. Rates are per 1000 population in each specified group.

	Year	Population of Continental United States[1]	Number of States[4]	Population[5]	Death-registration States[2] Deaths[3]										
					Number					Rate					
					Total	White		Non-white		Total	White		Non-white		
						Male	Female	Male	Female		Male	Female	Male	Female	
1	1954	162,414,000	48	161,195,000	1,481,000[6]	748,390[6]	559,760[6]	95,680[6]	77,170[6]	9.2[6]	10.5[6]	7.7[6]	11.4[6]	8.7[6]	
2	1953	159,629,000	48	158,306,000	1,517,541	766,703	569,132	100,397	81,309	9.6	11.0	8.0	12.2	10.1	
3	1952	157,022,000	48	155,755,000	1,496,838	753,571	561,451	100,356	81,460	9.6	11.0	8.0	12.5	9.6	
4	1951	154,360,000	48	153,384,000	1,482,099	747,049	555,920	98,184	80,946	9.7	11.0	8.0	12.5	9.8	
5	1950	151,132,000	48	150,697,361	1,452,454	731,366	544,719	96,383	79,986	9.6	11.0	8.0	12.5	9.9	
6	1949	149,188,000	48	148,665,000	1,443,607	726,169	542,679	95,122	79,637	9.7	11.0	8.1	12.5	10.0	
7	1948	146,631,000	48	146,093,000	1,444,337	725,818	544,771	95,113	78,635	9.9	11.2	8.3	12.7	10.1	
8	1947	144,126,000	48	143,446,000	1,445,370	726,104	548,789	92,130	78,347	10.1	11.4	8.5	12.5	10.3	
9	1946	141,389,000	48	140,054,000	1,395,617	697,323	535,014	88,366	74,914	10.0	11.2	8.5	12.2	10.0	
10	1945	139,928,000	48	132,481,000	1,401,719	697,698	536,191	90,365	77,465	10.6	12.5	8.6	13.5	10.5	
11	1944	138,397,000	48	132,885,000	1,411,338	697,731	541,098	92,130	80,379	10.6	12.2	8.8	13.8	11.1	
12	1943	136,739,000	48	134,245,000	1,459,544	721,777	559,110	95,708	82,949	10.9	12.2	9.2	14.0	11.6	
13	1942	134,860,000	48	133,920,000	1,385,187	685,468	524,476	94,986	80,257	10.3	11.4	8.7	14.0	11.4	
14	1941	133,402,000	48	133,121,000	1,397,642	685,672	527,839	99,361	84,770	10.5	11.4	8.9	14.8	12.2	
15	1940	131,820,000	48	131,669,000	1,417,269	690,901	540,322	100,102	85,944	10.8	11.6	9.2	15.1	12.6	
16	1939	130,879,718	48	130,879,718	1,387,897	672,047	535,031	96,830	83,989	10.6	11.3	9.2	14.7	12.4	
17	1938	129,824,939	48	129,824,939	1,381,391	665,559	529,872	99,343	86,617	10.6	11.3	9.2	15.2	12.9	
18	1937	128,824,829	48	128,824,829	1,450,427	702,630	552,157	106,204	89,436	11.3	12.0	9.6	16.4	13.4	
19	1936	128,053,180	48	128,053,180	1,479,228	712,126	566,253	109,313	91,536	11.6	12.3	9.9	16.9	13.9	
20	1935	127,250,232	48	127,250,232	1,392,752	671,298	536,061	100,022	85,371	10.9	11.6	9.5	15.6	13.0	
21	1934	126,373,773	48	126,373,773	1,396,903	670,476	536,671	102,119	87,587	11.1	11.7	9.6	16.0	13.5	
22	1933	125,578,763	48	125,578,763	1,342,106	641,725	520,673	95,587	84,121	10.7	11.2	9.3	15.1	13.1	
23	1932	124,840,471	47	118,903,899	1,293,269	614,093	508,377	90,413	80,386	10.9	11.3	9.6	15.4	13.5	
24	1931	124,039,648	47	118,148,987	1,307,273	621,120	504,257	96,510	85,386	11.1	11.5	9.6	16.5	14.5	
25	1930	123,076,741	47	117,238,278	1,327,240	625,792	511,092	100,888	89,468	11.3	11.7	9.8	17.4	15.3	
26	1929	121,769,939	46	115,317,450	1,369,757	642,463	533,027	103,028	91,239	11.9	12.2	10.4	18.0	15.8	
27	1928	120,501,115	44	113,636,160	1,361,987	637,063	531,206	101,828	91,890	12.0	12.3	10.8	18.0	16.2	
28	1927	119,038,062	42	107,084,532	1,211,627	572,061	478,297	84,636	76,633	11.3	11.6	10.0	17.2	15.6	
29	1926	117,399,225	41	103,822,683	1,257,256	590,852	502,998	86,180	77,226	12.1	12.3	10.8	18.7	16.9	
30	1925	115,831,963	40	102,031,555	1,191,809	559,356	476,144	82,041	74,268	11.7	11.8	10.4	18.2	16.6	
31	1924	114,113,463	39	99,318,098	1,151,076	539,303	458,314	80,571	72,888	11.6	11.8	10.3	17.9	16.3	
32	1923	111,949,945	38	96,788,197	1,174,065	549,623	478,478	75,636	70,328	12.1	12.3	11.0	17.0	16.0	
33	1922	110,054,778	37	92,702,901	1,083,952	507,567	443,885	68,360	64,140	11.7	11.9	10.7	15.7	14.8	
34	1921	108,541,489	34	87,814,447	1,009,673	475,172	420,421	58,095	55,985	11.5	11.6	10.6	15.7	15.4	
35	1920	106,466,420	34	86,079,263	1,118,070	521,440	469,419	64,696	62,515	13.0	13.0	12.1	17.8	17.5	
36	1919	105,062,747	33	83,157,982	1,072,263	502,968	442,468	64,217	62,610	12.9	13.0	11.8	18.1	17.8	
37	1918	104,549,886	30	79,008,412	1,430,079	706,613	575,920	77,694	69,852	18.1	19.3	15.8	26.7	24.4	
38	1917	103,413,743	27	70,234,775	981,239	486,208	396,527	52,315	46,189	14.0	14.6	12.4	21.4	19.4	
39	1916	101,965,984	26	66,971,177	924,971	461,432	381,165	43,455	38,919	13.8	14.4	12.4	19.9	18.4	
40	1915	100,549,013	24	61,894,847	815,500	415,476	346,813	28,452	24,759	13.2	13.7	12.0	20.8	19.5	
41	1914	99,117,567	24	60,963,309	810,914	415,493	343,107	28,129	24,185	13.3	13.9	12.1	20.9	19.4	
42	1913	97,226,814	23	58,156,740	802,909	413,225	339,040	27,122	23,522	13.8	14.5	12.5	21.0	19.6	
43	1912	95,331,300	22	54,847,700	745,771	388,302	321,229	19,791	16,449	13.6	14.3	12.4	21.3	19.7	
44	1911	93,867,814	22	53,929,644	749,918	388,238	325,006	19,895	16,779	13.9	14.5	12.8	21.9	20.6	
45	1910	92,406,536	20	47,470,437	696,856	365,042	304,433	15,031	12,350	14.7	15.4	13.6	22.3	21.0	
46	1909	90,491,525	18	44,223,513	630,057	327,153	276,398	14,398	12,108	14.2	14.9	13.2	22.3	21.2	
47	1908	88,708,976	17	38,634,759	567,245	294,173	248,627	13,186	11,259	14.7	15.3	13.6	22.8	22.0	
48	1907	87,000,271	15	34,552,837	550,245	286,269	238,990	13,530	11,456	15.9	16.8	14.5	25.0	23.5	
49	1906	85,436,556	15	33,782,288	531,005	274,579	231,974	13,112	11,340	15.7	16.5	14.4	24.7	23.6	

/1/ Estimates of armed forces overseas are included in the years 1917-19, 1940-54. /2/ Effective 1933, all of continental United States included. /3/ Exclusive of fetal deaths. For 1940-54, estimates exclusive of deaths among armed forces overseas; rates based on population excluding armed forces overseas. /4/ District of Columbia not included in "Number of States," though represented in all data shown for each year. /5/ Excludes armed forces overseas. /6/ Tentative.

433. AVERAGE REMAINING LIFETIME IN YEARS AT SPECIFIED AGES, BY RACE AND SEX: U.S.A., 1900-1953

For 1900-1902 and 1909-1911, data for the death-registration states of 1900, which consisted of 10 states and the District of Columbia; for 1919-1921, for the death-registration states of 1920, which consisted of 34 states and the District of Columbia; for 1929-1931, 1939-1941, 1949-1951, 1952 and 1953, for the entire continental United States.

	Age	1953	1952	1949-1951	1939-1941	1929-1931	1919-1921	1909-1911	1900-1902		Age	1953	1952	1949-1951	1939-1941	1929-1931	1919-1921	1909-1911	1900-1902
		White Male										White Female							
1	0	66.8	66.6	66.3	62.8	59.1	56.3	50.2	48.2	21	0	72.9	72.7	72.0	67.3	62.7	58.5	53.6	51.1
2	1	67.7	67.6	67.4	65.0	62.2	60.2	56.3	54.6	22	1	73.6	73.3	72.8	68.9	64.9	61.5	58.7	56.3
3	5	64.0	64.0	63.8	61.7	59.4	58.3	55.4	54.4	23	5	69.8	69.6	69.1	65.6	62.2	59.4	57.7	56.0
4	10	59.2	59.2	59.0	57.0	55.0	54.2	51.3	50.6	24	10	65.0	64.8	64.3	60.9	57.7	55.2	53.6	52.2
5	15	54.4	54.4	54.2	52.3	50.4	49.7	46.9	46.3	25	15	60.1	59.9	59.4	56.1	53.0	50.7	49.1	47.8
6	20	49.8	49.7	49.5	47.8	46.0	45.6	42.7	42.2	26	20	55.3	55.1	54.6	51.4	48.5	46.5	44.9	43.8
7	25	45.2	45.2	44.9	43.3	41.8	41.6	38.8	38.5	27	25	50.5	50.3	49.8	46.8	44.3	42.6	40.9	40.1
8	30	40.6	40.5	40.3	38.8	37.5	37.7	34.9	34.9	28	30	45.7	45.5	45.0	42.2	40.0	38.7	37.0	36.4
9	35	35.9	35.9	35.7	34.4	33.3	33.7	31.1	31.3	29	35	40.9	40.8	40.3	37.7	35.7	34.9	33.1	32.8
10	40	31.4	31.4	31.2	30.0	29.2	29.9	27.4	27.7	30	40	36.2	36.1	35.6	33.3	31.5	31.0	29.3	29.2
11	45	27.0	27.1	26.9	25.9	25.3	26.0	23.9	24.2	31	45	31.7	31.6	31.1	28.9	27.4	27.0	25.5	25.5
12	50	23.0	23.0	22.8	22.0	21.5	22.2	20.4	20.8	32	50	27.3	27.2	26.8	24.7	23.4	23.1	21.7	21.9
13	55	19.2	19.3	19.1	18.3	18.0	18.6	17.0	17.4	33	55	23.0	23.0	22.6	20.7	19.6	19.4	18.2	18.4
14	60	15.8	15.9	15.8	15.1	14.7	15.3	14.0	14.4	34	60	19.0	19.0	18.6	17.0	16.1	15.9	14.9	15.3
15	65	12.9	13.0	12.8	12.1	11.8	12.2	11.3	11.5	35	65	15.3	15.3	15.0	13.6	12.8	12.8	12.0	12.2
16	70	10.3	10.3	10.1	9.4	9.2	9.5	8.8	9.0	36	70	12.0	12.0	11.7	10.5	10.0	9.9	9.4	9.6
17	75	7.9	8.0	7.8	7.2	7.0	7.3	6.8	6.8	37	75	9.1	9.1	8.9	7.9	7.6	7.6	7.2	7.3
18	80	6.1	6.1	5.9	5.4	5.3	5.5	5.1	5.1	38	80	6.7	6.8	6.6	5.9	5.6	5.7	5.4	5.5
19	85	4.7	4.8	4.4	4.0	4.0	4.1	3.9	3.8	39	85	5.1	5.1	4.8	4.3	4.2	4.2	4.1	4.1
20	90	-	-	3.3	3.1	3.0	3.2	3.0	2.9	40	90	-	-	3.5	3.2	3.2	3.2	3.0	3.0

433. AVERAGE REMAINING LIFETIME IN YEARS AT SPECIFIED AGES, BY RACE AND SEX: U.S.A., 1900-1953 (Concluded)

For 1900-1902 and 1909-1911, data for the death-registration states of 1900, which consisted of 10 states and the District of Columbia; for 1919-1921, for the death-registration states of 1920, which consisted of 34 states and the District of Columbia; for 1929-1931, 1939-1941, 1949-1951, 1952 and 1953, for the entire continental United States.

	Age	1953	1952	1949-1951	1939-1941	1929-1931	1919-1921	1909-1911	1900-1902		Age	1953	1952	1949-1951	1939-1941	1929-1931	1919-1921	1909-1911	1900-1902
				Non-white Male[1]										Non-white Female[1] (concluded)						
41	0	59.7	59.1	58.9	52.3	47.6	47.1	34.1	32.5	71	45	26.9	26.8	26.1	23.9	21.4	22.6	20.4	21.4
42	1	61.7	61.4	61.1	55.9	51.1	51.6	42.5	42.5	72	50	23.4	23.2	22.7	21.0	18.6	19.8	17.7	18.7
43	5	58.3	58.0	57.7	53.0	48.7	50.2	44.3	45.0	73	55	20.3	20.2	19.6	18.4	16.3	17.1	15.0	15.9
44	10	53.5	53.3	53.0	48.3	44.3	46.0	40.7	41.9	74	60	17.4	17.4	17.0	16.1	14.2	14.7	12.8	13.6
45	15	48.8	48.5	48.2	43.7	39.8	41.8	36.8	38.3	75	65	14.7	14.8	14.5	13.9	12.2	12.4	10.8	11.4
46	20	44.2	44.0	43.7	39.5	36.0	38.4	33.5	35.1	76	70	12.9	12.9	12.3	11.8	10.4	10.3	9.2	9.6
47	25	39.9	39.7	39.5	35.7	32.7	35.5	30.4	32.2	77	75	10.8	10.8	10.2	9.8	8.6	8.4	7.6	7.9
48	30	35.7	35.6	35.3	32.1	29.5	32.5	27.3	29.3	78	80	9.1	9.1	8.2	8.0	6.9	6.6	6.1	6.5
49	35	31.6	31.4	31.2	28.5	26.4	29.5	24.4	26.2	79	85	7.6	7.3	6.2	6.4	5.5	5.2	5.1	5.1
50	40	27.6	27.5	27.3	25.1	23.4	26.5	21.6	23.1	80	90	-	-	4.1	5.0	4.2	4.1	4.5	4.0
51	45	23.8	23.8	23.6	21.9	20.6	23.6	18.9	20.1						Total Population					
52	50	20.4	20.4	20.3	19.1	17.9	20.5	16.2	17.3	81	0	68.8	68.6	68.1	63.6	59.2	56.4	51.5	49.2
53	55	17.5	17.5	17.4	16.6	15.5	17.5	13.8	14.7	82	1	69.8	69.6	69.2	65.8	61.9	59.9	57.1	55.2
54	60	14.9	15.0	14.9	14.4	13.2	14.7	11.7	12.6	83	5	66.1	66.0	65.5	62.5	59.3	58.0	56.2	55.0
55	65	12.7	12.8	12.8	12.2	10.9	12.1	9.7	10.4	84	10	61.3	61.1	60.7	57.8	54.8	53.8	52.2	51.1
56	70	11.2	11.1	10.7	10.1	8.8	9.6	8.0	8.3	85	15	56.5	56.3	55.9	53.1	50.3	49.4	47.7	46.8
57	75	9.5	9.3	8.8	8.2	7.0	7.6	6.6	6.6	86	20	51.7	51.6	51.2	48.5	45.9	45.3	43.5	42.8
58	80	8.0	8.0	7.1	6.6	5.4	5.8	5.5	5.1	87	25	47.1	47.0	46.6	44.1	41.9	41.5	39.6	39.1
59	85	6.9	6.8	5.4	5.3	4.3	4.5	4.5	4.0	88	30	42.4	42.3	41.9	39.7	37.8	37.7	35.7	35.5
60	90	-	-	3.8	4.2	3.4	3.6	4.0	3.2	89	35	37.8	37.7	37.3	35.3	33.7	33.9	31.9	31.9
				Non-white Female[1]						90	40	33.2	33.2	32.8	31.0	29.7	30.1	28.2	28.3
61	0	64.4	63.7	62.7	55.6	49.5	46.9	37.7	35.0	91	45	28.9	28.8	28.5	26.9	25.8	26.3	24.5	24.8
62	1	66.1	65.5	64.4	58.5	52.3	50.4	45.2	43.5	92	50	24.7	24.7	24.4	23.0	22.1	22.5	21.0	21.3
63	5	62.6	62.1	60.9	55.4	49.8	48.7	46.4	46.0	93	55	20.9	20.9	20.6	19.3	18.5	18.9	17.6	17.9
64	10	57.8	57.3	56.2	50.8	45.3	44.5	42.8	43.0	94	60	17.3	17.3	17.0	15.9	15.2	15.5	14.4	14.8
65	15	53.0	52.5	51.4	46.1	40.9	40.4	39.2	39.8	95	65	14.0	14.1	13.8	12.8	12.2	12.5	11.6	11.9
66	20	48.3	47.8	46.8	42.0	37.2	37.2	36.1	36.9	96	70	11.2	11.2	10.9	10.0	9.6	9.7	9.1	9.3
67	25	43.7	43.3	42.4	38.2	33.9	34.4	33.0	33.9	97	75	8.6	8.6	8.4	7.6	7.3	7.5	7.0	7.1
68	30	39.3	38.9	38.0	34.4	30.7	31.5	29.6	30.7	98	80	6.6	6.6	6.3	5.7	5.5	5.6	5.3	5.3
69	35	35.0	34.7	33.8	30.7	27.5	28.6	26.4	27.5	99	85	5.1	5.1	4.7	4.3	4.2	4.2	4.0	4.0
70	40	30.9	30.6	29.8	27.2	24.3	25.6	23.3	24.4										

/1/ Figures for the non-white groups cover only Negroes, who never comprised less than 95% of the corresponding non-white population.

434. LIFE EXPECTANCY: MAN, VARIOUS NATIONS
Values are years.

	Nation	Years Upon Which Data Are Based	Expectation of Life at Birth Male	Female		Nation	Years Upon Which Data Are Based	Expectation of Life at Birth Male	Female
	Africa and Adjacent Areas					Europe and Adjacent Areas			
1	Egypt	1936-1938	36.65	41.48	27	Austria	1930-1933	54.50	58.50
2	Mauritius[1]	1942-1946	32.25	33.83	28	Belgium	1946-1949	62.04	67.26
3	S. Rhodesia (Europeans)	1935-1937	58.52	62.57	29	Bulgaria	1925-1928	45.92	46.64
4	Union of South Africa (Europeans)	1945-1947	63.78	68.31	30	Czechoslovakia	1929-1932	51.92	55.18
	America, North and Adjacent Areas				31	Denmark	1946-1950	67.80	70.10
5	Barbados	1945-1947	49.17	52.94	32	Finland	1941-1945	54.62	61.14
6	British Honduras	1944-1948	44.99	48.97	33	France	1946-1949	61.90	67.40
7	Canada	1947	65.18	69.05	34	Germany, Federal Republic	1950	64.06	67.92
8	Guatemala	1939-1941	35.97	37.09	35	Greece	1926-1930	49.09	50.89
9	Jamaica	1945-1947	51.25	54.58	36	Hungary	1941	54.92	58.22
10	Mexico	1940	37.92	39.79	37	Iceland	1931-1940	60.90	65.60
11	Panama	1941-1943	50.54	53.46	38	Ireland	1945-1947	60.47	62.43
12	Trinidad and Tobago	1945-1947	52.98	56.03	39	Italy	1930-1932	53.76	56.00[3]
13	United States, White	1951	66.61	72.62	40	Luxembourg	1946-1948	61.69	65.75
14	United States, Non-white	1951	59.37	63.71	41	Malta and Gozo	1946	55.69	57.72
	America, South and Adjacent Areas				42	Netherlands	1947-1949	69.40	71.50
15	Brazil	1920	37.43[2]		43	Norway	1945-1948	67.76	71.68
16	British Guiana	1945-1947	49.32	52.05	44	Poland	1948	55.60	62.50
17	Chile	1939-1942	40.65	43.06	45	Portugal	1939-1942	48.58	52.82
18	Venezuela	1941-1942	45.83	47.55	46	Spain	1940	47.12	53.24
	Asia and Adjacent Areas				47	Sweden	1941-1945	67.06	69.71
19	Ceylon	1949	54.20	52.80	48	Switzerland	1939-1944	62.68	66.96
20	China (Formosa)	1936-1940	41.08	45.73	49	United Kingdom: England and Wales	1951	65.84	70.88
21	Cyprus	1931-1946	57.30	59.30	50	Northern Ireland	1936-1938	57.80	59.20
22	India	1931-1941	32.09	31.37	51	Scotland	1951	64.20	68.30
23	Israel	1951	67.30	70.10	52	USSR (Europe)	1926-1927	41.93	46.79
24	Japan	1949-1950	56.19	59.61		Oceania			
25	Korea	1938	47.20	50.59	53	Australia	1946-1948	66.07	70.63
26	Thailand, Bangkok	1937-1938	36.73	43.30	54	Hawaii	1919-1920	47.79	47.27
					55	New Zealand (Europeans)	1947	67.77	71.62

/1/ Exclusive of island dependencies. /2/ Total persons. /3/ Value for 1935-1937 was 57.49.

435. AVERAGE LIFE SPAN: MAN, NORTH AMERICA[1]
Values are years.

	Period	White Male	White Female	Negro Male	Negro Female		Period	White Male	White Female	Negro Male	Negro Female
1	1850	38.20[2,3]	40.50[2,3]			7	1920-1929[5]	57.85	60.62	46.90	47.95
2	1890	42.50[2,3]	44.46[2,3]			8	1929-1931	59.12	62.67	47.55	49.51
3	1900-1902[4]	48.23	51.08	32.54	35.04	9	1930-1939[6,7]	60.62	64.52	50.06	52.62
4	1901-1910[4]	49.32	52.54	32.57	35.65	10	1939-1941[6]	62.81	67.29	52.26	55.56
5	1909-1911[4]	50.23	53.62	34.05	37.67	11	1949[6]	65.88	71.51	58.57	62.93
6	1919-1921[5]	56.34	58.53	47.14	46.92	12	1951[6]	66.61	72.62	59.37	63.71

/1/ Increase in life expectancy at birth is mainly caused by decreased infant mortality; expectancy from age 30 was only about 6 years greater in 1949 than in 1850, and expectancy at age 60 was no greater in 1949 than in 1850. /2/ Massachusetts. /3/ Non-whites includes, about 1% of the total. /4/ Original death registration states. /5/ Death registration states in 1920. /6/ Continental United States. /7/ All non-whites.

436. POPULATION, ESTIMATED: VARIOUS WORLD REGIONS
Part I: WORLD POPULATION BY CONTINENTS AND REGIONS
Values in parentheses are ranges.

#	Continent and Region	Estimates of Midyear Population, Millions[1]					Area[2] sq km x 1000	Population Density, 1953 per sq km
		1920	1930	1940	1950	1953		
1	World total[3]	1813	1987	2213	2455	2547	135,168	19
2		(1753-1872)	(1937-2036)	(2157-2270)	(2370-2540)	(2459-2634)		
3	Africa, total	140	155	172	198	208	30,310	7
4		(130-151)	(145-164)	(163-181)	(190-207)	(199-216)		
5	Northern Africa	46	51	57	65	68	10,246	7
6		(40-53)	(45-56)	(52-62)	(60-69)	(63-72)		
7	Tropical and Southern Africa	94	104	115	134	140	20,064	7
8		(88-100)	(98-110)	(110-121)	(128-139)	(134-146)		
9	America, total	208	244	277	330	351	42,097	8
10		(204-212)	(240-247)	(274-280)	(326-334)	(347-355)		
11	North America	117	135	146	168	177	21,482	8
12		(115-118)	(134-136)	(145-147)	(167-169)	(176-179)		
13	Central America	30	34	41	51	55	2760	20
14		(29-31)	(33-35)	(40-42)	(50-52)	(54-56)		
15	South America	61	75	90	111	119	17,855	7
16		(59-64)	(72-77)	(88-92)	(108-114)	(116-122)		
17	Asia, total (except USSR)[4]	970	1047	1176	1321	1364	27,003	51
18		(922-1019)	(1007-1087)	(1128-1224)	(1247-1394)	(1288-1439)		
19	Southwest Asia	44	48	54	62	66	5543	12
20		(38-50)	(43-52)	(50-58)	(58-66)	(61-70)		
21	South Central Asia	326	362	410	464	482	5143	94
22		(320-333)	(355-369)	(403-417)	(459-470)	(476-488)		
23	Southeast Asia	110	128	155	171	179	4456	40
24		(106-113)	(125-132)	(151-160)	(165-176)	(173-186)		
25	East Asia	490	509	557	624	637	11,861	54
26		(449-531)	(476-542)	(517-597)	(558-690)	(570-705)		
27	Europe, total (except USSR)[4]	328	355	380	393	402	4930	82
28		(325-330)	(353-357)	(378-382)	(391-395)	(400-404)		
29	Northern and Western Europe	115	122	128	133	136	2252	60
30		(114-116)	(122-123)	(127-128)	(133-134)	(135-136)		
31	Central Europe	112	120	127	128	131	1014	129
32		(111-114)	(118-121)	(126-129)	(127-129)	(130-131)		
33	Southern Europe	101	113	125	131	135	1664	81
34		(99-102)	(112-114)	(124-126)	(130-133)	(134-136)		
35	Oceania	8.8	10.4	11.3	13.0	14.0	8557	2
36		(8.6-9.1)	(10.2-10.7)	(11.1-11.5)	(12.8-13.2)	(13.8-14.2)		

/1/ Estimates include adjustments for under-enumeration of various censuses. /2/ Land area including inland waters but excluding certain uninhabited polar regions and islands. /3/ Including allowance for the population and area of the USSR. /4/ European Turkey is included with Asia.

Part II: ESTIMATES OF TOTAL POPULATION: NORTH AMERICA, 1920-1954

#	Geographical Area	Estimated Population, Thousands								
		1920	1930	1940	1945	1950	1951	1952	1953	1954
1	Alaska[1], total	55	60	75	139	137	161	191	205	
2	Civilian population			74	79	111	123	141	155	
3	Bahama Islands		61	70	71	79	81	83	85	
4	Barbados		159	168	187	209	212	216		
5	Bermuda[2]	22[3]	32	32	35	37	38	39		
6	British Honduras	44[3]	51	56	59	67	70	72	75	
7	Canada[4]	8820	10,484	11,682	12,394	13,712	14,009	14,430	14,781	15,195
8	Excluding Yukon and N.W. Territories	8543[5]	10,195[5]	11,364[5]	12,055[5]	13,688	13,984	14,405	14,756	
9	Newfoundland	264	276	301	322					
10	Yukon and N.W. Territories	13	13	17	17	24	25	25	25	
11	Canal Zone, Panama, total[1]	23	40	57	88	53	56	58	57	
12	Civilian population			31	46	42	42	42	42	
13	Costa Rica	421[3]	499	619	695	800	825	850	881	915
14	Cuba[6]			4566	4940	5362	5471		5807	
15	Dominican Republic	879	1256	1674	1889	2131	2183	2236	2291	2347
16	El Salvador	1168	1443	1633	1742	1868	1920	1986	2052	2122
17	Greenland[7]	14	16	19	21	23	23	24	25	
18	Guatemala	1314[3]	1771	2222	2444	2802	2890	2975	3049	
19	Honduras		948	1146	1261	1428	1470	1513	1564	
20	Jamaica	830	997	1183	1266	1403	1430	1457	1486	
21	Cayman Islands		6	7	7	7	7	8		
22	Turks and Caicos Islands		5	6	6	7				
23	Leeward Islands		86	99	107	112	116	119	121	
24	Antigua		30	34	41	45	46	48	49	
25	Montserrat		13	15	15	14	14	13	13	
26	St. Kitts-Nevis and Anguilla		38	43	45	48	49	51	52	
27	Virgin Islands (British)		5	7	6	6	7	7	7	
28	Mexico[6]		16,589	19,763	22,233	25,791	26,332	26,992	28,053	28,850
29	Netherlands Antilles	55	72	107	131	161	166	172	178	
30	Nicaragua			825	923	1060	1093	1128	1166	1202
31	Panama[8]	447	471	620	703	797	817	841	863	
32	Puerto Rico[1]	1312	1552	1880	2099	2207	2233	2240	2229	
33	Civilian population			1876	2068	2202	2214	2214	2201	
34	St. Pierre and Miquelon				4	5	5			
35	Trinidad and Tobago		405	476	547	632	649	663	678	698
36	United States[9]		123,188	132,122	139,928	151,683	154,360	157,022	159,629	162,414
37	Excluding armed forces abroad	106,466	123,077	131,954	132,481	151,234	153,384	155,755	158,306	
38	Virgin Islands (USA)[1]		22	25	27	27	25	24	25	
39	Windward Islands[1] (Dominica Grenada, St. Lucia, St. Vincent)			259	263	276	284			

/1/ Legal population, but including U.S. Armed Forces stationed in the area. /2/ Civilian population, excluding tourists. /3/ For 31 December. /4/ Legal population. /5/ Prior to 1950, also excluding Newfoundland, which became the 10th province on 1 April 1949. /6/ Estimates for last intercensal period not yet revised to accord with census results. /7/ Indigenous population, representing approximately 98% of the total. /8/ Excluding Canal Zone shown separately above. /9/ Legal population, but excluding civilian citizens of continental U.S. absent from the country for extended periods of time.

437. POPULATION, PER CENT DISTRIBUTION BY AGE: U.S.A., 1850-1950

	Age (yr)	1950	1940	1930	1920	1910	1900	1890	1880	1870	1860	1850
1	<5	10.7	8.0	9.3	10.9	11.6	12.1	12.2	13.8	14.3	15.4	15.1
2	5-9	8.8	8.1	10.3	10.8	10.6	11.7	12.1	12.9	12.5	13.3	14.0
3	10-14	7.4	8.9	9.8	10.1	9.9	10.6	11.2	11.4	12.4	11.8	12.5
4	15-19	7.0	9.4	9.4	8.9	9.9	9.9	10.5	10.0	10.5	10.7	10.9
5	20-24	7.6	8.8	8.9	8.8	9.8	9.7	9.9	10.1	9.7	18.2	18.4
6	25-29	8.1	8.4	8.0	8.6	8.9	8.6	8.3	8.1	8.0		
7	30-34	7.6	7.8	7.4	7.6	7.6	7.3	7.3	6.7	6.6		
8	35-39	7.5	7.2	7.5	7.4	7.0	6.5	6.2	6.0	6.0	12.8	12.2
9	40-44	6.8	6.7	6.5	6.0	5.7	5.6	5.1	4.9	5.0		
10	45-49	6.0	6.3	5.7	5.5	4.9	4.5	4.4	4.2	4.1	8.3	8.0
11	50-54	5.5	5.5	4.9	4.5	4.2	3.9	3.7	3.7	3.5		
12	55-59	4.8	4.4	3.8	3.4	3.0	2.9	2.7	2.5	2.3	5.0	4.8
13	60-64	4.0	3.6	3.1	2.8	2.5	2.4	2.3	2.2	2.0		
14	65-69	3.3	2.9	2.3	2.0	1.8	1.7	1.6	1.4	1.3	2.8	2.6
15	70-74	2.3	2.0	1.6	1.3	1.2	1.2	1.1	1.0	0.9		
16	>74	2.6	2.0	1.6	1.4	1.3	1.2	1.1	1.0	0.8	1.4	1.5
17	Not reported			0.1	0.1	0.2	0.3	0.3			0.2	0.1

438. POPULATION, MALE-FEMALE RATIO: U.S.A., 1790-1950
Values are number of males per 100 females.

	Census Year	All Classes	White	Negro	Other Races
1	1950	98.6	99	94.3	131.7
2	1940	100.7	101.2	95	140.5
3	1930	102.5	102.9	97	150.6
4	1920	104	104.4	99.2	156.6
5	1910	106	106.6	98.9	185.7
6	1900	104.4	104.9	98.6	185.2
7	1890	105	105.4	99.5	182.5
8	1880	103.6	104	97.8	362.2
9	1870	102.2	102.8	96.2	400.7??
10	1860	104.7	105.3	99.6	260.8
11	1850	104.3	105.2	99.1	
12	1840	103.7	104.5	99.5	
13	1830	103.1	103.8	100.3	
14	1820	103.3	103.2	103.4	
15	1810	104			
16	1800	104			
17	1790	103.8			

439. POPULATION, LIVE BIRTHS AND BIRTH RATES, BY RACE: U.S.A., 1915-1954
Population estimated as of July 1 for 1916-1939, 1942-48 and 1952, and enumerated as of April 1 for 1940 and 1950. Rates are per 1000 population in each specified group.

	Year	Population of Continental United States[1]	Number of States[4]	Population[5]	Registered Births — Total	White	Non-white	Birth Rates[5] — Total	White	Non-white	Adjusted Number — White	Non-white	Adjusted Rates[6] — White	Non-white
1	1954	162,414,000	48	161,195,000	4,021,000[7]			24.9[7]						
2	1953[8]	159,629,000	48	158,306,000	3,902,120	3,356,772	545,348	24.8	23.7	32.3	3,389,000	575,000	24.0	34.1
3	1952[8]	157,022,000	48	155,755,000	3,846,986	3,322,658	524,328	24.7	23.9	31.8	3,358,000	555,000	24.1	33.6
4	1951[8]	154,360,000	48	153,384,000	3,750,850	3,237,072	513,778	24.5	23.6	31.8	3,277,000	546,000	23.9	33.8
5	1950	151,132,000	48	150,697,361	3,554,149	3,063,627	490,522	23.6	22.7	31.1	3,108,000	524,000	23.0	33.3
6	1949	149,188,000	48	148,665,000	3,559,529	3,083,721	475,808	23.9	23.2	30.6	3,136,000	513,000	23.6	33.0
7	1948	146,631,000	48	146,093,000	3,535,068	3,080,316	454,752	24.2	23.5	29.8	3,141,000	495,000	24.0	32.4
8	1947	144,126,000	48	143,446,000	3,699,940	3,274,620	425,320	25.8	25.5	28.3	3,347,000	469,000	26.1	31.2
9	1946	141,389,000	48	141,389,000	3,288,672	2,913,645	375,027	23.3	23.0	28.3	2,990,000	420,000	23.6	28.4
10	1945	139,928,000	48	139,928,000	2,735,456	2,395,563	339,893	19.5	19.1	23.2	2,471,000	388,000	19.7	26.5
11	1944	138,397,000	48	138,397,000	2,794,800	2,454,700	340,100	20.2	19.8	23.6	2,545,000	394,000	20.5	27.4
12	1943	136,739,000	48	136,739,000	2,934,860	2,594,763	340,097	21.5	21.2	24.1	2,704,000	400,000	22.1	28.3
13	1942	134,860,000	48	134,860,000	2,808,996	2,486,934	322,062	20.8	20.6	23.2	2,605,000	384,000	21.5	27.7
14	1941	133,402,000	48	133,402,000	2,513,427	2,204,903	308,524	18.8	18.4	22.6	2,330,000	374,000	19.5	27.3
15	1940	131,820,000	48	131,669,275	2,360,399	2,067,953	292,466	17.9	17.5	21.7	2,199,000	360,000	18.6	26.7
16	1939	130,879,718	48	130,879,718	2,265,588	1,982,671	282,917	17.3	16.9	21.2	2,177,000	349,000	18.0	26.1
17	1938	129,824,939	48	129,824,939	2,286,962	2,005,955	281,007	17.6	17.2	21.2	2,148,000	348,000	18.4	26.3
18	1937	128,824,829	48	128,824,829	2,203,337	1,928,437	274,900	17.1	16.7	20.9	2,071,000	342,000	17.9	26.0
19	1936	128,053,180	48	128,053,180	2,144,790	1,881,883	262,907	16.7	16.4	20.1	2,027,000	328,000	17.6	25.1
20	1935	127,250,232	48	127,250,232	2,155,105	1,888,012	267,093	16.9	16.5	20.6	2,042,000	334,000	17.9	25.8
21	1934	126,373,773	48	126,373,773	2,167,636	1,898,501	269,135	17.2	16.7	20.9	2,058,000	338,000	18.1	26.3
22	1933	125,578,763	48	125,578,763	2,081,232	1,823,531	257,701	16.6	16.2	20.2	1,982,000	325,000	17.6	25.5
23	1932	124,840,471	47	118,903,899	2,074,042	1,822,425	251,617	17.4	17.0	21.3	2,099,000	341,000	18.7	26.9
24	1931	124,039,648	46	117,455,229	2,112,760	1,867,245	245,515	18.0	17.7	21.0	2,170,000	335,000	19.5	26.9
25	1930	123,076,741	46	116,544,946	2,203,958	1,953,163	250,795	18.9	18.6	21.6	2,274,000	344,000	20.6	27.5
26	1929	121,769,939	46	115,317,450	2,169,920	1,924,475	245,445	18.8	18.5	21.3	2,244,000	339,000	20.5	27.3
27	1928	120,501,115	44	113,636,160	2,233,149	1,982,246	250,903	19.7	19.4	22.1	2,325,000	349,000	21.5	28.5
28	1927	119,038,062	40	104,320,830	2,137,836	1,925,585	212,251	20.5	20.2	23.6	2,425,000	377,000	22.7	31.1
29	1926	117,399,225	35	90,400,590	1,856,068	1,707,034	149,034	20.5	20.2	25.0	2,441,000	398,000	23.1	33.4
30	1925	115,831,963	33	88,294,564	1,878,880	1,731,669	147,211	21.3	21.0	25.4	2,506,000	403,000	24.1	34.2
31	1924	114,113,463	33	87,000,295	1,930,614	1,762,872	167,742	22.2	21.9	26.3	2,577,000	401,000	25.1	34.8
32	1923	111,949,945	30	81,072,123	1,792,646	1,644,034	148,612	22.1	21.9	25.2	2,531,000	380,000	25.2	33.2
33	1922	110,054,778	30	79,560,746	1,774,911	1,629,387	145,524	22.3	22.1	25.3	2,507,000	375,000	25.4	33.2
34	1921	108,541,489	27	70,807,090	1,714,261	1,565,446	148,815	24.2	23.9	27.6	2,657,000	398,000	27.3	35.8
35	1920	106,466,420	23	63,597,307	1,508,874	1,395,523	113,351	23.7	23.5	27.0	2,566,000	383,000	26.9	35.0
36	1919	105,062,747	22	61,212,076	1,373,438	1,269,363	104,075	22.4	22.3	24.9	2,387,000	353,000	25.3	32.4
37	1918	104,549,886	20	55,153,782	1,363,649	1,288,711	74,938	24.7	24.8	24.3	2,588,000	360,000	27.6	33.0
38	1917	103,413,743	20	55,197,952	1,353,792	1,280,288	73,504	24.5	24.3		2,587,000	357,000	27.9	32.9
39	1916	101,965,984	11	32,994,013	818,983			24.9						
40	1915	100,549,013	10	31,096,697	776,304			25.0						

/1/ Estimates of armed forces overseas are included in the years 1918, 1940-1954. /2/ Effective 1934, all of continental United States included. /3/ Adjustments on the basis of 48 states for lines 12 through 20. /4/ District of Columbia not included in the "Number of States," though represented in all data shown for each year. /5/ For 1942-46, estimates of population include armed forces overseas; rates based on population, including armed forces overseas. /6/ For 1917-19 and 1941-46 based on population including armed forces overseas. /7/ Tentative. /8/ Based on births from a 50% sample.

Values are males per 100 individuals. Values in parentheses are estimates "b" of the 95% range, unless otherwise indicated by superscripts (cf Introduction). Adult values should be considered with caution (particularly those for Invertebrates) because of extreme variation caused by geographical area, species considered, time of year, and population conditions.

Species	At Birth	Adult	Species	At Birth	Adult
Mammalia			**Aves** (concluded)		
1 Man, white, U.S.A.[1]	51.39		70 Crow (Corvus brachyrhynchos)		56
2 Man, non-white, U.S.A.[1]	50.28		71 Dove (Zenaidura macroura)	52(50-54)	60(57-63)
3 Ass (Equus asinus)	49(32-66)		72 Duck (Anas spp)	50(49-52)	
4 Badger (Meles meles)		54(34-75)	73 Canvasback	51(47-55)[d]	
5 Bat, big brown (Eptesicus fuscus)		68(32-78)[d]	74 Mallard	53(49-57)[d]	52(48-56)[d]
6 Bat (Myotis sodalis)		51(49-53)	75 Pintail	53(49-57)[d]	66(64-69)[d]
7 Bat (Pipistrellus subflavus)		74(68-80)	76 Redhead	53(48-58)[d]	
8 Beaver (Castor canadensis)		52(45-59)	77 Fowl (Gallus spp)	49(47-51)[d]	
Cattle (Bos taurus)			78 Rhode Island Red	50(46-54)	
9 Single birth	52(43-58)[d]		79 White Leghorn	49(48-51)	
10 Twin birth	49		80 Grackle (Quiscalus spp)		30(26-35)[d]
11 Triplet birth	46		81 Grouse, ruffed (Bonasa sp)	52(47-56)[d]	52(42-61)[d]
12 Ayrshire	49(45-53)		82 Grouse, sage		50(48-52)[d]
13 Brown alpine	50(47-52)		83 Grouse, sharp-tailed		63(54-72)[d]
14 Guernsey	44(41-48)		84 Hawk (Buteo spp)		50(46-54)
15 Hereford	51(49-53)		85 Parrot (Psittacus spp)		57(50-63)
16 Holstein	49(47-50)		86 Partridge (Perdix spp)	43(38-48)[d]	60(58-62)[d]
17 Jersey	52(48-56)		87 Pheasant, ring-necked (Phasianus sp)	50(46-54)[d]	52(50-55)
18 Shorthorn	49(47-51)		88 Pigeon (Columba spp)	50(48-52)[d]	
19 Welsh, black	50(48-52)		89 Quail, bobwhite (Colinus sp)		(59-66)
20 Zebu	51(50-52)		90 Quail, California (Lophortyx sp)		58(54-62)[d]
Dog (Canis familiaris)			91 Redwing (Agelaius sp)		77(73-81)
21 Collie, St. Bernard, spaniel	54(53-55)		92 Sparrow (Melospiza melodia)		52
22 German shepherd	55(51-58)[d]		93 Starling (Sturnus spp)		68
23 Greyhound	52(51-54)		94 Turkey (Meleagris gallopavo)		50(48-55)
24 Schnauzer	51(49-53)		**Reptilia**		
25 Terrier	56(53-59)		95 Lizards		58(55-62)
26 Elk, North American	51(46-56)[d]		96 Snakes		50(48-52)
27 Fox, red	50(41-59)	52(46-56)[d]	97 Tortoises, turtles		43(38-48)
28 Fox, silver	53(51-55)		**Amphibia**		
29 Goat, Angora	50(48-52)[d]		98 Frogs, toads		45(43-47)
30 Goat, crossbreeds	51(48-54)		99 Salamanders, newts		56(51-61)
31 Goat, Saanen (Britain)	55(50-61)		**Pisces**		
32 Goat, Toggenburg	50(46-55)		100 Elasmobranchs		47(45-48)
33 Guinea pig (Cavia porcellus)	52(51-53)[d]		101 Sturgeons and spoonbills		17(8-26)
34 Hare (Lepus americanus)		54(52-56)	True bony fishes		
35 Horse (Equus caballus)	52(50-55)[d]		102 Minnow (Gambusia holbrookii)	50(48-53)	
36 Horse, Thoroughbred	50		103 Walleye (Stezostedon vitreum)		72
37 Mink, ranch (Mustela spp)	51(49-53)[d]		**Arthropoda**		
38 Mink, hybrid, pastel	50(48-52)		Crustacea		
39 Mole (Scalopus aquaticus)		58(55-60)	104 Amphipoda		38(35-40)
40 Mouse (Mus musculus)		52(50-54)[d]	105 Cladocera		20(18-22)
41 Mouse, albino	50(48-52)[d]		106 Copepoda		28(27-29)
42 Mouse, Japanese and waltzing	51(48-52)[d]		107 Cumacea		37(29-45)
43 Mule	44(42-47)[d]		108 Decapoda		55
44 Muskrat (Ondatra zibethica)	54(42-66)[d]	56(55-57)[d]	109 Isopoda		33(31-35)
45 Opossum (Didelphis marsupialis)	57	57(50-68)[d]	110 Myriopoda		31(28-33)
46 Rabbit (Oryctolagus spp)	50(49-51)[d]		111 Ostracoda		39(35-43)
47 Rabbit, Flemish giant	57(46-68)[d]		112 Phyllopoda		28(27-29)
48 Rabbit, Polish	51(45-56)[d]		113 Stomatopoda		44(36-52)
49 Raccoon (Procyon lotor)		52(46-58)[d]	114 Xiphura		49(32-66)
50 Rat (Rattus norvegicus)	50(49-51)[d]		Insecta		
51 Rat, albino	50(49-51)		115 Anoplura and Mallophaga		(40-50)[d]
52 Rat, brown	51(48-55)	41(40-42)[d]	116 Coleoptera		77
53 Rat, hybrid and piebald	51(50-52)		117 Diptera		43(42-45)
54 Seal, harbor (Phoca groenlandica)		51(48-54)	118 Diptera (Drosophila melanogaster)		46
Sheep (Ovis aries)			119 Hemiptera		12(11-13)
55 Single birth	50(44-55)[d]		120 Lepidoptera		53(52-54)
56 Twin and triplet birth	49		121 Odonata		77(74-81)
57 Quadruplet birth	43		122 Orthoptera		44(43-45)
58 Cheviot	49(48-50)		123 Strepsiptera		65(62-68)
59 Karakul	52(47-57)		124 Thysanoptera		12(10-13)
60 Merino	47(44-50)		125 Thysanura		64(46-82)
61 Navajo	49(48-50)		126 Arachnida		48(46-49)
62 Swine (Sus scrofa)	52(51-53)[d]		127 Pycnogonida		36(35-38)
63 Berkshire	51(50-52)		**Mollusca**		
64 Duroc, Jersey	49(48-50)		128 Cephalapoda		46(43-49)
65 German improved	51(50-52)[d]		129 Gastropoda		47(46-48)
66 Inbred and linecross non-inbred	52(51-53)		130 Pelecypoda		50(49-51)
67 Weasel (Mustela nivalis)		73(63-83)	**Trochelminthes**		
Aves			131 Rotifera		33(32-34)
68 Canary (Serinus spp)	44(36-51)[d]		**Coelenterata**		
69 Cuckoo (Cuculus sp)		55(52-58)	132 Placophora		53(52-54)

/1/ Values based on 50% sample of 1952 registered live births.

441. ACREAGE AND YIELD, FIELD, FRUIT, AND VEGETABLE CROPS: U.S.A.

Part I: FIELD CROPS

Where plant part or product is specified, acreage values apply to the plants grown for the yield of that part or product.

	Crop Plant	Acreage Harvested				Yield per Acre			
		1930-1939[1]	1940-1949[1]	1950	1953	1930-1939[1]	1940-1949[1]	1950	1953
		Thousands of Acres[2]				Pounds[3]			
1	Alfalfa (Medicago sativa), seed	556	881	927	939	112	92	113	145
2	Barley (Hordeum vulgare), grain	10,707	12,569	11,153	8534	989	1172	1306	1354
3	Bean, edible (Phaseolus spp)[4]	1716	1882	1512	1398	781[5]	958[5]	1117[5]	1296[5]
4	Beet, sugar (Beta vulgaris)	815	750	925	745	2280	26,200	29,200	32,400
5	Buckwheat (Fagopyrum esculentum), grain	460	405	253	175	800	870	840	874
6	Clover, alsike (Trifolium hybridium), seed	172	132	96	63	119	153	146	192
7	Clover, red (T. pratense), seed	947	1755	2556	1415	70	56	58	59
8	Corn, all (Zea mays)	98,049	87,882	81,817	80,279	1316[5]	1898[5]	2094[5]	2218[5]
9	Cotton (Gossypium spp), lint	31,223	21,662	17,843	24,340	205	266	269	324
10	Cowpea (Vigna spp), peas	1140	854	420	318	384[5]	342[5]	390[5]	372[5]
11	Flaxseed (Linum spp)	1788	3919	4090	4380	358	526	549	470
12	Hay, all types	67,893	74,845	74,368	73,918	2320	2720	2760	2840
13	Hop,(Humulus spp), grain	30	37	39	28	1171	1267	1508	1488
14	Lespedeza (Lespedeza spp), seed	361	885	746	445	173	216	192	143
15	Oat (Avena sativa), grain	36,487	39,460	40,733	39,358	874	1062	1107	989
16	Peanut (Arachis hypogaea)	1486	2923	2268	1541	714[6]	704[6]	898[6]	1031[6]
17	Pea, field (Pisum sativum)	261	471	233	262	1008[5]	1230[5]	1376[5]	1279[5]
18	Rice (Oryza sativa), rough	942	1507	1620	2135	2178	2083	2388	2460
19	Rye (Secale cereale), grain	3320	2448	1744	1382	627	683	683	728
20	Sorghum (Sorghum spp), grain	7564	6737	10,335	6137	553	875	1266	997
21	Soybean (Glycine soja), bean	2052	9348	13,814	14,366	966[5]	1140[5]	1302[5]	1098[5]
22	Sugar cane (Saccharum officinarum), sirup	137	108	49	27	1809	1975	2134	2372
23	Sugar cane (S. officinarum), sugar	257	306	333	346	36,000	38,800	41,600	44,200
24	Sweetclover (Melilotus alba), seed	279	258	547	226	185	161	156	151
25	Timothy (Phleum pratense), seed	483	354	445	197	149	158	142	134
26	Tobacco (Nicotiana tabacum), leaves	1676	1613	1599	1634	834[7]	1100[7]	1269[7]	1259[7]
27	Velvetbean (Stizolobium spp)	1970	1486	580	311	806[8]	824[8]	890[8]	823[8]
28	Wheat, all (Triticum aestivum), grain	55,883	62,625	61,610	67,608	798	1026	990	1050
29	Wheat, winter (T. aestivum), grain	39,141	44,640	43,253	46,681	864	1,062	1,026	1128

/1/ Data applicable to 10-year averages. /2/ Acres x 0.4047 = hectares. /3/ Pounds per acre x 1.121 = kg per hectare. /4/ Besides the ordinary edible beans (kidney and lima) and beans grown for seed, data include blackeyes and garbonzos in California. /5/ Shelled. /6/ Picked and threshed. /7/ Farm sales-weight basis. /8/ Not shelled.

Part II: FRUIT AND VEGETABLE CROPS

	Crop Plant	Acreage Harvested				Yield per Acre			
		1930-1939[1]	1940-1949[1]	1950	1953	1930-1939[1]	1940-1949[1]	1950	1953
		Thousands of Acres[2]				Thousands of Pounds[3]			
1	Apple (Pyrus malus)[4]	1252[5]	884	817		5.6[5]	5.9	7.2	
2	Asparagus (Asparagus officinalis)	112	127	131	135	2.2	2.5	2.5	2.2
3	Avocado (Prunus gratissima)	9.5	15.3[6]			1.5	2.4[6]		
4	Bean, lima (Phaseolus lunatus macrocarpus)[7]	49	88	120	128	2.2[8]	2.5[8]	3.2[8]	3.7[8]
5	Bean, string (P. vulgaris)[9]	213	293	306	296	2.7	3.1	3.5	3.8
6	Beet, garden (Beta vulgaris)	19	28	30	25	10.4[10]	13.3[10]	15.3[10]	15.9[10]
7	Cabbage (Brassica oleraceae capitata)	176	192	186	169	13.3	14.6	17.5	17.1
8	Cantaloupe (Cucumis melo)[11]	108	109	134	141	6.7	7.6	7.6	7.8
9	Carrot (Daucus carota)	42	73	94	82	15.8[10]	16.8[10]	17[10]	19[10]
10	Cauliflower (Brassica oleracea botrytis)[12]	30	35	33	30	9.6	11.3	13.8	15.8
11	Celery (Apium graveolens)	37	41	36	37	26	31	37.2	39.1
12	Cherry (Prunus spp)	101	107[6]	29	26	2.8	3.3[6]		
13	Corn, sweet (Zea mays saccharata)[13]	319	465	557	718	4.2[14]	4.9[14]	5.5[14]	5.9[14]
14	Cucumber (Cucumis sativus)	127	160	158	200	3.7	4.2	4.2	5.1
15	Fig (Ficus carica), from California	42	35	29	26	3.8	6.7	5.8	6.5
16	Grape (Vitis spp)	680	627[6]			6.6	8.8[6]		
17	Grapefruit (Citrus paradisi)	154	193	175	146	12.3	20.6	21.2	26.5
18	Lemon (C. limonia), from California	43	61	54	55	15.6	16.7	19.5	22.8
19	Lettuce (Lactuca sativa)	159	173	227	210	8.8	11.6	11.7	13.4
20	Onion (Allium cepa)	128	130	136	132	11.9	14.6	16.9	18.7
21	Orange (Citrus spp)	426	539	562	564	10.5	15.3	18.7	20
22	Pea, garden (Pisum sativum)[7]	370	476	442	443	3.2[8]	5.2[8]	5.1[8]	5.3[8]
23	Peach (Prunus persica)	639	646[6]			4.2	5.2[6]		
24	Pear (Pyrus communis)	220	178[6]			6.1	8.4[6]		
25	Potato (Solanum tuberosum)	3238	2515	1696	1508	6.8	10.1	15.2	14.9
26	Prune (Prunus domestica)	224	183[6]			6.2	6.6[6]		
27	Spinach (Spinacia oleracea)	79	99	81	69	4.0	4.1	5.1	6.1
28	Strawberry (Fragaria spp)	170	121	127	112	2.3	2.6	3.1	4.0
29	Sweetpotato (Ipomoea batatas)	845	641	492	350	4.6	5.0	5.6	5.3
30	Tomato (Lycopersicon esculentum)	562	739	581	528	7.5	10.0	12.1	15.7
31	Watermelon (Citrullus vulgaris)	256	250	374	435	6.7	7.2	6.4	6.2

/1/ Data applicable to 10-year averages, unless otherwise specified. /2/ Acres x 0.4047 = hectares. /3/ Pounds per acre x 1.121 = kg per hectare. /4/ Commercial orchards only. /5/ Average for 1934-1939. /6/ Average for 1940-1946. /7/ Immature seeds. /8/ Not shelled. /9/ Immature edible pods. /10/ Without tops. /11/ Data include Casaba and Persian melons but not honey balls and honey dews. /12/ Data include headed types. /13/ Commercial crops used for processing. /14/ In husk.

442. SPECIFIED NOTIFIABLE DISEASES, REPORTED CASES AND DEATHS: U.S.A., 1945-1954

Data for 1949-1954 classified according to the Sixth Revision of the International List (1948); for 1945-1948 data classified according to the Fifth Revision of the International List (1938).

(-) = data not available.

	Disease		1954	1953	1952	1951	1950	1949	1948	1947	1946	1945
1	Amebiasis	Cases	3523	4444	4280	3550	4568	5543	4871	3365	4093	3412
2		Deaths	131	129	136	148	136	164	113	155	182	185
3	Anthrax	Cases	22	45	47	60	49	54	60	69	40	40
4		Deaths	0	0	3	3	5	0	5	3	7	6
5	Botulism	Cases	18	18	18	33	20	24	39	44	(-)	(-)
6		Deaths	14	17	14	31	16	22	(-)	(-)	(-)	(-)
7	Brucellosis (undulant fever)	Cases	1823	2032	2537	3139	3510	4235	4991	6321	5887	5049
8		Deaths	15	18	23	34	36	68	55	58	69	94
9	Dengue	Cases	6	8	5	16	26	46	24	35	40	106
10		Deaths	0	0	0	0	0	2	0	0	1	0
11	Diphtheria	Cases	2041	2355	2960	3983	5796	7969	9493	12,262	16,354	18,675
12		Deaths	145	156	217	302	410	574	634	799	1259	1598
13	Dysentery, bacillary (shigellosis)	Cases	13,846	16,533	23,197	32,215	23,367	29,080	23,753	17,048	24,286	34,943
14		Deaths	243	337	334	356	335	498	364	273	309	506
15	Encephalitis, acute infectious	Cases	2,606	1935	1912	1123	1135	903	730	785	728	785
16		Deaths	407	386	471	429	394	465	570	630	642	735
17	Hepatitis, infectious and serum	Cases	50,093	33,700	17,428	7349	2820	2027	709	1092	(-)	(-)
18		Deaths	821	821	794	675	552	560	(-)	(-)	(-)	(-)
19	Leprosy	Cases	56	60	57	57	44	41	63	56	43	40
20		Deaths	4	7	4	3	3	4	21	16	16	27
21	Leptospirosis	Cases	48	42	62	13	30	21	18	15	(-)	(-)
22		Deaths	14	17	12	13	16	21	13	15	13	31
23	Malaria	Cases	715	1310	7023	5600	2184	4151	9606	15,116	48,610	62,763
24		Deaths	24	32	25	64	76	118	170	214	341	443
25	Measles	Cases	682,720	449,146	683,077	530,118	319,124	625,281	615,104	222,375	695,843	146,013
26		Deaths	518	462	618	683	468	949	888	472	1310	307
27	Meningococcal infections	Cases	4436	5077	4884	4164	3788	3519	3376	3420	5693	8208
28		Deaths	1015	1325	1386	1124	974	917	873	917	1257	1728
29	Plague	Cases	0	0	0	1	3	3	0	1	0	0
30		Deaths	0	0	0	0	1	1	0	1	0	0
31	Poliomyelitis, acute	Cases	38,476	35,592	57,879	28,386	33,300	42,033	27,726	10,827	25,698	13,624
32		Deaths	1368	1450	3145	1551	1904	2720	1895	580	1845	1186
33	Psittacosis and ornithosis	Cases	563	169	135	25	26	35	32	27	26	27
34		Deaths	3	4	5	1	0	0	0	1	2	0
35	Q fever	Cases	8	4	7	8	0	2	1	0	(-)	(-)
36		Deaths	(-)	(-)	(-)	(-)	(-)	(-)	(-)	(-)	(-)	(-)
37	Rabies in man[1]	Cases	13	12	24	18	18	10	24	26	34	43
38		Deaths	13	12	24	18	18	10	24	26	34	43
39	Rabies in animals[2]	Cases	7297	8903	8445	8008	7901	7587	8495	8920	10,850	9928
40		Deaths	(-)	8903	8445	8008	7901	7587	8495	8920	10,850	9928
41	Rocky Mountain spotted fever	Cases	294	313	327	347	464	570	547	596	587	472
42		Deaths	10	21	20	26	31	36	94	105	124	128
43	Salmonellosis, paratyphoid fever	Cases	5375	3946	2596	1773	1233	1243	882	951	723	649
44		Deaths	48	72	42	31	43	37				
45	Scarlet fever and streptococcal	Cases	147,785	132,935	113,677	84,151	64,494	87,220	91,295	93,595	125,511	185,570
46	sore throat	Deaths	262	295	351	347	346	486	460	514	754	1094
47	Smallpox	Cases	9[3]	4	21	11	39	49	57	176	337	346
48		Deaths	0	0	0	1	1	2	5	5	25	12
49	Tetanus	Cases	524	506	484	506	486	579	601	560	(-)	(-)
50		Deaths	332	337	360	394	336	398	506	511	585	653
51	Trachoma	Cases	1172	773	3088	2916	1584	1475	2565	1540	(-)	(-)
52		Deaths	1	0	0	0	0	0	(-)	(-)	(-)	(-)
53	Trichiniasis	Cases	277	395	367	393	327	353	487	451	(-)	(-)
54		Deaths	1	7	10	10	9	9	15	14	16	20
55	Tuberculosis, all forms	Cases	100,589	106,925	109,837	118,491	121,742	134,865	137,006	134,946	119,256	114,931
56		Deaths	16,392	19,544	24,621	30,863	33,959	39,100	43,833	48,064	50,911	52,916
57	Tularemia	Cases	681	601	668	702	927	1179	1086	1401	1355	900
58		Deaths	4	7	8	9	15	18	46	113	113	122
59	Typhoid fever	Cases	2169	2252	2341	2128	2484	2795	2840	3075	3268	4211
60		Deaths	45	52	78	83	96	161	205	282	349	471
61	Typhus fever, endemic (murine)	Cases	163	221	205	378	685	985	1171	2050	3365	5193
62		Deaths	0	0	0	0	0	2	68	88	128	173
	Venereal diseases[4]											
63	Gonorrhea	Cases	249,883	246,311	253,839	254,057	286,746	317,950	345,501	380,666	415,855	313,363
64		Deaths	15	29	45	43	37	66	71	108	150	212
65	Syphilis	Cases	131,260	150,026	169,198	174,924	217,558	256,463	314,313	355,592	385,524	351,767
66		Deaths	4835	5273	5719	6274	7568	8581	11,616	12,671	12,955	14,062
67	Other specified venereal	Cases	4650	5209	6093	6885	8187	11,034	12,559	14,371	13,461	10,261
68	diseases	Deaths	29	36	38	42	43	50	47	68	83	84
69	Whooping cough (pertussis)	Cases	60,886	37,129	45,030	68,687	120,718	69,479	74,715	156,517	109,860	133,792
70		Deaths	373	270	402	951	1118	727	1146	1954	1241	1752

/1/ For 1945-53, figures represent registered deaths. /2/ For 1945-51, figures from the Animal Disease and Parasite Research Branch, Agricultural Research Service, U. S. Department of Agriculture. /3/ None of these cases fulfill the criteria for a diagnosis of smallpox. /4/ For 1945-51, figures (civilian cases only) from the Division of Venereal Diseases, U. S. Public Health Service.

Plant Diseases

#	Disease, Organism [Means of Dispersion]	Distances and Units Dispersed				
1	Celery mosaic [insects]	Ft from harborer plant	3	28	120	225
		Diseased plants, %	100	52	16	0
2	Chestnut blight (Endothia parasitica) [air currents]	Ft from spore source	27	85	180	265
		Ascospores, no.	23	11	8	8
3	Citrus psorosis [unknown]	Tree spaces from source	1	2	3	
		Diseased trees, %	32	20	14	
4	Cucurbit mosaic, cucumber [insects]	Yd from harborer plant	1	225	350	500
		Days to 1st symptoms	17	45	47	49
5	Curley top, sugar beet [beet leafhopper]	Mi. from breeding ground	57	315	430	
		Diseased plants, %	100	10	1	
6	Dutch elm disease (Ceratostomella ulmi) [beetle]	Ft from inoculum source	12.5	300	575	
		Diseased trees, no.	27	11	8	
7	Downy mildew (Pseudoperonospora humilis) [air currents]	Ft from spore source	10	100	200	400
		Leaves infected, %	26	12	7	3
8	Onion mildew (Peronospora destructor) [air currents]	Ft from onion sets	1100	100	2000	0
		Lesions/100 ft row, no.	100	0		
9	Potato calico [insects]	Rows from source	1	3	5	
		Diseased plants, no.	26	22	13	
10	Potato late blight (Phytophthora infestans) [air currents]	Ft from spore source	100	200	400	500
		Lesions/100 plants, no.	295	90	12	2
11	Potato leaf roll [aphids]	Rows from infected plants	1	2	4	5
		Diseased plants, %	21	12	5	1
12	Potato mosaic [insects]	Rows from diseased plants	1	3	6	
		Diseased plants, %	36	18	6	
13	Potato yellow dwarf (Macrosteles divisus) [insects]	Ft from old meadow	1	30	90	135
		Diseased plants, no.	80	23	9	4
14	Rust, cedar, apple (Gymnosporangium sp) [air currents]	Yd from infected trees	0	55	220	440
		Leaf infections, no.	64	40	26	19
15	Rust, wheat stem (Puccinia graminis) [air currents]	Mi. from known source	200	740	940	
		Spores collected, no.	13,000	8,000	7,000	
16	Rust, white pine blister (Cronartium ribicola) [air currents]	Ft from gooseberry bush	50	250	450	650
		Diseased trees, %	75	46	36	29
17	Severe streak, raspberries [insects]	Rows from wild brambles	3	8	18	23
		Diseased plants, no.	165	85	21	1
18	Smut, loose, wheat (Ustilago tritici) [air currents]	Mi. from spore source	2	4	24	80
		Smutted heads, %	240	235	115	0

Bacteria and Fungi (Miscellaneous)

#	Disease, Organism [Means of Dispersion]	Distances and Units Dispersed				
19	Bacterial colonies on sea water medium [air currents]	Mi. from land, over water	5	80	275	
		Bacterial colonies, no.	41	58	65	
20	Bacterial colonies on sea water medium [air currents]	Mi. from sea, over land	0	0.25	1	
		Bacterial colonies, no.	550	215	140	
21	Spores (Bovista plumbea) [air currents]	Mi. from release point	5	10	15	20
		Spores caught, no.	910	325	165	100
22	Spores (Tilletia tritici) [air currents]	Mi. from release point	5	10	15	20
		Spores caught, no.	800	170	50	30

Plants (Seeds and Pollen)

#	Disease, Organism [Means of Dispersion]	Distances and Units Dispersed				
23	Bean, common (Phaseolus vulgaris) [air currents; insects(?)]	Yd from lima bean	1	2	5	9
		Cross pollination, %	9	7	6	3
24	Bean, lima (P. lunatus) [air currents; insects(?)]	Yd from common bean	1	3	5	9
		Cross pollination, %	4	3	2	1
25	Cedar, western red (Juniperus scopularum) [air currents]	Yd from seed source	5	22	44	66	88
		Seedlings per acre	615	175	55	9
26	Clover, alsike (Trifolium hybridum) [honey bees]	Yd from bee colonies	5	5.5	38	440	880
		Seeds per head, no.	330	660	33	32
27	Corn (Zea mays) [air currents]	Ft from source	2	25	55.5	90
		Cross pollination, %	50	25	11	8
28	Fir, Douglas (Pseudotsuga taxifolia) [air currents]	Ft from seed trees	2	4	6	8
		Seedlings per acre	300	170	90	35

Insects (concluded)

#	Disease, Organism [Means of Dispersion]	Distances and Units Dispersed					
59	Curculio, plum (Conotrachelus nenuphar) [flight]	Ft from release point	50	136	335	670	
		Insects recovered, no.	48	13	2	1	
60	Earworm, corn (Heliothis armigera) [flight] convergence	Rows from light traps	1	5	10		
		Plants infested, %	32.4	31.9	31.6	31.9	31.3
61	Fly, apple maggot (Rhagoletis pomonella) [flight]	Ft from release point	37.5	137.5	237.5		
		Flies recovered, no.	47	26	17		
62	Fly, Hessian (Phytophaga destructor) [flight]	Ft from hibernation, %	7.5	27.5	47.5	97.5	
		Plants infested, %	44	16	9		
63	Fly, Hessian (P. destructor) [flight]	Ft from wheat field	100	400	600		
		Flies caught, no.	95	16	12		
64	Fly, house (Musca domestica) [flight]	Yd from release point	12.5	150	450	1050	
		Flies caught, no. /trap/da	3.6	1.2	0.8		
65	Fly, narcissus bulb (Merodon equestris) [flight]	Ft from old planting	7	85	200	300	
		Plants infested, %	42	21	13	10	
66	Fly, tsetse (Glossina morsitans) [flight]	Yd, following man	30	1000	4000	6000	
		Flies, no.	13	5	3		
67	Jointworm, wheat (Harmolita tritici) [flight]	Yd from wheat stubble	58	174	290	450	
		Adults caught, no.	18	9	4	0	
68	Leafhopper, beet (Circulifer tenellus) [flight]	Mi. from breeding area	15	35	105	215	
		Leafhoppers caught, no.	500	150	15	4	
69	Leafhopper, potato (Empoasca fabae) [flight]	Mi. from nearest land	3	6	9	10	
		Leafhoppers caught, no.	38	27	21	20	
70	Leafhopper, six-spotted (Macrosteles divisus) [flight, crawling]	Ft from release point	50	100	200		
		Leafhoppers caught, no.	9	3	1		
71	Leafhopper, six-spotted (M. divisus) [flight, crawling]	Ft from release point	30	225	450		
		Leafhoppers caught, no.	4	13	16		
		Days to first recovery	3	6	9	10	
72	Leafhopper, six-spotted (M. divisus) [flight]	Mi. from nearest land	37	125	225		
		Leafhoppers caught, no.	515	145	25		
73	Locust, migratory (Dissosteira longipennis and Melanoplus mexicanus) [flight]	Mi. from release point	8	6	5		
		Locusts recovered, no.	25				
74	Mosquito (Anopheles gambiae) [flight]	Mi. from release point	0.75	1.25	1.75	2.25	
		Mosquitoes caught, no.	3.0	2.2	1.6	1.2	
75	Mosquito (A. funestus) [flight]	Yd from river bank	100	600	1200	2400	
		Mosquitoes caught, no.	180	14	5	4	
76	Mosquito (A. quadrimaculatus)	Mi. from breeding area	0.1	0.5	2.0	2.5	
		Mosquitoes caught, no.	5000	1850	3500	6000	
77	Mosquito (Anopheles spp), incidence of malarial infections [flight]	Ft from mosquito source	500	1500	3500	6000	
		Infections, %	1	33	22	11	4
78	Mosquito, pest (Aedes and Culex spp) [flight]	Mi. from release point	4	8	12	16	
		Mosquitoes caught, no.	97	37	17	6.3	0.3
79	Mosquito, rice field (Psorophora confinnis) [flight]	Mi. from release point	2.5	4.5	8.5	11.5	
		Mosquitoes caught, no.	0.5	1.8	1.1	0.4	0
80	Mosquito, southern house (Culex quinquefasciatus) [flight]	Mi. from release point	1.4	2.0	2.6	3.1	
		Mosquitoes caught, no.	0.8	2.0	1.4	1.0	0.7
81	Mosquito, yellow fever (Aedes and other spp) [flight], incidence of yellow fever	Mi. from original case	17.5	32.5	47.5	92.5	
		Yellow fever cases, no.	14.6	4.6	1.7	0.6	
82	Moth (Catocala spp) [flight]	Ft from release point	13	88	240	365	
		Moths recovered, no.	8.1	3.7	1.5	0.6	
83	Moth, codling (Carpocapsa pomonella) [flight]	Ft from release point	75	190	265	330	
		Moths recovered, %	57	25	13	5	
84	Moth, gypsy, males (Porthetria dispar) [flight]	Ft from moth source	330	660	1300	2600	
		Moths recovered, no.	67	22	5	4	
85	Moth, gypsy, larva (P. dispar) [carried by wind]	Ft from source	50	150	250	350	600
		Larvae, no.	4.4	1.7	1.3	0.5	
86	Moth, oriental fruit (Grapholita molesta) [flight]	Ft from orchard	16	100	1300	2600	
		Moths recovered, no.	194	14	8		

(Insects, continued — distances and numbers of dispersed organisms)

No.	Organism [movement]	Measurement				
29	Fir, silver (Abies alba) [air currents]	Yd from seed trees		55	165	275
		Seedlings per acre		22	9	3
30	Hemlock, western (Tsuga heterophylla) [air currents]	Yd from seed trees	22	44	66	88
		Seedlings per acre	1400	3300	6200	8400
31	Pine (Pinus spp), stand [air currents]	Yd from seed trees		2000	1000	500
		Seedlings per acre		44	66	88
32	Pine, western white (P. monticola) [air currents]	Yd from seed source	22		175	
		Seedlings per acre	615	25	100	150
33	Pollen, apple (Malus pumila) [honey-bees]	Yd from bee colonies		7	6	4
		Set of apples, %		100	900	2000
34	Pollen, cotton (Gossypium hirsutum) [wind or insects]	Crossing, %	1	18	7	
		Ft from contaminant		95	190	335	420
35	Pollen, radish (Raphanus sativus) [wind or insects]	Crossing, %	18	10		
		Ft from contaminant		0.3	5.3	10.6
36	Rye (Secale cereale) [air currents]	Cross pollination, %	75	24	13	7
		Ft from pollen source		10	160	240
37	Spruce, black (Picea marianna) [air currents]	Seedlings per acre	6	30	54	72
		Ft from seed trees	1.1			
38	Tomato (Lycopersicon esculentum) [air currents; insects(?)]	Cross pollination, %		71,000	18,500	1,400
		Ft from contaminant		0.4	0.1	0
39	Walnut (Juglans regia) [air currents]	Ft from pollen source	60	500	1000	1600
		Pollen grs./sq mm/24 hr	4	1.4	0.6	0.6

Insects

No.	Organism [movement]	Measurement				
40	Bee, honey (Apis mellifera) [flight]	Yd from apiary	60	5	16	33
		Honeybees, no.	14	6.1	2.6	0.9	0.3
41	Beetle, convergent ladybird (Hippodamia convergens) [flight]	Mi. from release point	0.5	1.5	3.5	5.5
		Beetles recovered, no.	1.1	0.6	0.3	0.1
42	Beetle, elm bark, European (Scolytus multistriatus) [flight]	Ft from beetle source	63	50	200	1000
		Larvae recovered, no.		39	14	3
43	Beetle, elm bark, native (Hylurgopinus rufipes) [flight]	Twig crotches wounded, %		320	580	815
		Beetles/sq ft, no.		5	2	3
44	Beetle, flat grain (Laemophloeus minutum) [flight]	Beetles recovered, no.	50	100	200	400
		In. from release point	11	8	6	3
45	Beetle, Japanese, larva (Popillia japonica) [crawling]	Ft from field margin	22	42	62	84
		Beetles recovered, no.	79	44	23	7
46	Beetle, mountain pine (Dendroctonous monticolae) [flight]	Mi. from release point	2	5	10	15
		Beetles recovered, no.	63	26	11	3
47	Beetle, potato flea (Epitrix cucumeris) [flight]	Rows from field margin	3	9	33	50
		Insects recovered, no.	19	11	3	1
48	Beetle, red turpentine (Dendroctonous valens) [flight]	Ft from source logs	13	100	250	450
		Beetles recovered, no.		63	27	90
49	Beetle, spotted cucumber (Diabrotica duodecimpunctata) [flight]	Mi. from release point	560	11.5	105	273
		Beetles recovered, no.		0.32	1.33	0.17
50	Beetle, striped cucumber (D. vittita) [flight]	Ft from release point	0.25	0.75	1.25	1.75
		Beetles recovered, no.	31	11	4	
51	Billbug, maize (Calandra maidis) [crawling]	Rows from field margin		11	3	13
		Insects recovered, no.		9	1	8
52	Black scale (Saissetia oleae) [air currents]	Ft from source	19	100	250	450
		Insects caught, no.	13	5.5	1.20	1.16
53	Bollworm, pink (Pectinophora gossypiella) [flight]	Ft from moth source	560	1000	3500	6250
		Worms per boll, no.		0.75	1.25	1.75
54	Borer, roundheaded apple tree (Saperda candida) [flight]	Rows from release point	103	4	8	16
		Trees killed, %	2	47	39	39
55	Borer, European corn (Pyrausta nubilalis) [flight] convergence	Rows from light trap	85	3	4	36
		Plants infested, %	62	51	41	21
56	Borer, European corn, larva (P. nubilalis) [crawling]	Yd from source	56	80	89	103
		Larvae, no.	34	13	7	0
57	Borer, strawberry crown (Tyloderma fragariae) [crawling]	Yd from release point	25	68	125	300
		Insects recovered, no.		5	4	
58	Curculio, cowpea (Chalcodermus aeneus) [unknown]	Ft from field margin	6	1.0	37.5	138
		Insects recovered, no.		1.5	0.4	0.07

(Continued — insects and parasites)

No.	Organism [movement]	Measurement		100	900	3900	5100
87	Parasite, gypsy moth egg (Anastatus bifasciatus) [flight]	Yd from release point		100	900	3900	5100
		Eggs parasitized, % North		23	12	4	3
		Eggs parasitized, % South		32	20	13	12
88	Parasite, Japanese beetle (Tiphia vernalis) [flight]	Ft from feeding area	1	7	49	77	90
		Eggs/larva, no.	3	3.7	2.7	2.5	2.4
89	Psyllid, blackberry (Trioza tripunctata) [crawling]	Rows from field margin	10	5	10	20	25
		Psyllids per 10 bushes	5	3	9	3	2
90	Screwworm, primary larva (Cochliomyia americana) [crawling]	In. from carcass		3	9	15	21
		Larvae/sq ft, no.		320	47		
91	Screwworm, secondary (C. macellaria) [flight]	Mi. from release point		4.1	5.6	7.2	8.2
		Flies recovered, no.		37	22	10	2
92	Strawworm, wheat (Harmolita grandis) [crawling], spring form	Ft from wheat stubble		4.2	2.1	0.9	0.1
		Infestation, %		1	50	100	150
93	Strawworm, wheat (H. grandis) [flight], summer form	Ft from wheat stubble		52	19	13	10
		Infestation, %		25	220	880	1760
94	Weevil, cotton boll (Anthonomus grandis) [flight]	Yd from overwinter area		17	59	26	9
		Weevils trapped, no.		28	75	125	0
95	Weevil, cotton boll (A. grandis) [crawling]	Ft from release point			8	3	225
		Females recovered, no.			6	0	5
		Males recovered, no.			300	600	1400
96	Weevil, pea (Bruchus pisorum) [flight]	Ft from field margin		51	50	48
		Weevils, no.	1	2	5	3	2
97	Weevil, pea (B. pisorum) [flight]	Mi. from overwinter area	13	8	4	5	
		Weevils, no.					
98	Weevil, rice (Sitophilus oryzae) [crawling, probably]	Ft from source		50	100	200
		Weevils, no.			2	1	
99	Weevil, sugar cane, New Guinea (Rhabdocnemis obscura) [flight and crawling]	Ft from release point		265	600	825
		Beetles recovered, no.	10 5	26	8	1
		Days to recovery, no.		52	70	78

Vertical Dispersion

No.	Organism [movement]	Measurement				
100	Bacteria, miscellaneous [air currents]	Ft altitude	1,500	6,000	12,000	15,000
		Bacteria, no.	113	48	15	5
101	Azalea flower spot (Ovulinia azaleae) [air currents; water drip]	In. above ground	42	10	18	48
		Infections, no.		28	17	0
102	Onion mildew, spores (Peronospora destructor) [air currents]	Ft altitude	100	200	700	1200
		Spores/cu ft air	32	100	450	800
103	Rust, wheat stem (Puccinia graminis) [air currents]	Ft above barberry bushes		1,000	7,000	12,000
		Aeciospores caught, no.		19	5	5	
104	Pollen, sugar beet (Beta vulgaris) [air currents]	Ft altitude	1000	2000	3000	4000
		Grains caught, no.	56	26	14	3
105	Aphids [air currents and flight]	Mi. altitude	0.17	1.15	2.17	2.68
		Aphids caught, no.	2	9	16	19
106	Beetle, ladybird (Coccinellids) [flight]	Mi. altitude	0.17	1.15	2.17	2.68
		Beetles caught, no.	40	13	4	1
107	Beetle, tobacco flea (Epitrix hirtipennis) [flight]	Ft altitude		12	19	23
		Beetles caught, no.	96	41	18	
108	Borer, European corn, moth (Pyrausta nubilalis) [flight]	Ft altitude	5	10	15	15
		Moths caught, no.	915	545	330	
109	Fleahopper, cotton (Psallus seriatus) [flight; air currents]	Ft altitude	5.5	11.5	17.5	23.5
		Fleahoppers caught, no.	61	97	156	250
110	Fly, fruit [flight]	Mi. altitude	0.54	2.04	3.54	5.04
		Flies caught, no.	415	235	165	115
111	Insects, miscellaneous [flight; air currents]	Ft altitude		10	177	277
		Insects caught/cu ft air		239	51	21
112	Insects, miscellaneous [flight; air currents]	Ft altitude	20	1000	4000	7000
		Insects caught/10 min				
113	Leafhopper, sugar beet (Circulifer tenellus) [flight]	Ft altitude	26	6	3	1
		Leafhoppers caught, no.		275	210	170
114	Mosquito, malarial (Anopheles quadrimaculatus) [flight]	Ft altitude	1.5	3.0	6.0	7.5
		Mosquitoes caught, no.	14	11	5	3

Part I: PHYSICAL PROPERTIES AND CHEMICAL CONSTITUENTS

Values are per kg of water, unless otherwise indicated; values in parentheses are ranges.

	General Characteristics	Value
1	Density	1.02-1.03
2	Temperature	-1.5 to 30°C
3	pH, surface water	8.1-8.3
4	pH, at depth	7.5-8.1
5	Freezing point	-2°C[1]
6	Specific heat	0.93 Cal/g[2]
7	Velocity of sound	1450-1550 m/sec
8	Transparency, maximum[3]	66 m
9	Hydrostatic pressure[4]	1 atm/10 m

	Salinity[5]	g/kg
10	All oceans, average	35(33-37)
11	All oceans, below 1000 m (at -0.5 to 5°C)	34.6-35
12	Great depths (1-4°C)	34-35.2
13	At equator (average all oceans)	35
14	20th-40th parallel, N. Latitude	35.5
15	10th-30th parallel, S. Latitude	35.5
16	Average, 60°N. and S. Latitudes to the poles	35
17	North Pacific	34.5
18	North Sea, off Denmark	34
19	Indian Ocean, near Australia	35.5
20	South Pacific, off Peru	35.5
21	Arabian Sea	36-37
22	Sargasso Sea, N. Atlantic	36.5-37
23	South Atlantic, off Brazil	36-37
24	Red Sea (surface)	38-41
25	Mediterranean Sea (surface)	37-39
26	Gulf of Mexico (surface)	36-37
27	Antarctic Ocean (surface)	34-34.6
28	Arctic Ocean (surface)	32-33

Average Surface Temperature, °C

	Latitude	Atlantic Ocean	Indian Ocean	Pacific Ocean
46	70-60 N	5.60		
47	60-50 N	8.66		5.74
48	50-40 N	13.16		9.99
49	40-30 N	20.40		18.62
50	30-20 N	24.16	26.16	23.38
51	20-10 N	25.81	27.23	26.42
52	10-0 N	26.66	27.88	27.20
53	70-60 S	-1.30	-1.50	-1.30
54	60-50 S	1.76	1.63	5.00
55	50-40 S	8.68	8.67	11.16
56	40-30 S	16.90	17.00	16.98
57	30-20 S	21.20	22.53	21.53
58	20-10 S	23.16	25.85	25.11
59	10-0 S	25.18	27.41	26.01

Relation of Chlorinity and Salinity to Specific Gravity

	Chlorinity[7] g/kg	Salinity[5] g/kg	Specific Gravity at 17.5°C
60	0	0.00	1.00000
61	1	1.84	1.00144
62	2	3.64	1.00283
63	3	5.45	1.00421
64	4	7.25	1.00558
65	5	9.06	1.00696
66	6	10.86	1.00834
67	7	12.67	1.00971
68	8	14.47	1.01109
69	9	16.28	1.01246
70	10	18.08	1.01383
71	11	19.89	1.01521
72	12	21.69	1.01658
73	13	23.50	1.01795
74	14	25.30	1.01933
75	15	27.11	1.02070
76	16	28.91	1.02208
77	17	30.72	1.02346
78	18	32.52	1.02484
79	19	34.33	1.02622
80	20	36.13	1.02760
81	21	37.94	1.02899
82	22	39.74	1.03037

Major Constituents(concluded)

	Substance	Value
	Cations	
89	Sodium	10.56 g
90	Magnesium	1.27 g
91	Calcium	0.40 g
92	Potassium	0.38 g
93	Strontium	13 mg
	Element[8,9]	
94	Chlorine	18.98 g
95	Sodium	10.56 g
96	Magnesium	1.27 g
97	Sulfur	0.88 g
98	Calcium	0.40 g
99	Potassium	0.38 g
100	Bromine	65 mg
101	Carbon	28 mg
102	Strontium	13 mg
103	Boron	4.6 mg
104	Silicon	0.02-4.0 mg
105	Fluorine	1.4 mg
106	Nitrogen (comp.)	0.006-0.7 mg
107	Aluminum	70 µg
108	Rubidium	0.2 mg
109	Lithium	0.1 mg
110	Phosphorus	1-100 µg
111	Barium	54 µg
112	Iodine	50 µg
113	Arsenic	10-20 µg
114	Iron	2-50 µg
115	Manganese	1-10 µg
116	Copper	1-10 µg
117	Zinc	5 µg
118	Lead	5 µg
119	Selenium	4 µg
120	Cesium	2 µg
121	Uranium	2 µg
122	Molybdenum	0.7 µg
123	Gallium	0.5 µg
124	Thorium	0.4 µg
125	Cerium	0.4 µg
126	Silver	0.3 µg
127	Vanadium	0.3 µg
128	Lanthanum	0.3 µg
129	Yttrium	0.3 µg
130	Bismuth	0.2 µg
131	Nickel	0.1 µg
132	Scandium	0.04 µg
133	Mercury	0.03 µg
134	Gold	0.004 µg
135	Radium	0.2-0.3×10^{-10} µg
136	Cadmium	Present
137	Chromium	Present
138	Cobalt	0.1 µg
139	Tin	3 µg

Pressure-Depth Gradient[4]

	Depth m	Salinity g/kg	Temp °C	Latitude 30° atm/m	Latitude 60° atm/m
29	0	32	0	0.099141	0.099403
30	0	32	20	0.098831	0.099092
31	0	35	0	0.099375	0.099638
32	0	35	20	0.099052	0.099314
33	5000	35	0	0.101757	0.102026
34	5000	35	5	0.101660	0.101929
35	10,000	35	0	0.103952	0.104225

Oxygen Saturation Values from Normal Dry Atmosphere

36	Chlorinity	15	16	17	18	19	20
37	Salinity	27.11	28.91	30.72	32.52	34.33	36.11

	Temp °C	Oxygen ml/L[6]					
38	-2	9.01	8.89	8.76	8.64	8.52	8.39
39	0	8.55	8.43	8.32	8.20	8.08	7.97
40	5	7.56	7.46	7.36	7.26	7.16	7.07
41	10	6.77	6.69	6.60	6.52	6.44	6.35
42	15	6.14	6.07	6.00	5.93	5.86	5.79
43	20	5.63	5.56	5.50	5.44	5.38	5.31
44	25	5.17	5.12	5.06	5.00	4.95	4.86
45	30	4.74	4.68	4.63	4.58	4.52	4.46

Major Constituents[8]

	Substance	Value
	Anions	
83	Chloride	18.98 g
84	Sulfate	2.65 g
85	Bicarbonate	0.14 g
86	Bromide	65 mg
87	Fluoride	1.3 mg
88	Boric acid	26 mg

/1/ Value for water with salinity of slightly more 35 g/kg. /2/ Specific heat is a function of temperature, pressure and humidity; 0.93 approximates the value for sea water with a salinity of 34.85 g/kg at 20°C and atmospheric pressure (760 mm Hg). /3/ In Sargasso Sea, where a 30 cm Secchi disk disappears from sight at this depth. /4/ Hydrostatic pressure increases approximately 1 atmosphere (760 mm Hg) for each 10 m of depth, the exact value being affected by salinity, temperature and latitude. /5/ Total amount of solid material in g/kg of sea water when all carbonate has been converted to oxide, Br and I replaced by Cl, and all organic matter completely oxidized. /6/ mg-atoms of oxygen per liter = 0.08931 x ml/L (these values may be 3% too high). /7/ Chlorinity refers to total amount of Cl, Br and I in g/kg of sea water, and is equal to the mass, in grams, of "atomic weight silver" just necessary to precipitate the halogens in 0.3285233 kg. The standard chlorinity of sea water is 19, and equals salinity 34.325. /8/ Based on total salinity of 34.325. /9/ Nitrogen, oxygen, neon, helium and argon are also present as dissolved gases.

Part II: MARINE PLANT DISTRIBUTION

	Flora	Distribution
1	Seed plants (Spermatophyta)	None in deep oceans beyond continental shelves; 30 genera near coasts in 10-40 ft depths, all in 2 families (Hydrocharitaceae, Potamogetonaceae) as Halophila, Zostera, Thalassia, Phyllospadix.
2	Algae (Thallophyta)	Continental shelves all oceans with average salinity of 35, within 100 m depths; abundant near river mouths.
3	Blue-green (Myxophyceae)	Not abundant; nodularia in Norway fiords, Trichodesmium in Red Sea.
4	Green (Chlorophyceae)	Enteromorpha, Ulva in bays and harbors near surface; Codium, Halmeda (calcareous)[1] in tropics.
5	Brown (Phaeophyceae)	Ascophyllum, Fucus (smaller rock weeds); Laminaria, Nereocystis, Postelsia (large kelps), attached to rocks in deeper water; Sargassum floating in Central Atlantic.
6	Red (Rodophyceae)	Small forms can live beyond continental shelves in depths of 30 m or more; Corallina of tropics is calcareous.[1]
7	Fungi and bacteria	In mud and oozes of ocean floors - no other plant life.
8	Plankton	On surface all oceans; diatoms, dinoflagellates, coccolithophores; microscopic, important food for sea animals.

/1/ Contributing to sand (lime) deposits.

M = million; B = billion.

Era (Duration, yr)	Major Division	Period (Years Ago)	Epoch	Duration yr	Advances in Life	Dominant Life
1 Cenozoic (60 M)	Quaternary (2 M)		Recent	2 M	Rise of civilization.	Age of man and herbaceous plants.
			Pleistocene		Periodic glaciation; extinction of great mammals and many trees; rise of modern herbs; elevation of continents.	Age of modern life: mammals, birds, flowering plants.
	Tertiary	Late Tertiary	Pliocene	58 M	Continued cooling of climate; elevation of Andes; increasing restriction of plant distribution and forests; appearance of man.	
			Miocene		Climate changing greatly, becoming cool and semi-arid; elevation of Alps; restriction of distribution of plants; beginning of forest reduction; culmination of many mammals.	
		Early Tertiary	Oligocene		Climate warm, humid; elevation of Pyrenees; culmination of Eocene floras; world-wide distribution of tropical forests; primitive mammals disappear; rise of higher mammals and birds.	
		(60 M)	Eocene		Climate cool, semi-arid, then warm, humid; modernization of flowering plants; development of extensive forests, widespread in polar regions; modern birds and marine mammals appear.	
2 Mesozoic (125 M)		Cretaceous (125 M)	Upper Cretaceous	65 M	Climate fluctuating; angiosperms dominant in floras, dicotyledons and monocotyledons of numerous existing genera well developed; disappearance of Bennettitales; rise of primitive mammals.	Age of reptiles and higher gymnosperms.
			Middle Cretaceous		Climate fluctuating; rapid development of angiosperms, appearance of many existing genera; specialization and extinction of great reptiles.	
			Lower Cretaceous		Climate very warm; rise of angiosperms(?); conifers and cycads still dominant; earliest known pines (Pinaceae).	
		Jurassic (157 M)	Jurassic	32 M	Climate warm; beginning of Sierra Nevada Mountains; first certainly known angiosperms; conifers and cycads dominant; Ginkgoales and conifers world-wide; cordaites disappear; primitive birds and flying reptiles; rise of higher insects.	
		Triassic (185 M)	Triassic	28 M	Climate warm, semi-arid; floras not luxuriant; gymnosperms increase, spread of conifers, rise of cycads and Bennettitales; seed ferns disappear; diversification of modern fern families well started; first mammals; rise of giant reptiles (dinosaurs).	
3 Paleozoic (368 M)	Late Paleozoic	Carboniferous	Permian (223 M)	38 M	Climate dry; periodic glaciation, severe in southern hemisphere, elevation of Appalachians; dwindling of ancient groups, extinction of many; rise of ferns and conifers and land vertebrates; expansion of reptiles. Gondwana flora of southern hemisphere distinct from northern.	Age of amphibians, lycopods, and seed ferns.
			Pennsylvanian (271 M)	48 M	Dominant lycopods, seed ferns, horsetails; sphenophylls, Coniferales and calamites present; extensive coal formation.	
			Mississippian (309 M)	38 M	Dominant lycopods, horsetails, seed ferns; cordaites, sphenophylls, calamites present; rise of primitive reptiles and insects.	
	Middle Paleozoic	Devonian (354 M)	Devonian	45 M	Early land floras: Psilophytales (Rhynia, Horneophyton); lycopods; primitive horsetails, including sphenophylls; primitive gymnosperms (earliest Cordaites and seed ferns, their seeds not yet known); first forests; rise of amphibians and fishes.	Age of fishes and early land plants.
		Silurian (381 M)	Silurian	27 M	Algae dominant (e.g., Nematophyton hecksi); first known land plants: Psilophytales and Lycopodiales, e.g., Baragwanathia; rise of lungfishes and scorpions (first air-breathing animals).	
	Early Paleozoic	Ordovician (448 M)	Ordovician	67 M	Rise of corals, armored fishes (and land plants?); marine algae dominant; first known fresh-water fishes.	Age of higher invertebrates and algae.
		Cambrian (553 M)	Cambrian	105 M	Climate warm, uniform over earth; first abundant fossils; many groups of marine invertebrates; dominant trilobites; marine plants, few algae determinable; Cambrian spores, pollen, tracheids in India, north-central Europe and Scandinavia.	
4 Proterozoic (900 M)		Precambrian (1.5 B)	Precambrian		Rocks chiefly sedimentary, of enormous thickness; glaciation; first fossils: worms, crustaceans, brachiopods; evidence of algal and bacterial life described.	Age of primitive marine invertebrates; fossils rare.
5 Archeozoic (550 M+)		(3.5-5 B)			Igneous rocks: lavas, metamorphosed rocks; few sedimentary; no direct evidence of life; graphites of possible organic origin in sedimentary rocks of Grenville age.	Age of unicellular life (?); fossils unknown.

Appendix

Classification adapted from A. S. Pearse's "Zoological Names," Section F, American Association for the Advancement of Science, Durham, North Carolina, 1948. Extinct groups are indicated by an asterisk (*).

KINGDOM: ANIMALIA
Subkingdom: Protozoa
I. PHYLUM: PROTOZOA
Subphylum: Plasmodroma
 Class: Mastigophora
 Subclass: Phytomastigina
  Order: Chrysomonadina
   Suborder: Euchrysomonadina
   Suborder: Rhizochrysidina
   Suborder: Chrysocapsina
  Order: Cryptomonadina
   Suborder: Eucryptomonadina
   Suborder: Phoecapsina
  Order: Phytomonadina
  Order: Euglenoidina
  Order: Chloromonadina
  Order: Dinoflagellata
   Suborder: Porocentrinea
   Suborder: Peridiniinea
   Suborder: Cystoflagellata
 Subclass: Zoomastigina
  Order: Rhizomastigina
  Order: Protomonadina
  Order: Polymastigina
   Suborder: Monomonadina
   Suborder: Diplomonadina
   Suborder: Polymonadina
  Order: Hypermastigina
 Class: Sarcodina
 Subclass: Rhizopoda
  Order: Proteomyxa
  Order: Mycetozoa
   Suborder: Eumycetozoa
   Suborder: Sorophora
  Order: Amoebina
  Order: Testacea
  Order: Foraminifera
 Subclass: Actinopoda
  Order: Heliozoa
  Order: Radiolaria
 Class: Sporozoa
 Subclass: Telosporidia
  Order: Gregarinida
   Suborder: Eugregarinaria
   Suborder: Schizogregarinaria
  Order: Coccidia
   Suborder: Eimeridea
   Suborder: Adeleidea
  Order: Haemosporidia
 Subclass: Acnidosporidia
  Order: Sarcosporidia
  Order: Haplosporidia
 Subclass: Cnidosporidia
  Order: Myxosporidia
   Suborder: Eurysporea
   Suborder: Sphaerosporea
   Suborder: Platysporea
  Order: Actinomyxidia
  Order: Microsporidia
   Suborder: Monocnidea
   Suborder: Dicnidea
  Order: Helicosporidia
Subphylum: Ciliophora
 Class: Ciliata
 Subclass: Protociliata
 Subclass: Euciliata
  Order: Holotricha
   Suborder: Astomata
   Suborder: Gymnostomata
   Suborder: Trichostomata
   Suborder: Hymenostomata
   Suborder: Thigmotricha
   Suborder: Apostomea
  Order: Spirotricha
   Suborder: Heterotricha
   Suborder: Oligotricha
   Suborder: Ctenostomata
   Suborder: Hypotricha
  Order: Chonotricha
  Order: Peritricha
   Suborder: Sessilia
   Suborder: Mobilia
 Class: Suctoria
Subkingdom: Mesozoa
Subkingdom: Parazoa
II. PHYLUM: PORIFERA
 Class: Calcispongiae

 Order: Asconosa
 Order: Syconosa
 Class: Hyalospongiae
 Order: Hexasterophora
 Order: Amphidiscophora
 Class: Desmospongiae
 Order: Carnosa
 Order: Choristida
 Order: Epipolasida
 Order: Hadromerina
 Order: Poecilosclerina
 Order: Haplosclerina
 Order: Keratosa
III. PHYLUM: *ARCHAEOCYATHA
Subkingdom: Metazoa
Subkingdom: Enterozoa
IV. PHYLUM: COELENTERATA
 Class: Hydrozoa
  Order: Hydroida
  Order: Trachylina
  Order: Milleporina
  Order: Stylasterina
  Order: Siphonophora
 Class: Scyphozoa
  Order: Lucernariidea
  Order: Charybdeidea
  Order: Corona
  Order: Semaeostomaeae
  Order: Rhizostomeae
 Class: Anthozoa
 Subclass: Octocorallia
  Order: Stolonifera
  Order: Telestacea
  Order: Alcyonacea
  Order: *Trachypsammiacea
  Order: Coenothecalia
  Order: Gorgonacea
   Suborder: Scleraxonia
   Suborder: Holaxonia
  Order: Pennatulacea
   Suborder: Sessiliflorae
   Suborder: Subselliflorae
 Subclass: Zoantharia
  Order: Cerinthidea
  Order: Antipatharia
  Order: Zoanthidea
  Order: Actinaria
   Suborder: Ptychodactiaria
   Suborder: Corallimorpharia
   Suborder: Actiniaria
  Order: Scleractinia
   Suborder: Astrocoeniida
   Suborder: Fungiida
   Suborder: Faviida
   Suborder: Caryophylliida
   Suborder: Dendrophylliida
  Order: Rugosa
  Order: Tabulata
V. PHYLUM: CTENOPHORA
 Class: Tentaculata
  Order: Cydippidea
  Order: Lobata
  Order: Cestoidea
  Order: Platyctenea
 Class: Nuda
  Order: Beroidea
VI. PHYLUM: PLATYHELMINTHES
 Class: Turbellaria
  Order: Acoela
  Order: Rhabdocoela
   Suborder: Temnocephalida
  Order: Alloiocoela
  Order: Tricladida
  Order: Polycladida
 Class: Trematoda
 Subclass: Monogenea
  Order: Monopisthocotylea
  Order: Polyopisthocotylea
 Subclass: Aspidogastrea
 Subclass: Digenea
  Order: Gasterostoma
  Order: Prosostomata
 Class: Cestoidea
 Subclass: Cestoidaria
  Order: Amphilinidea
  Order: Gyrocotylidea
 Subclass: Cestoda

 Order: Pseudophyllidea
 Order: Cyclophyllidea
 Order: Tetraphyllidea
 Order: Trypanorhyncha
 Order: Heterophyllidea
VII. PHYLUM: NEMERTEA
 Class: Anopla
  Order: Paleonemertea
  Order: Heteronemertea
 Class: Enopla
  Order: Hoplonemertea
   Suborder: Monostilifera
   Suborder: Polystilifera
  Order: Bellonemertea
VIII. PHYLUM: ACANTHOCEPHALA
 Class: Eoacanthocephala
  Order: Gyracanthocephala
  Order: Neoacanthocephala
 Class: Metacanthocephala
  Order: Palaeacanthocephala
  Order: Archiacanthocephala
IX. PHYLUM: PROSOPYGIA
X. PHYLUM: ROTATORIA
 Class: Seisonidea
 Class: Bdelloidea
 Class: Monogononta
  Order: Ploima
  Order: Flosculariacea
  Order: Collothecacea
XI. PHYLUM: GASTROTRICHA
  Order: Macrodasyoidea
  Order: Chaetonotoidea
XII. PHYLUM: ECHINODERA
XIII. PHYLUM: NEMATOMORPHA
 Class: Gordididea
 Class: Nectonematoidea
XIV. PHYLUM: NEMATOIDEA
 Class: Phasmidia
  Order: Rhabditida
   Suborder: Rhabditata
   Suborder: Ascaridata
   Suborder: Strongylata
  Order: Spirurida
   Suborder: Spirurata
   Suborder: Camallanata
 Class: Aphasmidia
  Order: Enoplata
   Suborder: Enoplata
   Suborder: Dorylaimata
   Suborder: Dioctophymata
  Order: Chromadorida
   Suborder: Monohysterata
   Suborder: Desmoscolecata
   Suborder: Chromadorata
XV. PHYLUM: TARDIGRADA
 Class: Heterotardigrada
  Order: Arthrotardigrada
  Order: Echiniscoidea
 Class: Eutardigrada
XVI. PHYLUM: CHAETOGNATHA
XVII. PHYLUM: BRYOZOA
 Class: Entoprocta
 Class: Ectoprocta
 Subclass: Gymnolaemata
  Order: Cyclostomata
   Suborder: Tubipora
   Suborder: Cerioporina
   Suborder: Ceramoporoidea
   Suborder: Hederelloidea
  Order: Trepostomata
  Order: Cryptostomata
  Order: Ctenostoma
  Order: Cheilostomata
   Suborder: Anasca
   Suborder: Ascophora
 Subclass: Phylactolaemata
XVIII. PHYLUM: BRACHIOPODA
 Class: Inarticulata
  Order: Atremata
  Order: Neotremata
 Class: Articulata
  Order: *Paleotremata
  Order: Protremata
  Order: Telotremata
XIX. PHYLUM: PHORONIDEA
XX. PHYLUM: POEBIOIDEA
XXI. PHYLUM: POGONOPHORA

XXII. PHYLUM: PTEROBRANCHIA
XXIII. PHYLUM: ENTEROPNEUSTA
  Class: Balanoglossida
XXIV. PHYLUM: LINGUATULA
XXV. PHYLUM: ECHINODERMATA
Subphylum: Pelmatozoa
  Class: *Cystoidea
    Order: *Amphoridea
    Order: *Rhombifera
    Order: *Diploporita
    Order: *Aporita
    Order: *Edrioasteroida
  Class: *Blastoidea
    Order: *Protoblastoida
    Order: *Eublastoida
  Class: Crinoidea
    Order: *Camerata
    Order: *Adunata
    Order: Flexibilia
     Suborder: *Sagenocrinida
     Suborder: *Taxocrinida
    Order: *Inadunata
     Suborder: *Larviformia
     Suborder: *Fistulata
    Order: Articulata
     Suborder: Bourgueticrinida
     Suborder: Pentacrinida
     Suborder: Holopida
    Order: Comatulida
     Suborder: Oligophreata
     Suborder: Macrophreata
Subphylum: Asterozoa
  Class: Asteroidea
    Order: Phanerozonea
    Order: Spinulosa
    Order: Forcipulata
  Class: Ophiuroidea
  Subclass: *Aegophiurida
    Order: *Lysophiurida
  Subclass: Myophiurida
    Order: *Ophiocystiida
    Order: *Aganasterida
    Order: Phrynophiurida
    Order: Laemophiurida
    Order: Gnathophiurida
    Order: Chilophiurida
Subphylum: Echinozoa
  Class: Echinoidea
    Order: *Bothriocidaroida
    Order: Cidaroida
    Order: Centrechinoida
     Suborder: Aulodonta
     Suborder: Stirodonta
     Suborder: Camerodonta
    Order: Exocycloida
     Suborder: Holectypina
     Suborder: Echinoneina
     Suborder: Clypeastrina
     Suborder: Nucleolitina
     Suborder: Cassidulina
     Suborder: Urechinina
     Suborder: Spatangina
    Order: Perischoechinoida
    Order: Echinocystoida
    Order: Perichoechinoida
  Class: Holothurioidea
    Order: Dendrochirota
    Order: Elasipoda
    Order: Aspidochirota
    Order: Molpadonia
    Order: Apoda
XXVI. PHYLUM: PRIAPULOIDEA
XXVII. PHYLUM: ANNELIDA
  Class: Archiannelida
  Class: Polychaeta
    Order: Errantia
    Order: Sedentaria
  Class: Myzostoma
  Class: Oligochaeta
    Order: Plesiopora plesiotheca
    Order: Plesiopora prosotheca
    Order: Prosopora
    Order: Opisthopora
  Class: Hirudinea
    Order: Rhynchobdellida
    Order: Gnathobdellida
    Order: Pharyngobdellida
XXVIII. PHYLUM: ECHIUROIDEA
  Class: Echiurida

    Order: Echiuroinea
    Order: Xenopneusta
    Order: Heteromyota
  Class: Saccosomatida
XXIX. PHYLUM: SIPUNCULOIDEA
XXX. PHYLUM: ONYCHOPHORA
XXXI. PHYLUM: ARTHROPODA
Subphylum: *Trilobita
  Class: *Hypoparia
  Class: *Opisthoparia
  Class: *Proparia
Subphylum: Chelicerata
  Class: Merostomata
    Order: *Eurypterida
    Order: *Synxiphosura
    Order: Xiphosura
  Class: Pycnogonida
    Order: Colossendeomorpha
    Order: Nymphonomorpha
    Order: Ascorhynchomorpha
    Order: Pycnogonomorpha
  Class: Arachnida
  Subclass: Latigastra
    Order: Scorpiones
    Order: Pseudoscorpiones
    Order: Opiliones
    Order: *Architarbi
    Order: Acari
     Suborder: Notostigmata
     Suborder: Holothyroidea
     Suborder: Parasitiformes
     Suborder: Trombidiformes
     Suborder: Sarcoptiformes
     Suborder: Tetrapodili
  Subclass: Stethostomata
    Order: *Haptopoda
    Order: *Anthracomarti
  Subclass: Soluta
    Order: Trigonotarbi
  Subclass: Caulogastra
    Superorder: Latisterna
    Order: Palpigradi
    Superorder: Camarostomata
    Order: Schizomida
    Order: Telyphonida
    Order: Kustarachnae
    Superorder: Labellata
    Order: Phrynichida
    Order: Araneae
    Superorder: Cucullifera
    Order: Ricinulei
    Superorder: Rostrata
    Order: Solifugae
Subphylum: Mandibulata
  Superclass: Crustacea
  Class: Eucrustacea
  Subclass: Branchiopoda
    Order: Anostraca
    Order: Notostraca
    Order: Conchostraca
    Order: Cladocera
     Suborder: Calyptomera
     Suborder: Gymnomera
  Subclass: Ostracoda
    Order: Myodocopa
    Order: Cladocopa
    Order: Podocopa
    Order: Platycopa
  Subclass: Copepoda
    Order: Eucopepoda
     Suborder: Calanoida
     Suborder: Harpacticoida
     Suborder: Cyclopoida
     Suborder: Notodelphyoida
     Suborder: Monstrilloida
     Suborder: Caligoida
     Suborder: Lernaeopodoida
    Order: Branchiura
     Suborder: Arguloida
  Subclass: Cirripedia
    Order: Thoracica
     Suborder: Turrilepadomorpha
     Suborder: Lepadomorpha
     Suborder: Verrucomorpha
     Suborder: Balanomorpha
    Order: Ascothoracica
    Order: Apoda
    Order: Rhizocephala
  Subclass: Malacostraca

  Infraclass: Leptostraca
  Superorder: Phyllocarida
    Order: Nebaliacea
    Order: *Rhinocarina
    Order: *Ceratiocarina
    Order: *Hymenocarina
  Superorder: *Nahecarida
  Infraclass: Eumalacostraca
  Superorder: Syncarida
    Order: Anaspidacea
  Superorder: Peracarida
    Order: Mysidacea
    Order: Thermosbaenacea
    Order: Cumanea
    Order: Tanaidacea
    Order: Isopoda
     Suborder: Flabellifera
     Suborder: Valvifera
     Suborder: Asellota
     Suborder: Phreatoicidea
     Suborder: Epicaridea
     Suborder: Oniscoidea
    Order: Amphipoda
     Suborder: Gammaridea
     Suborder: Hyperiidea
     Suborder: Caprellidea
     Suborder: Ingolfiellidea
  Superorder: Eucarida
    Order: Euphausiacea
    Order: Decapoda
     Suborder: Natantia
     Suborder: Reptantia
  Superorder: Hoplocarida
    Order: Stomatopoda
  Superclass: Progoneata
  Class: Pauropoda
    Order: Pauropoda
     Suborder: Ectomorpha
     Suborder: Endomorpha
  Class: Symphyla
    Order: Symphyla
  Class: Diplopoda
  Subclass: Pselaphognatha
    Order: Ancyrotricha
    Order: *Lophotricha
  Subclass: Chilognatha
  Superorder: Opisthandria
    Order: Limacomorpha
    Order: Oniscomorpha
     Suborder: Sphaerotheria
     Suborder: Glomeridia
  Superorder: Proterandria
    Order: Colobognatha
    Order: Nematophora
     Suborder: Chordeumoidea
     Suborder: Stemmiuloidea
     Suborder: Striaroidea
     Suborder: Lysiopetaloidea
    Order: Proterospermophora
     Suborder: Polydesmoidea
     Suborder: Strongylosomoidea
    Order: Opisthospermophora
     Suborder: Juloidea
     Suborder: Spiroboloidea
     Suborder: Spirostreptoidea
     Suborder: Cambaloidea
  Superclass: Opisthogoneata
  Class: Chilopoda
  Subclass: Pleurostigmorphora
  Superorder: Epimorpha
    Order: Geophilomorpha
    Order: Scolopendromorpha
  Superorder: Anamorpha
    Order: Lithobiomorpha
    Order: Craterostigmorpha
  Subclass: Notostigmorphora
    Order: Scutigeromorpha
  Class: Insecta
  Subclass: Synaptera
    Order: Collembola
    Order: Protura
    Order: Entotrophi
    Order: Thysanura
  Subclass: Pterygota
    Order: Odonata
    Order: Ephemeroptera
    Order: Orthoptera
    Order: Isoptera
    Order: Dermaptera

Order: Plecoptera
Order: Embioptera
Order: Psocoptera
Order: Zoraptera
Order: Mallophaga
Order: Anoplura
Order: Hemiptera
  Suborder: Heteroptera
  Suborder: Homoptera
Order: Thysanoptera
Order: Neuroptera
  Suborder: Megaloptera
  Suborder: Raphidiodea
  Suborder: Planipennia
Order: Mecoptera
Order: Diptera
  Suborder: Nematocera
  Suborder: Brachycera
Order: Siphonaptera
Order: Trichoptera
Order: Lepidoptera
  Suborder: Jugatae
  Suborder: Frenatae
  Suborder: Rhopalocera
Order: Coleoptera
  Suborder: Adephaga
  Suborder: Polyphaga
Order: Hymenoptera
  Suborder: Chalastogastra
  Suborder: Clistogastra
Order: *Palaeodictyoptera
Order: *Megasecoptera
Order: *Protephemerida
Order: *Protodonata
Order: *Protoperlaria
Order: *Protelytroptera
Order: *Caloneurodea
Order: *Glosselytrodea
Order: *Protorthoptera
Order: *Protohemiptera
The following orders of insects are listed but
have dubious recognition.
Order: *Protoblattoidea
Order: *Hadentomoidea
Order: *Sypharopteroidea
Order: *Mixotermitoidea
Order: *Reculoidea
Order: *Hapalopteroidea
Order: *Protomecoptera
Order: *Paratrichoptera
Order: *Paramecoptera
Order: *Synarmogoidea
Order: *Diaphanopteroidea
Order: *Aeroplanoptera
Order: *Protohymenoptera
Order: *Protocoleoptera
Order: *Miomoptera
Order: *Pruvostitoptera
Order: *Meganisoptera
Order: *Permodonata
Order: *Archodonata
Order: *Protodiptera
Order: *Hemipsocoptera
Order: *Cnemidolestoidea
Order: *Paraplecoptera
Order: *Archaehymenoptera
Order: *Palaeohymenoptera
Order: *Protocicadida
Order: *Protofulgorida
Order: *Hemiodonata
Order: *Anisaxia
Order: *Perielytrodea
Order: *Permodictyoptera
Order: *Aphelophlebia
XXXII. PHYLUM: MOLLUSCA
Class: Crepipoda
Order: Eoplacophora
Order: Mesoplacophora
Order: Isoplacophora
Order: Teleoplacophora
Class: Gastropoda
Subclass: Prosobranchia
Order: Archaeogastropoda
Order: Mesogastropoda
Order: Neogastropoda
Subclass: Opisthobranchia
Order: Tectibranchia
Order: Pteropoda
  Suborder: Thecosomata

  Suborder: Gymnosomata
Order: Sacoglossa
Order: Acoela
  Suborder: Notaspidea
  Suborder: Nudibranchia
Subclass: Pulmonata
Order: Basommatophora
Order: Stylommatophora
Class: Scaphopoda
Class: Pelecypoda
Subclass: Prionodesmacea
Order: Palaeoconcha
Order: Taxodonta
Order: Schizodonta
Order: Dysodonta
Subclass: Anomalodesmacea
Order: Anomalobranchia
Order: Septibranchia
Subclass: Teleodesmacea
Order: *Pantodonta
Order: Diogenodonta
Order: Cyclodonta
Order: Teleodonta
Order: Asthenodonta
Class: Cephalopoda
Order: Tetrabranchia
  Suborder: Nautiloidea
  Suborder: *Ammonitoidea
Order: Dibranchia
  Suborder: Vampyromorpha
  Suborder: Decapoda
  Suborder: Octopoda
XXXIII. PHYLUM: CHORDATA
Subphylum: Tunicata
Class: Ascidiacea
Order: Stolidobranchiata
Order: Aspiraculata
Order: Phlebobranchiata
Order: Aplousobranchiata
Class: Larvacea
Class: Thaliacea
Subclass: Myosomata
Order: Salpida
Order: Doliolida
Subclass: Pyrosomata
Order: Pyrosomatida
Subphylum: Acrania
Class: Branchiostomi
Order: Branchiostomida
Subphylum: Craniata
Superclass: Agnatha
Class: *Cephalaspidomorphi
Order: *Osteostracida
Order: *Anaspida
Class: Petromyzontia
Order: Myxinida
Order: Petromyzontida
Class: *Pteraspidomorphi
Order: *Heterostracia
Order: *Coelolepida
Order: *Euphanerida
Superclass: Gnathostomata (Pisces)
Class: *Placodermi
Order: *Acanthodiida
Order: *Arthrodirida
  Suborder: *Euarthrodirina
  Suborder: *Arctolepina
  Suborder: *Brachythoracina
  Suborder: *Ptyctodontina
  Suborder: *Phyllolepina
Order: *Macropetalichthyida
Order: *Antiarchida
Order: *Stegoselachiida
  Suborder: *Stensioellina
  Suborder: *Rhenanina
Order: *Palaeospondylida
Class: Chondrichthyes
Subclass: *Xenacanthi
Order: *Xenacanthida
Subclass: *Cladoselachii
Order: *Cladoselachida
Subclass: Selachii
Superorder: Selachiica
Order: Hexanchida
  Suborder: Hexanchina
  Suborder: Chlamydoselachina
Order: Heterodontida
  Suborder: *Hybodontina
  Suborder: Heterodontina

Order: Galeida
  Suborder: Galeina
Order: Squalida
  Suborder: Squalina
Order: Squatinida
  Suborder: Squatinina
Order: Pristiophorida
Superorder: Rajica
Order: Rajida
  Suborder: Prostiina
  Suborder: Rhinobatina
  Suborder: Totpedinina
  Suborder: Rajina
  Suborder: Dasyatina
Subclass: Holocephali
Order: *Bradyodontida
Order: Chimaerida
Class: Osteichthyes
Subclass: Choanichthyes
Order: Neoceratodontida
Order: Crossopteryigida
  Suborder: *Rhipidistiina
  Suborder: Coelacanthina
Subclass: Actinopterygii
Superorder: Chondrosteica
Order: *Palaeoniscida
Order: Polypterida
Order: Acipenserida
Order: *Subholosteida
Superorder: Holosteica
Order: Lepisosteida
Order: *Pycnodontida
Order: *Aspidorhynchida
Order: Amiida
Order: *Pholidophorida
Superorder: Teleosteica
Order: Isospondylida
  Suborder: Clupeina
  Suborder: Salmonina
  Suborder: Opisthoproctina
  Suborder: Osteoglossina
  Suborder: Stomiatina
  Suborder: Gymnophotodermina
  Suborder: *Enchodontina
  Suborder: Iniomina
  Suborder: Berycomorphina
  Suborder: Esocina
Order: Bathyclupeida
Order: Mormyrida
Order: Ateleopida
Order: Giganturida
Order: Lyomerida
Order: Ostariophysida
  Suborder: Characina
  Suborder: Gymnotina
  Suborder: Cyprinina
  Suborder: Silurina
Order: Anguillida
Order: Heteromida
Order: Synbranchida
Order: Synentognathida
  Suborder: Scomberesocina
  Suborder: Exocoetina
Order: Cyprinodontida
  Suborder: Amblyopsina
  Suborder: Poeciliina
Order: Salmopercida
Order: Zeomorphida
Order: Solenichthyida
Order: Allotriognathida
Order: Anacanthida
Order: Gasterosteida
Order: Percomorphida
  Suborder: Sphyraenina
  Suborder: Phallostethina
  Suborder: Polynemina
  Suborder: Anabantina
  Suborder: Channina
  Suborder: Percina
  Suborder: Blenniina
  Suborder: Ophidiina
  Suborder: Ammodytina
  Suborder: Schindleriina
  Suborder: Callionymina
  Suborder: Trichiurina
  Suborder: Scombrina
  Suborder: Luvarina
  Suborder: Tetragonurina
  Suborder: Stromateina

Suborder: Kurtina
Suborder: *Ramphosina
Suborder: Gobiina
Order: Scorpaenida
Order: Cephalacanthida
Order: Pegasida
Order: Pleuronectida
  Suborder: Psettodina
  Suborder: Soleina
Order: Icosteida
Order: Chaudhurida
Order: Mastocembelida
Order: Echeneida
Order: Tetraodontida
  Suborder: Balistina
  Suborder: Ostraciontina
  Suborder: Tetraodontina
  Suborder: Diodontina
  Suborder: Molina
Order: Gobiesocida
Order: Batrachoidida
Order: Lophiida
  Suborder: Lophiina
  Suborder: Antennariina
  Suborder: Ceratiina
Superclass: Tetrapoda
Class: Amphibia
Superorder: *Labyrinthodontia
Order: *Ichthyostegalia
Order: *Rhachitomic
  Suborder: *Loxommoidea
  Suborder: *Edopsoidea
  Suborder: *Eryopsoidea
  Suborder: *Neorhachitomi
Order: *Stereospondyli
Order: *Embolomeri
Order: *Seymouriamorpha
Order: *Eoanura
Order: *Proanura
Order: Salientia
  Suborder: Amphicoela
  Suborder: Opisthocoela
  Suborder: Anomocoela
  Suborder: Procoela
  Suborder: Diplasiocoela
Subclass: *Lepospondyli
Order: *Aistopoda
Order: *Nectridia
Order: *Microsauria
Order: Caudata
  Suborder: Cryptobranchoidea
  Suborder: Ambystomoidea
  Suborder: Salamandroidea
  Suborder: Proteidea
Order: Apoda
Class: Reptilia
Subclass: Anapsida
Order: *Cotylosauria
  Suborder: *Captorhinomorpha
  Suborder: *Diadectomorpha
Order: Chelonia
  Suborder: *Eunotosauria
  Suborder: *Amphichelydia
  Suborder: Athecae
  Suborder: Thecophora
Subclass: *Ichthyopterygia
Subclass: *Synaptosauria
Order: *Protorosauria
Order: *Sauropterygia
  Suborder: *Nothsauria
  Suborder: *Plesiosauria
  Suborder: *Placodontia
Subclass: Lepidosauria
Order: *Eosuchia
  Suborder: *Younginiformes
  Suborder: *Choristodera
  Suborder: *Thalattosauria
  Suborder: *Acrosauria
Order: Rhynchocephalia
Order: Squamata
  Suborder: Lacertilia
  Suborder: Serpentes
Subclass: *Archosauria
Order: *Thecodontia
  Suborder: *Pseudosuchia
  Suborder: *Phytosauria
Order: Crocodilia
  Suborder: *Protosuchia
  Suborder: *Sebecosuchia
  Suborder: *Mesosuchia
  Suborder: Eusuchia

Order: *Pterosauri
  Suborder: *Rhamphorhynchoidea
  Suborder: *Pterodactyloidea
Order: *Saurischia
  Suborder: *Theropoda
  Suborder: *Sauropoda
Order: *Ornithischia
  Suborder: *Ornithopoda
  Suborder: *Ankylosauria
  Suborder: *Ceratopsia
Subclass: *Synapsida
Order: *Pelycosauria
  Suborder: *Ophiacodontia
  Suborder: *Sphenacodontia
  Suborder: *Edaphosauria
Order: *Therapsida
  Suborder: *Dinocephalia
  Suborder: *Dicynodontia
  Suborder: *Theriodontia
Order: *Ictidosauria
Class: Aves
Subclass: *Archaeornithes
Order: Archaeopterygiformes
Subclass: Neornithes
Superorder: *Odontognathae
Order: *Hesperornithiformes
Order: *Ichthyornithiformes
Superorder: Palaeognathae
Order: Caenagnathiformes
Order: Struthioniformes
Order: Rheiformes
Order: Casuariiformes
Order: *Dinornithiformes
Order: *Aepyornithiformes
Order: Tinamiformes
Order: Impennes
Superorder: Neognathae
Order: Gaviiformes
Order: Colymbiformes
  Suborder: Pterocletes
  Suborder: Columbae
Order: Procellariiformes
Order: Sphenisciformes
Order: Pelecaniformes
  Suborder: Phaëthontes
  Suborder: Pelecani
  Suborder: Fregatae
  Suborder: Odontopteryges
Order: Ciconiiformes
  Suborder: Ardeinae
  Suborder: Balaenicipites
  Suborder: Ciconiae
  Suborder: Phoenicopteri
Order: Anseriformes
  Suborder: Anhimae
  Suborder: Anseres
Order: Falconiformes
  Suborder: Cathartae
  Suborder: Falcones
Order: Galliformes
  Suborder: Galli
  Suborder: Opisthocomi
Order: Musophagi
Order: Gruiformes
  Suborder: Mesoenatides
  Suborder: Turnices
  Suborder: Grues
  Suborder: Heliornithes
  Suborder: Rhynocheti
  Suborder: Eurypygae
  Suborder: *Phororhaci
  Suborder: Cariamae
  Suborder: Otides
Order: *Diatrymiformes
Order: Charadriiformes
  Suborder: Charadrii
  Suborder: Lari
  Suborder: Alcae
Order: Psittaciformes
Order: Cuculiformes
Order: Strigiformes
Order: Caprimulgiformes
  Suborder: Steatornithes
  Suborder: Caprimulgi
Order: Apodiformes
  Suborder: Micropodi
  Suborder: Trochili
Order: Coliiformes
Order: Trogoniformes
Order: Coraciiformes
  Suborder: Alcedines

  Suborder: Meropes
  Suborder: Coracii
  Suborder: Bucerotes
Order: Piciformes
  Suborder: Galbulae
  Suborder: Pici
Order: Passeriformes
  Suborder: Eurylaimi
  Suborder: Tyranni
  Suborder: Menurae
  Suborder: Passeres
Class: Mammalia
Subclass: Prototheria
Order: Monotremata
Subclass: *Allotheria
Order: *Multituberculata
Order: *Triconodonta
Subclass: Theria
Infraclass: *Pantotheria
Order: *Pantotheria
Order: *Symmetrodonta
Infraclass: Metatheria
Order: Marsupialia
Infraclass: Eutheria
Cohort: Unguiculata
Order: Insectivora
Order: Dermoptera
Order: Chiroptera
  Suborder: Megachiroptera
  Suborder: Microchiroptera
Order: Primates
  Suborder: Prosimii
  Suborder: Anthropoidea
Order: *Tillodontia
Order: *Taeniodontia
Order: Edentata
  Suborder: *Palaeanodonta
  Suborder: Xenarthra
Order: Pholidota
Cohort: Glires
Order: Lagomorpha
Order: Rodentia
  Suborder: Sciuromorpha
  Suborder: Myomorpha
  Suborder: Hystricomorpha
Cohort: Mutica
Order: Cetacea
  Suborder: *Archaeoceti
  Suborder: Odontoceti
  Suborder: Mysticeti
Cohort: Ferungulata
Superorder: Ferae
Order: Carnivora
  Suborder: *Creodonta
  Suborder: Fissipeda
  Suborder: Pinnipedia
Superorder: *Protungulata
Order: *Condylarthra
Order: *Litopterna
Order: *Notoungulata
  Suborder: *Notioprogonia
  Suborder: *Toxodonta
  Suborder: *Typotheria
  Suborder: *Hegetotheria
Order: *Astrapotheria
  Suborder: *Trigonostylopoidea
  Suborder: *Astrapotherioidea
Order: Tubulidentata
Superorder: Paenungulata
Order: *Pantodonta
Order: *Dinocerata
Order: *Pyrotheria
Order: Proboscidia
  Suborder: *Moeritherioidea
  Suborder: Elephantoidea
  Suborder: *Deinotherioidea
  Suborder: *Barytherioidea
Order: *Embrithopoda
Order: Hyracoidea
Order: Sirenia
  Suborder: Trichechiformes
  Suborder: *Desmostyliformes
Superorder: Mesaxonia
Order: Perissodactyla
  Suborder: Hippomorpha
  Suborder: Ceratomorpha
Superorder: Paraxonia
Order: Artiodactyla
  Suborder: Suiformes
  Suborder: Tylopoda
  Suborder: Ruminantia

APPENDIX II. TAXONOMIC CLASSIFICATION: PLANTS

Classification adapted from that of Engler, A., and Diels, L. Roman numerals refer to divisions.

Part I: PLANT KINGDOM: MAJOR GROUPS

I. SCHIZOPHYTA (Bacteria)
  Class: Schizomycetes
    Order: Eubacteria
    Order: Thiobacteria
  Class: Schizophyceae
II. MYXOMYCETES (Slime molds)
  Order: Hydromyxales
  Order: Exosporales
  Order: Cribrariales
  Order: Enteridiales
  Order: Liceales
  Order: Stemonitales
  Order: Physarales
  Order: Margaritales
  Order: Trichiales
III. FLAGELLATAE (Flagellates)
  Order: Pantostomatales
  Order: Distomatales
  Order: Protomastigales
  Order: Chrysomonadales
  Order: Cryptomonadales
  Order: Chloromonadales
  Order: Euglenales
IV. DINOFLAGELLATAE
  Class: Adiniferidea
    Order: Athecatales
    Order: Thecatales
  Class: Diniferidea
    Order: Gymnodiniales
    Order: Peridiniales
V. SILICOFLAGELLATAE
  Order: Siphonotestales
  Order: Stereotestales
VI. HETEROCONTAE
VII. BACILLARIOPHYTA (Diatoms)
  Class: Centricae
  Class: Pennales
VIII. CONJUGATAE (Green algae)
IX. CHLOROPHYCEAE (Blue-green algae)
  Class: Protococcales
    Order: Volvocales
    Order: Euprotococcales
  Class: Ulotrichales
  Class: Siphonocladales
  Class: Siphonales
X. CHAROPHYTA (Yellow-green algae)
XI. PHAEOPHYCEAE (Brown algae)
  Order: Ectocarpales
  Order: Sphacelariales
  Order: Cutleriales
  Order: Dictyotales
  Order: Laminariales
  Order: Tilopteridales
  Order: Fucales
XII. RHODOPHYCEAE (Red algae)
  Class: Bangiales
  Class: Florideae
    Order: Nemalionales
    Order: Gelidiales
    Order: Cryptonemiales
    Order: Gigartinales
    Order: Rhodymeniales
    Order: Ceramiales
XIII. EUMYCETES (Fungi)
  Class: Phycomycetes
  Subclass: Oomycetes
    Order: Monoblepharidales
    Order: Saprolegniales
    Order: Ancylistales
    Order: Peronosporales
  Subclass: Zygomycetes
    Order: Mucorales

    Order: Entomophthorales
    Order: Endogonales
    Order: Basidiobolales
  Class: Ascomycetes
    Order: Spermophthorales
    Order: Euascales
    Order: Laboulbeniales
  Class: Protomycetes
  Class: Basidiomycetes
  Subclass: Hemibasidii
    Order: Ustilaginales
    Order: Uredinales
  Subclass: Eubasidii
    Order: Protobasidiomycetes
    Order: Autobasidiomycetes
Supplement a[1]: Fungi imperfecti
Supplement b[1]: Lichenes
  Subclass: Phycolichenes
  Subclass: Ascolichenes
    Order: Pyrenocarpeae
    Order: Gymnocarpeae
  Subclass: Basidiolichenes
XIV. ARCHEGONIATAE
XIVa. BRYOPHYTA (Mosses, liverworts)
  Class: Hepaticae
    Order: Marchantiales
    Order: Anthocerotales
    Order: Jungermanniales
  Class: Musci
  Subclass: Sphagnales
  Subclass: Andreaeales
  Subclass: Bryales
    Order Group: Eubryinales
    Order: Fissidentales
    Order: Dicranales
    Order: Pottiales
    Order: Grimmiales
    Order: Funariales
    Order: Schistostegales
    Order: Tetraphidales
    Order: Eubryales
    Order: Isobryales
    Order: Hookeriales
    Order: Hypnobryales
    Order Group: Buxbaumiinales
    Order: Buxbaumiales
    Order Group: Polytrichinales
    Order: Polytrichales
    Order: Dawsoniales
XIVb. PTERIDOPHYTA (Ferns and their allies)
  Class: Psilophytinae
  Class: Articulatae
  Subclass: Irotoarticulatales
  Subclass: Sphenophyllales
  Subclass: Cheirostrobales
  Subclass: Pseudoborniales
  Subclass: Equisetales
    Order: Euequisetales
    Order: Calamitales
  Class: Lycopodiinae
    Order: Lycopodiales
    Order: Selaginellales
      Suborder: Selaginellineae
      Suborder: Lepidophytineae
  Class: Psilotinae
  Class: Isoetinae
  Class: Filicinae
  Subclass: Eusporangiatae
    Order: Ophioglossales
    Order: Marattiales
  Subclass: Leptosporangiatae
    Order: Eufilicales

    Order: Hydropteridales
XV. EMBRYOPHYTA SIPHONOGAMA
    (Phanerogamae)
XVa. GYMNOSPERMAE (Conifers and their
    allies)
  Class: Cycadofilicales
  Class: Cycadales
  Class: Bennettitales
  Class: Ginkgoales
  Class: Cordaitales
  Class: Coniferae
  Class: Gnetales
XVb. ANGIOSPERMAE (Flowering plants)
  Class: Monocotyledoneae
    Order: Pandanales
    Order: Helobiae
    Order: Triuridales
    Order: Glumiflorae
    Order: Principes
    Order: Synanthae
    Order: Spathiflorae
    Order: Farinosae
    Order: Liliiflorae
    Order: Scitamineae
    Order: Microspermae
  Class: Dicotyledoneae
  Subclass: Archichlamydeae
    Order: Verticillatae
    Order: Piperales
    Order: Hydrostachyales
    Order: Salicales
    Order: Garryales
    Order: Myricales
    Order: Balanopsidales
    Order: Leitneriales
    Order: Juglandales
    Order: Julianiales
    Order: Batidales
    Order: Fagales
    Order: Urticales
    Order: Podostemonales
    Order: Proteales
    Order: Santalales
    Order: Aristolochiales
    Order: Balanophorales
    Order: Polygonales
    Order: Centrospermae
    Order: Ranales
    Order: Rhoeadales
    Order: Sarraceniales
    Order: Rosales
    Order: Pandales
    Order: Geraniales
    Order: Sapindales
    Order: Rhamnales
    Order: Malvales
    Order: Parietales
    Order: Opuntiales
    Order: Myrtiflorae
    Order: Umbelliflorae
  Subclass: Metachlamydeae
    Order: Diapensiales
    Order: Ericales
    Order: Primulales
    Order: Plumbaginales
    Order: Ebenales
    Order: Contortae
    Order: Tubiflorae
    Order: Plantaginales
    Order: Rubiales
    Order: Cucurbitales
    Order: Campanulatae

Part II: PHANEROGAMAE: FAMILIES

XV. EMBRYOPHYTA SIPHONOGAMA
XVa. GYMNOSPERMAE (Conifers and their
    allies)
  Class: Cycadofilicales
  Class: Cycadales
    Family: Cycadaceae
  Class: Bennettitales
    Family: Bennettitaceae
  Class: Ginkgoales
    Family: Ginkgoaceae
  Class: Cordaitales
    Family: Cordaitaceae
  Class: Coniferae
    Family: Taxaceae

    Family: Podocarpaceae
    Family: Araucariaceae
    Family: Cephalotaxaceae
    Family: Pinaceae
    Family: Taxodiaceae
    Family: Cupressaceae
  Class: Gnetales
    Family: Ephedraceae
    Family: Welwitschiaeceae
    Family: Gnetaceae
XVb. ANGIOSPERMAE (Flowering plants)
  Class: Monocotyledoneae
    Order: Pandanales
    Family: Typhaceae

    Family: Pandanaceae
    Family: Sparganiaceae
    Order: Helobiae
    Suborder: Potamogetonineae
      Family: Aponogetonaceae
      Family: Potamogetonaceae
      Family: Najadaceae
    Suborder: Scheuchzerineae
      Family: Scheuchzeriaceae
    Suborder: Alismatineae
      Family: Alismataceae
    Suborder: Butomineae
      Family: Butomaceae
      Family: Hydrocharitaceae

/1/ Supplement to classes Ascomycetes and Protomycetes.

531

Order: Triuridales	Family: Urticaceae	Family: Myrothamnaceae
Family: Triuridaceae	Order: Podostemonales	Family: Bruniaceae
Order: Glumiflorae	Family: Podostemonaceae	Family: Hamamelidaceae
Family: Gramineae	Order: Proteales	Family: Roridulaceae
Family: Cyperaceae	Family: Proteaceae	Family: Eucommiaceae
Order: Principes	Order: Santalales	Suborder: Rosineae
Family: Palmae	Suborder: Santalineae	Family: Platanaceae
Order: Synanthae	Family: Olacaceae	Family: Crossosomataceae
Family: Cyclanthaceae	Family: Opiliaceae	Family: Rosaceae
Order: Spathiflorae	Family: Octoknemataceae	Family: Connaraceae
Family: Araceae	Family: Grubbiaceae	Family: Leguminosae
Family: Lemnaceae	Family: Santalaceae	Order: Pandales
Order: Farinosae	Family: Myzodendraceae	Family: Pandaceae
Suborder: Flagellariineae	Suborder: Loranthineae	Order: Geraniales
Family: Flagellariaceae	Family: Loranthaceae	Suborder: Geraniineae
Suborder: Enantioblastae	Order: Aristolochiales	Family: Oxalidaceae
Family: Restionaceae	Family: Aristolochiaceae	Family: Geraniaceae
Family: Centrolepidaceae	Family: Rafflesiaceae	Family: Tropaeolaceae
Family: Mayacaceae	Family: Hydnoraceae	Family: Linaceae
Family: Xyridaceae	Order: Balanophorales	Family: Erythroxylaceae
Family: Eriocaulaceae	Family: Balanophoraceae	Family: Zygophyllaceae
Suborder: Bromeliineae	Order: Polygonales	Family: Cneoraceae
Family: Thurniaceae	Family: Polygonaceae	Family: Rutaceae
Family: Rapateaceae	Order: Centrospermae	Family: Simarubaceae
Family: Bromeliaceae	Suborder: Chenopodiineae	Family: Burseraceae
Suborder: Commelinineae	Family: Chenopodiaceae	Family: Meliaceae
Family: Commelinaceae	Family: Amaranthaceae	Family: Akariaceae
Suborder: Pontederiineae	Suborder: Phytolaccineae	Suborder: Malpighiineae
Family: Pontederiaceae	Family: Nyctaginaceae	Family: Malpighiaceae
Family: Cyanastraceae	Family: Phytolaccaceae	Family: Trigoniaceae
Suborder: Philydrineae	Family: Gyrostemonaceae	Family: Vochysiaceae
Family: Philydraceae	Family: Achatocarpaceae	Suborder: Polygalineae
Order: Liliiflorae	Family: Aizoaceae	Family: Tremandraceae
Suborder: Juncineae	Suborder: Portulacineae	Family: Polygalaceae
Family: Juncaceae	Family: Portulacaceae	Suborder: Dichapetalineae
Suborder: Liliineae	Family: Basellaceae	Family: Dichapetalaceae
Family: Stemonaceae	Suborder: Caryophyllineae	Suborder: Callitrichineae
Family: Liliaceae	Family: Caryophyllaceae	Family: Callitrichaceae
Family: Haemodoraceae	Order: Ranales	Order: Sapindales
Family: Amaryllidaceae	Suborder: Nymphaeineae	Suborder: Buxineae
Family: Velloziaceae	Family: Nymphaeaceae	Family: Buxaceae
Family: Taccaceae	Family: Ceratophyllaceae	Suborder: Empetrineae
Family: Dioscoreaceae	Suborder: Trochodendrineae	Family: Empetraceae
Suborder: Iridineae	Family: Trochodendraceae	Suborder: Coriariineae
Family: Iridaceae	Family: Cercidiphyllaceae	Family: Coriariaceae
Order: Scitamineae	Suborder: Ranunculineae	Suborder: Limnanthineae
Family: Musaceae	Family: Ranunculaceae	Family: Limnanthaceae
Family: Zingiberaceae	Family: Lardizabalaceae	Suborder: Anacardiineae
Family: Cannaceae	Family: Berberidaceae	Family: Anacardiaceae
Family: Marantaceae	Family: Menispermaceae	Suborder: Celastrineae
Order: Microspermae	Suborder: Magnoliineae	Family: Cyrillaceae
Suborder: Burmanniineae	Family: Magnoliaceae	Family: Pentaphylacaceae
Family: Burmanniaceae	Family: Himantandraceae	Family: Corynocarpaceae
Suborder: Gynandrae	Family: Calycanthaceae	Family: Aguifoliaceae
Family: Orchidaceae	Family: Lactoridaceae	Family: Celastraceae
Class: Dicotyledoneae	Family: Anonaceae	Family: Hippocrateaceae
Subclass: Archichlamydeae	Family: Eupomatiaceae	Family: Salvadoraceae
Order: Verticillatae	Family: Myristicaceae	Family: Stackhousiaceae
Family: Casuarinaceae	Family: Gomortegaceae	Family: Staphyleaceae
Order: Piperales	Family: Monimiaceae	Suborder: Icacinaceae
Family: Saururaceae	Family: Lauraceae	Family: Icacinaceae
Family: Piperaceae	Family: Hernandiaceae	Suborder: Sapindineae
Family: Chloranthaceae	Order: Rhoeadales	Family: Aextoxicaceae
Order: Hydrostachyales	Suborder: Rhoeadineae	Family: Aceraceae
Family: Hydrostachyaceae	Family: Papaveraceae	Family: Hippocastanaceae
Order: Salicales	Suborder: Capparidineae	Family: Sapindaceae
Family: Salicaceae	Family: Capparidaceae	Suborder: Sabiineae
Order: Garryales	Family: Cruciferae	Family: Sabiaceae
Family: Garryaceae	Family: Tovariaceae	Suborder: Melianthineae
Order: Myricales	Suborder: Resedineae	Family: Melianthaceae
Family: Myricaceae	Family: Resedaceae	Suborder: Didiereineae
Order: Balanopsidales	Suborder: Moringineae	Family: Didiereaceae
Family: Balanopsidaceae	Family: Moringaceae	Suborder: Balsaminineae
Order: Leitneriales	Suborder: Bretschneiderineae	Family: Balsaminaceae
Family: Leitneriaceae	Family: Bretschneideraceae	Order: Rhamnales
Order: Juglandales	Order: Sarraceniales	Family: Rhamnaceae
Family: Juglandaceae	Family: Sarraceniaceae	Family: Vitaceae
Order: Julianiales	Family: Nepenthaceae	Order: Malvales
Family: Julianiaceae	Family: Droseraceae	Suborder: Elaeocarpineae
Order: Batidales	Order: Rosales	Family: Elaeocarpaceae
Family: Batidaceae	Suborder: Saxifragineae	Suborder: Chlaenineae
Order: Fagales	Family: Crassulaceae	Family: Chlaenaceae
Family: Betulaceae	Family: Cephalotaceae	Suborder: Malvineae
Family: Fagaceae	Family: Saxifragaceae	Family: Tiliaceae
Order: Urticales	Family: Pittosporaceae	Family: Malvaceae
Family: Ulmaceae	Family: Byblidaceae	Family: Bombacaceae
Family: Rhoipteleaceae	Family: Brunelliaceae	Family: Sterculiaceae
Family: Moraceae	Family: Cunoniaceae	Suborder: Scytopetalineae

Part II: PHANEROGAMAE: FAMILIES (Concluded)

Family: Scytopetalaceae
Order: Parietales
  Suborder: Theineae
  Family: Dilleniaceae
  Family: Actinidiaceae
  Family: Eucryphiaceae
  Family: Medusagynaceae
  Family: Ochnaceae
  Family: Strasburgeriaceae
  Family: Caryocaraceae
  Family: Marcgraviaceae
  Family: Quinaceae
  Family: Theaceae
  Family: Guttiferae
  Family: Dipterocarpaceae
  Suborder: Tamaricineae
  Family: Elatinaceae
  Family: Frankeniaceae
  Family: Tamaricaceae
  Suborder: Cistineae
  Family: Cistaceae
  Family: Bixaceae
  Suborder: Cochlospermineae
  Family: Cochlospermaceae
  Suborder: Flacourtiineae
  Family: Canellaceae
  Family: Violaceae
  Family: Flacourtiaceae
  Family: Stachyuraceae
  Family: Turneraceae
  Family: Maleshserbiaceae
  Family: Passifloraceae
  Family: Achariaceae
  Suborder: Papayineae
  Family: Caricaceae
  Suborder: Loasineae
  Family: Loasaceae
  Suborder: Datiscineae
  Family: Datiscaceae
  Suborder: Begoniineae
  Family: Begoniaceae
  Suborder: Ancistrocladineae
  Family: Ancistrocladaceae
Order: Opuntiales
  Family: Cactaceae
Order: Myrtiflorae
  Suborder: Thymelaeineae
  Family: Geissolomataceae
  Family: Penaeaceae
  Family: Oliniaceae
  Family: Thymelaeaceae
  Family: Elaeagnaceae
  Suborder: Myrtineae
  Family: Lythraceae

Family: Heteropyxidaceae
Family: Sonneratiaceae
Family: Crypteroniaceae
Family: Punicaceae
Family: Lecythidaceae
Family: Rhizophoraceae
Family: Nyssaceae
Family: Alangiaceae
Family: Combretaceae
Family: Myrtaceae
Family: Melastomataceae
Family: Hydrocaryaceae
Family: Oenotheraceae
Family: Halorrhagaceae
  Suborder: Hippuridineae
  Family: Hippuridaceae
  Family: Thelygonaceae
  Suborder: Cynomoriineae
  Family: Cynomoriacae
Order: Umbelliflorae
  Family: Araliaceae
  Family: Umbelliferae
  Family: Cornaceae
Subclass: Metachlamydeae
Order: Diapensiales
  Family: Diapensiaceae
Order: Ericales
Subclass: Ericineae
  Family: Clethraceae
  Family: Pirolaceae
  Family: Ericaceae
Subclass: Epacridineae
  Family: Epacridaceae
Order: Primulales
  Family: Theophrastaceae
  Family: Myrsinaceae
  Family: Primulaceae
Order: Plumbaginales
  Family: Plumbaginaceae
Order: Ebenales
  Suborder: Sapotineae
  Family: Sapotaceae
  Family: Hoplestigmataceae
  Suborder: Diospyrineae
  Family: Ebenaceae
  Family: Diclidantheraceae
  Family: Symplocaceae
  Family: Styracaceae
  Family: Lissocarpaceae
Order: Contortae
  Suborder: Oleineae
  Family: Oleaceae
  Suborder: Gentianineae

Family: Desfontaineaceae
Family: Loganiaceae
Family: Gentianaceae
Family: Apocynaceae
Family: Asclepiadaceae
Order: Tubiflorae
  Suborder: Convolvulineae
  Family: Convolvulaceae
  Family: Polemoniaceae
  Family: Fouquieraceae
  Suborder: Lennoineae
  Family: Lennoaceae
  Suborder: Borraginineae
  Family: Hydrophyllaceae
  Family: Borraginaceae
  Suborder: Verbenineae
  Family: Verbenaceae
  Family: Labiatae
  Suborder: Solanineae
  Family: Nolanaceae
  Family: Solanaceae
  Family: Scrophulariaceae
  Family: Bignoniaceae
  Family: Pedaliaceae
  Family: Martyniaceae
  Family: Orobanchaceae
  Family: Gesnericeae
  Family: Columelliaceae
  Family: Lentibulariaceae
  Family: Globulariaceae
  Suborder: Acanthineae
  Family: Acanthaceae
  Suborder: Myoporineae
  Family: Myoporaceae
  Suborder: Phrymineae
  Family: Phrymaceae
Order: Plantaginales
  Family: Plantaginaceae
Order: Rubiales
  Family: Rubiaceae
  Family: Caprifoliaceae
  Family: Adoxaceae
  Family: Valerianaceae
  Family: Dipsacaceae
Order: Cucurbitales
  Family: Cucurbitaceae
Order: Campanulatae
  Family: Campanulaceae
  Family: Goodeniaceae
  Family: Brunoniaceae
  Family: Stylidiaceae
  Family: Calyceraceae
  Family: Compositae

APPENDIX III: ESTIMATED NUMBER OF SPECIES: ANIMAL, PLANT KINGDOM

Group	Number of Species[1]	Group	Number of Species[1]	Group	Number of Species[1]
Animal Kingdom		**Animal Kingdom (concluded)**		**Plant Kingdom (concluded)**	
1 Protozoa	15,000	27 Chordata	60,000	Eumycophyta (concluded)	
2 Porifera	5,000	28 Tunicata	700	49 Deuteromycetes	24,000
3 Coelenterata	10,000	29 Leptocarida	30	50 Lichenes	15,500
4 Ctenophora	100	Vertebrata		51 Bryophta	23,820
5 Platyhelminthes	6,000	30 Pisces	40,000[4]	52 Hepaticae	8,500
6 Nemertea	500	31 Amphibia	2,769[5]	53 Anthocerotae	320
7 Nemathelminthes	5,000	32 Reptilia	6,959[5]	54 Musci	15,000
8 Trochelminthes	2,000	33 Aves	8,600[6]	55 Pteridophyta	11,280
9 Bryozoa	3,000	34 Mammalia	3,000-5,000[7]	56 Psilotales	3
10 Brachiopoda	120	35 Total	938,000[8]	57 Lycopodiales	483
11 Phoronidea	15			58 Selaginellales	700
12 Chaetognatha	30	**Plant Kingdom**		59 Isoëtales	64
13 Annelida	6,500	36 Thallophyta	106,965	60 Equisetales	32
14 Arthropoda	750,000	37 Chlorophyta	5,700	61 Filicales	10,000
15 Crustacea	25,000	38 Euglenophyta	335	62 Spermatophyta	200,665
16 Arachnoidea	15,000	39 Pyrrophyta[9]	1,000	63 Gymnospermae	665
17 Onychophora	80	40 Chrysophyta[10]	5,700	64 Cycadales	100
18 Myripoda	7,000	41 Phaeophyta	900	65 Ginkgoales	1
19 Insecta	700,000[2]	42 Cyanophyta	1,400	66 Coniferae	520
20 Mollusca	70,000[3]	43 Rhodophyta	2,500	67 Gnetales	44
21 Echinodermata	5,000	44 Myxomycetes	430	68 Angiospermae	200,000
22 Crinoidea	635	45 Eumycophyta	73,500	69 Monocotyledones	34,000
23 Asteroidea	1,500	46 Phycomycetes	1,500	70 Dicotyledones	166,000
24 Ophiuroidea	1,500	47 Ascomycetes	25,000		
25 Echinoidea	771	48 Basidiomycetes	23,000	71 Total	342,730
26 Holothurioidea	600				

/1/ Exclusive of lower classification (subspecies, etc.), unless otherwise indicated. /2/ Estimated number of forms (species, subspecies, etc.), 900,000. /3/ Estimated number of forms, 100,000. /4/ Value includes "fish-like" vertebrates (Cyclostomata and Elasmobranchii). /5/ Applicable to number of forms. /6/ Estimated number of forms, 32,000. /7/ Estimated number of forms 20,000. /8/ Incomplete, recent estimates not available. /9/ Including Cryptophyceae, Desmokontae and Dinophyceae. /10/ Including Heterokontae and Chrysophyceae.

APPENDIX IV: SYMBOLS, UNITS, CONSTANTS, AND CONVERSION FACTORS

Although many of the values and symbols listed here may not be used as such in the Handbook, they will help the user translate values into units more applicable to his field, or to make a physical-chemical-biological correlation of data. Some of the tables include definitions and conversion factors which may not be listed here. In several instances two or more units of measurement may have the same symbol (e.g., M = mole; M= million); however, the possibility of confusion is remote because of the difference in the subject material where the units are applicable. The singular and plural forms of abbreviations are the same.

ABBREVIATIONS AND SYMBOLS USED IN THE HANDBOOK

mi = mile	lb = pound	yr = year	ev = electron volt
yd = yard	oz = ounce	mo = month	sp gr = specific gravity
ft = foot	kg = kilogram	wk = week	BP = boiling point
in. = inch	g = gram	da = day	MP = melting point
km = kilometer	dg = decigram	hr = hour	$[\alpha]_D$ = optical rotation
hm = hectometer	cg = centigram	min = minute	MW = molecular weight
m = meter	mg = milligram	sec = second	$\male$ = male
dm = decimeter	μg = microgram	msec = millisecond	$\female$ = female
cm = centimeter	gal = gallon	Cal = Calorie (kilocalorie)	mEq = milliequivalent
mm = millimeter	qt = quart	cal = calorie (gram calorie)	atm = atmosphere
μ = micron (10^{-3}mm)	pt = pint	^oF = degrees Fahrenheit	μ = micro- (10^{-6})
mμ = millimicron (10^{-6}mm)	kl = kiloliter	^oC = degrees centigrade	m = milli- (10^{-3})
Å = angstrom unit	hl = hectoliter	M = mole	c = centi- (10^{-2})
$\mu\mu$ = millionth micron (10^{-9}mm)	L = liter	F = farad	k = kilo- (10^3)
sq = square (e.g., sq m = square meter)	ml = milliliter	r = roentgen	M = mega- (10^6)
cu = cubic (e.g., cu cm = cubic centimeter)	μl = microliter	c = curie	B = billion (10^9)

SYSTEMS OF UNITS

In many tables units are indicated in relationship to other measurements, as, for example, calories per square centimeter per hour. As an expedient to conserve space, these are presented as cal/sq cm/hr. The slashes in such cases should always be interpreted as "per" rather than as fractional designations.

A. Mechanical

System	Length	Mass	Time	Force	Velocity	Acceleration	Torque	Pressure	Energy	Power	Momentum
Meter-Kilogram-Second	Meter (m)	Kilogram (kg)	Second (sec)	Newton (nt)	m/sec	m/sec^2	m·nt	nt/m^2	Joule	Watt	kg·m/sec
Centimeter-Gram-Second	Centimeter (cm)	Gram (g)	sec	Dyne	cm/sec	cm/sec^2	dyne·cm	dyne/cm^2	Erg	Erg/sec	g·cm/sec
Foot-Pound-Second	Foot (ft)	Pound (lb)	sec	Poundal (pd)	ft/sec	ft·sec^2	pdl·ft	pdl·ft	ft·pdl	ft·pdl/sec	ft·lb/sec

B. Electrical

System	Energy	Power	Current	Charge	Electric Potential	Resistance	Electric Intensity	Capacitance	Inductance
Meter-Kilogram-Second	Joule	Watt (Joule/sec)	Ampere	Coulomb	Volt	Ohm	Volt/meter	Farad	Henry
Electromagnetic	Erg	Erg/sec	Abampere	Abcoulomb	Abvolt	Abohm	Abvolt/cm	Abfarad	Abhenry
Electrostatic	Erg	Erg/sec	Statampere	Statcoulomb	Statvolt	Statohm	Statvolt/cm	Statfarad	Stathenry

SOME USEFUL CONSTANTS

Constant	Value	Reciprocal	Logarithm
$1/4\,\pi$	0.7853981634	1.2732395447	$\bar{1}$.8950898814
$1/2\,\pi$	1.5707963268	0.6366197724	0.1961198770
π	3.1415926536	0.3183098862	0.4971498727
2π	6.2831853072	0.1591549431	0.7981798684
$\sqrt{\pi}$	1.7724538509	0.5641895835	0.2485749363
$\sqrt{2\pi}$	2.5066282746	0.3989422804	0.3990899342
$\sqrt{1/2\pi}$	1.2533141373	0.7978845608	0.0980599385
$1/2\sqrt{\pi}$	0.8862269255	1.1283791671	$\bar{1}$.9475449407
e	2.7182818285	0.3678794412	0.4342944819
e^2	7.3890560989	0.1353352832	0.8685889638
$\sqrt{2}$	1.4142135624	0.7071067812	0.1505149978
$\sqrt{3}$	1.7320508076	0.5773502692	0.2385606274
$\sqrt{10}$	3.1622776602	0.3162277660	0.5000000000
$Log_{10}e$	0.4342944819	2.3025850930	$\bar{1}$.6377843113
Radian	57.2957795131^o	0.0174532925	1.7581226324

Binomial Coefficients
Value of n_x

4	5	6	7	8	9	10	11	12	1
1	1	1	1	1	1	1	1	1	0
4	5	6	7	8	9	10	11	12	1
6	10	15	21	28	36	45	55	66	2
4	10	20	35	56	84	120	165	220	3
1	5	15	35	70	126	210	330	495	4
	1	6	21	56	126	252	462	792	5
		1	7	28	84	210	462	924	6
			1	8	36	120	330	792	7
				1	9	45	165	495	8
					1	10	55	220	9
						1	11	66	10
							1	12	11
								1	12

Speed of light in a vacuum; also, ratio of emu to esu of electric charge (c) . . . . (2.99776±0.00004) x 10^8 m/sec
Charge of an electron (e) . . . . (1.6020±0.0002) x 10^{-19} coulomb
Faraday's constant; the charge transported by a gram atom of a univalent element (F) . . . . (96,522±7) coulombs/mole
Avogadro's number; the number of molecules in a gram molecule or of atoms in a gram atom (N_o) . . . . (6.0251±0.0004) x 10^{23}
Standard atmospheric pressure (P_o) . . . . (101,324.6±0.4) nt/sq m
Freezing point of water on the absolute (Kelvin) scale (T_o) . . . . (273.16±0.02) ^oK
Density of mercury at STP . . . . (13,595.04±0.06) kg/cu m
Atomic weight of oxygen, physical scale* . . . . (16.00436±0.00009)
Volume of a mole of perfect gas at STP (V_o) . . . . (22,420.7±0.6) cu cm
Universal gas constant (R_o) . . . . (8,316.6±0.4) joules/kg.^oK
Boltzmann's constant; gas constant per molecule (k) . . . . (1.3803±0.0001) x 10^{-23} joule/^oK
Mass of atom of unit atomic weight, physical scale* (m_1) . . . . (1.6589±0.0014) x 10^{-24}g
Mass of electron (m_e) . . . . (9.103±0.008) x 10^{-28} g
Mechanical equivalent of heat . . . . (4185.5±0.4) joules/Cal
Gravitation constant (G) . . . . (6.670±0.005) x 10^{-11} nt·sq m/sq kg
Planck's (quantum) constant (h) . . . . (6.623±0.001) x 10^{-34} joule·sec

*An atomic weight of 16 for oxygen (as determined by chemical analysis) is the basis for the chemical scale of atomic weights. In the physical scale the value of 16 is assigned to the most abundant isotope of oxygen. Physical scale atomic weights are larger than those in the chemical scale by a ratio of 1.00027 to 1.

Units expressed in Column A, when multiplied by the accompanying factor in Column B, are converted to units expressed in Column C.

Column A	x Column B	= Column C
Abamperes	10.0000	amperes
Abamperes	2.99796×10^{10}	statampere
Abcoulombs	10.0000	coulombs (Abs.)
Abcoulombs	2.99796×10^{10}	statcoulombs
Abcoulombs/kg	30577	statcoulombs/dyne
Abcoulombs/lb	6.7411×10^{4}	statcoulombs/dyne
Abfarads	1.0000×10^{9}	farads (Abs.)
Abfarads	1×10^{15}	microfarads
Abfarads	8.98776×10^{20}	statfarads
Abhenries	1.0000×10^{-9}	henries (Abs.)
Abhenries	1×10^{-6}	millihenries
Abhenries	1.11263×10^{-21}	stathenries
Abmhos/cu cm	1000	megmhos/cu cm
Abmhos/cu cm	1.00052×10^{9}	mhos,International/cu cm
Abmhos/cu cm	166.2	mhos/mil ft
Abohms	1×10^{-15}	megohms
Abohms	0.001	microhms
Abohms	1.0000×10^{-9}	ohms (Abs.)
Abohms	1.11263×10^{-21}	statohms
Abvolts	0.010000	microvolts
Abvolts	3.33560×10^{-1}	statvolts
Abvolts	1.0000×10^{-8}	volts (Abs.)
Abvolts/cm	1.0000×10^{-8}	volts (Abs.)/cm
Abvolts/°F	0.018000	microvolts/°C
Abvolts/in.	3.9370×10^{-9}	volts (Abs.)/cm
Acres (U. S.)	40.46873	ares (sq. dekameters)
Acres (U. S.)	0.4046873	hectares (sq. hectometers)
Acres (U. S.)	43560	sq ft
Acres (U. S.)	4046.873	sq m
Acres (U. S.)	0.0015625	sq mi
Acres (U. S.)	160	sq rods
Acres (U. S.)	4840	sq yd
Amperes (Abs.)	0.1	abamperes
Amperes (Abs.)	1.00007	amperes (International)
Amperes (Abs.)	1.0363×10^{-5}	faradays/sec
Amperes (Abs.)	2.99796×10^{9}	statampere
Ampere-hr (Abs.)	3600.0	coulombs (Abs.)
Angstrom units	3.937×10^{-9}	inches
Angstrom units	1×10^{-10}	meters
Angstrom units	100	micro-microns
Angstrom units	1×10^{-4}	microns
Angstrom units	0.1	milli-microns
Atmospheres	1.0133	bars
Atmospheres	76	cm Hg at 0°C
Atmospheres	1.01325×10^{6}	dynes/cm^2
Atmospheres	33.899	ft of water at 39.1°F
Atmospheres	1033.3	g/sq cm
Atmospheres	29.921	in. Hg at 32°F
Atmospheres	10333	kg/sq m
Atmospheres	760000	microns of Hg
Atmospheres	760	mm Hg
Atmospheres	2116.32	lb/sq ft
Atmospheres	14.696	lb/sq in.
Barrels (U.S., dry)	3.281	bushels
Barrels (U.S., dry)	7056	cu in.
Barrels (U.S., dry)	0.11562	cu m
Barrels (U.S., dry)	105.0	quarts (dry)
Barrels (U.S., liquid)	0.11924	cu m
Barrels (U.S., liquid)	31.5	gallons
BTU	252	gram calories
BTU	25030	foot poundals
BTU	777.9	ft lb
BTU	3.929×10^{-4}	horse power hr
BTU	1055	joules
Bushels (U.S., dry)	0.304785	barrels
Bushels (U.S., dry)	35239	cu cm
Bushels (U.S., dry)	1.2444	cu ft
Bushels (U.S., dry)	2150.42	cu in.
Bushels (U.S., dry)	0.035239	cu m
Bushels (U.S., dry)	0.35238329	hectoliters
Bushels (U.S., dry)	35.238329	liters
Bushels (U.S., dry)	4	pecks
Bushels (U.S., dry)/acre	0.870754	hectoliters/hectare
Calories, g	3.968×10^{-3}	BTU
Calories, g (mean)	0.001469	cu ft atm
Calories, g (mean)	99.334	foot-poundals
Calories, g (mean)	3.0874	ft lb
Calories, g	1.5591×10^{-6}	horse power hr
Calories, g (15°C)	4.185	joules (Abs.)
Calories, g (mean)	0.42685	kg m
Calories, g (mean)	4.1311×10^{-2}	L-atm
Calories, g (mean)	0.0011628	watt hr

Column A	x Column B	= Column C
Calorie (15°C) sec	6.3854×10^{33}	quanta
Calories (15°C)/ampere-hr	0.011625	joules/abcoulomb
Calories (15°C)/coulomb	41.850	joules/abcoulomb
Calories, gram (15°C)/°C	0.0022046	BTU (60°F)/°F
Calories, gram (15°C)/°C	4.185	joules/°C
Calories, gram (mean)/g	1.8	BTU (mean)/lb
Calories, gram (mean)/g/°C	1	BTU (60°F)/lb/°F
Calories, gram (mean)/g/°C	4.186	joules/g/°C
Calorie (15°C) sec/N_o*	1.0535×10^{10}	quanta
Calories, kg (mean)	3.9685	BTU (mean)
Calories, kg (mean)	1000	gram calories, (mean)
Calories, kg (mean)	4.186×10^{10}	ergs
Calories, kg (mean)	3087.4	ft lb
Calories, kg (mean)	4.2686×10^{7}	g cm
Calories, kg (mean)	0.0015593	horse power hr
Calories, kg (mean)	4186	joules
Calories, kg (mean)	426.85	kg m
Calories, kg (mean)	0.0011628	KW hr
Calories, kg (mean)/min	51.457	ft lb/sec
Calories, kg (mean)/min	0.093558	horse power
Calories, kg (mean)/min	69.769	watts
Calories, kg (mean)/sec	4.186	kilowatts
Candles (International)	1.0000	lumens (International)/steradian
Candle power (spherical)	12.566	lumens
Candles/sq cm	3.1416	lamberts
Candles/sq in.	0.48695	lamberts
Centigrade thermal unit (15°C)	1898.3	joules (Abs.)
Centimeters	1×10^{8}	angstrom units
Centimeters	0.032808	feet (British or U.S.)
Centimeters	0.393700	inches (U.S.)
Centimeters	10000	microns
Centimeters	393.70	mils
Centimeters	0.01093611	yards (U. S.)
Cm Hg at 0°C	0.013158	atmospheres
Cm Hg at 0°C	1.33322×10^{4}	dynes/sq cm
Cm Hg at 0°C	0.44604	ft of water at 39.1°F
Cm Hg at 0°C	135.95	kg/sq m
Cm Hg at 0°C	27.845	lb/sq ft
Cm Hg at 0°C	0.19337	lb/sq in.
Centimeters/sec	1.9685	ft/min
Centimeters/sec	0.03600	km/hr
Centimeters/sec	0.6000	m/min
Centimeters/sec	0.02237	mi/hr
Centimeters/sec	3.728×10^{-4}	mi/min
Centimeters/sec^2	0.036	km/hr/sec
Centimeters/sec^2	0.02237	mi/hr/sec
Circles	360	degrees
Circles	6.28319	radians
Circular in.	5.0671	sq cm
Circular in.	0.78540	sq in.
Circular mm	0.78540	sq mm
Circumferences	360	degrees
Circumferences	400	grades
Coulombs (Abs.)	0.1000	abcoulombs or electromagnetic cgs units
Coulombs (Abs.)	1.00010	coulombs (International)
Coulombs (Abs.)	6.281×10^{18}	electronic charges
Coulombs (Abs.)	2.99796×10^{9}	electrostatic cgs units or statcoulombs
Coulombs (International)	0.99990	coulombs (Abs.)
Coulombs/kg	3057.7	statcoulombs/dyne
Cubic cm	3.531445×10^{-5}	cu ft (U. S.)
Cubic cm	0.061023	cu in.
Cubic cm	1.3079×10^{-6}	cu yd
Cubic cm	0.27053	drams (U.S., fluid)
Cubic cm	2.6417×10^{-4}	gal (U.S.)
Cubic cm	9.9997×10^{-4}	liters
Cubic cm	16.231	minims (U.S.)
Cubic cm	0.033814	ounces (U.S., fluid)

* Avogadro's number.

Column A	x (Column B)	= (Column C)
Cubic cm	0.0021134	pints (U.S., liquid)
Cubic cm	9.0808×10^{-4}	quarts (U.S., dry)
Cubic cm	0.0010567	quarts (U.S., liquid)
Cubic cm atm (normal)	0.101325	joules (Abs.)
Cubic cm/sec	0.0021186	cu ft/min
Cubic ft (U.S.)	28317	cu cm
Cubic ft (U.S.)	1728	cu in.
Cubic ft (U.S.)	0.02831701	cu m
Cubic ft (U.S.)	0.037037	cu yd
Cubic ft (U.S.)	7.481	gallons (U.S.)
Cubic ft (U.S.)	28.316	liters
Cubic ft (U.S.)	25.714	quarts (U.S., dry)
Cubic ft (U.S.)	29.922	quarts (U.S., liquid)
Cubic ft atm	680.74	gram calories (mean)
Cubic ft atm	2116.3	ft lb
Cubic ft atm	2869.4	joules (Abs.)
Cubic ft atm	292.59	kg m
Cubic ft atm	28.316	L atm
Cubic ft of water (60°F)	62.37	pounds
Cubic ft/min	472.0	cu cm/sec
Cubic ft/min	0.1247	gal/sec
Cubic ft/min	0.4720	L/sec
Cubic ft/sec	2.22222	cu yd/min
Cubic in. (U.S.)	4.65025×10^{-4}	bushels (U.S.)
Cubic in. (British)	16.3870253	cu cm
Cubic in. (U.S.)	16.387162	cu cm
Cubic in. (British)	5.7870×10^{-4}	cu ft (British)
Cubic in. (U.S.)	5.78704×10^{-4}	cu ft (U.S.)
Cubic in. (U.S.)	1.63871×10^{-5}	cu m
Cubic in. (U.S.)	2.143347×10^{-5}	cu yards
Cubic in. (U.S.)	4.43322	drams (fluid)
Cubic in. (U.S.)	0.0043290	gallons (U.S.)
Cubic in. (U.S.)	0.0163868	liters
Cubic in. (U.S.)	0.5541	ounces (fluid) (U.S.)
Cubic in. (U.S.)	0.00186010	pecks (U.S.)
Cubic in. (U.S.)	0.0297616	pints (U.S., dry)
Cubic in. (U.S.)	0.0148808	quarts (U.S., dry)
Cubic in. (U.S.)	0.017316	quarts (U.S., liquid)
Cubic km	1×10^{9}	cu m
Cubic m	28.3776	bushels (U.S.)
Cubic m	1×10^{6}	cu cm
Cubic m	35.314445	cu ft (U.S.)
Cubic m	61023	cu in.
Cubic m	1.3079428	cu yd (U.S.)
Cubic m	999.973	liters
Cubic m	2113.4	pints (U.S., liquid)
Cubic m	1056.7	quarts (U.S., liquid)
Cubic mm	6.1023×10^{-5}	cu in.
Cubic mm	1×10^{-9}	cu m
Cubic mm	0.016231	minims (U.S.)
Cubic yd	764559.45	cu cm
Cubic yd (U.S.)	27	cu ft
Cubic yd (U.S.)	46656	cu in.
Cubic yd (U.S.)	0.76455945	cu m
Cubic yd (U.S.)	202.0	gallons (U.S.)
Cubic yd	764.54	liters
Cubic yd (U.S.)	1616	pints (U.S., liquid)
Cubic yd (U.S.)	807.9	quarts (U.S., liquid)
Days (mean solar)	24	hours (mean solar)
Days (mean solar)	1440	minutes (mean solar)
Days (mean solar)	86400	seconds (mean solar)
Days (siderial)	86164	seconds (mean solar)
Degrees	0.00277778	circumferences
Degrees	60	minutes
Degrees	1/90	quadrants
Degrees	0.0174533	radians
Degrees	0.00277778	revolutions
Degrees	3600	seconds
Degrees/sec	0.1667	revolutions/min
Degrees/sec	0.002778	revolutions/sec
Drams (apothecaries' or troy)	2.194286	drams (avoirdupois)
Drams (apothecaries' or troy)	60	grains
Drams (apothecaries' or troy)	3.8879351	grams
Drams (apothecaries' or troy)	0.1371429	ounces (avoirdupois)
Drams (apothecaries' or troy)	0.125	ounces (troy)
Drams (troy)	2.5	pennyweights
Drams (apothecaries' or troy)	0.008571429	pounds (avoirdupois)
Drams (apothecaries' or troy)	1/96	pounds (troy)
Drams (avoirdupois)	0.4557292	drams (apothecaries' or troy)

Column A	x (Column B)	= (Column C)
Drams (avoirdupois)	27.34375	grains
Drams (avoirdupois)	1.771845	grams
Drams (avoirdupois)	0.0625	ounces (avoirdupois)
Drams (avoirdupois)	0.056966146	ounces (troy)
Drams (avoirdupois)	1/256	pounds (avoirdupois)
Drams (avoirdupois)	0.0047471788	pounds (troy)
Drams (U.S., fluid or apoth.)	3.6967	cu cm
Drams (U.S., fluid or apoth.)	0.225570	cu in.
Drams (U.S., fluid or apoth.)	3.6966	milliliters
Drams (U.S., fluid or apoth.)	60	minims (U.S., fluid)
Drams (U.S., fluid or apoth.)	0.125	ounces (fluid)
Dynes	0.015368	grains
Dynes	0.00101972	grams
Dynes	2.2481×10^{-6}	pounds
Dyne-cm (torque)	1.0197×10^{-8}	kg m
Dyne-cm (torque)	7.3757×10^{-8}	lb ft
Dyne-cm (torque)	8.8511×10^{-7}	lb in.
Dynes/cm	1	ergs/sq cm
Dynes/cm	0.01	ergs/sq mm
Dynes/cm	2.5901	mg/in.
Dynes/cm	0.10197	mg/mm
Dynes/sq cm	9.8692×10^{-7}	atm
Dynes/sq cm	2.9530×10^{-5}	in. Hg at 32°F
Dynes/sq cm	4.0148×10^{-4}	in. of water at 39.2°F. (4°C.)
Dynes/sq cm	0.0101971	kg/sq m
Dynes/sq cm	7.5006×10^{-4}	mm Hg
Dynes/sq cm	0.0020886	lb/sq ft
Dynes/sq cm	1.4504×10^{-5}	lb/sq in.
Electromagnetic cgs unit of field strength	1.0000	gauss (Abs.)
Electromagnetic cgs units of magnetic permeability	8.9916×10^{20}	electrostatic cgs units of magnetic permeability
Electromagnetic cgs units of mass resistance	9.9948×10^{-6}	ohm, International-meter-gram
Electromagnetic cgs units of reluctance	1.0000	oersteds (Abs.)
Electronic charges	1.5921×10^{-20}	abcoulombs
Electronic charges	1.5921×10^{-19}	coulombs (Abs.)
Electronic charges	4.774×10^{-10}	statcoulombs
Electrons/kg	4.868×10^{-16}	statcoulombs/dyne
Electrostatic cgs units of field strength	3.33560×10^{-11}	gauss (Abs.)
Ergs	9.4805×10^{-11}	BTU (mean)
Ergs	2.3889×10^{-8}	gram calories (mean)
Ergs	2.3889×10^{-11}	kg calories (mean)
Ergs	7.3756×10^{-8}	ft lb
Ergs	0.00101972	g cm
Ergs	1×10^{-7}	joules
Ergs	1.0197×10^{-8}	kg m
Ergs/sec	5.6883×10^{-9}	BTU (mean)/min
Ergs/sec	1.4333×10^{-9}	kg calories (mean)/min
Ergs/sec	4.4254×10^{-6}	ft lb/min
Ergs/sec	7.3756×10^{-8}	ft lb/sec
Ergs/sec	1.3410×10^{-10}	horse power
Ergs/sec	1×10^{-10}	KW
Ergs/sec	1×10^{-7}	watts
Ergs/sq cm	1	dynes/cm
Ergs/sq cm	0.01	ergs/sq mm
Ergs/sq mm	100	dynes/cm
Ergs/sq mm	100	ergs/sq cm
Faradays	9.6500×10^{4}	coulombs (Abs.)
Faradays	9.6507×10^{4}	coulombs (International)
Faradays/kg	2.9507×10^{8}	statcoulombs/dyne
Faradays/sec	96500	amperes (Abs.)
Farads (Abs.)	1×10^{-9}	Abfarads
Farads (Abs.)	1.00052	farads (International)
Farads (Abs.)	1×10^{6}	microfarads
Farads (Abs.)	8.98776×10^{11}	statfarads
Farads (International)	0.99948	farads (Abs.)
Fathoms	6	feet
Feet (U.S.)	30.48006096	centimeters
Feet (U.S.)	0.3048006096	meters
Feet (U.S.)	1.6447×10^{-4}	miles (nautical)
Feet (U.S.)	1.893939×10^{-4}	miles (statute)
Feet (U.S.)	473404	wave lengths of red line of cadmium
Feet of water at 39.2°F. (4°C.)	0.029499	atm
Feet of water at 39.2°F. (4°C.)	0.88265	in. Hg at 32°F. (0°C.)

Column A	x Column B	= Column C
Feet of water at 39.2°F (4°C.)	304.79	kg/sq m
Feet of water at 39.2°F (4°C.)	0.43352	lb/sq in.
Feet of water at 39.2°F (4°C.)	62.427	lb/sq ft
Feet/min	0.508001	cm/sec
Feet/min	0.01829	km/hr
Feet/min	0.00508001	mi/sec
Feet/min	0.011364	m/hr
Feet/sec	1.0973	km/hr
Feet/sec	0.5921	knots/hr
Feet/sec	18.29	m/min
Feet/sec	0.6818	mi/hr
Feet/sec	0.011364	mi/min
Feet/sec²	1.0973	km/hr/sec
Foot candles	10.764	lumens/sq m
Foot pounds	0.32389	gram calories (mean)
Foot pounds	4.7253×10^{-4}	cu ft atm
Foot pounds	1.35582×10^{7}	ergs
Foot pounds	1.3825×10^{4}	g cm
Foot pounds	5.0505×10^{-7}	horse power hr
Foot pounds	1.35582	joules (Abs.)
Foot pounds	0.138255	kg m
Foot pounds	3.7662×10^{-7}	KW hr
Foot pounds	0.013381	L atm
Foot pounds/min	2.2597×10^{-5}	KW
Foot pounds/sec	0.0018182	horse power
Foot pounds/sec	0.00135582	KW
Foot pounds/sec	1.35582	watts (Abs.)
Gallons (U.S.)	3785.4	cu cm
Gallons (U.S.)	0.13368	cu ft
Gallons (U.S.)	231	cu in.
Gallons (U.S.)	0.0037854	cu m
Gallons (U.S.)	0.004951	cu yd
Gallons (U.S.)	3.78533	liters
Gallons (U.S.)	61440	minims
Gallons (U.S.)	128	ounces (U.S., fluid)
Gallons (U.S.)	8	pints (U.S., liquid)
Gallons (U.S.)	8.3378	pounds (avoirdupois) of water at 62°F (16.7°C)
Gallons (U.S.)	4	quarts (U.S., liquid)
Gallons (U.S.) water/min	6.0086	tons water/24 hours
Gallons (U.S.)/min	8.0208	cu ft/hr
Gallons (U.S.)/min	0.002228	cu ft/sec
Gallons (U.S.)/min	0.06308	L/sec
Grains	63.5453	dynes
Grains	0.064798918	grams
Grains	64.798918	milligrams
Grains	0.0022857	ounces (avoirdupois)
Grains	0.0020833	ounces (troy)
Grains	1/7000	pounds (avoirdupois)
Grains	1/5760	pounds (troy)
Grams	980.665	dynes
Grams	15.4324	grains
Grams	1×10^{6}	micrograms
Grams	1000	milligrams
Grams	0.0352739	ounces (avoirdupois)
Grams	0.0321507	ounces (troy)
Grams	0.00220462	pounds (avoirdupois)
Grams	0.00267923	pounds (troy)
Grams	1×10^{-6}	tons (metric)
Gram centimeters	2.3427×10^{-5}	gram calories (mean)
Gram centimeters	980.665	ergs
Gram centimeters	7.233×10^{-5}	ft lb
Gram centimeters	9.80665×10^{-5}	joules (Abs.)
Gram centimeters	1×10^{-5}	kg m
Gram centimeters/sec	9.80665×10^{-5}	watts (Abs.)
Gram sq cm (moment of inertia)	2.37305×10^{-6}	lb/sq ft
Gram sq cm (moment of inertia)	3.4172×10^{-4}	lb/sq in.
Grams/cu cm	62.43	lb/cu ft
Grams/cu cm	0.03613	lb/cu in.
Grams/cu cm	8.3454	lb/gal (U.S.)
Grams/cu m	0.35757	grains/cu ft
Grams/L	58.417	grains/gal (U.S.)
Grams/L	1000	parts per million
Grams/L	0.062427	lb/cu ft
Grams/L	8.345	lb/1000 gal (U.S.)
Grams/ml	0.999973	g/cu cm
Grams/sq cm	9.6784×10^{-4}	atm
Grams/sq cm	980.665	dynes/sq cm
Grams/sq cm	10	kg/sq m
Grams/sq cm	0.73556	mm Hg at 0°C
Grams/sq cm	2.04817	lb/sq ft

Column A	x Column B	= Column C
Grams/sq cm	0.0142234	lb/sq in.
Gravity	980.665	cm/sec²
Gravity	32.174	ft/sec²
Hectares	2.471044	acres (U.S.)
Hectares	10,000	sq m
Hectares	11959.85	sq yd (U.S.)
Horse power	42.418	BTU (mean)/min
Horse power	10.688	kg calories (mean)/min
Horse power	33,000	ft lb/min
Horse power	550	ft lb/sec
Horse power	1.0139	horse power (metric)
Horse power	0.74570	KW
Horse power	745.70	watts
Horse power (metric)	32549	ft lb/min
Horse power (metric)	0.98632	horse power (U.S.)
Horse power (metric)	75	kg m/sec
Horse power hr	641.304	kg calories (mean)
Horse power hr	1.9800×10^{6}	ft lb
Horse power hr	2.6845×10^{6}	joules (Abs.)
Horse power hr	2.7374×10^{5}	kg m
Horse power hr	0.7457	KW hr
Hours (mean solar)	0.041667	days (mean solar)
Hours (mean solar)	0.0059524	weeks
Inches (U.S.)	2.5400×10^{8}	angstrom units
Inches (U.S.)	2.540005	centimeters
Inches (U.S.)	1.57828×10^{-5}	miles
Inches (U.S.)	39450.45	wave length of the red line of cadmium
Inches Hg at 32°F	0.033421	atm
Inches Hg at 32°F	3.38639×10^{4}	dynes/sq cm
Inches Hg at 32°F	345.31	kg/sq m
Inches Hg at 32°F	70.727	lb/sq ft
Inches of water at 39.2°F (4°C)	0.0024583	atm
Inches of water at 39.2°F (4°C)	2490.82	dynes/sq cm
Inches of water at 39.2°F (4°C)	25.399	kg/sq m
Inches of water at 39.2°F (4°C)	5.2022	lb/sq ft
Joules (Abs.)	9.480×10^{-4}	BTU (mean)
Joules (Abs.)	0.23895	gram calories (mean)
Joules (Abs.)	0.23918	gram calories (20°C)
Joules (Abs.)	2.3889×10^{-4}	kg calories (mean)
Joules (Abs.)	3.485×10^{-4}	cu ft atm
Joules (Abs.)	1×10^{7}	ergs
Joules (Abs.)	0.73756	ft lb
Joules (Abs.)	1.0197×10^{4}	g cm
Joules (Abs.)	3.72508×10^{-7}	horse power hr
Joules (Abs.)	0.999680	joules (International)
Joules (Abs.)	0.101972	kg m
Joules (Abs.)	2.77778×10^{-7}	KW hr
Joules (Abs.)	0.0098689	L atm
Joules/°C	5.2679×10^{-4}	BTU (60°F)/°F
Joules/°C	0.23889	gram calories/°C
Joules/electron	6.2811×10^{19}	joules/abcoulomb
Joules/electron/°C	6.2811×10^{18}	joules/coulombs/°C
Joules/faraday	1.0363×10^{-4}	joules/abcoulomb
Joules/faraday/°C	1.0363×10^{-5}	joules/coulomb/°C
Joules/gram/°C	0.23889	gram calories (mean)/g/°C
Joule seconds	1.5258×10^{33}	quanta
Joule seconds/N_0*	2.5173×10^{9}	quanta
Kilograms	9.80665×10^{5}	dynes
Kilograms	2.204622341	pounds (avoirdupois)
Kilograms	2.6792285	pounds (troy)
Kilogram meters	0.00929667	BTU (mean)
Kilogram meters	2.3427	gram calories (mean)
Kilogram meters	0.0034177	cu ft atm
Kilogram meters	9.80665×10^{7}	ergs
Kilogram meters	232.71	foot poundals
Kilogram meters	7.2330	ft lb
Kilogram meters	3.6529×10^{-6}	horse power hr
Kilogram meters	2.72407×10^{-6}	KW hr
Kilograms/m	0.67197	lb/ft
Kilograms/sq cm	73.556	cm Hg at 0°C
Kilograms/sq cm	14.223	lb/sq in.
Kilograms/sq m	9.6777×10^{-5}	atm
Kilograms/sq m	98.0665	dynes/sq cm
Kilograms/sq m	0.0032809	ft of water
Kilograms/sq m	0.1	g/sq cm
Kilograms/sq m	0.0028959	in. Hg
Kilograms/sq m	0.073556	mm Hg
Kilograms/sq m	0.204817	lb/sq ft
Kilograms/sq m	0.00142234	lb/sq in.
Kilograms/sq mm	9.80665×10^{7}	dynes/sq cm
Kiloliters	35.317	cu ft

* Avogadro's number.

Column A	x	Column B	=	Column C
Kilometers	3280.83			feet
Kilometers	0.539593			miles (nautical)
Kilometers	0.6213699495			miles (U.S.)
Kilometers	0.1			myriameters
Kilometers	1093.6			yards
Kilometers/hr	27.7778			cm/sec
Kilometers/hr	54.68			ft/min
Kilometers/hr	0.9113			ft/sec
Kilometers/hr	0.5396			knots/hr
Kilometers/hr	16.667			m/min
Kilometers/hr	0.27778			m/sec
Kilometers/hr/sec	27.778			cm/sec^2
Kilometers/hr/sec	0.9113			ft/sec^2
Kilometers/hr/sec	0.27778			m/sec^2
Kilometers/min	1666.7			cm/sec
Kilometers/min	37.2822			mi/hr
Kilowatt hours	3413.0			BTU (mean)
Kilowatt hours	8.6001×10^5			gram calories (mean)
Kilowatt hours	2.6552×10^6			ft lb
Kilowatt hours	1.3410			horse power hr
Kilowatt hours	3.6000×10^6			joules (Abs.)
Kilowatt hours	3.6709×10^5			kg m
Kilowatts	56.884			BTU (mean)/min
Kilowatts	14.3334			kg calories (mean)/min
Kilowatts	2.6552×10^6			ft lb/hr
Kilowatts	1.3410			horse power
Knots/hr	51.479			cm/sec
Knots/hr	1.15155			mi/hr
Lamberts	0.3183			candles/sq cm
Lamberts	2.054			candles/sq in.
Lamberts	1			lumens emitted/sq cm (perfectly diffusing surface)
Liter atmospheres (normal)	24.206			gram calories (mean)
Liter atmospheres (normal)	0.035316			cu ft atm
Liters	0.028378			bushels (U.S.)
Liters	0.035316			cu ft
Liters	61.025			cu in.
Liters	0.001000027			cu m
Liters	0.0013080			cu yd
Liters	270.5179			drams (U.S., fluid)
Liters	0.26417762			gallons (U.S.)
Liters	33.8143			ounces (U.S., fluid)
Liters	1.816192			pints (U.S., dry)
Liters	2.11336			pints (U.S., liquid)
Liters	0.908096			quarts (U.S., dry)
Liters	1.056681869			quarts (U.S., liquid)
Liters/cm/da	0.011574			sq cm/sec
Liters/min	5.886×10^{-4}			cu ft/sec
Liters/min	0.004403			gal/sec
Liters/sec	2.11896			cu ft/min
Liters/sec	15.8507			gallons (U.S.)/min
Lumens	0.001496			watts
Lumens/sq ft	1			foot candles
Lumens/sq ft	10.764			lumens/sq m
Lumens/sq m	0.092902			foot candles (lumens)/sq ft
Lumens/sq m	1×10^{-4}			phots
Megmhos	0.001			abmhos
Megmhos	2.540			megmhos/cu in.
Megmhos/cu in.	0.39370			megmhos/cu cm
Mercury at 0°C	13.5951			g/cu cm
Meter candles	1.000			lumens/sq m
Meters	1×10^{10}			angstrom units
Meters	3.280833333			feet (U.S.)
Meters	39.3700			inches (U.S.)
Meters	5.39593×10^{-4}			miles (nautical)
Meters	6.2137×10^{-4}			miles (statute)
Meters	1×10^9			millimicrons
Meters	1×10^{12}			millionth microns
Meters	1.55316412×10^6			wave lengths of the red line of cadmium
Meters	1.093611			yards (U.S.)
Meters/min	1.6667			cm/sec
Meters/min	0.05468			ft/sec
Meters/min	0.06			km/hr
Meters/min	0.03728			mi/hr
Meters/sec	196.8			ft/min
Meters/sec	3.6000			km/hr
Meters/sec	0.060000			km/min
Meters/sec	2.2369			mi/hr
Meters/sec	0.03728			mi/min
Meters/sec^2	3.6			km/hr/sec
Meters/sec^2	2.2369			mi/hr/sec

Column A	x	Column B	=	Column C
Mhos, International/cu cm	0.99948			mhos (Abs.)/cu cm
Microfarads	1×10^{-15}			abfarads
Microns	1×10^4			angstrom units
Microns	1×10^{-4}			centimeters
Microns	3.937×10^{-5}			inches
Microns	0.001			millimeters
Microvolts/°F	1.8000			microvolts/°C
Miles (nautical)	6080.20			feet
Miles (nautical)	1.85325			kilometers
Miles (U.S., statute)	63360			inches
Miles (U.S., statute)	5280			feet
Miles (U.S., statute)	1.609347219			kilometers
Miles/hr	44.7041			cm/sec
Miles/hr	88			ft/min
Miles/hr	1.4667			ft/sec
Miles/hr	0.8684			knots/hr
Miles/hr	26.82			m/min
Miles/hr/min	0.74507			cm/sec^2
Miles/hr/sec	44.704			cm/sec^2
Miles/hr/sec	1.4667			ft/sec^2
Miles/hr/sec	0.44704			m/sec^2
Miles/min	2682.2			cm/sec
Miles/min	88			ft/sec
Milligrams	0.01543236			grains
Milligrams	5.64383×10^{-4}			drams (avoirdupois)
Milligrams	2.57206×10^{-4}			drams (troy)
Milligrams	3.52739×10^{-5}			ounces (avoirdupois)
Milligrams	3.215074×10^{-5}			ounces (troy)
Milligrams	2.2046×10^{-6}			pounds (avoirdupois)
Milligrams	2.67923×10^{-6}			pounds (troy)
Milligrams/in.	0.38609			dynes/cm
Milligrams/L	1.0			parts per million
Milligrams/mm	9.80665			dynes/cm
Millilamberts	0.929			lumens emitted/sq ft (with perfect diffusion)
Milliliters	1.000027			cu cm
Milliliters	0.061025			cu in.
Milliliters	0.2705179			drams (U.S., fluid)
Milliliters	16.2311			minims (U.S.)
Milliliters	0.0338147			ounces (U.F., fluid)
Millimeters	0.0393700			inches (U.S.)
Millimeters Hg at 0°C	0.00131579			atm
Millimeters Hg at 0°C	1333.22			dynes/sq cm
Millimeters Hg at 0°C	1.3595			g/sq cm
Millimeters Hg at 0°C	13.595			kg/sq m
Millimeters Hg at 0°C	1000			microns Hg at 0°C
Millimeters Hg at 0°C	2.7845			lb/sq ft
Millimeters Hg at 0°C	0.019337			lb/sq in.
Millimicrons (micromillimeters)	10			anstrom units
Millimicrons	1×10^{-7}			centimeters
Minims (U.S., fluid)	0.061612			cubic cm
Minims (U.S.)	61.612			cubic cm
Minims (U.S.)	1/60			drams (U.S., fluid)
Minims (U.S.)	0.0616102			milliliters
Minims (U.S.)	1/480			ounces (U.S., fluid)
Minutes (time)	6.94444×10^{-4}			days
Minutes (time)	9.9206×10^{-5}			weeks
Months (mean calender)	30.4202			days
Months (mean calender)	730.085			hours
Months (mean calender)	43805.1			minutes
Months (mean calender)	2.6283×10^6			seconds
Oersteds (Abs.)	1.00052			oersteds (International)
Ohm-mile-pounds	1.7513×10^{-4}			ohm-meter-grams
Ohms (Abs.)	0.99948			ohms (International)
Ounces (avoirdupois)	16			drams (avoirdupois)
Ounces (avoirdupois)	7.29166			drams (troy or apoth.)
Ounces (avoirdupois)	437.5			grains
Ounces (avoirdupois)	28.349527			grams
Ounces (avoirdupois)	0.9114583			ounces (troy or apoth.)
Ounces (avoirdupois)	1/16			pounds (avoirdupois)
Ounces (avoirdupois)	0.075954861			pounds (troy)
Ounces (troy or apoth.)	17.55428			drams (avoirdupois)
Ounces (troy or apoth.)	8			drams (troy or apoth.)
Ounces (troy or apoth.)	480			grains
Ounces (troy or apoth.)	31.103481			grams
Ounces (troy or apoth.)	1.09714			ounces (avoirdupois)
Ounces (troy or apoth.)	0.06857143			pounds (avoirdupois)
Ounces (troy or apoth.)	1/12			pounds (troy)
Ounces (U.S., fluid)	29.5737			cu cm
Ounces (U.S., fluid)	1.80469			cu in.
Ounces (U.S., fluid)	8			drams (fluid)
Ounces (U.S., fluid)	1/128			gallons (U.S.)
Ounces (U.S., fluid)	0.0295729			liters
Ounces (U.S., fluid)	480			minims (U.S.)
Ounces (U.S., fluid)	1/16			pints (U.S., liquid)

Column A	x	Column B	=	Column C	Column A	x	Column B	=	Column C
Pints (U.S., dry)		0.015625		bushels (U.S.)	Quarts (U.S., dry)		0.038889		cubic ft
Pints (U.S., dry		550.61		cu cm	Quarts (U.S., dry)		67.2006		cubic in.
Pints (U.S., dry		33.6003		cu in.	Quarts (U.S., dry)		1.10120		liters
Pints (U.S., dry		0.550599		liters	Quarts (U.S., dry)		0.125		pecks (U.S.)
Pints (U.S., dry		0.5		quarts (U.S., dry)	Quarts (U.S., dry)		2		pints (dry)
Pints (U.S., liquid)		473.179		cu cm	Quarts (U.S., liquid)		946.358		cubic cm
Pints (U.S., liquid)		0.016711		cu ft	Quarts (U.S., liquid)		57.749		cubic in.
Pints (U.S., liquid)		28.875		cu in.	Quarts (U.S., liquid)		0.033420		cu ft
Pints (U.S., liquid)		6.1881×10^{-4}		cu yd	Quarts (U.S., liquid)		256.00		drams (fluid)
Pints (U.S., liquid)		128		drams (fluid)	Quarts (U.S., liquid)		0.25		gallons (U.S.)
Pints (U.S., liquid)		0.125		gallons (U.S.)	Quarts (U.S., liquid)		0.946333		liters
Pints (U.S., liquid)		0.473168		liters	Quarts (U.S., liquid)		32		ounces (fluid, U.S.)
Pints (U.S., liquid)		7680		minims (U.S.)	Quarts (U.S., liquid)		1.96841		quintals (metric)
Pints (U.S., liquid)		16		ounces (U.S., fluid)	Square centimeters		0.0010764		sq ft
Pints (U.S., liquid)		0.5		quarts (U.S., liquid)	Square centimeters		0.15500		sq in.
Planck's quanta		6.554×10^{-27}		erg seconds	Square centimeters		0.00247107		sq. links (Gunter's)
Poises		1.000		g/cm/sec	Square centimeters		1×10^{-4}		sq m
Pounds (avoirdupois)		256		drams (avoirdupois)	Square centimeters		100		sq mm
Pounds (avoirdupois)		116.6667		drams (troy)	Square centimeters		1.1960×10^{-4}		sq yd
Pounds (avoirdupois)		4.44852×10^{5}		dynes	Square centimeters/day		1.1574×10^{-5}		sq cm/sec
Pounds (avoirdupois)		7000		grains	Square feet (U.S.)		2.29568×10^{-5}		acres
Pounds (avoirdupois)		453.5924277		grams	Square feet (U.S.)		929.0341		sq cm
Pounds (avoirdupois)		0.4535924277		kilograms	Square feet (U.S.)		144		sq in.
Pounds (avoirdupois)		16		ounces (avoirdupois)	Square feet (U.S.)		0.09290341		sq m
Pounds (avoirdupois)		14.5833		ounces (troy)	Square feet (U.S.)		3.58701×10^{-8}		sq mi
Pounds		32.174		poundals	Square feet (U.S.)		1/9		sq yd (U.S.)
Pounds (avoirdupois)		1.2152778		pounds (troy)	Square inches (U.S.)		6.4516258		sq cm
Pounds (avoirdupois)		4.464286×10^{-4}		tons (long)	Square inches (U.S.)		1/144		sq ft (U.S.)
Pounds (avoirdupois)		4.5359243×10^{-4}		tons (metric)	Square inches (U.S.)		6.4516258×10^{-4}		sq m
Pounds (avoirdupois)		5×10^{-4}		tons (short)	Square inches (U.S.)		1/1296		sq yd (U.S.)
Pounds (troy)		210.6514		drams (avoirdupois)	Square kilometers		247.1044		acres (U.S.)
Pounds (troy)		96		drams (troy)	Square kilometers		1.0764×10^{7}		sq ft
Pounds (troy)		5760		grains	Square kilometers		1×10^{6}		sq m
Pounds (troy)		373.2418		grams	Square kilometers		0.3861006		sq mi(U.S.)
Pounds (troy)		13.165714		ounces (avoirdupois)	Square kilometers		1.1960×10^{6}		sq yd
Pounds (troy)		12		ounces (troy)	Square meters		2.471044×10^{-4}		acres (U.S.)
Pounds (troy)		0.822857		pounds (avoirdupois)	Square meters		1×10^{4}		sq cm
Pounds (troy)		3.6735×10^{-4}		tons (long)	Square meters		10.76387		sq ft (U.S.)
Pounds (troy)		3.7324×10^{-4}		tons (metric)	Square meters		1550.0		sq. in.
Pounds (troy)		4.1143×10^{-4}		tons (short)	Square meters		1×10^{-6}		sq km
Pounds of water (62°F.)		0.016033		cu ft	Square meters		1×10^{6}		sq mm
Pounds of water		27.68		cu in.	Square meters		3.8610×10^{-7}		sq mi
Pounds of water		0.1198		gallons (U.S.)	Square meters		1.195985		sq yd (U.S.)
Pounds/cu in.		27.68		g/cu cm	Square miles		640		acres
Pounds/ft		1.48816		kg/m	Square miles		2.78784×10^{7}		sq ft
Pounds/in.		178.6		g/cm	Square miles		2.589998		sq km
Pounds/sq ft (moment of inertia)		4.2140×10^{5}		g/sq cm	Square miles		2589998		sq m
					Square miles		3.0976×10^{6}		sq yd
Pounds/sq ft (moment of inertia)		421.40		kg/sq cm	Square millimeters		0.01		sq cm
					Square millimeters		0.0015500		sq in.
Pounds/sq ft (moment of inertia)		144		lb/sq in.	Square millimeters		1×10^{-6}		sq m
Pound feet (torque)		1.3558×10^{7}		dyne cm	Square mils		6.4516×10^{-6}		sq cm
Pounds/sq in. (moment of inertia		2926.4		g/sq cm	Square mils		1×10^{-6}		sq in.
Pounds/sq in. (moment of inertia		2.9264		kg/sq cm	Square mils		6.4516×10^{-4}		sq mm
Pounds/sq in. (moment of inertia)		0.00694444		lb/sq ft	Square yards (U.S.)		2.06612×10^{-4}		acres (U.S.)
Pound inches (torque)		1.1298×10^{6}		dyne cm	Square yards (U.S.)		8361.31		sq cm
Pounds of water/min		0.016021		cu ft/min	Square yards (U.S.)		9		sq ft
Pounds of water/min		2.670×10^{-4}		cu ft/sec	Square yards (U.S.)		1296		sq in.
Pounds/cu ft		0.016018		g/cu cm	Square yards (U.S.)		0.83613		sq m
Pounds/cu ft		16.018		kg/cu m	Square yards (U.S.)		3.22831×10^{-7}		sq mi
Pounds/cu ft		5.787×10^{-4}		lb/cu in.	Statamperes		3.33560×10^{-10}		amperes (Abs.)
Pounds/cu in.		27.6800		g/cu cm	Statcoulombs		3.33560×10^{-10}		coulombs (Abs.)
Pounds/cu in.		2.768×10^{4}		kg/cu m	Statcoulombs		2.0947×10^{9}		electronic charges
Pounds/gal (British)		0.099776		g/cu cm	Statcoulombs/kg		1.0197×10^{-6}		statcoulombs/dyne
Pounds/gal (U.S.)		0.119826		g/cu cm	Statcoulombs/lb		2.2481×10^{-6}		statcoulombs/dyne
Pounds/sq ft		4.7252×10^{-4}		atm	Statfarads		1.11263×10^{-12}		farads (Abs.)
Pounds/sq ft		478.78		dynes/sq cm	Stathenries		8.98776×10^{11}		henries (Abs.)
Pounds/sq ft		0.016018		ft of water at 39.1°F	Statmhos		1.11263×10^{-12}		mohs, International/cu cm
Pounds/sq ft		0.48824		g/sq cm					
Pounds/sq ft		4.8824		kg/sq m	Statohms		8.98776×10^{11}		ohms (Abs.)
Pounds/sq ft		0.35913		mm of Hg at 0°C	Statvolts		299.796		volts (Abs.)
Pounds/sq ft		0.0069445		lb/sq in.	Tons (long)		1016.0470		kilograms
Pounds/sq in.		0.068046		atm	Tons (long)		2240		pounds (avoirdupois)
Pounds/sq in.		68946		dynes/sq cm	Tons (long)		2722.22		pounds (troy)
Pounds/sq in.		70.307		g/sq cm	Tons (metric)		1000		kilograms
Pounds/sq in.		27.673		in. of water at 39.2°F (4°C)	Tons (metric)		2204.62		pounds (avoirdupois)
					Tons (short)		8.8964×10^{8}		dynes
Pounds/sq in.		0.070307		kg/sq cm	Tons (short)		907.1846		kilograms
Pounds/sq in.		703.07		kg/sq m	Tons (short)		2000		pounds (avoirdupois)
Pounds/sq in.		51.715		mm of Hg	Tons (short)		2430.56		pounds (troy)
Pounds/sq in.		144		lb/sq ft	Tons (short)		0.892857		tons (long)
Quarts (U.S., dry)		0.03125		bushels (U.S.)	Tons (short)		0.907185		tons (metric)
Quarts (U.S., dry)		1101.23		cubic cm	Tons (short)/sq ft		0.94509		atmospheres
					Volts (Abs.)		1×10^{8}		abvolts
					Volts/°C		1.0000		joules/coulomb/°C
					Volts (Abs.)		0.0033356		statvolts
					Volts (Abs.)		0.99955		volts (International)

CONVERSION FACTORS (Concluded)

Column A	x	Column B	=	Column C	Column A	x	Column B	=	Column C
Watt hours		3.4130		BTU (mean)	Watts (Abs.)		1		joules/sec
Watt hours		860.01		calories, g (mean)	Watts (International)		1.00032		watts (Abs.)
Watt hours		0.86001		Calories, kg (mean)	Watts/sq in.		8.1913		BTU/sq ft/min
Watt hours		2655.3		foot pounds	Watts/sq in.		6372.6		ft lb/sq ft/min
Watt hours		0.0013410		horse power hr	Watts/sq in.		0.19310		horse power
Watt hours		3600		joules	Weeks		168		hours
Watt hours		367.09		kg meters	Weeks		10080		minutes
Watts (Abs.)		0.014333		Calories, kg(mean)/min	Weeks		604800		seconds
Watts (Abs.)		1 x 10^7		ergs/sec	Yards (U.S.)		91.440183		centimeters
Watts (Abs.)		44.254		ft lb/min	Yards (U.S.)		5.68182 x 10^{-4}		miles
Watts (Abs.)		0.73756		ft lb/sec	Years (sidereal)		365.256		days (mean solar)
Watts (Abs.)		0.0013410		horse power	Years (sidereal)		8766.144		hours (mean solar)
Watts (Abs.)		0.0013596		horse power (metric)					

ATOMIC WEIGHTS
Values in brackets are mass numbers of most stable isotopes.

Element	Symbol	Atomic No.	Atomic Wt.	Element	Symbol	Atomic No.	Atomic Wt.	Element	Symbol	Atomic No.	Atomic Wt.	Element	Symbol	Atomic No.	Atomic Wt.
Actinium	Ac	89	227	Erbium	Er	68	167.2	Neodymium	Nd	60	144.27	Scandium	Sc	21	44.96
Aluminum	Al	13	26.98	Europium	Eu	63	152.0	Neon	Ne	10	20.183	Selenium	Se	34	78.96
Americium	Am	95	[241]	Fluorine	F	9	19.00	Neptunium	Np	93	[237]	Silicon	Si	14	28.09
Antimony	Sb	51	121.76	Francium	Fr	87	[223]	Nickel	Ni	28	58.69	Silver	Ag	47	107.880
Argon	A	18	39.944	Gadolinium	Gd	64	156.9	Niobium (Columbium)	Nb	41	92.91	Sodium	Na	11	22.997
Arsenic	As	33	74.91	Gallium	Ga	31	69.72	Nitrogen	N	7	14.008	Strontium	Sr	38	87.63
Astatine	At	85	[210]	Germanium	Ge	32	72.60	Osmium	Os	76	190.2	Sulfur	S	16	32.066
Barium	Ba	56	137.36	Gold	Au	79	197.2	Oxygen	O	8	16.0000	Tantalum	Ta	73	180.88
Berkelium	Bk	97	[243]	Hafnium	Hf	72	178.6	Palladium	Pd	46	106.7	Technetium	Tc	43	[99]
Beryllium	Be	4	9.013	Helium	He	2	4.003	Phosphorus	P	15	30.975	Tellurium	Te	52	127.61
Bismuth	Bi	83	209.00	Holmium	Ho	67	164.94	Platinum	Pt	78	195.23	Terbium	Tb	65	159.2
Boron	B	5	10.82	Hydrogen	H	1	1.0080	Plutonium	Pu	94	[239]	Thallium	Tl	81	204.39
Bromine	Br	35	79.916	Indium	In	49	114.76	Polonium	Po	84	210	Thorium	Th	90	232.12
Cadmium	Cd	48	112.41	Iodine	I	53	126.91	Potassium	K	19	39.100	Thulium	Tm	69	169.4
Calcium	Ca	20	40.08	Iridium	Ir	77	193.1	Praseodymium	Pr	59	140.92	Tin	Sn	50	118.70
Californium	Cf	98	[244]	Iron	Fe	26	55.85	Promethium	Pm	61	[147]	Titanium	Ti	22	47.90
Carbon	C	6	12.010	Krypton	Kr	36	83.80	Protactinium	Pa	91	231	Tungsten (Wolfram)	W	74	183.92
Cerium	Ce	58	140.13	Lanthanum	La	57	138.92	Radium	Ra	88	226.05	Uranium	U	92	238.07
Cesium	Cs	55	132.91	Lead	Pb	82	207.21	Radon	Rn	86	222	Vanadium	V	23	50.95
Chlorine	Cl	17	35.457	Lithium	Li	3	6.940	Rhenium	Re	75	186.31	Xenon	Xe	54	131.3
Chromium	Cr	24	52.01	Lutetium	Lu	71	174.99	Rhodium	Rh	45	102.91	Ytterbium	Yb	70	173.04
Cobalt	Co	27	58.94	Magnesium	Mg	12	24.32	Rubidium	Rb	37	85.48	Yttrium	Y	39	88.92
Copper	Cu	29	63.54	Manganese	Mn	25	54.93	Ruthenium	Ru	44	101.7	Zinc	Zn	30	65.38
Curium	Cm	96	[242]	Mercury	Hg	80	200.61	Samarium	Sm	62	150.43	Zirconium	Zr	40	91.22
Dysprosium	Dy	66	162.46	Molybdenum	Mo	42	95.95								

WEIGHTS OF MULTIPLES

C = 12.01	H = 1.008	O = 16.000	N = 14.008	S = 32.066	P = 30.975	K = 39.100	Na = 22.997	Ca = 40.08	Mg = 24.32
2C = 24.02	2H = 2.016	2O = 32.000	2N = 28.016	2S = 64.132	2P = 61.950	2K = 78.200	2Na = 45.994	2Ca = 80.16	2Mg = 48.64
3C = 36.03	3H = 3.024	3O = 48.000	3N = 42.024	3S = 96.198	3P = 92.925	3K = 117.300	3Na = 68.991	3Ca = 120.24	3Mg = 72.96
4C = 48.04	4H = 4.032	4O = 64.000	4N = 56.032	4S = 128.264	4P = 123.900	4K = 156.400	4Na = 91.998	4Ca = 160.32	4Mg = 97.28
5C = 60.05	5H = 5.040	5O = 80.000	5N = 70.040	5S = 160.330	5P = 154.875	5K = 195.500	5Na = 118.985	5Ca = 200.40	5Mg = 121.60
6C = 72.06	6H = 6.048	6O = 96.000	6N = 84.048	6S = 192.396	6P = 185.850	6K = 234.600	6Na = 137.982	6Ca = 240.48	H$_2$O = 18.016
7C = 84.07	7H = 7.056	7O = 112.000	7N = 98.056	7S = 224.462	7P = 216.825	7K = 273.700	7Na = 160.979	7Ca = 280.56	2H$_2$O = 36.032
8C = 96.08	8H = 8.064	8O = 128.000	8N = 112.064	8S = 256.528	8P = 247.800	8K = 312.800	8Na = 183.976	8Ca = 320.64	3H$_2$O = 54.048
9C = 108.09	9H = 9.072	9O = 144.000	9N = 126.072	9S = 288.594	9P = 278.775	9K = 351.900	9Na = 206.973	9Ca = 360.72	4H$_2$O = 72.064
10C = 120.10	10H = 10.080	10O = 160.000	10N = 140.080	10S = 320.660	10P = 309.750	10K = 391.000	10Na = 229.970	10Ca = 400.80	5H$_2$O = 90.080

THERMOMETRIC EQUIVALENTS

$$F = \frac{9C}{5} + 32; \quad C = \frac{5\,(F-32)}{9}$$

°F ← (°C) Temp. (°F) → °C			°F ← (°C) Temp. (°F) → °C			°F ← (°C) Temp. (°F) → °C			°F ← (°C) Temp. (°F) → °C		
-40.0	- 40	-40.00	+35.6	+2	-16.67	+82.4	+28	-2.22	+129.2	+54	+12.22
-36.4	- 38	-38.89	+37.4	+3	-16.11	+84.2	+29	-1.67	+131.0	+55	+12.78
-32.8	- 36	-37.78	+39.2	+4	-15.56	+86.0	+30	-1.11	+132.8	+56	+13.33
-29.2	- 34	-36.67	+41.0	+5	-15.00	+87.8	+31	-0.56	+134.6	+57	+13.89
-25.6	- 32	-35.56	+42.8	+6	-14.44	+89.6	+32	±0.00	+136.4	+58	+14.44
-22.0	- 30	-34.44	+44.6	+7	-13.89	+91.4	+33	+0.56	+138.2	+59	+15.00
-18.4	- 28	-33.33	+46.4	+8	-13.33	+93.2	+34	+1.11	+140.0	+60	+15.56
-14.8	- 26	-32.22	+48.2	+9	-12.78	+95.0	+35	+1.67	+141.8	+61	+16.11
-11.2	- 24	-31.11	+50.0	+10	-12.22	+96.8	+36	+2.22	+143.6	+62	+16.67
-7.6	- 22	-30.00	+51.8	+11	-11.67	+98.6	+37	+2.78	+145.4	+63	+17.22
-4.0	- 20	-28.89	+53.6	+12	-11.11	+100.4	+38	+3.33	+147.2	+64	+17.78
-0.4	- 18	-27.78	+55.4	+13	-10.56	+102.2	+39	+3.89	+149.0	+65	+18.33
+3.2	- 16	-26.67	+57.2	+14	-10.00	+104.0	+40	+4.44	+150.8	+66	+18.89
+6.8	- 14	-25.56	+59.0	+15	-9.44	+105.8	+41	+5.00	+152.6	+67	+19.44
+10.4	- 12	-24.44	+60.8	+16	-8.89	+107.6	+42	+5.56	+154.4	+68	+20.00
+14.0	- 10	-23.33	+62.6	+17	-8.33	+109.4	+43	+6.11	+156.2	+69	+20.56
+17.6	- 8	-22.22	+64.4	+18	-7.78	+111.2	+44	+6.67	+158.0	+70	+21.11
+19.4	- 7	-21.67	+66.2	+19	-7.22	+113.0	+45	+7.22	+159.8	+71	+21.67
+21.2	- 6	-21.11	+68.0	+20	-6.67	+114.8	+46	+7.78	+161.6	+72	+22.22
+23.0	- 5	-20.56	+69.8	+21	-6.11	+116.6	+47	+8.33	+163.4	+73	+22.78
+24.8	- 4	-20.00	+71.6	+22	-5.56	+118.4	+48	+8.89	+165.2	+74	+23.33
+26.6	- 3	-19.44	+73.4	+23	-5.00	+120.2	+49	+9.44	+167.0	+75	+23.89
+28.4	- 2	-18.89	+75.2	+24	-4.44	+122.0	+50	+10.00	+168.8	+76	+24.44
+30.2	- 1	-18.33	+77.0	+25	-3.89	+123.8	+51	+10.56	+170.6	+77	+25.00
+32.0	+ 0	-17.78	+78.8	+26	-3.33	+125.6	+52	+11.11	+172.4	+78	+25.56
+33.8	+ 1	-17.22	+80.6	+27	-2.78	+127.4	+53	+11.67	+174.2	+79	+26.11

THERMOMETRIC EQUIVALENTS (Concluded)

°F ←	(°C) Temp. (°F)	→ °C	°F ←	(°C) Temp. (°F)	→ °C	°F ←	(°C) Temp. (°F)	→ °C	°F ←	(°C) Temp. (°F)	→ °C
+176.0	+80	+26.67	+237.2	+114	+45.56	+298.4	+148	+64.44	+359.6	+182	+83.33
+177.8	+81	+27.22	+239.0	+115	+46.11	+300.2	+149	+65.00	+361.4	+183	+83.89
+179.6	+82	+27.78	+240.8	+116	+46.67	+302.0	+150	+65.56	+363.2	+184	+84.44
+181.4	+83	+28.33	+242.6	+117	+47.22	+303.8	+151	+66.11	+365.0	+185	+85.00
+183.2	+84	+28.89	+244.4	+118	+47.78	+305.6	+152	+66.67	+366.8	+186	+85.56
+185.0	+85	+29.44	+246.2	+119	+48.33	+307.4	+153	+67.22	+368.6	+187	+86.11
+186.8	+86	+30.00	+248.0	+120	+48.89	+309.2	+154	+67.78	+370.4	+188	+86.67
+188.6	+87	+30.56	+249.8	+121	+49.44	+311.0	+155	+68.33	+372.2	+189	+87.22
+190.4	+88	+31.11	+251.6	+122	+50.00	+312.8	+156	+68.89	+374.0	+190	+87.78
+192.2	+89	+31.67	+253.4	+123	+50.56	+314.6	+157	+69.44	+375.8	+191	+88.33
+194.0	+90	+32.22	+255.2	+124	+51.11	+316.4	+158	+70.00	+377.6	+192	+88.89
+195.8	+91	+32.78	+257.0	+125	+51.67	+318.2	+159	+70.56	+379.4	+193	+89.44
+197.6	+92	+33.33	+258.8	+126	+52.22	+320.0	+160	+71.11	+381.2	+194	+90.00
+199.4	+93	+33.89	+260.6	+127	+52.78	+321.8	+161	+71.67	+383.0	+195	+90.56
+201.2	+94	+34.44	+262.4	+128	+53.33	+323.6	+162	+72.22	+384.8	+196	+91.11
+203.0	+95	+35.00	+264.2	+129	+53.89	+325.4	+163	+72.78	+386.6	+197	+91.67
+204.8	+96	+35.56	+266.0	+130	+54.44	+327.2	+164	+73.33	+388.4	+198	+92.22
+206.6	+97	+36.11	+267.8	+131	+55.00	+329.0	+165	+73.89	+390.2	+199	+92.78
+208.4	+98	+36.67	+269.6	+132	+55.56	+330.8	+166	+74.44	+392.0	+200	+93.33
+210.2	+99	+37.22	+271.4	+133	+56.11	+332.6	+167	+75.00	+393.8	+201	+93.89
+212.0	+100	+37.78	+273.2	+134	+56.67	+334.4	+168	+75.56	+395.6	+202	+94.44
+213.8	+101	+38.33	+275.0	+135	+57.22	+336.2	+169	+76.11	+397.4	+203	+95.00
+215.6	+102	+38.89	+276.8	+136	+57.78	+338.0	+170	+76.67	+399.2	+204	+95.56
+217.4	+103	+39.44	+278.6	+137	+58.33	+339.8	+171	+77.22	+401.0	+205	+96.11
+219.2	+104	+40.00	+280.4	+138	+58.89	+341.6	+172	+77.78	+402.8	+206	+96.67
+221.0	+105	+40.56	+282.2	+139	+59.44	+343.4	+173	+78.33	+404.6	+207	+97.22
+222.8	+106	+41.11	+284.0	+140	+60.00	+345.2	+174	+78.89	+406.4	+208	+97.78
+224.6	+107	+41.67	+285.8	+141	+60.56	+347.0	+175	+79.44	+408.2	+209	+98.33
+226.4	+108	+42.22	+287.6	+142	+61.11	+348.8	+176	+80.00	+410.0	+210	+98.89
+228.2	+109	+42.78	+289.4	+143	+61.67	+350.6	+177	+80.56	+411.8	+211	+99.44
+230.0	+110	+43.33	+291.2	+144	+62.22	+352.4	+178	+81.11	+413.6	+212	+100.00
+231.8	+111	+43.89	+293.0	+145	+62.78	+354.2	+179	+81.67	+415.4	+213	+100.56
+233.6	+112	+44.44	+294.8	+146	+63.33	+356.0	+180	+82.22	+417.2	+214	+101.11
+235.4	+113	+45.00	+296.6	+147	+63.89	+357.8	+181	+82.78	+419.0	+215	+101.67

APPENDIX V: LOGARITHMS AND ANTILOGARITHMS

FOUR-PLACE LOGARITHMS

N	0	1	2	3	4	5	6	7	8	9	Proportional Parts 1	2	3	4	5
10	0000	0043	0086	0128	0170	0212	0253	0294	0334	0374	4	8	12	17	21
11	0414	0453	0492	0531	0569	0607	0645	0682	0719	0755	4	8	11	15	19
12	0792	0828	0864	0899	0934	0969	1004	1038	1072	1106	3	7	10	14	17
13	1139	1173	1206	1239	1271	1303	1335	1367	1399	1430	3	6	10	13	16
14	1461	1492	1523	1553	1584	1614	1644	1673	1703	1732	3	6	9	12	15
15	1761	1790	1818	1847	1875	1903	1931	1959	1987	2014	3	6	8	11	14
16	2041	2068	2095	2122	2148	2175	2201	2227	2253	2279	3	5	8	11	13
17	2304	2330	2355	2380	2405	2430	2455	2480	2504	2529	2	5	7	10	12
18	2553	2577	2601	2625	2648	2672	2695	2718	2742	2765	2	5	7	9	12
19	2788	2810	2833	2856	2878	2900	2923	2945	2967	2989	2	4	7	9	11
20	3010	3032	3054	3075	3096	3118	3139	3160	3181	3201.	2	4	6	8	11
21	3222	3243	3263	3284	3304	3324	3345	3365	3385	3404	2	4	6	8	10
22	3424	3444	3464	3483	3502	3522	3541	3560	3579	3598	2	4	6	8	10
23	3617	3636	3655	3674	3692	3711	3729	3747	3766	3784	2	4	6	7	9
24	3802	3820	3838	3856	3874	3892	3909	3927	3945	3962	2	4	5	7	9
25	3979	3997	4014	4031	4048	4065	4082	4099	4116	4133	2	3	5	7	9
26	4150	4166	4183	4200	4216	4232	4249	4265	4281	4298	2	3	5	7	8
27	4314	4330	4346	4362	4378	4393	4409	4425	4440	4456	2	3	5	6	8
28	4472	4487	4502	4518	4533	4548	4564	4579	4594	4609	2	3	5	6	8
29	4624	4639	4654	4669	4683	4698	4713	4728	4742	4757	1	3	4	6	7
30	4771	4786	4800	4814	4829	4843	4857	4871	4886	4900	1	3	4	6	7
31	4914	4928	4942	4955	4969	4983	4997	5011	5024	5038	1	3	4	6	7
32	5051	5065	5079	5092	5105	5119	5132	5145	5159	5172	1	3	4	5	7
33	5185	5198	5211	5224	5237	5250	5263	5276	5289	5302	1	3	4	5	6
34	5315	5328	5340	5353	5366	5378	5391	5403	5416	5428	1	3	4	5	6
35	5441	5453	5465	5478	5490	5502	5514	5527	5539	5551	1	2	4	5	6
36	5563	5575	5587	5599	5611	5623	5635	5647	5658	5670	1	2	4	5	6
37	5682	5694	5705	5717	5729	5740	5752	5763	5775	5786	1	2	3	5	6
38	5798	5809	5821	5832	5843	5855	5866	5877	5888	5899	1	2	3	5	6
39	5911	5922	5933	5944	5955	5966	5977	5988	5999	6010	1	2	3	4	5
40	6021	6031	6042	6053	6064	6075	6085	6096	6107	6117	1	2	3	4	5
41	6128	6138	6149	6160	6170	6180	6191	6201	6212	6222	1	2	3	4	5
42	6232	6243	6253	6263	6274	6284	6294	6304	6314	6325	1	2	3	4	5
43	6335	6345	6355	6365	6375	6385	6395	6405	6415	6425	1	2	3	4	5
44	6435	6444	6454	6464	6474	6484	6493	6503	6513	6522	1	2	3	4	5
45	6532	6542	6551	6561	6571	6580	6590	6599	6609	6618	1	2	3	4	5
46	6628	6637	6646	6656	6665	6675	6684	6693	6702	6712	1	2	3	4	5
47	6721	6730	6739	6749	6758	6767	6776	6785	6794	6803	1	2	3	4	5
48	6812	6821	6830	6839	6848	6857	6866	6875	6884	6893	1	2	3	4	4
49	6902	6911	6920	6928	6937	6946	6955	6964	6972	6981	1	2	3	4	4
50	6990	6998	7007	7016	7024	7033	7042	7050	7059	7067	1	2	3	3	4
51	7076	7084	7093	7101	7110	7118	7126	7135	7143	7152	1	2	3	3	4
52	7160	7168	7177	7185	7193	7202	7210	7218	7226	7235	1	2	2	3	4
53	7243	7251	7259	7267	7275	7284	7292	7300	7308	7316	1	2	2	3	4
54	7324	7332	7340	7348	7356	7364	7372	7380	7388	7396	1	2	2	3	4
N	0	1	2	3	4	5	6	7	8	9	1	2	3	4	5

N	0	1	2	3	4	5	6	7	8	9	Proportional Parts 1	2	3	4	5
55	7404	7412	7419	7427	7435	7443	7451	7459	7466	7474	1	2	2	3	4
56	7482	7490	7497	7505	7513	7520	7528	7536	7543	7551	1	2	2	3	4
57	7559	7566	7574	7582	7589	7597	7604	7612	7619	7627	1	2	2	3	4
58	7634	7642	7649	7657	7664	7672	7679	7686	7694	7701	1	1	2	3	4
59	7709	7716	7723	7731	7738	7745	7752	7760	7767	7774	1	1	2	3	4
60	7782	7789	7796	7803	7810	7818	7825	7832	7839	7846	1	1	2	3	4
61	7853	7860	7868	7875	7882	7889	7896	7903	7910	7917	1	1	2	3	4
62	7924	7931	7938	7945	7952	7959	7966	7973	7980	7987	1	1	2	3	3
63	7993	8000	8007	8014	8021	8028	8035	8041	8048	8055	1	1	2	3	3
64	8062	8069	8075	8082	8089	8096	8102	8109	8116	8122	1	1	2	3	3
65	8129	8136	8142	8149	8156	8162	8169	8176	8182	8189	1	1	2	3	3
66	8195	8202	8209	8215	8222	8228	8235	8241	8248	8254	1	1	2	3	3
67	8261	8267	8274	8280	8287	8293	8299	8306	8312	8319	1	1	2	3	3
68	8325	8331	8338	8344	8351	8357	8363	8370	8376	8382	1	1	2	3	3
69	8388	8395	8401	8407	8414	8420	8426	8432	8439	8445	1	1	2	2	3
70	8451	8457	8463	8470	8476	8482	8488	8494	8500	8506	1	1	2	2	3
71	8513	8519	8525	8531	8537	8543	8549	8555	8561	8567	1	1	2	2	3
72	8573	8579	8585	8591	8597	8603	8609	8615	8621	8627	1	1	2	2	3
73	8633	8639	8645	8651	8657	8663	8669	8675	8681	8686	1	1	2	2	3
74	8692	8698	8704	8710	8716	8722	8727	8733	8739	8745	1	1	2	2	3
75	8751	8756	8762	8768	8774	8779	8785	8791	8797	8802	1	1	2	2	3
76	8808	8814	8820	8825	8831	8837	8842	8848	8854	8859	1	1	2	2	3
77	8865	8871	8876	8882	8887	8893	8899	8904	8910	8915	1	1	2	2	3
78	8921	8927	8932	8938	8943	8949	8954	8960	8965	8971	1	1	2	2	3
79	8976	8982	8987	8993	8998	9004	9009	9015	9020	9025	1	1	2	2	3
80	9031	9036	9042	9047	9053	9058	9063	9069	9074	9079	1	1	2	2	3
81	9085	9090	9096	9101	9106	9112	9117	9122	9128	9133	1	1	2	2	3
82	9138	9143	9149	9154	9159	9165	9170	9175	9180	9186	1	1	2	2	3
83	9191	9196	9201	9206	9212	9217	9222	9227	9232	9238	1	1	2	2	3
84	9243	9248	9253	9258	9263	9269	9274	9279	9284	9289	1	1	2	2	3
85	9294	9299	9304	9309	9315	9320	9325	9330	9335	9340	1	1	2	2	3
86	9345	9350	9355	9360	9365	9370	9375	9380	9385	9390	1	1	2	2	3
87	9395	9400	9405	9410	9415	9420	9425	9430	9435	9440	0	1	1	2	2
88	9445	9450	9455	9460	9465	9469	9474	9479	9484	9489	0	1	1	2	2
89	9494	9499	9504	9509	9513	9518	9523	9528	9533	9538	0	1	1	2	2
90	9542	9547	9552	9557	9562	9566	9571	9576	9581	9586	0	1	1	2	2
91	9590	9595	9600	9605	9609	9614	9619	9624	9628	9633	0	1	1	2	2
92	9638	9643	9647	9652	9657	9661	9666	9671	9675	9680	0	1	1	2	2
93	9685	9689	9694	9699	9703	9708	9713	9717	9722	9727	0	1	1	2	2
94	9731	9736	9741	9745	9750	9754	9759	9763	9768	9773	0	1	1	2	2
95	9777	9782	9786	9791	9795	9800	9805	9809	9814	9818	0	1	1	2	2
96	9823	9827	9832	9836	9841	9845	9850	9854	9859	9863	0	1	1	2	2
97	9868	9872	9877	9881	9886	9890	9894	9899	9903	9908	0	1	1	2	2
98	9912	9917	9921	9926	9930	9934	9939	9943	9948	9952	0	1	1	2	2
99	9956	9961	9965	9969	9974	9978	9983	9987	9991	9996	0	1	1	2	2
N	0	1	2	3	4	5	6	7	8	9	1	2	3	4	5

APPENDIX V: LOGARITHMS AND ANTILOGARITHMS

FOUR-PLACE ANTILOGARITHMS

Log_{10}	0	1	2	3	4	5	6	7	8	9	Proportional Parts 1	2	3	4	5
.00	1000	1002	1005	1007	1009	1012	1014	1016	1019	1021	0	0	1	1	1
.01	1023	1026	1028	1030	1033	1035	1038	1040	1042	1045	0	0	1	1	1
.02	1047	1050	1052	1054	1057	1059	1062	1064	1067	1069	0	0	1	1	1
.03	1072	1074	1076	1079	1081	1084	1086	1089	1091	1094	0	0	1	1	1
.04	1096	1099	1102	1104	1107	1109	1112	1114	1117	1119	0	1	1	1	1
.05	1122	1125	1127	1130	1132	1135	1138	1140	1143	1146	0	1	1	1	1
.06	1148	1151	1153	1156	1159	1161	1164	1167	1169	1172	0	1	1	1	1
.07	1175	1178	1180	1183	1186	1189	1191	1194	1197	1199	0	1	1	1	1
.08	1202	1205	1208	1211	1213	1216	1219	1222	1225	1227	0	1	1	1	1
.09	1230	1233	1236	1239	1242	1245	1247	1250	1253	1256	0	1	1	1	1
.10	1259	1262	1265	1268	1271	1274	1276	1279	1282	1285	0	1	1	1	1
.11	1288	1291	1294	1297	1300	1303	1306	1309	1312	1315	0	1	1	1	2
.12	1318	1321	1324	1327	1330	1334	1337	1340	1343	1346	0	1	1	1	2
.13	1349	1352	1355	1358	1361	1365	1368	1371	1374	1377	0	1	1	1	2
.14	1380	1384	1387	1390	1393	1396	1400	1403	1406	1409	0	1	1	1	2
.15	1413	1416	1419	1422	1426	1429	1432	1435	1439	1442	0	1	1	1	2
.16	1445	1449	1452	1455	1459	1462	1466	1469	1472	1476	0	1	1	1	2
.17	1479	1483	1486	1489	1493	1496	1500	1503	1507	1510	0	1	1	1	2
.18	1514	1517	1521	1524	1528	1531	1535	1538	1542	1545	0	1	1	1	2
.19	1549	1552	1556	1560	1563	1567	1570	1574	1578	1581	0	1	1	1	2
.20	1585	1589	1592	1596	1600	1603	1607	1611	1614	1618	0	1	1	1	2
.21	1622	1626	1629	1633	1637	1641	1644	1648	1652	1656	0	1	1	2	2
.22	1660	1663	1667	1671	1675	1679	1683	1687	1690	1694	0	1	1	2	2
.23	1698	1702	1706	1710	1714	1718	1722	1726	1730	1734	0	1	1	2	2
.24	1738	1742	1746	1750	1754	1758	1762	1766	1770	1774	0	1	1	2	2
.25	1778	1782	1786	1791	1795	1799	1803	1807	1811	1816	0	1	1	2	2
.26	1820	1824	1828	1832	1837	1841	1845	1849	1854	1858	0	1	1	2	2
.27	1862	1866	1871	1875	1879	1884	1888	1892	1897	1901	0	1	1	2	2
.28	1905	1910	1914	1919	1923	1928	1932	1936	1941	1945	0	1	1	2	2
.29	1950	1954	1959	1963	1968	1972	1977	1982	1986	1991	0	1	1	2	2
.30	1995	2000	2004	2009	2014	2018	2023	2028	2032	2037	0	1	1	2	2
.31	2042	2046	2051	2056	2061	2065	2070	2075	2080	2084	0	1	1	2	2
.32	2089	2094	2099	2104	2109	2113	2118	2123	2128	2133	0	1	1	2	2
.33	2138	2143	2148	2153	2158	2163	2168	2173	2178	2183	0	1	1	2	2
.34	2188	2193	2198	2203	2208	2213	2218	2223	2228	2234	1	1	2	2	3
.35	2239	2244	2249	2254	2259	2265	2270	2275	2280	2286	1	1	2	2	3
.36	2291	2296	2301	2307	2312	2317	2323	2328	2333	2339	1	1	2	2	3
.37	2344	2350	2355	2360	2366	2371	2377	2382	2388	2393	1	1	2	2	3
.38	2399	2404	2410	2415	2421	2427	2432	2438	2443	2449	1	1	2	2	3
.39	2455	2460	2466	2472	2477	2483	2489	2495	2500	2506	1	1	2	2	3
.40	2512	2518	2523	2529	2535	2541	2547	2553	2559	2564	1	1	2	2	3
.41	2570	2576	2582	2588	2594	2600	2606	2612	2618	2624	1	1	2	2	3
.42	2630	2636	2642	2649	2655	2661	2667	2673	2679	2685	1	1	2	2	3
.43	2692	2698	2704	2710	2716	2723	2729	2735	2742	2748	1	1	2	3	3
.44	2754	2761	2767	2773	2780	2786	2793	2799	2805	2812	1	1	2	3	3
.45	2818	2825	2831	2838	2844	2851	2858	2864	2871	2877	1	1	2	3	3
.46	2884	2891	2897	2904	2911	2917	2924	2931	2938	2944	1	1	2	3	3
.47	2951	2958	2965	2972	2979	2985	2992	2999	3006	3013	1	1	2	3	3
.48	3020	3027	3034	3041	3048	3055	3062	3069	3076	3083	1	1	2	3	4
.49	3090	3097	3105	3112	3119	3126	3133	3141	3148	3155	1	1	2	3	4
N	0	1	2	3	4	5	6	7	8	9	1	2	3	4	5

Log_{10}	0	1	2	3	4	5	6	7	8	9	Proportional Parts 1	2	3	4	5
.50	3162	3170	3177	3184	3192	3199	3206	3214	3221	3228	1	1	2	3	4
.51	3236	3243	3251	3258	3266	3273	3281	3289	3296	3304	1	2	2	3	4
.52	3311	3319	3327	3334	3342	3350	3357	3365	3373	3381	1	2	2	3	4
.53	3388	3396	3404	3412	3420	3428	3436	3443	3451	3459	1	2	2	3	4
.54	3467	3475	3483	3491	3499	3508	3516	3524	3532	3540	1	2	2	3	4
.55	3548	3556	3565	3573	3581	3589	3597	3606	3614	3622	1	2	2	3	4
.56	3631	3639	3648	3656	3664	3673	3681	3690	3698	3707	1	2	3	3	4
.57	3715	3724	3733	3741	3750	3758	3767	3776	3784	3793	1	2	3	3	4
.58	3802	3811	3819	3828	3837	3846	3855	3864	3873	3882	1	2	3	4	4
.59	3890	3899	3908	3917	3926	3936	3945	3954	3963	3972	1	2	3	4	5
.60	3981	3990	3999	4009	4018	4027	4036	4046	4055	4064	1	2	3	4	5
.61	4074	4083	4093	4102	4111	4121	4130	4140	4150	4159	1	2	3	4	5
.62	4169	4178	4188	4198	4207	4217	4227	4236	4246	4256	1	2	3	4	5
.63	4266	4276	4285	4295	4305	4315	4325	4335	4345	4355	1	2	3	4	5
.64	4365	4375	4385	4395	4406	4416	4426	4436	4446	4457	1	2	3	4	5
.65	4467	4477	4487	4498	4508	4519	4529	4539	4550	4560	1	2	3	4	5
.66	4571	4581	4592	4603	4613	4624	4634	4645	4656	4667	1	2	3	4	5
.67	4677	4688	4699	4710	4721	4732	4742	4753	4764	4775	1	2	3	4	5
.68	4786	4797	4808	4819	4831	4842	4853	4864	4875	4887	1	2	3	4	6
.69	4898	4909	4920	4932	4943	4955	4966	4977	4989	5000	1	2	3	5	6
.70	5012	5023	5035	5047	5058	5070	5082	5093	5105	5117	1	2	4	5	6
.71	5129	5140	5152	5164	5176	5188	5200	5212	5224	5236	1	2	4	5	6
.72	5248	5260	5272	5284	5297	5309	5321	5333	5346	5358	1	2	4	5	6
.73	5370	5383	5395	5408	5420	5433	5445	5458	5470	5483	1	3	4	5	6
.74	6495	5508	5521	5534	5546	5559	5572	5585	5598	5610	1	3	4	5	6
.75	5623	5636	5649	5662	5675	5689	5702	5715	5728	5741	1	3	4	5	7
.76	5754	5768	5781	5794	5808	5821	5834	5848	5861	5875	1	3	4	5	7
.77	5888	5902	5916	5929	5943	5957	5970	5984	5998	6012	1	3	4	5	7
.78	6026	6039	6053	6067	6081	6095	6109	6124	6138	6152	1	3	4	6	7
.79	6166	6180	6194	6209	6223	6237	6252	6266	6281	6295	1	3	4	6	7
.80	6310	6324	6339	6353	6368	6383	6397	6412	6427	6442	1	3	4	6	7
.81	6457	6471	6486	6501	6516	6531	6546	6561	6577	6592	2	3	5	6	8
.82	6607	6622	6637	6653	6668	6683	6699	6714	6730	6745	2	3	5	6	8
.83	6761	6776	6792	6808	6823	6839	6855	6871	6887	6902	2	3	5	6	8
.84	6918	6934	6950	6966	6982	6998	7015	7031	7047	7063	2	3	5	6	8
.85	7079	7096	7112	7129	7145	7161	7178	7194	7211	7228	2	3	5	7	8
.86	7244	7261	7278	7295	7311	7328	7345	7362	7379	7396	2	3	5	7	8
.87	7413	7430	7447	7464	7482	7499	7516	7534	7551	7568	2	3	5	7	9
.88	7586	7603	7621	7638	7656	7674	7691	7709	7727	7745	2	4	5	7	9
.89	7762	7780	7798	7816	7834	7852	7870	7889	7907	7925	2	4	6	7	9
.90	7943	7962	7980	7998	8017	8035	8054	8072	8091	8110	2	4	6	7	9
.91	8128	8147	8166	8185	8204	8222	8241	8260	8279	8299	2	4	6	8	9
.92	8318	8337	8356	8375	8395	8414	8433	8453	8472	8492	2	4	6	8	10
.93	8511	8531	8551	8570	8590	8610	8630	8650	8670	8690	2	4	6	8	10
.94	8710	8730	8750	8770	8790	8810	8831	8851	8872	8892	2	4	6	8	10
.95	8913	8933	8954	8974	8995	9016	9036	9057	9078	9099	2	4	6	8	10
.96	9120	9141	9162	9183	9204	9226	9247	9268	9290	9311	2	4	6	8	11
.97	9333	9354	9376	9397	9419	9441	9462	9484	9506	9528	2	4	7	9	11
.98	9550	9572	9594	9616	9638	9661	9683	9705	9727	9750	2	4	7	9	11
.99	9772	9795	9817	9840	9863	9886	9908	9931	9954	9977	2	5	7	9	11
N	0	1	2	3	4	5	6	7	8	9	1	2	3	4	5

APPENDIX VI: WORLD WEATHER EXTREMES

(Recorded Observations Only)

	Observation	Record
		Temperature
	Alaska	
1	Lowest recorded temperature	-78°F, Fort Yukon, January 14, 1934.
	United States	
2	Lowest recorded temperature	-66°F, at Riverside Ranger Station, Yellowstone Park, Wyo., Feb. 9, 1933.
3	Highest recorded temperature	134°F, Greenland Ranch, Death Valley, California, July 10, 1913.
	World	
4	Lowest recorded temperature	-90°F, Verkhoyansk, Siberia, February 5 and 7, 1892.
5	Highest recorded temperature	136°F, Azizia, Libya, North Africa, September 13, 1922.
6	Lowest mean annual temperature	-14°F, Framheim, Antarctica[1].
7	Highest mean annual temperature	86°F, Massawa, Eritrea, Africa.
		Precipitation
	United States	
8	Average annual precipitation	29 inches, approximately.
9	Wettest State	Louisiana, 55.11 inches annual average rainfall.
10	Driest State	Nevada, 8.81 inches annual average rainfall.
11	Highest local annual average rainfall	150.73 inches, Wynoochee, Oxbow, Washington (based on 13-year record).
12	Greatest 24-hour rainfall	23.22 inches, New Smyrna, Florida, October 10-11, 1924.
13	Extreme min. annual average rainfall	1.35 inches, Greenland Ranch, California
14	Extreme min. rainfall, 5 years	3.93 inches, Bagdad, California, 1909-1913.
15	Heavy snowfall record, 1 day	60.0 inches, Giant Forest, California.
16	2 days	42.0 inches, Angola, New York.
17	3 days	54.0 inches, The Dalles, Oregon.
18	4 days	96.0 inches, Vanceboro, Maine.
19	Greatest seasonal snowfall	884.0 inches (73+ feet), Tamarack, California, winter of 1906-07.
20	Largest definitely recorded hailstone	1.5 pounds, Potter, Nebraska, July 6, 1928.
	World	
21	Greatest 24-hour rainfall	46.0 inches, Baguio, Luzon, Philippine Islands, July 14-15, 1911.
22	Greatest monthly rainfall	241.0 inches, Cherrapunji, India, August 1841.[2]
23	Greatest annual average rainfall	460.20 inches, Waialeale, Hawaii.

/1/ The estimated mean temperature at the South Pole, elevation 8000 ft, is considerably below -22°C. /2/ 150 inches of rain fell in 5 consecutive days; the average annual in Cherrapunji is 426 inches.

APPENDIX VII:

THE GREEK ALPHABET

Α α - alpha
Β β - beta
Γ γ - gamma
Δ δ - delta
Ε ε - epsilon
Ζ ζ - zeta
Η η - eta
Θ θ - theta
Ι ι - iota
Κ κ - kappa
Λ λ - lambda
Μ μ - mu
Ν ν - nu
Ξ ξ - xi
Ο ο - omicron
Π π - pi
Ρ ρ - rho
Σ σ - sigma
Τ τ - tau
Υ υ - upsilon
Φ φ - phi
Χ χ - chi
Ψ ψ - psi
Ω ω - omega

INDEX

       This section is comprised of two parts, a Contributor-Reviewer Index and a Subject Index. On pages v - xxx there appears, in alphabetical order, a complete list of contributors and reviewers (not including advisers and members of the Panel of Appraisers), each with an accompanying reference number. In the table of contents each table title is followed, in parentheses, by the reference number(s) of the principal contributor(s) of that table. Single-source tables adapted directly from the literature have no such identifying numbers, but the literature citation is given in the headnote of that table. The Contributor-Reviewer Index lists, by number, all contributors and reviewers for each table. Table numbers are enclosed in "slashes," and are followed by appropriate reference numbers. For example, /1/ 211, 4036 indicates that Table 1, "Standard Solutions: pH_s," was contributed and/or reviewed by Roger G. Bates (number 211) and Claude E. ZoBell (number 4036).

       In an attempt to provide as useful a subject index as possible, and at the same time to strive for maximum economy of space, certain expediencies have been employed. The Subject Index is designed for use in correlation with the table of contents, eliminating the necessity for most of the usual secondary index entries. Because each table title appears in the Contents, such correlation is relatively simple. For example, GLUCOSE is accompanied by many page numbers, among which are (random selection) 8, 17, 52, 233, and 250. The table of contents reveals the following: page 8, characteristics of glucose; 17, glucose as a component of glycosides; 52, glucose content of human blood; 233, glycolytic metabolism of glucose; 250, the role of glucose in photosynthesis.

       Effort has been made to index scientific and common names for every organism and every chemical listed in the book. Unfortunately it has been impossible to adhere to any one standard system of nomenclature for either category--actually, "standard" systems themselves have undergone considerable change during the preparation of the Handbook. Consequently, it was decided that the nomenclature employed within the "text" of the book remain as in the data contributed by the many authorities and authenticated by other experts in the same fields. Wherever ambiguity appeared likely, entries were cross-referenced. Moreover, in most cases, synonyms (trade names, where applicable) and alternate designations accompany the nomenclature used within the tables.

       Organisms are indexed down to the genus level. Obviously, a listing of all species would not only quadruple the size of the index, but also would be redundant because in the majority of cases the several species of a given genus are grouped together within any one table. Common names of organisms have been indexed, wherever possible, in two ways, e.g., there is an entry EVERGREEN(S) after which appear the numbers of all pages containing information on evergreens in general; in addition, each evergreen, e.g., PINE(S), SPRUCE(S), FIR(S), is also indexed. Again, in most tables all species of each tree are grouped in alphabetical order.

       Indexing of table titles has been held to a minimum, and general subject headings appearing in the index apply to column headings or other sections of tables not directly indicated in the Contents.

Contributor - Reviewer Index

2770, 2784, 2811, 2875, 2923, 3015, 3164, 3286, 3290, 3368, 3453, 3561, 3589, 3614, 3647, 3776, 3945, 3958 /193/72, 722, 1041, 1200, 1365, 1565, 2564,
2756, 3811, 3875 /194/2756 /195/620, 2942, 3622, 3745, 3847 /196/ 744, 1401, 1792, 2006, 2504, 2702, 3436, 3682, 3900 /197/107, 588, 798, 1234,
1270, 2179, 2228, 3822 /198/574, 748, 1137, 1344, 1797, 1940, 2077, 2280, 2353, 2386, 2490, 2630, 2658, 2885, 2908, 2959, 3152, 3153, 3220, 3741
200 /199/1852, 2040, 2792, 3160, 3161 /200/556, 865, 1907, 2773, 2779, 3102, 3333, 3656, 3753, 3779, 3897 /201/1115, 1907, 2773, 2779, 3271, 3656, 3740
/202/1115, 1907, 3271, 3656, 3740 /203/556, 865, 1115, 1907, 2858, 3271, 3333, 3475, 3656, 3740, 3753, 3779, 3897 /204/223, 313, 438, 641, 646, 845,
1096, 1525, 1927, 1928, 2180, 2347, 2462, 2504, 2532, 2562, 2950, 3204, 3225, 3306, 3381, 3415, 3540, 3939, 4009 /205/312, 451, 720, 768, 1340, 1457,
1706, 1808, 1864, 2464, 2473, 2531, 2555, 3003, 3534, 3616, 3629, 3711, 3802 /206/312, 720, 733, 768, 857, 1693, 1706, 1911, 2522, 2646, 3101, 3340,
3534, 3616 /207/390, 733, 768, 810, 1040, 1457, 1706, 2455, 2464, 2473, 2497, 2555, 2775, 2815, 3519, 3534, 3616, 3629, 3802, 3930 /208/856, 1267,
1765, 1873, 2029, 2931, 3294, 3389, 3449, 3715 /209/856, 1267, 1765, 1873, 2029, 2931, 3294, 3389, 3449, 3715 /211/856, 1267, 1765, 1873, 2029,
2931, 3294, 3389, 3449, 3715 /211/319, 696, 1633, 2471, 3119, 4001 /212/376, 718, 745, 1351, 1465, 1661, 1787, 1955, 2173, 2272, 2530, 3039, 3453,
3612, 3730, 3759, 3833, 3846, 3850 /213/93, 114, 358, 609, 1216, 1300, 1308, 1499, 2374, 2695, 3007, 3408, 3424, 3692, 3831, 3832, 3949 /214/192,
319, 465, 1096, 1506, 1841, 2353, 2982, 3165, 3287, 3666, 4023 /215/192, 319, 465, 1096, 1506, 1841, 2353, 2982, 3165, 3287, 3666, 4023 /216/319,
376, 718, 754, 1465, 1661, 1955, 2272, 3039, 3121, 3453, 3612, 3692, 3730, 3759, 3833, 3846 /217/319, 376, 718, 754, 1465, 1661, 1955, 2272, 3121,
3453, 3692, 3730, 3846 /218/169, 614, 1506, 3492, 3759 /219/242, 614, 718, 1357, 1787, 2064, 2143, 2869, 3275, 3342, 3462 /220/402, 426, 1417, 1435,
1506, 3764 /221/588, 976, 1001, 1190, 1747, 2179, 2338, 2340, 2682, 2725, 3138, 3193, 3240, 3360, 3411, 3434, 3764 /222/485, 494, 846, 1022, 1145,
1313, 1396, 1408, 1953, 2100, 2122, 2211, 2217, 2281, 2721, 2776, 2794, 3079, 3280, 3407, 3707, 3932, 3941, 3956 /223/684, 1285,1456, 2253, 2629, 2639,
225 2767, 2879, 2952, 2971, 3163, 3199, 3331, 3363 /224/1421, 2142, 2532, 3287, 3990 /225/1421, 2142, 2532, 3287, 3990 /226/1592, 2417, 2583, 3491,
4001 /227/111, 1407, 1435, 2855, 3275, 3950 /228/111, 175, 273, 552, 3459, 3627 /229/111, 175, 273, 552, 3459, 3627 /230/307, 369, 511, 683, 1150,
1309, 2715, 2816, 3300, 3724, 3946 /231/369, 683, 1150, 1268 /232/3735, 3946 /233/36, 51, 99, 1116, 1754, 3228 /234/376, 3589 /235/1423, 2443,
2592, 2679, 2868, 2906, 3803 /236/1851, 1948, 2354, 2665 /237/1019, 1709, 1917, 2428, 2800, 2869, 2905, 3478, 3542, 3555, 3678, 3680, 3704, 3873
/238/451, 578, 717, 1279, 1555, 1582, 1999, 2138, 2171, 2232, 2425, 3007, 3028, 3516, 3930 /239/282, 383, 578, 995 /240/282, 383, 578, 995, 1858
/241/186, 787, 935, 1086, 1213, 1303, 1722, 1887, 1996, 2026, 2090, 2143, 2381, 2556, 2574, 2889, 3154, 3187, 3521, 3670 /242/1207, 1208, 2298, 2795,
2820, 3001 /243/348, 520, 631, 722, 769, 1185, 1239, 1319, 1379, 1392, 1501, 1665, 1977, 2028, 2325, 2409, 2619, 2645, 3022, 3186, 3311, 3377, 3592,
3675, 3857 /244/2346 /245/2346 /246/2346 /247/2346 /248/339, 1077, 1189, 1233, 1236, 1248, 1322, 1472, 1579, 1663, 2298, 2349, 2577, 2692, 2806,
2973, 3176, 3509, 3516, 3883 /249/339, 634, 875, 1077, 1189, 1248, 1318, 1322, 1443, 1472, 1579, 1663, 1873, 2187, 2305, 2577, 2578, 2722, 2733,
250 2806, 2903, 3001, 3883 /250/1873 /251/3247 /252/1233, 2298, 2346, 2692, 2879, 3176 /253/100, 564, 1677, 1865, 2720, 3169, 3324 /254/194, 227, 309,
723, 771, 983, 1626, 1654, 1707, 2016, 2070, 2132, 2733, 2787, 3324, 3711, 3969 /255/227, 1654, 2016, 3324, 3710 /256/198, 1664, 1707 /257/198,
1654, 1707 /258/2787, 4036 /259/20, 2305, 2787, 2903 /260/943, 2787, 2903 /261/2305, 2419, 2903, 3818 /262/65, 194, 297, 458, 712, 829, 904, 941,
956, 983, 1181, 1384, 1433, 1489, 1605, 1648, 1732, 2021, 2346, 2463, 2731, 2846, 2995, 3056, 3357, 3713, 3796, 3931, 3939, 4012 /263/65, 458, 694,
790, 941, 1010, 1109, 1384, 1561, 1590, 1605, 1732, 2240, 2463, 2728, 2846, 2956, 2995, 3357, 3516, 3796, 3931, 3939, 4012, 4041 /264/145, 464, 554,
830, 876, 946, 1330, 1695, 1918, 2071, 2105, 2270, 2544, 2576, 2629, 3013, 3234, 3299, 3771, 3891, 3975 /265/121, 451, 504, 1111, 1999, 2205, 2534,
3068, 3934 /266/183, 345, 628, 1010, 1178, 1464, 1480, 1773, 1793, 2168 /267/1247, 1363, 1828, 3222 /268/1473, 2306, 2479, 3253, 3584 /269/309,
1554, 2306, 2479, 3423, 3584 /270/894, 1277, 1613, 2449 /271/726, 1271, 1277, 1659, 2199, 2249, 3037, 3974 /272/1414 /273/10, 87, 321, 428, 1170,
275 1414, 1451, 1724, 1932, 1995, 2231, 2323, 2766, 2980, 3166, 3173, 3276, 3820, 4031 /274/284, 525, 1309 /275/360, 864, 2571, 2602, 3088, 3100, 3988
/276/207, 602, 1060, 1263, 2519, 3804 /277/2738, 2890, 3230, 3440, 3623 /278/1448, 1954, 2624, 2780, 2799, 3299, 3517 /279/706, 1283, 3203
/280/34, 63, 94, 95, 323, 398, 407, 469, 495, 608, 664, 780, 946, 1047, 1313, 1341, 1356, 1376, 1750, 1892, 1996, 2108, 2180, 2468, 2489, 2708, 2841,
3063, 3064, 3184, 3256, 3383, 3560, 3576, 3927, 3988 /281/2, 190, 495, 2035, 3006, 3064, 3815, 3835, 3902 /282/1416, 2519, 2579, 3519, 3655, 3967
/283/154, 197, 234, 364, 557, 688, 1678, 2668, 2895, 3467, 3528, 3744 /284/3467 /285/3467 /286/433, 1052, 1722, 2117, 2399, 3043, 3310, 3376, 3597,
3872, 4021 /287/789, 1643, 1838, 2326, 2519, 2927, 3146, 3872, 3977 /288/502, 529, 664, 910, 1044, 1121, 1313, 1466, 1750, 1854, 2108, 2489, 3063,
3170, 3506, 3667, 3987 /289/502, 1313, 2343, 2696 /290/157, 200, 365, 429, 714, 1162, 1251, 1467, 1567, 1609, 1816, 1930, 1939, 2083, 2250, 2267,
2289, 2293, 2327, 2496, 2547, 2566, 2589, 2976, 3288, 3557, 3687, 3757, 3762, 4026 /291/66, 569, 587, 871, 1063, 1074, 1075, 1321, 1337, 1402, 1920,
1934, 2166, 2315, 2479, 2537, 3062, 3309, 3466, 3859, 3964 /292/181, 551, 607, 709, 923, 1169, 1244, 1294, 1295, 2606, 2888, 3226 /293/251, 923,
1067, 1244, 1251, 1294, 1295, 1930, 2606, 2808, 3849 /294/238, 633, 1062, 1251, 1582, 2622 /295/1618, 3502 /296/1513, 3867 /297/464, 466, 2295,
300 2298, 2856, 3098, 3849, 3984 /298/3156 /299/53, 2432, 2715 /300/153, 654, 818, 1011, 1019, 1344, 2001, 2076, 2085, 2156, 2232, 3152, 3385 /301/170,
480, 1830, 2538, 3469 /302/268, 303, 1325, 2538 /303/78, 1556, 1812, 2218, 2538, 4006 /304/1144, 1207, 2879 /305/21, 1144, 1207, 1328, 1347, 1848,
2794, 3176, 3936, 3956 /306/205, 595, 649, 1172, 1674, 1704, 2088, 2104, 3207, 3774, 3822, 3826, 3854 /307/21, 189, 286, 337, 380, 450, 568, 753, 958,
1027, 1144, 1230, 1237, 1704, 1795, 1953, 2162, 2221, 2291, 2404, 2515, 2654, 2794, 2836, 3264, 3273, 3283, 3331, 3363, 3851, 3956 /308/21, 189, 286,
337, 380, 450, 568, 753, 958, 1027, 1144, 1230, 1237, 1704, 1795, 1953, 2162, 2221, 2291, 2404, 2515, 2654, 2794, 2836, 3235, 3264, 3283, 3331, 3363,
3851, 3956 /309/74, 691, 902, 1765, 1769, 1925, 1978, 2020, 2057, 2213, 2257, 2261, 2634, 2686, 2902, 3096, 3134, 3473 /310/1094, 1532, 1634, 1755,
1769, 2123, 2252, 3660 /311/431, 1056, 1292, 1471, 1605, 1744, 1746, 1910, 1986, 2030, 2576, 2788, 3037, 3186, 3476 /312/ 1744, 2321 /313/ 91,
163, 739, 1520, 2186, 2225, 2502, 2521, 3345 /314/446, 705, 1310, 1601, 1862, 2031 /315/457, 481, 532, 658, 1147, 1958, 2069, 2191, 2194, 2918, 3001,
3414, 3455, 3748 /316/123, 648, 963, 1672, 1905, 2560, 3006, 3315 /317/765, 1311, 1563, 1809, 3014, 3612 /318/124, 624, 700 /319/124, 624, 700
/320/124, 624, 700 /321/1430, 3357, 3924 /322/90, 359, 393, 871, 920 ,1368, 1461, 1482, 1704, 1730, 1825, 1973, 1998, 2016, 2063, 2071, 2133, 2707,
325 3289, 3314, 3584, 3696 /323/21 /324/21 /325/838, 996, 1724, 1736, 1992, 2437, 3032, 3071, 3287, 3940, 3980 /326/1596, 1802, 2310, 2372, 2678, 3558
/327/288, 449, 594, 1562, 2102, 2591, 3913, 4014 /328/302, 652, 1507, 1883 /329/575 /330/1, 112, 686, 1378, 1531, 1982, 2439 /331/713, 3568 /332/23,
112, 115, 618, 686, 1378, 1531, 1982, 2313 /333/134, 3173 /334/35, 410, 1586, 1859, 1873, 2234, 2762, 2877, 3104, 3151, 3231, 3419, 3846, 3903, 4020
/335/299 /336/642, 1673, 2062, 2078, 2220, 2978, 3571, 3840 /337/2978, 3571 /338/128, 254, 280, 306, 572, 762, 833, 999, 1028, 1517, 2055, 2210, 2698,
3139, 3272, 3923, 3978 /339/698, 784, 1030, 1888, 1975, 1976, 2525, 2626, 2755, 2934, 3086, 3269, 3905 /340/1888, 2287, 2527, 2755 /341/376, 2601,
3589, 4033 /342/376, 2601, 3589, 4033 /343/376, 2601, 3589, 4033 /344/891, 906, 1029, 1113, 1253, 2141, 2226, 2342, 2742, 2854, 2914, 2932, 3775, 3878
/345/891, 906, 1029, 1113, 1253, 2141, 2226, 2342, 2742, 2854, 2914, 2932, 3775, 3878 /346/ 453, 1092, 2153, 2472, 3182, 3291, 3525, 3598 /347/3175,
350 3355 /348/782, 930, 1487 /349/150, 460, 528, 964, 1495, 1541, 1647, 1913, 1984, 2095, 2513, 3045, 3918 /350/923, 1222, 1434, 2867, 3254, 3356 /351/1222,
2243, 2487, 3012, 3356 /352/276, 363, 2651, 2730, 2785, 3208, 3535 /353/252, 727, 944, 1449, 1969, 2438, 2626, 3284, 3852, 3960 /355/434, 859, 1053,
1832, 2871, 2992, 3320, 3393 /356/81, 385, 497, 656, 950, 1069, 1158, 1168, 1351, 1395, 1438, 1447, 1813, 1890, 2111, 2370, 2441, 2528, 2563, 2840,
2921, 3185, 3326, 3348, 3427, 3649 /357/643, 1351, 1682, 2528, 3258 /358/584, 1543, 3103 /359/52, 336, 825, 913, 1166, 1254, 1509, 1533, 1805, 1849,
1908, 2148, 2539, 2543, 2580, 2598, 3280, 3588, 3856, 4017 /360/509, 639, 643, 2415, 2864, 2909, 3352, 3461 /361/336, 518, 913, 1254, 1484, 1509,
1533, 1805, 1908, 2148, 2539, 2543, 2580, 3856, 4017 /362/21, 98, 137, 143, 155, 368, 430, 451, 623, 777, 788, 1165, 1420, 1605, 1629, 1630, 1712,
1791, 1986, 2043, 2302, 2502, 2511, 2516, 2540, 2554, 2754, 2967, 3037, 3040, 3227, 3405, 3516, 3567 /363/766, 788, 2302, 2499, 2502, 2511, 2754,
3040 /364/147, 253, 461, 1056, 1303, 1383, 2787, 3031, 3236, 3976, 3998 /365/21, 147, 461, 1056, 1303, 1383, 2787, 2913, 3031, 3176, 3236, 3976, 3998
/366/147, 461, 1056, 1303, 1383, 2787, 3031, 3236, 3976, 3998 /367/147, 461, 1056, 1303, 1383, 2787, 3031, 3236, 3976, 3998 /368/147, 461, 1056,
1303, 1383, 2787, 3031, 3236, 3976, 3998 /369/147, 248, 253, 461, 1056, 1303, 1383, 2184, 2787, 3031, 3236, 3405, 3872, 3976, 3998 /370/2765
/371/141, 1024, 1068, 1574, 1926, 2314 /372/29, 215, 240, 268, 335, 745, 1004, 1024, 1311, 1541, 1717, 1733, 1900, 1960, 2048, 2093, 2314, 2376,
2418, 2862, 2874, 3067, 3305, 3364, 3468, 3611, 3630, 3695, 4022 /373/191, 486, 825, 1025, 1131, 1159, 1298, 1324, 1926, 2492 /374/103, 513, 1081,
375 1298, 1717, 2174 /375/188, 1068, 1412, 1926, 2239, 2380, 3070, 3837, 3957 /376/650 /377/50, 78, 304, 436, 445, 872, 884, 932, 1224, 1589, 2080, 2218,
2535, 2619, 2753, 2827, 3401, 3531, 3637, 3643, 3848, 3879 /378/167, 3093 /379/49, 167, 201, 244, 852, 1514, 1660, 1943, 3093, 3632 /380/49, 627,
2401, 2529, 2723, 3093, 3531, 3761 /381/784, 1212, 1521, 1818, 3259, 3717, 3922 /382/1898, 2356, 2826, 2837, 3609, 3770, 3864 /383/136, 289, 985,
1045, 2356, 3604, 3896 /384/289, 750, 985, 1045, 2356, 3256, 3604, 3896 /385/448, 581, 605, 1494, 1653, 1783, 2054, 2618, 2946, 3263 /386/757, 2976,
3884 /387/3114, 3372, 3539, 3661 /388/159, 667, 1087, 2076, 3038 /389/159, 435, 667, 1087, 1148, 1306, 2076, 2230, 2979 /390/44, 244, 388, 749, 979,
1338, 1468, 1523, 3908 /391/44, 244, 388, 749, 869, 979, 1338, 1468, 1523, 1540, 1556, 1668, 2633, 2755, 3019, 3038, 3510, 4018 /392/ 852, 896, 1668,
3848, 3967 /393/2548, 2615, 3703 /394/463, 556, 1912, 2432, 2777 /395/3791 /396/15, 2565, 3329, 3602 /397/249, 2022, 3602 /398/1246, 2022, 2423,
400 2892, 3602 /399/1246 /400/15, 1246, 1550, 2106, 2423, 2892, 3329, 3602, 3739 /401/15, 249, 412, 1371, 1550, 1762, 2106, 2892, 3329, 3602, 3683, 3739
/402/412, 2022, 2892, 3602 /403/15, 412, 2892, 3602, 3739, 3792 /404/15, 1246, 2022, 2565, 2892, 3329, 3602 /405/15, 2565, 2892, 3602, 3809
/406/15, 249, 2423, 3602 /408/1246, 1550, 2892, 3602 /409/15, 249, 1141, 2423, 2999, 3097, 3107, 3602, 3683, 3792 /410/15, 527, 1506, 1604, 2844,
3129, 3602 /411/567, 2377 /412/15, 1065, 1155, 1371 /413/15, 249, 270, 527, 637, 2423, 2682, 2731, 3097, 3602, 3683 /414/3739 /415/708, 804, 996,
1880, 2763, 3117, 3489, 3683 /416/412, 1256, 1371, 2114, 2423, 2565, 2671, 2892 /417/955, 2635, 2647 /418/492, 955, 1323, 2329 /419/1036, 1168,
1307, 1350, 1790, 1959, 3312, 3971 /420/530, 970, 975, 1057, 1314, 1810, 2044, 2243, 2352, 2807, 3204, 3371 /421/54, 322, 982, 1756, 1810, 2041,
425 2243, 2352, 3371, 3432 /422/1026, 1824, 2314, 2528, 2585, 3292, 3600, 3708 /423/257, 815, 870, 1522, 2524, 2811, 3479 /424/814, 1522, 2811 /425/56,
103, 216, 513, 1015, 1081, 1979, 2736, 3375, 3438, 3768 /426/56, 76, 161, 216, 576, 939, 1015, 1876, 2292, 2553, 2736, 3387, 3671, 3768, 4028 /427/216
/428/233, 687, 792, 1168, 2103, 2149, 2215, 3622, 3847 /429/663, 3142, 3564, 3605 /430/1768 /431/724, 1105, 1290, 1355, 1529, 2835 /432/1483, 2567
/433/1483, 2567 /434/1020, 1483, 3410 /435/1020, 1483, 3410 /436/489, 1020, 1483 /437/489, 1020, 1483 /438/489, 1020, 1483 /439/1483, 2567
/440/118, 585, 627, 783, 1101, 1599, 1645, 1698, 1708, 1904, 2330, 2351, 2387, 3018, 3148, 3460, 3513, 3719 /441/736, 1016, 1800, 2546 /442/854, 1483,
1497, 2567 /443/657, 2010, 2525, 3754, 3963 /444/395, 1833, 1851, 2714, 2936, 2974, 3529, 3614, 4036 /445/177, 471, 1038, 1241, 2405, 3857, 4036

Subject Index

552

554

COPPERHEAD SNAKE(S), 183, 420-423
COPRINUS spp, 69, 131, 133, 135, 204, 262
COPROGEN, 209
COPROPORPHYRIN(S), 32, 62, 63, 242, 248
COPROPORPHYRINOGEN, 248
COPROSMA sp, 145
COPROSTANOL, and derivs., 22
COPROSTEROL, 231, 234
COPTIS sp, 458
COPTOCYCLA sp, 93
COPTOSOMA sp, 93
COPULATION, 128; algae, fungi, 132
CORACIIDAE, 117, 214
CORACIIFORMES, 117
CORACOBRACHIALIS MUSCLE, 296
CORACOHYOID, 295
CORACOID BONE(S), 168, 169; chondrification, 155
CORACOMANDIBULA, 295
CORAL(S), 184, 525
CORAL BELLS, 458
CORALBERRY, 142, 396, 458
CORALLINA sp, 524
CORALLORHIZA sp, 458
CORAL ROOT, 458
CORAL SNAKE(S), 420, 421
CORAL TREE, 430
CORBICULA sp, 22
CORBISTEROL, 22
CORCHORUS sp, 499
CORDAITES, 525
CORDYCEPS spp, 203, 204
CORDYLOBIA sp, 486
COREGONUS sp, 183
COREOPSIS spp, 38, 39, 394
CORETHRA sp, 339
CORIAMYRTIN, 432
CORIANDER, 43
CORIANDRUM sp, 43
CORIARIA sp, 432
CORI ESTER (see GLUCOSE-1-PHOSPHATE)
CORILAGIN, 41
CORIUM spp, 510
CORIXA spp, 92, 164
CORK, 19, 148, 149; -tree, 142
CORMORANT(S), 116, 182, 344
CORN, 82, 83, 86-88, 90, 91, 94, 107, 108, 110, 122, 134, 143-147, 186, 187, 189, 192, 193, 211-214, 224, 230, 250, 251, 264, 265, 336-338, 449-451, 453-455, 460, 489; -borers, 215, 490; -cross breeding, 110; -distillers grains, 188; -earworm, 122, 411, 522;-fodder, 189, 211; genetics of, 107, 110; -meal, 188; -oil, 20, 193, 211, 215; -starch, 211
CORNACEAE, 95
CORNARTIUM sp, 445
CORN BUNTING, 118
CORN COCKLE, 84, 394, 427
CORNEA, 76, 155, 316
CORNFLOWER, 394, 451, 460
CORNICULARIA sp, 263
CORNINELLUS sp, 133
CORNISH CHICKEN, 160
CORNUS spp, 85, 95, 138-140, 142, 145, 185, 250, 338, 396, 452, 454, 458
CORONA RADIATA, 123
CORONARY, -arteries, 286; - -innervation, 307, 310; -circulation, 283; -drugs, 376-381, 389; -veins, 287, 438
CORONILLA sp, 395
CORPORA CAVERNOSA, innervation of, 308, 310
CORPUS, -callosum, -striatum, 300
CORPUS LUTEUM, 126, 127, 130, 383, 385
CORROSIVE POISONS, 419
CORROSIVE SUBLIMATE, 410
CORRUGATOR MUSCLE(S), 296
CORTEXONE, 383, 385
CORTICIUM spp, 133, 445, 501, 503
CORTICO-HABENULAR TRACT, 302
CORTICOSPINAL TRACTS, 302
CORTICOSTEROIDS, of serous fluid, 55
CORTICOSTERONE, 383, 385
CORTICO-TEGMENTAL FASCICULUS TRACT, 302

CORTICOTROPIN, 376, 377, 382, 384, 385, 390, (see also ADRENO-CORTICOTROPIC HORMONE)
CORTINELLUS sp, 133
CORTISOL, 383, 385
CORTISONE, 383, 385, 391, 418; -acetate, 376, 377, 382, 390
CORVIDAE, 117, 214
CORVUS spp, 164, 182, 277, 344, 351, 519
CORYLINA spp, 498
CORYLUS spp, 134, 142, 145, 185, 186, 396, 499, 502
CORYNE sp, 204
CORYNEBACTERIUM spp, 89-91, 97, 209, 223, 236, 404, 405, 443, 444, 482, 496, 498-500
CORYNESPORA sp, 501
CORYNEUM sp, 501-503, 505
CORYNINE, 365, 369
CORYNOCEPHALUS spp, 328
CORYNORHINUS sp, 126
CORYPHAENA sp, 165
CORYTHUCHA sp, 490
COSMARIUM sp, 447
COSMIC RAYS, 467, 470, 478, 480
COSMOS spp, 39, 96, 451, 459, 460, 498
COSSUS sp, 66, 67, 78, 277
COSTA RICA, 420, 517
COTHURNIA, 339
COTINGAS, 117
COTINGIDAE, 117
COTINIS spp, 142, 489
COTO spp, 39
COTOIN, 39
COTONEASTER spp, 136, 185
COTTON, 44, 82-88, 95, 122, 135, 147, 186, 224, 264, 336, 358, 432, 451, 453-455, 460, 489-492, 498, 501, 508-510, 520, 523; -aphid, 411; -boll weevil, 122, 411, 523; -fleahopper, 523; -leafworm, 122, 411; -leaf-curl, 510; -mite, 411; -stainer, 436; -wax, 21
COTTONMOUTH(S), 119, 161, 183
COTTON RAT, 495
COTTONSEED, 22, 191; -feed, 188; -flour, 188; -meal, 211, 230; -oil, 20; -oil meal, 188
COTTONWOOD(S), 137-140, 147, 185, 338, 396, 452, 458
COTTUS sp, 277
COTULA sp, 394
COTURNIX sp, 182
COTYLORHIZA sp, 184
COUMARIN, 42, 43, 360, 391; derivs. of, 409; (see also ANTICOAGU-LANTS, DICOUMARIN, FUMARIN, WARFARIN)
COW (see CATTLE)
COWBIRD(S), 126, 164, 182, 244, 277
COWDRIA sp, 496
COWPEA, 85, 87, 122, 252, 336, 422, 451, 489, 492, 498, 509, 520; -curculio, 523; -hay, 189; -mosaic, 442; -weevil, 122
COWSLIP, 458
COXIELLA spp, 443, 484, 496
COXSACKIE, 493
COYOTE, 163, 182, 350, 494, 496
COYPU, 23
COZYMASE (see DIPHOSPHO-PYRIDINE NUCLEOTIDE)
CRAB(S), 25, 46, 70, 121, 184, 190, 243, 277, 282, 292, 295, 314, 320, 456, 484, 507; -meal, 188
CRABAPPLE, 85, 95, 142, 452, 458
CRABGRASS, 84, 94, 396
CRAB'S-EYE VINE, 432
CRACIDAE, 116
CRAG 974, 416
CRAGO sp, 456
CRANBERRY(IES), 17, 83, 96, 136, 187, 265, 458, 501, 510; -wax, 21
CRANCHIA spp, 328
CRANE(S), 116, 164, 182, 277, 344, 351
CRANESBILL, 395
CRANIAL GANGLIA, 152
CRANIAL NERVES, 154, 303, 312, (see also specific nerves)
CRANIAL VESSELS, innervation of, 305, 306
CRAPPIE, 161

CRASSOSTREA sp, 121, 456
CRASSULACEAE, 95
CRATAEGUS spp, 95, 136, 142, 185, 265, 396, 452, 458
CRAX spp, 344
CRAYFISH, 72, 121, 212, 243, 277, 295, 314, 315, 319, 339, 484, 507
CREAM, 190, 193
CREAM SPOT TIGER MOTH, 494
CREATINE, 52, 55, 59, 66, 71, 72, 76, 240, 242; -nitrogen, 77, 243; -phosphate, 240
CREATININE, 52, 53, 55-60, 76, 242, 346; -clearance, 341, 355; -nitrogen, 77, 243
CREEPER(S), 117, 396
CREEPING CHARLIE, 395
CREMASTER MUSCLE, 296
CRENICHTHYS sp, 261
CREOBROTER sp, 92
CREOSOL, 42
CREOSOTE(S), 417, 419
CREOSOTE BUSH, 358
CREPIDOBOTHRIUM sp, 440
CREPIDULA sp, 125
CREPIPODA, 125
CRESATIN, 416
CRESOL(S) (methylphenol), 331, 418, 419, (see also PHENOLS); -indo-phenol, 4
CRESS(ES), 395
CRESYL BLUE, 4
CRETACEOUS ERA, 525
CRICETUS spp, 69, 126, 182, 277
CRICKET(S), 67, 78, 319, 323, 325, 490
CRICOARYTENOIDEUS MUSCLE, 296
CRICONEMOIDES spp, 509
CRICOTHYROIDEUS MUSCLE, 296
CRINIPELLIS sp, 133
CRINOIDEA, 121, 125
CRIODRILUS sp, 125
CRISTIVOMER sp, 165
CRISTA BASILARIS, 322
CRISTULARIELLA sp, 504
CROAKER(S), 456
CROCETIN, 17; dimethyl ester, 356
CROCIN, 17
CROCODILE(S), 23, 119, 164, 173, 183, 270, 277, 282
CROCODILUS sp, 164, 183, 277
CROCUS spp, 17, 94, 134, 427
CROCUTA spp, 115, 163, 182, 212
CROMILEPTES sp, 456
CRONARTIUM spp, 133, 444, 504, 505, 522
CROP, 155
CROPS, field, 122, 450, 454, 460, 520, (see also specific crops)
CROSSASTER sp, 425
CROSSBILL(S), 344
CROTALARIA spp, 44, 134, 451
CROTALIDAE, 420-423
CROTALUS spp, 183, 261, 422, 423
CROTAPHYTUS sp, 119, 434
CROTIN, 427
CROTON, 427, 432; -oil, 317; -resin, 432
CROTOXIN, 24
CROW(S), 117, 164, 270, 277, 282, 344, 351, 519
CROWNBEARD, 147
CROWN GALL, 19, 143
CRUCIBULUM sp, 133
CRUCIFERAE, 95, 134, 144, 490, 491, 498, 502
CRUSTACEA, 68, 121, 184, 235, 339, 462, 484, 488, 519, 525, (see also specific Crustacea)
CRYOLITE, 410
CRYPTOBRANCHUS sp, 93, 120, 270
CRYPTOCERCUS sp, 261
CRYPTOCHITON sp, 277
CRYPTOCOCCUS spp, 404-406, 414, 415, 444, 482, 514
CRYPTOMERIA sp, 142
CRYPTONEMIA sp, 263
CRYPTOSPORELLA sp, 501
CRYPTOSTROBIN, 38
CRYPTOXANTHIN, 49, 226
CRYSTAL DENSITY, of proteins, 24

CRYSTALLIN(S), 76
CTENOCEPHALIDES spp, 412, 413, 484, 485, 487, 508
CTENOCEPHALUS sp, 93
CTENOPHORA, 125, 261, 328, 331, 332
CUBA, 517
CUBEB(S), 43
CUBE GAMBIER, 41
CUCKOO, 84, 117, 351, 519
CUCLOTOGASTER sp, 488
CUCULIDAE, 117
CUCULIFORMES, 117
CUCULUS spp, 93, 351, 519
CUCUMARIA spp, 121, 183
CUCUMBER, 88, 96, 146, 147, 187, 264, 265, 337, 394, 442, 450, 451, 453-455, 459, 460, 490, 491, 498, 502, 509, 510, 520; -mosaic, 89, 442, 510, 522; -virus, 90, 91
CUCUMBER-TREE, 95, 140, 185, 458
CUCUMIS spp, 88, 96, 146, 147, 187, 251, 264, 265, 337, 450, 451, 453-455, 459, 460, 498, 510, 520
CUCURBIT(S), 122, 489, 490, 498, 502; -mosaic, 510, 522
CUCURBITA spp, 87, 88, 96, 144, 147, 187, 264, 337, 391, 395, 449, 451, 453-455, 502
CUCURBITACEAE, 96, 135
CUCURBITALES, 85
CUDONIA spp, 96, 204
CULEX spp, 51, 66, 93, 166, 261, 411, 435, 485, 488, 508, 522
CULICOIDES spp, 484, 486
CULTERIA sp, 263
CULTURE MEDIA, 143, 216, 217, 440
CUMACEA, 519
CUMIN, 498
CUMINALDEHYDE, 42
CUMINGIA sp, 45
CUMINUM spp, 498
CUNEATE fasciculus tract, 302; -nucleus, 302
CUNNINGHAMELLA spp, 133, 204
CUPELOPAGIS sp, 184
CUPRESSUS spp, 136, 137, 140, 142, 185, 449, 452, 503
CURACIT, 371
CURARE, 268, 280, 331, 427, 431
CURARIFORM DRUGS, 367, 370
CURARIFORM DRUGS, 367, 370
CURASSOW(S), 344
CURCIN, 429
CURCULIO(S), 122, 522, 523
CURCUMA spp, 40, 46, 47
CURCUMIN, 40
CURINE, 427
CURIUM, 241
CURLEW, 351
CURLEY TOP, sugar beet, 522; -virus, 337
CURRANT(S), 95, 134, 187, 396, 458, 489, 498
CURTISIA sp, 92
CUSCUTA spp, 84, 337, 394
CUSHING'S SYNDROME, 280, 385
CUSTARD-APPLE, 95, 134
CUTANEOUS nerves, 312, 313; -blood, 271; - -pressure, 290
CUTASSFISH, 456
CUTCH, 41
CUTTLEFISH, 46, 277, 292, 314, 315
CUTWORM(S), 272, 411, 436, 490
CYANAMID, 206, 393
CYANATE, 241
CYANEA sp, 424
CYANIDE, 206, 241, 363, 418, 419
CYANOCITTA sp, 182, 344, 351
CYANOCOBALAMIN, 48, 50, 198, 227, 376, 377, 382, (see also COBALAMIN, VITAMIN B$_{12}$)
CYANOPHYTA, 131, 263, 447
CYANOSIS, 418
CYATHUS sp, 131, 133, 135, 204
CYBISTER sp, 184
CYCADACEAE, 94
CYCADS, 525
CYCLAMEN spp, 96, 186, 264, 432
CYCLAMIN, 432
CYCLANTHACEAE, 134
CYCLIC FATTY ACIDS, 19 (see also specific compounds)
CYCLIC OLIGOSACCHARIDES, 13 (see also specific compounds)

559

HORMISCIUM sp, 204
HORMODENDRUM spp, 204, 444, 514
HORMONE(S), 90, 91, 234, 242, 383-386, 390, (see also ENDOCRINES, GROWTH, -regulators; see also specific hormones)
HORN, composition of, 77
HORNBEAM(S), 84, 94, 134, 185, 396, 452, 454, 458
HORNBILL(S), 117, 182
HORNED LARK, 118
HORNED RATTLESNAKE, 422, 423
HORNET, bald-faced, 78
HORN FLY, 122, 411
HORNWORM(S), 122, 166, 436, 490, 491
HORSE(S), 25-27, 45, 47, 50, 51, 53-55, 57-62, 64, 70, 73, 77, 80, 90, 91, 109, 115, 123, 124, 126-129, 163, 167, 169, 171, 174, 175, 182, 196, 197, 211, 226, 228, 230, 258, 260, 261, 266, 267, 270, 271, 275-279, 282, 285, 304, 316, 339, 343, 350, 355, 428, 429, 437, 438, 485, 487, 488, 492-497, 508, 512-514, 519; -meat, 211-214; -serum, 260, 440
HORSE, -bean, 250; -bot-fly, 78; -chestnut, 17, 86, 88, 95, 142, 145, 265, 454, 458; -fly, 122; -mussel, 424
HORSENETTLE, 84
HORSERADISH, 27, 33, 134, 432, 499
HORSESHOE CRAB, 425
HORSETAIL(S), 251, 263, 395, 458, 525
HOSTA spp, 145, 458
HOSTIS spp, 493-495
HOSTONOMONAS sp, 507
HOTTINGER'S BROTH, 440
HOUND'S-TONGUE, 88, 395
HOUSE, -fly, 78, 122, 411, 522; -mouse, 409, 493; -sparrow, 119; -wren, 119
HOUSEHOLD POISONS, 418, 419
HOUSELEEK, 336
HOYA sp, 88, 96, 145
HUALLATA, 270
HUBL TEST, 21
HUMERUS, 168, 169
HUMIN, 88
HUMMINGBIRD(S), 117, 123, 164, 213, 261, 277, 345, 351
HUMULUS spp, 134, 453, 520
HUNGARY, 43, 516
HUTIA, 343
HYACINTH(S), 94, 134, 136, 395, 454, 499, 508
HYACINTH-BEAN, 134, 442; -enation mosaic, 442
HYAENA spp, 243, 277
HYAENANCHE sp, 432
HYAENANCHIN, 432
HYALODISCUS spp, 333
HYALOGONIUM sp, 202
HYALOMMA sp, 484
HYALOPHORA sp, 436
HYALOPTERUS sp, 92
HYALOSPORA sp, 503
HYALURONIC ACID (HUA), 31, 58, 76, 77; -ase, 29, 31, 59, 81, 421, 423
HYBORHYNCHUS sp, 435
HYBRID(S), fertility and infertility of, 109; -vigor, corn, 110
HYDERGINE, 365, 376, 377, 381
HYDNOCARPIC ACID, 19
HYDNOCARPUS spp, 432
HYDNUM spp, 204, 504
HYDRA spp, 68, 69, 92, 184, 320, 456, 462
HYDRA, -crylic acid, β-phenyl-ester, 412; -tropic acid, 359, 361; -zoic acid, 5
HYDRALAZINE, 376, 377, 380, 381
HYDRANGEA spp, 95, 224, 460
HYDRASTINE, 430
HYDRATROPOYL, -alcohol, 359; -glycine, 361
HYDRAZINE, 5
HYDRO, -chloric acid, 4, 61, 211, 225, 326, 331, 342; -cortisone, 383, 385; - -acetate, 390; -cotoin, 39;

-cyanic acid, 5, 42, 427; -ethyl-trimethylammonium chloride, 366, 369; -quinone, 5, 17, 358, 391; -sulfuric acid
HYDROBATES sp, 344
HYDROBATIDAE, 116
HYDROBILENES, 35
HYDROCHARIS sp, 146
HYDROCHARITACEAE, 94, 524
HYDROCOTYLE sp, 395
HYDRODICTYON-spp, 131
HYDROGEN, 26, 83, 89, 206, 221, 223, 331, 356, 357, 467, 478; -ase, 223; -bromide, 401; -constants, 5; -cyanide, 419; -electrode, 4; -ion concentration (see pH); -peroxide, 28, 29, 417; -peroxidase, 473; -sulfate, 326; -sulfide, 28, 29, 34, 419, 479
HYDROGENOMONAS spp, 223, 443
HYDROID, 456; -sting, 424
HYDROIDEA, 328
HYDROLAGUS sp, 425
HYDROLASE, 236
HYDROLYSATE, 91
HYDROMEDUSAE, 328
HYDROPHILUS spp, 51, 66, 67, 436
HYDROPHIS sp, 127
HYDROPHYTES, 338, 449
HYDROSTATIC PRESSURE, 281, 332; effects of, 335, 463, 464; of sea water, 524
HYDROUS spp, 78, 93, 436
HYDROXY, 57, 357; -acid, 473; -al-dehydes, 391; -amphetamine, 364, 368, 376, 377, 380, 381; -anthranil-ic acid, 246; -aspartic acid, 356; -benzoic acid, 209, 357, 415; -ben-zophenone, 39; -benzoyl, 356; bu-tyrate, 28; -butyryl-β-alanine, 357; -cerotic acid, 19; -cholenic acid, 23; -cholest-5-en-7-one; 472; -cholesterol, 22; -cobalamin, 48, 227; -cortisone, 383, 385; -cou-marin, 360, 376, 377, 382; -de-cosanoic acid, 19; -3, 7-dihydroxy-phenothiazine, 360; -diiodophenyl, 357; -1, 3-dimethylhydrouracil, 473; -N-α-dimethylphenethylamine, 364, 368; -dodecanoic acid, 19; -emodin, 253, 254; -ethyltrimethyl-ammonium chloride carbamate, 366, 369; -ethyltrimethylammonium hydroxide, 48; -fumigatin, 254; -glutamic acid, 356; -hemin, 33; -hexacosanoic acid, 19; -hexa-decanoic acid, 19; -indole, 360; [-β-iono-3, 7, 12, 16-tetramethyl-octo-deca-noene-2, 4, 6, 8, 10, 12, 14, 16, 18]-polyene, 40; -6-keto-allocholanic acid, 23; -kynurenine, 246; -leucotoin, 39; -lysine, 30; -methoxyflavone, 37; -methoxy-phenylacetic acid, 363; -methyl-aminomethylbenzyl alcohol, 364, 368; -methylenedioxybenzene, 358; -methyl-5-methoxyfuranochrome, 17; -α-methylphenethylamine, 364, 368; -6-methyl-3, 4-pyridinedi-methanol HCl, 49; -1-napthylidene-n-galactosamine, 9; -nervonic acid, 19; -9-octadecenoic acid, 19; -pan-tothenic acid, 357; -pentadecanoic acid, 19; -phenolmethylamino-ethanol tartrate, 364, 368; -phenyl-alanine, 356; -phenylpyruvic acid, 232; -phenyltrimethylammonium bromide, 366, 369; -progesterone, 257; -proline, 5, 30, 199, 200, 201, 216, 217, 232, 237, 238, 242, 473; -2-pyrrolidine carboxylic acid, 30; -pyruvic acid, 232; -quinoline, 414; -tetracosanoic acid, 19; -tetra-cosenoic acid, 19; -1, 2, 2, 6-tetra-methylpiperidinemandelate HCl, 367, 370; -triazolpyrimidine, 356; -tryptamine, 423, 479; -tyramine, 242
HYDROXYLAMINE, 34, 401, 479
HYDROXYL CONSTANTS, bases, 5
HYDROZOA, 121, 125, 184
HYENA(S), 115, 163, 182, 212, 243, 277

HYGOTRECHUS sp, 92
HYLA spp, 93, 120, 183, 434
HYLEMYA spp, 122, 215, 491
HYLOBATES spp, 115, 182, 304
HYLOCICHLA sp, 344
HYLOCOMIUM spp, 263
HYLOTRUPES spp, 184, 436
HYLURGOPINUS sp, 523
HYMENAEA spp, 41
HYMENOCHAETE sp, 504, 505
HYMENOLEPIS spp, 406, 484, 506
HYMENOPTERA, 122, 125, 166, 329, 346, 436
HYNOBIUS spp, 93, 120
HYODESOXYCHOLIC ACID, 23
HYOGLOSSUS MUSCLE, 297
HYOID BONES, 168, 169
HYOSCINE, 363, 366, 369, 431
HYOSCYAMINE, 366, 369, 419, 427-430
HYOSCYAMUS spp, 427, 431, 459, 460
HYPER, -parathyroidism, 280, 360; -tensinogen, 25; -tension, 290, 381, 418; -thermia, 418, 433-436; -thy-roidism, 385, 386; -trichosis, 101
HYPERICUM sp, 395
HYPERIDEA, 328
HYPHANTRIA sp, 492
HYPHOLOMA sp, 69, 133, 204
HYPNOTICS, 382, 389
HYPNUM sp, 263
HYPO, -chlorous acid, 5; -gastric nerves, plexuses, 305, 306, 311, 313; -glossal nerve, 313, 314; -glossus, 154; -nitrite, 206; -para-thyroidism, 280, 386; -phosphate, 241; -tension, 374, 418; -thalamus, 154, 260, 290, 300, 303; -thermia, 418, 438, 439, 479; -thyroidism, 385, 386, 390; -xanthine, 209, 235, 236, 244, 254, 356, 391, 473
HYPOCHNUS sp, 446
HYPODERMA spp, 122, 436, 485, 488, 503, 505
HYPODERMELLA sp, 503-505
HYPOMYCES spp, 96, 131, 135
HYPOPHYSEAL ARTERY, 287
HYPOPHYSIS, 22, 162, 300, (see also PITUITARY)
HYPOXIA, 274, 279, 282, 372-375, 479, (see also RESPIRATION)
HYPOXYLON sp, 204, 504, 505
HYRACOIDEA, 127, 214
HYRAX, 127, 163
HYSSOP, 43
HYSSOPUS sp, 43

IBERIS spp, 95
IBEX, Nubian, 182
IBIS(ES), 116, 344, 351
ICARITIN, 37
ICELAND, 516
ICERYA sp, 92
ICHNEUMIA sp, 163
ICHTHYOPHIS sp, 93
ICHTHYOSIS HYSTRIX GRAVIOR, 101
ICIUS sp, 92
ICTALURUS spp, 165, 243, 434, 456
ICTERIDAE, 117
ICTEROGENIN, 432
ICTERUS sp, 351
ICTERUS(IC) INDEX, 63, 342
ICTHYOSIS SIMPLEX, 101
ICTINUS sp, 92
ICTROGEN, 428
IDIOCY, 101
IDITOL, and derivs., 13
IDOSE, 254
IGUANA spp, 164, 183, 261, 271, 316
IGUANIDAE, 214
ILEAL ARTERIES, 287
ILEUM, 79, 260, 482
ILEX spp, 85, 95, 134, 136, 138, 140, 142, 146, 185, 454, 458, 460
ILIAC, -arteries, 287; -muscle, 297
ILIA NUCLEUS, 261
ILIDAR, 381
ILIO, -cecal sphincter, 308, 310; -costalis muscles, 297; -fibularis muscle, 293; -inguinal nerve, 312; -hypogastric nerve, 312; -lumbar

artery, 287
ILIUM, 170, 171
ILLICIUM sp, 42
ILLUMINATION, 321, 335, (see also LIGHT, DAYLIGHT)
ILLYANASSA sp, 45
ILOTYCIN, 256, 400, 401, 407
IMIDAZOLE, 54, 206, 356; -acetic acid, 362; -compounds, 232, 242, 473, (see also specific compounds)
IMIDE(S), acid, 206
IMMITIS, 184
IMPALLA, 350
IMPAR, -ganglia, 311; -tuberculum, 156
IMPATIENS spp, 95, 145; 338, 394, 449, 451, 454, 459, 460
INCENSE-CEDAR, 137, 139, 140, 185, 452, 503
INCILLARIA sp, 92
INCISORS, 73, 167
INCLUSION CONJUNCTIVITIS, 494
INCUBATION PERIODS, birds, 116, 117
INCUS, 322, 324
INDALONE, 412
INDANDIONE, 2-pivaloyl-, 409
INDENE-3-ACETIC ACID, 397
INDIA, 42, 43, 99, 273, 345, 420, 428-431, 488, 491, 506, 508, 511, 514, 516
INDIAN(S), American-, 100, 177, 318; Mexican-, 176
INDIAN CURRANT, 396
INDIAN-MEAL MOTH, 122
INDIAN OCEAN, 524
INDICAN, 17, 242
INDIELLA spp, 513
INDIGO, 394; -compounds, 4, 40, 394, 451
INDIGOBUSH, 142
INDIGOFERA spp, 17, 38, 40
INDIUM, 241
INDO-CHINA (-CHINESE), 176, 431
INDOLE, 206, 246, 357, 360, 473; -acetic acid, 209, 222, 242, 335, 337, 356, 391, 397, 473; -acetonitrile, 397; -acrylic acid, 357; -butyric acid, 397; -propi-onic acid, 397; -pyruvic acid, 232; -serine ligase, 246
INDOLY, -acetic acid, 361; -aceturic acid, 361
INDONESIA, 42, 420, 508, 509
INDO-PACIFIC, 121
INDOXYL, 17
INERMICAPSIFER sp, 484
INFANDIBULUM, 300
INFERIOR, -colliculus, 302, 304; -mesenteric ganglion, 305, 306; -olive, 304; -petrosal venous sinus, 287; -sagittal venous sinus, 287; -vena cava, 287; -vermis, 300
INFLUENZA, 89-91, 97, 441, 494
INFRAORBITAL, -artery, 287; -nerve, 312
INFRARED, -rays, 467; -receptor, 315
INFRASPINATUS MUSCLE, 297
INFRATROCHLEAR NERVE, 312
INIMICUS spp, 426
INIOTEUTHIS spp, 328
INJURY, cold-, 439
INKBERRY, 142
INNER EAR, 152, 322
INNER PHALANGEAL CELL, 322
INNOMINATE, -artery, 286; -vein, 287
INOCYBE sp, 133
INORGANIC, -fertilizers, 191; -phos-phorus, 78, 81
INOSINE, 215, 235, 236, 244, 473
INOSINIC ACID, 235, 236, 244
INOSITOL(S), 12-14, 29, 48, 50, 52, 56, 59, 76, 79, 192, 196, 197, 200-205, 208, 211, 215-217, 228, 231, 242, 356; and derivs., 12-14; -hexanitrate, 376, 377, 380, 381; -monomethyl ethers, 14; -phosphatides, 234
INOSOSE and derivs., 14
INSECTA, 29, 66, 68, 78, 109, 121, 122, 166, 184, 199-201, 206-210, 215, 235, 255, 339, 346, 356, 357, 411, 484-497, 519, 522, 523, 525, (see also specific insects); parasitic-, 484-497; -vectors of disease, 484-497, 510, 511

564

566

568

571

582